Just for New York!

W9-AUI-730

Pre-Algebra

Features of the New York Teacher Wraparound Edition

Exclusively from Glencoe

Additional New York Resources

New York Review Series, Grade 8 Mathematics   Reviews Post-March topics from Grade 7 and Pre-March topics from Grade 8. Lessons cover each performance indicator with fully worked out examples and exercises.

Preparing for the New York Tests CD-ROM   Includes questions that can help your students prepare for success on New York tests.

New York TeacherWorks™   An all-in-one lesson planner and resource center that helps you customize lesson plans and reproduce classroom resources quickly and easily.

New York StudentWorks™   This backpack solution CD-ROM allows students instant access to the Student Edition, lesson worksheet pages, and web resources.

New York Middle School Guide to Daily Intervention   A lesson-by-lesson guide to available resources to reach students in need of intervention/remediation.

Exam*View*® Pro   A customizable testmaker with built-in New York curriculum correlations.

New York Teacher Reviewers and Field Test School

Steven L. Arnofsky, Reviewer   Assistant Principal, Supervision, George W. Wingate High School, Brooklyn

Fay Bonacorsi, Reviewer   Math Teacher, LaFayette High School, Brooklyn

Field Test School   John F. Kennedy Middle School, Bethpage

For more information, visit: www.ny.pre-alg.com

New York Edition

Pre-Algebra

Covers the New York Grade 8 Performance Indicators

Teacher Wraparound Edition

State Bird
Bluebird

Contents

Glencoe

ISBN: 0-07-873315-4 *(New York Student Edition)*   0-07-869363-2 *(New York Teacher Wraparound Edition)*

New York Teacher Advisory Board

Photo Credits: NY1 Gary W. Carter/CORBIS; **NY2** Hisham Ibrahim/Photov.com/Alamy Images; **NY7** Terry Prekas/Alamy Images

Buffalo Skyline and Expressway

Test-Taking Tips

Go to bed early the night before the test. You will think more clearly after a good night's rest.

Read each problem carefully, underline key words, and think about ways to solve the problem before you try to answer the question.

Relax. Most people get nervous when taking a test. It's natural. Just do your best.

Answer questions you are sure about first. If you do not know the answer to a question, skip it and go back to that question later.

Become familiar with common formulas and when they should be used.

Think positively. Some problems may seem hard to you, but you may be able to figure out what to do if you read each question carefully.

If no figure is provided, draw one. If one is furnished, mark it up to help you solve the problem.

When you have finished each problem, reread it to make sure your answer is reasonable.

Make sure that the number of the question on the answer sheet matches the number of the question on which you are working in your test booklet.

New York State Mathematics Process Strands, Grade 8, Correlated to *Glencoe Pre-Algebra*

The lessons that address each Performance Indicator are listed, and those in which the Performance Indicator is the primary focus are indicated in **bold**.

Strands and Performance Indicators	Student Edition Lesson(s)
STRAND PROBLEM SOLVING	
Students will build new mathematical knowledge through problem solving.	
8.PS.1 Use a variety of strategies to understand new mathematical content and to develop more efficient methods	Used throughout the text, for example **1-4, 8-2, 13-1**
8.PS.2 Construct appropriate extensions to problem situations	Used throughout the text, for example **4-6F, 5-8, 8-5P, 9-5F**
8.PS.3 Understand and demonstrate how written symbols represent mathematical ideas	Used throughout the text, for example **1-3, 3-2, RM3**
Students will solve problems that arise in mathematics and in other contexts.	
8.PS.4 Observe patterns and formulate generalizations	Used throughout the text, for example **3-1, 5-8, 5-10, 10-6F**
8.PS.5 Make conjectures from generalizations	Used throughout the text, for example **3-7F, 9-4, 10-1, 10-5**
8.PS.6 Represent problem situations verbally, numerically, algebraically, and graphically	Used throughout the text, for example **8-3, 8-7, 12-3, 12-4**
Students will apply and adapt a variety of appropriate strategies to solve problems.	
8.PS.7 Understand that there is no one right way to solve mathematical problems but that different methods have advantages and disadvantages	Used throughout the text, for example **5-9, 7-1, 7-6, 8-8**
8.PS.8 Understand how to break a complex problem into simpler parts or use a similar problem type to solve a problem	Used throughout the text, for example **1-1, 7-2, 7-6, 8-2**
8.PS.9 Work backwards from a solution	Used throughout the text, for example **4-2, 4-3**

RM = Reading Mathematics Feature, P = Preview Lesson, F = Follow-Up Lesson, PS = Prerequisite Skills Appendix (pp. 706–723)

Strands and Performance Indicators		Student Edition Lesson(s)
8.PS.10	Use proportionality to model problems	Used throughout the text, for example **6-2, 6-3, 6-5**
8.PS.11	Work in collaboration with others to solve problems	Used throughout the text, for example **5-6F, 5-8P, 6-9P**

Students will monitor and reflect on the process of mathematical problem solving.

8.PS.12	Interpret solutions within the given constraints of a problem	Used throughout the text, for example **6-6, RM7, 8-8**
8.PS.13	Set expectations and limits for possible solutions	Used throughout the text, for example **8-7, 9-1, 9-5**
8.PS.14	Determine information required to solve the problem	Used throughout the text, for example **RM7, 8-3, 11-7, 12-5**
8.PS.15	Choose methods for obtaining required information	Used throughout the text, for example **8-8, 9-6, 10-3**
8.PS.16	Justify solution methods through logical argument	Used throughout the text, for example **1-1, 1-4**
8.PS.17	Evaluate the efficiency of different representations of a problem	Used throughout the text, for example **8-2P, 8-8, 12-9**

STRAND   REASONING AND PROOF

Students will recognize reasoning and proof as fundamental aspects of mathematics.

8.RP.1	Recognize that mathematical ideas can be supported by a variety of strategies	Used throughout the text, for example **1-1, 6-6, 9-5**

Students will make and investigate mathematical conjectures.

8.RP.2	Use mathematical strategies to reach a conclusion	Used throughout the text, for example **5-8, 9-2, 9-7**
8.RP.3	Evaluate conjectures by distinguishing relevant from irrelevant information to reach a conclusion or make appropriate estimates	Used throughout the text, for example **1-7, 4-2F, 9-8**

Students will develop and evaluate mathematical arguments and proofs.

8.RP.4	Provide supportive arguments for conjectures	Used throughout the text, for example **1-7, 8-8, 9-4**

RM = Reading Mathematics Feature, P = Preview Lesson, F = Follow-Up Lesson, PS = Prerequisite Skills Appendix (pp. 706–723)

Strands and Performance Indicators		Student Edition Lesson(s)
8.RP.5	Develop, verify, and explain an argument, using appropriate mathematical ideas and language	Used throughout the text, for example **1-1, 1-4**, 1-7

Students will select and use various types of reasoning and methods of proof.

8.RP.6	Support an argument by using a systematic approach to test more than one case	Used throughout the text, for example 1-1, **1-4**, 1-7
8.RP.7	Devise ways to verify results, or use counterexamples to refute incorrect statements	Used throughout the text, for example 1-1, 1-3, **1-4**
8.RP.8	Apply inductive reasoning in making and supporting mathematical conjectures	Used throughout the text, for example **1-1, 1-4**

STRAND COMMUNICATION

Students will organize and consolidate their mathematical thinking through communication.

8.CM.1	Provide a correct, complete, coherent, and clear rationale for thought process used in problem solving	Used throughout the text, for example **1-1, 1-4, 4-2, 4-3**
8.CM.2	Provide an organized argument which explains rationale for strategy selection	Used throughout the text, for example **10-3, 12-3, 12-6**
8.CM.3	Organize and accurately label work	Used throughout the text, for example **6-3, 9-7, 11-4, 11-7**

Students will communicate their mathematical thinking coherently and clearly to peers, teachers, and others.

8.CM.4	Share organized mathematical ideas through the manipulation of objects, numerical tables, drawings, pictures, charts, graphs, tables, diagrams, models and symbols in written and verbal form	Used throughout the text, for example **1-7, 4-4, 8-2, 9-8P**
8.CM.5	Answer clarifying questions from others	**12-5, RM12**

Students will analyze and evaluate the mathematical thinking and strategies of others.

8.CM.6	Analyze mathematical solutions shared by others	Used throughout the text, for example **5-10, 12-3**
8.CM.7	Compare strategies used and solutions found by others in relation to their own work	Used throughout the text, for example **8-3, 13-6**
8.CM.8	Formulate mathematical questions that elicit, extend, or challenge strategies, solutions, and/or conjectures of others	Used throughout the text, for example **5-8, 6-1, 9-2**

RM = Reading Mathematics Feature, P = Preview Lesson, F = Follow-Up Lesson, PS = Prerequisite Skills Appendix (pp. 706–723)

Strands and Performance Indicators		Student Edition Lesson(s)
Students will use the language of mathematics to express mathematical ideas precisely.		
8.CM.9	Increase their use of mathematical vocabulary and language when communicating with others	Used throughout the text, for example **1-4, RM2, RM9**
8.CM.10	Use appropriate language, representations, and terminology when describing objects, relationships, mathematical solutions, and rationale	Used throughout the text, for example **RM1, 1-3, 3-6, 8-3**
8.CM.11	Draw conclusions about mathematical ideas through decoding, comprehension, and interpretation of mathematical visuals, symbols, and technical writing	Used throughout the text, for example **2-6, 4-8, 6-3**
STRAND CONNECTIONS		
Students will recognize and use connections among mathematical ideas.		
8.CN.1	Understand and make connections among multiple representations of the same mathematical idea	Used throughout the text, for example **3-3P, 3-4P, 5-1, 5-8, 6-4**
8.CN.2	Recognize connections between subsets of mathematical ideas	Used throughout the text, for example **1-7, 4-4, 9-3F**
8.CN.3	Connect and apply a variety of strategies to solve problems	Used throughout the text, for example **1-1, 1-4, 4-2, 4-3**
Students will understand how mathematical ideas interconnect and build on one another to produce a coherent whole.		
8.CN.4	Model situations mathematically, using representations to draw conclusions and formulate new situations	Used throughout the text, for example **4-4, 6-3, 10-2, 12-3**
8.CN.5	Understand how concepts, procedures, and mathematical results in one area of mathematics can be used to solve problems in other areas of mathematics	Used throughout the text, for example **2-6, 5-10, 10-1**
Students will recognize and apply mathematics in contexts outside of mathematics.		
8.CN.6	Recognize and provide examples of the presence of mathematics in their daily lives	Used throughout the text, for example 5-5, **6-6, 6-8, 12-7**
8.CN.7	Apply mathematical ideas to problem situations that develop outside of mathematics	Used throughout the text, for example 2-4, **6-3**, 11-2
8.CN.8	Investigate the presence of mathematics in careers and areas of interest	Used throughout the text, for example 2-2, 5-4, 6-3, 7-6, 9-5, 9-8, 12-8, 13-1

RM = Reading Mathematics Feature, P = Preview Lesson, F = Follow-Up Lesson, PS = Prerequisite Skills Appendix (pp. 706–723)

Strands and Performance Indicators		Student Edition Lesson(s)
8.CN.9	Recognize and apply mathematics to other disciplines, areas of interest, and societal issues	Used throughout the text, for example 2-6, 5-7, 9-7

STRAND   REPRESENTATION

Students will create and use representations to organize, record, and communicate mathematical ideas.

8.R.1	Use physical objects, drawings, charts, tables, graphs, symbols, equations, and objects created using technology as representations	Used throughout the text, for example **4-4, 12-3, 12-4**
8.R.2	Explain, describe, and defend mathematical ideas using representations	Used throughout the text, for example **4-4, 9-3F, 13-6**
8.R.3	Recognize, compare, and use an array of representational forms	Used throughout the text, for example **1-7, 12-3, 13-1F**
8.R.4	Explain how different representations express the same relationship	Used throughout the text, for example **3-3P, 3-4P, 8-1, 12-5**
8.R.5	Use standard and non-standard representations with accuracy and detail	Used throughout the text, for example **5-10, 8-10, 10-6F**

Students will select, apply, and translate among mathematical representations to solve problems.

8.R.6	Use representations to explore problem situations	Used throughout the text, for example **8-2P, 8-6, 10-6F**
8.R.7	Investigate relationships between different representations and their impact on a given problem	Used throughout the text, for example **6-7, 8-6, 9-5**
8.R.8	Use representation as a tool for exploring and understanding mathematical ideas	Used throughout the text, for example **10-1F, 11-1P**

Students will use representations to model and interpret physical, social, and mathematical phenomena.

8.R.9	Use mathematics to show and understand physical phenomena (e.g., make and interpret scale drawings of figures or scale models of objects)	**6-3, 11-3, 11-5**
8.R.10	Use mathematics to show and understand social phenomena (e.g., determine profit from sale of yearbooks)	Used throughout the text, for example **6-5, 6-7, 6-8**
8.R.11	Use mathematics to show and understand mathematical phenomena (e.g., use tables, graphs, and equations to show a pattern underlying a function)	Used throughout the text, for example **6-7, 8-6, 13-6**

RM = Reading Mathematics Feature, P = Preview Lesson, F = Follow-Up Lesson, PS = Prerequisite Skills Appendix (pp. 706–723)

New York State Mathematics Content Strands, Grade 7, Post-March Indicators

These Indicators from Grade 7 are assessed on the Grade 8 Test.

7.A.2	Add and subtract monomials with exponents of one
7.A.3	Identify a polynomial as an algebraic expression containing one or more terms
7.A.4	Solve multi-step equations by combining like terms, using the distributive property, or moving variables to one side of the equation
7.A.7	Draw the graphic representation of a pattern from an equation or from a table of data
7.A.8	Create algebraic patterns using charts/tables, graphs, equations, and expressions
7.A.9	Build a pattern to develop a rule for determining the sum of the interior angles of polygons
7.A.10	Write an equation to represent a function from a table of values
7.G.5	Identify the right angle, hypotenuse, and legs of a right triangle
7.G.6	Explore the relationship between the lengths of the three sides of a right triangle to develop the Pythagorean Theorem
7.G.8	Use the Pythagorean Theorem to determine the unknown length of a side of a right triangle
7.G.9	Determine whether a given triangle is a right triangle by applying the Pythagorean Theorem and using a calculator
7.M.1	Calculate distance using a map scale
7.M.5	Calculate unit price using proportions
7.M.6	Compare unit prices
7.M.7	Convert money between different currencies with the use of an exchange rate table and a calculator

New York State Mathematics Content Strands, Grade 8, Correlated to *Glencoe Pre-Algebra*

The lessons that address each Performance Indicator are listed, and those in which the Performance Indicator is the primary focus are indicated in **bold**.

Strands and Performance Indicators	Student Edition Lesson(s)
STRAND NUMBER SENSE AND OPERATIONS	
Students will understand meanings of operations and procedures, and how they relate to one another.	
Operations	
8.N.1 Develop and apply the laws of exponents for multiplication and division	**4-6**
8.N.2 Evaluate expressions with integral exponents	**4-2**, 4-7
8.N.3 Read, write, and identify percents less than 1% and greater than 100%	6-4, 6-5, 6-6, 6-8

8.N.4 Apply percents to:
    Tax
    Percent increase/decrease
    Simple interest
    Sale price
    Commission
    Interest rates
    Gratuities
	6-6, **6-7**, **6-8**

Students will compute accurately and make reasonable estimates.	
Estimation	
8.N.5 Estimate a percent of quantity, given an application	6-4, 6-5P, **6-5**, 6-6, 6-7
8.N.6 Justify the reasonableness of answers using estimation	6-6, PS7, PS9, PS11, PS12
STRAND ALGEBRA	
Students will represent and analyze algebraically a wide variety of problem solving situations.	
Variables and Expressions	
8.A.1 Translate verbal sentences into algebraic inequalities	RM1, 1-3, RM3, 3-6, RM4, **RM7**, 7-3
8.A.2 Write verbal expressions that match given mathematical expressions	**1-3, RM3, 3-6,** RM4
8.A.3 Describe a situation involving relationships that matches a given graph	1-7P, 1-7, 1-7F, **8-8**

*Indicator is not tested on the Grade 8 Test.
RM = Reading Mathematics Feature, P = Preview Lesson, F = Follow-Up Lesson,
PS = Prerequisite Skills Appendix (pp. 706–723)

Strands and Performance Indicators		Student Edition Lesson(s)
8.A.4	Create a graph given a description or an expression for a situation involving a linear or nonlinear relationship	1-6, 1-7P, 1-7, 1-7F, **8-1, 8-2, 8-3, 8-4, 8-5, 8-6, 8-6F, 8-8**
8.A.5	Use physical models to perform operations with polynomials	**13-1F**, 13-2, 13-3, **13-4P**

Students will perform algebraic procedures accurately.

Variables and Expressions

8.A.6	Multiply and divide monomials	**4-5, 4-6, 13-4**
8.A.7	Add and subtract polynomials (integer coefficients)	**13-2, 13-3**
8.A.8	Multiply a binomial by a monomial or a binomial (integer coefficients)	**13-4**
8.A.9	Divide a polynomial by a monomial (integer coefficients) *Note: The degree of the denominator is less than or equal to the degree of the numerator for all variables.*	13-4, **13-4b** (p. NY35)
8.A.10	Factor algebraic expressions using the GCF	**4-1, 4-3, 4-4**
8.A.11	Factor a trinomial in the form $ax^2 + bx + c$; $a = 1$ and c having no more than three sets of factors	13-1, **13-1b** (p. NY32)

Equations and Inequalities

8.A.12	Apply algebra to determine the measure of angles formed by or contained in parallel lines cut by a transversal and by intersecting lines	**10-1**
8.A.13*	Solve multi-step inequalities and graph the solution set on a number line	**7-6**
8.A.14*	Solve linear inequalities by combining like terms, using the distributive property, or moving variables to one side of the inequality (include multiplication or division of inequalities by a negative number)	**7-3, 7-4, 7-5, 7-6**

Students will recognize, use, and represent algebraically patterns, relations, and functions.

Patterns, Relations, and Functions

8.A.15	Understand that numerical information can be represented in multiple ways: arithmetically, algebraically, and graphically	**1-1**, 1-7P, 1-7, **8-1, 8-2P, 8-2, 8-3, 8-5, 8-6, 8-6F, 8-8, 13-6, 13-6F**
8.A.16	Find a set of ordered pairs to satisfy a given linear numerical pattern (expressed algebraically); then plot the ordered pairs and draw the line	**1-6, 2-6**
8.A.17*	Define and use correct terminology when referring to function (domain and range)	**1-6, 8-1, RM8**
8.A.18*	Determine if a relation is a function	**8-1**
8.A.19*	Interpret multiple representations using equation, table of values, and graph	1-6, 1-7P, 1-7, 1-7F, **8-1, 8-2P, 8-2, 8-3, 8-4, 8-5, 8-6, 8-6F, 8-8, 13-6, 13-6F**

*Indicator is not tested on the Grade 8 Test.
RM = Reading Mathematics Feature, P = Preview Lesson, F = Follow-Up Lesson,
PS = Prerequisite Skills Appendix (pp. 706–723)

Strands and Performance Indicators	Student Edition Lesson(s)

STRAND GEOMETRY

Students will use visualization and spatial reasoning to analyze characteristics and properties of geometric shapes.

Constructions

8.G.0*	Construct the following using a straight edge and compass:
	    Segment congruent to a segment
	    Angle congruent to an angle
	    Perpendicular bisector
	    Angle bisector
		10-1F

Students will identify and justify geometric relationships, formally and informally.

Geometric Relationships

8.G.1	Identify pairs of vertical angles as congruent	10-1
8.G.2	Identify pairs of supplementary and complementary angles	10-1
8.G.3	Calculate the missing angle in a supplementary or complementary pair	10-1
8.G.4	Determine angle pair relationships when given two parallel lines cut by a transversal	10-1
8.G.5	Calculate the missing angle measurements when given two parallel lines cut by a transversal	10-1
8.G.6	Calculate the missing angle measurements when given two intersecting lines and an angle	10-1

Students will apply transformations and symmetry to analyze problem solving situations.

Transformational Geometry

8.G.7	Describe and identify transformations in the plane, using proper function notation (rotations, reflections, translations, and dilations)	10-3
8.G.8	Draw the image of a figure under rotations of 90 and 180 degrees	10-3
8.G.9	Draw the image of a figure under a reflection over a given line	10-3
8.G.10	Draw the image of a figure under a translation	10-3
8.G.11	Draw the image of a figure under a dilation	10-3F
8.G.12	Identify the properties preserved and not preserved under a reflection, rotation, translation, and dilation	10-3, 10-3F

Students will apply coordinate geometry to analyze problem solving situations.

Coordinate Geometry

8.G.13*	Determine the slope of a line from a graph and explain the meaning of slope as a constant rate of change	8-4, 8-5P, 8-5
8.G.14*	Determine the y-intercept of a line from a graph and be able to explain the y-intercept	8-3

*Indicator is not tested on the Grade 8 Test.
RM = Reading Mathematics Feature, P = Preview Lesson, F = Follow-Up Lesson,
PS = Prerequisite Skills Appendix (pp. 706–723)

Strands and Performance Indicators		Student Edition Lesson(s)
8.G.15*	Graph a line using a table of values	1-7P, 1-7, 1-7F, **2-6, 8-2**
8.G.16*	Determine the equation of a line given the slope and the y-intercept	**8-6, 8-6F, 8-7, 8-8**
8.G.17*	Graph a line from an equation in slope-intercept form ($y = mx + b$)	**8-6, 8-6F**
8.G.18*	Solve systems of equations graphically (only linear, integral solutions, $y = mx + b$ format, no vertical/horizontal lines)	**8-9**
8.G.19*	Graph the solution set of an inequality on a number line	**7-3, 7-4, 7-5, 7-6**
8.G.20*	Distinguish between linear and nonlinear equations $ax^2 + bx + c; a = 1$ (only graphically)	**13-5**
8.G.21*	Recognize the characteristics of quadratics in tables, graphs, equations, and situations	**13-6, 13-6F**

STRAND	MEASUREMENT

Students will determine what can be measured and how, using appropriate methods and formulas.

Units of Measurement

8.M.1	Solve equations/proportions to convert to equivalent measurements within metric and customary measurement systems *Note: Also allow Fahrenheit to Celsius and vice versa.*	PS13, PS14

*Indicator is not tested on the Grade 8 Test.
RM = Reading Mathematics Feature, P = Preview Lesson, F = Follow-Up Lesson,
PS = Prerequisite Skills Appendix (pp. 706–723)

Phillipsburg Manor, Sleepy Hollow

Prepare for the New York Test

Countdown to the New York Test

Pages NY10–NY30 of this text include a section called **Countdown to the New York Test.** The practice problems on these pages specifically address the New York Mathematics Performance Indicators that are assessed on the Grade 8 New York Test. Because the Grade 8 Test covers Indicators taught at the end of Grade 7 and Indicators taught at the beginning of Grade 8, the Countdown is written to address these Indicators.

Countdown to the New York Test

You should plan to complete one practice set each week to help you review the Grade 7 Post-March and Grade 8 Pre-March Mathematics Performance Indicators.

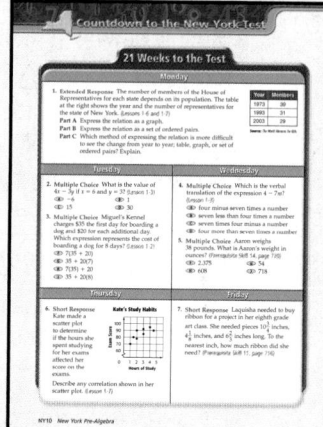

One-a-Day

Plan to spend a few minutes each day working on the practice problem(s) for that day unless your teacher asks you to do otherwise.

Reviewing Skills

If you have difficulty with any problem, you can refer to the lesson that is referenced in parentheses after the problem.

Record Answers

Your teacher can provide you with an answer sheet to record your work and your answers for each week. A printable answer sheet is also available at ny.pre-alg.com. At the end of the week, your teacher may want you to turn in the answer sheet.

Pacing

The questions in the Countdown to the New York Test are sequentially aligned with the sequence of the Student Edition so students may integrate this practice as they progress through the text.

Answer Sheet

The answer sheet shown is available at ny.pre-alg.com.

The Lessons

Each lesson tells you which New York Mathematics Performance Indicator is being covered. The **boldface** type pinpoints exactly what part(s) of the Indicator is addressed in the lesson.

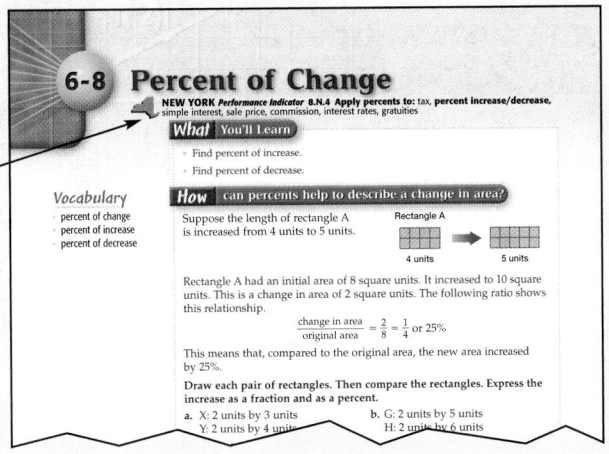

New York Review Series, Grade 8 Mathematics

The New York Review Series, Grade 8 Mathematics is an alternate student text that focuses on each of the New York Grade 8 Mathematics Performance Indicators. Worked-out examples and practice exercises in the format of the New York Test provide for content mastery.

Your textbook also gives you many opportunities to master the Grade 8 Mathematics Performance Indicators. Take time each day to do at least one sample problem either from the Countdown or from the lesson you are studying.

- **Each lesson** contains at least one practice problem that is similar to ones found on the New York test.

- **Worked-out examples** in each chapter show you step-by-step solutions of problems that are similar to ones found on the New York test. **Test-Taking Tips** are also included.

- The **Mid-Chapter Practice Test** and **Chapter Practice Test** also include practice test problems.

- Two pages of **Standardized Test Practice** are included at the end of each chapter. These problems may cover any of the content up to and including the chapter they follow.

- The **Preparing for the Standardized Tests** section of your textbook on pages 771–788 discusses various strategies for attacking questions like those that appear on the New York test. Additional practice problems are also available.

Monday

1A.

1B. (1973, 39), (1993, 31), (2003, 29)

1C. Answers will vary. Possible answer: ordered pairs. The ordered pairs do not show the data organized visually.

Thursday

6. As the number of hours increase, the scores on the exams increase. The data shows a positive correlation.

---

21 Weeks to the Test

Monday

1. Extended Response The number of members of the House of Representatives for each state depends on its population. The table at the right shows the year and the number of representatives for the state of New York. (Lessons 1-6 and 1-7) **See margin.**

Year	Members
1973	39
1993	31
2003	29

Source: *The World Almanac for Kids*

Part A Express the relation as a graph.
Part B Express the relation as a set of ordered pairs.
Part C Which method of expressing the relation is more difficult to see the change from year to year; table, graph, or set of ordered pairs? Explain.

Tuesday

2. Multiple Choice What is the value of $4x - 3y$ if $x = 6$ and $y = 3$? (Lesson 1-3) **C**
- Ⓐ −6
- Ⓑ 1
- Ⓒ 15
- Ⓓ 30

3. Multiple Choice Miguel's Kennel charges $35 the first day for boarding a dog and $20 for each additional day. Which expression represents the cost of boarding a dog for 8 days? (Lesson 1-2) **G**
- Ⓕ $7(35 + 20)$
- Ⓖ $35 + 20(7)$
- Ⓗ $7(35) + 20$
- Ⓙ $35 + 20(8)$

Wednesday

4. Multiple Choice Which is the verbal translation of the expression $4 - 7m$? (Lesson 1-3) **A**
- Ⓐ four minus seven times a number
- Ⓑ seven less than four times a number
- Ⓒ seven times four minus a number
- Ⓓ four more than seven times a number

5. Multiple Choice Aaron weighs 38 pounds. What is Aaron's weight in ounces? (Prerequisite Skill 14, page 720) **H**
- Ⓕ 2.375
- Ⓖ 54
- Ⓗ 608
- Ⓙ 718

Thursday

6. Short Response Kate made a scatter plot to determine if the hours she spent studying for her exams affected her score on the exams.

Kate's Study Habits

Describe any correlation shown in her scatter plot. (Lesson 1-7) **See margin.**

Friday

7. Short Response Laquisha needed to buy ribbon for a project in her eighth grade art class. She needed pieces $10\frac{3}{4}$ inches, $4\frac{1}{8}$ inches, and $6\frac{2}{3}$ inches long. To the nearest inch, how much ribbon did she need? (Prerequisite Skill 11, page 716)
22 inches

Performance Indicators Addressed

Monday	(1A) 8.A.15; (1B) 8.A.15; (1C) 8.A.15
Tuesday	(2) 8.N.2; (3) 8.A.2
Wednesday	(4) 8.A.2; (5) 8.M.1
Thursday	(6) 8.A.3
Friday	(7) 8.N.6

20 Weeks to the Test

Monday

1. **Extended Response** Juan compared the statistics for some of the softball teams in his league. He found that all teams in the league played 12 games. Let x represent the number of wins for each team and y represent the number of losses for each team. (Lessons 1-3 and 2-6) **See margin.**
   Part A Write an equation for the number of losses.
   Part B Make a table of four possible values for x and y. Explain how you determined these values for x and y.
   Part C Graph the ordered pairs in the first quadrant of a coordinate plane. Connect the ordered pairs to form a line. Explain what the line represents.

Tuesday

2. **Multiple Choice** Cara can run at a pace of 6.2 miles per hour. At this rate, about how far can she run in half an hour? (Prerequisite Skill 9, page 714) **B**
   Ⓐ 1 mile
   Ⓑ 3 miles
   Ⓒ 12 miles
   Ⓓ 18 miles

3. **Multiple Choice** Which is another way to express the relation shown in the graph? (Lesson 1-6) **J**

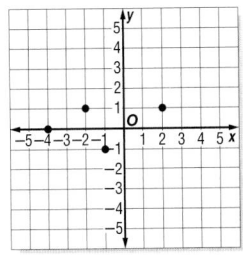

   Ⓕ {(−1, −1), (2, 1), (−2, −1), (−4, 0)}
   Ⓖ {(−1, 1), (2, 1), (−2, 1), (−4, 0)}
   Ⓗ {(−1, 1), (2, 1), (−2, −1), (−4, 0)}
   Ⓙ {(−1, −1), (2, 1), (−2, 1), (−4, 0)}

Wednesday

4. **Multiple Choice** The Statue of Liberty was built in France and brought to the United States in 350 pieces. The length of the statue's nose is 4 feet 6 inches. How many inches long is the nose? (Prerequisite Skill 14, page 720) **D**
   Ⓐ 10
   Ⓑ 46
   Ⓒ 48
   Ⓓ 54

5. **Multiple Choice** Which verbal sentence matches the equation $d - 15 = 73$? (Lesson 1-5) **H**
   Ⓕ Seventy-three is the sum of 15 and some number.
   Ⓖ Seventy-three and 15 is the difference of a number.
   Ⓗ Fifteen less than a number is seventy-three.
   Ⓙ A number less than 15 is 73.

Thursday

6. **Short Response** Li made 62 bracelets to sell at the beach. On Saturday, she sold 14 bracelets. On Sunday and Monday, she sold 31. At the end of Monday, Li stated that she had sold more than half of the bracelets made. Was her estimate reasonable? Explain. (Lesson 2-3) **See margin.**

Friday

7. **Short Response** Ving wanted the teller at the bank to exchange his 200 U.S. dollars for euros. The exchange rate board showed $1 U.S. = 0.775434 Euro. How much did Ving get from the teller in euros, to the nearest euro? Show your work. (Prerequisite Skill) **200 × 0.775434 = 155.087; 155 euros**

Performance Indicators Addressed

Monday	(1A) 8.A.15; (1B) 8.A.15; (1C) 8.A.16
Tuesday	(2) 8.N.6; (3) 8.A.15
Wednesday	(4) 8.M.1; (5) 8.A.2
Thursday	(6) 8.N.6
Friday	(7) 7.M.7

Monday

1A. Sample answer:
$y = 12 - x$

1B.

x	6	3	10	4
y	6	9	2	8

I chose a whole number less than 13 for x. Then I subtracted that whole number from 12 to get the value for y.

1C.

Choose any whole number along the x-axis. The y-coordinate of the point on the line tells the number of losses out of 12 games.

Thursday

6. Yes; possible explanation: half of 62 is 31. She sold 31 on Sunday and Monday. The bracelets she sold on Saturday puts her sales over half of 62.

19 Weeks to the Test

Thursday

6. $nx + ny$; the price of tickets and refreshments for Nia's family

Monday

1. **Extended Response** The difference between the length of the main span of the Verrazano-Narrows Bridge in lower New York Bay and the length of the main span of the Bronx-Whitestone Bridge in East River New York City is 1,960 feet. The Verrazano-Narrows Bridge is 4,260 feet long. (Lesson 3-3)

   Part A Write and simplify an expression to find the length of the main span of the Bronx-Whitestone Bridge. **4,260 − 1,960; 2,300 feet**

   Part B The main span of the Brooklyn Bridge in East River New York City is 704 feet shorter than the main span of the Bronx-Whitestone Bridge. Write and simplify an expression to find the length of the main span of the Brooklyn Bridge. **2,300 − 704; 1,596 feet**

Tuesday

2. **Multiple Choice** Sabrina spent $144 for 4 pairs of jeans each of equal cost. Which expression represents the cost of one pair of jeans? (Lesson 3-4) **A**
   - (A) $144 \div 4$
   - (B) $144 + 4$
   - (C) 144×4
   - (D) $144 - 4$

3. **Multiple Choice** What is the value of $-3rt$ if $r = 2$ and $t = -5$? (Lesson 2-4) **J**
   - (F) -30
   - (G) $\frac{6}{5}$
   - (H) $\frac{15}{2}$
   - (J) 30

Wednesday

4. **Multiple Choice** Carlos charges $20 to rent his lawn tiller plus $4 per hour. Which expression can be used to determine the cost of renting the tiller for h hours? (Lesson 3-5) **D**
   - (A) $20h + 4$
   - (B) $h + 20$
   - (C) $(20 + 4)h$
   - (D) $20 + 4h$

5. **Multiple Choice** What is $5f + 14 + 2f - 8$ simplified? (Lesson 3-2) **G**
   - (F) $10f + 6$
   - (G) $7f + 6$
   - (H) $10f + 22$
   - (J) $7f + 22$

Thursday

6. **Short Response** Tickets to an amusement park cost x dollars. Refreshments for one person at the park cost y dollars. If Nia has n family members, explain what $n(x + y)$ represents. Write the expression without parentheses. (Lesson 3-1) **See margin.**

Friday

7. **Short Response** The perimeter of a geometric figure is the sum of the measures of its sides. Write an expression in simplest form for the perimeter of the figure below. (Lesson 3-2) **5x − 1**

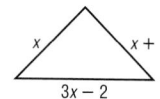

Performance Indicators Addressed	
Monday	(1A) 8.A.2; (1B) 8.A.2
Tuesday	(2) 8.A.2; (3) 8.N.2
Wednesday	(4) 8.A.2; (5) 7.A.2
Thursday	(6) 8.A.2
Friday	(7) 8.A.2

18 Weeks to the Test

Monday

1. **Extended Response** Let x represent the air mileage from New York City to Tokyo. The distance from San Francisco to Tokyo is 1,765 miles more than $\frac{1}{2}$ the distance from New York City to Tokyo. (Lesson 1-3)

   Part A Write an expression that represents the air mileage distance from San Francisco to Tokyo. $\frac{1}{2}x + 1,765$

   Part B Write an expression that represents the air mileage distance from New York City to Tokyo minus the air mileage distance from San Francisco to Tokyo. $x - \left(\frac{1}{2}x + 1,765\right)$, or $\frac{1}{2}x - 1,765$

   Part C The air mileage distance from New York City to Tokyo is 6,740 miles. What is the air mileage distance from San Francisco to Tokyo? **5,135 miles**

Friday

7. Isolate the variable terms on one side of the equals sign. Then divide each side by 5 so that the variable has a coefficient of 1.

$$12 - 2x = 2 + 3x$$
$$12 - 2x + 2x = 2 + 3x + 2x$$
$$12 - 2 = 2 - 2 + 5x$$
$$10 = 5x$$
$$2 = x$$
$$x = 2$$

Tuesday

2. **Multiple Choice** For which is the diagram below the best model? (Lesson 3-1) **D**

x	1	1
x	1	1
x	1	1

   Ⓐ $3(x + 2) = 3x$
   Ⓑ $3(x + 2) = 3x + 2$
   Ⓒ $x(3 + 2) = 3x + 2x$
   Ⓓ $3(x + 2) = 3x + 6$

3. **Multiple Choice** What is the fraction $\frac{6}{6,000}$ written as a percent? (Prerequisite Skill)
   Ⓕ 0.01%   **G**
   Ⓖ 0.1%
   Ⓗ 0.6%
   Ⓙ 6%

Wednesday

4. **Multiple Choice** Which set of ordered pairs is shown on the line in the coordinate grid below? (Lesson 2-6) **B**

   Ⓐ {(0, 0), (0, 1), (0, 2), (0, 3)}
   Ⓑ {(1, 2), (2, 3), (3, 4), (4, 5)}
   Ⓒ {(0, 1), (2, 4), (4, 2), (4, 0)}
   Ⓓ {(0, 1), (1, 0), (2, 4), (4, 2)}

5. **Multiple Choice** What is $11d - 8d$ simplified? (Lesson 3-2) **F**
   Ⓕ $3d$
   Ⓖ $19d$
   Ⓗ $3 + 2d$
   Ⓙ $11(d - 8)$

Thursday

6. **Short Response** At Milo's Grocery store, potato salad sold for $2 a pound. How many ounces could be bought for $1? (Prerequisite Skill 14, page 720) **8**

Friday

7. **Short Response** Describe in words how to solve the equation $12 - 2x = 2 + 3x$. Then solve the equation. Show your work. (Lesson 10-4) **See margin.**

New York Pre-Algebra NY13

Performance Indicators Addressed

Monday	(1A) 8.A.2; (1B) 7.A.2; (1C) 8.N.2
Tuesday	(2) 8.A.5; (3) 8.N.3
Wednesday	(4) 8.A.16; (5) 7.A.2
Thursday	(6) 8.M.1
Friday	(7) 7.A.4

Monday

1A. n^2

1B. The expression is $2 \cdot n \cdot n$, or $2n^2$.

1C. The expression is $(2n)^2$, or $4n^2$.

Friday

7. 6^3 times; Use the laws of exponents. $6^6 \div 6^3 = 6^3$

---

17 Weeks to the Test

Monday

1. **Extended Response** Alexis drew the plans for a garden she put in her backyard. The square garden was n feet by n feet. (Lesson 4-2) **See margin.**
   Part A Write an expression for the area of the garden.
   Part B If Alexis decided to double the length of one of the sides of the garden, by what factor will the area of her garden increase? Explain using an expression.
   Part C If Alexis decided to double the length of both sides of the garden, by what factor will the area of her garden increase? Explain using an expression.

Tuesday

2. **Multiple Choice** What is the value of $(mn)^{-2}$ if $m = 3$ and $n = 2$? (Lesson 4-7) **B**
   - Ⓐ -36
   - Ⓑ $\dfrac{1}{36}$
   - Ⓒ $\dfrac{1}{6}$
   - Ⓓ 36

3. **Multiple Choice** In 2003, the population of the state of New York was about 1.5 million more than 3 times the population of Tennessee. Which expression represents the population of New York in terms of the population of Tennessee t? (Lesson 1-3) **J**
   - Ⓕ $1 \times 6 + t$
   - Ⓖ $1,000,000t + 6$
   - Ⓗ $(6 + 1)t$
   - Ⓙ $6t + 1,000,000$

Wednesday

4. **Multiple Choice** What is the greatest common factor of $12m^2n^3$, $3mn$, and $15m^2n$? (Lesson 4-4) **A**
   - Ⓐ $3mn$
   - Ⓑ $15m^2n$
   - Ⓒ $24m^2n$
   - Ⓓ $60m^2n^3$

5. **Multiple Choice** Matthew made 102 cupcakes. On Wednesday he sold 13 cupcakes and made 9 more. On Thursday he sold 27 cupcakes. What is an estimate for the number of cupcakes he had left? (Lesson 2-3) **H**
   - Ⓕ 20
   - Ⓖ 50
   - Ⓗ 70
   - Ⓙ 80

Thursday

6. **Short Response** Evaluate the expression $a^2 + b^3$ if $a = -2$ and $b = 4$. Show your work and explain how you used the order of operations. (Lesson 4-2)
   $(-2)^2 + (4)^3 = 4 + 64 = 68$; The order of operations states to simplify the powers before adding.

Friday

7. **Short Response** How many times greater is the volume of the larger cylinder than the volume of the smaller cylinder? Explain your answer. (Lesson 4-6) **See margin.**

$v = 6^3 \pi$
cubic units

$v = 6^6 \pi$
cubic units

Performance Indicators Addressed

Day	Indicators
Monday	(1A) 8.A.2; (1B) 8.N.1; (1C) 8.N.1
Tuesday	(2) 8.N.2; (3) 8.A.2
Wednesday	(4) 8.A.10; (5) 8.N.6
Thursday	(6) 8.N.2
Friday	(7) 8.A.6, 8.N.1

16 Weeks to the Test

Monday

1. **Extended Response** Mishawn made a quilt made from squares that were equal in size. His finished quilt was 60 inches by 72 inches. (Lesson 4-4) **See margin.**
   Part A What possible sizes for quilt squares with whole number side lengths did Mishawn use so that he did not have to use part of a square? Explain.
   Part B How many quilt squares of each size answered in Part A did Mishawn need to make the quilt?

Tuesday

2. **Multiple Choice** What is the product of (r^4) and $(-3r^2)$? (Lesson 4-6) **B**
   - (A) $-3r^8$
   - (B) $-3r^6$
   - (C) $3r^2$
   - (D) $3r^6$

3. **Multiple Choice** Mr. James is fencing part of his yard to make a playground for his children. He knows the area of the part of the yard is $x^2 + 4x$. Which pair of factors could represent the length and the width of the fenced in part of the yard? (Lesson 4-4) **F**
   - (F) $x, x + 4$
   - (G) $x^2, 4x$
   - (H) $x, x + 2$
   - (J) $x, x + 4x$

Wednesday

4. **Multiple Choice** Which expression is equivalent to $\frac{(-3)(x^2)(x^3)}{x^4}$? (Lesson 4-5) **B**
   - (A) $-3x^2$
   - (B) $-3x$
   - (C) -3
   - (D) $\frac{-3}{x}$

5. **Multiple Choice** Which fraction shows $\frac{r^3 s^2 t}{r s^4 t^2}$ in simplest form? (Lesson 4-6) **F**
   - (F) $\frac{r^2}{s^2 t}$
   - (G) $r^4 s^6 t^3$
   - (H) $\frac{r^4}{s^6 t^3}$
   - (J) $\frac{r^2}{s^2}$

Thursday

6. **Short Response** In February 2005, *The Gates* were installed in New York City's Central Park. *The Gates* consisted of 7,503 saffron-colored fabric panels placed 5.5 to 18 feet apart along 23 miles of footpaths. Was the length of the footpath long enough for 15 feet to separate each panel? Explain your answer. (Lesson 4-4) **See margin.**

Friday

7. **Short Response** Carmen took a vacation to Niagara Falls. She spent part of the trip on the U.S. side and the other part on the Canadian side. Use the currency exchange rate table to determine the price in U.S. dollars of a $16 T-shirt bought on the Canadian side of the falls. (Prerequisite Skill) **$13.02**

Currency Exchange Rates February 2005	
1 U.S. Dollar	1.22910 Canadian Dollars

Monday

1A. 12 inches by 12 inches, 6 inches by 6 inches, 4 inches by 4 inches, 3 inches by 3 inches, 2 inches by 2 inches; 1 inch by 1 inch; The size of each square must divide evenly into 60 and 72.

1B. 30 12 inch by 12 inch squares, 120 6 inch by 6 inch squares, 270 4 inch by 4 inch squares, 480 3 inch by 3 inch squares, 1,080 2 inch by 2 inch squares, 4,320 1 inch by 1 inch squares

Thursday

6. Yes; 23 × 5,280 = 121,440 feet; 121,440 ÷ 15 = 8,096; There would be 8,096 − 7,503 or 593 feet left.

Performance Indicators Addressed

Monday	(1A) 8.A.10; (1B) 8.A.10
Tuesday	(2) 8.N.1, 8.A.6; (3) 8.A.10
Wednesday	(4) 8.A.6; (5) 8.N.1, 8.A.6
Thursday	(6) 8.M.1
Friday	(7) 7.M.7

15 Weeks to the Test

Monday

1. **Extended Response** Kevin decided to barbeque hamburgers for the student council picnic. Suppose that 1 hamburger used a pounds of ground beef and he bought a total of b pounds of ground beef. (Lesson 5-4)

   Part A Write an expression that can be used to find the number of hamburgers Kevin can make. $\dfrac{b}{a}$

   Part B Suppose each hamburger used $\dfrac{1}{3}$ pound of ground beef and Kevin bought $13\dfrac{2}{3}$ pounds of ground beef. How many hamburgers can he make? **41**

Tuesday

2. **Multiple Choice** Which shows the simplified form of $\dfrac{m}{6} \div \dfrac{m}{36}$? (Lesson 5-4) **B**

   (A) $\dfrac{m^2}{216}$

   (B) 6

   (C) $\dfrac{1}{6}$

   (D) $\dfrac{26}{m^2}$

3. **Multiple Choice** Which is the expression $8 \cdot 8 \cdot 8 \cdot m \cdot m \cdot m \cdot m$ written with exponents? (Lesson 4-2) **H**

   (F) $8m^4$

   (G) $8m$

   (H) $8^3 m^4$

   (J) $8^2 m^2$

Wednesday

4. **Multiple Choice** What is the value of $m - n$ if $m = 2\dfrac{1}{5}$ and $n = 1\dfrac{1}{6}$? (Lesson 5-5) **A**

   (A) $1\dfrac{1}{30}$

   (B) $1\dfrac{11}{30}$

   (C) $2\dfrac{17}{30}$

   (D) $3\dfrac{11}{30}$

5. **Multiple Choice** Gina's age is represented by the expression $3y - 4$. Jennifer's age is represented by the expression $2y + 8$. Which expression represents the sum of their ages? (Lesson 1-3) **F**

   (F) $5y + 4$ (G) $5y - 4$

   (H) $y + 8$ (J) $-y + 4$

Thursday

6. **Short Response** In Times Square on New Year's Eve, a 1,070 pound geodesic sphere begins to descend at 11:59 P.M. At midnight the ball reaches the bottom of the pole. How many inches does the ball descend each second? (Lesson 5-3)

   15.4 inches

   — 6 ft —

   77 ft

Friday

7. **Short Response** Is $(x^4)^{-2}$ equivalent to $(x^{-2})^4$? Explain your answer. (Lesson 4-7)

   Yes, $(x^4)^{-2} = x^{-8}$ and $(x^{-2})^4 = x^{-8}$.

Performance Indicators Addressed

Day	Indicators
Monday	(1A) 8.A.2; (1B) 8.N.2
Tuesday	(2) 8.A.6; (3) 8.N.1
Wednesday	(4) 8.N.2; (5) 7.A.2
Thursday	(6) 8.M.1
Friday	(7) 8.N.1

14 Weeks to the Test

Monday

1. **Extended Response** Ava sent her niece a present in a box that had a volume of $\frac{2}{3}$ cubic yard. (Lesson 5-3)

   Part A What is the volume of the box in cubic **feet**? **18 cubic feet**

   Part B After putting the gift in the box, Ava had 3 cubic feet of space left. How many cubic yards of space were left? $\frac{1}{9}$ **cubic yard**

   Part C One bag of packing peanuts fills $\frac{4}{5}$ of a cubic foot. How many bags will be needed to fill the rest of the box? **3.75 or 4 bags**

Tuesday

2. **Multiple Choice** Jerome used 20 cups of flour to make cookies. Each batch took $2\frac{1}{2}$ cups of flour. How many batches were made? (Lesson 5-4) **B**

   ⒜ 2 ⒝ 8
   ⒞ 10 ⒟ 50

3. **Multiple Choice** Which expression shows $(6x^4 \cdot x^3) \div 2x$ simplified? (Lesson 4-6) **H**

   ⒡ $12x^8$ ⒢ $12x^{12}$
   ⒣ $3x^6$ ⒥ $3x^{12}$

Wednesday

4. **Multiple Choice** What is the value of $\frac{m}{n}$ if $m = -2\frac{1}{4}$ and $n = 1\frac{1}{3}$? (Lesson 5-4) **B**

   ⒜ -3 ⒝ $-\frac{27}{16}$
   ⒞ $-\frac{16}{27}$ ⒟ 3

5. **Multiple Choice** What is the value of $6 \cdot n^2$ if $n = -\frac{1}{6}$? (Lesson 5-3) **H**

   ⒡ -1 ⒢ $-\frac{1}{6}$
   ⒣ $\frac{1}{6}$ ⒥ 1

Thursday

6. **Short Response** The graph shows the percent of people in New York City that used different types of transportation. Did **more** or **less** than $\frac{1}{4}$ of commuters drive alone? Explain your answer. (Lesson 5-1) **See margin.**

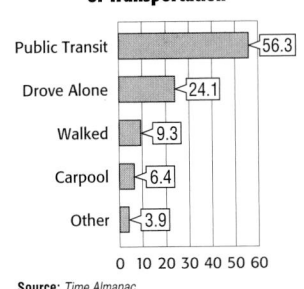

New York City Modes of Transportation

Public Transit 56.3
Drove Alone 24.1
Walked 9.3
Carpool 6.4
Other 3.9

0 10 20 30 40 50 60

Source: *Time Almanac*

Friday

7. **Short Response** The diagram below represents the state of New York. Albany is located near $(1, 0)$ on the grid and Buffalo is located near $(-2.5, 0)$. Plot these two cities on the grid. (Lesson 2-6) **See margin.**

Thursday

6. less; $\frac{1}{4} = 0.25$ and $0.241 < 0.25$

Friday

7.

Performance Indicators Addressed

Monday	(1A) 8.M.1; (1B) 8.M.1; (1C) 8.N.2
Tuesday	(2) 8.N.6; (3) 8.A.6
Wednesday	(4) 8.N.2; (5) 8.N.2
Thursday	(6) 8.N.5
Friday	(7) 8.A.15

Monday

1C. The jeans and the shirt would cost $(48 + 32)(0.75) = 60$ or $60. So he could afford them because $60 is less than $70.

Friday

7. Between 2 and 3 pounds; the price increases by $3.20.

Monday

1. **Extended Response** Tyler's department store is having a sale. Every item in the store is on sale for 25% off. (Lesson 6-6)

   Part A Keeli wants to buy a sweater that originally cost $44. What is the sale price of the sweater? **$33**

   Part B Miko spent $45 on a pair of shoes. What was the original price of the shoes? **$60**

   Part C Lee wanted to buy a pair of jeans that originally cost $48 and a shirt that originally cost $32. He had $70. Did he have enough to buy both items? Explain your answer. **See margin.**

Tuesday

2. **Multiple Choice** Which fraction is less than 1%? (Lesson 6-4) **A**

   Ⓐ $\frac{1}{150}$ Ⓑ $\frac{1}{60}$

   Ⓒ $\frac{3}{10}$ Ⓓ $\frac{6}{5}$

3. **Multiple Choice** Use the diagram of triangle QRS. Add 2 to each coordinate of the vertices of triangle QRS. What are the new coordinates of R? (Lesson 2-6) **F**

   Ⓕ $(5, 7)$ Ⓖ $(5, 5)$
   Ⓗ $(0, 3)$ Ⓙ $(7, 4)$

Wednesday

4. **Multiple Choice** Jorge drove to work at a speed of 25 miles per hour. How many feet per minute did he drive? (Lesson 6-1) **C**

   Ⓐ $\frac{25}{88}$ feet per minute

   Ⓑ $\frac{5}{12}$ feet per minute

   Ⓒ 2,200 feet per minute

   Ⓓ 132,000 feet per minute

5. **Multiple Choice** One of the largest subway systems in the world is located in New York City. It is nearly 850 miles long. How long is the subway system in feet? (Lesson 6-1) **J**

   Ⓕ about 0.16 feet

   Ⓖ about 6.21 feet

   Ⓗ 2,244,000 feet

   Ⓙ 4,488,000 feet

Thursday

6. **Short Response** Tameka invests $1,500 at an interest rate of 5% simple interest. How long will it take Tameka to earn $300? Show your work. (Lesson 6-7) **4 years;**
   $1500 \times 0.05 \times t = 300$
   $75t = 300$
   $t = 4$

Friday

7. **Short Response** The table shows the postage rate for mailing a letter from the post office to the addressee. Which pair of weights has the largest percent increase in price? Explain your answer. (Lesson 6-8)

Weight	2 lbs	3 lbs	4 lbs	5 lbs
Price	$17.85	$21.05	$24.20	$27.30

   Source: *Time Almanac*

   See margin.

Performance Indicators Addressed

Monday	(1A) 8.N.4; (1B) 8.N.4; (1C) 8.N.4
Tuesday	(2) 8.N.3; (3) 8.G.10
Wednesday	(4) 8.M.1; (5) 8.M.1
Thursday	(6) 8.N.4
Friday	(7) 8.N.4

12 Weeks to the Test

Monday

1. **Extended Response** Marcos is making a map of his neighborhood on a coordinate grid. (Lesson 2-6) **See margin.**

   Part A Marcos' house is located at $(-4, -2)$, and his school is located at $(4, 4)$. Plot these two locations on the coordinate grid.

   Part B Marcus used a scale of 1 unit = 50 yards on his map. How far does Marcus live from school? Explain how you found your answer and show your work.

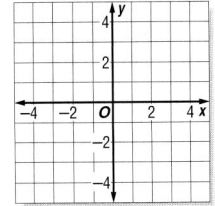

Tuesday

2. **Multiple Choice** What is the quotient of $(6m^3 - 4m^2 + 12)$ and $2m$? (Prerequisite Skill)

   Ⓐ $3m^2 - 2m + 6m$ **C**

   Ⓑ $3m - 2 + \frac{6}{m}$

   Ⓒ $3m^2 - 2m + \frac{6}{m}$

   Ⓓ $3m^3 - 2m^2 + 6m$

3. **Multiple Choice** Radio City Music Hall in New York City is the world's largest cinema with 5,910 seats. Jacquese went to a show on Friday when 76% of the seats were filled. About how many seats were filled? (Lesson 6-6) **J**

   Ⓕ 1,002   Ⓖ 1,478

   Ⓗ 4,120   Ⓙ 4,434

Wednesday

4. **Multiple Choice** Giselle had lunch at a restaurant. Her bill was $18. She left a 20% tip. How much money did she leave for the tip? (Lesson 6-6) **A**

   Ⓐ $3.60

   Ⓑ $4.00

   Ⓒ $8.00

   Ⓓ $21.60

5. **Multiple Choice** Which expression is equivalent to $15a + 9$? (Lesson 4-4) **H**

   Ⓕ $3(a + 3)$

   Ⓖ $9(a + 1)$

   Ⓗ $3(5a + 3)$

   Ⓙ $3a(5 + 3)$

Thursday

6. **Short Response** ESTIMATE the percent of the figure that is shaded. (Lesson 6-6)
   about 20%

Friday

7. **Short Response** Juanita can buy a 16-ounce box of cereal for $3.89 or a 21-ounce box of cereal for $4.50. Which is the better buy? Explain how you found your answer. (Lesson 6-5) **See margin.**

Monday

1A.

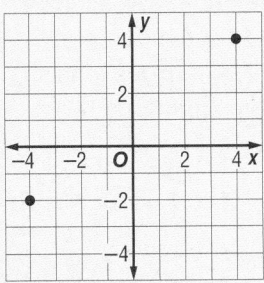

1B. Marco lives 500 yards from school.

Form a right triangle with length 8 units and height 6 units. Use the Pythagorean Theorem to determine the length of the hypotenuse to be 10 units.
$10 \times 50 = 500$

Friday

7. The 21-oz box is a better buy. The unit price for the 16-oz box is $3.89 \div 16$, or 0.243125. The unit price for the 21-oz box is $4.50 \div 21$, or 0.214286.

Performance Indicators Addressed

Day	Indicators
Monday	(1A) 8.A.15; (1B) 7.M.1
Tuesday	(2) 8.A.9; (3) 8.N.5
Wednesday	(4) 8.N.4; (5) 8.A.10
Thursday	(6) 8.N.5
Friday	(7) 7.M.6

Thursday

6. Between October and January; there was a decrease of 29.4 degrees over that four-month period.

11 Weeks to the Test

Monday

1. Extended Response Aaliyah spent *more than* $12 on refreshments at the amusement park on Friday. He bought some sodas for $2.50 each and a hamburger for $4.50. (Lesson 7-6)

Part A Write an inequality that describes this situation. Let x equal the number of sodas that he bought. **$12 < 4.50 + 2.50x$**

Part B How does the inequality change if *more than* is replaced with *at least*? **The inequality symbol changes to a less than or equal to symbol.**
$12 \leq 4.50 + 2.50x$

Tuesday

2. Multiple Choice Which shows $\left(\frac{3s^3}{t^3}\right) \div \left(\frac{6s}{t^3}\right)$ in simplest form? (Lesson 5-4) **D**

- **A** $\frac{18s^4}{t^5}$
- **B** $\frac{18s^2}{t}$
- **C** $3s^3t^5$
- **D** $\frac{s^2}{2}$

3. Multiple Choice What is the unit price of a 24-ounce sports drink that sells for $1.26? (Lesson 6-1) **H**

- **F** $0.65 per ounce
- **G** $0.525 per ounce
- **H** $0.0525 per ounce
- **J** $0.0025 per ounce

Wednesday

4. Multiple Choice Which inequality describes the following sentence? *Marcus needs to sell* at least *24 magazine subscriptions?* (Lesson 7-3) **B**

- **A** $x < 24$
- **B** $x \geq 24$
- **C** $x \leq 24$
- **D** $x > 24$

5. Multiple Choice Solve $3y - 9 = 6$ for y. (Lesson 3-5) **J**

- **F** $y = 10$
- **G** $y = 8$
- **H** $y = 6$
- **J** $y = 5$

Thursday

6. Short Response The line graph shows the average monthly temperature for Albany for four months. Between which two months shown was the largest decrease in temperature? (Lesson 6-8) **See margin.**

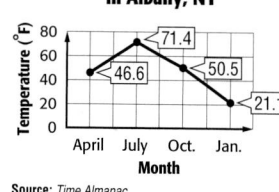

Average Temperatures in Albany, NY

Source: *Time Almanac*

Friday

7. Short Response In the year 2004, the New York state income tax for a married couple that makes $40,001 to $150,000 per year was 6.85%. Marsh and Todd's combined taxable income was $120,000 for 2004. How much did they pay in state income tax? (Lesson 6-7) **$8,220**

NY20   *New York Pre-Algebra*

Performance Indicators Addressed

Monday	(1A) 8.A.1; (1B) 8.A.1
Tuesday	(2) 8.A.6; (3) 7.M.5
Wednesday	(4) 8.A.1; (5) 7.A.4
Thursday	(6) 8.N.5
Friday	(7) 8.N.4

10 Weeks to the Test

Monday

1. **Extended Response** Terrell is making a rectangular platform to hold his science project. He wants the length of the platform to be 3 inches more than twice its width. He wants the perimeter of the platform to be no more than 6 feet. (Lesson 7-2) **See margin.**

   Part A Convert 6 feet to inches.

   Part B Write and solve an inequality for this situation.

Monday

1A. 6 feet = 6 × 12 = 72 inches

1B. $2(2w + 3 + w)$ < 72; $w < 11$; The width has to be less than 11 inches.

Friday

7. Each term is found by adding the two previous terms. The next three terms are 13, 21, and 34.

Tuesday

2. **Multiple Choice** What is the product of $\frac{m^2}{n}$ and $\frac{2n^2}{m}$ in simplest form? (Lesson 5-3) **A**

   Ⓐ $2mn$

   Ⓑ $\frac{m^3}{2n^3}$

   Ⓒ $2m^2n^2$

   Ⓓ $2mn^2$

3. **Multiple Choice** The perimeter of the rectangle below is less than 24 feet. Which inequality represents this situation? (Lesson 7-3) **G**

   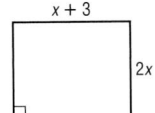

   Ⓕ $2x + x + 3 < 24$

   Ⓖ $2(2x) + 2(x + 3) < 24$

   Ⓗ $2(2x) + 2(x + 3) \le 24$

   Ⓙ $2(2x) + 2(x + 3) > 24$

Wednesday

4. **Multiple Choice** Regina can read 45 pages of a book in 30 minutes. What is her reading rate, in pages per minute? (Lesson 4-1) **D**

   Ⓐ 4.5 pages per minute

   Ⓑ 3.0 pages per minute

   Ⓒ 2.0 pages per minute

   Ⓓ 1.5 pages per minute

5. **Multiple Choice** Which inequality represents the situation below? (Lesson 7-3) **F**

   The Nine-spotted ladybug, which is the state insect of New York, is smaller than $\frac{1}{4}$ of an inch.

   Ⓕ $x < \frac{1}{4}$

   Ⓖ $x > \frac{1}{4}$

   Ⓗ $x \le \frac{1}{4}$

   Ⓙ $x \ge \frac{1}{4}$

Thursday

6. **Short Response** Melinda paid $210 for a set of 6 paintings. At this rate, how many paintings could Melinda buy for $1,000? Show your work. (Lesson 6-2)

   28; $\frac{210}{6} = \frac{1,000}{x}$; $210x = 6,000$; $x = 28.6$

Friday

7. **Short Response** A famous mathematical sequence is the Fibonacci sequence. The first few terms are 0, 1, 1, 2, 3, 5, 8, ... Describe the pattern used to generate each term of the sequence. What are the next three terms? (Lesson 5-10) **See margin.**

Performance Indicators Addressed

Day	
Monday	(1A) 8.M.1; (1B) 8.A.1
Tuesday	(2) 8.N.1; (3) 8.A.1
Wednesday	(4) 7.M.6; (5) 8.A.1
Thursday	(6) 7.M.5
Friday	(7) 7.A.8

9 Weeks to the Test

Monday

1. **Extended Response** A flea market charges $450 for each vendor to set up a booth. Meredith wants to rent a booth to sell her homemade rocking chairs. She earns a profit of $37.50 for each chair that she sells. (Lesson 8-5) **See margin.**

   Part A Write an expression for the net profit or loss if c chairs are sold.

   Part B How many chairs must Meredith sell in order to break even? Explain how you found your answer.

   Part C How much profit will Meredith earn if she sells 20 rocking chairs at the flea market?

Chairs Sold	Expression for Net Profit/Loss	Net Profit/Loss
0	37.50(0) − 450	−$450.00
1	37.50(1) − 450	−$412.50
2	37.50(2) − 450	−$375.00
3	37.50(3) − 450	−$337.50
⋮	⋮	⋮

Monday
1A. $37.50c - 450$

1B. $37.50c - 450 = 0$; Meredith must sell 12 rocking chairs in order to break even.

1C. $300

Thursday
6. $A(3, 3)$, $B(9, 9)$, $C(12, 6)$

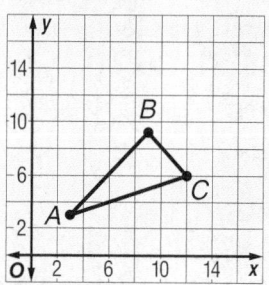

Tuesday

2. **Multiple Choice** What is the sum of the monomials $5a + 19a$? (Lesson 4-1) **D**
   - Ⓐ $14a$
   - Ⓑ $24 + 2a$
   - Ⓒ $24 + a$
   - Ⓓ $24a$

3. **Multiple Choice** Which segment represents the hypotenuse of right triangle ABC? (Lesson 9-4) **F**

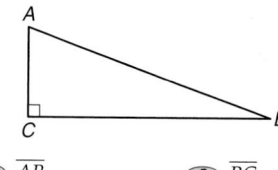

   - Ⓕ $\overline{AB}$
   - Ⓖ $\overline{BC}$
   - Ⓗ $\overline{AC}$
   - Ⓙ $\overline{BD}$

Wednesday

4. **Multiple Choice** What is the factored form of $x^2 + 5x + 6$? (Prerequisite Skill) **B**
   - Ⓐ $(x + 6)(x + 1)$
   - Ⓑ $(x + 2)(x + 3)$
   - Ⓒ $(x + 5)(x + 1)$
   - Ⓓ $(x + 6)(x + 6)$

5. **Multiple Choice** Deon bought a sweatshirt for $40. The New York sales tax on the shirt was 4%. About how much did he pay in sales tax? (Lesson 6-6) **G**
   - Ⓕ $0.50
   - Ⓖ $2.00
   - Ⓗ $38
   - Ⓙ $42

Thursday

6. **Short Response** Multiply each coordinate of the vertices of the triangle below by 3. Graph the dilation of $\triangle ABC$. (Lesson 10-3F) **See margin.**

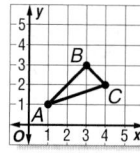

Friday

7. **Short Response** Tyrone is filling a goldfish pond at a rate of $4\frac{1}{2}$ gallons per minute using a hose. How long will it take him to fill the first 225 gallons of the pond? Show your work. (Lesson 6-1)

   $4.5x = 225$; $x = 50$ minutes

Performance Indicators Addressed

Monday	(1A) 8.A.2; (1B) 7.A.10; (1C) 7.A.4
Tuesday	(2) 7.A.2; (3) 7.G.5
Wednesday	(4) 8.A.11; (5) 8.N.5
Thursday	(6) 8.G.11
Friday	(7) 7.A.4

8 Weeks to the Test

Monday

1. **Extended Response** With each step, Antonio covers 2.5 feet of distance. (Lesson 8-2) **See margin.**

   Part A Use the table of values to write a function for the distance Antonio walks after taking s steps.

   Part B Plot the first ten data points of your function on a coordinate grid.

Steps	Distance (feet)
1	2.5
2	5
3	7.5
4	10
5	12.5

Tuesday

2. **Multiple Choice** Karen earned $150 for working 20 hours. What is her hourly rate of pay? (Lesson 6-1) **C**
   - Ⓐ $6.25 per hour
   - Ⓑ $6.75 per hour
   - Ⓒ $7.50 per hour
   - Ⓓ $9.40 per hour

3. **Multiple Choice** About how tall is the flagpole? (Lesson 9-5) **H**
   - Ⓕ 7.6 meters
   - Ⓖ 6.5 meters
   - Ⓗ 5.8 meters
   - Ⓙ 5.2 meters

   8.7 m
   6.5 m

Wednesday

4. **Multiple Choice** The average temperature in Buffalo for the month of May is 56 degrees. What is the average temperature in degrees Celsius to the nearest degree? (Lesson 3-7) **A**
   - Ⓐ 13°C
   - Ⓑ 93°C
   - Ⓒ 51°C
   - Ⓓ 133°C

5. **Multiple Choice** What is the value of $6x^2$ if $x = 5$? (Lesson 4-7) **G**
   - Ⓕ 60
   - Ⓖ 150
   - Ⓗ 600
   - Ⓙ 6,000

Thursday

6. **Short Response** Megan can buy an apple for $1 and a bottle of juice for $2. Find four solutions of the equation $x + 2y = 12$ to determine how many of each she can buy for $12. (Lesson 8-2)
   Sample: (2, 5), (4, 4), (6, 3), (8, 2)

Friday

7. **Short Response** Draw the image of the figure after it has been rotated 180 degrees. Write the new coordinates of each vertex. (Lesson 10-3) **See margin.**

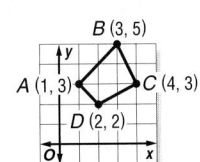

B (3, 5)
A (1, 3) C (4, 3)
D (2, 2)

Monday

1A. $f(s) = 2.5s$

1B.

Friday

7.

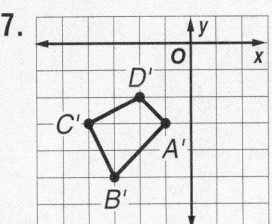

$A'(-1, -3)$,
$B'(-3, -5)$,
$C'(-4, -3)$,
$D'(-2, -2)$

Performance Indicators Addressed

Monday	(1A) 7.A.10; (1B) 7.A.7
Tuesday	(2) 7.M.5; (3) 7.G.8
Wednesday	(4) 8.M.1; (5) 8.N.2
Thursday	(6) 8.A.15
Friday	(7) 8.G.8

Countdown to the
New York Test

7 Weeks to the Test

Monday

1. **Extended Response** The area of the state of New York is 30,680,960 acres. The total area of federal land in New York state is 242,441.3 acres. (Lesson 6-4)
   Part A Estimate the percent of New York state that is federal land. **About 1%**
   Part B What is the actual percent of New York state that is federal land? Round to the nearest tenth of a percent. **0.8%**
   Part C Alaska is approximately 1,191% larger than New York. What is the area of Alaska in acres? Round to the nearest acre. **365,410,234 acres**

Thursday

6. Sample table:

x	−1	0	1	2
y	−4	−1	2	5

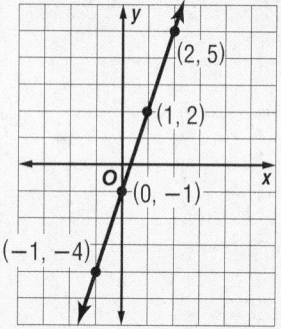

Tuesday

2. **Multiple Choice** Which expression can be used to find each value of b in the table? (Lesson 8-1) **B**

a	1	2	3	4	5
b	3	5	7	9	11

Ⓐ $2a - 1$
Ⓑ $2a + 1$
Ⓒ $3a$
Ⓓ $3a + 1$

3. **Multiple Choice** What value of x will form a right triangle? (Lesson 9-5) **H**

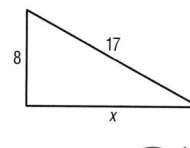

Ⓕ 11   Ⓖ 14
Ⓗ 15   Ⓙ 19

Wednesday

4. **Multiple Choice** Which equation can be used to find the lengths of the sides of $\triangle DEF$? (Lesson 9-5) **D**

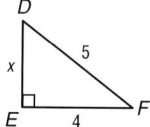

Ⓐ $x^2 = 5^2 + 4^2$
Ⓑ $5^2 = 4^2 - x^2$
Ⓒ $5^2 = (x + 4)^2$
Ⓓ $5^2 = x^2 + 4^2$

5. **Multiple Choice** Twice the sum of a number and 8 is greater than 42. Which inequality represents this situation? (Lesson 7-6) **H**
   Ⓕ $2n - 8 < 42$
   Ⓖ $2n + 8 > 42$
   Ⓗ $2(n + 8) > 42$
   Ⓙ $2n - 8 > 42$

Thursday

6. **Short Response** Make a table of ordered pairs for $y = 3x - 1$. Then graph the equation. (Lesson 8-2) **See margin.**

Friday

7. **Short Response** A school club earns money for each raffle ticket sold based on the table below. Write a function to show the amount of money raised for selling t tickets. (Lesson 8-7) **A = 1.5t**

Tickets	1	2	3	4
Amount Raised	$1.50	$3.00	$4.50	$6.00

NY24   *New York Pre-Algebra*

Performance Indicators Addressed

Monday	(1A) 8.N.5; (1B) 8.N.3; (1C) 8.N.4
Tuesday	(2) 7.A.8; (3) 7.G.9
Wednesday	(4) 7.G.6; (5) 8.A.1
Thursday	(6) 8.A.16
Friday	(7) 7.A.10

6 Weeks to the Test

Monday

1. **Extended Response** The graph at the right shows the sales of skateboards at Scott's Sports Store. (Lesson 8-4) **See margin.**

   Part A Which section of the graph shows the greatest increase in sales? Explain your answer.

   Part B Which section of the graph shows the greatest decrease in sales? Explain your answer.

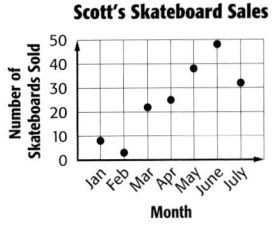

Scott's Skateboard Sales

Tuesday

2. **Multiple Choice** The New York Jets and New York Giants combined have won 3 Super Bowls. As of 2005, there have been 39 Super Bowls. About what percent of the Super Bowls have been won by the New York teams? (Lesson 6-6) **D**
   - ⓐ 0.8%
   - ⓑ 5%
   - ⓒ 7.7%
   - ⓓ 12%

3. **Multiple Choice** Which equation illustrates the use of the Pythagorean Theorem to determine if the given triangle is a right triangle? (Lesson 9-5) **H**

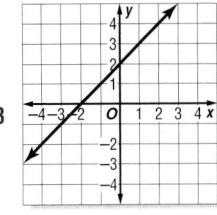

   - ⓕ $12.2 - 10 = 7$
   - ⓖ $12.2^2 - 10 = 7^2$
   - ⓗ $12.2^2 - 7^2 = 10^2$
   - ⓙ $100 + 49 = \sqrt{12.2}$

Wednesday

4. **Multiple Choice** Which equation represents the graph at the right? (Lesson 8-2) **B**
   - ⓐ $y = 2x - 2$
   - ⓑ $y = x + 2$
   - ⓒ $y = -2x + 2$
   - ⓓ $y = 2x + 2$

5. **Multiple Choice** Which statement is true about right triangles? (Lesson 9-4) **G**
   - ⓕ The hypotenuse is the short side of a right triangle.
   - ⓖ The right angle is opposite the hypotenuse in a right triangle.
   - ⓗ The legs of a right triangle must be equal lengths.
   - ⓙ The sum of the lengths of the legs of a right triangle must be less than the length of the hypotenuse.

Thursday

6. **Short Response** The 8th graders raised $320 more than half the amount raised by the 7th graders during a school fundraiser. If the 8th graders raised $910, how much did the 7th graders raise? Show your work. (Lesson 3-5)

   $1,180; $\frac{1}{2}x + 320 = 910$; $x = 1,180$

Friday

7. **Short Response** A rectangular soccer field has dimensions 80 yards by 120 yards. What is the distance from one corner of the field to the other corner across the diagonal of the rectangle? Show your work. (Lesson 9-4) **about 144.2 yards**; $80^2 + 120^2 = c^2$; $c = \sqrt{20.800}$

New York Pre-Algebra NY25

Countdown to the
New York Test

Monday

1A. Between February and March; there was an increase of 19 skateboards sold.

1B. Between June and July; there was a decrease of 16 skateboards sold.

Performance Indicators Addressed

Monday	(1A) 8.A.3; (1B) 8.A.3
Tuesday	(2) 8.N.3, 8.N.5; (3) 7.G.9
Wednesday	(4) 8.A.15; (5) 7.G.5
Thursday	(6) 7.A.4
Friday	(7) 7.G.8

Countdown to the
New York Test

5 Weeks to the Test

Monday

1. **Extended Response** Use the table at the right to answer each question. (Lesson 10-6)

   Part A What is the sum of the interior angles of a hexagon (6-sided figure)? **720 degrees**

   Part B What is the sum of the interior angles of a nonagon (9-sided figure)? **1,260 degrees**

   Part C Write an expression that can be used to find the interior angles sum for an n-sided figure. **180 $(n - 2)$**

Polygon	Number of Sides	Interior Angles Sum
triangle	3	180°
quadrilateral	4	360°
pentagon	5	540°
•	•	•
•	•	•
•	•	•

Tuesday

2. **Multiple Choice** Which type of angle pair is pictured at the right? (Lesson 10-1) **B**

   (A) alternate
   (B) complementary
   (C) supplementary
   (D) vertical

3. **Multiple Choice** Rectangle $MNPQ$ is drawn at the right. What are the coordinates of vertex M after the rectangle is rotated 180 degrees about the origin? (Lesson 10-3) **H**

   $M\,(1, 2)$ $N\,(3, 2)$
   $Q\,(1, 1)$
   $P\,(3, 1)$

   (F) $(-1, 2)$ (G) $(2, 1)$
   (H) $(-1, -2)$ (J) $(-2, -1)$

Wednesday

4. **Multiple Choice** Which of these transformations affects the size of the image? (Lesson 10-3) **A**

   (A) dilation
   (B) reflection
   (C) rotation of 90 degrees
   (D) rotation of 180 degrees

5. **Multiple Choice** What is the measure of angle A below? (Lesson 10-1) **H**

   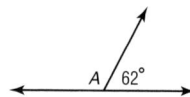
   $A\,/\,62°$

   (F) 28°
   (G) 62°
   (H) 118°
   (J) 242°

Thursday

6. **Short Response** The equation $y = 10x$ represents the cost, in dollars for x adults to take a ferry to the Statue of Liberty. Graph the equation. (Lesson 8-6)
   See margin.

Friday

7. **Short Response** Plot the values of the linear function $y = 2x - 1$ on a coordinate grid for the ordered pairs that have the following x-elements: -2, -1, 0, 1, 2. Explain how you found the data points. (Lesson 8-2) **See margin.**

Thursday

6.

Friday

7.

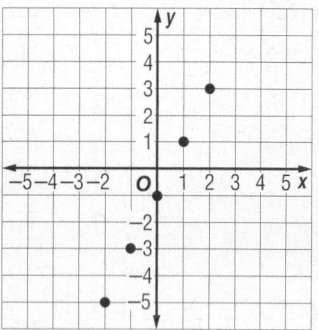

Substitute the values given for x into the equation and solve for y.

	Performance Indicators Addressed
Monday	(1A) 7.A.9; (1B) 7.A.9; (1C) 7.A.9
Tuesday	(2) 8.G.2; (3) 8.G.8
Wednesday	(4) 8.G.12; (5) 8.G.3
Thursday	(6) 8.A.4
Friday	(7) 7.A.7

Monday

1. **Extended Response** Pilar lives on the corner of Maple and Parker as shown at the right. Parker and Baylor are parallel streets. Maple and Oak are parallel streets. (Lesson 10-1)

   Part A Which other intersection meets at the same angle as the angle formed at Pilar's house? **See margin.**

   Part B If the angle formed in Pilar's yard by Maple and Parker is 96 degrees, what is the measure of the angle formed where Parker and Oak meet? Explain your answer.

   Part C List all of the angle measures that you know if the angle formed in Pilar's yard by Maple and Parker is 96 degrees.

Tuesday

2. **Multiple Choice** In the diagram at the right, which pair of angles is congruent? (Lesson 10-1) **D**

   Ⓐ 1 and 2   Ⓑ 2 and 3
   Ⓒ 3 and 4   Ⓓ 1 and 3

3. **Multiple Choice** Below is a map of the state of New York. If you reflect the map over the y-axis, what are the new coordinates of Albany? (Lesson 10-3) **F**

   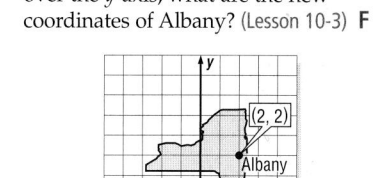

   Ⓕ (−2, 2)   Ⓖ (−2, 0)
   Ⓗ (2, −2)   Ⓙ (−2, −2)

Wednesday

4. **Multiple Choice** Ashley is building a bridge across a stream in her backyard. The pieces of wood marked A and B are parallel. Which of the statements below is true? (Lesson 10-1) **B**

   Ⓐ r is equal to s
   Ⓑ r is equal to u
   Ⓒ u is equal to s
   Ⓓ t is equal to u

5. **Multiple Choice** What is the value of x in the diagram? (Lesson 10-1) **H**

   $6x + 4$ $7x − 11$

   Ⓕ $\frac{15}{3}$ Ⓖ 3
   Ⓗ 15   Ⓙ 34

Thursday

6. **Short Response** What number is missing from the table of function values? Explain how you found your answer. (Lesson 11-2) **9; the function is $f(x) = 2x + 3$**

x	−3	−1	1	3	5
f(x)	−3	1	5	?	13

Friday

7. **Short Response** A drawing of Pedro's fence is shown at the right. Find all angle measures. Explain how you found the measures. (Lesson 10-1) **See margin.**

   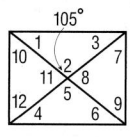

Monday

1A. angles *N* (vertical angle), *M* (corresponding angle), *J* (alternate exterior), *B* (corresponding), *D* (vertical to *B*), *G* (corresponding to *B*) and *H* (vertical to *G*)

1B. 96 degrees because it is a corresponding angle

1C. Angles *N, M, J, B, D, G,* and *H* are all 96 degrees. Angles *A, O, L, K, C, E, F,* and *I* are all 84 degrees.

Friday

7. Angle 5 = 105 degrees by vertical angles. Angles 11 and 8 = 75 degrees because they are supplementary angles.

Performance Indicators Addressed

Monday	(1A) 8.G.4; (1B) 8.G.5; (1C) 8.G.6
Tuesday	(2) 8.G.1; (3) 8.G.9
Wednesday	(4) 8.G.5; (5) 8.A.12, 8.G.1
Thursday	(6) 7.A.8
Friday	(7) 8.G.1, 8.G.2, 8.G.3, 8.G.4, 8.G.5, 8.G.6

3 Weeks to the Test

Monday

Monday

1A. The distance from the top of the building to the surveyor is the hypotenuse of a right triangle. The distance from the surveyor to the center of the building's base is one of the legs, and the height of the building is the other leg. The surveyor can use the Pythagorean Theorem to solve for the height of the Empire State Building.

1B. about 1,450 feet

Friday

7. $3x^2y - 4x + 2$; To find the length, divide the area by the width: $(9x^3y^2 - 12x^2y + 6xy) \div 3xy = 3x^2y - 4x + 2$

---

1. **Extended Response** The Empire State Building in Manhattan is one of the most prominent skyscrapers in the world. When a surveyor stands at a distance of 500 feet from the center of the building's base, her laser range finder calculates the distance to the top of the building as 1,533.8 feet. (Lesson 3-5) **See margin.**
   Part A Explain how the surveyor can use the properties of right triangles to solve for the height of the Empire State Building.
   Part B About how tall is the building?

1,533.8 ft
500 ft

Tuesday

2. **Multiple Choice**
   What are the measures of the angles at the right? (Lesson 10-1) **A**

   $15x + 30$ / $10x$
   - Ⓐ 60, 120
   - Ⓑ 30, 100
   - Ⓒ 90, 90
   - Ⓓ 80, 110

3. **Multiple Choice**
   When the figure at the right is dilated by a factor of 2, what are the coordinates of A? (Lesson 10-3) **G**

   A (1, 3)
   - Ⓕ (1, 6)
   - Ⓖ (2, 6)
   - Ⓗ (2, 3)
   - Ⓙ (3, 5)

Wednesday

4. **Multiple Choice**
   Corinna makes quilts as a hobby. Part of her quilt has the design at the right. What is the measure of angle A? (Lesson 10-1) **B**
   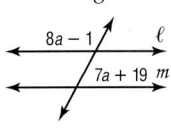
   A 94°
   - Ⓐ 36 degrees
   - Ⓑ 86 degrees
   - Ⓒ 94 degrees
   - Ⓓ 104 degrees

5. **Multiple Choice**
   Lines ℓ and m are parallel. What is the value of a in the diagram at the right? (Lesson 10-1) **H**

   $8a - 1$ ℓ
   $7a + 19$ m
   - Ⓕ 6
   - Ⓖ 10
   - Ⓗ 20
   - Ⓙ 159

Thursday

6. **Short Response** Diego is making a poster for his language arts project. He wants the width of the poster to be $x - 2$ feet. The area of the poster will be $x^2 + 4x - 12$ square feet. Factor the expression $x^2 + 4x - 12$ to find the length of his poster. (Lesson 13-1)
   $x^2 + 4x - 12 = (x + 6)(x - 2)$. **The length of the poster will be $x + 6$ feet.**

Friday

7. **Short Response** The area of the rectangle below is given by the polynomial $9x^3y^2 - 12x^2y + 6xy$. What is the length of the rectangle? Explain your answer. (Lesson 13-4) **See margin.**

   $3xy$ ▭

Performance Indicators Addressed

Monday	(1A) 7.G.6; (1B) 7.G.8
Tuesday	(2) 8.G.3; (3) 8.G.11
Wednesday	(4) 8.G.6; (5) 8.A.12
Thursday	(6) 8.A.11
Friday	(7) 8.A.11

2 Weeks to the Test

Monday

1. **Extended Response** Chloe designed a room above her garage. The length of the room was 5 feet shorter than twice the width. (Lesson 13-4) **See margin.**
   Part A Write an expression for the length of the room.
   Part B Write an expression for the perimeter of the room.
   Part C If the perimeter of the room is 110 feet, what are the dimensions of the room? Explain your answer.

Tuesday

2. **Multiple Choice** Suppose a figure is translated 2 units to the left and 3 units up. Which rule best describes this translation? (Lesson 10-3) **D**
   - (A) $(x, y) \rightarrow (x + 2, y + 3)$
   - (B) $(x, y) \rightarrow (x + 3, y - 2)$
   - (C) $(x, y) \rightarrow (x + 2, y - 3)$
   - (D) $(x, y) \rightarrow (x - 2, y + 3)$

3. **Multiple Choice** Which expression represents the area of the shaded portion of the figure at the right? (Lesson 13-1) **F**
   - (F) $3x - x^2$
   - (G) $x^2 - 3x$
   - (H) $x + 3 + x$
   - (J) $3x$

Wednesday

4. **Multiple Choice** What is the difference when $(2x - 1)$ is subtracted from $(5x - 2)$? (Lesson 13-3) **B**
   - (A) $-3x + 1$
   - (B) $3x - 1$
   - (C) $7x - 3$
   - (D) $7x - 1$

5. **Multiple Choice** Keenan saw that he could convert each of his U.S. dollars to 0.76 euros. How many euros could Keenan get for 500 U.S. dollars? (Prerequisite Skill) **H**
   - (F) 3,800
   - (G) 1,520
   - (H) 380
   - (J) 152

Thursday

6. **Short Response** Nadia paid $12x - 1$ dollars for a tea set 10 years ago. She sold it at a garage sale for $10x + 4$ dollars. In terms of x, how much money did she lose? Explain your answer. (Lesson 13-3)
   $2x - 5$

Friday

7. **Short Response** Below is a table of the attendance for different Broadway seasons. Make a graph of the data. Does the graph represent a linear or nonlinear situation? (Lesson 13-5) **See margin.**

Season	Attendance (millions)
2001–2002	11.0
2002–2003	11.4
2003–2004	11.6

Source: *The World Almanac*

Monday

1A. $2w - 5$

1B. $2(2w - 5 + w)$

1C. $w = 20$ and $\ell = 35$; solve the equation $2(2w - 5 + w) = 110$

Friday

7. **Broadway Attendance**

This represents a nonlinear situation because there is not a constant rate of change.

Performance Indicators Addressed

Monday	(1A) 8.A.2; (1B) 8.A.2; (1C) 8.A.15
Tuesday	(2) 8.G.7; (3) 8.A.8
Wednesday	(4) 7.A.2; (5) 7.M.5
Thursday	(6) 8.A.7
Friday	(7) 8.A.4

Countdown to the
New York Test

Monday

1A.

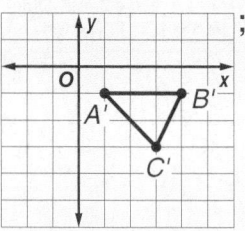

;

$A'(1, -1)$, $B'(4, -1)$,
$C'(3, -3)$

1B.

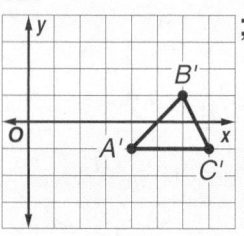

;

$A'(4, -1)$, $B'(6, 1)$,
$C'(7, -1)$

1C.

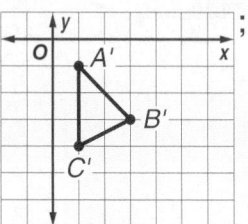

;

$A'(1, -1)$, $B'(3, -3)$,
$C'(1, -4)$

Thursday

6. A polynomial is an
expression containing
two or more terms.
Polynomial:
$7x^2 + 3x + 1$
Not a polynomial: 5

Friday

7. Nonlinear, there is
not a constant rate of
change.

---

1 Week to the Test

Monday

1. **Extended Response** Marianne is using the triangle pictured
at the right and transforming it to make a pattern on her wall.
(Lesson 10-3) **See margin.**

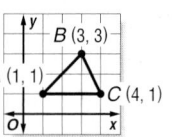

   Part A Draw the reflection of the triangle over the x-axis. Write
   the new coordinates of each vertex.

   Part B Draw the original triangle after it has been moved 3 units to
   the right and 2 units down. Write the coordinates of each
   vertex.

   Part C Draw the original triangle after a rotation of 90 degrees
   clockwise. Write the new coordinates of each vertex.

Tuesday

2. **Multiple Choice** Which of the following
expressions is a polynomial? (Lesson 13-1) **B**

   Ⓐ $\sqrt{3x}$ Ⓑ $9b^2 - 2b$

   Ⓒ $\dfrac{1}{2c + 8}$ Ⓓ $5^x - 1$

3. **Multiple Choice**
Ethan is making a
sandbox for his son.
What is the area
of the sandbox
pictured? (Lesson 13-4) **G**

   $3y - 2$

   $2y$

   Ⓕ $6y - 4$ Ⓖ $6y^2 - 4y$
   Ⓗ $5y - 2$ Ⓙ $10y - 4$

Wednesday

4. **Multiple Choice**
The perimeter
of the triangle
at the right is
$10x - 2$ units.
What is the length, in units, of the
missing side? (Lesson 13-3) **D**

   $6x + 1$ $3x - 1$?

   Ⓐ $x + 4$ Ⓑ $x - 4$
   Ⓒ $19x - 2$ Ⓓ $x - 2$

5. **Multiple Choice** What is the sum of
$(4x + 5)$ and $(x - 3)$? (Lesson 13-2) **G**

   Ⓕ $3x + 2$ Ⓖ $5x + 2$
   Ⓗ $x + 8$ Ⓙ $5x + 8$

Thursday

6. **Short Response** Define polynomial.
Give an example of a mathematical
expression that is a polynomial and an
example of one that is not a polynomial.
(Lesson 13-1) **See margin.**

Friday

7. **Short Response** The population of New
York for various years is listed below.
Suppose you graph the ordered pairs (year,
population). Would the graph be linear or
nonlinear? Explain your answer. (Lesson 13-5)

   See margin.

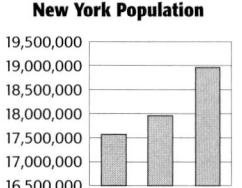

New York Population

Source: *The World Almanac*

Performance Indicators Addressed

Monday	(1A) 8.G.9; (1B) 8.G.10; (1C) 8.G.8
Tuesday	(2) 7.A.3; (3) 8.A.8
Wednesday	(4) 8.A.7; (5) 8.A.7
Thursday	(6) 7.M.6
Friday	(7) 8.A.4

Mathematics Reference Sheet—Grade 8

CONVERSIONS

Temperature Conversion

$F = \dfrac{9}{5}C + 32$

$C = \dfrac{5}{9}(F - 32)$

Measurement Conversions

1 mile = 5,280 feet

1 yard = 3 feet

FORMULAS

Pythagorean theorem

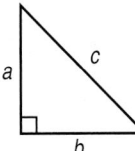

$c^2 = a^2 + b^2$

Simple Interest

$I = prt$

Distance Formula

$d = rt$

Slope-Intercept Form

$y = mx + b$

$m = slope$ and $b = y\text{-}intercept$

13-1b # Factoring Trinomials

NEW YORK *Performance Indicator* 8.A.11 Factor a trinomial in the form $ax^2 + bx + c$; $a = 1$ and c having no more than three sets of factors

How can factoring be used to find the dimensions of the garden?

$A = 54\ ft^2$

$P = 30\ ft$

Ask students:

• Why do you need to find two numbers whose product is 54 to find the dimensions of the garden? **The garden is a rectangle with an area of 54 ft². The area of a rectangle is equal to the length times the width. Since the area is 54 ft², the length and the width must be two numbers whose product is 54.**

• What two intergers have a product of 54? **1 and 54, 2 and 27, 3 and 18, 6 and 9**

• Which pair has a sum of 15? **6 and 9**

• What are the dimensions of the vegetable garden? **The garden is 6 ft by 9 ft.**

To factor some trinomials, you will use the pattern for multiplying two binomials. Study the following example.

$$\overset{F\quad O\quad I\quad L}{(x + 2)(x + 3)} = (x \cdot x) + (x \cdot 3) + (x \cdot 2) + (2 \cdot 3)$$
$$= x^2 + 3x + 2x + 6$$
$$= x^2 + (3 + 2)x + 6$$
$$= x^2 + 5x + 6$$

Use the FOIL method.
Simplify.
Distributive Property
Simplify.

Observe the following pattern in this multiplication.

$$(x + 2)(x + 3) = x^2 + (3 + 2)x + (2 \cdot 3)$$
$$(x + m)(x + n) = x^2 + (n + m)x + mn$$
$$= x^2 + \underline{(m + n)}x + \underline{mn}$$
$$x^2 + \quad bx \quad + c \qquad b = m + n \text{ and } c = mn$$

Notice that the coefficient of the middle term is the sum of m and n and the last term is the product of m and n. This pattern can be used to factor quadratic trinomials of the form $x^2 + bx + c$.

Key Concept — Factoring $x^2 + bx + c$

• **Words**   To factor quadratic trinomials of the form $x^2 + bx + c$, find two integers, m and n, whose sum is equal to b and whose product is equal to c. Then write $x^2 + bx + c$ using the pattern $(x + m)(x + n)$.

• **Symbols** $x^2 + bx + c = (x + m)(x + n)$ when $m + n = b$ and $mn = c$.

• **Example** $x^2 + 5x + 6 = (x + 2)(x + 3)$, since $2 + 3 = 5$ and $2 \cdot 3 = 6$.

Example 1 *b and c Are Positive*

Factor $x^2 + 7x + 12$.

In this trinomial, $b = 7$ and $c = 12$. You need to find two numbers whose sum is 7 and whose product is 12. Make an organized list of the factors of 12, and look for the pair of factors whose sum is 7.

Factors of 12	Sum of Factors
1, 12	13
2, 6	8
3, 4	7

The correct factors are 3 and 4.

Since 3 and 4 are factors of 12 and their sum is 7 we know that $m = 3$ and $n = 4$, so $x^2 + 7x + 12 = (x + 3)(x + 4)$.

NY32   *New York Pre-Algebra*

Tips for New Teachers

The concept of factoring trinomials as introduced in this lesson may seem somewhat abstract to some students. Whenever you introduce abstract concepts, it is good to reinforce them with a concrete example. After introducing factoring trinomials, refer students back to the lesson opener problem. Ask students to describe any similarities they notice between finding the dimensions of the garden and factoring a trinomial.

Example 2 *b Is Negative and c Is Positive*

Factor $x^2 - 22x + 21$.

In this trinomial, $b = -22$ and $c = 21$. This means that $m + n$ is negative and mn is positive. So m and n must both be negative. Therefore, make a list of the negative factors of 21, and look for the pair of factors whose sum is -22.

Factors of 21	Sum of Factors
$-1, -21$	-22
$-3, -7$	-10

The correct factors are -1 and -21.

So, $m = -1$ and $n = -21$.

$$x^2 - 22x + 21 = (x + (-1))(x + (x - 21))$$
$$= (x - 1)(x - 21)$$

Example 3 *b Is Positive and c Is Negative*

Factor $x^2 + x - 20$.

In this trinomial, $b = 1$ and $c = -20$. This means that $m + n$ is positive and mn is negative. So either m or n is negative, but not both. Therefore, make a list of the factors of -20, where one factor of each pair is negative. Look for the pair whose sum is one.

Factors of -21	Sum of Factors
$1, -20$	-19
$-1, 20$	19
$2, -10$	-8
$-2, 10$	8
$4, -5$	-1
$-4, 5$	1

The correct factors are -4 and 5.

So, $m = -4$ and $n = 5$.
$$x^2 + x - 20 = (x - 4)(x + 5)$$

In-Class Examples

1 Factor
$x^2 + 9x + 18$.
$(x + 3)(x + 6)$

Teaching Tip If students use the graphing calculator to check their factoring, make sure they clear all other functions from the Y= list, and clear all other drawings from the draw menu.

2 Factor
$x^2 - 12x + 27$.
$(x - 3)(x - 9)$

Teaching Tip Point out to students that whenever c is negative, either m or n must be negative, because if a product is negative, then one of the two factors must be negative.

3 Factor
$x^2 + 3x - 18$.
$(x + 6)(x - 3)$

4 Factor
$x^2 - x - 20$.
$(x - 5)(x + 4)$

4 Assess

Open-Ended Assessment

Speaking Ask volunteers to brainstorm a mnemonic device that will help them remember how to factor trinomials with different positive and negative values of b and c. Then write example trinomials on the chalkboard and have students factor them using the mnemonic devices as a guide.

Example 4 b and c Are Negative

Factor $x^2 + 18x - 40$.

Since $b = -18$ and $c = -40$, $m + n$ is negative and mn is negative. So either m or n is negative, but not both.

Factors of −40	Sum of Factors
1, −40	−39
−1, 40	39
2, −20	−18
−2, 20	18
4, −10	−6
−4, 10	6
5, −8	−3
5, 8	3

The correct factors are 2 and −20.

So, $m = 2$, $n = -20$, and $x^2 - 18x - 40 = (x + 2)(x - 20)$.

Exercises

Factor each trinomial.

1. $x^2 + 9x + 20$ $(x + 4)(x + 5)$

2. $x^2 - 7x + 10$ $(x - 5)(x - 2)$

3. $x^2 + 7x - 18$ $(x + 9)(x - 2)$

4. $x^2 - 2x - 3$ $(x - 3)(x + 1)$

5. $x^2 + 6x + 5$ $(x + 5)(x + 1)$

6. $x^2 - 10x + 21$ $(x - 7)(x - 3)$

7. $x^2 + x - 12$ $(x + 4)(x - 3)$

8. $x^2 - 13x - 14$ $(x - 14)(x + 1)$

9. $x^2 + 8x + 15$ $(x + 3)(x + 5)$

10. $x^2 - 4x + 4$ $(x - 2)(x - 2)$

11. $x^2 + 9x - 22$ $(x + 11)(x - 2)$

12. $x^2 - 6x - 7$ $(x - 7)(x + 1)$

13. $x^2 + 26x + 25$ $(x + 25)(x + 1)$

14. $x^2 - 12x - 13$ $(x - 13)(x + 1)$

15. $x^2 + 7x - 8$ $(x + 8)(x - 1)$

16. $x^2 - 2x - 35$ $(x + 5)(x - 7)$

Dividing Polynomials by Monomials

NEW YORK *Performance Indicator* **8.A.9 Divide a polynomial by a monomial (integer coefficients) Note: The degree of the denominator is less than or equal to the degree of the numerator for all variables.**

To divide a polynomial by a monomial, divide each term of the polynomial by the monomial.

Find $(3r^2 - 15r) \div 3r$.

$(3r^2 - 15r) \div 3r = \dfrac{3r^2 - 15r}{3r}$ Write as a rational expression.

$= \dfrac{3r^2}{3r} - \dfrac{15r}{3r}$ Divide each term by 3r.

$= \dfrac{\overset{r}{\cancel{3r^2}}}{\underset{1}{\cancel{3r}}} - \dfrac{\overset{5}{\cancel{15r}}}{\underset{1}{\cancel{3r}}}$ Simplify each term.

$= r - 5$ Simplify.

Exercises

Find each quotient.

1. $(3x^2 + 9x - 42x^3) \div 3x$ $x + 3 - 14x^2$

2. $(14a^2 + 7a - 28a^3) \div 7a$ $2a + 1 - 4a^2$

3. $\dfrac{9s^3t^2 - 15s^2t^3 + 24t^2s^4}{3s^2t^2}$ $3s - 5t + 8s^2$

4. $\dfrac{12a^3b + 16ab^3 - 8ab}{4ab}$ $3a^2 + 4b^2 - 2$

5. $15q^3 - 20q^2 + 10q \div 5q$ $3q^2 - 4q + 2$

6. $(12c^5d^6 + 36c^4d^4 - 42c^2d^5) \div 6c^2d^3$
   $2c^3d^3 + 6c^2d - 7d^2$

7. $\dfrac{33e^3f^5 - 11e^2 - f^2 + 22ef^5}{11ef^2}$ $3e^2f^3 - e + 2f^3$

8. $\dfrac{64x^4y^4 + 16x^3y^3 - 32x^2y^2 + 8xy}{8xy}$

   $8x^3y^3 + 2x^2y^2 - 4xy + 1$

9. $(12c^3d^5 - 24c^2d^6 + 48c^2d^7) \div 12c^2d$
   $cd^4 - 2d^5 + 4d^6$

10. $(72b^2c - 54b^2c^2 + 63b^3c - 18b^4) \div 9b$
    $8bc - 6bc^2 + 7b^2c - 2b^3$

11. $(39z^7 + 26z^6 - 52z^5) \div 13z^5$ $3z^2 + 2z - 4$

12. $(70r^3s^3 + 20r^4s^2 + 30r^7s^4 - 50r^8s^5) \div 10r^2s^2$
    $7rs + 2r^2 + 3r^5s^2 - 5r^6s^3$

13. $\dfrac{70m^5n^3 - 56m^3n + 84m}{14m}$ $5m^4n^3 - 4m^2n + 6$

14. $\dfrac{85k^4 - 51k^3n + 119k^2n^2}{17k}$ $5k^3 - 3k^2n + 7kn^2$

15. $(76p^6q^7 - 19p^5q^6 + 38p^3q^5 + 57p^2q^4) \div 19p^2q^3$
    $4p^4q^4 - p^3q^3 + 2pq^2 + 3q$

16. $\dfrac{14m^3no^2p^5 - 38m^2n^4op^8 + 6mn^7o^9p^{12}}{2mnop}$
    $7m^2op^4 - 19mn^3p^7 + 3n^6o^8p^{11}$

1 Focus

Have students discuss the definition of a monomial. A monomial is an expression that is a number, a variable, or the product of a number and one or more variables. Then have students describe how a polynomial and monomial are related. A polynomial is a monomial or sum of monomials.

2 Teach

In-Class Example

Find $(4x^2 - 18x) \div 2x$
$2x - 9$

3 Practice/Apply

About the Exercises . . .

Assignment Guide
Basic: 1–15 odd
Average: 2–16 even
Advanced: 1–16

4 Assess

Open-Ended Assessment

Speaking Have students work in pairs. Assign each student two polynomial division problems. Tell the students to study their problems for a few minutes to decide how the quotients should be found. Then ask the students to explain their decisions to each other, and discuss whether the methods chosen are correct.

GLENCOE
MATHEMATICS

New York
Edition

Pre-Algebra

Teacher Wraparound Edition

Malloy   Price

Willard   Sloan

 Glencoe

New York, New York
Columbus, Ohio
Chicago, Illinois
Peoria, Illinois
Woodland Hills, California

Teacher Handbook

Glencoe

The **McGraw·Hill** Companies

Send all inquiries to:
Glencoe/McGraw-Hill
8787 Orion Place
Columbus, OH 43240-4027

ISBN: 0-07-873315-4 (*New York Student Edition*)
ISBN: 0-07-869363-2 (*New York Teacher Wraparound Edition*)

Printed in the United States of America.

2 3 4 5 6 7 8 9 10 043/027 13 12 11 10 09 08 07 06

Contents in Brief

Authors

Carol Malloy, Ph.D.
Associate Professor of
    Mathematics Education
University of North Carolina
    at Chapel Hill
Chapel Hill, North Carolina

Jack Price, Ed.D.
Professor Emeritus,
    Mathematics Education
California State Polytechnic
    University
Pomona, California

Teri Willard, Ed.D.
Assistant Professor of
    Mathematics Education
Central Washington
    University
Ellensburg, Washington

**Leon L. "Butch"
Sloan, Ed.D.**
Secondary Mathematics
    Coordinator
Garland ISD
Garland, Texas

Contributing Authors

USA TODAY
The USA TODAY Snapshots®, created by
USA TODAY®, help students make the connection
between real life and mathematics.

Dinah Zike
Educational Consultant
Dinah-Might Activities, Inc.
San Antonio, Texas

Consultants

Mathematics Consultants

Rhonda Bailey
Mathematics Consultant
Mathematics by Design
DeSoto, Texas

Gunnar Carlsson, Ph.D.
Professor of Mathematics
Stanford University
Stanford, California

Ralph Cohen, Ph.D.
Professor of Mathematics
Stanford University
Stanford, California

William Leschensky
Former Mathematics Teacher
Glenbard South High School
College of DuPage
Glen Ellyn, Illinois

Yuria Orihuela
Mathematics Supervisor
Miami-Dade County Public Schools
Miami, Florida

Reading Consultants

Nancy Klores Welday
Language Arts Chairperson and
    Reading Resource Teacher
Hialeah-Miami Senior High School
Hialeah, Florida

Lynn T. Havens
Director
Project CRISS
Kalispell, Montana

ELL Consultant

Idania Dorta
Mathematics Educational Specialist
Miami–Dade County Public Schools
Miami, Florida

Teacher Reviewers

Teacher Reviewers

Each Teacher Reviewer reviewed at least two chapters of the Student Edition, giving feedback and suggestions for improving the effectiveness of the mathematics instruction.

Steven L. Arnofsky
Assistant Principal, Supervision
George W. Wingate High School
Brooklyn, New York

James M. Barr, Jr.
Teacher
Sells Middle School
Dublin, Ohio

Fay Bonacorsi
High School Mathematics Teacher
Lafayette High School
Brooklyn, New York

Rose H. Boothe
Subject Area Leader
A.J. Ferrell MST
Tampa, Florida

Diana L. Boyle
Mathematics Teacher, 6–8
Judson Middle School
Salem, Oregon

Beverly Burke
7th Grade Mathematics Teacher
USD 362
LaCygne, Kansas

Barbara A. Cain
Mathematics Teacher
Thomas Jefferson Middle School
Merritt Island, Florida

Rusty Campbell
Mathematics Instructor/Chairperson
North Marion High School
Farmington, West Virginia

Carol Caroff
Mathematics Department
  Chair/Teacher
Solon High School
Solon, Ohio

Vincent Ciraulo
Supervisor of Mathematics
J.P. Stevens High School
Edison, New Jersey

Lisa Cook
Mathematics Teacher
Kaysville Junior High School
Kaysville, Utah

Dianne Coppa
Mathematics Supervisor
Linden School District
Linden, New Jersey

Andrea L. Ellyson
Teacher/Department Chairperson
Great Bridge Middle School
Chesapeake, Virginia

James E. Ewing
7th Grade Pre-Algebra
Hiawatha Middle School
Hiawatha, Kansas

Eve Fingerett
Mathematics Teacher
Mountain Brook Junior High School
Mountain Brook, Alabama

Larry T. Gathers
Mathematics Teacher
Springfield South High School
Springfield, Ohio

Field Test Schools

Field Test Schools

Glencoe/McGraw-Hill wishes to thank the following schools that field-tested pre-publication manuscript during the 2001–2002 school year. They were instrumental in providing feedback and verifying the effectiveness of this program.

Burnett Middle School
Seffner, Florida

Carwise Middle School
Palm Harbor, Florida

Ft. Zumwalt Middle School
O'Fallon, Missouri

Graham Middle School
Bluefield, Virginia

John F. Kennedy Middle School
Bethpage, New York

McLane Middle School
Brandon, Florida

Martin Middle School
Raleigh, North Carolina

Parkway Southwest Middle School
Ballwin, Missouri

Safety Harbor Middle School
Safety Harbor, Florida

Teacher Handbook

Table of Contents

Designed to be in more

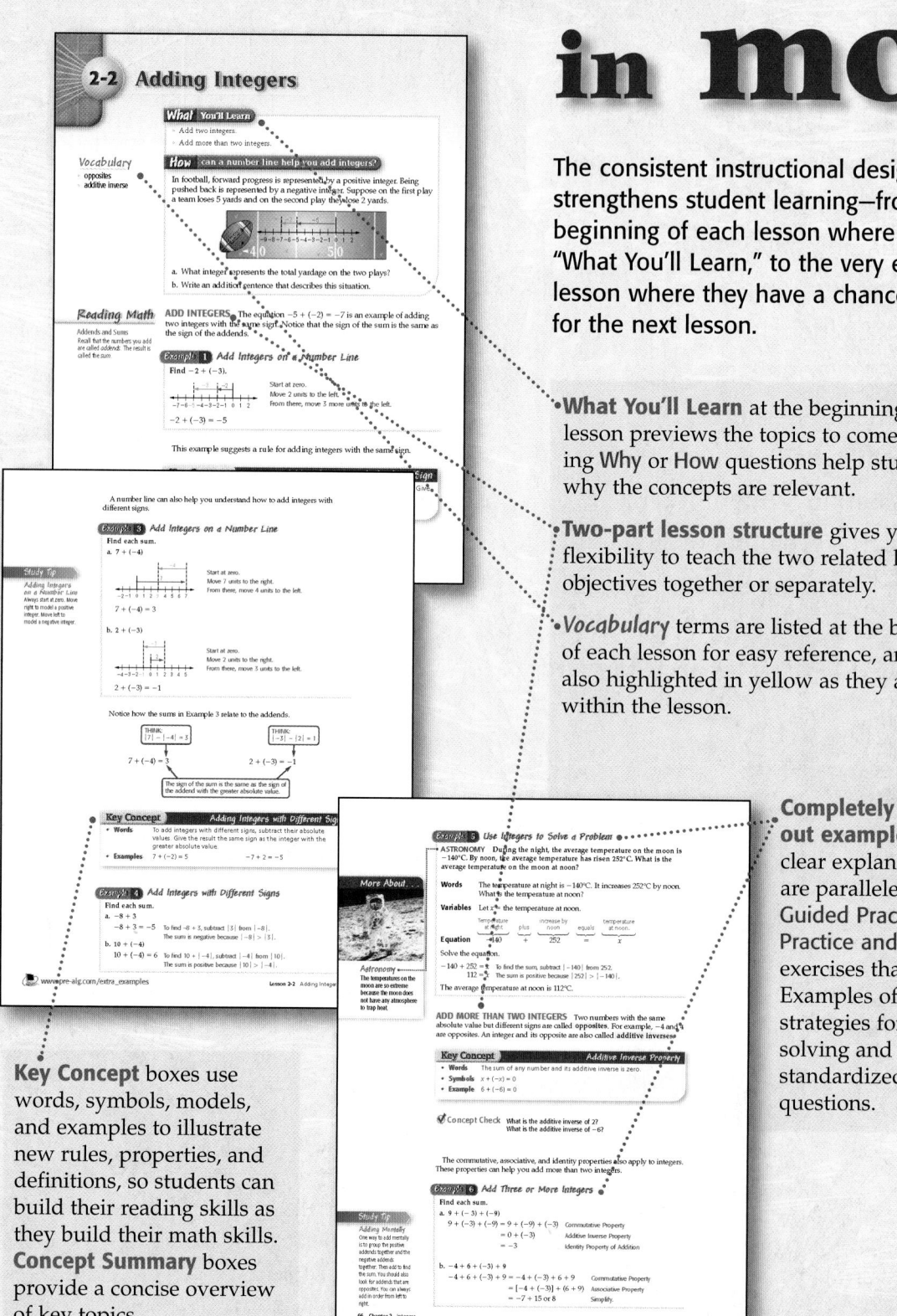

The consistent instructional design of the lessons strengthens student learning—from the very beginning of each lesson where students see "What You'll Learn," to the very end of each lesson where they have a chance to prepare for the next lesson.

• **What You'll Learn** at the beginning of each lesson previews the topics to come, and engaging Why or How questions help students see why the concepts are relevant.

• **Two-part lesson structure** gives you the flexibility to teach the two related lesson objectives together or separately.

• *Vocabulary* terms are listed at the beginning of each lesson for easy reference, and they're also highlighted in yellow as they appear within the lesson.

Completely worked-out examples with clear explanations are paralleled by the Guided Practice and Practice and Apply exercises that follow. Examples often include strategies for problem-solving and mastering standardized test questions.

Key Concept boxes use words, symbols, models, and examples to illustrate new rules, properties, and definitions, so students can build their reading skills as they build their math skills. **Concept Summary** boxes provide a concise overview of key topics.

effective, ways than one.

Check for Understanding

You can use this portion of exercises in class to ensure that all students understand the concepts.

- *Concept Check* exercises give students opportunities to define, describe, and explain the mathematical concepts they've just learned.

- *Guided Practice* presents a representative sample of the exercises in the Practice and Apply section. A key is provided in the **Teacher Wraparound Edition** that correlates the exercises with appropriate examples.

- *Application* problems give students the opportunity to use the skills they have learned in a real-world setting.

Practice and Apply

- **Skill Exercises** correspond to the Guided Practice exercises and are structured so that students practice the same concepts whether they are assigned odd- or even-numbered problems. Homework Help is provided so students can refer to examples in the lesson as they complete the exercises.

- **Applications** give students frequent opportunities to apply concepts to both real-life and mathematical situations.

- **CRITICAL THINKING** exercises in each lesson require students to explain, make conjectures, and prove mathematical relationships.

- *Standardized Test Practice* questions provide students with ongoing opportunities to sharpen their test-taking skills.
  (A) (B) (C) (D)

Maintain Your Skills

- *Mixed Review* includes spiraled, cumulative exercises from the two previous lessons as well as earlier lessons.

- *Getting Ready for the Next Lesson* exercises give students the chance to preview prerequisite skills for the coming lesson. A reference is provided should students need additional help.

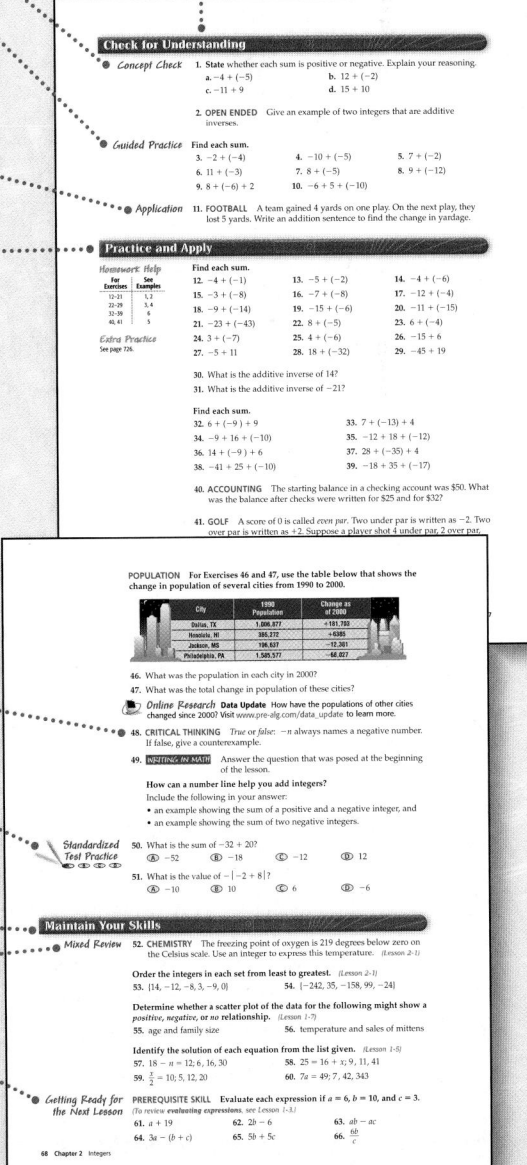

Accomplish more

Glencoe Pre-Algebra provides so many resources for lesson planning and teaching that you can create a complete, customized course in Pre-Algebra quickly...and easily.

This is where you start.

The **Teacher Wraparound Edition** is your key to all of the teaching resources in *Glencoe Pre-Algebra*. In addition to teaching suggestions, additional examples, and answers, the Teacher Wraparound Edition provides a guide for all of the print and software materials available for each lesson.

FAST FILE Chapter Resource
Masters contain all of the core supplements you'll need to begin teaching a chapter of *Glencoe Pre-Algebra*. Each chapter booklet features convenient tabs for easy filing.

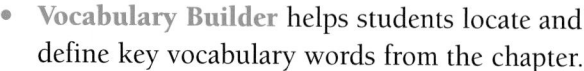

FAST FILE

- **Vocabulary Builder** helps students locate and define key vocabulary words from the chapter.
- **Study Guide and Intervention** summarizes key concepts and provides practice.
- **Skills Practice** provides ample exercises to help students develop basic computational skills, lesson by lesson.
- **Practice** mimics the computational and verbal problems in each lesson at an average level.
- **Reading to Learn Mathematics** provides students with various reading strategies to master the mathematics presented in each lesson.
- **Enrichment** activities extend students' knowledge and widen their appreciation of how mathematics relates to the world around them.
- **Assessment** options for each chapter include six forms of chapter tests, assessment tasks, quizzes, mid-chapter test, cumulative review, and standardized test practice.

Reading and Writing

WebQuest and Project Resources include teacher notes and answers for the Internet WebQuest projects with teaching notes, as well as other long-term projects that can be used with *Glencoe Pre-Algebra*.

Reading and Writing in the Mathematics Classroom features suggestions and activities for including reading as an integral part of the mathematics curriculum, as well as differentiated approaches to teaching mathematics that promote English learning and inclusion.

Teaching Mathematics with Foldables™ offers guidelines for

FOLDABLES Study Organizer

using Foldables interactive study organizers in your class. The booklet was written by Foldables creator Dinah Zike.

Applications

Science and Mathematics Lab Manual includes lab activity masters and teaching suggestions for integrating science into the mathematics classroom.

School-to-Career Masters feature activities showing how mathematics relates to careers.

Graphing Calculator and Spreadsheet Masters include activities to incorporate the TI-83 Plus calculator and spreadsheets into your Pre-Algebra course.

Real-World Transparencies and Masters feature colorful transparencies with accompanying student worksheets to show how mathematics relates to real-world topics.

Investigations for the Special Education Student includes investigations designed for students who are learning disabled, emotionally handicapped, autistic, or students with attention deficit disorder.

than you'd ever imagine

in less time than you'd ever believe

Assessment and Intervention

5-Minute Check Transparencies with Standardized Test Practice include a transparency for each lesson that evaluates what students have learned in the previous lesson. Each transparency also includes a standardized test practice question.

Closing the Gap for Absent Students provides an easy-to-use summary of all the materials you have covered in the chapter in a format that can be posted or distributed to students who have missed class.

DAILY INTERVENTION Guide to Daily Intervention offers suggestions for daily assessment and tips on how to help students succeed.

Prerequisite Skills Workbook: Remediation and Intervention includes worksheets to review the arithmetic skills needed in Pre-Algebra.

Staff Development

Answer Key Transparencies provide answers to Student Edition exercises.

Lesson Planning Guide features a daily resource guide for planning your curriculum, as well as pacing for block scheduling.

Solutions Manual includes completely worked-out solutions for all exercises in the Student Edition.

Using the Internet in the Mathematics Classroom provides guidelines for using the Internet, as well as a guide to additional mathematics resources available on the Internet.

Teaching Pre-Algebra with Manipulatives features activities and teaching suggestions to help you present algebraic concepts with manipulatives and hands-on materials.

Technology Support for Teachers

Glencoe offers many timesaving software products to help you develop creative classroom presentations...fast.

TeacherWorks All-in-One Lesson Planner and Resource Center CD-ROM includes a lesson planner and interactive Teacher Edition, so you can customize lesson plans and reproduce classroom resources quickly and easily, from just about anywhere.

Answer Key Maker software allows you to customize answer keys for your assignments from the Student Edition exercises.

Interactive Chalkboard CD-ROM includes fully worked-out examples, the 5-Minute Check Transparencies, and Your Turn problems in a customizable Microsoft® PowerPoint® format.

And more... Additional technology products and Internet resources for students, teachers, and parents are discussed on pages T6–T13 and T17.

HELP your students
become fluent

Glencoe Pre-Algebra makes it easy for you to incorporate constructive reading and writing strategies into every class you teach.

Reading Mathematics

Translating Verbal Problems into Equations

An important skill in algebra is translating verbal problems into equations. To do this accurately, analyze the statements until you completely understand the relationships among the given information. Look for key words and phrases.

> Jennifer is 6 years older than Akira. The sum of their ages is 20.

You can explore a problem situation by asking and answering questions.

Questions	Answers
a. Who is older?	**a.** Jennifer
b. How many years older?	**b.** 6 years
c. If Akira is x years old, how old is Jennifer?	**c.** $x + 6$
d. What expression represents the phrase *the sum of their ages*?	**d.** $x + (x + 6)$
e. What equation represents the sentence *the sum of their ages is 20*?	**e.** $x + (x + 6) = 20$

Reading to Learn

For each verbal problem, answer the related questions.

1. Lucas is 5 inches taller than Tamika, and the sum of their heights is 137 inches.
   a. Who is taller?
   b. How many inches taller?
   c. If x represents Tamika's height, how tall is Lucas?
   d. What expression represents *the sum of their heights*?
   e. What equation represents the sentence *the sum of their heights is 137*?

2. There are five times as many students as teachers on the field trip, and the sum of students and teachers is 132.
   a. Are there more students or teachers?
   b. How many times more?
   c. If x represents the number of teachers, how many students are there?
   d. What expression represents *the sum of students and teachers*?
   e. What equation represents the sentence *the sum of students and teachers is 132*?

Reading Mathematics   Translating Verbal Problems into Equations   **125**

Reading Mathematics activities help students master new mathematics vocabulary words and develop technical reading skills so they can understand and apply the language of math in their daily lives.

Student Edition

Foldables™ Study Organizers at the beginning of each chapter provide students with tools for organizing what they are reading and studying.

Reading Math Tips appear throughout each chapter, to help students learn and use the language of algebra.

Writing in Math questions in every lesson require students to use critical thinking skills to develop their answers.

Vocabulary terms are listed at the beginning of each lesson and highlighted when defined. The **Vocabulary and Concept Check** in each Study Guide and Review checks students' understanding of the key concepts of the chapter.

Key Concepts are illustrated using Words, Symbols, Models, and Examples, as appropriate. This approach improves reading comprehension by using multiple representations.

Concept Check provides an immediate opportunity to check students' comprehension before progressing to the next part of the lesson.

WebQuest Internet Projects are long-term projects that use problem-based learning to give students the opportunity to develop their research and creative writing skills.

in the Language of MATHEMATICS

Teacher Wraparound Edition

Study Notebook suggestions provide motivational ideas to help students create study notebooks that are thorough and effective.

Skill Check questions require students to describe, write, and explain the mathematical concepts they have learned in each lesson.

Modeling, Speaking, and **Writing** in every lesson require students to summarize what they have learned by responding to open-ended prompts.

ELL **Resources** highlight features and activities that help English-Language Learners grasp content.

Differentiated Instruction features help students at all points on the learning spectrum develop their reading, writing, and comprehension skills.

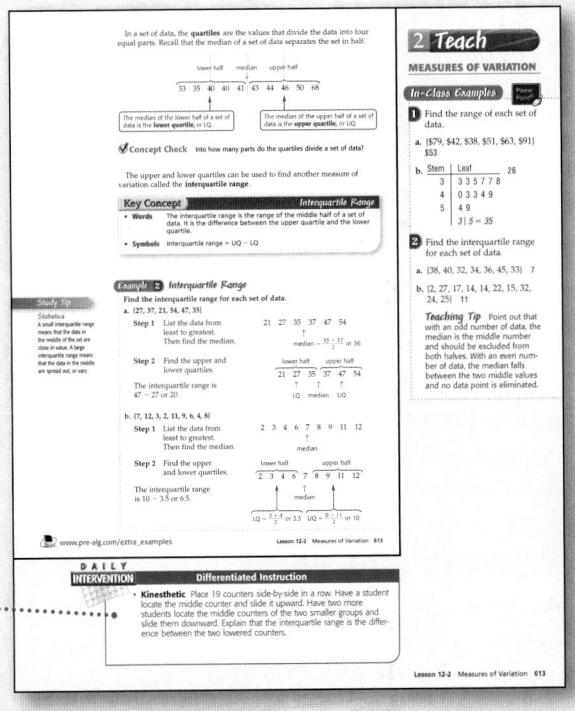

Technology Support

StudentWorks™, Glencoe's backpack solution, includes the entire Student Edition, formatted like the hardbound book, so students can study from just about anywhere—no book required. Students can also print their own lesson worksheet pages and get instant access to interactive web resources.

www.pre-alg.com/vocabulary_review is a Glencoe site that provides online study tools for reviewing the vocabulary of each chapter.

Vocabulary PuzzleMaker software creates crossword, jumble, and word search puzzles using vocabulary lists that you can customize.

Multimedia Applications: Virtual Activities CD-ROM provides in-depth interactive activities that help students explore the main concepts of each chapter in a real-world setting.

Additional Resources

Chapter Resource Masters

- Vocabulary Builder
- Reading to Learn Mathematics

Teaching Mathematics with Foldables™

Reading and Writing in the Mathematics Classroom

WebQuest and Project Resources

For more information on these products, see pp. T4–T5.

Quick Review Math Handbook: Hot Words, Hot Topics
is Glencoe's mathematical handbook for students. The Hot Words section includes a glossary of terms while the Hot Topics section consists of an explanation of key mathematical concepts. An exercise set is also included.

With these TOOLS,
you'll always know

Whether you need daily intervention resources integrated right into the program, or supplemental materials for after school and summer school programs, *Glencoe Pre-Algebra* puts it all right at your fingertips!

Diagnosis

Glencoe's **Diagnostic and Placement Tests** help you identify the key mathematical objectives that students are struggling with so you can make course placement decisions more effectively. A list of intervention resources is provided for each Glencoe program prior to and including *Glencoe Pre-Algebra*.

Prerequisite Skills

Students often struggle in Pre-Algebra because they have not mastered the prerequisite skills needed to be successful. *Glencoe Pre-Algebra* provides several opportunities to check student skills and determine which students need additional review and practice.

- The **Prerequisite Skills** at the beginning of every chapter help students identify and practice the skills they'll need for each new concept.

- Additional **prerequisite skills practice** is provided at the end of each lesson and includes page references to help students get extra review whenever they need it. More prerequisite skill practice appears in the Student Handbook section at the back of the Student Edition.

- The **Prerequisite Skills Workbook** provides extra practice on the basic skills needed for success in Pre-Algebra.

Daily Intervention Opportunities

Guide to Daily Intervention offers suggestions for using Glencoe materials to intercept students who are having difficulties and prescribe a system of reinforcement to promote student success.

The **Chapter Resource Masters** include several types of worksheets that can be used for daily intervention in each lesson. For a description of each worksheet, see page T4.

- **Study Guide and Intervention***
- **Skills Practice***
- **Practice***
- **Reading to Learn Mathematics**

  * *Each of these types of worksheets is available as a consumable workbook in both English and Spanish.*

The **Student Edition** contains additional problems to help students master each lesson before completing the chapter assessment.

- **Extra Practice**, located in the back of the Student Edition, provides additional, immediate practice with the concepts from each lesson.
- **Mixed Problem Solving**, also in the back of the Student Edition, includes numerous verbal problems to help students reinforce their problem-solving skills.

who needs EXTRA HELP.

And you'll be able to *DELIVER* it.

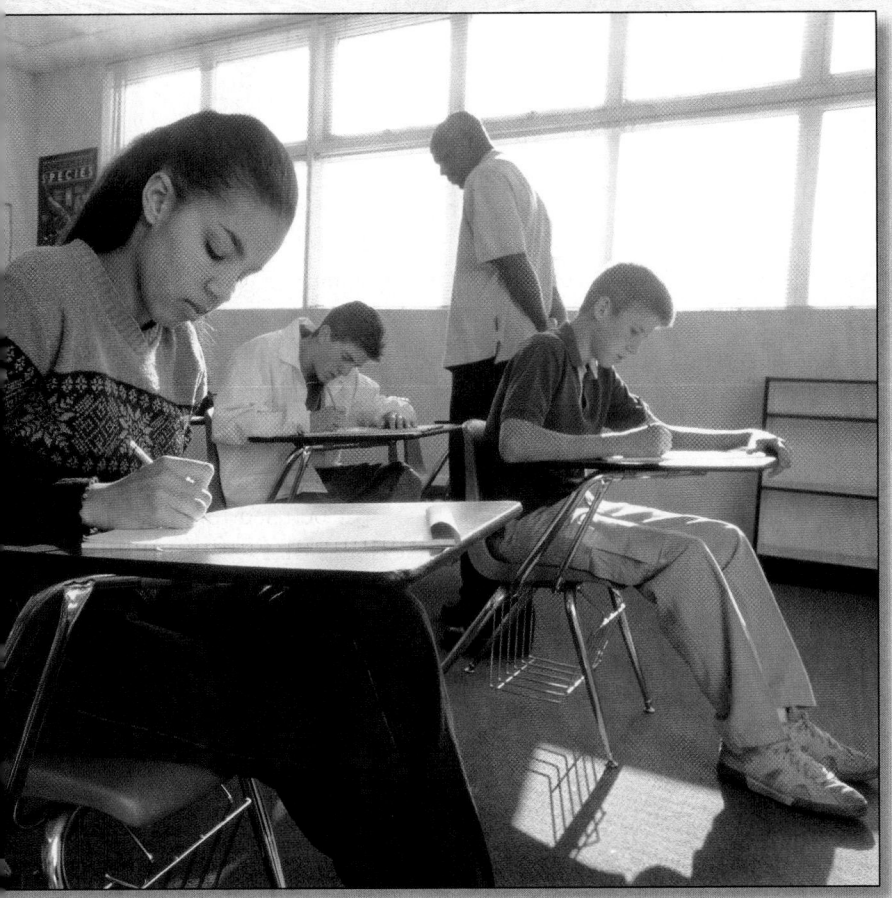

Technology Resources for Intervention

In addition to print resources, Glencoe offers a variety of timesaving technology tools to help students build their math skills more effectively.

Pre-AlgePASS: Tutorial Plus CD-ROM provides an interactive, self-paced tutorial for a complete Pre-Algebra curriculum. The 38 lessons are correlated directly to *Glencoe Pre-Algebra.* Each lesson, or concept, includes a pretest, tutorial, guided practice, and posttest. Students' answers to the pretests automatically determine whether they need the tutorial for each concept, so students can take responsibility for their own learning—without taking teacher time for grading.

Online Study Tools include comprehensive review and intervention tools that are available anytime, anyplace simply by logging on to

www.pre-alg.com.

Additional Teacher Resources

The following materials are available to help you determine which students need intervention and allow you to develop strategies for giving students the help they need. For a description of each feature, see page T5.

- **5-Minute Check Transparencies with Standardized Test Practice**
- **Daily Intervention** features in the Teacher Wraparound Edition
- **Closing the Gap for Absent Students**

Self-check quizzes are available for every lesson, and immediate feedback helps students check their progress and find specific pages and examples in the Student Edition whenever they need extra review. These Online Study Tools also include extra examples, chapter tests, standardized test practice, and vocabulary review.

ALEKS® is an online, intuitive, individualized tutor that students can take anywhere. This artificial intelligence-based system analyzes student answers and targets what the student is prepared to learn next. ALEKS is available by subscription only on the Internet.

www.k12.aleks.com

Give ASSESSMENT

Glencoe Pre-Algebra gives you all the tools you need to prepare students for success – including Standardized Test Practice in each lesson and the powerful ExamView® Pro CD-ROM.

Student Edition

Every lesson contains two Standardized Test Practice questions, and every chapter contains a completely worked-out standardized test example as well as two full pages of Standardized Test Practice with Test-Taking Tips.

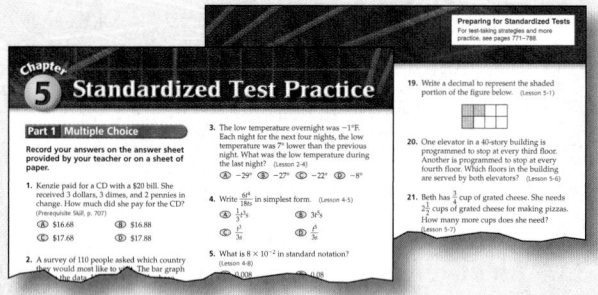

Preparing for Standardized Tests is designed
to help your students become better test-takers. Included are examples and practice for the types of questions and concepts commonly seen on standardized tests.

Chapter Study Guide and Review provides Vocabulary and Concept review—a Glencoe exclusive—and Lesson-by-Lesson Review, all at the point of use for students.

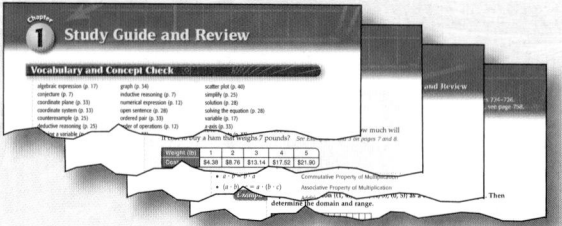

Practice Quizzes (2 per chapter) and a **Practice Test** for each chapter provide the variety of practice questions students need to succeed on tests.

Teacher Wraparound Edition

An **Open-Ended Assessment** activity is provided in each lesson in the margin of the Teacher Wraparound Edition.

the extra attention

it deserves, without the extra prep time.

Teacher Classroom Resources

5-Minute Check Transparencies with Standardized Test Practice provide full-size transparencies with questions covering the previous lesson or chapter. Standardized Test Practice Questions are also included.

Assessment Options in the Chapter Resource Masters

These assessment resources are available for each chapter in *Glencoe Pre-Algebra*.

- 6 Chapter Tests
- Open-Ended Assessment with Scoring Rubric
- Vocabulary Test and Review **Glencoe Exclusive!**
- 4 Quizzes
- Mid-Chapter Test
- Cumulative Review
- 2-page Standardized Test Practice

Unit Tests, Semester Tests, and a **Final Test** are also available at point of use in the Chapter Resource Masters.

Technology Support

Use the networkable **ExamView® Pro** to:

- Create **multiple versions** of tests.
- Create **modified** tests for *Inclusion* students.
- **Edit** existing questions and **add** your own questions.
- Use built-in **state curriculum correlations** to create tests aligned with state standards.
- Change **English** tests to **Spanish** and vice versa.

MindJogger Videoquizzes present chapter-by-chapter review sessions in a game show format to make review more interesting and active to students…especially great for reluctant readers. Available on VHS or on DVD with Real-Life Math Videos.

Online Study Tools

- Self-Check Quizzes
- Vocabulary Review
- Chapter Test Practice
- Standardized Test Practice

Introducing our new partner

USA TODAY® Education

USA TODAY Snapshots®

This is the same up-to-date data you know so well. But now, in an exclusive partnership with Glencoe/McGraw-Hill, USA TODAY® Education has brought its powerful, one-of-a-kind perspective and dynamic content to the pages of *Glencoe Pre-Algebra*. USA TODAY Snapshots® explode off the page to make Pre-Algebra come alive with current, relevant data.

- www.pre-alg.com/usa_today provides additional activities related to the topics presented in the USA TODAY Snapshots®.

- www.education.usatoday.com, USA TODAY® K-12 Education's Web site offers resources and interactive features connected to each day's newspaper. *Experience Today*, USA TODAY®'s daily lesson plan, is available on the site and delivered daily to subscribers. This plan provides instruction for integrating USA TODAY® graphics and key editorial features into your mathematics classroom.

Stay current with additional charts and graphs with USA TODAY®. Log on to www.education.usatoday.com, or call USA TODAY® at (800) 757-TEACH.

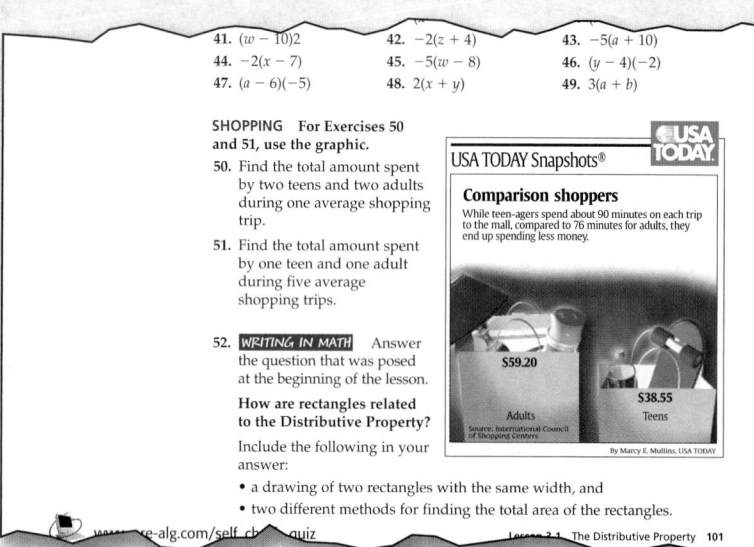

WebQuest: Online Projects

www.pre-alg.com/webquest gives students the chance to work through a long-term project to enable them to develop their research, creative writing, and presentation skills.

- WebQuests often utilize USA TODAY Snapshots® or USA TODAY® articles.

- Special features in the Student Edition prompt students to complete each stage of their WebQuest.

- Parents can use the guided instruction to help students become familiar with the Internet in a safe, productive manner.

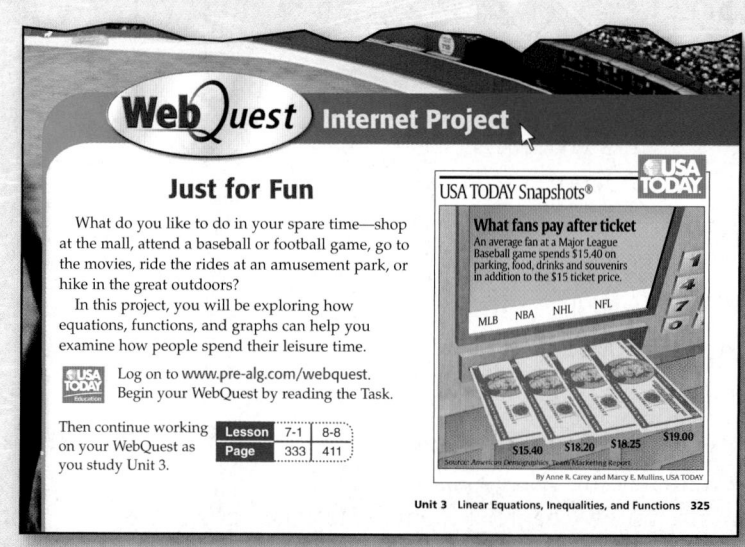

The INTERNET:
One TOOL.
Endless possibilities.

Many of your students may already be familiar with the Internet, but may not have discovered the full potential of this powerful research tool. With *Glencoe Pre-Algebra*, your students can use the Internet to build their algebra skills. And you can access a wide variety of resources to help you plan classes, extend lessons, even meet professional development requirements.

For Students

Online Study Tools, referenced on the Student Edition pages are keyed specifically to *Glencoe Pre-Algebra*.

- www.pre-alg.com/extra_examples features additional fully worked-out examples.
- www.pre-alg.com/self_check_quiz allows students to check their progress in each lesson.
- www.pre-alg.com/vocabulary_review lets students check their vocabulary comprehension.
- www.pre-alg.com/chapter_test provides additional practice in test taking.
- www.pre-alg.com/standardized_test simulates questions that appear on standardized and proficiency tests.

Other Online Resources

- www.pre-alg.com/webquest offers an online research project.
- www.pre-alg.com/usa_today provides additional activities related to the topics presented in the USA TODAY Snapshots®.
- www.pre-alg.com/data_update features links to updated statistical data presented in exercises.
- www.pre-alg.com/careers offers information about career opportunities.
- www.pre-alg.com/other_calculator_keystrokes provides keystroke instructions for various calculators to accompany graphing calculator activities and exercises in the Student Edition.

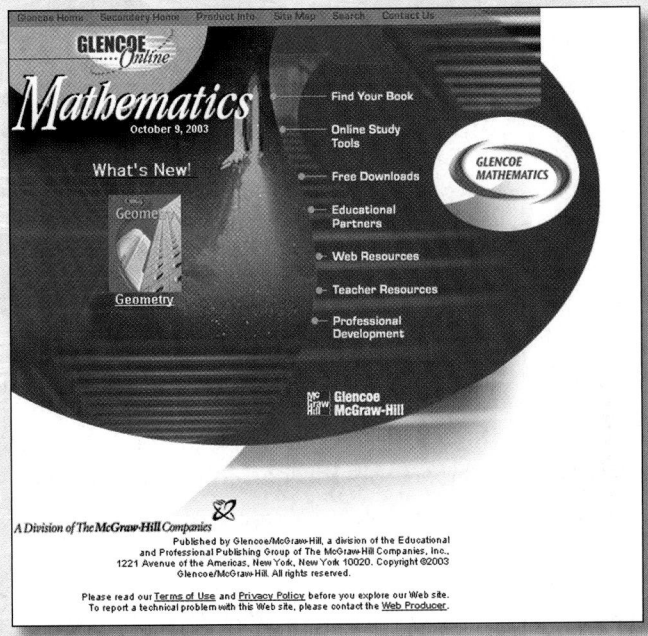

For Teachers

Powerful tools to make your job easier

- Classroom Games
- Key Concepts: Mathematical Background and Teaching Notes www.pre-alg.com/key_concepts
- USA TODAY® K-12 Education daily lesson plans
- Sharing Ideas with Other Teachers
- Cool Math Links
- State and National Resources

Staff Development Sites

- NCTM links
- Teaching Today link
- McGraw-Hill Learning Network link
- Cooperative learning suggestions
- Using the Internet in the Mathematics Classroom

For Parents

Help parents get involved with their child's learning

- Parent and Student Study Guide www.pre-alg.com/parent_student
- Involving Parents and Community in the Mathematics Classroom

DISCOVER how a simple sheet of paper can CHANGE the way your students THINK about math... forever.

Students love Foldables™ because they're fun. Teachers love them because they're effective.

Foldables are easy-to-make, three-dimensional interactive graphic organizers that students create out of simple sheets of paper. These unique hands-on tools for learning and reviewing were created exclusively for *Glencoe Pre-Algebra* by teaching specialist Dinah Zike.

Building Prereading Skills

At the beginning of each chapter, students construct one of a variety of Foldables. Each Foldable helps students create an interactive strategy for organizing what they read and observe. As they work through each chapter, students add more detail to their Foldable until they have created a comprehensive, interactive snapshot of the key concepts and vocabulary of the chapter.

Reading and Writing

Each Foldable helps students practice basic reading and writing skills, find and report main ideas, organize information, review key vocabulary terms, and more.

Review and Reinforcement

The completed Foldable is a comprehensive overview of the chapter concepts—perfect for preparing for chapter, unit, and even end-of-course tests.

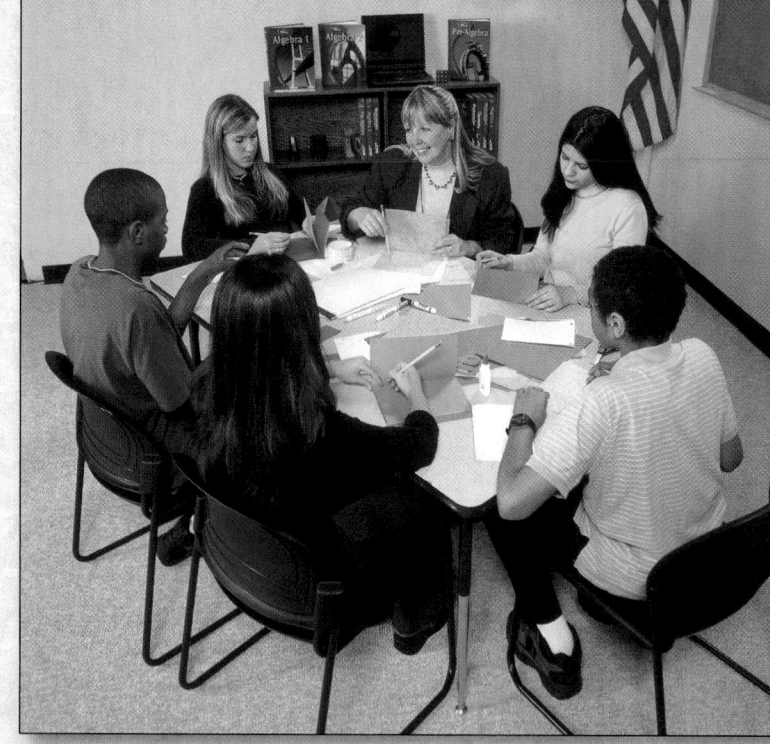

Assessment

Foldables present an ideal opportunity to probe the depth of your students' understanding of chapter concepts. You'll get detailed feedback on what your students know and what misconceptions they may have.

Staff Development

Teaching Mathematics with Foldables™ equips teachers to extend the use of Foldables in their classrooms by exploring the different Foldable formats and providing suggestions for using them throughout the mathematics curriculum.

Give students control,

so that they leave your classroom with *knowledge and power* over their *own learning.*

Study Skill

Project CRISS^SM (**CR**eating **I**ndependence through **S**tudent-owned **S**trategies) is a research-based staff development program created to help students better organize, understand, and retain course information. In short, students receiving the CRISS method of instruction will "LEARN HOW TO LEARN".

CRISS strategies are designed to develop thoughtful and independent readers and learners.

To enhance student learning, CRISS employs several concepts drawn from cognitive psychology.

- Students must be able to integrate new information with prior knowledge.
- Students need to be actively involved in their own learning by discussing, writing, and organizing information.
- Students must self-monitor to identify which strategies are the most effective for their own learning.

These behaviors need to be taught by content teachers to maximize student learning.

CReating Independence Through Student-Owned Strategies

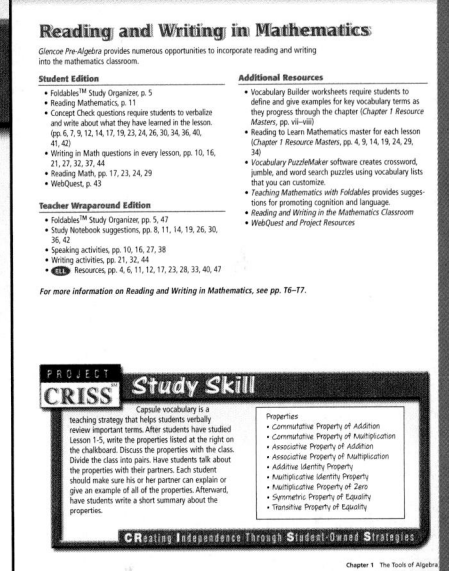

Reading and Writing in Mathematics

Glencoe Pre-Algebra provides numerous opportunities to incorporate reading and writing into the mathematics classroom.

Student Edition
- Foldables™ Study Organizer, p. 5
- Reading Mathematics, p. 11
- Concept Check questions require students to verbalize and write about what they have learned in the lesson. (pp. 6, 7, 9, 12, 14, 17, 19, 23, 24, 26, 30, 34, 36, 40, 41, 42)
- Writing in Math questions in every lesson, pp. 10, 16, 21, 27, 32, 37, 44
- Reading Math, pp. 17, 23, 24, 29
- WebQuest, p. 8

Teacher Wraparound Edition
- Foldables™ Study Organizer, pp. 5, 47
- Study Notebook suggestions, pp. 8, 11, 14, 19, 26, 30, 36, 42
- Speaking activities, pp. 10, 16, 27, 38
- Writing activities, pp. 21, 32, 44
- ELL Resources, pp. 4, 6, 11, 12, 17, 23, 28, 33, 40, 47

For more information on Reading and Writing in Mathematics, see pp. T6–T7.

Additional Resources
- Vocabulary Builder worksheets require students to define and give examples for key vocabulary terms as they progress through the chapter (*Chapter 1 Resource Masters*, pp. vii–viii)
- Reading to Learn Mathematics master for each lesson (*Chapter 1 Resource Masters*, pp. 4, 9, 14, 19, 24, 29, 34)
- *Vocabulary PuzzleMaker* software creates crossword, jumble, and word search puzzles using vocabulary lists that you can customize.
- *Teaching Mathematics with Foldables* provides suggestions for promoting cognition and language.
- *Reading and Writing in the Mathematics Classroom*
- *WebQuest and Project Resources*

PROJECT CRISS Study Skill

Capsule vocabulary is a teaching strategy that helps students verbally review important terms. After students have studied Lesson 1-5, write the properties listed at the right on the chalkboard. Discuss the properties with the class. Divide the class into pairs. Have students talk about the properties with their partners. Each student should make sure his or her partner can explain or give an example of all of the properties. Afterward, have students write a short summary about the properties.

Properties
- Commutative Property of Addition
- Commutative Property of Multiplication
- Associative Property of Addition
- Associative Property of Multiplication
- Additive Identity Property
- Multiplicative Identity Property
- Multiplicative Property of Zero
- Symmetric Property of Equality
- Transitive Property of Equality

CReating Independence Through Student-Owned Strategies

Chapter 1 The Tools of Algebra

Reading and Writing in Mathematics

Glencoe Pre-Algebra provides numerous opportunities to incorporate reading and writing into the mathematics classroom.

Student Edition
- Foldables™ Study Organizer, p. 55
- Reading Mathematics, p. 69
- Concept Check questions require students to verbalize and write about what they have learned in the lesson. (pp. 56, 57, 59, 66, 67, 71, 72, 77, 81, 83, 86, 87)
- Writing in Math questions in every lesson, pp. 61, 68, 74, 79, 84, 89
- Reading Math, pp. 56, 57, 64, 75, 80, 88
- WebQuest, p. 79

Teacher Wraparound Edition
- Foldables™ Study Organizer, pp. 55, 90
- Study Notebook suggestions, pp. 58, 63, 66, 69, 72, 77, 83, 87
- Modeling activities, pp. 61, 74
- Speaking activities, pp. 79, 89
- Writing activities, pp. 68, 84
- ELL Resources, pp. 54, 56, 64, 69, 70, 75, 80, 85, 90

For more information on Reading and Writing in Mathematics, see pp. T6–T7.

Additional Resources
- Vocabulary Builder worksheets require students to define and give examples for key vocabulary terms as they progress through the chapter (*Chapter 2 Resource Masters*, pp. vii–viii)
- Reading to Learn Mathematics master for each lesson (*Chapter 2 Resource Masters*, pp. 60, 65, 70, 75, 80, 85)
- *Vocabulary PuzzleMaker* software creates crossword, jumble, and word search puzzles using vocabulary lists that you can customize.
- *Teaching Mathematics with Foldables* provides suggestions for promoting cognition and language.
- *Reading and Writing in the Mathematics Classroom*
- *WebQuest and Project Resources*

Implementing CRISS Strategies

Project CRISS Study Skills were developed with leaders from Project CRISS to facilitate the teaching of each chapter of *Glencoe Pre-Algebra.* These strategies appear in the interleaf of the Teacher Wraparound Edition.

For more information on project CRISS^SM, visit www.projectcriss.com.

ELL ENGLISH LANGUAGE LEARNERS

English language learners may need specialized help in overcoming a language barrier to learn mathematics. Hands-on activities, modeling, working in flexible groups, and vocabulary building activities are particularly helpful to ELL students. Suggested strategies appear in the interleaf of the Teacher Wraparound Edition.

ELL ENGLISH LANGUAGE LEARNERS

Lesson 2-1
Flexible Groups

Give groups of six students a set of six cards with an integer on each card. Have the students order the numbers from least to greatest. On a wall of the room, mark 0, positive, and negative to denote a number line. Have the students come to the number line by group and position themselves in order on the number line. The students can check each other for accuracy.

Lesson 2-3
Higher-Level Thinking

Based on the patterns that students have seen modeled by the teacher, have them work in groups of three or four to come up with their own rules for adding integers with different signs. This same model can be used for subtracting, multiplying, and dividing integers.

Lesson 2-6
Using Models

Have students draw a coordinate plane on grid paper, labeling the x- and y- axes, the origin, and all four quadrants. Discuss with the students what an ordered pair is and how to locate one on the coordinate plane. For a large coordinate plane, use a shower curtain and masking tape to draw all the parts of the coordinate plane. Have students stand on points to graph ordered pairs.

Chapter 2 Integers

It's Staff Development,

As professional development continues to take on greater importance for educators across the country, teachers are constantly looking for easy-to-use tools to help them stay abreast of current trends and issues. At Glencoe, we know how valuable your time is, so we've developed a variety of staff development tools to help you meet your district's requirements.

Teacher Wraparound Edition

Mathematical Connections and Background found at the beginning of each chapter gives you an overview of the mathematics skills required in each lesson. Information about prior knowledge as well as future connections lets you see the continuity of instruction.

Building on Prior Knowledge provides you with information that links what students have previously learned to the content of the lesson.

Tips for New Teachers offers helpful suggestions for such things as classroom management, assessment, teaching techniques, and more.

Teaching Tips can be found not only in the margins but also on the reduced student pages at point of use.

Teacher Classroom Resources

Glencoe Mathematics Staff Development Series is a series of publications that allows you to stay current with issues that affect your teaching effectiveness. The series is intended to help you implement new mathematics strategies and enhance your classroom performance.

Available in print

- *Using the Internet in the Mathematics Classroom*
- *Reading and Writing in the Mathematics Classroom*
- *Teaching Mathematics with Foldables™*
- *Teaching Pre-Algebra with Manipulatives*

Available online at
www.math.glencoe.com

- *Graphing Calculators in the Mathematics Classroom*
- *Cooperative Learning in the Mathematics Classroom*
- *Alternative Assessment in the Mathematics Classroom*
- *Involving Parents and the Community in the Mathematics Classroom*

made convenient.

Technology Support

At www.math.glencoe.com, you'll find:

- a Staff Development site that addresses current issues in education.
- a Teacher Forum that allows teachers to discuss issues and ideas with colleagues.
- a State and National Resources site that links to math and math education resources, nationally and by state.

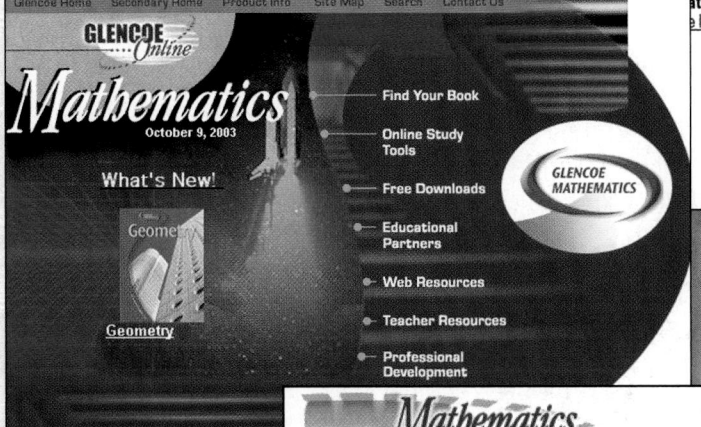

Glencoe Mathematics Programs—
Research-
Based and

Glencoe's mathematics programs are the product of ongoing classroom and educational research activities involving students, teachers, curriculum supervisors, administrators, parents, and college-level mathematics educators, mathematicians, and researchers.

SOUND

Prior to the publication of any Glencoe mathematics program, the following initial research is completed.

- Monitoring of national and state changes and trends such as graduation requirements, standardized test exams, and the latest NCTM and NAEP reports.

- Incorporating the most current and applicable educational research in which reported results show significant improvement on student learning and achievement.

- Analyzing returns from independently contracted mailing and telephone surveys.

- Reviewing all comments and correspondence on appropriate prior editions in terms of specific lessons. This helps Glencoe to build in staff development support, which makes the programs easy to implement from the first day of use.

Survey Results Responding Very Satisfied or Satisfied with Glencoe Pre-Algebra*

- Student Edition: 92%
- Teacher Wraparound Edition: 97%
- Overall Program: 93%

*Ratings for all other middle school math programs were 82%, 86%, and 78%, respectively.

Source: Middle School Mathematics Longitudinal Survey, 2003

tested to ensure success.

PROVEN

Prior to the publication of *Glencoe Pre-Algebra*, extensive research was conducted using manuscript and pre-publication versions of the program.

- Nationwide discussion groups were conducted, which involved mathematics teachers, department chairpersons, supervisors, and educational learning specialists.

- Face-to-face interviews were carried out with mathematics teachers.

- Reviewers and consultants reviewed *Glencoe Pre-Algebra* manuscripts for accuracy, content development, and thoroughness.

- Before the design of the Student Edition was completed, an independent research company was contracted to organize and conduct blind focus groups with pre-algebra teachers in various cities. The teachers' feedback was used for improvements.

- Follow-up interviews, observations, and surveys of users of Glencoe mathematics programs are continuously conducted and monitored.

- Glencoe conducts Learner Verification Research in which students and teachers use pre-publication manuscript in the classroom. The results, compiled by an independent contractor, for *Glencoe Pre-Algebra* are summarized below.

Top-Line Results

- The research indicates that test scores significantly increased among students using *Glencoe Pre-Algebra*.

- Roughly nine out of ten students earned higher scores after using the Glencoe program.

- The program was equally effective with boys and girls and with minority and non-minority students.

- Overall, the gap between the average pre-test score and a perfect score closed by 53%. Stated differently, on average, scores increased 48% after students used *Glencoe Pre-Algebra*.

EFFECTIVE

What do teachers say? Here are some testimonials from Learner Verification Research teachers.

- *great organization, great examples, and lots of extra practice*
- *program is mathematically correct, challenging, and age appropriate*
- *good balance of practice problems and word problems*
- *program is easy to follow for both teacher and student*
- *abundant resources and technology*

For more details of Glencoe's research, please contact us at www.math.glencoe.com.

Planning Your

Glencoe Pre-Algebra and the accompanying support materials allow you to create a Pre-Algebra course that meets the needs of each class of students. The charts shown on these two pages offer general suggestions for pacing your students through the book for average and advanced levels. Pacing for both standard class periods and block schedule class periods is given. A more detailed pacing chart appears on interleaf page A preceding each chapter in the *Teacher Wraparound Edition.*

The total number of days in each level of pacing is less than the typical 180-day school year and 90-day semester to allow for flexibility in planning due to testing, school cancellation, or shortened class periods.

AVERAGE PACING

Average Pacing is for those students who have a fairly good mathematical preparation for Pre-Algebra. You may want to use one of the six chapter tests provided in the Chapter Resource Masters as a pretest to determine how well your students are prepared for each chapter. If you find that they are well prepared, consider using the Study Guide and Review at the end of the chapter as a one-day lesson and proceed to the next chapter.

If your students are better prepared for Pre-Algebra, you may want to spend less time in the earlier chapters in order to explore Chapter 13.

Modifying Average Pacing for Basic Students

For those students who are less prepared for Pre-Algebra, spend more time on Units 1 and 2 (Chapters 1–6). Unit 5 (Chapters 12–13) may be omitted.

Year-Long Schedule
45–50 minute periods

Grading Period	Chapter	Days
1	1	11
	2	13
	3	12
	4 (through Lesson 4-4)	4
2	4 (Lesson 4-5 to end)	9
	5	14
	6	14
	7 (Lesson 7-1)	3
3	7 (Lesson 7-2 to end)	9
	8	19
	9	15
4	10	14
	11	12
	12	11
optional	13	0
	Total	160

Block Schedule
90 minute periods

Chapter	Days
1	5.5
2	7
3	6
4	7
5	7
6	7
7	6
8	10
9	7
10	7
11	6
12	6.5
13	0
Total	82

Pre-Algebra Course

Advanced Pacing is for those students who have a strong background in mathematics. These students are often sixth- or seventh-graders taking Pre-Algebra for the first time. In advanced pacing, students spend less time on introductory activities and more on the Follow-Up extension activities. They also cover Chapter 13. One of the six chapter tests provided in the Chapter Resource Masters can be used as a pretest for each chapter.

Year-Long Schedule
45–50 minute periods

Grading Period	Chapter	Days
1	1	11
	2	8
	3	11
	4	12
2	5	15
	6	13
	7	10
3	8	15
	9	15
	10	13
4	11	9
	12	15
	13	13
	Total	**160**

Block Schedule
90 minute periods

Chapter	Days
1	5.5
2	4
3	5
4	6
5	8
6	7
7	5
8	8
9	7
10	7
11	5
12	8
13	6.5
Total	**82**

Daily Planning

- A more detailed Suggested Pacing chart appears in the interleaf preceding each chapter in the *Teacher Wraparound Edition.*

- The *Lesson Planning Guide* offers further suggestions for the materials to be covered each day and how to adapt these for Block Scheduling.

- *TeacherWorks: All in One Lesson Planner and Resource Center* CD-ROM enables you to customize an entire course of study to meet your specific needs.

Implementing the NCTM Principles and Standards

In 1989, the National Council of Teachers of Mathematics (NCTM) published their *Curriculum and Evaluation Standards for School Mathematics*, which gave mathematics teachers their first set of goals toward a national mathematics curriculum. Teachers and supervisors have embraced these Standards and developed state standards based on this framework. In 2000, the National Council of Teachers of Mathematics published a revision of these guidelines entitled *NCTM Principles and Standards for School Mathematics*.

NCTM Principles for School Mathematics	Glencoe Pre-Algebra
Equity *Excellence in mathematics education requires equity—high expectations and strong support for all students.*	Glencoe's product line encourages high achievement at every level. Numerous teacher support materials provide activities for **differentiated instruction,** promotion of **reading and writing, pacing** for individual levels of achievement, and **daily intervention.**
Curriculum *A curriculum is more than a collection of activities: it must be coherent, focused on important mathematics, and well articulated across the grades.*	Glencoe authors developed a philosophy and scope and sequence to ensure a continuum of mathematical learning that builds on **prior knowledge** and extends concepts toward more **advanced mathematical thinking.**
Teaching *Effective mathematics teaching requires understanding what students know and need to learn and then challenging and supporting them to learn it well.*	Glencoe offers a plethora of teacher support materials. A comprehensive *Teacher Wraparound Edition* provides **mathematical background,** teaching tips, resource management guidelines, and **tips for new teachers.**
Learning *Students must learn mathematics with understanding, actively building new knowledge from experience and prior knowledge.*	The *Teacher Wraparound Edition* includes instruction on building from prior knowledge with materials in each interleaf and in **Building On Prior Knowledge** features. **Find the Error** and **Unlocking Misconception** teaching tips help to evaluate how students are thinking and learning.
Assessment *Assessment should support the learning of important mathematics and furnish useful information to both teachers and students.*	The **Practice Quizzes** and the **Chapter Practice Test** provide ways for students to check their own progress. Online Study Tools, such as **Self-Check Quizzes,** offer a unique way for students with Internet access to monitor their progress. The assessment tools in the *Chapter Resource Masters* contain different levels and formats for tests, as well as intermediate opportunities for assessment.
Technology *Technology is essential in teaching and learning mathematics; it influences the mathematics that is taught and enhances students' learning.*	The *Student Edition* includes opportunities to utilize graphing calculators and spreadsheets in the exploration of Pre-Algebra concepts. The *Teacher Wraparound Edition* offers teaching tips on using technology. *Graphing Calculator and Spreadsheet Masters* has additional activities. Glencoe's Web site is constantly updated to meet the needs of students and teachers in excelling in mathematics education.

NCTM Standards for School Mathematics

The Standards portion of the *NCTM Principles and Standards for School Mathematics* center upon ten areas of mathematics curriculum development. The number assigned to each standard is for easy reference and is not part of each standard's official title.

Instructional programs from prekindergarten through grade 12 should enable all students to:

1 Numbers and Operations

- Understand numbers, ways of representing numbers, relationships among numbers, and number systems
- Understand the meaning of operations and how they relate to each other
- Compute fluently and make reasonable estimates

Pages: 6-44, 56-84, 98-107, 148-190, 200-236, 238-242, 244-248, 264-315, 340-359, 436-445, 453-482, 506-511, 520-531, 533-543, 563-582, 584-594, 641-657, 674-686

2 Algebra

- Understand patterns, relations, and functions
- Represent and analyze mathematical situations and structures using algebraic symbols
- Use mathematical models to represent and understand quantitative relationships
- Analyze change in various contexts

Pages: 17-21, 40-44, 56-61, 64-89, 98-137, 148-190, 210-231, 237, 244-253, 264-280, 288-292, 298-302, 304-315, 328-359, 368-391, 393-423, 441-445, 453-482, 492-497, 500-504, 513-517, 563-582, 584-588, 669-697

3 Geometry

- Analyze characteristics and properties of two- and three-dimensional geometric shapes and develop mathematical arguments about geometric relationships
- Specify locations and describe spatial relationships using coordinate geometry and other representational systems
- Apply transformations and use symmetry to analyze mathematical situations
- Use visualization, spatial reasoning, and geometric modeling to solve problems

Pages: 85-89, 131-137, 175-179, 210-219, 249-253, 286-287, 304-308, 334-338, 393-397, 447-482, 492-543, 554-594, 673, 682, 687-697

4 Measurement

- Understand measurable attributes of objects and the units, systems, and processes of measurement
- Apply appropriate techniques, tools, and formulas to determine measurements

Pages: 23-27, 169-173, 186-190, 210-219, 238-242, 264-280, 286-287, 386, 392, 436-440, 447-482, 492-504, 512, 518-531, 533-543, 562-594, 673, 682

5 Data Analysis and Probability

- Formulate questions that can be addressed with data and collect, organize, and display relevant data to answer them
- Select and use appropriate statistical methods to analyze data
- Develop and evaluate inferences and predictions that are based on data
- Understand and apply basic concepts of probability

Pages: 40-44, 210-219, 237-243, 275, 303, 309-315, 409-413, 583, 606-657

Instructional programs from prekindergarten through grade 12 should enable all students to:

6 Problem Solving

- Build new mathematical knowledge through problem solving
- Solve problems that arise in mathematics and in other contexts
- Apply and adapt a variety of appropriate strategies to solve problems
- Monitor and reflect on the process of mathematical problem solving

Pages: 6-10, 28-32, 56-89, 98-107, 110-137, 148-185, 200-230, 232-236, 238-253, 270-280, 288-309, 330-338, 345-359, 369-385, 387-391, 393-401, 404-422, 436-440, 447-482, 492-497, 500-504, 513-517, 520-531, 533-543, 556-594, 606-621, 623-628, 635-639, 641-657, 697

7 Reasoning and Proof

- Recognize reasoning and proof as fundamental aspects of mathematics
- Make and investigate mathematical conjectures
- Develop and evaluate mathematical arguments and proofs
- Select and use various types of reasoning and methods of proof

Pages: 137, 148-152, 175-190, 205-209, 220-231, 249-253, 286-292, 368, 386, 392, 402-403, 458-464, 520-525, 533-538, 562, 583, 635-640, 650-657, 673, 697

8 Communication

- Organize and consolidate their mathematical thinking through communication
- Communicate their mathematical thinking coherently and clearly to peers, teachers, and others
- Analyze and evaluate the mathematical thinking and strategies of others
- Use the language of mathematics to express mathematical ideas precisely

Pages: 148-190, 249-253, 275, 288-297, 303, 309-314, 340-349, 404-408, 436-440, 453-481, 492-497, 500-504, 506-517, 520-531, 533-543, 556-561, 563-594, 630-633, 656-657, 682

9 Connections

- Recognize and use connections among mathematical ideas
- Understand how mathematical ideas build on one another to produce a coherent whole
- Recognize and apply mathematics in contexts outside of mathematics

Pages: 98-107, 110-137, 148-190, 249-253, 264-315, 355-359, 392-397, 402-403, 453-457, 471-482, 492-497, 500-504, 506-511, 513-517, 520-531, 533-543, 556-582, 584-594, 612-621, 641-657, 669-697

10 Representation

- Create and use representations to organize, record, and communicate mathematical ideas
- Select, apply, and translate among mathematical representations to solve problems
- Use representations to model and interpret physical, social, and mathematical phenomena

Pages: 56-61, 85-89, 108-109, 137, 148-190, 210-214, 232-236, 264-292, 298-315, 328-329, 368, 374-385, 387-423, 471-481, 520-532, 539-543, 554-561, 563-594, 606-611, 617-640, 669-697

1 Algebra and Integers

Chapter 1   The Tools of Algebra   4

Web**Quest** Internet Project ▶

• Introduction 3
• Follow-Ups 43, 79, 135
• Culmination 136

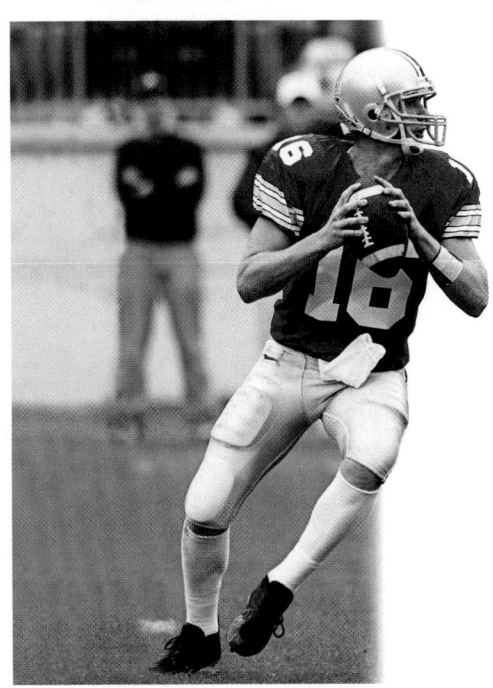

Lesson 1-2, page 15

Table of Contents

Prerequisite Skills
• Getting Started 5
• Getting Ready for the Next Lesson 10, 16, 21, 27, 32, 38

 Study Organizer 5

Reading and Writing Mathematics
• Translating Expressions into Words 11
• Reading Math Tips 17, 23, 24
• Writing in Math 10, 16, 21, 27, 32, 37, 44

Standardized Test Practice
• Multiple Choice 10, 16, 21, 27, 29, 30, 32, 38, 44, 51, 52
• Short Response/Grid In 53
• Extended Response 53

 Snapshots 3, 8, 16

Chapter ② Integers 54

Prerequisite Skills

FOLDABLES™

Study Organizer 55

Reading and Writing Mathematics

Standardized Test Practice

USA TODAY Snapshots 60

Lesson 2-4, page 78

Chapter ❸   Equations   96

Lesson 3-6, page 127

Prerequisite Skills

• Getting Started 97

• Getting Ready for the Next Lesson 102, 107, 114, 119,
124, 130

 Study Organizer 97

Reading and Writing Mathematics

• Translating Verbal Problems into Equations 125

• Reading Math Tips 98, 103

• Writing in Math 101, 106, 114, 119, 123, 130, 136

Standardized Test Practice

USA TODAY Snapshots 101

2 Algebra and Rational Numbers

Chapter 4 Factors and Fractions 146

Lesson 4-8, page 189

WebQuest Internet Project

- Introduction 145
- Follow-Ups 173, 242, 301
- Culmination 314

Prerequisite Skills

- Getting Started 147
- Getting Ready for the Next Lesson
  152, 157, 163, 168, 173, 179, 185

FOLDABLES™

Study Organizer 147

Reading and Writing Mathematics

- Powers 174
- Reading Math Tips 148, 149, 150, 159, 177
- Writing in Math 152, 157, 162, 168, 173, 179, 184, 190

Standardized Test Practice

- Multiple Choice 152, 157, 163, 168, 171, 173, 179, 184, 190, 195, 196
- Short Response/Grid In 197
- Extended Response 197

USA TODAY Snapshots 145, 156

Chapter 5   Rational Numbers   198

Algebra Activity, page 253

Prerequisite Skills
- Getting Started **199**
- Getting Ready for the Next Lesson **204, 209, 214, 219, 224, 230, 236, 242, 248**

 Study Organizer 199

Reading and Writing Mathematics
- Factors and Multiples **225**
- Reading Math Tips **200, 205, 206, 215**
- Writing in Math **204, 209, 214, 219, 223, 230, 236, 242, 247, 251**

Standardized Test Practice
- Multiple Choice **204, 209, 214, 219, 224, 230, 236, 240, 241, 242, 247, 252, 259, 260**
- Short Response/Grid In **240, 261**
- Extended Response **261**

USA TODAY Snapshots 203, 213

Chapter 6   Ratio, Proportion, and Percent   262

Lesson 6-7, page 299

Prerequisite Skills

- Getting Started 263
- Getting Ready for the Next Lesson 268, 274, 280, 285,
  292, 297, 302, 308

 Study Organizer 263

Reading and Writing Mathematics

- Making Comparisons 269
- Reading Math Tips 281, 300, 311
- Writing in Math 268, 274, 280, 285, 292, 297, 302,
  307, 314

Standardized Test Practice

- Multiple Choice 268, 274, 280, 285, 292, 297, 302,
  305, 306, 308, 314, 321, 322
- Short Response/Grid In 323
- Extended Response 323

 Snapshots 289, 290, 312, 314

3 Linear Equations, Inequalities, and Functions

Lesson 7-5, page 354

xv

Chapter ⑧   Functions and Graphing   366

Lesson 8-9, page 417

Chapter ⑨   Real Numbers and Right Triangles   434

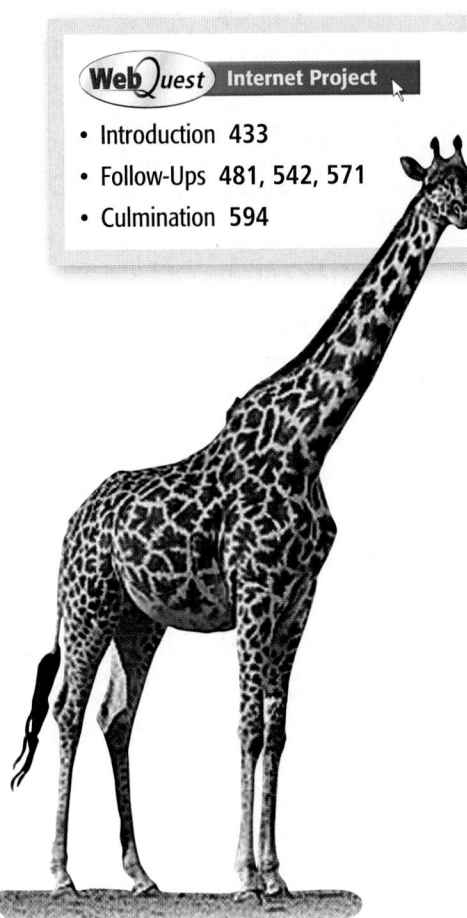

Web Quest   Internet Project

- Introduction 433
- Follow-Ups 481, 542, 571
- Culmination 594

Lesson 9-7, page 474

Prerequisite Skills
- Getting Started 435
- Getting Ready for the Next Lesson 440, 445, 451, 457, 464, 470, 475

FOLDABLES Study Organizer 435

Reading and Writing Mathematics
- Learning Geometry Vocabulary 446
- Reading Math Tips 437, 448, 453, 455, 471, 472, 477
- Writing in Math 440, 445, 451, 457, 464, 469, 475, 481

Standardized Test Practice
- Multiple Choice 440, 445, 451, 457, 461, 462, 464, 470, 475, 481, 487, 488
- Short Response/Grid In 489
- Extended Response 489

 USA TODAY Snapshots 433, 450

Chapter ⑩   Two-Dimensional Figures   490

Prerequisite Skills

FOLDABLES™

Study Organizer 491

Reading and Writing Mathematics

Standardized Test Practice

USA TODAY Snapshots 537

Lesson 10-5, page 524

Chapter ⑪ Three-Dimensional Figures 552

Lesson 11-2, page 564

Prerequisite Skills
- Getting Started **553**
- Getting Ready for the Next Lesson **561, 567, 572, 577, 582, 588**

FOLDABLES™ Study Organizer 553

Reading and Writing Mathematics
- Precision and Accuracy **589**
- Writing in Math **561, 567, 571, 577, 582, 588, 594**

Standardized Test Practice
- Multiple Choice **561, 564, 566, 567, 572, 577, 582, 588, 594, 599, 600**
- Short Response/Grid In **601**
- Extended Response **601**

 Snapshots 593

Extending Algebra to Statistics and Polynomials

Lesson 12-9, page 651

Prerequisite Skills
- Getting Started **605**
- Getting Ready for the Next Lesson **611, 616, 621, 628, 633, 639, 645, 649**

Reading and Writing Mathematics
- Dealing with Bias **634**
- Reading Math Tips **624, 641, 642, 643, 647, 650**
- Writing in Math **610, 616, 621, 627, 633, 639, 645, 649, 654**

FOLDABLES Study Organizer **605**

Standardized Test Practice
- Multiple Choice **611, 616, 621, 627, 633, 639, 645, 647, 648, 649, 655, 663, 664**
- Short Response/Grid In **665**
- Extended Response **665**

 Snapshots **603, 610, 649, 654**

Chapter 13 Polynomials and Nonlinear Functions 666

Prerequisite Skills

FOLDABLES

Study Organizer 667

Reading and Writing Mathematics

Standardized Test Practice

 Snapshots 690

Student Handbook

Skills

Reference

Lesson 13-2, page 675

One-Stop Internet Resources

Need extra help or information? Log on to math.glencoe.com or any of the Web addresses to learn more.

Online Study Tools

- www.pre-alg.com/extra_examples shows you additional worked-out examples that mimic the ones in your book.

- www.pre-alg.com/self_check_quiz provides you with a self-checking practice quiz for each lesson.

- www.pre-alg.com/vocabulary_review lets you check your understanding of the terms and definitions used in each chapter.

- www.pre-alg.com/chapter_test allows you to take a self-checking test before the actual test.

- www.pre-alg.com/standardized_test is another way to brush up on your standardized test-taking skills.

Research Options

- www.pre-alg.com/webquest walks you step-by-step through a long-term project using the Web. One WebQuest for each unit is explored using the mathematics from that unit.

- www.pre-alg.com/usa_today provides activities related to the concept of the lesson as well as up-to-date Snapshot data.

- www.pre-alg.com/careers links you to additional information about interesting careers.

- www.pre-alg.com/data_update links you to the most current data available for subjects such as basketball and family.

Calculator Help

- www.pre-alg.com/other_calculator_keystrokes provides you with keystrokes other than the TI-83 Plus used in your textbook.

Get Started

To help you learn how to use your math book, use the Scavenger Hunt at www.pre-alg.com.

FOLDABLES™

A Handy Way to Help You Study

As easy as 1-2-3! Just fold and you are ready to go! Each chapter provides you with a different Foldable that's easy to create. It's a fun way to organize what you learn and a great study tool.

FOLDABLES™ Study Organizer

Properties Make this Foldable to help you organize your notes. Add definitions and examples to it as you learn new properties throughout the year. Begin with eight half-sheets of plain paper.

Step 1 **Fold and Cut**

Fold a half sheet of paper in half. Cut a 1" tab along the left edge through one thickness.

Step 2 **Glue and Label**

Glue the 1" tab down. Write the name of the property on the front tab.

Distributive Property

Step 3 **Label**

Write the property in words and symbols under the tab.

Words:
Symbols:

Step 4 **Repeat and Staple**

Repeat Steps 1-3 for the remaining sheets of paper. Staple together to form a booklet.

Distributive Property

Foldables can be found on the following pages: 5, 55, 97, 147, 199, 263, 327, 367, 435, 491, 553, 605, and 667.

UNIT 1

Algebra and Integers

Introduction

In this unit, students will learn about the basic tools of algebra, including variables, integers, and equations. They will use a four-step plan to solve problems, translate verbal phrases and expressions into algebraic expressions, and use mathematical properties and the order of operations. They will compare and order integers and perform operations with integers. Students will evaluate and simplify algebraic expressions and write and solve two-step equations.

Students will use a coordinate plane to locate and graph ordered pairs and represent algebraic relationships.

Assessment Options

Unit 1 Test Pages 163–164 of the *Chapter 3 Resource Masters* may be used as a test or review for Unit 1. This assessment contains both multiple-choice and short answer items.

ExamView® Pro

This CD-ROM can be used to create additional unit tests and review worksheets.

Yearly Progress Pro

An online, research-based instructional, assessment, and intervention tool that provides specific feedback on student mastery of state and national standards, instant remediation, and a data management system to track performance. For more information, contact mhdigitallearning.com.

UNIT 1

The word *algebra* comes from the Arabic word *al-jebr*, which was part of the title of a book about equations and how to solve them. In this unit, you will lay the foundation for your study of algebra by learning about the language of algebra, its properties, and methods of solving equations.

Chapter 1
The Tools of Algebra

Chapter 2
Integers

Chapter 3
Equations

What's MATH Got To Do With It?

Real-Life Math Videos

What's Math Got to Do With It? Real-Life Math Videos engage students showing them how math is used in everyday situations. Use Video 1 with this unit.

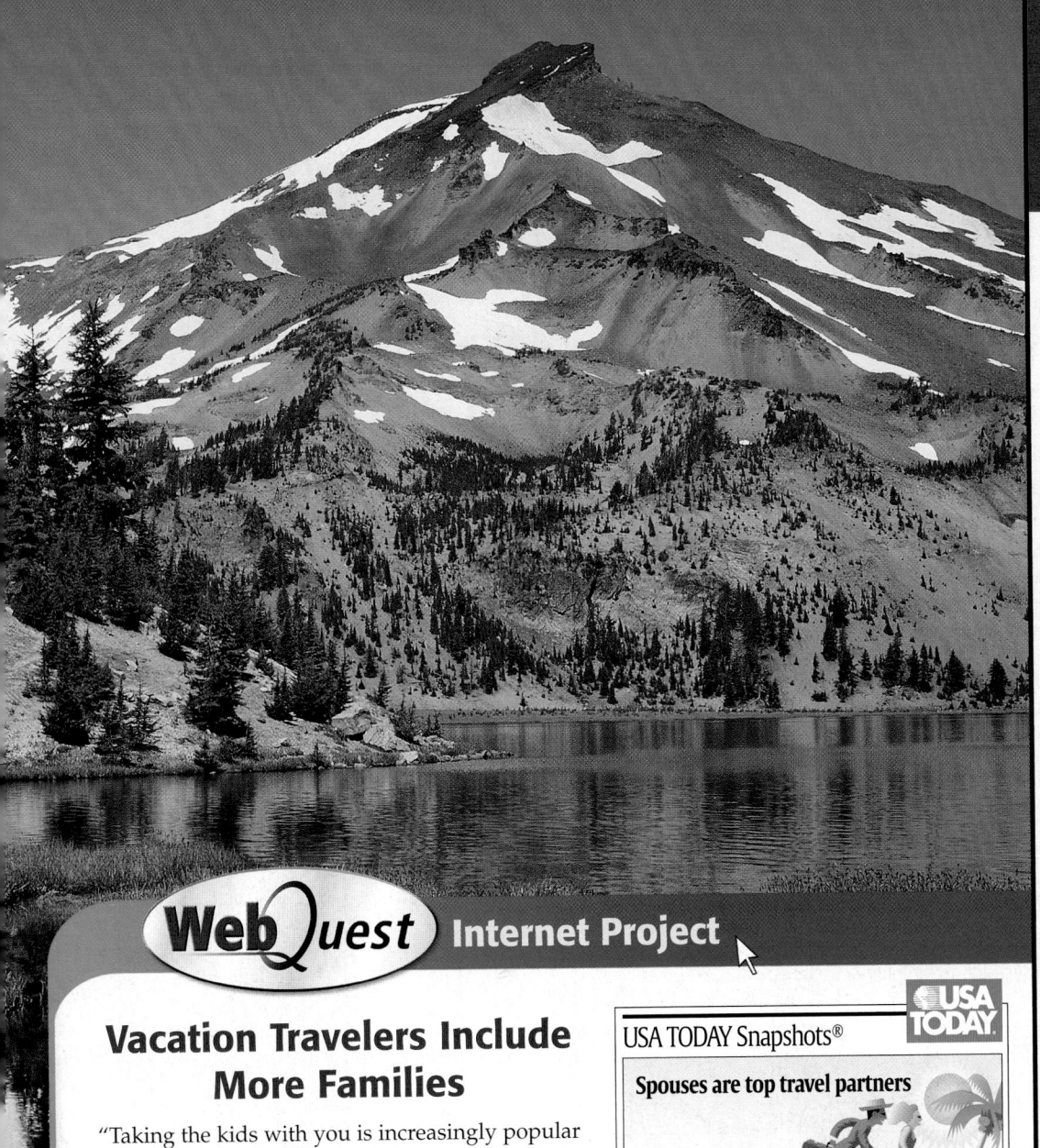

WebQuest Internet Project

Vacation Travelers Include More Families

"Taking the kids with you is increasingly popular among Americans, according to a travel report that predicts an expanding era of kid-friendly attractions and services." **Source:** *USA TODAY,* November 17, 1999

In this project, you will be exploring how graphs and formulas can help you plan a family vacation.

Log on to www.pre-alg.com/webquest. Begin your WebQuest by reading the Task.

Then continue working on your WebQuest as you study Unit 1.

Lesson	1-7	2-4	3-7
Page	43	79	135

USA TODAY Snapshots®

Spouses are top travel partners

Spouses	58%
Children/grandchildren	34%
Friends	18%
Other family members	14%
Solo	13%
Group tour	8%

Source: Travel Industry Association of America

By Cindy Hall and Sam Ward, USA TODAY

Unit 1 Algebra and Integers 3

WebQuest Internet Project

The Tools of Algebra
Chapter Overview and Pacing

Year-long pacing: pages T20–T21.

LESSON OBJECTIVES	PACING (days)			
	Regular		Block	
	Basic/ Average	Advanced	Basic/ Average	Advanced
1-1 Using a Problem-Solving Plan *(pp. 6–10)* • Use a four-step plan to solve problems. • Choose an appropriate method of computation.	1	1	0.5	0.5
1-2 Numbers and Expressions *(pp. 12–16)* • Use the order of operations to evaluate expressions. • Translate verbal phrases into numerical expressions.	1	1	0.5	0.5
1-3 Variables and Expressions *(pp. 17–22)* • Evaluate expressions containing variables. • Translate verbal phrases into algebraic expressions. *Follow-Up:* Use a spreadsheet to explore algebraic expressions.	1	2 (with 1-3 Follow-Up)	0.5	1 (with 1-3 Follow-Up)
1-4 Properties *(pp. 23–27)* • Identify and use properties of addition and multiplication. • Use properties of addition and multiplication to simplify algebraic expressions.	1	1	0.5	0.5
1-5 Variables and Equations *(pp. 28–32)* • Identify and solve open sentences. • Translate verbal sentences into equations.	2	1	1	0.5
1-6 Ordered Pairs and Relations *(pp. 33–38)* • Use ordered pairs to locate points. • Use tables and graphs to represent relations.	1	1	0.5	0.5
1-7 Scatter Plots *(pp. 39–46)* *Preview:* Use a scatter plot to investigate the relationship between two sets of data, height and arm span. • Construct scatter plots. • Interpret scatter plots. *Follow-Up:* Describe how a graphing calculator can help create a scatter plot.	2 (with 1-7 Preview)	2 (with 1-7 Follow-Up)	1 (with 1-7 Preview)	1 (with 1-7 Follow-Up)
Study Guide and **Practice Test** *(pp. 47–51)* **Standardized Test Practice** *(pp. 52–53)*	1	1	0.5	0.5
Chapter Assessment	1	1	0.5	0.5
TOTAL	11	11	5.5	5.5

*An electronic version of this chapter is available on **StudentWorks™**. This backpack solution CD-ROM allows students instant access to the Student Edition, lesson worksheet pages, and web resources.*

Chapter Resource Manager

Timesaving Tools

TeacherWorks™
All-In-One Planner and Resource Center
See pages T5 and T21.

CHAPTER 1 RESOURCE MASTERS

Study Guide and Intervention	Practice (Skills and Average)	Reading to Learn Mathematics	Enrichment	Assessment	Prerequisite Skills Workbook	Applications*	Parent and Student Study Guide Workbook	5-Minute Check Transparencies	Interactive Chalkboard	Pre-AlgePASS: Tutorial Plus (lessons)	Materials
1	2–3	4	5		1–8		1	1-1	1-1		
6	7–8	9	10	51	5–12		2	1-2	1-2	1	
11	12–13	14	15		5–12	GCS 19 SC 1	3	1-3	1-3	2	*Follow-Up:* spreadsheet software
16	17–18	19	20	51, 53	5–10		4	1-4	1-4		
21	22–23	24	25		5–10	SC 2 SM 1	5	1-5	1-5		
26	27–28	29	30	52			6	1-6	1-6		
31	32–33	34	35	52		GCS 20	7	1-7	1-7		*Preview:* graph paper, centimeter ruler *Follow-Up:* graphing calculator
				37–50 54–56							

* *Key to Abbreviations:* GCS = Graphing Calculator and Spreadsheet Masters
SC = School-to-Career Masters
SM = Science and Mathematics Lab Manual

ELL Study Guide and Intervention, Skills Practice, Practice, and Parent and Student Study Guide Workbooks are also available in Spanish.

Mathematical Connections and Background

Continuity of Instruction

Prior Knowledge

Prior to studying Pre-Algebra, students should have a basic knowledge of properties of operations, such as the Distributive Property. Students should be familiar with expressing variables as symbols and mathematical relationships using equations. They also should be able to represent and analyze patterns using words, tables, and graphs.

This Chapter

This chapter reinforces and extends the skills learned prior to beginning the Pre-Algebra course and lays the foundation for the studies of algebra, geometry, and statistics in the rest of the book. Students will learn to solve problems, to evaluate expressions, and to use variables and expressions when solving real-world problems.

Future Connections

The tools of algebra learned in this chapter will be used throughout students' math studies in both high school and college. The graphing techniques they learn are also used in geometry, statistics, and other disciplines such as science and social studies.

1-1 Using a Problem-Solving Plan

One method of problem solving is a four-step plan:

1. *Explore* the problem to see what information exists and what needs to be found out.
2. *Plan* the strategy to be used to solve the problem and estimate the answer.
3. *Solve* the problem using the plan.
4. *Examine* the answer to see whether it is reasonable and close to the estimate. If not, use another strategy to solve the problem.

Another problem-solving method, called inductive reasoning, uses a conjecture based on a pattern of examples or past events. When solving a problem, it is important to choose an appropriate method of computation. Depending on the problem, you will want to estimate, use a calculator, or use paper and pencil.

1-2 Numbers and Expressions

When evaluating an expression, find its numerical value using the accepted order of operations:

Step 1 Simplify the expressions inside grouping symbols.

Step 2 Do all multiplications and/or divisions from left to right.

Step 3 Do all additions and/or subtractions from left to right.

An important aspect of translating verbal expressions to numerical ones is the awareness of vocabulary that has mathematical meanings. Develop a list of words and their mathematical translations.

1-3 Variables and Expressions

Algebra is a language of symbols. A variable is a placeholder for any value. Any letter, such as x, can be used as a variable. An expression such as $x + 2$ is an algebraic expression because it contains sums and/or products of variables and numbers. Usually, mathematicians avoid the use of i and e for variables because they have other mathematical meanings ($i = \sqrt{-1}$, e is used with natural logarithms).

To evaluate an algebraic expression, replace the variable or variables with known values—demonstrating the Substitution Property of Equality—and then use the order of operations. Translate verbal phrases into algebraic expressions by first defining a variable: choose a variable and a quantity for the variable to represent. Algebraic expressions can be used to represent real-world situations.

1-4 Properties

In algebra, properties are statements that are true for any numbers. For example, the expression $3 + 8 = 8 + 3$ because each expression equals 11. This illustrates the Commutative Property of Addition. Likewise, $3 \cdot 8 = 8 \cdot 3$ illustrates the Commutative Property of Multiplication.

When evaluating expressions, it is often helpful to group or *associate* the numbers. The Associative Property says that the way in which numbers are grouped when added or multiplied does not change the sum or product.

The following properties are also true:

Additive Identity Property: When 0 is added to any number, the sum is the number.
Multiplicative Identity Property: When any number is multiplied by 1, the product is the number.
Multiplicative Property of Zero: When any number is multiplied by 0, the product is 0.

You can use the properties of numbers to find sums and products mentally. Look for sums or products that end in zero. You also can use the Associative or Commutative Properties to simplify expressions.

1-5 Variables and Equations

A mathematical sentence that contains an equals sign (=) is called an equation. An equation that contains a variable is an open sentence. An open sentence is neither true nor false. When the variable in an open sentence is replaced with a number, you can determine whether the sentence is true or false. A value for the variable that makes an equation true is called a solution. For $x + 7 = 19$, the solution is 12. The process of finding a solution is called solving the equation.

Two properties of equality are the Symmetric Property and the Transitive Property.

Symmetric: If one quantity equals a second quantity, then the second quantity also equals the first. That is, if $a = b$, then $b = a$.
Transitive: If one quantity equals a second quantity and the second quantity equals a third quantity, then the first equals the third. This means if $a = b$ and $b = c$, then $a = c$.

1-6 Ordered Pairs and Relations

The Cartesian coordinate system is used to locate points. The coordinate system is formed by two perpen-dicular number lines that intersect at their zero points. An ordered pair of numbers is used to locate any point on a coordinate plane. The first number is called the *x*-coordinate or abscissa, and tells how far left or right of the origin the point is located. The second number is called the *y*-coordinate or ordinate, and tells how far up or down from the origin the point is located.

A set of ordered pairs such as {(1, 2), (2, 4), (3, 0), (4, 5)} is a relation. The domain of the relation is the set of *x*-coordinates. The range of the relation is the set of *y*-coordinates. A relation can be shown as a set of ordered pairs, as a table, or as a graph.

1-7 Scatter Plots

A scatter plot is a graph that shows the relation-ship between two sets of data. In a scatter plot, two sets of data are graphed as ordered pairs on a coordinate system. Two sets of data can have a positive relation-ship (as *x* increases, *y* increases), a negative relationship (as *x* increases, *y* decreases), or no relationship (no obvious pattern is shown). Scatter plots can be used to spot trends, draw conclusions, and make predictions.

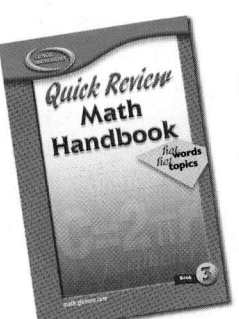

Quick Review Math Handbook

Hot Words includes a glossary of terms while Hot Topics consists of explanations of key mathematical concepts with exercises to test comprehension. This valuable resource can be used as a reference in the classroom or for home study.

Lesson	Hot Topics Section	Lesson	Hot Topics Section
GS 1	1.5	1-5	1.2, 6.1, 6.2, 6.3, 6.4, 6.7
1-1	1.1	1-6	1.5, 6.7
1-2	1.3, 1.5, 3.4	1-7P	4.3
1-3P	6.1, 6.2, 6.3	1-7	4.3
1-3	1.5, 6.1, 6.2, 6.3	1-7F	4.3
1-4	1.2, 1.5		

GS = Getting started, P = Preview, F = Follow-Up

 Additional mathematical information and teaching notes are available at www.pre-alg.com/key_concepts.

DAILY INTERVENTION and Assessment

Key to Abbreviations:
TWE = Teacher Wraparound Edition; CRM = Chapter Resource Masters

	Type	Student Edition	Teacher Resources	Technology/Internet
INTERVENTION	Ongoing	Prerequisite Skills, pp. 5, 10, 16, 21, 27, 32, 38 Practice Quiz 1, p. 21 Practice Quiz 2, p. 32	5-Minute Check Transparencies *Prerequisite Skills Workbook*, pp. 1–8, 5–12 Quizzes, CRM, pp. 51–52 Mid-Chapter Test, CRM, p. 53 Study Guide and Intervention, CRM, pp. 1, 6, 11, 16, 21, 26, 31	Pre-AlgePASS: Tutorial Plus, Lessons 1 and 2 www.pre-alg.com/self_check_quiz www.pre-alg.com/extra_examples
	Mixed Review	pp. 16, 21, 27, 32, 38, 44	Cumulative Review, CRM, p. 54	
	Error Analysis	Find the Error, pp. 14, 26	Find the Error, TWE, pp. 14, 26	
ASSESSMENT	Standardized Test Practice	pp. 10, 16, 21, 27, 29, 30, 32, 38, 44, 52–53	TWE, pp. 52–53 Standardized Test Practice, CRM, pp. 55–56	Standardized Test Practice CD-ROM www.pre-alg.com/standardized_test
	Open-Ended Assessment	Writing in Math, pp. 10, 16, 21, 27, 32, 37, 44 Open Ended, pp. 9, 14, 19, 26, 30, 36, 42 Standardized Test, p. 53	Speaking: TWE, pp. 10, 16, 27, 38 Writing: TWE, pp. 21, 32, 44 Open-Ended Assessment, CRM, p. 49	
	Chapter Assessment	Study Guide, pp. 47–50 Practice Test, p. 51	Multiple-Choice Tests (Forms 1, 2A, 2B), CRM, pp. 37–42 Free-Response Tests (Forms 2C, 2D, 3), CRM, pp. 43–48 Vocabulary Test/Review, CRM, p. 50	ExamView®Pro (see below) MindJogger Videoquizzes www.pre-alg.com/vocabulary_review www.pre-alg.com/chapter_test

 Yearly Progress Pro

For more information on Yearly ProgressPro, see p. 2.

Pre-Algebra Lesson	Yearly ProgressPro Skill Lesson(s)
1-1	Plan for Problem Solving
1-2	Evaluate Algebraic Expressions
1-3	Evaluate Algebraic Expressions
1-4	Commutative/Associative Properties of Addition Properties of Multiplication
1-5	Writing Expressions and Equations
1-6	Coordinate Locations: Level 3
1-7	Scatter Plots

 ExamView® Pro

Use the networkable **ExamView® Pro** to:
- Create **multiple versions** of tests.
- Create **modified** tests for *Inclusion* students.
- **Edit** existing questions and **add** your own questions
- Use built-in **state curriculum correlations** to create tests aligned with state standards.
- Change **English** tests to **Spanish** and vice versa.

For more information on Intervention and Assessment, see pp. T8–T11.

Reading and Writing in Mathematics

Glencoe Pre-Algebra provides numerous opportunities to incorporate reading and writing into the mathematics classroom.

Student Edition

- Foldables™ Study Organizer, p. 5
- Reading Mathematics, p. 11
- Concept Check questions require students to verbalize and write about what they have learned in the lesson. (pp. 6, 7, 9, 12, 14, 17, 19, 23, 24, 26, 30, 34, 36, 40, 41, 42)
- Writing in Math questions in every lesson, pp. 10, 16, 21, 27, 32, 37, 44
- Reading Math, pp. 17, 23, 24, 29
- WebQuest, p. 43

Teacher Wraparound Edition

- Foldables™ Study Organizer, pp. 5, 47
- Study Notebook suggestions, pp. 8, 11, 14, 19, 26, 30, 36, 42
- Speaking activities, pp. 10, 16, 27, 38
- Writing activities, pp. 21, 32, 44
- **ELL** Resources, pp. 4, 6, 11, 12, 17, 23, 28, 33, 40, 47

Additional Resources

- Vocabulary Builder worksheets require students to define and give examples for key vocabulary terms as they progress through the chapter (*Chapter 1 Resource Masters,* pp. vii–viii)
- Reading to Learn Mathematics master for each lesson (*Chapter 1 Resource Masters,* pp. 4, 9, 14, 19, 24, 29, 34)
- *Vocabulary PuzzleMaker* software creates crossword, jumble, and word search puzzles using vocabulary lists that you can customize.
- *Teaching Mathematics with Foldables* provides suggestions for promoting cognition and language.
- *Reading and Writing in the Mathematics Classroom*
- *WebQuest and Project Resources*

For more information on Reading and Writing in Mathematics, see pp. T6–T7.

PROJECT CRISS℠ Study Skill

Capsule vocabulary is a teaching strategy that helps students verbally review important terms. After students have studied Lesson 1-5, write the properties listed at the right on the chalkboard. Discuss the properties with the class. Divide the class into pairs. Have students talk about the properties with their partners. Each student should make sure his or her partner can explain or give an example of all of the properties. Afterward, have students write a short summary about the properties.

Properties
- Commutative Property of Addition
- Commutative Property of Multiplication
- Associative Property of Addition
- Associative Property of Multiplication
- Additive Identity Property
- Multiplicative Identity Property
- Multiplicative Property of Zero
- Symmetric Property of Equality
- Transitive Property of Equality

CReating **I**ndependence **T**hrough **S**tudent-**O**wned **S**trategies

What You'll Learn

Have students read over the list of objectives and make a list of any words with which they are not familiar.

Why It's Important

Point out to students that this is only one of many reasons why each objective is important. Others are provided in the introduction to each lesson.

The chart below correlates the objectives for each lesson to the NCTM Standards 2000. There is also space for you to reference your state and/or local objectives.

Lesson	NCTM Standards	Local Objectives
1-1	1, 6	
1-2	1	
1-3	1, 2	
1-3 Follow-Up	1, 2	
1-4	1, 4	
1-5	1, 6	
1-6	1	
1-7 Preview	1, 2, 5	
1-7	1, 2, 5	
1-7 Follow-Up	1, 2, 5	

Key to NCTM Standards:

1=Number & Operations, 2=Algebra,
3=Geometry, 4=Measurement,
5=Data Analysis & Probability, 6=Problem
Solving, 7=Reasoning & Proof,
8=Communication, 9=Connections,
10=Representation

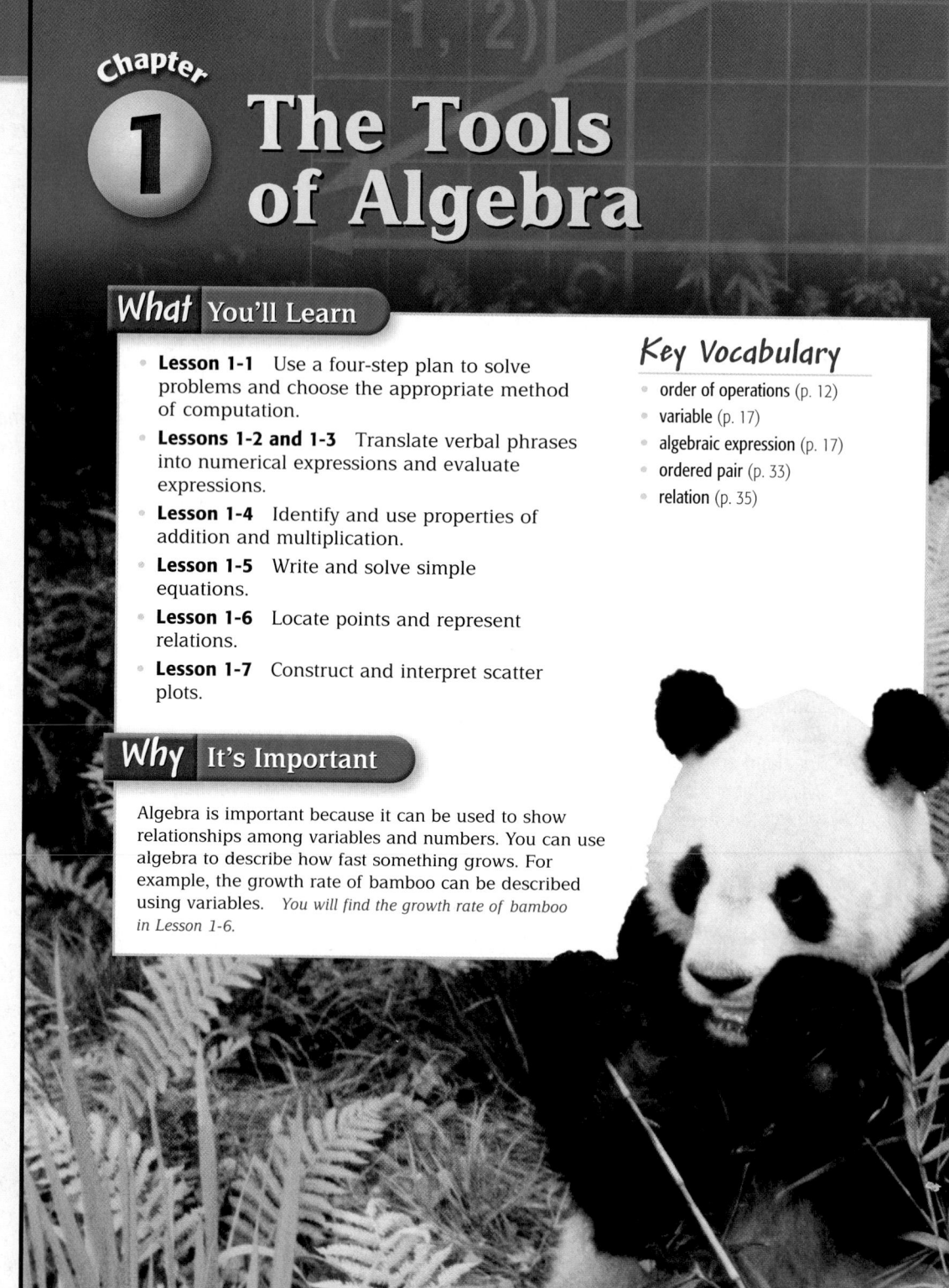

The Tools of Algebra

What You'll Learn

- **Lesson 1-1** Use a four-step plan to solve problems and choose the appropriate method of computation.
- **Lessons 1-2 and 1-3** Translate verbal phrases into numerical expressions and evaluate expressions.
- **Lesson 1-4** Identify and use properties of addition and multiplication.
- **Lesson 1-5** Write and solve simple equations.
- **Lesson 1-6** Locate points and represent relations.
- **Lesson 1-7** Construct and interpret scatter plots.

Key Vocabulary

- order of operations (p. 12)
- variable (p. 17)
- algebraic expression (p. 17)
- ordered pair (p. 33)
- relation (p. 35)

Why It's Important

Algebra is important because it can be used to show relationships among variables and numbers. You can use algebra to describe how fast something grows. For example, the growth rate of bamboo can be described using variables. *You will find the growth rate of bamboo in Lesson 1-6.*

Vocabulary Builder

ELL

The Key Vocabulary list introduces students to some of the main vocabulary terms included in this chapter. For a more thorough vocabulary list with pronunciations of new words, give students the Vocabulary Builder worksheets found on pages vii and viii of the *Chapter 1 Resource Masters*. Encourage them to complete the definition of each term as they progress through the chapter. You may suggest that they add these sheets to their study notebooks for future reference when studying for the Chapter 1 test.

▶ **Prerequisite Skills** To be successful in this chapter, you'll need to master these skills and be able to apply them in problem-solving situations. Review these skills before beginning Chapter 1.

For Lesson 1-1   **Add and Subtract Decimals**

Find each sum or difference.   *(For review, see page 713.)*

1. $6.6 + 8.2$ **14.8**   **2.** $4.7 + 8.5$ **13.2**   **3.** $5.4 - 2.3$ **3.1**

4. $8.6 - 4.9$ **3.7**   **5.** $2.65 + 0.3$ **2.95**   **6.** $1.08 + 1.2$ **2.28**

7. $4.25 - 0.7$ **3.55**   **8.** $4.3 - 2.89$ **1.41**   **9.** $9.06 - 1.18$ **7.88**

For Lessons 1-1 through 1-5   **Estimate with Whole Numbers**

Estimate each sum, difference, product, or quotient.

10. $1800 + 285$ **2300**   **11.** $328 + 879$ **1200**   **12.** $22{,}431 - 13{,}183$ **10,000**

13. $659 - 536$ **120**   **14.** 68×12 **700**   **15.** 189×89 **20,000**

16. $3845 \div 82$ **50**   **17.** $21{,}789 \div 97$ **220**   **18.** $\$1951 \div 49$ **\$40**

10–18. Sample answers are given.

For Lessons 1-1 through 1-5   **Estimate with Decimals**

Estimate each sum, difference, product, or quotient.   *(For review, see pages 712 and 714.)*

19. $8.8 + 5.3$ **14**   **20.** $47.2 + 9.75$ **57**   **21.** $\$7.34 - \$2.16$ **\$5**

22. $83.6 - 75.32$ **9**   **23.** 4.2×29.3 **120**   **24.** $18.8(5.3)$ **100**

25. $7.8 \div 2.3$ **4**   **26.** $54 \div 9.1$ **6**   **27.** $21.3 \div 1.7$ **10**

19–27. Sample answers are given.

 FOLDABLES™ Study Organizer

Problem Solving Make this Foldable to help you organize your notes. Begin with a sheet of unlined paper.

Step 1 **Fold**

Fold the short sides so they meet in the middle.

Step 2 **Fold Again**

Fold the top to the bottom.

Step 3 **Cut**

Unfold. Cut along the second fold to make four tabs.

Step 4 **Label**

Label each of the tabs as shown.

Reading and Writing As you read and study the chapter, you can write examples of each problem-solving step under the tabs.

This section provides a review of the basic concepts needed before beginning Chapter 1. Page references are included for additional student help.

Additional review is provided in the *Prerequisite Skills Workbook,* pages 1–12.

Prerequisite Skills in the Getting Ready for the Next Lesson section at the end of each lesson reviews a skill needed in the next lesson.

For Lesson	Prerequisite Skill
1-2	Round to Nearest Whole Number (p. 10)
1-3	Finding Sums (p. 16)
1-4	Finding Differences (p. 21)
1-5	Finding Products (p. 27)
1-6	Evaluating Expressions (p. 32)
1-7	Finding Quotients (p. 38)

Each chapter opens with Prerequisite Skills practice for lessons in the chapter. More Prerequisite Skill practice can be found at the end of each lesson.

Foldables™ are a unique way to enhance students' study skills. Encourage students to add to their Foldable as they work through the chapter, and use it to review for their chapter test.

FOLDABLES™ Study Organizer

For more information about Foldables, see *Teaching Mathematics with Foldables.*

Sequencing of Steps Under each tab of the Foldable, have students describe that step in detail and include examples of questions they might ask themselves during problem solving. Students can demonstrate their understanding and use of this problem-solving process by writing a problem under the explore tab, and using their Foldable to record how they plan, solve, and examine to reach a solution.

1-1 Using a Problem-Solving Plan

NEW YORK *Performance Indicator* **8.CM.1 Provide a correct, complete, coherent, and clear rationale for thought process used in problem solving**

1 Focus

5-Minute Check Transparency 1-1 Use as a quiz over prerequisite skills.

Mathematical Background notes are available for this lesson on page 4C.

Why is it helpful to use a problem-solving plan to solve problems?

The opening activity questions are repeated on page 4 of the *Chapter 1 Resource Masters.*

Reading to Learn Mathematics, p. 4   **ELL**

Pre-Activity *Why is it helpful to use a problem-solving plan to solve problems?*

Do the activity at the top of page 6 in your textbook. Write your answers below.

a. Find a pattern in the costs.   The cost increases by $0.21 for each additional ounce.

b. How can you determine the cost to mail a 6-ounce letter?   Add $0.21 to $1.18.

c. Suppose you were asked to find the cost of mailing a letter that weighs 8 ounces. What steps would you take to solve the problem? Sample answer: extend the pattern.

Reading the Lesson 1–2. See students' work.

Write a definition and give an example of each new vocabulary word or phrase.

Vocabulary	Definition	Example
1. conjecture		
2. inductive reasoning		

3. What is the next term: 3, 6, 12, 24 …? Explain.   48. Each number is two times the one before it, and 2 x 24 = 48.

4. Complete this sentence. In the ___examine___ step of the four-step problem-solving plan, you check the reasonableness of your answer.

Helping You Remember

5. Explain why each step of the four-step plan is important.   Students' answers will vary. Accept all reasonable answers.

Teaching Tip Encourage students to verbalize and write answers to the questions giving as many different explanations as possible.

Vocabulary
- conjecture
- inductive reasoning

a. The cost increases by $0.23 for each additional ounce.
b. Add $0.23 to $1.29.
c. Sample answer: extend the pattern.

Study Tip

Problem-Solving Strategies
Here are a few strategies you will use to solve problems in this book.
- Look for a pattern.
- Solve a simpler problem.
- Guess and check.
- Draw a diagram.
- Make a table or chart.
- Work backward.
- Make a list.

What You'll Learn
- Use a four-step plan to solve problems.
- Choose an appropriate method of computation.

Why is it helpful to use a problem-solving plan to solve problems?

The table shows the first-class mail rates in 2004.

Weight (oz)	Cost
1	$0.37
2	$0.60
3	$0.83
4	$1.06
5	$1.29

Source: www.ups.com

a. Find a pattern in the costs.
b. How can you determine the cost to mail a 6-ounce letter?
c. Suppose you were asked to find the cost of mailing a letter that weighs 8 ounces. What steps would you take to solve the problem?

FOUR-STEP PROBLEM-SOLVING PLAN   It is often helpful to have an organized plan to solve math problems. The following four steps can be used to solve any math problem.

1. Explore
- Read the problem quickly to gain a general understanding of it.
- Ask, "What facts do I know?" "What do I need to find out?"
- Ask, "Is there enough information to solve the problem? Is there extra information?"

2. Plan
- Reread the problem to identify relevant facts.
- Determine how the facts relate to each other.
- Make a plan to solve the problem.
- Estimate the answer.

3. Solve
- Use your plan to solve the problem.
- If your plan does not work, revise it or make a new plan.

4. Examine
- Reread the problem.
- Ask, "Is my answer reasonable and close to my estimate?"
- Ask, "Does my answer make sense?"
- If not, solve the problem another way.

 Concept Check Which step involves estimating the answer? Plan

Resource Manager

 Workbooks and Reproducible Masters

Chapter 1 Resource Masters
- Study Guide and Intervention, p. 1
- Skills Practice, p. 2
- Practice, p. 3
- Reading to Learn Mathematics, p. 4
- Enrichment, p. 5

Parent and Student Study Guide Workbook, p. 1
Prerequisite Skills Workbook, pp. 1–8

Transparencies
5-Minute Check Transparency 1-1
Answer Key Transparencies

Technology
Interactive Chalkboard

Example 1 Use the Four-Step Problem-Solving Plan

POSTAL SERVICE   Refer to page 6. How much would it cost to mail a 9-ounce letter first class?

Explore   The table shows the weight of a letter and the respective cost to mail it first class. We need to find how much it will cost to mail a 9-ounce letter.

Plan   Use the information in the table to solve the problem. Look for a pattern in the costs. Extend the pattern to find the cost for a 9-ounce letter.

Solve   First, find the pattern.

Weight (oz)	1	2	3	4	5
Cost	$0.37	$0.60	$0.83	$1.06	$1.29

+ 0.23   + 0.23   + 0.23   + 0.23

Each consecutive cost increases by $0.23. Next, extend the pattern.

Weight (oz)	5	6	7	8	9
Cost	$1.29	$1.52	$1.75	$1.98	$2.21

+ 0.23   + 0.23   + 0.23   + 0.23

It would cost $2.21 to mail a 9-ounce letter.

Examine   It costs $0.37 for the first ounce and $0.23 for each additional ounce. To mail a 9-ounce letter, it would cost $0.37 for the first ounce and $8 \times \$0.23$ or $1.84 for the eight additional ounces. Since $0.37 + $1.84 = $2.21, the answer is correct.

Study Tip

Reasonableness
Always check to be sure your answer is reasonable. If the answer seems unreasonable, solve the problem again.

A **conjecture** is an educated guess. When you make a conjecture based on a pattern of examples or past events, you are using **inductive reasoning**. In mathematics, you will use inductive reasoning to solve problems.

TEACHING TIP
Be sure to emphasize to students the importance of checking the reasonableness of the answer.

Example 2 Use Inductive Reasoning

a. Find the next term in 1, 3, 9, 27, 81, ...

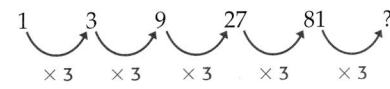

$$1 \quad 3 \quad 9 \quad 27 \quad 81 \quad ?$$
$$\times 3 \quad \times 3 \quad \times 3 \quad \times 3 \quad \times 3$$

Assuming the pattern continues, the next term is 81×3 or 243.

b. Draw the next figure in the pattern.

In the pattern, the shaded square moves counterclockwise. Assuming the pattern continues, the shaded square will be positioned at the bottom left of the figure.

✓ **Concept Check**   What type of reasoning is used when you make a conclusion based on a pattern? **inductive**

FOUR-STEP PROBLEM-SOLVING PLAN

Teaching Tip   A template for the four-step problem-solving plan is available on p. 18 of *Teaching Pre-Algebra with Manipulatives.*

In-Class Examples

1 **PIZZA** The price of a large cheese pizza at Paul's Pizza Place is $9.25. You receive a $0.50 discount for each additional pizza ordered, up to 10. So, one pizza costs $9.25, two pizzas cost $8.75 each, three pizzas cost $8.25 each, etc. If you need 8 pizzas for a party, what is the cost per pizza?   **$5.75**

2 **a.** Find the next term in 1, 4, 16, 64, 256, . . .   **1024**

b. Draw the next figure in the pattern.

CHOOSE THE METHOD OF COMPUTATION

In-Class Example

3 **PLANETS** The chart shows the distance of selected planets from the Sun. About how much farther is it from Earth to the Sun than from Mercury to the Sun?
about 57 million miles

Planet	Distance from Sun (millions of miles)
Mercury	36.0
Venus	67.24
Earth	92.9
Mars	141.71

Interactive Chalkboard
PowerPoint® Presentations

This CD-ROM is a customizable Microsoft® Power-Point® presentation that includes:
- Step-by-step, dynamic solutions of each In-Class Example from the Teacher Wraparound Edition
- Additional, Your Turn exercises for each example
- The 5-Minute Check Transparencies
- Hot links to Glencoe Online Study Tools

Study Notebook

Have students—
- add the definitions/examples of the vocabulary terms to their Vocabulary Builder worksheets for Chapter 1.
- copy the four-step problem-solving plan and write a brief explanation of each step.
- include any other item(s) that they find helpful in mastering the skills in this lesson.

Study Notebook tips offer suggestions for helping your students keep notes they can use to study this chapter.

About the Exercises . . .

Organization by Objective
- **Four Step Problem-Solving Plan:** 9–26
- **Choose the Method of Computation:** 21–26

Odd/Even Assignments
Exercises 9–20 are structured so that students practice the same concepts whether they are assigned odd or even problems.

Assignment Guide

Basic: 9, 10, 11–15 odd, 19–25 odd, 27–36

Average: 9, 10, 11–25 odd, 27–36

Advanced: 12–26 even, 27–30 (Optional: 31–36)

CHOOSE THE METHOD OF COMPUTATION Choosing the method of computation is also an important step in solving problems. Use the diagram below to help you decide which method is most appropriate.

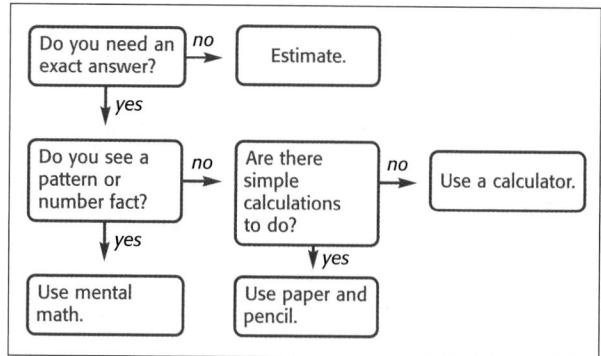

USA TODAY
Log on for:
- Updated data
- More activities on Using a Problem-Solving Plan
  www.pre-alg.com/usa_today

Glencoe's exclusive partnership with USA TODAY® provides actual USA TODAY Snapshots® that illustrate mathematical concepts.

Example 3 *Choose the Method of Computation*

TRAVEL The graph shows the seating capacity of certain baseball stadiums in the United States. About how many more seats does Comerica Park have than Fenway Park?

USA TODAY Snapshots®

Fenway has baseball's fewest seats
Boston's Fenway Park, opened in 1912, is Major League Baseball's oldest and smallest stadium, with a capacity of 33,871. Baseball's smallest stadiums in terms of capacity:

Fenway Park (Boston) 33,871
Wrigley Field (Chicago) 38,902
Comerica Park (Detroit) 40,000
Kauffman Stadium (Kansas City) 40,625
Pacific Bell Park (San Francisco) 40,800

Source: Major League Baseball

By Ellen J. Horrow and Bob Laird, USA TODAY

Explore You know the seating capacities of Comerica Park and Fenway Park. You need to find how many more seats Comerica Park has than Fenway Park.

Plan The question uses the word *about*, so an exact answer is not needed. We can solve the problem using estimation. Estimate the amount of seats for each park. Then subtract.

Solve Comerica Park: $40,000 \rightarrow 40,000$
Fenway Park: $33,871 \rightarrow 34,000$ Round to the nearest thousand.
$40,000 - 34,000 = 6000$ Subtract 34,000 from 40,000.

So, Comerica Park has about 6000 more seats than Fenway Park.

Examine Since $34,000 + 6000 = 40,000$, the answer makes sense.

DAILY
INTERVENTION **Differentiated Instruction**

- **Visual/Spatial** Give the students toothpicks to build the following models.

Ask students to build the models, then write down the number of toothpicks used to build each model. Finally, students should determine the number of toothpicks needed to build the tenth model. **21**

Concept Check

1. See margin.

1. **Tell** when it is appropriate to solve a problem using estimation.

2. **OPEN ENDED** Write a list of numbers in which four is added to get each succeeding term. **Sample answer: 0, 4, 8, 12, …**

Guided Practice

GUIDED PRACTICE KEY	
Exercises	Examples
4–7	2
3, 8	1, 3

3. **TIME** The ferry schedule at the right shows that the ferry departs at regular intervals. Use the four-step plan to find the earliest time a passenger can catch the ferry if he/she cannot leave until 1:30 P.M. **1:33 P.M.**

South Bass Island Ferry Schedule

Departures	Arrivals
8:45 A.M.	9:
9:33 A.M.	1
10:21 A.M.	
11:09 A.M.	

Find the next term in each list.

4. 10, 20, 30, 40, 50, … **60**

5. 37, 33, 29, 25, 21, … **17**

6. 12, 17, 22, 27, 32, … **37**

7. 3, 12, 48, 192, 768, … **3072**

Application

8. **MONEY** In 1999, the average U.S. household spent $12,057 on housing, $1891 on entertainment, $5031 on food, and $7011 on transportation. How much was spent on food each month? Round to the nearest cent.
Source: Bureau of Labor Statistics **$419.25**

★ **indicates increased difficulty**

Practice and Apply

Homework Help

For Exercises	See Examples
9, 10	1
11–20	2
21–26	3

Extra Practice
See page 724.

9. **178 beats per min**

HEALTH For Exercises 9 and 10, use the table that gives the approximate heart rate a person should maintain while exercising at 85% intensity.

Age	20	25	30	35	40	45
Heart Rate (beats/min)	174	170	166	162	158	154

9. Assume the pattern continues. Use the four-step plan to find the heart rate a 15-year-old should maintain while exercising at this intensity.

10. What heart rate should a 55-year old maintain while exercising at this intensity? **146 beats per min**

Find the next term in each list.

11. 2, 5, 8, 11, 14, … **17**

12. 4, 8, 12, 16, 20, … **24**

13. 0, 5, 10, 15, 20, … **25**

14. 2, 6, 18, 54, 162, … **486**

15. 54, 50, 46, 42, 38, … **34**

16. 67, 61, 55, 49, 43, … **37**

★17. 2, 5, 9, 14, 20, … **27**

★18. 3, 5, 9, 15, 23, … **33**

GEOMETRY Draw the next figure in each pattern. **19–20. See margin.**

19.

20.

21. **MONEY** Ryan needs to save $125 for a ski trip. He has $68 in his bank. He receives $15 for an allowance and earns $20 delivering newspapers and $16 shoveling snow. Does he have enough money for the trip? Explain. **See margin.**

 www.pre-alg.com/self_check_quiz/ny

Answers

1. **When an exact answer is not needed.**

19.

20.

21. **Since $68 + $15 + $20 + $16 = $119, Ryan does not have enough money for the ski trip.**

Open-Ended Assessment

Speaking Ask pairs of students to work through a given problem. Have each pair make a poster or transparency showing how they used the four-step problem-solving process. Have each pair present the results of their problem to the class.

New teachers, or teachers new to teaching mathematics, may especially appreciate the Tips for New Teachers.

Tips for New Teachers

Problem Solving Working through a four-step plan with students may take time. Some students find it difficult to plan the solution. You will want to model this process, encourage a variety of strategies, and work with students to estimate solutions. The problem-solving process will need to be reinforced frequently as you encounter new topics throughout the year.

Getting Ready for Lesson 1-2

BASIC SKILL Exercises 31–36 should be used to determine students' abilities to round decimal numbers to the nearest whole number. You may want to review rules for rounding before assigning these exercises.

---

22. Sample answer: 2 quarters, 1 dime, 5 pennies

25. Sample answer: about 21,800 transplants

More About . . .

Candy •
In 1981, $3\frac{1}{2}$ tons of red, blue, and white jelly beans were sent to the Presidential Inaugural Ceremonies for Ronald Reagan.
Source: www.jellybelly.com

NEW YORK Test Practice

Standardized Test Practice
Ⓐ Ⓑ Ⓒ Ⓓ

Getting Ready for the Next Lesson

---

22. MONEY Using eight coins, how can you make change for 65 cents that will not make change for a quarter?

23. TRANSPORTATION A car traveled 280 miles at 55 mph. About how many hours did it take for the car to reach its destination? **about 5 h**

24. CANDY A gourmet jelly bean company can produce 100,000 pounds of jelly beans a day. One ounce of these jelly beans contains 100 Calories. If there are 800 jelly beans in a pound, how many jelly beans can be produced in a day? **80,000,000 jelly beans**

25. MEDICINE The number of different types of transplants that were performed in the United States in 1999 are shown in the table. About how many transplants were performed?

Transplant	Number
heart	2185
liver	4698
kidney	12,483
heart-lung	49
lung	885
pancreas	363
intestine	70
kidney-pancreas	946

Source: *The World Almanac*

★ **26. COMMUNICATION** A telephone tree is set up so that every person calls three other people. Anita needs to tell her co-workers about a time change for a meeting. Suppose it takes 2 minutes to call 3 people. In 10 minutes, how many people will know about the change of time? **364 people**

27. CRITICAL THINKING Think of a 1 to 9 multiplication table.
  a. Are there more odd or more even products? How can you determine the answer without counting? **a–b. See margin.**
  b. Is this different from a 1 to 9 addition facts table?

28. WRITING IN MATH Answer the question that was posed at the beginning of the lesson. **See margin.**

  Why is it helpful to use a problem-solving plan to solve problems?
  Include the following in your answer:
  • an explanation of the importance of performing each step of the four-step problem-solving plan, and
  • an explanation of why it is beneficial to estimate the answer in the *Plan* step.

29. Find the next figure in the pattern shown below. **B**

30. A wagon manufacturing plant in Chicago, Illinois, can produce 8000 wagons a day at top production. Which of the following is a reasonable amount of wagons that can be produced in a year? **C**
  Ⓐ 24,000   Ⓑ 240,000   Ⓒ 2,400,000   Ⓓ 240,000,000

BASIC SKILL Round each number to the nearest whole number.

31. 2.8 **3**   **32.** 5.2 **5**   **33.** 35.4 **35**
34. 49.6 **50**   **35.** 109.3 **109**   **36.** 999.9 **1000**

Answers

27a. There are more even products; Since any even number multiplied by any number is even, and only an odd number multiplied by an odd number is odd, there are more even products in the table. There are about 3 times as many evens as odds.

27b. Yes; In the addition table, there is only one more even number than odd.

28. Sample answer: A problem-solving plan helps you to be organized in solving a math problem. Answers should include the following.

• It is important to perform each step. This enables you to understand the problem and its solution.

• By estimating the answer, you will know if your answer is reasonable.

Reading Mathematics

Reading Mathematics

NEW YORK *Performance Indicator* **8.A.2 Write verbal expressions that match given mathematical expressions**

Translating Expressions Into Words

Translating numerical expressions into verbal phrases is an important skill in algebra. Key words and phrases play an essential role in this skill.

The following table lists some words and phrases that suggest addition, subtraction, multiplication, and division.

Reading Mathematics features help students learn and use the language of mathematics.

Addition	Subtraction	Multiplication	Division
plus	minus	times	divided
sum	difference	product	quotient
more than	less than	multiplied	per
increased by	subtract	each	rate
in all	decreased by	of	ratio
	less	factors	separate

A few examples of how to write an expression as a verbal phrase are shown.

Expression	Key Word	Verbal Phrase
5×8	times	5 times 8
$2 + 4$	sum	the sum of 2 and 4
$16 \div 2$	quotient	the quotient of 16 and 2
$8 - 6$	less than	6 less than 8
2×5	product	the product of 2 and 5
$5 - 2$	less	5 less 2

Reading to Learn

1. Refer to the table above. Write a different verbal phrase for each expression.

1. Sample answer: the product of 5 and 8; 2 plus 4; 16 divided by 2; the difference of 8 and 6; 2 times 5; 2 less than 5

Choose the letter of the phrase that best matches each expression.

2. $9 - 3$ **c**

3. $3 \div 9$ **e**

4. $9 \cdot 3$ **d**

5. $3 + 9$ **a**

6. $9 \div 3$ **b**

   a. the sum of 3 and 9

   b. the quotient of 9 and 3

   c. 3 less than 9

   d. 9 multiplied by 3

   e. 3 divided by 9

11. 12 divided by 3; the quotient of 12 and 3

Write two verbal phrases for each expression. For Exercises 7–14, sample answers are given.

7. $5 + 1$ **5 plus 1; the sum of 5 and 1**

8. $8 + 6$ **the sum of 8 and 6; 6 more than 8**

9. 9×5 **9 times 5; the product of 9 and 5**

10. $2(4)$ **2 multiplied by 4; 2 times 4**

11. $12 \div 3$

12. $\frac{20}{4}$ **20 divided by 4; the quotient of 20 and 4**

13. $8 - 7$ **8 decreased by 7; 7 less than 8**

14. $11 - 5$ **11 minus 5; the difference of 11 and 5**

Before using this page, ask students to brainstorm any words or phrases they can think of that mean "add." Write the suggestions on the board. Repeat this activity for the words subtract, multiply, and divide.

Teach

- Ask students to look up the words *add, subtract, multiply,* and *divide* in a dictionary or thesaurus to further identify words or phrases that may be added to the list on the page. They can also investigate the origins of the words. Students can then practice translating numerical phrases into verbal phrases.
- Emphasize the difference between *decrease* and *decreased by,* and *less* and *less than.*

Assess

Study Notebook

Ask students to summarize what they have learned about translating expressions into words.

ELL English Language Learners may benefit from writing key concepts from this activity in their Study Notebooks in their native language and then in English.

ELL notations throughout the chapter indicate items that can assist English-Language Learners.

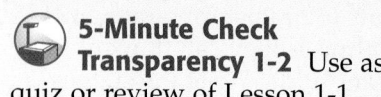

1 Focus

**5-Minute Check
Transparency 1-2** Use as a
quiz or review of Lesson 1-1.

Mathematical Background
notes are available for this lesson
on page 4C.

Why do we need to agree on
an order of operations?

The opening activity questions
are repeated on page 9 of the
Chapter 1 Resource Masters.

**Reading to Learn
Mathematics, p. 9**   **ELL**

Pre-Activity   *Why do we need to agree on an order of operations?*

Do the activity at the top of page 12 in your textbook. Write your
answers below.

a. Study the expressions and their respective values. For each expression,
tell the order in which the calculator performed the operations.
For $1 + 2 \times 5$, multiplication then addition; for $8 - 4 \div 2$,
division then subtraction; for $10 \div 5 + 14 \times 2$, division,
multiplication, then addition.

b. For each expression, does the calculator perform the operations in order
from left to right? **no**

c. Based on your answer to parts a and b, find the value of each
expression below. Check your answer with a scientific calculator.
$12 - 3 \times 2$ **6** $16 \div 4 - 2$ **2** $18 + 6 - 8 \div 2 \times 3$ **12**

d. **Make a conjecture** as to the order in which a scientific calculator
performs operations. Sample answer: Multiplication and
division first in the order they appear and then addition and
subtraction in the order they appear. The calculator performs
multiplication and division before addition and subtraction.

Reading the Lesson   1–3. See students' work.

Write a definition and give an example of each new vocabulary word or phrase.

Vocabulary	Definition	Example
1. numerical expression		
2. evaluate		
3. order of operations		

4. In the boxes below, write three different expressions using two operations that each have
a value of 6. Sample answers are given.

□ + □ × □ = 6   □ × □ − □ = 6   □ − □ × □ = 6

Helping You Remember

5. A mnemonic device helps you remember something. Create your own mnemonic device to
remember the order of operations. For example, list the operations in order, use the first
letter of each operation and create a phrase with words starting with the same letters.
Grouping symbols, Multiplication and Division, Addition and Subtraction
phrase: Give Me Dessert After Supper

Teaching Tip You may want to
demonstrate a calculation using
both a scientific calculator and a
four-function calculator to show that
one calculator uses the order of
operations and the other does not.

Resource Manager

📁 Workbooks and Reproducible Masters

Chapter 1 Resource Masters
• Study Guide and Intervention, p. 6
• Skills Practice, p. 7
• Practice, p. 8
• Reading to Learn Mathematics, p. 9
• Enrichment, p. 10
• Assessment, p. 51

**Parent and Student Study Guide
Workbook,** p. 2
Prerequisite Skills Workbook, pp. 5–12

📺 Transparencies
5-Minute Check Transparency 1-2
Answer Key Transparencies

💿 Technology
Interactive Chalkboard
Pre-AlgePASS: Tutorial Plus, Lesson 1

1-2 Numbers and Expressions

NEW YORK *Performance Indicator* **Reinforcement of 7.N.11 Simplify expressions using order of
operations** *Note: Expressions may include absolute value and/or integral exponents greater than 0.*

What You'll Learn

• Use the order of operations to evaluate expressions.
• Translate verbal phrases into numerical expressions.

Why do we need to agree on an order of operations?

Scientific calculators are programmed to find the value of an expression in
a certain order.

Expression	$1 + 2 \times 5$	$8 - 4 \div 2$	$10 \div 5 + 14 \times 2$
Value	11	6	30

a. Study the expressions and their respective values. For each expression,
tell the order in which the calculator performed the operations.

b. For each expression, does the calculator perform the operations in order
from left to right? **no**

c. Based on your answer to parts **a** and **b**, find the value of each expression
below. Check your answer with a scientific calculator.
$12 - 3 \times 2$ **6** $16 \div 4 - 2$ **2** $18 + 6 - 8 \div 2 \times 3$ **12**

d. **Make a conjecture** as to the order in which a scientific calculator
performs operations.

Vocabulary
• numerical expression
• evaluate
• order of operations

a. For $1 + 2 \times 5$,
multiplication then
addition; for
$8 - 4 \div 2$, division
then subtraction;
for $10 \div 5 + 14 \times 2$,
division, multiplication,
then addition.

TEACHING TIP

Nonscientific calculators
do not follow the order of
operations.

d. Sample answer:
Multiplication and
division first in the
order they appear and
then addition and
subtraction in the
order they appear.

Study Tip

Grouping Symbols
Grouping symbols include:
• parentheses ( ),
• brackets [ ], and
• fraction bars, as
in $\frac{6+4}{2}$, which
means $(6 + 4) \div 2$.

ORDER OF OPERATIONS   Expressions like $1 + 2 \times 5$ and $10 \div 5 + 14 \div 2$
are **numerical expressions**. Numerical expressions contain a combination of
numbers and operations such as addition, subtraction, multiplication, and
division.

When you **evaluate** an expression, you find its numerical value. To avoid
confusion, mathematicians have agreed upon the following **order of operations**.

Concept Summary   Order of Operations

Step 1   Simplify the expressions inside grouping symbols.
Step 2   Do all multiplications and/or divisions from left to right.
Step 3   Do all additions and/or subtractions from left to right.

Numerical expressions have only one value. Consider $6 + 4 \times 3$.

$$6 + 4 \times 3 = 6 + 12$$
$$= 18$$

Multiply,
then add.

$$6 + 4 \times 3 = 10 \times 3$$
$$= 30$$

Add, then
multiply.

Which is the correct value, 18 or 30? Using the order of operations, the correct
value of $6 + 4 \times 3$ is 18.

 Concept Check   Which operation should you perform first to evaluate
$10 - 2 + 3$? **subtraction**

Example 1 Evaluate Expressions

Find the value of each expression.

a. $3 + 4 \times 5$

$$3 + 4 \times 5 = 3 + 20 \quad \text{Multiply 4 and 5.}$$
$$= 23 \quad \text{Add 3 and 20.}$$

b. $18 \div 3 \times 2$

$$18 \div 3 \times 2 = 6 \times 2 \quad \text{Divide 18 by 3.}$$
$$= 12 \quad \text{Multiply 6 and 2.}$$

c. $6(2 + 9) - 3 \cdot 8$

$$6(2 + 9) - 3 \cdot 8 = 6(11) - 3 \cdot 8 \quad \text{Evaluate } (2 + 9) \text{ first.}$$
$$= 66 - 3 \cdot 8 \quad 6(11) \text{ means } 6 \times 11.$$
$$= 66 - 24 \quad 3 \cdot 8 \text{ means 3 times 8.}$$
$$= 42 \quad \text{Subtract 24 from 66.}$$

d. $4[(15 - 9) + 8(2)]$

$$4[(15 - 9) + 8(2)] = 4[6 + 8(2)] \quad \text{Evaluate } (15 - 9).$$
$$= 4(6 + 16) \quad \text{Multiply 8 and 2.}$$
$$= 4(22) \quad \text{Add 6 and 16.}$$
$$= 88 \quad \text{Multiply 4 and 22.}$$

e. $\dfrac{53 + 15}{17 - 13}$

$$\frac{53 + 15}{17 - 13} = (53 + 15) \div (17 - 13) \quad \text{Rewrite as a division expression.}$$
$$= 68 \div 4 \quad \text{Evaluate } 53 + 15 \text{ and } 17 - 13.$$
$$= 17 \quad \text{Divide 68 by 4.}$$

TRANSLATE VERBAL PHRASES INTO NUMERICAL EXPRESSIONS

You have learned to translate numerical expressions into verbal phrases. It is often necessary to translate verbal phrases into numerical expressions.

Example 2 Translate Phrases into Expressions

Write a numerical expression for each verbal phrase.

a. the product of eight and seven

Phrase	the product of eight and seven
Key Word	product
Expression	8×7

b. the difference of nine and three

Phrase	the difference of nine and three
Key Word	difference
Expression	$9 - 3$

www.pre-alg.com/extra_examples/ny   **Lesson 1-2** Numbers and Expressions   **13**

---

2 Teach

ORDER OF OPERATIONS

In-Class Example Power Point®

1 Find the value of each expression.

a. $6 + 8 \times 2$ **22**

b. $24 \div 8 \times 3$ **9**

c. $5(4 + 6) - 7 \cdot 7$ **1**

d. $3[(18 - 6) + 2(4)]$ **60**

e. $\dfrac{(49 + 31)}{(19 - 14)}$ **16**

Teaching Tip In Example 1e, you may want to show the division as a fraction to be simplified.

TRANSLATE VERBAL PHRASES INTO NUMERICAL EXPRESSIONS

In-Class Examples Power Point®

Teaching Tip Students may benefit from practicing verbal expressions orally.

2 Write a numerical expression for each verbal phrase.

a. the quotient of eighteen and six   **$18 \div 6$**

b. the sum of nine and five   **$9 + 5$**

3 **EARNINGS** Madison earns an allowance of $5 per week. She also earns $4 per hour babysitting, and usually babysits 6 hours each week. Write and evaluate an expression for the total amount of money she earns in one week.   **$5 + 4 \times 6$; $29**

About the Exercises . . .

Organization by Objective
• **Order of Operations:** 13–30, 40, 42, 48
• **Translate Verbal Phrases into Numerical Expressions:** 31–39, 41, 47

Odd/Even Assignments
Exercises 13–38 are structured so that students practice the same concepts whether they are assigned odd or even problems.

Assignment Guide
Basic: 13–23 odd, 29–35 odd, 39–42, 43, 45, 51–65
Average: 13–37 odd, 39–42, 43, 45, 51–65
Advanced: 14–38 even, 44, 46–61 (Optional: 62–65)

D A I L Y
INTERVENTION FIND THE ERROR
 Remind students that multiplication and division are performed in order from left to right. Multiplication is *not* automatically performed before division.

Answer

3. Emily; she followed the order of operations and divided first.

Example 3 *Use an Expression to Solve a Problem*

TRANSPORTATION A taxicab company charges a fare of $4 for the first mile and $2 for each additional mile. Write and then evaluate an expression to find the fare for a 10-mile trip.

Words	$4 for the first mile	and	$2 for each additional mile
Expression	4	+	2×9

TEACHING TIP
Be sure to explain why the number 9 is used. After the first mile of a 10-mile trip, there are 9 additional miles.

$$4 + 2 \times 9 = 4 + 18 \quad \text{Multiply.}$$
$$= 22 \quad \text{Add.}$$

The fare for a 10-mile trip is $22.

Check for Understanding

Concept Check

1. Sample answer: $(8 - 3) \cdot 2$
2. No; the value of $2 \times 4 + 3$ is 11 and the value of $2 \times (4 + 3)$ is 14.

1. **OPEN ENDED** Give an example of an expression involving multiplication and subtraction, in which you would subtract first.
2. **Tell** whether $2 \times 4 + 3$ and $2 \times (4 + 3)$ have the same value. Explain.
3. **FIND THE ERROR** Emily and Marcus are evaluating $24 \div 2 \times 3$.

Emily	Marcus
$24 \div 2 \times 3 = 12 \times 3$ $= 36$	$24 \div 2 \times 3 = 24 \div 6$ $= 4$

Who is correct? Explain your reasoning. **See margin.**

Guided Practice

Name the operation that should be performed first. Then find the value of each expression.

GUIDED PRACTICE KEY	
Exercises	Examples
4–9	1
10, 11	2
12	3

4. $3 \cdot 6 - 4$ ×; **14**
5. $32 - 24 \div 2$ ÷; **20**
6. $5(8) + 7$ ×; **47**
7. $6(15 - 4)$ −; **66**
8. $\frac{10 - 4}{1 + 2}$ − or +; **2**
9. $11 + 56 \div (2 \cdot 7)$ ×; **15**

Write a numerical expression for each verbal phrase.

10. the quotient of fifteen and five **15 ÷ 5**
11. the difference of twelve and nine **12 − 9**

Application

12. **MUSIC** Hector purchased 3 CDs for $13 each and 2 cassette tapes for $9 each. Write and then evaluate an expression for the total cost of the merchandise. **(3 × 13) + (2 × 9); $57**

★ indicates increased difficulty

Practice and Apply

Homework Help	
For Exercises	See Examples
13–28	1
31–38	2
39–42, 47, 48	3

Extra Practice
See page 724.

Find the value of each expression.

13. $2 \cdot 6 - 8$ **4**
14. $12 - 3 \times 3$ **3**
15. $12 \div 3 + 21$ **25**
16. $9 + 18 \div 3$ **15**
17. $8 + 5(6)$ **38**
18. $4(7) - 11$ **17**
19. $\frac{15 + 9}{32 - 20}$ **2**
20. $\frac{45 - 18}{9 \div 3}$ **9**
21. $11(6 - 1)$ **55**
22. $(9 - 7) \cdot 13$ **26**
23. $56 \div (7 \cdot 2) \times 6$ **24**
24. $75 \div (7 + 8) - 3$ **2**
★25. $2[5(11 - 3)] - 16$ **64**
★26. $5[4 + (12 - 4) \div 2]$ **40**
★27. $9[(22 - 17) + 5(1 + 2)]$ **180**
★28. $10[9(2 + 4) - 6 \cdot 2]$ **420**

USA TODAY Education

Online Lesson Plans

USA TODAY's Education Online site offers resources and interactive features connected to each day's newspaper. *Experience TODAY*, USA TODAY's daily lesson plan, is available on the site and delivered daily to subscribers. This plan provides instruction for integrating USA TODAY graphics and key editorial features into your mathematics classroom. Log on to **www.education.usatoday.com**

29. Find the value of *six added to the product of four and eleven.* **50**

30. What is the value of *sixty divided by the sum of two and ten?* **5**

Write a numerical expression for each verbal phrase.

31. six minus three **6 − 3**

32. seven increased by two **7 + 2**

33. nine multiplied by five **9 × 5**

34. eleven more than fifteen **15 + 11**

35. twenty-four divided by six **24 ÷ 6**

36. four less than eighteen **18 − 4**

★ **37.** the cost of 3 notebooks at $6 each **3 × $6**

★ **38.** the total amount of CDs if Erika has 4 and Roberto has 5 **4 + 5**

GARDENING For Exercises 39 and 40, use the following information.
A bag of potting soil sells for $2, and a bag of fertilizer sells for $13.

39. Write an expression for the total cost of 4 bags of soil and 2 bags of fertilizer. **(4 × 2) + (2 × 13)**

40. What is the total cost of the gardening supplies? **$34**

TRAVEL For Exercises 41 and 42, use the following information.
Miko is packing for a trip. The total weight of her luggage cannot exceed 200 pounds. She has 3 suitcases that weigh 57 pounds each and 2 sport bags that weigh 12 pounds each. **41. (3 × 57) + (2 × 12)**

41. Write an expression for the total weight of the luggage.

42. Is Miko's luggage within the 200-pound limit? Explain.
(3 × 57) + (2 × 12) is 195. So, Miko's luggage is within the limit.

Copy each sentence. Then insert parentheses to make each sentence true.

43. 61 − 15 + 3 = 43

44. 12 × 3 ÷ 1 + 2 = 12

45. 56 ÷ 2 + 6 − 4 = 3

46. 5 + 2 · 9 − 3 = 42

43–46. See margin.

FOOTBALL For Exercises 47 and 48, use the table and the following information. **47. (50 × 25) + (7 × 24) + (4 × 22) + (3 × 16)**
A national poll ranks college football teams using votes from sports reporters. Each vote is worth a certain number of points. Suppose The Ohio State University receives 50 first-place votes, 7 second-place votes, 4 fourth-place votes, and 3 tenth-place votes.

★ **47.** Write an expression for the number of points that Ohio State receives.

★ **48.** Find the total number of points. **1554**

Number of Points for Each Vote	
Vote	Points
1st place	25
2nd place	24
3rd place	23
4th place	22
5th place	21
⋮	⋮
25th place	1

More About . . .

Football •
The Ohio State University Buckeyes ended the 2002 season ranked No. 1 in NCAA Division I-A college football with a 14–0 record.
Source: www.espn.com

PUBLISHING For Exercises 49 and 50, use the following information.
An ISBN number is used to identify a published book. To determine if an ISBN number is correct, multiply each of the numbers in order by 10, 9, 8, 7, and so on. If the sum of the products can be divided by 11, with no remainder, the number is correct. **49–50. See margin.**

★ **49.** Find the ISBN number on the back cover of this book.

★ **50.** Is the number correct? Explain why or why not.

www.pre-alg.com/self_check_quiz/ny Lesson 1-2 Numbers and Expressions **15**

Answers

43. 61 − (15 + 3) = 43

44. 12 × 3 ÷ (1 + 2) = 12

45. 56 ÷ (2 + 6) − 4 = 3

46. (5 + 2) · (9 − 3) = 42

49. 0-07-825200-8

50. Yes; the total of the expression is 165, and 165 can be divided by 11 with no remainder.
(0 · 10) + (0 · 9) + (7 · 8) + (8 · 7) + (2 · 6) + (5 · 5) + (2 · 4) + (0 · 3) + (0 · 2) + (8 · 1)

Lesson 1-2 Numbers and Expressions **15**

Open-Ended Assessment

Speaking Show students the expression $3 + 4 \times 5 - 2$. Ask them to give two different verbal phrases for this expression. Then evaluate the expression, explaining their reasoning.

Getting Ready for Lesson 1-3

BASIC SKILL In Lesson 1-3, students will continue to evaluate expressions using addition, subtraction, multiplication, and division. Exercises 62–65 practice the basic skill of finding a sum.

Assessment Options

Quiz (Lessons 1-1 and 1-2) is available on p. 51 of the *Chapter 1 Resource Masters*.

Assessment Options lists the quizzes and tests that are available in the Chapter Resource Masters.

Answer

52. **Sample answer:** We need to agree on an order of operations so that each expression has one unique value. Answers should include the following.

• When evaluating a numerical expression, simplify any expressions inside grouping symbols. Then do all multiplication and/or division in order from left to right. Then do all addition and/or subtraction from left to right.

• When the order of operations is not followed, an incorrect value for the expression may result.

---

51. Sample answer:
$111 - (1 + 1 + 1) \times (11 + 1)$

NEW YORK Test Practice

Standardized Test Practice
Ⓐ Ⓑ Ⓒ Ⓓ

61. Sample answer: about 26 compact cars

Getting Ready for the Next Lesson

63. 126

---

51. **CRITICAL THINKING** Suppose only the 1, ➕, ➖, ✖, ➗, ⟮, ⟯, and ⟮ENTER⟯ keys on a calculator are working. How can you get a result of 75 if you are only allowed to push these keys fewer than 20 times?

52. ⟮WRITING IN MATH⟯ Answer the question that was posed at the beginning of the lesson. **See margin.**

Why do we need to agree on an order of operations?

Include the following in your answer:

• an explanation of how the order operations are performed, and
• an explanation of what will happen to the value of an expression if the order of operations are not followed.

53. Which expression has a value of 18? **C**

Ⓐ $2[2(6 - 3)] + 5$ Ⓑ $27 \div 3 + (12 - 4)$

Ⓒ $(9 \times 3) - 63 \div 7$ Ⓓ $6(3 + 2) \div (9 - 7)$

54. Identify the expression that represents *the quotient of ten and two.* **B**

Ⓐ $2 \div 10$ Ⓑ $\frac{10}{2}$ Ⓒ 10×2 Ⓓ $10 - 2$

Maintain Your Skills

Mixed Review   **Find the next term in each list.** *(Lesson 1-1)*

55. 2, 4, 8, 16, 32, … **64**   56. 45, 42, 39, 36, 33, … **30**

57. 1, 3, 6, 10, 15, 21, … **28**   58. 15, 18, 22, 25, 29, … **32**

Solve each problem. *(Lesson 1-1)*

59. **BUSINESS** Mrs. Lewis is a sales associate for a computer company. She receives a salary, plus a bonus for any computer package she sells. Find Mrs. Lewis' bonus if she sells 16 computer packages. **$275**

Packages	Bonus
2	$100
4	$125
6	$150
8	$175

60. **TRAVEL** The graph shows the projected number of travelers for 2020. How many more people will travel to the United States than to Spain? **31 million**

61. **SPACE SHUTTLE** The space shuttle can carry a payload of about 65,000 pounds. If a compact car weighs about 2450 pounds, about how many compact cars can the space shuttle carry?

BASIC SKILL   **Find each sum.**

62. $18 + 34$ **52**   63. $85 + 41$

64. $342 + 50$ **392**   65. $535 + 28$ **563**

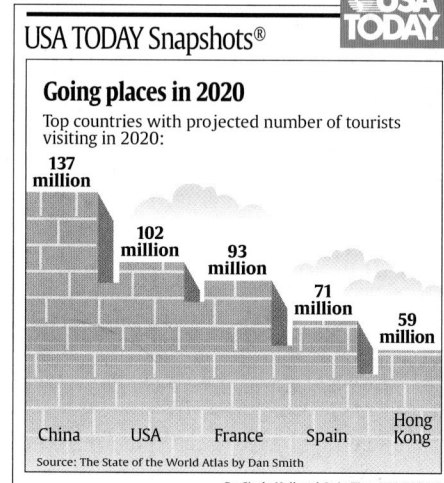
USA TODAY Snapshots®
Going places in 2020
Top countries with projected number of tourists visiting in 2020:
137 million — China
102 million — USA
93 million — France
71 million — Spain
59 million — Hong Kong
Source: The State of the World Atlas by Dan Smith
By Cindy Hall and Quin Tian, USA TODAY

16   Chapter 1   The Tools of Algebra

The Resource Manager lists all of the resources available for the lesson, including workbooks, blackline masters, transparencies, and technology.

1-3 Variables and Expressions

What You'll Learn

- Evaluate expressions containing variables.
- Translate verbal phrases into algebraic expressions.

How are variables used to show relationships?

A baby-sitter earns $5 per hour. The table shows several possibilities for number of hours and earnings.

a. Suppose the baby-sitter worked 10 hours. How much would he or she earn? **$50**

b. What is the relationship between the number of hours and the money earned? **The amount earned is five times the number of hours.**

c. If *h* represents *any number of hours,* what expression could you write to represent the amount of money earned? **5*h***

Number of Hours	Money Earned
2	5 · 2 or 10
5	5 · 5 or 25
8	5 · 8 or 40
11	5 · 11 or 55
h	?

Vocabulary

- variable
- algebraic expression
- defining a variable

Reading Math

Variable
Root Word: Vary
The word *variable* means *likely to change or vary.*

TEACHING TIP

The expression $\frac{y}{3}$ is an algebraic expression because it can be written as $\frac{1}{3}y$.

NEW YORK
Performance Indicator

Reinforcement of 7.A.1
Translate two-step verbal expressions into algebraic expressions

Reinforcement of 6.A.2
Use substitution to evaluate algebraic expressions (may include exponents of one, two, and three)

EVALUATE EXPRESSIONS Algebra is a language of symbols. One symbol that is frequently used is a variable. A **variable** is a placeholder for any value. As shown above, *h* represents some *unknown number of hours.*

Any letter can be used as a variable. Notice the special notation for multiplication and division with variables.

| The letter *x* is most often used as a variable. | $4h$ means $4 \times h$.
 mn means $m \times n$. | $\frac{y}{3}$ means $y \div 3$. |

$$x + 2 \qquad 4h - 5 \qquad mn \qquad \frac{y}{3}$$

An expression like $x + 2$ is an **algebraic expression** because it contains sums and/or products of variables and numbers.

✔ **Concept Check** *True or false:* 2*x* is an example of an algebraic expression. Explain your reasoning. **True; it is a combination of 2, *x*, and multiplication.**

To evaluate an algebraic expression, replace the variable or variables with known values and then use the order of operations.

Example 1 Evaluate Expressions

Evaluate $x + y - 9$ if $x = 15$ and $y = 26$.

$$\begin{aligned} x + y - 9 &= 15 + 26 - 9 &&\text{Replace } x \text{ with 15 and } y \text{ with 26.} \\ &= 41 - 9 &&\text{Add 15 and 26.} \\ &= 32 &&\text{Subtract 9 from 41.} \end{aligned}$$

Lesson 1-3 Variables and Expressions **17**

1-3 Lesson Notes

1 Focus

5-Minute Check Transparency 1-3 Use as a quiz or review of Lesson 1-2.

Mathematical Background notes are available for this lesson on page 4C.

How are variables used to show relationships?

The opening activity questions are repeated on page 14 of the *Chapter 1 Resource Masters.*

Reading to Learn Mathematics, p. 14   ELL

Pre-Activity *How are variables used to show relationships?*

Do the activity at the top of page 17 in your textbook. Write your answers below.

a. Suppose the baby-sitter worked 10 hours. How much would he or she earn? **$50**

b. What is the relationship between the number of hours and the money earned? **The amount earned is five times the number of hours.**

c. If *h* represents *any number of hours,* what expression could you write to represent the amount of money earned? **5*h***

Reading the Lesson 1–3. See students' work.

Write a definition and give an example of each new vocabulary word or phrase.

Vocabulary	Definition	Example
1. variable		
2. algebraic expression		
3. defining a variable		

4. Name three things that make an algebraic expression. **variables, numbers, and operations**

5. Why do you think replacing a variable with a number is called the Substitution Property of Equality? **If two quantities are equal, then one can be substituted, or replaced, for the other.**

Helping You Remember

6. *Variable* is a word used in everyday English.

a. Find the definition of *variable* in the dictionary. Write the definition. **able or apt to vary; subject to variation or changes**

b. Explain how the English definition can help you remember how *variable* is used in mathematics. **See students' answers.**

Resource Manager

📁 Workbooks and Reproducible Masters

Chapter 1 Resource Masters
- Study Guide and Intervention, p. 11
- Skills Practice, p. 12
- Practice, p. 13
- Reading to Learn Mathematics, p. 14
- Enrichment, p. 15

Graphing Calculator and Spreadsheet Masters, p. 19
Parent and Student Study Guide Workbook, p. 3
Prerequisite Skills Workbook, pp. 5–12
School-to-Career Masters, p. 1

Transparencies

5-Minute Check Transparency 1-3
Answer Key Transparencies

💿 Technology

Interactive Chalkboard
Pre-AlgePASS: Tutorial Plus, Lesson 2

2 Teach

EVALUATE EXPRESSIONS

In-Class Examples

1 Evaluate $x - y + 6$ if $x = 27$ and $y = 12$. **21**

Teaching Tip Make sure students remember that $4x$ means 4 times x. So if $x = 3$, $4x = 12$, not 43.

2 Evaluate each expression if $x = 3$, $y = 4$, and $z = 7$.

a. $6y - 4x$ **12**

b. $\dfrac{(z - x)}{y}$ **1**

c. $5z + (x + 4y) - 15$ **39**

TRANSLATE VERBAL PHRASES

In-Class Examples

3 Translate each phrase into an algebraic expression.

a. 35 more than the number of tickets sold $t + 35$

b. the difference of six times a number and 10 $6n - 10$

4 East Middle School sold tickets for a school play. The price of an adult ticket was $3, and the price of a student ticket was $1.

a. Write an expression that can be used to find the total amount of money collected. **3a + 1s**

b. Suppose 70 adult tickets and 85 students tickets were sold. How much money was collected? **$295**

Replacing a variable with a number demonstrates the **Substitution Property of Equality**.

> ### Key Concept — Substitution Property of Equality
> * **Words**   If two quantities are equal, then one quantity can be replaced by the other.
> * **Symbols**   For all numbers a and b, if $a = b$, then a may be replaced by b.

Example 2 Evaluate Expressions

Evaluate each expression if $k = 2$, $m = 7$, and $n = 4$.

a. $6m - 3k$

$$6m - 3k = 6(7) - 3(2) \quad \text{Replace } m \text{ with 7 and } k \text{ with 2.}$$
$$= 42 - 6 \quad \text{Multiply.}$$
$$= 36 \quad \text{Subtract.}$$

b. $\dfrac{mn}{2}$

$$\dfrac{mn}{2} = mn \div 2 \quad \text{Rewrite as a division expression.}$$
$$= (7 \cdot 4) \div 2 \quad \text{Replace } m \text{ with 7 and } n \text{ with 4.}$$
$$= 28 \div 2 \quad \text{Multiply.}$$
$$= 14 \quad \text{Divide.}$$

c. $n + (k + 5m)$

$$n + (k + 5m) = 4 + (2 + 5 \cdot 7) \quad \text{Replace } n \text{ with 4, } k \text{ with 2, and } m \text{ with 7.}$$
$$= 4 + (2 + 35) \quad \text{Multiply 5 and 7.}$$
$$= 4 + 37 \quad \text{Add 2 and 35.}$$
$$= 41 \quad \text{Add 4 and 37.}$$

TRANSLATE VERBAL PHRASES The first step in translating verbal phrases into algebraic expressions is to choose a variable and a quantity for the variable to represent. This is called **defining a variable**.

Example 3 Translate Verbal Phrases into Expressions

Translate each phrase into an algebraic expression.

a. twelve points more than the Dolphins scored

| **Words** | twelve points more than the Dolphins scored |
| **Variable** | Let p represent the points the Dolphins scored. |

	twelve points	more than	the Dolphins scored	
Expression	12	+	p	The expression is $p + 12$.

b. four times a number decreased by 6

| **Words** | four times a number decreased by 6 |
| **Variable** | Let n represent the number. |

	four times a number	decreased by	six	
Expression	$4n$	−	6	The expression is $4n - 6$.

DAILY INTERVENTION

Differentiated Instruction

* **Logical** Make a set of expression cards with numbers, operation symbols, and variables. Put one character on each card. Some students will hold number cards, some will hold operation symbol cards, and others will hold variable cards. Ask four or five students at a time to line up, making an expression using their cards. Have students with numbers interchange places with students who have variables, and so on, to create many different combinations and expressions.

Study Tip

Look Back
To review **key words and phrases**, see p. 11.

> Key Concept boxes highlight definitions, formulas, and other important ideas. Multiple representations— words, symbols, examples, models— reach students of all learning styles.

Algebraic expressions can be used to represent real-world situations.

Example 4 **Use an Expression to Solve a Problem**

More About. . .

Soccer

Soccer is the fastest growing and most popular sport in the world. It is estimated that more than 100,000,000 people in more than 150 countries play soccer.

Source: *The World Almanac for Kids*

SOCCER The Johnstown Soccer League ranks each team in their league using points. A team gets three points for a win and one point for a tie.

a. Write an expression that can be used to find the total number of points a team receives.

Words	three points for a win and one point for a tie
Variables	Let w = number of wins and t = number of ties.

three points for a win   and   one point for a tie

Expression $3w$ $+$ $1t$

The expression $3w + 1t$ can be used to find the total number of points a team will receive.

b. Suppose in one season, the North Rockets had 17 wins and 4 ties. How many points did they receive?

$$3w + 1t = 3(17) + 1(4) \quad \text{Replace } w \text{ with 17 and } t \text{ with 4.}$$
$$= 51 + 4 \quad \text{Multiply.}$$
$$= 55 \quad \text{Add.}$$

The North Rockets received 55 points.

Check for Understanding

Concept Check

1. Sample answer: $7n$ and $3x - 1$; $2 + 3$ and 3×8

1. **OPEN ENDED**   Give two examples of an algebraic expression and two examples of expressions that are *not* algebraic.

2. **Define** *variable.* **A variable is a placeholder for a number.**

3. **Write** an expression that is the same as $4cd$. **Sample answer: $4 \times c \times d$**

Guided Practice

GUIDED PRACTICE KEY	
Exercises	Examples
4–7	1, 2
8–11	3
12	4

ALGEBRA   Evaluate each expression if $a = 5$, $b = 12$, and $c = 4$.

4. $b + 6$ **18**
5. $18 - 3c$ **6**
6. $\dfrac{2b}{8}$ **3**
7. $5a - (b - c)$ **17**

ALGEBRA   Translate each phrase into an algebraic expression.

8. eight more than the amount Kira saved $s + 8$

9. five goals less than the Pirates scored $g - 5$

10. the quotient of a number and four, minus five $k \div 4 - 5$

11. seven increased by the quotient of a number and eight $7 + n \div 8$

Application

12. **SPACE**   Due to gravity, objects weigh three times as much on Earth as they do on Mercury.

a. Suppose the weight of an object on Mercury is w. Write an expression for the object's weight on Earth. $3w$

b. How much would an object weigh on Earth if it weighs 25 pounds on Mercury? **75 lb**

Lesson 1-3 Variables and Expressions **19**

3 Practice/Apply

Study Notebook

Have students—
• add the definitions/examples of the vocabulary terms to their Vocabulary Builder worksheets for Chapter 1.
• record the different ways to show multiplication and division in algebraic expressions.
• include any other item(s) that they find helpful in mastering the skills in this lesson.

About the Exercises . . .

Organization by Objective
• **Evaluate Expressions:** 13–32, 43–44, 50
• **Translate Verbal Phrases:** 33–42, 48, 49

Odd/Even Assignments
Exercises 13–44 are structured so that students practice the same concepts whether they are assigned odd or even problems.

Alert! Exercises 8–11 and 33–42 can have different variables from given answers.

Assignment Guide
Basic: 13–29 odd, 31, 32, 33–39 odd, 45, 47, 51–62
Average: 13–29 odd, 31, 32, 33–47 odd, 51–62
Advanced: 14–30 even, 34–48 even, 49–58 (Optional: 59–62)
All: Practice Quiz 1 (1–5)

★ indicates increased difficulty

Practice and Apply

ALGEBRA Evaluate each expression if $x = 7$, $y = 3$, and $z = 9$.

13. $z + 2$ **11**
14. $5 + x$ **12**
15. $2 + 4z$ **38**
16. $15 - 2x$ **1**
17. $\frac{6y}{z}$ **2**
18. $\frac{9x}{y}$ **21**
19. $\frac{xy}{3} + 2$ **9**
20. $10 - \frac{xz}{9}$ **3**
21. $4z - 3y$ **27**
22. $3x - 2y$ **15**
23. $2x + 3z + 5y$ **56**
24. $5z - 3x - 2y$ **18**
25. $7z - (y + x)$ **53**
26. $(8y + 5) - 2z$ **11**
27. $3y + (7z - 4x)$ **44**
28. $6x - (z - 2y) + 15$ **54**
29. $2x + (4z - 13) - 5$ **32**
30. $(9 - 3y) + 4z - 5$ **31**

SCIENCE For Exercises 31 and 32, use the following information.
The number of times a cricket chirps can be used to estimate the temperature in degrees Fahrenheit. Use $c \div 4 + 37$ where c is the number of chirps in one minute.

31. Find the approximate temperature if a cricket chirps 136 times in a minute.   **71° F**

32. What is the temperature if a cricket chirps 100 times in a minute?   **62° F**

ALGEBRA Translate each phrase into an algebraic expression.

33. Mark's salary plus a $200 bonus $s + \$200$
34. three more than the number of cakes baked $c + 3$
35. six feet shorter than the mountain's height $h - 6$
36. two seconds faster than Sarah's time $t + 2$
37. five times a number, minus four $5q - 4$
38. seven less than a number times eight $8n - 7$
39. nine more than a number divided by six $n \div 6 + 9$
40. the quotient of eight and twice a number $8 \div 2b$
★ 41. the difference of seventeen and four times a number $17 - 4w$
★ 42. three times the product of twenty-five and a number $3(25 \times n)$

★ 43. Evaluate $\frac{10mn}{3p - 3}$ if $m = 6$, $n = 3$, and $p = 7$.   **10**

★ 44. What is the value of $\frac{3(4a - 3b)}{b - 4}$ if $a = 6$ and $b = 7$?   **3**

ALGEBRA Write an algebraic expression that represents the relationship in each table.   45. $x + 3$ 46. $5n$ 47. $p - 4$

45.

Age Now	Age in Three Years
10	13
12	15
15	18
20	23
x	▪

46.

Number of Items	Total Cost
5	25
6	30
8	40
10	50
n	▪

47.

Regular Price	Sale Price
$12	8
$15	11
$18	14
$24	20
$p	▪

There is a Study Guide and Intervention, Skills Practice, Practice, Reading to Learn Mathematics, and Enrichment Master for every lesson in the Student Edition. These masters can be found in the Chapter Resource Masters.

48. **BUSINESS** Cornet Cable charges $32.50 a month for basic cable television. Each premium channel selected costs an additional $4.95 per month. Write an expression to find the cost of a month of cable service. **32.50 + 4.95c**

SALES For Exercises 49 and 50, use the following information.
The selling price of a sweater is the cost plus the markup minus the discount.

49. Write an expression to show the selling price s of a sweater. Use c for cost, m for markup, and d for discount. **$s = c + m - d$**

50. Suppose the cost of a sweater is $25, the markup is $20, and the discount is $6. What is the selling price of the sweater? **$39**

51. **CRITICAL THINKING** What value of t makes the expressions $6t$, $t + 5$, and $2t + 4$ equal? **1**

52. WRITING IN MATH   Answer the question that was posed at the beginning of the lesson. **See margin.**

How are variables used to show relationships?

Include the following in your answer:
- an explanation of variables and what they represent, and
- an example showing how variables are used to show relationships.

NEW YORK
Test Practice

Standardized
Test Practice
Ⓐ Ⓑ Ⓒ Ⓓ

53. If the value of $c + 5$ is 18, what is the value of c? **D**
   Ⓐ 3   Ⓑ 8   Ⓒ 7   Ⓓ 13

54. Which expression represents *four less than twice a number*? **B**
   Ⓐ $4n - 2$ Ⓑ $2n - 4$ Ⓒ $4(2 + n)$ Ⓓ $2n + 4$

Maintain Your Skills

Mixed Review   Find the value of each expression.   *(Lesson 1-2)*

55. $3 + (6 \times 2) - 8$ **7**   56. $5(16 - 5 \times 3)$ **5**   57. $36 \div (9 \cdot 2) + 7$ **9**

58. **FOOD** The table shows the amount in pounds of certain types of pasta sold in a recent year. About how many million pounds of these types of pasta were sold?   *(Lesson 1-1)*
Sample answer: about 660 million lb

Pasta	Amount (millions)
Spaghetti	308
Elbow	121
Noodles	70
Twirl	52
Penne	51
Lasagna	35
Fettuccine	24

Source: *National Pasta Association*

Getting Ready for the Next Lesson   **BASIC SKILL**   Find each difference.

59. $53 - 17$ **36**   60. $97 - 28$ **69**   61. $104 - 82$ **22**   62. $152 - 123$ **29**

Practice Quiz 1   Lessons 1-1 through 1-3

1. What is the next term in the list 4, 5, 7, 10, …?   *(Lesson 1-1)* **14**

Find the value of each expression.   *(Lesson 1-2)*

2. $28 \div 4 \times 2$ **14**   3. $7(3 + 10) - 2 \cdot 6$ **79**   4. $3[6(12 - 3)] - 17$ **145**

5. Evaluate $7x - 3y$ if $x = 4$ and $y = 2$.   *(Lesson 1-3)* **22**

Answer

52. **Expressions show relationships, and the variables in the relationships are placeholders for numbers. Answers should include the following.**

- **Variables are placeholders that are represented by letters.**
- **For example, $x + y = 2$. This shows that the sum of two numbers is equal to 2.**

4 Assess

Open-Ended Assessment

Writing Ask students to write an algebraic expression involving two variables and two or more operations. They can then assign values to the variables and evaluate them, showing how the result was determined.

Each lesson ends with Open-Ended Assessment strategies for closing the lesson. These include writing, modeling, and speaking.

Getting Ready for Lesson 1-4

BASIC SKILL Lesson 1-4 continues to utilize algebraic expressions as properties are introduced. Exercises 59–62 practice the basic skill of finding differences. The algebraic expressions can involve all four operations, including subtraction.

Assessment Options

Practice Quiz 1 The quiz provides students with a brief review of the concepts and skills in Lessons 1-1 through 1-3. Lesson numbers are given to the right of exercises or instruction lines so students can review concepts not yet mastered.

Spreadsheet Investigation

Getting Started

Objective Use a spreadsheet to explore algebraic expressions.

Materials
spreadsheet application

Teaching Tip Before starting this activity, you may want to familiarize students with the layout of a spreadsheet. Provide students with a copy of a blank spreadsheet template from p. 2 of the *Graphing Calculator and Spreadsheet Masters*. Ask them to locate specific cells.

Teaching Tip Review the formulas that appear in each B cell of the spreadsheet in the Example so that students understand what they mean.

Teach

- Before students enter each spreadsheet command, you may want them to guess what will happen and how the page will look.
- You may want students to work in pairs to discuss their ideas and help each other troubleshoot any problems they may have getting used to the software.

Assess

In **Exercises 6–8**, students should:

- discover that using any type of number in the example problem gives a result of 3.
- verify with algebra tiles that the result of the example problem is 3 unit tiles.
- extend their thinking about expressions and spreadsheets to create their own example problem.

Spreadsheet Investigation

NEW YORK *Performance Indicator* **8.R.1 Use** physical objects, drawings, charts, **tables**, graphs, symbols, equations, and **objects created using technology as representations**

Expressions and Spreadsheets

One of the most common computer applications is a spreadsheet program. A **spreadsheet** is a table that performs calculations. It is organized into boxes called **cells**, which are named by a letter and a number. In the spreadsheet below, cell B2 is highlighted.

An advantage of using a spreadsheet is that values in the spreadsheet are recalculated when a number is changed. You can use a spreadsheet to investigate patterns in data.

Example

Here's a mind-reading trick! Think of a number. Then double it, add six, divide by two, and subtract the original number. What is the result?

You can use a spreadsheet to test different numbers. Suppose we start with the number 10.

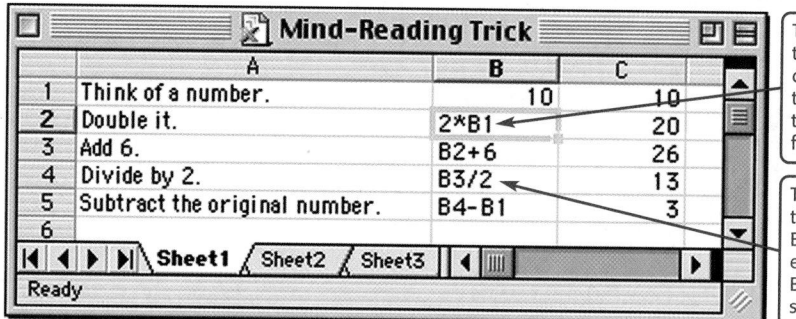

The spreadsheet takes the value in B1, doubles it, and enters the value in B2. Note the * is the symbol for multiplication.

The spreadsheet takes the value in B3, divides by 2, and enters the value in B4. Note that / is the symbol for division.

The result is 3.

Exercises

To change information in a spreadsheet, move the cursor to the cell you want to access and click the mouse. Then type in the information and press Enter. Find the result when each value is entered in B1.

1. 6 **3**   **2.** 8 **3**   **3.** 25 **3**   **4.** 100 **3**   **5.** 1500 **3**

Make a Conjecture

6. What is the result if a decimal is entered in B1? a negative number? **3, 3**

7. Explain why the result is always 3. **See margin.**

8. Make up your own mind-reading trick. Enter it into a spreadsheet to show that it works. **See margin.**

Answers

7. Let *x* represent the number. When you double the number the result is 2*x*. Adding 6 you get 2*x* + 6. Dividing by 2, *x* + 3 results. Subtracting the original number, you get 3. Thus, regardless of what *x* represents, the result is always 3.

8. Sample answer: Think of a number. Double it, add 4, divide by 2, and subtract the original number. The result is always 2.

1-4 Properties

What You'll Learn

- Identify and use properties of addition and multiplication.
- Use properties of addition and multiplication to simplify algebraic expressions.

Vocabulary
- properties
- counterexample
- simplify
- deductive reasoning

NEW YORK
Performance Indicator

Reinforcement of 6.N.2 Define and identify the commutative and associative properties of addition and multiplication

Reinforcement of 6.N.4 Define and identify the identity and inverse properties of addition and multiplication

Reinforcement of 6.N.5 Define and identify the zero property of multiplication

How are real-life situations commutative?

Abraham Lincoln delivered the Gettysburg Address more than 130 years ago. The table lists the number of words in certain historic documents.

Historical Document	Words
Preamble to The U.S. Constitution	52
Mayflower Compact	196
Atlantic Charter	375
Gettysburg Address (Nicolay Version)	238

Source: U.S. Historical Documents Archive

a. Suppose you read the Preamble to The U.S. Constitution first and then the Gettysburg Address. Write an expression for the total number of words read. **52 + 238**

b. Suppose you read the Gettysburg Address first and then the Preamble to the U.S. Constitution. Write an expression for the total number of words read. **238 + 52**

c. Find the value of each expression. What do you observe? **c. 290; 290; The values are the same.**

d. Does it matter in which order you add any two numbers? Why or why not? **no; the result is always the same**

PROPERTIES OF ADDITION AND MULTIPLICATION

In algebra, **properties** are statements that are true for any numbers. For example, the expressions 3 + 8 and 8 + 3 have the same value, 11. This illustrates the **Commutative Property of Addition**. Likewise, 3 · 8 and 8 · 3 have the same value, 24. This illustrates the **Commutative Property of Multiplication**.

Reading Math

Commutative

Root Word: Commute
The everyday meaning of the word *commute* means *to change or exchange.*

Key Concept — Commutative Property of Addition

- **Words**   The order in which numbers are added does not change the sum.

- **Symbols**   For any numbers a and b, $a + b = b + a$.
- **Example** $2 + 3 = 3 + 2$
  $5 = 5$

Commutative Property of Multiplication

- **Words**   The order in which numbers are multiplied does not change the product.

- **Symbols**   For any numbers a and b, $a \cdot b = b \cdot a$.
- **Example** $2 \cdot 3 = 3 \cdot 2$
  $6 = 6$

✔ **Concept Check**   Write an example that shows the Commutative Property of Multiplication.   **Sample answer: 4 · 5 = 5 · 4**

Lesson 1-4 Properties   23

---

1 Focus

5-Minute Check Transparency 1-4 Use as a quiz or review of Lesson 1-3.

Mathematical Background notes are available for this lesson on page 4D.

How are real-life situations commutative?

The opening activity questions are repeated on page 19 of the *Chapter 1 Resource Masters*.

Reading to Learn Mathematics, p. 19   ELL

Pre-Activity   How are real-life situations commutative?

Do the activity at the top of page 23 in your textbook. Write your answers below.

a. Suppose you read the Preamble to the U.S. Constitution first and then the Gettysburg Address. Write an expression for the total number of words read. **52 + 238**

b. Suppose you read the Gettysburg Address first and then the Preamble to the U.S. Constitution. Write an expression for the total number of words read. **238 + 52**

c. Find the value of each expression. What do you observe? **290; The values are the same.**

d. Does it matter in which order you add any two numbers? Why or why not? **no; The result is always the same.**

Reading the Lesson   1–4. See students' work.

Write a definition and give an example of each new vocabulary word or phrase.

Vocabulary	Definition	Example
1. properties		
2. counterexample		
3. simplify		
4. deductive reasoning		

Helping You Remember

5. Tell what a counterexample is in your own words. Tell how it is used in mathematics and why it is important. **A counterexample is an example that shows a statement is false. It is used in mathematics to disprove ideas or conjectures. If a counterexample is found for a conjecture, then it must be false and there is no need to try and prove the statement true.**

Resource Manager

Transparencies

5-Minute Check Transparency 1-4
Answer Key Transparencies

Technology

Interactive Chalkboard

📁 **Workbooks and Reproducible Masters**

Chapter 1 Resource Masters
- Study Guide and Intervention, p. 16
- Skills Practice, p. 17
- Practice, p. 18
- Reading to Learn Mathematics, p. 19
- Enrichment, p. 20
- Assessment pp. 51, 53

Parent and Student Study Guide Workbook, p. 4
Prerequisite Skills Workbook, pp. 5–10

PROPERTIES OF ADDITION AND MULTIPLICATION

In-Class Examples [Power Point®]

1 Name the property shown by each statement.

a. $3 \cdot 10 \cdot 2 = 3 \cdot 2 \cdot 10$
Commutative Property (×)

b. $(2 + 5) + m = 2 + (5 + m)$
Associative Property (+)

c. $17 \cdot 1 = 17$ **Multiplicative Identity**

Teaching Tip To help students remember the identity properties, remind them that adding 0 to any number or multiplying any number by 1 maintains the number's identity.

2 Find $(18 \cdot 20) \cdot 5$ mentally.
$18 \cdot (20 \cdot 5) = 18 \cdot 100 = 1800$

Teaching Tip When using properties to do computations mentally, it may be helpful to review compatible numbers with students.

3 State whether the following conjecture is true or false. If false, provide a counter-example.

Division of whole numbers is commutative.

False; $12 \div 6 \neq 6 \div 12$

SIMPLIFY ALGEBRAIC EXPRESSIONS

In-Class Example [Power Point®]

4 Simplify each expression.

a. $5 \cdot (3 \cdot r)$ **15r**

b. $12 + (x + 18)$ **30 + x**

TEACHING TIP
The order of operations tells you to simplify the expression in parentheses first.

TEACHING TIP
The Multiplicative Identity Property allows you to write 1x as x.

When evaluating expressions, it is often helpful to group or *associate* the numbers. The **Associative Property** says that the way in which numbers are grouped when added or multiplied does not change the sum or the product.

Key Concept — **Associative Property of Addition**

- **Words** — The way in which numbers are grouped when added does not change the sum.
- **Symbols** — For any numbers a, b, and c, $(a + b) + c = a + (b + c)$.
- **Example** — $(5 + 8) + 2 = 5 + (8 + 2)$
  $13 + 2 = 5 + 10$
  $15 = 15$

Associative Property of Multiplication

- **Words** — The way in which numbers are grouped when multiplied does not change the product.
- **Symbols** — For any numbers a, b, and c, $(a \cdot b) \cdot c = a \cdot (b \cdot c)$.
- **Example** — $(4 \cdot 6) \cdot 3 = 4 \cdot (6 \cdot 3)$
  $24 \cdot 3 = 4 \cdot 18$
  $72 = 72$

☑ **Concept Check** Write an example showing the Associative Property of Addition.
Sample answer: $4 + (1 + 3) = (4 + 1) + 3$

The following properties are also true.

Key Concept — **Properties of Numbers**

Property	Words	Symbols	Examples
Additive Identity	When 0 is added to any number, the sum is the number.	For any number a, $a + 0 = 0 + a = a$.	$5 + 0 = 5$ $0 + 9 = 9$
Multiplicative Identity	When any number is multiplied by 1, the product is the number.	For any number a, $a \cdot 1 = 1 \cdot a = a$.	$7 \cdot 1 = 7$ $1 \cdot 6 = 6$
Multiplicative Property of Zero	When any number is multiplied by 0, the product is 0.	For any number a, $a \cdot 0 = 0 \cdot a = 0$.	$4 \cdot 0 = 0$ $0 \cdot 2 = 0$

Example 1 Identify Properties

Name the property shown by each statement.

a. $3 + 7 + 9 = 7 + 3 + 9$

The order of the numbers changed. This is the Commutative Property of Addition.

b. $(a \cdot 6) \cdot 5 = a \cdot (6 \cdot 5)$

The grouping of the numbers and variables changed. This is the Associative Property of Multiplication.

c. $0 \cdot 12 = 0$

The number was multiplied by zero. This is the Multiplicative Property of Zero.

In-Class Examples, which are included for every example in the Student Edition, exactly parallel the examples in the text. Teaching Tips about the examples in the Student Edition are included where appropriate.

You can use the properties of numbers to find sums and products mentally. Look for sums or products that end in zero.

Example 2 Mental Math

Find $4 \cdot (25 \cdot 11)$ mentally.

Group 4 and 25 together because $4 \cdot 25 = 100$. It is easy to multiply by 100 mentally.

$$
\begin{aligned}
4 \cdot (25 \cdot 11) &= (4 \cdot 25) \cdot 11 && \text{Associative Property of Multiplication} \\
&= 100 \cdot 11 && \text{Multiply 4 and 25 mentally.} \\
&= 1100 && \text{Multiply 100 and 11 mentally.}
\end{aligned}
$$

Study Tip

Counterexample
You can disprove a statement by finding only one counterexample.

You may wonder whether these properties apply to subtraction. One way to find out is to look for a counterexample. A **counterexample** is an example that shows a conjecture is not true.

Example 3 Find a Counterexample

State whether the following conjecture is *true* or *false*. If false, provide a counterexample.

Subtraction of whole numbers is associative.

Write two subtraction expressions using the Associative Property, and then check to see whether they are equal.

$$
\begin{aligned}
9 - (5 - 3) &\overset{?}{=} (9 - 5) - 3 && \text{State the conjecture.} \\
9 - 2 &\overset{?}{=} 4 - 3 && \text{Simplify within the parentheses.} \\
7 &\neq 1 && \text{Subtract.}
\end{aligned}
$$

We found a counterexample. That is, $9 - (5 - 3) \neq (9 - 5) - 3$. So, subtraction is *not* associative. The conjecture is false.

ALGEBRA CONNECTION

SIMPLIFY ALGEBRAIC EXPRESSIONS To **simplify** algebraic expressions means to write them in a simpler form. You can use the Associative or Commutative Properties to simplify expressions.

Example 4 Simplify Algebraic Expressions

Simplify each expression.

a. $(k + 2) + 7$

$$
\begin{aligned}
(k + 2) + 7 &= k + (2 + 7) && \text{Associative Property of Addition} \\
&= k + 9 && \text{Substitution Property of Equality; } 2 + 7 = 9
\end{aligned}
$$

b. $5 \cdot (d \cdot 9)$

$$
\begin{aligned}
5 \cdot (d \cdot 9) &= 5 \cdot (9 \cdot d) && \text{Commutative Property of Multiplication} \\
&= (5 \cdot 9)d && \text{Associative Property of Multiplication} \\
&= 45d && \text{Substitution Property of Equality; } 5 \cdot 9 = 45
\end{aligned}
$$

Study Tip

Inductive Reasoning
In inductive reasoning, conclusions are made based on past events or patterns.

Notice that each step in Example 4 was justified by a property. The process of using facts, properties, or rules to justify reasoning or reach valid conclusions is called **deductive reasoning**.

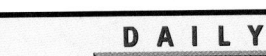

www.pre-alg.com/extra_examples/ny

Lesson 1-4 Properties 25

Lesson 1-4 Properties 25

Study Notebook

Have students—
- add the definitions/examples of the vocabulary terms to their Vocabulary Builder worksheets for Chapter 1.
- write down each property and a corresponding example.
- include any other item(s) that they find helpful in mastering the skills in this lesson.

Daily Intervention notes help you help students when they need it most.

DAILY
INTERVENTION **FIND THE ERROR** You may need to discuss with students that Carlos's problem involves both addition and multiplication so the Associative Property does not apply.

About the Exercises . . .

Organization by Objective
- **Properties of Addition and Multiplication:** 14–25
- **Simplify Algebraic Expressions:** 26–34, 39–47

Odd/Even Assignments
Exercises 14–34 and 39–47 are structured so that students practice the same concepts whether they are assigned odd or even problems.

Assignment Guide

Basic: 15–21 odd, 27–45 odd, 48–65

Average: 15–47 odd, 48–65

Advanced: 14–46 even, 48–59 (Optional: 60–65)

Check for Understanding

Concept Check

1. **OPEN ENDED** Write a numerical sentence that illustrates the Commutative Property of Multiplication. **Sample answer:** $3 \cdot 4 = 4 \cdot 3$

2. **Tell** the difference between the Commutative and Associative Properties.

3. **FIND THE ERROR** Kimberly and Carlos are using the Associative Properties of Addition and Multiplication to rewrite expressions.

Kimberly	Carlos
$(4 + 3) + 6 = 4 + (3 + 6)$	$(2 + 7) \cdot 5 = 2 + (7 \cdot 5)$

Who is correct? Explain your reasoning. **2–3. See margin.**

Guided Practice

GUIDED PRACTICE KEY	
Exercises	Examples
4–6, 13	1
7–9	2
10	3
11, 12	4

Name the property shown by each statement.

4. $7 + 5 = 5 + 7$ **Comm. (+)**
5. $8 + 0 = 8$ **Identity (+)**
6. $8 \cdot 4 \cdot 13 = 4 \cdot 8 \cdot 13$ **Comm. (×)**

Find each sum or product mentally.

7. $13 + 8 + 7$ **28**
8. $6 \cdot 9 \cdot 5$ **270**
9. $8 + 11 + 22 + 4$ **45**

10. State whether the conjecture *division of whole numbers is commutative* is *true* or *false*. If false, provide a counterexample. **False, $4 \div 2 \neq 2 \div 4$.**

ALGEBRA Simplify each expression.

11. $6 + (n + 7)$ **$n + 13$**
12. $(3 \cdot w) \cdot 9$ **$27w$**

Application

13. **SHOPPING** Denyce purchased a pair of jeans for $26, a T-shirt for $12, and a pair of socks for $4. What is the total cost of the items? Explain how the Commutative Property of Addition can be used to find the total. **See margin.**

★ indicates increased difficulty

Practice and Apply

Homework Help

For Exercises	See Examples
14–25	1
26–34	2
35–37	3
39–47	4

Extra Practice
See page 725.

Name the property shown by each statement. **14–25. See margin.**

14. $5 \cdot 3 = 3 \cdot 5$
15. $1 \cdot 4 = 4$
16. $6 \cdot 2 \cdot 0 = 0$
17. $12 \cdot 8 = 8 \cdot 12$
18. $0 + 13 = 13 + 0$
19. $(4 + 5) + 15 = 4 + (5 + 15)$
20. $1h = h$
21. $7k + 0 = 7k$
★ 22. $(5 + x) + 6 = 5 + (x + 6)$
★ 23. $4(mn) = (4m)(n)$
★ 24. $9(gh) = (9g)h$
★ 25. $(3a + b) + 2c = 2c + (3a + b)$

Find each sum or product mentally.

26. $11 + 8 + 19$ **38**
27. $17 + 5 + 33$ **55**
28. $15 \cdot 0 \cdot 2$ **0**
29. $5 + 18 + 15 + 2$ **40**
30. $2 \cdot 7 \cdot 30$ **420**
31. $11 \cdot 9 \cdot 10$ **990**
32. $23 + 3 + 17 + 7$ **50**
33. $125 \cdot 4 \cdot 0$ **0**
★ 34. $16 + 57 + 94 + 33$ **200**

State whether each conjecture is *true* or *false*. If false, provide a counterexample. **35–37. See margin.**

35. Division of whole numbers is associative.

36. The sum of two whole numbers is always greater than either addend.

37. Subtraction of whole numbers is commutative.

Answers

2. The Commutative Property states that the order in which numbers are added or multiplied does not change the sum or product. The Associative Property states that the way numbers are grouped when added or multiplied does not change the sum or product.

3. Kimberly; the Associative Property only holds true if all numbers are added or all numbers are multiplied, not a combination of the two.

More About . . .

Science •

A water molecule is composed of two atoms of hydrogen and one atom of oxygen. Thus, in chemistry, the formula for water is H_2O.

Source: *Merrill Chemistry*

NEW YORK
Test Practice

Standardized Test Practice
Ⓐ Ⓑ Ⓒ Ⓓ

38. SCIENCE In chemistry, water is used to dilute acid. Since pouring water into acid could cause spattering and burns, it's important to pour the acid into the water. Is combining acid and water commutative? Explain. **See margin.**

ALGEBRA Simplify each expression.

39. $(m + 8) + 4$ **$m + 12$**   **40.** $(17 + p) + 9$ **$p + 26$**   **41.** $15 + (12 + a)$ **$a + 27$**

42. $21 + (k + 16)$ **$k + 37$**   **43.** $6 \cdot (y \cdot 2)$ **$12y$**   **44.** $7 \cdot (d \cdot 4)$ **$28d$**

45. $(6 \cdot c) \cdot 8$ **$48c$**   **46.** $(3 \cdot w) \cdot 5$ **$15w$**   ★**47.** $25s(3)$ **$75s$**

48. CRITICAL THINKING The **Closure Property** states that because the sum or product of two whole numbers (0, 1, 2, 3, …) is also a whole number, the set of whole numbers is *closed* under addition and multiplication. Tell whether the set of whole numbers is closed under subtraction and division. If not, give counterexamples. **See margin.**

49. WRITING IN MATH Answer the question that was posed at the beginning of the lesson. **See pp. 53A–53B.**

How are real-life situations commutative?

Include the following in your answer:
- an example of a real-life situation that is commutative,
- an example of a real-life situation that is not commutative, and
- an explanation of why each situation is or is not commutative.

50. The statement $e + (f + g) = (f + g) + e$ is an example of which property of addition? **A**
Ⓐ Commutative   Ⓑ Associative
Ⓒ Identity   Ⓓ Substitution

51. Rewrite the expression $(7 \cdot m) \cdot 8$ using the Associative Property. **B**
Ⓐ $(8 \cdot 7) \cdot m$ Ⓑ $7 \cdot (m \cdot 8)$
Ⓒ $8 \cdot (7 \cdot m)$ Ⓓ $7 \cdot m \cdot 8$

Maintain Your Skills

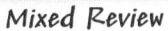

Mixed Review **ALGEBRA** Evaluate each expression if $a = 6$, $b = 4$, and $c = 5$. *(Lesson 1-3)*

52. $a + c - b$ **7**   **53.** $8a - 3b$ **36**   **54.** $4a - (b + c)$ **15**

55. Translate the phrase *the difference of w and 12* into an algebraic expression. *(Lesson 1-3)* **$w - 12$**

Find the value of each expression. *(Lesson 1-2)*

56. $7 - 2 \times 3$ **1**   **57.** $21 \div 3 \times 5$ **35**   **58.** $4 \cdot (8 + 9) + 6$ **74**

59. Find the next two terms in the list 0, 1, 3, 6, 10, … *(Lesson 1-1)* **15, 21**

Getting Ready for the Next Lesson **BASIC SKILL** Find each product.

60. 48×5 **240**   **61.** 8×37 **296**   **62.** 16×12 **192**

63. 25×42 **1050**   **64.** 106×13 **1378**   **65.** 59×127 **7493**

Open-Ended Assessment

Speaking Ask students to summarize at least two ways in which properties can help them perform tasks in mathematics. The explanation should include examples, and should identify which properties are used.

Getting Ready for Lesson 1-5

BASIC SKILL Lesson 1-5 presents variables and equations. A number next to a variable means multiply that variable by the number. Exercises 60–65 should be used to determine your students' familiarity with multiplication.

Assessment Options

Quiz (Lessons 1-3 and 1-4) is available on p. 51 of the *Chapter 1 Resource Masters.*

Mid-Chapter Test (Lessons 1-1 through 1-4) is available on p. 53 of the *Chapter 1 Resource Masters.*

Answers

20. Multiplicative Identity
21. Additive Identity
22. Associative Property (+)
23. Associative Property (×)
24. Associative Property (×)
25. Commutative Property (+)
35. false; $(100 \div 10) \div 2 \neq 100 \div (10 \div 2)$
36. false; $2 + 0 = 2$ and 2 is not greater than 2.
37. false; $9 - 3 = 3 - 9$
38. No; The acid can be poured into the water, but the water cannot be poured into the acid.
48. The set of whole numbers is not closed under subtraction and division. $2 - 3 = -1$ and -1 is not a whole number. $1 \div 2 = 0.5$ and 0.5 is not a whole number.

Answers

13. $42; To find the total cost, add the three costs together. Since the order in which the costs are added does not matter, the Commutative Property of Addition holds true and makes the addition easier. By adding 4 and 26, the result is 30, and $30 + 12$ is 42.

14. Commutative Property (×)
15. Multiplicative Identity
16. Multiplicative Property of Zero
17. Commutative Property (×)
18. Commutative Property (+)
19. Associative Property (+)

NEW YORK *Performance Indicator* **Reinforcement of 6.A.3 Translate two-step verbal sentences into algebraic equations**

1 Focus

 5-Minute Check Transparency 1-5 Use as a quiz or review of Lesson 1-4.

Mathematical Background notes are available for this lesson on page 4D.

How is solving an open sentence similar to evaluating an expression?

The opening activity questions are repeated on page 24 of the *Chapter 1 Resource Masters*.

Reading to Learn Mathematics, p. 24 **ELL**

Pre-Activity *How is solving an open sentence similar to evaluating an expression?*

Do the activity at the top of page 28 in your textbook. Write your answers below.

a. If Rebecca is *x* years old, what expression represents Emilio's age? *x + 7*

b. What two expressions are equal? *x + 7 and 19*

c. If Emilio is 19, how old is Rebecca? **12**

Reading the Lesson 1–4. See students' work.

Write a definition and give an example of each new vocabulary word or phrase.

Vocabulary	Definition	Example
1. equation		
2. open sentence		
3. solution		
4. solving the equation		

5. Complete this sentence. When the __variable__ in an open sentence is replaced with a number, you can determine whether the sentence is true or false.

6. Consider $x - 4 = 6$. Find a value for x that makes the sentence true and another value that makes it false. If $x = 10$, the sentence is true; If x is any other value, the sentence is false.

Helping You Remember

7. Explain how an open sentence is different from an algebraic expression. **An open sentence is an equation that contains a variable. Therefore, an open sentence has an equal sign. An algebraic expression does not.**

Vocabulary

- equation
- open sentence
- solution
- solving the equation

Study Tip

Symbols
The symbol $\neq$ means *is not equal to.*

What You'll Learn

- Identify and solve open sentences.
- Translate verbal sentences into equations.

How is solving an open sentence similar to evaluating an expression?

Emilio is seven years older than his sister Rebecca. **a. *x* + 7**

a. If Rebecca is *x* years old, what expression represents Emilio's age?

Suppose Emilio is 19 years old. You can write a mathematical sentence that shows two expressions are equal.

Words Emilio's age is 19.

Symbols $x + 7 = 19$

b. What two expressions are equal? **$x + 7$ and 19**

c. If Emilio is 19, how old is Rebecca? **12**

EQUATIONS AND OPEN SENTENCES A mathematical sentence that contains an equals sign (=) is called an **equation**. A few examples are shown.

$$5 + 9 = 14 \qquad 2(6) - 3 = 9 \qquad x + 7 = 19 \qquad 2m - 1 = 13$$

An equation that contains a variable is an **open sentence**. An open sentence is neither true nor false. When the variable in an open sentence is replaced with a number, you can determine whether the sentence is true or false.

$$x + 7 = 19$$
$$11 + 7 \stackrel{?}{=} 19 \quad \text{Replace } x \text{ with 11.}$$
$$18 \neq 19 \quad \text{false}$$

When $x = 11$, this sentence is false.

$$x + 7 = 19$$
$$12 + 7 \stackrel{?}{=} 19 \quad \text{Replace } x \text{ with 12.}$$
$$19 = 19 \quad \text{true}$$

When $x = 12$, this sentence is true.

A value for the variable that makes an equation true is called a **solution**. For $x + 7 = 19$, the solution is 12. The process of finding a solution is called **solving the equation**.

Example 1 *Solve an Equation*

Find the solution of $12 - m = 8$. Is it 2, 4, or 7?

Replace *m* with each value.

Value for *m*	$12 - m = 8$	True or False?
2	$12 - 2 \stackrel{?}{=} 8$	false
4	$12 - 4 \stackrel{?}{=} 8$	true ✓
7	$12 - 7 \stackrel{?}{=} 8$	false

Therefore, the solution of $12 - m = 8$ is 4.

Resource Manager

 Workbooks and Reproducible Masters

Chapter 1 Resource Masters
- Study Guide and Intervention, p. 21
- Skills Practice, p. 22
- Practice, p. 23
- Reading to Learn Mathematics, p. 24
- Enrichment, p. 25

Parent and Student Study Guide Workbook, p. 5
Prerequisite Skills Workbook, pp. 5–10
School-to-Career Masters, p. 2
Science and Mathematics Lab Manual, pp. 1–4

 Transparencies
5-Minute Check Transparency 1-5
Answer Key Transparencies

Technology
Interactive Chalkboard

Standardized Test Practice
Ⓐ Ⓑ Ⓒ Ⓓ

Most standardized tests include questions that ask you to solve equations.

Example 2 *Solve an Equation*

Multiple-Choice Test Item

> Which value is the solution of $2x + 1 = 7$?
> Ⓐ 6   Ⓑ 5   Ⓒ 4   Ⓓ 3

Read the Test Item

The *solution* is the value that makes the equation true.

Solve the Test Item Test each value.

$2x + 1 = 7$
$2(6) + 1 = 7$ Replace x with 6.
$13 \neq 7$

$2x + 1 = 7$
$2(5) + 1 = 7$ Replace x with 5.
$11 \neq 7$

$2x + 1 = 7$
$2(4) + 1 = 7$ Replace x with 4.
$9 \neq 7$

$2x + 1 = 7$
$2(3) + 1 = 7$ Replace x with 3.
$7 = 7$ ✓

Since 3 makes the equation true, the answer is D.

Test-Taking Tip
The strategy of testing each value is called *backsolving*. You can also use this strategy with complex equations.

Example 3 *Solve Simple Equations Mentally*

Solve each equation mentally.

a. $5x = 30$
$5 \cdot 6 = 30$ Think: What number times 5 is 30?
$x = 6$ The solution is 6.

b. $\frac{72}{d} = 8$
$\frac{72}{9} = 8$ Think: 72 divided by what number is 8?
$d = 9$ The solution is 9.

In Lesson 1-4, you learned that certain properties are true for any number. Two properties of equality are shown below.

Key Concept			*Properties of Equality*
Property	**Words**	**Symbols**	**Example**
Symmetric	If one quantity equals a second quantity, then the second quantity also equals the first.	For any numbers a and b, if $a = b$, then $b = a$.	If $10 = 4 + 6$, then $4 + 6 = 10$.
Transitive	If one quantity equals a second quantity and the second quantity equals a third quantity, then the first equals the third.	For any numbers a, b, and c, if $a = b$ and $b = c$, then $a = c$.	If $3 + 5 = 8$ and $8 = 2(4)$, then $3 + 5 = 2(4)$.

DAILY INTERVENTION

Differentiated Instruction

- **Intrapersonal** Have students write in their journals a number of open sentences using all four operations in their samples. Then for each example they should write a question like that in the text to help them solve mentally ("What number times 2 is 10?"). Ask students to examine their equations and decide which operation is most difficult for them to do mentally. In their journals, they should describe a strategy to help themselves solve such problems more quickly.

---

2 Teach

EQUATIONS AND OPEN SENTENCES

Building on Prior Knowledge

In elementary school, students saw problems like □ + 5 = 8. Remind them that the box was the variable and discuss what processes they used to determine the number to put in the box.

In-Class Examples Power Point®

1 Find the solution of $44 + p = 53$. Is it 11, 9, or 7? **9**

2 **Multiple-Choice Test Item** Which value is the solution of $4x - 1 = 11$? **c**
A 5   B 4   C 3   D 2

3 Solve each equation mentally.
a. $7x = 56$ **8**
b. $x - 15 = 40$ **55**

4 Name the property of equality shown by each statement.
a. If $3x + 1 = 10$, then $10 = 3x + 1$. **Symmetric Property of Equality**
b. If $z + 6 = 8$ and $8 = 2 + 6$, then $z + 6 = 2 + 6$. **Transitive Property of Equality**

 Skills Check

Equations and Open Sentences Show the equation $4x + 1 = 25$. Ask students how they would determine if 5 is a solution. They should then do the problem. Students should explain their method, work through the problem, and state if 5 is the solution. They could even try to find the correct solution if 5 is incorrect. **The solution is not 5. The correct solution is 6.**

5 The quotient of a number and four is nine. Find the number. $\frac{n}{4} = 9$; 36

Teaching Tip Emphasize to students that "is" most often translates to "equals" in mathematics problems.

3 Practice/Apply

Study Notebook

Have students—
- add the definitions/examples of the vocabulary terms to their Vocabulary Builder worksheets for Chapter 1.
- include any other item(s) that they find helpful in mastering the skills in this lesson.

About the Exercises . . .

Organization by Objective
- **Equations and Open Sentences:** 14–23, 26–47, 49, 55
- **Translate Verbal Sentences into Equations:** 42–48, 54

Odd/Even Assignments
Exercises 14–47 are structured so that students practice the same concepts whether they are assigned odd or even problems.

Assignment Guide

Basic: 15–47 odd, 48, 49, 51, 56–59, 61–73

Average: 15–47 odd, 48, 49, 51, 53, 56–59, 61–73 (Optional: 60)

Advanced: 14–46 even, 50, 52, 54–67 (Optional: 68–73)

All: Practice Quiz 2 (1–5)

Example 4 *Identify Properties of Equality*

Name the property of equality shown by each statement.

a. If $5 = x + 2$, then $x + 2 = 5$.

If $a = b$, then $b = a$. This is the Symmetric Property of Equality.

b. If $y + 8 = 15$ and $15 = 7 + 8$, then $y + 8 = 7 + 8$.

If $a = b$ and $b = c$, then $a = c$. This is the Transitive Property of Equality.

TRANSLATE VERBAL SENTENCES INTO EQUATIONS Just as verbal phrases can be translated into algebraic expressions, verbal sentences can be translated into equations and then solved.

Example 5 *Translate Sentences Into Equations*

The difference of a number and ten is seventeen. Find the number.

Words	The difference of a number and ten is seventeen.
Variables	Let n = the number. *Define the variable.*

	The difference of a number and ten	is	seventeen.
Equation	$n - 10$	$=$	17

$n - 10 = 17$ Write the equation.

$27 - 10 = 17$ Think: What number minus 10 is 17?

$n = 27$ The solution is 27.

Check for Understanding exercises are intended to be completed in class. Concept Check exercises ensure that students understand the concepts in the lesson. The rest of the exercises are representative of the exercises used for homework or seatwork.

Check for Understanding

Concept Check

1. **OPEN ENDED** Write two different equations whose solutions are 5.

2. **Tell** what it means to *solve an equation*. **1–2. See margin.**

Guided Practice

ALGEBRA Find the solution of each equation from the list given.

3. $h + 15 = 21$; 5, <u>6</u>, 7

4. $13 - m = 4$; 7, 8, <u>9</u>

ALGEBRA Solve each equation mentally.

5. $a + 8 = 13$ **5**

6. $12 - d = 9$ **3**

7. $3x = 18$ **6**

8. $4 = \frac{36}{t}$ **9**

Name the property of equality shown by each statement.

9. If $x + 4 = 9$, then $9 = x + 4$. **Symmetric**

10. If $5 + 7 = 12$ and $12 = 3 \cdot 4$, then $5 + 7 = 3 \cdot 4$. **Transitive**

11. Let n = the number.

12. Let d = the number.

ALGEBRA Define a variable. Then write an equation and solve.

11. A number increased by 8 is 23. $n + 8 = 23$; 15

12. Twenty-five is 10 less than a number. $25 = d - 10$; 35

NEW YORK Test Practice

Standardized Test Practice Ⓐ Ⓑ Ⓒ Ⓓ

13. Find the value that makes $6 = \frac{48}{k}$ true. **C**

Ⓐ 6   Ⓑ 7   Ⓒ 8   Ⓓ 12

The Assignment Guides provide suggestions for the exercises that are appropriate for basic, average, or advanced students. Many of the homework exercises are paired, so that students could do the odds one day and the evens the next day.

Answers

1. Sample answer: $b + 7 = 12$ and $8 - h = 3$

2. To solve an equation, find a value for the variable that makes a true statement.

★ indicates increased difficulty

Practice and Apply

Homework Help

For Exercises	See Examples
14–23	1
26–41	3
42–49, 54, 55	5
50–53	4

Extra Practice
See page 725.

ALGEBRA   Find the solution of each equation from the list given.

14. $c + 12 = 30$; 8, 16, <u>18</u>

15. $g + 17 = 28$; 9, <u>11</u>, 13

16. $23 - m = 14$; 7, <u>9</u>, 11

17. $18 - k = 6$; 8, 10, <u>12</u>

18. $14k = 42$; 2, <u>3</u>, 4

19. $75 = 15n$; 3, 4, <u>5</u>

20. $\frac{51}{z} = 3$; 15, 16, <u>17</u>

21. $\frac{60}{p} = 4$; <u>15</u>, 16, 17

22. What is the solution of $3n + 13 = 25$; 2, 3, <u>4</u>?

23. Find the solution of $7 = 4w - 29$. Is it 8, <u>9</u>, or 10?

Tell whether each sentence is *sometimes*, *always*, or *never* true.

24. An equation is an open sentence. **sometimes**

25. An open sentence contains a variable. **always**

ALGEBRA   Solve each equation mentally.

26. $d + 7 = 12$ **5**

27. $19 = 4 + y$ **15**

28. $8 + j = 27$ **19**

29. $22 + b = 22$ **0**

30. $20 - p = 11$ **9**

31. $15 - m = 0$ **15**

32. $16 = x - 7$ **23**

33. $12 = y - 5$ **17**

34. $7s = 49$ **7**

35. $8c = 88$ **11**

36. $63 = 9h$ **7**

37. $72 = 8w$ **9**

38. $\frac{30}{r} = 3$ **10**

39. $\frac{24}{y} = 8$ **3**

40. $12 = \frac{36}{p}$ **3**

41. $14 = \frac{56}{d}$ **4**

ALGEBRA   Define a variable. Then write an equation and solve.

42. The sum of 7 and a number is 23. $7 + k = 23$; **16**

43. A number minus 10 is 27. $h - 10 = 27$; **37**

44. Twenty-four is the product of 8 and a number. $24 = 8a$; **3**

45. The sum of 9 and a number is 36. $9 + w = 36$; **27**

46. The difference of a number and 12 is 54. $z - 12 = 54$; **66**

47. A number times 3 is 45. $3x = 45$; **15**

42–47. See margin for definitions.

MOVIE INDUSTRY   For Exercises 48 and 49, use the following information.
Megan purchased movie tickets for herself and two friends. The cost was $24.

48. Define a variable. Then write an equation that can be used to find how much Megan paid for each ticket. **Let c = cost of each ticket; $3c = 24$.**

49. What was the cost of each ticket? **$8**

Name the property of equality shown by each statement.

50. If $2 + 3 = 5$ and $5 = 1 + 4$, then $2 + 3 = 1 + 4$. **Transitive**

51. If $3 + 4 = 7$ then $7 = 3 + 4$. **Symmetric**

★ **52.** If $(1 + 2) + 6 = 9$, then $9 = (1 + 2) + 6$. **Symmetric**

★ **53.** If $m + n = p$, then $p = m + n$. **Symmetric**

HEIGHT   For Exercises 54 and 55, use the following information.
Sean grew from a height of 65 inches to a height of 68 inches.

54. Define a variable. Then write an equation that can be used to find the increase in height. **Let h = the increase in height; $65 + h = 68$**

55. How many inches did Sean grow? **3**

 www.pre-alg.com/self_check_quiz/ny

More About. . .

Movie Industry
In 1990, the total number of indoor movie screens was about 22,000. Today, there are over 37,000 indoor movie screens and the number keeps rising.
Source: National Association of Theatre Owners

Answers

42. Let k = the number.

43. Let h = the number.

44. Let a = the number.

45. Let w = the number.

46. Let z = the number.

47. Let x = the number.

Every effort is made to show the Answers to exercises (1) on the reduced Student Edition page, or (2) in the margin of the Teacher Wraparound Edition. However, answers that do not fit in either of these places can be found in pages at the end of each chapter.

Study Guide and Intervention, p. 21

An equation that contains a variable is called an **open sentence**. When the variable is replaced with a number, you can determine whether the sentence is true or false. A value that makes the sentence true is called a **solution**.

Example 1   ALGEBRA   Find the solution of $27 - p = 14$. Is it 11, 13, or 15?

Value for p	$27 - p = 14$	True or False?
11	$27 - 11 \overset{?}{=} 15$	false
13	$27 - 13 \overset{?}{=} 14$	true
15	$27 - 15 \overset{?}{=} 14$	false

Verbal sentences can be translated into equations and then solved.

Example 2   ALGEBRA   The sum of a number and six is twenty-one. Find the number.
Let n = the number.
Words   The sum of a number and six is twenty-one.
Variables   Let n = the number.
Equation $n + 6 = 21$ Write the equation.
$15 + 6 = 21$ Think: What number added to 6 is 21?
$n = 15$ The solution is 15.

Exercises

ALGEBRA   Find the solution of each equation from the list given.

1. $b + 11 = 29$; 16, <u>18</u>, 20
2. $h + 7 = 42$; <u>35</u>, 37, 39
3. $37 - x = 24$; 9, 11, <u>13</u>
4. $26 - m = 18$; 6, <u>8</u>, 10
5. $v - 6 = 5$; 7, 9, <u>11</u>
6. $6r = 48$; 6, <u>8</u>, 10
7. $\frac{63}{a} = 9$; <u>7</u>, 9, 11
8. $k - 16 = 15$; <u>31</u>, 33, 35
9. $121 = 11p$; 9, <u>11</u>, 13
10. $\frac{x}{5} = 15$; 70, <u>75</u>, 80
11. $2n + 1 = 7$; <u>3</u>, 4, 5
12. $11 = 3y - 25$; 10, 11, <u>12</u>

ALGEBRA   Define the variable. Then write the equation and solve.

13. The product of seven and a number is fifty-six. **Let n = the number; $7n = 56$; 8**
14. The quotient of eighty-two and a number is two. **Let n = the number; $82 \div n = 2$; 41**
15. The difference between a number and four is twelve. **Let n = the number; $n - 4 = 12$; 16**

Skills Practice, p. 22 and Practice, p. 23 (shown)

ALGEBRA Find the solution of each equation from the list given.

1. $w + 16 = 31$; 13, <u>15</u>, 17
2. $z + 31 = 72$; 37, 39, <u>41</u>
3. $25 - p = 0$; 21, 23, <u>25</u>
4. $s - 14 = 2$; 12, 14, <u>16</u>
5. $19 = t - 21$; <u>40</u>, 42, 44
6. $b = 15 - 3$; <u>12</u>, 14, 16
7. $9q = 72$; 6, <u>8</u>, 10
8. $35 = 5m$; <u>7</u>, 9, 11
9. $\frac{78}{n} = 15$; <u>5</u>, 7, 9
10. $\frac{p}{8} = 10$; <u>80</u>, 84, 88

ALGEBRA Solve each equation mentally.

11. $g + 19 = 29$ **10**
12. $26 + h = 35$ **9**
13. $n - 6 = 12$ **18**
14. $36 + a = 12$ **3**
15. $\frac{90}{45} = u$ **2**
16. $3t = 39$ **13**
17. $15 + r = 30$ **15**
18. $34 - v = 20$ **14**

ALGEBRA Define a variable. Then write an equation and solve.

19. The sum of 3, 5, and a number is 15. **Let n = the number; $3 + 5 + n = 15$; 7**
20. The difference of a number and 16 is 5. **Let k = the number; $k - 16 = 5$; 21**
21. The quotient of 56 and a number is 7. **Let r = the number; $56 \div r = 7$; 8**
22. A number increased by 30 is 63. **Let g = the number; $g + 30 = 63$; 33**
23. Eight times a number is 32. **Let j = the number; $8j = 32$; 4**
24. A number decreased by 4 is 41. **Let c = the number; $c - 4 = 41$; 45**
25. **WEATHER** During the month of July, meteorologists recorded 5 inches of rainfall. This is 6 inches below average. Define a variable and write an equation that can be used to determine the average rainfall for July. Find the average rainfall for July. **Let r = the average rainfall for July. So, $r - 6 = 5$. The average rainfall is 11 inches.**
26. **FOOD** Junot and Lisa ordered a pizza and cut it into six slices. If Junot ate one slice and Lisa ate one slice, how many slices are left? **Let s = the number of slices. So, $1 + 1 + s = 6$. There are 4 slices left.**

Enrichment, p. 25

Solution Sets

Consider the following open sentence.
It is a robot that starred in STAR WARS.

You know that a replacement for the word *It* must be found in order to determine if the sentence is true or false. If *It* is replaced by either R2D2 or C3PO, the sentence is true.

The set {R2D2, C3PO} can be thought of as the *solution set* of the open sentence given above. This set includes all replacements for the word *It* that make the sentence true.

Write the solution set of each open sentence.

1. *It* is the name of a state beginning with the letter A. {Alabama, Alaska, Arkansas, Arizona}
2. *It* is a primary color. {red, yellow, blue}
3. *Its* capital is Harrisburg. {Pennsylvania}
4. *It* is a New England state. {Connecticut, Maine, Massachusetts, New Hampshire, Rhode Island, Vermont}
5. He was one of the Seven Dwarfs. {Doc, Happy, Sleepy, Bashful, Grumpy, Sneezy, Dopey}
6. *It* is the name of a month that contains the letter q. ∅
7. During the 1990s, she was the wife of a U.S. President. {Barbara Bush, Hillary Clinton}
8. *It* is an even number between 1 and 13. {2, 4, 6, 8, 10, 12}
9. $x + 4 = 10$ {6}
10. $31 = 72 - k$ {41}
11. *It* is the square of 2, 3, or 4. {4, 9, 16}

Write a description of each set.

12. {A, E, I, O, U} the vowels
13. {1, 3, 5, 7, 9} the odd numbers between 0 and 10
14. {June, July, August} the months between May and September
15. {Atlantic, Pacific, Indian, Arctic} the oceans

4 Assess

Open-Ended Assessment

Writing Have students prepare a quiz of five questions covering equations, open sentences, and translating verbal sentences. Each question must include instructions and an answer key with complete solutions. The questions can then be exchanged and practiced or collected and a class quiz can be compiled.

Getting Ready for Lesson 1-6

PREREQUISITE SKILL Lesson 1-6 presents ordered pairs and relations, which can often be described by algebraic expressions. Exercises 68–73 review evaluating expressions.

Assessment Options

Practice Quiz 2 The quiz provides students with a brief review of the concepts and skills in Lessons 1-4 and 1-5. Lesson numbers are given to the right of exercises or instruction lines so students can review concepts not yet mastered.

---

56. CRITICAL THINKING Write three different equations in which there is no solution that is a whole number. **See margin.**

57. WRITING IN MATH Answer the question that was posed at the beginning of the lesson. **See margin.**

How is solving an open sentence similar to evaluating an expression?

Include the following in your answer:
- an explanation of how to evaluate an expression, and
- an explanation of what makes an open sentence true.

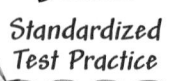

Standardized Test Practice
Ⓐ Ⓑ Ⓒ Ⓓ

58. Find the solution of $9m = 54$. **D**
Ⓐ 4   Ⓑ 7   Ⓒ 5   Ⓓ 6

59. Which value satisfies $2n - 5 = 19$? **B**
Ⓐ 11   Ⓑ 12   Ⓒ 13   Ⓓ 14

Extending the Lesson

60. The table shows equations that have one variable or two variables.

a. Find as many whole number solutions as you can for each equation. **See students' work.**

One Variable	Two Variables
$4 + x = 7$	$z + y = 7$
$3t = 24$	$ab = 24$
$s - 5 = 2$	$m - n = 2$

60b. See margin.

b. **Make a conjecture** about the relationship between the number of variables in equations like the ones above and the number of solutions.

Maintain Your Skills

Mixed Review **Simplify each expression.** *(Lesson 1-4)*

61. $16 + (7 + d)$ **$23 + d$**   **62.** $(4 \cdot p) \cdot 6$ **$24p$**

ALGEBRA Translate each phrase into an algebraic expression. *(Lesson 1-3)*

63. ten decreased by a number **$10 - n$**

64. the sum of three times a number and four **$3n + 4$**

Find the value of each expression. *(Lesson 1-2)*

65. $3 \cdot 7 - 2(1 + 4)$ **11**   **66.** $3[(17 - 7) - 2(3)]$ **12**

67. What is the next term in $67, 62, 57, 52, 47, \ldots$? *(Lesson 1-1)* **42**

Getting Ready for the Next Lesson **PREREQUISITE SKILL Evaluate each expression for the given value.**
(To review evaluating expressions, see Lesson 1-5.)

68. $4x; x = 3$ **12**   **69.** $3m; m = 6$ **18**   **70.** $2d; d = 8$ **16**

71. $5c; c = 10$ **50**   **72.** $8a; a = 9$ **72**   **73.** $6y; y = 15$ **90**

Practice Quiz 2 — Lessons 1-4 and 1-5

Name the property shown by each statement. *(Lesson 1-4)*

1. $6 \cdot 1 = 6$ **Identity (×)**   **2.** $9 + 6 = 6 + 9$ **Comm. (+)**

3. Simplify $8 \cdot (h \cdot 3)$. *(Lesson 1-4)* **$24h$**

4. Find the solution of $2w - 6 = 14$. Is it 8, 10, or 12? *(Lesson 1-4)* **10**

5. Solve $72 = 9x$ mentally. *(Lesson 1-5)* **8**

Answers

56. Sample answer: $4a = 21$; $7z = 3$; $14 = 5g$

57. Sample answer: Once the variable(s) are replaced in the open sentence, the order of operations is used to find the value of the expression. Answers should include the following.

- To evaluate an expression, replace the variable(s) with the given values, and then find the value of the expression.

- To solve an open sentence, find the value of the variable that makes the sentence true.

60b. For equations like those in the table, an equation with one variable has one unique solution; an equation with more than one variable has more than one solution.

1-6 Ordered Pairs and Relations

NEW YORK *Performance Indicator* **8.A.19** Interpret multiple representations using equation, **table of values,** and **graph**

What You'll Learn

- Use ordered pairs to locate points.
- Use tables and graphs to represent relations.

Vocabulary

- coordinate system
- *y*-axis
- coordinate plane
- origin
- *x*-axis
- ordered pair
- *x*-coordinate
- *y*-coordinate
- graph
- relation
- domain
- range

a. Sample answer: 3 over and 2 up; this move would block Hiroshi.

d. See students' work. It depends on where the third X is placed.

How are ordered pairs used to graph real-life data?

Maria and Hiroshi are playing a game. The player who gets four Xs or Os in a row wins.

1st move   Maria places an X at 1 over and 3 up.

2nd move   Hiroshi places an O at 2 over and 2 up.

3rd move   Maria places an X at 1 over and 1 up.

4th move   Hiroshi places an O at 1 over and 2 up.

Starting Position

a. Where should Maria place an X now? Explain your reasoning.

b. Suppose (1, 2) represents 1 over and 2 up. How could you represent 3 over and 2 up? **(3, 2)**

c. How are (5, 1) and (1, 5) different?

d. Where is a good place to put the next O?

e. Work with a partner to finish the game. **See students' work.**

c. (5, 1) is 5 over and 1 up; (1, 5) is 1 over and 5 up.

ORDERED PAIRS In mathematics, a **coordinate system** is used to locate points. The coordinate system is formed by the intersection of two number lines that meet at right angles at their zero points.

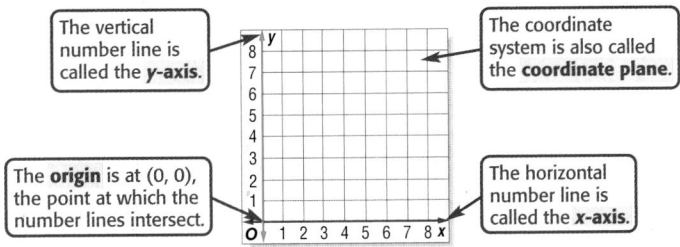

The vertical number line is called the **y-axis**.

The coordinate system is also called the **coordinate plane**.

The **origin** is at (0, 0), the point at which the number lines intersect.

The horizontal number line is called the **x-axis**.

An **ordered pair** of numbers is used to locate any point on a coordinate plane. The first number is called the **x-coordinate**. The second number is called the **y-coordinate**.

The *x*-coordinate corresponds to a number on the *x*-axis.

(3, 2)

The *y*-coordinate corresponds to a number on the *y*-axis.

1-6 Lesson Notes

1 Focus

5-Minute Check Transparency 1-6 Use as a quiz or review of Lesson 1-5.

Mathematical Background notes are available for this lesson on page 4D.

How are ordered pairs used to graph real-life data?

The opening activity questions are repeated on page 29 of the *Chapter 1 Resource Masters*.

Reading to Learn Mathematics, p. 29 **ELL**

Pre-Activity How are ordered pairs used to graph real-life data?

Do the activity at the top of page 33 in your textbook. Write your answers below.

a. Where should Maria place an X now? Explain your reasoning. Sample answer: 3 over and 2 up; this move would block Hiroshi.

b. Suppose (1, 2) represents 1 over and 2 up. How could you represent 3 over and 2 up? (3, 2)

c. How are (5, 1) and (1, 5) different? (5, 1) is 5 over and 1 up; (1, 5) is 1 over and 5 up.

d. Where is a good place to put the next O? It depends on where the next X is placed.

e. Work with a partner to finish the game. See students' work.

Reading the Lesson 1–12. See students' work.

Write a definition and give an example of each new vocabulary word or phrase.

Vocabulary	Definition	Example
1. coordinate system		
2. y-axis		
3. coordinate plane		
4. origin		
5. x-axis		
6. ordered pair		
7. x-coordinate		
8. y-coordinate		
9. graph		
10. relation		
11. domain		
12. range		

Teaching Tip Remind students that the starting position is 0, not 1. You must move over a place to reach 1.

Resource Manager

Workbooks and Reproducible Masters

Chapter 1 Resource Masters
- Study Guide and Intervention, p. 26
- Skills Practice, p. 27
- Practice, p. 28
- Reading to Learn Mathematics, p. 29
- Enrichment, p. 30
- Assessment, p. 52

Parent and Student Study Guide Workbook, p. 6

Transparencies

5-Minute Check Transparency 1-6
Answer Key Transparencies

Technology
Interactive Chalkboard

ORDERED PAIRS

1 Graph each ordered pair on a coordinate system.

a. (3, 4)   **b.** (0, 2)

2 Write the ordered pair that names each point.

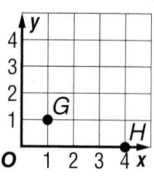

a. *G* **(1, 1)**

b. *H* **(4, 0)**

Study Tip

Coordinate System
You can assume that each unit on the *x*- and *y*-axis represents 1 unit. *Axes* is the plural of *axis*.

Study Tips offer students helpful information about the topics they are studying.

To **graph** an ordered pair, draw a dot at the point that corresponds to the ordered pair. The coordinates are your directions to locate the point.

Example 1 *Graph Ordered Pairs*

Graph each ordered pair on a coordinate system.

a. (4, 1)

Step 1 Start at the origin.

Step 2 Since the *x*-coordinate is 4, move 4 units to the right.

Step 3 Since the *y*-coordinate is 1, move 1 unit up. Draw a dot.

b. (3, 0)

Step 1 Start at the origin.

Step 2 The *x*-coordinate is 3. So, move 3 units to the right.

Step 3 Since the *y*-coordinate is 0, you will not need to move up. Place the dot on the axis.

✓ **Concept Check** Where is the graph of (0, 4) located? **4 units up on the *y*-axis**

Sometimes a point on a graph is named by using a letter. To identify its location, you can write the ordered pair that represents the point.

Example 2 *Identify Ordered Pairs*

Write the ordered pair that names each point.

a. *M*

Step 1 Start at the origin.

Step 2 Move right on the *x*-axis to find the *x*-coordinate of point *M*, which is 2.

Step 3 Move up the *y*-axis to find the *y*-coordinate, which is 5.

The ordered pair for point *M* is (2, 5).

b. *N*

The *x*-coordinate of *N* is 4, and the *y*-coordinate is 4.

The ordered pair for point *N* is (4, 4).

c. *P*

The *x*-coordinate of *P* is 7, and the *y*-coordinate is 0.

The ordered pair for point *P* is (7, 0).

Differentiated Instruction suggestions are keyed to eight commonly-accepted learning styles.

DAILY INTERVENTION

Differentiated Instruction

- **Kinesthetic** Use masking tape to mark an *x*-axis and *y*-axis on the floor. Make up cards with ordered pairs. Give each of several students a card and ask them to start at the origin and walk to the location of their point. Make sure they follow the over, up procedure.

RELATIONS   A set of ordered pairs such as {(1, 2), (2, 4), (3, 0), (4, 5)} is a **relation**. The **domain** of the relation is the set of *x*-coordinates. The **range** of the relation is the set of *y*-coordinates.

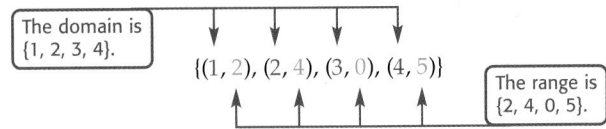

The domain is {1, 2, 3, 4}.

{(1, 2), (2, 4), (3, 0), (4, 5)}

The range is {2, 4, 0, 5}.

A relation can be shown in several ways.

Ordered Pairs	Table	Graph
(1, 2)		
(2, 4)		
(3, 0)		
(4, 5)		

x	y
1	2
2	4
3	0
4	5

Example 3   Relations as Tables and Graphs

Express the relation {(0, 0), (2, 1), (1, 3), (5, 2)} as a table and as a graph. Then determine the domain and range.

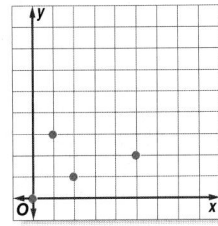

x	y
0	0
2	1
1	3
5	2

The domain is {0, 2, 1, 5}, and the range is {0, 1, 3, 2}.

Example 4   Apply Relations

PLANTS   Some species of bamboo grow 3 feet in one day.

a. Make a table of ordered pairs in which the *x*-coordinate represents the number of days and the *y*-coordinate represents the amount of growth for 1, 2, 3, and 4 days.

b. Graph the ordered pairs.

x	y	(x, y)
1	3	(1, 3)
2	6	(2, 6)
3	9	(3, 9)
4	12	(4, 12)

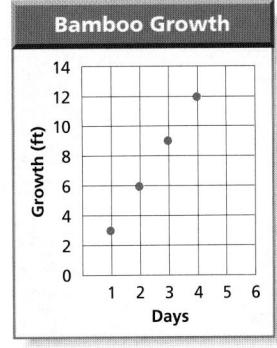

Bamboo Growth

c. Describe the graph.
   The points appear to fall in a line.

www.pre-alg.com/extra_examples/ny

RELATIONS

In-Class Examples Power Point®

3 Express the relation {(1, 4), (2, 2), (3, 0), (0, 2)} as a table and as a graph. Then determine the domain and range.
D = {0, 1, 2, 3}, R = {0, 2, 4}

x	y
1	4
2	2
3	0
0	2

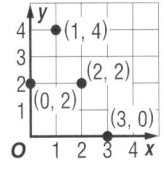

4 **EARNINGS**   Austin earns $5 an hour doing yard work. Suppose *x* represents the number of hours Austin works.

a. Make a table of ordered pairs in which the *x*-coordinate represents the hours worked and *y* represents the amount of money Austin earns for 1, 2, 3, 4, and 5 hours of work.

x	y
1	5
2	10
3	15
4	20
5	25

b. Graph the ordered pairs.

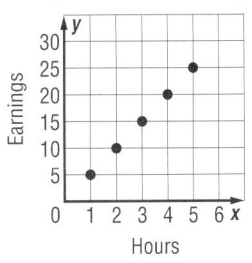

c. Describe the graph.   **The points fall in a line.**

Teacher to Teacher

Rhonda Bailey   Mathematics Consultant, Richardson, TX

"We practice graphing points by playing tic-tac-toe on an overhead-projected coordinate plane. Use two different colors of overhead counters. Students take turns calling out ordered pairs (counters) to be graphed. The first team to get 4 of their counters in a row wins the game. Play the best 2 out of 3."

Study Notebook

Have students—
- add the definitions/examples of the vocabulary terms to their Vocabulary Builder worksheets for Chapter 1.
- draw and label a coordinate plane as shown on page 33.
- include any other item(s) that they find helpful in mastering the skills in this lesson.

About the Exercises . . .

Organization by Objective
- **Ordered Pairs:** 12–24
- **Relations:** 26–42

Odd/Even Assignments
Exercises 12–23 and 31–36 are structured so that students practice the same concepts whether they are assigned odd or even problems.

Assignment Guide

Basic: 13–23 odd, 26–30, 31–35 odd, 37–39, 44, 45, 47, 48, 50–65

Average: 13–25 odd, 26–30, 31–35 odd, 37–39, 44, 45, 47, 48, 50–65 (Optional: 49)

Advanced: 12–24 even, 32–36 even, 40–57 (Optional: 58–65)

Check for Understanding

Concept Check

1. **OPEN ENDED** Give an example of an ordered pair, and identify the x- and y-coordinate. **See margin.**

2. **Name** three ways to represent a relation. **ordered pairs, table, graph**

3. **Define** *domain* and *range*. **See margin.**

Guided Practice

GUIDED PRACTICE KEY	
Exercises	Examples
4, 5	1
6, 7	2
8, 9	3
10, 11	4

Graph each point on a coordinate system.

4. $H(5, 3)$ 5. $D(6, 0)$
4–5. See margin.

Refer to the coordinate system shown at the right. Write the ordered pair that names each point.

6. Q **(2, 3)**   7. P **(6, 5)**

Express each relation as a table and as a graph. Then determine the domain and range. **8–9. See pp. 53A–53B.**

8. $\{(2, 5), (0, 2), (5, 5)\}$ 9. $\{(1, 6), (6, 4), (0, 2), (3, 1)\}$

Application

ENTERTAINMENT For Exercises 10 and 11, use the following information. It costs \$4 to buy a student ticket to the movies. **10–11. See pp. 53A–53B.**

10. Make a table of ordered pairs in which the x-coordinate represents the number of student tickets and the y-coordinate represents the cost for 2, 4, and 5 tickets.

11. Graph the ordered pairs (number of tickets, cost).

★ indicates increased difficulty

Practice and Apply

Homework Help

For Exercises	See Examples
12–17	1
18–23	2
26–30, 37–43	4
31–36	3

Extra Practice
See page 725.

Graph each point on a coordinate system. **12–17. See pp. 53A–53B.**

12. $A(3, 3)$ 13. $D(1, 8)$ 14. $G(2, 7)$
15. $X(7, 2)$ 16. $P(0, 6)$ 17. $N(4, 0)$

Refer to the coordinate system shown at the right. Write the ordered pair that names each point.

18. C **(1, 7)**   19. J **(7, 3)**
20. N **(0, 4)**   21. T **(6, 6)**
22. Y **(2, 1)**   23. B **(3, 4)**

24. What point lies on both the x-axis and y-axis? **(0, 0)**

★25. Where are all of the possible locations for the graph of (x, y) if $y = 0$?, if $x = 0$? **on the x-axis; on the y-axis**

SCIENCE For Exercises 26 and 27, use the following information. The average speed of a house mouse is 12 feet per second.
Source: *Natural History Magazine*

26. Find the distance traveled in 3, 5, and 7 seconds.

27. Graph the ordered pairs (time, distance). **26–27. See pp. 53A–53B.**

Answers

1. Sample answer: (3, 5); the x-coordinate is 3, and the y-coordinate is 5.

3. The domain of a relation is the set of x-coordinates. The range is the set of y-coordinates.

4.

5.

SCIENCE For Exercises 28–30, use the following information.
Keyson is conducting a physics experiment. He drops a tennis ball from a height of 100 centimeters and then records the height after each bounce. The results are shown in the table. **28–30. See pp. 53A–53B.**

Bounce	0	1	2	3	4
Height (cm)	100	50	25	13	6

28. Write a set of ordered pairs for the data.

29. Graph the data.

30. How high do you think the ball will bounce on the fifth bounce? Explain.

Express each relation as a table and as a graph. Then determine the domain and range. 31–36. See pp. 53A–53B.

31. {(4, 5), (5, 2), (1, 6)}

32. {(6, 8), (2, 9), (0, 1)}

33. {(7, 0), (3, 2), (4, 4), (5, 1)}

34. {(2, 4), (1, 3), (5, 6), (1, 1)}

35. {(0, 1), (0, 3), (0, 5), (2, 0)}

36. {(4, 3), (3, 4), (1, 2), (2, 1)}

AIR PRESSURE For Exercises 37–39, use the table and the following information.
The air pressure decreases as the distance from Earth increases. The table shows the air pressure for certain distances.

Height (mi)	Pressure (lb/in²)
sea level	14.7
1	10.2
2	6.4
3	4.3
4	2.7
5	1.6

37. **(0, 14.7), (1, 10.2), (2, 6.4), (3, 4.3), (4, 2.7), (5, 1.6)** Write a set of ordered pairs for the data.

38. Graph the data. **See pp. 53A–53B.**

39. State the domain and the range of the relation.
domain = {0, 1, 2, 3, 4, 5}; range = {14.7, 10.2, 6.4, 4.3, 2.7, 1.6}

SCIENCE For Exercises 40–43, use the following information and the information at the left. **40–43. See pp. 53A–53B.**
★
Water boils at sea level at 100°C. The boiling point of water decreases about 5°C for every mile above sea level.

40. Make a table that shows the boiling point at sea level and at 1, 2, 3, 4, and 5 miles above sea level.

41. Show the data as a set of ordered pairs.

42. Graph the ordered pairs.

43. At about what temperature does water boil in Albuquerque, New Mexico? in Alpine, Texas? (*Hint:* 1 mile = 5280 feet)

44. **CRITICAL THINKING** Where are all of the possible locations for the graph of (x, y) if $x = 4$? **the vertical line where $x = 4$**

45. **WRITING IN MATH** Answer the question that was posed at the beginning of the lesson. **See margin.**

How are ordered pairs used to graph real-life data?

Include the following in your answer:
- an explanation of how an ordered pair identifies a specific point on a graph, and
- an example of a situation where ordered pairs are used to graph data.

More About . . .

Science •·············
Albuquerque, New Mexico, is at 7200 feet above sea level. Alpine, Texas, is at 4490 feet above sea level.
Source: *The World Almanac*

www.pre-alg.com/self_check_quiz/ny   Lesson 1-6 Ordered Pairs and Relations **37**

Answer

45. Ordered pairs can be used to graph real-life data by expressing the data as ordered pairs and then graphing the ordered pairs. Answers should include the following.
- The *x*- and *y*-coordinate of an ordered pair specifies the point on the graph.
- longitude and latitude lines

Study Guide and Intervention, p. 26

In mathematics, a **coordinate system** is used to locate points. The horizontal number line is called the **x-axis** and the vertical number line is called the **y-axis**. The point where the two axes intersect is the **origin** (0, 0). An **ordered pair** of numbers is used to locate points in the coordinate plane. The point (4, 3) has an **x-coordinate** of 4 and a **y-coordinate** of 3.

Example 1 Graph A(4, 3) on the coordinate system.
Step 1 Start at the origin.
Step 2 Since the x-coordinate is 4, move 4 units to the right.
Step 3 Since the y-coordinate is 3, move 3 units up. Draw a dot.
A set of ordered pairs is called a **relation**. The set of x-coordinates is called the **domain**. The set of y-coordinates is called the **range**.

Example 2 Express the relation {(0, 0), (2, 1), (4, 2), (3, 5)} as a table and as a graph. Then determine the domain and range.

x	y
0	0
2	1
4	2
3	5

The domain is {0, 2, 4, 3}, and the range is {0, 1, 2, 5}.

Exercises

Graph each point on the coordinate system.
1. A(4,1)   2. B(2,0)
3. C(1,3)   4. D(5,2)
5. E(0,3)   6. F(6,4)

7. Express the relation {(4,6), (0,3), (1,4)} as a table and a graph. Then determine the domain and range. domain: {4, 0, 1}, range: {6, 3, 4}

x	y
4	6
0	3
1	4

Skills Practice, p. 27 and Practice, p. 28 (shown)

Graph each point on the coordinate system.
1. Q(4, 2)   2. V(3, 7)
3. T(0, 3)   4. B(8, 6)
5. R(5, 0)   6. L(4, 4)

Write the ordered pair that names each point.
7. J (4, 1)   8. X (0, 7)
9. R (2, 2)   10. B (8, 5)
11. K (3, 4)   12. H (8, 0)
13. D (1, 6)   14. N (7, 3)

Express each relation as a table and as a graph. Then determine the domain and range.
15. {(3, 7), (1, 1), (6, 5), (2, 4)}

x	y
3	7
1	1
6	5
2	4

domain = {3, 1, 6, 2}
range = {7, 1, 5, 4}

16. {(0, 2), (4, 6), (3, 7)}

x	y
0	2
4	6
3	7

domain = {0, 4, 3}
range = {2, 6, 7}

17. **GEOMETRY** Graph (2, 1), (2, 4), and (5,1) on the coordinate system.
a. Connect the points with line segments. What figure is formed? **a right triangle**
b. Multiply each number in the set of ordered pairs by 2. Graph and connect the new ordered pairs. What figure is formed? **a right triangle**
c. Compare the two figures you drew. Write a sentence that tells how the figures are the same and how they are different. **Sample answer: Both figures are right triangles, but one is twice as large as the other.**

Enrichment, p. 30

The Hidden Animal

Graph the following sets of points. Join successive points by a line segment. Begin a new line segment with each numbered set of ordered pairs. When you finish, you will have a picture of an animal.

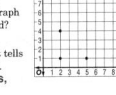

1. (10, 12), (8, 12), (2, 11½), (½, 10), (½, 5)

2. (½, 8), (1, 6½), (1, 5½), (1½, 3), (1½, 1), (4, 1), (3½, 2), (3½, 5½)

3. (8½, 6½), (8, 6), (8½, 4), (8½, 1), (10½, 1), (10, 2), (10, 6)

4. (10, 5), (12, 3), (12, 1½), (10½, 1½), (10½, 2½), (10, 3)

5. (8, 6), (6, 5½), (3, 5½), (3, 2), (3½, 1)

6. (12, 12), (11, 12½), (9, 11½), (8½, 10½), (8½, 9½), (9, 8½), (10, 8), (11, 9)

7. (12, 12), (13, 12), (14, 11), (14, 9), (13½, 8), (13½, 7), (13, 3), (12½, 2), (12, 2½), (12½, 3), (12½, 6), (12, 7), (11, 7½), (10½, 7), (10, 6)

8. Suppose you multiply both coordinates of each ordered pair by 2 and graph the resulting pairs on graph paper using the same scale on the axes as for the drawing above. How would the drawings compare? **Each segment in the new figure would be twice as long.**

Open-Ended Assessment

Speaking Ask students to explain how to set up a coordinate plane and locate the points of a given relation. Encourage students to use as many vocabulary words from this section of the textbook as possible.

Getting Ready for Lesson 1-7

BASIC SKILL Exercises 58–65 review finding a quotient. These exercises continue to review basic operations necessary for working with algebraic expressions.

Assessment Options

Quiz (Lessons 1-5 and 1-6) is available on p. 52 of the *Chapter 1 Resource Masters.*

Answers

46a.

(9, 10)

46b.

(8, 2)

49a.

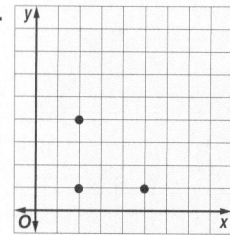

49e. The figures have the same shape but not the same size.

★ **46.** Graph each relation on a coordinate system. Then find the coordinates of another point that follows the pattern in the graph. **46a–b. See margin.**

a.

x	1	3	5	7
y	2	4	6	8

b.

x	0	2	4	6
y	10	8	6	4

Standardized Test Practice
Ⓐ Ⓑ Ⓒ Ⓓ

47. State the domain of the relation shown in the graph. **D**

Ⓐ {0, 1, 4, 5, 8}

Ⓑ {A, G, P, S, Z}

Ⓒ {0, 1, 2, 4, 5}

Ⓓ {1, 2, 5, 6, 7}

48. What relationship exists between the x- and y-coordinates of each of the data points shown on the graph? **D**

Ⓐ The y-coordinate varies, and the x-coordinate is always 4.

Ⓑ The y-coordinate is 4 more than the x-coordinate.

Ⓒ The sum of the x- and y-coordinate is always 4.

Ⓓ The x-coordinate varies, and the y-coordinate is always 4.

Extending the Lesson
49. Draw a coordinate grid. **49b. triangle** **49c. (4, 2), (4, 8), (10, 2)**

a. Graph (2, 1), (2, 4), and (5, 1). **See margin.**

b. Connect the points with line segments. Describe the figure formed.

c. Multiply each coordinate in the set of ordered pairs by 2.

d. Graph the new ordered pairs. Connect the points with line segments. What figure is formed? **triangle**

e. **MAKE A CONJECTURE** How do the figures compare? Write a sentence explaining the similarities and differences of the figures. **See margin.**

Maintain Your Skills

Mixed Review **ALGEBRA** Solve each equation mentally. *(Lesson 1-5)*

50. $a + 6 = 17$ **11** **51.** $7t = 42$ **6** **52.** $\frac{54}{n} = 6$ **9**

53. Name the property shown by $4 \cdot 1 = 4$. *(Lesson 1-4)* **Multiplicative Identity**

ALGEBRA Evaluate each expression if $a = 5$, $b = 1$, and $c = 3$. *(Lesson 1-3)*

54. $ca - cb$ **12** **55.** $5a - 6c$ **7**

Write a numerical expression for each verbal phrase. *(Lesson 1-2)*

56. fifteen less than twenty-one **21 − 15**

57. the product of ten and thirty **10 · 30**

Getting Ready for the Next Lesson **BASIC SKILL** Find each quotient.

58. $74 \div 2$ **37** **59.** $96 \div 8$ **12** **60.** $102 \div 3$ **34** **61.** $112 \div 4$ **28**

62. $80 \div 16$ **5** **63.** $91 \div 13$ **7** **64.** $132 \div 22$ **6** **65.** $153 \div 17$ **9**

Algebra Activity

A Preview of Lesson 1-7

NEW YORK *Performance Indicator* **8.A.4 Create a graph given a description or an expression for a situation involving a linear or nonlinear relationship**

Scatter Plots

Sometimes, it is difficult to determine whether a relationship exists between two sets of data by simply looking at them. To determine whether a relationship exists, we can write the data as a set of ordered pairs and then graph the ordered pairs on a coordinate system.

Collect the Data

Let's investigate whether a relationship exists between height and arm span.

Step 1 Work with a partner. Use a centimeter ruler to measure the length of your partner's height and arm span to the nearest centimeter. Record the data in a table like the one shown.

Name	Height (cm)	Arm Span (cm)

Step 2 Extend the table. Combine your data with that of your classmates.

Step 3 Make a list of ordered pairs in which the x-coordinate represents height and the y-coordinate represents arm span.

Step 4 Draw a coordinate grid like the one shown and graph the ordered pairs (height, arm span).

Analyze the Data

1. Does there appear to be a trend in the data? If so, describe the trend.
   Yes; as height increases, arm span increases.

Make a Conjecture 2–4. See margin.

2. Estimate the arm span of a person whose height is 60 inches. 72 inches.

3. How does a person's arm span compare to his or her height?

4. Suppose the variable x represents height, and the variable y represents arm span. Write an expression for arm span.

Extend the Activity

5. Collect and graph data to determine whether a relationship exists between height and shoe length. Explain your results. **See margin.**

Algebra Activity   Scatter Plots   **39**

Getting Started

Objective Use a scatter plot to investigate the relationship between two sets of data, height and arm span.

Materials
grid paper
centimeter ruler or tape measure

Teach

- Make sure students understand how to measure arm span. With arms outstretched, measure the distance from the tips of the middle fingers.
- As students look for trends in the data, ask them to discuss any points that may not follow the trend.

Assess

In **Exercises 1–4**, students should

- discover that height and arm span are somewhat equal.
- make up a problem about how the relationship between height and shoe length can be used by a detective. Then solve the problem.

Answers

2. about 60 inches; about 72 inches

3. A person's arm span is about equal to his/her height.

4. $y = x$

5. See student's work; generally, as height increases, shoe length increases.

Resource Manager

Teaching Pre-Algebra with Manipulatives

- p. 1 (master for grid paper)
- p. 22 (rulers)
- p. 33 (student recording sheet)

Glencoe Mathematics Classroom Manipulative Kit

- centimeter rulers
- tape measures

1 Focus

 5-Minute Check Transparency 1-7 Use as a quiz or review of Lesson 1-6.

Mathematical Background notes are available for this lesson on page 4D.

How can scatter plots help spot trends?

The opening activity questions are repeated on page 34 of the *Chapter 1 Resource Masters*.

Reading to Learn Mathematics, p. 34 **ELL**

Pre-Activity *How can scatter plots help spot trends?*

Do the activity at the top of page 40 in your textbook. Write your answers below.

a. What appears to be the trend in sales of movies on videocassette?
   Sample answer: Consumers are buying less movies on videocassette.

b. Estimate the number of movies on videocassette sold for 2003. about 40

Reading the Lesson

Write a definition and give an example of the new vocabulary term.

Vocabulary	Definition	Example
1. scatter plot	See students' work.	

Helping You Remember

2. Scatter plots are used to show relationships.

   a. For a positive relationship, as *x* increases, *y* __increases__.

   b. For a negative relationship, as *x* increases, *y* __decreases__.

3. The scatter plot compares the weights and heights of the players on a high school football team.

   Heights of Football Players

   a. What type of relationship exists, if any? In general, as the heights of the players increase, so do the weights. The scatter plot shows a positive relationship.

   b. Based on the scatter plot, predict the weight of a 5' 5" player who decided to join the team. approximately 145 pounds

Teaching Tip Make sure students understand how to set up the scale on the axes using equal increments along each axis. The two axes need not have the same scale.

What You'll Learn

- Construct scatter plots.
- Interpret scatter plots.

Vocabulary
- scatter plot

a. Sample answer: Consumers are buying less movies on videocassette.
b. about 40

TEACHING TIP
Ask students why they think the sales of videocassettes have fallen.

NEW YORK *Performance Indicator*

8.A.3 Describe a situation involving relationships that matches a given graph

8.A.4 Create a graph given a description or an expression for a situation involving a linear or nonlinear relationship

How can scatter plots help spot trends?

Suppose you work in the video department of a home entertainment store. The number of movies on videocassettes you have sold in a five-year period is shown in the graph.

a. What appears to be the trend in sales of movies on videocassette?

b. Estimate the number of movies on videocassette sold for 2005.

Videocassette Sales

CONSTRUCT SCATTER PLOTS A **scatter plot** is a graph that shows the relationship between two sets of data. In a scatter plot, two sets of data are graphed as ordered pairs on a coordinate system.

Example 1 Construct a Scatter Plot

TEST SCORES The table shows the average SAT math scores from 1993–2002. Make a scatter plot of the data.

Year	'93	'94	'95	'96	'97	'98	'99	'00	'01	'02
Score	503	504	506	508	511	512	511	514	514	516

Source: *The College Board*

Let the horizontal axis, or *x*-axis, represent the year. Let the vertical axis, or *y*-axis, represent the score. Then graph ordered pairs (year, score).

Average SAT Scores, 1993–2002

✓ **Concept Check** *True or false*: A scatter plot represents one set of data. Explain.
False; it shows two sets of data.

Resource Manager

📁 Workbooks and Reproducible Masters

Chapter 1 Resource Masters
- Study Guide and Intervention, p. 31
- Skills Practice, p. 32
- Practice, p. 33
- Reading to Learn Mathematics, p. 34
- Enrichment, p. 35
- Assessment, p. 52

Graphing Calculator and Spreadsheet Masters, pp. 20, 45
Parent and Student Study Guide Workbook, p. 7

📺 Transparencies
5-Minute Check Transparency 1-7
Real-World Transparency 1
Answer Key Transparencies

⚙️ Technology
Interactive Chalkboard

INTERPRET SCATTER PLOTS The following scatter plots show the types of relationships or patterns of two sets of data.

Concept Summary | **Types of Relationships**

Positive Relationship
As *x* increases, *y* increases.

Negative Relationship
As *x* increases, *y* decreases.

No Relationship
No obvious pattern.

✓ **Concept Check** What type of relationship is shown on a graph that shows as the values of *x* increase, the values of *y* decrease? **negative**

Example 2 *Interpret Scatter Plots*

Determine whether a scatter plot of the data for the following might show a *positive*, *negative*, or *no* relationship. Explain your answer.

a. age of car and value of car

As the age of a car increases, the value of the car decreases. So, a scatter plot of the data would show a negative relationship.

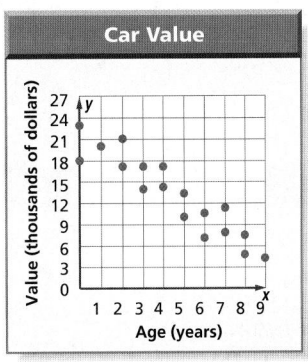

b. birth month and birth weight

A person's birth weight is not affected by their birth month. Therefore, a scatter plot of the data would show no relationship.

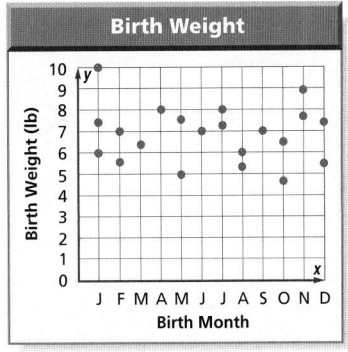

You can also use scatter plots to spot trends, draw conclusions, and make predictions about the data.

www.pre-alg.com/extra_examples/ny

Lesson 1-7 Scatter Plots **41**

b. shoe size and math test score
no relationship

---

2 Teach

CONSTRUCT SCATTER PLOTS

In-Class Example Power Point®

1 The table shows the average cost of a loaf of bread from 1920–2000. Make a scatter plot of the data.

Year	1920	1930	1940	1950	1960
Cents	12	9	8	14	20

Year	1970	1980	1990	2000
Cents	24	52	72	99

Source: *Time Almanac*

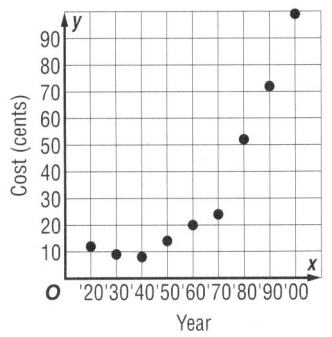

INTERPRET SCATTER PLOTS

In-Class Example Power Point®

2 Determine whether a scatter plot of the data for the following might show a *positive*, *negative* or *no* relationship. Explain your answer.

a. height of basketball player and number of rebounds

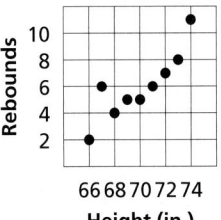

As height increases, number of rebounds increases; positive relationship.

Lesson 1-7 Scatter Plots **41**

3 The table shows temperatures in degrees Celsius and the corresponding temperatures in Fahrenheit.

°F	32	41	50	59	68	77	86
°C	0	5	10	15	20	25	30

a. Make a scatter plot of the data.

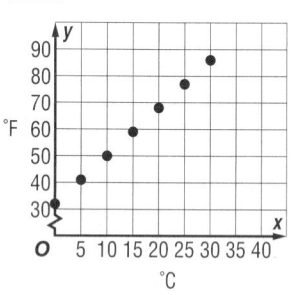

b. Does the scatter plot show a relationship between °C and °F? Explain.   **Yes, a positive relationship. As °C increase, so do °F.**

c. Predict the Fahrenheit temperature for 35°C. **about 95°**

---

3 Practice/Apply

Study Notebook

Have students—
• complete the definition/example for the remaining term on the Vocabulary Builder worksheets for Chapter 1.
• include any other item(s) that they find helpful in mastering the skills in this lesson.

Biologist ·············

Wildlife biologists work in the field of fish and wildlife conservation. Duties may include studying animal populations and monitoring trends of migrating animals.

Online Research
For information about a career as a wildlife biologist, visit: www.pre-alg.com/careers

---

Example 3 *Use Scatter Plots to Make Predictions*

BIOLOGY A biologist recorded the lengths and weights of some largemouth bass. The table shows the results.

Length (in.)	9.2	10.9	12.3	12.0	14.1	15.5	16.4	16.9	17.7	18.4	19.8
Weight (lb)	0.5	0.8	0.9	1.3	1.7	2.2	2.5	3.2	3.6	4.1	4.8

a. Make a scatter plot of the data.

Let the horizontal axis represent length, and let the vertical axis represent weight. Graph the data.

b. Does the scatter plot show a relationship between the length and weight of a largemouth bass? Explain.

As the length of the bass increases, so does its weight. So, the scatter plot shows a positive relationship.

c. Predict the weight of a bass that measures 22 inches.

By looking at the pattern in the graph, we can predict that the weight of a bass measuring 22 inches would be between 5 and 6 pounds.

Check for Understanding

Concept Check

1. Sample answer: make predictions, draw conclusions, spot trends

Guided Practice

Application

GUIDED PRACTICE KEY	
Exercises	Examples
4, 5	2
6, 7	1, 3

1. List three ways a scatter plot can be used.

2. OPEN ENDED Draw a scatter plot with ten ordered pairs that show a negative relationship. **See margin.**

3. Name the three types of relationships shown by scatter plots. **negative, positive, and none**

Determine whether a scatter plot of the data for the following might show a *positive*, *negative*, or *no* relationship. Explain your answer. **4–5. See margin.**

4. hours worked and earnings   **5.** hair color and height

SCHOOL For Exercises 6 and 7, use the table that shows the heights and grade point averages of the students in Mrs. Stanley's class. **6. See pp. 53A–53B.**

6. Make a scatter plot of the data.

7. Does there appear to be a relationship between the scores? Explain. **Since the points appear to be random, there is no relationship.**

Name	Height (in.)	GPA
Jenna	66	3.6
Michael	61	3.2
Laura	59	3.9
Simon	64	2.8
Marcus	61	3.8
Timothy	65	3.1
Brandon	70	2.6
Emily	64	2.2
Eduardo	65	4.0

About the Exercises . . .

Organization by Objective
• **Construct Scatter Plots:** 17
• **Interpret Scatter Plots:** 8–16, 18, 19, 21

Alert! Exercise 20 involves research on the Internet or other reference materials.

Odd/Even Assignments
Exercises 8–13 are structured so that students practice the same concepts whether they are assigned odd or even problems.

Assignment Guide
Basic: 9–13 odd, 14–16, 21–37
Average: 9–13 odd, 17–37
Advanced: 8–12 even, 17–37

Practice and Apply

Homework Help

For Exercises	See Examples
8–13	2
14–20	1, 3

Extra Practice
See page 726.

Determine whether a scatter plot of the data for the following might show a *positive*, *negative*, or *no* relationship. Explain your answer.

8. size of household and amount of water bill **positive**

9. number of songs on a CD and cost of a CD **no**

10. size of a car's engine and miles per gallon **negative**

11. speed and distance traveled **positive**

12. outside temperature and amount of heating bill **negative**

13. size of a television screen and the number of channels it receives **no**
8–13. See pp. 53A–53B for explanations.

ANIMALS For Exercises 14–16, use the scatter plot shown.

14. Do the data show a *positive*, *negative*, or *no* relationship between the year and the number of bald eagle hatchlings?

15. What appears to be the trend in the number of hatchlings between 1965 and 1972?

16. What appears to be the trend between 1972 and 1985?
The number increases.

14. There is no obvious pattern, so the graph shows no relationship.

15. The number decreases.

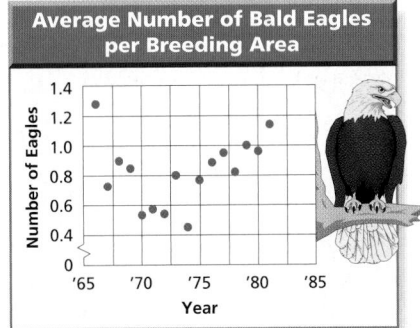

Average Number of Bald Eagles per Breeding Area

Source: *CHANCE*

 Online Research **Data Update** How has the total number of bald eagle pairs in the United States changed since 1980? Visit www.pre-alg.com/data_update to learn more.

WebQuest

The high and low temperatures for your vacation destinations can be shown in a scatter plot. Visit www.pre-alg.com/webquest to continue work on your WebQuest project.

BASKETBALL For Exercises 17–19, use the following information.
The number of minutes played and the number of field goal attempts for certain players of the Indiana Pacers for the 1999–2000 season is shown below.

Player	Minutes Played	Field Goal Attempts	Player	Minutes Played	Field Goal Attempts
Rose	2978	1196	Best	1691	561
Miller	2987	1041	Jackson	2190	570
Smits	1852	890	Perkins	1620	441
Croshere	1885	653	Mullin	582	187
Davis	2127	602	McKey	634	108

17. Make a scatter plot of the data. **See pp. 53A–53B.**

18. Does the scatter plot show any relationship? If so, is it positive or negative? Explain your reasoning.

19. Suppose a player played 2500 minutes. Predict the number of field goal attempts for that player. **about 800**

18. Yes; positive; as the number of minutes increases, the number of field goal attempts increases.

20. **RESEARCH** Use the Internet or another source to find two sets of sports statistics that can be shown in a scatter plot. Identify any trends in the data. **See students' work.**

 www.pre-alg.com/self_check_quiz/ny

Answers (p. 42)

2. Sample answer:

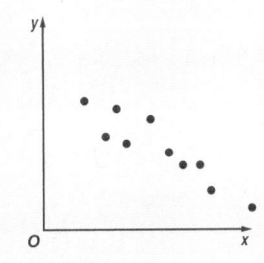

4. **Positive; as the number of hours worked increases, so do the earnings.**

5. **No; hair color is not related to height.**

Open-Ended Assessment

Writing Provide students with a scatter plot of interesting sports data such as the record 100 m relay times for the last several years. Ask students to write a paragraph describing the graph, any trends or relationships in the data, and any predictions they could make from the past of the future.

Assessment Options

Quiz (Lesson 1-7) is available on p. 52 of the *Chapter 1 Resource Masters.*

Answers

21. Sample answer: Yes; as more emphasis is placed on standard-ized tests, students will become more comfortable taking the tests, and scores will increase.

22. Sample answer: By studying scatter plots and identifying the type of relationship the scatter plot shows, you can determine trends. Answers should include the following:

   • A positive relationship means that as one set of data increases, the other set also increases. A negative rela-tionship means that as one set of data increases, the other set decreases. No rela-tionship means that one set of data is not related to the other set of data.

   • The amount of money spent and the amount of money saved would be an example of a negative relationship. The number of hours spent studying and test scores would represent a positive relationship. The number of days in a month and the num-ber of rainy days is an example of no relationship.

21. **CRITICAL THINKING** Refer to Example 1 on page 40. Do you think the trend in the test scores would continue in the years to come? Explain your reasoning. **See margin.**

22. **WRITING IN MATH** Answer the question that was posed at the beginning of the lesson. **See margin.**

   How can scatter plots help us spot trends?

   Include the following in your answer:
   • definitions of positive relationship, negative relationship, and no relationship, and
   • examples of real-life situations that would represent each type of relationship.

The scatter plot shows the study time and test scores for the students in Mr. Mock's history class.

23. Based on the results, which of the following is an appropriate score for a student who studies for 1 hour? **C**
   Ⓐ 68   Ⓑ 98
   Ⓒ 87   Ⓓ 72

24. Which of the following is an appropriate score for a student who studies for 1.5 hours? **B**
   Ⓐ 78   Ⓑ 92
   Ⓒ 81   Ⓓ 74

Study Time and Test Scores

Maintain Your Skills

Mixed Review

Graph each ordered pair on a coordinate system. *(Lesson 1-6)*
25. $M(3, 2)$ 26. $X(5, 0)$ 27. $K(0, 2)$
25–27. See margin.

Write the ordered pair that names each point. *(Lesson 1-6)*

28. (2, 3)

29. (0, 4)

30. (3, 0)

31. Determine the domain and range of the relation $\{(0, 9), (4, 8), (2, 3), (6, 1)\}$. *(Lesson 1-6)* **domain = {0, 4, 2, 6}; range = {9, 8, 3, 1}**

ALGEBRA Solve each equation mentally. *(Lesson 1-5)*
32. $3c = 81$ **27**   33. $15 - x = 8$ **7**   34. $8 = \dfrac{32}{m}$ **4**

35. **ALGEBRA** Simplify $15 + (b + 3)$. *(Lesson 1-4)* **b + 18**

ALGEBRA Evaluate each expression if $m = 8$ and $y = 6$. *(Lesson 1-3)*
36. $(2m + 3y) - m$ **26**   37. $3m + (y - 2) + 3$ **31**

25.

26.

27.

Graphing Calculator Investigation

A Follow-Up of Lesson 1-7

NEW YORK *Performance Indicator* **8.R.1 Use** physical objects, drawings, charts, **tables,** graphs, symbols, equations, **and objects created using technology as representations**

Scatter Plots

You have learned that graphing ordered pairs as a scatter plot on a coordinate plane is one way to make it easier to "see" if there is a relationship. You can use a TI-83 Plus graphing calculator to create scatter plots.

SCIENCE A zoologist studied extinction times (in years) of island birds. The zoologist wanted to see if there was a relationship between the average number of nests and the time needed for each bird to become extinct on the islands. Use the table of data below to make a scatter plot.

Bird Name	Bird Size	Average Number of Nests	Extinction Time
Buzzard	Large	2.0	5.5
Quail	Large	1.0	1.5
Curlew	Large	2.8	3.1
Cuckoo	Large	1.4	2.5
Magpie	Large	4.5	10.0
Swallow	Small	3.8	2.6
Robin	Small	3.3	4.0
Stonechat	Small	3.6	2.4
Blackbird	Small	4.7	3.3
Tree-sparrow	Small	2.2	1.9

Step 1 *Enter the data.*

• Clear any existing lists.

KEYSTROKES: STAT ENTER ▲ CLEAR ENTER

• Enter the average number of nests as L1 and extinction times as L2.

KEYSTROKES: STAT ENTER 2 ENTER 1 ENTER ... 2.2 ENTER ► 5.5 ENTER 1.5 ENTER ... 1.9 ENTER

The first data pair is (2, 5.5).

Step 2 *Format the graph.*

• Turn on the statistical plot.

KEYSTROKES: 2nd [STAT PLOT] ENTER ENTER

• Select the scatter plot, L1 as the Xlist and L2 as the Ylist.

KEYSTROKES: ▼ ENTER ▼ 2nd [L1] ENTER 2nd [L2] ENTER

A Follow-Up of Lesson 1-7

Getting Started

Know Your Calculator Besides creating scatter plots, a graphing calculator can plot statistical data such as histograms, box-and-whisker plots, and other types of displays. The calculator organizes lists of numbers for each type of statistical measure, making it possible to see various displays of a data set.

Teach

• Make sure students have deactivated or cleared out any equations stored in the Y= list before graphing the scatter plot.

• Students should double check that all data have been entered correctly and that each list contains the same number of entries. Only the ordered pairs from the data set should be in L1 and L2.

• Have students complete Exercises 1–9.

Graphing Calculator and Spreadsheet Investigations empower students to use technology tools to solve problems.

Help students describe how the calculator helps create a scatter plot. Also have them describe any features of the calculator that help them analyze the graph.

Answers

1. The *x*-coordinate represents average number of nests and the *y*-coordinate represents extinction time for each bird.

2. Sample answer: The points seem to be slanting up from left to right. One point seems much higher than the others.

3. Sample answer: Generally, as the number of nests increases, the time it takes to become extinct increases also. There is a positive relationship.

5.

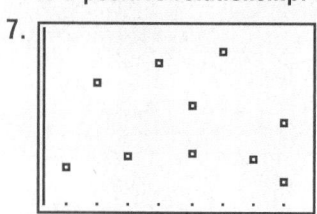

The plot shows larger birds tend to have longer extinction lines.

6.

As *x* increases, *y* increases. There is a positive relationship.

7.

No relationship

8.

As *x* increases, *y* decreases. There is a negative relationship

---

Step 3 *Graph the data.*

• Display the scatter plot.
  KEYSTROKES: ZOOM 9

• Use the TRACE feature and the left and right arrow keys to move from one point to another.

Exercises **1–3. See margin.**

1. Press TRACE . Use the left and right arrow keys to move from one point to another. What do the coordinates of each data point represent?

2. Describe the scatter plot.

3. Is there a relationship between the average number of nests and extinction times? If so, write a sentence or two that describes the relationship.

4. Are there any differences between the extinction times of large birds versus small birds? **Sample answer: Large birds tend to have longer extinction times.**

5. Separate the data by bird size. Enter average number of nests and extinction times for large birds as lists L1 and L2 and for small birds as lists L3 and L4. Use the graphing calculator to make two scatter plots with different marks for large and small birds. Does your scatter plot agree with your answer in Exercise 4? Explain.

5. See margin for graph. The plot shows larger birds tend to have longer extinction times.

For Exercises 6–8, make a scatter plot for each set of data and describe the relationship, if any, between the *x*- and *y*-values. **6–8. See margin for graphs.**

6.

x	y
70	323
80	342
40	244
50	221
30	121
80	399
60	230
60	200
50	215
40	170

As *x* increases, *y* increases. There is a positive relationship.

7.

x	y
8	89
5	32
9	30
10	18
3	26
4	72
10	51
7	34
6	82
7	60

no relationship

8.

x	5.2	5.8	6.3	6.7	7.4	7.6	8.4	8.5	9.1
y	12.1	11.9	11.5	9.8	10.2	9.6	8.8	9.1	8.5

As *x* increases, *y* decreases. There is a negative relationship.

9. **RESEARCH** Find two sets of data on your own. Then determine whether a relationship exists between the data. **Sample data: year vs. 100-meter dash times; year vs. school enrollment.**

Vocabulary and Concept Check

algebraic expression (p. 17)	graph (p. 34)	scatter plot (p. 40)
conjecture (p. 7)	inductive reasoning (p. 7)	simplify (p. 25)
coordinate plane (p. 33)	numerical expression (p. 12)	solution (p. 28)
coordinate system (p. 33)	open sentence (p. 28)	solving the equation (p. 28)
counterexample (p. 25)	ordered pair (p. 33)	variable (p. 17)
deductive reasoning (p. 25)	order of operations (p. 12)	x-axis (p. 33)
defining a variable (p. 18)	origin (p. 33)	x-coordinate (p. 33)
domain (p. 35)	properties (p. 23)	y-axis (p. 33)
equation (p. 28)	range (p. 35)	y-coordinate (p. 33)
evaluate (p. 12)	relation (p. 35)	

Choose the letter of the term that best matches each statement or phrase. Use each letter once.

1. $m + 3n - 4$ **d**
2. to find the value of a numerical expression **b**
3. the set of all y-coordinates of a relation **e**
4. $20 + 12 \div 4 - 1 \times 2$ **a**
5. the set of all x-coordinates of a relation **c**

> a. numerical expression
> b. evaluate
> c. domain
> d. algebraic expression
> e. range

Lesson-by-Lesson Review

1-1 Using a Problem-Solving Plan

See pages 6–10.

Concept Summary

- The four steps of the four-step problem-solving plan are *explore, plan, solve,* and *examine.*
- Some problems can be solved using inductive reasoning.

Example What is the next term in the list 1, 5, 9, 13, 17, …?

Explore We know the first five terms. We need to find the next term.

Plan Use inductive reasoning to determine the next term.

Solve Each term is 4 more than the previous term.

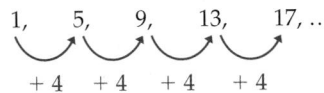

$$1, \quad 5, \quad 9, \quad 13, \quad 17, \dots$$
$$+4 \quad +4 \quad +4 \quad +4$$

By continuing the pattern, the next term is $17 + 4$ or 21.

Examine Subtract 4 from each term. $21 - 4 = 17$, $17 - 4 = 13$, $13 - 4 = 9$, $9 - 4 = 5$, and $5 - 4 = 1$. So, the answer is correct.

Chapter 1 Study Guide and Review

Vocabulary and Concept Check

- This alphabetical list of vocabulary terms in Chapter 1 includes a page reference where each term was introduced.
- **Assessment** A vocabulary review/test for Chapter 1 is available on p. 50 of the *Chapter 1 Resource Masters.*

Lesson-by-Lesson Review

For each lesson,
- the main ideas are summarized,
- additional examples review concepts, and
- practice exercises are provided.

Vocabulary PuzzleMaker

ELL The Vocabulary PuzzleMaker software improves students' mathematics vocabulary using four puzzle formats—crossword, scramble, word search using a word list, and word search using clues. Students can work on a computer screen or from a printed handout.

MindJogger Videoquizzes

ELL MindJogger Videoquizzes provide an alternative review of concepts presented in this chapter. Students work in teams in a game show format to gain points for correct answers. The questions are presented in three rounds.

Round 1 Concepts (5 questions)
Round 2 Skills (4 questions)
Round 3 Problem Solving (4 questions)

FOLDABLES™ Study Organizer

For more information about Foldables, see *Teaching Mathematics with Foldables.*

Have students reexamine their Foldables to make sure all examples they have written are correct. Suggest that they refer to their Foldables if needed when working through the Study Guide exercises or preparing for the Chapter Test.

Exercises   **Find the next term in each list.**   *See Example 2 on page 7.*

6. 2, 4, 6, 8, 10, ... **12**

7. 5, 8, 11, 14, 17, ... **20**

8. 2, 6, 18, 54, 162, ... **486**

9. 1, 2, 4, 7, 11, 16, ... **22**

10. FOOD   The table below shows the cost of various-sized hams. How much will it cost to buy a ham that weighs 7 pounds?   *See Examples 1 and 3 on pages 7 and 8.*

Weight (lb)	1	2	3	4	5
Cost	$4.38	$8.76	$13.14	$17.52	$21.90

$30.66

1-2 Numbers and Expressions

See pages 12–16.

Concept Summary

- When evaluating an expression, follow the order of operations.

  Step 1   Simplify the expressions inside grouping symbols.

  Step 2   Do all multiplications and/or divisions from left to right.

  Step 3   Do all additions and/or subtractions from left to right.

Example   Find the value of $3[(10 - 7) + 2]$.

$3[(10 - 7) + 2] = 3[3 + 2]$ Evaluate $(10 - 7)$.

$\qquad\qquad\qquad = 3[5]$ Add 3 and 2.

$\qquad\qquad\qquad = 15$ Multiply 3 and 5.

Exercises   **Find the value of each expression.**   *See Example 1 on page 13.*

11. $7 + 3 \cdot 5$ **22**

12. $36 \div 9 - 3$ **1**

13. $5 \cdot (7 - 2) - 9$ **16**

14. $\dfrac{2(17 + 4)}{3}$ **14**

15. $18 \div (7 - 4) + 6$ **12**

16. $4[9 + (1 \cdot 16) - 8]$ **68**

1-3 Variables and Expressions

See pages 17–21.

Concept Summary

- To evaluate an algebraic expression, replace each variable with its known value, and then use the order of operations.

Example   Evaluate $5a + 2$ if $a = 7$.

$5a + 2 = 5(7) + 2$ Replace a with 7.

$\qquad\quad = 35 + 2$ Multiply 5 and 7.

$\qquad\quad = 37$ Add 35 and 2.

Exercises   **ALGEBRA**   **Evaluate each expression if $x = 3$, $y = 8$, and $z = 5$.**

See Examples 1 and 2 on pages 17 and 18.

17. $y + 6$ **14**

18. $17 - 2x$ **11**

19. $z - 3 + y$ **10**

20. $6x - 2z + 7$ **15**

21. $\dfrac{6y}{x} + 9$ **25**

22. $9x - (y + z)$ **14**

1-4 Properties

See pages 23–27.

Concept Summary

For any numbers a, b, and c:

- $a + b = b + a$ Commutative Property of Addition
- $(a + b) + c = a + (b + c)$ Associative Property of Addition
- $a \cdot b = b \cdot a$ Commutative Property of Multiplication
- $(a \cdot b) \cdot c = a \cdot (b \cdot c)$ Associative Property of Multiplication
- $a + 0 = 0 + a = a$ Additive Identity
- $a \cdot 0 = 0 \cdot a = 0$ Multiplicative Property of Zero
- $a \cdot 1 = 1 \cdot a = a$ Multiplicative Identity

Example Name the property shown by each statement.

$8 \cdot 1 = 8$	Multiplicative Identity
$(2 + 3) + 6 = 2 + (3 + 6)$	Associative Property of Addition
$1 \cdot 6 \cdot 9 = 6 \cdot 1 \cdot 9$	Commutative Property of Multiplication

Exercises Name the property shown by each statement.
See Example 1 on page 24.

23. $1 + 9 = 9 + 1$ **Comm. (+)**

24. $6 + 0 = 6$ **Identity (+)**

25. $15 \times 0 = 0$ **Mult. Zero**

26. $(x \cdot 8) \cdot 2 = x \cdot (8 \cdot 2)$ **Assoc. (×)**

1-5 Variables and Equations

See pages 28–32.

Concept Summary

- To solve an equation, find the value for the variable that makes the equation true.

Example Find the solution of $26 = 33 - w$. Is it 5, 6, or 7?

Replace w with each value.

Value for w	$26 = 33 - w$	True or False?
5	$26 \stackrel{?}{=} 33 - 5$	false
6	$26 \stackrel{?}{=} 33 - 6$	false
7	$26 \stackrel{?}{=} 33 - 7$	true ✓

Therefore, the solution of $26 = 33 - w$ is 7.

ALGEBRA Solve each equation mentally. *See Example 3 on page 29.*

27. $n + 3 = 13$ **10**

28. $9 = k - 6$ **15**

29. $24 = 7 + g$ **17**

30. $6x = 48$ **8**

31. $54 = 9h$ **6**

32. $\dfrac{56}{a} = 14$ **4**

Study Guide and Review

Chapter 1 For More ...
• Extra Practice, see pages 724–726.
• Mixed Problem Solving, see page 758.

Answers

33.

x	y
2	3
6	1
7	5

domain: {2, 6, 7}; range: {3, 1, 5}

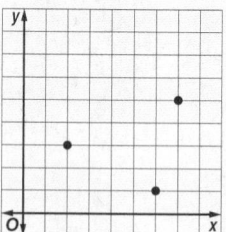

34.

x	y
0	2
1	7
5	2
6	5

domain: {0, 1, 5, 6}; range: {2, 5, 7}

35. Positive; as the height increases, the circumference increases.

36. about 90–95 feet

Answers (p. 51)

2. Simplify the expressions inside grouping symbols. Do all multiplication and/or division in order from left to right. Do all addition and/or subtraction in order from left to right.

17.

1-6 Ordered Pairs and Relations

See pages 33–38.

Concept Summary

• Ordered pairs are used to graph a point on a coordinate system.
• A relation is a set of ordered pairs. The set of x-coordinates is the domain, and the set of y-coordinates is the range.

Example Express the relation {(1, 4), (3, 2), (4, 3), (0, 5)} as a table and as a graph. Then determine the domain and range.

x	y
1	4
3	2
4	3
0	5

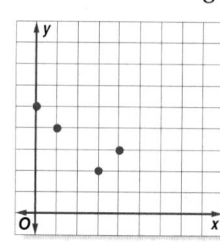

The domain is {1, 3, 4, 0}, and the range is {4, 2, 3, 5}.

Exercises Express each relation as a table and as a graph. Then determine the domain and range. *See Example 3 on page 35.* **33–34. See margin.**

33. {(2, 3), (6, 1), (7, 5)}   **34.** {(0, 2), (1, 7), (5, 2), (6, 5)}

1-7 Scatter Plots

See pages 40–44.

Concept Summary

• A scatter plot is a graph that shows the relationship between two sets of data.

Example The scatter plot shows the approximate heights and circumferences of various giant sequoia trees.

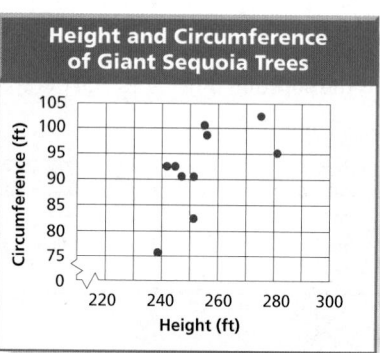

Height and Circumference of Giant Sequoia Trees

35–36. See margin.

Exercises Refer to the scatter plot. *See Example 3 on page 42.*

35. Does the scatter plot show a *positive, negative,* or *no* relationship? Explain.

36. Predict the circumference of a 245-foot sequoia. Explain your reasoning.

20.

x	y
8	5
4	3
2	2
6	1

domain: {8, 4, 2, 6}; range: {5, 3, 2, 1}

Vocabulary and Concepts

1. **Write** the steps of the four-step problem-solving plan. **Explore, Plan, Solve, Examine**

2. **List** the order of operations used to find the value of a numerical expression. **See margin.**

Skills and Applications

Find the value of each expression.

3. $24 - 8 \div 2 \cdot 3$ **12**

4. $16 \div 4 + 3(9 - 7)$ **10**

5. $3[18 - 5(7 - 5 + 1)]$ **9**

Write a numerical expression for each verbal phrase.

6. three less than fifteen **15 − 3**

7. twelve increased by seven **12 + 7**

8. the quotient of twelve and six **12 ÷ 6**

ALGEBRA Evaluate each expression if $a = 7$, $b = 3$, and $c = 5$.

9. $4a - 3c$ **13**

10. $42 \div [a(c - b)]$ **3**

11. $5c + (a + 2b) - 8$ **30**

12. What property is shown by $(5 \cdot 6) \cdot 8 = 5 \cdot (6 \cdot 8)$? **Assoc. (×)**

ALGEBRA Simplify each expression.

13. $9 + (p + 3)$ **$p + 12$**

14. $6 \cdot (7 \cdot k)$ **$42k$**

ALGEBRA Solve each equation mentally.

15. $4m = 20$ **5**

16. $16 - a = 9$ **7**

17. Graph $A(2, 5)$ on a coordinate system. **See margin.**

Refer to the coordinate system shown at the right. Write the ordered pair that names each point.

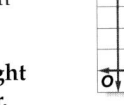

18. C **(3, 0)**

19. D **(1, 3)**

20. Express $\{(8, 5), (4, 3), (2, 2), (6, 1)\}$ as a table and as a graph. Then determine the domain and range. **See margin.**

Determine whether a scatter plot of the data for the following might show a positive, negative, or no relationship. Explain your answer.

21. outside temperature and air conditioning bill **positive**

22. number of siblings and height **no**

23. Find the next three terms in the list 3, 5, 9, 15, …. **23, 33, 45**

24. **MONEY** Mrs. Adams rents a car for a week and pays $79 for the first day and $49 for each additional day. Mr. Lowe rents a car for $350 a week. Which was the better deal? Explain.
Renting a car for $350/week was the better deal. It was $23 cheaper.

YORK Practice

25. **STANDARDIZED TEST PRACTICE** Katie purchased 6 loaves of bread at the grocery store and paid a total of $12. Which equation can be used to find how much Katie paid for each loaf of bread? **B**

Ⓐ $x + 6 = 12$ Ⓑ $6x = 12$ Ⓒ $x - 6 = 12$ Ⓓ $x \div 6 = 12$

www.pre-alg.com/chapter_test/ny

Chapter 1 Practice Test **51**

Assessment Options

Vocabulary Test A vocabulary review/test for Chapter 1 can be found on p. 50 of the *Chapter 1 Resource Masters.*

Chapter Tests There are six Chapter 1 Tests and an Open-Ended Assessment task available in the *Chapter 1 Resource Masters.*

Chapter 1 Tests			
Form	Type	Level	Pages
1	MC	basic	37–38
2A	MC	average	39–40
2B	MC	average	41–42
2C	FR	average	43–44
2D	FR	average	45–46
3	FR	advanced	47–48

MC = multiple-choice questions
FR = free-response questions

Open-Ended Assessment
Performance tasks for Chapter 1 can be found on p. 49 of the *Chapter 1 Resource Masters.* A sample scoring rubric for these tasks appears on p. A25.

ExamView® PRO

Use the networkable **ExamView® Pro** to:

- Create **multiple versions** of tests.

- Create **modified** tests for *Inclusion* students.

- **Edit** existing questions and **add** your own questions

- Use built-in **state curriculum correlations** to create tests aligned with state standards.

- Change **English** tests to **Spanish** and vice versa.

Portfolio Suggestion

Introduction Variables are used as placeholders for numbers and quantities that are unknown or can change. Variables, numbers, and at least one operation make up an algebraic expression.

Ask Students to find a problem from their work in this chapter and explain how they used variables to show relationships.

These two pages contain practice questions in the various formats that can be found on the most frequently given standardized tests.

A practice answer sheet for these two pages can be found on page A1 of the *Chapter 1 Resource Masters*.

Standardized Test Practice
Student Recording Sheet, p. A1

Part 1 *Multiple Choice*

Select the best answer from the choices given and fill in the corresponding oval.

1 Ⓐ Ⓑ Ⓒ Ⓓ   4 Ⓐ Ⓑ Ⓒ Ⓓ   7 Ⓐ Ⓑ Ⓒ Ⓓ   9 Ⓐ Ⓑ Ⓒ Ⓓ
2 Ⓐ Ⓑ Ⓒ Ⓓ   5 Ⓐ Ⓑ Ⓒ Ⓓ   8 Ⓐ Ⓑ Ⓒ Ⓓ   10 Ⓐ Ⓑ Ⓒ Ⓓ
3 Ⓐ Ⓑ Ⓒ Ⓓ   6 Ⓐ Ⓑ Ⓒ Ⓓ

Part 2 *Short Response/Grid In*

Solve the problem and write your answer in the blank.

For Questions 13–15, also enter your answer by writing each number or symbol in a box. Then fill in the corresponding oval for that number or symbol.

11 _____   13 ⌷⌷⌷⌷   14 ⌷⌷⌷⌷
12 _____
13 _____ (grid in)
14 _____ (grid in)
15 _____ (grid in)
16 _____   15 ⌷⌷⌷⌷

Part 3 *Extended Response*

Record your answers for Questions 17–18 on the back of this paper.

Additional Practice

See pp. 55–56 of the *Chapter 1 Resource Masters* for additional standardized test practice.

The items on the Standardized Test Practice pages were created to closely parallel those on actual state proficiency tests and college entrance exams, like PSAT, ACT, and SAT.

NEW YORK
Test Practice

Part 1   Multiple Choice

Record your answers on the answer sheet provided by your teacher or on a sheet of paper.

1. Find the next two terms in the pattern 4, 12, 36, 108, … . (Lesson 1-1) **D**
   Ⓐ 116 and 124   Ⓑ 116 and 140
   Ⓒ 324 and 648   Ⓓ 324 and 972

2. Evaluate $2(15 - 3 \cdot 4)$. (Lesson 1-2) **A**
   Ⓐ 6   Ⓑ 16   Ⓒ 18   Ⓓ 96

3. Of the six books in a mystery series, four have 200 pages and two have 300 pages. Which expression represents the total number of pages in the series? (Lesson 1-3) **C**
   Ⓐ $200 + 300$ Ⓑ $6(200 + 300)$
   Ⓒ $4(200) + 2(300)$ Ⓓ $6(200) + 6(300)$

4. The postage for a first-class letter is $0.34 for the first ounce and $0.21 for each additional ounce. Which expression best represents the cost of postage for a letter that weighs 5 ounces? (Lesson 1-3) **D**
   Ⓐ $0.34 + 0.21(5)$ Ⓑ $0.21 + 0.34(4)$
   Ⓒ $0.34(5)$ Ⓓ $0.34 + 0.21(4)$

5. Which property is represented by the equation below? (Lesson 1-4) **C**
   $$8 \cdot (5 \cdot 3) = (8 \cdot 5) \cdot 3$$
   Ⓐ Commutative Property of Addition
   Ⓑ Commutative Property of Multiplication
   Ⓒ Associative Property of Multiplication
   Ⓓ Identity Property of Multiplication

6. Which number is the solution of the equation $17 - 2x = 9$? (Lesson 1-5) **B**
   Ⓐ 2   Ⓑ 4   Ⓒ 6   Ⓓ 8

Test-Taking Tip   Ⓐ Ⓑ Ⓒ Ⓓ
Question 6
To solve an equation, you can replace the variable in the equation with the values given in each answer choice. The answer choice that results in a true statement is the correct answer.

52   Chapter 1   The Tools of Algebra

---

7. Which sentence does the equation $n + 9 = 15$ represent? (Lesson 1-5) **D**
   Ⓐ A number is the sum of 9 and 15.
   Ⓑ A number decreased by 9 is 15.
   Ⓒ The product of a number and 9 is 15.
   Ⓓ Nine more than a number is 15.

8. What are the coordinates of point P? (Lesson 1-6) **B**
   Ⓐ $(3, 5)$
   Ⓑ $(5, 3)$
   Ⓒ $(3, 3)$
   Ⓓ $(5, 5)$
   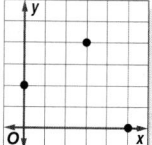

9. Which table shows the set of ordered pairs that represents the points graphed on the grid below? (Lesson 1-6) **C**

   Ⓐ
x	y
2	0
3	4
0	5

   Ⓑ
x	y
0	2
4	3
5	0

   Ⓒ
x	y
0	2
3	4
5	0

   Ⓓ
x	y
2	0
4	3
0	5

10. What type of relationship does the scatter plot below show? (Lesson 1-7) **B**

    Ⓐ positive   Ⓑ negative
    Ⓒ associative   Ⓓ none

ExamView® Pro

Special banks of standardized test questions similar to those on the SAT, ACT, TIMSS 8, NAEP 8, and Pre-Algebra End-of-Course tests can be found on this CD-ROM.

Part 2 | Short Response/Grid In

Record your answers on the answer sheet provided by your teacher or on a sheet of paper. **11. Thursday**

11. The graph below shows the number of students absent from school each day of one week. On what day were the fewest students absent? (Prerequisite Skill, p. 722)

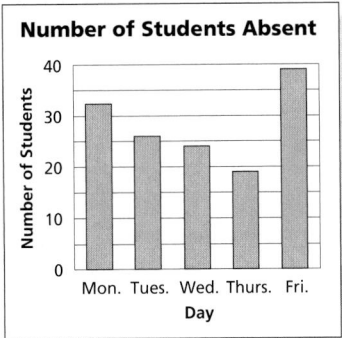

Number of Students Absent

12. The number of Olympic events for women is shown. About how many more events for women were held in 2000 than in 1980? (Prerequisite Skill, p. 722) **about 80**

Olympic Events for Women

13. Six tables positioned in a row will be used to display science projects. Each table is 8 feet long. How many yards of fabric are needed to make a banner that will extend from one end of the row of tables to the other? (Lesson 1-1) **16**

x yd

www.pre-alg.com/standardized_test/ny

14. What is the value of the expression $5 + 4 \times 6 \div 3$? (Lesson 1-2) **13**

15. Evaluate $x(xy + 3)$ if $x = 5$ and $y = 2$. (Lesson 1-3) **65**

16. Write *14 is 12 less than twice the value of x* as an equation. (Lesson 1-5) **14 = 2x − 12**

Part 3 | Extended Response

Record your answers on a sheet of paper. Show your work.

17. Kenneth is recording the time it takes him to run various distances. The results are shown. (Lesson 1-6)

Distance (mi)	2	3	5	7	9
Time (min)	13	20	35	53	72

   a. Write a set of ordered pairs for the data.
   b. Graph the data. **a–c. See margin.**
   c. How many minutes do you think it will take Kenneth to run 4 miles? Explain.
   d. Predict how far Kenneth will run if he runs for 1 hour. **about 8 mi**

18. The table below shows the results of a survey about the average time that individual students spend studying on weekday evenings. (Lesson 1-7)

Grade	Time (min)	Grade	Time (min)
2	20	6	60
2	15	6	45
2	20	6	55
4	30	6	60
4	20	8	70
4	25	8	80
4	40	8	75
4	30	8	60

   a. Make a scatter plot of the data. **See margin.**
   b. What are the coordinates of the point that represents the longest time spent on homework? **(8, 80)**
   c. Does a relationship exist between grade level and time spent studying? If so, write a sentence to describe the relationship. If not, explain why not. **See margin.**

Evaluating Extended Response Questions

Extended Response questions are graded by using a multilevel rubric that guides you in assessing a student's knowledge of a particular concept.

Goal: Create and interpret a scatter plot of given data.

Sample Scoring Rubric: The following rubric is a sample scoring device. You may wish to add more detail to this sample to meet your individual scoring needs.

Score	Criteria
4	A correct solution that is supported by well-developed, accurate explanations
3	A generally correct solution, but may contain minor flaws in reasoning or computation
2	A partially correct interpretation and/or solution to the problem
1	A correct solution with no supporting evidence or explanation
0	An incorrect solution indicating no mathematical understanding of the concept or task, or no solution is given

17b.

Running Distance and Time

Answers

17a. {(2, 13), (3, 20), (5, 35), (7, 53), (9, 72)}

17b. See graph at right.

17c. About 25–30 minutes because the time it takes to run 4 miles would be between the time it takes to run 3 and 5 miles.

18a. See graph at right.

18c. Yes, there is a positive relationship between grade and time spent on homework. As the grade level increases, the time spent on homework increases.

18a. **Study Time**

Page 27, Lesson 1-4

49. Sample answer: There are many real-life situations in which the order in which things are completed does not matter. For example, you can read the sports page and then the comics, or you can read the comics and then the sports page. No matter the order, both parts of the newspaper will be read. However, some situations are not commutative. For example, when washing clothes, you would add the detergent and then wash the clothes, not wash the clothes and then add the detergent.

Pages 36–37, Lesson 1-6

8.

x	y
2	5
0	2
5	5

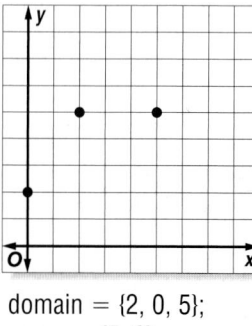

domain = {2, 0, 5};
range = {5, 2}

9.

x	y
1	6
6	4
0	2
3	1

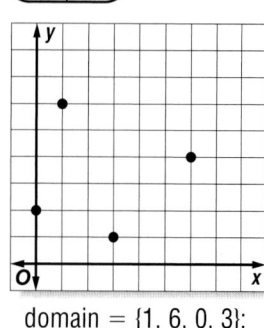

domain = {1, 6, 0, 3};
range = {6, 4, 2, 1}

10.

x	y
2	8
4	16
5	20

11.

12.

13.

14.

15.

16.

17.

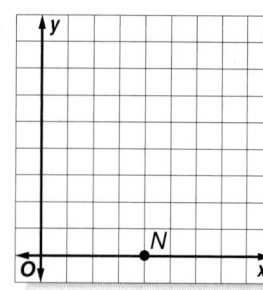

26. 36 ft; 60 ft; 84 ft

27. Speed of a House Mouse

28. (0, 100), (1, 50), (2, 25), (3, 13), (4, 6)

29. Science Experiment

30. The height of each successive bounce is about half of the previous. Since the 4th bounce is 6 cm, the 5th bounce will be about 6 ÷ 2 or 3 cm.

31.

x	y
4	5
5	2
1	6

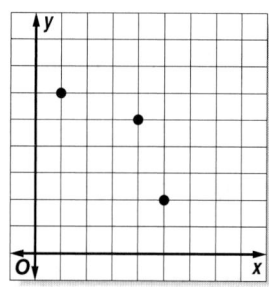

domain = {4, 5, 1}; range = {5, 2, 6}

32.

x	y
6	8
2	9
0	1

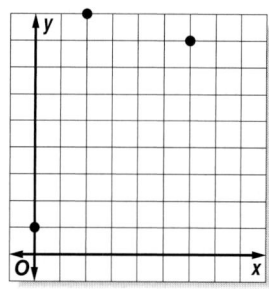

domain = {6, 2, 0}; range = {8, 9, 1}

33.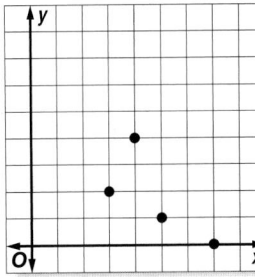

domain = {7, 3, 4, 5}; range = {0, 2, 4, 1}

34.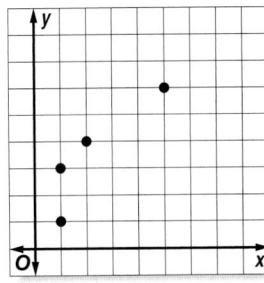

domain = {2, 1, 5}; range = {4, 3, 6, 1}

35.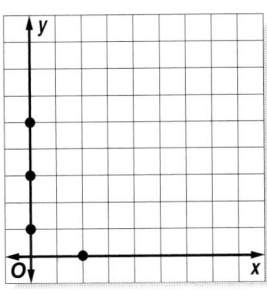

domain = {0, 2}; range = {1, 3, 5, 0}

36.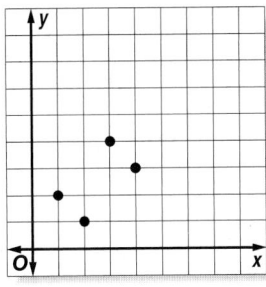

domain = {4, 3, 1, 2}; range = {3, 4, 2, 1}

38.

40.

x	y
0	100
1	95
2	90
3	85
4	80
5	75

41. {(0, 100), (1, 95), (2, 90), (3, 85), (4, 80), (5, 75)}

42.

43. about 93°C; about 96°C

Page 42, Lesson 1-7

6.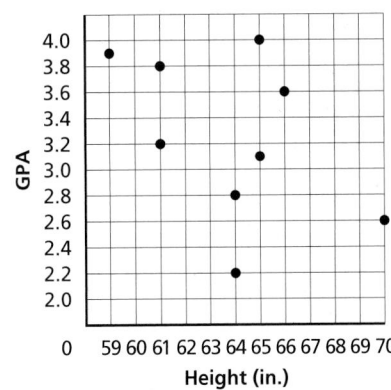

Page 43, Lesson 1-7

8. As a household size increases, the amount of the water bill increases.

9. The number of songs on a CD usually does not affect the cost of the CD.

10. As the size of a car's engine increases, the miles per gallon decrease.

11. As speed increases, distance traveled increases.

12. As the outside temperature increases, the amount of the heating bill decreases.

13. The size of a television screen and the number of channels it receives are not related.

17.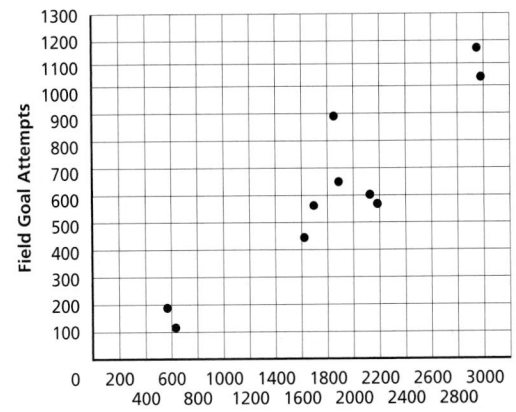

Integers
Chapter Overview and Pacing

Year-long pacing: pages T20–T21.

LESSON OBJECTIVES

LESSON OBJECTIVES	PACING (days)			
	Regular		**Block**	
	Basic/ Average	Advanced	Basic/ Average	Advanced
2-1 Integers and Absolute Value *(pp. 56–61)* • Compare and order integers. • Find the absolute value of an expression.	2	1	1	0.5
2-2 Adding Integers *(pp. 62–68)* *Preview:* Model operations with integers with algebra tiles and an integer mat. • Add two integers. • Add more than two integers.	2 (with 2-2 Preview)	1	1.5 (with 2-2 Preview)	0.5
2-3 Subtracting Integers *(pp. 70–74)* • Subtract integers. • Evaluate expressions containing variables.	2	1	1	0.5
2-4 Multiplying Integers *(pp. 75–79)* • Multiply integers. • Simplify algebraic expressions.	2	1	1	0.5
2-5 Dividing Integers *(pp. 80–84)* • Divide integers. • Find the average of a set of data.	2	1	1	0.5
2-6 The Coordinate System *(pp. 85–89)* • Graph points on a coordinate plane. • Graph algebraic relationships.	1	1	0.5	0.5
Study Guide and **Practice Test** *(pp. 90–93)* **Standardized Test Practice** *(pp. 94–95)*	1	1	0.5	0.5
Chapter Assessment	1	1	0.5	0.5
TOTAL	13	8	7	4

*An electronic version of this chapter is available on **StudentWorks**™. This backpack solution CD-ROM allows students instant access to the Student Edition, lesson worksheet pages, and web resources.*

Chapter Resource Manager

TeacherWorks™
All-In-One Planner
and Resource Center
See pages T5 and T21.

CHAPTER 2 RESOURCE MASTERS

Study Guide and Intervention	Practice (Skills and Average)	Reading to Learn Mathematics	Enrichment	Assessment	Prerequisite Skills Workbook	Applications*	Parent and Student Study Guide Workbook	5-Minute Check Transparencies	Interactive Chalkboard	Pre-AlgePASS: Tutorial Plus (lessons)	Materials
57	58–59	60	61		1–2, 5–8	SC 3 SM 2	9	2-1	2-1		
62	63–64	65	66	101	5–8		10	2-2	2-2		*Preview:* algebra tiles, integer mat
67	68–69	70	71	101, 103	5–8	SC 4	11	2-3	2-3		
72	73–74	75	76		9–10		12	2-4	2-4		
77	78–79	81	81	102	11–12	GCS 12	13	2-5	2-5	3	
82	83–84	85	86	102		GCS 22	14	2-6	2-6		
				87–100 104–106							

* *Key to Abbreviations:* GCS = Graphing Calculator and Spreadsheet Masters
SC = School-to-Career Masters
SM = Science and Mathematics Lab Manual

 ELL Study Guide and Intervention, Skills Practice, Practice, and Parent and Student Study Guide Workbooks are also available in Spanish.

Chapter 2 Integers **54B**

Mathematical Connections and Background

Continuity of Instruction

Prior Knowledge

Students bring their previous experience adding, subtracting, multiplying, and dividing whole numbers, as well as finding patterns, to the study of integers in this chapter. In Chapter 1, students learned to evaluate algebraic expressions. They also learned how to graph points on a coordinate grid.

This Chapter

Students will learn to compare and order integers, find the absolute value of an expression, and find the average of a set of data. They apply the rules for adding, subtracting, multiplying, and dividing integers to evaluating algebraic expressions. Students also use the Cartesian coordinate system to graph points in all four quadrants of the coordinate grid.

Future Connections

The basic rules for adding, subtracting, multiplying, and dividing integers will be used in Chapter 3 as students solve equations. In Chapter 8, students will graph linear equations, systems of linear equations, and linear inequalities on a coordinate plane.

2-1 Integers and Absolute Value

A negative number is a number less than zero. Negative numbers like -8, positive numbers like $+6$, and zero are members of the set of integers. Integers can be represented as points on a number line. This set of integers can be written $\{ \ldots, -3, -2, -1, 0, 1, 2, 3, \ldots \}$ where $\ldots$ means "continues indefinitely." When graphing integers, locate the points named by the integers on a number line. The number that corresponds to a point is called the coordinate of that point. The numbers on a number line increase from left to right. This can help determine which of two numbers is greater. Any mathematical sentence containing $<$ (less than) or $>$ (greater than) is called an inequality. An inequality compares numbers or quantities.

In mathematics, when two integers on a number line are on opposite sides of zero, and they are the same distance from zero, they have the same absolute value. The symbol for absolute value is two vertical bars on either side of the number. For example, $|-5| = 5$. Since variables represent numbers, absolute value notation can be used in algebraic expressions involving variables.

2-2 Adding Integers

The equation $-5 + (-2) = -7$ is an example of adding two integers with the same sign. To add integers with the same sign, add their absolute values. The sum takes the same sign as the addends. To add integers with different signs, subtract their absolute values. The sum takes the same sign as the addend with the greater absolute value.

Two numbers with the same absolute value but different signs are called *opposites*. For example, -4 and 4 are opposites. An integer and its opposite are also called *additive inverses*. The Additive Inverse Property says that the sum of any number and its additive inverse is zero. The Commutative, Associative, and Identity Properties also apply to integers. These properties help when adding more than two integers.

2-3 Subtracting Integers

In this lesson, the rules for adding integers are extended to the subtraction of integers. To subtract an integer, add its additive inverse. For example, to find the difference $2 - 5$, add the additive inverse of 5 to 2: $2 + (-5) = -3$. The rule for subtracting integers can be used to solve real-world problems and to evaluate algebraic expressions.

2-4 Multiplying Integers

Since multiplication is repeated addition, $3(-7)$ means that -7 is used as an addend 3 times. By the Commutative Property of Multiplication, $3(-7) = -7(3)$. The product of two integers with different signs is always negative. Students use this fact and the fact that the product of two positive integers is positive to find inductively that the product of two integers with the same sign is positive.

2-5 Dividing Integers

The quotient of two integers can be found by using the related multiplication sentence. For example, the division sentence $-12 \div (-4) = 3$ is related to the multiplication sentence $-4 \times 3 = -12$. Students use examples such as this one, their study of the multiplication of integers in Lesson 2-4, and their prior experience with dividing whole numbers to determine that the quotient of two integers with the same sign is positive. By examining multiplication sentences involving integers with different signs, students learn that the quotient of two integers with different signs is negative.

The division of integers is extended to statistics to find the average, or mean, of a set of data. When finding the mean of a set of numbers, find the sum of the numbers and then divide by the number in the set.

2-6 The Coordinate System

In the Cartesian coordinate system, the y-axis extends above and below the origin and the x-axis extends to the right and left of the origin, which is the point at which the x- and y-axes intersect. Numbers below and to the left of the origin are negative. A point graphed on the coordinate grid is said to have an x-coordinate and a y-coordinate. For example, the point $(1, -2)$, has as its x-coordinate the number 1, and has as its y-coordinate the number -2. This point is graphed by locating the position on the grid that is 1 unit to the right of the origin and 2 units below the origin.

The x-axis and the y-axis separate the coordinate plane into four regions, called *quadrants*. The axes and points located on the axes themselves are not located in any of the quadrants. The quadrants are labeled I to IV, starting in the upper right and proceeding counterclockwise. In quadrant I, both coordinates are positive. In quadrant II, the x-coordinate is negative and the y-coordinate is positive. In quadrant III, both coordinates are negative. In quadrant IV, the x-coordinate is positive and the y-coordinate is negative. A coordinate graph can be used to show algebraic relationships among numbers.

Quick Review Math Handbook

Hot Words includes a glossary of terms while Hot Topics consists of explanations of key mathematical concepts with exercises to test comprehension. This valuable resource can be used as a reference in the classroom or for home study.

Lesson	Hot Topics Section	Lesson	Hot Topics Section
GS 2	6.3, 6.7	2-4	1.5
2-1	1.5	2-5	1.5, 6.7
2-2	1.5, 6.3	2-6	6.7
2-3	1.5		

GS = Getting Started

 Additional mathematical information and teaching notes are available at www.pre-alg.com/key_concepts.

DAILY
INTERVENTION and Assessment

Key to Abbreviations:
TWE = Teacher Wraparound Edition; CRM = Chapter Resource Masters

Type	Student Edition	Teacher Resources	Technology/Internet
INTERVENTION Ongoing	Prerequisite Skills, pp. 55, 61, 68, 74, 79, 84 Practice Quiz 1, p. 74 Practice Quiz 2, p. 84	5-Minute Check Transparencies *Prerequisite Skills Workbook*, pp. 1–2, 5–12 Quizzes, *CRM*, pp. 101, 102 Mid-Chapter Test, *CRM*, p. 103 Study Guide and Intervention, *CRM*, pp. 57, 62, 67, 72, 77, 82	Pre-AlgePASS: Tutorial Plus, Lesson 3 www.pre-alg.com/ self_check_quiz www.pre-alg.com/ extra_examples
Mixed Review	pp. 61, 68, 74, 79, 84, 89	Cumulative Review, *CRM*, p. 104	
Error Analysis	Find the Error, pp. 72, 87	Find the Error, *TWE*, pp. 72, 87 Unlocking Misconceptions, *TWE*, pp. 58, 65, 82	
Standardized Test Practice	pp. 61, 68, 74, 76, 77, 79, 84, 89, 94–95	*TWE*, pp. 94–95 Standardized Test Practice, *CRM*, pp. 105–106	Standardized Test Practice CD-ROM www.pre-alg.com/ standardized_test
ASSESSMENT Open-Ended Assessment	Writing in Math, pp. 61, 68, 74, 79, 84, 89 Open Ended, pp. 59, 67, 72, 77, 83, 87 Standardized Test, p. 95	Modeling: *TWE*, pp. 61, 74 Speaking: *TWE*, pp. 79, 89 Writing: *TWE*, pp. 68, 84 Open-Ended Assessment, *CRM*, p. 99	
Chapter Assessment	Study Guide, pp. 90–92 Practice Test, p. 93	Multiple-Choice Tests (Forms 1, 2A, 2B), *CRM*, pp. 87–92 Free-Response Tests (Forms 2C, 2D, 3), *CRM*, pp. 93–98 Vocabulary Test/Review, *CRM*, p. 100	ExamView® Pro (see below) MindJogger Videoquizzes www.pre-alg.com/ vocabulary_review www.pre-alg.com/chapter_test

For more information on Yearly ProgressPro, see p. 2.

Pre-Algebra Lesson	Yearly ProgressPro Skill Lesson(s)
2-1	Writing Integers Absolute Value
2-2	Add Integers
2-3	Subtracting Integers
2-4	Multiply Integers
2-5	Divide Integers
2-6	Coordinate Locations: Level 3

ExamView® Pro

Use the networkable **ExamView® Pro** to:
• Create **multiple versions** of tests.
• Create **modified** tests for *Inclusion* students.
• **Edit** existing questions and **add** your own questions.
• Use built-in **state curriculum correlations** to create tests aligned with state standards.
• Change **English** tests to **Spanish** and vice versa.

For more information on Intervention and Assessment, see pp. T8–T11.

Reading and Writing in Mathematics

Glencoe Pre-Algebra provides numerous opportunities to incorporate reading and writing into the mathematics classroom.

Student Edition

- Foldables™ Study Organizer, p. 55
- Reading Mathematics, p. 69
- Concept Check questions require students to verbalize and write about what they have learned in the lesson. (pp. 56, 57, 59, 66, 67, 71, 72, 77, 81, 83, 86, 87)
- Writing in Math questions in every lesson, pp. 61, 68, 74, 79, 84, 89
- Reading Math, pp. 56, 57, 64, 75, 80, 88
- WebQuest, p. 79

Teacher Wraparound Edition

- Foldables™ Study Organizer, pp. 55, 90
- Study Notebook suggestions, pp. 58, 63, 66, 69, 72, 77, 83, 87
- Modeling activities, pp. 61, 74
- Speaking activities, pp. 79, 89
- Writing activities, pp. 68, 84
- **ELL** Resources, pp. 54, 56, 64, 69, 70, 75, 80, 85, 90

Additional Resources

- Vocabulary Builder worksheets require students to define and give examples for key vocabulary terms as they progress through the chapter (*Chapter 2 Resource Masters,* pp. vii–viii)
- Reading to Learn Mathematics master for each lesson (*Chapter 2 Resource Masters,* pp. 60, 65, 70, 75, 80, 85)
- *Vocabulary PuzzleMaker* software creates crossword, jumble, and word search puzzles using vocabulary lists that you can customize.
- *Teaching Mathematics with Foldables* provides suggestions for promoting cognition and language.
- *Reading and Writing in the Mathematics Classroom*
- *WebQuest and Project Resources*

For more information on Reading and Writing in Mathematics, see pp. T6–T7.

ENGLISH LANGUAGE LEARNERS

Lesson 2-1
Flexible Groups

Give groups of six students a set of six cards with an integer on each card. Have the students order the numbers from least to greatest. On a wall of the room, mark 0, positive, and negative to denote a number line. Have the students come to the number line by group and position themselves in order on the number line. The students can check each other for accuracy.

Lesson 2-2
Higher-Level Thinking

Based on the patterns that students have seen modeled by the teacher, have them work in groups of three or four to come up with their own rules for adding integers with different signs. This same model can be used for subtracting, multiplying, and dividing integers.

Lesson 2-6
Using Models

Have students draw a coordinate plane on grid paper, labeling the *x*- and *y*- axes, the origin, and all four quadrants. Discuss with the students what an ordered pair is and how to locate one on the coordinate plane. For a large coordinate plane, use a shower curtain and masking tape to draw all the parts of the coordinate plane. Have students stand on points to graph ordered pairs.

Chapter 2 Notes

What You'll Learn

Have students read over the list of objectives and make a list of any words with which they are not familiar.

Why It's Important

Point out to students that this is only one of many reasons why each objective is important. Others are provided in the introduction to each lesson.

Lesson	NCTM Standards	Local Objectives
2-1	1, 2, 6, 10	
2-2 Preview	1, 6	
2-2	1, 2, 6	
2-3	1, 2, 6	
2-4	1, 2, 6	
2-5	1, 2, 6	
2-6	2, 3, 6, 10	

Key to NCTM Standards:

1=Number & Operations, 2=Algebra,
3=Geometry, 4=Measurement,
5=Data Analysis & Probability, 6=Problem Solving, 7=Reasoning & Proof,
8=Communication, 9=Connections,
10=Representation

Chapter 2 Integers

What You'll Learn

- **Lesson 2-1** Compare and order integers, and find the absolute value of an expression.
- **Lessons 2-2 through 2-5** Add, subtract, multiply, and divide integers.
- **Lessons 2-3 and 2-4** Evaluate and simplify algebraic expressions.
- **Lesson 2-5** Find the average of a set of data.
- **Lesson 2-6** Graph points, and show algebraic relationships on a coordinate plane.

Key Vocabulary

- integer (p. 56)
- inequality (p. 57)
- absolute value (p. 58)
- additive inverse (p. 66)
- quadrants (p. 86)

Why It's Important

In both mathematics and everyday life, there are many situations where integers are used. Some examples include temperatures, sports such as golf and football, and measuring the elevation of points on Earth or the depth below sea level. *You will represent real-world situations with integers in Lesson 2-1.*

Vocabulary Builder ELL

The Key Vocabulary list introduces students to some of the main vocabulary terms included in this chapter. For a more thorough vocabulary list with pronunciations of new words, give students the Vocabulary Builder worksheets found on pages vii and viii of the *Chapter 2 Resource Masters*. Encourage them to complete the definition of each term as they progress through the chapter. You may suggest that they add these sheets to their study notebooks for future reference when studying for the Chapter 2 test.

Getting Started

▶ **Prerequisite Skills** To be successful in this chapter, you'll need to master these skills and be able to apply them in problem-solving situations. Review these skills before beginning Chapter 2.

For Lesson 2-1   **Evaluate Expressions**

Evaluate each expression if $a = 4$, $b = 10$, and $c = 8$.   *(For review, see Lesson 1-3.)*

1. $a + b + c$ **22**   **2.** $bc - ab$ **40**   **3.** $b + ac$ **42**

4. $4c + 3b$ **62**   **5.** $2b - (a + c)$ **8**   **6.** $2c - b + a$ **10**

For Lesson 2-3   **Patterns**

Find the next term in each list.   *(For review, see Lesson 1-1.)*

7. 34, 28, 22, 16, 10, … **4**   **8.** 120, 105, 90, 75, … **60**

For Lesson 2-6   **Graph Points**

Use the grid to name the point for each ordered pair.
(For review, see Lesson 1-6.)

9. (1, 3) *T*   **10.** (5, 2) *L*   **11.** (5, 5) *V*

12. (3, 4) *U*   **13.** (0, 2) *Q*   **14.** (6, 1) *R*

FOLDABLES™
Study Organizer

Operations with Integers Make this Foldable to help you organize your notes. Begin with a piece of graph paper.

Step 1 **Fold in Half**

Fold the graph paper in half lengthwise.

Step 2 **Fold Again in Fourths**

Fold the top to the bottom twice.

Step 3 **Cut**

Open. Cut along the second fold to make four tabs.

Step 4 **Label**

Fold lengthwise. Draw a number line on the outside. Label each tab as shown.

Reading and Writing As you read and study the chapter, write rules and examples for each integer operation under the tabs.

Getting Started

This section provides a review of the basic concepts needed before beginning Chapter 2. Page references are included for additional student help.

Additional review is provided in the *Prerequisite Skills Workbook*, pages 1–2 and 5–12.

Prerequisite Skills in the Getting Ready for the Next Lesson section at the end of each lesson reviews a skill needed in the next lesson.

For Lesson	Prerequisite Skill
2-2	Adding and Subtracting Whole Numbers (p. 61)
2-3	Evaluating Expressions (p. 68)
2-4	Multiplying Whole Numbers (p. 74)
2-5	Dividing Whole Numbers (p. 79)
2-6	Ordered Pairs (p. 84)

FOLDABLES™
Study Organizer

For more information about Foldables, see *Teaching Mathematics with Foldables.*

Reading for Main Ideas and Note Taking Ask students to read and determine the main ideas for each lesson. When searching for the main idea, encourage students to ask themselves, "What is this paragraph or lesson telling me? What is its intent?" After students have determined the main idea, they can also find supporting details or words that give more information about the main idea.

1 Focus

**5-Minute Check
Transparency 2-1** Use as a
quiz or review of Chapter 1.

Mathematical Background notes
are available for this lesson on
page 54C.

How are integers used to
model real-world
situations?

The opening activity questions
are repeated on page 60 of the
Chapter 2 Resource Masters.

Reading to Learn Mathematics, p. 60 — ELL

Pre-Activity How are integers used to model real-world situations?
Do the activity at the top of page 56 in your textbook.
Write your answers below.

a. What does a value of −7 represent? **7 inches below normal**

b. Which city was farthest from its normal rainfall? **Jackson, MS**

c. How could you represent 5 inches above normal rainfall? **+5**

Reading the Lesson   1–5. See students' work.
Write a definition and give an example of each new vocabulary word or phrase.

Vocabulary	Definition	Example
1. negative number		
2. integers		
3. coordinate		
4. inequality		
5. absolute value		

Helping You Remember

6. *Absolute* is a word that is used frequently in the English language.

a. Find the definition of *absolute* in a dictionary. Write the definition that most closely relates to mathematics.   **independent of arbitrary standards of measurement**

b. Explain how the English definition can help you remember the meaning of *absolute value* in mathematics.
The absolute value of an integer is independent of the sign of the number.

2-1 Integers and Absolute Value

NEW YORK *Performance Indicator* Reinforcement of 6.N.13 Define absolute value and determine the absolute value of rational numbers (including positive and negative), Reinforcement of 6.N.14 Locate rational numbers on a number line (including positive and negative), Reinforcement of 6.N.15 Order rational numbers (including positive and negative)

What You'll Learn

* Compare and order integers.
* Find the absolute value of an expression.

Vocabulary

* negative number
* integers
* coordinate
* inequality
* absolute value

a. 7 in. below normal

b. Jackson, MS

How are integers used to model real-world situations?

The summer of 1999 was
unusually dry in parts of the
United States. In the graph,
a value of −8 represents
8 inches below the normal
rainfall.

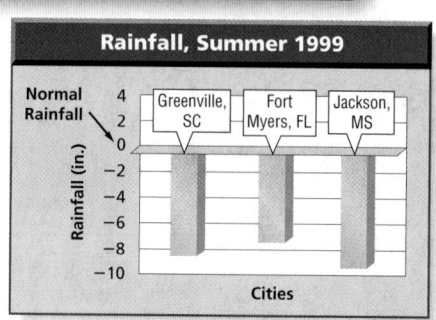

Rainfall, Summer 1999

a. What does a value
of −7 represent?

b. Which city was farthest
from its normal rainfall?

c. How could you represent
5 inches above normal
rainfall? **+5**

Reading Math

Integers

Read −8 as *negative 8*. A
positive integer like 6 can be
written as +6. It is usually written
without the + sign, as 6.

COMPARE AND ORDER INTEGERS   With normal rainfall as the
starting point of 0, you can express 8 inches below normal as 0 − 8, or −8.
A **negative number** is a number less than zero.

Negative numbers like −8, positive numbers like +6, and zero are members
of the set of **integers**. Integers can be represented as points on a number line.

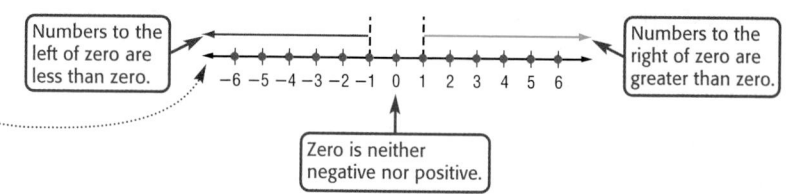

Numbers to the
left of zero are
less than zero.

Numbers to the
right of zero are
greater than zero.

Zero is neither
negative nor positive.

TEACHING TIP

Remind students that the
arrowheads on the num-
ber line indicate that the
set of numbers continues
indefinitely.

This set of integers can be written $\{\ldots, -3, -2, -1, 0, 1, 2, 3, \ldots\}$ where …
means continues indefinitely.

Example 1 Write Integers for Real-World Situations

Write an integer for each situation.

a. 500 feet below sea level   The integer is −500.

b. a temperature increase of 12°   The integer is +12.

c. a loss of $240   The integer is −240.

✓ **Concept Check** Which integer is neither positive nor negative? **zero**

Resource Manager

📂 Workbooks and Reproducible Masters

Chapter 2 Resource Masters
• Study Guide and Intervention, p. 57
• Skills Practice, p. 58
• Practice, p. 59
• Reading to Learn Mathematics, p. 60
• Enrichment, p. 61

**Parent and Student Study Guide
Workbook**, p. 9
Prerequisite Skills Workbook, pp. 1–2,
5–8
School-to-Career Masters, p. 3
**Science and Mathematics Lab
Manual**, pp. 5–10

📖 Transparencies

5-Minute Check Transparency 2-1
Real-World Transparency 2
Answer Key Transparencies

⚙ Technology

Interactive Chalkboard

To graph integers, locate the points named by the integers on a number line. The number that corresponds to a point is called the **coordinate** of that point.

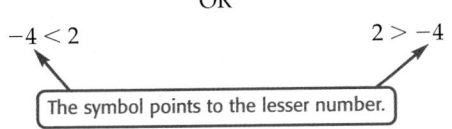

graph of a point with coordinate −4

graph of a point with coordinate 2

Notice that the numbers on a number line increase as you move from left to right. This can help you determine which of two numbers is greater.

Reading Math

Inequality Symbols
Read the symbol < as *is less than*. Read the symbol > as *is greater than*.

Words	−4 is less than 2.	2 is greater than −4.
	OR	
Symbols	−4 < 2	2 > −4

The symbol points to the lesser number.

Any mathematical sentence containing < or > is called an inequality. An **inequality** compares numbers or quantities.

Example 2 **Compare Two Integers**

Use the integers graphed on the number line below.

−6−5−4−3−2−1 0 1 2 3 4 5 6

a. Write two inequalities involving −3 and 4.
Since −3 is to the left of 4, write −3 < 4.
Since 4 is to the right of −3, write 4 > −3.

b. Replace the ● with < or > in −5 ● −1 to make a true sentence.
−1 is greater since it lies to the right of −5. So write −5 < −1.

Integers are used to compare numbers in many real-world situations.

Example 3 **Order Integers**

More About. . .

Golf
Annika Sorenstam won the 2003 LPGA Championship at 6 under par. She was the LPGA's leading money winner in 2001 and 2002.
Source: www.LPGA.com

GOLF The top ten fourth round scores of the 2003 LPGA Championship tournament were 0, +1, −4, −2, −1, +4, +2, +3, +5, and −3. Order the scores from least to greatest.

Graph each integer on a number line.

−5 −4 −3 −2 −1 0 1 2 3 4 5

Write the numbers as they appear from left to right.
The scores −4, −3, −2, −1, 0, +1, +2, +3, +4, +5 are in order from least to greatest.

It has the > symbol and compares two numbers.
✓ Concept Check Why is the sentence 5 > 2 an inequality?

COMPARE AND ORDER INTEGERS

In-Class Examples Power Point®

Teaching Tip The integers can be described as the natural numbers, their opposites, and zero.

1 Write an integer for each situation.
a. 32 feet under ground   **−32**
b. 8 weeks after birth   **+8**
c. a loss of 6 pounds   **−6**

Teaching Tip You may want to suggest that the < and > symbols "point to the lesser number and open to the greater number."

2 Use the integers graphed on the number line below for each question.

−4 −2 0 2 4 6 8

a. Write two inequalities involving 7 and −4.
7 > −4; −4 < 7

b. Replace the ● with <, >, or = in −2 ● 3 to make a true sentence.   **<**

3 **WEATHER** The high temperatures for the first seven days of January were −8°, 10°, 2°, −3°, −11°, 0°, and 1°. Order the temperatures from least to greatest.
−11, −8, −3, 0, 1, 2, 10

✓ Skills Check

Compare and Order Integers
Order the integers in each set from least to greatest.

a. {2, −7, 0, 1, −3}
  {−7, −3, 0, 1, 2}

b. {123, −54, 27, −48, 115}
  {−54, −48, 27, 115, 123}

Interactive Chalkboard
PowerPoint® Presentations

This CD-ROM is a customizable Microsoft® Power-Point® presentation that includes:
• Step-by-step, dynamic solutions of each In-Class Example from the Teacher Wraparound Edition
• Additional, Your Turn exercises for each example
• The 5-Minute Check Transparencies
• Hot links to Glencoe Online Study Tools

Building on Prior Knowledge

In Chapter 1, students learned how to evaluate algebraic expressions with whole numbers. In Example 5, they will extend this knowledge to evaluate expressions involving integers.

ABSOLUTE VALUE

In-Class Examples

4 Evaluate each expression.

a. $|5|$ **5**

b. $|-8| + |-1|$ **9**

c. $|6| - |-4|$ **2**

Teaching Tip Explain that in expressions such as the one in Example 5, the absolute value symbol cannot be removed from the variables before evaluating the expression.

5 **ALGEBRA** Evaluate the expression $|x| - 8$ if $x = -2$.
–6

3 Practice/Apply

Study Notebook

Have students—
• add the definitions/examples of the vocabulary terms to their Vocabulary Builder worksheets for Chapter 2.
• make a list of words and phrases that indicate positive and negative numbers.
• include any other item(s) that they find helpful in mastering the skills in this lesson.

ABSOLUTE VALUE   On the number line, notice that -5 and 5 are on opposite sides of zero, and they are the same distance from zero. In mathematics, we say they have the same **absolute value**, 5.

The symbol for absolute value is two vertical bars on either side of the number.

$|5| = 5$ The absolute value of 5 is 5.
$|-5| = 5$ The absolute value of -5 is 5.

Key Concept   **Absolute Value**

• **Words**   The absolute value of a number is the distance the number is from zero on the number line. The absolute value of a number is always greater than or equal to zero.

• **Examples** $|5| = 5$ $|-5| = 5$

Study Tip

Common Misconception
It is not always true that the absolute value of a number is the opposite of the number. Remember that absolute value is always positive or zero.

Example 4 Expressions with Absolute Value

Evaluate each expression.

a. $|-8|$

$|-8| = 8$ The graph of -8 is 8 units from 0.

b. $|9| + |-7|$ The absolute value of 9 is 9.
$|9| + |-7| = 9 + 7$ The absolute value of -7 is 7.
$= 16$ Simplify.

c. $|-4| - |3|$
$|-4| - |3| = 4 - 3$ $|-4| = 4, |3| = 3$
$= 1$ Simplify.

ALGEBRA CONNECTION

Since variables represent numbers, you can use absolute value notation with algebraic expressions involving variables.

Example 5 Algebraic Expressions with Absolute Value

ALGEBRA   Evaluate $|x| - 3$ if $x = -5$.
$|x| - 3 = |-5| - 3$ Replace x with -5.
$= 5 - 3$ The absolute value of -5 is 5.
$= 2$ Simplify.

DAILY INTERVENTION

Unlocking Misconceptions

• **Absolute Value**   Watch for students who think that the absolute value of a positive number is negative. Remind them that the absolute value of either a positive or negative number represents a distance, and distances are always positive.

Concept Check

1. **Explain** how you would graph −4 on a number line. **See margin.**

2. **OPEN ENDED** Write two inequalities using integers. **See margin.**

3. **Define** *absolute value*. **See margin.**

Guided Practice

GUIDED PRACTICE KEY	
Exercises	Examples
4–6	1
7–12	2
12, 19	3
13–15	4
16–18	5

Write an integer for each situation. Then graph on a number line.

4. 8° below zero **−8**
5. a 15-yard gain **+15**

4–5. See margin for graphs.

6. Graph the set of integers {0, −3, 6} on a number line. **See margin.**

Write two inequalities using the numbers in each sentence. Use the symbols < or >.

7. −4° is colder than 2°. **−4 < 2; 2 > −4**
8. −6 is greater than −10. **−6 > −10; −10 < −6**

Replace each ● with <, >, or = to make a true sentence.

9. −18 ● −8 **<**
10. 0 ● −3 **>**
11. 9 ● −9 **>**

12. Order the integers {28, −6, 0, −2, 5, −52, 115} from least to greatest. **{−52, −6, −2, 0, 5, 28, 115}**

Evaluate each expression.

13. |−10| **10**
14. |10| − |−4| **6**
15. |16| + |−5| **21**

ALGEBRA Evaluate each expression if $a = -8$ and $b = 5$.

16. 9 + |a| **17**
17. |a| − b **3**
18. 2|a| **16**

Application

19. **WEATHER** The table shows the record low temperatures in °F for selected states. Order the temperatures from least to greatest.

State	AL	CA	FL	IN	KY	NY	NC	OK	OR
Temperature	−27	−45	−2	−36	−37	−52	−34	−27	−54

−54, −52, −45, −37, −36, −34, −27, −27, −2

★ indicates increased difficulty

Homework Help	
For Exercises	See Examples
20–25, 66	1
26–43	2
44–47, 67–70	3
48–59	4
60–65	5

Extra Practice
See page 726.

Write an integer for each situation. Then graph on a number line.

20. a bank withdrawal of $100 **−100**
21. a loss of 6 pounds **−6**

22. a salary increase of $250 **+250**
23. a gain of 9 yards **+9**

24. 12° above zero **+12**
25. 5 seconds before liftoff **−5**

20–25. See margin for graphs.

Graph each set of integers on a number line. **26–29. See pp. 95A–95B.**

26. {0, −2, 4}
27. {−3, 1, 2, 5}

28. {−2, −4, −5, −8}
29. {−4, 0, 6, −7, −1}

Write two inequalities using the numbers in each sentence. Use the symbols < or >. **31. −5 > −10; −10 < −5**

30. 3 meters is taller than 2 meters. **3 > 2; 2 < 3**

31. A temperature of −5°F is warmer than a temperature of −10°F.

32. 55 miles per hour is slower than 65 miles per hour. **55 < 65; 65 > 55**

DAILY
INTERVENTION

Differentiated Instruction

- **Auditory/Musical** Bring to class several bars of music in the key of C to distribute to small groups or to individual students. Let middle C correspond to 0 on a number line. Have students plot the notes in the bar of music onto a number line. Let each whole step count as 1; the first F above middle C would equal 3, and the first A before middle C would equal −2. Have students play or sing the music, and then play the notes ordered from least to greatest on the number line.

Organization by Objective
- **Compare and Order Integers:** 20–47, 66–70
- **Absolute Value:** 48–65

Odd/Even Assignments
Exercises 20–65 are structured so that students practice the same concepts whether they are assigned odd or even problems.

Assignment Guide
Basic: 21–41 odd, 45–57 odd, 61–65 odd, 67–89

Average: 21–65 odd, 67–89

Advanced: 22–66 even, 67–83 (Optional: 84–89)

Answers

1. Draw a number line. Draw a dot at −4.

2. Sample answer: 3 > −2, |−5| < |−8|

3. The absolute value of a number is its distance from 0 on a number line.

4. (number line from −8 to 0, dot at −4)

5. (number line from 8 to 16, dot at 15)

6. (number line from −3 to 6, dots at −3, 0, 6)

20. (number line −100 to 100, dot at −100)

21. (number line −8 to 0, dot at −6)

22. (number line 0 to 300, dot at 250)

23. (number line 5 to 13, dot at 9)

24. (number line 0 to 16, dot at 12)

25. (number line −8 to 0, dot at −5)

Study Guide and Intervention, p. 57

The set of **integers** can be written {..., −3, −2, −1, 0, 1, 2, 3, ...} where ... means continues indefinitely. Two integers can be compared using an **inequality**, which is a mathematical sentence containing < or >.

Example 1 Use the integers graphed on the number line below for each question.

Replace each ● with < or > to make a true sentence.

a. −6 ● −2
b. 3 ● −4

−2 is greater since it lies to the right of −6. So write −6 < −2.
3 is greater since it lies to the right of −4. So write 3 > −4.

Numbers on opposite sides of zero and the same distance from zero have the same **absolute value**.

The symbol for absolute value is two vertical bars on either side of the number. $|2| = 2$ and $|-2| = 2$

Example 2 Evaluate each expression.

a. $|-4|$
$|-4| = 4$

b. $|-3| + |6|$
$|-3| + |6| = 3 + 6$ $|-3| = 3, |6| = 6$
$= 9$ Simplify.

Exercises

Replace each ● with <, >, or = to make a true sentence.

1. 4 ● −4 >
2. 8 ● 12 <
3. −7 ● −5 <
4. 2 ● 5 <
5. −1 ● 1 <
6. 4 ● −3 >
7. 6 ● 8 <
8. −2 ● 12 <
9. 9 ● −1 >
10. −6 ● −6 =
11. 5 ● −3 >
12. −10 ● 2 <

Evaluate each expression.

13. $|-6|$ 6
14. $|15|$ 15
15. $|-12|$ 12
16. $|21|$ 21
17. $|4| - |2|$ 2
18. $|-8| + |-3|$ 11
19. $|-10| - |-6|$ 4
20. $|12| + |-4|$ 16

Skills Practice, p. 58 and Practice, p. 59 (shown)

NAME _____ DATE _____ PERIOD _____

2-1 Practice

Integers and Absolute Value

Replace each ● with <, >, or = to make a true sentence.
1. 0 ● −5 >
2. 10 ● −10 >
3. −8 ● 3 <
4. 11 ● 11 =
5. −18 ● −18 =
6. −18 ● 18 <
7. 18 ● −18 >
8. 18 ● 18 =
9. −120 ● −95 <
10. 35 ● −12 >
11. −35 ● 12 <
12. 41 ● 17 >

Order the integers in each set from least to greatest.
13. {−14, −6, −22, 0}   14. {−3, 19, 0, −5}   15. {−7, 20, −21, 7}
{−22, −14, −6, 0}   {−5, −3, 0, 19}   {−21, −7, 7, 20}
16. {15, −1, 4, −3}   17. {0, −1, 2, −3, 4}   18. {55, 0, −60, 12}
{−3, −1, 4, 15}   {−3, −1, 0, 2, 4}   {−60, 0, 12, 55}
19. {−48, −30, −49, −8, 3, −4}   20. {27, −9, 3, 0, −2, 29}
{−49, −48, −30, −8, −4, 3}   {−9, −2, 0, 3, 27, 29}

Evaluate each expression.
21. $|-7|$ 22. $|14|$ 23. $|-11|$
7   14   11
24. $|-9| - |6|$ 25. $|-18| - |-8|$ 26. $|-12| + |1|$
3   10   13
27. $|8-4|$ 28. $|23| - |18|$ 29. $-|-16| + |-22|$
4   5   38

Evaluate each expression if $a = -3$, $b = 0$, and $c = 1$.
30. $|a| - |c|$ 31. $|a| + |c|$ 32. $|ab| + c$
2   4   1
33. $5 - |ac|$ 34. $c + |-5|$ 35. $c + |5|$
2   6   6

36. **WEATHER** At 6:15 a.m. the temperature was −8°F. At 12:15 p.m. the temperature was −12°F. At 6:16 p.m. the temperature was −10°F. Order the temperatures from least to greatest.
−12°F, −10°F, −8°F

© Glencoe/McGraw-Hill   59   Glencoe Pre-Algebra

Enrichment, p. 61

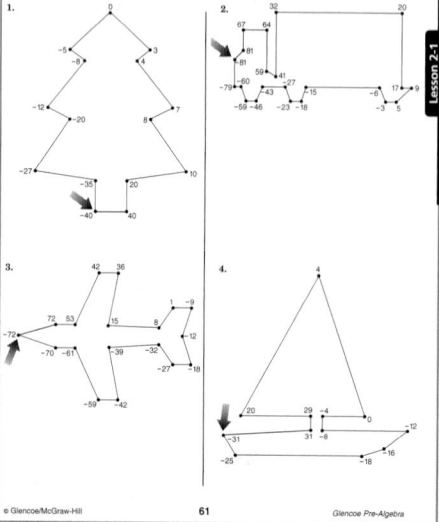

Integers in Order

Connect the dots in each exercise in the order of the integers shown, from least to greatest. The least integer in each exercise is indicated by the arrow.

Write two inequalities using the numbers in each sentence. Use the symbols < or >. 33. 248 < 425; 425 > 248   34. −2 < 23; 23 > −2

33. Yesterday's pollen count was 248. Today's count is 425.

34. Yesterday's low temperature was −2°F. The high temperature was 23°F.

35. Water boils at 212°F, and it freezes at 32°F. **212 > 32; 32 < 212**

Replace each ● with <, >, or = to make a true sentence.

36. −6 ● −2 <
37. −10 ● −13 >
38. 0 ● −9 >
39. 14 ● 0 >
40. −18 ● 8 <
41. 5 ● −23 >
★42. $|9| ● |-9|$ =
★43. $|-20| ● |-4|$ >

Order the integers in each set from least to greatest. 45. {−15, −4, −2, −1}

44. {5, 0, −8} **{−8, 0, 5}**
45. {−15, −1, −2, −4}
46. {24, 5, −46, 9, 0, −3} **{−46, −3, 0, 5, 9, 24}**
47. {98, −57, −60, 38, 188} **{−60, −57, 38, 98, 188}**

Evaluate each expression.

48. $|-15|$ **15**
49. $|46|$ **46**
50. $-|20|$ **−20**
51. $-|5|$ **−5**
52. $|0|$ **0**
53. $|7|$ **7**
54. $|-5| + |4|$ **9**
55. $|0| + |-2|$ **2**
56. $|15| - |-1|$ **14**
57. $|0 + 9|$ **9**
★58. $-|-24|$ **−24**
★59. $-||-6| + |14||$ **−20**

ALGEBRA Evaluate each expression if $a = 0$, $b = 3$, and $c = -4$.

60. $14 + |b|$ **17**
61. $|c| - a$ **4**
62. $a + b + |c|$ **7**
63. $ab + |-40|$ **40**
64. $|c| - b$ **1**
65. $|ab| + b$ **3**

66. **GEOGRAPHY** The Caribbean Sea has an average depth of 8685 feet below sea level. Use an integer to express this depth. **−8685 ft**

WEATHER For Exercises 67–70, use the graphic.

67. Graph the temperatures on a number line. **See margin.**

68. Compare the lowest temperature in the United States and the lowest temperature east of the Mississippi using the < symbol. **−80 < −54**

69. Compare the lowest temperatures of the contiguous 48 states and east of the Mississippi using the > symbol. **−54 > −70**

70. Write the temperatures in order from greatest to least. **−54°, −70°, −80°**

71. How many units apart are −4 and 3 on a number line? **7**

72. **CRITICAL THINKING** Consider any two points on the number line where $X > Y$. Is it *always*, *sometimes*, or *never* true that $|X| > |Y|$? Explain. **See margin.**

Study Tip

Contiguous States
Contiguous states are those states that touch each other. Alaska and Hawaii are *not* contiguous states.

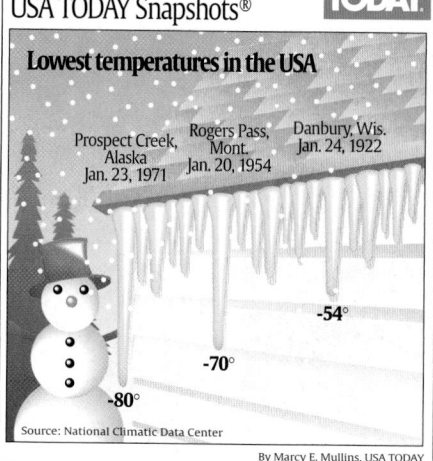

USA TODAY Snapshots®

Lowest temperatures in the USA

Prospect Creek, Alaska
Jan. 23, 1971

Rogers Pass, Mont.
Jan. 20, 1954

Danbury, Wis.
Jan. 24, 1922

−54°
−70°
−80°

Source: National Climatic Data Center

By Marcy E. Mullins, USA TODAY

---

73. CRITICAL THINKING Consider two numbers A and B on a number line. Is it *always*, *sometimes*, or *never* true that the distance between A and B equals the distance between $|A|$ and $|B|$? Explain. **See margin.**

74. WRITING IN MATH   Answer the question that was posed at the beginning of the lesson. **See margin.**

How are integers used to model real-world situations?

Include the following in your answer:
- an explanation of how integers are used to describe rainfall, and
- some situations in the real world where negative numbers are used.

75. Which of the following describes the absolute value of $-2°$? **B**
Ⓐ It is the distance from -2 to 2 on a thermometer.
Ⓑ It is the distance from -2 to 0 on a thermometer.
Ⓒ It is the actual temperature outside when a thermometer reads $-2°$.
Ⓓ None of these describes the absolute value of $-2°$.

76. What is the temperature shown on the thermometer at the right? **D**
Ⓐ 8
Ⓑ 7
Ⓒ -7
Ⓓ -8

Maintain Your Skills

Mixed Review   **Determine whether a scatter plot of the data for the following might show a *positive*, *negative*, or *no* relationship. Explain your answer.** *(Lesson 1-7)*

77. height and arm length **positive**   **78.** birth month and weight **none**
77–78. See margin for explanations.

Express each relation as a table and as a list of ordered pairs. *(Lesson 1-6)*

79–80.
See pp. 95A–95B.

79.

80.
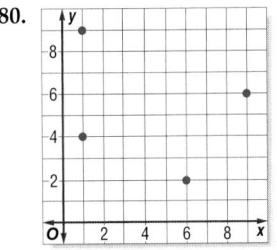

Name the property shown by each statement. *(Lesson 1-4)*

81. $20 \cdot 18 = 18 \cdot 20$
   Comm. $(\times)$

82. $9 \cdot 8 \cdot 0 = 0$
   Mult. Prop. of 0

83. $3ab = 3ba$
   Comm. $(\times)$

Getting Ready for the Next Lesson   **BASIC SKILL   Find each sum or difference.** **86. 2107**

84. $18 + 29 + 46$ **93**   **85.** $232 + 156$ **388**   **86.** $451 + 629 + 1027$

87. $36 - 19$ **17**   **88.** $479 - 281$ **198**   **89.** $2011 - 962$ **1049**

Answers (p. 60)

67.

$-90 \quad -70 \quad -50 \quad -30 \quad -10$

72. Sometimes true; if X and Y are both negative it will not be true.

73. Sometimes true; if A and B are both positive, both negative, or one is 0, it is always true. If one number is negative and the other is positive, it is never true.

Answers

74. Sample answer: Integers describe real-world situations involving measures above and below zero. Answers should include the following.
- Rainfall above normal is described using positive integers, below normal by negative integers.
- Some examples are: accounting uses + for deposits and − for withdrawals; gains are represented by +, losses by −; in golf, scores above par are +, below par are −, temperatures above zero are +, below zero are −.

77. As height increases, so does arm length.

78. Birth month and weight are not related.

Getting Started

Objective Model operations with integers with algebra tiles and an integer mat.

Materials
algebra tiles
integer mat

Teach

Activity 1

- Encourage students to line their tiles up neatly in side-by-side lines to help them see zero pairs.

Activity 2

- Reproduce the addition table on a transparency. Shade positive integers one color, negative integers another, and the zeros yet another color to make the patterns easier for the class to see. The student recording sheet has this table on it. Students could use colored pencils to do the same color scheme on their own papers.

Answers (p. 63)

1.

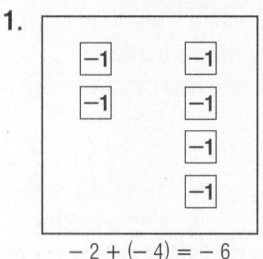

$$-2 + (-4) = -6$$

Algebra Activity

A Preview of Lesson 2-2

NEW YORK *Performance Indicator* Reinforcement of **7.N.12 Add,** subtract, multiply, and divide **integers**

Adding Integers

In a set of algebra tiles, $\boxed{1}$ represents the integer 1, and $\boxed{-1}$ represents the integer -1. You can use algebra tiles and an integer mat to model operations with integers.

Activity 1

The following example shows how to find the sum $-3 + (-2)$ using algebra tiles. Remember that addition means *combining*. $-3 + (-2)$ tells you to combine a set of 3 negative tiles with a set of 2 negative tiles.

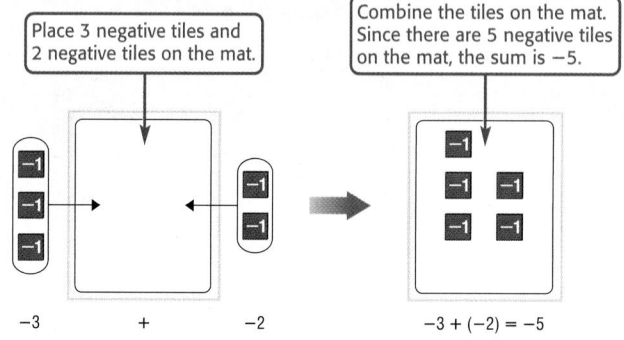

Therefore, $-3 + (-2) = -5$.

There are two important properties to keep in mind when you model operations with integers.

- When one positive tile is paired with one negative tile, the result is called a **zero pair**.
- You can add or remove zero pairs from a mat because removing or adding zero does not change the value of the tiles on the mat.

The following example shows how to find the sum $-4 + 3$.

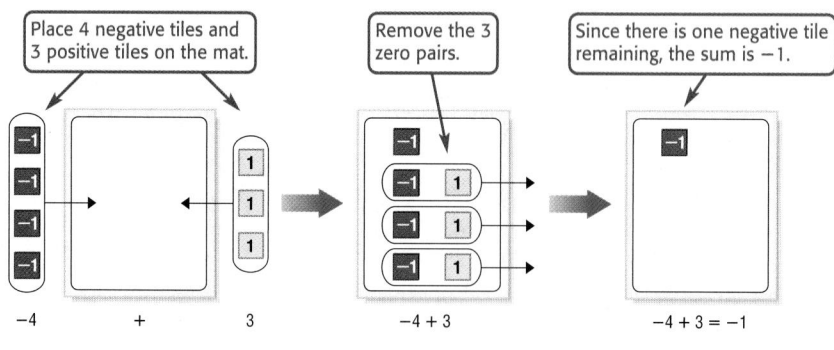

Therefore, $-4 + 3 = -1$.

2.

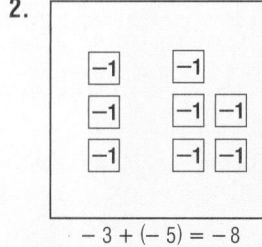

$$-3 + (-5) = -8$$

3.

$$-6 + (-1) = -7$$

4.

$$-4 + (-5) = -9$$

5.

$$-4 + 2 = -2$$

6.

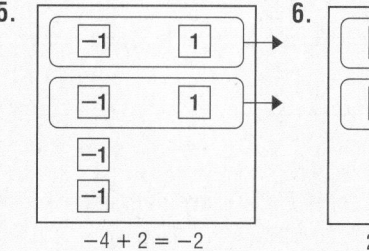

$$2 + (-5) = -3$$

Model

Use algebra tiles to model and find each sum. **1–8. See margin for models.**

1. $-2 + (-4)$ **−6**　2. $-3 + (-5)$ **−8**　3. $-6 + (-1)$ **−7**　4. $-4 + (-5)$ **−9**
5. $-4 + 2$ **−2**　6. $2 + (-5)$ **−3**　7. $-1 + 6$ **5**　8. $4 + (-4)$ **0**

Activity 2

The Addition Table was completed using algebra tiles. In the highlighted portion of the table, the addends are −3 and 1, and the sum is −2. So, $-3 + 1 = -2$. You can use the patterns in the Addition Table to learn more about integers.

Addition Table

+	4	3	2	1	0	−1	−2	−3	−4	← addends
4	8	7	6	5	4	3	2	1	0	
3	7	6	5	4	3	2	1	0	−1	
2	6	5	4	3	2	1	0	−1	−2	
1	5	4	3	2	1	0	−1	−2	−3	
0	4	3	2	1	0	−1	−2	−3	−4	} sums
−1	3	2	1	0	−1	−2	−3	−4	−5	
−2	2	1	0	−1	−2	−3	−4	−5	−6	
−3	1	0	−1	−2	−3	−4	−5	−6	−7	
−4	0	−1	−2	−3	−4	−5	−6	−7	−8	

addends ⌐

Make a Conjecture

9. Locate all of the positive sums in the table. Describe the addends that result in a positive sum.

10. Locate all of the negative sums in the table. Describe the addends that result in a negative sum.

11. Locate all of the sums that are zero. Describe the addends that result in a sum of zero. **They are additive inverses.**

12. The Identity Property says that when zero is added to any number, the sum is the number. Does it appear that this property is true for addition of integers? If so, write two examples that illustrate the property. If not, give a counterexample. **Yes; see margin for examples.**

13. The Commutative Property says that the order in which numbers are added does not change the sum. Does it appear that this property is true for addition of integers? If so, write two examples that illustrate the property. If not, give a counterexample. **Yes; see margin for examples.**

14. The Associative Property says that the way numbers are grouped when added does not change the sum. Is this property true for addition of integers? If so, write two examples that illustrate the property. If not, give a counterexample.

9. The addends are both +, or one is + and one − with the + addend having the greater absolute value.
10. The addends are both −, or one is + and one − with the − addend having the greater absolute value
14. Yes; see margin for examples.

Algebra Activity　Adding Integers　**63**

Answers

7.

$-1 + 6 = 5$

8.

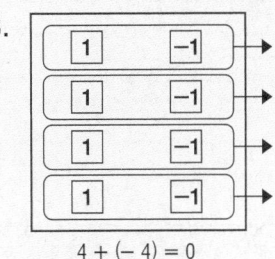

$4 + (-4) = 0$

12. Sample examples: $-1 + 0 = -1$; $0 + (-2) = -2$

13. Sample examples: $-1 + 3 = 2$ and $3 + (-1) = 2$; $-2 + (-1) = -3$ and $-1 + (-2) = -3$

14. Sample examples:

$$[3 + (-2)] + (-1) = 3 + [(-2) + (-1)]$$
$$1 + (-1) = 3 + (-3)$$
$$0 = 0$$

and

$$[1 + (-2)] + 2 = 1 + [-2 + 2]$$
$$-1 + 2 = 1 + 0$$
$$1 = 1$$

2-2 Lesson Notes

1 Focus

5-Minute Check Transparency 2-2 Use as a quiz or review of Lesson 2-1.

Mathematical Background notes are available for this lesson on page 54C.

How can a number line help you add integers?

The opening activity questions are repeated on page 65 of the *Chapter 2 Resource Masters*.

Reading to Learn Mathematics, p. 65   **ELL**

Pre-Activity   *How can a number line help you add integers?*

Do the activity at the top of page 64 in your textbook. Write your answers below.

a. What integer represents the total yardage on the two plays?   −7

b. Write an addition sentence that describes this situation.
−5 + (−2) = −7

Reading the Lesson   1–2. See students' work.
Write a definition and give an example of each new vocabulary word or phrase.

Vocabulary	Definition	Example
1. opposites		
2. additive inverse		

3. Draw a number line model that shows how to find the sum −4 + (−2). Explain your model.

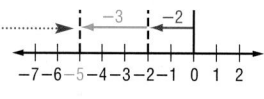

Start at zero on the number line. Move 4 units to the left because −4 is negative. Then move 2 more units to the left because −2 is negative. Then land on −6, so the sum is −6.

4. The sum of any number and its ___additive inverse___ is zero.

Helping You Remember

5. Suppose that one of your classmates was absent the day you learned how to add integers.

a. Explain to your classmate how to add two integers with the same sign.
Add their absolute values. Give the result the same sign as the integers.

b. Explain to your classmate how to add two integers with different signs.
Subtract their absolute values. Give the result the same sign as the integer with the greater absolute value.

2-2 Adding Integers

NEW YORK *Performance Indicator* **Reinforcement of 7.N.13 Add** and subtract **two integers** (with and without the use of a number line)

What You'll Learn

- Add two integers.
- Add more than two integers.

Vocabulary
- opposites
- additive inverse

How can a number line help you add integers?

In football, forward progress is represented by a positive integer. Being pushed back is represented by a negative integer. Suppose on the first play a team loses 5 yards and on the second play they lose 2 yards.

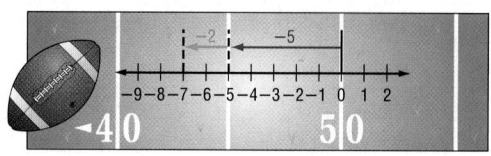

a. What integer represents the total yardage on the two plays? −7

b. Write an addition sentence that describes this situation. −5 + (−2) = −7

Reading Math

Addends and Sums
Recall that the numbers you add are called *addends*. The result is called the *sum*.

ADD INTEGERS   The equation −5 + (−2) = −7 is an example of adding two integers with the same sign. Notice that the sign of the sum is the same as the sign of the addends.

Example 1 Add Integers on a Number Line

Find −2 + (−3).

Start at zero.
Move 2 units to the left.
From there, move 3 more units to the left.

−2 + (−3) = −5

This example suggests a rule for adding integers with the same sign.

TEACHING TIP

Point out that the length of each arrow on the number line represents the absolute value of the addend.

Key Concept   Adding Integers with the Same Sign

- **Words**   To add integers with the same sign, add their absolute values. Give the result the same sign as the integers.

- **Examples**   −5 + (−2) = −7   6 + 3 = 9

Example 2 Add Integers with the Same Sign

Find −4 + (−5).

−4 + (−5) = −9   Add |−4| and |−5|. Both numbers are negative, so the sum is negative.

Resource Manager

📂 Workbooks and Reproducible Masters

Chapter 2 Resource Masters
- Study Guide and Intervention, p. 62
- Skills Practice, p. 63
- Practice, p. 64
- Reading to Learn Mathematics, p. 65
- Enrichment, p. 66
- Assessment, p. 101

Parent and Student Study Guide Workbook, p. 10
Prerequisite Skills Workbook, pp. 5–8

📺 Transparencies
5-Minute Check Transparency 2-2
Answer Key Transparencies

💿 Technology
Interactive Chalkboard

A number line can also help you understand how to add integers with different signs.

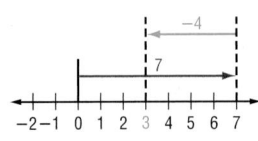 **Example 3** *Add Integers on a Number Line*

Find each sum.

a. 7 + (−4)

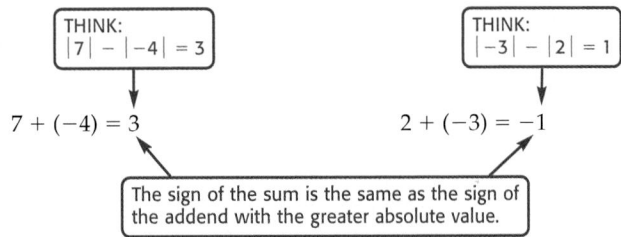

Start at zero.
Move 7 units to the right.
From there, move 4 units to the left.

7 + (−4) = 3

b. 2 + (−3)

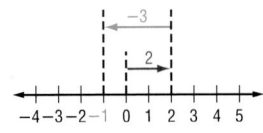

Start at zero.
Move 2 units to the right.
From there, move 3 units to the left.

2 + (−3) = −1

Notice how the sums in Example 3 relate to the addends.

THINK:
|7| − |−4| = 3

7 + (−4) = 3

THINK:
|−3| − |2| = 1

2 + (−3) = −1

The sign of the sum is the same as the sign of the addend with the greater absolute value.

Key Concept *Adding Integers with Different Signs*

- **Words** To add integers with different signs, subtract their absolute values. Give the result the same sign as the integer with the greater absolute value.

- **Examples** 7 + (−2) = 5   −7 + 2 = −5

Example 4 *Add Integers with Different Signs*

Find each sum.

a. −8 + 3

−8 + 3 = −5   To find −8 + 3, subtract |3| from |−8|.
The sum is negative because |−8| > |3|.

b. 10 + (−4)

10 + (−4) = 6   To find 10 + |−4|, subtract |−4| from |10|.
The sum is positive because |10| > |−4|.

 www.pre-alg.com/extra_examples/ny   **Lesson 2-2** Adding Integers   **65**

Study Tip

Adding Integers on a Number Line
Always start at zero. Move right to model a positive integer. Move left to model a negative integer.

---

2 Teach

ADD INTEGERS

In-Class Examples   Power Point®

Teaching Tip Tell students that positive indicates a movement right, and negative is a movement left. When adding a positive integer to a positive or negative integer, move right on the number line. When adding a negative integer to a positive or negative integer, move left on the number line.

1 Find 3 + 4. **7**

2 Find −5 + (−4). **−9**

3 Find each sum.

a. 7 + (−11) **−4**

b. −2 + 9 **7**

4 Find each sum.

a. −9 + 10 **1**

b. 8 + (−15) **−7**

✓ Skills Check

Add Integers Find each sum.
a. 5 + (−6) **−1**
b. 8 + 5 **13**
c. −8 + (−9) **−17**
d. −3 + 9 **6**
e. −11 + 5 **−6**

DAILY
INTERVENTION **Unlocking Misconceptions**

- **Add Integers** After presenting Example 4, some students may mistakenly assume the sign of the first addend is the sign of the sum. Emphasize that the sum has the same sign of the number that is farthest from 0 on the number line.

More About. . .

Astronomy
The temperatures on the moon are so extreme because the moon does not have any atmosphere to trap heat.

Example 5 *Use Integers to Solve a Problem*

ASTRONOMY During the night, the average temperature on the moon is −140°C. By noon, the average temperature has risen 252°C. What is the average temperature on the moon at noon?

Words The temperature at night is −140°C. It increases 252°C by noon. What is the temperature at noon?

Variables Let x = the temperature at noon.

Temperature at night	plus	increase by noon	equals	temperature at noon.

Equation -140 $+$ 252 $=$ x

Solve the equation.

$-140 + 252 = x$ To find the sum, subtract $|-140|$ from 252.

$112 = x$ The sum is positive because $|252| > |-140|$.

The average temperature at noon is 112°C.

ADD MORE THAN TWO INTEGERS Two numbers with the same absolute value but different signs are called **opposites**. For example, −4 and 4 are opposites. An integer and its opposite are also called **additive inverses**.

> **Key Concept** — *Additive Inverse Property*
> • **Words** The sum of any number and its additive inverse is zero.
> • **Symbols** $x + (-x) = 0$
> • **Example** $6 + (-6) = 0$

☑ **Concept Check** What is the additive inverse of 2? **−2**
What is the additive inverse of −6? **6**

The commutative, associative, and identity properties also apply to integers. These properties can help you add more than two integers.

Example 6 *Add Three or More Integers*

Find each sum.

a. $9 + (-3) + (-9)$

$9 + (-3) + (-9) = 9 + (-9) + (-3)$ Commutative Property
$= 0 + (-3)$ Additive Inverse Property
$= -3$ Identity Property of Addition

b. $-4 + 6 + (-3) + 9$

$-4 + 6 + (-3) + 9 = -4 + (-3) + 6 + 9$ Commutative Property
$= [-4 + (-3)] + (6 + 9)$ Associative Property
$= -7 + 15$ or 8 Simplify.

Study Tip

Adding Mentally
One way to add mentally is to group the positive addends together and the negative addends together. Then add to find the sum. You should also look for addends that are opposites. You can always add in order from left to right.

66 Chapter 2 Integers

D A I L Y
INTERVENTION — **Differentiated Instruction**

• **Visual/Spatial** To illustrate the concept of opposites on a number line, bring a small unbreakable mirror to class. Draw a number line on a piece of paper and hold the mirror perpendicular to the number line at the zero position. Have students come up a few at a time to observe what happens as a counter is moved along the positive side of a number line. **The counter's opposite value appears on the number line in the mirror, exactly the same distance from zero as the real counter.**

Check for Understanding

Concept Check

GUIDED PRACTICE KEY	
Exercises	Examples
3, 4	1, 2
5–8	3, 4
9, 10	6
11	5

1. **State** whether each sum is positive or negative. Explain your reasoning.
    a. $-4 + (-5)$ **negative**   b. $12 + (-2)$ **positive**
    c. $-11 + 9$ **negative**   d. $15 + 10$ **positive**
1a–d. See margin for explanations.

2. **OPEN ENDED** Give an example of two integers that are additive inverses. **Sample answer: −1 and 1**

Guided Practice

Find each sum.

3. $-2 + (-4)$ **−6**   4. $-10 + (-5)$ **−15**   5. $7 + (-2)$ **5**

6. $11 + (-3)$ **8**   7. $8 + (-5)$ **3**   8. $9 + (-12)$ **−3**

9. $8 + (-6) + 2$ **4**   10. $-6 + 5 + (-10)$ **−11**

11. 4 + (−5) = −1

Application

11. **FOOTBALL** A team gained 4 yards on one play. On the next play, they lost 5 yards. Write an addition sentence to find the change in yardage.

★ indicates increased difficulty

Practice and Apply

Homework Help	
For Exercises	See Examples
12–21	1, 2
22–29	3, 4
32–39	6
40, 41	5

Extra Practice
See page 726.

Find each sum.

12. $-4 + (-1)$ **−5**   13. $-5 + (-2)$ **−7**   14. $-4 + (-6)$ **−10**

15. $-3 + (-8)$ **−11**   16. $-7 + (-8)$ **−15**   17. $-12 + (-4)$ **−16**

18. $-9 + (-14)$ **−23**   19. $-15 + (-6)$ **−21**   20. $-11 + (-15)$ **−26**

21. $-23 + (-43)$ **−66**   22. $8 + (-5)$ **3**   23. $6 + (-4)$ **2**

24. $3 + (-7)$ **−4**   25. $4 + (-6)$ **−2**   26. $-15 + 6$ **−9**

27. $-5 + 11$ **6**   28. $18 + (-32)$ **−14**   29. $-45 + 19$ **−26**

30. What is the additive inverse of 14? **−14**

31. What is the additive inverse of −21? **21**

TEACHING TIP

Refer students to the Study Tip on page 66 for strategies to use when adding more than two integers.

Find each sum.

32. $6 + (-9) + 9$ **6**   33. $7 + (-13) + 4$ **−2**

34. $-9 + 16 + (-10)$ **−3**   35. $-12 + 18 + (-12)$ **−6**

36. $14 + (-9) + 6$ **11**   37. $28 + (-35) + 4$ **−3**

38. $-41 + 25 + (-10)$ **−26**   39. $-18 + 35 + (-17)$ **0**

40. **ACCOUNTING** The starting balance in a checking account was $50. What was the balance after checks were written for $25 and for $32? **−$7**

41. **GOLF** A score of 0 is called *even par*. Two under par is written as −2. Two over par is written as +2. Suppose a player shot 4 under par, 2 over par, even par, and 3 under par in four rounds of a tournament. What was the player's final score? **−5**

Find each sum.

★ 42. $|18 + (-13)|$ **5**   ★ 43. $|-27 + 19|$ **8**

★ 44. $|-25 + (-12)|$ **37**   ★ 45. $|-28 + (-12)|$ **40**

www.pre-alg.com/self_check_quiz/ny

Lesson 2-2 Adding Integers **67**

Study Guide and Intervention, p. 62

Adding Integers with the Same Sign	Add their absolute values. Give the result the same sign as the integers.

Example 1 Find the sum $-3 + (-4)$.
$-3 + (-4) = -7$ Add -3 and -4. Both numbers are negative so the sum is negative.

Adding Integers with Different Signs	Subtract their absolute values. Give the result the same sign as the integer with the greater absolute value.

Example 2 Find each sum.
a. $-5 + 4$
$-5 + 4 = |-5| - |4|$ Subtract $|4|$ from $|-5|$.
$= 5 - 4$ or 1   Simplify.
$= -1$ The sum is negative because $|-5| > |4|$.
b. $6 + (-2)$
$6 + (-2) = |6| - |-2|$ Subtract $|-2|$ from $|6|$.
$= 6 - 2$ or 4   Simplify.
$= 4$ The sum is positive because $|6| > |-2|$.

Exercises

Find each sum.

1. $6 + (-3)$ **3**   2. $-3 + (-5)$ **−8**   3. $7 + (-3)$ **4**
4. $-4 + (-4)$ **−8**   5. $-8 + 5$ **−3**   6. $-12 + (-10)$ **−22**
7. $6 + (-13)$ **−7**   8. $-14 + 4$ **−10**   9. $6 + (-6)$ **0**
10. $-15 + (-5)$ **−20**   11. $-9 + 8$ **−1**   12. $20 + (-8)$ **12**
13. $-19 + (-11)$ **−30**   14. $17 + (-9)$ **8**   15. $-16 + (-5)$ **−21**
16. $-12 + 14$ **2**   17. $9 + (-25)$ **−16**   18. $-36 + 19$ **−17**
19. $7 + (-18)$ **−11**   20. $-12 + (-15)$ **−27**   21. $10 + (-14)$ **−4**
22. $-33 + 19$ **−14**   23. $-20 + (-5)$ **−25**   24. $-12 + (-10)$ **−22**
25. $-15 + 4$ **−11**   26. $-34 + 29$ **−5**   27. $46 + (-32)$ **14**

Skills Practice, p. 63 and Practice, p. 64 (shown)

Find each sum.

1. $-19 + (-7)$ **−26**   2. $-29 + 30$ **1**   3. $-32 + 9$ **−23**   4. $10 + 37$ **47**
5. $34 + 22$ **56**   6. $-16 + (-28)$ **−44**   7. $-4 + (-50)$ **−54**   8. $-12 + (-63)$ **−75**
9. $26 + (-9)$ **17**   10. $-17 + (-23)$ **−40**   11. $12 + (-22)$ **−10**   12. $18 + (-56)$ **−38**
13. $-36 + (-36)$ **−72**   14. $-54 + 45$ **−9**   15. $-34 + 17$ **−17**   16. $-16 + (-24)$ **−40**
17. $70 + (-108)$ **−38**   18. $-52 + 36$ **−16**   19. $-71 + (-86)$ **−157**   20. $-39 + (-40)$ **−79**
21. $25 + 18 + (-23)$ **20**   22. $-65 + (-2) + 9$ **−58**   23. $80 + 15 + (-26)$ **69**
24. $-5 + 4 + (-27)$ **−28**   25. $-29 + 12 + 44$ **27**   26. $-1 + (-8) + (-49)$ **−58**
27. $-16 + (-56) + (-90)$ **−162**   28. $-18 + 13 + (-35)$ **−40**   29. $10 + (-34) + 17$ **−7**
30. $30 + (-9) + 1$ **22**   31. $-24 + 7 + 47$ **30**   32. $51 + (-21) + (-12)$ **18**

33. **TEMPERATURE** At 4:00 A.M., the outside temperature was $-28°$F. By 4:00 P.M. it rose 38 degrees. What was the temperature at 4:00 P.M.? **+10°F**

34. **HEALTH** Three friends decided to exercise together four times a week to lose fat and increase muscle mass. While all three were healthier after six weeks, one had lost 5 pounds, another had gained 3 pounds, and one had lost 4 pounds. What was the total number of pounds gained or lost by the three friends? **−6 pounds**

35. **ROLLER COASTERS** The latest thrill ride at a popular theme park takes roller coaster fans on an exciting ride. In the first 20 seconds, it carries its passengers up a 100-meter hill, plunges them 72 meters down, and quickly takes them back up a 48-meter rise. How much higher or lower from the start of the ride are they after these 20 seconds? **76 m higher**

Enrichment, p. 66

Modular Arithmetic

In modular arithmetic, there is a finite set of numbers. An example of a finite set would be the numbers on the face of a clock. No matter how many numbers are added together, the answer will still be one of the twelve numbers found on the face of the clock.

Example 1 In mod 12, $5 + 8 + 2 = 3$.
To find the sum, start at 0. Count 5 units in a clockwise direction, then 8 units, and then 2 units. You should end at the number 3.

Find each sum in mod 12.

1. $6 + 8 + 4$ **6**   2. $7 + 9 + 11 + 5$ **8**
3. $6 + 4 + 11 + 12 + 5$ **2**   4. $1 + 4 + 9 + 11 + 6$ **7**
5. $7 + 10 + 9 + 12 + 10$ **0**   6. $6 + 12 + 5 + 12 + 8 + 12$ **7**
7. $12 + 12 + 12 + 12 + 6$ **6**   8. $4 + 9 + 3 + 7 + 8 + 11 + 5$ **11**
9. $6 + 10 + 7 + 8 + 4 + 3 + 9$ **11**   10. $9 + 2 + 4 + 3 + 10 + 12 + 4 + 11$ **7**

Example 2 In mod 7, $3 + 5 + 2 = 3$.
To find the sum, start at 0. Count 3 units in a clockwise direction, then 5 units, and then 2 units. You should end at the number 3.

Find each sum in mod 7.

11. $2 + 4 + 3$ **2**   12. $5 + 1 + 6 + 3$ **1**
13. $2 + 2 + 4 + 6 + 7$ **0**   14. $5 + 3 + 4 + 6 + 1$ **5**
15. $7 + 7 + 7 + 7 + 5$ **5**   16. $6 + 5 + 1 + 2 + 4$ **4**
17. $4 + 3 + 1 + 5 + 6 + 2$ **0**   18. $4 + 2 + 1 + 6 + 7 + 5 + 4 + 3$ **4**
19. $6 + 5 + 4 + 3 + 2 + 1 + 7 + 6$ **6**   20. $5 + 7 + 4 + 4 + 2 + 6 + 1 + 2$ **3**

21. Can you find a pattern to these exercises? Explain. **Yes; the sum in mod x is the remainder when the sum is divided by x.**

Intervention If there is any doubt whether your students thoroughly understand the adding of integers, consider spending an extra day on this lesson. Use the Extra Practice on p. 726. You can also use the Study Guide and Intervention masters or the Practice masters in the *Chapter 2 Resource Masters* to reinforce this concept.

4 Assess

POPULATION For Exercises 46 and 47, use the table below that shows the change in population of several cities from 1990 to 2000.

City	1990 Population	Change as of 2000
Dallas, TX	1,006,877	+181,703
Honolulu, HI	365,272	+6385
Jackson, MS	196,637	−12,381
Philadelphia, PA	1,585,577	−68,027

46. Dallas: 1,188,580; Honolulu: 371,657; Jackson: 184,256; Philadelphia: 1,517,550

46. What was the population in each city in 2000?

47. What was the total change in population of these cities? **+107,680**

Online Research **Data Update** How have the populations of other cities changed since 2000? Visit www.pre-alg.com/data_update to learn more.

48. False; sample counterexample: If $n = -2$, then $-(-2)$ is positive.

48. CRITICAL THINKING *True or false*: $-n$ always names a negative number. If false, give a counterexample.

49. **WRITING IN MATH** Answer the question that was posed at the beginning of the lesson. **See margin.**

How can a number line help you add integers?

Include the following in your answer:
- an example showing the sum of a positive and a negative integer, and
- an example showing the sum of two negative integers.

Standardized Test Practice

50. What is the sum of $-32 + 20$? **C**
Ⓐ −52   Ⓑ −18   Ⓒ −12   Ⓓ 12

51. What is the value of $-|-2 + 8|$? **D**
Ⓐ −10   Ⓑ 10   Ⓒ 6   Ⓓ −6

Maintain Your Skills

Mixed Review

52. CHEMISTRY The freezing point of oxygen is 219 degrees below zero on the Celsius scale. Use an integer to express this temperature. *(Lesson 2-1)* **−219°C**

Order the integers in each set from least to greatest. *(Lesson 2-1)*

53. {14, −12, −8, 3, −9, 0}
{−12, −9, −8, 0, 3, 14}

54. {−242, 35, −158, 99, −24}
{−242, −158, −24, 35, 99}

Determine whether a scatter plot of the data for the following might show a *positive*, *negative*, or *no* relationship. *(Lesson 1-7)*

55. age and family size
no relationship

56. temperature and sales of mittens
negative

Identify the solution of each equation from the list given. *(Lesson 1-5)*

57. $18 - n = 12$; <u>6</u>, 16, 30

58. $25 = 16 + x$; <u>9</u>, 11, 41

59. $\frac{x}{2} = 10$; 5, 12, <u>20</u>

60. $7a = 49$; <u>7</u>, 42, 343

Getting Ready for the Next Lesson

PREREQUISITE SKILL Evaluate each expression if $a = 6$, $b = 10$, and $c = 3$.
*(To review **evaluating expressions**, see Lesson 1-3.)*

61. $a + 19$ **25**

62. $2b - 6$ **14**

63. $ab - ac$ **42**

64. $3a - (b + c)$ **5**

65. $5b + 5c$ **65**

66. $\frac{6b}{c}$ **20**

Answer

49. To add integers on a number line, start at 0. Move right to show positive integers and left to show negative integers.

- Sample answer:

- Sample answer:

Learning Mathematics Vocabulary

Some words used in mathematics are also used in English and have similar meanings. For example, in mathematics *add* means *to combine*. The meaning in English is *to join or unite*.

Some words are used only in mathematics. For example, *addend* means *a number to be added to another*.

Some words have more than one mathematical meaning. For example, an *inverse* operation *undoes the effect of another operation*, and an additive *inverse* is *a number that when added to a given number gives zero*.

The list below shows some of the mathematics vocabulary used in Chapters 1 and 2.

Vocabulary	Meaning	Examples
algebraic expression	an expression that contains at least one variable and at least one mathematical operation	$2 + x$, $\frac{4}{c}$, $3b$
evaluate	to find the value of an expression	$2 + 5 = 7$
simplify	to find a simpler form of an expression	$3b + 2b = 5b$
integer	a whole number, its inverse, or zero	$-3, 0, 2$
factor	a number that is multiplied by another number	$3(4) = 12$ 3 and 4 are factors.
product	the result of multiplying	$3(4) = 12 \longleftarrow$ product
quotient	the result of dividing two numbers	$\frac{12}{4} = 3 \longleftarrow$ quotient
dividend	the number being divided	$\frac{12}{4} = 3$ dividend
divisor	the number being divided into another number	$\frac{12}{4} = 3$ divisor
coordinate	a number that locates a point	$(5, 2)$

Reading to Learn 1–3. See margin.

1. Name two of the words above that are also used in everyday English. Use the Internet, a dictionary, or another reference to find their everyday definition. How do the everyday definitions relate to the mathematical definitions?

2. Name two words above that are used only in mathematics.

3. Name two words above that have more than one mathematical meaning. List their meanings.

Answers

1. Sample answer: Simplify – make simpler; coordinate – put in the same order

2. Answers should include two of the following: divisor, quotient, integer, algebraic expression.

3. Sample answer: Simplify – also means to simplify a fraction; factor – also means to find the factors of a number.

Getting Started

Read each word to the class. Have students think of sentences using the word in a non-mathematical way, if possible. For the first one, just have them use the word *expression*.

Teach

Students may not be aware of all of the possible meanings of the words listed just by reading the list. Keep an ear open to cases where a hint needs to be given or an instruction to consult the dictionary for more meanings.

Assess

Study Notebook

- Ask students to include any non-mathematical definitions of the words listed that might help them remember the mathematical meanings. Suggest that they include sentences for both the mathematical usage and the everyday usage for each word that they include.

ELL English Language Learners may benefit from writing key concepts from this activity in their Study Notebooks in their native language and then in English.

1 Focus

5-Minute Check Transparency 2-3 Use as a quiz or review of Lesson 2-2.

Mathematical Background notes are available for this lesson on page 54C.

How are addition and subtraction of integers related?

The opening activity questions are repeated on page 70 of the *Chapter 2 Resource Masters.*

Reading to Learn Mathematics, p. 70   ELL

Pre-Activity *How are addition and subtraction of integers related?*
  Do the activity at the top of page 70 in your textbook. Write your answers below.
  a. What is 6 − 8? −2
  b. What direction do you move to indicate subtracting a positive integer?
  left
  c. What addition sentence is also modeled by the number line on page 70?
  6 + (−8) = −2

Reading the Lesson
1. To subtract an integer, add its ___additive inverse___.
2. Draw a number line model that shows how to find the difference −4 − 2. Explain your model.
  To subtract 2 from −4, add −2 to −4. Start at zero. Move 4 units left to show −4. Then move 2 units left to add −2. The difference −4 −2 is −6.
3. Can 9 − (−3) be rewritten as 9 + 3? Explain. Yes; to subtract −3, you add 3.

Helping You Remember
4. You have learned how use addition to subtract both positive and negative integers. Write one example of each difference described below. Then show how to use addition to find the difference. **Sample answers are given.**
  a. subtracting a positive integer from a positive integer
  4 − 7 = 4 + (−7) = −3
  b. subtracting a positive integer from a negative integer
  −5 − 3 = −5 + (−3) = −8
  c. subtracting a negative integer from a positive integer
  3 − (−6) = 3 + 6 = 9
  d. subtracting a negative integer from a negative integer
  −7 − (−2) = −7 + 2 = −5

Teaching Tip Point out that the part of the arrow for −8 that extends beyond the arrow for +5 represents the difference.

---

c. 6 + (−8) = −2

TEACHING TIP
Remind students of the definition of additive inverse as given in Lesson 2-2.

Study Tip

Subtracting a Positive Integer
To subtract a positive integer, think about moving left on a number line from the starting integer. In Example 1a, start at 8, then move left 13. You'll end at −5. In Example 1b, start at −4, then move left 10. You'll end at −14.

2-3 Subtracting Integers

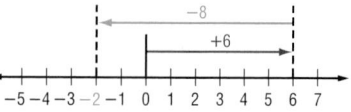
NEW YORK *Performance Indicator* Reinforcement of 7.N.13 Add and **subtract two integers (with and without the use of a number line)**

What You'll Learn
- Subtract integers.
- Evaluate expressions containing variables.

How are addition and subtraction of integers related?

You can use a number line to subtract integers. The model below shows how to find 6 − 8.

Step 1 Start at 0. Move 6 units right to show positive 6.

Step 2 From there, move 8 units left to subtract positive 8.

a. What is 6 − 8? −2

b. What direction do you move to indicate subtracting a positive integer? left

c. What addition sentence is also modeled by the number line above?

SUBTRACT INTEGERS   When you subtract 6 − 8, as shown on the number line above, the result is the same as adding 6 + (−8). When you subtract −3 − 5, the result is the same as adding −3 + (−5).

   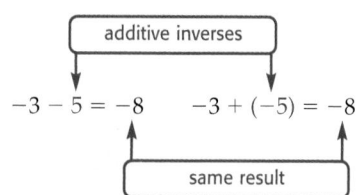

These examples suggest a method for subtracting integers.

Key Concept   Subtracting Integers
- **Words**   To subtract an integer, add its additive inverse.
- **Symbols** $a - b = a + (-b)$
- **Examples** $5 - 9 = 5 + (-9)$ or -4 $-2 - 7 = -2 + (-7)$ or -9

Example 1 *Subtract a Positive Integer*
Find each difference.
a. $8 - 13$
  $8 - 13 = 8 + (-13)$ To subtract 13, add −13.
  $\qquad\;\; = -5$ Simplify.
b. $-4 - 10$
  $-4 - 10 = -4 + (-10)$ To subtract 10, add −10.
  $\qquad\quad = -14$ Simplify.

Resource Manager

 Workbooks and Reproducible Masters

Chapter 2 Resource Masters
- Study Guide and Intervention, p. 67
- Skills Practice, p. 68
- Practice, p. 69
- Reading to Learn Mathematics, p. 70
- Enrichment, p. 71
- Assessment, pp. 101, 103

Parent and Student Study Guide Workbook, p. 11
Prerequisite Skills Workbook, pp. 5–8
School-to-Career Masters, p. 4

Transparencies
5-Minute Check Transparency 2-3
Answer Key Transparencies

Technology
Interactive Chalkboard

In Example 1, you subtracted a positive integer by adding its additive inverse. Use inductive reasoning to see if the method also applies to subtracting a negative integer.

Study Tip

Look Back
To review **inductive reasoning**, see Lesson 1-1.

Subtracting an Integer	↔	Adding Its Additive Inverse
$2 - 2 = 0$		$2 + (-2) = 0$
$2 - 1 = 1$		$2 + (-1) = 1$
$2 - 0 = 2$		$2 + 0 = 2$
$2 - (-1) = ?$		$2 + 1 = 3$

Continuing the pattern in the first column, $2 - (-1) = 3$. The result is the same as when you add the additive inverse. This suggests that the method also works for subtracting a negative integer.

Example 2 **Subtract a Negative Integer**

Find each difference.

a. $7 - (-3)$

$7 - (-3) = 7 + 3$ To subtract -3,
$ = 10$ add 3.

b. $-2 - (-4)$

$-2 - (-4) = -2 + 4$ To subtract -4,
$ = 2$ add 4.

✓ **Concept Check**   How do you find the difference $9 - (-16)$? **Add 9 and 16.**

Example 3 **Subtract Integers to Solve a Problem**

WEATHER The table shows the record high and low temperatures recorded in selected states through 1999. What is the range, or difference between the highest and lowest temperatures, for Virginia?

State	Lowest Temp. °F	Highest Temp. °F
Utah	−69	117
Vermont	−50	105
Virginia	−30	110
Washington	−48	118
West Virginia	−37	112
Wisconsin	−54	114
Wyoming	−66	114

Source: *The World Almanac*

Explore   You know the highest and lowest temperatures. You need to find the range for Virginia's temperatures.

Plan   To find the range, or difference, subtract the lowest temperature from the highest temperature.

Solve $110 - (-30) = 110 + 30$ To subtract -30, add 30.
$ = 140$ Add 110 and 30.
The range for Virginia is 140°.

Examine   Think of a thermometer. The difference between 110° above zero and 30° below zero must be $110 + 30$ or 140°. The answer appears to be reasonable.

---

2 Teach

Building on Prior Knowledge

In Chapter 1, students studied patterns. In this lesson, students will examine patterns in the subtraction of integers.

SUBTRACT INTEGERS

In-Class Examples   Power Point®

1 Find each difference.

a. $9 - 14$ **−5**

b. $-10 - 8$ **−18**

2 Find each difference.

a. $15 - (-4)$ **19**

b. $-10 - (-7)$ **−3**

3 **WEATHER** Refer to the table in the Student Edition. What is the range for Wyoming? **180°**

✓ Skills Check

Subtract Integers Find each difference.

a. $-13 - 9$ **−22**

b. $20 - (-15)$ **35**

c. $-1 - (-10)$ **9**

d. $-16 - (-3)$ **−13**

EVALUATE EXPRESSIONS

In-Class Example   Power Point®

4 a. Evaluate $m - (-2)$ if $m = 4$.   **6**

b. Evaluate $x - y$ if $x = -14$ and $y = -2$.   **−12**

c. Evaluate $p + q - r$ if $p = -11$, $q = 6$, and $r = -12$.   **7**

Teacher to Teacher

Kurt Parchment   Homestead M.S., Homestead, FL

"I use pre-printed response cards (numbers and signs), along with the overhead projector, to guide the whole class through evaluating expressions that involve integers."

Study Notebook

Have students—
- write a paragraph comparing subtraction of integers with addition of integers.
- give samples that illustrate subtraction of integers.
- include any other item(s) that they find helpful in mastering the skills in this lesson.

DAILY

INTERVENTION **FIND THE ERROR**
Help students understand that subtracting −2 is not the same as adding −2, as Reiko's work shows.

About the Exercises . . .

Organization by Objective
- **Subtract Integers:** 14–39, 52–53
- **Evaluate Expressions:** 40–51, 54

Odd/Even Assignments
Exercises 14–53 are structured so that students practice the same concepts whether they are assigned odd or even problems.

Alert! For Exercises 52 and 53, you may wish to have students use a calculator.

Assignment Guide

Basic: 15–33 odd, 39–51 odd, 55–74

Average: 15–51 odd, 52, 53, 55–74

Advanced: 14–50 even, 54–70 (Optional: 71–74)

All: Practice Quiz 1 (1–10)

ALGEBRA CONNECTION

EVALUATE EXPRESSIONS You can use the rule for subtracting integers to evaluate expressions.

Example 4 *Evaluate Algebraic Expressions*

a. Evaluate $x - (-6)$ if $x = 12$.

$$x - (-6) = 12 - (-6)$$ Write the expression. Replace x with 12.
$$= 12 + 6$$ To subtract −6, add its additive inverse, 6.
$$= 18$$ Add 12 and 6.

b. Evaluate $s - t$ if $s = -9$ and $t = -3$.

$$s - t = -9 - (-3)$$ Replace s with −9 and t with −3.
$$= -9 + 3$$ To subtract −3, add 3.
$$= -6$$ Add −9 and 3.

c. Evaluate $a - b + c$ if $a = 15$, $b = 5$, and $c = -8$.

$$a - b + c = 15 - 5 + (-8)$$ Replace a with 15, b with 5, and c with −8.
$$= 10 + (-8)$$ Order of operations
$$= 2$$ Add 10 and −8.

Concept Check: Find the sum of the first integer and the additive inverse of the second integer.

✓ **Concept Check** How do you subtract integers using additive inverses?

Check for Understanding

Concept Check

1. **OPEN ENDED** Write examples of a positive and a negative integer and their additive inverses. **Sample answer: 5, −5; −9, 9**

2. **FIND THE ERROR** José and Reiko are finding $8 - (-2)$.

José	Reiko
$8 - (-2) = 8 + 2$ $= 10$	$8 - (-2) = 8 + (-2)$ $= 6$

Who is correct? Explain your reasoning. **See margin.**

Guided Practice

GUIDED PRACTICE KEY	
Exercises	Examples
3, 4	1
5–8	2
9–11	4
12, 13	3

Find each difference.

3. $8 - 11$ **−3**
4. $-9 - 3$ **−12**
5. $5 - (-4)$ **9**
6. $7 - (-10)$ **17**
7. $-6 - (-4)$ **−2**
8. $-2 - (-8)$ **6**

ALGEBRA Evaluate each expression if $x = 10$, $y = -4$, and $z = -15$.

9. $x - (-10)$ **20**
10. $y - x$ **−14**
11. $x + y - z$ **21**

Application

WEATHER For Exercises 12 and 13, use the table in Example 3 on page 71.

12. Find the range in temperature for Vermont. **155°**

13. Name a state that has a greater range than Vermont's. **Utah, Washington, Wisconsin, or Wyoming**

Answer

2. José; Reiko added −2 instead of its additive inverse.

Practice and Apply

Homework Help

For Exercises	See Examples
14–21, 30–33	1
22–29, 34–37	2
38, 39	3
40–51	4

Extra Practice
See page 727.

Find each difference.

14. $3 - 8$ **−5**
15. $4 - 5$ **−1**
16. $2 - 9$ **−7**
17. $9 - 12$ **−3**
18. $-3 - 1$ **−4**
19. $-5 - 4$ **−9**
20. $-6 - 7$ **−13**
21. $-4 - 8$ **−12**
22. $6 - (-8)$ **14**
23. $4 - (-6)$ **10**
24. $7 - (-4)$ **11**
25. $9 - (-3)$ **12**
26. $-9 - (-7)$ **−2**
27. $-7 - (-10)$ **3**
28. $-11 - (-12)$ **1**
29. $-16 - (-7)$ **−9**
30. $10 - 24$ **−14**
31. $45 - 59$ **−14**
32. $-27 - 14$ **−41**
33. $-16 - 12$ **−28**
34. $48 - (-50)$ **98**
★ 35. $125 - (-114)$ **239**
★ 36. $-320 - (-106)$ **−214**
★ 37. $-2200 - (-3500)$ **1300**

38. **WEATHER** During January, the normal high temperature in Duluth, Minnesota, is 16°F, and the normal low temperature is −2°F. Find the difference between the temperatures. **18°F**

39. **GEOGRAPHY** The highest point in California is Mount Whitney, with an elevation of 14,494 feet. The lowest point is Death Valley, elevation −282 feet. Find the difference in the elevations. **14,776 ft**

ALGEBRA Evaluate each expression if $x = -3$, $y = 8$, and $z = -12$.

40. $y - 10$ **−2**
41. $12 - z$ **24**
42. $3 - x$ **6**
43. $z - 24$ **−36**
44. $x - y$ **−11**
45. $z - x$ **−9**
46. $y - z$ **20**
47. $z - y$ **−20**
48. $x + y - z$ **17**
49. $z - y + x$ **−23**
50. $x - y - z$ **1**
51. $z - y - x$ **−17**

52. **+59; −4242; −1769; −1899; −3039; +68**

PETS For Exercises 52 and 53, use the following table.

52. Describe the change in the number of dogs of each breed registered from Year 1 to Year 2.

53. What was the total change in the number of dogs of these breeds registered from Year 1 to Year 2? **−10,822**

Registration in American Kennel Club		
Breed	Year 1	Year 2
Airedale Terrier	2891	2950
Beagle	53,322	49,080
Chinese Shar-Pei	8614	6845
Chow Chow	6241	4342
Labrador Retriever	157,936	154,897
Pug	21,487	21,555

Source: www.akc.org

54. **BUSINESS** The formula $P = I - E$ is used to find the profit (P) when income (I) and expenses (E) are known. One month a small business has income of $19,592 and expenses of $20,345.

a. What is the profit for the month? **−$753**

b. What does a negative profit mean? **expenses > income**

55. **CRITICAL THINKING** Determine whether each statement is *true* or *false*. If false, give a counterexample.

a. Subtraction of integers is commutative. **False; $3 - 4 \neq 4 - 3$**

b. Subtraction of integers is associative. **False; $(5 - 2) - 1 \neq 5 - (2 - 1)$**

www.pre-alg.com/self_check_quiz/ny

Career Choices

Veterinarian

Veterinarians work with animals to diagnose, treat, and prevent disease, disorders, and injuries.

Online Research
For information about a career as a veterinarian, visit: www.pre-alg.com/careers

---

Study Guide and Intervention, p. 67

Subtracting Integers	To subtract an integer, add its additive inverse.

Example 1 Find each difference.

a. $9 - 17$
$9 - 17 = 9 + (-17)$ To subtract 17, add −17.
$= -8$ Simplify.

b. $-7 - 3$
$-7 - 3 = -7 + (-3)$ To subtract 3, add −3.
$= -10$ Simplify.

Example 2 Find each difference.

a. $4 - (-5)$
$4 - (-5) = 4 + 5$ To subtract −5, add +5.
$= 9$ Simplify.

b. $-6 - (-2)$
$-6 - (-2) = -6 + 2$ To subtract −2, add +2.
$= -4$ Simplify.

Exercises

Find each difference.

1. $9 - 16$ **−7**
2. $7 - 19$ **−12**
3. $12 - 21$ **−9**
4. $-5 - 3$ **−8**
5. $-8 - 9$ **−17**
6. $-13 - 17$ **−30**
7. $7 - (-4)$ **11**
8. $9 - (-9)$ **18**
9. $-11 - (-2)$ **−9**
10. $-6 - (-9)$ **3**
11. $-6 - 4$ **−10**
12. $-16 - (-20)$ **4**
13. $-14 - 4$ **−18**
14. $8 - (-6)$ **14**
15. $-10 - (-6)$ **−4**
16. $13 - (-17)$ **30**
17. $24 - (-16)$ **40**
18. $17 - (-9)$ **26**
19. $-24 - 8$ **−32**
20. $18 - (-9)$ **27**
21. $26 - 49$ **−23**
22. $-45 - (-26)$ **−19**
23. $-15 - (-25)$ **10**
24. $29 - (-6)$ **35**

Skills Practice, p. 68 and Practice, p. 69 (shown)

Find each difference.

1. $-26 - (-30)$ **4**
2. $25 - 32$ **−7**
3. $-18 - 54$ **−72**
4. $59 - (-19)$ **78**
5. $-41 - (-19)$ **−22**
6. $-20 - 13$ **−33**
7. $31 - (-56)$ **87**
8. $15 - (-40)$ **55**
9. $-32 - 28$ **−60**
10. $10 - (-23)$ **33**
11. $-14 - 64$ **−78**
12. $-12 - (-36)$ **24**
13. $-81 - 4$ **−85**
14. $9 - 30$ **−21**
15. $-44 - (-21)$ **−23**
16. $140 - (-9)$ **149**

Evaluate each expression if $a = -11$, $b = 8$, and $c = -6$.

17. $a - 17$ **−28**
18. $10 - b$ **2**
19. $-30 - c$ **−24**
20. $b - a$ **19**
21. $a - b$ **−19**
22. $c - b$ **−14**
23. $b - c + a$ **3**
24. $b - c - a$ **25**
25. $c - a - b$ **−3**
26. $b + a - c$ **3**
27. $b + c - a$ **13**
28. $c - a + b$ **13**
29. $a - b + c$ **−25**
30. $b - a + c$ **13**
31. $a - b - c$ **−13**
32. $c + b - a$ **13**
33. $c - b + a$ **−25**
34. $a + b - c$ **3**
35. $18 + a + c$ **−1**
36. $a - b + a$ **−5**

37. **ELEVATORS** Linda entered an elevator on floor 9. She rode down 8 floors. Then she rode up 11 floors and got off. What floor was she on when she left the elevator? **12**

38. **INVESTMENTS** The NASDAQ lost 36 points on a Monday, but rebounded the next day, gaining 24 points. What was the total change in points? **−12 points**

39. **OFFICE BUILDINGS** Randi takes the stairs at work whenever possible instead of the elevator. She must climb up 51 steps from her office to get to the accounting department. The human resources department is 34 steps below her office. How many steps are there between human resources and accounting? **85 steps**

Enrichment, p. 71

Subtracting in a Finite Number System

To subtract in a finite number system, add a number's additive inverse. The additive inverse of a number in a finite number system is that number which, when added to the first number, results in a sum that is the mod of the number.

Example 1 What is the additive inverse of 4 in mod 7?

$-(4) = 3$ What is added to 4 to equal 7? The answer is 3.
The additive inverse of 4 in mod 7 is 3.

The additive inverses for 1, 2, 3, 5, and 6 are 6, 5, 4, 2, and 1, respectively. In mod 7, subtraction is the same as adding the additive inverse.

Example 2
$3 - 4 = 3 + (-4) = 3 + 3 = 6$ Subtract 4 by adding its additive inverse, 3.
$1 - 6 = 1 + (-6) = 1 + 1 = 2$ Subtract 6 by adding its additive inverse, 1.

Solve each equation in mod 7.

1. $x = 1 - 3$
$x = 1 + 4 = 5$
2. $5 - 6 = y$
$y = 5 + 1 = 6$
3. $2 - 5 = z$
$z = 2 + 2 = 4$
4. $q = 6 - 4$
$q = 6 + 3 = 2$
5. $b = 2 - 6$
$b = 2 + 1 = 3$
6. $3 - 4 = z$
$z = 3 + 3 = 6$
7. $y = 0 - 4$
$y = 0 + 3 = 3$
8. $3 - 6 = x$
$x = 3 + 1 = 4$
9. $4 - 5 = p$
$p = 4 + 2 = 6$

Solve each equation in mod 12.

10. $y = 2 - 9$
$y = 2 + 3 = 5$
11. $x = 1 - 8$
$x = 1 + 4 = 5$
12. $3 - 5 = r$
$r = 3 + 7 = 10$
13. $z = 0 - 4$
$z = 0 + 8 = 8$
14. $q = 4 - 10$
$q = 4 + 2 = 6$
15. $6 - 11 = p$
$p = 6 + 1 = 7$
16. $5 - 3 = k$
$k = 5 + 9 = 2$
17. $7 - 11 = z$
$z = 7 + 1 = 8$
18. $2 - 3 = b$
$b = 2 + 9 = 11$
19. $8 - 10 = r$
$r = 8 + 2 = 10$
20. $9 - 7 = f$
$f = 9 + 5 = 2$
21. $4 - 7 = w$
$w = 4 + 5 = 9$
22. $m = 1 - 11$
$m = 1 + 1 = 2$
23. $z = 3 - 8$
$z = 3 + 4 = 7$
24. $g = 5 - 9$
$g = 5 + 3 = 8$

DAILY INTERVENTION

Differentiated Instruction

• **Interpersonal** Have students make 4 cards with a different positive integer on each one and 4 other cards with a different negative integer on each. Then have them ask another student to draw 2 cards randomly and subtract the second card from the first card drawn. Students can work in pairs, small groups, or circulate around the room.

4 Assess

Open-Ended Assessment

Modeling Have students use a number line to show how to find the differences $8 - (-3)$ and $-8 - (-3)$.

Getting Ready for Lesson 2-4

PREREQUISITE SKILL Lesson 2-4 presents multiplying integers. Exercises 71–74 should be used to determine your students' familiarity with finding the products of positive integers.

Assessment Options

Practice Quiz 1 The quiz provides students with a brief review of the concepts and skills in Lessons 2-1 through 2-3. Lesson numbers are given to the right of exercises or instruction lines so students can review concepts not yet mastered.

Quiz (Lesson 2-3) is available on p. 101 of the *Chapter 2 Resource Masters.*

Mid-Chapter Test (Lessons 2-1 through 2-3) is available on p. 103 of the *Chapter 2 Resource Masters.*

Answer

56. Addition and subtraction of integers are related because a subtraction problem can be rewritten as an addition problem. Answers should include the following.

• $4 - 10$ is rewritten as the addition expression $4 + (-10)$.

---

56. **WRITING IN MATH** Answer the question that was posed at the beginning of the lesson. **See margin.**

How are addition and subtraction of integers related?

Include the following in your answer:
• a model that shows how to find the difference $4 - 10$, and
• the expression $4 - 10$ rewritten as an addition expression.

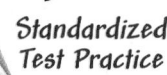

NEW YORK Test Practice

Standardized Test Practice
(A)(B)(C)(D)

57. The terms in a pattern are given in the table. What is the value of the 5th term? **A**

Term	1	2	3	4	5
Value	13	8	3	−2	?

(A) −7   (B) −5
(C) 7   (D) 5

58. When 5 is subtracted from a number, the result is −4. What is the number? **B**

(A) 9   (B) 1   (C) −1   (D) −9

Maintain Your Skills

Mixed Review

59. **OCEANOGRAPHY** A submarine at 1300 meters below sea level descends an additional 1150 meters. What integer represents the submarine's position with respect to sea level? *(Lesson 2-2)* **−2450**

60. **ALGEBRA** Evaluate $|b| - |a|$ if $a = 2$ and $b = -4$. *(Lesson 2-1)* **2**

ALGEBRA Solve each equation mentally. *(Lesson 1-5)*

61. $x + 9 = 12$ **3**   62. $18 = w - 2$ **20**   63. $5a = 35$ **7**   64. $\frac{64}{b} = 8$ **8**

ALGEBRA Translate each phrase into an algebraic expression. *(Lesson 1-3)*

65. a number divided by 5 $\frac{x}{5}$ 66. the sum of t and 9 $t + 9$

67. the quotient of eighty-six and b $\frac{86}{b}$ 68. s decreased by 8 $s - 8$

Find the value of each expression. *(Lesson 1-2)*

69. $2 \times (5 + 8) - 6$ **20**   70. $96 \div (6 \times 8) \div 2$ **1**

Getting Ready for the Next Lesson

BASIC SKILL Find each product.

71. $5 \cdot 15$ **75**   72. $8 \cdot 12$ **96**   73. $3 \cdot 5 \cdot 8$ **120**   74. $2 \cdot 7 \cdot 5 \cdot 9$ **630**

Practice Quiz 1   Lessons 2-1 through 2-3

1. **WEATHER** The three states with the lowest recorded temperatures are Alaska at −80°F, Utah at −69°F, and Montana at −70°F. Order the temperatures from least to greatest. *(Lesson 2-1)* **−80, −70, −69**

Find each sum. *(Lesson 2-2)*

2. $-5 + (-15)$ **−20**   3. $-5 + 11$ **6**   4. $-6 + 9 + (-8)$ **−5**

Find each difference. *(Lesson 2-3)*

5. $16 - 23$ **−7**   6. $-15 - 8$ **−23**   7. $25 - (-7)$ **32**

ALGEBRA Evaluate each expression if $x = 5$, $y = -2$, and $z = -3$. *(Lesson 2-3)*

8. $x - y$ **7**   9. $z - 6$ **−9**   10. $x - y - z$ **10**

2-4 Multiplying Integers

NEW YORK *Performance Indicator* Reinforcement of **7.N.12** Add, subtract, **multiply,** and divide **integers**

What You'll Learn

- Multiply integers.
- Simplify algebraic expressions.

How are the signs of factors and products related?

The temperature drops 7°C for each 1 kilometer increase in altitude. A drop of 7°C is represented by -7. So, the temperature change equals the altitude times -7. The table shows the change in temperature for several altitudes.

Altitude (km)	Altitude × Rate of Change	Temperature Change (°C)
1	1(−7)	−7
2	2(−7)	−14
3	3(−7)	−21
...	...	...
11	11(−7)	−77

a. Suppose the altitude is 4 kilometers. Write an expression to find the temperature change. **4(−7)**

b. Use the pattern in the table to find 4(−7). **−28**

Reading Math

Parentheses
Recall that a product can be written using parentheses. Read 3(−7) as *3 times negative 7.*

MULTIPLY INTEGERS   Multiplication is repeated addition. So, 3(−7) means that −7 is used as an addend 3 times.

$$3(-7) = (-7) + (-7) + (-7)$$
$$= -21$$

By the Commutative Property of Multiplication, $3(-7) = -7(3)$.

This example suggests the following rule.

Key Concept   Multiplying Two Integers with Different Signs

- **Words**   The product of two integers with different signs is negative.
- **Examples** $4(-3) = -12$ $-3(4) = -12$

Example 1   Multiply Integers with Different Signs

Find each product.

a. **5(−6)**

   $5(-6) = -30$ The factors have different signs. The product is negative.

b. **−4(16)**

   $-4(16) = -64$ The factors have different signs. The product is negative.

2-4 Lesson Notes

1 Focus

**5-Minute Check
Transparency 2-4** Use as a quiz or review of Lesson 2-3.

Mathematical Background notes are available for this lesson on page 54D.

How are the signs of factors and products related?

The opening activity questions are repeated on page 75 of the *Chapter 2 Resource Masters.*

Reading to Learn Mathematics, p. 75   **ELL**

Pre-Activity   *How are the signs of factors and products related?*

Do the activity at the top of page 75 in your textbook. Write your answers below.

a. Suppose the altitude is 4 kilometers. Write an expression to find the temperature change.   4(−7)

b. Use the pattern in the table on page 75 to find 4(−7).   −28

Reading the Lesson

1. The product of two integers with ___different___ sign(s) is negative.

2. The product of two integers with ___the same___ sign(s) is positive.

3. Draw a number line model that shows how to find the product 4(−2). Explain your model.

   Start at zero. Move 2 units to the left to show −2. Do this three more times to show that −2, moved 4 times, equals −8.

4. Show how to use a pattern to find (−5)(−1).
   (−5)(1) = −5 } + 5
   (−5)(0) = 0 } + 5
   (−5)(−1) = 5

5. You can use the ___Associative Property of Multiplication___ when you multiply more than two integers.

Helping You Remember

6. In your own words, describe how to tell the sign of the product of two integers. Sample answer is given. If the two integers have different signs, the product is negative. If the two integers have the same sign, the product is positive.

Resource Manager

Workbooks and Reproducible Masters

Chapter 2 Resource Masters
- Study Guide and Intervention, p. 72
- Skills Practice, p. 73
- Practice, p. 74
- Reading to Learn Mathematics, p. 75
- Enrichment, p. 76

Parent and Student Study Guide Workbook, p. 12
Prerequisite Skills Workbook, pp. 9–10

Transparencies
5-Minute Check Transparency 2-4
Answer Key Transparencies

Technology
Interactive Chalkboard

Teaching Tip Use a transparency of a Celsius thermometer with the gradients clearly visible. Prepare cut-outs to represent 7° on the drawing. Place one cut-out on the thermometer. Show how the addition of each subsequent cut-out below the previous one pushes the temperature down by 7°.

MULTIPLY INTEGERS

In-Class Examples Power Point®

1 Find each product.

a. $8(-12)$ **−96**

b. $-9(11)$ **−99**

2 Find $-4(-16)$. **64**

3 Find $-7(11)(-2)$. **154**

Teaching Tip Write several problems multiplying more than two integers on the chalkboard. Vary the number of total factors, as well as the number of negatives and positives. Then group the factors in each problem by pairs and keep multiplying pairs, so students see what is happening with the signs. Lead students to discover the rule that if the number of negative integers is odd, the product is negative, and if the number of negative integers is even, then the product is positive.

4 **Multiple-Choice Test Item**
A student missed only 4 problems on a test, each worth 20 points. What is the total number of points missed? **D**

A -5 **B** -20 **C** 24 **D** –80

✓ Skills Check

Multiply Integers Find each product.

a. $21(-6)$ **−126**

b. $-8(-4)$ **32**

c. $-10(7)$ **−70**

d. $-3(-4)(5)$ **60**

e. $-9(-5)(-2)$ **−90**

The product of two positive integers is positive. What is the sign of the product of two negative integers? Use a pattern to find $(-4)(-2)$.

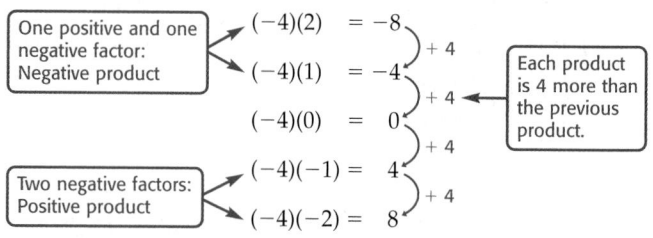

One positive and one negative factor: Negative product

$(-4)(2) = -8$
$(-4)(1) = -4$ } $+4$
$(-4)(0) = 0$ } $+4$
$(-4)(-1) = 4$ } $+4$
$(-4)(-2) = 8$ } $+4$

Each product is 4 more than the previous product.

Two negative factors: Positive product

This example suggests the following rule.

Key Concept Multiplying Two Integers with the Same Sign

- **Words** The product of two integers with the same sign is positive.
- **Examples** $4(3) = 12$ $-4(-3) = 12$

Example 2 Multiply Integers with the Same Sign

Find $-6(-12)$.

$-6(-12) = 72$ The two factors have the same sign. The product is positive.

Study Tip

Look Back
To review the **Associative Property**, see Lesson 1-4.

Example 3 Multiply More Than Two Integers

Find $-4(-5)(-8)$.

$-4(-5)(-8) = [(-4)(-5)](-8)$ Associative Property

$= 20(-8)$ $(-4)(-5) = 20$

$= -160$ $20(-8) = -160$

NEW YORK Test Practice

Standardized Test Practice Ⓐ Ⓑ Ⓒ Ⓓ

Example 4 Use Integers to Solve a Problem

Multiple-Choice Test Item

A glacier was receding at a rate of 300 feet per day. What is the glacier's movement in 5 days?

Ⓐ 305 feet   Ⓑ −1500 feet   Ⓒ −300 feet   Ⓓ −60 feet

Read the Test Item

The word *receding* means moving backward, so the rate per day is represented by −300. Multiply 5 times −300 to find the movement in 5 days.

Solve the Test Item

$5(-300) = -1500$ The product is negative.

The answer is B.

Test-Taking Tip
Read the problem. Try to picture the situation. Look for words that suggest mathematical concepts.

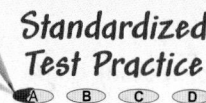

Standardized Test Practice Ⓐ Ⓑ Ⓒ Ⓓ

Example 4 By understanding that receding means a negative movement, students can immediately eliminate choice A from the answers given. Since the glacier recedes over 300 feet, answers C and D can also be eliminated, leaving choice B.

ALGEBRAIC EXPRESSIONS You can use the rules for multiplying integers to simplify and evaluate algebraic expressions.

Example 5 *Simplify and Evaluate Algebraic Expressions*

a. Simplify $-4(9x)$.

$$-4(9x) = (-4 \cdot 9)x \quad \text{Associative Property of Multiplication}$$
$$= -36x \quad \text{Simplify.}$$

b. Simplify $-2x(3y)$.

$$-2x(3y) = (-2)(x)(3)(y) \quad -2x = (-2)(x), 3y = (3)(y)$$
$$= (-2 \cdot 3)(x \cdot y) \quad \text{Commutative Property of Multiplication}$$
$$= -6xy \quad -2 \cdot 3 = -6, x \cdot y = xy$$

c. Evaluate $4ab$ if $a = 3$ and $b = -5$.

$$4ab = 4(3)(-5) \quad \text{Replace } a \text{ with 3 and } b \text{ with } -5.$$
$$= [4(3)](-5) \quad \text{Associative Property of Multiplication}$$
$$= 12(-5) \quad \text{The product of 4 and 3 is positive.}$$
$$= -60 \quad \text{The product of 12 and } -5 \text{ is negative.}$$

Check for Understanding

Concept Check

1. Write the product that is modeled on the number line below. $3(-5) = -15$

2. State whether each product is positive or negative.
  a. $-5 \cdot 8$ **neg.**
  b. $6(-4)$ **neg.**
  c. $8 \cdot 24$ **pos.**
  d. $-9(-7)$ **pos.**
  e. $-2(9)(-3)$ **pos.**
  f. $-7(-5)(-11)$ **neg.**

3. OPEN ENDED Give an example of three integers whose product is negative. **Sample answer: $(-4)(9)(2)$**

Guided Practice

Find each product.

GUIDED PRACTICE KEY	
Exercises	Examples
4, 5	1
6, 7	2
8, 9	3
10–14	5
15	4

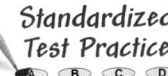

NEW YORK *Test Practice*

Standardized Test Practice

Ⓐ Ⓑ Ⓒ Ⓓ

4. $-3 \cdot 8$ **-24**
5. $5(-8)$ **-40**
6. $4 \cdot 30$ **120**
7. $-7(-4)$ **28**
8. $-4(2)(-6)$ **48**
9. $-5(-9)(-12)$ **-540**

ALGEBRA Simplify each expression.
10. $-4 \cdot 3x$ **$-12x$**
11. $7(-3y)$ **$-21y$**
12. $-8a(-3b)$ **$24ab$**

ALGEBRA Evaluate each expression.
13. $-6h$, if $h = -20$ **120**
14. $-4st$, if $s = -9$ and $t = 3$ **108**

15. The research submarine *Alvin*, used to locate the wreck of the *Titanic*, descends at a rate of about 100 feet per minute. Which integer describes the distance *Alvin* travels in 5 minutes? **A**
  Ⓐ -500 ft
  Ⓑ -100 ft
  Ⓒ -20 ft
  Ⓓ 100 ft

www.pre-alg.com/extra_examples/ny

Lesson 2-4 Multiplying Integers **77**

In-Class Example   Power Point®

5 a. Simplify $-7(6k)$. **$-42k$**

  b. Simplify $8a(-5b)$. **$-40ab$**

  c. Evaluate $-3xy$ if $x = -4$ and $y = 9$. **108**

3 Practice/Apply

Study Notebook

Have students—
• write a paragraph about how to multiply integers. They should use examples to illustrate their explanations.
• include any other item(s) that they find helpful in mastering the skills in this lesson.

About the Exercises...

Organization by Objective
• **Multiply Integers:** 16–35, 54–55
• **Algebraic Expressions:** 36–53

Odd/Even Assignments
Exercises 16–55 are structured so that students practice the same concepts whether they are assigned odd or even problems.

Assignment Guide

Basic: 17–53 odd, 54–85
Average: 17–53 odd, 54–85
Advanced: 16–52 even, 54–79
(Optional: 80–85)

Tips for New Teachers

Mental Math Have the class look over Exercises 16–33. Without having them do any calculations, have students tell whether a product will be positive or negative just by examining the signs of the factors.

Practice and Apply

Homework Help

For Exercises	See Examples
16–21	1
22–25	2
26–33	3
34, 35, 54, 55	4
36–53	5

Extra Practice See page 727.

Find each product.
16. $-3 \cdot 4$ -12
17. $-7 \cdot 6$ -42
18. $4(-8)$ -32
19. $9 \cdot (-8)$ -72
20. $-12 \cdot 3$ -36
21. $14(-5)$ -70
22. $6 \cdot 19$ 114
23. $4(32)$ 128
24. $-8(-11)$ 88
25. $-15(-3)$ 45
26. $-5(-4)(6)$ 120
27. $5(-13)(-2)$ 130
28. $-7(-8)(-3)$ -168
29. $-11(-4)(-7)$ -308
30. $-12(-9)(6)$ 648
31. $-6(-8)(11)$ 528
32. $2(-8)(-9)(10)$ 1440
33. $4(-7)(-4)(-12)$ -1344

34. **FLOODS** In 1993, the Mississippi River was so high that it caused the Illinois River to flow backward. If the Illinois River flowed at the rate of -1500 feet per hour, how far would the water travel in 24 hours? $-36,000$ ft or about -6.8 mi

35. **TEMPERATURE** During a 10-hour period, the temperature in Browning, Montana, changed at a rate of $-10°F$ per hour, starting at $44°F$. What was the ending temperature? $-56°F$

ALGEBRA Simplify each expression.
36. $-5 \cdot 7x$ $-35x$
37. $-8 \cdot 12y$ $-96y$
38. $6(-8a)$ $-48a$
39. $5(-11b)$ $-55b$
40. $-7s(-8t)$ $56st$
41. $-12m(-9n)$ $108mn$
42. $2ab(3)(-7)$ $-42ab$
43. $3x(5y)(-9)$ $-135xy$
44. $-4(-p)(-q)$ $-4pq$
45. $-8(-11b)(-c)$ $-88bc$
46. $9(-2c)(3d)$ $-54cd$
47. $-6j(3)(5k)$ $-90jk$

ALGEBRA Evaluate each expression.
48. $-7n$, if $n = -4$ 28
49. $9s$, if $s = -11$ -99
50. ab, if $a = 9$ and $b = 8$ 72
51. $-2xy$, if $x = -8$ and $y = 5$ 80
52. $-16cd$, if $c = 4$ and $d = -5$ 320
53. $18gh$, if $g = -3$ and $h = 4$ -216

More About...

Tides

It takes about 6 hours for the ocean to move from low to high tide. High tide can change the width of the beach at a rate of -17 feet an hour.

TIDES For Exercises 54 and 55, use the information below and at the left.
In Wrightsville, North Carolina, during low tide, the beachfront in some places is about 350 feet from the ocean to the homes. At high tide, the water is much closer to the homes. 54. -102 ft

54. What is the change in the width of the beachfront from low to high tide?

55. What is the distance from the ocean to the homes at high tide? 248 ft

56. **CRITICAL THINKING** Write a rule that will help you determine the sign of the product if you are multiplying two or more integers. See margin.

57. **CRITICAL THINKING** Determine whether each statement is *true* or *false*. If false, give a counterexample. If true, give an example.
a. Multiplication of integers is commutative. True; $3(-5) = -5(3)$
b. Multiplication of integers is associative. True; $-2(3 \cdot 5) = (-2 \cdot 3)(5)$

Answer

56. If there is an even number of negative numbers being multiplied, the product will be positive. If there is an odd number of negative numbers being multiplied, the product will be negative.

58. WRITING IN MATH   Answer the question that was posed at the beginning of the lesson. **See margin.**

How are the signs of factors and products related?

Include the following in your answer:
- a model of $2(-4)$,
- an explanation of why the product of a positive and a negative integer must be negative, and
- a pattern that explains why the product $-3(-3)$ is positive.

Standardized Test Practice
(A) (B) (C) (D)

59. The product of two negative integers is— **B**
- (A) always negative.
- (B) always positive.
- (C) sometimes negative.
- (D) never positive.

60. Which values complete the table at the right for $y = -3x$? **D**

x	−2	−1	0	1
y				

- (A) $-6, -3, 0, 3$
- (B) $-6, -2, 0, 2$
- (C) $6, 2, 0, -2$
- (D) $6, 3, 0, -3$

Maintain Your Skills

Mixed Review   ALGEBRA   Evaluate each expression if $a = -2$, $b = -6$, and $c = 14$.
(Lesson 2-3)

61. $a - c$ **−16**   **62.** $b - a$ **−4**   **63.** $a - b$ **4**

64. $a + b + c$ **6**   **65.** $b - a + c$ **10**   **66.** $a - b - c$ **−10**

67. WEATHER RECORDS   The highest recorded temperature in Columbus, Ohio, is 104°F. The lowest recorded temperature is $-22°$F. What is the difference between the highest and lowest temperatures?   *(Lesson 2-3)* **126°F**

The cost of a trip to a popular amusement park can be determined with integers. Visit www.pre-alg.com/webquest to continue work on your WebQuest project.

Find each sum.   *(Lesson 2-2)*

68. $-10 + 8 + 4$ **2**   **69.** $-4 + (-3) + (-7)$ **−14**   **70.** $9 + (-14) + 2$ **−3**

Refer to the coordinate system. Write the ordered pair that names each point.
(Lesson 1-6)

71. E **(6, 2)**   **72.** C **(3, 4)**

73. B **(1, 5)**   **74.** F **(8, 0)**

75. D **(5, 5)**   **76.** A **(0, 3)**

Find each sum or product mentally.   *(Lesson 1-4)*

77. $3 \cdot 8 \cdot 20$ **480**   **78.** $8 + 98 + 102$ **208**   **79.** $5 \cdot 11 \cdot 10$ **550**

Getting Ready for the Next Lesson   BASIC SKILL   Find each quotient.

80. $40 \div 8$ **5**   **81.** $90 \div 15$ **6**   **82.** $45 \div 3$ **15**

83. $105 \div 7$ **15**   **84.** $240 \div 6$ **40**   **85.** $96 \div 24$ **4**

www.pre-alg.com/self_check_quiz/ny

Lesson 2-4 Multiplying Integers **79**

---

4 Assess

Open-Ended Assessment
Speaking Have students explain the difference in rules between addition of integers and multiplication of integers.

Getting Ready for Lesson 2-5
PREREQUISITE SKILL Lesson 2-5 presents the division of integers, for which the students need to know how to divide whole numbers. Exercises 80–85 should be used to determine your students' familiarity with finding quotients.

Answer

58. When you multiply two integers with the same sign, the product is positive; when you multiply two integers with different signs, the product is negative. Answers should include the following.

- [number line model showing -4 and -4 from -8 to 0]

- If the positive integer represents the number of groups made up of the negative integer, the total will be negative.

- $-3 \cdot 2 = -6$
  $-3 \cdot 1 = -3$
  $-3 \cdot 0 = 0$
  $-3 \cdot (-1) = 3$
  $-3 \cdot (-2) = 6$
  $-3 \cdot (-3) = 9$

D A I L Y

INTERVENTION   **Differentiated Instruction**

- **Logical** On a blank transparency, draw a multiplication table similar to the addition table shown on p. 63. Have students find the products for two positive factors. Then have them find a pattern for the values in the table and extend the pattern to complete the table.

Lesson 2-4 Multiplying Integers **79**

NEW YORK *Performance Indicator* **Reinforcement of 7.N.12** Add, subtract, multiply, and **divide integers**

1 Focus

5-Minute Check Transparency 2-5 Use as a quiz or review of Lesson 2-4.

Mathematical Background notes are available for this lesson on page 54D.

How is dividing integers related to multiplying integers?

The opening activity questions are repeated on page 80 of the *Chapter 2 Resources Masters*.

Vocabulary
- average (mean)

c. −4 · 3 = −12

d.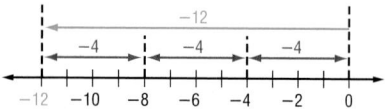

Reading Math

Parts of a Division Sentence
In a division sentence, like 15 ÷ 5 = 3, the number you are dividing, 15, is called the *dividend*. The number you are dividing by, 5, is called the *divisor*. The result, 3, is called the *quotient*.

What You'll Learn
- Divide integers.
- Find the average of a set of data.

How is dividing integers related to multiplying integers?

You can find the quotient −12 ÷ (−4) using a number line. To find how many groups of −4 there are in −12, show −12 on a number line. Then divide it into groups of −4.

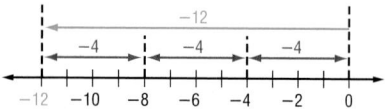

a. How many groups are there? **3**

b. What is the quotient of −12 ÷ (−4)? **3**

c. What multiplication sentence is also shown on the number line?

d. Draw a number line and find the quotient −10 ÷ (−2). **5**

DIVIDE INTEGERS   You can find the quotient of two integers by using the related multiplication sentence.

Think of this factor   to find this quotient.

$$-4 \times 3 = -12 \quad \rightarrow \quad -12 \div (-4) = 3$$
$$-2 \times 5 = -10 \quad \rightarrow \quad -10 \div (-2) = 5$$

In the division sentences −12 ÷ (−4) = 3 and −10 ÷ (−2) = 5, notice that the dividends and divisors are both negative. In both cases, the quotient is positive.

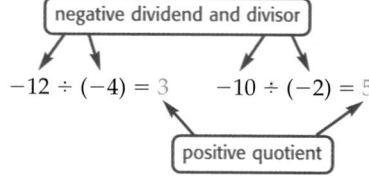

negative dividend and divisor

$$-12 \div (-4) = 3 \qquad -10 \div (-2) = 5$$

positive quotient

You already know that the quotient of two positive integers is positive.

$$12 \div 4 = 3 \qquad 10 \div 2 = 5$$

These and similar examples suggest the following rule for dividing integers with the same sign.

Key Concept   *Dividing Integers with the Same Sign*

- **Words**   The quotient of two integers with the same sign is positive.
- **Examples**   −12 ÷ (−3) = 4   12 ÷ 3 = 4

Resource Manager

 Workbooks and Reproducible Masters

Chapter 2 Resource Masters
- Study Guide and Intervention, p. 77
- Skills Practice, p. 78
- Practice, p. 79
- Reading to Learn Mathematics, p. 80
- Enrichment, p. 81
- Assessment, p. 102

Graphing Calculator and Spreadsheet Masters, p. 21
Parent and Student Study Guide Workbook, p. 13
Prerequisite Skills Workbook, pp. 11–12

Transparencies
5-Minute Check Transparency 2-5
Answer Key Transparencies

Technology
Interactive Chalkboard
Pre-AlgePASS: Tutorial Plus, Lesson 3

Example 1 — Divide Integers with the Same Sign

Find each quotient.

a. $-32 \div (-8)$ — The dividend and the divisor have the same sign.

$-32 \div (-8) = 4$ — The quotient is positive.

b. $\dfrac{75}{5}$

$\dfrac{75}{5} = 75 \div 5$ — The dividend and divisor have the same sign.

$= 15$ — The quotient is positive.

What is the sign of the quotient of a positive and a negative integer? Look for a pattern in the following related sentences.

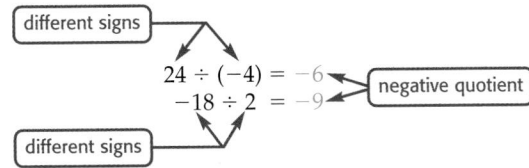

Think of this factor   to find this quotient.

$-4 \times (-6) = 24 \quad \rightarrow \quad 24 \div (-4) = -6$
$2 \times (-9) = -18 \quad \rightarrow \quad -18 \div 2 = -9$

Notice that the signs of the dividend and divisor are different. In both cases, the quotient is negative.

different signs

$24 \div (-4) = -6$
$-18 \div 2 = -9$ → negative quotient

different signs

These and other similar examples suggest the following rule.

Key Concept — Dividing Integers with Different Signs

- **Words** — The quotient of two integers with different signs is negative.
- **Examples** — $-12 \div 4 = -3$ $\qquad$ $12 \div (-4) = -3$

✓ **Concept Check** How do you know the sign of the quotient of two integers?

Example 2 — Divide Integers with Different Signs

Find each quotient.

a. $-42 \div 3$

$-42 \div 3 = -14$ — The signs are different. The quotient is negative.

b. $\dfrac{48}{-6}$

$\dfrac{48}{-6} = 48 \div (-6)$ — The signs are different. The quotient is negative.

$= -8$ — Simplify.

 www.pre-alg.com/extra_examples/ny

Lesson 2-5 Dividing Integers **81**

DAILY INTERVENTION

Differentiated Instruction

- **Kinesthetic** Have students model "average." Write $-7 + 2 + 10 + (-6) + (-9) + (-8)$ on the board. One student holds a sign with "(+)" on one side and "(−)" on the other. Then 7 students come up and the sign bearer shows the negative sign. Two students then leave. In order to add 10, after the remaining 5 students sit down, 5 more must come up, and the sign changes to positive. After all the terms are added, the students divide into 6 equal groups to find the average. **−3**

---

2 Teach

DIVIDE INTEGERS

In-Class Examples Power Point®

1 Find each quotient.

a. $-28 \div (-4)$ **7**

b. $\dfrac{96}{8}$ **12**

2 Find each quotient.

a. $54 \div (-3)$ **−18**

b. $\dfrac{-42}{6}$ **−7**

3 Evaluate $6x \div y$, if $x = -4$ and $y = -8$. **3**

✓ Skills Check

Divide Integers Find each quotient.

a. $-18 \div -9$ **2**

b. $40 \div (-8)$ **−5**

c. $-30 \div 6$ **−5**

d. $60 \div 10$ **6**

AVERAGE (MEAN)

In-Class Example Power Point®

4 a. Sam had quiz scores of 89, 98, 96, 97, and 95. Find the average (mean) of his test scores. **95**

b. Find the average (mean) of 10, −12, 9, 15, −4, 0, −1, and 7. **3**

ALGEBRA CONNECTION

You can use the rules for dividing integers to evaluate algebraic expressions.

Example 3 *Evaluate Algebraic Expressions*

Evaluate $ab \div (-4)$ if $a = -6$ and $b = -8$.

$ab \div (-4) = -6(-8) \div (-4)$ Replace a with -6 and b with -8.
$= 48 \div (-4)$ The product of -6 and -8 is positive.
$= -12$ The quotient of 48 and -4 is negative.

AVERAGE (MEAN) Division is used in statistics to find the **average**, or **mean**, of a set of data. To find the mean of a set of numbers, find the sum of the numbers and then divide by the number in the set.

Example 4 *Find the Mean*

a. **Rachel had test scores of 84, 90, 89, and 93. Find the average (mean) of her test scores.**

$\frac{84 + 90 + 89 + 93}{4} = \frac{356}{4}$ Find the sum of the test scores. Divide by the number of scores.
$= 89$ Simplify.

The average of her test scores is 89.

b. **Find the average (mean) of -2, 8, 5, -9, -12, and -2.**

$\frac{-2 + 8 + 5 + (-9) + (-12) + (-2)}{6} = \frac{-12}{6}$ Find the sum of the set of integers. Divide by the number in the set.
$= -2$ Simplify.

The average is -2.

You can refer to the following table to review operations with integers.

Concept Summary	**Operations with Integers**
Words	**Examples**
Adding Integers	
To add integers with the same sign, add their absolute values. Give the result the same sign as the integers.	$-5 + (-4) = -9$ $5 + 4 = 9$
To add integers with different signs, subtract their absolute values. Give the result the same sign as the integer with the greater absolute value.	$-5 + 4 = -1$ $5 + (-4) = 1$
Subtracting Integers To subtract an integer, add its additive inverse.	$5 - 9 = 5 + (-9)$ or -4 $5 - (-9) = 5 + 9$ or 14
Multiplying Integers The product of two integers with the same sign is positive. The product of two integers with different signs is negative.	$5 \cdot 4 = 20$ $-5 \cdot (-4) = 20$ $-5 \cdot 4 = -20$ $5 \cdot (-4) = -20$
Dividing Integers The quotient of two integers with the same sign is positive. The quotient of two integers with different signs is negative.	$20 \div 5 = 4$ $-20 \div (-5) = 4$ $-20 \div 5 = -4$ $20 \div (-5) = -4$

DAILY INTERVENTION   **Unlocking Misconceptions**

- From the answer in Example 4, students may assume that the average is always a number from the set of data. Use In-Class Example 4b to dispel these wrong assumptions.

Check for Understanding

Concept Check
1. **OPEN ENDED** Write an equation with three integers that illustrates dividing integers with different signs. **See margin.**

2. **Explain** how to find the average of a set of numbers. **See margin.**

Guided Practice

Find each quotient.

3. $88 \div 8$ **11**

4. $-20 \div (-5)$ **4**

5. $-18 \div 6$ **−3**

6. $\dfrac{-36}{-4}$ **9**

7. $\dfrac{70}{-7}$ **−10**

8. $\dfrac{-81}{9}$ **−9**

ALGEBRA Evaluate each expression.

9. $x \div 4$, if $x = -52$ **−13**

10. $\dfrac{s}{t}$, if $s = -45$ and $t = 5$ **−9**

Application
11. **WEATHER** The low temperatures for 7 days in January were $-2, 0, 5, -1, -4, 2$, and 0. Find the average for the 7-day period. **0**

★ indicates increased difficulty

Practice and Apply

Find each quotient.

12. $54 \div 9$ **6**

13. $45 \div 5$ **9**

14. $-27 \div (-3)$ **9**

15. $-64 \div (-8)$ **8**

16. $-72 \div (-9)$ **8**

17. $-60 \div (-6)$ **10**

18. $-77 \div 7$ **−11**

19. $-300 \div 6$ **−50**

20. $480 \div (-12)$ **−40**

★ 21. $\dfrac{132}{-12}$ **−11**

★ 22. $\dfrac{175}{-25}$ **−7**

★ 23. $\dfrac{143}{-13}$ **−11**

24. What is -91 divided by -7? **13**

25. Divide -76 by -4. **19**

ALGEBRA Evaluate each expression.

26. $\dfrac{x}{-5}$, if $x = 85$ **−17**

27. $\dfrac{108}{m}$, if $m = -9$ **−12**

28. $\dfrac{c}{d}$, if $c = -63$ and $d = -7$ **9**

29. $\dfrac{s}{t}$, if $s = 52$ and $t = -4$ **−13**

30. $xy \div (-3)$ if $x = 9$ and $y = -7$ **21**

31. $ab \div 6$ if $a = -12$ and $b = -8$ **16**

32. **STATISTICS** Find the average (mean) of $4, -8, 9, -3, -7, 10$, and 2. **1**

33. **BASKETBALL** In their first five games, the Jefferson Middle School basketball team scored 46, 52, 49, 53, and 45 points. What was their average number of points per game? **49 points**

ENERGY For Exercises 34–36, use the information below.

The formula $d = \left| 65 - \dfrac{h + l}{2} \right|$ can be used to find degree days, where h is the high and l is the low temperature.

34. If Baltimore had a high of $81°$ and a low of $65°$, find the degree days. **8**

35. If Milwaukee had a high of $8°$ and a low of $0°$, find the degree days. **61**

36. **RESEARCH** Use the Internet or another resource to find the high and low temperature for your city for a day in January. Find the degree days. **See students' work.**

Study Notebook

Have students—
- add the definition/example of the vocabulary term to their Vocabulary Builder worksheets for Chapter 2.
- describe how to find the average (mean) and include 2 examples.
- copy the "Concept summary" table into their notebooks, including the examples.
- include any other item(s) that they find helpful in mastering the skills in this lesson.

About the Exercises . . .

Organization by Objective
- **Divide Integers:** 12–31, 34, 35
- **Average (Mean):** 32, 33

Odd/Even Assignments
Exercises 12–35 are structured so that students practice the same concepts whether they are assigned odd or even problems.

Alert! Exercise 36 involves research on the Internet or other reference materials.

Assignment Guide

Basic: 13–19 odd, 25–35 odd, 36–40, 42–50

Average: 13–35 odd, 36–50

Advanced: 12–34 even, 36–46 (Optional: 47–50)

All: Practice Quiz 2 (1–10)

Answers

1. Sample answer: $-16 \div 4 = -4$

2. Find the sum of the numbers. Divide by the number in the set.

Open-Ended Assessment

Writing Have students write a paragraph explaining how they know whether a quotient should be positive or negative. How does this compare with products of multiplication?

Getting Ready for Lesson 2-6

PREREQUISITE SKILL In Lesson 2-6, students need to understand how points are named in ordered pairs in order to graph them. Exercises 47–50 should be used to determine your students' familiarity with ordered pairs.

Assessment Options

Practice Quiz 2 The quiz provides students with a brief review of the concepts and skills in Lessons 2-4 and 2-5. Lesson numbers are given to the right of exercises or instruction lines so students can review concepts not yet mastered.

Quiz (Lessons 2-4 and 2-5) is available on p. 102 of the *Chapter 2 Resource Masters*.

Answers

37. Sample answer: $x = -144$; $y = 12$; $z = -12$

39. Sample answer: When the signs of the integers are the same, both a product and a quotient are positive; when the signs are different, the product and quotient are negative. Answers should include the following.

• Sample answer: $4 \cdot (-6) = -24$ and $-24 \div 4 = -6$; $-3 \cdot 2 = -6$ and $-6 \div (-3) = 2$

• Sample answers: same sign: $-30 \div (-5) = 6$, $30 \div 5 = 6$ different signs: $-24 \div 8 = -3$, $24 \div (-8) = 3$

---

37. **CRITICAL THINKING** Find values for x, y, and z, so that all of the following statements are true. **See margin.**
   • $y > x$, $z < y$, and $x < 0$ • $z \div 2$ and $z \div 3$ are integers.
   • $x \div z = -z$ • $x \div y = z$

38. **CRITICAL THINKING** Addition and multiplication are said to be closed for whole numbers, but subtraction and division are not. That is, when you add or multiply any two whole numbers, the result is a whole number. Which operations are closed for integers? **add., subt., and mult.**

39. WRITING IN MATH   Answer the question that was posed at the beginning of the lesson. **See margin.**

   How is dividing integers related to multiplying integers?
   Include the following in your answer:
   • two related multiplication and division sentences, and
   • an example of each case (same signs, different signs) of dividing integers.

NEW YORK
Test Practice

Standardized Test Practice
Ⓐ Ⓑ Ⓒ Ⓓ

40. On Saturday, the temperature fell $10°$ in 2 hours. Which expresses the temperature change per hour? **C**
   Ⓐ $5°$ Ⓑ $-2°$ Ⓒ $-5°$ Ⓓ $-10°$

★ 41. Mark has quiz scores of 8, 7, 8, and 9. What is the lowest score he can get on the remaining quiz to have a final average (mean) score of at least 8? **B**
   Ⓐ 7   Ⓑ 8   Ⓒ 9   Ⓓ 10

Maintain Your Skills

Mixed Review Find each difference or product. *(Lessons 2-3 and 2-4)* 44. $-4ab$ 45. $-50cd$
42. $-8 - (-25)$ **17** 43. $75 - 114$ **-39** 44. $2ab \cdot (-2)$ 45. $(-10c)(5d)$

46. **PATTERNS** Find the next two numbers in the pattern $5, 4, 2, -1, …$ *(Lesson 1-1)* **$-5, -10$**

Getting Ready for the Next Lesson **PREREQUISITE SKILL** Use the grid to name the point for each ordered pair. *(To review ordered pairs, see Lesson 1-6.)*
47. $(1, 5)$ **B**   48. $(6, 2)$ **F**
49. $(4, 5)$ **D**   50. $(0, 3)$ **A**

Practice Quiz 2   Lessons 2-4 and 2-5

Find each product. *(Lesson 2-4)*
1. $-12 \cdot 7$ **-84**   2. $-6(-15)$ **90**   3. $-3(-7)(-6)$ **-126**   4. $3(-8)(-5)$ **120**

Find each quotient. *(Lesson 2-5)*
5. $-124 \div 4$ **-31**   6. $-90 \div (-6)$ **15**   7. $125 \div (-5)$ **-25**   8. $-126 \div (-9)$ **14**

9. Simplify $4x(-5y)$. *(Lesson 2-4)* **$-20xy$**

10. Evaluate $-9a$ if $a = -6$. *(Lesson 2-4)* **54**

2-6 The Coordinate System

What You'll Learn

- Graph points on a coordinate plane.
- Graph algebraic relationships.

How is a coordinate system used to locate places on Earth?

A GPS, or Global Positioning System, can be used to find a location anywhere on Earth by identifying its latitude and longitude. Several cities are shown on the map below. For example, Sydney, Australia, is located at approximately 30°S, 150°E.

a. Latitude is measured north and south of the equator. What is the latitude of New Orleans? **30°N**

b. Longitude is measured east and west of the prime meridian. What is the longitude of New Orleans? **90°W**

c. What does the location 30°N, 90°W mean?

c. 30° north of the equator; 90° west of the prime meridian

GRAPH POINTS Latitude and longitude are a kind of coordinate system. The coordinate system you used in Lesson 1-6 can be extended to include points below and to the left of the origin.

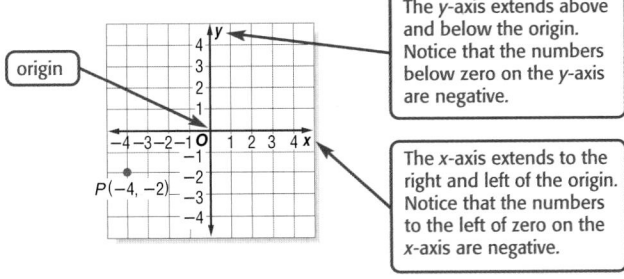

The *y*-axis extends above and below the origin. Notice that the numbers below zero on the *y*-axis are negative.

The *x*-axis extends to the right and left of the origin. Notice that the numbers to the left of zero on the *x*-axis are negative.

Recall that a point graphed on the coordinate system has an *x*-coordinate and a *y*-coordinate. The dot at the ordered pair $(-4, -2)$ is the graph of point *P*.

x-coordinate   *y*-coordinate

$(-4, -2)$

ordered pair

Vocabulary

- quadrants

NEW YORK
Performance Indicator

8.A.16 Find a set of ordered pairs to satisfy a given linear numerical pattern (expressed algebraically); then plot the ordered pairs and draw the line

8.G.15 Understand that numerical information can be represented in multiple ways: arithmetically, **algebraically, and graphically**

TEACHING TIP

Ask: Is $(-2, -4)$ the same point? Locate $(-2, -4)$ on the coordinate system. Emphasize the idea of order in ordered pairs.

---

1 Focus

 5-Minute Check Transparency 2-6 Use as a quiz or review of Lesson 2-5.

Mathematical Background notes are available for this lesson on page 54D.

How is a coordinate system used to locate places on Earth?

The opening activity questions are repeated on page 85 of the *Chapter 2 Resource Masters*.

Reading to Learn Mathematics, p. 85 — ELL

Pre-Activity *How is a coordinate system used to locate places on Earth?*

Do the activity at the top of page 85 in your textbook. Write your answers below.

a. Latitude is measured north and south of the equator. What is the latitude of New Orleans? **30°N**

b. Longitude is measured east and west of the prime meridian. What is the longitude of New Orleans? **90°W**

c. What does the location 30°N, 90°W mean?
30° north of the equator; 90° west of the prime meridian

Reading the Lesson

Write a definition and give an example of the new vocabulary word.

	Vocabulary	Definition	Example
1.	quadrants	See students' work.	

2. A point graphed on the coordinate system has a(n) **x-coordinate** and a(n) **y-coordinate** .

3. In which quadrant does the point $A(4, -2)$ lie? **IV**

Helping You Remember

4. Draw a coordinate grid with points to represent your classroom and where your classmates sit. Explain how to name the locations of your classmates.

Sample answer. Let the center row of desks be the *y*-axis, and the center column of desks be the *x*-axis. Have the front of the class be positive. A student sitting at $(3, -22)$ would be 3 desks to the right of the center desk, and 2 desks behind the center desk.

Resource Manager

Workbooks and Reproducible Masters

Chapter 2 Resource Masters
- Study Guide and Intervention, p. 82
- Skills Practice, p. 83
- Practice, p. 84
- Reading to Learn Mathematics, p. 85
- Enrichment, p. 86
- Assessment, p. 102

Graphing Calculator and Spreadsheet Masters, p. 22
Parent and Student Study Guide Workbook, p. 14

Transparencies
5-Minute Check Transparency 2-6
Answer Key Transparencies

Technology
Interactive Chalkboard
Multimedia Applications

Building on Prior Knowledge

Students will apply the same skills for graphing points from Chapter 1 to graph points in all four quadrants.

GRAPH POINTS

Teaching Tip Have students look at the *x*-axis and ask what this represents. **a number line** Ask them to examine the *y*-axis and ask the same question. For those who cannot see that the *y*-axis is a number line, have them rotate their books 90° clockwise and look at the *y*-axis again.

1 Write the ordered pair that names each point.

a. *P*	b. *Q*	c. *R*
(4, −2)	(−3, −1)	(2, 0)

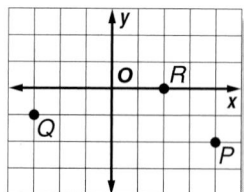

Teaching Tip Just as *x* and *y* are in alphabetical order in the ordered pair (*x*, *y*), so are the directions from the origin that they represent (horizontal, vertical) or (across, up and down).

2 Graph and label each point on a coordinate plane. Then name the quadrant in which each point lies.

a. *S*(−1, −5)
   Quadrant III

b. *U*(−2, 3)
   Quadrant II

c. *T*(0, −3)
   not in any quadrant

Example 1 **Write Ordered Pairs**

Write the ordered pair that names each point.

a. *A*

The *x*-coordinate is −3.
The *y*-coordinate is 2.
The ordered pair is (−3, 2).

b. *B*

The *x*-coordinate is 4.
The *y*-coordinate is –2.
The ordered pair is (4, −2).

c. *C*

The point lies on the *y*-axis, so its *x*-coordinate is 0.
The *y*-coordinate is −3. The ordered pair is (0, −3).

The *x*-axis and the *y*-axis separate the coordinate plane into four regions, called **quadrants**. The axes and points on the axes are not located in any of the quadrants.

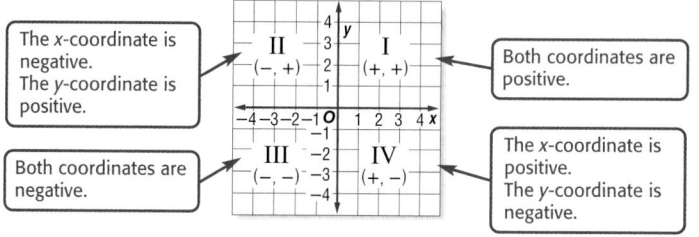

The *x*-coordinate is negative. The *y*-coordinate is positive. [II (−, +)]

Both coordinates are positive. [I (+, +)]

Both coordinates are negative. [III (−, −)]

The *x*-coordinate is positive. The *y*-coordinate is negative. [IV (+, −)]

Example 2 **Graph Points and Name Quadrant**

Graph and label each point on a coordinate plane. Name the quadrant in which each point lies.

a. *D*(2, 4)

Start at the origin. Move 2 units right.
Then move 4 units up and draw a dot.
Point *D*(2, 4) is in Quadrant I.

b. *E*(−3, −2)

Start at the origin. Move 3 units left.
Then move 2 units down and draw a dot.
Point *E*(−3, −2) is in Quadrant III.

c. *F*(4, 0)

Start at the origin. Move 4 units right. Since the *y*-coordinate is 0, the point lies on the *x*-axis. Point *F*(4, 0) is not in any quadrant.

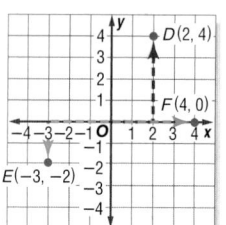

✓ **Concept Check** What parts of a coordinate graph do not lie in any quadrant?
the two axes

DAILY INTERVENTION · **Differentiated Instruction**

• **Visual/Spatial** Have students create a line design extending beyond a single quadrant, on a coordinate grid. Have them list each "corner" or vertex of the design as an ordered pair. They should list the ordered pairs in sequence as they progress around the outline of the objects in the designs. Then have them give their ordered lists to their partners to plot on a coordinate grid. As the partners "connect the dots," they will see the designs take shape.

GRAPH ALGEBRAIC RELATIONSHIPS You can use a coordinate graph to show relationships between two numbers.

Example 3 *Graph an Algebraic Relationship*

The sum of two numbers is 5. If x represents the first number and y represents the second number, make a table of possible values for x and y. Graph the ordered pairs and describe the graph.

First, make a table.
Choose values for x and y that have a sum of 5.

$x + y = 5$		
x	y	(x, y)
2	3	(2, 3)
1	4	(1, 4)
0	5	(0, 5)
−1	6	(−1, 6)
−2	7	(−2, 7)

Then graph the ordered pairs on a coordinate plane.

The points on the graph are in a line that slants downward to the right. The line crosses the y-axis at $y = 5$.

Check for Understanding

Concept Check

1. **Explain** why the point (3, 6) is different from the point (6, 3). **See pp. 95A–95B.**

2. **OPEN ENDED** Name two ordered pairs whose graphs are *not* located in one of the four quadrants. **Sample answer: (0, 0), (4, 0)**

3. **FIND THE ERROR** Keisha says that if you interchange the coordinates of any point in Quadrant I, the new point would still be in Quadrant I. Jason says the new point would be in Quadrant 3. Who is correct? Explain your reasoning. **See pp. 95A–95B.**

Guided Practice

Name the ordered pair for each point graphed at the right.

GUIDED PRACTICE KEY	
Exercises	Examples
4–7	1
8–11	2
12	3

4. A (−4, 5)   5. C (1, 3)

6. G (−3, −2)   7. K (5, −4)

Graph and label each point on a coordinate plane. Name the quadrant in which each point is located.

8–11. See pp. 95A–95B for graphs.

8. $J(3, −4)$ **IV**   9. $K(−2, 2)$ **II**

10. $L(0, 4)$ **none**   11. $M(−1, −2)$ **III**

Application

12. **ALGEBRA** Make a table of values and graph six ordered integer pairs where $x + y = 3$. Describe the graph. **See pp. 95A–95B.**

GRAPH ALGEBRAIC RELATIONSHIPS

In-Class Example

3. The difference between two integers is 4. If x represents the first integer and y is subtracted from it, make a table of possible values for x and y. Then graph the ordered pairs and describe the graph.

$x − y = 4$		
x	y	(x, y)
2	−2	(2, −2)
1	−3	(1, −3)
0	−4	(0, −4)
−1	−5	(−1, −5)
−2	−6	(−2, −6)

The points on the graph are in a line that slants upward to the right. The line crosses the y-axis at $y = −4$.

---

3 Practice/Apply

Study Notebook

Have students—

• complete the definition/example for the remaining term on the Vocabulary Builder Worksheets for Chapter 2.

• include any other item(s) that they find helpful in mastering the skills in this lesson.

DAILY

INTERVENTION **FIND THE ERROR** Have students review the illustration of the quadrants shown on p. 86. Ask them which quadrants, when the ordered pairs defining their points are interchanged, retain the resulting points, and which quadrants do not. **I and III; II and IV**

Study Guide and Intervention, p. 82

Example

Graph and label each point on a coordinate plane. Name the quadrant in which each point lies.

a. $M(-2, 5)$
Start at the origin. Move 2 units left.
Then move 5 units up and draw a dot.
Point $M(-2, 5)$ is in Quadrant II.

b. $N(4, -4)$
Start at the origin. Move 4 units right.
Then move 4 units down and draw a dot.
Point $N(4, -4)$ is in Quadrant IV.

Exercises

Graph and label each point on the coordinate plane. Name the quadrant in which each point is located.

1. $A(2, 6)$ I
2. $B(-1, 4)$ II
3. $C(0, -5)$ none
4. $D(-4, -3)$ III
5. $E(2, 0)$ none
6. $F(3, -2)$ IV
7. $G(-4, 4)$ II
8. $H(2, -5)$ IV
9. $I(6, 3)$ I
10. $J(-5, -8)$ III
11. $K(3, -5)$ IV
12. $L(-7, -3)$ III

Skills Practice, p. 83 and Practice, p. 84 (shown)

Graph and label each point on the coordinate plane. Name the quadrant in which each point is located.

1. $A(8, 6)$ I
2. $B(-8, 6)$ II
3. $C(-4, -11)$ III
4. $D(3, -6)$ IV
5. $E(9, 0)$ none
6. $F(-4, 1)$ II
7. $G(-10, -10)$ III
8. $H(0, -8)$ none
9. $I(6, -2)$ IV
10. $J(2, 13)$ I

11. **ALGEBRA** Make a table of values and graph six sets of ordered pairs for the equation $y = 5 - x$. Describe the graph.

	$y = 5 - x$	
x	y	(x, y)
3	2	(3, 2)
2	3	(2, 3)
1	4	(1, 4)
0	5	(0, 5)
−1	6	(−1, 6)
−2	7	(−2, 7)

The points are along a line slanting down to the right, crossing the y-axis at 5 and the x-axis at 5.

12. **GEOMETRY** On the coordinate plane, draw a rectangle $ABCD$ with vertices at $A(1, 4)$, $B(5, 4)$, $C(5, 1)$, and $D(1, 1)$. Then graph and describe the new rectangle formed when you subtract 3 from each coordinate of the vertices in rectangle $ABCD$.

The new rectangle is the same size as rectangle $ABCD$ and is shifted to the left 3 units and down 3 units, with vertices at (−2, 1), (2, 1), (2, −2), and (−2, −2).

Enrichment, p. 86

Polar Coordinates

In a rectangular coordinate system, the ordered pair (x, y) describes the location of a point x units from the origin along the x-axis and y units from the origin along the y-axis.

In a polar coordinate system, the ordered pair (r, θ) describes the location of a point r units from the pole on the ray (vector) whose endpoint is the pole and which forms an angle of θ with the polar axis.

The graph of $(2, 30°)$ is shown on the polar coordinate system at the right below. Note that the concentric circles indicate the number of units from the pole.

Locate each point on the polar coordinate system below.

1. $(3, 45°)$
2. $(1, 135°)$
3. $\left(2\frac{1}{2}, 60°\right)$
4. $(4, 120°)$
5. $(2, 225°)$
6. $(3, -30°)$
7. $(1, -90°)$
8. $(-2, 30°)$

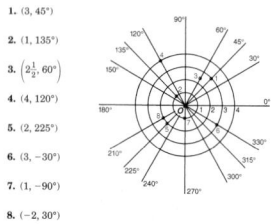

★ indicates increased difficulty

Practice and Apply

Homework Help

For Exercises	See Examples
13–22	1
23–34, 41, 42	2
35–40, 43, 44	3

Extra Practice
See page 728.

Name the ordered pair for each point graphed at the right.

13. R $(-2, 4)$
14. G $(-4, 2)$
15. M $(4, -2)$
16. B $(1, -4)$
17. V $(2, 2)$
18. H $(4, 3)$
19. U $(0, -2)$
20. W $(3, 0)$
21. A $(-3, -5)$
22. T $(-2, -2)$

Graph and label each point on a coordinate plane. Name the quadrant in which each point is located. 23–34. See pp. 95A–95B for graphs.

23. $A(4, 5)$ I
24. $K(-5, 1)$ II
25. $M(4, -2)$ IV
26. $B(-5, -5)$ III
27. $S(2, -5)$ IV
28. $R(-3, 5)$ II
29. $E(0, 3)$ none
30. $H(0, -3)$ none
31. $G(5, 0)$ none
32. $C(6, -1)$ IV
33. $D(0, 0)$ none
34. $F(-4, 0)$ none

ALGEBRA Make a table of values and graph six sets of ordered integer pairs for each equation. Describe the graph. 35–40. See pp. 95A–95B.

35. $x + y = 5$
36. $x + y = -2$
37. $y = 2x$
38. $y = -2x$
39. $y = x + 2$
40. $y = x - 1$

Graph each point. Then connect the points in alphabetical order and identify the figure. 41–42. See pp. 95A–95B for graphs.

41. $A(0, 6)$, $B(4, -6)$, $C(-6, 2)$, $D(6, 2)$, $E(-4, -6)$, $F(0, 6)$ **5-point star**

42. $A(5, 8)$, $B(1, 13)$, $C(5, 18)$, $D(9, 13)$, $E(5, 8)$, $F(5, 6)$, $G(3, 7)$, $H(3, 5)$, $I(7, 7)$, $J(7, 5)$, $K(5, 6)$, $L(5, 3)$, $M(3, 4)$, $N(3, 2)$, $P(7, 4)$, $Q(7, 2)$, $R(5, 3)$, $S(5, 1)$ **kite**

★ 43. Graph eight ordered integer pairs where $|x| > 3$. Describe the graph.

★ 44. Graph all ordered integer pairs that satisfy the condition $|x| < 4$ and $|y| < 3$.
43–44. See pp. 95A–95B.

Reading Math

Vertex, Vertices

A *vertex* of a triangle is a point where two sides of a triangle meet. *Vertices* is the plural of *vertex*.

GEOMETRY On a coordinate plane, draw a triangle ABC with vertices at $A(3, 1)$, $B(4, 2)$, and $C(2, 4)$. Then graph and describe each new triangle formed in Exercises 45–48. 45–48. See pp. 95A–95B.

45. Multiply each coordinate of the vertices in triangle ABC by 2.

46. Multiply each coordinate of the vertices in triangle ABC by -1.

47. Add 2 to each coordinate of the vertices in triangle ABC.

48. Subtract 4 from each coordinate of the vertices in triangle ABC.

49. **MAPS** Find a map of your school and draw a coordinate grid on the map with the library as the center. Locate the cafeteria, principal's office, your math classroom, gym, counselor's office, and the main entrance on your grid. Write the coordinates of these places. How can you use these points to help visitors find their way around your school?
See students' work.

About the Exercises . . .

Organization by Objective
• **Graph Points:** 13–34, 41, 42, 45–48
• **Graph Algebraic Relationships:** 35–40, 43, 44

Alert! Exercises 8–12 and 23–49 require graph paper.

Odd/Even Assignments
Exercises 13–42 are structured so that students practice the same concepts whether they are assigned odd or even problems.

50. CRITICAL THINKING   If the graph of A(x, y) satisfies the given condition, name the quadrant in which point A is located.

a. $x > 0$, $y > 0$ **I**   **b.** $x < 0$, $y < 0$ **III**   **c.** $x < 0$, $y > 0$ **II**

51. CRITICAL THINKING   Graph eight sets of integer coordinates that satisfy $|x| + |y| > 3$. Describe the location of the points. **See margin.**

52. WRITING IN MATH   Answer the question that was posed at the beginning of the lesson. **See margin.**

How is a coordinate system used to locate places on Earth?

Include the following in your answer:
- an explanation of how coordinates can describe a location, and
- a description of how latitude and longitude are related to the x- and y-axes on a coordinate plane. Include what corresponds to the origin on a coordinate plane.

NEW YORK Test Practice

Standardized Test Practice
Ⓐ Ⓑ Ⓒ Ⓓ

53. On the coordinate plane at the right, what are the coordinates of the point that shows the location of the library? **D**

Ⓐ (4, −2)   Ⓑ (−2, −4)
Ⓒ (4, 2)   Ⓓ (−4, −2)

54. On the coordinate plane at the right, what location has coordinates (5, −2)? **B**

Ⓐ Park   Ⓑ School
Ⓒ Library   Ⓓ Grocery Store

Maintain Your Skills

Mixed Review   **Find each quotient.**   *(Lesson 2-5)*

55. $-24 \div 8$ **−3**   **56.** $105 \div (-5)$ **−21**   **57.** $-400 \div (-50)$ **8**

ALGEBRA   **Evaluate each expression if $f = -9$, $g = -6$, and $h = 8$.**
(Lesson 2-4)

58. $-5fg$ **−270**   **59.** $2gh$ **−96**   **60.** $-10fh$ **720**

61. WEATHER   In the newspaper, Amad read that the low temperature for the day was expected to be −5°F and the high temperature was expected to be 8°F. What was the difference in the expected high and low temperature?   *(Lesson 2-3)* **13°F**

ALGEBRA   **Simplify each expression.**   *(Lesson 1-4)*

62. $(a + 8) + 6$ **$a + 14$**   **63.** $4(6h)$ **24h**   **64.** $(n \cdot 7) \cdot 8$ **56n**
65. $(b \cdot 9) \cdot 5$ **45b**   **66.** $(16 + 3y) + y$ **$4y + 16$** **67.** $0(4z)$ **0**

---

4 Assess

Open-Ended Assessment
Speaking Give a set of ordered pairs to the class, including at least one point in each quadrant, and have students explain step-by-step how to graph each one.

Assessment Options
Quiz (Lesson 2-6) is available on p. 102 of the *Chapter 2 Resource Masters.*

Answers

51. Sample answer:

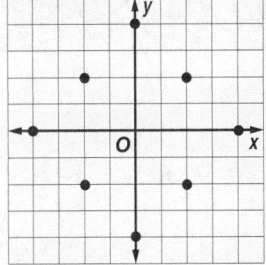

Description: The points lie outside a rhombus defined by (0, 4), (4, 0), (0, −4), and (−4, 0).

52. Latitude and longitude lines are similar to a coordinate system. Answers should include the following.
- Coordinates describe a location by telling how far and in what direction the location is from a given starting point.
- In the latitude and longitude system, longitude is similar to the x-coordinate of a point in a coordinate plane. Latitude is similar to the y-coordinate. The point where the prime meridian and the equator meet is similar to the origin in the coordinate system.

Assignment Guide
Basic: 13–41 odd, 45–48, 50–67
Average: 13–43 odd, 45–48, 50–67
Advanced: 12–44 even, 45–67

Chapter 2 Study Guide and Review

Vocabulary and Concept Check

- This alphabetical list of vocabulary terms in Chapter 2 includes a page reference where each term was introduced.
- **Assessment** A vocabulary review/test for Chapter 2 is available on p. 100 of the *Chapter 2 Resource Masters*.

Lesson-by-Lesson Review

For each lesson,
- the main ideas are summarized,
- additional examples review concepts, and
- practice exercises are provided.

Vocabulary PuzzleMaker

ELL The Vocabulary PuzzleMaker software improves students' mathematics vocabulary using four puzzle formats—crossword, scramble, word search using a word list, and word search using clues. Students can work on a computer screen or from a printed handout.

MindJogger Videoquizzes

ELL MindJogger Videoquizzes provide an alternative review of concepts presented in this chapter. Students work in teams in a game show format to gain points for correct answers. The questions are presented in three rounds.

Round 1 Concepts (5 questions)
Round 2 Skills (4 questions)
Round 3 Problem Solving (4 questions)

Vocabulary and Concept Check

absolute value (p. 58)	inequality (p. 57)	opposites (p. 66)
additive inverse (p. 66)	integers (p. 56)	quadrants (p. 86)
average (p. 82)	mean (p. 82)	
coordinate (p. 57)	negative number (p. 56)	

Complete each sentence with the correct term. Choose from the list above.

1. A(n) _____ is a number less than zero. **negative number**
2. The four regions separated by the axes on a coordinate plane are called _____. **quadrants**
3. The number that corresponds to a point on the number line is called the _____ of that point. **coordinate**
4. An integer and its opposite are also called _____ of each other. **additive inverses**
5. The set of _____ includes positive whole numbers, their opposites, and zero. **integers**
6. The _____ of a number is the distance the number is from zero on the number line. **absolute value**
7. A(n) _____ is a mathematical sentence containing < or >. **inequality**

Lesson-by-Lesson Review

2-1 Integers and Absolute Value

See pages 56–61.

Concept Summary
- Numbers on a number line increase as you move from left to right.
- The absolute value of a number is the distance the number is from zero on the number line.

Examples

1 Replace the ● with <, >, or = in −3 ● 2 to make a true sentence.

$$-4\,-3\,-2\,-1\;0\;1\;2\;3\;4$$

Since −3 is to the left of 2, write −3 < 2.

2 Evaluate $|-4|$.

4 units

$$-5\,-4\,-3\,-2\,-1\,0\;1\;2$$

The graph of −4 is 4 units from 0. So, $|-4| = 4$.

Exercises Replace each ● with <, >, or = to make a true sentence. *See Example 2 on page 57.*

8. 8 ● −8 **>**   9. −3 ● −3 **=**   10. −2 ● 0 **<**   11. −12 ● −21 **>**

Evaluate each expression. *See Example 4 on page 58.*

12. $|-32|$ **32**   13. $|25|$ **25**   14. $-|15|$ **−15**   15. $|-8| + |-14|$ **22**

 www.pre-alg.com/vocabulary_review

FOLDABLES Study Organizer

For more information about Foldables, see *Teaching Mathematics with Foldables.*

Have students reexamine their Foldables to make sure all examples they have written are correct. Have them refer to their Foldables if needed when working through the Study Guide exercises.

2-2 Adding Integers

See pages 64–68.

Concept Summary

- To add integers with the same sign, add their absolute values. Give the result the same sign as the integers.
- To add integers with different signs, subtract their absolute values. Give the result the same sign as the integer with the greater absolute value.

Examples Find each sum.

1. $-3 + (-4)$

   $-3 + (-4) = -7$ The sum is negative.

2. $5 + (-2)$

   $5 + (-2) = 3$ The sum is positive.

Exercises Find each sum. *See Examples 2, 4, and 6 on pages 64–66.*

16. $-6 + (-3)$ **−9**
17. $-4 + (-1)$ **−5**
18. $-2 + 7$ **5**
19. $4 + (-8)$ **−4**
20. $6 + (-9) + (-8)$ **−11**
21. $4 + (-7) + (-3) + (-4)$ **−10**

2-3 Subtracting Integers

See pages 70–74.

Concept Summary

- To subtract an integer, add its additive inverse.

Examples Find each difference.

1. $-5 - 2$

   $-5 - 2 = -5 + (-2)$ To subtract 2,
   $\quad\quad = -7$ add −2.

2. $8 - (-4)$

   $8 - (-4) = 8 + 4$ To subtract −4,
   $\quad\quad = 12$ add 4.

Exercises Find each difference. *See Examples 1 and 2 on pages 70–71.*

22. $4 - 9$ **−5**
23. $-3 - 5$ **−8**
24. $7 - (-2)$ **9**
25. $-1 - (-6)$ **5**
26. $-7 - 8$ **−15**
27. $6 - 10$ **−4**
28. $-3 - (-7)$ **4**
29. $6 - (-3)$ **9**

2-4 Multiplying Integers

See pages 75–79.

Concept Summary

- The product of two integers with different signs is negative.
- The product of two integers with the same sign is positive.

Examples Find each product.

1. $6(-4)$

   $6(-4) = -24$ The factors have different signs, so the product is negative.

2. $-8(-2)$

   $-8(-2) = 16$ The factors have the same sign, so the product is positive.

Chapter 2 **For More ...**
- Extra Practice, see pages 726–728.
- Mixed Problem Solving, see page 759.

Answers

40–43.

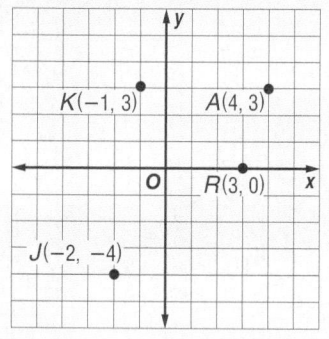

Answers (p. 93)

1. Find the difference of their absolute values. Give the result the sign of the integer having the larger absolute value.

2. Add the additive inverse of the integer being subtracted.

3.

28–30.

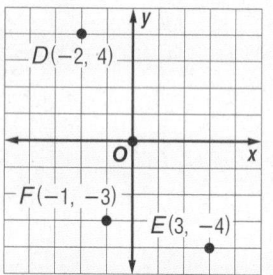

Exercises Find each product. *See Examples 1 and 2 on pages 75–76.*

30. $-9(5)$ **−45**   **31.** $11(-6)$ **−66**   **32.** $-4(-7)$ **28**   **33.** $-3(-16)$ **48**

34. Simplify $-2a(4b)$.   *See Example 5 on page 77.* **−8ab**

2-5 Dividing Integers

See pages 80–84.

Concept Summary

- The quotient of two integers with the same sign is positive.
- The quotient of two integers with different signs is negative.

Examples Find each quotient.

1 $-30 \div (-5)$.

$-30 \div (-5) = 6$ The signs are the same, so the quotient is positive.

2 $27 \div (-3)$

$27 \div (-3) = -9$ The signs are different, so the quotient is negative.

Exercises Find each quotient. *See Examples 1 and 2 on page 81.*

35. $-14 \div (-2)$ **7**   **36.** $-52 \div (-4)$ **13**   **37.** $-36 \div 9$ **−4**   **38.** $88 \div (-4)$ **−22**

39. Find the average (mean) of $-3, -6, 9, -3$, and 13.   *See Example 4 on page 82* **2**

2-6 The Coordinate System

See pages 85–89.

Concept Summary

- The x-axis and the y-axis separate the coordinate plane into four quadrants.
- The axes and points on the axes are not located in any of the quadrants.

Examples Graph and label each point on a coordinate plane. Name the quadrant in which each point is located.

1 $F(5, -3)$

Point $F(5, -3)$ is in quadrant IV.

2 $G(0, 4)$

Point $G(0, 4)$ is not in any quadrant.

40–43. See margin for graphs.

Exercises Graph and label each point on a coordinate plane. Name the quadrant in which each point is located. *See Example 2 on page 86.*

40. $A(4, 3)$ **I**   **41.** $J(-2, -4)$ **III**   **42** $K(-1, 3)$ **II**   **43.** $R(3, 0)$ **none**

Vocabulary and Concepts

1. **Explain** how to add two integers with different signs. **See margin.**

2. **State** a rule used for subtracting integers. **See margin.**

3. **Graph** the set of integers $\{-6, 2, -1, 1\}$ on a number line. **See margin.**

Skills and Applications

Write two inequalities using the numbers in each sentence. Use the symbols $<$ and $>$.

4. -5 is less than 2. **$-5 < 2$; $2 > -5$**

5. 12 is greater than -15. **$12 > -15$; $-15 < 12$**

Replace each ● with $<$, $>$, or $=$ to make a true sentence.

6. $-5 ● -3$ **$<$**

7. $-5 ● -14$ **$>$**

8. $4 ● |-7|$ **$<$**

Find each sum or difference.

9. $-4 + (-8)$ **-12**
10. $-9 + 15$ **6**
11. $12 + (-15)$ **-3**
12. $14 + (-7) + -11$ **-4**

13. $4 - 13$ **-9**
14. $8 - (-6)$ **14**
15. $-6 - (-10)$ **4**
16. $-14 - (-7)$ **-7**

Find each product or quotient.

17. $6(-8)$ **-48**
18. $-9(8)$ **-72**
19. $-7(-5)$ **35**
20. $2(-4)(11)$ **-88**

21. $54 \div (-9)$ **-6**
22. $-64 \div (-4)$ **16**
23. $-250 \div 25$ **-10**
24. $-144 \div (-6)$ **24**

ALGEBRA Evaluate each expression if $a = -5$, $b = 3$, and $c = -10$.

25. $ab - c$ **-5**
26. $c \div a$ **2**
27. $4c + |a|$ **-35**

Graph and label each point on a coordinate plane. Name the quadrant in which each point is located. **28–30. See margin for graphs.**

28. $D(-2, 4)$ **II**
29. $E(3, -4)$ **IV**
30. $F(-1, -3)$ **III**

31. **WEATHER** The table shows the low temperatures during one week in Anchorage, Alaska. Find the average low temperature for the week. **$-3°F$**

Day	S	M	T	W	T	F	S
Temperature (°F)	-12	3	-7	0	-4	1	-2

32. **SPORTS** During the first play of the game, the Brownville Tigers football team lost seven yards. On each of the next three plays, an additional four yards were lost. Express the total yards lost at the end of the first four plays as an integer. **-19 yd**

33. **STANDARDIZED TEST PRACTICE** Suppose Jason's home represents the origin on a coordinate plane. If Jason leaves his home and walks two miles west and then four miles north, what is the location of his destination as an ordered pair? In which quadrant is his destination? **A**

Ⓐ $(-2, 4)$; II Ⓑ $(2, 4)$; I Ⓒ $(-2, -4)$; II Ⓓ $(4, -2)$; IV

www.pre-alg.com/chapter_test/ny

Chapter 2 Practice Test **93**

Portfolio Suggestion

Introduction The rules for operations on integers are fundamental to algebra as they apply to operations on variables as well.

Ask Students to include a summary of the rules for operations on integers. They should organize the information in the way that best suits them, such as in a chart, on a foldable, or in a paragraph.

Chapter
2 Practice Test

Assessment Options

Vocabulary Test A vocabulary review/test for Chapter 2 can be found on p. 100 of the *Chapter 2 Resource Masters.*

Chapter Tests There are six Chapter 2 Tests and an Open-Ended Assessment task available in the *Chapter 2 Resource Masters.*

Chapter 2 Tests			
Form	Type	Level	Pages
1	MC	basic	87–88
2A	MC	average	89–90
2B	MC	average	91–92
2C	FR	average	93–94
2D	FR	average	95–96
3	FR	advanced	97–98

MC = multiple-choice questions
FR = free-response questions

Open-Ended Assessment
Performance tasks for Chapter 2 can be found on p. 99 of the *Chapter 2 Resource Masters,* along with a sample scoring rubric for these tasks on p. A22.

 ExamView® Pro

Use the networkable **ExamView® Pro** to:

- Create **multiple versions** of tests.
- Create **modified** tests for *Inclusion* students.
- **Edit** existing questions and **add** your own questions.
- Use built-in **state curriculum correlations** to create tests aligned with state standards.
- Change **English** tests to **Spanish** and vice versa.

These two pages contain practice questions in the various formats that can be found on the most frequently given standardized tests.

A practice answer sheet for these two pages can be found on page A1 of the *Chapter 2 Resource Masters*.

Standardized Test Practice
Student Recording Sheet, p. A1

Part 1 *Multiple Choice*

Select the best answer from the choices given and fill in the corresponding oval.

1. Ⓐ Ⓑ Ⓒ Ⓓ   4. Ⓐ Ⓑ Ⓒ Ⓓ   7. Ⓐ Ⓑ Ⓒ Ⓓ   9. Ⓐ Ⓑ Ⓒ Ⓓ
2. Ⓐ Ⓑ Ⓒ Ⓓ   5. Ⓐ Ⓑ Ⓒ Ⓓ   8. Ⓐ Ⓑ Ⓒ Ⓓ   10. Ⓐ Ⓑ Ⓒ Ⓓ
3. Ⓐ Ⓑ Ⓒ Ⓓ   6. Ⓐ Ⓑ Ⓒ Ⓓ

Part 2 *Short Response/Grid In*

Solve the problem and write your answer in the blank.

For Questions 11, 12, 14, and 15 also enter your answer by writing each number or symbol in a box. Then fill in the corresponding oval for that number or symbol.

11 ___ (grid in)
12 ___ (grid in)
13 ___
14 ___ (grid in)
15 ___ (grid in)
16 ___

Part 3 *Extended Response*

Record your answers for Question 17 on the back of this paper.

Teaching Tip In part 2, only Exercises 10 and 11 could appear as grid-in questions on a standardized test.

Additional Practice

See pp. 105–106 of the *Chapter 2 Resource Masters* for additional standardized test practice.

NEW YORK Test Practice

Part 1 | Multiple Choice

Record your answers on the answer sheet provided by your teacher or on a sheet of paper.

1. The table below shows the number of cells present after a certain form of bacteria multiplies for a number of hours. How many cells will be present in five hours? (Lesson 1-1) **C**

Number of Hours	Number of Cells
0	1
1	3
2	9
3	27

Ⓐ 81   Ⓑ 91

Ⓒ 243   Ⓓ 279

2. Suppose your sister has 3 more CDs than you do. Which equation represents the number of CDs that you have? Let y represent your CDs and s represent your sister's CDs. (Lesson 1-5) **B**

Ⓐ $y = s + 3$ Ⓑ $y = s - 3$

Ⓒ $y = 3 - s$ Ⓓ $y = 3s$

3. Which expression represents the greatest integer? (Lesson 2-1) **C**

Ⓐ $|4|$ Ⓑ $|-3|$

Ⓒ $|-8|$ Ⓓ -9

4. The water level of a local lake is normally 0 feet above sea level. In a flood, the water level rose 4 feet above normal. A month later, the water level had gone down 5 feet. Which integer best represents the water level at that time? (Lesson 2-1) **B**

Ⓐ -3 Ⓑ -1

Ⓒ 4   Ⓓ 9

5. What is the sum of -5 and 2? (Lesson 2-2) **B**

Ⓐ -7 Ⓑ -3

Ⓒ 3   Ⓓ 7

6. Find the value of x if $x = 7 - (-3)$. (Lesson 2-3) **D**

Ⓐ -10 Ⓑ -4

Ⓒ 4   Ⓓ 10

7. If $t = -5$, what is the value of the expression $-3t + 7$? (Lesson 2-4) **D**

Ⓐ -8 Ⓑ -6

Ⓒ 8   Ⓓ 22

8. If $a = -2$ and $b = 5$, what is the value of $\frac{b - 13}{a}$? (Lesson 2-5) **D**

Ⓐ -4 Ⓑ -9

Ⓒ 9   Ⓓ 4

For Questions 9 and 10, use the following graph.

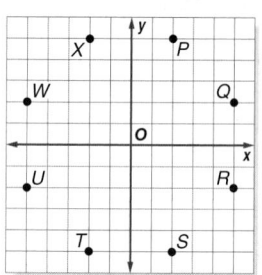

9. Which letter represents the ordered pair $(-2, 5)$? (Lesson 2-6) **B**

Ⓐ R   Ⓑ X

Ⓒ T   Ⓓ W

10. Which ordered pair represents point U? (Lesson 2-6) **C**

Ⓐ $(5, -2)$ Ⓑ $(-2, -5)$

Ⓒ $(-5, -2)$ Ⓓ $(-2, 5)$

 ExamView® Pro

Special banks of standardized test questions similar to those on the SAT, ACT, TIMSS 8, NAEP 8, and Pre-Algebra End-of-Course tests can be found on this CD-ROM.

Preparing for Standardized Tests
For test-taking strategies and more
practice, see pages 771–788.

Part 2 | Short Response/Grid In

Record your answers on the answer sheet
provided by your teacher or on a sheet of
paper.

11. The bar graph shows the numbers of girls
and boys in each grade at Muir Middle
School. In which grade is the difference
between the number of girls and the number
of boys the greatest? (Prerequisite Skill, p. 722) **6**

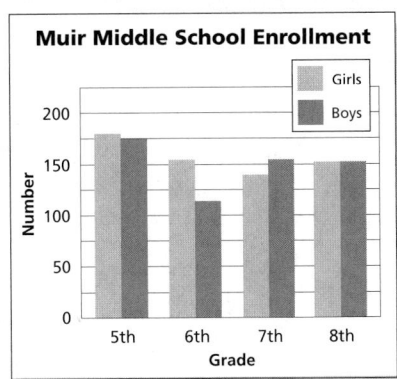

Muir Middle School Enrollment

12. Nine less than a number is 15. Find the
number. (Lesson 1-5) **24**

13. The Springfield High School football team
gained 7 yards on one play. On the next
play, they lost 11 yards. Write an integer that
represents the net result of these two plays.
(Lesson 2-2) **−4**

14. The low temperature one winter night in
Bismarck, North Dakota, was −15°F. The
next day the high temperature was 3°F. How
many degrees had the temperature risen?
(Lesson 2-3) **18**

15. The table below was used to change values
of x into values of y.

x	$y = x - 7$
6	−1
7	0
8	1

What value of x can be used to obtain
a y-value equal to 5? (Lesson 2-3) **12**

www.pre-alg.com/standardized_test/ny

16. The low temperatures in Minneapolis
during four winter days were +2°F, −7°F,
−12°F, and +9°F. What was the average low
temperature during these four days?
(Lesson 2-5) **−2°F**

Part 3 | Extended Response

Record your answers on a sheet of paper.
Show your work.

17. On graph paper, graph the points $A(4, 2)$,
$B(-3, 7)$, and $C(-3, 2)$. Connect the points to
form a triangle. (Lesson 2-6)

  a. Add 6 to the x-coordinate of each
  coordinate pair. Graph and connect the
  new points to form a new figure. Is the
  new figure the same size and shape as the
  original triangle? Describe how the size,
  shape, and position of the new triangle
  relate to the size, shape, and position of
  the original triangle. **See margin.**

  b. If you add −6 to each original
  x-coordinate, and graph and connect the
  new points to create a new figure, how
  will the position of the new figure relate
  to that of the original one? **See margin.**

  c. Multiply the y-coordinate of each original
  ordered pair by −1. Graph and connect
  the new points to form a new figure.
  Describe how the size, shape, and
  position of the new triangle relate to the
  size, shape, and position of the original
  triangle. **See margin.**

  d. If you multiply each original x-coordinate
  by −1, and graph and connect the new
  points to create a new figure, how will
  the position of the new figure relate to
  that of the original one? **See margin.**

Test-Taking Tip Ⓐ Ⓑ Ⓒ Ⓓ

Question 17
When answering open-ended items on standardized tests,
follow these steps:
1. Read the item carefully.
2. Show all of your work. You may receive points for
   items that are only partially correct.
3. Check your work.

Chapter 2 Standardized Test Practice **95**

Evaluating Extended Response Questions

Extended Response questions
are graded by using a multilevel
rubric that guides you in assessing a student's knowledge of a
particular concept.

Goal: Graph geometric figures
on a coordinate grid and analyze
the relationships among figures,
points, and mathematical
operations.

Sample Scoring Rubric: The
following rubric is a sample
scoring device. You may wish
to add more detail to this sample
to meet your individual scoring
needs.

Score	Criteria
4	A correct solution that is supported by well-developed, accurate explanations
3	A generally correct solution, but may contain minor flaws in reasoning or computation
2	A partially correct interpretation and/or solution to the problem
1	A correct solution with no supporting evidence or explanation
0	An incorrect solution indicating no mathematical understanding of the concept or task, or no solution is given

Answer

17a–d.

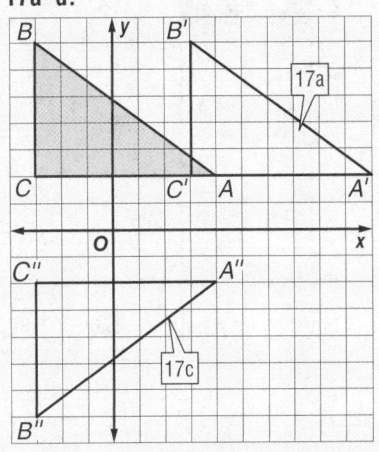

17a. Yes, the new figure is the same size and
shape as the original triangle. The original triangle could be slid (translated)
6 units to the right to create the new
figure.

17b. If −6 were added to each x-coordinate,
the original triangle could be slid 6 units
to the left (or slid −6 units) to create the
new figure.

17c. Yes, the new figure is the same size and
shape as the original triangle. The original triangle could be flipped (reflected)
across the x-axis to create the new
figure.

17d. If you multiplied the x-coordinate of
each original coordinate pair by −1, the
original triangle would be flipped
(reflected) over the y-axis.

Page 59, Lesson 2-1

26. ![number line with points at -3, -1, 1, 3]
$-4 -3 -2 -1 \ 0 \ 1 \ 2 \ 3 \ 4$

27. ![number line]
$-3 -2 -1 \ 0 \ 1 \ 2 \ 3 \ 4 \ 5$

28. ![number line]
$-8 -7 -6 -5 -4 -3 -2 -1 \ 0$

29. ![number line]
$-8 -6 -4 -2 \ 0 \ 2 \ 4 \ 6 \ 8$

Page 61, Lesson 2-1

79. {(3, 2), (3, 4), (2, 1), (2, 4)}   **80.** {(1, 4), (6, 2), (9, 6), (1, 9)}

x	y
3	2
3	4
2	1
2	4

x	y
1	4
6	2
9	6
1	9

Page 87, Lesson 2-6

1. Sample answer: (3, 6) represents a point 3 units to the right and 6 units up from the origin. (6, 3) represents a point 6 units to the right and 3 units up from the origin.

3. Keisha; a point in Quadrant I has two positive coordinates. Interchanging the coordinates will still result in two positive coordinates, and the point will be in Quadrant I.

8–11.

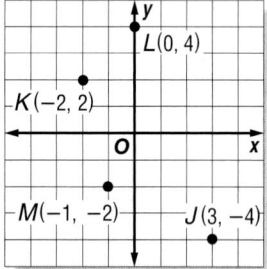

12. Sample answer:

x	y
-2	5
-1	4
0	3
1	2
2	1
3	0

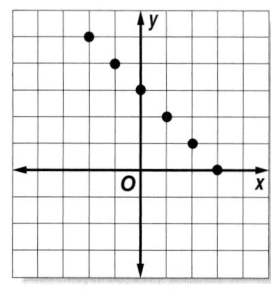

The points are along a diagonal line that crosses the y-axis at $y = 3$ and the x-axis at $x = 3$.

23–34.

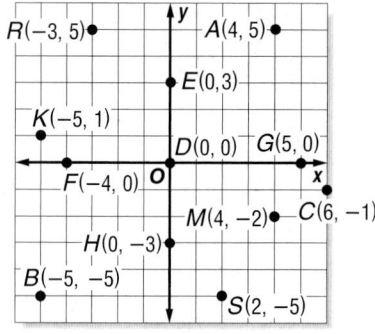

35–40. Sample answers given.

35.

x	y
1	4
2	3
3	2
4	1
5	0
6	-1

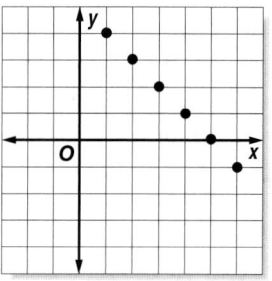

The points are along a line slanting down to the right, crossing the y-axis at 5 and the x-axis at 5.

36.

x	y
-2	0
-1	-1
0	-2
1	-3
2	-4
3	-5

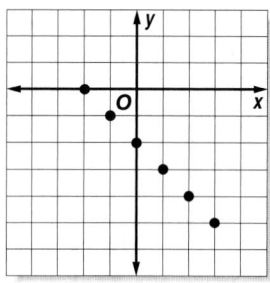

The points are along a line slanting down, crossing the x-axis at -2 and the y-axis at -2.

37.

x	y
-2	-4
-1	-2
0	0
1	2
2	4
3	6

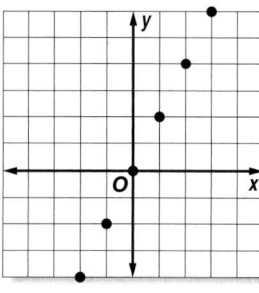

The points are along a line slanting up, through the origin

38.

x	y
-2	4
-1	2
0	0
1	-2
2	-4
3	-6

The points are along a line slanting down, through the origin

39.

x	y
-3	-1
-2	0
-1	1
0	2
1	3
2	4

The points are along a line slanting up, crossing the y-axis at 2 and the x-axis at -2

40.

x	y
-2	-3
-1	-2
0	-1
1	0
2	1
3	2

The points are along a line slanting up, crossing the y-axis at -1 and the x-axis at 1

41.

42.

43. Sample answer:

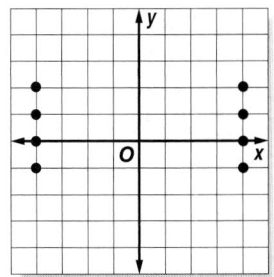

The graph can include any ordered pair in which $x > 3$ or $x < -3$.

44.

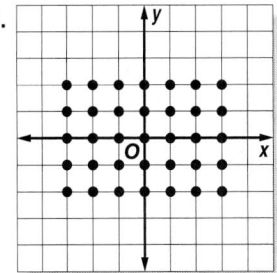

The graph can include any integer pairs where $x > 4$ or $x < -4$.

45.

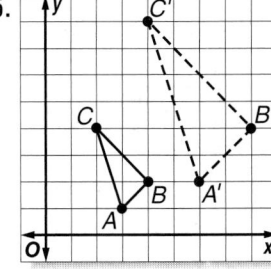

The new triangle is twice the size of the original triangle, and is moved to the right and up.

46.

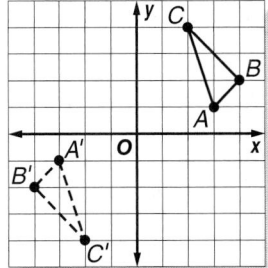

The new triangle is reflected over the x- and y-axes; it is the same size as the original triangle.

47.

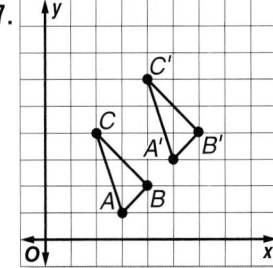

The new triangle is translated right 2 units and up 2 units; it is the same size as the original triangle.

48.

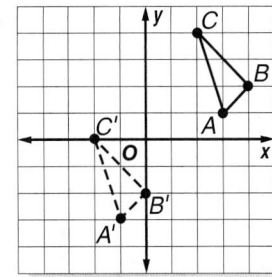

The new triangle is translated left 4 and down 4; it is the same size as the original triangle.

Equations
Chapter Overview and Pacing

Year-long pacing: pages T20–T21.

LESSON OBJECTIVES	Regular		Block	
	Basic/ Average	Advanced	Basic/ Average	Advanced
3-1 The Distributive Property *(pp. 98–102)* • Use the Distributive Property to write equivalent numerical expressions. • Use the Distributive Property to write equivalent algebraic expressions.	1	1	0.5	0.5
3-2 Simplifying Algebraic Expressions *(pp. 103–107)* • Use the Distributive Property to simplify algebraic expressions.	1	1	0.5	0.5
3-3 Solving Equations by Adding or Subtracting *(pp. 108–114)* *Preview:* Solve equations using algebra tiles. • Solve equations by using the Subtraction Property of Equality. • Solve equations by using the Addition Property of Equality.	2 (with 3-3 Preview)	1	1 (with 3-3 Preview)	0.5
3-4 Solving Equations by Multiplying or Dividing *(pp. 115–119)* • Solve equations by using the Division Property of Equality. • Solve equations by using the Multiplication Property of Equality.	1	1	0.5	0.5
3-5 Solving Two-Step Equations *(pp. 120–124)* • Solve two-step equations.	2	2	1	0.5
3-6 Writing Two-Step Equations *(pp. 126–130)* • Write verbal sentences as two-step equations. • Solve verbal problems by writing and solving two-step equations.	2	1	1	0.5
3-7 Using Formulas *(pp. 131–137)* • Solve problems by using formulas. • Solve problems involving the perimeters and areas of rectangles. *Follow-Up:* Use a spreadsheet to find perimeter and area.	1	2 (with 3-7 Follow-Up)	0.5	1 (with 3-7 Follow-Up)
Study Guide and **Practice Test** *(pp. 138–141)* **Standardized Test Practice** *(pp. 142–143)*	1	1	0.5	0.5
Chapter Assessment	1	1	0.5	0.5
TOTAL	12	11	6	5

Chapter Resource Manager

CHAPTER 3 RESOURCE MASTERS

Study Guide and Intervention	Practice (Skills and Average)	Reading to Learn Mathematics	Enrichment	Assessment	Prerequisite Skills Workbook	Applications*	Parent and Student Study Guide Workbook	5-Minute Check Transparencies	Interactive Chalkboard	Pre-AlgePASS: Tutorial Plus (lessons)	Materials
107	108–109	110	111		9–10		16	3-1	3-1		
112	113–114	115	116	157			17	3-2	3-2		
117	118–119	120	121		5–8	SC 5	18	3-3	3-3		*Preview:* algebra tiles, equation mat
122	123–124	125	126	157, 159	9–12		19	3-4	3-4	4	
127	128–129	130	131		21–26	SM 9 GCS 23	20	3-5	3-5	5, 6	
132	133–134	135	136	158			21	3-6	3-6		
137	138–139	140	141	158		SC 6 GCS 24	22	3-7	3-7		*Follow-Up:* spreadsheet software
				143–156, 160–162 163–164							

* *Key to Abbreviations:* GCS = Graphing Calculator and Spreadsheet Masters
SC = School-to-Career Masters
SM = Science and Mathematics Lab Manual

 ELL Study Guide and Intervention, Skills Practice, Practice, and Parent and Student Study Guide Workbooks are also available in Spanish.

Chapter 3 — Mathematical Connections and Background

Continuity of Instruction

Prior Knowledge

Prior to beginning the Pre-Algebra course, students learned addition, subtraction, multiplication, and division of whole numbers. In Chapter 1 they learned to solve equations mentally, to use addition and subtraction properties, and to translate verbal expressions into algebraic expressions. In Chapter 2 students learned addition, subtraction, multiplication, and division of integers.

This Chapter

In this chapter, students will study how to use the Distributive Property to combine like terms in order to simplify algebraic expressions. They solve equations using properties of equality. Students will learn how to write and solve two-step equations and they will use formulas to solve real-world problems such as finding the area and perimeter of rectangles.

Future Connections

Skill in solving equations will be needed in Chapter 6 when students learn to solve proportion and percent problems and in Chapter 7 when they learn to solve inequalities. Solving two-step equations will be extended to include solving equations with variables on each side in Chapter 8. The study of area of rectangles in this chapter forms the basis of the formulas for area of parallelograms, triangles, and trapezoids in Chapter 10.

3-1 The Distributive Property

Two expressions are said to be equivalent if they have the same value. The Distributive Property says that to multiply a number by a sum, multiply each number inside the parentheses by the number outside the parentheses. For example, the expression $3(x - 4) = 3x - 12$. Algebra tiles can be used to demonstrate the Distributive Property by showing that two equivalent algebraic expressions will always have the same value, no matter what variables are used in the expression.

3-2 Simplifying Algebraic Expressions

The Distributive Property can be used to simplify algebraic expressions. When plus or minus signs separate an algebraic expression into parts, each part is a term. The numerical part of a term that contains a variable is called the *coefficient* of the variable. Like terms are terms that contain the same variables, such as $2n$ and $5n$ or $6xy$ and $4xy$. A term without a variable is called a *constant*. Constant terms are also like terms. Rewriting a subtraction expression using addition helps identify the terms of an expression. An algebraic expression is in simplest form if it has no like terms and no parentheses.

3-3 Solving Equations by Adding or Subtracting

Inverse operations often can be used to solve equations. Inverse operations reverse one another. For example, the inverse of the addition of 4 in the expression $x + 4$ is the subtraction of 4. The Addition and Subtraction Properties of Equality say that if you add or subtract the same number from each side of an equation, the two sides remain equal. Two equations are equivalent equations if they have the same solution. When solving an equation, check to be sure that the first and last equations are equivalent. If an equation has a subtraction expression, first rewrite the expression as an addition expression. Then add the additive inverse to each side.

3-4 Solving Equations by Multiplying or Dividing

Multiplication and division are inverse operations of one another. Some equations can be solved by multiplying or dividing each side by the same number. The Division Property of Equality says that when you divide each side of an equation by the same nonzero number, the two sides remain equal. For example, when solving $4x = 20$, $\frac{4x}{4} = \frac{20}{4}$, which simplifies to $x = 5$. The Multiplication Property of Equality says that when you multiply each side of an equation by the same number, the two sides remain equal. For example, when solving $\frac{x}{3} = 5$, $3\left(\frac{x}{3}\right) = 3(5)$, which simplifies to $x = 15$.

3-5 Solving Two-Step Equations

A two-step equation contains two operations. In the equation $2x + 1 = 9$, x is multiplied by 2 and then 1 is added. When solving two-step equations, use inverse operations to undo each operation in reverse order. The equation $2x + 1 = 9$ can be solved in two steps. First, subtract 1 from each side. Second, divide each side by 2. When two-step equations have terms with negative coefficients, rewrite subtraction expressions as addition expressions before solving. Sometimes it also is necessary to combine like terms before solving.

3-6 Writing Two-Step Equations

An equation is a statement that two expressions are equal. The expressions are joined with an equals sign (=). Words such as *is, equals,* or *is equal to* can be used when you translate sentences into equations. For example, the sentence "The difference between 3 times some number and 78 is −33" can be expressed by the equation $3n - 78 = -33$.

Many real-world situations can be represented by two-step equations. For example, a savings account may be started with a deposit of $100, and added to at the rate of $25 a month. To show how many months it would take to save $500, you could write the equation $25x + 100 = 500$.

3-7 Using Formulas

A formula is an equation that shows a relationship among certain quantities. A formula usually contains two or more variables. One of the most commonly used formulas shows the relationship between distance, rate (or speed), and time. The distance formula $d = rt$ means that "distance equals the rate multiplied by the time."

Other formulas find geometric quantities. For example, the distance around a geometric figure is called the *perimeter*. One method of finding the perimeter P of a rectangle is to add the measures of the four sides. The formula for the perimeter of a rectangle expresses this as $P = 2(\ell + w)$. Likewise, the measure of the surface enclosed by a figure is its area. The formula for the area of a rectangle is $A = \ell w$.

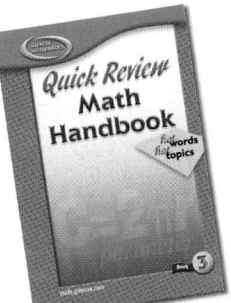

Quick Review Math Handbook

Hot Words includes a glossary of terms while Hot Topics consists of explanations of key mathematical concepts with exercises to test comprehension. This valuable resource can be used as a reference in the classroom or for home study.

Lesson	Hot Topics Section	Lesson	Hot Topics Section
GS 3	1.5, 6.1	3-4	1.5, 6.4
3-1	1.2, 1.5, 6.2	3-5	6.1, 6.4
3-2	1.2, 1.5, 6.2	3-6	6.1, 6.4
3-3	1.5, 6.4	3-7	6.3, 6.4, 7.4, 7.5

GS = Getting Started

 Additional mathematical information and teaching notes are available at www.pre-alg.com/key_concepts.

Chapter 3

DAILY INTERVENTION and Assessment

Key to Abbreviations:
TWE = Teacher Wraparound Edition; CRM = Chapter Resource Masters

	Type	Student Edition	Teacher Resources	Technology/Internet
INTERVENTION	Ongoing	Prerequisite Skills, pp. 97, 102, 107, 114, 119, 124, 130 Practice Quiz 1, p. 107 Practice Quiz 2, p. 130	5-Minute Check Transparencies *Prerequisite Skills Workbook*, pp. 5–12, 21–26 Quizzes, *CRM*, pp. 157, 158 Mid-Chapter Test, *CRM*, p. 159 Study Guide and Intervention, *CRM*, pp. 107, 112, 117, 122, 127, 132, 137	Pre-AlgePASS: Tutorial Plus, Lessons 4, 5, and 6 www.pre-alg.com/self_check_quiz www.pre-alg.com/extra_examples
	Mixed Review	pp. 102, 107, 114, 119, 124, 130, 136	Cumulative Review, *CRM*, p. 160	
	Error Analysis	Find the Error, pp. 100, 105, 128	Find the Error, *TWE*, pp. 100, 105, 128 Unlocking Misconceptions, *TWE*, pp. 104, 116	
ASSESSMENT	Standardized Test Practice	pp. 102, 107, 112, 113, 114, 119, 124, 130, 136, 142–143	*TWE*, pp. 142–143 Standardized Test Practice, *CRM*, pp. 161–162	Standardized Test Practice CD-ROM www.pre-alg.com/standardized_test
	Open-Ended Assessment	Writing in Math, pp. 101, 106, 114, 119, 123, 130, 136 Open Ended, pp. 100, 105, 113, 117, 122, 128, 133 Standardized Test, p. 143	Speaking: *TWE*, pp. 107, 114 Writing: *TWE*, p. 130 Modeling: *TWE*, pp. 102, 119, 124, 136 Open-Ended Assessment, *CRM*, p. 155	
	Chapter Assessment	Study Guide, pp. 138–140 Practice Test, p. 141	Multiple-Choice Tests (Forms 1, 2A, 2B), *CRM*, pp. 143–148 Free-Response Tests (Forms 2C, 2D, 3), *CRM*, pp. 149–154 Vocabulary Test/Review, *CRM*, p. 156	ExamView® Pro (see below) MindJogger Videoquizzes www.pre-alg.com/vocabulary_review www.pre-alg.com/chapter_test

For more information on Yearly ProgressPro, see p. 2.

Pre-Algebra Lesson	Yearly ProgressPro Skill Lesson(s)
3-1	Distributive Property
3-2	Simplifying Algebraic Expressions
3-3	Solving Addition/Subtraction Equations
3-4	Solving Multiplication Equations Solving Equations with Division
3-5	Solving Two-Step Equations
3-6	Writing Two-Step Equations
3-7	Area of Rectangles Perimeters of Rectangles/Squares/Triangles

ExamView® Pro

Use the networkable **ExamView® Pro** to:
- Create **multiple versions** of tests.
- Create **modified** tests for *Inclusion* students.
- **Edit** existing questions and **add** your own questions.
- Use built-in **state curriculum correlations** to create tests aligned with state standards.
- Change **English** tests to **Spanish** and vice versa.

For more information on Intervention and Assessment, see pp. T8–T11.

Reading and Writing in Mathematics

Glencoe Pre-Algebra provides numerous opportunities to incorporate reading and writing into the mathematics classroom.

Student Edition

- Foldables™ Study Organizer, p. 97
- Reading Mathematics, p. 125
- Concept Check questions require students to verbalize and write about what they have learned in the lesson. (pp. 98, 99, 100, 103, 104, 105, 110, 111, 113, 116, 117, 121, 122, 126, 128, 131, 133)
- Writing in Math questions in every lesson, pp. 101, 106, 114, 119, 123, 130, 136
- Reading Math, pp. 98, 103
- WebQuest, pp. 135, 136

Teacher Wraparound Edition

- Foldables™ Study Organizer, pp. 97, 138
- Study Notebook suggestions, pp. 100, 105, 109, 112, 117, 122, 125, 128, 133
- Modeling activities, pp. 102, 119, 124, 136
- Speaking activities, pp. 107, 114
- Writing activities, p. 130
- Differentiated Instruction, (Verbal/ Linguistic), p. 129
- **ELL** Resources, pp. 96, 98, 103, 110, 115, 120, 125, 126, 129, 131, 138

Additional Resources

- Vocabulary Builder worksheets require students to define and give examples for key vocabulary terms as they progress through the chapter (*Chapter 3 Resource Masters,* pp. vii–viii)
- Reading to Learn Mathematics master for each lesson (*Chapter 3 Resource Masters*, pp. 110, 115, 120, 125, 130, 135, 140)
- *Vocabulary PuzzleMaker* software creates crossword, jumble, and word search puzzles using vocabulary lists that you can customize.
- *Teaching Mathematics with Foldables* provides suggestions for promoting cognition and language.
- *Reading and Writing in the Mathematics Classroom*
- *WebQuest and Project Resources*

For more information on Reading and Writing in Mathematics, see pp. T6–T7.

ELL ENGLISH LANGUAGE LEARNERS

Lesson 3-1
Flexible Groups

Give groups of students a set of index cards with several examples of the properties mentioned. Students can come to consensus and write the name of the property on the back of each card. Students can add their own mathematical or real-world examples of the properties and explain them in their own words.

Lesson 3-5
Using Modeling

Model solving a two-step equation. For example, to solve $5x + 4 = 29$, first cover the coefficient to show the students the equation $x + 4 = 29$. Ask students how they would solve this equation. Subtract 4 from each side. Now the equation is $5x = 25$. Ask students to solve this equation. Then solve for x. This method allows students to see that two steps are involved and that the addition or subtraction occurs first, followed by the multiplication or division. You may wish to do several examples the same way until students see a pattern and make a conjecture about how to solve two-step equations.

Lesson 3-6
Peer Tutoring

Write the words *addition, subtraction, multiplication,* and *division* on the chalkboard. Have students come to the chalkboard and write words that signify each operation. Allow for spelling/grammatical errors. Help students with the translation between verbal sentences and mathematical sentences by writing a verbal sentence on the chalkboard and highlighting text and translating each piece until they have formed the equation. Have the students then practice with a partner, pairing English Language Learners with bilingual students whenever possible.

What You'll Learn

Have students read over the list of objectives and make a list of any words with which they are not familiar.

Why It's Important

Point out to students that this is only one of many reasons why each objective is important. Others are provided in the introduction to each lesson.

Lesson	NCTM Standards	Local Objectives
3-1	1, 2, 6, 9	
3-2	1, 2, 6, 9	
3-3 and 3-4 Preview	2, 10	
3-3	2, 6, 9	
3-4	2, 6, 9	
3-5	2, 6, 9	
3-6	2, 6, 9	
3-7	2, 3, 6, 9	
3-7 Follow-Up	2, 3, 6, 7, 10	

Key to NCTM Standards:

1=Number & Operations, 2=Algebra,
3=Geometry, 4=Measurement,
5=Data Analysis & Probability, 6=Problem
Solving, 7=Reasoning & Proof,
8=Communication, 9=Connections,
10=Representation

Chapter 3 Equations

What You'll Learn

- **Lessons 3-1 and 3-2** Use the Distributive Property to simplify expressions.
- **Lessons 3-3 and 3-4** Solve equations using the Properties of Equality.
- **Lessons 3-5 and 3-6** Write and solve two-step equations.
- **Lesson 3-7** Use formulas to solve real-world and geometry problems.

Key Vocabulary

- equivalent expressions (p. 98)
- coefficient (p. 103)
- constant (p. 103)
- perimeter (p. 132)
- area (p. 132)

Why It's Important

As you continue to study algebra, you will learn how to describe quantitative relationships using variables and equations. For example, the equation $d = rt$ shows the relationship between the variables d (distance), r (rate or speed), and t (time). *You will solve a problem about ballooning in Lesson 3-7.*

Vocabulary Builder   ELL

The Key Vocabulary list introduces students to some of the main vocabulary terms included in this chapter. For a more thorough vocabulary list with pronunciations of new words, give students the Vocabulary Builder worksheets found on pages vii and viii of the *Chapter 3 Resource Masters*. Encourage them to complete the definition of each term as they progress through the chapter. You may suggest that they add these sheets to their study notebooks for future reference when studying for the Chapter 3 test.

▶ **Prerequisite Skills**   To be successful in this chapter, you'll need to master these skills and be able to apply them in problem-solving situations. Review these skills before beginning Chapter 3.

For Lesson 3-1   Multiply Integers

Find each product.   *(For review, see Lesson 2-4.)*

1. $2(-3)$ **−6**   **2.** $-4(3)$ **−12**   **3.** $-5(-2)$ **10**   **4.** $-4(6)$ **−24**

For Lesson 3-2   Write Addition Expressions

Write each subtraction expression as an addition expression.   *(For review, see Lesson 2-3.)*

5. $5 - 7$ **5 + (−7)**   **6.** $6 - 10$ **6 + (−10)**   **7.** $-5 - 9$ **−5 + (−9)** **8.** $11 - 10$
                                                                                        11 + (−10)

For Lessons 3-3 and 3-5   Add Integers

Find each sum.   *(For review, see Lesson 2-2.)*

9. $6 + (-9)$ **−3**   **10.** $-8 + 4$ **−4**   **11.** $4 + (-4)$ **0**   **12.** $7 + (-10)$ **−3**

For Lesson 3-6   Write Algebraic Expressions

Write an algebraic expression for each verbal expression.   *(For review, see Lesson 1-3.)*

13. five more than twice a number **5 + 2n**   **14.** the difference of a number and 15 **n − 15**

15. three less than a number **n − 3**   **16.** the quotient of a number and 10 **n ÷ 10**

Writing and Solving Equations   Make this Foldable to help you organize your notes. Begin with four sheets of $8\frac{1}{2}"\times 11"$ paper.

Step 1   Stack Pages

Place 4 sheets of paper $\frac{3}{4}$ inch apart.

Step 2   Roll Up Bottom Edges

All tabs should be the same size.

Step 3   Crease and Staple

Staple along the fold.

Step 4   Label

Label the tabs with topics from the chapter.

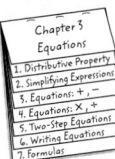

Reading and Writing   As you read and study the chapter, record examples under each tab.

This section provides a review of the basic concepts needed before beginning Chapter 3. Page references are included for additional student help.

Additional review is provided in the *Prerequisite Skills Workbook*, pages 5–12 and 21–26.

Prerequisite Skills in the Getting Ready for the Next Lesson section at the end of each lesson reviews a skill needed in the next lesson.

For Lesson	Prerequisite Skill
3-2	Subtraction Expressions (p. 102)
3-3	Adding Integers (p. 107)
3-4	Dividing Integers (p. 114)
3-5	Subtracting Integers (p. 119)
3-6	Algebraic Expressions (p. 124)
3-7	Solving Equations (p. 130)

FOLDABLES ™
Study Organizer

For more information about Foldables, see *Teaching Mathematics with Foldables.*

Descriptive Writing and Organizing Data   Students use their Foldables to take notes, define terms, record concepts, and write examples. At the end of the appropriate lessons, ask students to write a descriptive paragraph about each method of solution and what equations can be solved that way. Encourage students to see the connectivity of the methods with the operations in the equation. Their writings should help them develop a deeper understanding of the algebraic processes being used.

3-1 The Distributive Property

1 Focus

5-Minute Check Transparency 3-1 Use as a quiz or review of Chapter 2.

Mathematical Background notes are available for this lesson on page 96C.

How are rectangles related to the Distributive Property?

The opening activity questions are repeated on page 110 of the *Chapter 3 Resource Masters*.

Reading to Learn Mathematics, p. 110   ELL

Pre-Activity   *How are rectangles related to the Distributive Property?*

Do the activity at the top of page 98 in your textbook. Write your answers below.

a. Draw a 2-by-5 and a 2-by-4 rectangle. Find the total area in two ways.
$2 \cdot 5 + 2 \cdot 4 = 10 + 8$ or 18; $2(5 + 4) = 2(9)$ or 18

b. Draw a 4-by-4 and a 4-by-1 rectangle. Find the total area in two ways.
$4 \cdot 4 + 4 \cdot 1 = 16 + 4$ or 20; $4(4 + 1) = 4(5)$ or 20

c. Draw any two rectangles that have the same width. Find the total area in two ways. **Sample answer: $3(2 + 2) = 12$;**
$3 \cdot 2 + 3 \cdot 2 = 12$

d. What did you notice about the total area in each case?
The areas are equal.

Reading the Lesson

Write a definition and give an example of the new vocabulary term.

Vocabulary	Definition	Example
1. equivalent expressions	See students' work.	

2. In rewriting $3(x + 2)$, which term is "distributed" to the other terms in the expression? **3**

Helping You Remember

3. *Distribute* is a word that is used frequently in the English language.
   a. Find the definition of *distribute* in a dictionary. Write the definition. **to give out or deliver especially to members of a group**
   b. Explain how the English definition can help you remember how the word *distributive* relates to mathematics. **The number outside the parentheses is "distributed" to each number inside.**

Vocabulary

- equivalent expressions

TEACHING TIP

Remind students how to find the area of a rectangle. They will learn more about the formula for the area of a rectangle in Lesson 3-7.

Reading Math

Distributive
Root Word: Distribute
To *distribute* means to deliver to each member of a group.

3-1 The Distributive Property

NEW YORK *Performance Indicator* Reinforcement of 6.N.3 Define and identify the distributive property of multiplication over addition

What You'll Learn

- Use the Distributive Property to write equivalent numerical expressions.
- Use the Distributive Property to write equivalent algebraic expressions.

How are rectangles related to the Distributive Property?

To find the area of a rectangle, multiply the length and width. You can find the total area of the blue and yellow rectangles in two ways.

Method 1
Put them together. Add the lengths, then multiply.

$3(4 + 2) = 3 \cdot 6$ Add.
$\qquad\quad = 18$ Multiply.

Method 2
Separate them. Multiply to find each area, then add.

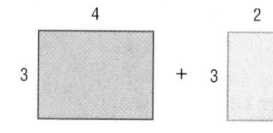

$3 \cdot 4 + 3 \cdot 2 = 12 + 6$ Multiply.
$\qquad\qquad\quad = 18$ Add.

a. Draw a 2-by-5 and a 2-by-4 rectangle. Find the total area in two ways.

b. Draw a 4-by-4 and a 4-by-1 rectangle. Find the total area in two ways.

c. Draw any two rectangles that have the same width. Find the total area in two ways. **a–c. See margin.**

d. What did you notice about the total area in each case? **d. The areas are equal.**

DISTRIBUTIVE PROPERTY The expressions $3(4 + 2)$ and $3 \cdot 4 + 3 \cdot 2$ are **equivalent expressions** because they have the same value, 18. This example shows how the **Distributive Property** combines addition and multiplication.

Key Concept   Distributive Property

- **Words**   To multiply a number by a sum, multiply each number inside the parentheses by the number outside the parentheses.
- **Symbols** $a(b + c) = ab + ac$ $(b + c)a = ba + ca$
- **Examples** $3(4 + 2) = 3 \cdot 4 + 3 \cdot 2$ $(5 + 3)2 = 5 \cdot 2 + 3 \cdot 2$

✓ **Concept Check**   Name two operations that are combined by the Distributive Property. **multiplication, addition**

Resource Manager

📂 **Workbooks and Reproducible Masters**

Chapter 3 Resource Masters
- Study Guide and Intervention, p. 107
- Skills Practice, p. 108
- Practice, p. 109
- Reading to Learn Mathematics, p. 110
- Enrichment, p. 111

Parent and Student Study Guide Workbook, p. 16
Prerequisite Skills Workbook, pp. 9–10

📽 **Transparencies**
5-Minute Check Transparency 3-1
Answer Key Transparencies

💿 **Technology**
Interactive Chalkboard

Example 1 Use the Distributive Property

Use the Distributive Property to write each expression as an equivalent expression. Then evaluate the expression.

a. $2(6 + 4)$

$2(6 + 4) = 2 \cdot 6 + 2 \cdot 4$
$= 12 + 8$ Multiply.
$= 20$ Add.

b. $(8 + 3)5$

$(8 + 3)5 = 8 \cdot 5 + 3 \cdot 5$
$= 40 + 15$ Multiply.
$= 55$ Add.

Example 2 Use the Distributive Property to Solve a Problem

AMUSEMENT PARKS A one-day pass to an amusement park costs $40. A round-trip bus ticket to the park costs $5.

a. Write two equivalent expressions to find the total cost of a one-day pass and a bus ticket for 15 students.

Method 1 Find the cost for 1 person, then multiply by 15.

$$15(\$40 + \$5)$$
$\longrightarrow$ cost for 1 person

Method 2 Find the cost of 15 passes and 15 tickets. Then add.

$$15(\$40) + 15(\$5)$$
cost of 15 passes $\longleftarrow$ $\longrightarrow$ cost of 15 tickets

b. Find the total cost.

Evaluate either expression to find the total cost.

$15(\$40 + 5) = 15(\$40) + 15(\$5)$ Distributive Property
$= \$600 + \$75$ Multiply.
$= \$675$ Add.

The total cost is $675.

CHECK You can check your results by evaluating $15(\$45)$.

More About. . .

Amusement Parks

Attendance at U.S. amusement parks increased 22% in the 1990s. In 1999, over 300 million people attended these parks.

Source: *International Association of Amusement Parks and Attractions*

ALGEBRAIC EXPRESSIONS You can also model the Distributive Property by using algebra tiles.

ALGEBRA CONNECTION

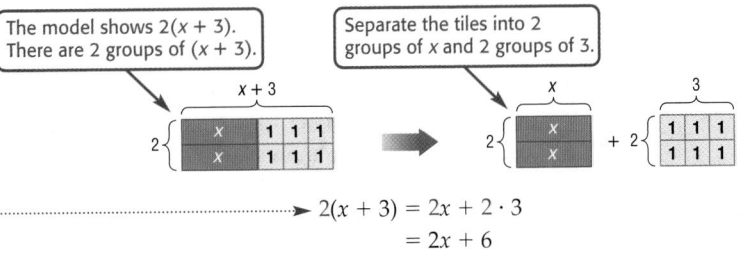

The model shows $2(x + 3)$. There are 2 groups of $(x + 3)$.

Separate the tiles into 2 groups of x and 2 groups of 3.

$x + 3$

$2(x + 3) = 2x + 2 \cdot 3$
$= 2x + 6$

TEACHING TIP

Ask students to evaluate $2(x + 3)$ and $2x + 6$ for different values of x to convince them the expressions are equivalent.

The expressions $2(x + 3)$ and $2x + 6$ are equivalent expressions because no matter what x is, these expressions have the same value.

✓ **Concept Check** Are $3(x + 1)$ and $3x + 1$ equivalent expressions? Explain. No; if $x = 1$, $3(x + 1) = 6$ and $3x + 1 = 4$.

www.pre-alg.com/extra_examples/ny

Lesson 3-1 The Distributive Property **99**

Building on Prior Knowledge

In Chapter 2, students studied operations with integers. These skills will be used in Lesson 3-1.

DISTRIBUTIVE PROPERTY

In-Class Examples Power Point®

1 Use the Distributive Property to write each expression as an equivalent expression. Then evaluate the expression.

a. $4(5 + 8)$ $4 \cdot 5 + 4 \cdot 8$; 52

b. $(6 + 9)2$ $6 \cdot 2 + 9 \cdot 2$; 30

2 **RECREATION** North Country Rivers of York, Maine, offers one-day white-water rafting trips on the Kennebec River. The trip costs $69 per person, and wet suits are $15 each.

a. Write two equivalent expressions to find the total cost of one trip for a family of four if each person uses a wet suit. $4(69 + 15)$; $4 \cdot 69 + 4 \cdot 15$

b. Find the total cost. **$336**

ALGEBRAIC EXPRESSIONS

In-Class Examples Power Point®

3 Use the Distributive Property to write each expression as an equivalent algebraic expression.

a. $2(x + 4)$ $2x + 8$

b. $(y + 3)6$ $6y + 18$

Teaching Tip Watch for students who miss steps when working Example 4. Have them do a few problems, writing out the explanation for each step as in the Example.

4 Use the Distributive Property to write each expression as an equivalent algebraic expression.

a. $4(x - 2)$ $4x - 8$

b. $-2(n - 3)$ $-2n + 6$

Study Notebook

Have students—
- add the definition/example of the vocabulary term to their Vocabulary Builder worksheets for Chapter 3.
- use the Distributive Property to show examples of equivalent expressions.
- give an example of the Distributive Property. Use arrows to show which numbers or variables are multiplied.
- include any other item(s) that they find helpful in mastering the skills in this lesson.

D A I L Y
INTERVENTION **FIND THE ERROR**
Have students replace x with 8 in $3(x + 2)$, $3x + 2$, and $3x + 6$ to determine which is correct. Then ask what the error is. **Julia forgot to multiply the second number by 3.**

About the Exercises . . .
Organization by Objective
- Distributive Property: 12–25, 50, 51
- Algebraic Expressions: 26–49

Odd/Even Assignments
Exercises 12–51 are structured so that students practice the same concepts whether they are assigned odd or even problems.

Assignment Guide
Basic: 13–21 odd, 25–47 odd, 51–55, 64–77

Average: 13–51 odd, 52–55, 64–77 (Optional: 56–63)

Advanced: 12–52 even, 53–71 (Optional: 72–77)

TEACHING TIP
You may want to point out that when students replace $3 \cdot 1$ with 3, they are using the Substitution Property.

Example 3 Simplify Algebraic Expressions

Use the Distributive Property to write each expression as an equivalent algebraic expression.

a. $3(x + 1)$

$3(x + 1) = 3x + 3 \cdot 1$
$ = 3x + 3$ Simplify.

b. $(y + 4)5$

$(y + 4)5 = y \cdot 5 + 4 \cdot 5$
$ = 5y + 20$ Simplify.

Example 4 Simplify Expressions with Subtraction

Use the Distributive Property to write each expression as an equivalent algebraic expression.

Study Tip
Look Back
To review **subtraction expressions**, see Lesson 2-3.

a. $2(x - 1)$

$2(x - 1) = 2[x + (-1)]$ Rewrite $x - 1$ as $x + (-1)$.
$ = 2x + 2(-1)$ Distributive Property
$ = 2x + (-2)$ Simplify.
$ = 2x - 2$ Definition of subtraction

b. $-3(n - 5)$

$-3(n - 5) = -3[n + (-5)]$ Rewrite $n - 5$ as $n + (-5)$.
$ = -3n + (-3)(-5)$ Distributive Property
$ = -3n + 15$ Simplify.

Check for Understanding

Concept Check

1. **OPEN ENDED** Write an equation using three integers that is an example of the Distributive Property. **Sample answer:** $2(3 + 4) = 2 \cdot 3 + 2 \cdot 4$

2. **FIND THE ERROR** Julia and Catelyn are using the Distributive Property to simplify $3(x + 2)$. Who is correct? Explain your reasoning.

2. Catelyn; each number inside the parentheses should be multiplied by 3.

Julia
$3(x + 2) = 3x + 2$

Catelyn
$3(x + 2) = 3x + 6$

Guided Practice

Use the Distributive Property to write each expression as an equivalent expression. Then evaluate it.

GUIDED PRACTICE KEY	
Exercises	Examples
3–5	1
6–9	3, 4
10, 11	2

3. $5(7 + 8)$
   $5 \cdot 7 + 5 \cdot 8, 75$

4. $2(9 + 1)$
   $2 \cdot 9 + 2 \cdot 1, 20$

5. $(2 + 4)6$
   $2 \cdot 6 + 4 \cdot 6, 36$

ALGEBRA Use the Distributive Property to write each expression as an equivalent algebraic expression.

6. $4(x + 3)$
   $4x + 12$

7. $(n + 2)3$
   $3n + 6$

8. $8(y - 2)$
   $8y - 16$

9. $-6(x - 5)$
   $-6x + 30$

Application

MONEY For Exercises 10 and 11, use the following information.
Suppose you work in a grocery store 4 hours on Friday and 5 hours on Saturday. You earn $6.25 an hour.

10. $6.25(4 + 5),
$6.25(4) + $6.25(5)

10. Write two different expressions to find your wages.

11. Find the total wages for that weekend. **$56.25**

D A I L Y
INTERVENTION **Differentiated Instruction**

- **Visual/Spatial** Have students write the equations shown in the definition of the Distributive Property in the Key Concept box on page 98. Then have them use colored pencils or markers to color each number or variable in an equation using the same unique color each time it appears. Have students describe the pattern shown by the colors and use the Distributive Property to explain the pattern.

Practice and Apply

Use the Distributive Property to write each expression as an equivalent expression. Then evaluate it. 12–23. See pp. 143A–143B.

12. $2(6 + 1)$ **13.** $5(7 + 3)$ **14.** $(4 + 6)9$

15. $(4 + 3)3$ **16.** $(9 + 2)4$ **17.** $(8 + 8)2$

18. $7(3 - 2)$ **19.** $6(8 - 5)$ **20.** $-5(8 - 4)$

21. $-3(9 - 2)$ ★**22.** $(8 - 4)(-2)$ ★**23.** $(10 - 3)(-5)$

24. MOVIES One movie ticket costs $7, and one small bag of popcorn costs $3. Write two equivalent expressions for the total cost of four movie tickets and four bags of popcorn. Then find the cost.
4($7 + $3), 4($7) + 4($3); $40

25. SPORTS A volleyball uniform costs $15 for the shirt, $10 for the pants, and $8 for the socks. Write two equivalent expressions for the total cost of 12 uniforms. Then find the cost.
12($15 + $10 + $8), 12($15) + 12($10) + 12($8); $396

ALGEBRA Use the Distributive Property to write each expression as an equivalent algebraic expression. **26–49. See pp. 143A–143B.**

26. $2(x + 3)$ **27.** $5(y + 6)$ **28.** $3(n + 1)$

29. $7(y + 8)$ **30.** $(x + 3)4$ **31.** $(y + 2)10$

32. $(3 + y)6$ **33.** $(2 + x)5$ **34.** $3(x - 2)$

35. $9(m - 2)$ **36.** $8(z - 3)$ **37.** $15(s - 3)$

38. $(r - 5)6$ **39.** $(x - 3)12$ **40.** $(t - 4)5$

41. $(w - 10)2$ **42.** $-2(z + 4)$ **43.** $-5(a + 10)$

44. $-2(x - 7)$ **45.** $-5(w - 8)$ **46.** $(y - 4)(-2)$

47. $(a - 6)(-5)$ ★**48.** $2(x + y)$ ★**49.** $3(a + b)$

SHOPPING For Exercises 50 and 51, use the graphic.

50. Find the total amount spent by two teens and two adults during one average shopping trip. **$195.50**

51. Find the total amount spent by one teen and one adult during five average shopping trips. **$488.75**

52. WRITING IN MATH   Answer the question that was posed at the beginning of the lesson.

How are rectangles related to the Distributive Property?

Include the following in your answer: **See pp. 143A–143B.**

• a drawing of two rectangles with the same width, and
• two different methods for finding the total area of the rectangles.

USA TODAY Snapshots®

Comparison shoppers

While teen-agers spend about 90 minutes on each trip to the mall, compared to 76 minutes for adults, they end up spending less money.

$59.20 Adults

$38.55 Teens

Source: International Council of Shopping Centers

By Marcy E. Mullins, USA TODAY

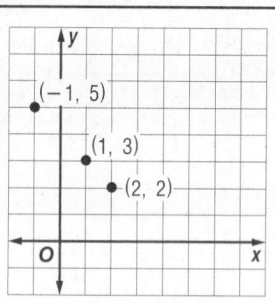

4 Assess

Open-Ended Assessment

Modeling Ask students to use algebra tiles or draw a model to explain the Distributive Property to another student.

Getting Ready for Lesson 3-2

PREREQUISITE SKILL In Lesson 3-2, students use the Distributive Property to simplify algebraic expressions involving addition and subtraction of integers. Exercises 72–77 should be used to determine your students' familiarity with writing a subtraction expression as an addition expression.

Answer

64a.

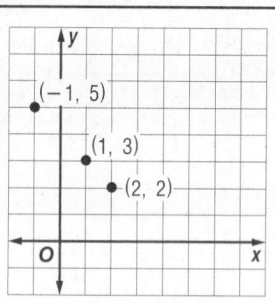

---

53. CRITICAL THINKING Is $3 + (x \cdot y) = (3 + x) \cdot (3 + y)$ a true statement? If so, explain your reasoning. If not, give a counterexample.
No; $3 + (4 \cdot 5) = 23$, $(3 + 4)(3 + 5) = 56$

54. One ticket to a baseball game costs t dollars. A soft drink costs s dollars. Which expression represents the total cost of a ticket and soft drink for p people? **D**
Ⓐ pst　　Ⓑ $p + (ts)$　　Ⓒ $t(p + s)$　　Ⓓ $p(t + s)$

55. Which equation is always true? **C**
Ⓐ $5(a + b) = 5a + b$　　Ⓑ $5(ab) = (5a)(5b)$
Ⓒ $5(a + b) = 5(b + a)$　　Ⓓ $5(a + 0) = 5a + 5$

Extending the Lesson

MENTAL MATH The Distributive Property allows you to find certain products mentally. Replace one factor with the sum of a number and a multiple of ten. Then apply the Distributive Property.

Example Find $15 \cdot 12$ mentally.

$$15 \cdot 12 = 15(10 + 2) \quad \text{Think: 12 is 10 + 2.}$$
$$= 15 \cdot 10 + 15 \cdot 2 \quad \text{Distributive Property}$$
$$= 150 + 30 \quad \text{Multiply mentally.}$$
$$= 180 \quad \text{Add mentally.}$$

Rewrite each product so it is easy to compute mentally. Then find the product.

56. $7(10 + 4) = 98$
57. $8(20 + 3) = 184$
58. $9(30 + 2) = 288$
59. $16(10 + 1) = 176$
60. $14(10 + 2) = 168$
61. $9(100 + 3) = 927$
62. $11(100 + 2) = 1122$
63. $12(1000 + 4) = 12,048$

56. $7 \cdot 14$	**57.** $8 \cdot 23$	**58.** $9 \cdot 32$	**59.** $16 \cdot 11$
60. $14 \cdot 12$	**61.** $9 \cdot 103$	**62.** $11 \cdot 102$	**63.** $12 \cdot 1004$

Maintain Your Skills

Mixed Review

64. The table shows several solutions of the equation $x + y = 4$. *(Lesson 2-6)* **a. See margin.**
  a. Graph the ordered pairs on a coordinate plane.
  b. Describe the graph. **The points are in a straight line.**

x + y = 4		
x	**y**	**(x, y)**
−1	5	(−1, 5)
1	3	(1, 3)
2	2	(2, 2)

65. ALGEBRA Evaluate $\dfrac{-4y}{x}$ if $x = 2$ and $y = -3$. *(Lesson 2-5)* **6**

ALGEBRA Find the solution of each equation if the replacement set is {1, 2, 3, 4, 5}. *(Lesson 1-5)*

66. $2n + 3 = 9$ **3**　　67. $3n - 4 = 8$ **4**　　68. $4x - 9 = -5$ **1**

Find the next three terms in each pattern. *(Lesson 1-1)*

69. 5, 9, 13, 17, . . .　　70. 20, 22, 26, 32, . . .　　71. 5, 10, 20, 40, . . .
21, 25, 29　　**40, 50, 62**　　**80, 160, 320**

Getting Ready for the Next Lesson

PREREQUISITE SKILL Write each subtraction expression as an addition expression. *(To review subtraction expressions, see Lesson 2-3.)*

72. $5 - 3$ **5 + (−3)**　　73. $-8 - 4$ **−8 + (−4)**　　74. $10 - 14$ **10 + (−14)**
75. $3 - 9$ **3 + (−9)**　　76. $-2 - (-5)$ **−2 + 5**　　77. $-7 - 10$ **−7 + (−10)**

Interactive Chalkboard
PowerPoint® Presentations

This CD-ROM is a customizable Microsoft® Power-Point® presentation that includes:
• Step-by-step, dynamic solutions of each In-Class Example from the Teacher Wraparound Edition
• Additional, Your Turn exercises for each example
• The 5-Minute Check Transparencies
• Hot links to Glencoe Online Study Tools

Simplifying Algebraic Expressions

 NEW YORK *Performance Indicator* 8.PS.3
Understand and demonstrate how written symbols represent mathematical ideas

What You'll Learn

• Use the Distributive Property to simplify algebraic expressions.

How can you use algebra tiles to simplify an algebraic expression?

You can use algebra tiles to represent expressions. You can also sort algebra tiles by their shapes and group them.

The drawing on the left represents the expression $2x + 3 + 3x + 1$. On the right, the algebra tiles have been sorted and combined.

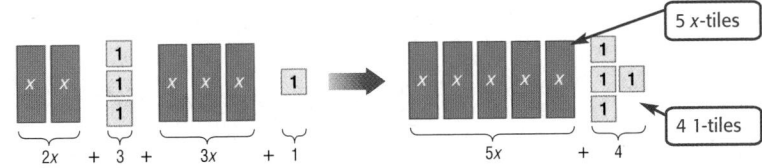

5 x-tiles

4 1-tiles

Therefore, $2x + 3 + 3x + 1 = 5x + 4$.

Model each expression with algebra tiles or a drawing. Then sort them by shape and write an expression represented by the tiles.

a. $3x + 2 + 4x + 3$ **$7x + 5$**   b. $2x + 5 + x$ **$3x + 5$**

c. $4x + 5 + 3$ **$4x + 8$**   d. $x + 2x + 4x$ **$7x$**

Vocabulary

• term
• coefficient
• like terms
• constant
• simplest form
• simplifying an expression

TEACHING TIP

If an expression has no plus or minus signs, the entire expression is a term.

SIMPLIFY EXPRESSIONS When plus or minus signs separate an algebraic expression into parts, each part is a **term**. The numerical part of a term that contains a variable is called the **coefficient** of the variable.

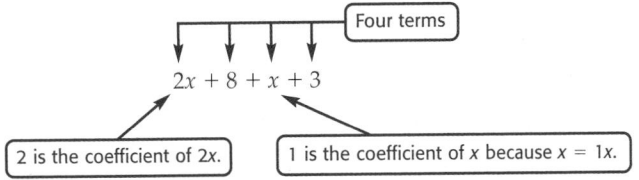

Four terms

$2x + 8 + x + 3$

2 is the coefficient of 2x.

1 is the coefficient of x because $x = 1x$.

Reading Math

Constant
Everyday Meaning: unchanging
Math Meaning: fixed value in an expression

Like terms are terms that contain the same variables, such as $2n$ and $5n$ or $6xy$ and $4xy$. A term without a variable is called a **constant**. Constant terms are also like terms.

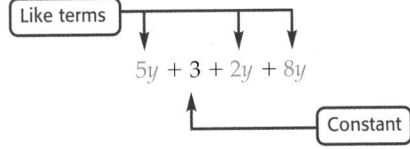

Like terms

$5y + 3 + 2y + 8y$

Constant

✓ **Concept Check** Are 5x and 5y like terms? Explain. **No; they contain different variables.**

Lesson 3-2 Simplifying Algebraic Expressions **103**

3-2 **Lesson Notes**

1 Focus

 5-Minute Check
Transparency 3-2 Use as a quiz or review of Lesson 3-1.

Mathematical Background notes are available for this lesson on page 96C.

How can you use algebra tiles to simplify an algebraic expression?

The opening activity questions are repeated on page 115 of the *Chapter 3 Resource Masters*.

Reading to Learn Mathematics, p. 115 **ELL**

Pre-Activity *How can you use algebra tiles to simplify an algebraic expression?*

Do the activity at the top of page 103 in your textbook. Write your answers below.

a. $3x + 2 + 4x + 3$ **$7x + 5$**   b. $2x + 5 + x$ **$3x + 5$**

c. $4x + 5 + 3$ **$4x + 8$**   d. $x + 2x + 4x$ **$7x$**

Reading the Lesson 1–6. See students' work.

Write a definition and give an example of each new vocabulary word or phrase.

Vocabulary	Definition	Example
1. term		
2. coefficient		
3. like terms		
4. constant		
5. simplest form		
6. simplifying an expression		

7. Is $2(r + 1)$ in simplest form? Explain.
No; the expression contains parentheses.

Helping You Remember

8. *Constant* is a word used in everyday English as well as in mathematics.
  a. Find the definition of *constant* in a dictionary. Write the definition. **something invariable or unchanging**
  b. Explain how the English definition can help you remember how *constant* is used in mathematics. **In mathematics, because a constant has no variable, its value is not subject to change.**

Resource Manager

Workbooks and Reproducible Masters

Chapter 3 Resource Masters
• Study Guide and Intervention, p. 112
• Skills Practice, p. 113
• Practice, p. 114
• Reading to Learn Mathematics, p. 115
• Enrichment, p. 116
• Assessment, p. 157

Parent and Student Study Guide Workbook, p. 17

 Transparencies
5-Minute Check Transparency 3-2
Answer Key Transparencies

 Technology
Interactive Chalkboard

SIMPLIFY EXPRESSIONS

In-Class Examples Power Point®

1 Identify the terms, like terms, coefficients, and constants in the expression $4x - x + 2y - 3$. **terms: 4x, −x, 2y, −3; coefficients: 4, −1, 2; like terms: 4x, −x; constant: −3**

Teaching Tip Remind students that the order of the addends does not affect the sum.

2 Simplify each expression.

a. $5x + 4x$ **9x**

b. $8n + 4 + 4n$ **12n + 4**

c. $6x + 4 - 5x - 7$ **x − 3**

d. $-y + 2(x + 3y)$ **2x + 5y**

3 **WORK** You and a friend worked in the school store last week. You worked 4 hours more than your friend. Write an expression in simplest form that represents the total number of hours you both worked. **2h + 4, where h is the number of hours your friend worked**

 Skills Check

Simplify Expressions
Simplify each expression.

a. $2x + 5x$ **7x**

b. $2x - 2(y + 5x)$ **−8x − 2y**

c. $3x + 7(5 - x)$ **−4x + 35**

> **Study Tip**
>
> *Equivalent Expressions*
> To check whether $2x + 8x$ and $10x$ are equivalent expressions, substitute any value for x and see whether the expressions have the same value.

TEACHING TIP

Substituting one value for x does not *guarantee* that the expressions are equivalent. But if the expressions do *not* have the same value, you'll know that the expressions are *not* equivalent.

TEACHING TIP

When students understand that $m = 1 \cdot m$, have them try to perform this step mentally.

Rewriting a subtraction expression using addition will help you identify the terms of an expression.

Example 1 *Identify Parts of Expressions*

Identify the terms, like terms, coefficients, and constants in the expression $3x - 4x + y - 2$.

$$3x - 4x + y - 2 = 3x + (-4x) + y + (-2) \quad \text{Definition of subtraction}$$
$$= 3x + (-4x) + 1y + (-2) \quad \text{Identity Property}$$

The terms are $3x$, $-4x$, y, and -2. The like terms are $3x$ and $-4x$.

The coefficients are 3, −4, and 1. The constant is −2.

An algebraic expression is in **simplest form** if it has no like terms and no parentheses. When you use the Distributive Property to combine like terms, you are **simplifying the expression**.

Example 2 *Simplify Algebraic Expressions*

Simplify each expression.

a. $2x + 8x$

$2x$ and $8x$ are like terms.

$$2x + 8x = (2 + 8)x \quad \text{Distributive Property}$$
$$= 10x \quad \text{Simplify.}$$

b. $6n + 3 + 2n$

$6n$ and $2n$ are like terms.

$$6n + 3 + 2n = 6n + 2n + 3 \quad \text{Commutative Property}$$
$$= (6 + 2)n + 3 \quad \text{Distributive Property}$$
$$= 8n + 3 \quad \text{Simplify.}$$

c. $3x - 5 - 8x + 6$

$3x$ and $-8x$ are like terms. -5 and 6 are also like terms.

$$3x - 5 - 8x + 6 = 3x + (-5) + (-8x) + 6 \quad \text{Definition of subtraction}$$
$$= 3x + (-8x) + (-5) + 6 \quad \text{Commutative Property}$$
$$= [3 + (-8)]x + (-5) + 6 \quad \text{Distributive Property}$$
$$= -5x + 1 \quad \text{Simplify.}$$

d. $m + 3(n + 4m)$

$$m + 3(n + 4m) = m + 3n + 3(4m) \quad \text{Distributive Property}$$
$$= m + 3n + 12m \quad \text{Associative Property}$$
$$= 1m + 3n + 12m \quad \text{Identity Property}$$
$$= 1m + 12m + 3n \quad \text{Commutative Property}$$
$$= (1 + 12)m + 3n \quad \text{Distributive Property}$$
$$= 13m + 3n \quad \text{Simplify.}$$

Concept Check Expressions like $4(x - 3)$, $4x - 12$, and $x + 3x - 12$ are equivalent expressions. Which is in simplest form? **4x − 12**

DAILY INTERVENTION   **Unlocking Misconceptions**

- **Simplify Expressions** When expressions include coefficients of 1, students may forget to include all of the terms. For example, they may mistakenly simplify $5n + n$ as $5n$, forgetting about the unwritten 1 before the second n. Have them first rewrite the expression as $5n + 1n$ before combining like terms.

Example 3 *Translate Verbal Phrases into Expressions*

BASEBALL CARDS Suppose you and your brother collect baseball cards. He has 15 more cards in his collection than you have. Write an expression in simplest form that represents the total number of cards in both collections.

Words   You have some cards. Your brother has 15 more.

Variables Let x = number of cards you have.

Let $x + 15$ = number of cards your brother has.

Expression To find the total, add the expressions.

$$x + (x + 15) = (x + x) + 15 \qquad \text{Associative Property}$$
$$= (1x + 1x) + 15 \qquad \text{Identity Property}$$
$$= (1 + 1)x + 15 \qquad \text{Distributive Property}$$
$$= 2x + 15 \qquad \text{Simplify.}$$

The expression $2x + 15$ represents the total number of cards, where x is the number of cards you have.

More About. . .

Baseball Cards ·····

Honus Wagner is considered by many to be baseball's greatest all-around player. In July, 2000, one of his baseball cards sold for $1.1 million.

Source: CMG Worldwide

Check for Understanding

Concept Check

1. Define *like terms*. **terms that contain the same variable or are constants**

2. Sample answer:
$4x + 5y - 1$

2. OPEN ENDED Write an expression containing three terms that is in simplest form. One of the terms should be a constant.

3. FIND THE ERROR Koko and John are simplifying the expression $5x - 4 + x + 2$.

Koko
$5x - 4 + x + 2 =$
$6x - 2$

John
$5x - 4 + x + 2 =$
$5x - 2$

Who is correct? Explain your reasoning. **Koko; $5x + x = 6x$, not $5x$.**

Guided Practice

GUIDED PRACTICE KEY

Exercises	Examples
4–6	1
7–15	2
16	3

Identify the terms, like terms, coefficients, and constants in each expression. 4–6. See margin.

4. $4x + 3 + 5x + y$ **5.** $2m - n + 6m$ **6.** $4y - 2x - 7$

Simplify each expression. 9. $7c + 12$ 12. $-2x + 3$

7. $6a + 2a$ **8a**   **8.** $x + 9x + 3$ **10x + 3**   **9.** $6c + 4 + c + 8$

10. $7m - 2m$ **5m**   **11.** $9y + 8 - 8$ **9y**   **12.** $2x - 5 - 4x + 8$

13. $5 - 3(y + 7)$ **$-3y - 16$** **14.** $3x + 2y + 4y$ **15.** $x + 3(x + 4y)$
                                     $3x + 6y$ **$4x + 12y$**

Application

16. MONEY You have saved some money. Your friend has saved $20 more than you. Write an expression in simplest form that represents the total amount of money you and your friend have saved. **$2x + 20$**

---

3 Practice/Apply

Study Notebook

Have students—

• add the definitions/examples of the vocabulary terms to their Vocabulary Builder worksheets for Chapter 3.

• write a checklist for the things to look for when simplifying expressions.

• include any other item(s) that they find helpful in mastering the skills in this lesson.

DAILY
INTERVENTION FIND THE ERROR

Ask students why John made the error and how they would teach him to add the x-term in such expressions.

About the Exercises . . .

Odd/Even Assignments

Exercises 17–55 are structured so that students practice the same concepts whether they are assigned odd or even problems.

Assignment Guide

Basic: 17–45 odd, 51–55 odd, 56–73

Average: 17–55 odd, 56–73

Advanced: 18–56 even, 57–67 (Optional: 68–73)

All: Quiz 1 (1–5)

Answers

4. terms: $4x$, 3, $5x$, y; like terms: $4x$, $5x$; coefficients: 4, 5, 1; constant: 3

5. terms: $2m$, $-1n$, $6m$; like terms: $2m$, $6m$; coefficients: 2, -1, 6; constant: none

6. terms: $4y$, $-2x$, -7; like terms: none; coefficients: 4, -2; constant: -7

DAILY
INTERVENTION   **Differentiated Instruction**

• **Kinesthetic** Have students work in groups to model combining like terms. Call out an everyday school item, such as "pencil." Each student in the group then places the pencils in his or her possession in a pile on the table or desk. Then the group writes an expression to show, for example, that each person in turn had 4, 3, 1, and 0 pencils: $4p + 3p + 1p + 0$. Finally, the group simplifies the expression: $8p$.

Study Guide and Intervention, p. 112

term: a number, a variable, or a product of numbers and variables
coefficient: the numerical part of a term that also contains a variable
constant: term without a variable
like terms: terms that contain the same variables

Example 1 Identify the terms, like terms, coefficients, and constants in the expression $4m - 5m + n - 7$.

$4m - 5m + n - 7 = 4m + (-5m) + n + (-7)$ Definition of subtraction
$= 4m + (-5m) + 1n + (-7)$ Identity Property
terms $4m, -5m, 1n, -7$; like terms: $4m, -5m$; coefficients: $4, -5, 1$; constants: -7

When an algebraic expression has no like terms and no parentheses, we say that it is in **simplest form**.

Example 2 Simplify $6x - 5 - 2x + 7$.

$6x - 5 - 2x + 7 = 6x + (-5) + (-2x) + 7$ Definition of subtraction
$= 6x + (-2x) + (-5) + 7$ Commutative Property
$= [6 + (-2)]x + (-5) + 7$ Distributive Property
$= 4x + 2$ Simplify

Exercises

Identify the terms, like terms, coefficients, and constants in each expression.

1. $2 + 6a + 4a$
2, 6a, 4a; 6a, 4a; 6, 4; 2

2. $m + 4m + 2m + 5$
m, 4m, 2m, 5; m, 4m, 2m; 1, 4, 2; 5

3. $3c + 4d - c + 2$
3c, 4d, −c, 2; 3c, −c; 3, 4, −1; 2

4. $5h - 3g + 2g - h$
5h, −3g, 2g, −h; 5h, −h and −3g, 2g; 5, −3, 2, −1; none

5. $3w + 4u - 6$
3w, 4u, −6; none; 3, 4; −6

6. $4r - 5s + 5s - 2r$
4r, −5s, 5s, −2r; 4r, −2r and −5s, 5s; 4, −5, 5, −2; none

Simplify each expression.

7. $9m + 3m$ $12m$
8. $5x - x$ $4x$
9. $8y + 2y + 3y$ $13y$
10. $4 + m - 3m$ $-2m + 4$
11. $13a + 7a + 2a$ $22a$
12. $3y + 1 + 5 + 4y$ $7y + 6$
13. $8d - 4 - d + 5$ $7d + 1$
14. $10 - 4s + 2s - 3$ $7 - 2s$

Skills Practice, p. 113 and Practice, p. 114 (shown)

Simplify each expression.

1. $6y - 4 + y$ $7y - 4$
2. $8u + 2u - 3u$ $7u$
3. $-12 + 5g + 8 - g$ $4g - 4$
4. $-21w + 5 + 3w - 1$ $-18w + 4$
5. $r + r + r + r + r$ $5r$
6. $f - 3f + 2 - f + 1$ $-3f + 3$
7. $-8q + 6 + 5q - 3$ $-3q + 3$
8. $h + 5h - 3 - 6h$ -3
9. $2a - 5(a + 1)$ $-3a - 5$
10. $b - 2(b - 2)$ $-b + 4$
11. $9 - t - 3(t + 3)$ $-4t$
12. $-8 + 5(g + 2) - 2$ $5g$
13. $12m + 9 - 2m - 16$ $10m - 7$
14. $4(y - 3) + 9 - 3y$ $y - 3$
15. $8a + b - 3a + 4b$ $5a + 5b$
16. $-11x + 4 + 8x - 4 + 3x$ 0
17. $-14y + 12(x + y) - 12x$ $-2y$
18. $15y - 4h + 4 - 20(g - 1)$ $-g - 4h + 24$
19. $-5(c + d) - 4d + 5c - d$ $-10d$
20. $(8 - b)(-3) + 6b + 12 - 10b$ $-b - 12$
21. $-p + q + 2(p + q) - p - q$ $2q$
22. $-55n + 28n + 21n + 7n - n$ 0
23. $-12z + 4(z - 9) + 30 + z$ $-7z - 6$
24. $-9 + w - v + 5w + 2v + 5$ $v + 6w - 4$
25. $-6(y - 1) + 2y + 7 - y + 4$ $-5y + 17$
26. $x - 10 + y - 2(x + y) + y$ $-x - 10$

Write an expression in simplest form that represents the total amount in each situation.

27. **LUNCH** You bought 3 pieces of chicken that cost x dollars each, a salad for $3, and a drink for $1. $3x + 4$

28. **SOCCER** Sal has scored g goals this season. Ben has scored four times as many goals as Sal. Chun has scored three fewer goals than Ben. $9g - 3$

Enrichment, p. 116

Algebraic Proof

Recall that properties are statements that are true for any numbers. These properties are used to prove theorems. Use the properties you have learned to complete each proof.

Abbreviations for some properties you may need to use are listed below.
Commutative Property—Addition (CPA)
Commutative Property—Multiplication (CPM)
Associative Property—Addition (APA)
Associative Property—Multiplication (APM)
Additive Identity Property (AIP)
Multiplicative Identity Property (MIP)
Inverse Property of Addition (IPA)
Inverse Property of Multiplication (IPM)
Multiplicative Property of Zero (MPZ)
Distributive Property (DP)

Write the reason for each statement.

1. Prove: $-(y - x) = x - y$

Statement	Reason
$-(y - x) = -1(y - x)$	MIP
$= -1y - (-1x)$	a. DP
$= -y - (-x)$	b. MIP
$= -y + x$	c. Definition of Subtraction
$= x + (-y)$	d. CPA
$= x - y$	e. Definition of Subtraction

2. Prove: $3x - 4 - x = 2x - 4$

Statement	Reason
$3x - 4 - x = 3x + (-4) + (-x)$	a. Definition of Subtraction
$= 3x + (-x) + (-4)$	b. CPA
$= 3x + (-1x) + (-4)$	c. MIP
$= [3 + (-1)]x + (-4)$	d. DP
$= 2x + (-4)$	e. Simplify
$= 2x - 4$	f. Definition of Subtraction

3. Prove: $-2x + 6 + 2x = 6$

Statement	Reason
$-2x + 6 + 2x = -2x + 2x + 6$	a. CPA
$= (-2 + 2)x + 6$	b. DP
$= 0x + 6$	c. IPA
$= 0 + 6$	d. MPZ
$= 6$	e. AIP

★ indicates increased difficulty

Practice and Apply

Homework Help

For Exercises	See Examples
17–22	1
23–49	2
50–53	3

Extra Practice
See page 728.

Identify the terms, like terms, coefficients, and constants in each expression. **17–22. See margin.**

17. $3 + 7x + 3x + x$
18. $y + 3y + 8y + 2$
19. $2a + 5c - a + 6a$
20. $5c - 2d + 3d - d$
21. $6m - 2n + 7$
22. $7x - 3y + 3z - 2$

Simplify each expression. **28. $4 + 3m$**   **29. $7y + 9$**   **30. $10x + 12$**

23. $2x + 5x$ **$7x$**
24. $7b + 2b$ **$9b$**
25. $y + 10y$ **$11y$**
26. $5y + y$ **$6y$**
27. $2a + 3 + 5a$ **$7a + 3$**
28. $4 + 2m + m$
29. $2y + 8 + 5y + 1$
30. $8x + 5 + 7 + 2x$
31. $5x - 3x$ **$2x$**
32. $10b - 2b$ **$8b$**
33. $4y - 5y$ **$-y$**
34. $r - 3r$ **$-2r$**
35. $8 + x - 5x$ **$-4x + 8$**
36. $6x + 4 - 7x$
37. $8y - 7 + 7$ **$8y$**
38. $9x + 2 - 2$ **$9x$**
39. $2x + 3 - 3x + 9$
40. $5t - 3 - t + 2$
41. $3(b + 2) + 2b$
42. $5(x + 3) + 8x$
43. $-3(a + 2) - a$
44. $-2(x + 3) + 2x$ **-6**
45. $4x - 4(2 + x)$ **-8**
46. $8a - 2(a - 7)$
★ 47. $6m + 2n + 10m$ **$16m + 2n$**
★ 48. $-2y + x + 3y$ **$x + y$**
★ 49. $c + 2(d - 5c)$ **$-9c + 2d$**

36. $4 - x$ or $-x + 4$
39. $-x + 12$
40. $4t - 1$
41. $5b + 6$
42. $13x + 15$
43. $-4a - 6$
46. $6a + 14$

For Exercises 50–53, write an expression in simplest form that represents the total amount in each situation.

50. **SCHOOL SUPPLIES** You bought 5 folders that each cost x dollars, a calculator for $45, and a set of pens for $3.   **$5x + 48$**

51. **SHOPPING** Suppose you buy 3 shirts that each cost s dollars, a pair of shoes for $50, and jeans for $30.   **$3s + 80$**

52. **BIRTHDAYS** Today is your friend's birthday. She is y years old. Her sister is 5 years younger.   **$2y - 5$**

53. **BABY-SITTING** Alicia earned d dollars baby-sitting. Her friend earned twice as much. You earned $2 less than Alicia's friend earned.   **$5d - 2$**

GEOMETRY You can find the perimeter of a geometric figure by adding the measures of its sides. Write an expression in simplest form for the perimeter of each figure.

54. $12x$
$3x$ $5x$
$4x$

55. $6x + 2$
$2x + 1$
x x
$2x + 1$

56. **WRITING IN MATH** Answer the question that was posed at the beginning of the lesson. **See pp. 143A–143B.**

How can you use algebra tiles to simplify an algebraic expression?

Include the following in your answer:
- a drawing that shows how to simplify the expression $4x + 2 + 3x + 1$ using algebra tiles,
- a definition of *like terms*, and
- an explanation of how you use the Commutative and Distributive Properties to simplify $4x + 2 + 3x + 1$.

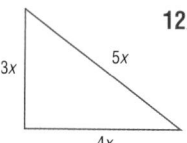

Baby-sitting

In a recent survey, 10% of students in grades 6–12 reported that most of their spending money came from baby-sitting.
Source: *USA WEEKEND*

Answers

17. terms: $3, 7x, 3x, x$; like terms: $7x, 3x, x$; coefficients: $7, 3, 1$; constant: 3

18. terms: $y, 3y, 8y, 2$; like terms: $y, 3y, 8y$; coefficients: $1, 3, 8$; constant: 2

19. terms: $2a, 5c, -1a, 6a$; like terms: $2a, -1a, 6a$; coefficients: $2, 5, -1, 6$; constant: none

20. terms: $5c, -2d, 3d, -1d$; like terms: $-2d, 3d, -1d$; coefficients: $5, -2, 3, -1$; constant: none

21. terms: $6m, -2n, 7$; like terms: none; coefficients: $6, -2$; constant: 7

22. terms: $7x, -3y, 3z, -2$; like terms: none; coefficients: $7, -3, 3$; constant: -2

57. CRITICAL THINKING You use *deductive reasoning* when you base a conclusion on mathematical rules or properties. Indicate the property that justifies each step that was used to simplify $3(x + 4) + 5(x + 1)$.

a. $3(x + 4) + 5(x + 1) = 3x + 12 + 5x + 5$ **Distributive**
b. $= 3x + 5x + 12 + 5$ **Commutative**
c. $= 3x + 5x + 17$ **Substitution**
d. $= 8x + 17$ **Distributive**

58. Which expression is *not* equivalent to the other three? **C**

  Ⓐ $-6(x - 2)$ Ⓑ $x + 12 - 7x$

  Ⓒ $-6x - 12$ Ⓓ $-x - 5x + 12$

59. Katie practiced the clarinet for m minutes. Her sister practiced 10 minutes less. Which expression represents the total time they spent practicing? **C**

  Ⓐ $m - 10$ Ⓑ $m + 10$ Ⓒ $2m - 10$ Ⓓ $2m + 10$

Maintain Your Skills

Mixed Review   **ALGEBRA**   Use the Distributive Property to write each expression as an equivalent expression. *(Lesson 3-1)*

60. $3(a + 5)$ **$3a + 15$**   **61.** $-2(y + 8)$ **$-2y - 16$**   **62.** $-3(x - 1)$ **$-3x + 3$**

63. Name the quadrant in which $P(-5, -6)$ is located. *(Lesson 2-6)* **III**

64. CRUISES The table shows the number of people who took a cruise in various years. Make a scatter plot of the data. *(Lesson 1-7)* **See margin.**

	People Taking Cruises			
Year	1970	1980	1990	2000
Number (millions)	0.5	1.4	3.6	6.5

Source: Cruise Lines International Association

Evaluate each expression. *(Lesson 1-2)*

65. $2 + 3 \cdot 5$ **17**   **66.** $8 \div 2 \cdot 4$ **16**   **67.** $10 - 2 \cdot 4$ **2**

Getting Ready for the Next Lesson   **PREREQUISITE SKILL**   Find each sum. *(To review **adding integers**, see Lesson 2-2.)*

68. $-5 + 4$ **-1**   **69.** $-8 + (-3)$ **-11**   **70.** $10 + (-1)$ **9**
71. $4 + (-9)$ **-5**   **72.** $11 + (-7)$ **4**   **73.** $-4 + (-9)$ **-13**

Practice Quiz 1   Lessons 3-1 and 3-2

Simplify each expression. *(Lessons 3-1 and 3-2)*

1. $6(x + 2)$ **$6x + 12$**   **2.** $5(x - 7)$ **$5x - 35$**   **3.** $6y - 4 + y$ **$7y - 4$**   **4.** $2a + 4(a - 9)$ **$6a - 36$**

5. SCHOOL You spent m minutes studying on Monday. On Tuesday, you studied 15 more minutes than you did on Monday. Write an expression in simplest form that represents the total amount of time spent studying on Monday and Tuesday. *(Lesson 3-2)* **$2m + 15$**

---

4 Assess

Open-Ended Assessment

Speaking Have pairs of students take turns challenging each other to simplify algebraic expressions by combining like terms. Have one student state an expression to simplify. Then have the other student state which are the like terms, and then state the simplified expression. Students should then switch roles.

Getting Ready for Lesson 3-3

PREREQUISITE SKILL In Lesson 3-3, students will solve equations by adding or subtracting. Exercises 68–73 should be used to determine your students' familiarity with adding integers.

Assessment Options

Practice Quiz 1 The quiz provides students with a brief review of the concepts and skills in Lessons 3-1 and 3-2. Lesson numbers are given to the right of exercises or instruction lines so students can review concepts not yet mastered.

Quiz (Lessons 3-1 and 3-2) is available on p. 157 of the *Chapter 3 Resource Masters*.

Answer

64. People Taking Cruises

Getting Started

Objective Solve equations using algebra tiles.

Materials
algebra tiles
equation mat

Teaching Tip If algebra tiles and an equation mat are unavailable, students could draw the tiles on the chalkboard or an erasable board, or make their own tiles from stiff paper or cardboard.

Teach

Activity 1
• Relate the adding or removing of the same number of tiles to each side of the equation to keeping a scale in balance.

Activity 2
• Remind students that they need to add counters to each side of an equation to make enough zero pairs to leave the x-tile alone on one side of the mat.

Activity 3
• Remind students that they need to match each x-tile with an equal number of counters.

Algebra Activity
A Preview of Lessons 3-3 and 3-4

NEW YORK *Performance Indicator* Reinforcement of 5.A.5 Solve and explain simple one-step equations using inverse operations involving whole numbers

Solving Equations Using Algebra Tiles

Activity 1

In a set of algebra tiles, x represents the variable x, 1 represents the integer 1,

and -1 represents the integer -1. You can use algebra tiles and an equation mat to model equations.

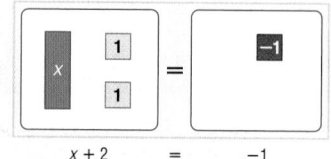

When you solve an equation, you are trying to find the value of x that makes the equation true. The following example shows how to solve $x + 3 = 5$ using algebra tiles.

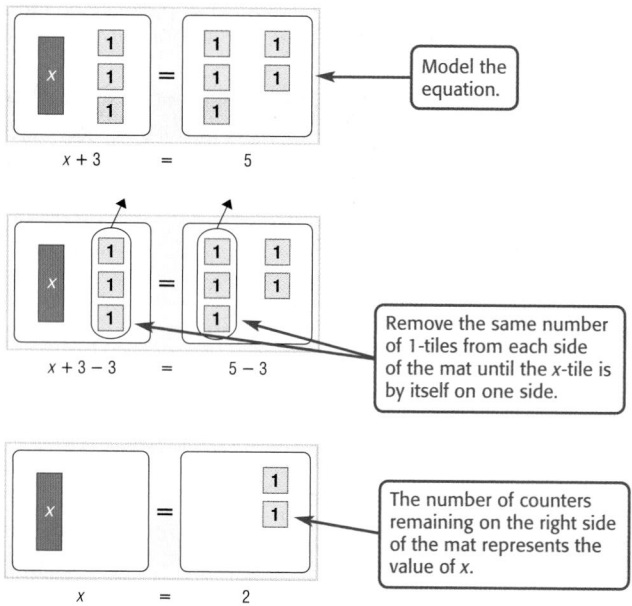

Model the equation.

Remove the same number of 1-tiles from each side of the mat until the x-tile is by itself on one side.

The number of counters remaining on the right side of the mat represents the value of x.

Therefore, $x = 2$. Since $2 + 3 = 5$, the solution is correct.

Model **1–4. See margin for models.**

Use algebra tiles to model and solve each equation.

1. $3 + x = 7$ **4**   **2.** $x + 4 = 5$ **1**   **3.** $6 = x + 4$ **2**   **4.** $5 = 1 + x$ **4**

Resource Manager

📁 Teaching Pre-Algebra with Manipulatives
• pp. 7–8 (Master for algebra tiles)
• p. 13 (Master for equation mat)
• p. 51 (student recording sheet)

Glencoe Mathematics Classroom Manipulative Kit
• algebra tiles
• equation mat

Activity 2

Some equations are solved by using zero pairs. You may add or subtract a zero pair from either side of an equation mat without changing its value. The following example shows how to solve $x + 2 = -1$ by using zero pairs.

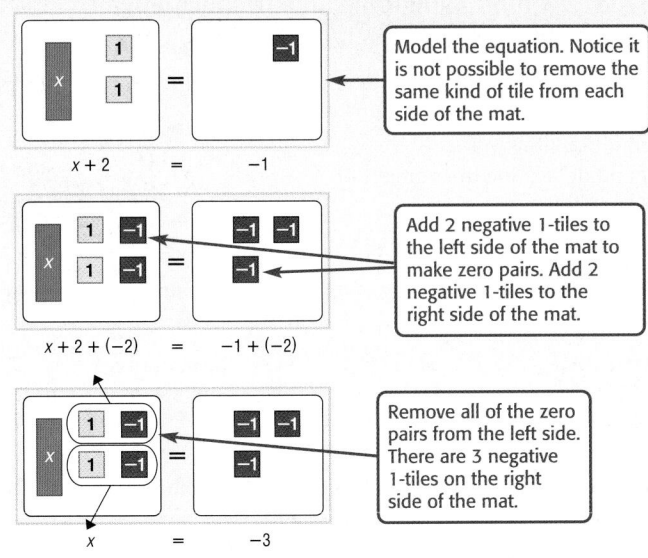

> **TEACHING TIP**
> Remind students that a zero pair is one positive counter paired with a negative counter.

Model the equation. Notice it is not possible to remove the same kind of tile from each side of the mat.

$x + 2 = -1$

Add 2 negative 1-tiles to the left side of the mat to make zero pairs. Add 2 negative 1-tiles to the right side of the mat.

$x + 2 + (-2) = -1 + (-2)$

Remove all of the zero pairs from the left side. There are 3 negative 1-tiles on the right side of the mat.

$x = -3$

Therefore, $x = -3$. Since $-3 + 2 = -1$, the solution is correct.

Model

Use algebra tiles to model and solve each equation. 5–8. See pp. 143A–143B for models.

5. $x + 2 = -2$ **−4**   **6.** $x - 3 = 2$ **5**   **7.** $0 = x + 3$ **−3**   **8.** $-2 = x + 1$ **−3**

Activity 3

Some equations are modeled using more than one x-tile. The following example shows how to solve $2x = -6$ using algebra tiles.

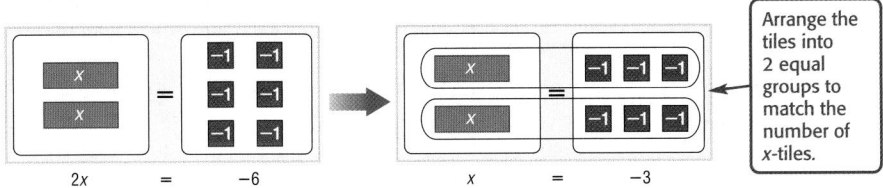

Arrange the tiles into 2 equal groups to match the number of x-tiles.

$2x = -6$ $x = -3$

Therefore, $x = -3$. Since $2(-3) = -6$, the solution is correct.

Model

Use algebra tiles to model and solve each equation. 9–12. See pp. 143A–143B for models.

9. $3x = 3$ **1**   **10.** $2x = -8$ **−4**   **11.** $6 = 3x$ **2**   **12.** $-4 = 2x$ **−2**

Algebra Activity Solving Equations Using Algebra Tiles **109**

4.

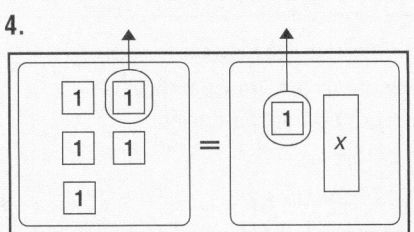

Assess

In **Exercises 1–4**, students should subtract the same number from each side of the equation.

In **Exercises 5–8**, students should add enough counters to each side to make zero pairs with all the counters on the side with the x-tile.

In **Exercises 9–12**, ask students to solve equations by division.

Study Notebook

Have students write how using algebra tiles can help them better understand how to solve equations.

Answers

1.

2.

3.

1 Focus

5-Minute Check Transparency 3-3 Use as a quiz or review of Lesson 3-2.

Mathematical Background notes are available for this lesson on page 96C.

How is solving an equation similar to keeping a scale in balance?

The opening activity questions are repeated on page 120 of the *Chapter 3 Resource Masters.*

Reading to Learn Mathematics, p. 120 — ELL

Pre-Activity *How is solving an equation similar to keeping a scale in balance?*

Do the activity at the top of page 110 in your textbook. Write your answers below.

a. Without looking in the bag, how can you determine the number of blocks in the bag? Remove 4 blocks from each side. There are 3 blocks left on the right, so there must be 3 blocks in the bag.

b. Explain why your method works. Removing the same number of blocks from each side keeps the scale in balance.

Reading the Lesson 1–2. See students' work.

Write a definition and give an example of each new vocabulary phrase.

Vocabulary	Definition	Example
1. inverse operations		
2. equivalent equations		

3. Are $x - 2 = 8$ and $x = 6$ equivalent equations? Explain. No; they do not have the same solution. The solution of $x - 2 = 8$ is 10, and the solution of $x = 6$ is 6.

Helping You Remember

4. How is adding 2 blocks to each side of a balanced scale like the Addition Property of Equality? Adding 2 blocks to each side keeps the scale in balance. Adding the same number on each side of an equation keeps the two sides of the equation equal.

Teaching Tip Use an overhead projector to model the equation $x + 4 = 7$ using overhead algebra tiles on an equation mat transparency.

What You'll Learn

- Solve equations by using the Subtraction Property of Equality.
- Solve equations by using the Addition Property of Equality.

Vocabulary
- inverse operation
- equivalent equations

a. Remove 4 blocks from each side. There are 3 blocks left on the right, so there must be 3 blocks in the bag.

NEW YORK— Performance Indicator
Reinforcement of 5.A.5 Solve and explain simple one-step equations using inverse operations involving whole numbers

How is solving an equation similar to keeping a scale in balance?

On the balance below, the paper bag contains a certain number of blocks. (Assume that the paper bag weighs nothing.)

a. Without looking in the bag, how can you determine the number of blocks in the bag?

b. Explain why your method works.

b. Removing the same number of blocks from each side keeps the scale in balance.

SOLVE EQUATIONS BY SUBTRACTING The equation $x + 4 = 7$ is a model of the situation shown above. You can use inverse operations to solve the equation. **Inverse operations** "undo" each other. For example, to undo the addition of 4 in the expression $x + 4$, you would subtract 4.

To solve the equation $x + 4 = 7$, subtract 4 from each side.

$$x + 4 = 7$$
$$x + 4 - 4 = 7 - 4$$
$$x + 0 = 3$$
$$x = 3$$

Subtract 4 from the left side of the equation to isolate the variable.

Subtract 4 from the right side of the equation to keep it balanced.

The solution is 3.

You can use the **Subtraction Property of Equality** to solve any equation like $x + 4 = 7$.

Key Concept — Subtraction Property of Equality

- **Words** If you subtract the same number from each side of an equation, the two sides remain equal.

- **Symbols** For any numbers a, b, and c, if $a = b$, then $a - c = b - c$.

- **Examples**

$5 = 5$	$x + 2 = 3$
$5 - 3 = 5 - 3$	$x + 2 - 2 = 3 - 2$
$2 = 2$	$x = 1$

✓ **Concept Check** Which integer would you subtract from each side of $x + 7 = 20$ to solve the equation? 7

Resource Manager

Workbooks and Reproducible Masters

Chapter 3 Resource Masters
- Study Guide and Intervention, p. 117
- Skills Practice, p. 118
- Practice, p. 119
- Reading to Learn Mathematics, p. 120
- Enrichment, p. 121

Parent and Student Study Guide Workbook, p. 18
Prerequisite Skills Workbook, pp. 5–8
School-to-Career Masters, p. 5

Transparencies
5-Minute Check Transparency 3-3
Answer Key Transparencies

Technology
Interactive Chalkboard

The equations $x + 4 = 7$ and $x = 3$ are **equivalent equations** because they have the same solution, 3. When you solve an equation, you should always check to be sure that the first and last equations are equivalent.

✓ **Concept Check** Are $x + 4 = 15$ and $x = 4$ equivalent equations? Explain.
No; the solution of $x + 4 = 15$ is 11, not 4.

Example 1 Solve Equations by Subtracting

Solve $x + 8 = -5$. Check your solution.

$x + 8 = -5$	Write the equation.
$x + 8 - 8 = -5 - 8$	Subtract 8 from each side.
$x + 0 = -13$	$8 - 8 = 0, -5 - 8 = -13$
$x = -13$	Identity Property; $x + 0 = x$

To check your solution, replace x with -13 in the original equation.

CHECK	$x + 8 = -5$	Write the equation.
	$-13 + 8 \overset{?}{=} -5$	Check to see whether this sentence is true.
	$-5 = -5 \checkmark$	The sentence is true.

The solution is -13.

Example 2 Graph the Solutions of an Equation

Graph the solution of $16 + x = 14$ on a number line.

$16 + x = 14$	Write the equation.
$x + 16 = 14$	Commutative Property; $16 + x = x + 16$
$x + 16 - 16 = 14 - 16$	Subtract 16 from each side.
$x = -2$	Simplify.

The solution is -2. To graph the solution, draw a dot at -2 on a number line.

SOLVE EQUATIONS BY ADDING Some equations can be solved by adding the same number to each side. This property is called the **Addition Property of Equality**.

Key Concept	**Addition Property of Equality**
• **Words**	If you add the same number to each side of an equation, the two sides remain equal.
• **Symbols**	For any numbers a, b, and c, if $a = b$, then $a + c = b + c$.
• **Examples**	$6 = 6$ $\qquad\qquad$ $x - 2 = 5$
	$6 + 3 = 6 + 3$ $\qquad$ $x - 2 + 2 = 5 + 2$
	$9 = 9$ $\qquad\qquad$ $x = 7$

www.pre-alg.com/extra_examples/ny $\qquad$ Lesson 3-3 Solving Equations by Adding or Subtracting $\quad$ **111**

---

2 Teach

Building on Prior Knowledge

In Chapter 2, students learned how to add and subtract integers. In this lesson, students will use the Addition Property of Equality and the Subtraction Property of Equality with integers to solve equations.

SOLVE EQUATIONS BY SUBTRACTING

In-Class Examples

Teaching Tip Point out that this method of checking solutions can save time when solving similar problems on standardized tests.

1 Solve $x + 4 = -3$. Check your solution. $\quad -7$

2 Graph the solution of $x + 8 = 7$ on a number line.

SOLVE EQUATIONS BY ADDING

In-Class Examples

3 Solve $y - 3 = -14$. $\quad -11$

4 **ENTERTAINMENT** Movie *A* earned $225 million at the box office. That is $38 million less than Movie *B* earned. Write and solve an equation to find the amount Movie *B* earned.
$B - 38 = 225$; Movie *B* earned $263 million at the box office.

5 **Multiple-Choice Test Item** What value of x makes $x - 1 = 8$ a true statement?

A 9 $\quad$ **B** 7 $\quad$ **C** -7 $\quad$ **D** -9
A

✓ **Skills Check**

Solve Equations by Subtracting or Adding Solve and check each equation.

a. $m - 4 = -5$ $\quad -1$

b. $r + 7 = -23$ $\quad -30$

c. $11 = t - 8$ $\quad 19$

d. $4 = -21 + k$ $\quad 25$

About the Exercises . . .

Organization by Objective
• Solve Equations by Subtracting: 12–19, 28–29
• Solve Equations by Adding: 20–27, 30–32

Odd/Even Assignments
Exercises 12–42 are structured so that students practice the same concepts whether they are assigned odd or even problems.

Alert! Exercises 45–47 require access to the Internet or other research materials.

Assignment Guide

Basic: 13–31 odd, 37–45 odd, 46–67
Average: 13–45 odd, 46–67
Advanced: 12–44 even, 45–61 (Optional: 62–67)

If an equation has a subtraction expression, first rewrite the expression as an addition expression. Then add the additive inverse to each side.

Example 3 Solve Equations by Adding

Solve $y - 7 = -25$.

$y - 7 = -25$	Write the equation.
$y + (-7) = -25$	Rewrite $y - 7$ as $y + (-7)$.
$y + (-7) + 7 = -25 + 7$	Add 7 to each side.
$y + 0 = -25 + 7$	Additive Inverse Property; $(-7) + 7 = 0$.
$y = -18$	Identity Property; $y + 0 = y$

The solution is -18.   Check your solution.

Example 4 Use an Equation to Solve a Problem

• **AVIATION** Use the information at the left. Write and solve an equation to find the length of Wilbur Wright's flight.

More About. . .

Aviation •
On December 17, 1903, the Wright brothers made the first flights in a power-driven airplane. Orville's flight covered 120 feet, which was 732 feet shorter than Wilbur's.
Source: www.infoplease.com

Words   Orville's flight was 732 feet shorter than Wilbur's.

Variables   Let x = the length of Wilbur's flight.

Orville's flight	was	732 feet shorter than Wilbur's flight.
Equation 120	=	$x - 732$

Solve the equation.

$120 = x - 732$	Think of $x - 732$ as $x + (-732)$.
$120 + 732 = x - 732 + 732$	Add 732 to each side.
$852 = x$	Simplify.

Wilbur's flight was 852 feet.

Almost all standardized tests have items involving equations.

NEW YORK Test Practice

Standardized Test Practice
Ⓐ Ⓑ Ⓒ Ⓓ

Example 5 Solve Equations

Multiple-Choice Test Item

What value of x makes $x - 4 = -2$ a true statement?
Ⓐ 6   Ⓑ 2   Ⓒ -2 Ⓓ -6

Read the Test Item   To find the value of x, solve the equation.

Solve the Test Item

$x - 4 = -2$	Write the equation.
$x - 4 + 4 = -2 + 4$	Add 4 to each side.
$x = 2$	Simplify.

The answer is B.

Standardized Test Practice
Ⓐ Ⓑ Ⓒ Ⓓ

Example 5 Tell students to eliminate choices whenever possible. For example, in the equation $x - 4 = -2$, $x - 4$ must be negative, so choice **A** can be eliminated without solving the equation.

Check for Understanding

Concept Check

1. Addition Property of Equality

1. **Tell** what property you would use to solve $x - 15 = -3$.

2. **OPEN ENDED** Write two equations that are equivalent. Then write two equations that are *not* equivalent. **See pp. 143A–143B.**

Guided Practice

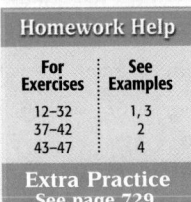
NEW YORK
Test Practice

Standardized Test Practice
Ⓐ Ⓑ Ⓒ Ⓓ

ALGEBRA Solve each equation. Check your solution.

3. $x + 14 = 25$ **11**　　**4.** $w + 4 = -10$ **−14**　　**5.** $16 = y + 20$ **−4**

6. $n - 8 = 5$ **13**　　**7.** $k - 25 = 30$ **55**　　**8.** $r - 4 = -18$ **−14**

ALGEBRA Graph the solution of each equation on a number line.

9. $-8 = x - 6$ 　　　　　　　**10.** $y - 3 = -1$ **9–10. See pp. 143A–143B.**

11. What value of x makes $x - 10 = -5$ a true statement? **C**
　Ⓐ -5　　　Ⓑ 15　　　Ⓒ 5　　　Ⓓ -15

★ indicates increased difficulty

Practice and Apply

ALGEBRA Solve each equation. Check your solution.

12. $y + 7 = 21$ **14**　　**13.** $x + 5 = 18$ **13**　　**14.** $m + 10 = -2$ **−12**

15. $x + 5 = -3$ **−8**　　**16.** $a + 10 = -4$ **−14**　　**17.** $t + 6 = -9$ **−15**

18. $y + 8 = 3$ **−5**　　**19.** $9 = 10 + b$ **−1**　　**20.** $k - 6 = 13$ **19**

21. $r - 5 = 10$ **15**　　**22.** $8 = r - 5$ **13**　　**23.** $19 = g - 5$ **24**

24. $x - 6 = -2$ **4**　　**25.** $y - 49 = -13$ **36**　　**26.** $-15 = x - 16$ **1**

27. $-8 = t - 4$ **−4**　　**28.** $23 + y = 14$ **−9**　　**29.** $59 = s + 90$ **−31**

30. $x - 27 = -63$ **−36**　　**31.** $84 = r - 34$ **118**　　**32.** $y - 95 = -18$ **77**

ALGEBRA Write and solve an equation to find each number.

★ **33.** The sum of a number and 9 is –2. $n + 9 = -2$; **−11**

★ **34.** The sum of –5 and a number is –15. $-5 + n = -15$; **−10**

★ **35.** The difference of a number and 3 is –6. $n - 3 = -6$; **−3**

★ **36.** When 5 is subtracted from a number, the result is 16. $n - 5 = 16$; **21**

ALGEBRA Graph the solution of each equation on a number line.

37. $8 + w = 3$　　　**38.** $z - 5 = -8$　　　**39.** $8 = x - 2$

40. $9 + x = 12$　　　**41.** $-11 = y - 7$　　　**42.** $x - (-1) = 0$

37–42. See pp. 143A–143B.

43. **ELECTIONS** In the 2000 presidential election, Indiana had 12 electoral votes. That was 20 votes fewer than the number of electoral votes in Texas. Write and solve an equation to find the number of electoral votes in Texas. $12 = x - 20$; **32**

44. **WEATHER** The difference between the record high and low temperatures in Charlotte, North Carolina, is 109°F. The record low temperature was −5°F. Write and solve an equation to find the record high temperature. $x - (-5) = 109$; **104°**

45. See students' work.　**45.** **RESEARCH** Use the Internet or another source to find record temperatures in your state. Use the data to write a problem.

www.pre-alg.com/self_check_quiz/ny

DAILY INTERVENTION

Differentiated Instruction

- **Interpersonal** Have students work with a partner. First, one student writes an equation such as $x + 6 = -2$ or $x - 5 = 8$. Then the other student solves the equation using algebra tiles. The partners should then switch roles and repeat the activity.

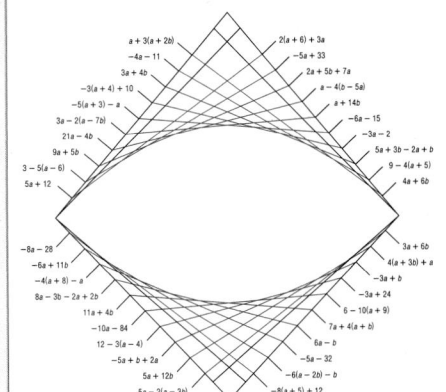

Open-Ended Assessment

Speaking Working in pairs, have students take turns presenting one another with simple equations such as $x + 4 = 8$. The second student should state which Property of Equality to use to solve the equation and what the first step would be, for example, "Subtract 4 from each side."

Getting Ready for Lesson 3-4

PREREQUISITE SKILL Lesson 3-4 presents solving equations by multiplying or dividing. Exercises 62–67 should be used to determine your students' familiarity with dividing integers.

Answer

49. When you solve an equation, you perform the same operation on each side so that the two sides remain equal. Answers should include the following.

- In an equation, both sides are equal. In a balance scale, the weight of the items on both sides are equal.

- The Addition and Subtraction Properties of Equality allow you to add or subtract the same number from each side of an equation. The two sides of the equation remain equal.

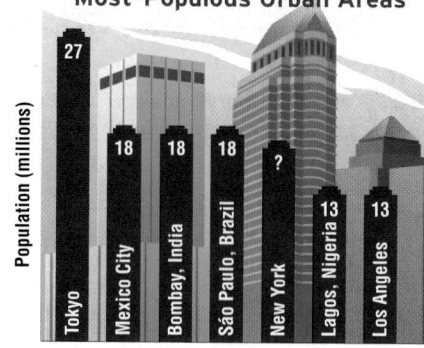

Most-Populous Urban Areas

Source: United Nations

POPULATION For Exercises 46 and 47, use the graph and the following information.
Tokyo's population is 10 million greater than New York's population. Los Angeles' population is 4 million less than New York's population.

46. Write two different equations to find New York's population.

47. Solve the equations.
17 million
46. $27 = x + 10$, $13 = x - 4$

 Online Research **Data Update** How are the populations of these cities related today? Visit www.pre-alg.com/data_update to learn more.

48. **CRITICAL THINKING** Write two equations in which the solution is -5.
Sample answer: $x - 2 = -7$, $x + 2 = -3$

49. **WRITING IN MATH** Answer the question that was posed at the beginning of the lesson. **See margin.**

Why is solving an equation similar to keeping a scale in balance?

Include the following in your answer:
- a comparison of an equation and a balanced scale, and
- an explanation of the Addition and Subtraction Properties of Equality.

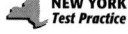 **NEW YORK Test Practice**

Standardized Test Practice

★50. If $x + 4 = -2$, the numerical value of $-3x - 2$ is **B**
(A) -20. (B) 16. (C) 4. (D) -8.

★51. When 7 is subtracted from a number 5 times, the result is 3. What is the number? **C**
(A) 10 (B) -2 (C) 38 (D) 35

Maintain Your Skills

Mixed Review **ALGEBRA** Simplify each expression. *(Lessons 3-1 and 3-2)*

52. $-2(x + 5)$ $-2x - 10$
53. $(t + 4)3$ $3t + 12$
54. $-4(x - 2)$ $-4x + 8$
55. $6z - 3 - 10z + 7$ $-4z + 4$
56. $2(x + 6) + 4x$ $6x + 12$
57. $3 - 4(m + 1)$ $-4m - 1$

ALGEBRA What property is shown by each statement? *(Lessons 2-2 and 1-4)*

58. $9a + b = b + 9a$ **Commutative (+)**
59. $x[y + (-y)] = x(0)$ **Additive Inverse**
60. $6(3x) = (6 \cdot 3)x$ **Associative (×)**

61. **ALGEBRA** Evaluate $9a + 4b$ if $a = 8$ and $b = 3$. *(Lesson 1-3)* **84**

Getting Ready for the Next Lesson **PREREQUISITE SKILL** Divide. *(To review dividing integers, see Lesson 2-5.)*

62. $-100 \div 10$ -10
63. $50 \div (-2)$ -25
64. $-49 \div (-7)$ 7
65. $\frac{72}{-8}$ -9
66. $\frac{-18}{-6}$ 3
67. $\frac{-36}{9}$ -4

Solving Equations by Multiplying or Dividing

What You'll Learn

- Solve equations by using the Division Property of Equality.
- Solve equations by using the Multiplication Property of Equality.

How are equations used to find the U.S. value of foreign currency?

NEW YORK
Performance Indicator
Reinforcement of 5.A.5
Solve and explain simple one-step equations using inverse operations involving whole numbers

In Mexico, about 9 *pesos* can be exchanged for $1 of U.S. currency, as shown in the table.

In general, if we let d represent the number of U.S. dollars and p represent the number of pesos, then $9d = p$.

U.S. Value ($)	Number of Pesos
1	9(1) = 9
2	9(2) = 18
3	9(3) = 27
4	9(4) = 36

a. Suppose lunch in Mexico costs 72 pesos. Write an equation to find the cost in U.S. dollars. **$9d = 72$**

b. How can you find the cost in U.S. dollars? **Divide by 9.**

TEACHING TIP
You may want to refer students to Activity 3 on page 109.

SOLVE EQUATIONS BY DIVIDING The equation $9x = 72$ is a model of the relationship described above. To undo the multiplication operation in $9x$, you would divide by 9.

To solve the equation $9x = 72$, divide each side by 9.

$$9x = 72$$

Divide the left side of the equation by 9 to undo the multiplication $9 \cdot x$.

$$\frac{9x}{9} = \frac{72}{9}$$

Divide the right side of the equation by 9 to keep it balanced.

$$1x = 8$$
$$x = 8$$

The solution is 8.

You can use the **Division Property of Equality** to solve any equation like $9x = 72$.

TEACHING TIP
Point out that division by 0 is undefined, so $c \neq 0$.

Key Concept — Division Property of Equality

- **Words** When you divide each side of an equation by the same nonzero number, the two sides remain equal.

- **Symbols** For any numbers a, b, and c, where $c \neq 0$, then $\frac{a}{c} = \frac{b}{c}$.

- **Examples**

$14 = 14$	$3x = -12$
$\frac{14}{7} = \frac{14}{7}$	$\frac{3x}{3} = \frac{-12}{3}$
$2 = 2$	$x = -4$

1 Focus

5-Minute Check Transparency 3-4 Use as a quiz or review of Lesson 3-3.

Mathematical Background notes are available for this lesson on page 96D.

How are equations used to find the U.S. value of foreign currency?

The opening activity questions are repeated on page 125 of the *Chapter 3 Resource Masters*.

Reading to Learn Mathematics, p. 125 — ELL

Pre-Activity *How are equations used to find the U.S. value of foreign currency?*

Do the activity at the top of page 115 in your textbook. Write your answers below.

a. Suppose lunch in Mexico costs 72 pesos. Write an equation to find the cost in U.S. dollars. **$9d = 72$**

b. How can you find the cost in U.S. dollars? **Divide by 9.**

Reading the Lesson

1. How do you undo multiplication in an expression? **use division**

2. What does the expression $\frac{x}{2}$ mean? **x divided by 2**

3. Explain how to find the value of x in the equation $\frac{x}{4} = 3$. How do you check your answer?

Multiply both sides by 4. $\frac{x}{\cancel{4}} \cdot \frac{\cancel{4}}{1} = 3 \cdot 4$, **$x = 12$** **Substitute 12 for the x in**

the original equation to check whether this equation is correct. $\frac{12}{4} = 3$

Helping You Remember

4. You have learned about four properties of equalities: Addition Property of Equality, Subtraction Property of Equality, Multiplication Property of Equality, and Division Property of Equality. In each circle, write three equations that can be solved by using the given property. Include at least one negative integer in each circle. **Sample answers given.**

These equations can be solved by using the given property.

Addition Property	Subtraction Property	Multiplication Property	Division Property
$x - 1 = 15$	$x + 4 = 9$	$\frac{y}{2} = 8, \frac{y}{3} = 4$	$2x = -6$
$y - 3 = -2$	$y + 11 = -3$	$\frac{z}{5} = -4$	$-5y = 25$
$z - 5 = 0$	$r + 25 = 13$		$-7z = -49$

Teaching Tip Have students act out the exchange in the opening activity by using algebra tiles and counters.

Resource Manager

Transparencies

5-Minute Check Transparency 3-4
Real-World Transparency 3
Answer Key Transparencies

Technology

Interactive Chalkboard
Pre-AlgePASS: Tutorial Plus, Lesson 4
Multimedia Applications

Workbooks and Reproducible Masters

Chapter 3 Resource Masters
- Study Guide and Intervention, p. 122
- Skills Practice, p. 123
- Practice, p. 124
- Reading to Learn Mathematics, p. 125
- Enrichment, p. 126
- Assessment, pp. 157, 159

Parent and Student Study Guide Workbook, p. 19
Prerequisite Skills Workbook, pp. 9–12

SOLVE EQUATIONS BY DIVIDING

1 Solve $7x = -56$. Check your solution and graph it on a number line. $x = -8$;

$$\begin{array}{ccccc} & & & & \\ \hline -10 & -8 & -6 & -4 & -2 \end{array}$$

2 **HOBBIES** Esteban spent $112 on boxes of baseball cards. If he paid $14 per box, how many boxes of cards did Esteban buy? **8 boxes**

Skills Check

Solve Equations by Dividing

Solve each equation. Check your solution.

a. $8a = -48$ -6

b. $-3b = 27$ -9

c. $12c = -48$ -4

SOLVE EQUATIONS BY MULTIPLYING

Teaching Tip Ask students to make a rule to identify equations that can be solved by multiplying.

3 Solve $\dfrac{y}{-5} = -12$.   **60**

More About. . .

Parks •..................

The Columbia River Highway, built in 1913, is a historic route in Oregon that curves around twenty waterfalls through the Cascade Mountains.

Source: *USA TODAY*

Example 1 **Solve Equations by Dividing**

Solve $5x = -30$. Check your solution and graph it on a number line.

$5x = -30$ Write the equation.

$\dfrac{5x}{5} = \dfrac{-30}{5}$ Divide each side by 5 to undo the multiplication in $5 \cdot x$.

$1x = -6$ $5 \div 5 = 1$, $-30 \div 5 = -6$

$x = -6$ Identity Property; $1x = x$

To check your solution, replace x with -6 in the original equation.

CHECK $5x = -30$ Write the equation.

$5(-6) \stackrel{?}{=} -30$ Check to see whether this statement is true.

$-30 = -30 \;\checkmark$ The statement is true.

The solution is -6.

To graph the solution, draw a dot at -6 on a number line.

$$\begin{array}{ccccccccc} & & & & & & & & \\ \hline -7 & -6 & -5 & -4 & -3 & -2 & -1 & 0 \end{array}$$

Concept Check
Explain how you could find the value of x in $3x = 18$. **Divide each side by 3.**

Example 2 **Use an Equation to Solve a Problem**

•**PARKS** It costs $3 per car to use the hiking trails along the Columbia River Highway. If income from the hiking trails totaled $1275 in one day, how many cars entered the park?

Words $3 times the number of cars equals the total.

Variables   Let x represent the number of cars.

The cost per car	times	the number of cars	equals	the total.
Equation $3	$\cdot$	x	$=$	$1275

Solve the equation.

$3x = 1275$ Write the equation.

$\dfrac{3x}{3} = \dfrac{1275}{3}$ Divide each side by 3.

$x = 425$ Simplify.

CHECK $3x = 1275$ Write the equation.

$3(425) \stackrel{?}{=} 1275$ Check to see whether this statement is true.

$1275 = 1275 \;\checkmark$ The statement is true.

Therefore, 425 cars entered the park.

Concept Check
Suppose it cost $5 per car to use the hiking trails and the total income was $1275. What equation would you solve? $5x = 1275$

DAILY INTERVENTION

Unlocking Misconceptions

• **Solve Equations by Multiplying** Many students mistakenly switch dividends and divisors when solving equations by multiplying. Have them check their answers by substituting the found value into the equation.

SOLVE EQUATIONS BY MULTIPLYING   Some equations can be solved by multiplying each side by the same number. This property is called the **Multiplication Property of Equality**.

Key Concept — Multiplication Property of Equality

- **Words**   When you multiply each side of an equation by the same number, the two sides remain equal.
- **Symbols**   For any numbers a, b, and c, if $a = b$, then $ac = bc$.
- **Examples**

$$8 = 8 \qquad\qquad \frac{x}{6} = 7$$

$$8(-2) = 8(-2) \qquad \left(\frac{x}{6}\right)6 = (7)6$$

$$-16 = -16 \qquad\qquad x = 42$$

Study Tip

Division Expressions
Remember, $\frac{y}{-4}$ means y divided by -4.

Example 3   Solve Equations by Multiplying

Solve $\dfrac{y}{-4} = -9$. Check your solution.

$$\frac{y}{-4} = -9 \qquad \text{Write the equation.}$$

$$\frac{y}{-4}(-4) = -9(-4) \qquad \text{Multiply each side by } -4 \text{ to undo the division in } \frac{y}{-4}.$$

$$y = 36 \qquad \text{Simplify.}$$

CHECK $\dfrac{y}{-4} = -9$ Write the equation.

$$\frac{36}{-4} \stackrel{?}{=} -9 \qquad \text{Check to see whether this statement is true.}$$

$$-9 = -9 \checkmark \qquad \text{The statement is true.}$$

The solution is 36.

Check for Understanding

Concept Check

1. Multiplication Property of Equality
2. Divide each side by -5; $y = 9$.

1. **State** what property you would use to solve $\dfrac{x}{-9} = -36$.

2. **Explain** how to find the value of y in $-5y = -45$.

3. **OPEN ENDED**   Write an equation of the form $ax = c$ where a and c are integers and the solution is 4. **Sample answer: $-5x = -20$**

Guided Practice

GUIDED PRACTICE KEY	
Exercises	Examples
4–9	1, 3
10	2

ALGEBRA   Solve each equation. Check your solution.

4. $4x = 24$ **6**

5. $-2a = 10$ **-5**

6. $-42 = -7t$ **6**

7. $\dfrac{k}{3} = 9$ **27**

8. $\dfrac{y}{5} = -8$ **-40**

9. $-11 = \dfrac{n}{-6}$ **66**

Application

10. $80x = 4000$; 50 toys

10. **TOYS**   A spiral toy that can bounce down a flight of stairs is made from 80 feet of wire. Write and solve an equation to find how many of these toys can be made from a spool of wire that contains 4000 feet.

www.pre-alg.com/extra_examples/ny   **Lesson 3-4**   Solving Equations by Multiplying or Dividing   **117**

★ indicates increased difficulty

Practice and Apply

ALGEBRA Solve each equation. Check your solution.

11. $3t = 21$ 7
12. $8x = 72$ 9
13. $-32 = 4y$ -8
14. $5n = -95$ -19
15. $-56 = -7p$ 8
16. $-8j = -64$ 8
17. $\dfrac{h}{4} = 6$ 24
18. $\dfrac{c}{9} = 4$ 36
19. $\dfrac{g}{-2} = -7$ 14
20. $-42 = \dfrac{x}{-2}$ 84
21. $11 = \dfrac{b}{-3}$ -33
22. $\dfrac{h}{-7} = 20$ -140
23. $45 = 5x$ 9
24. $3u = 51$ 17
25. $86 = -2v$ -43
26. $-8a = 144$ -18
27. $\dfrac{m}{45} = -3$ -135
28. $\dfrac{d}{3} = -3$ -9
29. $\dfrac{f}{-13} = -10$ 130
30. $\dfrac{v}{-11} = -132$ 1452
31. $-116 = -4w$ 29
32. $-68 = -4m$ 17
33. $-21 = \dfrac{k}{8}$ -168
34. $-56 = \dfrac{t}{9}$ -504

ALGEBRA Write and solve an equation for each sentence.

★ 35. The product of a number and 6 is -42. $6x = -42$; -7
★ 36. The product of -7 and a number is -35. $-7x = -35$; 5
★ 37. The quotient of a number and -4 is 8. $\dfrac{x}{-4} = 8$; -32
★ 38. When you divide a number by -5, the result is -2. $\dfrac{x}{-5} = -2$; 10

39–44. See margin.

ALGEBRA Graph the solution of each equation on a number line.

39. $48 = -6x$
40. $-32t = 64$
41. $-6r = -18$
42. $-42 = -7x$
43. $\dfrac{n}{12} = 3$
44. $\dfrac{y}{-4} = -1$

45. **RANCHING** The largest ranch in the world is in the Australian Outback. It is about 12,000 square miles, which is five times the size of the largest United States ranch. Write and solve an equation to find the size of the largest United States ranch. $12,000 = 5x$; 2400 mi²

46. **RANCHING** In the driest part of an Outback ranch, each cow needs about 40 acres for grazing. Write and solve an equation to find how many cows can graze on 720 acres of land. $40x = 720$; 18 cows

★ 47. **PAINTING** A **person-day** is a unit of measure that represents one person working for one day. A painting contractor estimates that it will take 24 person-days to paint a house. Write and solve an equation to find how many painters the contractor will need to hire to paint the house in 6 days. $6p = 24$, 4 painters

★ 48. **MEASUREMENT** The chart shows several conversions in the customary system. Write and solve an equation to find each quantity.
   a. the number of feet in 132 inches $12f = 132$; 11 ft
   b. the number of yards in 15 feet $3y = 15$; 5 yd
   c. the number of miles in 10,560 feet $5280m = 10,560$; 2 mi

Customary System (length)
1 mile = 5280 feet
1 mile = 1760 yards
1 yard = 3 feet
1 foot = 12 inches
1 yard = 36 inches

Answers

39.
   $-9\ -8\ -7\ -6\ -5\ -4\ -3\ -2$

40.
   $-3\ -2\ -1\ \ 0\ \ 1\ \ 2\ \ 3\ \ 4$

41.
   $-3\ -2\ -1\ \ 0\ \ 1\ \ 2\ \ 3\ \ 4$

42.
   $0\ \ 1\ \ 2\ \ 3\ \ 4\ \ 5\ \ 6\ \ 7$

43.
   $30\ 31\ 32\ 33\ 34\ 35\ 36\ 37$

44.
   $-3\ -2\ -1\ \ 0\ \ 1\ \ 2\ \ 3\ \ 4$

49a. True; one pyramid balances two cubes, so this is the same as adding one cube to each side.

49b. True; one pyramid and one cube balance three cubes, which balance one cylinder.

49. **CRITICAL THINKING**   Suppose that one pyramid balances two cubes and one cylinder balances three cubes. Determine whether each statement is *true* or *false*. Justify your answers.

a. One pyramid and one cube balance three cubes.

b. One pyramid and one cube balance one cylinder.

c. One cylinder and one pyramid balance four cubes.
   False; one cylinder and one pyramid balance five cubes.

50. WRITING IN MATH   Answer the question that was posed at the beginning of the lesson. **See margin.**

   How are equations used to find the U.S. value of foreign currency?

   Include the following in your answer:

   • the cost in U.S. dollars of a 12-*pound* bus trip in Egypt, if 4 *pounds* can be exchanged for one U.S. dollar, and

   • the cost in U.S. dollars of a 3040-*schilling* hotel room in Austria, if 16 *schillings* can be exchanged for one U.S. dollar.

 Online Research **Data Update** How many pounds and schillings can be exchanged for a U.S. dollar today? Visit www.pre-alg.com/data_update to learn more.

NEW YORK Test Practice

Standardized Test Practice
Ⓐ Ⓑ Ⓒ Ⓓ

★ 51. Solve $\frac{mx}{n} = p$ for x. **B**

   Ⓐ $x = \frac{m}{pn}$ Ⓑ $x = \frac{pn}{m}$ Ⓒ $x = \frac{p-n}{m}$ Ⓓ $x = pn - m$

52. A number is divided by -6, and the result is 24. What is the original number? **C**

   Ⓐ -4 Ⓑ 4 Ⓒ -144 Ⓓ 144

Maintain Your Skills

Mixed Review   **ALGEBRA**   Solve each equation.   *(Lesson 3-3)*

53. $3 + y = 16$ **13**   54. $29 = n + 4$ **25**   55. $k - 12 = -40$ **−28**

ALGEBRA   Simplify each expression.   *(Lesson 3-2)*

56. $4x + 7x$ **11x**   57. $2y + 6 + 5y$ **7y + 6**   58. $3 - 2(y + 4)$ **−2y − 5**

59. **ALGEBRA**   Evaluate $3ab$ if $a = -6$ and $b = 2$.   *(Lesson 2-4)* **−36**

60. Replace ● in -14 ● -4 with $<$, $>$, or $=$ to make a true sentence.
   (Lesson 2-1) **<**

Getting Ready for the Next Lesson   **PREREQUISITE SKILL**   Find each difference.
*(To review **subtracting integers**, see Lesson 2-3.)*

61. $8 - (-2)$ **10**   62. $-5 - 5$ **−10**   63. $-10 - (-8)$ **−2**
64. $-18 - 4$ **−22**   65. $-3 - (-5)$ **2**   66. $-45 - (-9)$ **−36**
67. $-24 - (-5)$ **−19**   68. $-15 - (-15)$ **0**   69. $-8 - 19$ **−27**

Open-Ended Assessment

Modeling Have students use algebra tiles and an equation mat to model these equations. Identify which of the equations can be solved by dividing and which can be solved by multiplying. Then solve.

1. $48 = 24m$ dividing; 2
2. $6j = 54$ dividing; 9
3. $\frac{k}{7} = 5$ multiplying; 35

Getting Ready for Lesson 3-5

PREREQUISITE SKILL Lesson 3-5 presents solving two-step equations, in which students will need to know how to subtract integers. Exercises 61–69 should be used to determine your students' familiarity with subtracting integers.

Assessment Options

Quiz (Lessons 3-3 and 3-4) is available on p. 157 of the *Chapter 3 Resource Masters*.

Mid-Chapter Test (Lessons 3-1 through 3-4) is available on p. 159 of the *Chapter 3 Resource Masters*.

Answer

50. Sample answer: You can use the exchange rate to write and solve an equation involving foreign currency. Answers should include the following.

   • The equation is $4d = 12$, where d is the number of U.S. dollars. The bus trip costs $3 U.S. dollars.

   • The equation is $16d = 3040$, where d is the number of U.S. dollars. The hotel room costs $190 U.S. dollars.

NEW YORK *Performance Indicator* **Reinforcement of 7.A.4 Solve multi-step equations by combining like terms,** using the distributive property, **or moving variables to one side of the equation**

What You'll Learn

- Solve two-step equations.

How can algebra tiles show the properties of equality?

1 Focus

5-Minute Check Transparency 3-5 Use as a quiz or review of Lesson 3-4.

Mathematical Background notes are available for this lesson on page 96D.

How can algebra tiles show the properties of equality?

The opening activity questions are repeated on page 130 of the *Chapter 3 Resource Masters.*

Vocabulary
- two-step equation

The equation $2x + 1 = 9$, modeled below, can be solved with algebra tiles.

$$2x + 1 \quad = \quad 9$$

You can use the steps shown at the right to solve the equation.

Step 1 Remove 1 tile from each side of the mat.

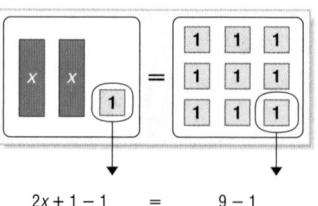

$$2x + 1 - 1 \quad = \quad 9 - 1$$

Step 2 Separate the remaining tiles into two equal groups.

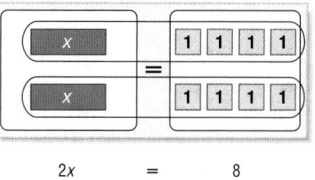

$$2x \quad = \quad 8$$

a. Subtraction Property of Equality
b. Division Property of Equality

a. What property is shown by removing a tile from each side?
b. What property is shown by separating the tiles into two groups?
c. What is the solution of $2x + 1 = 9$? **4**

SOLVE TWO-STEP EQUATIONS A **two-step equation** contains two operations. In the equation $2x + 1 = 9$, x is multiplied by 2 and then 1 is added. To solve two-step equations, use inverse operations to undo each operation in reverse order. You can solve $2x + 1 = 9$ in two steps.

Step 1 First, undo addition.

$$2x + 1 = 9$$
$$2x + 1 - 1 = 9 - 1$$
$$2x = 8$$

 Subtract 1 from each side.

Step 2 Then, undo multiplication.

$$2x = 8$$
$$\frac{2x}{2} = \frac{8}{2}$$
$$x = 4$$

 Divide each side by 2.

The solution is 4.

Resource Manager

Workbooks and Reproducible Masters

Chapter 3 Resource Masters
- Study Guide and Intervention, p. 127
- Skills Practice, p. 128
- Practice, p. 129
- Reading to Learn Mathematics, p. 130
- Enrichment, p. 131

Graphing Calculator and Spreadsheet Masters, p. 23
Parent and Student Study Guide Workbook, p. 20
Prerequisite Skills Workbook, pp. 21–26
Science and Mathematics Lab Manual, pp. 39–42

Transparencies
5-Minute Check Transparency 3-5
Answer Key Transparencies

Technology
Interactive Chalkboard
Pre-AlgePASS: Tutorial Plus, Lessons 5 and 6

Example 1 — Solve Two-Step Equations

a. Solve $5x - 2 = 13$. Check your solution.

$$5x - 2 = 13 \qquad \text{Write the equation.}$$
$$5x - 2 + 2 = 13 + 2 \qquad \text{Undo subtraction. Add to each side.}$$
$$5x = 15 \qquad \text{Simplify.}$$
$$\frac{5x}{5} = \frac{15}{5} \qquad \text{Undo multiplication. Divide each side by 5.}$$
$$x = 3 \qquad \text{Simplify.}$$

CHECK
$$5x - 2 = 13 \qquad \text{Write the equation.}$$
$$5(3) - 2 \stackrel{?}{=} 13 \qquad \text{Check to see whether this statement is true.}$$
$$13 = 13 \; \checkmark \qquad \text{The statement is true.}$$

The solution is 3.

b. Solve $4 = \dfrac{n}{6} + 11$.

$$4 = \frac{n}{6} + 11 \qquad \text{Write the equation.}$$
$$4 - 11 = \frac{n}{6} + 11 - 11 \qquad \text{Undo addition. Subtract 11 from each side.}$$
$$-7 = \frac{n}{6} \qquad \text{Simplify.}$$
$$6(-7) = 6\left(\frac{n}{6}\right) \qquad \text{Undo division. Multiply each side by 6.}$$
$$-42 = n \qquad \text{Simplify.}$$

The solution is -42. $\qquad$ Check your solution.

☑ **Concept Check** Explain how inverse operations can be used to solve a two-step equation. **You undo each operation in reverse order.**

Many real-world situations can be modeled with two-step equations.

Example 2 — Use an Equation to Solve a Problem

SALES Mandy bought a DVD player. The sales clerk says that if she pays $80 now, her monthly payments will be $32. The total cost will be $400. Solve $80 + 32x = 400$ to find how many months she will make payments.

$$80 + 32x = 400 \qquad \text{Write the equation.}$$
$$80 - 80 + 32x = 400 - 80 \qquad \text{Subtract 80 from each side.}$$
$$32x = 320 \qquad \text{Simplify.}$$
$$\frac{32x}{32} = \frac{320}{32} \qquad \text{Divide each side by 32.}$$
$$x = 10 \qquad \text{Simplify.}$$

The solution is 10.

Therefore, Mandy will make payments for 10 months.

Study Tip

Checking Your Solution
Use estimation to determine whether your solution is reasonable: $80 + 30(10) = 380$. Since $380 is close to $400, the solution is reasonable.

 www.pre-alg.com/extra_examples/ny

Teacher to Teacher

Jack Price $\qquad$ Author, Pomona, CA

"It often helps to show how an expression in an equation was 'built' graphically, so you can show how to 'unbuild' it. To solve an equation like $2x + 1 = 13$, you must undo the + 1 first because it is the last thing you built in forming the expression."

Example: $2x + 1 = 13$

| x | → x
| x | + | x | → 2x
| x | + | x | + | 1 | → 2x + 1

Power Point®

3 Solve $5 - x = 7$.   **−2**

4 Solve $b - 3b + 8 = 18$.   **−5**

✓ Skills Check

Solve Two-Step Equations

Solve each equation. Check your solution.

a. $3y + 4 = 13$ **3**

b. $20 - z = 11$ **9**

c. $3n + n - 4 = 12$ **4**

3 Practice/Apply

Study Notebook

Have students—

• add the definition/example of the vocabulary term to their Vocabulary Builder worksheets for Chapter 3.

• draw models of the equations they write for Exercise 2.

• include any other item(s) that they find helpful in mastering the skills in this lesson.

About the Exercises . . .

Odd/Even Assignments

Exercises 13–48 are structured so that students practice the same concepts whether they are assigned odd or even problems.

Assignment Guide

Basic: 13–49 odd, 50–74

Average: 13–49 odd, 50–74

Advanced: 14–48 even, 50–69 (Optional: 70–74)

Some two-step equations have terms with negative coefficients.

TEACHING TIP

You may want to have students write the equation as $(-1x) + 4 = 10$ before adding -4 to each side.

Example 3   Equations with Negative Coefficients

Solve $4 - x = 10$.

$4 - x = 10$	Write the equation.
$4 - 1x = 10$	Identity Property; $x = 1x$
$4 + (-1x) = 10$	Definition of subtraction
$-4 + 4 + (-1x) = -4 + 10$	Add -4 to each side.
$-1x = 6$	Simplify.
$\dfrac{-1x}{-1} = \dfrac{6}{-1}$	Divide each side by -1.
$x = -6$	Simplify.

The solution is -6.   Check your solution.

Sometimes it is necessary to combine like terms before solving.

Study Tip

Mental Computation
You use the Distributive Property to simplify $1m - 5m$.
$1m - 5m = (1 - 5)m$
         $= -4m$
You can also simplify the expression mentally.

Example 4   Combine Like Terms Before Solving

Solve $m - 5m + 3 = 47$.

$m - 5m + 3 = 47$	Write the equation.
$1m - 5m + 3 = 47$	Identity Property; $m = 1m$
$-4m + 3 = 47$	Combine like terms, $1m$ and $-5m$.
$-4m + 3 - 3 = 47 - 3$	Subtract 3 from each side.
$-4m = 44$	Simplify.
$\dfrac{-4m}{-4} = \dfrac{44}{-4}$	Divide each side by -4.
$m = -11$	Simplify.

The solution is -11.   Check your solution.

Check for Understanding

Concept Check

1. You undo the operations in reverse order.

1. Explain how you can work backward to solve a two-step equation.

2. OPEN ENDED Write a two-step equation that could be solved by using the Addition and Multiplication Properties of Equality.

Sample answer: $\frac{x}{2} - 3 = 5$

Guided Practice

GUIDED PRACTICE KEY	
Exercises	Examples
3–8	1
9–11	2, 3
12	4

ALGEBRA   Solve each equation. Check your solution.

3. $2x - 7 = 9$ **8**

4. $3t + 5 = 2$ **−1**

5. $-16 = 6a - 4$ **−2**

6. $\frac{y}{3} + 2 = 10$ **24**

7. $1 + \frac{k}{4} = -9$ **−40**

8. $8 = \frac{n}{-7} - 5$ **−91**

9. $3 - c = 7$ **−4**

10. $2a - 8a = 24$ **−4**

11. $8y - 9y + 6 = -4$ **10**

Application

12. MEDICINE For Jillian's cough, her doctor says that she should take eight tablets the first day and then four tablets each day until her prescription runs out. There are 36 tablets. Solve $8 + 4d = 36$ to find the number of days she will take four tablets. **7 days**

ALGEBRA Solve each equation. Check your solution.

13. $3x + 1 = 7$ **2**

14. $5x - 4 = 11$ **3**

15. $4h + 6 = 22$ **4**

16. $8n + 3 = -5$ **−1**

17. $37 = 4d + 5$ **8**

18. $9 = 15 + 2p$ **−3**

19. $2n - 5 = 21$ **13**

20. $3j - 9 = 12$ **7**

21. $-1 = 2r - 7$ **3**

22. $12 = 5k - 8$ **4**

23. $10 = 6 + \frac{y}{7}$ **28**

24. $14 = 6 + \frac{n}{5}$ **40**

25. $3 + \frac{t}{2} = 35$ **64**

26. $13 + \frac{p}{3} = -4$ **−51**

27. $\frac{k}{5} - 10 = 3$ **65**

28. $\frac{w}{8} - 4 = -7$ **−24**

29. $8 = \frac{c}{-3} + 15$ **21**

30. $\frac{b}{-4} + 8 = -42$ **200**

ALGEBRA Find each number.

31. Five more than twice a number is 27. Solve $2n + 5 = 27$. **11**

32. Three less than four times a number is -7. Solve $4n - 3 = -7$. **−1**

33. Ten less than the quotient of a number and 2 is 5. Solve $\frac{n}{2} - 10 = 5$. **30**

34. Six more than the quotient of a number and 6 is -3. Solve $\frac{n}{6} + 6 = -3$. **−54**

ALGEBRA Solve each equation. Check your solution.

35. $8 - t = -25$ **33**

36. $3 - y = 13$ **−10**

37. $-5 - b = 8$ **−13**

38. $10 = -9 - x$ **−19**

39. $2w - 4w = -10$ **5**

40. $3x - 5x = 22$ **−11**

41. $x + 4x + 6 = 31$ **5**

42. $5r + 3r - 6 = 10$ **2**

43. $1 - 3y + y = 5$ **−2**

44. $16 = w - 2w + 9$ **−7**

45. $23 = 4t - 7 - t$ **10**

46. $-4 = -a + 8 - 2a$ **4**

47. **POOLS** There were 640 gallons of water in a 1600-gallon pool. Water is being pumped into the pool at a rate of 320 gallons per hour. Solve $1600 = 320t + 640$ to find how many hours it will take to fill the pool. **3 h**

48. **PHONE CALLING CARDS** A telephone calling card allows for 25¢ per minute plus a one-time service charge of 75¢. If the total cost of the card is $5, solve $25m + 75 = 500$ to find the number of minutes you can use the card. **17 min**

49. **BUSINESS** Twelve-year old Aaron O'Leary of Columbus, Ohio, bought old bikes at an auction for $350. He fixed them and sold them for $50 each. He made a $6200 profit. Solve $6200 = 50b - 350$ to determine how many bikes he sold. **131 bikes**

50. Answer the question that was posed at the beginning of the lesson. **See pp. 143A–143B.**

How can algebra tiles show the properties of equality?

Include the following in your answer:

- a drawing that shows how to solve $2x + 3 = 7$ using algebra tiles, and
- a list of the properties of equality that you used to solve $2x + 3 = 7$.

Open-Ended Assessment

Modeling Have students use algebra tiles and an equation mat to solve the following equations.

1. $2x + 6 = 14$ **4**
2. $3x - 5 = -2$ **1**
3. $9 = -4x - 3$ **−3**

Getting Ready for Lesson 3-6

PREREQUISITE SKILL Lesson 3-6 presents writing two-step equations. Exercises 70–74 should be used to determine your students' familiarity with writing algebraic expressions from verbal expressions.

---

51. CRITICAL THINKING Write a two-step equation with a variable using the numbers 2, 5, and 8, in which the solution is 2. $5x - 2 = 8$

New York Test Practice — Standardized Test Practice

52. GRID IN The charge to park at an art fair is a flat rate plus a per hour fee. The graph shows the charge for parking for up to 4 hours. If x represents the number of hours and y represents the total charge, what is the charge for parking for 7 hours? **$4.50**

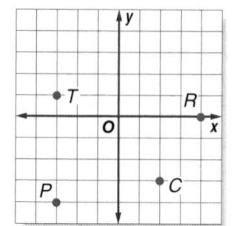

53. A local health club charges an initial fee of $45 for the first month and then a $32 membership fee each month after the first. The table shows the cost to join the health club for up to 6 months.

Months	1	2	3	4	5	6
Cost (dollars)	45	77	109	141	173	205

What is the cost to join the health club for 10 months? **C**

(A) $215   (B) $320   (C) $333   (D) $450

Maintain Your Skills

Mixed Review   **ALGEBRA   Solve each equation. Check your solution.** *(Lessons 3-3 and 3-4)*

54. $5y = 60$ **12**   55. $14 = -2n$ **−7**   56. $\frac{x}{3} = -9$ **−27**

57. $x - 4 = -6$ **−2**   58. $-13 = y + 5$ **−18**   59. $18 = 20 + x$ **−2**

ALGEBRA   Simplify each expression. *(Lesson 3-1)*

60. $4(x + 1)$ **4x + 4**   61. $-5(y + 3)$ **−5y − 15**   62. $3(k - 10)$ **3k − 30**

63. $-9(y - 4)$ **−9y + 36**   64. $7(a - 2)$ **7a − 14**   65. $-8(r - 5)$ **−8r + 40**

Name the ordered pair for each point graphed on the coordinate plane at the right. *(Lesson 2-6)*

66. T **(−3, 1)**
67. C **(2, −3)**
68. R **(4, 0)**
69. P **(−3, −4)**

Getting Ready for the Next Lesson   **PREREQUISITE SKILL   Write an algebraic expression for each verbal expression.** *(To review algebraic expressions, see Lesson 1-3.)*

70. two times a number less six **2x − 6**

71. the quotient of a number and 15 **x ÷ 15**

72. the difference between twice a number and 8 **2x − 8**

73. twice a number increased by 10 **2x + 10**

74. the sum of $2x$, $7x$, and 4 **9x + 4**

DAILY

INTERVENTION   **Differentiated Instruction**

- **Auditory/Musical** Have groups of students each write a two-step equation and then perform solving it for the class. For example, have them sing or shout in unison a catchy phrase for each step in the solution, such as "To each side, add a 2," and "Now it's time to simplify!"

Translating Verbal Problems into Equations

An important skill in algebra is translating verbal problems into equations. To do this accurately, analyze the statements until you completely understand the relationships among the given information. Look for key words and phrases.

> Jennifer is 6 years older than Akira. The sum of their ages is 20.

You can explore a problem situation by asking and answering questions.

Questions	Answers
a. Who is older?	**a.** Jennifer
b. How many years older?	**b.** 6 years
c. If Akira is *x* years old, how old is Jennifer?	**c.** $x + 6$
d. What expression represents the phrase *the sum of their ages*?	**d.** $x + (x + 6)$
e. What equation represents the sentence *the sum of their ages is 20*?	**e.** $x + (x + 6) = 20$

Reading to Learn

For each verbal problem, answer the related questions.

1. Lucas is 5 inches taller than Tamika, and the sum of their heights is 137 inches.
   a. Who is taller? **Lucas**
   b. How many inches taller? **5 inches**
   c. If *x* represents Tamika's height, how tall is Lucas? $x + 5$
   d. What expression represents *the sum of their heights*? $x + (x + 5)$ **or** $2x + 5$
   e. What equation represents the sentence *the sum of their heights is 137*?
      $2x + 5 = 137$

2. There are five times as many students as teachers on the field trip, and the sum of students and teachers is 132.
   a. Are there more students or teachers? **students**
   b. How many times more? **5 times**
   c. If *x* represents the number of teachers, how many students are there? $5x$
   d. What expression represents *the sum of students and teachers*? $x + 5x$ **or** $6x$
   e. What equation represents *the sum of students and teachers is 132*? $6x = 132$

3-6 Writing Two-Step Equations

NEW YORK *Performance Indicator* **8.PS.3 Understand and demonstrate how written symbols represent mathematical ideas, 8.PS.6 Represent problem situations verbally, numerically, algebraically, and graphically**

1 Focus

5-Minute Check Transparency 3-6 Use as a quiz or review of Lesson 3-5.

Mathematical Background notes are available for this lesson on page 96D.

How are equations used to solve real-world problems?

The opening activity questions are repeated on page 135 of the *Chapter 3 Resource Masters*.

Reading to Learn Mathematics, p. 135 — ELL

Pre-Activity *How are equations used to solve real-world problems?*
Do the activity at the top of page 126 in your textbook. Write your answers below.

a. Let *n* represent the number of minutes. Write an expression that represents the cost when your call lasts *n* minutes $4n + 99$

b. Suppose your monthly cost was 299¢. Write and solve an equation to find the number of minutes you used the calling card. $4n + 99 = 299$

c. Why is your equation considered to be a two-step equation? It has two operations, multiplication and addition.

Reading the Lesson
Refer to Example 3 on page 127. Read the Explore and Plan steps. Then complete the following.

1. Suppose you have already saved $75 and plan to save $5 a week.
   a. Complete the table below.

Week	Amount Saved ($)
0	$5(0) + 75 = 75$
1	$5(1) + 75 = 80$
2	$5(2) + 75 = 85$
3	$5(3) + 75 = 90$
n	$5(n) + 75 = 5n + 75$

   b. Write an equation that represents how many weeks it will take you to save $100. $5n + 75 = 100$

2. Suppose you have already saved $25 and plan to save $10 each week.
   a. Complete the table below.

Week	Amount Saved ($)
0	$10(0) + 25 = 25$
1	$10(1) + 25 = 35$
2	$10(2) + 25 = 45$
3	$10(3) + 25 = 55$
n	$10(n) + 25 = 10n + 25$

   b. Write an equation that represents how many weeks it will take you to save $175. $10n + 25 = 175$

What You'll Learn

- Write verbal sentences as two-step equations.
- Solve verbal problems by writing and solving two-step equations.

How are equations used to solve real-world problems?

A phone company advertises that you can call anywhere in the United States for 4¢ per minute plus a monthly fee of 99¢ with their calling card. The table shows how to find your total monthly cost.

Time (minutes)	Monthly Cost (cents)
0	$4(0) + 99 = 99$
5	$4(5) + 99 = 119$
10	$4(10) + 99 = 139$
15	$4(15) + 99 = 159$
20	$4(20) + 99 = 179$

a. Let *n* represent the number of minutes. Write an expression that represents the cost when your call lasts *n* minutes.

a. $4n + 99$

TEACHING TIP
Point out that the monthly cost must be expressed in cents. A monthly cost of $2.99 is 299¢.

b. Suppose your monthly cost was 299¢. Write and solve an equation to find the number of minutes you used the calling card. $4n + 99 = 299$; 50

c. Why is your equation considered to be a two-step equation?

c. It has two operations, multiplication and addition.

WRITE TWO-STEP EQUATIONS In Chapter 1, you learned how to write verbal phrases as expressions.

Phrase the sum of 4 times some number and 99

Expression $4n + 99$

An equation is a statement that two expressions are equal. The expressions are joined with an equals sign. Look for the words *is*, *equals*, or *is equal to* when you translate sentences into equations.

Sentence The sum of 4 times some number and 99 is 299.

Equation $4n + 99 = 299$

Study Tip

Expression
An expression is any combination of numbers and operations.

Example 1 Translate Sentences into Equations

Translate each sentence into an equation.

Sentence	Equation
a. Six more than twice a number is −20.	$2n + 6 = -20$
b. Eighteen is 6 less than four times a number.	$18 = 4n - 6$
c. The quotient of a number and 5, increased by 8, is equal to 14.	$\frac{n}{5} + 8 = 14$

Concept Check: An expression is any combination of numbers and operations; an equation is a statement that two expressions are equal.

✓ **Concept Check** What is the difference between an expression and an equation?

126 Chapter 3 Equations

Resource Manager

📂 Workbooks and Reproducible Masters

Chapter 3 Resource Masters
- Study Guide and Intervention, p. 132
- Skills Practice, p. 133
- Practice, p. 134
- Reading to Learn Mathematics, p. 135
- Enrichment, p. 136
- Assessment, p. 158

Parent and Student Study Guide Workbook, p. 21

📽 Transparencies
5-Minute Check Transparency 3-6
Answer Key Transparencies

Technology
Interactive Chalkboard

Example 2 *Translate and Solve an Equation*

Seven more than three times a number is 31. Find the number.

Words	Seven more than three times a number is 31.
Variables	Let n = the number.

Equation

$$3n + 7 = 31 \qquad \text{Write the equation.}$$
$$3n + 7 - 7 = 31 - 7 \qquad \text{Subtract 7 from each side.}$$
$$3n = 24 \qquad \text{Simplify.}$$
$$n = 8 \qquad \text{Mentally divide each side by 3.}$$

Therefore, the number is 8.

Study Tip

Solving Equations Mentally
When solving a simple equation like $3n = 24$, mentally divide each side by 3.

TWO-STEP VERBAL PROBLEMS   There are many real-world situations in which you start with a given amount and then increase it at a certain rate. These situations can be represented by two-step equations.

Example 3 *Write and Solve a Two-Step Equation*

SCOOTERS   Suppose you are saving money to buy a scooter that costs $100. You have already saved $60 and plan to save $5 each week. How many weeks will you need to save?

Explore	You have already saved $60. You plan to save $5 each week until you have $100.
Plan	Organize the data for the first few weeks in a table. Notice the pattern.

Week	Amount
0	$5(0) + 60 = 60$
1	$5(1) + 60 = 65$
2	$5(2) + 60 = 70$
3	$5(3) + 60 = 75$

Write an equation to represent the situation.

Let x = the number of weeks.

$$\underbrace{5x}_{\substack{\$5 \text{ each week} \\ \text{for } x \text{ weeks}}} \underbrace{+}_{\text{plus}} \underbrace{60}_{\substack{\text{amount already} \\ \text{saved}}} \underbrace{=}_{\text{equals}} \underbrace{100}_{\$100.}$$

Solve

$$5x + 60 = 100 \qquad \text{Write the equation.}$$
$$5x + 60 - 60 = 100 - 60 \qquad \text{Subtract 60 from each side.}$$
$$5x = 40 \qquad \text{Simplify.}$$
$$x = 8 \qquad \text{Mentally divide each side by 5.}$$

You need to save $5 each week for 8 weeks.

Examine   If you save $5 each week for 8 weeks, you'll have an additional $40. The answer appears to be reasonable.

More About...

Scooters

Most scooters are made of aircraft aluminum. They can transport over 200 pounds easily, yet are light enough to carry.

Source: www.emazing.com

---

2 Teach

WRITE TWO-STEP EQUATIONS

In-Class Examples

1 Translate each sentence into an equation.

a. Twice a number, increased by 5, equals −25.
$2n + 5 = -25$

b. Four times a number minus 8 equals 28. $4n − 8 = 28$

c. When five is added to the product of a number and 8, the result is 12. $5 + 8n = 12$

2 Nine more than four times a number is 41. Find the number. $9 + 4n = 41; 8$

✓ Skills Check

Write Two-Step Equations
Translate each sentence into an equation. Then find each number.

a. The product of 6 and a number, less 7, equals 11.
$6n − 7 = 11; 3$

b. When four is added to a number that has been divided by 3, the result is 1.
$\dfrac{n}{3} + 4 = 1; -9$

c. Four less than 8 times a number is 12. $8n − 4 = 12; 2$

TWO-STEP VERBAL PROBLEMS

In-Class Example

3 **EARNINGS**   Ms. Blake earns $48,400 per year. That is $4150 more than three times as much as her daughter earns. How much does her daughter earn?   **$14,750**

Teaching Tip   Write the Example on the board and have a student circle the unknown. Let that value be x. Then have another student circle the known number that will stand alone on one side of the equals sign. Finally, have a student circle the other numbers and have the class help place them in the equation.

4 **COMMUNITY SERVICE** In a canned food drive, Sam collected 12 more cans than Louise. Together, they collected 128 cans. How many cans did Sam collect? **70**

3 Practice/Apply

Study Notebook

Have students—
- list several words or phrases in verbal problems that can be translated into each of the four basic operations.
- write about the process they used to translate verbal problems into equations.
- include any other item(s) that they find helpful in mastering the skills in this lesson.

About the Exercises . . .
Organization by Objective
- **Write Two-Step Equations:** 8–19
- **Two-Step Verbal Problems:** 20–23

Odd/Even Assignments
Exercises 8–23 are structured so that students practice the same concepts whether they are assigned odd or even problems.

Assignment Guide
Basic: 9–15 odd, 21, 23, 26–42
Average: 9–25 odd, 26–42
Advanced: 8–24 even, 26–36 (Optional: 37–42)
All: Quiz 2 (1–5)

Example 4 **Write and Solve a Two-Step Equation**

OLYMPICS In the 2000 Summer Olympics, the United States won 9 more medals than Russia. Together they won 185 medals. How many medals did the United States win?

Words   Together they won 185 medals.

Variables   Let x = number of medals won by Russia.
             Then $x + 9$ = number of medals won by United States.

Equation

$x + (x + 9) = 185$	Write the equation.
$(x + x) + 9 = 185$	Associative Property
$2x + 9 = 185$	Combine like terms.
$2x + 9 - 9 = 185 - 9$	Subtract 9 from each side.
$2x = 176$	Simplify.
$\dfrac{2x}{2} = \dfrac{176}{2}$	Divide each side by 2.
$x = 88$	Simplify.

Since x represents the number of medals won by Russia, Russia won 88 medals. The United States won $88 + 9$ or 97 medals.

> **Study Tip**
> **Alternative Method**
> Let x = number of U.S. medals. Then $x - 9$ = number of Russian medals.
> $x + (x - 9) = 185$
> $x = 97$
> In this case, x is the number of U.S. medals, 97.

Check for Understanding

Concept Check
1. **List** three words or phrases in a verbal problem that can be translated into an equals sign in an equation. **is, equals, is equal to**

2. **OPEN ENDED** Write a verbal sentence involving an unknown number and two operations. **Sample answer: Three more than twice a number is 15.**

3. **FIND THE ERROR** Alicia and Ben are translating the following sentence into an equation: *Three less than two times a number is 15.*

Alicia	Ben
$3 - 2x = 15$	$2x - 3 = 15$

Who is correct? Explain your reasoning. **Ben;** *Three less than* **means that three is subtracted** *from* **a number.**

GUIDED PRACTICE KEY

Exercises	Examples
4, 5	1
6	2
7	3

Guided Practice
Translate each sentence into an equation. Then find each number.
4. Three more than four times a number is 23. **$4n + 3 = 23$, 5**

5. Four less than twice a number is –2. **$2n - 4 = -2$, 1**

Applications
Solve each problem by writing and solving an equation.
6. **METEOROLOGY** Suppose the current temperature is 17°F. It is expected to rise 3°F each hour for the next several hours. In how many hours will the temperature be 32°F? **$17 + 3x = 32$, 5 h**

7. **AGES** Lawana is five years older than her brother Cole. The sum of their ages is 37. How old is Lawana? **$2x + 5 = 37$, 21 yr**

D A I L Y
INTERVENTION **FIND THE ERROR**
       To choose whether Alicia or Ben is correct, translate each mathematical equation back into a verbal sentence without looking at the original sentence. Then compare sentences.

Practice and Apply

Homework Help

For Exercises	See Examples
8–19	1, 2
20, 21	3
22–24	4

Extra Practice
See page 730.

Translate each sentence into an equation. Then find each number.

8. Seven more than twice a number is 17. $2n + 7 = 17, 5$

9. Twenty more than three times a number is −4. $3n + 20 = -4, -8$

10. Four less than three times a number is 20. $3n - 4 = 20, 8$

11. Eight less than ten times a number is 82. $10n - 8 = 82, 9$

12. Ten more than the quotient of a number and −2 is three. $\frac{n}{-2} + 10 = 3, 14$

13. The quotient of a number and −4, less 8, is −42. $\frac{n}{-4} - 8 = -42, 136$

14. The difference between twice a number and 9 is 17. $2n - 9 = 17, 13$

15. The difference between three times a number and 8 is −2. $3n - 8 = -2, 2$

★ 16. If 5 is decreased by 3 times a number, the result is −4. $5 - 3n = -4, 3$

★ 17. If 17 is decreased by twice a number, the result is 5. $17 - 2n = 5, 6$

★ 18. Three times a number plus twice the number plus 1 is −4.

★ 19. Four times a number plus five more than three times the number is 47.
$4n + 3n + 5 = 47, 6$ 18. $3n + 2n + 1 = -4, -1$

Solve each problem by writing and solving an equation.

20. **WILDLIFE** Your friend bought 3 bags of wild bird seed and an $18 bird feeder. Each bag of birdseed costs the same amount. If your friend spent $45, find the cost of one bag of birdseed. $3x + 18 = 45, \$9$

21. **METEOROLOGY** The temperature is 8°F. It is expected to fall 5° each hour for the next several hours. In how many hours will the temperature be −7°F? $8 - 5x = -7, 3\text{ h}$

22. **FOOD SERVICE** You and your friend spent a total of $15 for lunch. Your friend's lunch cost $3 more than yours did. How much did you spend for lunch? $2x + 3 = 15, \$6$

23. **POPULATION** By 2020, California is expected to have 2 million more senior citizens than Florida, and the sum of the number of senior citizens in the two states is expected to be 12 million. Find the expected senior citizen population of Florida in 2020. $2x + 2 = 12. 5$ million people

★ 24. **NATIVE AMERICANS** North Carolina's Native-American population is 22,000 greater than New York's. New York's Native-American population is 187,000 less than Oklahoma's. If the total population of all three is 437,000, find each state's Native-American population. NC: 98,000; NY: 76,000; OK: 263,000

Native-American Populations (thousands)

California	309
Arizona	256
New Mexico	163
Washington	103
Alaska	100
Texas	96
Michigan	60
Oklahoma	?
New York	?
North Carolina	?

Source: U.S. Census Bureau

Career Choices

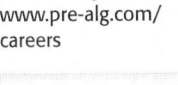

Meteorologist •········

Meteorologists are best known for forecasting the weather. However, they also work in the fields of air pollution, agriculture, and defense.

📖 **Online Research**
For information about a career as a meteorologist, visit:
www.pre-alg.com/careers

Study Guide and Intervention, p. 132

You can use two-step equations to represent situations in which you start with a given amount and then increase it at a certain rate.

Example **PRINTING:** A laser printer prints 9 pages per minute. Liza refilled the paper tray after it had printed 92 pages. In how many more minutes will there be a total of 245 pages printed?

EXPLORE You know the number of pages printed and the total number of pages to be printed. You need to find the number of minutes required to print the remaining pages.

PLAN Let m = the number of minutes. Write and solve an equation. The remaining pages to print is $9m$.
remaining pages + pages printed = total pages
$9m$ + 92 = 245

SOLVE
$9m + 92 = 245$
$9m + 92 - 92 = 245 - 92$
$9m = 153$
$\frac{9m}{9} = \frac{153}{9}$
$m = 17$

EXAMINE The remaining 153 pages will print in 17 minutes. Since $245 - 153 = 92$, the answer is correct.

Exercises

Solve each problem by writing and solving an equation.

1. **METEOROLOGY** During one day in 1918, the temperature in Granville, North Dakota, began at −33° and rose for 12 hours. The high temperature was about 51°. About how many degrees per hour did the temperature rise? $-33 + 12d = 51$; about 7 degrees

2. **SAVINGS** John has $825 in his savings account. He has decided to deposit $65 per month until he has a total of $1800. In how many months will this occur? $65m + 825 = 1800$; 15 months

3. **SKYDIVING** A skydiver jumps from an airplane at an altitude of 12,000 feet. After 42 seconds, she reaches 4608 feet and opens her parachute. What was her average velocity during her descent? $12,000 - 42f = 4608$; 176 feet per second

4. **FLOODING** The water level of a creek has risen 4 inches above its flood stage. If it continues to rise steadily at 2 inches per hour, how long will it take for the creek to be 12 inches above its flood stage? $4 + 2h = 12$; 4 hours

---

Skills Practice, p. 133 and Practice, p. 134 (shown)

Translate each sentence into an equation. Then find each number.

1. Eight less than 7 times a number is −29.
$7n - 8 = -29; -3$

2. Twenty more than twice a number is 52.
$20 + 2n = 52; 16$

3. The difference between three times a number and 11 is 10.
$3n - 11 = 10; 7$

4. One more than the difference between 18 and seven times a number is −9.
$1 + 18 - 7n = -9; 4$

5. Eight times a number plus 6 less than twice the number is 34.
$8n + 2n - 6 = 34; 4$

6. 26 more than the product of a number and 17 is −42.
$17n + 26 = -42; -4$

7. Twelve less than the quotient of a number and 8 is −1.
$\frac{n}{8} - 12 = -1; 88$

Solve each problem by writing and solving an equation.

8. **ANIMAL TRAINING** Last summer, Gary trained 32 more dogs than Zina. Together they trained 126 dogs. How many dogs did Gary train? $g + (g - 32) = 126; 79$ dogs

9. **SALES** Julius sold five times as many computers as Sam sold last year. In total, they sold 78 computers. How many computers did Julius sell? $5s + s = 78; 65$ computers

10. **TRACK** In one season, Ana ran 18 races. This was four fewer races than twice the number of races Kelly ran. How many races did Kelly run? $18 = 2r - 4; 11$ races

11. **BASEBALL** André hit four more home runs than twice the number of home runs Larry hit. Together they hit 10 home runs. How many home runs did André hit? $h + 2h + 4 = 10; 8$ home runs

---

Enrichment, p. 136

Systems of Equations

A **system of equations** is a set of equations with the same variables. The equations shown below are an example of one kind of system of equations.

$y = x + 2$
$3x - 5 = 16$

The solution of this system must be a pair of numbers, x and y, that make both equations true.

To solve this type of system, first solve the equation that contains only one variable. Then substitute that answer into the second equation and solve for the remaining variable.

Example Solve each system of equations.

a. $y = x + 2$
   $3x - 5 = 16$

Solve $3x - 5 = 16$ first.
$3x - 5 = 16$
$3x - 5 + 5 = 16 + 5$
$3x = 21$
$\frac{3x}{3} = \frac{21}{3}$
$x = 7$

Substitute 7 for x in the other equation.
$y = x + 2$
$y = 7 + 2$ or 9
The solution is $x = 7$ and $y = 9$.

b. $4d - 1 = 19$
   $c = d - 3$

Solve $4d - 1 = 19$ first.
$4d - 1 = 19$
$4d - 1 + 1 = 19 + 1$
$4d = 20$
$\frac{4d}{4} = \frac{20}{4}$
$d = 5$

Substitute 5 for d in the other equation.
$c = d - 3$
$c = 5 - 3$ or 2
The solution is $c = 2$ and $d = 5$.

Solve each system of equations.

1. $40 - 2t = 10$
   $3t - s = 35$
   $t = 15, s = 10$

2. $4a + 2b = 22$
   $25 = 11a - 8$
   $a = 3, b = 5$

3. $82.5 = 1.5s$
   $d = 3s + 35$
   $s = 55, d = 200$

4. $\frac{m}{5} + 1.5 = 2$
   $7m + n = 17.5$
   $m = 2.5, n = 0$

5. $6x + \frac{y}{2} = 43$
   $22 + 3x = 43$
   $x = 7, y = 2$

6. $\frac{c}{5} + p = 4$
   $20 = 4p - 3$
   $p = 5.75, c = -8.75$

DAILY INTERVENTION

Differentiated Instruction **ELL**

• **Verbal/Linguistic** Have students make a chart of mathematical expressions and the different phrases they can be translated into. For example, the phrase *is increased by* indicates addition and the phrase *separated into equal parts* indicates division.

Open-Ended Assessment

Writing Have students write a verbal problem that can be solved by the equation $2x - 5 = 19$. **Sample answer: Olga scored five less than twice as many points as Tricia scored in the basketball game. If Tricia scored 19 points, how many did Olga score?**

Tips for New Teachers

Intervention Make sure that students get into the habit of stating what the variable represents. It's the first thing to check if they make an error.

Getting Ready for Lesson 3-7

PREREQUISITE SKILL Lesson 3-7 presents solving problems by using formulas. Exercises 37–42 should be used to determine your students' familiarity with solving equations.

Assessment Options

Practice Quiz 2 The quiz provides students with a brief review of the concepts and skills in Lessons 3-3 through 3-6. Lesson numbers are given to the right of exercises or instruction lines so students can review concepts not yet mastered.

Quiz (Lessons 3-5 and 3-6) is available on p. 158 of the *Chapter 3 Resource Masters.*

---

25. See margin.

★ 25. **WRITE A PROBLEM** The table shows the expected population age 85 or older for certain states in 2020. Use the data to write a problem that can be solved by using a two-step equation.

Population (age 85 or older)	
State	Number (thousands)
CA	809
FL	735
TX	428
NY	418

26. **CRITICAL THINKING** If you begin with an even integer and count by two, you are counting *consecutive even integers*. Write and solve an equation to find two consecutive even integers whose sum is 50. **$2x + 2 = 50$, 24 and 26**

27. 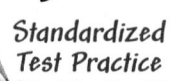 **WRITING IN MATH** Answer the question that was posed at the beginning of the lesson. **See margin.**

How are equations used to solve real-world problems?

Include the following in your answer:
- an example that starts with a given amount and increases, and
- an example that involves the sum of two quantities.

NEW YORK Test Practice

Standardized Test Practice
Ⓐ Ⓑ Ⓒ Ⓓ

28. Which verbal expression represents the phrase *three less than five times a number*? **C**
  Ⓐ $3 - 5n$ Ⓑ $n - 3$ Ⓒ $5n - 3$ Ⓓ $5 + n - 3$

29. The Bank of America building in San Francisco is 74 feet shorter than the Transamerica Pyramid. If their combined height is 1632 feet, how tall is the Transamerica Pyramid? **D**
  Ⓐ 41 ft   Ⓑ 779 ft   Ⓒ 781 ft   Ⓓ 853 ft

Maintain Your Skills

Mixed Review **ALGEBRA** Solve each equation. *(Lessons 3-3, 3-4, and 3-5)*

30. $6 - 2x = 10$ **−2**   31. $-4x = -16$ **4**   32. $y - 7 = -3$ **4**

Evaluate each expression if $x = -12$, $y = 4$, and $z = -1$. *(Lesson 2-1)*

33. $|x| - 7$ **5**   34. $|x| + |y|$ **16**   35. $|z| - |x|$ **−11**

36. Name the property shown by $(2 + 6) + 9 = 2 + (6 + 9)$. *(Lesson 1-4)*
  Associative Property of Addition

Getting Ready for the Next Lesson

PREREQUISITE SKILL Solve each equation. Check your solution.
*(To review **solving equations**, see Lesson 3-4.)*

37. $2x = -8$ **−4**   38. $24 = 6y$ **4**   39. $5w = -25$ **−5**

40. $15s = 75$ **5**   41. $108 = 18x$ **6**   42. $25z = 175$ **7**

Practice Quiz 2   Lessons 3-3 through 3-6

ALGEBRA Solve each equation. *(Lessons 3-3, 3-4, and 3-5)*

1. $4h = -52$ **−13**   2. $\frac{x}{-3} = 4$ **−12**   3. $y - 5 = -23$ **−18**   4. $2v - 11 = -5$ **3**

5. **ALGEBRA** Twenty more than three times a number is 32. Write and solve an equation to find the number. *(Lesson 3-6)* **$3n + 20 = 32$, 4**

Answers

25. Sample answer: By 2020, Texas is expected to have 10,000 more people age 85 or older than New York will have. Together, they are expected to have 846,000 people age 85 or older. Find the expected number of people age 85 or older in New York by 2020.

27. Sample answer: Two-step equations can be used when you start with a certain amount and increase or decrease at a certain rate. Answers should include the following.
- You've been running 15 minutes each day as part of a fitness program. You plan to increase your time by 5 minutes each week.

After how many weeks do you plan to run 30 minutes each day? ($5w + 15 = 30$; 3 weeks)

- You are three years older than your sister is. Together the sum of your ages is 21. How old is your sister? ($2x + 3 = 21$; 9 years old)

3-7 Using Formulas

NEW YORK *Performance Indicator* **Reinforcement of 7.A.6 Evaluate formulas for given input values** (surface area, rate, and density problems)

What You'll Learn

- Solve problems by using formulas.
- Solve problems involving the perimeters and areas of rectangles.

Vocabulary
- formula
- perimeter
- area

Why are formulas important in math and science?

The top recorded speed of a mallard duck in level flight is 65 miles per hour. You can make a table to record the distances that a mallard could fly at that rate.

a. Write an expression for the distance traveled by a duck in *t* hours. **65t**

b. What disadvantage is there in showing the data in a table?

c. Describe an easier way to summarize the relationship between the speed, time, and distance.

b. You cannot show all of the possible relationships in a table

Speed (mph)	Time (hr)	Distance (mi)
65	1	65
65	2	130
65	3	195
65	t	?

c. Write an equation that relates speed, time, and distance.

TEACHING TIP
Point out that a formula also shows how one quantity can be computed from other quantities.

FORMULAS A **formula** is an equation that shows a relationship among certain quantities. A formula usually contains two or more variables. One of the most commonly-used formulas shows the relationship between distance, rate (or speed), and time.

Words Distance equals the rate multiplied by the time.

Variables Let d = distance, r = rate, and t = time.

Equation $d = rt$

Example 1 Use the Distance Formula

SCIENCE What is the rate in miles per hour of a dolphin that travels 120 miles in 4 hours?

$d = rt$ Write the formula.

$120 = r \cdot 4$ Replace d with 120 and t with 4.

$\dfrac{120}{4} = \dfrac{r \cdot 4}{4}$ Divide each side by 4.

$30 = r$ Simplify.

The dolphin travels at a rate of 30 miles per hour.

✓ **Concept Check** Name an advantage of using a formula to show a relationship among quantities. **A formula is a concise way to describe a relationship among quantities.**

Lesson 3-7 Using Formulas **131**

3-7 Lesson Notes

1 Focus

5-Minute Check Transparency 3-7 Use as a quiz or review of Lesson 3-6.

Mathematical Background notes are available for this lesson on page 96D.

Why are formulas important in math and science?

The opening activity questions are repeated on page 140 of the *Chapter 3 Resource Masters*.

Reading to Learn Mathematics, p. 140 **ELL**

Pre-Activity Why are formulas important in math and science?

Do the activity at the top of page 131 in your textbook. Write your answers below.

  a. Write an expression for the distance traveled by a duck in *t* hours. **65t**

  b. What disadvantage is there in showing the data in a table? **You cannot show all of the possible relationships in a table.**

  c. Describe an easier way to summarize the relationship between the speed, time, and distance. **Write an equation that relates speed, time, and distance.**

Reading the Lesson 1–3. See students' work.

Write a definition and give an example of each new vocabulary word.

Vocabulary	Definition	Example
1. formula		
2. perimeter		
3. area		

Helping You Remember

4. The word *perimeter* is composed of the prefix *peri-* and the suffix *-meter*.

  a. Find the definitions of *peri-* and *-meter* in a dictionary. Write their definitions. **Enclosing or surrounding; means for measuring**

  b. Find two other words in a dictionary that begin with the prefix *peri-*. Write their definitions. **Sample answers: peripheral: of, relating to, or being the outer part of the field of vision; pericardium: the membrane that encloses the heart of vertebrates**

  c. Explain how your definitions can help you remember how perimeter is used in mathematics. **The definitions relate to the outer edge of something, just as perimeter is a measure of the distance around a figure.**

Teaching Tip Ask students to list formulas they have used in the past. Ask what each is used for. Discuss the importance of formulas in real-world situations.

Resource Manager

Workbooks and Reproducible Masters

Chapter 3 Resource Masters
- Study Guide and Intervention, p. 137
- Skills Practice, p. 138
- Practice, p. 139
- Reading to Learn Mathematics, p. 140
- Enrichment, p. 141
- Assessment, p. 158

Graphing Calculator and Spreadsheet Masters, p. 24
Parent and Student Study Guide Workbook, p. 22
School-to-Career Masters, p. 6

 Transparencies

5-Minute Check Transparency 3-7
Answer Key Transparencies

Technology

Interactive Chalkboard

2 Teach

FORMULAS

In-Class Example

Teaching Tip In the example below, have students identify which parts of the distance formula correspond to each number in the problem. **135 mi = *d*; 3 h = *t***

1 **TRAVEL** If you travel 135 miles in 3 hours, what is your average speed in miles per hour? **45 mph**

PERIMETER AND AREA

In-Class Examples

2 Find the perimeter of the rectangle.

15 cm

20 cm

70 cm

Teaching Tip Have students sketch a rectangle and label what is known on the rectangle. In the example below, two opposing sides each measure 9 feet, and the other two sides have the same length, ℓ. This will help students write the equation $P = 2\ell + 2(9)$.

3 The perimeter of a rectangle is 60 feet. Its width is 9 feet. Find its length. **21 ft**

Study Tip

Common Misconception
Although the length of a rectangle is usually greater than the width, it does not matter which side you choose to be the length.

PERIMETER AND AREA The distance around a geometric figure is called the **perimeter**. One method of finding the perimeter P of a rectangle is to add the measures of the four sides.

Key Concept — *Perimeter of a Rectangle*

- **Words** The perimeter of a rectangle is twice the sum of the length and width.

- **Symbols** $P = \ell + \ell + w + w$
  $P = 2\ell + 2w$ or $2(\ell + w)$

- **Model**

  ℓ

  w

Example 2 *Find the Perimeter of a Rectangle*

Find the perimeter of the rectangle.

$P = 2(\ell + w)$	Write the formula.
$P = 2(11 + 5)$	Replace ℓ with 11 and w with 5.
$P = 2(16)$	Add 11 and 5.
$P = 32$	Simplify.

11 in.

5 in.

The perimeter is 32 inches.

Example 3 *Find a Missing Length*

The perimeter of a rectangle is 28 meters. Its width is 8 meters. Find the length.

$P = 2(\ell + w)$	Write the formula.
$P = 2\ell + 2w$	Distributive Property
$28 = 2\ell + 2(8)$	Replace P with 28 and w with 8.
$28 = 2\ell + 16$	Simplify.
$28 - 16 = 2\ell + 16 - 16$	Subtract 16 from each side.
$12 = 2\ell$	Simplify.
$6 = \ell$	Mentally divide each side by 2.

The length is 6 meters.

The measure of the surface enclosed by a figure is its **area**.

Key Concept — *Area of a Rectangle*

- **Words** The area of a rectangle is the product of the length and width.

- **Symbols** $A = \ell w$

- **Model**

  ℓ

  w

Example 4 Find the Area of a Rectangle

Find the area of a rectangle with length 15 meters and width 7 meters.

$A = \ell w$ Write the formula.
$A = 15 \cdot 7$ Replace ℓ with 15 and w with 7.
$A = 105$ Simplify.

The area is 105 square meters.

15 m
7 m

Example 5 Find a Missing Width

The area of a rectangle is 45 square feet. Its length is 9 feet. Find its width.

$A = \ell w$ Write the formula.
$45 = 9w$ Replace A with 45 and ℓ with 9.
$5 = w$ Mentally divide each side by 9.

The width is 5 feet.

✓ **Concept Check** Which is measured in square units, area or perimeter? **area**

Check for Understanding

Concept Check 1. **Write** the formula that shows the relationship among distance, rate, and time. **d = rt**

2. See margin.   2. **Explain** the difference between the perimeter and area of a rectangle.

3. **OPEN ENDED** Draw and label a rectangle that has a perimeter of 18 inches. **See margin.**

Guided Practice **GEOMETRY** Find the perimeter and area of each rectangle.

GUIDED PRACTICE KEY	
Exercises	Examples
4–6	2, 3
7, 8	3, 5
9	1

4.

8 ft
3 ft
22 ft, 24 ft²

5.

15 km
2 km
34 km, 30 km²

6. a rectangle with length 15 feet and width 6 feet **42 ft, 90 ft²**

GEOMETRY Find the missing dimension in each rectangle.

7.

12 in.
w
Perimeter = 32 in.
4 in.

8.

8 m
Area = 96 m²
ℓ
12 m

Application 9. **MILITARY** How long will it take an Air Force jet fighter to fly 5200 miles at 650 miles per hour? **8 h**

---

4 Find the area of a rectangle with length 14 feet and width 6 feet. **84 ft²**

Teaching Tip Point out that area is measured in square units. Students can internalize this by remembering that a line, such as the side of a rectangle or its perimeter, has one dimension, but a plane, such as the area of a rectangle, has two dimensions. This will help students place values into the area equation correctly.

5 The area of a rectangle is 40 square meters. Its length is 8 meters. Find its width. **5 m**

✓ Skills Check

Perimeter and Area Find the perimeter and area of a rectangle that is 3 centimeters wide and 7 centimeters long. **20 cm, 21 cm²**

3 Practice/Apply

Study Notebook

Have students—
• add the definitions/examples for the remaining terms on the Vocabulary Builder Worksheets for Chapter 3.
• write about the difference between area and perimeter.
• include any other item(s) that they find helpful in mastering the skills in this lesson.

Answers

2. Perimeter is the measure of the distance around a rectangle; area is the measure of the surface the perimeter encloses.

3. Sample answer:
5 in.
4 in.

Answers (p. 135)

37.

4 ft
3 ft

38.

6 m
2 m

39.

4 cm
4 cm

40.

4 in.
2 in.

Answer (Differentiated Instruction)

12 m
6 m
x   32 m²   A
8 m

$x = 4$ m, $A = 16$ m², $P = 44$ m

★ indicates increased difficulty

Practice and Apply

Homework Help

For Exercises	See Examples
10–11	1
12–19	2, 4
20–27	3, 5

Extra Practice
See page 730.

10. TRAVEL Find the distance traveled by driving at 55 miles per hour for 3 hours. **165 mi**

11. BALLOONING What is the rate, in miles per hour, of a balloon that travels 60 miles in 4 hours? **15 mph**

GEOMETRY Find the perimeter and area of each rectangle.

12. 3 mi, 2 mi **10 mi, 6 mi²**

13. 9 cm, 18 cm **54 cm, 162 cm²**

14. 12 ft, 5 ft **34 ft, 60 ft²**

15. 18 in., 50 in. **136 in., 900 in²**

16. 6 m, 17 m **46 m, 102 m²**

17. 12 m, 12 m **48 m, 144 m²**

18. a rectangle that is 38 meters long and 10 meters wide **96 m, 380 m²**

19. a square that is 5 meters on each side **20 m, 25 m²**

GEOMETRY Find the missing dimension in each rectangle.

20. 15 cm, Area = 270 cm², ℓ **18 cm**

21. w, Area = 176 yd², 16 yd **11 yd**

22. ℓ, 11 m, Perimeter = 70 m **24 m**

23. 7 m, w, Perimeter = 24 m **5 m**

24. w, Area = 154 in², 14 in. **11 in.**

25. 12 ft, Area = 468 ft², ℓ **39 ft**

26. GEOMETRY The perimeter of a rectangle is 46 centimeters. Its width is 5 centimeters. Find the length. **18 cm**

27. GEOMETRY The area of a rectangle is 323 square yards. Its length is 17 yards. Find the width. **19 yd**

28. COMMUNITY SERVICE Each participant in a community garden is allotted a rectangular plot that measures 18 feet by 45 feet. How much fencing is needed to enclose each plot? **126 ft**

29. SOCCER Find the perimeter and area of the soccer field described at the left. **390 yd, 9000 yd²**

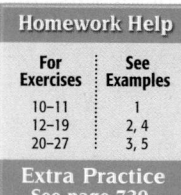

DAILY
INTERVENTION   **Differentiated Instruction**

- **Logical** Have students sketch this shape and find the missing values: "One large rectangle is divided into 3 smaller rectangles. The largest rectangle of these is 12 meters long and 6 meters wide. Underneath it, side-by-side, lie the other 2 rectangles. One of these measures 8 meters long and has an area of 32 square meters. Its width is x. Find x as well as the area A of the last smaller rectangle, and the perimeter P of the large rectangle that contains the 3 rectangles."

Using a formula can help you find the cost of a vacation. Visit www.pre-alg.com/webquest to continue work on your WebQuest project.

For Exercises 30 and 31, translate each sentence into a formula.

30. SALES The sale price of an item s is equal to the list price ℓ minus the discount d. $s = \ell - d$

31. GEOMETRY In a circle, the diameter d is twice the length of the radius r. $d = 2r$

32. RUNNING The *stride rate r* of a runner is the number of strides n that he or she takes divided by the amount of time t, or $r = \frac{n}{t}$. The best runners usually have the greatest stride rate. Use the table to determine which runner has the greater stride rate. **A**

Runner	Number of Strides	Time (s)
A	20	5
B	30	10

LANDSCAPING   For Exercises 33 and 34, use the figure at the right.

33. 4300 ft²

33. What is the area of the lawn?

34. Suppose your family wants to fertilize the lawn that is shown. If one bag of fertilizer covers 2500 square feet, how many bags of fertilizer should you buy? **2 bags**

80 ft

Lawn

House
28 ft x 50 ft

75 ft

Driveway
15 ft x 20 ft

★ **BICYCLING   For Exercises 35 and 36, use following information.**
American Lance Armstrong won the 2000 Tour De France, completing the 2178-mile race in 92 hours 33 minutes 8 seconds.

35. Find Armstrong's average rate in miles per hour for the race. **≈ 23.5 mph**

36. Armstrong also won the 1999 Tour de France. He completed the 2213-mile race in 91 hours 32 minutes 16 seconds. Without calculating, determine which race was completed with a faster average speed. Explain. **1999; he traveled a greater distance in less time.**

★ **GEOMETRY   Draw and label the dimensions of each rectangle whose perimeter and area are given. 37–40. See margin.**

37. $P = 14$ ft, $A = 12$ ft²   **38.** $P = 16$ m, $A = 12$ m²

39. $P = 16$ cm, $A = 16$ cm²   **40.** $P = 12$ in., $A = 8$ in²

41. CRITICAL THINKING Is it *sometimes*, *always*, or *never* true that the perimeter of a rectangle is numerically greater than its area? Give an example. **See margin.**

42. CRITICAL THINKING An airplane flying at a rate of 500 miles per hour leaves Los Angeles. One-half hour later, a second airplane leaves Los Angeles in the same direction flying at a rate of 600 miles per hour. How long will it take the second airplane to overtake the first? **2.5 h**

 www.pre-alg.com/self_check_quiz/ny

Answer

41. Sometimes; a 3-inch by 4-inch rectangle has a perimeter of 14 inches and an area of 12 square inches; a 6-inch by 8-inch rectangle has a perimeter of 28 inches and an area of 48 square inches.

Open-Ended Assessment

Modeling Cut out rectangles of various sizes and shapes and give one to each student. Then have the students find the perimeters of their rectangles by measuring the sides with a ruler and applying the formulas for perimeter and area.

Assessment Options

Quiz (Lesson 3-7) is available on p. 158 of the *Chapter 3 Resource Masters*.

Answer

43. Formulas are important in math and science because they summarize the relationships among quantities. Answers should include the following.

- Sample answer: The formula to find acceleration is $a = \dfrac{v_f - v_i}{t}$ where v_f is the final velocity and v_i is the initial velocity.

- You can find the acceleration of an automobile with this formula.

---

43. **WRITING IN MATH** Answer the question that was posed at the beginning of the lesson. **See margin.**

Why are formulas important in math and science?

Include the following in your answer:

- an example of a formula from math or science that you have used, and
- an explanation of how you used the formula.

NEW YORK Test Practice

Standardized Test Practice
Ⓐ Ⓑ Ⓒ Ⓓ

★ 44. The formula $d = rt$ can be rewritten as $\dfrac{d}{t} = r$. How is the rate affected if the time t increases and the distance d remains the same? **B**

Ⓐ It increases.　　　　Ⓑ It decreases.
Ⓒ It remains the same.　Ⓓ There is not enough information.

45. The area of each square in the figure is 16 square units. Find the perimeter. **C**

Ⓐ 16 units　　　　Ⓑ 32 units
Ⓒ 48 units　　　　Ⓓ 64 units

Maintain Your Skills

Mixed Review

46. Eight more than five times a number is 78. Find the number. *(Lesson 3-6)*
14

ALGEBRA Solve each equation. Check your solution. *(Lessons 3-3, 3-4, and 3-5)*

47. $-5x + 8 = 53$ **−9**　　48. $4y = -24$ **−6**　　49. $m + 5 = -3$ **−8**

ALGEBRA Simplify each expression. *(Lesson 3-2)*

50. $3y + 5 - 2y$ **y + 5**　51. $9 + x - 5x$ **−4x + 9**　52. $3(r + 2) + 6r$ **9r + 6**

53a. {(1870, 14), (1881, 600), (1910, 1000), (2000, 1500)}
53b. domain: {1870, 1881, 1910, 2000}, range: {14, 600, 1000, 1500}

53. **LIGHT BULBS** The table shows the average life of an incandescent bulb for selected years. *(Lesson 1-6)*

  a. Write a set of ordered pairs for the data.

  b. State the domain and the range of the relation.

Incandescent Light Bulbs

 WebQuest Internet Project

Vacation Travelers Include More Families
It's time to complete your Internet project. Use the information and data you have gathered about the costs of lodging, transportation, and entertainment for each of the vacations. Prepare a brochure or Web page to present your project. Be sure to include graphs and/or tables in the presentation.
www.pre-alg.com/webquest

Spreadsheet Investigation

A Follow-Up of Lesson 3-7

Perimeter and Area

A spreadsheet allows you to use formulas to investigate problems. When you change a numerical value in a cell, the spreadsheet recalculates the formula and automatically updates the results.

Example

Suppose a gardener wants to enclose a rectangular garden using part of a wall as one side and 20 feet of fencing for the other three sides. What are the dimensions of the largest garden she can enclose?

If w represents the length of each side attached to the wall, $20 - 2w$ represents the length of the side opposite the wall. These values are listed in column B. The areas are listed in column C.

Garden Dimensions

	A	B	C
1	Length of Fence	20	
2	Length of Side Attached to Wall	Length of Side Opposite Wall	Area
3	1	18	18
4	2	16	32
5	3	14	42
6	4	12	48
7	5	10	50
8	6	8	48
9	7	6	42
10	8	4	32
11	9	2	18
12			

Sheet1 / Sheet2

The spreadsheet evaluates the formula B1 − 2 × A3.

The spreadsheet evaluates the formula A9 × B9.

The greatest possible area is 50 square feet. It occurs when the length of each side attached to the wall is 5 feet, and the length of the side opposite the wall is 10 feet.

Exercises

1. What is the area if the length of the side attached to the wall is 10 feet? 11 feet? **0, −22**

2. Are the answers to Exercise 1 reasonable? Explain. **No; area cannot be zero or a negative number.**

3. Suppose you want to find the greatest area that you can enclose with 30 feet of fencing. Which cell should you modify to solve this problem? **B1**

4. Use a spreadsheet to find the dimensions of the greatest area you can enclose with 40 feet, 50 feet, and 60 feet of fencing. **10 ft by 20 ft; 12.5 ft by 25 ft; 15 ft by 30 ft**

5. **MAKE A CONJECTURE** Use any pattern you may have observed in your answers to Exercise 4 to find the dimensions of the greatest area you can enclose with 100 feet of fencing. Explain. **25 ft by 50 ft; the opposite wall is twice the attached wall.**

Spreadsheet Investigation

A Follow-Up of Lesson 3-7

Getting Started

Before students turn to this page in class, present the Example problem on a transparency. Ask a few students to sketch out some possible dimensions for the garden as described in the Example. Then ask for a formula to represent the garden's possible dimensions.

Teach

- Explain to students that spreadsheet programs use column letters and row numbers to designate the location of cells, and that these designations are used as variables in spreadsheet formulas. To reinforce this, point to a few cells, one at a time, and have the class call out the cells' "names."

- If students need to review using formulas to solve problems, have them revisit Lesson 3-7.

Assess

Have students complete Exercises 1–5. If any students have difficulty with Exercise 3, have them sketch or cut out the dimensions on paper. You may wish to have students discuss Exercise 5 in small groups.

Chapter 3 Study Guide and Review

Vocabulary and Concept Check

- This alphabetical list of vocabulary terms in Chapter 3 includes a page reference where each term was introduced.

- **Assessment** A vocabulary review/test for Chapter 3 is available on p. 156 of the *Chapter 3 Resource Masters*.

Lesson-by-Lesson Review

For each lesson,

- the main ideas are summarized,
- additional examples review concepts, and
- practice exercises are provided.

Vocabulary PuzzleMaker

ELL The Vocabulary PuzzleMaker software improves students' mathematics vocabulary using four puzzle formats—crossword, scramble, word search using a word list, and word search using clues. Students can work on a computer screen or from a printed handout.

MindJogger Videoquizzes

ELL MindJogger Videoquizzes provide an alternative review of concepts presented in this chapter. Students work in teams in a game show format to gain points for correct answers. The questions are presented in three rounds.

Round 1 Concepts (5 questions)
Round 2 Skills (4 questions)
Round 3 Problem Solving (4 questions)

Vocabulary and Concept Check

area (p. 132)	inverse operations (p. 110)	Properties of Equality
coefficient (p. 103)	like terms (p. 103)	Multiplication (p. 117)
constant (p. 103)	perimeter (p. 132)	Subtraction (p. 110)
Distributive Property (p. 98)	Properties of Equality	simplest form (p. 104)
equivalent equations (p. 111)	Addition (p. 111)	simplifying an expression (p. 104)
equivalent expression (p. 98)	Division (p. 115)	term (p. 103)
formula (p. 131)		two-step equation (p. 120)

Complete each sentence with the correct term.

1. Terms that contain the same variables are called _____ . **like terms**

2. The _____ of a geometric figure is the measure of the distance around it. **perimeter**

3. The _____ states that when you multiply each side of an equation by the same number, the two sides remain equal. **Multiplication Property (=)**

4. The equations $x + 3 = 8$ and $x = 5$ are _____ because they have the same solution. **equivalent**

5. You could use the _____ Property to rewrite $9(t - 2)$ as $9t - 18$. **Distributive**

6. In the term $4b$, 4 is the _____ of the expression. **coefficient**

7. The solution of $2y + 5 = 13$ is a _____ of a point on a number line. **coordinate**

8. The measure of the surface enclosed by a geometric figure is its _____ . **area**

9. In the expression $10x + 6$, the number 6 is the _____ term. **constant**

10. Addition and subtraction are _____ because they "undo" each other.

10. **inverse operations**

Lesson-by-Lesson Review

3-1 The Distributive Property

See pages 98–102.

Concept Summary

- The Distributive Property combines addition and multiplication.
- For any numbers a, b, and c, $a(b + c) = ab + ac$ and $(b + c)a = ba + ca$.

Example Use the Distributive Property to rewrite $2(t - 3)$.

$$2(t - 3) = 2[(t + (-3)] \quad \text{Rewrite } t - 3 \text{ as } t + (-3).$$
$$= 2t + 2(-3) \quad \text{Distributive Property}$$
$$= 2t + (-6) \quad \text{Simplify.}$$
$$= 2t - 6 \quad \text{Definition of subtraction}$$

11. $3h + 18$
12. $7x + 14$
13. $-5k - 5$
14. $-2a - 16$
15. $9t - 45$
16. $7x - 21$
17. $-2b + 8$
18. $-6y + 18$

Exercises Use the Distributive Property to rewrite each expression.
See Examples 3 and 4 on page 100.

11. $3(h + 6)$
12. $7(x + 2)$
13. $-5(k + 1)$
14. $-2(a + 8)$
15. $(t - 5)9$
16. $(x - 3)7$
17. $-2(b - 4)$
18. $-6(y - 3)$

 www.pre-alg.com/vocabulary_review

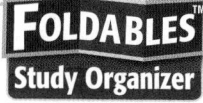

Study Organizer

For more information about Foldables, see *Teaching Mathematics with Foldables.*

Have students review their Foldables to be sure they have included notes on every lesson in this chapter.

Encourage students to refer to their Foldables while completing the Study Guide and Review and to use them in preparing for the Chapter Test.

3-2 Simplifying Algebraic Expressions

See pages 103–107.

Concept Summary

- Simplest form means no like terms and no parentheses.

Example **Simplify** $9x + 3 - 7x$.

$$
\begin{aligned}
9x + 3 - 7x &= 9x + 3 + (-7x) &&\text{Definition of subtraction} \\
&= 9x + (-7x) + 3 &&\text{Commutative Property} \\
&= [9 + (-7)]x + 3 &&\text{Distributive Property} \\
&= 2x + 3 &&\text{Simplify.}
\end{aligned}
$$

Exercises **Simplify each expression.** *See Example 2 on page 104.*

19. $4a + 5a$ **20.** $3x + 7 + x$ **21.** $8(n - 1) - 10n$ **22.** $6w + 2(w + 9)$

$9a$ $4x + 7$ $-2n - 8$ $8w + 18$

3-3 Solving Equations by Adding or Subtracting

See pages 110–114.

Concept Summary

- When you add or subtract the same number from each side of an equation, the two sides remain equal.

Examples **1 Solve** $x + 3 = 7$.

$$
\begin{aligned}
x + 3 &= 7 \\
x + 3 - 3 &= 7 - 3 &&\text{Subtract 3 from each side.} \\
x &= 4
\end{aligned}
$$

2 Solve $y - 5 = -2$.

$$
\begin{aligned}
y - 5 &= -2 \\
y - 5 + 5 &= -2 + 5 &&\text{Add 5 to each side.} \\
y &= 3
\end{aligned}
$$

Exercises **Solve each equation.** *See Examples 1 and 3 on pages 111 and 112.*

23. $t + 5 = 8$ **3**   **24.** $12 = x + 4$ **8**   **25.** $k - 1 = 4$ **5**   **26.** $-7 = n - 6$ **−1**

3-4 Solving Equations by Multiplying or Dividing

See pages 115–119.

Concept Summary

- When you multiply or divide each side of an equation by the same nonzero number, the two sides remain equal.

Examples **1 Solve** $-5x = -30$.

$$
\begin{aligned}
-5x &= -30 &&\text{Write the equation.} \\
\frac{-5x}{-5} &= \frac{-30}{-5} &&\text{Divide each side by −5.} \\
x &= 6 &&\text{Simplify.}
\end{aligned}
$$

2 Solve $\dfrac{a}{-8} = 3$.

$$
\begin{aligned}
\frac{a}{-8} &= 3 &&\text{Write the equation.} \\
-8\left(\frac{a}{-8}\right) &= -8(3) &&\text{Multiply each side by −8.} \\
a &= -24 &&\text{Simplify.}
\end{aligned}
$$

Exercises **Solve each equation.** *See Examples 1 and 3 on pages 116 and 117.*

27. $6n = 48$ **8**   **28.** $-3x = 30$ **−10**   **29.** $\dfrac{t}{2} = -9$ **−18**   **30.** $\dfrac{r}{-5} = -2$ **10**

Study Guide and Review

Chapter 3 For More ... • Extra Practice, see pages 728–730.
• Mixed Problem Solving, see page 760.

3-5 Solving Two-Step Equations

See pages 120–124.

Concept Summary

• To solve a two-step equation undo operations in reverse order.

Example Solve $6k - 4 = 14$.

$$6k - 4 = 14 \qquad \text{Write the equation.}$$
$$6k - 4 + 4 = 14 + 4 \qquad \text{Undo subtraction. Add 4 to each side.}$$
$$6k = 18 \qquad \text{Simplify.}$$
$$k = 3 \qquad \text{Mentally divide each side by 6.}$$

Exercises Solve each equation. *See Examples 1, 3, and 4 on pages 121 and 122.*

31. $6 + 2y = 8$ **1** **32.** $3n - 5 = -17$ **33.** $\frac{t}{3} + 4 = 2$ **−6** **34.** $\frac{c}{9} - 3 = 2$ **45**
−4

3-6 Writing Two-Step Equations

See pages 126–130.

Concept Summary

• The words *is, equals,* or *is equal to,* can be translated into an equals sign.

Example Seven less than three times a number is −22. Find the number.

$$3n - 7 = -22 \qquad \text{Write the equation.}$$
$$3n - 7 + 7 = -22 + 7 \qquad \text{Add 7 to each side.}$$
$$3n = -15 \qquad \text{Simplify.}$$
$$n = -5 \qquad \text{Mentally divide each side by 3.}$$

Exercises Translate the sentence into an equation. Then find the number.
See Examples 1 and 2 on pages 126 and 127.

35. Three more than twice n is 53. **36.** Four times x minus 16 is 52.

$2n + 3 = 53; 25$ $4x - 16 = 52; 17$

3-7 Using Formulas

See pages 131–136.

Concept Summary

• Perimeter of a rectangle: $P = 2(\ell + w)$ • Area of a rectangle: $A = \ell w$

Example Find the perimeter and area of a 14-meter by 6-meter rectangle.

$P = 2(\ell + w)$ Formula for perimeter $\qquad A = \ell w$ Formula for area
$P = 2(14 + 6)$ $\ell = 14$ and $w = 6$. $\qquad A = 14 \cdot 6$ $\ell = 14$ and $w = 6$.
$P = 40$ Simplify. $\qquad A = 84$ Simplify.

Exercises Find the perimeter and area of each rectangle whose dimensions
are given. *See Examples 2 and 4 on pages 132 and 133.*

37. 8 feet by 9 feet **34 ft, 72 ft²** **38.** 5 meters by 15 meters **40 m, 75 m²**

Answers (p. 141)

1. Sample answer: like terms—$2x$ and $3x$,
not like terms—$5y$ and 2.

2. To multiply a number by a sum, multiply
the number outside the parentheses by
each number inside the parentheses.

Vocabulary and Concepts

1. **OPEN ENDED** Give an example of two terms that are like terms and two terms that are *not* like terms. **See margin.**
2. **State** the Distributive Property in your own words. **See margin.**
3. **Explain** the difference between perimeter and area. **Perimeter is the distance around a figure; area is a measure of the surface the perimeter encloses.**

Skills and Applications

Simplify each expression.

4. $9x + 5 - x + 3$ **$8x + 8$**   5. $-3(a - 8)$ **$-3a + 24$**   6. $10(y + 3) - 4y$ **$6y + 30$**

Solve each equation. Check your solution.

7. $19 = f + 5$ **14**

8. $-15 + z = 3$ **18**

9. $x - 7 = 16$ **23**

10. $g - 9 = -10$ **-1**

11. $-8y = 72$ **-9**

12. $\frac{n}{-30} = -6$ **180**

13. $25 = 2d - 9$ **17**

14. $4w - 18 = -34$ **-4**

15. $6v + 10 = -62$ **-12**

16. $-7 = \frac{d}{-5} + 1$ **40**

17. $7 - x = 18$ **-11**

18. $b - 7b + 6 = -30$ **6**

Translate each sentence into an equation. Then find each number.

19. The quotient of a number and 8, decreased by 17 is -15. $\frac{n}{8} - 17 = -15$, **16**
20. Five less than 3 times a number is 25. **$3n - 5 = 25$, 10**

Find the perimeter and area of each rectangle.

21. 48 m ; 20 m **136 m, 960 m²**

22. 100 yd ; 75 yd **350 yd, 7500 yd²**

23. **ENTERTAINMENT** Suppose you pay $15 per hour to go horseback riding. You ride 2 hours today and plan to ride 4 more hours this weekend.
    a. Write two different expressions to find the total cost of horseback riding.
    b. Find the total cost. **$90**

    23a. $15(2 + 4)$, $15 \cdot 2 + 15 \cdot 4$

24. **HEIGHT** Todd is 5 inches taller than his brother. The sum of their heights is 139 inches. Find Todd's height. **72 in.**

25. **STANDARDIZED TEST PRACTICE** A carpet store advertises 16 square yards of carpeting for $300, which includes the $60 installation charge. Which equation could be used to determine the cost of one square yard of carpet x? **D**

  YORK Practice

  Ⓐ $16x = 300$ Ⓑ $x + 60 = 300$
  Ⓒ $60x + 16 = 300$ Ⓓ $16x + 60 = 300$

Portfolio Suggestion

Introduction Equations are used to solve many different types of problems. Sometimes special types of equations called formulas are used.

Ask Students to find a problem from their work in this chapter and explain how they used an equation or formula to solve it.

Assessment Options

Vocabulary Test A vocabulary review/test for Chapter 3 can be found on p. 156 of the *Chapter 3 Resource Masters*.

Chapter Tests There are six Chapter 3 Tests and an Open-Ended Assessment task available in the *Chapter 3 Resource Masters*.

Chapter 3 Tests			
Form	Type	Level	Pages
1	MC	basic	143–144
2A	MC	average	145–146
2B	MC	average	147–148
2C	FR	average	149–150
2D	FR	average	151–152
3	FR	advanced	153–154

MC = multiple-choice questions
FR = free-response questions

Open-Ended Assessment
Performance tasks for Chapter 3 can be found on p. 155 of the *Chapter 3 Resource Masters*, along with a sample scoring rubric for these tasks on p. A25.

Unit 1 Test/Review Pages 163–164 of the *Chapter 3 Resource Masters* provide a cumulative review of Unit 1, which can be used as a Unit Review or a Unit Test.

 ExamView® Pro

Use the networkable **ExamView® Pro** to:

- Create **multiple versions** of tests.
- Create **modified** tests for *Inclusion* students.
- **Edit** existing questions and **add** your own questions.
- Use built-in **state curriculum correlations** to create tests aligned with state standards.
- Change **English** tests to **Spanish** and vice versa.

These two pages contain practice questions in the various formats that can be found on the most frequently given standardized tests.

A practice answer sheet for these two pages can be found on page A1 of the *Chapter 3 Resource Masters*.

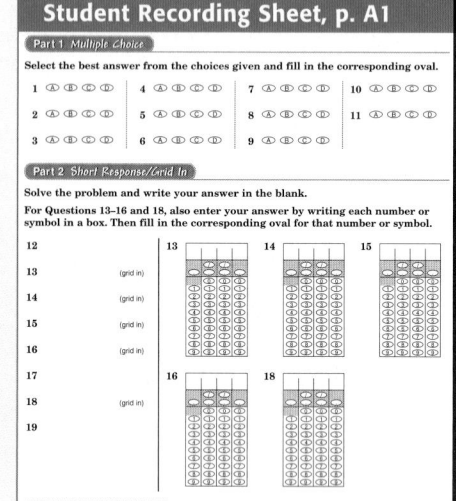

Additional Practice

See pp. 161–162 of the *Chapter 3 Resource Masters* for additional standardized test practice.

Part 1 Multiple Choice

Record your answers on the answer sheet provided by your teacher or on a sheet of paper.

1. Ms. Bauer notices that her car's gas tank is nearly empty. Gasoline costs $1.59 a gallon. *About* how many gallons can she buy with a $20 bill?   (Prerequisite Skills, p. 714) **C**
   - Ⓐ 10
   - Ⓑ 30
   - Ⓒ 12
   - Ⓓ 20

2. Which is equivalent to $3 \times 8 - 6 \div 2$? (Lesson 1-2) **D**
   - Ⓐ 3
   - Ⓑ 9
   - Ⓒ 13
   - Ⓓ 21

3. Which statement illustrates the Commutative Property of Multiplication? (Lesson 1-4) **B**
   - Ⓐ $5 + w + 8 = 5 + 8 + w$
   - Ⓑ $5 \cdot w \cdot 8 = 5 \cdot 8 \cdot w$
   - Ⓒ $(5 \cdot w) \cdot 8 = 5 \cdot (w \cdot 8)$
   - Ⓓ $(5 + w) + 8 = 5 + (w + 8)$

4. Which point on the graph below represents the ordered pair (4, 3)?   (Lesson 1-6) **B**

   - Ⓐ M
   - Ⓑ N
   - Ⓒ P
   - Ⓓ Q

5. The temperature at 6:00 A.M. was $-5°F$. What was the temperature at 8:00 A.M. if it had risen 7 degrees?   (Lesson 2-2) **A**
   - Ⓐ 2°F
   - Ⓑ $-2°F$
   - Ⓒ 12°F
   - Ⓓ $-12°F$

6. Suppose points at (x, y) are graphed using the values in the table. Which statement is true about the graphs? (Lesson 2-6) **B**

x	y
−1	5
−3	10
−5	6

   - Ⓐ The graphs are located in Quadrant I.
   - Ⓑ The graphs are located in Quadrant II.
   - Ⓒ The graphs are located in Quadrant III.
   - Ⓓ The graphs are located in Quadrant IV.

7. Which expression is equivalent to $5 \times 3 + 5 \times 12$?   (Lesson 3-1) **C**
   - Ⓐ $5 \times 8 \times 12$
   - Ⓑ $3 + (5 \times 12)$
   - Ⓒ $5 \times (3 + 12)$
   - Ⓓ $5 + (3 \times 12)$

8. Simplify $x - 4(x + 3)$.   (Lesson 3-2) **B**
   - Ⓐ $5x + 12$
   - Ⓑ $-3x - 12$
   - Ⓒ $-3x + 12$
   - Ⓓ $5x - 12$

9. Solve $y - (-4) = 6 - 8$.   (Lesson 3-3) **A**
   - Ⓐ -6
   - Ⓑ -2
   - Ⓒ 2
   - Ⓓ 6

10. Mr. Samuels is a car sales associate. He makes a salary of $400 per week. He also earns a bonus of $100 for each car he sells. Which equation represents the total amount of money Mr. Samuels earns in a week when he sells n cars?   (Lesson 3-6) **C**
    - Ⓐ $T = 400n + 100$
    - Ⓑ $T = n(100 + 400)$
    - Ⓒ $T = 100n + 400$
    - Ⓓ $T = 400 + 100 + n$

11. Tiffany's Gift Shop has fixed monthly expenses, E, of $1850. If the owner wants to make a profit, P, of $4000 next month, how many dollars in sales, S, does the shop need to earn? Use the formula $P = S - E$.   (Lesson 3-7) **C**
    - Ⓐ 2150
    - Ⓑ 4000
    - Ⓒ 5850
    - Ⓓ 7400

ExamView® Pro

Special banks of standardized test questions similar to those on the SAT, ACT, TIMSS 8, NAEP 8, and Pre-Algebra End-of-Course tests can be found on this CD-ROM.

Part 2 Short Response/Grid In

Record your answers on the answer sheet provided by your teacher or on a sheet of paper.

12. The charge to enter a nature preserve is a flat amount per vehicle plus a fee for each person in the vehicle. The table shows the charge for vehicles holding up to 4 people.

Number of People	Charge (dollars)
1	1.50
2	2.00
3	2.50
4	3.00

What is the charge, in dollars, for a vehicle holding 8 people?   (Lesson 1-1) **$5**

13. Evaluate $-2(-8 + 5)$.   (Lesson 1-2) **6**

14. Last week, the stock market rose 10 points in two days. What number expresses the average change in the stock market per day?   (Lesson 2-1) **5**

15. The ordered pairs $(-7, -2)$, $(-3, 5)$, and $(-3, -2)$ are coordinates of three of the vertices of a rectangle. What is the y-coordinate of the ordered pair that represents the fourth vertex?   (Lesson 2-6) **5**

16. What value of x makes $x - 4 = -2$ a true statement?   (Lesson 3-3) **2**

17. Cara filled her car's gas tank with 15 gallons of gas. Her car usually gets 24 miles per gallon. How many miles can she drive using 15 gallons of gas? (Lesson 3–7) **360 mi**

www.pre-alg.com/standardized_test/ny

18. A mail-order greeting card company charges $3 for each box of greeting cards plus a handling charge of $2 per order. How many boxes of cards can you order from this company if you want to spend $26?   (Lesson 3-6) **8**

19. Mr. Ruiz owns a health club and is planning to increase the floor area of the weight room. In the figure below, the rectangle with the solid border represents the floor area of the existing room, and the rectangle with the dashed border represents the floor area to be added. What will be the length, in feet, of the new weight room? (Lesson 3-7) **30 ft**

18 ft   360 ft²   180 ft²

Part 3 Extended Response

Record your answers on a sheet of paper. Show your work.

20. The overnight low in Fargo, North Dakota, was $-14°F$. The high the next day was $6°F$. (Lesson 3-3)

  a. Draw a number line to represent the increase in temperature. **See margin.**

  b. How many degrees did the temperature rise from the low to the high? **20°F**

  c. Explain how the concept of absolute value relates to this question. **See margin.**

21. In a school basketball game, each field goal is worth 2 points, and each free throw is worth 1 point. Josh heard the Springdale Stars scored a total of 63 points in their last game. Soledad says that they made a total of 12 free throws in that game.   (Lesson 3-6)

  a. Write an equation to represent the total points scored p. Use f for the number of free throws and g for the number of field goals. **$f + 2g = p$**

  b. Can both Josh and Soledad be correct? Explain. **No; a team can't score half of a basket.**

Chapter 3 Standardized Test Practice 143

Evaluating Extended Response Questions

Extended Response questions are graded by using a multilevel rubric that guides you in assessing a student's knowledge of a particular concept.

Goal: Use knowledge of integers and algebraic equations to solve real-world problems.

Sample Scoring Rubric: The following rubric is a sample scoring device. You may wish to add more detail to this sample to meet your individual scoring needs.

Score	Criteria
4	A correct solution that is supported by well-developed, accurate explanations
3	A generally correct solution, but may contain minor flaws in reasoning or computation
2	A partially correct interpretation and/or solution to the problem
1	A correct solution with no supporting evidence or explanation
0	An incorrect solution indicating no mathematical understanding of the concept or task, or no solution is given

Answers

20a.

20 degree rise

-14 -12 -10 -8 -6 -4 -2 0 2 4 6 8

20c. The increase from the low temperature to 0° is the absolute value of the low temperature. The increase from 0° to the high temperature is the absolute value of the high temperature. The total increase can be found by adding the absolute values of the two temperatures. $|-14| + |6| = 20$.

Page 101, Lesson 3-1

12. $2 \cdot 6 + 2 \cdot 1, 14$

13. $5 \cdot 7 + 5 \cdot 3, 50$

14. $4 \cdot 9 + 6 \cdot 9, 90$

15. $4 \cdot 3 + 3 \cdot 3, 21$

16. $9 \cdot 4 + 2 \cdot 4, 44$

17. $8 \cdot 2 + 8 \cdot 2, 32$

18. $7 \cdot 3 + 7(-2), 7$

19. $6 \cdot 8 + 6(-5), 18$

20. $-5 \cdot 8 + (-5)(-4), -20$

21. $-3 \cdot 9 + (-3)(-2), -21$

22. $8(-2) - 4(-2), -8$

23. $10(-5) - 3(-5), -35$

26. $2x + 6$

27. $5y + 30$

28. $3n + 3$

29. $7y + 56$

30. $4x + 12$

31. $10y + 20$

32. $18 + 6y$

33. $10 + 5x$

34. $3x - 6$

35. $9m - 18$

36. $8z - 24$

37. $15s - 45$

38. $6r - 30$

39. $12x - 36$

40. $5t - 20$

41. $2w - 20$

42. $-2z - 8$

43. $-5a - 50$

44. $-2x + 14$

45. $-5w + 40$

46. $-2y + 8$

47. $-5a + 30$

48. $2x + 2y$

49. $3a + 3b$

52. Sample answer: You can compute the area of two rectangles with the same width in two ways. You can put them together and multiply to find the total area or find each area separately and then add to find the total. The Distributive Property states that the expressions $a(b + c)$, and $ab + ac$ are equivalent.

- $2(5 + 4) = 18; 2 \cdot 5 + 2 \cdot 4 = 18$

Page 106, Lesson 3-2

56. Sample answer: You can use algebra tiles to simplify an algebraic expression by grouping the tiles with the same size and shape together.

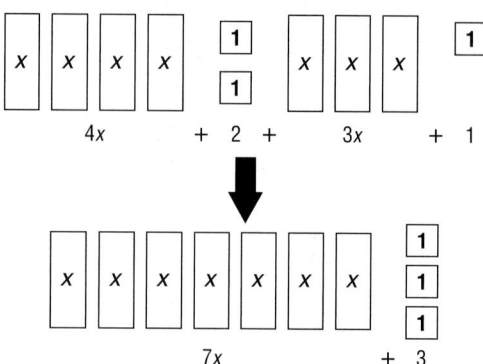

- *Like terms* are terms that have the same variable(s) or are constants.

- You use the Commutative Property when you change the order of 2 and $3x$. You use the Distributive Property when you write $4x + 3x$ as $7x$.

Page 109, Algebra Activity

5.

6.

7.

8.

9.

10.

11.

12.

Page 113, Lesson 3-3

2. Sample answer: equivalent—$x + 3 = 5$, $x = 2$; not equivalent—$x + 5 = 2$, $x + 1 = 5$

9.
```
 ───┼───●───┼───┼───┼───┼───┼───┼───
   -3  -2  -1   0   1   2   3   4
```

10.
```
 ───┼───┼───┼───┼───┼───●───┼───┼───
   -3  -2  -1   0   1   2   3   4
```

37.
```
 ───┼───●───┼───┼───┼───┼───┼───┼───
   -6  -5  -4  -3  -2  -1   0   1
```

38.
```
 ───●───┼───┼───┼───┼───┼───┼───┼───
   -3  -2  -1   0   1   2   3   4
```

39.
```
 ───┼───┼───┼───┼───┼───●───┼───┼───
    5   6   7   8   9  10  11  12
```

40.
```
 ───┼───┼───┼───┼───┼───┼───●───┼───
   -3  -2  -1   0   1   2   3   4
```

41.
```
 ───●───┼───┼───┼───┼───┼───┼───┼───
   -4  -3  -2  -1   0   1   2   3
```

42.
```
 ───┼───┼───●───┼───┼───┼───┼───┼───
   -3  -2  -1   0   1   2   3   4
```

Page 123, Lesson 3-5

50. Sample answer: You can add or remove tiles from each side of a mat. This models the Addition and Subtraction Properties of Equality. Also, separating tiles into groups models the Division Property of Equality.

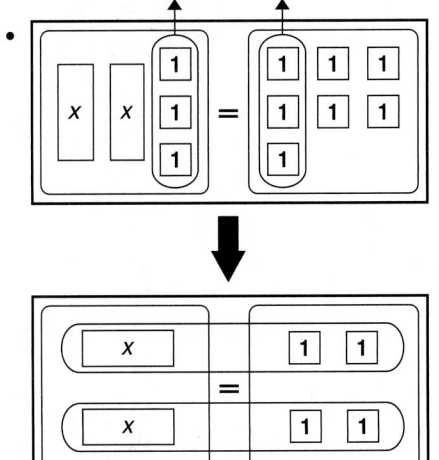

- Subtraction Property of Equality, Division Property of Equality

UNIT 2

Algebra and Rational Numbers

Introduction

In this unit, students explore rational numbers. They will learn to use prime factorization and greatest common factor to solve real-world problems and simplify algebraic equations.

Students will examine exponents, multiply and divide monomials, and use scientific notation. Students will also compute and solve equations with rational numbers. They will use measures of central tendency. Students will apply ratios and proportions to problems involving fractions, decimals, and percents. Students will use percent equations, calculate percent of change, and make predictions based on probability.

Assessment Options

📁 **Unit 2 Test** Pages 365–366 of the *Chapter 6 Resource Masters* may be used as a test or review for Unit 2. This assessment contains both multiple-choice and short answer items.

💿 **ExamView® Pro**
This CD-ROM can be used to create additional unit tests and review worksheets.

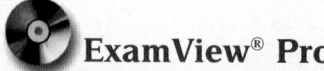
Yearly Progress Pro

An online, research-based instructional, assessment, and intervention tool that provides specific feedback on student mastery of state and national standards, instant remediation, and a data management system to track performance. For more information, contact mhdigitallearning.com.

Most of the numbers you encounter in the real world are *rational numbers*—fractions, decimals, and percents. In this unit, you will build on your foundation of algebra so that it includes rational numbers.

Chapter 4
Factors and Fractions

Chapter 5
Rational Numbers

Chapter 6
Ratio, Proportion, and Percent

What's MATH Got To Do With It?

Real-Life Math Videos

What's Math Got to Do With It? Real-Life Math Videos engage students showing them how math is used in everyday situations. Use Video 1 with this unit.

Teaching Suggestions

Have students study the USA TODAY Snapshot®.

- Ask them whether the survey data are based on the use of mean, median, or mode.
  mean

- How much does the average teenager spend per week on fast food? **\$12.18**

- Students eat 7 percent of their meals at fast-food restaurants. What does 1 percent of their meals represent in dollars? **\$1,814,285,714**

Additional USA TODAY Snapshots® appearing in Unit 2:

Chapter 4 Our daily time behind the wheel (p. 156)

Chapter 5 Favorite subjects (p. 203)

Discussing school at home (p. 213)

Chapter 6 Number of threatened species in USA (p. 289)

Kids don't enjoy cleaning their rooms (p. 290)

Monster cookies (p. 312)

Chocolate cravings (p. 314)

WebQuest Internet Project

Kids Gobbling Empty Calories

"Teens are eating 150 more calories a day in snacks than they did two decades ago. And kids of all ages are munching on more of the richer goodies between meals than children did in the past."

Source: *USA TODAY*, April 30, 2001

In this project, you will be exploring how rational numbers are related to nutrition.

 Log on to www.pre-alg.com/webquest. Begin your WebQuest by reading the Task.

Then continue working on your WebQuest as you study Unit 2.

Lesson	4-5	5-8	6-7
Page	173	242	301

USA TODAY Snapshots®

Teen fuel

Kids ages 12-17 eat an average of 7% of their meals at fast-food restaurants, spending \$12.7 billion a year. Teens and fast food:

Fast-food visits per week	**2.13**
Average spent per visit	**\$5.72**
Favorite order	**Hamburger (46%)**
Time of day	**5-8 p.m. (38%)**

Source: David Michaelson & Associates for Channel One Network

By Anne R. Carey and Jerry Mosemak, USA TODAY

Unit 2 Algebra and Rational Numbers 145

WebQuest Internet Project

Problem-Based Learning A WebQuest is an online project in which students do research on the Internet, gather data, and make presentations using word processing, graphing, page-making, or presentation software. In each chapter, students advance to the next step in their WebQuest. At the end of Chapter 6, the project culminates with a presentation of their findings.

Teaching suggestions and sample answers are available in the *WebQuest and Project Resources*.

Chapter 4

Factors and Fractions
Chapter Overview and Pacing

Year-long pacing: pages T20–T21.

LESSON OBJECTIVES	Regular Basic/ Average	Regular Advanced	Block Basic/ Average	Block Advanced
4-1 Factors and Monomials (pp. 148–152) • Determine whether one number is a factor of another. • Determine whether an expression is a monomial.	1	1	0.5	0.5
4-2 Powers and Exponents (pp. 153–158) • Write expressions using exponents. • Evaluate expressions containing exponents. *Follow-Up:* Investigate writing numerals in base 2.	1	2 (with 4-2 Follow-Up)	0.5	1 (with 4-2 Follow-Up)
4-3 Prime Factorization (pp. 159–163) • Write the prime factorizations of composite numbers. • Factor monomials.	1	1	0.5	0.5
4-4 Greatest Common Factor (GCF) (pp. 164–168) • Find the greatest common factor of two or more numbers or monomials. • Use the Distributive Property to factor algebraic expressions.	1	1	0.5	0.5
4-5 Simplifying Algebraic Fractions (pp. 169–173) • Simplify fractions using the GCF. • Simplify algebraic fractions.	2	1	1	0.5
4-6 Multiplying and Dividing Monomials (pp. 175–180) • Multiply monomials. • Divide monomials. *Follow-Up:* Model and investigate radioactive half-lives.	2	2 (with 4-6 Follow-Up)	1.5	1 (with 4-6 Follow-Up)
4-7 Negative Exponents (pp. 181–185) • Write expressions using negative exponents. • Evaluate numerical expressions containing negative exponents.	2	1	1	0.5
4-8 Scientific Notation (pp. 186–190) • Express numbers in standard form and in scientific notation. • Compare and order numbers written in scientific notation.	1	1	0.5	0.5
Study Guide and **Practice Test** (pp. 191–195) **Standardized Test Practice** (pp. 196–197)	1	1	0.5	0.5
Chapter Assessment	1	1	0.5	0.5
TOTAL	**13**	**12**	**7**	**6**

*An electronic version of this chapter is available on **StudentWorks**™. This backpack solution CD-ROM allows students instant access to the Student Edition, lesson worksheet pages, and web resources.*

Chapter Resource Manager

Timesaving Tools

TeacherWorks™

All-In-One Planner and Resource Center

See pages T5 and T21.

| CHAPTER 4 RESOURCE MASTERS | | | | | | | | | | | | | |
Study Guide and Intervention	Practice (Skills and Average)	Reading to Learn Mathematics	Enrichment	Assessment	Prerequisite Skills Workbook	Applications*	Parent and Student Study Guide Workbook	5-Minute Check Transparencies	Interactive Chalkboard	Pre-AlgePASS: Tutorial Plus (lessons)	Materials
165	166–167	168	169		13–14	GCS 26	24	4-1	4-1		
170	171–172	173	174	219		SC 7 GCS 25	25	4-2	4-2		*Follow-Up:* grid paper
175	176–177	178	179		13–14		26	4-3	4-3		
180	181–182	183	184	219, 221			27	4-4	4-4	7	
185	186–187	188	189				28	4-5	4-5		
190	191–192	193	194	220		SC 8	29	4-6	4-6		*Follow-Up:* 50 pennies, grid paper, shoebox with lid
195	196–197	198	199				30	4-7	4-7		
200	201–202	203	204	220	33–36		31	4-8	4-8	8	
				205–218 222–224							

* *Key to Abbreviations:* GCS = Graphing Calculator and Spreadsheet Masters
SC = School-to-Career Masters
SM = Science and Mathematics Lab Manual

 ELL Study Guide and Intervention, Skills Practice, Practice, and Parent and Student Study Guide Workbooks are also available in Spanish.

Chapter 4

Mathematical Connections and Background

Continuity of Instruction

Prior Knowledge

In Chapter 3, students learned to simplify algebraic expressions. They solved equations by adding, subtracting, multiplying, or dividing. They also learned to apply equations to real-world problems and to write and solve two-step equations. Students used formulas to find the perimeter and area of rectangles and squares.

This Chapter

Students examine factors and monomials. They learn to evaluate expressions containing powers and exponents. They use greatest common factor to simplify expressions and algebraic fractions. They also learn to multiply and divide monomials and express numbers using positive and negative exponents and scientific notation.

Future Connections

Prime factorization, greatest common factor, powers, exponents, and multiplying and dividing monomials are important elements of algebraic manipulation in Pre-Algebra and Algebra I. Powers, exponents, and scientific notation are utilized in various sciences, including astronomy, chemistry, physics, archaeology, and geology.

4-1 Factors and Monomials

Two or more numbers that are multiplied to form a product are called factors. Divisibility rules can be used to determine whether 2, 3, 5, 6, or 10 are factors of a given number. Divisibility rules can be used to solve real-world problems and to identify factors suitable for simplifying equations.

A monomial is a number, a variable, or a product of numbers and/or variables. So, $3abc$ is a monomial, but $6 + 4n$ is not because it involves addition.

4-2 Powers and Exponents

An expression such as $3 \cdot 3 \cdot 3 \cdot 3$ can be written as a power. A power has two parts, a base and an exponent. The base is the number that is multiplied (3). The exponent tells how many times the base is used as a factor (4 times). Thus, $3 \cdot 3 \cdot 3 \cdot 3$ can be written as 3^4. Numbers and variables can be written using exponents. For example, $8 \cdot 8 \cdot 8 \cdot m \cdot m \cdot m \cdot m \cdot m$ can be expressed as $8^3 m^5$. Exponents also can be used with place value to express numbers in expanded form. Using this method, 1462 can be written as $(1 \times 10^3) + (4 \times 10^2) + (6 \times 10^1) + (2 \times 10^0)$.

4-3 Prime Factorization

A prime number is a whole number that has exactly two factors, 1 and itself. A composite number is a whole number that has more than two factors. Zero and 1 are neither prime nor composite. When a composite number is expressed as the product of prime factors, it is called the prime factorization of the number. The prime factorization of 40 is $2 \cdot 2 \cdot 2 \cdot 5$ or $2^3 \cdot 5$, each factor being a prime number.

A monomial also may be factored. The monomial $27ab^3$ is factored as $3 \cdot 3 \cdot 3 \cdot a \cdot b \cdot b \cdot b$.

4-4 Greatest Common Factor (GCF)

Often numbers have some of the same factors. The greatest number that is a factor of two or more numbers is called the greatest common factor (GCF). There are two methods to find the GCF. One way is to list the factors of the numbers and identify the largest factor they have in common. The other method uses prime factorization to express each number as the product of prime factors. The GCF is then found by multiplying the common prime factors.

4-5 Simplifying Algebraic Fractions

A fraction is in simplest form when the GCF of the numerator and the denominator is 1. One way to write a fraction in simplest form is to write the prime factorization of the numerator and the denominator and then divide each by the GCF. For example, $\frac{12}{76}$ can be reduced to simplest form by factoring the numerator ($12 = 2 \cdot 2 \cdot 3$) and the denominator ($76 = 2 \cdot 2 \cdot 19$) and then dividing each by the GCF (in this case, $2 \cdot 2$). The resulting fraction, $\frac{3}{19}$, is in simplest form. Note that the value of the fraction remains the same; it just is expressed with simpler numbers.

4-6 Multiplying and Dividing Monomials

The rule for multiplying monomials is the same as that for multiplying powers with the same base: the base remains the same and the exponents are added. Thus, $6^3 \cdot 6^4$ equals 6^7, and $b^2 \cdot b^7$ equals b^9. This rule also can be used with the Commutative and Associative Properties. For example, $(-3m^3)(5m^5)$ can be expressed as $(-3 \cdot 5)(m^5 \cdot m^3)$ or $-15m^8$. Powers and monomials with the same base may be divided by subtracting their exponents.

4-7 Negative Exponents

Very small numbers can be expressed using negative exponents. For example, $\frac{1}{625}$ can be written as 5^{-4}. A negative power indicates that the base is the denominator of a fraction. One way to write a fraction as an equivalent expression with negative exponents is to use prime factorization. The fraction $\frac{1}{32}$ can be expressed as $\frac{1}{2} \cdot \frac{1}{2} \cdot \frac{1}{2} \cdot \frac{1}{2} \cdot \frac{1}{2} = \frac{1}{2^5}$ or 2^{-5}. Negative exponents often are used in science to express small numbers, usually as a power of 10. In this way, $\frac{1}{100,000}$ can be written as 10^{-5}.

Algebraic expressions containing negative exponents also can be written as fractions and then evaluated. For example, if $w = 3$, then $w^{-3} = \frac{1}{w^3}$ or $\frac{1}{27}$. While positive exponents are a notation for repeated multiplication, a negative exponent can be thought of as the reciprocal of the number expressed, or as repeated division. For example, $3^{-6} = \frac{1}{3^6} = \frac{1}{3} \cdot \frac{1}{3} \cdot \frac{1}{3} \cdot \frac{1}{3} \cdot \frac{1}{3} \cdot \frac{1}{3}$.

$$a^1 \cdot a^{-1} = a^0 \quad \text{Product of powers}$$
$$a \cdot a^{-1} = 1 \quad \text{Definition of } a^1 \text{ and } a^0$$
$$a^{-1} = \frac{1}{a} \quad \text{Divide each side by } a.$$
$$\text{So, } a^{-n} = \underbrace{\frac{1}{a} \cdot \frac{1}{a} \cdot \frac{1}{a} \ldots \frac{1}{a}}_{n \text{ factors}} \text{where } a \neq 0.$$
$$= \frac{1}{a^n}$$

4-8 Scientific Notation

When dealing with very large numbers like 1,500,000 or very small numbers like 0.000015, it is helpful to keep track of the place value by writing the numbers in scientific notation. Powers of 10 with positive exponents are used with a decimal to express large numbers. The exponent represents the number of places the decimal point is to be moved to the right. So, 528,000 is written in scientific notation as 5.28×10^5. Powers of 10 with negative exponents are used to express small numbers. The exponent represents the number of places the decimal point is to be moved to the left. The number 0.00047 is expressed as 4.7×10^{-4}. Numbers can be converted between standard form and scientific notation. Scientific notation is used in all the sciences.

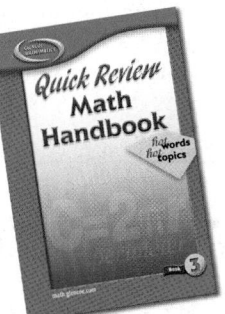

Quick Review Math Handbook

Hot Words includes a glossary of terms while Hot Topics consists of explanations of key mathematical concepts with exercises to test comprehension. This valuable resource can be used as a reference in the classroom or for home study.

Lesson	Hot Topics Section	Lesson	Hot Topics Section
GS 4	2.6, 6.2, 6.3	4-5	2.1, 6.2
4-1	1.4, 1.5	4-6	2.1, 2.9
4-2	1.4, 3.1, 3.4	4-7	2.6, 3.3
4-3	1.2, 1.4, 6.1	4-8	3.3
4-4	1.4, 8.2		

GS = Getting Started

 Additional mathematical information and teaching notes are available at www.pre-alg.com/key_concepts.

Chapter 4

DAILY INTERVENTION and Assessment

Key to Abbreviations:
TWE = Teacher Wraparound Edition; CRM = Chapter Resource Masters

	Type	Student Edition	Teacher Resources	Technology/Internet
INTERVENTION	Ongoing	Prerequisite Skills, pp. 147, 152, 157, 163, 168, 173, 179, 185 Practice Quiz 1, p. 163 Practice Quiz 2, p. 185	5-Minute Check Transparencies *Prerequisite Skills Workbook,* pp. 13–14, 33–36 Quizzes, *CRM,* pp. 219, 220 Mid-Chapter Test, *CRM,* p. 221 Study Guide and Intervention, *CRM,* pp. 165, 170, 175, 180, 185, 190, 195, 200	Pre-AlgePASS: Tutorial Plus, Lessons 7 and 8 www.pre-alg.com/self_check_quiz www.pre-alg.com/extra_examples
	Mixed Review	pp. 152, 157, 163, 168, 173, 179, 185, 190	Cumulative Review, *CRM,* p. 222	
	Error Analysis	Find the Error, pp. 161, 166	Find the Error, *TWE,* pp. 161, 166	
ASSESSMENT	Standardized Test Practice	pp. 152, 157, 163, 168, 171, 173, 179, 184, 190, 196–197	*TWE,* pp. 196–197 Standardized Test Practice, *CRM,* pp. 223–224	Standardized Test Practice CD-ROM www.pre-alg.com/standardized_test
	Open-Ended Assessment	Writing in Math, pp. 152, 157, 162, 168, 173, 179, 184, 190 Open Ended, pp. 150, 155, 161, 166, 171, 177, 183, 188 Standardized Test, p. 197	Speaking: *TWE,* pp. 157, 185, 190 Writing: *TWE,* pp. 168, 173, 179 Modeling: *TWE,* pp. 152, 163 Open-Ended Assessment, *CRM,* p. 217	
	Chapter Assessment	Study Guide, pp. 191–194 Practice Test, p. 195	Multiple-Choice Tests (Forms 1, 2A, 2B), *CRM,* pp. 205–210 Free-Response Tests (Forms 2C, 2D, 3), *CRM,* pp. 211–216 Vocabulary Test/Review, *CRM,* p. 218	ExamView® Pro (see below) MindJogger Videoquizzes www.pre-alg.com/vocabulary_review www.pre-alg.com/chapter_test

For more information on Yearly ProgressPro, see p. 144.

Pre-Algebra Lesson	Yearly ProgressPro Skill Lesson
4-1	Divide Integers
4-2	Evaluate Expressions with Exponents: Level 3
4-3	Prime Factorization with Algebraic Expressions
4-4	Greatest Common Factor with Algebraic Expressions
4-5	Prime Factorization with Algebraic Expressions
4-6	Multiplying and Dividing Monomials
4-7	Negative Exponents
4-8	Scientific Notation: Level 1

ExamView® Pro

Use the networkable **ExamView® Pro** to:
- Create **multiple versions** of tests.
- Create **modified** tests for *Inclusion* students.
- **Edit** existing questions and **add** your own questions.
- Use built-in **state curriculum correlations** to create tests aligned with state standards.
- Change **English** tests to **Spanish** and vice versa.

For more information on Intervention and Assessment, see pp. T8–T11.

Reading and Writing in Mathematics

Glencoe Pre-Algebra provides numerous opportunities to incorporate reading and writing into the mathematics classroom.

Student Edition

- Foldables™ Study Organizer, p. 147
- Reading Mathematics, p. 174
- Concept Check questions require students to verbalize and write about what they have learned in the lesson. (pp. 148, 150, 154, 155, 160, 161, 166, 170, 171, 176, 177, 182, 183, 186, 188)
- Writing in Math questions in every lesson, pp. 152, 157, 162, 168, 173, 179, 184, 190
- Reading Math, pp. 148, 149, 150, 159, 177
- WebQuest, p. 173

Teacher Wraparound Edition

- Foldables™ Study Organizer, pp. 147, 191
- Study Notebook suggestions, pp. 150, 155, 158, 161, 166, 171, 174, 178, 183, 188
- Modeling activities, pp. 152, 163
- Speaking activities, pp. 157, 185, 190
- Writing activities, pp. 168, 173, 179
- Differentiated Instruction (Verbal/Linguistic), p. 155
- **ELL** Resources, pp. 148, 153, 159, 164, 169, 175, 181, 186, 191

Additional Resources

- Vocabulary Builder worksheets require students to define and give examples for key vocabulary terms as they progress through the chapter (*Chapter 4 Resource Masters*, pp. vii–viii)
- Reading to Learn Mathematics master for each lesson (*Chapter 4 Resource Masters*, pp. 168, 173, 178, 183, 188, 193, 198, 203)
- *Vocabulary PuzzleMaker* software creates crossword, jumble, and word search puzzles using vocabulary lists that you can customize.
- *Teaching Mathematics with Foldables* provides suggestions for promoting cognition and language.
- *Reading and Writing in the Mathematics Classroom*
- *WebQuest and Project Resources*

For more information on Reading and Writing in Mathematics, see pp. T6–T7.

PROJECT CRISS℠ Study Skill

A problem-solution graphic structure can be used by students to develop a step-by-step plan for solving a problem. Students begin by writing details of the problem. Next, they write the steps that are necessary to solve the problem. Finally, they solve the problem and write out their result.

The graphic structure at the right applies the four-step plan presented in Chapter 1 to solving a problem containing an exponent. Have students develop a similar structure to solve factorization problems and other types of problems they encounter in this chapter.

Problem

Evaluate the expression $5x^3$ if $x = -2$.

↓

Steps to Solution

Step	Result
1. Explore	1. The exponent means that -2 is used as a factor 3 times
2. Plan	2. Replace x with -2.
3. Solve	3. $5x^3 = 5(-2)^3$ $= 5(-8)$ $= -40$
4. Examine	4. $5(-2)^3 = -40$ is a reasonable answer.

End Result

$5(-2)^3 = -40$

CReating **I**ndependence **T**hrough **S**tudent-**O**wned **S**trategies

What You'll Learn

Have students read over the list of objectives and make a list of any words with which they are not familiar.

Why It's Important

Point out to students that this is only one of many reasons why each objective is important. Others are provided in the introduction to each lesson.

Lesson	NCTM Standards	Local Objectives
4-1	1, 2, 6, 7, 8, 9, 10	
4-2	1, 2, 6, 8, 9, 10	
4-2 Follow-Up	1, 6, 7, 8, 9, 10	
4-3	1, 2, 6, 8, 9, 10	
4-4	1, 2, 6, 8, 9, 10	
4-5	1, 2, 4, 6, 8, 9, 10	
4-6	1, 2, 3, 6, 7, 8, 9, 10	
4-6 Follow-Up	1, 4, 5, 6, 7, 8, 9, 10	
4-7	1, 2, 6, 7, 8, 9, 10	
4-8	1, 2, 4, 7, 8, 9, 10	

Key to NCTM Standards:

1=Number & Operations, 2=Algebra,
3=Geometry, 4=Measurement,
5=Data Analysis & Probability, 6=Problem
Solving, 7=Reasoning & Proof,
8=Communication, 9=Connections,
10=Representation

What You'll Learn

- **Lessons 4-1, 4-3, and 4-6** Identify, factor, multiply, and divide monomials.
- **Lessons 4-2 and 4-7** Evaluate expressions containing exponents.
- **Lesson 4-4** Factor algebraic expressions by finding the GCF.
- **Lesson 4-5** Simplify fractions using the GCF.
- **Lesson 4-8** Write numbers in scientific notation.

Key Vocabulary

- factors (p. 148)
- monomial (p. 150)
- power (p. 153)
- prime factorization (p. 160)
- scientific notation (p. 186)

Why It's Important

Fractions can be used to analyze and compare real-world data. For example, does a hummingbird or a tiger eat more, in relation to its size? You can use fractions to find the answer. *You will compare eating habits of these and other animals in Lesson 4-5.*

Vocabulary Builder

The Key Vocabulary list introduces students to some of the main vocabulary terms included in this chapter. For a more thorough vocabulary list with pronunciations of new words, give students the Vocabulary Builder worksheets found on pages vii and viii of the *Chapter 4 Resource Masters*. Encourage them to complete the definition of each term as they progress through the chapter. You may suggest that they add these sheets to their study notebooks for future reference when studying for the Chapter 4 test.

▶ **Prerequisite Skills** To be successful in this chapter, you'll need to master these skills and be able to apply them in problem-solving situations. Review these skills before beginning Chapter 4.

For Lesson 4-1   **Distributive Property**

Simplify. *(For review, see Lesson 3-1.)*

1. $2(x + 1)$ **$2x + 2$**   **2.** $3(n - 1)$ **$3n - 3$**   **3.** $-2(k + 8)$ **$-2k - 16$**   **4.** $-4(x - 5)$ **$-4x + 20$**

5. $6(2c + 4)$ **6.** $5(-3s + t)$ **7.** $7(a + b)$ **$7a + 7b$**   **8.** $9(b - 2c)$
    $12c + 24$ **$-15s + 5t$**   **$9b - 18c$**

For Lesson 4-2   **Order of Operations**

Evaluate each expression if $x = 2$, $y = 5$, and $z = -1$. *(For review, see Lesson 1-3.)*

9. $x + 12$ **14**   **10.** $z + (-5)$ **-6**   **11.** $4y + 8$ **28**   **12.** $10 + 3z$ **7**

13. $(2 + y)9$ **63**   **14.** $6(x - 4)$ **-12**   **15.** $3xy$ **30**   **16.** $2z + y$ **3**

For Lesson 4-8   **Product of Decimals**

Find each product. *(For review, see page 715.)*

17. $4.5 \cdot 10$ **45**   **18.** $3.26 \cdot 100$ **326**   **19.** $0.1 \cdot 780$ **78**   **20.** $15 \cdot 0.01$ **0.15**

21. $3.9 \cdot 0.1$ **0.39**   **22.** $63.2 \cdot 0.1$ **6.32**   **23.** $0.01 \cdot 0.5$ **0.005**   **24.** $301.8 \cdot 0.001$
                                                                   0.3018

FOLDABLES™ Study Organizer

Factors and Monomials Make this Foldable to help you organize your notes. Begin with four sheets of notebook paper.

Step 1   Fold

Fold four sheets of notebook paper in half from top to bottom.

Step 2   Cut and Staple

Cut along the fold. Staple the eight half-sheets together to form a booklet.

Step 3   Cut Tabs into Margin

Make the top tab 2 lines wide, the next tab 4 lines wide, and so on.

Step 4   Label

Label each of the tabs with the lesson number and title.

Reading and Writing As you read and study the chapter, write notes and examples on each page.

This section provides a review of the basic concepts needed before beginning Chapter 4. Page references are included for additional student help.

Additional review is provided in the *Prerequisite Skills Workbook*, pages 13–14, and 33–36.

Prerequisite Skills in the Getting Ready for the Next Lesson section at the end of each lesson reviews a skill needed in the next lesson.

For Lesson	Prerequisite Skill
4-2	Multiplying Integers (p. 152)
4-3	Factoring (p. 157)
4-4	Distributive Property (p. 163)
4-5	Converting Measurements (p. 168)
4-6	Properties of Multiplication (p. 173)
4-7	Evaluating Expressions (p. 179)
4-8	Multiplying Decimals (p. 185)

FOLDABLES™ Study Organizer

For more information about Foldables, see *Teaching Mathematics with Foldables.*

Organization of Data: Write a Summary After students make their Foldables, have them label the side tabs to correspond to the eight lessons in this chapter. Students use their Foldables to take notes, define terms, record concepts, and write examples. At the end of each lesson, ask students to write a summary of the lesson, or write in their own words what the lesson was about. Summaries are useful for condensing data.

1 Focus

5-Minute Check
Transparency 4-1 Use as a quiz or review of Chapter 3.

Mathematical Background notes are available for this lesson on page 146C.

How are side lengths of rectangles related to factors?

The opening activity questions are repeated on page 168 of the *Chapter 4 Resource Masters*.

Reading to Learn Mathematics, p. 168 ELL

Pre-Activity	How are side lengths of rectangles related to factors?

Do the activity at the top of page 148 in your textbook. Write your answers below.

a. Use grid paper to draw as many other rectangles as possible with an area of 36 square units. Label the length and width of each rectangle. **Students should draw rectangles with dimensions 1 × 36, 2 × 18, 3 × 12, and 6 × 6.**

b. Did you draw a rectangle with a length of 5 units? Why or why not? **No, if the length were 5, there is no whole number width that would give an area of 36.**

c. List all of the pairs of whole numbers whose product is 36. Compare this list to the lengths and widths of all the rectangles that have an area of 36 square units. What do you observe? **1 and 36, 2 and 18, 3 and 12, 4 and 9, 6 and 6; they are the same.**

d. Predict the number of rectangles that can be drawn with an area of 64 square units. Explain how you can predict without actually drawing them. **4 rectangles; find the factor pairs whose product is 64: 1 × 64, 2 × 32, 4 × 16, 8 × 8.**

Reading the Lesson 1–3. See students' work.

Write a definition and give an example of each new vocabulary word.

Vocabulary	Definition	Example
1. factors		
2. divisible		
3. monomial		

4. Is the expression 2x − 1 a monomial? Explain. **2x − 1 is not a monomial because it is the difference of two terms.**

Helping You Remember

5. Explain in your own words how to determine whether an expression is a monomial. **Sample answer: A monomial is a number, a variable, or the product of numbers and/or variables.**

Teaching Tip Point out that all measurements are whole number quantities.

NEW YORK *Performance Indicator* Reinforcement of 5.N.14 Identify the factors of a given number

What You'll Learn

- Determine whether one number is a factor of another.
- Determine whether an expression is a monomial.

Vocabulary
- factors
- divisible
- monomial

How are side lengths of rectangles related to factors?

The rectangle at the right has an area of $9 \cdot 4$ or 36 square units.

a. Use grid paper to draw as many other rectangles as possible with an area of 36 square units. Label the length and width of each rectangle.

b. Did you draw a rectangle with a length of 5 units? Why or why not?

c. List all of the pairs of whole numbers whose product is 36. Compare this list to the lengths and widths of all the rectangles that have an area of 36 square units. What do you observe?

d. Predict the number of rectangles that can be drawn with an area of 64 square units. Explain how you can predict without drawing.

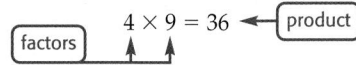

Area = 36 units²

FIND FACTORS Two or more numbers that are multiplied to form a product are called **factors**.

$$4 \times 9 = 36 \leftarrow \text{product}$$
factors

So, 4 and 9 are factors of 36 because they each divide 36 with a remainder of 0. We can say that 36 is **divisible** by 4 and 9. However, 5 is not a factor of 36 because $36 \div 5 = 7$ with a remainder of 1.

Sometimes you can test for divisibility mentally. The following rules can help you determine whether a number is divisible by 2, 3, 5, 6, or 10.

Reading Math

Even and Odd Numbers

A number that is divisible by 2 is called an *even number*. A number that is not divisible by 2 is called an *odd number*.

Concept Summary **Divisibility Rules**

A number is divisible by:	Examples		Reasons
• 2 if the ones digit is divisible by 2.	54	→	4 is divisible by 2.
• 3 if the sum of its digits is divisible by 3.	72	→	$7 + 2 = 9$, and 9 is divisible by 3.
• 5 if the ones digit is 0 or 5.	65	→	The ones digit is 5.
• 6 if the number is divisible by 2 and 3.	48	→	48 is divisible by 2 and 3.
• 10 if the ones digit is 0.	120	→	The ones digit is 0.

 Concept Check Is 51 divisible by 3? Why or why not?
Yes; $5 + 1 = 6$, and 6 is divisible by 3.

Resource Manager

Workbooks and Reproducible Masters

Chapter 4 Resource Masters
- Study Guide and Intervention, p. 165
- Skills Practice, p. 166
- Practice, p. 167
- Reading to Learn Mathematics, p. 168
- Enrichment, p. 169

Parent and Student Study Guide Workbook, p. 24
Prerequisite Skills Workbook, pp. 13–14

 Transparencies
5-Minute Check Transparency 4-1
Answer Key Transparencies

Technology
Interactive Chalkboard

Example 1 Use Divisibility Rules

Determine whether 138 is divisible by 2, 3, 5, 6, or 10.

Number	Divisible?	Reason
2	yes	The ones digit is 8, and 8 is divisible by 2.
3	yes	The sum of the digits is $1 + 3 + 8$ or 12, and 12 is divisible by 3.
5	no	The ones digit is 8, not 0 or 5.
6	yes	138 is divisible by 2 and 3.
10	no	The ones digit is not 0.

So, 138 is divisible by 2, 3, and 6.

More About . . .

Weddings •

On average, it costs four times more to book reception sites in Los Angeles than in the Midwest.

Source: newschannel5.
webpoint.com/wedding

Example 2 Use Divisibility Rules to Solve a Problem

• **WEDDINGS** A bride must choose whether to seat 5, 6, or 10 people per table at her reception. If there are 192 guests and she wants all the tables to be full, which should she choose?

Seats Per Table	Yes/No	Reason
5	no	The ones digit of 192 does not end in 0 or 5, so 192 is not divisible by 5. There would be empty seats.
6	yes	192 is divisible by 2 and 3, so it is also divisible by 6. Therefore, all the tables would be full.
10	no	The ones digit of 192 does not end in 0, so 192 is not divisible by 10. There would be empty seats.

The bride should choose tables that seat 6 people.

You can also use the rules for divisibility to find the factors of a number.

Example 3 Find Factors of a Number

Reading Math

Divisible/Factor
The following statements mean the same thing.

• 72 is divisible by 2.
• 2 is a factor of 72.

List all the factors of 72.
Use the divisibility rules to determine whether 72 is divisible by 2, 3, 5, and so on. Then use division to find other factors of 72.

Number	72 Divisible by Number?	Factor Pairs
1	yes	$1 \cdot 72$
2	yes	$2 \cdot 36$
3	yes	$3 \cdot 24$
4	yes	$4 \cdot 18$
5	no	—
6	yes	$6 \cdot 12$
7	no	—
8	yes	$8 \cdot 9$
9	yes	$9 \cdot 8$

Use division to find the other factor in each factor pair. $72 \div 2 = 36$

You can stop finding factors when the numbers start repeating.

So, the factors of 72 are 1, 2, 3, 4, 6, 8, 9, 12, 18, 24, 36, and 72.

www.pre-alg.com/extra_examples/ny   **Lesson 4-1** Factors and Monomials   **149**

Interactive Chalkboard
PowerPoint® Presentations

This CD-ROM is a customizable Microsoft® Power-Point® presentation that includes:

• Step-by-step, dynamic solutions of each In-Class Example from the Teacher Wraparound Edition
• Additional, Your Turn exercises for each example
• The 5-Minute Check Transparencies
• Hot links to Glencoe Online Study Tools

---

2 Teach

FIND FACTORS

Teaching Tip Point out that a number is divisible by 9 if the sum of the digits is divisible by 9.

In-Class Examples Power Point®

1 Determine whether 435 is divisible by 2, 3, 5, 6, or 10.
435 is divisible by 3 and 5.

2 Sonya is running for student council president. She wants to give out campaign flyers with a pen to each student in the school. She can buy "Vote for Sonya" pens in packages of 5, 6, or 10. If there are 306 students in the school and she wants no pens left over, which size packages should she buy?
She should buy pens in packages of 6.

3 List all the factors of 64.
1, 2, 4, 8, 16, 32, 64

MONOMIALS

In-Class Example Power Point®

Teaching Tip An expression that is not a monomial may simplify to two or more terms. When simplifying expressions, you may need to review the Distributive Property.

4 Determine whether each expression is a monomial.

a. $4(n + 3)$ **This expression is not a monomial because in its simplest form, $4n + 12$, it involves two terms that are added.**

b. $\frac{x}{3}$ **This expression is a monomial because it is the product of a rational number and a variable.**

3 Practice/Apply

ALGEBRA CONNECTION

Study Notebook

Have students—
- add the definitions/examples of the vocabulary terms to their Vocabulary Builder worksheets for Chapter 4.
- copy the divisibility rules for 2, 3, 5, 6, and 10 along with a simple example of each.
- include any other item(s) that they find helpful in mastering the skills in this lesson.

About the Exercises . . .

Organization by Objective
- **Find Factors:** 16–35, 48–55
- **Monomials:** 36–47

Odd/Even Assignments
Exercises 16–53 are structured so that students practice the same concepts whether they are assigned odd or even problems.

Alert! Exercise 3 requires a calculator. Exercise 51 involves research on the Internet or other reference materials.

Assignment Guide

Basic: 17–25 odd, 29–47 odd, 48, 49, 56–72

Average: 17–47 odd, 50, 51, 53, 56–72

Advanced: 16–46 even, 50–66 (Optional: 67–72)

Answer

1. Use the rules for divisibility to determine whether 18,450 is divisible by both 2 and 3. If it is, then the number is also divisible by 6 and there is no remainder.

MONOMIALS A number such as 80 or an expression such as $8x$ is called a monomial. A **monomial** is a number, a variable, or a product of numbers and/or variables.

$$8 \cdot 10 = 80 \qquad\qquad 8 \cdot x = 8x$$

8 and 10 are factors of 80.

8 and x are factors of $8x$.

Reading Math

Monomial
The prefix *mono* means one. A monomial is an expression with one term.

Monomials		Not Monomials	
4	a number	$2 + x$	two terms are added
y	a variable	$5c - 6$	one term is subtracted from another term
$-2rs$	the product of a number and variables	$3(a + b)$	two terms are added $3(a + b) = 3a + 3b$

TEACHING TIP

Clarify that a monomial is the product of variables and rational numbers and may have a number as a denominator, but not a variable. For example, $\frac{x}{2}$ is a monomial, but $\frac{2}{x}$ is not.

✓ **Concept Check** Explain why $7q \cdot n$ is a monomial, but $7q + n$ is not.
$7q \cdot n$ **is a product;** $7q + n$ **is the sum of two terms.**

Before you determine whether an expression is a monomial, be sure the expression is in simplest form.

Example 4 Identify Monomials

Determine whether each expression is a monomial.

a. $2(x - 3)$

$\quad 2(x - 3) = 2x + 2(-3) \quad$ Distributive Property
$\qquad\qquad\;\; = 2x - 6 \qquad$ Simplify.

This expression is not a monomial because it has two terms involving subtraction.

b. $-48xyz$

This expression is a monomial because it is the product of integers and variables.

Check for Understanding

Concept Check

2. No; 132 is divisible by 3, but 125 is not.

GUIDED PRACTICE KEY	
Exercises	Examples
4–7	1
8–10	3
11–14	4
15	2

Guided Practice

1. **Explain** how you can mentally determine whether there is a remainder when 18,450 is divided by 6. **See margin.**

2. **Determine** whether 3 is a common factor of 125 and 132. Explain.

3. **OPEN ENDED** Use mental math, paper and pencil, or a calculator to find at least one number that satisfies each condition.
   a. a 3-digit number that is divisible by 2, 3, and 6 **102** b. **1035**
   b. a 4-digit number that is divisible by 3 and 5, but is not divisible by 10.
   c. a 3-digit number that is not divisible by 2, 3, 5, or 10 **343**
   3a–c. Sample answers are given.

Use divisibility rules to determine whether each number is divisible by 2, 3, 5, 6, or 10.

4. 51 **3**   5. 146 **2**   6. 876 **2, 3, 6**   7. 3050 **2, 5, 10**

150 Chapter 4 Factors and Fractions

D A I L Y

INTERVENTION

Differentiated Instruction

- **Logical** Try the following game. Give each pair of students a hundreds chart and a calculator (optional). Have students take turns crossing one number off the chart until each student has crossed off 5 numbers. Each student should use a different color pencil or pen for this activity. Then have students find all factors of the numbers they selected. The winner is the student who compiled the most factors overall. Repeat the activity with the winner compiling the least number of factors overall.

List all the factors of each number. **9. 1, 2, 4, 5, 8, 10, 16, 20, 40, 80**

8. 203 **1, 7, 29, 203**   9. 80   10. 115 **1, 5, 23, 115**

ALGEBRA Determine whether each expression is a monomial. Explain why or why not. **11–14. See margin for explanations.**

11. 38 **yes**   12. $2n - 2$ **no**   13. $5(x + y)$ **no**   14. $17(4)k$ **yes**

Application 15. **CALENDARS** Years that are divisible by 4, called *leap years*, are 366 days long. Also, years ending in "00" that are divisible by 400 are leap years. Use the rule given below to determine whether 2000, 2004, 2015, 2018, 2022, and 2032 are leap years. **2000, 2004, and 2032 are leap years.**

> If the last two digits form a number that is divisible by 4, then the number is divisible by 4.

★ indicates increased difficulty

Practice and Apply

Homework Help

For Exercises	See Examples
16–27	1
28–35	3
36–47	4
48–51	2

Extra Practice
See page 730.

Use divisibility rules to determine whether each number is divisible by 2, 3, 5, 6, or 10. **19. 2, 3, 5, 6, 10**

16. 39 **3**   17. 135 **3, 5**   18. 82 **2**   19. 120
20. 250 **2, 5, 10**   21. 118 **2**   22. 378 **2, 3, 6**   23. 955 **5**
24. 5010   25. 684   ★ 26. 10,523   ★ 27. 24,640
   2, 3, 5, 6, 10   **2, 3, 6**   **none**   **2, 5, 10**

List all the factors of each number. **28–35. See margin.**

28. 75   29. 114   30. 57   31. 65
32. 90   33. 124   34. 102   35. 135

ALGEBRA Determine whether each expression is a monomial. Explain why or why not. **36–47. See p. 197A for explanations.**

36. m **yes**   37. 110 **yes**   38. $s + t$ **no**   39. $g - h$ **no**
40. $-12 + 12x$ **no**   41. $3c + 6$ **no**   42. $7(a + 1)$ **no**   43. $4(2t - 1)$ **no**
44. $4b$ **yes**   45. $10(-t)$ **yes**   46. $-25abc$ **yes**   47. $8j(4k)$ **yes**

MUSIC For Exercises 48 and 49, use the following information.
The band has 72 students who will march during halftime of the football game. For one drill, they need to march in rows with the same number of students in each row. **48–49. See p. 197A.**

48. Can the whole band be arranged in rows of 7? Explain.

49. How many different ways could students be arranged? Describe the arrangements.

More About. . .

History •
In 1912, when there were 48 states, the stars of the flag were arranged in equal rows. In 1959, after Alaska joined the Union, a new arrangement was proposed.
Source: www.usflag.org

HISTORY For Exercises 50 and 51, use the following information.
★ Each star on the U.S. flag represents a state. As states joined the Union, the rectangular arrangement of the stars changed. **50–51. See p. 197A.**

50. Use the information at the left to make a conjecture about how you think the stars of the flag were arranged in 1912 and in 1959.

51. **Research** What is the correct arrangement of stars on the U.S. flag? Explain why the arrangement is not rectangular.

www.pre-alg.com/self_check_quiz/ny   **Lesson 4-1** Factors and Monomials **151**

Answers

11. a number

12. one term is subtracted from another term

13. two terms are added

14. the product of numbers and a variable

28. 1, 3, 5, 15, 25, 75

29. 1, 2, 3, 6, 19, 38, 57, 114

30. 1, 3, 19, 57

31. 1, 5, 13, 65

32. 1, 2, 3, 5, 6, 9, 10, 15, 18, 30, 45, 90

33. 1, 2, 4, 31, 62, 124

34. 1, 2, 3, 6, 17, 34, 51, 102

35. 1, 3, 5, 9, 15, 27, 45, 135

Open-Ended Assessment

Modeling Have students work in pairs using 42 rainbow or centimeter cubes. Students will use these blocks to model the factors of 42. Show students that one row of 42 blocks is the same thing as two rows of 21 blocks, because both use 42 blocks. Have students model all of the factors of 42 in this way.

Getting Ready for Lesson 4-2

PREREQUISITE SKILL Lesson 4-2 presents powers and exponents. To evaluate a power, students must be able to find products of integers. Exercises 67–72 should be used to determine your students' familiarity with multiplying integers.

Answers

52. If a number is divisible by 3 and by 2, then it is also divisible by 6. If a number is divisible by 3, but not divisible by 2, then it is not divisible by 6.

53. A number that has 10 as a factor is divisible by $2 \cdot 5$, so it is always divisible by 5.

54. A number that has a factor of 10 is divisible by $2 \cdot 5$. Since such a number is divisible by 2, it must be even.

57. The side lengths or dimensions of a rectangle are factors of the number that is the area of the rectangle. Answers should include the following.

- A rectangle with dimensions and area labeled; for example, a 4×5 rectangle would have length 5 units, width 4 units, and area 20 square units.

- Factors are numbers that are multiplied to form a product. The dimensions of a rectangle are factor pairs of the area since they are multiplied to form the area.

Determine whether each statement is *sometimes*, *always*, or *never* true. Explain your reasoning. 52–54. See margin for explanations.

★**52.** A number that is divisible by 3 is also divisible by 6. **sometimes**

★**53.** A number that has 10 as a factor is not divisible by 5. **never**

★**54.** A number that has a factor of 10 is an even number. **always**

★**55.** **MONEY** The homecoming committee can spend $144 on refreshments for the dance. Soft drinks cost $6 per case, and cookies cost $4 per bag.

  a. How many cases of soft drinks can they buy with $144? **24 cases**

  b. How many bags of cookies can they buy with $144? **36 bags**

  c. Suppose they want to buy approximately the same amounts of soft drinks and cookies. How many of each could they buy with $144?

55c. Sample answers:
12 cases, 18 bags;
14 cases, 15 bags;
16 cases, 12 bags

56. **CRITICAL THINKING** Write a number that satisfies each set of conditions.

  a. the greatest three-digit number that is not divisible by 2, 3, or 10 **997**

  b. the least three-digit number that is not divisible by 2, 3, 5, or 10 **101**

57. `WRITING IN MATH` Answer the question that was posed at the beginning of the lesson. **See margin.**

How are side lengths of rectangles related to factors?

Include the following in your answer:

- a drawing of a rectangle with its dimensions and area labeled, and
- a definition of *factors* and a description of the relationship between rectangle dimensions and factor pairs of a number.

NEW YORK Test Practice

Standardized Test Practice
Ⓐ Ⓑ Ⓒ Ⓓ

58. Which number is divisible by 3? **B**

  Ⓐ 133　　Ⓑ 444　　Ⓒ 53　　Ⓓ 250

59. Determine which expression is *not* a monomial. **C**

  Ⓐ $6d$　　Ⓑ $6d \cdot 5$　　Ⓒ $6d - 5$　　Ⓓ 5

Maintain Your Skills

Mixed Review **GEOMETRY** Find the perimeter and area of each rectangle. *(Lesson 3-7)*

60. 3.5 m, 4.9 m
16.8 m, 17.15 m²

61. 5 in., 12 in.
34 in., 60 in²

ALGEBRA Translate each sentence into an equation. Then find each number. *(Lesson 3-6)*

62. Eight more than twice a number is -16. $2n + 8 = -16$; **-12**

63. Two less than 5 times a number equals 3. $5n - 2 = 3$; **1**

ALGEBRA Solve each equation. Check your solution. *(Lesson 3-5)*

64. $2x - 1 = 9$ **5**　　**65.** $14 = 8 + 3n$ **2**　　**66.** $7 + \frac{k}{5} = -1$ **-40**

Getting Ready for the Next Lesson **PREREQUISITE SKILL** Find each product.
*(To review **multiplying integers**, see Lesson 2-4.)*

67. $4 \cdot 4 \cdot 4$ **64**　　**68.** $10 \cdot 10 \cdot 10 \cdot 10$ **10,000** **69.** $(-3)(-3)(-3)$ **-27**

70. $(-2)(-2)(-2)(-2)$ **16** **71.** $8 \cdot 8 \cdot 6 \cdot 6$ **2304**　　**72.** $(2)(2)(-5)(-5)(-5)$ **-500**

4-2 Powers and Exponents

NEW YORK *Performance Indicator* 8.N.2 Evaluate expressions with integral exponents

What You'll Learn

- Write expressions using exponents.
- Evaluate expressions containing exponents.

Why are exponents important in comparing computer data?

Computer data are measured in small units called *bytes*. These units are based on factors of 2.

a. Write 16 as a product of factors of 2. How many factors are there?

b. How many factors of 2 form the product 128?

c. One megabyte is 1024 kilobytes. How many factors of 2 form the product 1024?

Personal Computers

Year	Amount of Memory
1980	16 kilobytes
1983	1 megabyte
1992	16 megabytes
1998	32 megabytes
1999	128 megabytes
2002	512 megabytes

Source: www.islandnet.com

EXPONENTS An expression like $2 \times 2 \times 2 \times 2$ can be written as a power. A power has two parts, a base and an exponent. The expression $2 \times 2 \times 2 \times 2$ can be written as 2^4.

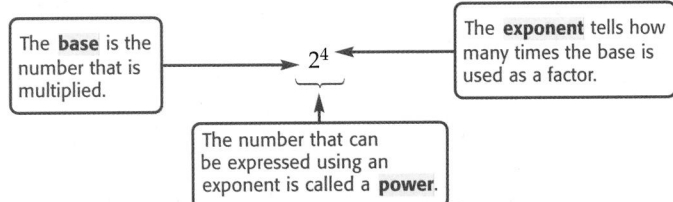

The **base** is the number that is multiplied.

The **exponent** tells how many times the base is used as a factor.

2^4

The number that can be expressed using an exponent is called a **power**.

The table below shows how to write and read powers with positive exponents.

Powers	Words	Repeated Factors
2^1	2 to the first power	2
2^2	2 to the second power or 2 squared	$2 \cdot 2$
2^3	2 to the third power or 2 cubed	$2 \cdot 2 \cdot 2$
2^4	2 to the fourth power or 2 to the fourth	$2 \cdot 2 \cdot 2 \cdot 2$
⋮	⋮	⋮
2^n	2 to the *n*th power or 2 to the *n*th	$2 \cdot 2 \cdot 2 \cdot \ldots \cdot 2$

n factors

Any number, except 0, raised to the zero power is defined to be 1.

$$1^0 = 1 \qquad 2^0 = 1 \qquad 3^0 = 1 \qquad 4^0 = 1 \qquad 5^0 = 1 \qquad x^0 = 1, x \neq 0$$

---

2 Teach

Building on Prior Knowledge

In Chapter 1, students learned order of operations. In this lesson they will add a step to the order that involves evaluating exponents.

EXPONENTS

In-Class Examples

1 Write each expression using exponents.

a. $6 \cdot 6 \cdot 6 \cdot 6$ 6^4

b. p p^1

c. $(-1)(-1)(-1)$ $(-1)^3$

d. $(5x + 1)(5x + 1)$ $(5x + 1)^2$

e. $\frac{1}{2} \cdot x \cdot x \cdot x \cdot x \cdot y \cdot y \cdot y$

$\frac{1}{2}x^4y^3$

2 Express 235,016 in expanded form. $235{,}016 = (2 \times 10^5) + (3 \times 10^4) + (5 \times 10^3) + (0 \times 10^2) + (1 \times 10^1) + (6 \times 10^0)$

✓ Skills Check

Exponents Ask students to explain the meaning of

a. $(23)^5$ b. $2a^3$ c. $(2a)^3$

EVALUATE EXPRESSIONS

In-Class Example

3 Evaluate each expression.

a. 4^2 16

b. $r^3 - 3$ if $r = -2$ -11

c. $x(y + 2)^2$ if $x = 2$ and $y = -2$ 0

Teaching Tip Emphasize that the value of x^5 increases more rapidly than $5x$ when evaluated for positive numbers. Substitute values to verify this.

Example 1 **Write Expressions Using Exponents**

Write each expression using exponents.

a. $3 \cdot 3 \cdot 3 \cdot 3 \cdot 3$

The base is 3. It is a factor 5 times, so the exponent is 5.
$3 \cdot 3 \cdot 3 \cdot 3 \cdot 3 = 3^5$

b. $t \cdot t \cdot t \cdot t$

The base is t. It is a factor 4 times, so the exponent is 4.
$t \cdot t \cdot t \cdot t = t^4$

c. $(-9)(-9)$

The base is -9. It is a factor 2 times, so the exponent is 2.
$(-9)(-9) = (-9)^2$

d. $(x + 1)(x + 1)(x + 1)$

The base is $x + 1$. It is a factor 3 times, so the exponent is 3.
$(x + 1)(x + 1)(x + 1) = (x + 1)^3$

e. $7 \cdot a \cdot a \cdot a \cdot b \cdot b$

First, group the factors with like bases. Then, write using exponents.
$7 \cdot a \cdot a \cdot a \cdot b \cdot b = 7 \cdot (a \cdot a \cdot a) \cdot (b \cdot b)$
$= 7a^3b^2$ $a \cdot a \cdot a = a^3$ and $b \cdot b = b^2$

✓ Concept Check   How would you write *ten to the fourth* using an exponent? 10^4

The number 13,548 is in **standard form** because it does not contain exponents. You can use place value and exponents to express a number in **expanded form**.

Example 2 **Use Exponents in Expanded Form**

Express 13,048 in expanded form.

Step 1 Use place value to write the value of each digit in the number.
$13{,}048 = 10{,}000 + 3000 + 0 + 40 + 8$
$= (1 \times 10{,}000) + (3 \times 1000) + (0 \times 100) + (4 \times 10) + (8 \times 1)$

Step 2 Write each place value as a power of 10 using exponents.
$13{,}048 = (1 \times 10^4) + (3 \times 10^3) + (0 \times 10^2) + (4 \times 10^1) + (8 \times 10^0)$

Recall that $10^0 = 1$.

EVALUATE EXPRESSIONS   Since powers are forms of multiplication, they need to be included in the rules for order of operations.

Concept Summary		Order of Operations
	Words	**Example**
Step 1	Simplify the expressions inside grouping symbols. Start with the innermost grouping symbols.	$(3 + 4)^2 + 5 \cdot 2 = 7^2 + 5 \cdot 2$
Step 2	Evaluate all powers.	$= 49 + 5 \cdot 2$
Step 3	Do all multiplications or divisions in order from left to right.	$= 49 + 10$
Step 4	Do all additions or subtractions in order from left to right.	$= 59$

Teacher to Teacher

Jenny L. Miller   Tuttle M.S., Crawfordsville, IN

"Students have trouble understanding the effect a power has on a number. I have my students use blocks to build visual images of powers such as 2^1, 2^2, 2^3, and so on."

Follow the order of operations to evaluate algebraic expressions.

Example 3 Evaluate Expressions

Evaluate each expression.

a. 2^3

$$2^3 = 2 \cdot 2 \cdot 2 \qquad \text{2 is a factor 3 times.}$$
$$= 8 \qquad\qquad \text{Multiply.}$$

b. $y^2 + 5$ if $y = -3$

$$y^2 + 5 = (-3)^2 + 5 \qquad \text{Replace } y \text{ with } -3.$$
$$= (-3)(-3) + 5 \qquad -3 \text{ is a factor two times.}$$
$$= 9 + 5 \qquad\qquad \text{Multiply.}$$
$$= 14 \qquad\qquad \text{Add.}$$

c. $3(x + y)^4$ if $x = -2$ and $y = 1$

$$3(x + y)^4 = 3(-2 + 1)^4 \qquad \text{Replace } x \text{ with } -2 \text{ and } y \text{ with } 1.$$
$$= 3(-1)^4 \qquad\qquad \text{Simplify the expression inside the parentheses.}$$
$$= 3(1) \qquad\qquad \text{Evaluate } (-1)^4.$$
$$= 3 \qquad\qquad \text{Simplify.}$$

Check for Understanding

Concept Check

1. Sample answer:
2^5, x^5
2–3. See margin.

1. **OPEN ENDED** Use exponents to write a numerical expression and an algebraic expression in which the base is a factor 5 times.

2. **Explain** how the expression *6 cubed* is repeated multiplication.

3. **Make a conjecture** about the value of 1^n and the value of $(-1)^n$ for any value of n. Explain.

Guided Practice

GUIDED PRACTICE KEY	
Exercises	Examples
4–6, 11	1
7	2
8–10	3

Write each expression using exponents.

4. $n \cdot n \cdot n$ n^3
5. $7 \cdot 7$ 7^2
6. $3 \cdot 3 \cdot x \cdot x \cdot x \cdot x$ $3^2 x^4$

7. Express 2695 in expanded form. $(2 \times 10^3) + (6 \times 10^2) + (9 \times 10^1) + (5 \times 10^0)$

ALGEBRA Evaluate each expression.

8. 2^4 **16**
9. $x^3 - 3$ if $x = -2$ **−11**
10. $5(y - 1)^2$ if $y = 4$ **45**

Application

11. **SOUND** Fireworks can easily reach a sound of 169 decibels, which can be dangerous if prolonged. Write this number using exponents and a smaller base. **13^2**

★ indicates increased difficulty

Practice and Apply

Write each expression using exponents. 15. $(-8)^4$ 20. $a^2 b^4$ 23. $9(p + 1)^2$

12. $4 \cdot 4 \cdot 4 \cdot 4 \cdot 4 \cdot 4$ 4^6
13. 6 6^1
14. $(-5)(-5)(-5)$ $(-5)^3$
15. $(-8)(-8)(-8)(-8)$
16. $k \cdot k$ k^2
17. $(-t)(-t)(-t)$ $(-t)^3$
18. $(r \cdot r)(r \cdot r)$ r^4
19. $m \cdot m \cdot m \cdot m$ m^4
20. $a \cdot a \cdot b \cdot b \cdot b \cdot b$
21. $2 \cdot x \cdot x \cdot y \cdot y$ $2x^2 y^2$
22. $7 \cdot 7 \cdot 7 \cdot n \cdot n \cdot n \cdot n$ $7^3 n^4$
23. $9 \cdot (p + 1) \cdot (p + 1)$

Lesson 4-2 Powers and Exponents **155**

Lesson 4-2 Powers and Exponents **155**

25. $(8 \times 10^2) + (0 \times 10^1) + (3 \times 10^0)$
26. $(6 \times 10^3) + (9 \times 10^2) + (9 \times 10^1) + (4 \times 10^0)$
27. $(2 \times 10^4) + (3 \times 10^3) + (7 \times 10^2) + (8 \times 10^1) + (1 \times 10^0)$

Express each number in expanded form.   24. $(4 \times 10^2) + (5 \times 10^1) + (2 \times 10^0)$

24. 452   25. 803   26. 6994   27. 23,781

ALGEBRA Evaluate each expression if $a = 2$, $b = 4$, and $c = -3$.

28. 7^2 49
29. 10^3 1000
30. $(-9)^3$ -729
31. $(-2)^5$ -32
32. b^4 256
33. c^4 81
34. $5a^4$ 80
35. ac^3 -54
36. $b^0 - 10$ -9
37. $c^2 + a^2$ 13
★ 38. $3a + b^3$ 70
★ 39. $a^2 + 3a - 1$ 9
★ 40. $b^2 - 2b + 6$ 14
★ 41. $3(b - 1)^4$ 243
★ 42. $2(3c + 7)^2$ 8

43. **TRAVEL** Write each number in the graphic as a power. $81 = 9^2$ or 3^4, $64 = 8^2$ or 4^3 or 2^6

44. Write *7 cubed times x squared* as repeated multiplication. $7 \cdot 7 \cdot 7 \cdot x \cdot x$

45. Write *negative eight, cubed* using exponents, as a product of repeated factors, and in standard form. $(-8)^3$; $(-8)(-8)(-8)$; -512

46. Without using a calculator, order 96, 96^2, 96^{10}, 96^5, and 96^0 from least to greatest. Explain your reasoning. **See margin.**

47. **NUMBER THEORY** Explain whether the square of any nonzero number is *sometimes*, *always*, or *never* a positive number.
Always; the product of two negative numbers is always positive.

48. **BIOLOGY** A man burns approximately 121 Calories by standing for an hour. A woman burns approximately 100 Calories per hour when standing. Write each of these numbers as a power with an exponent other than 1. $121 = 11^2$; $100 = 10^2$

HISTORY For Exercises 49–51, use the following information.

★ In an ancient Chinese tradition, a chef stretches and folds dough to make long, thin noodles called *so*. After the first fold, he makes 2 noodles. He stretches and folds it a second time to make 4 noodles. Each time he repeats this process, the number of noodles doubles.

49. Use exponents to express the number of noodles after each of the first five folds. 2^1, 2^2, 2^3, 2^4, 2^5

50. Legendary chefs have completed as many as thirteen folds. How many noodles is this? $2^{13} = 8192$ noodles

51. If the noodles are laid end to end and each noodle is 5 feet long, after how many of these folds will the length be more than a mile?   **See margin.**

Replace each ● with <, >, or = to make a true statement.

52. $3^7 ● 7^3$ $>$
53. $2^4 ● 4^2$ $=$
54. $6^3 ● 4^4$ $<$

More About. . .

History •

The *so* noodles are about a yard long and as thin as a piece of yarn. Very few chefs still know how to make these noodles.

Source: *The Mathematics Teacher*

USA TODAY Snapshots®

Our daily time behind the wheel

Men   81 minutes
Women   64 minutes

Source: Federal Highway Administration, American Automobile Manufacturers Association

By Anne R. Carey and Marcy E. Mullins, USA TODAY

Answers

46. 96^0, 96, 96^2, 96^5, 96^{10}; As the exponents increase, the additional factors of 96, and therefore the values of the expressions, increase. Since $96^0 = 1$, it has the least value.

51. After 10 folds, the noodles are $5(2^{10}) = 5(1024)$ or 5120 feet long, which is slightly less than a mile. So, after 11 folds the length of the noodles will be greater than a mile.

GEOMETRY For Exercises 55–57, use the cube below.

55. The *surface area* of a cube is the sum of the areas of the faces. Use exponents to write an expression for the surface area of the cube. **6 · 3² cm²**

56. The *volume* of a cube, or the amount of space that it occupies, is the product of the length, width, and height. Use exponents to write an expression for the volume of the cube. **3³ cm³**

3 cm
3 cm   3 cm

57. No; the surface area is multiplied by 4. The volume is multiplied by 8.

57. If you double the length of each edge of the cube, are the surface area and volume also doubled? Explain.

58a. The perimeter is doubled and the area is four times the area of the original square.
58b. original area: n^2, new area: $(3n)^2$ or $9n^2$
58c. original volume: n^3, new volume: $(3n)^3$ or $27n^3$

58. **CRITICAL THINKING** Suppose the length of a side of a square is n units and the length of an edge of a cube is n units.

   a. If all the side lengths of a square are doubled, are the perimeter and the area of the square doubled? Explain.

   b. If all the side lengths of a square are tripled, show that the area of the new square is 9 times the area of the original square.

   c. If all the edge lengths of a cube are tripled, show that the volume of the new cube is 27 times the volume of the original cube.

59. **WRITING IN MATH** Answer the question that was posed at the beginning of the lesson. **See margin.**

   Why are exponents important in comparing computer data?

   Include the following in your answer:
   • an explanation of how factors of 2 describe computer memory, and
   • a sentence explaining the advantage of using exponents.

   Online Research Data Update How many megabytes of memory are common today? Visit www.pre-alg.com/data_update to learn more.

NEW YORK Test Practice

Standardized Test Practice
Ⓐ Ⓑ Ⓒ Ⓓ

60. Write *ten million* as a power of ten. **C**
   Ⓐ 10^5 Ⓑ 10^6 Ⓒ 10^7 Ⓓ 10^8

61. What value of x will make $256 = 2^x$ true? **B**
   Ⓐ 7   Ⓑ 8   Ⓒ 9   Ⓓ 128

Maintain Your Skills

State whether each number is divisible by 2, 3, 5, 6, or 10. *(Lesson 4-1)*

62. 128 **2**   63. 370 **2, 5, 10**   64. 945 **3, 5**

65. **METEOROLOGY** A tornado travels 300 miles in 2 hours. Use the formula $d = rt$ to find the tornado's speed in miles per hour. *(Lesson 3-7)* **150 mph**

ALGEBRA Solve each equation. Check your solution. *(Lesson 3-5)*

66. $2x + 1 = 7$ **3**   67. $16 = 5k - 4$ **4**   68. $\frac{n}{3} + 8 = 6$ **−6**

69. **ALGEBRA** Simplify $4(y + 2) - y$. *(Lesson 3-2)* **3y + 8**

PREREQUISITE SKILL List all the factors for each number.
*(To review **factoring**, see Lesson 4-1.)*

70. 11 **1, 11**   71. 5 **1, 5**   72. 9 **1, 3, 9**

73. 16 **1, 2, 4, 8, 16**   74. 19 **1, 19**   75. 35 **1, 5, 7, 35**

---

4 Assess

Open-Ended Assessment

Speaking Give students the expression $6a^2 - a - 2$. Ask them to select a value for a, then explain how to evaluate the expression.

Getting Ready for Lesson 4-3

PREREQUISITE SKILL Lesson 4-3 presents prime factorization. Exercises 70–75 should be used to determine your students' familiarity with finding factors.

Assessment Options

Quiz (Lessons 4-1 and 4-2) is available on p. 219 of the *Chapter 4 Resource Masters*.

Answer

59. As the capacity of computer memory increases, the number of factors of 2 in the number of megabytes increases. Answers should include the following.

   • Computer data are measured in small units that are based on factors of 2.

   • In describing the amount of memory in modern computers, it would be impractical to list all the factors of 2. Using exponents is a more efficient way to describe and compare computer data.

Algebra Activity

NEW YORK *Performance Indicator* **8.R.5** Use standard and non-standard representations with accuracy and detail

Getting Started

Objective Investigate writing numerals in base 2.

Materials
paper and pencil
grid paper

Teach

- If students find base 2 difficult, try using sticks (or toothpicks) to represent the numbers. If you have 13 toothpicks, ask what is the largest base 2 bundle you could make. Since you could make 1 bundle of 8, you have 5 left. Now make 1 bundle of 4 and 1 bundle of 1. Thus, $(1 \times 8) + (1 \times 4) + (0 \times 2) + (1 \times 1) = 1101_2$.

Assess

After completing **Exercises 1–7**, students should be able to write any base 10 number in another base using the rules for place value.

Study Notebook

You may wish to have students summarize this activity and what they learned from it.

Base 2

Activity

A computer contains a large number of tiny electronic switches that can be turned ON or OFF. The digits 0 and 1, also called *bits*, are the alphabet of computer language. This **binary** language uses a **base two** system of numbers.

$$10110_2 = (1 \times 2^4) + (0 \times 2^3) + (1 \times 2^2) + (1 \times 2^1) + (0 \times 2^0)$$
$$= 16 + 0 + 4 + 2 + 0$$
$$= 22$$

So, $10110_2 = 22_{10}$ or 22.

You can also reverse the process and express base ten numbers as equivalent numbers in base two.

> **TEACHING TIP**
> Base 10 numbers are called *decimal* numbers. Base 2 numbers are called *binary* numbers.

Express the decimal number 13 as a number in base two.

Step 1 Make a base 2 place-value chart. Find the greatest factor of 2 that is less than 13. Place a 1 in that place value.

16	8	4	2	1
	1			

Step 2 Subtract $13 - 8 = 5$. Now find the greatest factor of 2 that is less than 5. Place a 1 in that place value.

16	8	4	2	1
	1	1		

Step 3 Subtract $5 - 4 = 1$. Place a 1 in that place value.

Step 4 There are no factors of 2 left, so place a 0 in any unfilled spaces.

16	8	4	2	1
	1	1	0	1

So, 13 in the base 10 system is equal to 1101 in the base 2 system. Or, $13 = 1101_2$.

Exercises

1. Express 1011_2 as an equivalent number in base 10. **11**

Express each base 10 number as an equivalent number in base 2.

2. 6 **110_2**
3. 9 **1001_2**
4. 15 **1111_2**
5. 21 **10101_2**

Extend the Activity

625	125	25	5	1

6. The first five place values for base 5 are shown. Any digit from 0 to 4 can be used to write a base 5 number. Write 179 in base 5. **1204_5**

7. **OPEN ENDED** Write 314 as an equivalent number in a base other than 2, 5, or 10. Include a place-value chart. **See margin.**

8. **OPEN ENDED** Choose a base 10 number and write it as an equivalent number in base 8. Include a place-value chart. **See margin.**

Answers

7. Sample answer: Write 314 in base 4.

256	64	16	4	1
1	0	3	2	2

$314 = 10322_4$

8. Sample answer: Write 5123 in base 8.

4096	512	64	8	1
1	2	0	0	3

$5123 = 12003_8$

Resource Manager

Teaching Pre-Algebra with Manipulatives

- p. 1 (master for grid paper)
- p. 60 (student recording sheet)

Prime Factorization

NEW YORK *Performance Indicator* **8.A.10 Factor algebraic expressions** using the GCF

What You'll Learn

- Write the prime factorizations of composite numbers.
- Factor monomials.

How can models be used to determine whether numbers are prime?

There are two ways that 10 can be expressed as the product of whole numbers. This can be shown by using 10 squares to form rectangles.

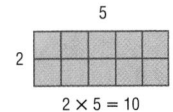

$1 \times 10 = 10$

$2 \times 5 = 10$

a. Use grid paper to draw as many different rectangular arrangements of 2, 3, 4, 5, 6, 7, 8, and 9 squares as possible. **See students' work.**

b. Which numbers of squares can be arranged in more than one way?

c. Which numbers of squares can only be arranged one way? **2, 3, 5, 7**

d. What do the rectangles in part **c** have in common? Explain.

Vocabulary

- prime number
- composite number
- prime factorization
- factor tree
- factor

b. 4, 6, 8, 9
d. They all have a width of 1 because no other pair of factors can be found.

Reading Math

Composite

Everyday Meaning: materials that are made up of many substances

Math Meaning: numbers having many factors

PRIME NUMBERS AND COMPOSITE NUMBERS A **prime number** is a whole number that has exactly two factors, 1 and itself. A **composite number** is a whole number that has more than two factors. Zero and 1 are neither prime nor composite.

Whole Numbers	Factors	Number of Factors
Prime Numbers		
2	1, 2	2
3	1, 3	2
5	1, 5	2
7	1, 7	2
Composite Numbers		
4	1, 2, 4	3
6	1, 2, 3, 6	4
8	1, 2, 4, 8	4
9	1, 3, 9	3
Neither Prime nor Composite		
0	all numbers	infinite
1	1	1

Example 1 Identify Numbers as Prime or Composite

a. Determine whether 19 is prime or composite.

Find factors of 19 by listing the whole number pairs whose product is 19.

$19 = 1 \times 19$

The number 19 has only two factors. Therefore, 19 is a prime number.

Workbooks and Reproducible Masters

Chapter 4 Resource Masters
- Study Guide and Intervention, p. 175
- Skills Practice, p. 176
- Practice, p. 177
- Reading to Learn Mathematics, p. 178
- Enrichment, p. 179

Graphing Calculator and Spreadsheet Masters, p. 26
Parent and Student Study Guide Workbook, p. 26
Prerequisite Skills Workbook, pp. 13–14

4-3 Lesson Notes

1 Focus

5-Minute Check Transparency 4-3 Use as a quiz or review of Lesson 4-2.

Mathematical Background notes are available for this lesson on page 146C.

How can models be used to determine whether numbers are prime?

The opening activity questions are repeated on page 178 of the *Chapter 4 Resource Masters.*

Reading to Learn Mathematics, p. 178 **ELL**

Pre-Activity *How can models be used to determine whether numbers are prime?*

Do the activity at the top of page 159 in your textbook. Write your answers below.

a. Use grid paper to draw as many different rectangular arrangements of 2, 3, 4, 5, 6, 7, 8, and 9 squares as possible. See students' answers.

b. Which numbers of squares can be arranged in more than one way? **4, 6, 8, 9**

c. Which numbers of squares can only be arranged one way? **2, 3, 5, 7**

d. What do all rectangles that you listed in part **c** have in common? Explain. They all have a width of 1 because no other pair of factors can be found.

Reading the Lesson 1–5. See students' work.

Write a definition and give an example of each new vocabulary word or phrase.

Vocabulary	Definition	Example
1. composite number		
2. factor		
3. factor tree		
4. prime factorization		
5. prime number		

Helping You Remember

6. *Composite* is a word used in everyday English.

a. Find the definition of *composite* in the dictionary. Write the definition. made up of distinct parts

b. Explain how the English definition can help you remember how composite is used in mathematics. Sample answer: Composite numbers are made up of many distinct parts, or factors.

Resource Manager

Transparencies

5-Minute Check Transparency 4-3
Answer Key Transparencies

Technology

Interactive Chalkboard

2 Teach

PRIME NUMBERS AND COMPOSITE NUMBERS

In-Class Examples

Power Point®

1 Determine whether each number is prime or composite.

a. 31   The number 31 has only two factors. Therefore, 31 is a prime number.

b. 36   The factors of 36 are 1, 2, 3, 4, 6, 9, 12, 18, and 36. Since there are more than two factors, the number is composite.

2 Write the prime factorization of 56. $2^3 \cdot 7$

Teaching Tip   Make sure students carry any prime numbers down to the bottom of the factor tree. Otherwise, they may lose track of these factors.

✓ Skills Check

Prime Factorization   Ask students to describe the similarities and differences between two factor trees made for the same number.

FACTOR MONOMIALS

In-Class Example

Power Point®

3 Factor each monomial.

a. $16p^2q^4$ $2 \cdot 2 \cdot 2 \cdot 2 \cdot p \cdot p \cdot q \cdot q \cdot q \cdot q$

b. $-21x^2y$ $-1 \cdot 3 \cdot 7 \cdot x \cdot x \cdot y$

Study Tip

Mental Math
To determine whether a number is prime or composite, you can mentally use the rules for divisibility rather than listing factors.

b. Determine whether 28 is prime or composite.

Find factors of 28 by listing the whole number pairs whose product is 28.

$28 = 1 \times 28$
$28 = 2 \times 14$
$28 = 4 \times 7$

The factors of 28 are 1, 2, 4, 7, 14, and 28. Since the number has more than two factors, it is composite.

TEACHING TIP

Emphasize that factors are natural numbers.

When a composite number is expressed as the product of prime factors, it is called the **prime factorization** of the number. One way to find the prime factorization of a number is to use a **factor tree**.

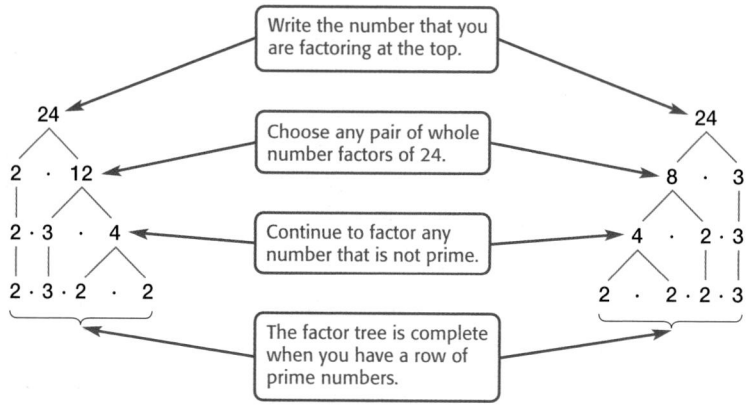

Study Tip

Commutative
The order of the factors does not matter because the operation of multiplication is commutative.

Both trees give the same prime factors, except in different orders. There is exactly one prime factorization of 24. The prime factorization of 24 is $2 \cdot 2 \cdot 2 \cdot 3$ or $2^3 \cdot 3$.

✓ Concept Check   Could a different factor tree have been used to write the prime factorization of 24? If so, would the result be the same?
Yes, the first factor pair could have been 4 · 6.

Example 2   Write Prime Factorization

Write the prime factorization of 36.

```
      36
     /  \
    6  ·  6      36 = 6 · 6
   / \   / \
  2·3·2·3        6 = 2 · 3
```

The factorization is complete because 2 and 3 are prime numbers.
The prime factorization of 36 is $2 \cdot 2 \cdot 3 \cdot 3$ or $2^2 \cdot 3^2$.

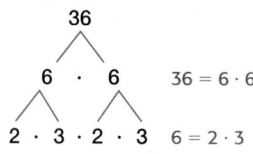

Teacher to Teacher

Butch Sloan   Garland ISD, Garland, TX

"Another way to factor is to use what we call the L method. To find the factors of 210, you divide by a prime factor and write the quotient underneath. Then divide the quotient by another prime factor, and so on until the result is 1. This method transfers well to two or more numbers and finding the GCF and LCM later in this chapter."

2	210
3	105
5	35
7	7
	1

You can also use a strategy involving division called the *cake method* to find a prime factorization. The prime factorization of 210 is shown below using the cake method.

Study Tip

Remainders
If you get a remainder when using the cake method, choose a different prime number to divide the quotient.

Step 1
Begin with the smallest prime that is a factor of 210, in this case, 2. Divide 210 by 2.

$$2\overline{)210} \atop 105$$

→

Step 2
Divide the quotient 105 by the smallest possible prime factor, 3.

$$\begin{array}{r} 35 \\ 3\overline{)105} \\ 2\overline{)210} \end{array}$$

→

Step 3
Repeat until the quotient is prime.

$$\begin{array}{r} 7 \\ 5\overline{)35} \\ 3\overline{)105} \\ 2\overline{)210} \end{array}$$

The prime factorization of 210 is $2 \cdot 3 \cdot 5 \cdot 7$. Multiply to check the result.

ALGEBRA CONNECTION

FACTOR MONOMIALS To **factor** a number means to write it as a product of its factors. A monomial can also be factored as a product of prime numbers and variables with no exponent greater than 1. Negative coefficients can be factored using -1 as a factor.

Example 3 *Factor Monomials*

Factor each monomial.

a. $8ab^2$
$8ab^2 = 2 \cdot 2 \cdot 2 \cdot a \cdot b^2 \qquad 8 = 2 \cdot 2 \cdot 2$
$\quad\quad = 2 \cdot 2 \cdot 2 \cdot a \cdot b \cdot b \quad a \cdot b^2 = a \cdot b \cdot b$

b. $-30x^3y$
$-30x^3y = -1 \cdot 2 \cdot 3 \cdot 5 \cdot x^3 \cdot y \qquad -30 = -1 \cdot 2 \cdot 3 \cdot 5$
$\quad\quad\quad = -1 \cdot 2 \cdot 3 \cdot 5 \cdot x \cdot x \cdot x \cdot y \quad x^3 \cdot y = x \cdot x \cdot x \cdot y$

TEACHING TIP

Since all numbers have 1 as a factor, students should not include 1 when they factor monomials. However, point out that students should include -1 when they factor negative monomials.

Check for Understanding

Concept Check

1. A prime number has exactly two factors: 1 and itself. A composite number has more than two factors.

1. **Explain** the difference between a prime and composite number.

2. **OPEN ENDED** Write a 2-digit number with prime factors that include 2 and 3. **Sample answer: 12**

3. **FIND THE ERROR** Cassidy and Francisca each factored 88.

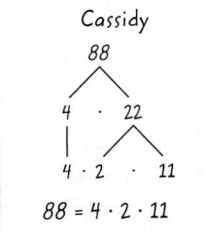

Cassidy

88
4 · 22
4 · 2 · 11
$88 = 4 \cdot 2 \cdot 11$

Francisca

$$\begin{array}{r} 11 \\ 2\overline{)22} \\ 2\overline{)44} \\ 2\overline{)88} \end{array}$$

$88 = 2 \cdot 2 \cdot 2 \cdot 11$

Who is correct? Explain your reasoning. **Francisca; 4 is not prime.**

www.pre-alg.com/extra_examples/ny

Lesson 4-3 Prime Factorization **161**

3 Practice/Apply

Study Notebook

Have students—
• add the definitions/examples of the vocabulary terms to their Vocabulary Builder worksheets for Chapter 4.
• copy an example of finding a prime factorization using both a factor tree and the cake method.
• include any other item(s) that they find helpful in mastering the skills in this lesson.

DAILY INTERVENTION FIND THE ERROR
When students write their prime factorization, encourage them to (a) multiply the factors to check the result and (b) use the rules for divisibility to check that each factor is prime.

About the Exercises . . .
Organization by Objective
• **Prime and Composite Numbers:** 14–29, 42, 44
• **Factor Monomials:** 30–41, 43

Odd/Even Assignments
Exercises 14–41 are structured so that students practice the same concepts whether they are assigned odd or even problems.

Assignment Guide
Basic: 15–37 odd, 43, 45–63
Average: 15–43 odd, 45–63
Advanced: 14–44 even, 45–57, (Optional 58–63)
All: Practice Quiz 1 (1–10)

DAILY INTERVENTION

Differentiated Instruction

• **Visual/Spatial** Have students find prime numbers using a hundreds chart. Have them cross off number 1. Circle number 2 (the first prime) then cross off all other numbers divisible by 2. Go back and circle the next prime, which is 3. Now cross off all numbers divisible by 3. Continue until all numbers showing are circled, and are therefore prime. This method is called the *sieve of Eratosthenes*, named for Eratosthenes of Cyrene (*circa* 276–194 B.C.).

Study Guide and Intervention, p. 175

A **prime number** is a whole number that has exactly two factors, 1 and itself. A **composite number** is a whole number that has more than two factors. Zero and 1 are neither prime nor composite.

Example 1 Determine whether 29 is prime or composite.

Find the factors of 29.

$29 = 1 \cdot 29$

The only factors of 29 are 1 and 29, therefore 29 is a prime number.

Any composite number can be written as a product of prime numbers. A factor tree can be used to find the prime factorization.

Example 2 Find the prime factorization of 48.

48 is the number to be factored.
Find any pair of whole number factors of 48.
Continue to factor any number that is not prime.
The factor tree is complete when there is a row of prime numbers.

The prime factorization of 48 is $2 \cdot 2 \cdot 2 \cdot 2 \cdot 3$ or $2^4 \cdot 3$.

In algebra, monomials can be factored as a product of prime numbers and variables with no exponent greater than 1. So, $8x^2$ factors as $2 \cdot 2 \cdot 2 \cdot x \cdot x$.

Exercises

Determine whether each number is *prime* or *composite*.

1. 27 composite
2. 151 prime
3. 77 composite
4. 25 composite

Write the prime factorization for each number. Use exponents for repeated factors.

5. 16 2^4
6. 45 $3^2 \cdot 5$
7. 78 $2 \cdot 3 \cdot 13$
8. 70 $2 \cdot 5 \cdot 7$

Factor each monomial.

9. $6m^3$ $2 \cdot 3 \cdot m \cdot m \cdot m$
10. $-20xy^2$ $-1 \cdot 2 \cdot 2 \cdot 5 \cdot x \cdot y \cdot y$
11. $a^2b^2c^3$ $a \cdot a \cdot b \cdot b \cdot c \cdot c \cdot c$
12. $25h$ $5 \cdot 5 \cdot h$

Skills Practice, p. 176 and Practice, p. 177 (shown)

Determine whether each number is *prime* or *composite*.

1. 11 prime
2. 63 composite
3. 73 prime
4. 75 composite
5. 49 composite
6. 69 composite
7. 53 prime
8. 83 prime

Write the prime factorization of each number. Use exponents for repeated factors.

9. 33 $3 \cdot 11$
10. 24 $2^3 \cdot 3$
11. 72 $2^3 \cdot 3^2$
12. 276 $2^2 \cdot 3 \cdot 23$
13. 85 $5 \cdot 17$
14. 1024 2^{10}
15. 95 $5 \cdot 19$
16. 200 $2^3 \cdot 5^2$
17. 243 3^5
18. 735 $3 \cdot 5 \cdot 7^2$

Factor each monomial.

19. $35v$ $5 \cdot 7 \cdot v$
20. $49c^2$ $7 \cdot 7 \cdot c \cdot c$
21. $-14b^3$ $-1 \cdot 2 \cdot 7 \cdot b \cdot b \cdot b$
22. $-81h^2$ $-1 \cdot 3 \cdot 3 \cdot 3 \cdot 3 \cdot h \cdot h$
23. $33wz$ $3 \cdot 11 \cdot w \cdot z$
24. $-56ghj$ $-1 \cdot 2 \cdot 2 \cdot 2 \cdot 7 \cdot g \cdot h \cdot j$

25. **NUMBER THEORY** *Twin primes* are a pair of primes, which differ by 2. For example, 3 and 5 are twin primes. Find the twin primes less than 100. (*Hint:* There are 8 pairs of twins less than 100.) 3, 5; 5, 7; 11, 13; 17, 19; 29, 31; 41, 43; 59, 61; 71, 73

Enrichment, p. 179

Prime Pyramid

A **prime number** is a whole number that has exactly two factors—itself and 1. The pyramid below is called a *prime pyramid*. Each row begins with 1 and ends with the number of that row. So, row 2 begins with 1 and ends with 2, row 3 begins with 1 and ends with 3, and so on. In each row, the numbers from 1 to the row number are arranged such that the sum of any two adjacent numbers is a prime number.

For example, look at row 4:
- It must contain the numbers 1, 2, 3, and 4.
- It must begin with 1 and end with 4.
- The sum of adjacent pairs must be a prime number:
  $1 + 2 = 3$, $2 + 3 = 5$, $3 + 4 = 7$

```
                      1   2
                   1   2   3
                1   4   3   2   5
             1   4   3   2   5   6
          1   4   3   2   5   6   7
       1   2   3   4   7   6   5   8
    1   2   3   4   7   6   5   8   9
 1   2   3   4   7   6   5   8   9   10
1   4   3   2   5   6   7   10  9   8   11
1   4   3   2   5   6   7   10  9   8   11  12
```

1. Complete the pyramid by filling in the missing numbers.

2. Extend the pyramid to row 13.
   1, 4, 3, 2, 5, 6, 7, 10, 9, 8, 11, 12, 13

3. Explain the patterns you see in the completed pyramid.
   Sample answer: Each row alternates odd and even numbers. Multiples of 3 form diagonals that are constant.

Guided Practice

GUIDED PRACTICE KEY	
Exercises	Examples
4–6, 13	1
7–9	2
10–12	3

Determine whether each number is *prime* or *composite*.

4. 7 prime
5. 23 prime
6. 15 composite

Write the prime factorization of each number. Use exponents for repeated factors.

7. 18 $2 \cdot 3^2$
8. 39 $3 \cdot 13$
9. 50 $2 \cdot 5^2$

ALGEBRA Factor each monomial.

10. $4c^2$ $2 \cdot 2 \cdot c \cdot c$
11. $5a^2b$ $5 \cdot a \cdot a \cdot b$
12. $-70xyz$ $-1 \cdot 2 \cdot 5 \cdot 7 \cdot x \cdot y \cdot z$

Application

13. **NUMBER THEORY** One mathematical conjecture that is unproved states that there are infinitely many *twin primes*. Twin primes are prime numbers that differ by 2, such as 3 and 5. List all the twin primes that are less than 50. 3 and 5, 5 and 7, 11 and 13, 17 and 19, 29 and 31, 41 and 43

★ indicates increased difficulty

Practice and Apply

Homework Help	
For Exercises	See Examples
14–21	1
22–29	2
30–41	3

Extra Practice
See page 731.

Determine whether each number is *prime* or *composite*.

14. 21 composite
15. 33 composite
16. 23 prime
17. 70 composite
18. 17 prime
19. 51 composite
20. 43 prime
21. 31 prime

Write the prime factorization of each number. Use exponents for repeated factors.

22. 26 $2 \cdot 13$
23. 81 3^4
24. 66 $2 \cdot 3 \cdot 11$
25. 63 $3^2 \cdot 7$
26. 56 $2^3 \cdot 7$
27. 100 $2^2 \cdot 5^2$
28. 392 $2^3 \cdot 7^2$
29. 110 $2 \cdot 5 \cdot 11$

ALGEBRA Factor each monomial. 30–41. See margin.

30. $14w$
31. $9t^2$
32. $-7c^2$
33. $-25z^3$
34. $20st$
35. $-38mnp$
36. $28x^2y$
37. $21gh^3$
38. $13q^2r^2$
★ 39. $64n^3$
★ 40. $-75ab^2$
★ 41. $-120r^2st^3$

42. Is the value of $n^2 - n + 41$ prime or composite if $n = 3$? prime

43. **OPEN ENDED** Write a monomial whose factors include -1, 5, and x.
Sample answer: $-25x$

44. **TECHNOLOGY** *Mersenne primes* are prime numbers in the form $2^n - 1$. In 2001, a computer programmer used special software to discover the largest prime number so far, $2^{13,466,917} - 1$. Write the prime factorization of each number, or write *prime* if the number is a Mersenne prime.

a. $2^5 - 1$ prime
b. $2^6 - 1$ $3^2 \cdot 7$
c. $2^7 - 1$ prime
d. $2^8 - 1$ $3 \cdot 5 \cdot 17$

45. WRITING IN MATH Answer the question that was posed at the beginning of the lesson. See margin.

How can models be used to determine whether numbers are prime?
Include the following in your answer:
- the number of rectangles that can be drawn to represent prime and composite numbers, and
- an explanation of how one model can show that a number is *not* prime.

Answers

30. $2 \cdot 7 \cdot w$
31. $3 \cdot 3 \cdot t \cdot t$
32. $-1 \cdot 7 \cdot c \cdot c$
33. $-1 \cdot 5 \cdot 5 \cdot z \cdot z \cdot z$
34. $2 \cdot 2 \cdot 5 \cdot s \cdot t$
35. $-1 \cdot 2 \cdot 19 \cdot m \cdot n \cdot p$

36. $2 \cdot 2 \cdot 7 \cdot x \cdot x \cdot y$
37. $3 \cdot 7 \cdot g \cdot h \cdot h \cdot h$
38. $13 \cdot q \cdot q \cdot r \cdot r$
39. $2 \cdot 2 \cdot 2 \cdot 2 \cdot 2 \cdot 2 \cdot n \cdot n \cdot n$
40. $-1 \cdot 3 \cdot 5 \cdot 5 \cdot a \cdot b \cdot b$
41. $-1 \cdot 2 \cdot 2 \cdot 2 \cdot 3 \cdot 5 \cdot r \cdot r \cdot s \cdot t \cdot t \cdot t$

46. CRITICAL THINKING Find the prime factors of these numbers that are divisible by 12: 12, 60, 84, 132, and 180. Then, write a rule to determine when a number is divisible by 12. **See margin.**

47. Which table of values represents the following rule? **C**
Add the input number to the square of the input number.

(A)
Input (x)	Output (y)
0	1
2	3
4	5

(B)
Input (x)	Output (y)
1	1
2	6
4	8

(C)
Input (x)	Output (y)
1	2
2	6
4	20

(D)
Input (x)	Output (y)
1	2
2	4
4	8

48. Determine which number is *not* a prime factor of 70. **D**
(A) 2   (B) 5   (C) 7   (D) 10

Maintain Your Skills

Mixed Review

49. Write $(-5) \cdot (-5) \cdot (-5) \cdot h \cdot h \cdot k$ using exponents. *(Lesson 4-2)* $(-5)^3 h^2 k$

Determine whether each expression is a monomial. *(Lesson 4-1)*

50. $14cd$ **yes**   **51.** -5 **yes**   **52.** $x - y$ **no**   **53.** $3(1 + 3r)$ **no**

ALGEBRA Solve each equation. Check your solution. *(Lesson 3-4)*

54. $\frac{n}{8} = -4$ **−32**   **55.** $2x = -18$ **−9**   **56.** $30 = 6n$ **5**   **57.** $-7 = \frac{y}{4}$ **−28**

Getting Ready for the Next Lesson

PREREQUISITE SKILL Use the Distributive Property to rewrite each expression. *(To review the Distributive Property, see Lesson 3-1.)*

58. $2(n + 4)$ **2n + 8**   **59.** $5(x - 7)$ **5x − 35**   **60.** $-3(t + 4)$ **−3t − 12**

61. $(a + 6)10$ **10a + 60**   **62.** $(b - 3)(-2)$ **−2b + 6**   **63.** $8(9 - y)$ **72 − 8y**

Practice Quiz 1   Lessons 4-1 through 4-3

Use divisibility rules to determine whether each number is divisible by 2, 3, 5, 6, or 10. *(Lesson 4-1)*

1. 105 **3, 5**   **2.** 270 **2, 3, 5, 6, 10**   **3.** 511 **none**   **4.** 1368 **2, 3, 6**

5. ALGEBRA Evaluate $b^2 - 4ac$ if $a = -1$, $b = 5$, and $c = 3$. *(Lesson 4-2)* **37**

6. LITERATURE In a story, a knight received a reward for slaying a dragon. He received 1 cent on the first day, 2 cents on the second day, 4 cents on the third day, and so on, continuing to double the amount for 30 days. *(Lesson 4-2)*

a. Express his reward on each of the first three days as a power of 2. $2^0, 2^1, 2^2$

b. Express his reward on the 8th day as a power of 2. Then evaluate. $2^7 = 128$ **cents**

Factor each monomial. *(Lesson 4-3)*

7. $77x$ **7 · 11 · x**   **8.** $18st$ **2 · 3 · 3 · s · t**   **9.** $-23n^3$ **−1 · 23 · n · n · n**   **10.** $30cd^2$ **2 · 3 · 5 · c · d · d**

---

4 Assess

Open-Ended Assessment

Modeling Have students find the prime factorization of a number using index cards and string. At the top of the model, place the index card with the number written on it. Have students use cards to write the whole number factors for the number until they have expressed the prime factors. Then, make a factor tree by attaching the factor cards to the original number with the string.

Getting Ready for Lesson 4-4

PREREQUISITE SKILL Lesson 4-4 presents the greatest common factor. Finding the greatest common factor of two terms of an algebraic expression requires the Distributive Property. Exercises 58–63 should be used to determine your students' familiarity with using the Distributive Property.

Answer

46. $12 = 2^2 \cdot 3$
$60 = 2^2 \cdot 3 \cdot 5$
$84 = 2^2 \cdot 3 \cdot 7$
$132 = 2^2 \cdot 3 \cdot 11$
$180 = 2^2 \cdot 3^2 \cdot 5$

Sample answer: A number is divisible by 12 if the number is divisible by 3 and 4.

Answer (p.162)

45. The number of rectangles that can be modeled to represent a number indicate whether the number is prime or composite. Answers should include the following.

- If a number is prime, then only one rectangle can be drawn to represent the number. If a number is composite, then more than one rectangle can be drawn to represent the number.

- If a model has a length or width of 1, then the number may be prime or composite. If a model does not have a length or width of 1, then the number must be composite.

4-4 Greatest Common Factor (GCF)

1 Focus

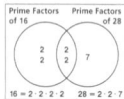

5-Minute Check Transparency 4-4 Use as a quiz or review of Lesson 4-3.

Mathematical Background notes are available for this lesson on page 146C.

How can a diagram be used to find the greatest common factor?

The opening activity questions are repeated on page 183 of the *Chapter 4 Resource Masters.*

Reading to Learn Mathematics, p. 183 **ELL**

Pre-Activity *How can a diagram be used to find the greatest common factor?*

Do the activity at the top of page 164 in your textbook. Write your answers below.

a. Which numbers are in both circles? **2, 2**

b. Find the product of the numbers that are in both circles. **4**

c. Is the product also a factor of 12 and 20? **yes**

d. Make a Venn diagram showing the prime factors of 16 and 28. Then use it to find the common factors of the numbers. **2, 2**

Prime Factors of 16 | Prime Factors of 28
2 2 | 2 2 | 7
16 = 2 · 2 · 2 · 2   28 = 2 · 2 · 7

Reading the Lesson 1–2. See students' work.
Write a definition and give an example of each new vocabulary word or phrase.

Vocabulary	Definition	Example
1. Venn diagram		
2. greatest common factor		

Helping You Remember

3. Summarize in your own words how to find the greatest common factor of two numbers using each method.

a. prime factorization Write the prime factorization of each number, then look for the prime factors common to both numbers. The greatest common factor is the product of the common factors.

b. lists of factors Make a list of all factors of both numbers. The largest factor that is in both lists is the greatest common factor.

c. a Venn diagram Make a Venn diagram with the prime factors of each number in a circle. The GCF is the product of the factors in the overlapping section of the diagram.

4-4 Greatest Common Factor (GCF)

NEW YORK *Performance Indicator* **8.A.10 Factor algebraic expressions using the GCF**

What You'll Learn

- Find the greatest common factor of two or more numbers or monomials.
- Use the Distributive Property to factor algebraic expressions.

Vocabulary
- Venn diagram
- greatest common factor

How can a diagram be used to find the greatest common factor?

A **Venn diagram** shows the relationships among sets of numbers or objects by using overlapping circles in a rectangle.

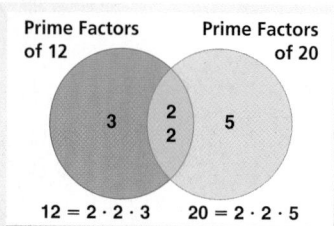

Prime Factors of 12   Prime Factors of 20

3   2 2   5

12 = 2 · 2 · 3   20 = 2 · 2 · 5

The Venn diagram at the right shows the prime factors of 12 and 20. The common prime factors are in both circles.

a. Which numbers are in both circles? **2, 2**

b. Find the product of the numbers that are in both circles. **4**

c. Is the product also a factor of 12 and 20? **yes**

d. Make a Venn diagram showing the prime factors of 16 and 28. Then use it to find the common factors of the numbers. **See margin.**

GREATEST COMMON FACTOR   Often, numbers have some of the same factors. The greatest number that is a factor of two or more numbers is called the **greatest common factor (GCF)**. Below are two ways to find the GCF of 12 and 20.

Example 1 Find the GCF

Find the GCF of 12 and 20.

Method 1   List the factors.

factors of 12: 1, 2, 3, ④, 6, 12 ← Common factors of 12 and 20: 1, 2, 4
factors of 20: 1, 2, ④, 5, 10, 20 ←

The greatest common factor of 12 and 20 is 4.

Method 2   Use prime factorization.

$12 = \boxed{2} \cdot \boxed{2} \cdot 3$ ← Common prime factors of 12 and 20: 2, 2
$20 = \boxed{2} \cdot \boxed{2} \cdot 5$ ←

The GCF is the product of the common prime factors.
$2 \cdot 2 = 4$

Again, the GCF of 12 and 20 is 4.

Study Tip

Choosing a Method
To find the GCF of two or more numbers, it is easier to
- list the factors if the numbers are small, or
- use prime factorization if the numbers are large.

Resource Manager

📁 Workbooks and Reproducible Masters

Chapter 4 Resource Masters
- Study Guide and Intervention, p. 180
- Skills Practice, p. 181
- Practice, p. 182
- Reading to Learn Mathematics, p. 183
- Enrichment, p. 184
- Assessment, pp. 219, 221

Parent and Student Study Guide Workbook, p. 27

📖 Transparencies

5-Minute Check Transparency 4-4
Answer Key Transparencies

Technology

Interactive Chalkboard
Pre-AlgePASS: Tutorial Plus, Lesson 7

Example 2 Find the GCF

Find the GCF of each set of numbers.

a. 30, 24

First, factor each number completely. Then circle the common factors.

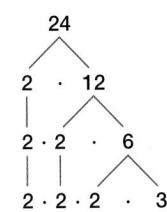

$30 = \boxed{2} \cdot \boxed{3} \cdot 5$ The common prime
$24 = \boxed{2} \cdot 2 \cdot 2 \cdot \boxed{3}$ factors are 2 and 3.

The GCF of 30 and 24 is $2 \cdot 3$ or 6.

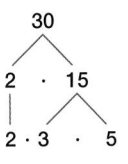

Study Tip

Writing Prime Factors
Try to line up the common prime factors so that it is easier to circle them.

b. 54, 36, 45

$54 = 2 \cdot \boxed{3} \cdot \boxed{3} \cdot 3$ The common
$36 = 2 \cdot 2 \cdot \boxed{3} \cdot \boxed{3}$ prime factors
$45 = \boxed{3} \cdot \boxed{3} \cdot 5$ are 3 and 3.

The GCF is $3 \cdot 3$ or 9.

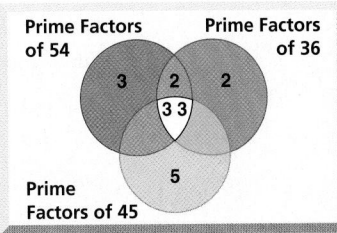

Example 3 Use the GCF to Solve Problems

TRACK AND FIELD There are 208 boys and 240 girls participating in a field day competition.

a. What is the greatest number of teams that can be formed if each team has the same number of girls and each team has the same number of boys?

Find the GCF of 208 and 240.

$208 = \boxed{2} \cdot \boxed{2} \cdot \boxed{2} \cdot \boxed{2} \cdot 13$ The common prime factors
$240 = \boxed{2} \cdot \boxed{2} \cdot \boxed{2} \cdot \boxed{2} \cdot 3 \cdot 5$ are 2, 2, 2, and 2.

The greatest common factor of 208 and 240 is $2 \cdot 2 \cdot 2 \cdot 2$ or 16. So, 16 teams can be formed.

b. How many boys and girls will be on each team?

$208 \div 16 = 13$
$240 \div 16 = 15$

So, each team will have 13 boys and 15 girls.

More About. . .

Track and Field
In some events such as sprints and the long jump, if the wind speed is greater than 2 meters per second, then the time or mark cannot be considered for record purposes.

Source: www.encarta.msn.com

www.pre-alg.com/extra_examples/ny   **Lesson 4-4** Greatest Common Factor (GCF) **165**

---

2 Teach

GREATEST COMMON FACTOR

In-Class Examples Power Point®

1 Find the GCF of 16 and 24. **8**

   Teaching Tip Remind students that for two numbers that do not appear to have any common factors, the greatest common factor is 1, not 0.

2 Find the GCF of each set of numbers.

   a. 28, 35 **7**

   b. 12, 48, 72 **12**

3 Parents donated 150 chocolate chip cookies and 120 molasses cookies for a school bake sale.

   a. If the cookies are arranged on plates, and each plate has the same number of chocolate chip cookies and each plate has the same number of molasses cookies, what is the largest number of plates possible? **30**

   b. How many chocolate chip and molasses cookies will be on each plate? **5 chocolate chip, 4 molasses**

FACTOR ALGEBRAIC EXPRESSIONS

In-Class Examples Power Point®

4 Find the GCF of $18x^3y^2$ and $42xy^2$. **$6xy^2$**

5 Factor $3x + 12$. **$3(x + 4)$**

DAILY
INTERVENTION

Differentiated Instruction

- **Visual/Spatial** Give students rectangles cut from grid paper. Their task is to cut the rectangle into equal squares with no material left. Discuss their results. What is the connection between the sizes of squares and the length and width of the original rectangle? Students should discover that a side on a square will be a factor of the length and width. The side of the largest square will give the GCF of the length and width.

3 Practice/Apply

Study Notebook

Have students—
- add the definitions/examples of the vocabulary terms to their Vocabulary Builder worksheets for Chapter 4.
- write down examples of each method for finding greatest common factors.
- include any other item(s) that they find helpful in mastering the skills in this lesson.

D A I L Y
INTERVENTION **FIND THE ERROR**
Some students have difficulty identifying common prime factors when the factors are written with exponents. Students may benefit from writing prime factorizations without exponents until they learn to pick out common factors.

About the Exercises . . .
Organization by Objective
- **Greatest Common Factor:** 17–43, 53–55
- **Factor Algebraic Expressions:** 44–52

Odd/Even Assignments
Exercises 17–42 and 44–52 are structured so that students practice the same concepts whether they are assigned odd or even problems.

Assignment Guide
Basic: 17–37 odd, 45–49 odd, 53, 55, 57–60, 67–81

Average: 17–55 odd, 57–60, 67–81 (Optional: 61–66)

Advanced: 18–56 even, 57–75 (Optional: 76–81)

ALGEBRA CONNECTION

FACTOR ALGEBRAIC EXPRESSIONS You can also find the GCF of two or more monomials by finding the product of their common prime factors.

Example 4 *Find the GCF of Monomials*

Find the GCF of $16xy^2$ and $30xy$.

Completely factor each expression.

$$16xy^2 = \boxed{2} \cdot 2 \cdot 2 \cdot 2 \cdot \boxed{x} \cdot \boxed{y} \cdot y$$
$$30xy = \boxed{2} \cdot 3 \cdot 5 \cdot \boxed{x} \cdot \boxed{y} \quad \text{Circle the common factors.}$$

The GCF of $16xy^2$ and $30xy$ is $2 \cdot x \cdot y$ or $2xy$.

Study Tip

Look Back
To review the **Distributive Property**, see Lesson 3-1.

In Lesson 3-1, you used the Distributive Property to rewrite $2(x + 3)$ as $2x + 6$. You can also use this property to factor an algebraic expression such as $2x + 6$.

Example 5 *Factor Expressions*

Factor $2x + 6$.

First, find the GCF of $2x$ and 6.

$$2x = \boxed{2} \cdot x$$
$$6 = \boxed{2} \cdot 3 \qquad \text{The GCF is 2.}$$

Now write each term as a product of the GCF and its remaining factors.
$$2x + 6 = 2(x) + 2(3)$$
$$= 2(x + 3) \qquad \text{Distributive Property}$$

So, $2x + 6 = 2(x + 3)$.

✓ **Concept Check** Which property allows you to factor $3x + 9$?
Distributive Property

Check for Understanding

Concept Check
1. **Explain** how to find the greatest common factor of two or more numbers. **See margin.**

2. Sample answer: 12 and 24

3. Jack; the common prime factors of the expressions are 2 and 11, so the GCF is $2 \cdot 11$ or 22.

2. **OPEN ENDED** Name two different numbers whose GCF is 12.

3. **FIND THE ERROR** Christina and Jack both found the GCF of $2 \cdot 3^2 \cdot 11$ and $2^3 \cdot 5 \cdot 11$.

Who is correct? Explain your reasoning.

Answer

1. Sample answer: Find the prime factorization of each number. Multiply the factors that are common to both.

Guided Practice

GUIDED PRACTICE KEY

Exercises	Examples
4–10	1, 2
11, 12	4
13–15	5
16	3

Find the GCF of each set of numbers or monomials.

4. 6, 8 **2**
5. 21, 45 **3**
6. 16, 56 **8**
7. 28, 42 **14**
8. 7, 30 **1**
9. 108, 144 **36**
10. 12, 24, 36 **12**
11. $14n, 42n^2$ **14n**
12. $36a^3b, 56ab^2$ **4ab**

Factor each expression.

13. $3n + 9$ **3(n + 3)**
14. $t^2 + 4t$ **t(t + 4)**
15. $15 + 20x$ **5(3 + 4x)**

Application

16. **PARADES** In the parade, 36 members of the color guard are to march in front of 120 members of the high school marching band. Both groups are to have the same number of students in each row. Find the greatest number of students in each row. **12 students**

★ indicates increased difficulty

Practice and Apply

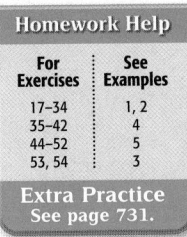

Homework Help

For Exercises	See Examples
17–34	1, 2
35–42	4
44–52	5
53, 54	3

Extra Practice
See page 731.

Find the GCF of each set of numbers or monomials.

17. 12, 8 **4**
18. 3, 9 **3**
19. 24, 40 **8**
20. 21, 14 **7**
21. 20, 30 **10**
22. 12, 18 **6**
23. 18, 45 **9**
24. 22, 21 **1**
25. 16, 40 **8**
26. 42, 56 **14**
27. 30, 35 **5**
28. 12, 60 **12**
29. 116, 100 **4**
30. 135, 315 **45**
31. 9, 15, 24 **3**
32. 20, 21, 25 **1**
33. 20, 28, 36 **4**
34. 66, 90, 150 **6**
35. $12x, 40x^2$ **4x**
36. $18, 45mn$ **9**
37. $4st, 10s$ **2s**
38. $5ab, 6b^2$ **b**
★ 39. $14b, 56b^2$ **14b**
★ 40. $30a^3b^2, 24a^2b$ **6a²b**

★ 41. What is the greatest common factor of $32mn^2$, $16n$, and $12n^3$? **4n**

★ 42. Name the GCF of $15v^2$, $70vw$, and $36w^2$. **1**

★ 43. Name two monomials whose GCF is $2x$. **Sample answer: 2x, 6x²**

Factor each expression.

44. $2x + 8$ **2(x + 4)**
45. $3r + 12$ **3(r + 4)**
46. $8 + 32a$ **8(1 + 4a)**
47. $6 + 3y$ **3(2 + y)**
48. $9 + 3t$ **3(3 + t)**
49. $14 + 21c$ **7(2 + 3c)**
★ 50. $k^2 + 5k$ **k(k + 5)**
★ 51. $4y - 16$ **4(y - 4)**
★ 52. $5n - 10$ **5(n - 2)**

53. **PATTERNS** Consider the pattern 7, 14, 21, 28, 35, … . **a. See margin.**
    a. Find the GCF of the terms in the pattern. Explain how you know.
    b. Write the next two terms in the pattern. **42, 49**

54. **CARPENTRY** Tamika is helping her father make shelves to store her sports equipment in the garage. How many shelves measuring 12 inches by 16 inches can be cut from a 48-inch by 72-inch piece of plywood so that there is no waste? **18 shelves**

55. **DESIGN** Lauren is covering the surface of an end table with equal-sized ceramic tiles. The table is 30 inches long and 24 inches wide.
    a. What is the largest square tile that Lauren can use and not have to cut any tiles? **6-in. squares**
    b. How many tiles will Lauren need? **20 tiles**

 www.pre-alg.com/self_check_quiz/ny

Lesson 4-4 Greatest Common Factor (GCF) **167**

Answer

53a. 7; Sample answer:

```
7    14   21   28   35
↓    ↓    ↓    ↓    ↓
7(1) 7(2) 7(3) 7(4) 7(5)
```

The terms increase by a factor of 7.

Lesson 4-4 Greatest Common Factor (GCF) **167**

Open-Ended Assessment

Writing Have students write a paragraph relating any two of the following ideas—use of Venn diagrams, finding greatest common factors, and applying the Distributive Property.

Getting Ready for Lesson 4-5

PREREQUISITE SKILL Lesson 4-5 presents simplifying fractions. Students will also determine what fraction one measurement is of another. Exercises 76–81 should be used to determine your students' familiarity with converting measurements.

Assessment Options

Quiz (Lessons 4-3 and 4-4) is available on p. 219 of the *Chapter 4 Resource Masters.*

Mid-Chapter Test (Lessons 4-1 through 4-4) is available on p. 221 of the *Chapter 4 Resource Masters.*

★ **56. HISTORY** *The Nine Chapters on the Mathematical Art* is a Chinese math book written during the first century. It describes a procedure for finding the greatest common factors. Follow each step below to find the GCF of 86 and 110. **b. 86 − 24 = 62**

 a. Subtract the lesser number, *a*, from the greater number, *b*. **24**

 b. If the result in part **a** is a factor of both numbers, it is the GCF. If the result is not a factor of both numbers, subtract the result from *a* or subtract *a* from the result so that the difference is a positive number.

 c. Continue subtracting and checking the results until you find a number that is a factor of both numbers. **2**

57. CRITICAL THINKING Can the GCF of a set of numbers be equal to one of the numbers? Give an example or a counterexample to support your answer. **Yes; the GCF of 2 and 8 is 2.**

58. **WRITING IN MATH** Answer the question that was posed at the beginning of the lesson. **See margin.**

 How can a diagram be used to find the greatest common factor?

 Include the following in your answer:
 - a description of how a Venn diagram can be used to display the prime factorization of two or more numbers, and
 - the part of a Venn diagram that is used to find the greatest common factor.

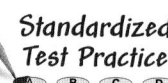

NEW YORK Test Practice

Standardized Test Practice
(A)(B)(C)(D)

59. Write $6y + 21$ in factored form. **D**
 Ⓐ $6(y + 3)$ Ⓑ $2(3y + 7)$ Ⓒ $3(y + 7)$ Ⓓ $3(2y + 7)$

60. Find the GCF of $42x^2y$ and $38xy^2$. **C**
 Ⓐ $2x^2y$ Ⓑ $3xy$ Ⓒ $2xy$ Ⓓ $6x^2y^2$

Extending the Lesson
Two numbers are **relatively prime** if their only common factor is 1. Determine whether the numbers in each pair are relatively prime. Write *yes* or *no*.

61. 7 and 8 **yes**   **62.** 13 and 11 **yes**   **63.** 27 and 18 **no**

64. 20 and 25 **no**   **65.** 22 and 23 **yes**   **66.** 8 and 12 **no**

Maintain Your Skills

Mixed Review   **ALGEBRA   Factor each monomial.** *(Lesson 4-3)*

70. $2 \cdot 11 \cdot a \cdot b \cdot b \cdot b$

67. $9n$ $3 \cdot 3 \cdot n$ **68.** $15x^2$ $3 \cdot 5 \cdot x \cdot x$ **69.** $-5jk$ $-1 \cdot 5 \cdot j \cdot k$ **70.** $22ab^3$

71. ALGEBRA Evaluate $7x^2 + y^3$ if $x = -2$ and $y = 4$. *(Lesson 4-2)* **92**

Find each quotient. *(Lesson 2-5)*

72. $69 \div 23$ **3**   **73.** $48 \div (-8)$ **−6**   **74.** $-24 \div (-12)$ **2**   **75.** $-50 \div 5$ **−10**

Getting Ready for the Next Lesson   **PREREQUISITE SKILL   Find each equivalent measure.**
*(To review **converting measurements**, see pages 718–721.)*

76. 1 ft = _?_ in. **12**   **77.** 1 yd = _?_ in. **36**   **78.** 1 lb = _?_ oz **16**

79. 1 day = _?_ h **24**   **80.** 1 m = _?_ cm **100**   **81.** 1 kg = _?_ g **1000**

Answer

58. A Venn diagram can be used to display the prime factorizations of two or more numbers. Answers should include the following.

 - Each circle in a Venn diagram represents a number. The prime factors of each number are listed inside its circle. The overlapping part(s) of the circles contain the common prime factors.

 - The overlapping area in the Venn diagram is used to find the greatest common factor. Multiply the numbers found in this area.

Simplifying Algebraic Fractions

NEW YORK *Performance Indicator* **8.A.6 Multiply and divide monomials**

What You'll Learn

- Simplify fractions using the GCF.
- Simplify algebraic fractions.

Vocabulary
- simplest form
- algebraic fraction

How are simplified fractions useful in representing measurements?

You can use a fraction to compare a *part* of something to a *whole*. The figures below show what part 15 minutes is of 1 hour.

$\frac{15}{60}$ is shaded.

$\frac{3}{12}$ is shaded.

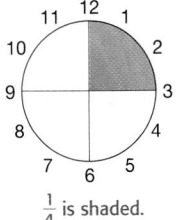
$\frac{1}{4}$ is shaded.

a. Are the three fractions equivalent? Explain your reasoning.

b. Which figure is divided into the least number of parts? **the third figure**

c. Which fraction would you say is written in simplest form? Why?

a. Yes; the same portion of each circle is shaded.

c. $\frac{1}{4}$; The shaded part is not divided into smaller parts.

SIMPLIFY NUMERICAL FRACTIONS
A fraction is in **simplest form** when the GCF of the numerator and the denominator is 1.

Fractions in Simplest Form	Fractions *not* in Simplest Form
$\frac{1}{4}, \frac{1}{3}, \frac{3}{4}, \frac{17}{50}$	$\frac{3}{12}, \frac{15}{60}, \frac{6}{8}, \frac{5}{20}$

One way to write a fraction in simplest form is to write the prime factorization of the numerator and the denominator. Then divide the numerator and denominator by the GCF.

Study Tip

Use a Venn Diagram To simplify fractions, let one circle in a Venn diagram represent the numerator and let another circle represent the denominator. The number or product of numbers in the intersection is the GCF.

Example 1 Simplify Fractions

Write $\frac{9}{12}$ in simplest form.

$9 = 3 \cdot \boxed{3}$ Factor the numerator.
$12 = 2 \cdot 2 \cdot \boxed{3}$ Factor the denominator.

The GCF of 9 and 12 is 3.

$\frac{9}{12} = \frac{9 \div 3}{12 \div 3}$ Divide the numerator and the denominator by the GCF.

$= \frac{3}{4}$ Simplest form

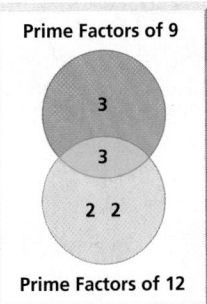
Prime Factors of 9
3
3
2 2
Prime Factors of 12

---

1 Focus

5-Minute Check Transparency 4-5 Use as a quiz or review of Lesson 4-4.

Mathematical Background notes are available for this lesson on page 146D.

How are simplified fractions useful in representing measurements?

The opening activity questions are repeated on page 188 of the *Chapter 4 Resource Masters*.

Reading to Learn Mathematics, p. 188 **ELL**

Pre-Activity	How are simplified fractions useful in representing measurements?

Do the activity at the top of page 169 in your textbook. Write your answers below.

a. Are the three fractions equivalent? Explain your reasoning.
  Yes; the same portion of each circle is shaded.

b. Which figure is divided into the least number of parts?
  the third figure

c. Which fraction would you say is written in simplest form? Why? $\frac{1}{4}$;
  The shaded part is not divided into smaller parts.

Reading the Lesson 1–2. See students' work.

Write a definition and give an example of each new vocabulary phrase.

Vocabulary	Definition	Example
1. simplest form		
2. algebraic fraction		

3. Use a Venn diagram to explain how to simplify $\frac{18}{45}$. The prime factors of the numerator are 3, 3, and 2. The prime factors of the denominator are 3, 3, and 5. The GCF of the numbers, 9, is shown by the intersection. So, the simplified fraction is $\frac{2}{5}$.

18   45
  2   3 3   5
  3·3·2   3·3·5

Helping You Remember

4. Explain the similarities and differences between simplifying a numerical fraction and simplifying an algebraic fraction. Both fractions are simplified by dividing the numerator and denominator by the GCF. The only difference is that an algebraic fraction has variables as factors in the numerator and/or the denominator.

Resource Manager

Workbooks and Reproducible Masters

Chapter 4 Resource Masters
- Study Guide and Intervention, p. 185
- Skills Practice, p. 186
- Practice, p. 187
- Reading to Learn Mathematics, p. 188
- Enrichment, p. 189

Parent and Student Study Guide Workbook, p. 28

Transparencies
5-Minute Check Transparency 4-5
Answer Key Transparencies

Technology
Interactive Chalkboard
Multimedia Applications

SIMPLIFY NUMERICAL FRACTIONS

In-Class Examples Power Point®

1 Write $\frac{16}{24}$ in simplest form.
$\frac{2}{3}$

2 Write $\frac{72}{120}$ in simplest form.
$\frac{3}{5}$

3 250 pounds is what part of 1 ton? **There are 2000 pounds in 1 ton, so** $\frac{250}{2000} = \frac{1}{8}$.

Teaching Tip You can have students multiply the numerator and denominator of the simplified fraction by the GCF. The result should be the original fraction. This is often helpful when checking work.

SIMPLIFY ALGEBRAIC FRACTIONS

In-Class Examples Power Point®

4 Simplify $\frac{20m^3n^2}{65mn}$. $\quad \frac{4m^2n}{13}$

5 **Multiple-Choice Test Item**

Which fraction is $\frac{x^3y^2}{x^2y^3}$ written in simplest form? **C**

A $\quad \frac{y}{x}$

B $\quad \frac{y^2}{x^2}$

C $\quad \frac{x}{y}$

D $\quad \frac{x^2}{y^2}$

The division in Example 1 can be represented in another way.

TEACHING TIP
This method is sometimes called *canceling*.

$$\frac{9}{12} = \frac{\overset{1}{\cancel{3}} \cdot 3}{2 \cdot 2 \cdot \underset{1}{\cancel{3}}}$$ The slashes mean that the numerator and the denominator are both divided by the GCF, 3.

$$= \frac{3}{2 \cdot 2} \text{ or } \frac{3}{4} \quad \text{Simplify.}$$

TEACHING TIP
Emphasize that if a common factor other than the GCF is used to simplify a fraction, the resulting fraction will not be in simplest form.

Example 2 *Simplify Fractions*

Write $\frac{15}{60}$ in simplest form.

$$\frac{15}{60} = \frac{\overset{1}{\cancel{3}} \cdot \overset{1}{\cancel{5}}}{2 \cdot 2 \cdot \underset{1}{\cancel{3}} \cdot \underset{1}{\cancel{5}}} \quad \text{Divide the numerator and denominator by the GCF, } 3 \cdot 5.$$

$$= \frac{1}{4} \quad \text{Simplify.}$$

✓**Concept Check** How do you know when a fraction is in simplest form? **The GCF of the numerator and the denominator is 1.**

Simplifying fractions is a useful tool in measurement.

Study Tip

Alternative Method
You can also divide the numerator and denominator by common factors until the fraction is in simplest form.
$$\frac{88}{5280} = \frac{44}{2640}$$
$$= \frac{22}{1320}$$
$$= \frac{11}{660} \text{ or } \frac{1}{60}$$

Example 3 *Simplify Fractions in Measurement*

MEASUREMENT **Eighty-eight feet is what part of 1 mile?**

There are 5280 feet in 1 mile. Write the fraction $\frac{88}{5280}$ in simplest form.

$$\frac{88}{5280} = \frac{\overset{1}{\cancel{2}} \cdot \overset{1}{\cancel{2}} \cdot \overset{1}{\cancel{2}} \cdot \overset{1}{\cancel{11}}}{\underset{1}{\cancel{2}} \cdot \underset{1}{\cancel{2}} \cdot \underset{1}{\cancel{2}} \cdot 2 \cdot 2 \cdot 3 \cdot 5 \cdot \underset{1}{\cancel{11}}} \quad \text{Divide the numerator and denominator by the GCF, } 2 \cdot 2 \cdot 2 \cdot 11.$$

$$= \frac{1}{60} \quad \text{Simplify.}$$

So, 88 feet is $\frac{1}{60}$ of a mile.

ALGEBRA CONNECTION

SIMPLIFY ALGEBRAIC FRACTIONS A fraction with variables in the numerator or denominator is called an **algebraic fraction**. Algebraic fractions can also be written in simplest form.

Example 4 *Simplify Algebraic Fractions*

Simplify $\frac{21x^2y}{35xy}$.

$$\frac{21x^2y}{35xy} = \frac{3 \cdot \overset{1}{\cancel{7}} \cdot \overset{1}{\cancel{x}} \cdot x \cdot \overset{1}{\cancel{y}}}{5 \cdot \underset{1}{\cancel{7}} \cdot \underset{1}{\cancel{x}} \cdot \underset{1}{\cancel{y}}} \quad \text{Divide the numerator and denominator by the GCF, } 7 \cdot x \cdot y.$$

$$= \frac{3x}{5} \quad \text{Simplify.}$$

D A I L Y
INTERVENTION   **Differentiated Instruction**

• **Intrapersonal** Have students evaluate how well they understand each example. Have them make a list of questions that they have about the examples that they do not understand completely. Use the Guided Practice or the Study Guide master to reteach any concept that they have identified as a weakness.

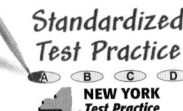
Example 5 Simplify Algebraic Fractions

Multiple-Choice Test Item

Which fraction is $\dfrac{abc^3}{a^2b}$ written in simplest form?

Ⓐ $\dfrac{bc^3}{a}$ Ⓑ $\dfrac{bc^2}{a}$ Ⓒ $\dfrac{c^3}{a}$ Ⓓ $\dfrac{c^2}{a}$

Read the Test Item *In simplest form* means that the GCF of the numerator and the denominator is 1.

Solve the Test Item

$$\frac{abc^3}{a^2b} = \frac{ab\!\!\!/c^3}{a^2b\!\!\!/}$$

Without factoring, you can see that the variable b will not appear in the simplified fraction. That eliminates choices A and B.

$$\frac{abc^3}{a^2b} = \frac{\overset{1}{\cancel{a}} \cdot \overset{1}{\cancel{b}} \cdot c \cdot c \cdot c}{\underset{1}{\cancel{a}} \cdot a \cdot \underset{1}{\cancel{b}}} \qquad \text{Factor.}$$

$$= \frac{c^3}{a} \qquad \text{Multiply.}$$

The answer is C.

Check for Understanding

Concept Check

1. **Explain** what it means to express a fraction in simplest form.
   The GCF of the numerator and denominator is 1.

2. **OPEN ENDED** Write examples of a numerical fraction and an algebraic fraction in simplest form and examples of a numerical fraction and an algebraic fraction not in simplest form. **See margin.**

Guided Practice

Write each fraction in simplest form. If the fraction is already in simplest form, write *simplified*.

3. $\dfrac{2}{14}$ $\dfrac{1}{7}$ 4. $\dfrac{9}{15}$ $\dfrac{3}{5}$ 5. $\dfrac{5}{11}$ **simp.**   6. $\dfrac{25}{40}$ $\dfrac{5}{8}$ 7. $\dfrac{64}{68}$ $\dfrac{16}{17}$

GUIDED PRACTICE KEY	
Exercises	Examples
3–7	1, 2
8–11	4
12	3
13	5

ALGEBRA Simplify each fraction. If the fraction is already in simplest form, write *simplified*.

8. $\dfrac{x}{x^3}$ $\dfrac{1}{x^2}$ 9. $\dfrac{8a^2}{16a}$ $\dfrac{a}{2}$ 10. $\dfrac{12c}{15d}$ $\dfrac{4c}{5d}$ 11. $\dfrac{24}{5k}$ **simp.**

12. **MEASUREMENT** Nine inches is what part of 1 yard? $\dfrac{1}{4}$

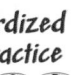
13. Which fraction is $\dfrac{25mn}{65n}$ written in simplest form? **B**

Ⓐ $\dfrac{2m}{6}$ Ⓑ $\dfrac{5m}{13}$ Ⓒ $\dfrac{5m}{13n}$ Ⓓ $\dfrac{25mn}{65}$

---

3 Practice/Apply

Study Notebook

Have students—

- add the definitions/examples of the vocabulary terms to their Vocabulary Builder worksheets for Chapter 4.
- record several measurement conversions for use with application problems. For example 1 mile = 5280 feet; 3 feet = 1 yard; 2000 pound = 1 ton, etc.
- include a fully worked example of simplifying an algebraic fraction.

Answer

2. Sample answer: $\dfrac{2}{3}$ and $\dfrac{x}{4}$ are in simplest form; $\dfrac{2}{4}$ and $\dfrac{3n}{n^2}$ are not in simplest form.

About the Exercises . . .

Organization by Objective
- **Simplify Numerical Fractions:** 14–29, 42–49
- **Simplify Algebraic Fractions:** 30–41

Odd/Even Assignments

Exercises 14–28 and 30–43 are structured so that students practice the same concepts whether they are assigned odd or even problems.

Assignment Guide

Basic: 15–25 odd, 29–39 odd, 43, 45, 47–68

Average: 15–45 odd, 47–68

Advanced: 14–46 even, 47–64 (Optional: 65–68)

★ indicates increased difficulty

Practice and Apply

Write each fraction in simplest form. If the fraction is already in simplest form, write *simplified*.

14. $\frac{3}{18}$ $\frac{1}{6}$ 15. $\frac{10}{12}$ $\frac{5}{6}$ 16. $\frac{15}{21}$ $\frac{5}{7}$ 17. $\frac{8}{36}$ $\frac{2}{9}$ 18. $\frac{17}{20}$ simp.

19. $\frac{18}{44}$ $\frac{9}{22}$ 20. $\frac{16}{64}$ $\frac{1}{4}$ 21. $\frac{30}{37}$ simp.   22. $\frac{34}{38}$ $\frac{17}{19}$ 23. $\frac{17}{51}$ $\frac{1}{3}$

24. $\frac{51}{60}$ $\frac{17}{20}$ 25. $\frac{25}{60}$ $\frac{5}{12}$ 26. $\frac{36}{96}$ $\frac{3}{8}$ ★27. $\frac{133}{140}$ $\frac{19}{20}$ ★28. $\frac{765}{2023}$ $\frac{45}{119}$

29. **AIRCRAFT** A model of Lindbergh's *Spirit of St. Louis* has a wingspan of 18 inches. The wingspan of the actual airplane is 46 feet. Write a fraction in simplest form comparing the wingspan of the model and the wingspan of the actual airplane. (*Hint:* convert 46 feet to inches.) $\frac{3}{92}$

ALGEBRA Simplify each fraction. If the fraction is already in simplest form, write *simplified*.

30. $\frac{a}{a^4}$ $\frac{1}{a^3}$ 31. $\frac{y^3}{y}$ $\frac{y^2}{1}$ or y^2 32. $\frac{12m}{15m}$ $\frac{4}{5}$ 33. $\frac{40d}{42d}$ $\frac{20}{21}$

34. $\frac{4k}{19m}$ simp.   35. $\frac{8t}{64t^2}$ $\frac{1}{8t}$ 36. $\frac{16n}{18n^2p}$ $\frac{8}{9np}$ 37. $\frac{28z^3}{16z}$ $\frac{7z^2}{4}$

38. $\frac{6r}{15rs}$ $\frac{2}{5s}$ 39. $\frac{12cd}{19e}$ simp.   40. $\frac{30x^2}{51xy}$ $\frac{10x}{17y}$ ★41. $\frac{17g^2h}{51g}$ $\frac{gh}{3}$

42. **MEASUREMENT** Fifteen hours is what part of one day? $\frac{5}{8}$

43. **MEASUREMENT** Ninety-six centimeters is what part of a meter? $\frac{24}{25}$

44. **MEASUREMENT** Twelve ounces is what part of a pound? (*Hint:* 1 lb = 16 oz) $\frac{3}{4}$

45. **MUSIC** Musical notes C and A sound harmonious together because of their *frequencies*, or vibrations. The fraction that is formed by the two frequencies can be simplified, as shown below.

$$\frac{C}{A} = \frac{264}{440} \text{ or } \frac{3}{5}$$

When a fraction formed by two frequencies *cannot* be simplified, the notes sound like noise. Determine whether each pair of notes would sound harmonious together. Explain why or why not.

a. E and A
b. D and F
c. first C and last C

a–c. See margin.

Note	Frequency (hz)
C	264
D	294
E	330
F	349
G	392
A	440
B	494
C	528

46. **ANIMALS** The table shows the average amount of food each animal can eat in a day and its average weight. What fraction of its weight can each animal eat per day?

elephant, $\frac{1}{20}$; hummingbird, $\frac{2}{3}$; polar bear, $\frac{1}{60}$; tiger, $\frac{1}{25}$

Animal	Daily Amount of Food	Weight of Animal
elephant	450 lb	9000 lb
hummingbird	2 g	3 g
polar bear	25 lb	1500 lb
tiger	20 lb	500 lb

Source: *Animals as Our Companions, Wildlife Fact File*

Answer

45a. yes; $\frac{330}{440} = \frac{3}{4}$

45b. No; $\frac{294}{349}$ cannot be simplified.

45c. yes; $\frac{264}{528} = \frac{1}{2}$

MONEY For Exercises 47–49, use the graph to write each fraction in simplest form.

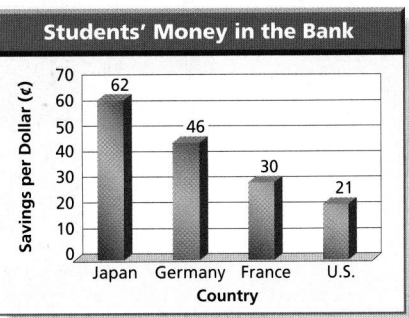

Students' Money in the Bank

47. the fraction of a dollar that students in Japan save $\frac{31}{50}$

48. the fraction of a dollar that students in the U.S. save $\frac{21}{100}$

49. a fraction showing the amount of a dollar that students in the U.S. save compared to students in France $\frac{7}{10}$

50. **CRITICAL THINKING** Is it true that $\frac{23}{53} = \frac{\cancel{23}}{\cancel{53}}$ or $\frac{2}{5}$? Explain. No, $23 \neq 2 \cdot 3$ and $53 \neq 5 \cdot 3$.

51. **WRITING IN MATH** Answer the question that was posed at the beginning of the lesson. **See margin.**

How are simplified fractions useful in representing measurements?

Include the following in your answer:
- an explanation of how measurements represent parts of a whole, and
- examples of fractions that represent measurements.

52. Which fraction represents the shaded area written in simplest form? **B**

Ⓐ $\frac{9}{30}$ Ⓑ $\frac{3}{10}$ Ⓒ $\frac{6}{20}$ Ⓓ $\frac{30}{100}$

53. Write $\frac{15ab}{25b^2}$ in simplest form. **A**

Ⓐ $\frac{3a}{5b}$ Ⓑ $\frac{15a}{25b}$ Ⓒ $\frac{3ab}{5}$ Ⓓ $\frac{15a}{25b^2}$

Maintain Your Skills

Mixed Review

Find the greatest common factor of each set of numbers or monomials. *(Lesson 4-4)*

54. 9, 15 **3**   55. 4, 12, 10 **2**   56. $40x^2$, $16x$ **8x**   57. $25a$, $30b$ **5**

Determine whether each number is *prime* or *composite*. *(Lesson 4-3)*

58. 13 **prime**   59. 34 **comp.**   60. 99 **comp.**   61. 79 **prime**

ALGEBRA Solve each equation. Check your solution. *(Lesson 3-3)*

62. $t - 18 = 24$ **42**   63. $30 = 3 + y$ **27**   64. $-7 = x + 11$ **−18**

Getting Ready for the Next Lesson

PREREQUISITE SKILL For each expression, use parentheses to group the numbers together and to group the powers with like bases together.
*(To review **properties of multiplication**, see Lesson 1-4.)* 68. $(5 \cdot 2)(n^3 \cdot n)(p \cdot p)$

Example: $a \cdot 4 \cdot a^3 \cdot 2 = (4 \cdot 2)(a \cdot a^3)$

65. $6 \cdot 7 \cdot k^3$ **$(6 \cdot 7)(k^3)$**   66. $s \cdot t^2 \cdot s \cdot t$ **$(s \cdot s)(t^2 \cdot t)$**

67. $3 \cdot x^4 \cdot (-5) \cdot x^2$ **$(3 \cdot -5)(x^4 \cdot x^2)$**   68. $5 \cdot n^3 \cdot p \cdot 2 \cdot n \cdot p$

Lesson 4-5 Simplifying Algebraic Fractions **173**

Open-Ended Assessment

Writing Have each student write three questions about simplifying fractions. The questions should cover what they think are the main ideas. Each student must provide a detailed answer key. Teachers can use students' work to assess their understanding, then select questions to give to the class.

Tips for New Teachers

Problem Solving Some students may continue to simplify fractions one step at a time rather than using the GCF. This is acceptable, especially if this is a time saving strategy. However, understanding how to use the GCF is important, so verify that all students understand using the GCF.

Getting Ready for Lesson 4-6

PREREQUISITE SKILL Lesson 4-6 presents multiplying and dividing monomials. Students will be required to group certain terms to find the product or quotient. Exercises 65–68 should be used to determine your students' familiarity with properties of multiplication.

Answer

51. Fractions represent parts of a whole. So, measurements that contain parts of units can be represented using fractions. Answers should include the following.

- Measurements can be given as parts of a whole because smaller units make up larger units. For example, inches make up feet.

- Twelve inches equals 1 foot. So, 3 inches equals $\frac{3}{12}$ or $\frac{1}{4}$ foot.

Lesson 4-5 Simplifying Algebraic Fractions **173**

Reading Mathematics

Getting Started

Before you begin this activity, you may want students to review their study notebook entries for Lesson 4-2. Be sure to mention the vocabulary such as base, power, squared, and cubed.

Teach

Powers Have students use a dictionary to find the meaning of *quantity* in English. Ask them to discuss why we use *the quantity* in mathematics to indicate parentheses.

For Exercises 11–16, remind students about expanding a power so that they might better determine whether the two expressions are equivalent.

Assess

Study Notebook

Ask students to summarize what they have learned about reading and writing verbal expressions from this activity.

ELL English Language Learners may benefit from writing key concepts from this activity in their Study Notebooks in their native language and then in English.

Powers

The phrase *the quantity* is used to indicate parentheses when reading expressions. Recall that an exponent indicates the number of times that the base is used as a factor. Suppose you are to write each of the following in symbols.

Words	Symbols	Examples (Let $x = 2$.)
three times x squared	$3x^2$	$3x^2 = 3 \cdot 2^2$ $= 3 \cdot 4$ Evaluate 2^2. $= 12$ Multiply $3 \cdot 4$.
three times x the quantity squared	$(3x)^2$	$(3x)^2 = (3 \cdot 2)^2$ $= 6^2$ Evaluate $3 \cdot 2$. $= 36$ Square 6.

In the expression $(3x)^2$, parentheses are used to show that $3x$ is used as a factor twice.

$$(3x)^2 = (3x)(3x)$$

The quantity can also be used to describe division of monomials.

Words	Symbols	Examples (Let $x = 2$.)
eight divided by x squared	$\dfrac{8}{x^2}$	$\dfrac{8}{x^2} = \dfrac{8}{2^2}$ $= \dfrac{8}{4}$ Evaluate 2^2. $= 2$ Divide $8 \div 4$.
eight divided by x the quantity squared	$\left(\dfrac{8}{x}\right)^2$	$\left(\dfrac{8}{x}\right)^2 = \left(\dfrac{8}{2}\right)^2$ $= 4^2$ Evaluate $8 \div 2$. $= 16$ Square 4.

Reading to Learn

State how you would read each expression. 1–10. See margin.

1. $4a^2$
2. $(10x)^5$
3. $\dfrac{5}{n^3}$
4. $\left(\dfrac{4}{r}\right)^2$
5. $(m + n)^3$
6. $(a - b)^4$
7. $a - b^4$
8. $\dfrac{a}{b^4}$
9. $(4c^2)^3$
10. $\left(\dfrac{8}{c^2}\right)^3$

Determine whether each pair of expressions is equivalent. Write *yes* or *no*.

11. $4ab^5$ and $4(ab)^5$ **no**
12. $(2x)^3$ and $8x^3$ **yes**
13. $(mn)^4$ and $m^4 \cdot n^4$ **yes**
14. c^3d^3 and cd^3 **no**
15. $\dfrac{x}{y^2}$ and $\left(\dfrac{x}{y}\right)^2$ **no**
16. $\dfrac{n^2}{r^2}$ and $\left(\dfrac{n}{r}\right)^2$ **yes**

Answers

1–10. Sample answers are given.

1. four times a squared
2. ten times x the quantity to the fifth power
3. five divided by n cubed
4. four divided by r the quantity squared
5. the sum of m and n the quantity cubed
6. a minus b the quantity to the fourth power
7. a minus b to the fourth power
8. a divided by b to the fourth power
9. four times c squared the quantity cubed
10. eight divided by c squared the quantity cubed

Multiplying and Dividing Monomials

NEW YORK *Performance Indicator* **8.N.1 Develop and apply the laws of exponents for multiplication and division, 8.A.6 Multiply and divide monomials**

What You'll Learn

- Multiply monomials.
- Divide monomials.

How are powers of monomials useful in comparing earthquake magnitudes?

For each increase on the Richter scale, an earthquake's vibrations, or *seismic waves*, are 10 times greater. So, an earthquake of magnitude 4 has seismic waves that are 10 times greater than that of a magnitude 3.

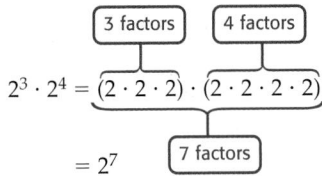

Richter Scale	Times Greater than Magnitude 3 Earthquake	Written Using Powers
4	10	10^1
5	$10 \times 10 = 100$	$10^1 \times 10^1 = 10^2$
6	$10 \times 100 = 1000$	$10^1 \times 10^2 = 10^3$
7	$10 \times 1000 = 10,000$	$10^1 \times 10^3 = 10^4$
8	$10 \times 10,000 = 100,000$	$10^1 \times 10^4 = 10^5$

a. The exponents of the factors are added to get the exponent of each product.
b. Sample answer: Add the exponents.

a. Examine the exponents of the factors and the exponents of the products in the last column. What do you observe?

b. Make a conjecture about a rule for determining the exponent of the product when you multiply powers with the same base. Test your rule by multiplying $2^2 \cdot 2^4$ using a calculator.

MULTIPLY MONOMIALS Recall that exponents are used to show repeated multiplication. You can use the definition of exponent to help find a rule for multiplying powers with the same base.

$$2^3 \cdot 2^4 = \underbrace{(2 \cdot 2 \cdot 2)}_{\text{3 factors}} \cdot \underbrace{(2 \cdot 2 \cdot 2 \cdot 2)}_{\text{4 factors}}$$

$$= 2^7 \quad \underbrace{}_{\text{7 factors}}$$

Notice the sum of the original exponents and the exponent in the final product. This relationship is stated in the following rule.

Study Tip

Common Misconception
When multiplying powers, do not multiply the bases.
$3^2 \cdot 3^4 = 3^6$, not 9^6

Key Concept   Product of Powers

- **Words**   You can multiply powers with the same base by adding their exponents.

- **Symbols** $a^m \cdot a^n = a^{m+n}$

- **Example** $3^2 \cdot 3^4 = 3^{2+4}$ or 3^6

Lesson 4-6 Multiplying and Dividing Monomials **175**

4-6 Lesson Notes

1 Focus

5-Minute Check Transparency 4-6 Use as a quiz or review of Lesson 4-5.

Mathematical Background notes are available for this lesson on page 146D.

How are powers of monomials useful in comparing earthquake magnitudes?

The opening activity questions are repeated on page 193 of the *Chapter 4 Resource Masters*.

Reading to Learn Mathematics, p. 193   ELL

Pre-Activity   *How are powers of monomials useful in comparing earthquake magnitudes?*

Do the activity at the top of page 175 in your textbook. Write your answers below.

a. Examine the exponents of the factors and the exponents of the products in the last column. What do you observe? The exponents of the factors are added to get the exponent of the product.

b. Make a conjecture about a rule for determining the exponent of the product when you multiply powers with the same base. Test your rule by multiplying $2^2 \cdot 2^4$ using a calculator. Sample answer: Add the exponents.

Reading the Lesson

1. When multiplying powers with like bases, **add** the exponents.

2. When dividing powers with like bases, **subtract** the exponents.

3. Write a division expression whose quotient is 7^2. Sample answer: $\frac{7^3}{7}$

4. Write a multiplication expression whose product is v^5. Sample answer: $v^2 \cdot v^3$

5. Find each product.
   a. $4 \cdot 4^3$ 4^4 **b.** $y^7 \cdot y^5$ y^{12}
   c. $(-2x^2)(5x^2)$ $-10x^4$ **d.** $-3r^2 \cdot r$ $-3r^3$

6. Find each quotient.
   a. $\frac{7^4}{7^2}$ 7^2 **b.** $\frac{v^8}{v^2}$ v^6
   c. $\frac{6^7}{6^6}$ 6^1 or 6   **d.** $\frac{a^2b^3}{b^2}$ a^2

Helping You Remember

7. Explain how dividing powers is related to simplifying fractions. Provide an example as part of your explanation. Sample answer: When dividing powers with like bases, subtracting the exponents is equivalent to simplifying fractions. For example, $3^4 \div 3^2 = 3^{4-2}$ or 3^2 by the Quotient of Powers rule. When simplifying $\frac{3^4}{3^2}$, divide the numerator and denominator by the GCF, 3^2, to get $\frac{3^2}{1}$ or 3^2.

Resource Manager

Workbooks and Reproducible Masters

Chapter 4 Resource Masters
- Study Guide and Intervention, p. 190
- Skills Practice, p. 191
- Practice, p. 192
- Reading to Learn Mathematics, p. 193
- Enrichment, p. 194
- Assessment, p. 220

Parent and Student Study Guide Workbook, p. 29
School-to-Career Masters, p. 8

 Transparencies
5-Minute Check Transparency 4-6
Answer Key Transparencies

 Technology
Interactive Chalkboard

2 Teach

Teaching Tip Students may be tempted to multiply exponents when multiplying monomials. Be sure to emphasize that we add the exponents because we want to know how many times each factor is used.

MULTIPLY MONOMIALS

In-Class Examples

1 Find $3^4 \cdot 3^6$. **3^{10}**

2 Find each product.

a. $y^4 \cdot y$ **y^5**

b. $(3p^4)(-2p^3)$ **$-6p^7$**

Teaching Tip Some students will benefit initially from writing out all factors until they understand why exponents are added.

3 Find each quotient.

a. $\dfrac{8^{11}}{8^5}$ **8^6**

b. $\dfrac{x^{12}}{x}$ **x^{11}**

4 **FOLDING PAPER** If you fold a sheet of paper in half, you have a thickness of 2 sheets. Folding again, you have a thickness of 4 sheets. Continue folding in half and recording the thickness. How many times thicker is a sheet that has been folded 4 times than a sheet that has not been folded?

$\dfrac{2^4}{2^0} = 2^{4-0}$ **or 16 times**

Example 1 **Multiply Powers**

Find $7^3 \cdot 7$.

$$7^3 \cdot 7 = 7^3 \cdot 7^1 \qquad 7 = 7^1$$
$$= 7^{3+1} \qquad \text{The common base is 7.}$$
$$= 7^4 \qquad \text{Add the exponents.}$$

CHECK $7^3 \cdot 7 = (7 \cdot 7 \cdot 7)(7)$
$$= 7 \cdot 7 \cdot 7 \cdot 7 \text{ or } 7^4 \checkmark$$

☑ Concept Check Can you simplify $2^3 \cdot 3^3$ using the Product of Powers rule? Explain. **No; the bases are different.**

> **ALGEBRA CONNECTION**

Monomials can also be multiplied using the rule for the product of powers.

Example 2 **Multiply Monomials**

Find each product.

a. $x^5 \cdot x^2$

$x^5 \cdot x^2 = x^{5+2}$ The common base is x.
$\qquad = x^7$ Add the exponents.

b. $(-4n^3)(2n^6)$

$(-4n^3)(2n^6) = (-4 \cdot 2)(n^3 \cdot n^6)$ Use the Commutative and Associative Properties.
$\qquad = (-8)(n^{3+6})$ The common base is n.
$\qquad = -8n^9$ Add the exponents.

> **Study Tip**
>
> **Look Back**
> To review the **Commutative and Associative Properties of Multiplication**, see Lesson 1-4.

DIVIDE MONOMIALS

You can also write a rule for finding quotients of powers.

$$\dfrac{2^6}{2^1} = \dfrac{2 \cdot 2 \cdot 2 \cdot 2 \cdot 2 \cdot 2}{2} \qquad \boxed{6 \text{ factors}} \quad \boxed{1 \text{ factor}}$$

$$= \dfrac{2 \cdot 2 \cdot 2 \cdot 2 \cdot 2 \cdot \overset{1}{\cancel{2}}}{\underset{1}{\cancel{2}}} \qquad \text{Divide the numerator and the denominator by the GCF, 2.}$$

$$= 2^5 \qquad \boxed{5 \text{ factors}} \quad \text{Simplify.}$$

Compare the difference between the original exponents and the exponent in the final quotient. This relationship is stated in the following rule.

Key Concept — *Quotient of Powers*

- **Words** You can divide powers with the same base by subtracting their exponents.
- **Symbols** $\dfrac{a^m}{a^n} = a^{m-n}$, where $a \neq 0$
- **Example** $\dfrac{4^5}{4^2} = 4^{5-2}$ or 4^3

DAILY
INTERVENTION **Differentiated Instruction**

- **Auditory/Musical** The phrase *Please Excuse My Dear Aunt Sally* indicates the correct order of operations: Parentheses, Exponents, Multiplication, Division, Addition, Subtraction. Challenge students to create a catchy phrase, rhyme, or rap that articulates the rules for multiplying and dividing monomials with powers. Share ideas with the class.

Example 3 Divide Powers

Find each quotient.

a. $\dfrac{5^7}{5^4}$

$\dfrac{5^7}{5^4} = 5^{7-4}$ The common base is 5.

$= 5^3$ Subtract the exponents.

b. $\dfrac{y^5}{y^3}$

$\dfrac{y^5}{y^3} = y^{5-3}$ The common base is y.

$= y^2$ Subtract the exponents.

✓ **Concept Check**   Can you simplify $\dfrac{x^7}{y^2}$ using the Quotient of Powers rule? Why or why not? **No; the bases are different.**

Example 4 Divide Powers to Solve a Problem

Reading Math

How Many/How Much

How many times faster indicates that division is to be used to solve the problem. If the question had said *how much faster*, then subtraction ($10^9 - 10^8$) would have been used to solve the problem.

COMPUTERS The table compares the processing speeds of a specific type of computer in 1993 and in 1999. Find how many times faster the computer was in 1999 than in 1993.

Write a division expression to compare the speeds.

$\dfrac{10^9}{10^8} = 10^{9-8}$ Subtract the exponents.

$= 10^1$ or 10   Simplify.

So, the computer was 10 times faster in 1999 than in 1993.

Year	Processing Speed (instructions per second)
1993	10^8
1999	10^9

Source: *The Intel Microprocessor Quick Reference Guide*

Check for Understanding

Concept Check

GUIDED PRACTICE KEY	
Exercises	Examples
4–7	1, 2
8–11	3
12	4

1. **State** whether you could use the Product of Powers rule, Quotient of Powers rule, or neither to find $m^5 \cdot n^4$. Explain.
   Neither; the factors have different bases.

2. **Explain** whether $4^8 \cdot 4^6$ and $4^4 \cdot 4^{10}$ are equivalent expressions.
   Yes; they both equal 4^{14}.

3. **OPEN ENDED** Write a multiplication expression whose product is 5^3.
   Sample answer: $5 \cdot 5^2 = 5^3$

Guided Practice

Find each product or quotient. Express using exponents.   7. $-12x^5$

4. $9^3 \cdot 9^2$ 9^5 5. $a \cdot a^5$ a^6 6. $(n^4)(n^4)$ n^8 7. $-3x^2(4x^3)$

8. $\dfrac{3^8}{3^5}$ 3^3 9. $\dfrac{10^5}{10^3}$ 10^2 10. $\dfrac{x^3}{x}$ x^2 11. $\dfrac{a^{10}}{a^6}$ a^4

Application

12. **EARTHQUAKES** In 2000, an earthquake measuring 8 on the Richter scale struck Indonesia. Two months later, an earthquake of magnitude 5 struck northern California. How many times greater were the seismic waves in Indonesia than in California? (*Hint:* Let 10^8 and 10^5 represent the earthquakes, respectively.) **10^3 or 1000 times greater**

 www.pre-alg.com/extra_examples/ny   **Lesson 4-6** Multiplying and Dividing Monomials   **177**

Lesson 4-6 Multiplying and Dividing Monomials   **177**

Study Notebook

Have students—

• copy the rules for multiplying and dividing monomials, including an example of each.

• include any other item(s) that they find helpful in mastering the skills in this lesson.

About the Exercises . . .

Organization by Objective
• **Multiplying Monomials:** 13–24, 37, 39
• **Dividing Monomials:** 25–36, 38, 41–44

Odd/Even Assignments
Exercises 13–40 are structured so that students practice the same concepts whether they are assigned odd or even problems.

Assignment Guide

Basic: 13–21 odd, 25–31 odd, 37, 45, 46, 50–69

Average: 13–39 odd, 45–47, 50–69

Advanced: 14–40 even, 41–44, 47–63 (Optional: 64–69)

Practice and Apply

Homework Help

For Exercises	See Examples
13–24	1, 2
25–36	3
41–44	4

Extra Practice
See page 732.

24. $-20x^4y^3$
31. $(-2)^1$ or -2

TEACHING TIP

In multiplication or division exercises, students may actually multiply or divide exponents rather than add or subtract them. Review the rules with students.

Find each product or quotient. Express using exponents. 23. $8a^3b^{10}$

13. $3^3 \cdot 3^2$ **3^5**   14. $6 \cdot 6^7$ **6^8**   15. $d^4 \cdot d^6$ **d^{10}**   16. $10^4 \cdot 10^3$ **10^7**

17. $n^8 \cdot n$ **n^9**   18. $t^2 \cdot t^4$ **t^6**   19. $9^4 \cdot 9^5$ **9^9**   20. $a^6 \cdot a^6$ **a^{12}**

21. $2y \cdot 9y^4$ **$18y^5$**   22. $(5r^3)(4r^4)$ **$20r^7$** ★23. $ab^5 \cdot 8a^2b^5$ ★24. $10x^3y \cdot (-2xy^2)$

25. $\dfrac{5^5}{5^2}$ **5^3**   26. $\dfrac{8^4}{8^3}$ **8^1 or 8**   27. $b^6 \div b^3$ **b^3**   28. $10^{10} \div 10^2$ **10^8**

29. $\dfrac{m^{20}}{m^8}$ **m^{12}**   30. $\dfrac{a^8}{a^8}$ **a^0 or 1**   31. $\dfrac{(-2)^6}{(-2)^5}$ 32. $\dfrac{(-x)^5}{(-x)}$ **$(-x)^4$**

★33. $\dfrac{n^3(n^5)}{n^2}$ **n^6** ★34. $\dfrac{s^7}{s \cdot s^2}$ **s^4** ★35. $\left(\dfrac{k^3}{k}\right)\left(\dfrac{m^2}{m}\right)$ **k^2m** ★36. $\left(\dfrac{15}{5}\right)\left(\dfrac{n^9}{n}\right)$ **$3n^8$**

37. the product of nine to the fourth power and nine cubed **9^7**

38. the quotient of k to the fifth power and k squared **k^3**

★39. What is the product of 7^3, 7^5, and 7? **7^9**

★40. Find $a^4 \cdot a^6 \div a^2$. **a^8**

More About . . .

Chemistry •············

The pH values of different kitchen items are shown below.

Item	pH
lemon juice	2
vinegar	3
tomatoes	4
baking soda	9

Source: *Biology*, Raven

•····**CHEMISTRY**   **For Exercises 41–43, use the following information.**

★The pH of a solution describes its acidity. Neutral water has a pH of 7. Each one-unit *decrease* in the pH means that the solution is 10 times more acidic. For example, a pH of 4 is 10 times more acidic than a pH of 5.

41. Suppose the pH of a lake is 5 due to acid rain. How much more acidic is the lake than neutral water? **10^2 or 100 times**

42. Use the information at the left to find how much more acidic vinegar is than baking soda. **10^6 or 1,000,000 times**

43. Cola is 10^4 times more acidic than neutral water. What is the pH value of cola? **3**

★44. **LIFE SCIENCE**   When bacteria reproduce, they split so that one cell becomes two. The number of cells after t cycles of reproduction is 2^t.

   a. *E. coli* reproduce very quickly, about every 15 minutes. If there are 100 *E. coli* in a dish now, how many will there be in 30 minutes? **400**

   b. How many times more *E. coli* are there in a population after 3 hours than there were after 1 hour? **256 times more**

GEOMETRY   **For Exercises 45 and 46, use the information in the figures.**

45. How many times greater is the length of the edge of the larger cube than the smaller one? **2 times**

46. How many times greater is the volume of the larger cube than the smaller one? **2^3 or 8 times**

Volume = 2^3 cubic units

Volume = 2^6 cubic units

★**Find each missing exponent.**

47. $(4^{\bullet})(4^3) = 4^{11}$ **8**   48. $\dfrac{t^{\bullet}}{t^2} = t^{14}$ **16**   49. $\dfrac{13^5}{13^{\bullet}} = 1$ **5**

50. CRITICAL THINKING Use the laws of exponents to show why the value of *any* nonzero number raised to the zero power equals 1. **See margin.**

51. **WRITING IN MATH** Answer the question that was posed at the beginning of the lesson. **See margin.**

How are powers of monomials useful in comparing earthquake magnitudes?

Include the following in your answer:
- a description of the Richter scale, and
- a comparison of two earthquakes of different magnitudes by using the Quotient of Powers rule.

NEW YORK Test Practice

Standardized Test Practice
ⒶⒷⒸⒹ

52. Multiply $7xy$ and $x^{14}z$. **A**

Ⓐ $7x^{15}yz$ Ⓑ $7x^{15}y$ Ⓒ $7x^{13}yz$ Ⓓ $x^{15}yz$

53. Find the quotient $a^5 \div a$. **B**

Ⓐ a^5 Ⓑ a^4 Ⓒ a^6 Ⓓ a

Maintain Your Skills

Mixed Review Write each fraction in simplest form. If the fraction is already in simplest form, write *simplified*. *(Lesson 4-5)*

54. $\frac{12}{40}$ $\frac{3}{10}$ **55.** $\frac{20}{53}$ **simplified**   **56.** $\frac{8n^2}{32n}$ $\frac{n}{4}$ **57.** $\frac{6x^3}{4x^2y}$ $\frac{3x}{2y}$

Find the greatest common factor of each set of numbers or monomials. *(Lesson 4-4)*

58. 36, 4 **4**   **59.** 18, 28 **2**   **60.** 42, 54 **6**   **61.** $9a$, $10a^3$ **a**

62. Evaluate $|a| - |b| \cdot |c|$ if $a = -16$, $b = 2$, and $c = 3$. *(Lesson 2-1)* **10**

63. ENERGY The graph shows the high temperature and the maximum amount of electricity that was used during each of fifteen summer days. Do the data show a *positive*, *negative*, or *no* relationship? Explain.
(Lesson 1-7)
Positive; as the high temperature increases, the amount of electricity that is used also increases.

Energy Used

Getting Ready for the Next Lesson **PREREQUISITE SKILL** Evaluate each expression if $x = 10$, $y = -5$, and $z = 4$. Write as a fraction in simplest form.
*(To review **evaluating expressions**, see Lesson 1-3.)*

64. $\frac{1}{x}$ $\frac{1}{10}$ **65.** $\frac{y}{50}$ $-\frac{1}{10}$ **66.** $\frac{z}{100}$ $\frac{1}{25}$

67. $\frac{1}{zy}$ $-\frac{1}{20}$ **68.** $\frac{1}{x \cdot x}$ $\frac{1}{100}$ **69.** $\frac{1}{(z)(z)(z)}$ $\frac{1}{64}$

Open-Ended Assessment

Writing Have students write an explanation of how to simplify (a.) $x^3y \cdot x^2$ and (b.) $x^3y \div x^2$.

Tips for New Teachers

Intervention If there is any doubt whether your students thoroughly understand multiplying and dividing monomials with powers, consider spending an extra day on this lesson. Use the Extra Practice on p. 732. You can also use the Study Guide and Intervention masters or the Practice masters in the *Chapter 4 Resource Masters* to reinforce this concept.

Getting Ready for Lesson 4-7

PREREQUISITE SKILL Lesson 4-7 presents negative exponents. A negative exponent is another way to write a fraction. Exercises 64–69 should be used to determine your students' familiarity with evaluating expressions written with fractions.

Assessment Options

Quiz (Lessons 4-5 and 4-6) is available on p. 220 of the *Chapter 4 Resource Masters*.

Answers

50. Sample answer: By the law of exponents,
$\frac{a^n}{a^n} = a^{n-n}$ or a^0 for $a \neq 0$.
Since $\frac{a^n}{a^n} = 1$, then $a^0 = 1$. So, any number raised to the zero power must equal 1. Or, $a^0 \cdot a^m = a^{0+m}$ or a^m. Therefore, by the Identity Property of Multiplication, a^0 must equal 1.

51. Each level on the Richter scale is 10 times greater than the previous level. So, powers of 10 can be used to compare earthquake magnitudes. Answers should include the following.

- On the Richter scale, each whole-number increase represents a 10-fold increase in the magnitude of seismic waves.

- An earthquake of magnitude 7 is 10^5 times greater than an earthquake of magnitude 2 because $10^7 \div 10^2 = 10^{7-2}$ or 10^5.

Getting Started

Objective Model and investigate radioactive half-lives.

Materials
50 pennies   grid paper
shoebox with lid   pencil

Teach

• Ask students to predict how many pennies will remain after each half-life. Discuss discrepancies between their predictions and the actual number of pennies.
• Combine everyone's data to make a classroom data set. How does the classroom data fit the anticipated result?

Assess

In **Exercises 1–2,** students should create a scatter plot and describe the relationship between the number of half-lives and number of pennies.

In **Exercises 3–4,** students should relate the expressions to the experiment.

Answer

1. Sample answer:

Number of Half-Lives	Number of Pennies That Remain
1	27
2	14
3	6
4	3
5	1

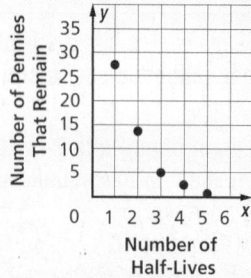

Algebra Activity

A Follow-Up of Lesson 4-6

NEW YORK *Performance Indicator* **8.PS.4 Observe patterns and formulate generalizations, 8.PS.5 Make conjectures from generalizations**

A Half-Life Simulation

A radioactive material such as uranium decomposes or decays in a regular manner best described as a *half-life*. A half-life is the time it takes for half of the atoms in the sample to decay.

Collect the Data

Step 1 Place 50 pennies heads up in a shoebox. Put the lid on the box and shake it up and down one time. This simulates one half-life.

Step 2 Open the lid of the box and remove all the pennies that are now tails up. In a table like the one at the right, record the number of pennies that remain.

Step 3 Put the lid back on the box and again shake the box up and down one time. This represents another half-life.

Step 4 Open the lid. Remove all the tails up pennies. Count the pennies that remain.

Step 5 Repeat the half-life of decay simulation until less than five pennies remain in the shoebox.

Number of Half-Lives	Number of Pennies That Remain
1	
2	
3	
4	
5	

Analyze the Data

1. On grid paper, draw a coordinate grid in which the *x*-axis represents the number of half-lives and the *y*-axis represents the number of pennies that remain. Plot the points (number of half-lives, number of remaining pennies) from your table. **See margin.**

2. Describe the graph of the data. **Points descend from left to right in a curve.**

After each half-life, you expect to remove about one-half of the pennies. So, you expect about one-half to remain. The expressions at the right represent the average number of pennies that remain if you start with 50, after one, two, and three half-lives.

$$\text{one half-life:} \qquad 50\left(\tfrac{1}{2}\right) = 50\left(\tfrac{1}{2}\right)^1$$

$$\text{two half-lives:} \qquad 50\left(\tfrac{1}{2}\right)\left(\tfrac{1}{2}\right) = 50\left(\tfrac{1}{2}\right)^2$$

$$\text{three half-lives:} \qquad 50\left(\tfrac{1}{2}\right)\left(\tfrac{1}{2}\right)\left(\tfrac{1}{2}\right) = 50\left(\tfrac{1}{2}\right)^3$$

Make a Conjecture **3. 6.25 or about 6 pennies; see students' work.**

3. Use the expressions to predict how many pennies remain after three half-lives. Compare this number to the number in the table above. Explain any differences.

4. Suppose you started with 1000 pennies. Predict how many pennies would remain after three half-lives. **125 pennies**

Resource Manager

 Teaching Pre-Algebra with Manipulatives

• p. 1 (master for grid paper)
• p. 63 (student recording sheet)

Negative Exponents

 NEW YORK *Performance Indicator* **8.N.2** Evaluate expressions with integral exponents

What You'll Learn

- Write expressions using negative exponents.
- Evaluate numerical expressions containing negative exponents.

How do negative exponents represent repeated division?

Copy the table at the right.

a. The exponents decrease by 1.

b. Each number is divided by 2.

c. See students' work.

a. Describe the pattern of the powers in the first column. Continue the pattern by writing the next two powers in the table.

b. Describe the pattern of values in the second column. Then complete the second column.

c. Verify that the powers you wrote in part **a** are equal to the values that you found in part **b**.

d. Determine how 3^{-1} should be defined. $\frac{1}{3}$

Power	Value
2^6	64
2^5	32
2^4	16
2^3	8
2^2	4
2^1	2
? 2^0	? 1
? 2^{-1}	? $\frac{1}{2}$

ALGEBRA CONNECTION

NEGATIVE EXPONENTS Extending the pattern at the right shows that 2^{-1} can be defined as $\frac{1}{2}$.

You can apply the Quotient of Powers rule and the definition of a power to $\frac{x^3}{x^5}$ and write a general rule about negative powers.

$$2^2 = 4$$
$$\Big\downarrow \div 2$$
$$2^1 = 2$$
$$\Big\downarrow \div 2$$
$$2^0 = 1$$
$$\Big\downarrow \div 2$$
$$2^{-1} = \frac{1}{2}$$

Method 1 Quotient of Powers

$$\frac{x^3}{x^5} = x^{3-5}$$
$$= x^{-2}$$

Method 2 Definition of Power

$$\frac{x^3}{x^5} = \frac{\overset{1}{\cancel{x}} \cdot \overset{1}{\cancel{x}} \cdot \overset{1}{\cancel{x}}}{\underset{1}{\cancel{x}} \cdot \underset{1}{\cancel{x}} \cdot \underset{1}{\cancel{x}} \cdot x \cdot x}$$
$$= \frac{1}{x \cdot x}$$
$$= \frac{1}{x^2}$$

Since $\frac{x^3}{x^5}$ cannot have two different values, you can conclude that $x^{-2} = \frac{1}{x^2}$. This suggests the following definition.

Key Concept — Negative Exponents

- **Symbols** $a^{-n} = \frac{1}{a^n}$, for $a \neq 0$ and any integer n

- **Example** $5^{-4} = \frac{1}{5^4}$

---

1 Focus

5-Minute Check Transparency 4-7 Use as a quiz or review of Lesson 4-6.

Mathematical Background notes are available for this lesson on page 146D.

How do negative exponents represent repeated division?

The opening activity questions are repeated on page 198 of the *Chapter 4 Resource Masters*.

Reading to Learn Mathematics, p. 198 **ELL**

Pre-Activity *How do negative exponents represent repeated division?*
Do the activity at the top of page 181 in your textbook. Write your answers below.

a. Describe the pattern of powers in the first column. Continue the pattern by writing the next two powers in the table. **The exponents decrease by 1; 2^0, 2^{-1}.**

b. Describe the pattern of values in the second column. Then complete the second column. **Each number is divided by 2; 1, $\frac{1}{2}$.**

c. Verify that the powers you wrote in part **a** are equal to the values that you found in part **b**. **See students' work.**

d. Determine how 3^{-1} should be defined. $\frac{1}{3}$

Reading the Lesson

1. Explain the value of 5^{-3} using a pattern. **Sample answer: The value in each row is the previous value divided by 5, so 5^{-3} is $\frac{1}{125}$.**

Power	Value
5^1	5
5^0	1
5^{-1}	$\frac{1}{5}$
5^{-2}	$\frac{1}{25}$
5^{-3}	$\frac{1}{125}$

2. Using what you know about the Quotient of Powers rule, fill in the missing number. $5^{-3} = \frac{?}{5^5}$ $5^{-3} = \frac{5^2}{5^5}$

Helping You Remember

3. Are $-x^2$ and x^{-2} equivalent? Explain. **Sample answer: No; let $x = 3$. $-3^2 = -9$, but $3^{-2} = \frac{1}{3^2} = \frac{1}{9}$.**

Resource Manager

Workbooks and Reproducible Masters

Chapter 4 Resource Masters
- Study Guide and Intervention, p. 195
- Skills Practice, p. 196
- Practice, p. 197
- Reading to Learn Mathematics, p. 198
- Enrichment, p. 199

Parent and Student Study Guide Workbook, p. 30

Transparencies
5-Minute Check Transparency 4-7
Answer Key Transparencies

Technology
Interactive Chalkboard

NEGATIVE EXPONENTS

1 Write each expression using a positive exponent.

a. 3^{-4} $\dfrac{1}{3^4}$

b. m^{-2} $\dfrac{1}{m^2}$

2 Write $\dfrac{1}{125}$ as an expression using a negative exponent.
5^{-3}

3 An atom is an incredibly small unit of matter. The smallest atom has a diameter of approximately $\dfrac{1}{10}$th of a nanometer, or 0.0000000001 meter. Write the decimal as a fraction and as a power of 10.

$$\frac{1}{10,000,000,000} = \frac{1}{10^{10}} = 10^{-10}$$

Teaching Tip Remind students that saying a decimal properly will automatically give the fraction. So, 0.001 is 1 one thousandth or $\dfrac{1}{1000}$.

EVALUATE EXPRESSIONS

4 Evaluate r^{-2} if $r = -4$. $\dfrac{1}{16}$

Example 1 **Use Positive Exponents**

Write each expression using a positive exponent.

a. 6^{-2}

$6^{-2} = \dfrac{1}{6^2}$ Definition of negative exponent

b. x^{-5}

$x^{-5} = \dfrac{1}{x^5}$ Definition of negative exponent

One way to write a fraction as an equivalent expression with negative exponents is to use prime factorization.

Example 2 **Use Negative Exponents**

Write $\dfrac{1}{9}$ as an expression using a negative exponent.

$\dfrac{1}{9} = \dfrac{1}{3 \cdot 3}$ Find the prime factorization of 9.

$= \dfrac{1}{3^2}$ Definition of exponent

$= 3^{-2}$ Definition of negative exponent

✓ **Concept Check** How can $\dfrac{1}{9}$ be written as an expression with a negative exponent other than 3^{-2}? 9^{-1}

Negative exponents are often used in science when dealing with very small numbers. Usually the number is a power of ten.

Example 3 **Use Exponents to Solve a Problem**

WATER A molecule of water contains two hydrogen atoms and one oxygen atom. A hydrogen atom is only 0.00000001 centimeter in diameter. Write the decimal as a fraction and as a power of ten.

The digit 1 is in the 100-millionths place.

$0.00000001 = \dfrac{1}{100,000,000}$ Write the decimal as a fraction.

$= \dfrac{1}{10^8}$ $100,000,000 = 10^8$

$= 10^{-8}$ Definition of negative exponent

EVALUATE EXPRESSIONS Algebraic expressions containing negative exponents can be written using positive exponents and evaluated.

Example 4 **Algebraic Expressions with Negative Exponents**

Evaluate n^{-3} if $n = 2$.

$n^{-3} = 2^{-3}$ Replace n with 2.

$= \dfrac{1}{2^3}$ Definition of negative exponent

$= \dfrac{1}{8}$ Find 2^3.

TEACHING TIP
Remind students that the negative exponent in n^{-3} does not change the sign of the expression.

More About . . .

Water
A single drop of water contains about 10^{20} molecules.

Source: www.composite.about.com

DAILY INTERVENTION   Differentiated Instruction

• **Intrapersonal** To insure that students understand the difference between negative numbers and numbers with negative exponents, have them write a paragraph about each of these in their Math Study Notebooks. Check their explanations to make sure each student has described the difference successfully.

Concept Check

1–2. See margin.

1. **OPEN ENDED** Write a convincing argument that $3^0 = 1$ using the fact that $3^4 = 81$, $3^3 = 27$, $3^2 = 9$, and $3^1 = 3$.

2. Order 8^{-8}, 8^3 and 8^0 from greatest to least. Explain your reasoning.

Guided Practice

GUIDED PRACTICE KEY	
Exercises	Examples
3–6	1
7–10	2
11, 12	4
13	3

Write each expression using a positive exponent.

3. 5^{-2} $\quad \frac{1}{5^2}$

4. $(-7)^{-1}$ $\quad \frac{1}{(-7)^1}$ or $\frac{1}{-7}$

5. t^{-6} $\quad \frac{1}{t^6}$

6. n^{-2} $\quad \frac{1}{n^2}$

Write each fraction as an expression using a negative exponent other than -1.

7. $\frac{1}{3^4}$ $\quad 3^{-4}$

8. $\frac{1}{9^2}$ $\quad 9^{-2}$

9. $\frac{1}{49}$ $\quad 7^{-2}$

10. $\frac{1}{8}$ $\quad 2^{-3}$

ALGEBRA Evaluate each expression if $a = 2$ and $b = -3$.

11. a^{-5} $\quad \frac{1}{32}$

12. $(ab)^{-2}$ $\quad \frac{1}{36}$

Application

13. **MEASUREMENT** A unit of measure called a *micron* equals 0.001 millimeter. Write this number using a negative exponent. $\mathbf{10^{-3}}$

★ indicates increased difficulty

Practice and Apply

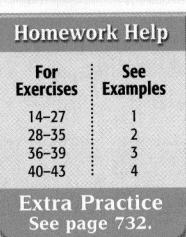

Homework Help

For Exercises	See Examples
14–27	1
28–35	2
36–39	3
40–43	4

Extra Practice
See page 732.

20. $\frac{1}{p^1}$ or $\frac{1}{p}$

Write each expression using a positive exponent.

14. 4^{-1} $\quad \frac{1}{4^1}$ or $\frac{1}{4}$

15. 5^{-3} $\quad \frac{1}{5^3}$

16. $(-6)^{-2}$ $\quad \frac{1}{(-6)^2}$

17. $(-3)^{-3}$ $\quad \frac{1}{(-3)^3}$

18. 3^{-5} $\quad \frac{1}{3^5}$

19. 10^{-4} $\quad \frac{1}{10^4}$

20. p^{-1}

21. a^{-10} $\quad \frac{1}{a^{10}}$

22. d^{-3} $\quad \frac{1}{d^3}$

23. q^{-4} $\quad \frac{1}{q^4}$

★ 24. $2s^{-5}$ $\quad 2\left(\frac{1}{s^5}\right)$

★ 25. $\frac{1}{x^{-2}}$ $\quad x^2$

For Exercises 26 and 27, write each expression using a positive exponent. Then write as a decimal.

26. A snowflake weighs 10^{-6} gram. $\quad \frac{1}{10^6}$; **0.000001**

27. A small bird uses 5^{-4} Joules of energy to sing a song. $\quad \frac{1}{5^4}$; **0.0016**

Write each fraction as an expression using a negative exponent other than -1.

28. $\frac{1}{9^4}$ $\quad 9^{-4}$

29. $\frac{1}{5^5}$ $\quad 5^{-5}$

30. $\frac{1}{8^3}$ $\quad 8^{-3}$

31. $\frac{1}{13^2}$ $\quad 13^{-2}$

32. $\frac{1}{100}$ $\quad 10^{-2}$

33. $\frac{1}{81}$ $\quad 9^{-2}$

★ 34. $\frac{1}{27}$ $\quad 3^{-3}$

★ 35. $\frac{1}{16}$ $\quad 2^{-4}$ or 4^{-2}

Write each decimal using a negative exponent.

36. 0.1 $\quad 10^{-1}$

37. 0.01 $\quad 10^{-2}$ or 100^{-1}

38. 0.0001 $\quad 10^{-4}$ or 100^{-2}

39. 0.00001 $\quad 10^{-5}$

ALGEBRA Evaluate each expression if $w = -2$, $x = 3$, and $y = -1$.

40. x^{-4} $\quad \frac{1}{81}$

41. w^{-7} $\quad -\frac{1}{128}$

42. 8^w $\quad \frac{1}{64}$

★ 43. $(xy)^{-6}$ $\quad \frac{1}{729}$

Lesson 4-7 Negative Exponents **183**

Study Notebook

Have students—

• copy the rule for negative exponents. (See key concept in the box on p. 181.)

• include any other item(s) that they find helpful in mastering the skills in this lesson.

About the Exercises . . .

Organization by Objective
• **Negative Exponents:** 14–39
• **Evaluate Expressions:** 40–43

Odd/Even Assignments
Exercises 14–43 and 45–52 are structured so that students practice the same concepts whether they are assigned odd or even problems.

Assignment Guide

Basic: 15–23 odd, 27–33 odd, 37–41 odd, 45, 53–56, 61–74

Average: 15–53 odd, 54–56, 61–74 (Optional: 57–60)

Advanced: 14–52 even, 53–68 (Optional: 69–74)

All: Practice Quiz 2 (1–10)

Answers

1. To get each successive power, divide the previous power by 3. Therefore, $3^0 = 3 \div 3$ or 1.

2. 8^3, 8^0, 8^{-8}; Sample answer: 8^3 is the greatest because its exponent is positive. 8^0 is next because it equals 1. The expression 8^{-8} is a fraction less than 1.

Lesson 4-7 Negative Exponents **183**

44. **PHYSICAL SCIENCE** A nanometer is equal to a billionth of a meter. The visible range of light waves ranges from 400 nanometers (violet) to 740 nanometers (red).

400 nm	430 nm	500 nm	560 nm	600 nm	650 nm	740 nm

    a. Write one billionth of a meter as a fraction and with a negative exponent.

    b. Use the information at the left to express the greatest wavelength of an X ray in meters. Write the expression using a negative exponent. 10^{-8} m

    a. $\frac{1}{1,000,000,000}$ m; 10^{-9} m

45. **ANIMALS** A common flea 2^{-4} inch long can jump about 2^3 inches high. How many times its body size can a flea jump? **128 times**

★ 46. **MEDICINE** Which type of molecule in the table has a greater mass? How many times greater is it than the other type? **penicillin; 10^5 times greater**

Molecule	Mass (kg)
penicillin	10^{-18}
insulin	10^{-23}

Use the Product of Power and Quotient of Power rules to simplify each expression.

★ 47. $x^{-2} \cdot x^{-3}$ x^{-5} ★ 48. $r^{-5} \cdot r^9$ r^4 ★ 49. $\frac{x^4}{x^7}$ x^{-3}

★ 50. $\frac{y^6}{y^{-10}}$ y^{16} ★ 51. $\frac{a^4 b^{-4}}{ab^{-2}}$ $a^3 b^{-2}$ or $\frac{a^3}{b^2}$ ★ 52. $\frac{36 s^3 t^5}{12 s^6 t^{-3}}$ $3 s^{-3} t^8$ or $\frac{3 t^8}{s^3}$

53. **CRITICAL THINKING** Using what you learned about exponents, is $(x^3)^{-2} = (x^{-2})^3$? Why or why not? **Yes; see margin for explanation.**

54. **WRITING IN MATH** Answer the question that was posed at the beginning of the lesson. **See margin.**

How do negative exponents represent repeated division?

Include the following in your answer:
- an example of a power containing a negative exponent written in fraction form, and
- a discussion about whether the value of a fraction such as $\frac{1}{2^n}$ increases or decreases as the value of n increases.

55. Which is 15^{-5} written as a fraction? **C**

    Ⓐ $\frac{1}{5^5}$ Ⓑ $\frac{1}{15}$

    Ⓒ $\frac{1}{15^5}$ Ⓓ $-\frac{1}{15^5}$

56. One square millimeter equals $\underline{\ ?\ }$ square centimeter(s). (*Hint*: 1 cm = 10 mm) **B**

    Ⓐ 10^{-1} Ⓑ 10^{-2}

    Ⓒ 10^{-3} Ⓓ 10^3

□ 1 mm   1 cm
1 mm
1 cm

More About. . .

Physical Science ····
The wavelengths of X rays are between 1 and 10 nanometers.
Source: *Biology*, Raven

Answer

53. $(x^3)^{-2} = \frac{1}{(x^3)^2}$ $(x^{-2})^3 = (x^{-2})(x^{-2})(x^{-2})$

$\qquad\qquad = \frac{1}{x^3 \cdot x^3}$ or $\frac{1}{x^6}$ $= x^{-6}$ or $\frac{1}{x^6}$

Extending the Lesson

58. $(2 \times 10^{-1}) +$
(4×10^{-2})
59. $(1 \times 10^{-1}) +$
$(7 \times 10^{-2}) +$
(3×10^{-3})

Numbers less than 1 can also be expressed in expanded form.

Example: $0.568 = 0.5 + 0.06 + 0.008$
$\qquad = (5 \times 10^{-1}) + (6 \times 10^{-2}) + (8 \times 10^{-3})$

Express each number in expanded form.

57. 0.9 9×10^{-1} **58.** 0.24 **59.** 0.173 **60.** 0.5875
60. $(5 \times 10^{-1}) + (8 \times 10^{-2}) + (7 \times 10^{-3}) + (5 \times 10^{-4})$

Maintain Your Skills

Mixed Review Find each product or quotient. Express your answer using exponents.
(Lesson 4-6)

61. $3^6 \cdot 3$ $\mathbf{3^7}$ **62.** $x^2 \cdot x^4$ $\mathbf{x^6}$ **63.** $\dfrac{5^5}{5^2}$ $\mathbf{5^3}$

64. ALGEBRA Write $\dfrac{16n^3}{8n}$ in simplest form. *(Lesson 4-5)* $\mathbf{2n^2}$

ALGEBRA Use the Distributive Property to rewrite each expression. *(Lesson 3-1)*

65. $8(y + 6)$ $\mathbf{8y + 48}$ **66.** $(9 + k)(-2)$ $\mathbf{-18 - 2k}$ **67.** $(n - 3)5$ $\mathbf{5n - 15}$

68. Write the ordered pair that names point P. *(Lesson 2-6)* $\mathbf{(1, -4)}$

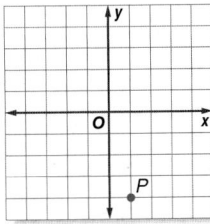

Getting Ready for the Next Lesson

PREREQUISITE SKILL Find each product.
*(To review **multiplying decimals**, see page 715.)*

69. 7.2×100 **720** **70.** 1.6×1000 **1600** **71.** 4.05×10 **40.5**

72. 3.8×0.01 **0.038** **73.** 5.0×0.0001 **0.0005** **74.** 9.24×0.1 **0.924**

Practice Quiz 2 — Lessons 4-4 through 4-7

Find the GCF of each set of numbers or monomials. *(Lesson 4-4)*

1. 15, 20 **5** **2.** 24, 30 **6** **3.** $2ab, 6a^2$ **2a**

Write each fraction in simplest form. *(Lesson 4-5)*

4. SCHOOL What fraction of days were you absent from school this nine-week period if you were absent twice out of 44 days? $\dfrac{1}{22}$

5. COMMUNICATION What fraction of E-mail messages did you respond to, if you responded to 6 out of a total of 15 messages? $\dfrac{2}{5}$

ALGEBRA Find each product or quotient. Express using exponents. *(Lesson 4-6)*

6. $4^2 \cdot 4^4$ $\mathbf{4^6}$ **7.** $(n^4)(-2n^3)$ $\mathbf{-2n^7}$ **8.** $\dfrac{q^9}{q^4}$ $\mathbf{q^5}$

9. ALGEBRA Write b^{-6} as an expression using a positive exponent. *(Lesson 4-7)* $\dfrac{1}{b^6}$

10. ALGEBRA Evaluate x^{-5} if $x = -2$. *(Lesson 4-7)* $-\dfrac{1}{32}$

Open-Ended Assessment

Speaking Have students explain how to simplify an expression with negative exponents using the rules for multiplying monomials. For example, $2x^{-2} \cdot 3x$ could be simplified. Then ask students to evaluate the expression if $x = 3$.

Getting Ready for Lesson 4-8

PREREQUISITE SKILL Lesson 4-8 presents scientific notation, which expresses numbers as the product of a number and a power of 10. Exercises 69–74 should be used to determine your students' familiarity with multiplying by powers of 10.

Assessment Options

Practice Quiz 2 The quiz provides students with a brief review of the concepts and skills in Lessons 4-4 through 4-7. Lesson numbers are given to the right of exercises or instruction lines so students can review concepts not yet mastered.

Answer (p.184)

54. Exponents are used to represent repeated factors in a multiplication. If the exponent is a negative number, then the repeated factors act as repeated divisors in the denominator. Answers should include the following.

- $4^{-2} = \dfrac{1}{4^2} = \dfrac{1}{4 \cdot 4}$ or $\dfrac{1}{16}$

- In 2^{-3}, the negative sign indicates that the factor 2 is repeated three times in the denominator, or 1 is divided by 2 three times. So, $2^{-3} = \dfrac{1}{2 \cdot 2 \cdot 2}$. If the exponent were -4, then 1 would be divided by 2 four times, and so on. So, as the value of n increases, the value of $\dfrac{1}{2^n}$ decreases.

4-8 Scientific Notation

NEW YORK *Performance Indicator* Reinforcement of **7.N.5** Write numbers in scientific notation, Reinforcement of **7.N.6** Translate numbers from scientific notation into standard form, Reinforcement of **7.N.7** Compare numbers written in scientific notation

What You'll Learn

- Express numbers in standard form and in scientific notation.
- Compare and order numbers written in scientific notation.

Why is scientific notation an important tool in comparing real-world data?

A compact disc or CD has a single spiral track that stores data. It circles from the inside of the disc to the outside. If the track were stretched out in a straight line, it would be 0.5 micron wide and over 5000 meters long.

Track Length	Track Width
5000 meters	0.5 micron

a. Write the track length in millimeters. **5,000,000 mm**

b. Write the track width in millimeters. (1 micron = 0.001 millimeter.)

---

1 Focus

5-Minute Check
Transparency 4-8 Use as a quiz or review of Lesson 4-7.

Mathematical Background
notes are available for this lesson on page 146D.

Why is scientific notation an important tool in comparing real-world data?

The opening activity questions are repeated on page 203 of the *Chapter 4 Resource Masters*.

Reading to Learn Mathematics, p. 203 ELL

Pre-Activity *Why is scientific notation an important tool in comparing real-world data?*

Do the activity at the top of page 186 in your textbook. Write your answers below.

a. Write the track length in millimeters. **5,000,000 mm**

b. Write the track width in millimeters. (1 micron = 0.001 millimeter) **0.0005 mm**

Reading the Lesson

Write a definition and give an example of the new vocabulary phrase.

Vocabulary	Definition	Example
1. slope intercept form	See students' work.	

2. To multiply by a power of 10, move the decimal point to the __right__ if the exponent is positive.

3. Which is larger, -2.1×10^4 or -2.1×10^{-4}? Explain. **-2.1×10^{-4} is larger, since the numbers are negative and it is closer to zero.**

Helping You Remember

4. Explain how to express each number in scientific notation.

a. a number greater than 1 **Place the decimal point after the first nonzero digit, then multiply by the appropriate positive power of 10.**

b. a number less than one **Place the decimal point after the first nonzero digit, then multiply by the appropriate negative power of 10.**

c. the number 1 **Place the decimal point after the 1, then multiply by 10^0 (1.0 x 10^0).**

Vocabulary
- scientific notation

b. 0.0005 mm

TEACHING TIP

Emphasize the difference between scientific notation and standard form. Students should feel comfortable with the terminology.

Study Tip

Powers of Ten

To multiply by a power of 10,
- move the decimal point to the right if the exponent is positive, and
- move the decimal point to the left if the exponent is negative.

In each case, the exponent tells you how many places to move the decimal point.

SCIENTIFIC NOTATION When you deal with very large numbers like 5,000,000 or very small numbers like 0.0005, it is difficult to keep track of the place value. Numbers such as these can be written in **scientific notation**.

Key Concept — Scientific Notation

- **Words** A number is expressed in scientific notation when it is written as the product of a factor and a power of 10. The factor must be greater than or equal to 1 and less than 10.
- **Symbols** $a \times 10^n$, where $1 \le a < 10$ and n is an integer
- **Examples** $5{,}000{,}000 = 5.0 \times 10^6$ $0.0005 = 5.0 \times 10^{-4}$

✓ **Concept Check** Is 13.0×10^2 written in scientific notation? Why or why not? **No; 13.0 is not a factor between 1 and 10. It should be 1.3×10^3.**

You can express numbers that are in scientific notation in standard form.

Example 1 Express Numbers in Standard Form

Express each number in standard form.

a. 3.78×10^6

$3.78 \times 10^6 = 3.78 \times 1{,}000{,}000$ $10^6 = 1{,}000{,}000$

$= 3{,}780{,}000$ Move the decimal point 6 places to the right.

b. 5.1×10^{-5}

$5.1 \times 10^{-5} = 5.1 \times 0.00001$ $10^{-5} = 0.00001$

$= 0.000051$ Move the decimal point 5 places to the left.

Resource Manager

 Workbooks and Reproducible Masters

Chapter 4 Resource Masters
- Study Guide and Intervention, p. 200
- Skills Practice, p. 201
- Practice, p. 202
- Reading to Learn Mathematics, p. 203
- Enrichment, p. 204
- Assessment, p. 220

Parent and Student Study Guide Workbook, p. 31
Prerequisite Skills Workbook, pp. 33–36

 Transparencies
5-Minute Check Transparency 4-8
Real-World Transparency 4
Answer Key Transparencies

Technology
Interactive Chalkboard
Pre-AlgePASS: Tutorial Plus, Lesson 8

To write a number in scientific notation, place the decimal point after the first nonzero digit. Then find the power of 10.

Example 2   Express Numbers in Scientific Notation

Express each number in scientific notation.

a. 60,000,000

$$60{,}000{,}000 = 6.0 \times 10{,}000{,}000 \quad \text{The decimal point moves 7 places.}$$
$$= 6.0 \times 10^7 \quad \text{The exponent is positive.}$$

b. 32,800

$$32{,}800 = 3.28 \times 10{,}000 \quad \text{The decimal point moves 4 places.}$$
$$= 3.28 \times 10^4 \quad \text{The exponent is positive.}$$

c. 0.0049

$$0.0049 = 4.9 \times 0.001 \quad \text{The decimal point moves 3 places.}$$
$$= 4.9 \times 10^{-3} \quad \text{The exponent is negative.}$$

People who make comparisons or compute with extremely large or extremely small numbers use scientific notation.

Example 3   Use Scientific Notation to Solve a Problem

SPACE The table shows the planets and their distances from the Sun. Light travels 300,000 kilometers per second. Estimate how long it takes light to travel from the Sun to Pluto. (*Hint:* Recall that distance = rate × time.)

Planet	Distance from the Sun (km)
Mercury	5.80×10^7
Venus	1.03×10^8
Earth	1.55×10^8
Mars	2.28×10^8
Jupiter	7.78×10^8
Saturn	1.43×10^9
Uranus	2.87×10^9
Neptune	4.50×10^9
Pluto	5.90×10^9

Explore You know that the distance from the Sun to Pluto is 5.90×10^9 kilometers and that the speed of light is 300,000 kilometers per second.

Plan To find the time, solve the equation $d = rt$. Since you are estimating, round the distance 5.90×10^9 to 6.0×10^9. Write the rate 300,000 as 3.0×10^5.

Solve

$$d = rt \quad \text{Write the formula.}$$

$$6.0 \times 10^9 = (3.0 \times 10^5)t \quad \text{Replace } d \text{ with } 6.0 \times 10^9 \text{ and } r \text{ with } 3.0 \times 10^5.$$

$$\frac{6.0 \times 10^9}{3.0 \times 10^5} \approx \frac{(3.0 \times 10^5)t}{3.0 \times 10^5} \quad \text{Divide each side by } 3.0 \times 10^5.$$

$$2.0 \times 10^4 \approx t \quad \text{Divide 6.0 by 3.0 and } 10^9 \text{ by } 10^5.$$

So, it would take about 2.0×10^4 seconds or about 6 hours for light to travel from the Sun to Pluto.

Examine Use estimation to check the reasonableness of these results.

SCIENTIFIC NOTATION

In-Class Examples Power Point®

1 Express each number in standard form.

a. 4.395×10^4 **43,950**

b. 6.79×10^{-6} **0.00000679**

2 Express each number in scientific notation.

a. 800,000 **8.0×10^5**

b. 1,320,000 **1.32×10^6**

c. 0.0119 **1.19×10^{-2}**

3 **SPACE** Use the table in Example 3 in the textbook. Estimate how many times farther Pluto is from the Sun than Mercury is from the Sun. **Pluto is about 100 times farther from the Sun than Mercury.**

Teaching Tip Emphasize to students that using scientific notation instead of standard form requires them to use the rules for multiplying and dividing monomials. Since the numbers are typically very large or small, estimation is often encouraged.

COMPARE AND ORDER NUMBERS

In-Class Example Power Point®

4 **SPACE** The diameters of Mercury, Saturn, and Pluto are 4.9×10^3 km, 1.2×10^5 km, and 2.3×10^3 km, respectively. List the planets in order of increasing diameter. **Pluto, Mercury, Saturn**

DAILY INTERVENTION

Differentiated Instruction

- **Naturalist** Have students research the sizes of very small or very large quantities in nature. Have them illustrate these and write the quantities in scientific notation.

Study Notebook

Have students—
• complete the definitions/examples
  for the remaining terms on the
  Vocabulary Builder worksheets for
  Chapter 4.
• copy the rules for writing numbers
  in scientific notation from p. 186.
• include any other item(s) that
  they find helpful in mastering the
  skills in this lesson.

About the Exercises . . .

Organization by Objective
• **Scientific Notation:** 12–34
• **Compare and Order Numbers:** 35–41

Odd/Even Assignments
Exercises 12–33, 35–40, 42–45, and 47–48 are structured so that students practice the same concepts whether they are assigned odd or even problems.

Alert! Exercises 44–46 require a scientific calculator.

Assignment Guide
Basic: 13–41 odd, 49–59
Average: 13–45 odd, 49–59
Advanced: 12–46 even, 47–59

Answers

1. Sample answer: Numbers that are greater than 1 can be expressed as the product of a factor and a positive power of 10. So, these numbers are written in scientific notation using positive exponents. Numbers between 0 and 1 cannot be expressed as the product of a factor and a whole number power of 10, so they are written in scientific notation using negative exponents.

COMPARE AND ORDER NUMBERS To compare and order numbers in scientific notation, first compare the exponents. With positive numbers, any number with a greater exponent is greater. If the exponents are the same, compare the factors.

Example 4 *Compare Numbers in Scientific Notation*

SPACE **Refer to the table in Example 3. Order Mars, Jupiter, Mercury, and Saturn from least to greatest distance from the Sun.**

First, order the numbers according to their exponents. Then, order the numbers with the same exponent by comparing the factors.

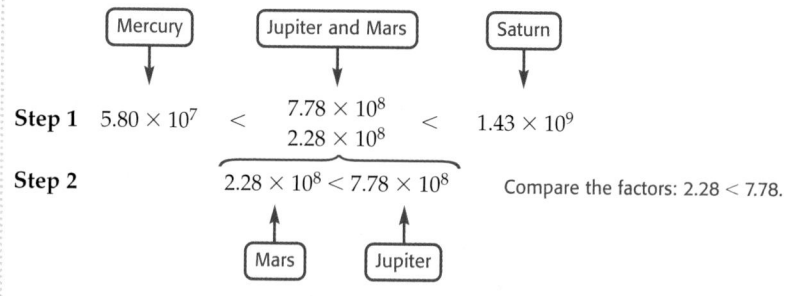

So, the order is Mercury, Mars, Jupiter, and Saturn.

Check for Understanding

Concept Check
1–2. See margin.

1. **Explain** the relationship between a number in standard form and the sign of the exponent when the number is written in scientific notation.

2. **OPEN ENDED** Write a number in standard form and then write the number in scientific notation, explaining each step that you used.

Guided Practice

GUIDED PRACTICE KEY	
Exercises	Examples
3–5	1
6–9	2
10	3
11	4

Express each number in standard form.
3. 3.08×10^{-4} **0.000308**   4. 1.4×10^2 **140**   5. 8.495×10^5 **849,500**

Express each number in scientific notation.
6. 80,000,000 $\mathbf{8.0 \times 10^7}$ 7. 697,000 $\mathbf{6.97 \times 10^5}$ 8. 0.059 $\mathbf{5.9 \times 10^{-2}}$
9. the diameter of a spider's thread, 0.001 inch $\mathbf{1.0 \times 10^{-3}}$

Applications

10. **SPACE** Refer to the table in Example 3 on page 187. To the nearest second, how long does it take light to travel from the Sun to Earth? **517 s**

11. **SPACE** Rank the planets in the table at the right by diameter, from least to greatest.
Mars, Venus, Earth

Planet	Diameter (km)
Earth	1.276×10^4
Mars	6.790×10^3
Venus	1.208×10^4

2. Sample answer: 312 is in standard form. First, move the decimal point in 312 two places to the left, 3.12×100. Next, write 100 using a positive exponent, 3.12×10^2.

Practice and Apply

Homework Help

For Exercises	See Examples
12–20	1
21–33	2
34	3
39–41	4

Extra Practice
See page 733.

Express each number in standard form. 15. 0.005689

12. 4.24×10^2 **424**   **13.** 5.72×10^4 **57,200**   **14.** 3.347×10^{-1} **0.3347**

15. 5.689×10^{-3} **16.** 6.1×10^4 **61,000**   **17.** 9.01×10^{-2} **0.0901**

18. 1.399×10^5 **139,900**   **19.** 2.505×10^3 **2505**   **20.** 1.5×10^{-4} **0.00015**

Express each number in scientific notation. 30. 3.1×10^{-4}

21. 2,000,000 2.0×10^6 **22.** 499,000 4.99×10^5 **23.** 0.006 6.0×10^{-3}

24. 0.0125 1.25×10^{-2} **25.** 50,000,000 5.0×10^7 **26.** 39,560 3.956×10^4

27. 5,894,000 5.894×10^6 **28.** 0.000078 7.8×10^{-5} **29.** 0.000425 4.25×10^{-4}

30. The flow rate of some Antarctic glaciers is 0.00031 mile per hour.

31. Humans blink about 6.25 million times a year. 6.25×10^6

32. The number of possible ways that a player can play the first four moves in a chess game is 3 billion. 3.0×10^9

33. A particle of dust floating in the air weighs 0.000000753 gram. 7.53×10^{-7}

34. SPACE Refer to the table in Example 3 on page 187. To the nearest second, how long does it take light to travel from the Sun to Venus? **343 s**

Choose the greater number in each pair.

35. $\underline{2.3 \times 10^5}$, 1.7×10^5 **36.** $\underline{1.8 \times 10^3}$, 1.9×10^{-1}

37. 5.2×10^2, $\underline{5000}$ **38.** 0.012, $\underline{1.6 \times 10^{-1}}$

More About...

Oceans

In 2000, the International Hydrographic Organization named a fifth world ocean near Antarctica, called the *Southern Ocean*. It is larger than the Arctic Ocean and smaller than the Indian Ocean.

Source: www.geography.about.com

39. OCEANS Rank the oceans in the table at the right by area from least to greatest. **Arctic, Indian, Atlantic, Pacific**

Ocean	Area (sq mi)
Arctic	5.44×10^6
Atlantic	3.18×10^7
Indian	2.89×10^7
Pacific	6.40×10^7

40. petameter, gigameter, kilometer, nanometer, picometer, attometer

40. MEASUREMENT The table at the right shows the values of different prefixes that are used in the metric system. Write the units attometer, gigameter, kilometer, nanometer, petameter, and picometer in order from greatest to least measure.

Metric Measures	
Prefix	**Meaning**
atto	10^{-18}
giga	10^9
kilo	10^3
nano	10^{-9}
peta	10^{15}
pico	10^{-12}

41. Order 6.1×10^4, 6100, 6.1×10^{-5}, 0.0061, and 6.1×10^{-2} from least to greatest. $\mathbf{6.1 \times 10^{-5}}$, **0.0061**, $\mathbf{6.1 \times 10^{-2}}$, **6100**, $\mathbf{6.1 \times 10^4}$

★ 42. Write $(6 \times 10^0) + (4 \times 10^{-3}) + (3 \times 10^{-5})$ in standard form. **6.00403**

★ 43. Write $(4 \times 10^4) + (8 \times 10^3) + (3 \times 10^2) + (9 \times 10^1) + (6 \times 10^0)$ in standard form. **48,396**

44. 2.0×10^6; 2,000,000
45. 2.52×10^5; 252,000
46. 1.6575×10^{-5}; 0.000016575

Convert the numbers in each expression to scientific notation. Then evaluate the expression. Express in scientific notation and in decimal notation.

★ 44. $\dfrac{20{,}000}{0.01}$ **★ 45.** $\dfrac{(420{,}000)(0.015)}{0.025}$ **★ 46.** $\dfrac{(0.078)(8.5)}{0.16(250{,}000)}$

Study Guide and Intervention, p. 200

When you deal with very large numbers like 5,000,000 or very small numbers like 0.0005, it is difficult to keep track of place value. Numbers such as these can be written in **scientific notation**. A number is expressed in scientific notation when it is written as a product of a factor and a power of 10. The factor must be greater than or equal to 1 and less than 10.

By definition, a number in scientific notation is written as $a \cdot 10^n$, where $1 \le a < 10$ and n is an integer.

Example 1 Express each number in standard form.
a. 6.32×10^5
 $6.32 \times 10^5 = 632000$ Move the decimal point 5 places to the right.
b. 7.8×10^{-6}
 $7.8 \times 10^{-6} = 0.0000078$ Move the decimal point 6 places to the left.

Example 2 Express each number in scientific notation.
a. 62,000,000
 To write in scientific notation, place the decimal point after the first nonzero digit, then find the power of 10.
 $62000000 = 6.2 \times 10^7$ The decimal point moves 7 places. The power of 10 is 7.
b. 0.00025
 $0.00025 = 2.5 \times 10^{-4}$ Place the decimal point after the first nonzero digit. The power of 10 is −4.

Exercises

1. 4.12×10^6 4,120,000   2. 5.8×10^2 580   3. 9.01×10^{-3} 0.00901
4. 6.72×10^{-7} 0.000000672   5. 8.72×10^4 87,200   6. 4.44×10^{-5} 0.0000444

Express each number in scientific notation.
7. 12,000,000,000 1.2×10^{10} 8. 5000 5.0×10^3 9. 0.00475 4.75×10^{-3}
10. 0.00007463 7.463×10^{-5} 11. 235,000 2.35×10^5 12. 0.000377 3.77×10^{-4}

Choose the greater number in each pair.
13. $\underline{4.9 \times 10^4}$, 9.9×10^{-4} 14. $\underline{2.004 \times 10^3}$, 2.005×10^{-2}
15. 3.2×10^2, $\underline{700}$ 16. $\underline{0.002}$, 3.6×10^{-4}

Skills Practice, p. 201 and Practice, p. 202 (shown)

Express each number in standard form.
1. 2.4×10^4 24,000   2. 9.0×10^3 9000
3. 4.385×10^7 43,850,000   4. 1.03×10^8 103,000,000
5. 3.05×10^2 305   6. 5.11×10^{10} 51,100,000,000
7. 6.000032×10^6 6,000,032   8. 1.0×10^1 10
9. 8.75×10^5 875,000   10. 8.49×10^{-2} 0.0849
11. 7.1×10^{-6} 0.0000071   12. 1.0×10^{-3} 0.001
13. 4.39×10^{-7} 0.000000439   14. 1.25×10^{-4} 0.000125

Express each number in scientific notation.
15. 40,000 4.0×10^4 16. 16 1.6×10^1
17. 876,000,000 8.76×10^8 18. 4500 4.5×10^3
19. 151 1.51×10^2 20. 0.00037 3.7×10^{-4}
21. 83,000,000 8.3×10^7 22. 919,100 9.191×10^5
23. 5,000,000,000,000 5.0×10^{12} 24. 0.13 1.3×10^{-1}
25. 0.0000007 7.0×10^{-7} 26. 0.0067 6.7×10^{-3}

NIAGARA FALLS For Exercises 27 and 28, use the following information.

Every minute, 840,000,000,000 drops of water flow over Niagara Falls.

27. Write this number in scientific notation. 8.4×10^{11}
28. How many drops flow over the falls in a day? 1.2096×10^{15}

Enrichment, p. 204

Scientific Notation

It is sometimes necessary to multiply and divide very large or very small numbers using scientific notation.

To multiply numbers in scientific notation, use the following rule.

For any numbers a and b, and any numbers c and d,
$(c \times 10^a)(d \times 10^b) = (c \times d) \times 10^{a+b}$.

Example 1 $(3.0 \times 10^4)(-5.0 \times 10^{-2}) = [3.0 \times (-5.0)] \times 10^{4+(-2)}$
$= -15.0 \times 10^2$
$= -1.5 \times 10^3$ or -1500

To divide numbers in scientific notation, use the following rule.

For any numbers a and b, and any numbers c and d, $(d \ne 0)$
$(c \times 10^a) \div (d \times 10^b) = (c \div d) \times 10^{a-b}$.

Example 2 $(24 \times 10^{-4}) \div (1.5 \times 10^2) = (24 \div 1.5) \times 10^{-4-2}$
$= 16 \times 10^{-6}$
$= 1.6 \times 10^{-5}$ or 0.000016

Multiply or divide. Express each product or quotient in scientific notation.
1. $(2.7 \times 10^9) \times (3.1 \times 10^2)$ 8.37×10^{11} 2. $(6.1 \times 10^{-2}) \times (1.3 \times 10^5)$ 7.93×10^3
3. $(5.4 \times 10^{-3}) \div (1.8 \times 10^2)$ 3.0×10^{-5} 4. $(6.9 \times 10^{-3}) \div (3.0 \times 10^{-8})$ 2.3×10^5
5. $(1.1 \times 10^{-5}) \times (9.9 \times 10^{-1})$ 1.089×10^{-5} 6. $(4.0 \times 10^9) \div (1.0 \times 10^{-2})$ 4.0×10^2

Solve. Write your answers in standard form.
7. The distance from Earth to the Moon is about 2.0×10^5 miles. The distance from Earth to the Sun is about 9.3×10^7 miles. How many times farther is it to the Sun than to the Moon? 465
8. If each of the 3.0×10^4 people employed by Sunny Motors earned 4.0×10^4 dollars last year, how much money did the company pay out to its employees? $1,200,000,000

Open-Ended Assessment

Speaking Have students explain orally how to convert a number in standard form to scientific notation and vice versa.

Assessment Options

Quiz (Lessons 4-7 and 4-8) is available on p. 220 of the *Chapter 4 Resource Masters*.

Answers

47. Bezymianny; Santa Maria; Agung; Mount St. Helens tied with Hekla 1947; Hekla, 1970; Ngauruhoe

50. Scientific notation is a shorthand way of writing very large or very small numbers. Answers should include the following.

  • Examples of data that can be written in scientific notation, such as the surface area of planets and the diameter of atoms.

  • Scientific notation is useful because you can compare quantities by simply looking at the exponent of the power of 10, rather than counting decimal places.

PHYSICAL SCIENCE For Exercises 47 and 48, use the graph.

The graph shows the maximum amounts of lava in cubic meters per second that erupted from seven volcanoes in the last century.

Eruption Rates

Mount St. Helens, 1980	2.0×10^4
Ngauruhoe, 1975	2.0×10^3
Hekla, 1970	4.0×10^3
Agung, 1963	3.0×10^4
Bezymianny, 1956	2.0×10^5
Hekla, 1947	2.0×10^4
Santa Maria, 1902	4.0×10^4

Source: University of Alaska

47. Rank the volcanoes in order from greatest to least eruption rate. **See margin.**

48. How many times larger was the Santa Maria eruption than the Mount St. Helens eruptions? **2 times**

 Online Research **Data Update** How do the eruption rates of other volcanoes compare with those in the graph? Visit www.pre-alg.com/data_update to learn more.

49. **CRITICAL THINKING** In standard form, $3.14 \times 10^{-4} = 0.000314$, and $3.14 \times 10^4 = 31,400$. What is 3.14×10^0 in standard form? **3.14**

50. WRITING IN MATH Answer the question that was posed at the beginning of the lesson. **See margin.**

Why is scientific notation an important tool in comparing real-world data?

Include the following in your answer:
  • some real-world data that is written in scientific notation, and
  • the advantages of using scientific notation to compare data.

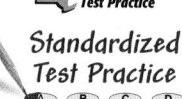

NEW YORK Test Practice

Standardized Test Practice
Ⓐ Ⓑ Ⓒ Ⓓ

51. If the bodies of water in the table are ordered from least to greatest area, which would be third in the list? **B**

  Ⓐ Lake Huron   Ⓑ Lake Victoria
  Ⓒ Red Sea   Ⓓ Great Salt Lake

Body of Water	Area (km²)
Lake Huron	5.7×10^4
Lake Victoria	6.9×10^4
Red Sea	4.4×10^5
Great Salt Lake	4.7×10^3

52. Which is 5.80×10^{-4} written in standard form? **D**

  Ⓐ 58,000   Ⓑ 5800   Ⓒ 0.58   Ⓓ 0.00058

Maintain Your Skills

Mixed Review **ALGEBRA** Evaluate each expression if $s = -2$ and $t = 3$. *(Lesson 4-7)*

53. t^{-4} $\dfrac{1}{81}$ 54. s^{-5} $-\dfrac{1}{32}$ 55. 7^s $\dfrac{1}{49}$

ALGEBRA Find each product or quotient. Express using exponents. *(Lesson 4-6)*

56. $4^4 \cdot 4^7$ **4^{11}**   57. $3a^2 \cdot 5a^2$ **$15a^4$**   58. $c^5 \div c^2$ **c^3**

59. **BUSINESS** Online Book Distributors add a $2.50 shipping and handling charge to the total price of every order. If the cost of books in an order is c, write an expression for the total cost. *(Lesson 1-3)* **$c + \$2.50$**

Vocabulary and Concept Check

algebraic fraction (p. 170)
base (p. 153)
base two (p. 158)
binary (p. 158)
composite number (p. 159)
divisible (p. 148)
expanded form (p. 154)

exponent (p. 153)
factor (p. 161)
factors (p. 148)
factor tree (p. 160)
greatest common factor (GCF) (p. 164)
monomial (p. 150)

power (p. 153)
prime factorization (p. 160)
prime number (p. 159)
scientific notation (p. 186)
simplest form (p. 169)
standard form (p. 154)
Venn diagram (p. 164)

Determine whether each statement is *true* or *false*. If false, replace the underlined word or number to make a true statement. 4. false; product

1. A prime number is a whole number that has exactly two factors, 1 and itself. **true**

2. Numbers expressed using exponents are called powers. **true**

3. The number 7 is a factor of 49 because it divides 49 with a remainder of zero. **true**

4. A monomial is a number, a variable, or a sum of numbers and/or variables.

5. The number 64 is a composite number. **true**

6. The number 9,536 is written in standard form. **true**

7. To write a fraction in simplest form, divide the numerator and the denominator by the GCF. **true**

8. A fraction is in simplest form when the GCF of the numerator and the denominator is 2. **false; 1**

Lesson-by-Lesson Review

4-1 Factors and Monomials

See pages 148–152.

Concept Summary

- Numbers that are multiplied to form a product are called factors.

 Example **Determine whether 102 is divisible by 2, 3, 5, 6, or 10.**

2: Yes, the ones digit is divisible by 2.
3: Yes, the sum of the digits is 3, and 3 is divisible by 3.
5: No, the ones digit is not 0 or 5.
6: Yes, the number is divisible by 2 and by 3.
10: No, the ones digit is not 0.

Exercises Use divisibility rules to determine whether each number is divisible by 2, 3, 5, 6, or 10. *See Example 1 on page 149.*

9. 111 **3**
10. 405 **3, 5**
11. 635 **5**
12. 863 **none**
13. 582 **2, 3, 6**
14. 2124 **2, 3, 6**
15. 700 **2, 5, 10**
16. 4200 **2, 3, 5, 6, 10**

 www.pre-alg.com/vocabulary_review

Vocabulary and Concept Check

- This alphabetical list of vocabulary terms in Chapter 4 includes a page reference where each term was introduced.

- **Assessment** A vocabulary review/test for Chapter 4 is available on p. 218 of the *Chapter 4 Resource Masters*.

Lesson-by-Lesson Review

For each lesson,

- the main ideas are summarized,
- additional examples review concepts, and
- practice exercises are provided.

Vocabulary PuzzleMaker

ELL The Vocabulary PuzzleMaker software improves students' mathematics vocabulary using four puzzle formats—crossword, scramble, word search using a word list, and word search using clues. Students can work on a computer screen or from a printed handout.

MindJogger Videoquizzes

ELL MindJogger Videoquizzes provide an alternative review of concepts presented in this chapter. Students work in teams in a game show format to gain points for correct answers. The questions are presented in three rounds.

Round 1 Concepts (5 questions)
Round 2 Skills (4 questions)
Round 3 Problem Solving (4 questions)

FOLDABLES™
Study Organizer

For more information about Foldables, see *Teaching Mathematics with Foldables.*

Have students reread the lesson notes and summaries they wrote in their Foldables. Ask them to highlight the ideas they consider most difficult.

Encourage students to refer to their Foldables while completing the Study Guide and Review and to use them in preparing for the Chapter Test.

4-2 Powers and Exponents

See pages 153–157.

Concept Summary

- An exponent is a shorthand way of writing repeated multiplication.
- A number can be written in expanded form by using exponents.
- Follow the order of operations to evaluate algebraic expressions containing exponents.

Example Evaluate $4(a + 2)^3$ if $a = -5$.

$$
\begin{aligned}
4(a + 2)^3 &= 4(-5 + 2)^3 && \text{Replace } a \text{ with } -5. \\
&= 4(-3)^3 && \text{Simplify the expression inside the parentheses.} \\
&= 4(-27) && \text{Evaluate } (-3)^3. \\
&= -108 && \text{Simplify.}
\end{aligned}
$$

Exercises Evaluate each expression if $x = -3$, $y = 4$, and $z = -2$.
See Example 3 on page 155.

17. 3^3 **27**   18. 10^4 **10,000**   19. $(-5)^2$ **25**   20. y^3 **64**

21. $10x^2$ **90**   22. xy^3 **−192**   23. $7y^0z^4$ **112**   24. $2(3z + 4)^5$ **−64**

4-3 Prime Factorization

See pages 159–163.

Concept Summary

- A prime number is a whole number that has exactly two factors, 1 and itself.
- A composite number is a whole number that has more than two factors.

Example Write the prime factorization of 40.

```
        40
       /  \
      4  · 10        40 = 4 · 10
     / \   / \
    2 · 2 · 2 · 5    4 = 2 · 2 and 10 = 2 · 5
```

The prime factorization of 40 is $2 \cdot 2 \cdot 2 \cdot 5$ or $2^3 \cdot 5$.

Example Factor $9s^3t^2$.

$$
\begin{aligned}
9s^3t^2 &= 3 \cdot 3 \cdot s^3 \cdot t^2 && 9 = 3 \cdot 3 \\
&= 3 \cdot 3 \cdot s \cdot s \cdot s \cdot t \cdot t && s^3 \cdot t^2 = s \cdot s \cdot s \cdot t \cdot t
\end{aligned}
$$

Exercises Write the prime factorization of each number. Use exponents for repeated factors. *See Example 2 on page 160.*

25. 45 $3^2 \cdot 5$ 26. 55 $5 \cdot 11$ 27. 68 $2^2 \cdot 17$ 28. 200 $2^3 \cdot 5^2$

30. $-1 \cdot 3 \cdot 5 \cdot n \cdot n$

Factor each monomial. *See Example 3 on page 161.* 31. $2 \cdot 13 \cdot p \cdot p \cdot p$

29. $49k$ $7 \cdot 7 \cdot k$ 30. $-15n^2$ 31. $26p^3$ 32. $10a^2b$ $2 \cdot 5 \cdot a \cdot a \cdot b$

4-4 Greatest Common Factor (GCF)

See pages 164–168.

Concept Summary

- The greatest number or monomial that is a factor of two or more numbers or monomials is the GCF.
- The Distributive Property can be used to factor algebraic expressions.

Examples

1 Find the GCF of $12a^2$ and $15ab$.

$12a^2 = 2 \cdot 2 \cdot \boxed{3} \cdot \boxed{a} \cdot a$
$15ab = \qquad \boxed{3} \cdot 5 \cdot \boxed{a} \cdot b$ The GCF of $12a^2$ and $15ab$ is $3 \cdot a$ or $3a$.

2 Factor $4n + 8$.

Step 1 Find the GCF of $4n$ and 8.

$4n = \boxed{2} \cdot \boxed{2} \cdot n$
$8 \ = \boxed{2} \cdot \boxed{2} \cdot 2$ The GCF is $2 \cdot 2$ or 4.

Step 2 Write the product of the GCF and its remaining factors.

$4n + 8 = 4(n) + 4(2)$ Rewrite each term using the GCF.
$\qquad = 4(n + 2)$ Distributive Property

Exercises Find the GCF of each set of numbers or monomials.
See Examples 2 and 4 on pages 165 and 166.

33. 6, 48 **6** **34.** 16, 24 **8** **35.** $4n, 5n^2$ **n** **36.** $20c^3d, 12cd$ **$4cd$**

Factor each expression. *See Example 5 on page 166.*

37. $2t + 20$ **$2(t + 10)$** **38.** $3x + 24$ **$3(x + 8)$** **39.** $30 + 4n$ **$2(15 + 2n)$**

4-5 Simplifying Algebraic Fractions

See pages 169–173.

Concept Summary

- Algebraic fractions can be written in simplest form by dividing the numerator and the denominator by the GCF.

Example Simplify $\dfrac{8np}{18n^2}$.

$$\frac{8np}{18n^2} = \frac{\overset{1}{2} \cdot 2 \cdot 2 \cdot \overset{1}{n} \cdot p}{\underset{1}{2} \cdot 3 \cdot 3 \cdot \underset{1}{n} \cdot n}$$ Divide the numerator and the denominator by the GCF, $2 \cdot n$.

$$= \frac{4p}{9n}$$ Simplify.

Exercises Write each fraction in simplest form. If the fraction is already in simplest form, write *simplified*. *See Examples 2 and 4 on page 170.*

40. $\dfrac{6}{21}$ **$\dfrac{2}{7}$** **41.** $\dfrac{24}{40}$ **$\dfrac{3}{5}$** **42.** $\dfrac{15}{16}$ **simplified** **43.** $\dfrac{30}{51}$ **$\dfrac{10}{17}$**

44. $\dfrac{st}{t^4}$ **$\dfrac{s}{t^3}$** **45.** $\dfrac{23x}{32y}$ **simplified** **46.** $\dfrac{9mn}{18n^2}$ **$\dfrac{m}{2n}$** **47.** $\dfrac{15ac^2}{24ab}$ **$\dfrac{5c^2}{8b}$**

Study Guide and Review

Chapter **4** For More ...
• Extra Practice, see pages 730–733.
• Mixed Problem Solving, see page 761.

Additional Answers (p. 195)

1. A number is divisible by: 2 if the ones digit is even; 3 if the sum of its digits is divisible by 3; 5 if the ones digit is 0 or 5; 6 if the number is divisible by 2 and 3; 10 if the ones digit is 0.

2. A prime number has only two factors, 1 and the number itself. A composite number has more than two factors.

4-6 Multiplying and Dividing Monomials

See pages 175–179.

Concept Summary

• Powers with the same base can be multiplied by adding their exponents.
• Powers with the same base can be divided by subtracting their exponents.

Examples

1 Find $x^3 \cdot x^2$.

$$x^3 \cdot x^2 = x^{3+2}$$ The common base is x.
$$= x^5$$ Add the exponents.

2 Find $\frac{4^5}{4^3}$.

$$\frac{4^5}{4^3} = 4^{5-3}$$ The common base is 4.
$$= 4^2$$ Subtract the exponents.

Exercises Find each product or quotient. Express using exponents.
See Examples 1–3 on pages 176 and 177.

48. $8^4 \cdot 8^5$ **8^9**   49. $c \cdot c^3$ **c^4**   50. $\frac{3^7}{3^2}$ **3^5**   51. $\frac{r^{11}}{r^9}$ **r^2**   52. $7x \cdot 2x^6$ **$14x^7$**

4-7 Negative Exponents

See pages 181–185.

Concept Summary

• For $a \neq 0$ and any integer n, $a^{-n} = \frac{1}{a^n}$.

Example Write 3^{-4} as an expression using a positive exponent.

$$3^{-4} = \frac{1}{3^4}$$ Definition of negative exponent

Exercises Write each expression using a positive exponent.
See Example 1 on page 182.

53. 7^{-2} **$\frac{1}{7^2}$**   54. 10^{-1} **$\frac{1}{10^1}$ or $\frac{1}{10}$**   55. b^{-4} **$\frac{1}{b^4}$**   56. t^{-8} **$\frac{1}{t^8}$**   57. $(-4)^{-3}$ **$\frac{1}{(-4)^3}$**

4-8 Scientific Notation

See pages 186–190.

Concept Summary

• A number in scientific notation contains a factor and a power of 10.

Examples

1 Express 3.5×10^{-2} in standard form.

$$3.5 \times 10^{-2} = 3.5 \times 0.01$$ $10^{-2} = 0.01$
$$= 0.035$$ Move the decimal point 2 places to the left.

2 Express 269,000 in scientific notation.

$$269,000 = 2.69 \times 100,000$$ The decimal point moves 5 places.
$$= 2.69 \times 10^5$$ The exponent is positive.

Exercises Express each number in standard form. See Example 1 on page 186.

58. 6.1×10^2 **610**   59. 2.9×10^{-3} **0.0029**   60. 1.85×10^{-2} **0.0185**   61. 7.045×10^4 **70,450**

Express each number in scientific notation. See Example 2 on page 187.

62. 1200 **1.2×10^3**   63. 0.008 **8.0×10^{-3}**   64. 0.000319 **3.19×10^{-4}**   65. 45,710,000 **4.571×10^7**

Vocabulary and Concepts

1. **Explain** how to use the divisibility rules to determine whether a number is divisible by 2, 3, 5, 6, or 10. **1–2. See margin.**

2. **Explain** the difference between a prime number and a composite number.

3. **OPEN ENDED** Write an algebraic fraction that is in simplest form. **Sample answer:** $\frac{x}{2}$

Skills and Applications

Determine whether each expression is a monomial. Explain why or why not.

4. $6xyz$ **yes; product of a number and variables**

5. $-2m + 9$ **no; sum of two terms**

Write each expression using exponents.

6. $3 \cdot 3 \cdot 3 \cdot 3$ **3^4**

7. $-2 \cdot -2 \cdot -2 \cdot a \cdot a \cdot a \cdot a$ **$(-2)^3 a^4$**

Factor each expression.

8. $12r^2$ **$2 \cdot 2 \cdot 3 \cdot r \cdot r$**

9. $50xy^2$ **$2 \cdot 5 \cdot 5 \cdot x \cdot y \cdot y$**

10. $7 + 21p$ **$7(1 + 3p)$**

Find the GCF of each set of numbers or monomials.

11. $70, 28$ **14**

12. $36, 90, 180$ **18**

13. $12a^3b, 40ab^4$ **$4ab$**

Write each fraction in simplest form. If the fraction is already in simplest form, write *simplified*.

14. $\frac{57}{95}$ **$\frac{3}{5}$**

15. $\frac{240}{360}$ **$\frac{2}{3}$**

16. $\frac{56m^3n}{32mn}$ **$\frac{7m^2}{4}$**

Find each product or quotient. Express using exponents.

17. $5^3 \cdot 5^6$ **5^9**

18. $(4x^7)(-6x^3)$ **$-24x^{10}$**

19. $w^9 \div w^5$ **w^4**

Write each expression using a positive exponent.

20. 4^{-2} **$\frac{1}{4^2}$**

21. t^{-6} **$\frac{1}{t^6}$**

22. $(yz)^{-3}$ **$\frac{1}{(yz)^3}$**

Write each number in standard form.

23. 9.0×10^{-2} **0.09**

24. 5.206×10^{-3} **0.005206**

25. 3.71×10^4 **37,100**

Write each number in scientific notation.

26. $345,000$ **3.45×10^5**

27. $1,680,000$ **1.68×10^6**

28. 0.00072 **7.2×10^{-4}**

29. **BAKING** A recipe for butter cookies requires 12 tablespoons of sugar for every 16 tablespoons of flour. Write this as a fraction in simplest form. **$\frac{3}{4}$**

30. **STANDARDIZED TEST PRACTICE** Earth is approximately 93 million miles away from the Sun. Express this distance in scientific notation. **A**

   Ⓐ 9.3×10^7 mi
   Ⓑ 9.3×10^6 mi
   Ⓒ 93×10^6 mi
   Ⓓ $93,000,000$ mi

www.pre-alg.com/chapter_test/ny

Portfolio Suggestion

Introduction In mathematics, many quantities are expressed as fractions. Some fractions may be very large or very small. Other fractions may be algebraic.

Ask Students to locate one numerical and one algebraic fraction in Chapter 4. Write a portfolio entry that explains how factors and related concepts such as divisibility are used to write the fractions in simplest form.

Assessment Options

Vocabulary Test A vocabulary review/test for Chapter 4 can be found on p. 218 of the *Chapter 4 Resource Masters*.

Chapter Tests There are six Chapter 4 Tests and an Open-Ended Assessment task available in the *Chapter 4 Resource Masters*.

Chapter 4 Tests			
Form	Type	Level	Pages
1	MC	basic	205–206
2A	MC	average	207–208
2B	MC	average	209–210
2C	FR	average	211–212
2D	FR	average	213–214
3	FR	advanced	215–216

MC = multiple-choice questions
FR = free-response questions

Open-Ended Assessment Performance tasks for Chapter 4 can be found on p. 217 of the *Chapter 4 Resource Masters*. A sample scoring rubric for these tasks appears on p. A27.

 ExamView® Pro

Use the networkable **ExamView® Pro** to:

- Create **multiple versions** of tests.
- Create **modified** tests for *Inclusion* students.
- **Edit** existing questions and **add** your own questions.
- Use built-in **state curriculum correlations** to create tests aligned with state standards.
- Change **English** tests to **Spanish** and vice versa.

These two pages contain practice questions in the various formats that can be found on the most frequently given standardized tests.

A practice answer sheet for these two pages can be found on page A1 of the *Chapter 4 Resource Masters*.

Standardized Test Practice
Student Recording Sheet, p. A1

Part 1 *Multiple Choice*

Select the best answer from the choices given and fill in the corresponding oval.

1	Ⓐ Ⓑ Ⓒ Ⓓ	4	Ⓐ Ⓑ Ⓒ Ⓓ	7	Ⓐ Ⓑ Ⓒ Ⓓ	10	Ⓐ Ⓑ Ⓒ Ⓓ
2	Ⓐ Ⓑ Ⓒ Ⓓ	5	Ⓐ Ⓑ Ⓒ Ⓓ	8	Ⓐ Ⓑ Ⓒ Ⓓ	11	Ⓐ Ⓑ Ⓒ Ⓓ
3	Ⓐ Ⓑ Ⓒ Ⓓ	6	Ⓐ Ⓑ Ⓒ Ⓓ	9	Ⓐ Ⓑ Ⓒ Ⓓ		

Part 2 *Short Response/Grid In*

Solve the problem and write your answer in the blank.

For Questions 15, 17, and 19, also enter your answer by writing each number or symbol in a box. Then fill in the corresponding oval for that number or symbol.

12 _____
13 _____
14 _____
15 _____ (grid in)
16 _____
17 _____ (grid in)
18 _____
19 _____ (grid in)
20 _____
21 _____

Part 3 *Extended Response*

Record your answers for Question 22 on the back of this paper.

Additional Practice

See pp. 223–224 of the *Chapter 4 Resource Masters* for additional standardized test practice.

NEW YORK
Test Practice

Part 1 | Multiple Choice

Record your answers on the answer sheet provided by your teacher or on a sheet of paper.

1. Andy has 7 fewer computer games than Ling. Carlos has twice as many computer games as Andy. If Ling has x computer games, which of these represents the number of computer games that Carlos has? (Lesson 1-3) **D**
   - Ⓐ $7 - 2x$
   - Ⓑ $x - 7$
   - Ⓒ $2x - 7$
   - Ⓓ $2(x - 7)$

2. Which of the following statements is *false*, when r, s, and t are different integers? (Lesson 1-4) **D**
   - Ⓐ $(rs)t = r(st)$
   - Ⓑ $r + s = s + r$
   - Ⓒ $rs = sr$
   - Ⓓ $r - s = s - r$

3. The low temperatures during the past five days are given in the table. Find the average (mean) of the temperatures. (Lesson 2-5) **B**

Day	1	2	3	4	5
Temperature (°F)	−2	0	4	5	4

   - Ⓐ 3°F
   - Ⓑ 2.2°F
   - Ⓒ 13°F
   - Ⓓ 2.75°F

4. Which coordinates are most likely to be the coordinates of point P? (Lesson 2-6) **A**
   - Ⓐ $(-13, 7)$
   - Ⓑ $(7, -13)$
   - Ⓒ $(13, 7)$
   - Ⓓ $(7, 13)$

Test-Taking Tip Ⓐ Ⓑ Ⓒ Ⓓ
Question 2
When a multiple-choice question asks you to verify statements that include variables, you can substitute numbers into the variables to determine which statements are true and which are false.

---

5. Solve $3n - 6 = -39$ for n. (Lesson 3-5) **B**
   - Ⓐ -15
   - Ⓑ -11
   - Ⓒ 11
   - Ⓓ 15

6. For every order purchased from an Internet bookstore, the shipping and handling charges include a base fee of $5 plus a fee of $3 per item purchased in the order. Which equation represents the shipping and handling charge for ordering n items? (Lesson 3-6) **D**
   - Ⓐ $S = 5(3n)$
   - Ⓑ $S = 3n - 5$
   - Ⓒ $S = 5 + \frac{3}{n}$
   - Ⓓ $S = 5 + 3n$

7. The area of the rectangle below is 18 square units. Use the formula $A = \ell w$ to find its width. (Lesson 3-7) **C**
   - Ⓐ $\frac{1}{3}$ unit
   - Ⓑ 2 units
   - Ⓒ 3 units
   - Ⓓ 12 units

   6 units

8. Write the prime factorization of 84. (Lesson 4-3) **D**
   - Ⓐ $2 \cdot 3 \cdot 7$
   - Ⓑ $4 \cdot 21$
   - Ⓒ $3 \cdot 4 \cdot 7$
   - Ⓓ $2 \cdot 2 \cdot 3 \cdot 7$

9. What is the greatest common factor of 28 and 42? (Lesson 4-4) **C**
   - Ⓐ 2
   - Ⓑ 7
   - Ⓒ 14
   - Ⓓ 28

10. Write 3^{-3} as a fraction. (Lesson 4-7) **C**
    - Ⓐ $-\frac{1}{9}$
    - Ⓑ $-\frac{1}{27}$
    - Ⓒ $\frac{1}{27}$
    - Ⓓ $\frac{1}{9}$

11. Asia is the largest continent. It has an area of 17,400,000 square miles. What is 17,400,000 expressed in scientific notation? (Lesson 4-8) **B**
    - Ⓐ 174×10^5
    - Ⓑ 1.74×10^7
    - Ⓒ 174×10^7
    - Ⓓ 1.74×10^8

ExamView® Pro

Special banks of standardized test questions similar to those on the SAT, ACT, TIMSS 8, NAEP 8, and Pre-Algebra End-of-Course tests can be found on this CD-ROM.

Record your answers on the answer sheet provided by your teacher or on a sheet of paper.

12. A health club charges an initial fee of $60 for the first month, and then a $28 membership fee each month after the first month, as shown in the table. What is the total membership cost for 9 months? (Lesson 1-1) **$284**

Number of Months	Total Cost ($)
1	60
2	88
3	116
4	144
5	172

13. The temperature in Concord at 5 P.M. was -3 degrees. By midnight, the temperature had dropped 9 degrees. What was the temperature at midnight? (Lesson 2-3) **-12 or -12 degrees**

14. A skating rink charges $2.00 to rent a pair of skates and $1.50 per hour of skating. Jeff wants to spend no more than $8.00 and he needs to rent skates. How many hours can he skate? (Lesson 3-5) **4 h**

15. At a birthday party, Maka gave 30 gel pens to her friends as prizes. Everyone got at least 1 gel pen. Six friends got just 1 gel pen each, 4 friends got 3 gel pens each for winning games, and the rest of the friends got 2 gel pens each. How many friends got 2 gel pens? (Lesson 3-6) **6**

16. A table 8 feet long and 2 feet wide is to be covered for the school bake sale. If organizers want the covering to hang down 1 foot on each side, what is the area of the covering that they need? (Lesson 3-7) **40 square feet**

17. What is the least 3-digit number that is divisible by 3 and 5? (Lesson 4-1) **105**

18. Write $10 \cdot 10 \cdot 10 \cdot 10$ using an exponent. (Lesson 4-2) **10^4**

19. Find the greatest common factor of 18, 44, and 12. (Lesson 4-4) **2**

20. Write $\dfrac{1}{5 \cdot 5 \cdot 5}$ using a negative exponent. (Lesson 4-7) **5^{-3}**

21. The Milky Way galaxy is made up of about 200 billion stars, including the Sun. Write this number in scientific notation. (Lesson 4-8) **2.0×10^{11}**

Part 3 Extended Response

Record your answers on a sheet of paper. Show your work.

22. Chandra plans to order CDs from an Internet shopping site. She finds that the CD prices are the same at three different sites, but that the shipping costs vary. The shipping costs include a fee per order, plus an additional fee for each item in the order, as shown in the table below. (Lesson 3-6) **a–c. See margin.**

	Shipping Cost	
Company	Per Order	Per Item
CDBargains	$4.00	$1.00
WebShopper	$6.00	$3.00
EverythingStore	$2.50	$1.50

a. For each company, write an equation that represents the shipping cost. In each of your three equations, use S to represent the shipping cost and n to represent the number of items purchased.

b. If Chandra orders 2 CDs, which company will charge the least for shipping? Use the equations you wrote and show your work.

c. If Chandra orders 10 CDs, which company will charge the least for shipping? Use the equations you wrote and show your work.

d. For what number of CDs do both CDBargains and EverythingStore charge the same amount for shipping and handling costs? **3 CDs**

Evaluating Extended Response Questions

Extended Response questions are graded by using a multilevel rubric that guides you in assessing a student's knowledge of a particular concept.

Goal: Use mathematical equations to solve a realistic word problem.

Sample Scoring Rubric: The following rubric is a sample scoring device. You may wish to add more detail to this sample to meet your individual scoring needs.

Score	Criteria
4	A correct solution that is supported by well-developed, accurate explanations
3	A generally correct solution, but may contain minor flaws in reasoning or computation
2	A partially correct interpretation and/or solution to the problem
1	A correct solution with no supporting evidence or explanation
0	An incorrect solution indicating no mathematical understanding of the concept or task, or no solution is given

Answer

22a. CDBargains $S = 4 + n$
WebShopper $S = 6 + 3n$
EverythingStore $S = 2.5 + 1.5n$

22b. Let $n = 2$.
CD Bargains $S = 4 + 2$ or $6
WebShopper $S = 6 + 3(2)$ or $12
EverythingStore $S = 2.5 + 1.5(2)$ or $5.50; EverythingStore has the least shipping cost.

22c. Let $n = 10$.
CD Bargains $S = 4 + 10$ or $14
WebShopper $S = 6 + 3(10)$ or $36
EverythingStore $S = 2.5 + 1.5(10)$ or $17.50; CD Bargains has the least shipping cost.

Page 151, Lesson 4-1

36. a variable

37. a number

38. two terms are added

39. one term is subtracted from another term

40. two terms are added

41. two terms are added

42. two terms are added

43. one term is subtracted from another term

44. the product of a number and a variable

45. the product of a number and a variable

46. the product of a number and variables

47. the product of numbers and variables

48. No; 72 is not divisible by 7.

49. 6 ways; 1×72, 2×36, 3×24, 4×18, 6×12, 8×9

50. 1912, a 6-by-8 arrangement; 1959, a 7-by-7 arrangement

51. Alternating rows of a flag contain 6 stars and 5 stars, respectively. 50 is not divisible by a number that would make the arrangement of stars in an appropriate-sized rectangle.

Chapter 5

Rational Numbers
Chapter Overview and Pacing

*An electronic version of this chapter is available on **StudentWorks**™. This backpack solution CD-ROM allows students instant access to the Student Edition, lesson worksheet pages, and web resources.*

Year-long pacing: pages T20–T21.

LESSON OBJECTIVES

	PACING (days)			
	Regular		Block	
	Basic/ Average	Advanced	Basic/ Average	Advanced
5-1 Writing Fractions as Decimals (pp. 200–204) • Write fractions as terminating or repeating decimals. • Compare fractions and decimals.	1	1	0.5	0.5
5-2 Rational Numbers (pp. 205–209) • Write rational numbers as fractiions. • Identify and classify rational numbers.	1	1	0.5	0.5
5-3 Multiplying Rational Numbers (pp. 210–214) • Multiply fractions. • Use dimensional analysis to solve problems.	1	1	0.5	0.5
5-4 Dividing Rational Numbers (pp. 215–219) • Divide fractions using multiplicative inverses. • Use dimensional analysis to solve problems.	1	1	0.5	0.5
5-5 Adding and Subtracting Like Fractions (pp. 220–224) • Add like fractions. • Subtract like fractions.	1	1	0.5	0.5
5-6 Least Common Multiple (pp. 226–231) • Find the least common multiple of two or more numbers. • Find the least common denominator of two or more fractions. *Follow-Up:* Participate in a strategic game utilizing factors and multiples.	2 (with 5-6 Follow-Up)	2 (with 5-6 Follow-Up)	1	1.5 (with 5-6 Follow-Up)
5-7 Adding and Subtracting Unlike Fractions (pp. 232–236) • Add unlike fractions. • Subtract unlike fractions.	1	1	0.5	0.5
5-8 Measures of Central Tendency (pp. 237–243) *Preview:* Determine a number that best represents or describes a set of data. • Use the mean, median, and mode as measures of central tendency. • Analyze data using mean, median, and mode. *Follow-Up:* Describe how a graphing calculator can be used to store data in a list.	2 (with 5-8 Preview)	2 (with 5-8 Follow-Up)	1	1.5 (with 5-8 Follow-Up)
5-9 Solving Equations with Rational Numbers (pp. 244–248) • Solve equations containing rational numbers.	1	1	0.5	0.5
5-10 Arithmetic and Geometric Sequences (pp. 249–253) • Find the terms of arithmetic sequences. • Find the terms of geometric sequences. *Follow-Up:* Become familiar with the Fibonacci Sequence.	1	2 (with 5-10 Follow-Up)	0.5	0.5
Study Guide and Practice Test (pp. 254–259) **Standardized Test Practice** (pp. 260–261)	1	1	0.5	0.5
Chapter Assessment	1	1	0.5	0.5
TOTAL	14	15	7	8

Chapter Resource Manager

Timesaving Tools

TeacherWorks™

All-In-One Planner and Resource Center

See pages T5 and T21.

CHAPTER 5 RESOURCE MASTERS

Study Guide and Intervention	Practice (Skills and Average)	Reading to Learn Mathematics	Enrichment	Assessment	Prerequisite Skills Workbook	Applications*	Parent and Student Study Guide Workbook	5-Minute Check Transparencies	Interactive Chalkboard	Pre-AlgePASS: Tutorial Plus (lessons)	Materials
225	226–227	228	229		15–18	GCS 28	33	5-1	5-1		
230	231–232	233	234			SC 9	34	5-2	5-2		
235	236–237	238	239	289		SM 3	35	5-3	5-3		
240	241–242	243	244			SC 10	36	5-4	5-4		
245	246–247	248	249	289, 291	37–44		37	5-5	5-5		
250	251–252	253	254				38	5-6	5-6		*Follow-Up:* hundreds chart, colored markers
255	256–257	258	259		37–44	GCS 27	39	5-7	5-7		
260	261–262	263	264	290	19–22, 29–30		40	5-8	5-8	9	*Preview:* weather data, graph or data table/newspaper, small box of raisins *Follow-Up:* graphing calculator
265	266–267	268	269		21–24, 27–28, 31–32, 47–62		41	5-9	5-9		
270	271–272	273	274	290	1–2, 45–48		42	5-10	5-10	10, 11	*Follow-Up:* artichoke, pinecone, pineapple, or sunflower, markers
				275–288 292–298							

* *Key to Abbreviations:* GCS = Graphing Calculator and Spreadsheet Masters
SC = School-to-Career Masters
SM = Science and Mathematics Lab Manual

ELL Study Guide and Intervention, Skills Practice, Practice, and Parent and Student Study Guide Workbooks are also available in Spanish.

Chapter 5
Mathematical Connections and Background

Continuity of Instruction

Prior Knowledge

In the previous chapter, students examined factors and monomials and learned to evaluate expressions containing powers and exponents. They learned to simplify expressions and algebraic fractions using greatest common factor. They also multiplied and divided monomials and expressed numbers using positive and negative integers and exponents.

This Chapter

Students will explore rational numbers, learning to multiply and divide fractions and add and subtract like and unlike fractions. They will also learn to convert fractions to decimals, factor numbers, and determine least common multiple (LCM). They will examine measures of central tendency. Students will learn to solve equations and identify sequences.

Future Connections

The study of rational numbers is essential for real-world problem solving and lays the groundwork for future classwork in algebra, business mathematics, and number theory. Measures of central tendency are important in statistical analysis and research sciences. Arithmetic and geometric sequences are used to develop formulas in higher mathematics.

5-1 Writing Fractions as Decimals

Any fraction $\frac{a}{b}$, where $b \neq 0$, can be written as a decimal by dividing the numerator by the denominator. So, $\frac{a}{b} = a \div b$. If the division ends, or terminates, when the remainder is zero, the decimal is a terminating decimal. Not all fractions can be written as terminating decimals. Some have a repeating decimal. A bar indicates that the decimal repeats forever. For example, the fraction $\frac{4}{9}$ can be converted to a repeating decimal, $0.\overline{4}$.

5-2 Rational Numbers

A number that can be written as a fraction is called a rational number. Terminating and repeating decimals are rational numbers because both can be written as fractions. Decimals that are neither terminating nor repeating are called irrational numbers because they cannot be written as fractions. Terminating decimals can be converted to fractions by placing the number (without the decimal point) in the numerator. Count the number of places to the right of the decimal point and in the denominator, place a 1 followed by a number of zeros equal to the number of places that you counted. The fraction can then be reduced to simplest form.

5-3 Multiplying Rational Numbers

To multiply fractions (rational numbers), multiply the numerators and multiply the denominators. If the fractions have common factors in the numerators and denominators, they can be simplified before multiplication. If one of the fractions is negative, then the product will be negative. Mixed numbers can be multiplied in the same manner, after first being renamed as improper fractions. A fraction that contains one or more variables in the numerator or the denominator is called an algebraic fraction. Algebraic fractions may be multiplied using the same method described above.

5-4 Dividing Rational Numbers

Rational numbers have all of the properties of whole numbers and integers. Another property is shown by $\frac{7}{4} \cdot \frac{4}{7} = 1$. Two numbers whose product is 1 are called multiplicative inverses or reciprocals. To divide by a fraction (rational number), multiply by its multiplicative inverse. When dividing by a mixed number, first rename the number as an improper fraction, and then multiply by its multiplicative inverse. This process of multiplying by a number's reciprocal can also be used when dividing algebraic fractions and in dimensional analysis.

5-5 Adding and Subtracting Like Fractions

Fractions with the same denominator are called like fractions. To add like fractions, add the numerators and write the sum over the denominator. To add mixed numbers with like fractions, add the whole numbers and fractions separately, adding the numerators of the fractions, then simplifying if necessary. The rule for subtracting fractions with like denominators is similar to the rule for addition. The numerators can be subtracted and the difference written over the denominator. Mixed numbers are written as improper fractions before subtracting. These same rules apply to adding or subtracting like algebraic fractions.

5-6 Least Common Multiple

A multiple of a number is a product of that number and a whole number. Sometimes different numbers have some of the same multiples. These are called common multiples. The smallest of the nonzero common multiples is called the least common multiple (LCM). When numbers are large, an easy way of finding the least common multiple is to use prime factorization. The LCM is the smallest product that contains the prime factors of each number.

5-7 Adding and Subtracting Unlike Fractions

Fractions with different denominators are called unlike fractions. The LCM of the denominators is used to rename the fractions with a common denominator. After a common denominator is found, the numerators can then be added or subtracted. To add mixed numbers with unlike fractions, rename the mixed numbers as improper fractions. Then find a common denominator, add the numerators, and simplify the answer.

5-8 Measures of Central Tendency

It is often helpful to use one or more numbers to represent a whole set of data. These numbers are measures of central tendency. The mean is the sum of the data divided by the number of items in the data set. The median is the middle number of the ordered data (or the mean of the two middle numbers). The mode is the number or numbers that occur most often. These measures allow data to be analyzed.

5-9 Solving Equations with Rational Numbers

Rational number equations can be solved using the same method used to solve integer equations, by applying opposite operations to each side of the equation. Addition, subtraction, multiplication, and division (reciprocal) can be used. For example, to solve $4.9 = b + 8.5$, subtract 8.5 from each side to get $b = -3.6$. The skill of solving equations with rational numbers may be applied to many real-world problems.

5-10 Arithmetic and Geometric Sequences

A sequence is an ordered list of numbers. An arithmetic sequence is a sequence in which the difference between any two consecutive terms is the same. A geometric sequence is a sequence in which the quotient of any two consecutive terms is the same. The next term in a geometric sequence can be found by multiplying the previous term by the same number. So, the sequence 7, 3, −1, −5 is arithmetic because the difference between the terms is the same number, −4. The sequence 2, −4, 8, −16 is geometric because the quotient of any two consecutive numbers is the same, −2.

Quick Review Math Handbook

Hot Words includes a glossary of terms while Hot Topics consists of explanations of key mathematical concepts with exercises to test comprehension. This valuable resource can be used as a reference in the classroom or for home study.

Lesson	Hot Topics Section	Lesson	Hot Topics Section
5-1	2.1, 2.9	5-5, 5-6	1.4, 2.3
5-2	2.1, 2.2, 2.4	5-7	1.5, 2.3
5-3	1.4, 2.4	5-8	2.6, 4.4
5-4	2.1, 2.4	5-9	1.5, 6.4

 Additional mathematical information and teaching notes are available at www.pre-alg.com/key_concepts.

DAILY
INTERVENTION and Assessment

Key to Abbreviations:
TWE = Teacher Wraparound Edition; CRM = Chapter Resource Masters

	Type	Student Edition	Teacher Resources	Technology/Internet
INTERVENTION	Ongoing	Prerequisite Skills, pp. 199, 204, 209, 214, 219, 224, 230, 236, 242, 248 Practice Quiz 1, p. 224 Practice Quiz 2, p. 248	5-Minute Check Transparencies *Prerequisite Skills Workbook*, pp. 1–2, 15–24, 27–32, 37–62 Quizzes, *CRM*, pp. 289, 290 Mid-Chapter Test, *CRM*, p. 291 Study Guide and Intervention, *CRM*, pp. 225, 230, 235, 240, 245, 250, 255, 260, 265, 270	Pre-AlgePASS: Tutorial Plus, Lessons 9, 10, and 11 www.pre-alg.com/ self_check_quiz www.pre-alg.com/ extra_examples
	Mixed Review	pp. 204, 209, 214, 219, 224, 230, 236, 242, 248, 252	Cumulative Review, *CRM*, p. 292	
	Error Analysis	Find the Error, pp. 212, 222, 234, 246	Find the Error, *TWE*, pp. 212, 222, 234, 246 Unlocking Misconceptions, *TWE*, p. 211	
ASSESSMENT	Standardized Test Practice	pp. 204, 209, 214, 219, 224, 230, 236, 240, 241, 242, 247, 252, 260–261	*TWE*, pp. 260–261 Standardized Test Practice, *CRM*, pp. 293–294	Standardized Test Practice CD-ROM www.pre-alg.com/ standardized_test
	Open-Ended Assessment	Writing in Math, pp. 204, 209, 214, 219, 223, 230, 236, 242, 247, 251 Open Ended, pp. 202, 207, 212, 217, 222, 228, 234, 241, 246, 251 Standardized Test, p. 261	Speaking: *TWE*, pp. 209, 224, 248 Writing: *TWE*, pp. 204, 219, 230, 242 Modeling: *TWE*, pp. 214, 236, 252 Open-Ended Assessment, *CRM*, p. 287	
	Chapter Assessment	Study Guide, pp. 254–258 Practice Test, p. 259	Multiple-Choice Tests (Forms 1, 2A, 2B), *CRM*, pp. 275–280 Free-Response Tests (Forms 2C, 2D, 3), *CRM*, pp. 281–286 Vocabulary Test/Review, *CRM*, p. 288	ExamView® Pro (see below) MindJogger Videoquizzes www.pre-alg.com/ vocabulary_review www.pre-alg.com/chapter_test

For more information on Yearly ProgressPro, see p. 144.

Pre-Algebra Lesson	Yearly ProgressPro Skill Lesson
5-1	Compare/Order Positive and Negative Rational Numbers
5-2	Fraction/Decimal/Percent Conversions: Level 2
5-3	Multiply Fractions
5-4	Divide Fractions
5-5	Add/Subtract Fractions with Like Denominatios: Level 3
5-6	Least Common Multiple: Level 2
5-7	Add/Subtract Fractions with Unlike Denominators: Level 3
5-8	Mean; Median; Mode: Level 2
5-9	Solve One-Step Equations with Rational Numbers
5-10	Sequences

ExamView® Pro

Use the networkable **ExamView® Pro** to:
- Create **multiple versions** of tests.
- Create **modified** tests for *Inclusion* students.
- **Edit** existing questions and **add** your own questions.
- Use built-in **state curriculum correlations** to create tests aligned with state standards.
- Change **English** tests to **Spanish** and vice versa.

For more information on Intervention and Assessment, see pp. T8–T11.

Reading and Writing in Mathematics

Glencoe Pre-Algebra provides numerous opportunities to incorporate reading and writing into the mathematics classroom.

Student Edition

- Foldables™ Study Organizer, p. 199
- Reading Mathematics, p. 225
- Concept Check questions require students to verbalize and write about what they have learned in the lesson. (pp. 201, 202, 205, 207, 212, 216, 217, 221, 222, 227, 228, 232, 239, 241, 245, 246, 250, 251)
- Writing in Math questions in every lesson, pp. 204, 209, 214, 219, 223, 230, 236, 242, 247, 251
- Reading Math, pp. 200, 205
- WebQuest, p. 242

Teacher Wraparound Edition

- Foldables™ Study Organizer, pp. 199, 254
- Study Notebook suggestions, pp. 202, 207, 212, 217, 222, 225, 228, 231, 234, 237, 240, 246, 251, 253
- Modeling activities, pp. 214, 236, 252
- Speaking activities, pp. 209, 224, 248
- Writing activities, pp. 204, 219, 230, 242
- Differentiated Instruction (Verbal/Linguistic), p. 228
- **ELL** Resources, pp. 198, 200, 205, 210, 215, 220, 225, 226, 232, 238, 244, 249, 254

For more information on Reading and Writing in Mathematics, see pp. T6–T7.

Additional Resources

- Vocabulary Builder worksheets require students to define and give examples for key vocabulary terms as they progress through the chapter (*Chapter 5 Resource Masters*, pp. vii–viii)
- Reading to Learn Mathematics master for each lesson (*Chapter 5 Resource Masters*, pp. 228, 233, 238, 243, 248, 253, 258, 263, 268, 273)
- *Vocabulary PuzzleMaker* software creates crossword, jumble, and word search puzzles using vocabulary lists that you can customize.
- *Teaching Mathematics with Foldables* provides suggestions for promoting cognition and language.
- *Reading and Writing in the Mathematics Classroom*
- *WebQuest and Project Resources*

 ENGLISH LANGUAGE LEARNERS

Lesson 5-1
Using Manipulatives

Give each group of students a bag with fraction cards inside. Have one student draw a card and find a decimal equivalent for the fraction using a calculator. Make sure students know how to input the numbers into the calculator. Have students write down the answer from the calculator and ask them what they notice. Have the students categorize the quotients as terminating or repeating decimals.

Lesson 5-4
Reading and Writing

Write the term *reciprocal* on the chalkboard and give students examples of how to find the reciprocal of a number. Be sure to include finding reciprocals of whole numbers as well as fractions.

Lesson 5-9
Building on Prior Knowledge

Students who know how to solve equations involving intergers oftern have trouble solving equations with rational numbers because of the more complex computations. In order to help them with this transition, have students solve an equation with whole numbers, than with integers, and then integrate the rational numbers. When students need to perform an operation with the rational numbers, take the operation out of the problem or equation, perform it and then let the variable equal the answer.

What You'll Learn

Have students read over the list of objectives and make a list of any words with which they are not familiar.

Why It's Important

Point out to students that this is only one of many reasons why each objective is important. Others are provided in the introduction to each lesson.

Lesson	NCTM Standards	Local Objectives
5-1	1, 6	
5-2	1, 6, 7	
5-3	1–6, 10	
5-4	1–6	
5-5	1, 2, 6, 7	
5-6	1, 2, 6, 7	
5-6 Follow-Up	1, 2, 7	
5-7	1, 6, 10	
5-8 Preview	2, 5	
5-8	1, 4, 5, 6	
5-8 Follow-Up	5, 6	
5-9	1, 2, 6	
5-10	2, 3, 6–9	
5-10 Follow-Up	2, 3, 6–9	

Key to NCTM Standards:

1=Number & Operations, 2=Algebra, 3=Geometry, 4=Measurement, 5=Data Analysis & Probability, 6=Problem Solving, 7=Reasoning & Proof, 8=Communication, 9=Connections, 10=Representation

Chapter 5 Rational Numbers

What You'll Learn

- **Lessons 5-1 and 5-2** Write fractions as decimals and write decimals as fractions.
- **Lessons 5-3, 5-4, 5-5, and 5-7** Add, subtract, multiply, and divide rational numbers.
- **Lessons 5-6 and 5-9** Use the least common denominator to compare fractions and to solve equations.
- **Lesson 5-8** Use the mean, median, and mode to analyze data.
- **Lesson 5-10** Find the terms of arithmetic and geometric sequences.

Key Vocabulary

- rational number (p. 205)
- algebraic fraction (p. 211)
- multiplicative inverse (p. 215)
- measures of central tendency (p. 238)
- sequence (p. 249)

Why It's Important

Rational numbers are the numbers used most often in the real world. They include fractions, decimals, and integers. Understanding rational numbers is important in understanding and analyzing real-world occurrences, such as changes in barometric pressure during a storm. *You will compare the barometric pressure before and after a storm in Lesson 5-9.*

Vocabulary Builder

ELL

The Key Vocabulary list introduces students to some of the main vocabulary terms included in this chapter. For a more thorough vocabulary list with pronunciations of new words, give students the Vocabulary Builder worksheets found on pages vii and viii of the *Chapter 5 Resource Masters.* Encourage them to complete the definition of each term as they progress through the chapter. You may suggest that they add these sheets to their study notebooks for future reference when studying for the Chapter 5 test.

▶ **Prerequisite Skills** To be successful in this chapter, you'll need to master these skills and be able to apply them in problem-solving situations. Review these skills before beginning Chapter 5.

For Lessons 5-1 through 5-4 — Multiply and Divide Integers

Find each product or quotient. If necessary, round to the nearest tenth.
(For review, see Lessons 2-4 and 2-5.)

1. $3 \div 5$ **0.6**
2. $-1 \div 8$ **−0.1**
3. $2 \cdot 17$ **34**
4. $-12 \cdot 3$ **−36**
5. $-2 \div (-9)$ **0.2**
6. $-4(-6)$ **24**
7. $5(-15)$ **−75**
8. $4 \div (-15)$ **−0.3**
9. $-24 \div 14$ **−1.7**

For Lesson 5-5 — Simplify Fractions Using the GCF

Write each fraction in simplest form. If the fraction is already in simplest form, write *simplified*. *(For review, see Lesson 4-5.)*

10. $\frac{5}{40}$ **$\frac{1}{8}$**
11. $\frac{12}{20}$ **$\frac{3}{5}$**
12. $\frac{14}{39}$ **simplified**
13. $\frac{36}{50}$ **$\frac{18}{25}$**

For Lessons 5-8 through 5-10 — Add and Subtract Integers

Find each sum or difference. *(For review, see Lessons 2-2 and 2-3.)*

14. $4 + (-9)$ **−5**
15. $-10 + 16$ **6**
16. $20 - 12$ **8**
17. $19 - 32$ **−13**
18. $7 + (-5)$ **2**
19. $26 - 11$ **15**
20. $(-3) + (-8)$ **−11**
21. $-1 - (-10)$ **9**

Rational Numbers Make this Foldable to help you organize your notes. Begin with three sheets of $8\frac{1}{2}$" by 11" paper.

Step 1 — Fold and Cut Two Sheets

Fold each sheet in half from top to bottom. Cut along the fold from the edges to the margin.

Step 2 — Fold and Cut the Other Sheet

Fold in half from top to bottom. Cut along fold between the margins.

Step 3 — Fold

Insert the first two sheets through the third sheet and align the folds.

Step 4 — Label

Label each page with a lesson number and title. Write the chapter title on the front.

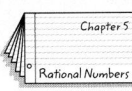

Chapter 5
Rational Numbers

Reading and Writing As you read and study the chapter, fill the journal with notes, diagrams, and examples for rational numbers.

Getting Started

This section provides a review of the basic concepts needed before beginning Chapter 5. Page references are included for additional student help.

Additional review is provided in the *Prerequisite Skills Workbook*, pages 1–2, 15–24, 27–32, and 37–62.

Prerequisite Skills in the Getting Ready for the Next Lesson section at the end of each lesson reviews a skill needed in the next lesson.

For Lesson	Prerequisite Skill
5-2	Simplifying Fractions (p. 204)
5-3	Estimating Products (p. 209)
5-4	GCF of Monomials (p. 214)
5-5	Simplifying Fractions (p. 219)
5-6	Prime Factorization (p. 224)
5-7	Estimating with Fractions (p. 230)
5-8	Adding Integers (p. 236)
5-9	Dividing Decimals (p. 242)
5-10	Dividing Integers (p. 248)

FOLDABLES™ Study Organizer

For more information about Foldables, see *Teaching Mathematics with Foldables.*

Journal Writing Have students write about rational numbers. For example, they might compare fractions and decimals in writing, or they might rename decimals as fractions. Math journals can also be used to record the direction and progress of learning, to describe positive and negative experiences during learning, to write about personal associations and experiences during learning, and to list examples of ways in which new knowledge has or will be used in their daily life.

5-1 Writing Fractions as Decimals

NEW YORK *Performance Indicator* Reinforcement of 6.N.20 Represent fractions as terminating or repeating decimals

What You'll Learn

- Write fractions as terminating or repeating decimals.
- Compare fractions and decimals.

Vocabulary

- terminating decimal
- mixed number
- repeating decimal
- bar notation
- period

How were fractions used to determine the size of the first coins?

In the 18th century, a silver dollar contained $1 worth of silver. The sizes of all other coins were based on this coin.

a. A half dollar contained half the silver of a silver dollar. What was it worth? **$0.50**

b. Write the decimal value of each coin in the table. **$0.25, $0.10, $0.05**

c. Order the fractions in the table from least to greatest. (*Hint:* Use the values of the coins.)

Coin	Fraction of Silver of $1 Coin
quarter-dollar (quarter)	$\frac{1}{4}$
10-cent (dime)	$\frac{1}{10}$
half-dime* (nickel)	$\frac{1}{20}$

* In 1866, nickels were enlarged for convenience

c. $\frac{1}{20}, \frac{1}{10}, \frac{1}{4}$

Reading Math

Terminating
Everyday Meaning: bringing to an end
Math Meaning: a decimal whose digits end

WRITE FRACTIONS AS DECIMALS Any fraction $\frac{a}{b}$, where $b \neq 0$, can be written as a decimal by dividing the numerator by the denominator. So, $\frac{a}{b} = a \div b$. If the division ends, or terminates, when the remainder is zero, the decimal is a **terminating decimal**.

Example 1 Write a Fraction as a Terminating Decimal

Write $\frac{3}{8}$ as a decimal.

Method 1 Use paper and pencil.

$$\begin{array}{r} 0.375 \\ 8)\overline{3.000} \\ \underline{-24} \\ 60 \\ \underline{-56} \\ 40 \\ \underline{-40} \\ 0 \end{array}$$

Division ends when the remainder is 0.

0.375 is a terminating decimal.

Method 2 Use a calculator.

3 ÷ 8 **ENTER** .375

$\frac{3}{8} = 0.375$

A **mixed number** such as $3\frac{1}{2}$ is the sum of a whole number and a fraction. Mixed numbers can also be written as decimals.

Example 2 Write a Mixed Number as a Decimal

Write $3\frac{1}{2}$ as a decimal.

$3\frac{1}{2} = 3 + \frac{1}{2}$ Write as the sum of an integer and a fraction.

$= 3 + 0.5$ $\frac{1}{2} = 0.5$

$= 3.5$ Add.

Not all fractions can be written as terminating decimals.

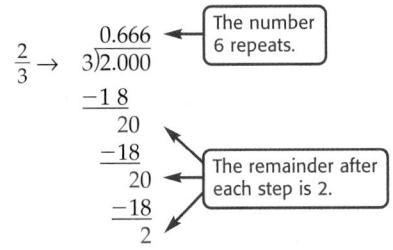

$\frac{2}{3} \rightarrow$

$3\overline{)2.000}$ 0.666 ← The number 6 repeats.

-18

20

-18 ← The remainder after each step is 2.

20

-18

2

CHECK 2 ÷ 3 [ENTER] .6666666667 ✓ The last digit is rounded.

So, $\frac{2}{3} = 0.6666666666\ldots$. This decimal is called a **repeating decimal**. You can use **bar notation** to indicate that the 6 repeats forever.

$0.6666666666\ldots = 0.\overline{6}$ The digit 6 repeats, so place a bar over the 6.

The **period** of a repeating decimal is the digit or digits that repeat. So, the period of $0.\overline{6}$ is 6.

Decimal	Bar Notation	Period
0.13131313...	$0.\overline{13}$	13
6.855555...	$6.8\overline{5}$	5
19.1724724...	$19.1\overline{724}$	724

✓ **Concept Check** Is $0.\overline{75}$ a terminating or a repeating decimal? Explain.
Repeating; the digits 75 repeat.

Example 3 Write Fractions as Repeating Decimals

a. Write $-\frac{6}{11}$ as a decimal.

$-\frac{6}{11} \rightarrow 11\overline{)6.0000\ldots}$ 0.5454... The digits 54 repeat.

So, $-\frac{6}{11} = -0.\overline{54}$.

b. Write $\frac{2}{15}$ as a decimal.

$\frac{2}{15} \rightarrow 15\overline{)2.0000\ldots}$ 0.1333... The digit 3 repeats.

So, $\frac{2}{15} = 0.1\overline{3}$.

 www.pre-alg.com/extra_examples/ny

Lesson 5-1 Writing Fractions as Decimals **201**

Lesson 5-1 Writing Fractions as Decimals **201**

Study Notebook

Have students—

- add the definitions/examples of the vocabulary terms to their Vocabulary Builder worksheets for Chapter 5.
- write a list of commonly used fractions and their decimal equivalents. These may be memorized for convenience. Students should also include an example of expressing a fraction as a decimal using division.
- include any other item(s) that they find helpful in mastering the skills in this lesson.

About the Exercises . . .
Organization by Objective
- **Write Fractions as Decimals:** 13–30
- **Compare Fractions and Decimals:** 31–44

Odd/Even Assignments
Exercises 13–30 and 32–44 are structured so that students practice the same concepts whether they are assigned odd or even problems.

Assignment Guide
Basic: 13–39 odd, 46–73
Average: 13–45 odd, 46–73
Advanced: 14–44 even, 45–65 (Optional: 66–73)

Answer

2. $0.5 = 0.50$ and $0.\overline{5} = 0.55...$; $0.\overline{5}$ is greater because in the hundredths place, $5 > 0$.

COMPARE FRACTIONS AND DECIMALS   It may be easier to compare numbers when they are written as decimals.

Example 4 Compare Fractions and Decimals

Replace ● with <, >, or = to make $\frac{3}{5}$ ● 0.75 a true sentence.

$\frac{3}{5}$ ● 0.75   Write the sentence.

0.6 ● 0.75   Write $\frac{3}{5}$ as a decimal.

$0.6 < 0.75$ In the tenths place, $6 < 7$.

On a number line, 0.6 is to the left of 0.75, so $\frac{3}{5} < 0.75$.

Example 5 Compare Fractions to Solve a Problem

BREAKFAST In a survey of students, $\frac{13}{20}$ of the boys and $\frac{17}{25}$ of the girls make their own breakfast. Of those surveyed, do a greater fraction of boys or girls make their own breakfast?

Write the fractions as decimals and then compare the decimals.

boys: $\frac{13}{20} = 0.65$

girls: $\frac{17}{25} = 0.68$

On a number line, 0.65 is to the left of 0.68. Since $0.65 < 0.68$, $\frac{13}{20} < \frac{17}{25}$. So, a greater fraction of girls make their own breakfast.

Check for Understanding

Concept Check

1. **Describe** the steps you should take to order $\frac{5}{8}$, 0.8, and $\frac{3}{5}$.

1. Sample answer: write the fractions as decimals and then compare.

2. **Explain** how 0.5 and $0.\overline{5}$ are different. Which is greater? **See margin.**

3. **OPEN ENDED** Give an example of a repeating decimal whose period is 14. **Sample answer: $0.\overline{14}$**

Guided Practice

GUIDED PRACTICE KEY	
Exercises	Examples
4, 5	1, 2
6, 7	3
8–11	4
12	5

Write each fraction or mixed number as a decimal. Use a bar to show a repeating decimal.

4. $\frac{7}{8}$ **0.875**   5. $2\frac{2}{25}$ **2.08**   6. $-\frac{5}{9}$ **$-0.\overline{5}$**   7. $\frac{4}{15}$ **$0.2\overline{6}$**

Replace each ● with <, >, or = to make a true sentence.

8. $\frac{9}{10}$ ● 0.90 **=**   9. 0.3 ● $\frac{1}{3}$ **<**   10. $\frac{1}{4}$ ● $\frac{1}{3}$ **<**   11. $-\frac{3}{4}$ ● $-\frac{7}{8}$ **>**

Application

12. **TRUCKS** Of all the passenger trucks sold each year in the United States, $\frac{1}{5}$ are pickups and 0.17 are SUVs. Are more SUVs or pickups sold? Explain. **Source:** U.S. Department of Energy, EPA **Pickups; $\frac{1}{5} = 0.2$, and $0.2 > 0.17$.**

DAILY
INTERVENTION   **Differentiated Instruction**

- **Kinesthetic** Give each student a large index card with a fraction or mixed number on one side. Each student should rewrite the number as a decimal on the back side of the card. Then have students line up in the front of the classroom in order from least value to greatest value.

★ indicates increased difficulty

Practice and Apply

Homework Help

For Exercises	See Examples
13–20	1, 2
21–28	3
32–43	4
46, 47	5

Extra Practice
See page 733.

Write each fraction or mixed number as a decimal. Use a bar to show a repeating decimal.

13. $\frac{1}{5}$ 0.2

14. $\frac{3}{20}$ 0.15

15. $\frac{8}{25}$ 0.32

16. $-\frac{5}{8}$ −0.625

17. $7\frac{3}{10}$ 7.3

18. $1\frac{1}{2}$ 1.5

19. $5\frac{1}{8}$ 5.125

20. $-3\frac{3}{4}$ −3.75

21. $\frac{1}{9}$ $0.\overline{1}$

22. $-\frac{2}{9}$ $-0.\overline{2}$

23. $-\frac{5}{11}$ $-0.\overline{45}$

24. $\frac{4}{11}$ $0.\overline{36}$

25. $\frac{1}{6}$ $0.1\overline{6}$

26. $\frac{7}{15}$ $0.4\overline{6}$

27. $\frac{5}{16}$ 0.3125

★ 28. $\frac{7}{12}$ $0.58\overline{3}$

29. **ANIMALS** A marlin can swim $\frac{5}{6}$ mile in one minute. Write $\frac{5}{6}$ as a decimal rounded to the nearest hundredth. **0.83**

30. **COMPUTERS** In a survey, 17 students out of 20 said they use a home PC as a reference source for school projects. Write 17 out of 20 as a decimal.
Source: NPD Online Research **0.85**

31. Order $\frac{7}{8}$, 0.8, and $\frac{7}{9}$ from least to greatest. $\frac{7}{9}$, **0.8**, $\frac{7}{8}$

Replace each ● with <, >, or = to make a true sentence.

32. 0.3 ● $\frac{1}{4}$ >

33. $\frac{5}{8}$ ● 0.65 <

34. $\frac{2}{5}$ ● 0.4 =

35. $\frac{1}{3}$ ● $\frac{1}{2}$ <

36. $\frac{1}{5}$ ● $0.\overline{5}$ <

37. $1\frac{1}{20}$ ● 1.01 >

38. $\frac{7}{8}$ ● $\frac{8}{9}$ <

39. $3\frac{4}{9}$ ● $3.\overline{4}$ =

40. 6.18 ● $6\frac{1}{5}$ <

★ 41. -0.75 ● $-\frac{7}{9}$ >

★ 42. $0.3\overline{4}$ ● $\frac{34}{99}$ >

★ 43. $-2\frac{1}{12}$ ● −2.09 >

44. On a number line, would $\frac{11}{15}$ be graphed to the right or to the left of $\frac{3}{4}$? Explain. **To the left;** $\frac{11}{15} = 0.7\overline{3}$ **and** $\frac{3}{4} = 0.75$; **since** $0.7\overline{3} < 0.75$, $\frac{11}{15} < \frac{3}{4}$.

★ 45. Find a terminating and a repeating decimal between $\frac{1}{6}$ and $\frac{8}{9}$. Explain how you found them. **See margin.**

SCHOOL For Exercises 46 and 47, use the graphic at the right and the information below.

28% = 0.28	21% = 0.21
16% = 0.16	15% = 0.15
13% = 0.13	5% = 0.05

46. More than; $\frac{1}{4}$ **=**
0.25 and 0.28 > 0.25.

46. Did more or less than one-fourth of the students surveyed choose math as their favorite subject? Explain.

47. This is greater than those who chose English in the survey because $\frac{1}{7} \approx 0.14$, **and 0.14 > 0.13.**

47. Suppose $\frac{1}{7}$ of the students in your class choose English as their favorite subject. How does this compare to the results of the survey? Explain.

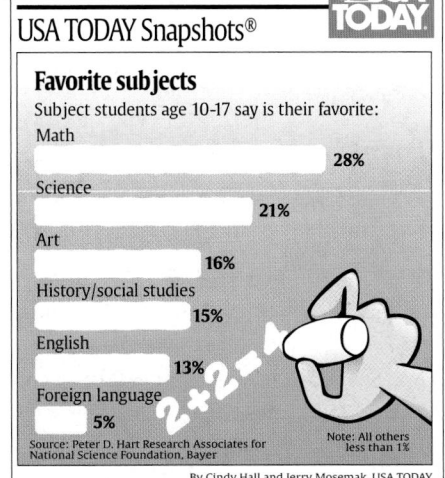

USA TODAY Snapshots®

Favorite subjects
Subject students age 10-17 say is their favorite:

Math **28%**
Science **21%**
Art **16%**
History/social studies **15%**
English **13%**
Foreign language **5%**

Source: Peter D. Hart Research Associates for National Science Foundation, Bayer
Note: All others less than 1%

By Cindy Hall and Jerry Mosemak, USA TODAY

Answer

45. **Sample answer: 0.7 and** $0.\overline{7}$; $\frac{1}{6} = 0.1\overline{6}$
and $\frac{8}{9} = 0.\overline{8}$; **0.7 and** $0.\overline{7}$ **are both greater than** $0.1\overline{6}$ **and less than** $0.\overline{8}$.

Study Guide and Intervention, p. 225

Fractions can be written as decimals by dividing the numerator by the denominator. If the division ends, or terminates, when the remainder is 0, it is a terminating decimal. If the decimal number repeats without end, it is a repeating decimal.

Example 1 Write each fraction as a decimal.

a. $\frac{7}{8}$

$$\begin{array}{r} 0.875 \\ 8\overline{)7.000} \\ \underline{6\,4} \\ 60 \\ \underline{56} \\ 40 \\ \underline{40} \\ 0 \end{array}$$

b. $\frac{4}{9}$

$$\begin{array}{r} 0.444 \\ 9\overline{)4.000} \\ \underline{3\,6} \\ 40 \\ \underline{36} \\ 40 \\ \underline{36} \\ 0 \end{array}$$

0.875 is a terminating decimal.

0.4... or $0.\overline{4}$ is a repeating decimal.

It may be easier to compare numbers if they are written as decimals.

Example 2 Replace ● with <, >, or = to make $\frac{3}{8}$ ● 0.28 a true sentence.

$\frac{3}{8} = 0.375$, so $\frac{3}{8}$ ● 0.28 can be written as 0.375 ● 0.28. Since 0.375 > 0.28, $\frac{3}{8}$ > 0.28.

Exercises

Write each fraction or mixed number as a decimal. Use a bar to show a repeating decimal.

1. $\frac{7}{20}$ 0.35
2. $\frac{2}{11}$ $0.\overline{18}$
3. $\frac{5}{9}$ $0.\overline{5}$
4. $\frac{5}{6}$ $0.8\overline{3}$
5. $\frac{6}{25}$ 0.24
6. $\frac{5}{20}$ 0.25
7. $8\frac{3}{5}$ 8.6
8. $3\frac{7}{25}$ 3.28
9. $1\frac{4}{15}$ $1.2\overline{6}$
10. $\frac{12}{32}$ 0.375
11. $-6\frac{9}{10}$ −6.9
12. $1\frac{5}{11}$ $1.\overline{45}$

Replace each ● with <, >, or = to make a true sentence.

13. $\frac{5}{8}$ ● $\frac{6}{9}$ <
14. $1\frac{4}{5}$ ● 1.8 =
15. $-2\frac{7}{8}$ ● $-2\frac{4}{5}$ <
16. 5.09 ● $5\frac{1}{2}$ <
17. 9.3 ● $\frac{28}{3}$ <
18. $\frac{28}{20}$ ● $\frac{31}{23}$ >

Skills Practice, p. 226 and Practice, p. 227 (shown)

Write each fraction or mixed number as a decimal. Use a bar to show a repeating decimal.

1. $\frac{3}{5}$ 0.6
2. $\frac{1}{8}$ 0.125
3. $\frac{9}{11}$ $0.\overline{81}$
4. $-\frac{3}{16}$ −0.1875
5. $\frac{3}{40}$ 0.075
6. $\frac{8}{11}$ $0.\overline{72}$
7. $\frac{5}{12}$ $0.41\overline{6}$
8. $\frac{1}{3}$ $0.\overline{3}$
9. $\frac{7}{9}$ $0.\overline{7}$
10. $-\frac{11}{15}$ $-0.7\overline{3}$
11. $-\frac{12}{16}$ −0.75
12. $\frac{13}{60}$ $0.21\overline{6}$
13. $\frac{1}{45}$ $0.0\overline{2}$
14. $-\frac{5}{24}$ $-0.208\overline{3}$
15. $\frac{13}{20}$ 0.65
16. $\frac{17}{18}$ $0.9\overline{4}$
17. $-11\frac{1}{4}$ −11.25
18. $23\frac{5}{11}$ $23.\overline{45}$
19. $-18\frac{2}{3}$ $-18.\overline{6}$
20. $5\frac{7}{8}$ 5.875

Replace each ● with <, >, or = to make a true sentence.

21. $-\frac{13}{2}$ ● −6.4 <
22. $\frac{6}{7}$ ● $\frac{5}{9}$ >
23. −0.75 ● $-\frac{15}{20}$ =
24. $-4\frac{3}{8}$ ● −4.40 >
25. $\frac{7}{8}$ ● $\frac{8}{9}$ <
26. $-\frac{33}{100}$ ● $-0.\overline{3}$ >

27. Order $\frac{4}{9}$, $\frac{444}{1000}$, and 0.4 from least to greatest. 0.4, $\frac{444}{1000}$, $\frac{4}{9}$

28. Order $-\frac{8}{9}$, $-\frac{8}{10}$, and $-0.\overline{80}$ from least to greatest. $-\frac{8}{9}$, $-0.\overline{80}$, $-\frac{8}{10}$

29. **OPINION** In a school survey, 787 out of 1000 students preferred hip-hop music to techno. Is this figure more or less than $\frac{7}{9}$ of those surveyed? Explain.
More; $\frac{787}{1000} = 0.787$ **and** $\frac{7}{9} = 0.\overline{7}$, **so** $\frac{787}{1000}$ **is greater than** $\frac{7}{9}$.

Enrichment, p. 229

GCF, LCM, and Ladders
When two or more numbers have common factors, the greatest of these is called the **greatest common factor (GCF)**. When two or more numbers have nonzero common multiples, the least of these is called the **least common multiple (LCM)** of the numbers. A method of determining the GCF and LCM for two or more numbers is the ladder.

Example Find the GCF and LCM of 24 and 36.

6	24	36	Find any number that will divide into both numbers.
2	4	6	Both 24 and 36 can be divided evenly by 6.
1	2	3	Continue to choose divisors until the only remaining divisor is 1.
	2	3	

To find the GCF, multiply all the divisors.
6 · 2 · 1 = 12 The GCF is 12.

To find the LCM, multiply the GCF and the numbers remaining on the bottom of the ladder.
12 · 2 · 3 = 72 The LCM is 72.

Find the GCF and LCM for each pair of numbers by using a ladder. The numbers used as divisors in the ladder may vary.

1. 18, 27
GCF: 9
LCM: 54

2. 24, 42
GCF: 6
LCM: 168

3. 44, 66
GCF: 22
LCM: 132

4. 36, 81
GCF: 9
LCM: 324

5. 42, 48
GCF: 6
LCM: 336

6. 100, 125
GCF: 25
LCM: 500

7. 64, 72
GCF: 8
LCM: 576

8. 90, 150
GCF: 30
LCM: 450

9. 250, 300
GCF: 50
LCM: 1500

Open-Ended Assessment

Writing Have students write three fractions. They should express each as a decimal, explain whether they are terminating or repeating, then order them. Encourage students to utilize as many math terms as possible in their explanations.

Getting Ready
for Lesson 5-2

PREREQUISITE SKILL Lesson 5-2 presents rational numbers. Students will need to be able to write rational numbers as fractions. Exercises 66–73 should be used to determine your students' familiarity with simplifying fractions.

Answers

48a. $2 = 2$, $3 = 3$, $4 = 2^2$, $5 = 5$,
  $6 = 2 \cdot 3$, $8 = 2^3$, $9 = 3^2$,
  $10 = 2 \cdot 5$, $12 = 2^2 \cdot 3$,
  $15 = 3 \cdot 5$, $20 = 2^2 \cdot 5$

48b. $\frac{1}{2} = 0.5$, $\frac{1}{3} = 0.\overline{3}$, $\frac{1}{4} = 0.25$,

  $\frac{1}{5} = 0.2$, $\frac{1}{6} = 0.1\overline{6}$, $\frac{1}{8} = 0.125$,

  $\frac{1}{9} = 0.\overline{1}$, $\frac{1}{10} = 0.1$, $\frac{1}{12} = 0.083\overline{3}$,

  $\frac{1}{15} = 0.0\overline{6}$, $\frac{1}{20} = 0.05$

48c. Sample answer: Fractions whose denominators have only 2 or 5 as prime factors are terminating decimals. Fractions whose denominators have 3 as a prime factor are repeating decimals.

49. All coins were made with a fraction of silver that was contained in a silver dollar. Answers should include the following.

  • A quarter had one-fourth the amount of silver as a silver dollar, a dime had one-tenth the amount, and a nickel had one-twentieth the amount.

  • It is easier to perform arithmetic operations using decimals rather than using fractions.

---

48. CRITICAL THINKING a–c. See margin.

  a. Write the prime factorization of each denominator in the fractions listed below.

  $$\frac{1}{2}, \frac{1}{3}, \frac{1}{4}, \frac{1}{5}, \frac{1}{6}, \frac{1}{8}, \frac{1}{9}, \frac{1}{10}, \frac{1}{12}, \frac{1}{15}, \frac{1}{20}$$

  b. Write the decimal equivalent of each fraction.

  c. **Make a conjecture** relating prime factors of denominators and the decimal equivalents of fractions.

49. Answer the question that was posed at the beginning of the lesson. **See margin.**

  How were fractions used to determine the size of the first coins?

  Include the following in your answer:

  • a description of the first coins, and

  • an explanation of why decimals rather than fractions are used in money exchange today.

NEW YORK
Test Practice

Standardized
Test Practice
Ⓐ Ⓑ Ⓒ Ⓓ

50. Which decimal is equivalent to $\frac{1}{100}$? **B**

  Ⓐ 0.001   Ⓑ 0.01   Ⓒ 0.1   Ⓓ $0.\overline{1}$

51. Write the shaded portion of the figure at the right as a decimal. **D**

  Ⓐ 0.6   Ⓑ $0.\overline{6}$
  Ⓒ 0.63   Ⓓ $0.6\overline{3}$

Maintain Your Skills

Mixed Review **Write each number in scientific notation.** *(Lesson 4-8)*

52. 854,000,000
  8.54×10^8

53. 0.077
  7.7×10^{-2}

54. 0.00016
  1.6×10^{-4}

55. 925,000
  9.25×10^5

Write each expression using a positive exponent. *(Lesson 4-7)*

56. 10^{-5} $\frac{1}{10^5}$

57. $(-2)^{-7}$ $\frac{1}{(-2)^7}$

58. x^{-4} $\frac{1}{x^4}$

59. y^{-3} $\frac{1}{y^3}$

60. ALGEBRA Write $(a \cdot a \cdot a)(a \cdot a)$ using an exponent. *(Lesson 4-2)* a^5

61. TRANSPORTATION A car can travel an average of 464 miles on one tank of gas. If the tank holds 16 gallons of gasoline, how many miles per gallon does it get? *(Lesson 3-7)* **29**

ALGEBRA **Solve each equation. Check your solution.** *(Lesson 3-4)*

62. $4n = 32$ **8**

63. $-64 = 2t$ **−32**

64. $\frac{a}{5} = -9$ **−45**

65. $-8 = \frac{x}{-7}$ **56**

Getting Ready for
the Next Lesson

PREREQUISITE SKILL **Simplify each fraction.**
*(To review **simplifying fractions**, see Lesson 4-5.)*

66. $\frac{4}{30}$ $\frac{2}{15}$

67. $\frac{5}{65}$ $\frac{1}{13}$

68. $\frac{36}{60}$ $\frac{3}{5}$

69. $\frac{12}{18}$ $\frac{2}{3}$

70. $\frac{21}{24}$ $\frac{7}{8}$

71. $\frac{16}{28}$ $\frac{4}{7}$

72. $\frac{32}{48}$ $\frac{2}{3}$

73. $\frac{125}{1000}$ $\frac{1}{8}$

What You'll Learn

• Write rational numbers as fractions.

• Identify and classify rational numbers.

Vocabulary

• rational number

NEW YORK
Performance Indicator
Reinforcement of 7.N.1
Distinguish between the various subsets of real numbers (counting/natural numbers, whole numbers, integers, rational numbers, and irrational numbers)

b. The set of rational numbers includes natural numbers, whole numbers, and integers.
c. Yes; any natural number can be written as a fraction with a denominator of 1. No; $\frac{8}{9}$ is rational, but it is not a natural number.

How are rational numbers related to other sets of numbers?

The solution of $2x = 4$ is 2. It is a member of the set of *natural numbers* N = {1, 2, 3, ...}.

The solution of $x + 3 = 3$ is 0. It is a member of the set of *whole numbers* W = {0, 1, 2, 3, ...}.

The solution of $x + 5 = 2$ is -3. It is a member of the set of *integers* I = {..., −3, −2, −1, 0, 1, 2, 3, ...}.

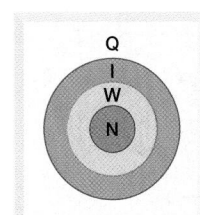

The solution of $2x = 3$ is $\frac{3}{2}$, which is neither a natural number, a whole number, nor an integer. It is a member of the set of *rational numbers* Q. ⟶

Rational numbers include fractions and decimals as well as natural numbers, whole numbers, and integers.

a. Is 7 a natural number? a whole number? an integer? **yes; yes; yes**

b. How do you know that 7 is also a rational number?

c. Is every natural number a rational number? Is every rational number a natural number? Give an explanation or a counterexample to support your answers.

Reading Math

Rational
Root Word: Ratio
A *ratio* is the comparison of two quantities by division. Recall that $\frac{a}{b} = a \div b$, where $b \neq 0$.

WRITE RATIONAL NUMBERS AS FRACTIONS
A number that can be written as a fraction is called a **rational number**. Some examples of rational numbers are shown below.

$$0.75 = \frac{3}{4} \qquad -0.\overline{3} = -\frac{1}{3} \qquad 28 = \frac{28}{1} \qquad 1\frac{1}{4} = \frac{5}{4}$$

Example 1 Write Mixed Numbers and Integers as Fractions

a. Write $5\frac{2}{3}$ as a fraction.

$5\frac{2}{3} = \frac{17}{3}$ Write $5\frac{2}{3}$ as an improper fraction.

b. Write -3 as a fraction.

$-3 = \frac{-3}{1}$ or $-\frac{3}{1}$

✓ **Concept Check** Explain why any integer n is a rational number.
It can be written as a fraction $\frac{n}{1}$.

---

1 Focus

5-Minute Check Transparency 5-2 Use as a quiz or review of Lesson 5-1.

Mathematical Background notes are available for this lesson on page 198C.

How are rational numbers related to other sets of numbers?

The opening activity questions are repeated on page 233 of the *Chapter 5 Resource Masters*.

Reading to Learn Mathematics, p. 233 **ELL**

Pre-Activity How are rational numbers related to other sets of numbers?

Do the activity at the top of page 205 in your textbook. Write your answers below.

a. Is 7 a natural number? a whole number? an integer?
yes; yes; yes

b. How do you know that 7 is also a rational number?
The set of rational numbers includes natural numbers, whole numbers, and integers.

c. Is every natural number a rational number? Is every rational number a natural number? Give an explanation or a counterexample to support your answers. Yes; any natural number can be written as a fraction with a denominator of 1. No; $\frac{8}{9}$ is rational, but it is not a natural number.

Reading the Lesson

Write a definition and give an example of the new vocabulary term.

	Vocabulary	Definition	Example
1.	rational number	See students' work.	

2. **Terminating** decimals can be written as fractions with a denominator of 10, 100, 1000, and so on.

3. A number such as π is called **irrational** because it cannot be written as a fraction.

4. Is −3 a rational number? Explain. Yes, any integer is a rational number.

Helping You Remember

5. *Irrational* is a word that is used in everyday English.

a. Find the definition of *irrational* in the dictionary. Write the definition. not endowed with reason or understanding

b. Explain how the English definition can help you remember how irrational and rational are used in mathematics. The decimal form of an irrational number has no repeating pattern or terminating features, whereas rational numbers do.

Resource Manager

Workbooks and Reproducible Masters

Chapter 5 Resource Masters
• Study Guide and Intervention, p. 230
• Skills Practice, p. 231
• Practice, p. 232
• Reading to Learn Mathematics, p. 233
• Enrichment, p. 234

Parent and Student Study Guide Workbook, p. 34
School-to-Career Masters, p. 9

Transparencies

5-Minute Check Transparency 5-2
Answer Key Transparencies

Technology

Interactive Chalkboard

WRITE RATIONAL NUMBERS AS FRACTIONS

1 a. Write $-4\frac{3}{8}$ as a fraction.

$-\frac{35}{8}$

b. Write 10 as a fraction. $\frac{10}{1}$

2 Write each decimal as a fraction or mixed number in simplest form.

a. 0.26 $\frac{13}{50}$

b. 2.875 $2\frac{7}{8}$

3 Write $0.\overline{39}$ as a fraction in simplest form. $\frac{13}{33}$

Teaching Tip Remind students that reading a decimal number properly gives a fraction, so 0.12 is 12 hundredths or $\frac{12}{100}$.

 Skills Check

Write Rational Numbers as Fractions Ask students to explain whether each of the following is a rational number. If so, how do you express the decimals as fractions?

a. 0.125   b. $0.\overline{125}$

IDENTIFY AND CLASSIFY RATIONAL NUMBERS

 In-Class Example

4 Identify all sets to which each number belongs.

a. 15   whole number, integer, and rational

b. $\frac{1}{8}$ rational

c. 0.30303030 . . .   rational

Terminating decimals are rational numbers because they can be written as a fraction with a denominator of 10, 100, 1000, and so on.

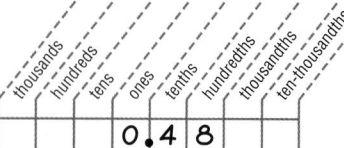 Write Terminating Decimals as Fractions

Write each decimal as a fraction or mixed number in simplest form.

a. **0.48**

$0.48 = \frac{48}{100}$ 0.48 is 48 hundredths.

$= \frac{12}{25}$ Simplify. The GCF of 48 and 100 is 4.

b. **6.375**

$6.375 = 6\frac{375}{1000}$ 6.375 is 6 and 375 thousandths.

$= 6\frac{3}{8}$ Simplify. The GCF of 375 and 1000 is 125.

Reading Math

Decimals
Use the word *and* to represent the decimal point.
- Read 0.375 as three hundred seventy-five thousandths.
- Read 300.075 as three hundred *and* seventy-five thousandths.

Any repeating decimal can be written as a fraction, so repeating decimals are also rational numbers.

Study Tip

Repeating Decimals
When *two* digits repeat, multiply each side by 100. Then subtract *N* from 100*N* to eliminate the repeating part.

 Write Repeating Decimals as Fractions

Write $0.\overline{8}$ as a fraction in simplest form.

$N = 0.888\ldots$ Let N represent the number.

$10N = 10(0.888\ldots)$ Multiply each side by 10 because one digit repeats.
$10N = 8.888\ldots$

Subtract N from 10N to eliminate the repeating part, 0.888... .

$\begin{aligned} 10N &= 8.888\ldots \\ -(N &= 0.888\ldots) \\ \hline 9N &= 8 \end{aligned}$ $10N - N = 10N - 1N$ or $9N$

$\frac{9N}{9} = \frac{8}{9}$ Divide each side by 9.

$N = \frac{8}{9}$ Simplify.

Therefore, $0.\overline{8} = \frac{8}{9}$.

CHECK 8 ÷ 9 [ENTER] .8888888889 ✓

IDENTIFY AND CLASSIFY RATIONAL NUMBERS All rational numbers can be written as terminating or repeating decimals. Decimals that are neither terminating nor repeating, such as the numbers below, are called *irrational* because they cannot be written as fractions. *You will learn more about irrational numbers in Chapter 9.*

$\pi = 3.141592654\ldots$ → The digits do not repeat.

$4.232232223\ldots$ → The same block of digits do not repeat.

Teacher to Teacher

Teri Willard   **Mathematics Consultant, Belgrade, MT**

"I like for students to see the patterns that develop in the rational numbers before simplifying. For example, $0.\overline{2} = \frac{2}{9}$, $0.\overline{35} = \frac{35}{99}$, $0.\overline{625} = \frac{625}{999}$, and $0.\overline{7123} = \frac{7123}{9999}$. The number of 9s in the denominator is the same as the number of repeated digits."

The following model can help you classify rational numbers.

Concept Summary   *Rational Numbers*

- **Words** A rational number is any number that can be expressed as the quotient $\frac{a}{b}$ of two integers, a and b, where $b \neq 0$.

- **Model**

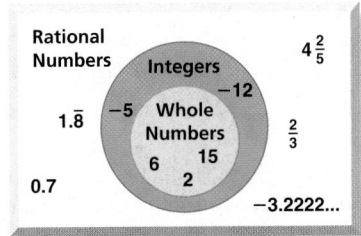

Example 4 *Classify Numbers*

Identify all sets to which each number belongs.

a. -6

   -6 is an integer and a rational number.

b. $2\frac{4}{5}$

   Because $2\frac{4}{5} = \frac{14}{5}$, it is a rational number. It is neither a whole number nor an integer.

c. $0.914114111…$

   This is a nonterminating, nonrepeating decimal. So, it is not a rational number.

TEACHING TIP
Point out that the decimal in Example 4c is nonrepeating because the 1 does not repeat the same number of times.

Check for Understanding

Concept Check

1. **Define** *rational number* in your own words.

2. **OPEN ENDED** Give an example of a number that is not rational. Explain why it is not rational. **See margin.**

1. any number that can be written as a fraction

Guided Practice **Write each number as a fraction.**

3. $-2\frac{1}{3}$ $-\frac{7}{3}$ 4. 10 $\frac{10}{1}$

GUIDED PRACTICE KEY

Exercises	Examples
3, 4	1
5, 6, 11	2
7, 8	3
9, 10	4

Write each decimal as a fraction or mixed number in simplest form.

5. 0.8 $\frac{4}{5}$ 6. 6.35 $6\frac{7}{20}$ 7. $-0.\overline{7}$ $-\frac{7}{9}$ 8. $0.\overline{45}$ $\frac{5}{11}$

Identify all sets to which each number belongs.

9. -5 I, Q   10. 6.05 Q

Application 11. **MEASUREMENT** A *micron* is a unit of measure that is approximately 0.000039 inch. Express this as a fraction. $\frac{39}{1,000,000}$

Study Notebook

Have students—
- add the definition/example of the vocabulary term to their Vocabulary Builder worksheets for Chapter 5.
- copy the Venn diagram on page 207 showing the relationships among the sets of numbers.
- include any other item(s) that they find helpful in mastering the skills in this lesson.

About the Exercises . . .

Organization by Objective
- **Write Rational Numbers as Fractions:** 12–33, 42–43
- **Identify and Classify Rational Numbers:** 34–41, 44–46

Odd/Even Assignments
Exercises 12–43 are structured so that students practice the same concepts whether they are assigned odd or even problems.

Assignment Guide

Basic: 13–25 odd, 29–41 odd, 45, 47, 50–75

Average: 13–49 odd, 50–75

Advanced: 12–48 even, 49–69 (Optional: 70–75)

Answer

2. Sample answer: 1.242442444… is not rational because it is nonrepeating and nonterminating.

DAILY
INTERVENTION   **Differentiated Instruction**

- **Visual/Spatial** Make a transparency of the Venn diagram shown on page 207 (omit the example numbers). Call a student to the front to place a number on the diagram. The class then identifies the sets to which the number belongs. Continue in this manner until each section has at least two examples.

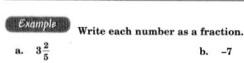

Study Guide and Intervention, p. 230

A number that can be written as a fraction is called a **rational number**. Mixed numbers, integers, and many decimals can be written as fractions. Only decimals that terminate or repeat can be written as fractions. Other decimal numbers such as $\pi = 3.14159265\ldots$ are infinite and nonrepeating. They are called **irrational numbers**.

Example Write each number as a fraction.

a. $3\frac{2}{5}$

$3\frac{2}{5} = \frac{17}{5}$ Write the mixed number as an improper fraction.

b. -7

$-7 = -\frac{7}{1}$ The denominator is 1.

c. 0.14

0.14 is 14 hundredths.

$0.14 = \frac{14}{100}$ or $\frac{7}{50}$ Simplify.

d. $0.\overline{5}$

$0.\overline{5} = 0.555\ldots$

$N = 0.555\ldots$ Let N represent the number.

$10N = 5.555\ldots$ Multiply each side by 10 because one digit repeats.

$\begin{array}{l}10N = 5.555\ldots \\ -(N = 0.555\ldots) \\ \hline 9N = 5\end{array}$ Subtract N from $10N$.

$\frac{9N}{9} = \frac{5}{9}$ Divide each side by 9.

$N = \frac{5}{9}$ Simplify.

The diagram at the right illustrates the relationships among whole numbers, integers, and rational numbers.

Exercises

Write each number as a fraction.

1. $1\frac{1}{5}$ $\frac{6}{5}$ 2. -2 $-\frac{2}{1}$ 3. 0.7 $\frac{7}{10}$

4. 0.32 $\frac{8}{25}$ 5. $-0.\overline{1}$ $-\frac{1}{9}$ 6. $0.\overline{49}$ $\frac{49}{99}$

Identify all sets to which each number belongs (N = natural numbers, W = whole numbers, I = integers, Q = rational numbers).

7. -12 I, Q   8. 8.5 Q   9. 582 W, N, Q

Skills Practice, p. 231 and Practice, p. 232 (shown)

Write each number as a fraction.

1. 29 $\frac{29}{1}$ 2. 0 $\frac{0}{1}$

3. $3\frac{7}{8}$ $\frac{31}{8}$ 4. -47 $-\frac{47}{1}$

5. $-5\frac{6}{7}$ $-\frac{41}{7}$ 6. $4\frac{3}{20}$ $\frac{83}{20}$

7. $-7\frac{2}{15}$ $-\frac{107}{15}$ 8. $10\frac{2}{9}$ $\frac{92}{9}$

Write each decimal as a fraction or mixed number in simplest form.

9. 0.32 $\frac{8}{25}$ 10. 0.42 $\frac{21}{50}$

11. $0.\overline{8}$ $\frac{8}{9}$ 12. $-6.\overline{3}$ $-6\frac{1}{3}$

13. 0.91 $\frac{91}{100}$ 14. 17.875 $17\frac{7}{8}$

15. $-0.666\ldots$ $-\frac{2}{3}$ 16. 0.07 $\frac{7}{100}$

17. $9.\overline{7}$ $9\frac{7}{9}$ 18. 7.75 $7\frac{3}{4}$

19. 0.525 $\frac{21}{40}$ 20. -8.26 $-8\frac{13}{50}$

21. $6.\overline{5}$ $6\frac{5}{9}$ 22. -4.12 $-4\frac{3}{25}$

23. 13.006 $13\frac{3}{500}$ 24. $3.\overline{34}$ $3\frac{34}{99}$

Identify all sets to which each number belongs (N = natural numbers, W = whole numbers, I = integers, Q = rational numbers).

25. 15 W, N, I, Q   26. $-3.\overline{8}$ Q

27. -5.075 Q   28. $\frac{50}{25}$ W, N, I, Q

29. π not rational   30. $-\frac{4}{2}$ I, Q

31. **BOTANY** The smallest flowering plant is the flowering aquatic duckweed found in Australia. It is 0.0236 inch long and 0.0129 inch wide. Write these dimensions as fractions in simplest form.

$\frac{59}{2500}$ in. long and $\frac{129}{10,000}$ in. wide

Enrichment, p. 234

Irrational Numbers

Decimals in which a digit or group of digits repeats are called **repeating decimals**.

Example
$0.333\ldots = 0.\overline{3}$
$1.454545\ldots = 1.\overline{45}$ The bar indicates the repeating digit or digits.

Decimals in which only a 0 repeats are called **terminating decimals**.

Example
$0.5000\ldots = 0.5$
$42.19500\ldots = 42.195$

Consider the decimal $0.757757775\ldots$ It does not terminate in zero nor does it have a group of digits that repeat. Numbers that are represented by nonterminating, nonrepeating decimals are **irrational numbers**.

Example
$\pi = 3.14159\ldots$
$\sqrt{5} = 2.236068\ldots$

Determine whether each decimal is repeating or nonrepeating.

1. $0.373373337\ldots$ nonrepeating   2. $24.15971597\ldots$ repeating   3. $5.71571571\ldots$ repeating

4. $0.5795579555\ldots$ nonrepeating   5. $8.3121121112\ldots$ nonrepeating

Name the next three digits in the following irrational numbers.

6. $0.13141516\ldots$ 171   7. $0.96796679666\ldots$ 796

Name an irrational number between each pair of numbers. Answers will vary. Sample answers given.

8. 6.7 and 6.8 $6.7121221222\ldots$ 9. 17.3 and 17.4 $17.353553555\ldots$

10. $0.1231233\ldots$ and $0.1231134111\ldots$ $0.1231152552555\ldots$

11. $2.333\ldots$ and $2.444\ldots$ $2.43344333444\ldots$

Find each sum.

12. $0.232232223\ldots + 0.323323332\ldots$ $0.555555555\ldots$ or $0.\overline{5}$

13. $0.131131113\ldots + 0.868868886\ldots$ $0.999999999\ldots$ or $0.\overline{9}$

Practice and Apply

Homework Help

For Exercises	See Examples
12–15	1
16–21, 28–33	2
22–27	3
34–41	4

Extra Practice
See page 733.

Write each number as a fraction.

12. $5\frac{2}{3}$ $\frac{17}{3}$ 13. $-1\frac{4}{7}$ $-\frac{11}{7}$ 14. -21 $-\frac{21}{1}$ 15. 60 $\frac{60}{1}$

Write each decimal as a fraction or mixed number in simplest form.

16. 0.4 $\frac{2}{5}$ 17. 0.09 $\frac{9}{100}$ 18. 5.22 $5\frac{11}{50}$ 19. 1.68 $1\frac{17}{25}$

20. 0.625 $\frac{5}{8}$ 21. 8.004 $8\frac{1}{250}$ 22. $0.\overline{2}$ $\frac{2}{9}$ 23. $-0.333\ldots$ $-\frac{1}{3}$

24. $4.\overline{5}$ $4\frac{5}{9}$ 25. $5.\overline{6}$ $5\frac{2}{3}$ ★ 26. $0.\overline{32}$ $\frac{32}{99}$ ★ 27. $2.\overline{25}$ $2\frac{25}{99}$

28. **WHITE HOUSE** The White House covers an area of 0.028 square mile. What fraction of a square mile is this? $\frac{7}{250}$

29. **RECYCLING** In 1999, 0.06 of all recycled newspapers were used to make tissues. What fraction is this? $\frac{3}{50}$

GEOGRAPHY Africa makes up $\frac{1}{5}$ of all the land on Earth. Use the table to find the fraction of Earth's land that is made up by other continents. Write each fraction in simplest form.

30. Antarctica $\frac{19}{200}$ 31. Asia $\frac{59}{200}$

32. Europe $\frac{7}{100}$ 33. North America $\frac{4}{25}$

Continent	Decimal Portion of Earth's Land
Antarctica	0.095
Asia	0.295
Europe	0.07
North America	0.16

Source: *Incredible Comparisons*

Identify all sets to which each number belongs.

34. 4 N, W, I, Q   35. -7 I, Q   36. $-2\frac{5}{8}$ Q   37. $\frac{6}{3}$ N, W, I, Q

38. 15.8 Q   39. $9.0202020\ldots$ Q   40. $1.2345\ldots$ not rational   41. $30.151151115\ldots$ not rational

42. Write 125 thousandths as a fraction in simplest form. $\frac{1}{8}$

★ 43. Express *two hundred and nineteen hundredths* as a fraction or mixed number in simplest form. $200\frac{19}{100}$

Determine whether each statement is *sometimes*, *always*, or *never* true. Explain by giving an example or a counterexample.

44. An integer is a rational number.   **always**

45. A rational number is an integer.   **sometimes**

46. A whole number is not a rational number.   **never**

44–46. See margin for explanations.

47. **MANUFACTURING** A garbage bag has a thickness of 0.8 mil. This is 0.0008 inch. What fraction of an inch is this? $\frac{1}{1250}$ in.

48. **GEOMETRY** Pi (π) to six decimal places has a value of 3.141592. Pi is often estimated as $\frac{22}{7}$. Is the estimate for π greater than or less than the actual value of π? Explain.   greater than; $\frac{22}{7} \approx 3.142857 > 3.141592$

More About...

Recycling

The portions of recycled newspapers used for other purposes are shown below.

Newsprint: 0.34
Exported for recycling: 0.22
Paperboard: 0.17
Other products: 0.18

Source: American Forest and Paper Association, Newspaper Association of America

---

Answers

44. Every integer can be written as a fraction with 1 as the denominator; $5 = \frac{5}{1}$, so 5 is a rational number.

45. $\frac{1}{2}$ and 2 are both rational numbers, but only 2 is an integer.

46. Every whole number can be written as a fraction with 1 as the denominator. 3 is a whole number and $3 = \frac{3}{1}$, so it is a rational number.

★ **49. MACHINERY** Will a steel peg 2.37 inches in diameter fit in a $2\frac{3}{8}$-inch diameter hole? How do you know? **Yes; $2\frac{3}{8}$ = 2.375 and 2.375 > 2.37.**

50. CRITICAL THINKING Show that $0.999\ldots = 1$. **See margin.**

51. WRITING IN MATH Answer the question that was posed at the beginning of the lesson. **See margin.**

How are rational numbers related to other sets of numbers?

Include the following in your answer:
- examples of numbers that belong to more than one set, and
- examples of numbers that are only rational.

52. There are infinitely many ___?___ between S and T on the number line. **A**

```
        S           T
 ┼─┼─┼─┼─┼─┼─┼─┼─┼─┼─┼─┼
 −2 −1  0  1  2  3  4  5  6  7  8
```

Ⓐ rational numbers   Ⓑ integers

Ⓒ whole numbers   Ⓓ natural numbers

53. Express 0.56 as a fraction in simplest form. **C**

Ⓐ $\frac{56}{100}$ Ⓑ $\frac{28}{50}$ Ⓒ $\frac{14}{25}$ Ⓓ $\frac{7}{12}$

Maintain Your Skills

Mixed Review   Write each fraction or mixed number as a decimal. Use a bar to show a repeating decimal. *(Lesson 5-1)*

54. $\frac{2}{5}$ **0.4**   **55.** $-7\frac{4}{5}$ **−7.8**   **56.** $-\frac{13}{20}$ **−0.65**   **57.** $2\frac{5}{9}$ **$2.\overline{5}$**

Write each number in standard form. *(Lesson 4-8)*

58. 2×10^3 **2000**   **59.** 3.05×10^6 **3,050,000**   **60.** 7.4×10^{-4} **0.00074**   **61.** 1.681×10^{-2} **0.01681**

62. ALGEBRA Write $\frac{12n^2}{3an}$ in simplest form. *(Lesson 4-5)* **$\frac{4n}{a}$**

63. Use place value and exponents to express 483 in expanded form. *(Lesson 4-2)*
$(4 \times 10^2) + (8 \times 10^1) + (3 \times 10^0)$

Find the perimeter and area of each rectangle. *(Lesson 3-7)*

64. **46 in.; 112 in²**
7 in.
16 in.

65. **24 cm; 27 cm²**
3 cm
9 cm

Use the Distributive Property to rewrite each expression. *(Lesson 3-1)*

66. $3(5 + 9)$ **67.** $(8 + 1)2$ **68.** $6(b − 5)$ **69.** $(x + 4)7$
$3 \cdot 5 + 3 \cdot 9$ $8 \cdot 2 + 1 \cdot 2$ $6b − 30$ $7x + 28$

Getting Ready for the Next Lesson   **PREREQUISITE SKILL** Estimate each product.
*(To review **estimating products**, see page 717.)* **70–75. Sample answers are given.**

Example: $-3\frac{1}{4} \cdot 5\frac{7}{8} \approx -3 \cdot 6$ or -18 **71.** $-5 \cdot 4 = -20$

70. $1\frac{2}{3} \cdot 4\frac{1}{8}$ **$2 \cdot 4 = 8$**   **71.** $-5\frac{2}{5} \cdot 3\frac{4}{5}$ **72.** $2\frac{1}{4} \cdot 2\frac{1}{9}$ **$2 \cdot 2 = 4$**

73. $6\frac{7}{8} \cdot 1\frac{9}{10}$ **$7 \cdot 2 = 14$**   **74.** $9\frac{1}{8} \cdot \left(-4\frac{3}{4}\right)$ **$9 \cdot (-5) = -45$**   **75.** $15\frac{5}{7} \cdot 2\frac{1}{3}$ **$16 \cdot 2 = 32$**

---

4 Assess

Open-Ended Assessment

Speaking Have students explain how to express terminating and repeating decimals as fractions. They can pair off and explain their reasoning to a partner or engage in a whole class discussion. Each student should practice explaining until the listener understands the thinking.

Getting Ready for Lesson 5-3

PREREQUISITE SKILL Lesson 5-3 presents multiplication with rational numbers. Estimating products is a useful skill for this lesson. Exercises 70–75 should be used to determine your students' familiarity with estimating products of mixed numbers.

Answers

50. Let $N = 0.999\ldots$ and let $10N = 9.999\ldots$.

$$10N = 9.999\ldots$$
$$-\;(N = 0.999\ldots)$$
$$\overline{9N = 9}$$

$$\frac{9N}{9} = \frac{9}{9}$$

$$N = 1$$

51. The set of rational numbers includes the set of natural numbers, whole numbers, and integers. In the same way, natural numbers are part of the set of whole numbers and the set of whole numbers is part of the set of integers. Answers should include the following.

- The number 5 belongs to the set of natural numbers, whole numbers, integers, and rational numbers.
- The number $\frac{1}{2}$ belongs only to the set of rational numbers.

1 Focus

5-Minute Check Transparency 5-3 Use as a quiz or review of Lesson 5-2.

Mathematical Background notes are available for this lesson on page 198C.

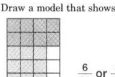

How is multiplying fractions related to areas of rectangles?

The opening activity questions are repeated on page 238 of the *Chapter 5 Resource Masters*.

Reading to Learn Mathematics, p. 238   ELL

Pre-Activity How is multiplying fractions related to areas of rectangles?

Do the activity at the top of page 210 in your textbook. Write your answers below.

a. The overlapping green area represents the product $\frac{2}{3}$ and $\frac{3}{4}$. What is the product? $\frac{6}{12}$ or $\frac{1}{2}$

Use an area model to find each product.

b. $\frac{1}{2} \cdot \frac{1}{3}$ $\frac{1}{6}$ **c.** $\frac{3}{5} \cdot \frac{1}{4}$ $\frac{3}{20}$ **d.** $\frac{3}{4} \cdot \frac{1}{3}$ $\frac{3}{12}$ or $\frac{1}{4}$

e. What is the relationship between the numerators and denominators of the factors and the numerator and denominator of the product?
The numerator of the product equals the product of the numerators of the factors. The denominator of the product equals the product of the denominators of the factors.

Reading the Lesson 1–2. See students' work.

Write a definition and give an example of each new vocabulary phrase.

Vocabulary	Definition	Example
1. algebraic fraction		
2. dimensional analysis		

3. Draw a model that shows $\frac{2}{5} \cdot \frac{3}{4}$.

$\frac{6}{20}$ or $\frac{3}{10}$

Helping You Remember

4. Compare the process of multiplying numerical fractions and algebraic fractions.
The process of multiplying numerical fractions and algebraic fractions is the same. The only difference is that algebraic fractions contain variables.

5-3 Multiplying Rational Numbers

NEW YORK *Performance Indicator* **8.A.6 Multiply** and divide **monomials**

What You'll Learn

- Multiply fractions.
- Use dimensional analysis to solve problems.

Vocabulary
- dimensional analysis

How is multiplying fractions related to areas of rectangles?

To find $\frac{2}{3} \cdot \frac{3}{4}$, think of using an area model to find $\frac{2}{3}$ of $\frac{3}{4}$.

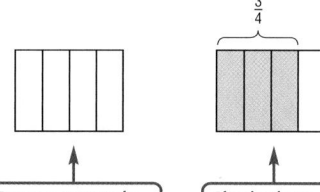

| Draw a rectangle with four columns. | Shade three fourths of the rectangle blue. | Divide the rectangle into three rows. Shade two thirds of the rectangle yellow. |

a. The overlapping green area represents the product of $\frac{2}{3}$ and $\frac{3}{4}$. What is the product? $\frac{6}{12}$ or $\frac{1}{2}$

Use an area model to find each product.

b. $\frac{1}{2} \cdot \frac{1}{3}$ $\frac{1}{6}$ **c.** $\frac{3}{5} \cdot \frac{1}{4}$ $\frac{3}{20}$ **d.** $\frac{3}{4} \cdot \frac{1}{3}$ $\frac{3}{12}$ or $\frac{1}{4}$

e. What is the relationship between the numerators and denominators of the factors and the numerator and denominator of the product?

e. The numerator of the product equals the product of the numerators of the factors. The denominator of the product equals the product of the denominators of the factors.

MULTIPLY FRACTIONS These and other similar models suggest the following rule for multiplying fractions.

> ### Key Concept   Multiplying Fractions
>
> - **Words**   To multiply fractions, multiply the numerators and multiply the denominators.
> - **Symbols** $\frac{a}{b} \cdot \frac{c}{d} = \frac{a \cdot c}{b \cdot d}$, where $b, d \neq 0$
> - **Example** $\frac{1}{3} \cdot \frac{2}{5} = \frac{1 \cdot 2}{3 \cdot 5}$ or $\frac{2}{15}$

Example 1 Multiply Fractions

Find $\frac{2}{3} \cdot \frac{3}{4}$. Write the product in simplest form.

 $\frac{2}{3} \cdot \frac{3}{4} = \frac{2 \cdot 3}{3 \cdot 4}$ ← Multiply the numerators.
  ← Multiply the denominators.

 $= \frac{6}{12}$ or $\frac{1}{2}$ Simplify. The GCF of 6 and 12 is 6.

Study Tip

Look Back
To review **GCF**, see Lesson 4-4.

Resource Manager

📁 Workbooks and Reproducible Masters

Chapter 5 Resource Masters
- Study Guide and Intervention, p. 235
- Skills Practice, p. 236
- Practice, p. 237
- Reading to Learn Mathematics, p. 238
- Enrichment, p. 239
- Assessment, p. 289

Parent and Student Study Guide Workbook, p. 35
Science and Mathematics Lab Manual, pp. 11–14

📄 Transparencies
5-Minute Check Transparency 5-3
Answer Key Transparencies

💿 Technology
Interactive Chalkboard

If the fractions have common factors in the numerators and denominators, you can simplify before you multiply.

Example 2 *Simplify Before Multiplying*

Find $\frac{4}{7} \cdot \frac{1}{6}$. Write the product in simplest form.

$$\frac{4}{7} \cdot \frac{1}{6} = \frac{\overset{2}{\cancel{4}}}{7} \cdot \frac{1}{\underset{3}{\cancel{6}}} \qquad \text{Divide 4 and 6 by their GCF, 2.}$$

$$= \frac{2 \cdot 1}{7 \cdot 3} \qquad \text{Multiply the numerators and multiply the denominators.}$$

$$= \frac{2}{21} \qquad \text{Simplify.}$$

Study Tip

Negative Fractions
$-\frac{5}{12}$ can be written as $\frac{-5}{12}$ or as $\frac{5}{-12}$.

Example 3 *Multiply Negative Fractions*

Find $-\frac{5}{12} \cdot \frac{3}{8}$. Write the product in simplest form.

$$-\frac{5}{12} \cdot \frac{3}{8} = \frac{-5}{\underset{4}{\cancel{12}}} \cdot \frac{\overset{1}{\cancel{3}}}{8} \qquad \text{Divide 3 and 12 by their GCF, 3.}$$

$$= \frac{-5 \cdot 1}{4 \cdot 8} \qquad \text{Multiply the numerators and multiply the denominators.}$$

$$= -\frac{5}{32} \qquad \text{Simplify.}$$

Example 4 *Multiply Mixed Numbers*

Find $1\frac{2}{5} \cdot 2\frac{1}{2}$. Write the product in simplest form.   Estimate: $1 \cdot 3 = 3$

$$1\frac{2}{5} \cdot 2\frac{1}{2} = \frac{7}{5} \cdot \frac{5}{2} \qquad \text{Rename } 1\frac{2}{5} \text{ as } \frac{7}{5} \text{ and rename } 2\frac{1}{2} \text{ as } \frac{5}{2}.$$

$$= \frac{7}{5} \cdot \frac{\overset{1}{\cancel{5}}}{2} \qquad \text{Divide by the GCF, 5.}$$

$$= \frac{7 \cdot 1}{1 \cdot 2} \qquad \text{Multiply.}$$

$$= \frac{7}{2} \text{ or } 3\frac{1}{2} \qquad \text{Simplify.}$$

ALGEBRA CONNECTION

Algebraic fractions are multiplied in the same manner as numeric fractions.

TEACHING TIP
In this text, assume the denominator in an algebraic fraction is not equal to zero.

Example 5 *Multiply Algebraic Fractions*

Find $\frac{2a}{b} \cdot \frac{b^2}{d}$. Write the product in simplest form.

$$\frac{2a}{b} \cdot \frac{b^2}{d} = \frac{2a}{\cancel{b}} \cdot \frac{\overset{1}{\cancel{b}} \cdot b}{d} \qquad \text{The GCF of } b \text{ and } b^2 \text{ is } b.$$

$$= \frac{2ab}{d} \qquad \text{Simplify.}$$

---

2 Teach

MULTIPLY FRACTIONS

In-Class Examples

1 Find $\frac{2}{5} \cdot \frac{5}{8}$. Write the product in simplest form.
$\frac{1}{4}$

2 Find $\frac{8}{9} \cdot \frac{5}{6}$. Write the product in simplest form.
$\frac{20}{27}$

3 Find $-\frac{1}{4} \cdot \frac{2}{7}$. Write the product in simplest form.
$-\frac{1}{14}$

4 Find $1\frac{1}{2} \cdot 3\frac{2}{3}$. Write the product in simplest form.
$\frac{11}{2}$ or $5\frac{1}{2}$

5 Find $\frac{3p^2}{q} \cdot \frac{q^2}{r}$. Write the product in simplest form.
$\frac{3p^2 q}{r}$

✓ **Skills Check**
Multiply Fractions Ask students to find $\frac{4}{9} \cdot \frac{3}{8}$ two ways: simplify before multiplying and simplify after multiplying. Which do they prefer? Why?

DIMENSIONAL ANALYSIS

In-Class Example

6 **RUNNING TRACK** The track at Cole's school is $\frac{1}{4}$ mile around. If Cole runs one lap in two minutes, how far (in miles) does he run in 30 minutes? $3\frac{3}{4}$ miles

---

DAILY INTERVENTION

Unlocking Misconceptions

- From Example 3, students may think that the negative sign in a fraction always goes with the numerator. Point out that $-\frac{5}{12} = \frac{-5}{12} = \frac{5}{-12}$, but NOT $\frac{-5}{-12}$.

- Point out that dimensional analysis is not just a math skill but one used in science classes such as chemistry and physics.

Study Notebook

Have students—

• add the definitions/examples of the vocabulary terms to their Vocabulary Builder worksheets for Chapter 5.

• include any other item(s) that they find helpful in mastering the skills in this lesson.

DAILY
INTERVENTION **FIND THE ERROR**
If students are having difficulty with Exercise 2, remind them that the numerator and denominator must be simplified by the same factor. You may want to show them that $\frac{18}{24} \neq \frac{9}{4}$ by expressing each fraction as a decimal.

About the Exercises . . .

Organization by Objective
• **Multiply Fractions:** 13–33, 38–45
• **Dimensional Analysis:** 34–37, 49–52

Odd/Even Assignments
Exercises 13–33 are structured so that students practice the same concepts whether they are assigned odd or even problems.

Assignment Guide

Basic: 13–41 odd, 45, 47, 53–56, 60–74

Average: 13–51 odd, 53–56, 60–74 (Optional: 57–59)

Advanced: 14–52 even, 53–68 (Optional: 69–74)

Answer

2. **Terrence; Marie incorrectly divided the 18 in the numerator of the second fraction.**

DIMENSIONAL ANALYSIS **Dimensional analysis** is the process of including units of measurement when you compute. You can use dimensional analysis to check whether your answers are reasonable.

Example 6 *Use Dimensional Analysis*

SPACE TRAVEL The landing speed of the space shuttle is about 216 miles per hour. How far does the shuttle travel in $\frac{1}{3}$ hour during landing?

Words	Distance equals the rate multiplied by the time.

Variables Let d = distance, r = rate, and t = time.

Formula
$d = rt$ Write the formula.

$d = 216$ miles per hour $\cdot \frac{1}{3}$ hour   Include the units.

$= \dfrac{\overset{72}{\cancel{216} \text{ miles}}}{1 \text{ hour}} \cdot \frac{1}{\underset{1}{\cancel{3}}} \text{ hour}$ Divide by the common factors and units.

$= 72$ miles   Simplify.

The space shuttle travels 72 miles in $\frac{1}{3}$ hour during landing.

CHECK The problem asks for the distance. When you divide the common units, the answer is expressed in miles. So, the answer is reasonable.

✔ **Concept Check** What is the final unit when you multiply feet per second by seconds? **feet**

Check for Understanding

Concept Check
1. **OPEN ENDED** Choose two rational numbers whose product is a number between 0 and 1. **Sample answer:** $\frac{1}{2}, \frac{1}{3}$

2. **FIND THE ERROR** Terrence and Marie are finding $\frac{5}{24} \cdot \frac{18}{25}$.

Terrence	Marie
$\dfrac{\overset{1}{\cancel{5}}}{\underset{4}{\cancel{24}}} \cdot \dfrac{\overset{3}{\cancel{18}}}{\underset{5}{\cancel{25}}} = \dfrac{3}{20}$	$\dfrac{\overset{1}{\cancel{5}}}{\underset{4}{\cancel{24}}} \cdot \dfrac{\overset{9}{\cancel{18}}}{\underset{5}{\cancel{25}}} = \dfrac{9}{20}$

Who is correct? Explain your reasoning. **See margin.**

Guided Practice **Find each product. Write in simplest form.**

GUIDED PRACTICE KEY	
Exercises	Examples
3–6	1–3
7, 8	4
9–11	5
12	6

3. $\frac{1}{4} \cdot \frac{3}{5}$ $\frac{3}{20}$

4. $\frac{1}{2}\left(-\frac{5}{6}\right)$ $-\frac{5}{12}$

5. $-\frac{2}{3}\left(-\frac{5}{6}\right)$ $\frac{5}{9}$

6. $7\left(\frac{8}{21}\right)$ $2\frac{2}{3}$

7. $3\frac{1}{4} \cdot \frac{2}{11}$ $\frac{13}{22}$

8. $-5\frac{1}{3} \cdot 3\frac{3}{8}$ -18

ALGEBRA **Find each product. Write in simplest form.**

9. $\frac{2}{x} \cdot \frac{3x}{7}$ $\frac{6}{7}$

10. $\frac{a}{b} \cdot \frac{5b}{c}$ $\frac{5a}{c}$

11. $\frac{4t}{9r} \cdot \frac{18r}{t^2}$ $\frac{8}{t}$

Application
12. **TRAVEL** A car travels 65 miles per hour for $3\frac{1}{2}$ hours. What is the distance traveled? Use the formula $d = rt$ and show how you can divide by the common units. $d = 65 \frac{\text{mi}}{\cancel{h}} \cdot \frac{7}{2}\cancel{h}$ or $227\frac{1}{2}$ mi

---

DAILY
INTERVENTION **Differentiated Instruction**

• **Intrapersonal** Ask students to extend the area model for multiplying fractions to multiplying a mixed number by a proper fraction, such as $4\frac{3}{5} \cdot \frac{2}{3}$. In their Math Journals, have students draw 5 rectangles, divide into fifths, and shade $4\frac{3}{5}$; divide each rectangle into thirds and shade two-thirds of each; state what the overlapping areas represent.

★ indicates increased difficulty

Practice and Apply

Homework Help

For Exercises	See Examples
13–24	1–3
25–33	4
37–42	5
47–50	6

Extra Practice
See page 734.

Find each product. Write in simplest form.

13. $\dfrac{6}{7} \cdot \dfrac{2}{7}$ **$\dfrac{12}{49}$**

14. $\dfrac{4}{9} \cdot \dfrac{2}{3}$ **$\dfrac{8}{27}$**

15. $\dfrac{1}{5}\left(-\dfrac{1}{8}\right)$ **$-\dfrac{1}{40}$**

16. $-\dfrac{3}{4} \cdot \dfrac{3}{5}$ **$-\dfrac{9}{20}$**

17. $\dfrac{5}{9} \cdot \dfrac{8}{25}$ **$\dfrac{8}{45}$**

18. $-\dfrac{1}{2}\left(-\dfrac{2}{7}\right)$ **$\dfrac{1}{7}$**

19. $\dfrac{2}{5} \cdot \dfrac{5}{6}$ **$\dfrac{1}{3}$**

20. $\dfrac{8}{9} \cdot \dfrac{27}{28}$ **$\dfrac{6}{7}$**

21. $\dfrac{3}{4}\left(-\dfrac{1}{3}\right)$ **$-\dfrac{1}{4}$**

22. $-\dfrac{7}{8} \cdot \dfrac{2}{5}$ **$-\dfrac{7}{20}$**

23. $\dfrac{3}{5} \cdot \dfrac{15}{24}$ **$\dfrac{3}{8}$**

24. $\dfrac{3}{32} \cdot \dfrac{24}{39}$ **$\dfrac{3}{52}$**

25. $2 \cdot \dfrac{7}{12}$ **$1\dfrac{1}{6}$**

26. $\dfrac{6}{15}(-3)$ **$-1\dfrac{1}{5}$**

27. $6\dfrac{2}{3} \cdot \dfrac{1}{2}$ **$3\dfrac{1}{3}$**

28. $\dfrac{5}{12} \cdot 3\dfrac{1}{9}$ **$1\dfrac{8}{27}$**

29. $2\dfrac{2}{6} \cdot 6\dfrac{2}{7}$ **$14\dfrac{2}{3}$**

30. $3\dfrac{1}{3} \cdot 2\dfrac{5}{8}$ **$8\dfrac{3}{4}$**

31. $-6\dfrac{2}{3}\left(-1\dfrac{1}{2}\right)$ **10**

32. $1\dfrac{3}{7}\left(-9\dfrac{4}{5}\right)$ **-14**

33. $-1\dfrac{1}{4} \cdot 3\dfrac{5}{9}$ **$-4\dfrac{4}{9}$**

MEASUREMENT Complete.

34. $\underline{\quad?\quad}$ feet $= \dfrac{5}{6}$ mile **4400**
(*Hint:* 1 mile = 5280 feet)

35. $\underline{\quad?\quad}$ ounces $= \dfrac{3}{8}$ pound **6**
(*Hint:* 1 pound = 16 ounces)

36. $\dfrac{2}{3}$ hour $= \underline{\quad?\quad}$ minutes **40**

37. $\dfrac{3}{4}$ yard $= \underline{\quad?\quad}$ inches **27**

ALGEBRA Find each product. Write in simplest form.

38. $\dfrac{4a}{5} \cdot \dfrac{3}{a}$ **$2\dfrac{2}{5}$**

39. $\dfrac{3x}{y} \cdot \dfrac{9y}{x}$ **27**

40. $\dfrac{12}{jk} \cdot \dfrac{3k}{4}$ **$\dfrac{9}{j}$**

41. $\dfrac{8}{c} \cdot \dfrac{c^2}{11}$ **$\dfrac{8c}{11}$**

42. $\dfrac{n}{18} \cdot \dfrac{6}{n^4}$ **$\dfrac{1}{3n^3}$**

★ 43. $\dfrac{x}{2z} \cdot \dfrac{2z^3}{3}$ **$\dfrac{xz^2}{3}$**

44. **ALGEBRA** Evaluate x^2 if $x = -\dfrac{1}{2}$. **$\dfrac{1}{4}$**

45. **ALGEBRA** Evaluate $(xy)^2$ if $x = \dfrac{3}{4}$ and $y = -\dfrac{4}{5}$. **$\dfrac{9}{25}$**

SCHOOL For Exercises 46 and 47, use the graphic at the right.

46. Five-eighths of an eighth grade class are boys. Predict approximately what fraction of the eighth graders are boys who talk about school at home.
$\left(\textit{Hint: } 40\% = \dfrac{2}{5}\right)$ **$\dfrac{1}{4}$**

47. In a 12th grade class, five-ninths of the students are girls. Predict about what fraction of twelfth graders are girls who talk about school at home.
$\left(\textit{Hint: } 33\% = \dfrac{33}{100}\right)$ **$\dfrac{11}{60}$**

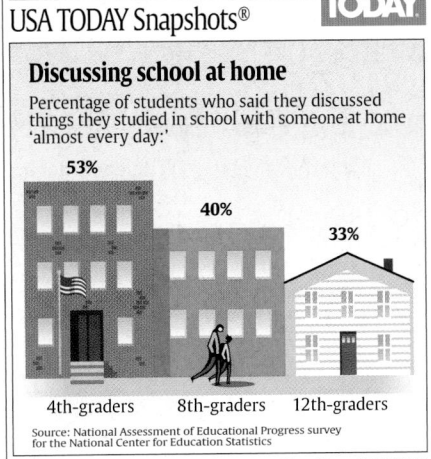

USA TODAY Snapshots®

Discussing school at home
Percentage of students who said they discussed things they studied in school with someone at home 'almost every day:'

53% 4th-graders
40% 8th-graders
33% 12th-graders

Source: National Assessment of Educational Progress survey for the National Center for Education Statistics

By Mark Pearson and Jerry Mosemak, USA TODAY

48. **GARDENING** Jamal's lawn is $\dfrac{2}{3}$ of an acre. If $7\dfrac{1}{2}$ bags of fertilizer are needed for 1 acre, how much will he need to fertilize his lawn? **5 bags**

Online Lesson Plans

USA TODAY Education's Online site offers resources and interactive features connected to each day's newspaper. *Experience TODAY*, USA TODAY's daily lesson plan, is available on the site and delivered daily to subscribers. This plan provides instruction for integrating USA TODAY graphics and key editorial features into your mathematics classroom. Log on to www.education.usatoday.com

---

Open-Ended Assessment

Modeling Ask students to use an area model to show $\frac{7}{8} \cdot \frac{4}{5}$. Verify the result by multiplying. Students should explain the process of simplifying their answers.

Getting Ready for Lesson 5-4

PREREQUISITE SKILL Lesson 5-4 presents division of rational numbers. Exercises 69–74 should be used to determine your students' familiarity with finding greatest common factors, which is used in simplifying answers.

Assessment Options

Quiz (Lessons 5-1 through 5-3) is available on p. 289 of the *Chapter 5 Resource Masters*.

Answer

54. Fractions can be used to represent parts of rectangles. The product of the fractions equals a portion of the rectangle's area. Answers should include the following.

 • A rectangle that is divided into rows and columns; one fraction represents the fraction of columns that are shaded and another fraction represents the fraction of rows that are shaded.

 • The product of the fractions is the overlapping shaded area.

More About . . .

Converting Measures

In 1998, a Mars probe was lost because scientists did not convert a customary measure of force to a metric measure.

Source: *Newsday*

NEW YORK Test Practice

Standardized Test Practice
Ⓐ Ⓑ Ⓒ Ⓓ

Extending the Lesson

Maintain Your Skills

Mixed Review

Getting Ready for the Next Lesson

• CONVERTING MEASURES Use dimensional analysis and the fractions in the table to find each missing measure.

Conversion Factors	
Customary → Metric	Metric → Customary
$\frac{2.54 \text{ cm}}{1 \text{ in.}}$	$\frac{0.39 \text{ in.}}{1 \text{ cm}}$
$\frac{1.61 \text{ km}}{1 \text{ mi}}$	$\frac{0.62 \text{ mi}}{1 \text{ km}}$
$\frac{0.09 \text{ m}^2}{1 \text{ ft}^2}$	$\frac{10.76 \text{ ft}^2}{1 \text{ m}^2}$

★ 49. 5 inches = _?_ centimeters **12.7**

★ 50. 10 kilometers = _?_ miles **6.2**

★ 51. 26.3 centimeters = _?_ inches **10.257**

★ 52. $8\frac{2}{3}$ square feet = _?_ square meters **0.78**

53. **CRITICAL THINKING** Use the digits 3, 4, 5, 6, 8, and 9 to make true sentences. **a–b. Sample answers are given.**

 a. $\frac{\square}{\square} \times \frac{\square}{\square} = \frac{6}{5}$ $\frac{8}{4} \times \frac{3}{5}$

 b. $\frac{\square}{\square} \times \frac{\square}{\square} = \frac{5}{8}$ $\frac{3}{4} \times \frac{5}{6}$

54. **WRITING IN MATH** Answer the question that was posed at the beginning of the lesson. **See margin.**

 How is multiplying fractions related to areas of rectangles?

 Include the following in your answer:

 • an area model of a multiplication problem involving fractions, and

 • an explanation of how rectangles can be used to show multiplication of fractions.

55. The product of $\frac{8}{15}$ and $\frac{3}{8}$ is a number **A**

 Ⓐ between 0 and 1.   Ⓑ between 1 and 2.

 Ⓒ between 2 and 3.   Ⓓ greater than 3.

56. What is the equivalent length of a chain that is 52 feet long? **C**

 Ⓐ 4 yards 5 feet   Ⓑ 4.5 yards

 Ⓒ 17 yards 1 foot   Ⓓ 17.1 yards

Evaluate each expression if $n = 2$ and $p = -4$.

57. $5n^{-3}$ $\frac{5}{8}$ 58. $7 \cdot 3^p$ $\frac{7}{81}$ 59. $13n^{-1}p^{-2}$ $\frac{13}{32}$

Write each decimal as a fraction or mixed number in simplest form. *(Lesson 5-2)*

60. 0.18 $\frac{9}{50}$ 61. -0.2 $-\frac{1}{5}$ 62. 3.04 $3\frac{1}{25}$ 63. $0.\overline{7}$ $\frac{7}{9}$

Write each fraction or mixed number as a decimal. Use a bar to show a repeating decimal. *(Lesson 5-1)*

64. $\frac{17}{20}$ **0.85**   65. $\frac{1}{6}$ **$0.1\overline{6}$**   66. $2\frac{2}{11}$ **$2.\overline{18}$**   67. $-4\frac{7}{8}$ **−4.875**

68. **ALGEBRA** What is the product of x^2 and x^4? *(Lesson 4-6)* **x^6**

PREREQUISITE SKILL Find the GCF of each pair of monomials. *(To review the GCF of monomials, see Lesson 4-4.)*

69. $8n, 16n$ **$8n$**   70. $5ab, 8b$ **b**   71. $12t, 10t$ **$2t$**

72. $2rs, 3rs$ **rs**   73. $9k, 27$ **9**   74. $4p^2, 6p$ **$2p$**

Dividing Rational Numbers

NEW YORK *Performance Indicator* **8.A.6** Multiply and **divide monomials**

What You'll Learn

- Divide fractions using multiplicative inverses.
- Use dimensional analysis to solve problems.

How is dividing by a fraction related to multiplying?

The model shows $4 \div \frac{1}{3}$. Each of the 4 circles is divided into $\frac{1}{3}$-sections.

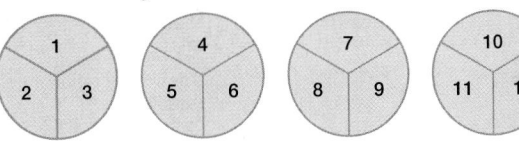

There are twelve $\frac{1}{3}$-sections, so $4 \div \frac{1}{3} = 12$. Another way to find the number of sections is $4 \times 3 = 12$.

Use a model to find each quotient. Then write a related multiplication problem. c. 12; $3 \times 4 = 12$

a. $2 \div \frac{1}{3}$ 6; $2 \times 3 = 6$ b. $4 \div \frac{1}{2}$ 8; $4 \times 2 = 8$ c. $3 \div \frac{1}{4}$

d. **Make a conjecture** about how dividing by a fraction is related to multiplying.

Vocabulary
- multiplicative inverses
- reciprocals

d. Dividing by a fraction with 1 in the numerator is the same as multiplying by the number that is in the denominator.

DIVIDE FRACTIONS   Rational numbers have all of the properties of whole numbers and integers. Another property is shown by $\frac{1}{3} \cdot \frac{3}{1} = 1$. Two numbers whose product is 1 are called **multiplicative inverses** or **reciprocals**.

Study Tip

Reading Math
Multiplicative inverse and reciprocal are different terms for the same concept. They may be used interchangeably.

Key Concept — Inverse Property of Multiplication

- **Words**   The product of a number and its multiplicative inverse is 1.
- **Symbols**   For every number $\frac{a}{b}$, where $a, b \neq 0$,
  there is exactly one number $\frac{b}{a}$ such that $\frac{a}{b} \cdot \frac{b}{a} = 1$.
- **Example** $\frac{3}{4}$ and $\frac{4}{3}$ are multiplicative inverses because $\frac{3}{4} \cdot \frac{4}{3} = 1$.

Example 1 Find Multiplicative Inverses

Find the multiplicative inverse of each number.

a. $-\frac{3}{8}$

$-\frac{3}{8}\left(-\frac{8}{3}\right) = 1$ The product is 1.

The multiplicative inverse or reciprocal of $-\frac{3}{8}$ is $-\frac{8}{3}$.

b. $2\frac{1}{5}$

$2\frac{1}{5} = \frac{11}{5}$ Write as an improper fraction.

$\frac{11}{5} \cdot \frac{5}{11} = 1$ The product is 1.

The reciprocal of $2\frac{1}{5}$ is $\frac{5}{11}$.

---

1 Focus

 5-Minute Check Transparency 5-4 Use as a quiz or review of Lesson 5-3.

Mathematical Background notes are available for this lesson on page 198C.

How is dividing by a fraction related to multiplying?

The opening activity questions are repeated on page 243 of the *Chapter 5 Resource Masters*.

Reading to Learn Mathematics, p. 243   **ELL**

Pre-Activity   *How is dividing by a fraction related to multiplying?*

Do the activity at the top of page 215 in your textbook. Write your answers below. Use a model to find each quotient. Then write a related multiplication problem.

a. $2 \div \frac{1}{3}$ 6; $2 \times 3 = 6$

b. $4 \div \frac{1}{2}$ 8; $4 \times 2 = 8$

c. $3 \div \frac{1}{4}$ 12; $3 \times 4 = 12$

d. Make a conjecture about how dividing by a fraction is related to multiplying.   Dividing by a fraction with 1 in the numerator is the same as multiplying by the number that is in the denominator.

Reading the Lesson 1–2. See students' work.

Write a definition and give an example of each new vocabulary word or phrase.

Vocabulary	Definition	Example
1. multiplicative inverses		
2. reciprocals		

Helping You Remember

3. Explain in your own words how to relate dividing rational numbers to multiplication. Give an example.   Sample answer: Dividing by a fraction is equivalent to multiplying by its reciprocal. $8 \div 4 = \frac{8}{1} \cdot \frac{1}{4}$, $\frac{2}{5} \div \frac{5}{5} = \frac{2}{5} \cdot \frac{5}{3}$

Teaching Tip   Remind students that for any numbers a, b, c ($b \neq 0$), $a \div b = c$ if and only if $b \cdot c = a$. For example, $10 \div 5 = 2$ since $2 \cdot 5 = 10$.

Resource Manager

Workbooks and Reproducible Masters

Chapter 5 Resource Masters
- Study Guide and Intervention, p. 240
- Skills Practice, p. 241
- Practice, p. 242
- Reading to Learn Mathematics, p. 243
- Enrichment, p. 244

Parent and Student Study Guide Workbook, p. 36
School-to-Career Masters, p. 10

 Transparencies

5-Minute Check Transparency 5-4
Real-World Transparency 5
Answer Key Transparencies

Technology

Interactive Chalkboard

DIVIDE FRACTIONS

1 Find the multiplicative inverse of each number.

a. $\dfrac{6}{7}$ $\dfrac{7}{6}$

b. $3\dfrac{2}{5}$ $\dfrac{5}{17}$

2 Find $\dfrac{4}{5} \div \dfrac{3}{10}$. Write the quotient in simplest form. $\dfrac{8}{3}$ or $2\dfrac{2}{3}$

3 Find $\dfrac{5}{6} \div 3$. Write the quotient in simplest form. $\dfrac{5}{18}$

Teaching Tip Encourage students to check their answers using multiplication. In Example 3, $\dfrac{5}{8} \div 6 = \dfrac{5}{48}$; $\dfrac{5}{48} \cdot 6 = \dfrac{5}{8}$.

4 Find $4\dfrac{2}{3} \div -3\dfrac{1}{9}$. Write the quotient in simplest form. $-\dfrac{3}{2}$ or $-1\dfrac{1}{2}$

5 Find $\dfrac{5x}{8y} \div \dfrac{10}{16y}$. Write the quotient in simplest form. x

✓ Skills Check

Divide Fractions Have students explain how to divide by an algebraic fraction. Then ask them to discuss the similarities and differences between dividing by an algebraic fraction and dividing by a numerical fraction.

Dividing by 2 is the same as multiplying by $\frac{1}{2}$, its multiplicative inverse. This is true for any rational number.

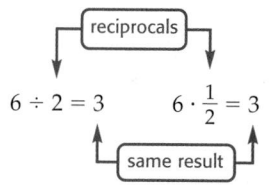

$$6 \div 2 = 3 \qquad 6 \cdot \dfrac{1}{2} = 3$$

reciprocals

same result

Key Concept — Dividing Fractions

- **Words** — To divide by a fraction, multiply by its multiplicative inverse.
- **Symbols** — $\dfrac{a}{b} \div \dfrac{c}{d} = \dfrac{a}{b} \cdot \dfrac{d}{c}$, where $b, c, d \neq 0$
- **Example** — $\dfrac{1}{4} \div \dfrac{5}{7} = \dfrac{1}{4} \cdot \dfrac{7}{5}$ or $\dfrac{7}{20}$

Concept Check: No; 0 does not have a reciprocal because the product of 0 and any number is 0.

✓ Concept Check Does every rational number have a multiplicative inverse? Explain.

Example 2   Divide by a Fraction

Find $\dfrac{1}{3} \div \dfrac{5}{9}$. Write the quotient in simplest form.

$$\dfrac{1}{3} \div \dfrac{5}{9} = \dfrac{1}{3} \cdot \dfrac{9}{5} \qquad \text{Multiply by the multiplicative inverse of } \dfrac{5}{9}, \dfrac{9}{5}.$$

$$= \dfrac{1}{\cancel{3}} \cdot \dfrac{\cancel{9}^{\,3}}{5} \qquad \text{Divide 3 and 9 by their GCF, 3.}$$

$$= \dfrac{3}{5} \qquad \text{Simplify.}$$

Study Tip

Dividing By a Whole Number
When dividing by a whole number, always rename it as an improper fraction first. Then multiply by its reciprocal.

Example 3   Divide by a Whole Number

Find $\dfrac{5}{8} \div 6$. Write the quotient in simplest form.

$$\dfrac{5}{8} \div 6 = \dfrac{5}{8} \div \dfrac{6}{1} \qquad \text{Write 6 as } \dfrac{6}{1}.$$

$$= \dfrac{5}{8} \cdot \dfrac{1}{6} \qquad \text{Multiply by the multiplicative inverse of } \dfrac{6}{1}, \dfrac{1}{6}.$$

$$= \dfrac{5}{48} \qquad \text{Multiply the numerators and multiply the denominators.}$$

TEACHING TIP

You may want to encourage students to write the negative sign with the numerator so that it does not get left out in the final answer. $\dfrac{-15}{2}$

Example 4   Divide by a Mixed Number

Find $-7\dfrac{1}{2} \div 2\dfrac{1}{10}$. Write the quotient in simplest form.

$$-7\dfrac{1}{2} \div 2\dfrac{1}{10} = -\dfrac{15}{2} \div \dfrac{21}{10} \qquad \text{Rename the mixed numbers as improper fractions.}$$

$$= -\dfrac{15}{2} \cdot \dfrac{10}{21} \qquad \text{Multiply by the multiplicative inverse of } \dfrac{21}{10}, \dfrac{10}{21}.$$

$$= -\dfrac{\cancel{15}^{\,5}}{\cancel{2}_{1}} \cdot \dfrac{\cancel{10}^{\,5}}{\cancel{21}_{7}} \qquad \text{Divide out common factors.}$$

$$= -\dfrac{25}{7} \text{ or } -3\dfrac{4}{7} \qquad \text{Simplify.}$$

You can divide algebraic fractions in the same way that you divide numerical fractions.

Example 5 *Divide by an Algebraic Fraction*

Find $\dfrac{3xy}{4} \div \dfrac{2x}{8}$. Write the quotient in simplest form.

$\dfrac{3xy}{4} \div \dfrac{2x}{8} = \dfrac{3xy}{4} \cdot \dfrac{8}{2x}$ Multiply by the multiplicative inverse of $\dfrac{2x}{8}$, $\dfrac{8}{2x}$.

$= \dfrac{3xy}{\overset{}{\underset{1}{4}}} \cdot \dfrac{\overset{2}{8}}{\underset{1}{2x}}$ Divide out common factors.

$= \dfrac{6y}{2}$ or $3y$ Simplify.

DIMENSIONAL ANALYSIS   Dimensional analysis is a useful way to examine the solution of division problems.

Example 6 *Use Dimensional Analysis*

• **CHEERLEADING**   How many cheerleading uniforms can be made with $22\dfrac{3}{4}$ yards of fabric if each uniform requires $\dfrac{7}{8}$-yard?

To find how many uniforms, divide $22\dfrac{3}{4}$ by $\dfrac{7}{8}$.

$22\dfrac{3}{4} \div \dfrac{7}{8} = 22\dfrac{3}{4} \cdot \dfrac{8}{7}$ Multiply by the reciprocal of $\dfrac{7}{8}$, $\dfrac{8}{7}$.

$= \dfrac{91}{4} \cdot \dfrac{8}{7}$ Write $22\dfrac{3}{4}$ as an improper fraction.

$= \dfrac{\overset{13}{91}}{\underset{1}{4}} \cdot \dfrac{\overset{2}{8}}{\underset{1}{7}}$ Divide out common factors.

$= 26$ Simplify.

So, 26 uniforms can be made.

CHECK   Use dimensional analysis to examine the units.

$$\text{yards} \div \frac{\text{yards}}{\text{uniform}} = \text{yards} \cdot \frac{\text{uniform}}{\text{yards}} \quad \text{Divide out the units.}$$
$$= \text{uniform} \quad \text{Simplify.}$$

The result is expressed as uniforms. This agrees with your answer of 26 uniforms.

More About. . .

Cheerleading •⋯⋯⋯⋯
In the 1930s, both men and women cheerleaders began wearing cheerleading uniforms.
Source: www.umn.edu

TEACHING TIP
In Example 6, point out that students could also include the units when solving the problem. Stress that the reciprocal of $\dfrac{\text{yards}}{\text{uniform}}$ is $\dfrac{\text{uniform}}{\text{yards}}$.

Check for Understanding

Concept Check   1. **Explain** how reciprocals are used in division of fractions.
Dividing by a fraction is the same as multiplying by its reciprocal.
2. **OPEN ENDED**   Write a division expression that can be simplified by using the multiplicative inverse $\dfrac{7}{5}$. **Sample answer: $14 \div \dfrac{5}{7}$**

www.pre-alg.com/extra_examples/ny   Lesson 5-4 Dividing Rational Numbers   **217**

DIMENSIONAL ANALYSIS

In-Class Example   Power Point

6 **TRAVEL** How many gallons of gas are needed to travel $78\dfrac{3}{4}$ miles if a car gets $25\dfrac{1}{2}$ miles per gallon? $\dfrac{105}{34}$ or $3\dfrac{3}{34}$ gallons

Teaching Tip Dimensional analysis, examining the units, can help students set up the problem correctly. The values in the problem must be divided so that the correct unit remains.

3 Practice/Apply

Study Notebook

Have students—
• add the definitions/examples of the vocabulary terms to their Vocabulary Builder worksheets for Chapter 5.
• include any other item(s) that they find helpful in mastering the skills in this lesson.

About the Exercises . . .

Organization by Objective
• **Divide Fractions:** 16–45, 48–49
• **Dimensional Analysis:** 46–47, 50–51

Odd/Even Assignments
Exercises 16–51 are structured so that students practice the same concepts whether they are assigned odd or even problems.

Assignment Guide
Basic: 17–43 odd, 51–74
Average: 17–51 odd, 52–74
Advanced: 16–50 even, 52–65 (Optional: 66–74)

Study Guide and Intervention, p. 240

Two numbers whose product is 1 are called multiplicative inverses or reciprocals. For any fraction $\frac{a}{b}$, where $a, b \neq 0$, $\frac{b}{a}$ is the multiplicative inverse and $\frac{a}{b} \cdot \frac{b}{a} = 1$. This means that $\frac{2}{3}$ and $\frac{3}{2}$ are multiplicative inverses because $\frac{2}{3} \cdot \frac{3}{2} = 1$.

To divide by a fraction, multiply by its multiplicative inverse: $\frac{a}{b} \div \frac{c}{d} = \frac{a}{b} \cdot \frac{d}{c} = \frac{ad}{bc}$, where $b, c, d \neq 0$.

Example Find each quotient. Write in simplest form.

a. $\frac{3}{4} \div \frac{5}{8}$

$\frac{3}{4} \div \frac{5}{8} = \frac{3}{4} \cdot \frac{8}{5}$ — Multiply by the multiplicative inverse of $\frac{5}{8}$, $\frac{8}{5}$.

$= \frac{3}{4} \cdot \frac{8}{5}$ — Divide 4 and 8 by their GCF, 4.

$= \frac{6}{5}$ or $1\frac{1}{5}$ — Simplify.

b. $6\frac{2}{5} \div 2\frac{1}{5}$

$6\frac{2}{5} \div 2\frac{1}{5} = \frac{32}{5} \div \frac{11}{5}$ — Rename mixed numbers as improper fractions.

$= \frac{32}{5} \cdot \frac{5}{11}$ — Multiply by the multiplicative inverse of $\frac{11}{5}$, $\frac{5}{11}$.

$= \frac{32}{5} \cdot \frac{5}{11}$ — Divide out common factors.

$= \frac{32}{11}$ or $2\frac{10}{11}$ — Simplify.

Exercises

Find each quotient. Write in simplest form.

1. $\frac{5}{16} \div \frac{5}{8}$ $\frac{1}{2}$
2. $\frac{7}{9} \div \frac{2}{3}$ $1\frac{1}{6}$
3. $\frac{16}{21} \div \left(-\frac{2}{7}\right)$ $-2\frac{2}{3}$
4. $-\frac{4}{5} \div \frac{3}{10}$ $-2\frac{2}{3}$
5. $1\frac{1}{4} \div 2\frac{3}{8}$ $\frac{10}{19}$
6. $-8\frac{4}{7} \div 2\frac{1}{7}$ -4
7. $\frac{18}{21} \div 3$ $\frac{2}{7}$
8. $-4\frac{5}{8} \div \left(-3\frac{1}{3}\right)$ $1\frac{31}{80}$
9. $\frac{2x}{y} \div \frac{3}{y}$ $\frac{2x}{3}$
10. $\frac{c}{4d} \div \frac{3}{8d}$ $\frac{2c}{3}$
11. $\frac{4a}{b} \div \frac{2ac}{b}$ $\frac{2}{c}$
12. $\frac{m}{9} \div \frac{mn^2}{3}$ $\frac{1}{3n^2}$

Skills Practice, p. 241 and Practice, p. 242 (shown)

Find each quotient. Write in simplest form.

1. $\frac{1}{2} \div \frac{1}{10}$ 5
2. $-\frac{3}{8} \div \frac{9}{24}$ -1
3. $-\frac{15}{16} \div \frac{7}{12}$ $-1\frac{17}{28}$
4. $\frac{17}{20} \div \left(-\frac{3}{10}\right)$ $-2\frac{5}{6}$
5. $-\frac{3}{8} \div \left(-\frac{3}{9}\right)$ $1\frac{1}{8}$
6. $\frac{25}{32} \div \frac{15}{56}$ $2\frac{11}{12}$
7. $0 \div \frac{17}{18}$ 0
8. $-1\frac{1}{2} \div \frac{1}{4}$ -6
9. $\frac{8}{9} \div \frac{22}{81}$ $3\frac{3}{11}$
10. $8\frac{4}{9} \div 2\frac{1}{9}$ 4
11. $4\frac{3}{5} \div \frac{2}{5}$ $11\frac{1}{2}$
12. $-\frac{100}{63} \div \frac{10}{81}$ $-12\frac{6}{7}$
13. $18\frac{1}{3} \div \left(-4\frac{1}{6}\right)$ $-4\frac{2}{5}$
14. $-3\frac{2}{9} \div \frac{4}{27}$ $-21\frac{3}{4}$
15. $-2\frac{5}{6} \div \frac{3}{51}$ $-48\frac{1}{6}$
16. $4\frac{11}{12} \div 4\frac{5}{6}$ $1\frac{1}{58}$
17. $\frac{2x}{3} \div \frac{1}{9}$ $6x$
18. $\frac{a}{4} \div \frac{a}{8}$ 2
19. $\frac{4k}{5} \div \frac{25}{2k}$ $\frac{8k^2}{125}$
20. $\frac{ab}{8} \div \frac{b}{a}$ $\frac{a^2}{8}$
21. $\frac{2c}{b} \div \frac{4a}{b}$ $\frac{c}{2a}$
22. $\frac{y}{x} \div y^2$ $\frac{1}{xy}$
23. $\frac{3st}{r} \div \frac{4t}{r}$ $\frac{3s}{4}$
24. $\frac{a^2}{b^2} \div \frac{c^2}{b^2}$ $\frac{a^2}{c^2}$
25. $-\frac{2x}{y} \div \frac{4}{y}$ $-\frac{x}{2}$
26. $\frac{m^2}{2ap} \div \frac{n}{4p}$ $\frac{2m^2}{n^2}$

27. Evaluate $x \div y$ if $x = 3\frac{1}{2}$ and $y = \frac{3}{4}$. $4\frac{2}{3}$

28. Evaluate $w \div z$ if $w = \frac{6}{7}$ and $z = 3$. $\frac{2}{7}$

29. **TRAVEL** What is the average speed that Robin must drive to reach her friend's house 170 miles away in $2\frac{1}{2}$ hours? **68 mph**

30. **SEWING** How many choir robes can be made from $20\frac{1}{4}$ yards of fabric if each robe needs $1\frac{1}{8}$ yards? **18 choir robes**

Enrichment, p. 244

Number Theory Proof

Use your knowledge of properties to demonstrate why the reciprocal of the opposite of a number multiplied by the opposite of that number is equal to 1. In other words, show why $-\frac{1}{a} \cdot (-a) = 1$.

Write the reason for each statement.

1. Prove: $-\frac{1}{a} \cdot -a = 1$

Statement	Reason
Let a be any number.	a. Given
$-\frac{1}{a} \cdot (-a) = -a^{-1} \cdot (-a)$	b. Definition of Negative Exponents
$-\frac{1}{a} \cdot (-a) = -1a^{-1} \cdot (-1a)$	c. Identity Property of Multiplication
$-\frac{1}{a} \cdot (-a) = 1a^{-1+1}$	d. Product of Powers
$-\frac{1}{a} \cdot (-a) = 1a^0$	e. Inverse Property of Addition
$-\frac{1}{a} \cdot (-a) = 1 \cdot 1$	f. Definition of Zero Exponents
$-\frac{1}{a} \cdot (-a) = 1$	g. Simplify.

Use fractions to write an example showing each property of multiplication.
2–5. Sample answers are given.

2. Commutative Property
$\frac{1}{2} \cdot \frac{1}{3} = \frac{1}{3} \cdot \frac{1}{2}$

3. Associative Property
$\left(\frac{1}{2} \cdot \frac{1}{3}\right) \cdot \frac{1}{4} = \frac{1}{2}\left(\frac{1}{3} \cdot \frac{1}{4}\right)$

4. Identity Property
$\frac{1}{2} \cdot 1 = \frac{1}{2}$

5. Inverse Property
$\frac{1}{2} \cdot 2 = 1$

Guided Practice

GUIDED PRACTICE KEY	
Exercises	Examples
3–5	1
6–11	2–4
12–14	5
15	6

Find the multiplicative inverse of each number.

3. $\frac{4}{5}$ $\frac{5}{4}$
4. -16 $-\frac{1}{16}$
5. $3\frac{1}{8}$ $\frac{8}{25}$

Find each quotient. Write in simplest form.

6. $\frac{1}{2} \div \frac{6}{7}$ $\frac{7}{12}$
7. $-\frac{2}{3} \div \left(-\frac{5}{6}\right)$ $\frac{4}{5}$
8. $\frac{7}{9} \div \frac{2}{3}$ $1\frac{1}{6}$
9. $7\frac{1}{3} \div 5$ $1\frac{7}{15}$
10. $-\frac{8}{9} \div 3\frac{1}{5}$ $-\frac{5}{18}$
11. $2\frac{1}{6} \div \left(-1\frac{1}{5}\right)$ $-1\frac{29}{36}$

ALGEBRA Find each quotient. Write in simplest form.

12. $\frac{14}{n} \div \frac{1}{n}$ 14
13. $\frac{ab}{4} \div \frac{b}{6}$ $\frac{3a}{2}$
14. $\frac{x^2}{5} \div \frac{ax}{2}$ $\frac{2x}{5a}$

Application 15. **CARPENTRY** How many boards, each 2 feet 8 inches long, can be cut from a board 16 feet long if there is no waste? **6 boards**

★ indicates increased difficulty

Practice and Apply

Homework Help

For Exercises	See Examples
16–21	1
22–39	2–4
40–45	5
46, 47	6

Extra Practice
See page 734.

Find the multiplicative inverse of each number.

16. $\frac{6}{11}$ $\frac{11}{6}$
17. $-\frac{1}{5}$ $-\frac{5}{1}$ or -5
18. -7 $-\frac{1}{7}$
19. 24 $\frac{1}{24}$
20. $5\frac{1}{4}$ $\frac{4}{21}$
21. $-3\frac{2}{9}$ $-\frac{9}{29}$

Find each quotient. Write in simplest form.

22. $\frac{1}{4} \div \frac{3}{5}$ $\frac{5}{12}$
23. $\frac{2}{9} \div \frac{1}{4}$ $\frac{8}{9}$
24. $-\frac{1}{2} \div \frac{5}{6}$ $-\frac{3}{5}$
25. $\frac{6}{11} \div \left(-\frac{4}{5}\right)$ $-\frac{15}{22}$
26. $\frac{8}{9} \div \frac{4}{3}$ $\frac{2}{3}$
27. $\frac{7}{8} \div \frac{14}{15}$ $\frac{15}{16}$
28. $\frac{3}{4} \div \frac{3}{4}$ 1
29. $\frac{2}{9} \div \left(-\frac{2}{9}\right)$ -1
30. $\frac{3}{5} \div \frac{5}{9}$ $1\frac{2}{25}$
31. $\frac{3}{10} \div \frac{1}{5}$ $1\frac{1}{2}$
32. $12 \div \frac{4}{9}$ 27
33. $-8 \div \frac{4}{5}$ -10
34. $-\frac{5}{8} \div (-4)$ $\frac{5}{32}$
35. $6\frac{2}{3} \div 5$ $1\frac{1}{3}$
36. $-1\frac{1}{9} \div \frac{2}{3}$ $-1\frac{2}{3}$
37. $-\frac{2}{3} \div \left(-\frac{1}{3}\right)$ 2
38. $3\frac{3}{10} \div 1\frac{5}{6}$ $1\frac{4}{5}$
39. $7\frac{1}{2} \div \left(-1\frac{1}{5}\right)$ $-6\frac{1}{4}$

ALGEBRA Find each quotient. Write in simplest form.

40. $\frac{a}{7} \div \frac{a}{42}$ 6
41. $\frac{10}{3x} \div \frac{5}{2x}$ $\frac{4}{3}$
42. $\frac{c}{8} \div \frac{cd}{5}$ $\frac{5}{8d}$
43. $\frac{5s}{t} \div \frac{6rs}{t}$ $\frac{5}{6r}$
44. $\frac{k^3}{9} \div \frac{k}{24}$ $\frac{8k^2}{3}$
★ 45. $\frac{2s}{t^2} \div \frac{st^3}{8}$ $\frac{16}{t^5}$

46. **COOKING** How many $\frac{1}{4}$-pound hamburgers can be made from $2\frac{3}{4}$ pounds of ground beef? **11 hamburgers**

★ 47. **SEWING** How many 9-inch ribbons can be cut from $1\frac{1}{2}$ yards of ribbon? **6 ribbons**

ALGEBRA Evaluate each expression.

48. $m \div n$ if $m = -\frac{8}{9}$ and $n = \frac{7}{18}$ $-2\frac{2}{7}$
★ 49. $r^2 \div s^2$ if $r = -\frac{3}{4}$ and $s = 1\frac{1}{3}$ $\frac{81}{256}$

More About...

Travel •••••••••

Trains in Europe can travel faster than 125 miles per hour.

Source: www.geography. about.com

For Exercises 50 and 51, solve each problem. Then check your answer using dimensional analysis.

• 50. **TRAVEL** How long would it take a train traveling 80 miles per hour to go 280 miles? **3.5 h**

51. **FOOD** The average young American woman drinks $1\frac{1}{2}$ cans of cola each day. At this rate, in how many days would it take to drink a total of 12 cans? **Source:** U.S. Department of Agriculture **8 days**

52. **CRITICAL THINKING** **b. The quotient increases.**
   a. Divide $\frac{3}{4}$ by $\frac{1}{2}$, $\frac{1}{4}$, $\frac{1}{8}$, and $\frac{1}{12}$. $1\frac{1}{2}$, **3, 6, 9**
   b. What happens to the quotient as the value of the divisor decreases?
   c. **Make a conjecture** about the quotient when you divide $\frac{3}{4}$ by fractions that increase in value. Test your conjecture. **The quotient decreases.**

53. WRITING IN MATH Answer the question that was posed at the beginning of the lesson. **See margin.**

   How is dividing by a fraction related to multiplying?

   Include the following in your answer:
   • a model of a whole number divided by a fraction, and
   • an explanation of how division of fractions is related to multiplication.

NEW YORK
Test Practice

Standardized Test Practice
Ⓐ Ⓑ Ⓒ Ⓓ

54. Carla baby-sits for $2\frac{1}{4}$ hours and earns \$11.25. What is her rate? **D**
   Ⓐ \$4.00/h   Ⓑ \$5.50/h   Ⓒ \$4.50/h   Ⓓ \$5.00/h

55. What is $\frac{3}{10}$ divided by $1\frac{4}{5}$? **C**
   Ⓐ $\frac{1}{2}$ Ⓑ $\frac{3}{8}$ Ⓒ $\frac{1}{6}$ Ⓓ $\frac{27}{50}$

Maintain Your Skills

Mixed Review **Find each product. Write in simplest form.** *(Lesson 5-3)* 59. $-\frac{10}{21}$

56. $\frac{3}{5} \cdot \frac{1}{3}$ $\frac{1}{5}$ 57. $\frac{2}{9} \cdot \frac{15}{16}$ $\frac{5}{24}$ 58. $2\frac{4}{5} \cdot \frac{3}{8}$ $1\frac{1}{20}$ 59. $-\frac{5}{12} \cdot 1\frac{1}{7}$

Identify all sets to which each number belongs. *(Lesson 5-2)*

60. 16 **N, W, I, Q**   61. $-2.8888\ldots$ **Q**   62. $0.\overline{9}$ **Q**   63. $5.121221222\ldots$ **not rational**

64. Write the prime factorization of 150. Use exponents for repeated factors. *(Lesson 4-3)* $2 \cdot 3 \cdot 5^2$

65. **ALGEBRA** Solve $3x - 5 = 16$. *(Lesson 3-5)* **7**

Getting Ready for the Next Lesson **PREREQUISITE SKILL** Write each improper fraction as a mixed number in simplest form. *(To review simplifying fractions, see Lesson 4-5.)*

66. $\frac{9}{4}$ $2\frac{1}{4}$ 67. $\frac{8}{7}$ $1\frac{1}{7}$ 68. $\frac{17}{2}$ $8\frac{1}{2}$

69. $\frac{25}{4}$ $6\frac{1}{4}$ 70. $\frac{24}{5}$ $4\frac{4}{5}$ 71. $\frac{22}{6}$ $3\frac{2}{3}$

72. $\frac{15}{6}$ $2\frac{1}{2}$ 73. $\frac{30}{18}$ $1\frac{2}{3}$ 74. $\frac{18}{15}$ $1\frac{1}{5}$

www.pre-alg.com/self_check_quiz/ny   Lesson 5-4 Dividing Rational Numbers **219**

4 Assess

Open-Ended Assessment

Writing Have students write an outline describing a procedure to divide fractions. Students should include at least one example to illustrate their ideas.

Getting Ready for Lesson 5-5

PREREQUISITE SKILL Lesson 5-5 presents adding and subtracting like fractions. Exercises 66–74 should be used to determine your students' familiarity with simplifying fractions.

Answer

53. Dividing by a fraction is the same as multiplying by its reciprocal. Answers should include the following.
   • For example, a model of two circles, each divided into four sections, represents $2 \div \frac{1}{4}$. Since there are 8 sections, $2 \div \frac{1}{4} = 8$.
   • Division of fractions and multiplication of fractions are inverse operations. So, $2 \div \frac{1}{4}$ equals $2 \cdot 4$ or 8.

1 Focus

5-Minute Check Transparency 5-5 Use as a quiz or review of Lesson 5-4.

Mathematical Background notes are available for this lesson on page 198D.

Why are fractions important when taking measurements?

The opening activity questions are repeated on page 248 of the *Chapter 5 Resource Masters*.

Reading to Learn Mathematics, p. 248 **ELL**

Pre-Activity *Why are fractions important when taking measurements?*

Do the activity at the top of page 220 in your textbook. Write your answers below. Use a ruler to find each measure.

a. $\frac{1}{8}$ in. $+ \frac{3}{8}$ in. $\frac{4}{8}$ or $\frac{1}{2}$ in.

b. $\frac{3}{8}$ in. $+ \frac{4}{8}$ in. $\frac{7}{8}$ in.

c. $\frac{4}{8}$ in. $+ \frac{4}{8}$ in. $\frac{8}{8}$ or 1 in.

d. $\frac{6}{8}$ in. $- \frac{3}{8}$ in. $\frac{3}{8}$ in.

Reading the Lesson

1. Like fractions have like __denominators__ .

2. Find two fractions whose sum is $\frac{7}{8}$. Sample answer: $\frac{3}{8}, \frac{4}{8}$

3. Find two fractions whose difference is $\frac{2}{7}$. Sample answer: $\frac{6}{7}, \frac{4}{7}$

4. To add or subtract like fractions, you __add or subtract__ the numerators and keep the __denominators__ the same.

5. Explain how to use a ruler to add $\frac{3}{8} + \frac{7}{8}$.
Sample answer: Starting at zero, count over $\frac{3}{8}$ inch. Continue counting for an additional $\frac{7}{8}$ inch. The ending location is $1\frac{2}{8}$ or $1\frac{1}{4}$ inches.

Helping You Remember

6. Sketch a model to show each sum or difference.

a. $\frac{3}{10} + \frac{6}{10}$

$\frac{3}{10} + \frac{6}{10} = \frac{9}{10}$

b. $\frac{6}{7} - \frac{3}{7}$

$\frac{6}{7} - \frac{3}{7} = \frac{3}{7}$

Reinforcement of 7.A.2 Add and subtract monomials with exponents of one

a. $\frac{4}{8}$ or $\frac{1}{2}$ in.

b. $\frac{7}{8}$ in.

c. $\frac{8}{8}$ or 1 in.

d. $\frac{3}{8}$ in.

What You'll Learn

- Add like fractions.
- Subtract like fractions.

Why are fractions important when taking measurements?

Measures of different parts of an insect are shown in the diagram. The sum of the parts is $\frac{6}{8}$ inch. Use a ruler to find each measure.

a. $\frac{1}{8}$ in. $+ \frac{3}{8}$ in.

b. $\frac{3}{8}$ in. $+ \frac{4}{8}$ in.

c. $\frac{4}{8}$ in. $+ \frac{4}{8}$ in.

d. $\frac{6}{8}$ in. $- \frac{3}{8}$ in.

ADD LIKE FRACTIONS Fractions with the same denominator are called *like fractions*. The rule for adding like fractions is stated below.

Key Concept   *Adding Like Fractions*

- **Words** To add fractions with like denominators, add the numerators and write the sum over the denominator.

- **Symbols** $\frac{a}{c} + \frac{b}{c} = \frac{a+b}{c}$, where $c \neq 0$

- **Example** $\frac{1}{5} + \frac{2}{5} = \frac{1+2}{5}$ or $\frac{3}{5}$

Example 1 Add Fractions

Find $\frac{3}{7} + \frac{5}{7}$. Write the sum in simplest form.   **Estimate:** $0 + 1 = 1$

$\frac{3}{7} + \frac{5}{7} = \frac{3+5}{7}$ The denominators are the same. Add the numerators.

$= \frac{8}{7}$ or $1\frac{1}{7}$ Simplify and rename as a mixed number.

Example 2 Add Mixed Numbers

Find $6\frac{5}{8} + 1\frac{1}{8}$. Write the sum in simplest form.   **Estimate:** $7 + 1 = 8$

$6\frac{5}{8} + 1\frac{1}{8} = (6+1) + \left(\frac{5}{8} + \frac{1}{8}\right)$ Add the whole numbers and fractions separately.

$= 7 + \frac{5+1}{8}$ Add the numerators.

$= 7\frac{6}{8}$ or $7\frac{3}{4}$ Simplify.

Study Tip

Alternative Method
You can also stack the mixed numbers vertically to find the sum.

$6\frac{5}{8}$
$+1\frac{1}{8}$
_____
$7\frac{6}{8}$ or $7\frac{3}{4}$

Resource Manager

📁 Workbooks and Reproducible Masters

Chapter 5 Resource Masters
- Study Guide and Intervention, p. 245
- Skills Practice, p. 246
- Practice, p. 247
- Reading to Learn Mathematics, p. 248
- Enrichment, p. 249
- Assessment, pp. 289, 291

Parent and Student Study Guide Workbook, p. 37
Prerequisite Skills Workbook,
  pp. 37–44

Transparencies

5-Minute Check Transparency 5-5
Answer Key Transparencies

Technology

Interactive Chalkboard

SUBTRACT LIKE FRACTIONS The rule for subtracting fractions with like denominators is similar to the rule for addition.

> **Key Concept** — **Subtracting Like Fractions**
>
> - **Words** To subtract fractions with like denominators, subtract the numerators and write the difference over the denominator.
> - **Symbols** $\frac{a}{c} - \frac{b}{c} = \frac{a-b}{c}$, where $c \neq 0$
> - **Example** $\frac{5}{7} - \frac{1}{7} = \frac{5-1}{7}$ or $\frac{4}{7}$

Concept Check: It is the same, except the numerators are subtracted rather than added.

✓ **Concept Check** How is the rule for subtracting fractions with like denominators similar to the rule for adding fractions with like denominators?

Example 3 Subtract Fractions

Find $\frac{9}{20} - \frac{13}{20}$. Write the difference in simplest form. **Estimate:** $\frac{1}{2} - 1 = -\frac{1}{2}$

$\frac{9}{20} - \frac{13}{20} = \frac{9-13}{20}$ The denominators are the same. Subtract the numerators.

$\phantom{\frac{9}{20} - \frac{13}{20}} = \frac{-4}{20}$ or $-\frac{1}{5}$ Simplify.

You can write the mixed numbers as improper fractions before adding or subtracting.

Example 4 Subtract Mixed Numbers

Evaluate $a - b$ if $a = 9\frac{1}{6}$ and $b = 5\frac{2}{6}$.   **Estimate:** $9 - 5 = 4$

$a - b = 9\frac{1}{6} - 5\frac{2}{6}$ Replace a with $9\frac{1}{6}$ and b with $5\frac{2}{6}$.

$ = \frac{55}{6} - \frac{32}{6}$ Write the mixed numbers as improper fractions.

$ = \frac{23}{6}$ Subtract the numerators.

$ = 3\frac{5}{6}$ Simplify.

 ALGEBRA CONNECTION

You can use the same rules for adding or subtracting like algebraic fractions as you did for adding or subtracting like numerical fractions.

Example 5 Add Algebraic Fractions

Find $\frac{n}{8} + \frac{5n}{8}$. Write the sum in simplest form.

$\frac{n}{8} + \frac{5n}{8} = \frac{n+5n}{8}$ The denominators are the same. Add the numerators.

$\phantom{\frac{n}{8} + \frac{5n}{8}} = \frac{6n}{8}$ Add the numerators.

$\phantom{\frac{n}{8} + \frac{5n}{8}} = \frac{3n}{4}$ Simplify.

 www.pre-alg.com/extra_examples/ny   Lesson 5-5 Adding and Subtracting Like Fractions   **221**

✓ **Skills Check**

Add and Subtract Like Fractions Write each answer in simplest form.

a. $\frac{4}{9} + \frac{5}{9}$ 1 **b.** $3\frac{1}{4} - 2\frac{3}{4}$ $\frac{1}{2}$

c. $2\frac{5}{14} + 3\frac{3}{14}$ $5\frac{4}{7}$

Study Notebook

Have students—
- record the key concepts for adding like fractions and subtracting like fractions.
- include any other item(s) that they find helpful in mastering the skills in this lesson.

D A I L Y
INTERVENTION FIND THE ERROR
If students are having difficulty with negative numbers, suggest that they keep negative signs with the numerators. Emphasize that if the rest of the work is correct, the answer will be incorrect if the negative sign is omitted.

About the Exercises . . .
Odd/Even Assignments
Exercises 15–46 are structured so that students practice the same concepts whether they are assigned odd or even problems.

Assignment Guide
Basic: 15–31 odd, 35–45 odd, 48–65

Average: 15–47 odd, 48–65

Advanced: 16–46 even, 47–59 (Optional: 60–65)

All: Practice Quiz 1 (1–10)

Answer

1.

$$\frac{2}{7} \qquad \frac{4}{7}$$

$$\frac{6}{7}$$

Check for Understanding

Concept Check 1. **Draw** a model to show the sum $\frac{2}{7} + \frac{4}{7}$. **See margin.**

2. **OPEN ENDED** Write a subtraction expression in which the difference of two fractions is $\frac{18}{25}$. **Sample answer:** $\frac{19}{25} - \frac{1}{25}$

3. **FIND THE ERROR** Kayla and Ethan are adding $-2\frac{1}{8}$ and $-4\frac{3}{8}$.

Kayla	Ethan
$-2\frac{1}{8} + \left(-4\frac{3}{8}\right) = -\frac{17}{8} + \left(-\frac{35}{8}\right)$ $= -\frac{52}{8}$ or $-6\frac{1}{2}$	$-2\frac{1}{8} + \left(-4\frac{3}{8}\right) = \frac{17}{8} + \left(-\frac{35}{8}\right)$ $= -\frac{18}{8}$ or $-2\frac{1}{4}$

Who is correct? Explain your reasoning.
Kayla; Ethan incorrectly left out the negative sign on the first term.

GUIDED PRACTICE KEY

Exercises	Examples
4–9, 14	1–3
10	4
11–13	5

Guided Practice Find each sum or difference. Write in simplest form.

4. $\frac{1}{7} + \frac{5}{7}$ $\frac{6}{7}$ 5. $\frac{11}{14} - \frac{3}{14}$ $\frac{4}{7}$ 6. $\frac{3}{10} + \frac{3}{10}$ $\frac{3}{5}$

7. $-\frac{1}{8} - \frac{5}{8}$ $-\frac{3}{4}$ 8. $-2\frac{4}{5} + \left(-\frac{2}{5}\right)$ $-3\frac{1}{5}$ 9. $7\frac{1}{8} - \left(-1\frac{3}{8}\right)$ $8\frac{1}{2}$

TEACHING TIP
Remind students that answers to application problems should be given in simplest form.

10. **ALGEBRA** Evaluate $x + y$ if $x = 2\frac{4}{9}$ and $y = 8\frac{7}{9}$. $11\frac{2}{9}$

ALGEBRA Find each sum or difference. Write in simplest form.

11. $\frac{6r}{11} + \frac{2r}{11}$ $\frac{8r}{11}$ 12. $\frac{19}{a} - \frac{12}{a}, a \neq 0$ $\frac{7}{a}$ 13. $\frac{5}{3x} - \frac{6}{3x}, x \neq 0$ $-\frac{1}{3x}$

Application 14. **MEASUREMENT** Hoai was $62\frac{1}{8}$ inches tall at the end of school in June. He was $63\frac{7}{8}$ inches tall in September. How much did he grow during the summer? $1\frac{3}{4}$ in.

★ indicates increased difficulty

Practice and Apply

Homework Help

For Exercises	See Examples
15–24	1–3
25–38, 45, 46	4
39–44	5

Extra Practice
See page 734.

Find each sum or difference. Write in simplest form.

15. $\frac{2}{5} + \frac{1}{5}$ $\frac{3}{5}$ 16. $\frac{10}{11} - \frac{8}{11}$ $\frac{2}{11}$ 17. $\frac{17}{18} - \frac{5}{18}$ $\frac{2}{3}$

18. $\frac{3}{10} + \frac{7}{10}$ 1 19. $\frac{1}{12} + \left(-\frac{7}{12}\right)$ $-\frac{1}{2}$ 20. $\frac{9}{20} - \left(-\frac{7}{20}\right)$ $\frac{4}{5}$

21. $-\frac{3}{4} + \left(-\frac{3}{4}\right)$ $-1\frac{1}{2}$ 22. $-\frac{13}{16} + \left(-\frac{9}{16}\right)$ $-1\frac{3}{8}$ 23. $-\frac{7}{9} + \frac{5}{9}$ $-\frac{2}{9}$

24. $-\frac{17}{20} + \frac{9}{20}$ $-\frac{2}{5}$ 25. $7\frac{2}{5} + 4\frac{2}{5}$ $11\frac{4}{5}$ 26. $-4\frac{5}{8} - \frac{3}{8}$ -5

27. $5\frac{7}{9} - \left(-3\frac{5}{9}\right)$ $9\frac{1}{3}$ 28. $2\frac{5}{12} + \left(-2\frac{7}{12}\right)$ $-\frac{1}{6}$ 29. $2\frac{3}{8} - 1\frac{5}{8}$ $\frac{3}{4}$

30. $8\frac{9}{10} - 6\frac{1}{10}$ $2\frac{4}{5}$ 31. $7\frac{4}{7} - 2\frac{5}{7}$ $4\frac{6}{7}$ 32. $-8\frac{6}{11} - \left(-2\frac{5}{11}\right)$ $-6\frac{1}{11}$

★33. Find $12\frac{7}{8} - 7\frac{3}{8} + 2\frac{5}{8}$. $8\frac{1}{8}$ ★34. Find $5\frac{5}{6} + 3\frac{5}{6} - 2\frac{1}{6}$. $7\frac{1}{2}$

D A I L Y
INTERVENTION   **Differentiated Instruction**

- **Visual/Spatial** Have students use rectangles divided into parts to model addition and subtraction of fractions. Students can draw rectangles on paper (or grid paper), then shade in the fractions to be added or subtracted.

ALGEBRA Evaluate each expression if $x = \frac{8}{15}$, $y = 2\frac{1}{15}$, and $z = \frac{11}{15}$. Write in simplest form.

35. $x + y$ $2\frac{3}{5}$

36. $z + y$ $2\frac{4}{5}$

37. $z - x$ $1\frac{1}{5}$

38. $y - x$ $1\frac{8}{15}$

ALGEBRA Find each sum or difference. Write in simplest form.

39. $\frac{x}{8} + \frac{4x}{8}$ $\frac{5x}{8}$

40. $\frac{3r}{10} + \frac{3r}{10}$ $\frac{3r}{5}$

41. $\frac{12}{m} - \frac{9}{m}$, $m \neq 0$ $\frac{3}{m}$

★ 42. $\frac{10a}{3b} - \frac{7a}{3b}$, $b \neq 0$ $\frac{a}{b}$

43. $5\frac{4}{7}c - 3\frac{1}{7}c$ $2\frac{3}{7}c$

44. $-2\frac{1}{6}y + 8\frac{5}{6}y$ $6\frac{2}{3}y$

45. **CARPENTRY** A 5-foot long kitchen countertop is to be installed between two walls that are $54\frac{5}{8}$ inches apart. How much of the countertop must be cut off so that it fits between the walls? $5\frac{3}{8}$ in.

46. **SEWING** Chumani is making a linen suit. The portion of the pattern envelope that shows the yards of fabric needed for different sizes is shown at the right. If Chumani is making a size 6 jacket and skirt from 45-inch fabric, how much fabric should she buy? $3\frac{1}{2}$ yd

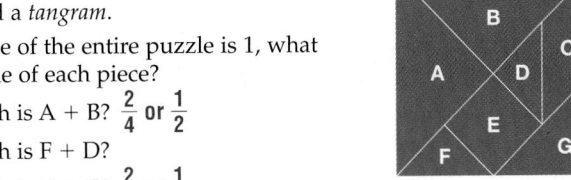

Size	(6	8	10)
JACKET			
45"	$2\frac{5}{8}$	$2\frac{3}{4}$	$2\frac{3}{4}$
60"	2	2	2
SKIRT			
45"	$\frac{7}{8}$	$1\frac{1}{8}$	$1\frac{1}{8}$
60"	$\frac{7}{8}$	$\frac{7}{8}$	$\frac{7}{8}$

★ 47. **GARDENING** Melanie's flower garden has a perimeter of 25 feet. She plans to add 2 feet 9 inches to the width and 3 feet 9 inches to the length. What is the new perimeter in feet? **38 ft**

48. **CRITICAL THINKING** The 7-piece puzzle at the right is called a *tangram*.

48a. $A = \frac{1}{4}$, $B = \frac{1}{4}$,
$C = \frac{1}{8}$, $D = \frac{1}{16}$, $E = \frac{1}{8}$,
$F = \frac{1}{16}$, $G = \frac{1}{8}$

48c. $\frac{2}{16}$ or $\frac{1}{8}$

a. If the value of the entire puzzle is 1, what is the value of each piece?

b. How much is A + B? $\frac{2}{4}$ or $\frac{1}{2}$

c. How much is F + D?

d. How much is C + E? $\frac{2}{8}$ or $\frac{1}{4}$

e. Which pieces each equal the sum of E and G? **A and B**

49. **WRITING IN MATH** Answer the question that was posed at the beginning of the lesson. **See margin.**

Why are fractions important when taking measurements?

Include the following in your answer:

• the fraction of an inch that each mark on a ruler or tape measure represents, and

• some real-world examples in which fractional measures are used.

Answer

49. When you use a ruler or a tape measure, measurements are usually a fraction of an inch. Answers should include the following.

• The marks on a ruler represent $\frac{1}{16}$ of an inch, $\frac{1}{8}$ of an inch, $\frac{1}{4}$ of an inch, and $\frac{1}{2}$ of an inch.

• Fractional measures are used in sewing and construction.

Open-Ended Assessment

Speaking Show students the following diagram:

Have them explain the problem shown and tell how to find the sum. They should explain how to give the sum in simplest form. Repeat with several similar examples including subtraction.

Getting Ready for Lesson 5-6

PREREQUISITE SKILL Lesson 5-6 presents least common multiple. Exercises 60–65 should be used to determine your students' familiarity with finding prime factorization, which can be used to find LCM.

Assessment Options

Practice Quiz 1 The quiz provides students with a brief review of the concepts and skills in Lessons 5-1 through 5-5. Lesson numbers are given to the right of exercises or instruction lines so students can review concepts not yet mastered.

Quiz (Lessons 5-4 and 5-5) is available on p. 289 of the *Chapter 5 Resource Masters*.

Mid-Chapter Test (Lessons 5-1 through 5-5) is available on p. 291 of the *Chapter 5 Resource Masters*.

---

50. Find $\frac{13}{20} - \frac{7}{20}$. Write in simplest form. **D**

(A) $\frac{6}{10}$ (B) $\frac{3}{5}$ (C) $\frac{6}{20}$ (D) $\frac{3}{10}$

51. A piece of wood is $1\frac{9}{16}$ inches thick. A layer of padding $\frac{15}{16}$ inch thick is placed on top. What is the total thickness of the wood and the padding? **A**

(A) $2\frac{1}{2}$ in.   (B) $1\frac{1}{2}$ in.   (C) $1\frac{24}{16}$ in.   (D) $1\frac{3}{8}$ in.

Maintain Your Skills

Mixed Review   **Find each quotient. Write in simplest form.**   *(Lesson 5-4)*

52. $\frac{1}{6} \div \frac{3}{4}$ **$\frac{2}{9}$**   53. $-\frac{5}{8} \div \frac{1}{3}$ **$-1\frac{7}{8}$**   54. $\frac{2}{5} \div 1\frac{1}{2}$ **$\frac{4}{15}$**

Find each product. Write in simplest form.   *(Lesson 5-3)*

55. $\frac{2}{5} \cdot \frac{3}{4}$ **$\frac{3}{10}$**   56. $\frac{1}{6} \cdot \left(-\frac{8}{9}\right)$ **$-\frac{4}{27}$**   57. $\frac{4}{7} \cdot 2\frac{1}{3}$ **$1\frac{1}{3}$**

58. Find the product of $4y^2$ and $8y^5$. *(Lesson 4-6)* **$32y^7$**

59. **GEOMETRY** Find the perimeter and area of the rectangle. *(Lesson 3-7)* **42 cm; 90 cm²**

6 cm

15 cm

Getting Ready for the Next Lesson   **PREREQUISITE SKILL** Use exponents to write the prime factorization of each number or monomial. *(To review prime factorization, see Lesson 4-3.)*

60. 60 **$2^2 \cdot 3 \cdot 5$**   61. 175 **$5^2 \cdot 7$**   62. 112 **$2^4 \cdot 7$**
63. $12n$ **$2^2 \cdot 3 \cdot n$**   64. $24s^2$ **$2^3 \cdot 3 \cdot s^2$**   65. $42a^2b$ **$2 \cdot 3 \cdot 7 \cdot a^2 \cdot b$**

Practice Quiz 1   Lessons 5-1 through 5-5

Write each fraction or mixed number as a decimal. Use a bar to show a repeating decimal.   *(Lesson 5-1)*

1. $\frac{4}{25}$ **0.16**   2. $-\frac{2}{9}$ **$-0.\overline{2}$**   3. $3\frac{1}{8}$ **3.125**

Write each decimal as a fraction or mixed number in simplest form. *(Lesson 5-2)*

4. -6.75 **$-6\frac{3}{4}$**   5. 0.12 **$\frac{3}{25}$**   6. 0.5555… **$\frac{5}{9}$**

Simplify each expression. *(Lessons 5-3, 5-4, and 5-5)*

7. $\frac{5}{18} \cdot \frac{4}{15}$ **$\frac{2}{27}$**   8. $\frac{7}{8} \div \left(-\frac{1}{4}\right)$ **$-3\frac{1}{2}$**   9. $\frac{11}{12} - \frac{6}{12}$ **$\frac{5}{12}$**

10. **ALGEBRA** Find $6\frac{3}{5}a + 2\frac{4}{5}a$. Write in simplest form. *(Lesson 5-5)* **$9\frac{2}{5}a$**

Factors and Multiples

Many words used in mathematics are also used in everyday language. You can use the everyday meaning of these words to better understand their mathematical meaning. The table shows both meanings of the words *factor* and *multiple*.

Term	Everyday Meaning	Mathematical Meaning
factor	something that contributes to the production of a result • The weather was not a *factor* in the decision. • The type of wood is one *factor* that contributes to the cost of the table.	one of two or more numbers that are multiplied together to form a product
multiple	involving more than one or shared by many • *multiple* births • *multiple* ownership	the product of a quantity and a whole number

Source: *Merriam Webster's Collegiate Dictionary*

When you count by 2, you are listing the multiples of 2. When you count by 3, you are listing the multiples of 3, and so on, as shown in the table below.

Number	Factors	Multiples
2	1, 2	2, 4, 6, 8, …
3	1, 3	3, 6, 9, 12, …
4	1, 2, 4	4, 8, 12, 16, …

Notice that the mathematical meaning of each word is related to the everyday meaning. The word *multiple* means many, and in mathematics, a number has infinitely many multiples.

1. Sample answer: a factor is found by dividing a number; a multiple is found by multiplying a number.

3. Sample answer: words with fact- generally mean make or do, and words with multi- mean many.

Reading to Learn

1. Write your own rule for remembering the difference between *factor* and *multiple*.

2. RESEARCH Use the Internet or a dictionary to find the everyday meaning of each word listed below. Compare them to the mathematical meanings of *factor* and *multiple*. Note the similarities and differences. **a–c. See margin.**
  a. factotum   **b.** multicultural   **c.** multimedia

3. Make lists of other words that have the prefixes fact- or multi-. Determine what the words in each list have in common.

Sample Answers

2a. A factotum is a person that has many diverse activities or responsibilities. A factotum produces results, just as factors produce products.

2b. Multicultural means many diverse cultures, just as a multiple is one of many numbers that can be formed.

2c. Multimedia means using several media, or multiple media.

Before starting this activity, ask students to count by 2's, 3's, 4's, 5's, and 6's, writing down the numbers. Then have students describe any patterns they see. To see patterns, encourage students to write down at least 10 numbers each time.

Teach

Factors and Multiples Neal and Rayna name numbers related to the number 18. Neal names 1, 2, 3, 6, 9, and 18. Rayna names 18, 36, 54, 72, 90, and 180. Ask students to classify the numbers named by each person. **Neal named factors; Rayna named multiples.**

Assess

Study Notebook

Ask students to look up *factor* and *multiple* in a thesaurus. Have them write the synonyms that relate to the mathematical meanings of the words. Then ask them to summarize what they learned about the words *factor* and *multiple*.

ELL English Language Learners may benefit from writing key concepts from this activity in their Study Notebooks in their native language and then in English.

1 Focus

How can you use prime factors to find the least common multiple?

The opening activity questions are repeated on page 253 of the *Chapter 5 Resource Masters*.

Reading to Learn Mathematics, p. 253 | ELL

Pre-Activity *How can you use prime factors to find the least common multiple?*
Do the activity at the top of page 226 in your textbook. Write your answers below.

   a. List the next three years in which the voter can vote for a president. **2004, 2008, 2012**

   b. List the next three years in which the voter can vote for a senator. **2006, 2012, 2018**

   c. What will be the next year in which the voter has a chance to vote for a president and a senator? **2012**

Reading the Lesson 1–4. See students' work.

Write a definition and give an example of each new vocabulary word or phrase.

Vocabulary	Definition	Example
1. multiple		
2. common multiples		
3. least common multiple (LCM)		
4. least common denominator (LCD)		

5. Find two numbers whose LCM is 24. **Sample answer: 6 and 8**

6. Find two fractions whose LCD is 2a. **Sample answer: $\frac{1}{2}$ and $\frac{1}{a}$**

7. Explain what happens if a common multiple is used to find a common denominator, but the multiple is not the LCM. **Sample answer: The fractions formed will be equivalent to fractions written with the LCD.**

Helping You Remember

8. Use a Venn diagram to show multiples of 3 and multiples of 4. Explain how to use the diagram to find common multiples and the LCM. **Sample answer: The overlapping circles show the common multiples. The LCM is the smallest of these numbers.**

5-6 Least Common Multiple

 NEW YORK *Performance Indicator* Reinforcement of **7.N.9 Determine multiples and least common multiple of two or more numbers**

What You'll Learn

- Find the least common multiple of two or more numbers.
- Find the least common denominator of two or more fractions.

Vocabulary
- multiple
- common multiples
- least common multiple (LCM)
- least common denominator (LCD)

a. 2004, 2008, 2012
b. 2006, 2012, 2018

How can you use prime factors to find the least common multiple?

A voter voted for both president and senator in the year 2000.

a. List the next three years in which the voter can vote for president.

b. List the next three years in which the voter can vote for senator.

c. What will be the next year in which the voter has a chance to vote for both president and senator? **2012**

Candidate	Length of Term (years)
President	4
Senator	6

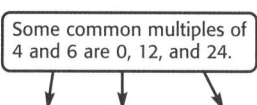

LEAST COMMON MULTIPLE A **multiple** of a number is a product of that number and a whole number.

Sometimes numbers have some of the same multiples. These are called **common multiples**.

Multiples of 5
$5 \cdot 0 = 0$
$5 \cdot 1 = 5$
$5 \cdot 2 = 10$
$5 \cdot 3 = 15$
⋮   ⋮

> Some common multiples of 4 and 6 are 0, 12, and 24.

multiples of 4:   0, 4, 8, 12, 16, 20, 24, 28, …
multiples of 6:   0, 6, 12, 18, 24, 30, 36, 42, …

The least of the *nonzero* common multiples is called the **least common multiple (LCM)**. So, the LCM of 4 and 6 is 12.

When numbers are large, an easier way of finding the least common multiple is to use prime factorization. The LCM is the smallest product that contains the prime factors of each number.

Study Tip

Prime Factors
If a prime factor appears in both numbers, use the factor with the greatest exponent.

Example 1 Find the LCM

Find the LCM of 108 and 240.

Number	Prime Factorization	Exponential Form
108	$2 \cdot 2 \cdot 3 \cdot 3 \cdot 3$	$2^2 \cdot 3^3$
240	$2 \cdot 2 \cdot 2 \cdot 2 \cdot 3 \cdot 5$	$2^4 \cdot 3 \cdot 5$

Resource Manager

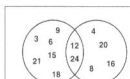 **Workbooks and Reproducible Masters**

Chapter 5 Resource Masters
- Study Guide and Intervention, p. 250
- Skills Practice, p. 251
- Practice, p. 252
- Reading to Learn Mathematics, p. 253
- Enrichment, p. 254

Parent and Student Study Guide Workbook, p. 38

 Transparencies
5-Minute Check Transparency 5-6
Answer Key Transparencies

 Technology
Interactive Chalkboard
Multimedia Applications

The prime factors of both numbers are 2, 3, and 5. Multiply the greatest power of 2, 3, and 5 appearing in either factorization.

$$LCM = 2^4 \cdot 3^3 \cdot 5$$
$$= 2160$$

So, the LCM of 108 and 240 is 2160.

☑ **Concept Check**   What is the LCM of 6 and 12? **12**

The LCM of two or more monomials is found in the same way as the LCM of two or more numbers.

Example 2 *The LCM of Monomials*

Find the LCM of $18xy^2$ and $10y$.

$$18xy^2 = 2 \cdot 3^2 \cdot x \cdot y^2$$
$$10y = 2 \cdot 5 \cdot y$$

$$LCM = 2 \cdot 3^2 \cdot 5 \cdot x \cdot y^2 \quad \text{Multiply the greatest power of each prime factor.}$$
$$= 90xy^2$$

The LCM of $18xy^2$ and $10y$ is $90xy^2$.

LEAST COMMON DENOMINATOR   The **least common denominator (LCD)** of two or more fractions is the LCM of the denominators.

Example 3 *Find the LCD*

Find the LCD of $\frac{5}{9}$ and $\frac{11}{21}$.

$$9 = 3^2 \longleftarrow$$
$$21 = 3 \cdot 7 \longleftarrow$$

> Write the prime factorization of 9 and 21.
> Highlight the greatest power of each prime factor.

$$LCM = 3^2 \cdot 7 \quad \text{Multiply.}$$
$$= 63$$

The LCD of $\frac{5}{9}$ and $\frac{11}{21}$ is 63.

The LCD for algebraic fractions can also be found.

Example 4 *Find the LCD of Algebraic Fractions*

Find the LCD of $\frac{5}{12b^2}$ and $\frac{3}{8ab}$.

$$12b^2 = 2^2 \cdot 3 \cdot b^2$$
$$8ab = 2^3 \cdot a \cdot b$$

$$LCM = 2^3 \cdot 3 \cdot a \cdot b^2 \text{ or } 24ab^2$$

Thus, the LCD of $\frac{5}{12b^2}$ and $\frac{3}{8ab}$ is $24ab^2$.

☑ **Concept Check**   What is the LCD of $\frac{1}{x^2}$ and $\frac{1}{xy}$? x^2y

 www.pre-alg.com/extra_examples/ny

Lesson 5-6   Least Common Multiple   **227**

Lesson 5-6   Least Common Multiple   **227**

Study Notebook

Have students—

- add the definitions/examples of the vocabulary terms to their Vocabulary Builder worksheets for Chapter 5.
- record an example of finding an LCM two ways—by listing the multiples and by using the prime factorizations of the numbers.
- include any other item(s) that they find helpful in mastering the skills in this lesson.

About the Exercises . . .

Organization by Objective
- **Least Common Multiple:** 16–33
- **Least Common Denominator:** 34–41

Odd/Even Assignments

Exercises 16–54 are structured so that students practice the same concepts whether they are assigned odd or even problems.

Assignment Guide

Basic: 17–25 odd, 31–49 odd, 53, 59–80

Average: 17–57 odd, 59–80

Advanced: 16–54 even, 55–74 (Optional: 75–80)

Answer

1. The LCM involves the common multiples of a set of numbers; the LCD is the LCM of the denominators of two or more fractions.

One way to compare fractions is to write them using the LCD. We can multiply the numerator and the denominator of a fraction by the same number, because it is the same as multiplying the fraction by 1.

 Example 5 Compare Fractions

Replace ● with <, >, or = to make $\frac{1}{6}$ ● $\frac{7}{15}$ a true statement.

The LCD of the fractions is $2 \cdot 3 \cdot 5$ or 30. Rewrite the fractions using the LCD and then compare the numerators.

$\frac{1}{6} = \frac{1 \cdot 5}{2 \cdot 3 \cdot 5} = \frac{5}{30}$ Multiply the fraction by $\frac{5}{5}$ to make the denominator 30.

$\frac{7}{15} = \frac{7 \cdot 2}{3 \cdot 5 \cdot 2} = \frac{14}{30}$ Multiply the fraction by $\frac{2}{2}$ to make the denominator 30.

Since $\frac{5}{30} < \frac{14}{30}$, then $\frac{1}{6} < \frac{7}{15}$.

$$\frac{1}{6} \qquad\qquad \frac{7}{15}$$

$$\frac{2}{30} \quad \frac{4}{30} \quad \frac{6}{30} \quad \frac{8}{30} \quad \frac{10}{30} \quad \frac{12}{30} \quad \frac{14}{30} \quad \frac{16}{30}$$

$\frac{1}{6}$ is to the left of $\frac{7}{15}$ on the number line.

Check for Understanding

Concept Check

1. **Compare and contrast** least common multiple (LCM) and least common denominator (LCD). **See margin.**

2. **OPEN ENDED** Write two fractions whose least common denominator (LCD) is 35. **Sample answer:** $\frac{1}{7}$ **and** $\frac{1}{5}$

Guided Practice

Find the least common multiple (LCM) of each pair of numbers or monomials.

GUIDED PRACTICE KEY	
Exercises	Examples
3–7, 15	1
8	2
9, 10	3
11	4
12–14	5

3. 6, 8 **24**   4. 7, 9 **63**   5. 10, 14 **70**

6. 12, 30 **60**   7. 16, 24 **48**   8. $36ab$, $4b$ **36ab**

Find the least common denominator (LCD) of each pair of fractions.

9. $\frac{1}{2}, \frac{3}{8}$ **8**   10. $\frac{2}{3}, \frac{7}{10}$ **30**   11. $\frac{2}{25x}, \frac{13}{20x}$ **100x**

Replace each ● with <, >, or = to make a true statement.

12. $\frac{1}{4}$ ● $\frac{3}{16}$ **>**   13. $\frac{10}{45}$ ● $\frac{2}{9}$ **=**   14. $\frac{5}{7}$ ● $\frac{7}{9}$ **<**

Application

15. **CYCLING** The front bicycle gear has 52 teeth and the back gear has 20 teeth. How many revolutions must each gear make for them to align again as shown? (*Hint:* First, find the number of teeth. Then divide to find the final answers.)
front gear: 5; back gear: 13

back gear   front gear

DAILY INTERVENTION   **Differentiated Instruction**   **ELL**

- **Verbal/Linguistic** Give students several pairs of fractions. Ask them to explain how they would find the LCD in each case. Also, ask them to discuss what would happen if they used a common denominator that wasn't the LCD.

★ indicates increased difficulty

Practice and Apply

Homework Help

For Exercises	See Examples
16–29	1
30–33	2
34–39	3
40, 41	4
44–54	5

Extra Practice
See page 735.

Find the least common multiple (LCM) of each set of numbers or monomials.

16. 4, 10 **20**
17. 20, 12 **60**
18. 2, 9 **18**

19. 16, 3 **48**
20. 15, 75 **75**
21. 21, 28 **84**

22. 14, 28 **28**
23. 20, 50 **100**
24. 18, 32 **288**

25. 24, 32 **96**
★ 26. 10, 20, 40 **40**
★ 27. 7, 21, 84 **84**

★ 28. 9, 12, 15 **180**
★ 29. 45, 30, 35 **630**
30. $20c, 12c$ **$60c$**

31. $16a^2, 14ab$ **$112a^2b$**
32. $7x, 12x$ **$84x$**
33. $75n^2, 25n^4$ **$75n^4$**

Find the least common denominator (LCD) of each pair of fractions.

34. $\frac{1}{4}, \frac{7}{8}$ **8**
35. $\frac{8}{15}, \frac{1}{3}$ **15**
36. $\frac{4}{5}, \frac{1}{2}$ **10**
37. $\frac{2}{5}, \frac{6}{7}$ **35**

38. $\frac{4}{9}, \frac{5}{12}$ **36**
39. $\frac{3}{8}, \frac{5}{6}$ **24**
40. $\frac{1}{3t}, \frac{4}{5t^2}$ **$15t^2$**
41. $\frac{7}{8cd}, \frac{5}{16c^2}$ **$16c^2d$**

42. **PLANETS** The table shows the number of Earth years it takes for some of the planets to revolve around the Sun. Find the least common multiple of the revolution times to determine approximately how often these planets align. **420 yr**

Planet	Revolution Time (Earth Years)
Jupiter	12
Saturn	30
Uranus	84

43. **AUTO RACING** One driver can circle a one-mile track in 30 seconds. Another driver takes 20 seconds. If they both start at the same time, in how many seconds will they be together again at the starting line? **60 s**

Replace each ● with <, >, or = to make a true statement.

44. $\frac{1}{2} ● \frac{5}{12}$ **>**
45. $\frac{7}{9} ● \frac{5}{6}$ **<**
46. $\frac{3}{5} ● \frac{4}{7}$ **>**

47. $\frac{21}{100} ● \frac{1}{5}$ **>**
48. $\frac{17}{34} ● \frac{1}{2}$ **=**
49. $\frac{12}{17} ● \frac{36}{51}$ **=**

50. $\frac{8}{9} ● \frac{19}{21}$ **<**
★ 51. $-\frac{9}{11} ● -\frac{5}{6}$ **>**
★ 52. $-\frac{14}{15} ● -\frac{9}{10}$ **<**

53. **ANIMALS** Of all the endangered species in the world, $\frac{7}{39}$ of the reptiles and $\frac{5}{9}$ of the amphibians are in the United States. Is there a greater fraction of endangered reptiles or amphibians in the U.S.? **amphibians**

 Online Research **Data Update** How many endangered species are in the United States today? Visit www.pre-alg.com/data_update to learn more.

54. **TELEPHONES** Eleven out of 20 people in Chicago, Illinois, have cell phones, and $\frac{14}{25}$ of the people in Anchorage, Alaska, have cell phones. In which city do a greater fraction of people have cell phones? **Source:** Polk Research **Anchorage**

★ 55. Find two composite numbers between 10 and 20 whose least common multiple (LCM) is 36. **12 and 18**

 www.pre-alg.com/self_check_quiz/ny

Lesson 5-6 Least Common Multiple **229**

Open-Ended Assessment

Writing Have each student write a five-question quiz that covers the concepts of this lesson. Each student must provide a fully worked answer key. The questions can be used later for review.

Getting Ready for Lesson 5-7

PREREQUISITE SKILL Lesson 5-7 presents adding and subtracting unlike fractions. Estimating an answer before doing the problem will help students see if their answer is reasonable. Exercises 75–80 should be used to determine your students' familiarity with estimating sums of fractions.

Answers

56. Sample answer: the LCM of 2, 4, and 8 is 8, which is one of the numbers. The LCM of 2, 3, and 4 is 12, which is not one of the numbers.

57. Sample answer: 5 and 6 do not contain any factors in common, and the LCM of 5 and 6 is 30.

58. Sample answer: the GCF of 6 and 12 is 6 and the LCM is 12. The GCF of 3 and 5 is 1 and the LCM is 15. In each case, LCM > GCF.

59a. If two numbers are relatively prime, then their LCM is the product of the two numbers. For example, the LCM of 4 and 5 is $2^2 \cdot 5$ or 20; the LCM of 6 and 25 is $2 \cdot 3 \cdot 5^2$ or 150.

59b. Always; the LCM contains all of the factors of both numbers. Therefore, it must contain any common factors.

Determine whether each statement is *sometimes*, *always*, **or** *never* **true. Give an example to support your answer.** 56–58. See margin for examples.

56. The LCM of three numbers is one of the numbers. **sometimes**

57. If two numbers do not contain any factors in common, then the LCM of the two numbers is 1. **never**

58. The LCM of two numbers is greater than the GCF of the numbers. **always**

59. CRITICAL THINKING a–b. See margin.

   a. If two numbers are relatively prime, what is their LCM? Give two examples and explain your reasoning.

   b. Determine whether the LCM of two whole numbers is *always*, *sometimes*, or *never* a multiple of the GCF of the same two numbers. Explain.

60. **WRITING IN MATH** Answer the question that was posed at the beginning of the lesson. **See margin.**

How can you use prime factors to find the least common multiple?

Include the following in your answer:

* a definition of least common multiple, and
* a description of the steps you take to find the LCM of two or more numbers.

NEW YORK Test Practice

Standardized Test Practice
Ⓐ Ⓑ Ⓒ Ⓓ

61. Find the least common multiple of $12a^2b$ and $9ac$. **B**

   Ⓐ $36a^2b$ Ⓑ $36a^2bc$ Ⓒ $3a^2bc$ Ⓓ $3abc$

62. A $\frac{7}{8}$-inch wrench is too large to tighten a bolt. Of these, which is the next smaller size? **D**

   Ⓐ $\frac{3}{4}$-inch   Ⓑ $\frac{5}{8}$-inch   Ⓒ $\frac{7}{16}$-inch   Ⓓ $\frac{13}{16}$-inch

Maintain Your Skills

Mixed Review **Find each sum or difference. Write in simplest form.** *(Lesson 5-5)*

63. $\frac{7}{8} - \frac{3}{8}$ $\frac{1}{2}$ **64.** $3\frac{9}{11} - \frac{5}{11}$ $3\frac{4}{11}$ **65.** $\frac{13}{14} + \frac{3}{14}$ $1\frac{1}{7}$ **66.** $2\frac{5}{6} + 4\frac{1}{6}$ 7

ALGEBRA **Find each quotient. Write in simplest form.** *(Lesson 5-4)*

67. $\frac{3}{n} \div \frac{1}{n}$ 3   **68.** $\frac{x}{8} \div \frac{x}{6}$ $\frac{3}{4}$ **69.** $\frac{ac}{5} \div \frac{c}{d}$ $\frac{ad}{5}$ **70.** $\frac{6k}{7m} \div \frac{3}{14m}$ $4k$

71. ALGEBRA Translate *the sum of 7 and two times a number is 11* into an equation. Then find the number. *(Lesson 3-6)* $7 + 2n = 11$; 2

ALGEBRA **Solve each equation. Check your solution.** *(Lessons 3-3 and 3-4)*

72. $9 = x - 4$ **13**   **73.** $\frac{a}{-2} = 10$ **−20**   **74.** $-5c = -105$ **21**

Getting Ready for the Next Lesson

PREREQUISITE SKILL **Estimate each sum.**
(To review ***estimating with fractions***, *see page 716.)* 75–80. Sample answers are given.

75. $\frac{3}{8} + \frac{3}{4}$ $0 + 1 = 1$ **76.** $\frac{9}{10} + \frac{14}{15}$ $1 + 1 = 2$ **77.** $\frac{4}{7} + 2\frac{1}{5}$ $1 + 2 = 3$

78. $5\frac{7}{8} + \frac{2}{3}$ $6 + 1 = 7$ **79.** $8\frac{3}{11} + 7\frac{2}{9}$ $8 + 7 = 15$ **80.** $20\frac{5}{16} + 6\frac{1}{9}$ $20 + 6 = 26$

60. The LCM of two or more numbers involves the product of prime factors. Answers should include the following.

* The LCM of two numbers is the least number into which both of the numbers will divide evenly.

* Write the prime factorization of each number in exponential form. Multiply each factor the greatest number of times that it appears in either factorization. If the same factors appear in more than one number, multiply the greatest power of the factor that appears.

Study Tip

Relatively Prime
Recall that two numbers that are relatively prime have a GCF of 1.

Algebra Activity

A Follow-Up of Lesson 5-6

NEW YORK *Performance Indicator* 8.PS.11 Work in collaboration with others to solve problems

Juniper Green

Juniper Green is a game that was invented by a teacher in England.

Getting Ready
This game is for two people, so students should divide into pairs.

Rules of the Game
- The first player selects an even number from the hundreds chart and circles it with a colored marker.
- The next player selects any remaining number that is a factor or multiple of this number and circles it.
- Players continue taking turns circling numbers, as shown below.
- When a player cannot select a number or circles a number incorrectly, then the game is over and the other player wins.

2nd move
Player 2 circles 7 because it is a factor of 42.

1st move
Player 1 circles 42.

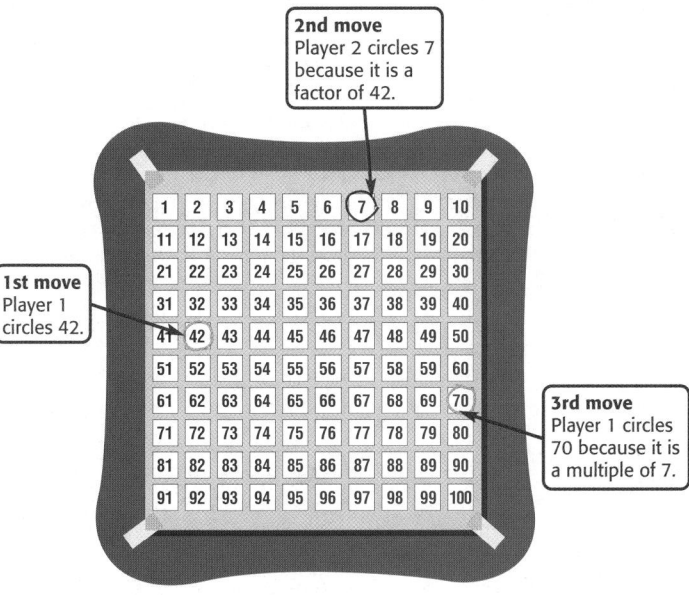

3rd move
Player 1 circles 70 because it is a multiple of 7.

Analyze the Strategies 1–2. See margin.
Play the game several times and then answer the following questions.
1. Why do you think the first player must select an even number? Explain.
2. Describe the kinds of moves that were made just before the game was over.

Answers

1. The first number selected must be even to guarantee that the second player can circle a number; for example, if the first number were 97, there is no factor or multiple on the hundreds chart.

2. Sample answer: finding patterns in the chart

Resource Manager

📂 **Teaching Pre-Algebra with Manipulatives**
- p. 70 (student recording sheet)

Algebra Activity

A Follow-Up of Lesson 5-6

Getting Started

Objective Participate in a strategic game utilizing factors and multiples.

Materials
hundreds chart
colored markers

Teach

- Before starting, review briefly factors and multiples. Discuss numbers with many factors as well as prime numbers.
- Remind students to consider the restriction of using only the numbers on the chart and plan their moves accordingly. For example, larger numbers will have no other multiples on the chart.
- Encourage students to reflect on their choices of numbers and try to create a strategy to win. You may want to have a class discussion of their findings.

Assess

In **Exercises 1 and 2,** students should
- reflect on their experience playing the game.
- articulate strategies for winning or playing a competitive game.

Study Notebook

Have students summarize the rules of the game and any strategies for success that they learned.

1 *Focus*

How can the LCM be used to add and subtract fractions with different denominators?

The opening activity questions are repeated on page 258 of the *Chapter 5 Resource Masters*.

Reading to Learn Mathematics, p. 258 **ELL**

Pre-Activity *How can the LCM be used to add and subtract fractions with different denominators?*

Do the activity at the top of page 232 in your textbook. Write your answers below.

a. What is the LCM of the denominators? **6**

b. If you partition the model into six parts, what fraction of the model is shaded? **5/6**

c. How many parts are $\frac{1}{2}$, $\frac{1}{3}$? **3; 2**

d. Describe a model that you could use to add $\frac{1}{3}$ and $\frac{1}{4}$. Then use it to find the sum. **a figure with 12 parts; 7/12**

Reading the Lesson

1. Fractions with different denominators are called ___unlike fractions___.

2. To add unlike fractions, you must first find a(n) ___common denominator___.

3. Name a common denominator of $\frac{3}{5}$ and $\frac{9}{12}$. **60**

4. To subtract unlike fractions, you must first find a(n) ___common denominator___.

5. Monique rewrote $\frac{6}{4} - \frac{1}{3}$ as $\frac{36}{24} - \frac{8}{24}$. Is she correct? Explain.
   Monique correctly rewrote the fractions using a common denominator. However, she did not choose the LCD, which is 12. The problem can be finished and simplified correctly.

Helping You Remember

6. Describe two methods that can be used to add $1\frac{1}{2} + 3\frac{2}{3}$. Then find the sum.
   Either add the whole numbers separately from the fractions, or write the mixed numbers as improper fractions and then add. In both cases, use a common denominator. The sum is $5\frac{1}{6}$.

What You'll Learn

- Add unlike fractions.
- Subtract unlike fractions.

How can the LCM be used to add and subtract fractions with different denominators?

The sum $\frac{1}{2} + \frac{1}{3}$ is modeled at the right. We can use the LCM to find the sum.

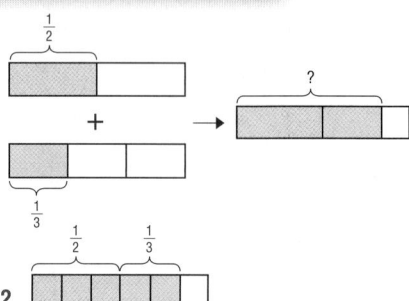

a. What is the LCM of the denominators? **6**

b. If you partition the model into six parts, what fraction of the model is shaded? **5/6**

c. How many parts are $\frac{1}{2}$? $\frac{1}{3}$? **3; 2**

d. Describe a model that you could use to add $\frac{1}{3}$ and $\frac{1}{4}$. Then use it to find the sum. **a figure with 12 parts;** $\frac{7}{12}$

ADD UNLIKE FRACTIONS Fractions with different denominators are called *unlike fractions*. In the activity above, you used the LCM of the denominators to rename the fractions. You can use any common denominator.

Key Concept *Adding Unlike Fractions*

- **Words** To add fractions with unlike denominators, rename the fractions with a common denominator. Then add and simplify.

- **Example** $\frac{1}{3} + \frac{2}{5} = \frac{1}{3} \cdot \frac{5}{5} + \frac{2}{5} \cdot \frac{3}{3}$

  $= \frac{5}{15} + \frac{6}{15}$ or $\frac{11}{15}$

Example 1 Add Unlike Fractions

Find $\frac{1}{4} + \frac{2}{3}$.

$\frac{1}{4} + \frac{2}{3} = \frac{1}{4} \cdot \frac{3}{3} + \frac{2}{3} \cdot \frac{4}{4}$ 　Use $4 \cdot 3$ or 12 as the common denominator.

$= \frac{3}{12} + \frac{8}{12}$ 　Rename each fraction with the common denominator.

$= \frac{11}{12}$ 　Add the numerators.

✓ **Concept Check** Name a common denominator of $\frac{5}{9}$ and $\frac{4}{5}$. **45**

Resource Manager

📂 Workbooks and Reproducible Masters

Chapter 5 Resource Masters
- Study Guide and Intervention, p. 255
- Skills Practice, p. 256
- Practice, p. 257
- Reading to Learn Mathematics, p. 258
- Enrichment, p. 259

Graphing Calculator and Spreadsheet Masters, p. 27
Parent and Student Study Guide Workbook, p. 39
Prerequisite Skills Workbook, pp. 37–44

🗔 Transparencies
5-Minute Check Transparency 5-7
Answer Key Transparencies

💿 Technology
Interactive Chalkboard

You can rename unlike fractions using any common denominator. However, it is usually simpler to use the least common denominator.

Example 2 Add Fractions

Find $\dfrac{3}{8} + \dfrac{7}{12}$.　**Estimate:** $\dfrac{1}{2} + \dfrac{1}{2} = 1$

$$\dfrac{3}{8} + \dfrac{7}{12} = \dfrac{3}{8} \cdot \dfrac{3}{3} + \dfrac{7}{12} \cdot \dfrac{2}{2}$$ 　The LCD is $2^3 \cdot 3$ or 24.

$$= \dfrac{9}{24} + \dfrac{14}{24}$$ 　Rename each fraction with the LCD.

$$= \dfrac{23}{24}$$ 　Add the numerators.

Example 3 Add Mixed Numbers

Find $1\dfrac{2}{9} + \left(-2\dfrac{1}{3}\right)$. **Write in simplest form.** **Estimate:** $1 + (-2) = -1$

$$1\dfrac{2}{9} + \left(-2\dfrac{1}{3}\right) = \dfrac{11}{9} + \left(-\dfrac{7}{3}\right)$$ 　Write the mixed numbers as improper fractions.

$$= \dfrac{11}{9} + \left(-\dfrac{7}{3}\right) \cdot \dfrac{3}{3}$$ 　Rename $-\dfrac{7}{3}$ using the LCD, 9.

$$= \dfrac{11}{9} + \left(\dfrac{-21}{9}\right)$$ 　Simplify.

$$= \dfrac{-10}{9}$$ 　Add the numerators.

$$= -1\dfrac{1}{9}$$ 　Simplify.

Study Tip

Negative Signs
When adding or subtracting a negative fraction, place the negative sign in the numerator.

SUBTRACT UNLIKE FRACTIONS The rule for subtracting fractions with unlike denominators is similar to the rule for addition.

Key Concept 　　　 Subtracting Unlike Fractions

- **Words** 　To subtract fractions with unlike denominators, rename the fractions with a common denominator. Then subtract and simplify.

- **Example** 　$\dfrac{6}{7} - \dfrac{2}{3} = \dfrac{6}{7} \cdot \dfrac{3}{3} - \dfrac{2}{3} \cdot \dfrac{7}{7}$

　　　　　　　$= \dfrac{18}{21} - \dfrac{14}{21}$ or $\dfrac{4}{21}$

Example 4 Subtract Fractions

Find $\dfrac{5}{21} - \dfrac{6}{7}$.

$$\dfrac{5}{21} - \dfrac{6}{7} = \dfrac{5}{21} - \dfrac{6}{7} \cdot \dfrac{3}{3}$$ 　The LCD is 21.

$$= \dfrac{5}{21} - \dfrac{18}{21}$$ 　Rename $\dfrac{6}{7}$ using the LCD.

$$= \dfrac{-13}{21} \text{ or } -\dfrac{13}{21}$$ 　Subtract the numerators.

 www.pre-alg.com/extra_examples/ny
Lesson 5-7 Adding and Subtracting Unlike Fractions 　**233**

---

2 Teach

ADD UNLIKE FRACTIONS

In-Class Examples Power Point®

Teaching Tip To emphasize the importance of a common denominator, ask students to find $\dfrac{1}{2} + \dfrac{1}{3}$ without referring to a common denominator.

Teaching Tip Another way to rename fractions with the LCD is to divide the LCD by the denominator and multiply that number by the numerator.

1 Find $\dfrac{3}{4} + \dfrac{1}{7}$. 　$\dfrac{25}{28}$

2 Find $\dfrac{5}{6} + \dfrac{3}{10}$. 　$1\dfrac{2}{15}$

3 Find $2\dfrac{1}{8} + \left(-3\dfrac{2}{3}\right)$. Write in simplest form. 　$-1\dfrac{13}{24}$

Teaching Tip Encourage students to write mixed numbers as improper fractions before adding or subtracting. This method produces fewer errors than adding or subtracting the whole numbers and fractions separately.

SUBTRACT UNLIKE FRACTIONS

In-Class Examples Power Point®

4 Find $\dfrac{9}{16} - \dfrac{5}{8}$. 　$-\dfrac{1}{16}$

5 Find $4\dfrac{2}{3} - 3\dfrac{6}{7}$. 　$\dfrac{17}{21}$

6 **JOGGING** Juyong jogged three days this week. She jogged $3\dfrac{1}{2}$ miles, $4\dfrac{1}{4}$ miles, and $4\dfrac{1}{10}$ miles. How far did she jog altogether? 　$11\dfrac{17}{20}$ miles

---

✓ **Skills Check**
Add and Subtract Unlike Fractions

a. Have students explain how they would find $4 + 8\dfrac{5}{12} + 2\dfrac{1}{3} + \left(21\dfrac{1}{6}\right)$.

b. Have students explain how they would find $7\dfrac{1}{9} - 4\dfrac{5}{6}$.

Study Notebook

Have students—
• record the key concepts for adding and subtracting unlike fractions.
• include any other item(s) that they find helpful in mastering the skills in this lesson.

DAILY

INTERVENTION **FIND THE ERROR**
If students are having difficulty with Exercise 3, remind them they can add the numerators only when there is a common denominator. Estimating the answer before adding will help students understand that Daniel cannot be correct.

About the Exercises . . .
Odd/Even Assignments
Exercises 11–34 are structured so that students practice the same concepts whether they are assigned odd or even problems.

Assignment Guide
Basic: 11–25 odd, 31, 33, 35–39, 43–56
Average: 11–33 odd, 35–39, 43–56 (Optional: 40–42)
Advanced: 12–34 even, 35–52 (Optional: 53–56)

Answers

2. Sample answer: A piece of string $15\frac{3}{4}$ inches long is cut so that it is $2\frac{1}{8}$ inches shorter. How long is the piece of string after it is cut?

3. José; he finds a common denominator by multiplying the denominators. Daniel incorrectly adds the numerators and the denominators of unlike fractions.

Example 5 **Subtract Mixed Numbers**

Find $6\frac{1}{2} - 4\frac{1}{5}$. Write in simplest form.

$$6\frac{1}{2} - 4\frac{1}{5} = \frac{13}{2} - \frac{21}{5}$$ Write the mixed numbers as improper fractions.

$$= \frac{13}{2} \cdot \frac{5}{5} - \frac{21}{5} \cdot \frac{2}{2}$$ Rename the fractions using the LCD.

$$= \frac{65}{10} - \frac{42}{10}$$ Simplify.

$$= \frac{23}{10} \text{ or } 2\frac{3}{10}$$ Subtract.

Example 6 **Use Fractions to Solve a Problem**

HOUSES The diagram shows a cross-section of an outside wall. How thick is the wall?

Explore   You know the measure of each layer of the wall.

Plan   Add the measures to find the total thickness of the wall. Estimate your answer.

$$\frac{1}{2} + 5\frac{1}{2} + 1 + 1 = 8$$

Solve $\frac{5}{8} + 5\frac{1}{2} + \frac{3}{4} + \frac{7}{8} = \frac{5}{8} + 5\frac{4}{8} + \frac{6}{8} + \frac{7}{8}$ Rename the fractions with the LCD, 8.

$$= 5\frac{22}{8}$$ Add the like fractions.

$$= 7\frac{6}{8} \text{ or } 7\frac{3}{4} \text{ in.}$$ Simplify.

The wall is $7\frac{3}{4}$ inches thick.

Examine   Since $7\frac{3}{4}$ is close to 8, the answer is reasonable.

$\frac{5}{8}$-inch drywall

$5\frac{1}{2}$-inch insulation

$\frac{3}{4}$-inch wall sheathing

$\frac{7}{8}$-inch siding

Check for Understanding

Concept Check
1. **Describe** the first step in adding or subtracting fractions with unlike denominators. **Find the least common denominator.**

2. **OPEN ENDED** Write a real-world problem that you could solve by subtracting $2\frac{1}{8}$ from $15\frac{3}{4}$. **See margin.**

3. **FIND THE ERROR** José and Daniel are finding $\frac{9}{10} + \frac{7}{12}$.

José

$$\frac{9}{10} + \frac{7}{12} = \frac{9}{10} \cdot \frac{12}{12} + \frac{7}{12} \cdot \frac{10}{10}$$

Daniel

$$\frac{9}{10} + \frac{7}{12} = \frac{9+7}{10+12}$$

Who is correct? Explain your reasoning. **See margin.**

DAILY

INTERVENTION **Differentiated Instruction**

• **Naturalist** Students often learn best when mathematics is applied to the world around them. Have students examine a log or tree stump and study the growth rings. Have them measure the exact widths of five consecutive rings in inches. Have them total the growth for the five-year period. Are the rings the same width? Explain.

Note: If a tree stump is unavailable, an enlarged picture of the tree rings can be used.

Guided Practice

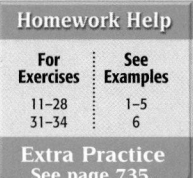

GUIDED PRACTICE KEY	
Exercises	Examples
4–9	1–5
10	6

Find each sum or difference. Write in simplest form.

4. $\frac{1}{10} + \frac{1}{3}$ **$\frac{13}{30}$**

5. $-\frac{1}{6} + \frac{7}{18}$ **$\frac{2}{9}$**

6. $\frac{1}{4} - \frac{2}{3}$ **$-\frac{5}{12}$**

7. $-\frac{7}{10} - \frac{2}{15}$ **$-\frac{5}{6}$**

8. $6\frac{4}{5} + \left(-1\frac{3}{4}\right)$ **$5\frac{1}{20}$**

9. $-9\frac{3}{4} - \left(-5\frac{1}{2}\right)$ **$-4\frac{1}{4}$**

Application

10. **SEWING** Jessica needs $1\frac{5}{8}$ yards of fabric to make a skirt and $3\frac{1}{2}$ yards to make a coat. How much fabric does she need in all? **$5\frac{1}{8}$ yd**

★ **indicates increased difficulty**

Practice and Apply

Homework Help	
For Exercises	See Examples
11–28	1–5
31–34	6

Extra Practice
See page 735.

Find each sum or difference. Write in simplest form.

11. $\frac{3}{5} + \frac{3}{10}$ **$\frac{9}{10}$**

12. $\frac{9}{26} + \frac{3}{13}$ **$\frac{15}{26}$**

13. $\frac{3}{7} + \left(-\frac{1}{4}\right)$ **$\frac{5}{28}$**

14. $-\frac{5}{8} + \left(-\frac{1}{3}\right)$ **$-\frac{23}{24}$**

15. $\frac{7}{8} - \left(-\frac{3}{16}\right)$ **$1\frac{1}{16}$**

16. $-\frac{2}{5} - \frac{7}{8}$ **$-1\frac{11}{40}$**

17. $\frac{3}{4} - \frac{5}{8}$ **$\frac{1}{8}$**

18. $\frac{5}{7} + \left(-\frac{10}{21}\right)$ **$\frac{5}{21}$**

19. $-\frac{1}{2} + \frac{3}{8}$ **$-\frac{1}{8}$**

20. $-\frac{2}{3} + \frac{7}{12}$ **$-\frac{1}{12}$**

21. $1\frac{2}{5} - \frac{1}{3}$ **$1\frac{1}{15}$**

22. $\frac{7}{8} + 4\frac{1}{24}$ **$4\frac{11}{12}$**

23. $-6\frac{2}{3} - \frac{8}{9}$ **$-7\frac{5}{9}$**

24. $2\frac{16}{30} - \frac{7}{15}$ **$2\frac{1}{15}$**

25. $-4\frac{1}{6} + \left(-7\frac{11}{18}\right)$ **$-11\frac{7}{9}$**

26. $3\frac{1}{2} - \left(-7\frac{1}{3}\right)$ **$10\frac{5}{6}$**

★ 27. $-19\frac{3}{8} - \left(-4\frac{3}{4}\right)$ **$-14\frac{5}{8}$**

★ 28. $-3\frac{2}{5} - \left(-2\frac{4}{7}\right)$ **$-\frac{29}{35}$**

★ 29. **ALGEBRA** Evaluate $x - y$ if $x = 4\frac{7}{18}$ and $y = 1\frac{1}{12}$. **$3\frac{11}{36}$**

★ 30. **ALGEBRA** Solve $\frac{64}{143} - \frac{21}{208} = a$. **$\frac{61}{176}$**

31. **EARTH SCIENCE** Did you know that water has a greater density than ice? Use the information in the table to find how much more water weighs per cubic foot. **$5\frac{3}{5}$ lb**

1 Cubic Foot	Weight (lb)
water	$62\frac{1}{2}$
ice	$56\frac{9}{10}$

32. **GRILLING** Use the table to find the fraction of people who grill two, three, or four times per month. **$\frac{7}{10}$**

33. **PUBLISHING** The length of a page in a yearbook is 10 inches. The top margin is $\frac{1}{2}$ inch, and the bottom margin is $\frac{3}{4}$ inch. What is the length of the page inside the margins? **$8\frac{3}{4}$ in.**

34. **VOTING** In the class election, Murray received $\frac{1}{3}$ of the votes and Sara received $\frac{2}{5}$ of the votes. Makayla received the rest. What fraction of the votes did Makayla receive? **$\frac{4}{15}$**

Barbecuing in the Summer

Times Per Month	Fraction of People
Less than 1	$\frac{11}{50}$
1	$\frac{2}{25}$
2-3	$\frac{4}{25}$
4	$\frac{27}{50}$

Source: American Plastics Council

www.pre-alg.com/self_check_quiz/ny

Lesson 5-7 Adding and Subtracting Unlike Fractions **235**

Study Guide and Intervention, p. 255

To add fractions with unlike denominators, rename the fractions with a common denominator. Then add and simplify.

Example 1 Find $\frac{4}{7} + \frac{1}{3}$.

$\frac{4}{7} + \frac{1}{3} = \frac{4}{7} \cdot \frac{3}{3} + \frac{1}{3} \cdot \frac{7}{7}$ Use 7 · 3 or 21 as the common denominator.

$= \frac{12}{21} + \frac{7}{21}$ Rename each fraction with the common denominator.

$= \frac{19}{21}$ Add the numerators.

To subtract fractions with unlike denominators, rename the fractions with a common denominator. Then subtract and simplify.

Example 2 Find $9\frac{2}{9} - 8\frac{5}{6}$.

$9\frac{2}{9} - 8\frac{5}{6} = \frac{83}{9} - \frac{53}{6}$ Write the mixed numbers as improper fractions.

$= \frac{83}{9} \cdot \frac{2}{2} - \frac{53}{6} \cdot \frac{3}{3}$ Rename fractions using the LCD, 18.

$= \frac{166}{18} - \frac{159}{18}$ Simplify.

$= \frac{7}{18}$ Subtract the numerators.

Exercises

Find each sum or difference. Write in simplest form.

1. $\frac{8}{9} + \frac{2}{5}$ $1\frac{13}{45}$

2. $\frac{7}{15} - \frac{3}{4}$ $\frac{1}{6}$

3. $-\frac{2}{3} + \frac{1}{4}$ $-\frac{5}{12}$

4. $-\frac{6}{11} - \frac{6}{11}$ $-1\frac{1}{11}$

5. $\frac{7}{8} + \frac{1}{4}$ $1\frac{1}{8}$

6. $\frac{13}{15} - \frac{2}{5}$ $\frac{7}{15}$

7. $3\frac{1}{5} + 2\frac{3}{4}$ $5\frac{19}{20}$

8. $7\frac{5}{8} + \left(-3\frac{1}{8}\right)$ $4\frac{1}{2}$

9. $\frac{3}{8} - \frac{1}{12}$ $\frac{7}{24}$

10. $4\frac{3}{10} - \left(-2\frac{4}{5}\right)$ $7\frac{1}{10}$

11. $6\frac{3}{8} + 3\frac{1}{2}$ $10\frac{1}{4}$

12. $7\frac{4}{9} + 9\frac{1}{6}$ $16\frac{11}{18}$

13. $4\frac{1}{6} - 3\frac{1}{8}$ $1\frac{1}{24}$

14. $5\frac{8}{9} - \left(-2\frac{1}{3}\right)$ $8\frac{2}{9}$

15. $5\frac{1}{10} - 3\frac{2}{3}$ $1\frac{13}{30}$

Skills Practice, p. 256 and Practice, p. 257 (shown)

Find each sum or difference. Write in simplest form.

1. $\frac{9}{10} + \frac{1}{2}$ $1\frac{2}{5}$

2. $\frac{7}{8} + \frac{1}{10}$ $\frac{39}{40}$

3. $-\frac{3}{4} + \frac{5}{16}$ $-\frac{7}{16}$

4. $\frac{4}{5} - \frac{2}{6}$ $\frac{7}{15}$

5. $\frac{5}{8} - \frac{3}{16}$ $\frac{7}{16}$

6. $\frac{1}{3} + \frac{5}{36}$ $\frac{17}{36}$

7. $\frac{7}{10} - \frac{14}{100}$ $\frac{14}{25}$

8. $\frac{17}{21} - \frac{4}{7}$ $\frac{1}{6}$

9. $\frac{11}{14} - \frac{1}{6}$ $\frac{13}{21}$

10. $\frac{4}{15} - \left(-\frac{3}{12}\right)$ $\frac{31}{60}$

11. $\frac{7}{15} + \frac{3}{6}$ $\frac{29}{30}$

12. $-\frac{7}{8} + \frac{9}{10}$ $\frac{1}{40}$

13. $10\frac{1}{2} + 7\frac{1}{3}$ $17\frac{5}{6}$

14. $7\frac{1}{2} - 2\frac{7}{10}$ $4\frac{4}{5}$

15. $8\frac{1}{6} + 5\frac{3}{4}$ $13\frac{11}{12}$

16. $7\frac{7}{12} - 5\frac{1}{3}$ $2\frac{1}{4}$

17. $6\frac{4}{5} + \left(-2\frac{3}{8}\right)$ $4\frac{17}{40}$

18. $16\frac{3}{5} + 3\frac{11}{15}$ $20\frac{1}{3}$

19. $18\frac{2}{5} - 7\frac{1}{4}$ $11\frac{7}{20}$

20. $12\frac{2}{7} - 3\frac{5}{6}$ $8\frac{19}{42}$

21. $2\frac{5}{8} + 6\frac{3}{4}$ $9\frac{3}{8}$

22. $29\frac{5}{33} + \left(-3\frac{1}{2}\right)$ $25\frac{10}{11}$

23. $-6\frac{2}{7} - 5\frac{3}{14}$ $11\frac{1}{2}$

24. $-16\frac{2}{7} - 3\frac{20}{21}$ $-20\frac{5}{21}$

25. $-10\frac{1}{9} + 9\frac{7}{45}$ $-\frac{43}{45}$

26. $\frac{1}{3} + \frac{5}{6} + \frac{1}{2}$ $1\frac{2}{3}$

27. $9\frac{2}{7} - 11\frac{18}{21}$ $-2\frac{12}{21}$

28. $-17\frac{2}{9} - \left(-5\frac{4}{18}\right)$ $-12\frac{4}{9}$

29. $11\frac{3}{16} - 5\frac{1}{12}$ $6\frac{5}{48}$

30. $\frac{64}{143} - \frac{21}{208}$ $\frac{61}{176}$

31. **SEWING** The inseam on Juan's pants is $34\frac{1}{4}$ inches. If he has them shortened by $2\frac{7}{8}$ inches, what is the new length? **$31\frac{3}{8}$ in.**

Enrichment, p. 259

Adding and Subtracting Fractions

Solve each problem. The first one is done for you.

1. $\frac{7}{14} + \frac{3}{14}$ $\frac{5}{7}$ I

2. $\frac{5}{6} + \frac{7}{8}$ $1\frac{17}{24}$ K

3. $\frac{3}{5} + \frac{7}{10} + \frac{1}{15}$ $1\frac{11}{30}$ U

4. $\frac{3}{8} - \frac{1}{8}$ $\frac{1}{4}$ A

5. $\frac{6}{10} + \frac{2}{5}$ $\frac{1}{5}$ G

6. $2\frac{2}{3} + \frac{3}{5}$ $3\frac{4}{15}$ D

7. $8\frac{1}{2} - 6\frac{1}{3}$ $2\frac{1}{6}$ H

8. $25\frac{1}{9} - 14\frac{5}{18}$ $10\frac{5}{18}$ S

9. $15\frac{3}{8} + 13\frac{1}{4}$ $28\frac{5}{8}$ L

10. $5\frac{3}{4} + 6\frac{2}{3}$ $12\frac{5}{12}$ F

11. $8 - 2\frac{2}{3}$ $5\frac{1}{3}$ E

12. $5\frac{7}{9} - 3\frac{1}{6}$ $2\frac{23}{42}$ N

13. $1\frac{5}{24} + \frac{11}{24}$ $2\frac{1}{8}$ O

14. $8\frac{1}{4} - 3\frac{5}{8}$ $4\frac{13}{24}$ T

15. $15\frac{11}{30} + 5\frac{4}{15}$ $20\frac{19}{30}$ C

16. $15 - 8\frac{2}{3}$ $6\frac{1}{3}$ R

Write the letter that is next to each solution above on the corresponding line shown below to complete the following question. The first letter is completed.

Did you hear about the football player who . . .

A S K E D   H I S   C O A C H   T O
$\frac{1}{4}$ $6\frac{1}{3}$ $1\frac{17}{24}$ $5\frac{1}{3}$ $3\frac{4}{15}$ $2\frac{1}{6}$ $\frac{5}{7}$ $6\frac{1}{3}$ $20\frac{19}{30}$ $2\frac{1}{8}$ $\frac{1}{4}$ $20\frac{19}{30}$ $4\frac{13}{24}$ $2\frac{1}{8}$ $\frac{7}{5}$ $\frac{1}{4}$

F L O O D   T H E   F I E L D
$12\frac{5}{12}$ $28\frac{5}{8}$ $2\frac{1}{8}$ $2\frac{1}{8}$ $3\frac{4}{15}$ $4\frac{13}{24}$ $2\frac{1}{6}$ $5\frac{1}{3}$ $12\frac{5}{12}$ $\frac{5}{7}$ $5\frac{1}{3}$ $28\frac{5}{8}$ $3\frac{4}{15}$

S O   H E   C O U L D   G O   I N
$6\frac{1}{3}$ $2\frac{1}{8}$ $\frac{1}{6}$ $5\frac{1}{3}$ $20\frac{19}{30}$ $2\frac{1}{8}$ $1\frac{11}{30}$ $28\frac{5}{8}$ $3\frac{4}{15}$ $\frac{1}{5}$ $2\frac{1}{8}$ $\frac{5}{7}$ $2\frac{23}{42}$

A S   A   S U B ?
$\frac{1}{4}$ $6\frac{1}{3}$ $\frac{1}{4}$ $11\frac{1}{30}$ $10\frac{5}{18}$

Open-Ended Assessment

Modeling Have students model the addition of unlike fractions using the problem of their choice. They may shade in rectangles as shown in the opening activity or use any commercial fraction model. Students should explain their reasoning and then write the corresponding problem using fractions.

Getting Ready for Lesson 5-8

PREREQUISITE SKILL Lesson 5-8 presents measures of central tendency. Exercises 53–56 should be used to determine your students' familiarity with finding sums of integers. This is a necessary skill when finding the mean.

Answers

35. Sample answer: Fill the $\frac{1}{2}$-cup.

From the $\frac{1}{2}$-cup, fill the $\frac{1}{3}$-cup.

$\frac{1}{6}$ cup will be left in the $\frac{1}{2}$-cup because $\frac{1}{2} - \frac{1}{3} = \frac{1}{6}$.

36. Rational numbers are closed under addition, subtraction, and multiplication because the sum, difference, or product of two rational numbers is a rational number. They are not closed under division because a rational number divided by zero is undefined.

---

35. **CRITICAL THINKING** A set of measuring cups has measures of 1 cup, $\frac{3}{4}$ cup, $\frac{1}{2}$ cup, $\frac{1}{3}$ cup, and $\frac{1}{4}$ cup. How could you get $\frac{1}{6}$ cup of milk by using these measures? **See margin.**

36. **CRITICAL THINKING** Do you think the rational numbers are closed under *addition, subtraction, multiplication,* or *division*? Explain. **See margin.**

37. **WRITING IN MATH** Answer the question that was posed at the beginning of the lesson. **See margin.**

How can the LCM be used to add and subtract fractions with different denominators?

Include the following in your answer:
- an example using the LCM, and
- an explanation of how prime factorization is a helpful way to add and subtract fractions that have different denominators.

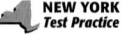

NEW YORK Test Practice

Standardized Test Practice
Ⓐ Ⓑ Ⓒ Ⓓ

38. For an art project, Halle needs $11\frac{3}{8}$ inches of red ribbon and $6\frac{7}{9}$ inches of white ribbon. Which is the best estimate for the total amount of ribbon that she needs? **A**

  Ⓐ 18 in.   Ⓑ 26 in.   Ⓒ 10 in.   Ⓓ 8 in.

39. How much less is $\frac{6}{15}$ than $9\frac{1}{2}$? **B**

  Ⓐ $9\frac{27}{30}$ Ⓑ $9\frac{1}{10}$ Ⓒ $1\frac{11}{30}$ Ⓓ $9\frac{3}{10}$

Extending the Lesson More than a thousand years ago, the Greeks wrote all fractions as the sum of *unit fractions*. A unit fraction is a fraction that has a numerator of 1, such as $\frac{1}{5}, \frac{1}{7},$ or $\frac{1}{4}$. Express each fraction below as the sum of two different unit fractions. **40–42. Sample answers are given.**

40. $\frac{7}{12}$ $\frac{1}{3} + \frac{1}{4}$ 41. $\frac{3}{5}$ $\frac{1}{2} + \frac{1}{10}$ 42. $\frac{2}{9}$ $\frac{1}{18} + \frac{1}{6}$

Maintain Your Skills

Mixed Review **Find the LCD of each pair of fractions.** *(Lesson 5-6)*

43. $\frac{4}{9}, \frac{7}{12}$ **36**   44. $\frac{3}{15t}, \frac{2}{5t}$ **15t**   45. $\frac{1}{3n}, \frac{7}{6n^3}$ **6n³**

Find each sum or difference. Write in simplest form. *(Lesson 5-5)*

46. $\frac{4}{7} + \frac{6}{7}$ $1\frac{3}{7}$ 47. $2\frac{3}{4} + 6\frac{3}{4}$ $9\frac{1}{2}$ 48. $\frac{7}{8} - \frac{5}{8}$ $\frac{1}{4}$

49. $3\frac{2}{5} - \frac{3}{5}$ $2\frac{4}{5}$ 50. $4\frac{1}{6} + 5\frac{5}{6}$ **10**   51. $8 - 6\frac{1}{5}$ $1\frac{4}{5}$

52. Write the prime factorization of 124. *(Lesson 4-3)* $2^2 \cdot 31$

Getting Ready for the Next Lesson **PREREQUISITE SKILL Find each sum.**
*(To review **adding integers**, see Lesson 2-2.)*

53. $24 + (-12) + 15$ **27**   54. $(-2) + 5 + (-3)$ **0**

55. $4 + (-9) + (-9) + 5$ **−9**   56. $-10 + (-9) + (-11) + (-8)$ **−38**

---

37. Find the LCM of the denominators. Then rename the fractions as like fractions with the LCM as the denominators. Answers should include the following.

- For example, the LCM of 4 and 6 is 12. So, $\frac{1}{4} + \frac{5}{6} = \frac{3}{12} + \frac{10}{12} = \frac{13}{12}$ or $1\frac{1}{12}$.

- Writing the prime factorization of the denominators is the first step in finding the LCM of the denominators, which is the LCD. Then the fractions can be added or subtracted.

Algebra Activity

A Preview of Lesson 5-8

NEW YORK *Performance Indicator* **8.PS.15 Choose methods for obtaining required information**

Analyzing Data

Often, it is useful to describe or represent a set of data by using a single number. The table shows the daily maximum temperatures for twenty days during a recent April in Norfolk, Virginia.

One number to describe this data set might be 68. Some reasons for choosing this number are listed below.

- It occurs four times, more often than any other number.
- If the numbers are arranged in order from least to greatest, 68 falls in the center of the data set.

Norfolk, Virginia Maximum Temperatures (nearest °F)			
48	71	61	66
80	83	64	53
54	57	70	68
66	68	68	72
68	76	84	76

There is an equal number of data above and below 68.

48 53 54 57 61 64 66 66 68 68 68 68 70 71 72 76 76 80 83 84

So, if you wanted to describe a typical high temperature for Norfolk during April, you could say 68°F.

Collect the Data

Collect a group of data. Use one of the suggestions below, or use your own method.

- Research data about the weather in your city or in another city, such as temperatures, precipitation, or wind speeds.
- Find a graph or table of data in the newspaper or a magazine. Some examples include financial data, population data, and so on.
- Conduct a survey to gather some data about your classmates.
- Count the number of raisins in a number of small boxes.

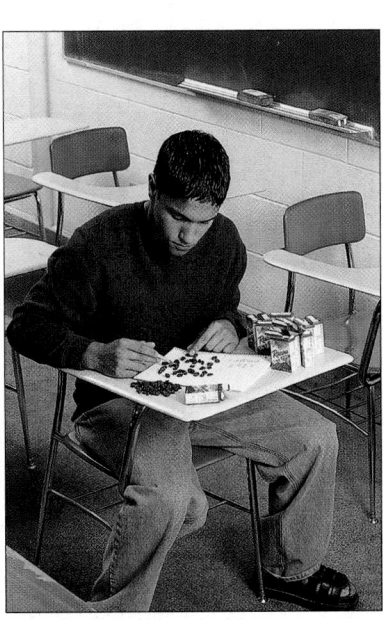

Analyze the Data 1–3. See students' work.

1. Choose a number that best describes all of the data in the set.
2. Explain what your number means, and explain which method you used to choose your number.
3. Describe how your number might be useful in real life.

Algebra Activity Analyzing Data **237**

A Preview of Lesson 5-8

Getting Started

Objective Determine a number that best represents or describes a set of data.

Possible Materials
weather data from newspaper or Internet
graph or data table from newspaper
small boxes of raisins

Teach

- Before starting this activity, ask students why it is desirable to have a number that describes an entire set of data. Who would use such a number?
- Encourage students to record their data in a chart or table.

Assess

In **Exercises 1–3,** students should
- organize the data in order (usually least to greatest).
- identify the value(s) in the middle.
- look for data that are repeated.

Study Notebook

Have students summarize their activities and write a brief description of the number that best described their data.

Resource Manager

📁 *Teaching Pre-Algebra with Manipulatives*
- p. 71 (student recording sheet)

5-8 **Measures of Central Tendency**

NEW YORK *Performance Indicator* **Reinforcement of 7.S.5 Select the appropriate measure of central tendency**

1 Focus

5-Minute Check Transparency 5-8 Use as a quiz or review of Lesson 5-7.

Mathematical Background notes are available for this lesson on page 198D.

How are measures of central tendency used in the real world?

The opening activity questions are repeated on page 263 of the *Chapter 5 Resource Masters*.

Reading to Learn Mathematics, p. 263 **ELL**

Pre-Activity *How are measures of central tendency used in the real world?*

Do the activity at the top of page 238 in your textbook. Write your answers below.

a. Which number appears most often? **11**

b. If you list in order from least to greatest, which number is in the middle? **12**

c. What is the sum of all the numbers divided by 28? If necessary, round to the nearest tenth. **13.0**

d. If you had to give one number that best represents the winning times, which would you choose? Explain. **Sample answer: 11, because it occurs more often than any other number; 12, because it is the middle value in the data set; 13, because it is the sum of the data values divided by the number of values.**

Reading the Lesson 1–4. See students' work.

Write a definition and give an example of each new vocabulary word or phrase.

Vocabulary	Definition	Example
1. measures of central tendency		
2. mean		
3. median		
4. mode		

5. How do you find the median if the data have an even number of items? **Find the mean of the two middle numbers.**

6. Describe a situation in which no mode exists. **There is no mode if each number occurs once in the set.**

7. An extreme value will affect which measure of central tendency the most? **mean**

Helping You Remember

8. You have learned about mean, median, and mode. In each circle, write three numbers that satisfy the given information. **Sample answers are given.**

mean = 5 median = 5 mode = 5
4, 5, 6   2, 5, 8   3, 5, 5

Vocabulary

- measures of central tendency
- mean
- median
- mode

d. Sample answer: 11, because it occurs more often than any other number.

Study Tip

Mean, Median, Mode

- The mean and median do not have to be part of the data set.
- If there is a mode, it is always a member of the data set.

What You'll Learn

- Use the mean, median, and mode as measures of central tendency.
- Analyze data using mean, median, and mode.

How are measures of central tendency used in the real world?

The *Iditarod* is a 1150-mile dogsled race across Alaska. The winning times for 1973–2000 are shown in the table.

a. Which number appears most often? **11**

b. If you list the data in order from least to greatest, which number is in the middle? **12**

c. What is the sum of all the numbers divided by 28? If necessary, round to the nearest tenth. **13.0**

d. If you had to give one number that best represents the winning times, which would you choose? Explain.

Winning Times (days)

20	21	15	19	17	15	15
14	12	16	13	13	18	12
11	11	11	11	13	11	11
11	9	9	9	9	10	9

Source: Anchorage Daily News

MEAN, MEDIAN, AND MODE When you have a list of numerical data, it is often helpful to use one or more numbers to represent the whole set. These numbers are called **measures of central tendency**. You will study three types.

Key Concept	**Measures of Central Tendency**
Statistic	**Definition**
mean	the sum of the data divided by the number of items in the data set
median	the middle number of the ordered data, or the mean of the middle two numbers
mode	the number or numbers that occur most often

Example 1 Find the Mean, Median, and Mode

SPORTS The heights of the players on the girls' basketball team are shown in the chart. Find the mean, median, and mode.

$$\text{mean} = \frac{\text{sum of heights}}{\text{number of players}}$$

$$= \frac{130 + 154 + 148 + \ldots + 150}{12}$$

$$= \frac{1824}{12} \text{ or } 152$$

The mean height is 152 centimeters.

Height of Players (cm)

130	154	148
155	172	153
160	162	140
149	151	150

Resource Manager

📂 Workbooks and Reproducible Masters

Chapter 5 Resource Masters
- Study Guide and Intervention, p. 260
- Skills Practice, p. 261
- Practice, p. 262
- Reading to Learn Mathematics, p. 263
- Enrichment, p. 264
- Assessment, p. 290

Parent and Student Study Guide Workbook, p. 40
Prerequisite Skills Workbook, pp. 19–22, 29–30

📖 Transparencies
5-Minute Check Transparency 5-8
Answer Key Transparencies

💿 Technology
Interactive Chalkboard
Pre-AlgePASS: Tutorial Plus, Lesson 9

To find the median, order the numbers from least to greatest.

130, 140, 148, 149, 150, 151, 153, 154, 155, 160, 162, 172

$$\frac{151 + 153}{2} = 152$$

There is an even number of items. Find the mean of the two middle numbers.

The median height is 152.

There is no mode because each number in the set occurs once.

Example 2 — Use a Line Plot

HURRICANES The line plot shows the number of Atlantic hurricanes that occurred each year from 1974–2000. Find the mean, median, and mode.

Source: Colorado State/Tropical Prediction Center

$$mean = \frac{2 + 3(4) + 4(5) + 5(5) + 6(2) + 7(3) + 8(3) + 9(2) + 10 + 11}{27} \approx 5.7$$

There are 27 numbers. So the middle number, which is the median, is the 14th number, or 5.

You can see from the graph that 4 and 5 both occur most often in the data set. So there are two modes, 4 and 5.

✓ **Concept Check**   If 4 were added to the data set, what would be the new mode?
4 only

A number in a set of data that is much greater or much less than the rest of the data is called an *extreme value*. An extreme value can affect the mean of the data.

Example 3 — Find Extreme Values that Affect the Mean

NUTRITION The table shows the number of Calories per serving of each vegetable. Identify an extreme value and describe how it affects the mean.

Vegetable	Calories	Vegetable	Calories
asparagus	14	cauliflower	10
beans	30	celery	17
bell pepper	20	corn	66
broccoli	25	lettuce	9
cabbage	17	spinach	9
carrots	28	zucchini	17

The data value 66 appears to be an extreme value. Calculate the mean with and without the extreme value to find how it affects the mean.

mean with extreme value

$$\frac{\text{sum of values}}{\text{number of values}} = \frac{262}{12}$$

$$\approx 21.8$$

mean without extreme value

$$\frac{\text{sum of values}}{\text{number of values}} = \frac{196}{11}$$

$$\approx 17.8$$

The extreme value increases the mean by 21.8 − 17.8 or about 4.

TEACHING TIP
Have students explain whether 66 affects the median.

 www.pre-alg.com/extra_examples/ny

---

2 Teach

MEAN, MEDIAN, AND MODE

In-Class Examples Power Point®

Teaching Tip Make sure students order their data before locating the median and mode. Also, emphasize that more than one mode or no mode are possibilities.

1 MOVIES The revenue of the 10 highest grossing movies as of June 2000 are given in the table. Find the mean, median, and mode of the revenues.
mean, $379.8 million; median, $343.5 million; no mode

Top 10 Movie Revenues (millions of $)	
601	330
461	313
431	309
400	306
357	290

Source: *World Almanac*

2 OLYMPICS The line plot below shows the number of gold medals earned by each country that participated in the 1998 Winter Olympic Games in Nagano, Japan. Find the mean, median, and mode for the gold medals won.   **mean, 2.875; median, 2; mode, 0**

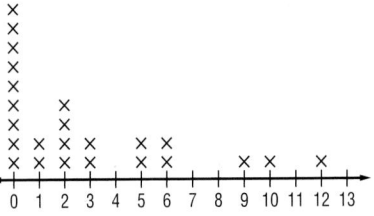

Source: *Time Almanac*

3 QUIZ SCORES The quiz scores for a math class are 8, 7, 6, 10, 8, 8, 9, 8, 7, 9, 8, 0, and 10. Identify an extreme value and describe how it affects the mean. **0; it lowers the mean by about $\frac{2}{3}$.**

In-Class Examples

4 The table shows the monthly salaries of the employees at two bookstores. Find the mean, median, and mode for each set of data. Based on the averages, which bookstore pays its employees better?

Bob's Books	The Reading Place
1290	1400
1400	1450
1400	1550
1600	1600
3650	2000

Bob's Books: $1868, $1400, $1400; The Reading Place: $1600, $1550, no mode; The Reading Place

5 Jenny's bowling average is 146. Today she bowled 138, 140, and 145. What does she need to score on her fourth game to maintain her average?   **at least a 161**

3 Practice/Apply

Study Notebook

Have students—
- add the definitions/examples of the vocabulary terms to their Vocabulary Builder worksheets for Chapter 5.
- include any other item(s) that they find helpful in mastering the skills in this lesson.

ANALYZE DATA   You can use measures of central tendency to analyze data.

Example 4 *Use Mean, Median, and Mode to Analyze Data*

HOURLY PAY   Compare and contrast the central tendencies of the salaries for the two stores. Based on the averages, which store pays its employees better?

Hourly Salaries ($)	
Sports Superstore	Extreme Sports
7, 24, 7, 6, 8, 8, 8, 6	8, 9, 10, 10, 9, 8, 10, 10

Sports Superstore

mean:
$$= \frac{7 + 24 + 7 + 6 + 8 + 8 + 8 + 6}{8}$$
$$= \$9.25$$

median: 6, 6, 7, 7, 8, 8, 8, 24
$$\frac{7+8}{2} \text{ or } \$7.50$$

mode: $8

Extreme Sports

mean:
$$= \frac{8 + 9 + 10 + 10 + 9 + 8 + 10 + 10}{8}$$
$$= \$9.25$$

median: 8, 8, 9, 9, 10, 10, 10, 10
$$\frac{9+10}{2} \text{ or } \$9.50$$

mode: $10

The $24 per hour salary at Sports Superstore is an extreme value that increases the mean salary. However, the employees at Extreme Sports are generally better paid, as shown by the higher median and mode salaries.

If you know the value of the mean, you can work backward to find a missing value in the data set.

Example 5 *Work Backward*

Grid-In Test Item

Francisca needs an average score of 92 on five quizzes to earn an A. The mean of her first four scores was 91. What is the lowest score that she can receive on the fifth quiz to earn an A?

Read the Test Item   To find the lowest score, write an equation to find the sum of the first four scores. Then write an equation to find the fifth score.

Solve the Test Item

Step 1   Find the sum of the first four scores x.

mean of first four scores → $91 = \frac{x}{4}$ ← sum of first four scores

$(91)4 = \left(\frac{x}{4}\right)4$ Multiply each side by 4.

$364 = x$ Simplify.

Step 2   Find the fifth score y.

mean $= \frac{\text{sum of the first four scores} + \text{fifth score}}{5}$ Write an equation.

$92 = \frac{364 + y}{5}$ Substitution

$460 = 364 + y$ Multiply each side by 5 and simplify.

$96 = y$ Subtract 364 from each side and simplify.

TEACHING TIP

Suppose that for this grading period you were to allow students to choose whether you should use the mean, the median, or the mode of their test and quiz scores to determine their grade. Ask them which they would choose and why.

Test-Taking Tip

Substituting   Check that your answer satisfies the conditions of the original problem.

About the Exercises . . .

Organization by Objective
- **Mean, Median, and Mode:** 10–15
- **Analyze Data:** 16–18

Odd/Even Assignments
Exercises 10–15 are structured so that students practice the same concepts whether they are assigned odd or even problems.

Assignment Guide

Basic: 11–15 odd, 19–35

Average: 11–17 odd, 19–35

Advanced: 10–16 even, 17–31 (Optional: 32–35)

Check for Understanding

Concept Check

1. **Explain** which measure of central tendency is most affected by an extreme value. **See margin.**

2. **OPEN ENDED** Write a set of data with at least four numbers that has a mean of 8 and a median that is *not* 8. **Sample answer: 4, 7, 9, 10, 10**

Guided Practice

Find the mean, median, and mode for each set of data. If necessary, round to the nearest tenth.

3. 4, 5, 7, 3, 9, 11, 23, 37 **12.4; 8; none**

4. 7.2, 3.6, 9.0, 5.2, 7.2, 6.5, 3.6 **6.0; 6.5; 3.6 and 7.2**

5.

```
              X
      X   X   X           X
  X   X   X   X           X
  X   X   X   X       X   X
 ─┼───┼───┼───┼───┼───┼───┼───┼─
  1   2   3   4   5   6   7   8
```

3.6; 3.5; 4

GUIDED PRACTICE KEY	
Exercises	Examples
3, 4, 6	1
5	2
7	3
8	4
9	5

Application

VACATIONS For Exercises 6–8, use the table. **6. 29.4; 28; 25**

6. Find the mean, median, and mode.

7. Identify any extreme values and describe how they affect the mean.

7–8. See margin.

8. Which statistic would you say best represents the data? Explain.

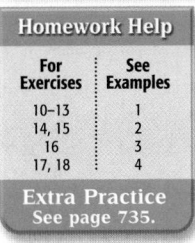

NEW YORK Test Practice

Standardized Test Practice
Ⓐ Ⓑ Ⓒ Ⓓ

9. Brad's average for five quizzes is 86. If he wants to have an average of 88 for six quizzes, what is the lowest score he can receive on his sixth quiz? **98**

Annual Vacation Days	
Country	Number of Days
Brazil	34
Canada	26
France	37
Germany	35
Italy	42
Japan	25
Korea	25
United Kingdom	28
United States	13

Source: World Tourism Organization

★ indicates increased difficulty

Practice and Apply

Homework Help

For Exercises	See Examples
10–13	1
14, 15	2
16	3
17, 18	4

Extra Practice
See page 735.

Find the mean, median, and mode for each set of data. If necessary, round to the nearest tenth. **13. 7.6; 7.5; 7.1 and 7.4 15. 4.3; 4.2; 4.1 and 4.2**

10. 41, 37, 43, 43, 36 **40; 41; 43**

11. 2, 8, 16, 21, 3, 8, 9, 7, 6 **8.9; 8; 8**

12. 14, 6, 8, 10, 9, 5, 7, 13 **9; 8.5; none**

13. 7.5, 7.1, 7.4, 7.6, 7.4, 9.0, 7.9, 7.1

14.

```
      X           X       X
      X           X       X
      X   X   X   X   X   X
 ─┼───┼───┼───┼───┼───┼───┼───┼─
  15  16  17  18  19  20  21  22
```

18.3; 18; 16, 18, and 20

15.

```
  X   X
  X   X
  X   X
  X   X   X   X                       X
 ─┼───┼───┼───┼───┼───┼───┼───┼─
 4.1 4.2 4.3 4.4 4.5 4.6 4.7 4.8
```

16. Mean; the height of the tallest basketball player increases the mean height of the team.

16. **BASKETBALL** Refer to the cartoon at the right. Which measure of central tendency would make opponents believe that the height of the team is much taller than it really is? Explain.

★ 17. **TESTS** Which measure of central tendency best summarizes the test scores shown below? Explain.

97, 99, 95, 89, 99, 100, 87, 85, 89, 92, 96, 95, 60, 97, 85 **See margin.**

www.pre-alg.com/self_check_quiz/ny

Answers

1. Mean; when an extreme value is added to the other data, it can raise or lower the sum, and therefore the mean.

7. Sample answer: 13 could be an extreme value because it is 12 less than the next value. It lowers the mean by 2.1.

8. Sample answer: median, because half the data are less than the median and half are greater than the median.

17. Sample answer: the median, 95, or the modes, 95 and 97, because most students scored higher than mean, which is 91.

Open-Ended Assessment

Writing Give students a data set to analyze. They should write a short report of their analysis including use of mean, median, mode, and extreme value.

Getting Ready for Lesson 5-9

PREREQUISITE SKILL Lesson 5-9 presents solving equations with rational numbers. Some problems will require using division of decimals. Exercises 32–35 should be used to determine your students' familiarity with finding quotients of decimals.

Assessment Options

Quiz (Lessons 5-6 through 5-8) is available on p. 290 of the *Chapter 5 Resource Masters.*

Answers

18. **Sample answer: The mean is greater than the median because of the high salaries of the top baseball players. These are the extreme values that affect the mean.**

19. **Sample answer: The median home price would be useful because it is not affected by the cost of the very expensive homes. The cost of half the homes in the county would be greater than the median cost and half would be less.**

20. **Measures of central tendency are used to describe or represent real-world data. Answers should include the following.**

    • **Test scores, heights of students, and number of hours worked per week can be described using the mean, median, or mode.**

    • **Newspaper articles may discuss the average cost of living, the average family size, or the average income for people in a certain age bracket.**

★ 18. **SALARIES** The graph shows the mean and median salaries of baseball players from 1983 to 2000. Explain why the mean is so much greater than the median. **See margin.**

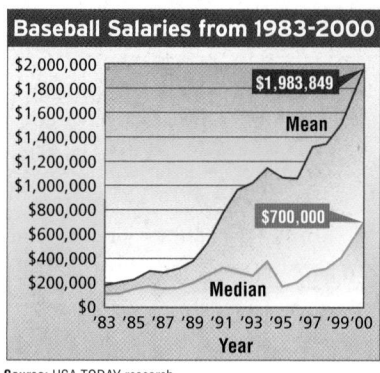

Baseball Salaries from 1983-2000

$1,983,849 — Mean

$700,000

Median

'83 '85 '87 '89 '91 '93 '95 '97 '99 '00
Year

Source: USA TODAY research

WebQuest

Using measures of central tendency can help you analyze the data from fast-food restaurants. Visit www.pre-alg.com/webquest to continue work on your WebQuest project.

19. **CRITICAL THINKING** A real estate guide lists the "average" home prices for counties in your state. Do you think the mean, median, or mode would be the most useful average for homebuyers? Explain. **See margin.**

20. **WRITING IN MATH** Answer the question that was posed at the beginning of the lesson. **See margin.**

How are measures of central tendency used in the real world?

Include the following in your answer:

• examples of real-life data from home or school that can be described using the mean, median, or mode, and

• one or more newspaper articles in which averages are used.

NEW YORK Test Practice

Standardized Test Practice
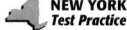
Ⓐ Ⓑ Ⓒ Ⓓ

21. If 18 were added to the data set below, which statement is true? **C**

16, 14, 22, 16, 16, 18, 15, 25

Ⓐ The mode increases.   Ⓑ The mean decreases.

Ⓒ The mean increases.   Ⓓ The median increases.

22. Jonelle's tips as a waitress are shown in the table. On Friday, her tips were $74. Which measure of central tendency will change the *most* as a result? **A**

Ⓐ mean   Ⓑ median

Ⓒ mode   Ⓓ no measure

Day	Tips
Monday	$36
Tuesday	$32
Wednesday	$40
Thursday	$36

Maintain Your Skills

Mixed Review

Find each sum or difference. Write in simplest form. *(Lesson 5-7)*

23. $9\frac{2}{3} + \frac{1}{6}$ **$9\frac{5}{6}$**

24. $\frac{7}{8} - \frac{3}{10}$ **$\frac{23}{40}$**

25. $-2\frac{3}{4} - 1\frac{1}{8}$ **$-3\frac{7}{8}$**

Replace each ● with <, >, or = to make a true statement. *(Lesson 5-6)*

26. $\frac{1}{2} ● \frac{5}{12}$ **>**

27. $\frac{16}{50} ● \frac{9}{30}$ **>**

28. $\frac{4}{5} ● \frac{48}{60}$ **=**

ALGEBRA   Solve each equation. Check your solution. *(Lessons 3-3 and 3-4)*

29. $y - 5 = 13$ **18**

30. $10 = 14 + n$ **−4**

31. $-4w = 20$ **−5**

Getting Ready for the Next Lesson

PREREQUISITE SKILL Find each quotient. If necessary, round to the nearest tenth. *(To review **dividing decimals**, see page 715.)*

32. $25.6 \div 3$ **8.5**   33. $37 \div 4.7$ **7.9**   34. $30.5 \div 11.2$ **2.7**   35. $46.8 \div 15.6$ **3**

DAILY INTERVENTION   **Differentiated Instruction**

• **Kinesthetic** Have students use a stack of blocks to represent each number in a data set. To represent the mean, have students "even out" each stack of blocks until each stack is equal. How tall is each stack? Students should try this several times, then write a journal entry, complete with diagrams, describing the averaging process.

Graphing Calculator Investigation

A Follow-Up of Lesson 5-8

NEW YORK *Performance Indicator* Reinforcement of 7.S.5 Select the appropriate measure of central tendency

Mean and Median

A graphing calculator is able to perform operations on large data sets efficiently. You can use a TI-83 Plus graphing calculator to find the mean and median of a set of data.

SURVEYS Fifteen seventh graders were surveyed and asked what was their weekly allowance (in dollars). The results of the survey are shown at the right.

20	10	5	5	10
15	5	10	5	10
5	5	5	5	5

Find the mean and median allowance.

Step 1 *Enter the data.*

- Clear any existing lists.

  KEYSTROKES: STAT ENTER ▲ CLEAR
  ENTER

- Enter the allowances as L1.

  KEYSTROKES: 20 ENTER 10 ENTER ... 5 ENTER

Step 2 *Find the mean and median.*

- Display a list of statistics for the data.

  KEYSTROKES: STAT ▶ ENTER ENTER

The first value, $\bar{x}$, is the mean.

Use the down arrow key to locate "Med." The median allowance is $5 and the mean allowance is $8.

Exercises

Clear list L1 and find the mean and median of each data set. Round decimal answers to the nearest hundredth.

1. 6.4, 5.6, 7.3, 1.2, 5.7, 8.9 **5.85; 6.05**

2. −23, −13, −16, −21, −15, −34, −22 **−20.57; −21**

3. 123, 423, 190, 289, 99, 178, 156, 217, 217 **210.22; 190**

4. 8.4, 2.2, −7.3, −5.3, 6.7, −4.3, 5.1, 1.3, −1.1, −3.2, 2.2, 2.9, 1.4, 68 **5.5; 1.8**

5. Look back at the medians found. When is the median a member of the data set? **See margin.**

6. Refer to Exercise 4. **a–c. See margin.**

   a. Which statistic better represents the data, the mean or median? Explain.

   b. Suppose the number 68 should have been 6.8. Recalculate the mean and median. Is there a significant difference between the first pair of values and the second pair?

   c. When there is an error in one of the data values, which statistic is less likely to be affected? Why?

 www.pre-alg.com/other_calculator_keystrokes   **Graphing Calculator Investigation** Mean and Median **243**

Answers

5. The median is a term when the number of terms is odd.

6a. Median; 68 in the data set increases the mean so that it does not best represent the data.

6b. 1.13; 1.8; There is a significant difference between the pair of means. The second mean is 4.37 less than the first mean. The median remains the same.

6c. Median; an error can change the mean significantly because it affects the sum of the data. However, the median could remain the same.

Getting Started

Know Your Calculator The graphing calculator will store data in a list. The data will remain in the list until it is deleted.

Teach

- If students make an error entering data, simply use the arrow keys within the list to change and correct. To delete an entry completely, use DEL.

- Have students complete Exercises 1–6.

Assess

Have students describe when the mean best represents the data and when the median best represents the data. Students should be able to provide a list of numbers to illustrate their ideas.

1 Focus

5-Minute Check Transparency 5-9 Use as a quiz or review of Lesson 5-8.

Mathematical Background notes are available for this lesson on page 198D.

How are reciprocals used in solving problems involving music?

The opening activity questions are repeated on page 268 of the *Chapter 5 Resource Masters*.

Reading to Learn Mathematics, p. 268 ELL

Pre-Activity *How are reciprocals used in solving problems involving music?*

Do the activity at the top of page 244 in your textbook. Write your answers below.

a. A guitar string vibrates 440 times per second to produce the A above middle C. Write an equation to find the number of vibrations per second to produce middle C. If you multiply each side by 3, what is the result? $\frac{5}{3}n = 440$; $5n = 1320$

b. How would you solve the second equation you wrote in part a? Divide each side by 5.

c. How can you combine the steps in parts a and b into one step? Multiply each side by $\frac{3}{5}$.

d. How many vibrations per second are needed to produce middle C? 264

Reading the Lesson

1. Dividing by a fraction is the same as multiplying by the ___reciprocal___.

2. Write the first step in solving each equation.
   a. $y - 1.1 = 6.8$ Add 1.1 to each side.
   b. $6 + x = -9$ Subtract 6 from each side.
   c. $\frac{c}{6} = \frac{1}{2}$ Multiply each side by 6.
   d. $-\frac{2}{3}p = -\frac{2}{3}$ Divide each side by $-\frac{2}{3}$ or multiply by $-\frac{3}{2}$.

Helping You Remember

3. You learned to solve equations. Addition equations are solved using subtraction; subtraction equations are solved using addition; multiplication equations are solved using division; division equations are solved using multiplication. In the table below, write three equations that can be solved using the given operations. Be sure to use a variety of rational numbers.

Sample answers are given.

Addition	Subtraction	Multiplication	Division
1. $x - 3 = 6$	1. $m + 6 = 11$	1. $\frac{b}{8} = 10$	1. $-6x = 12$
2. $x - 2.5 = 3.6$	2. $3.8 + p = 6$	2. $\frac{q}{1.1} = 9$	2. $\frac{5}{8}a = 16$
3. $t - \frac{1}{2} = \frac{2}{3}$	3. $x + \frac{3}{7} = \frac{9}{14}$	3. $-\frac{v}{6} = \frac{2}{3}$	3. $8.9h = -20$

Teaching Tip You may want students to estimate solutions to the equations before solving.

NEW YORK Performance Indicator

Reinforcement of 7.A.4 Solve multi-step equations by combining like terms, using the distributive property, **or moving variables to one side of the equation**

a. $\frac{5}{3}n = 440$; $5n = 1320$

b. Divide each side by 5.

c. Multiply each side by $\frac{3}{5}$.

d. 264

Study Tip

Look Back
To review **solving equations**, see Lessons 3-3 and 3-4.

TEACHING TIP
You may want to introduce the use of rational numbers in equations by first solving problems using whole numbers. Then replace whole numbers with decimals and fractions and solve.

Solving Equations with Rational Numbers

What You'll Learn
- Solve equations containing rational numbers.

How are reciprocals used in solving problems involving music?

Musical sounds are made by vibrations. If n represents the number of vibrations for middle C, then the approximate vibrations for the other notes going up the scale are given below.

Notes	Middle C	D	E	F	G	A	B	C
Number of Vibrations	n	$\frac{9}{8}n$	$\frac{5}{4}n$	$\frac{4}{3}n$	$\frac{3}{2}n$	$\frac{5}{3}n$	$\frac{15}{8}n$	$\frac{2}{1}n$

a. A guitar string vibrates 440 times per second to produce the A above middle C. Write an equation to find the number of vibrations per second to produce middle C. If you multiply each side by 3, what is the result?

b. How would you solve the second equation you wrote in part **a**?

c. How can you combine the steps in parts **a** and **b** into one step?

d. How many vibrations per second are needed to produce middle C?

SOLVE ADDITION AND SUBTRACTION EQUATIONS
You can solve rational number equations the same way you solved equations with integers.

Example 1 Solve by Using Addition

Solve $2.1 = t - 8.5$. Check your solution.

$2.1 = t - 8.5$	Write the equation.
$2.1 + 8.5 = t - 8.5 + 8.5$	Add 8.5 to each side.
$10.6 = t$	Simplify.

CHECK

$2.1 = t - 8.5$	Write the original equation.
$2.1 \stackrel{?}{=} 10.6 - 8.5$	Replace t with 10.6.
$2.1 = 2.1$ ✓	Simplify.

Example 2 Solve by Using Subtraction

Solve $x + \frac{3}{5} = \frac{2}{3}$.

$x + \frac{3}{5} = \frac{2}{3}$	Write the equation.
$x + \frac{3}{5} - \frac{3}{5} = \frac{2}{3} - \frac{3}{5}$	Subtract $\frac{3}{5}$ from each side.
$x = \frac{2}{3} - \frac{3}{5}$	Simplify.
$x = \frac{10}{15} - \frac{9}{15}$ or $\frac{1}{15}$	Rename the fractions using the LCD and subtract.

Resource Manager

📂 Workbooks and Reproducible Masters

Chapter 5 Resource Masters
- Study Guide and Intervention, p. 265
- Skills Practice, p. 266
- Practice, p. 267
- Reading to Learn Mathematics, p. 268
- Enrichment, p. 269

Parent and Student Study Guide Workbook, p. 41
Prerequisite Skills Workbook, pp. 21–24, 27–28, 31–32, 47–62

Transparencies
5-Minute Check Transparency 5-9
Answer Key Transparencies

Technology
Interactive Chalkboard

Study Tip

Reciprocals
Recall that dividing by a fraction is the same as multiplying by its multiplicative inverse.

SOLVE MULTIPLICATION AND DIVISION EQUATIONS To solve $\frac{1}{2}x = 3$, you can divide each side by $\frac{1}{2}$ or multiply each side by the multiplicative inverse of $\frac{1}{2}$, which is 2.

$$\frac{1}{2}x = 3 \qquad \text{Write the equation.}$$

$$2 \cdot \frac{1}{2}x = 2 \cdot 3 \qquad \text{Multiply each side by 2.}$$

The product of any number and its multiplicative inverse is 1.

$$1x = 6 \qquad \text{Simplify.}$$

$$x = 6$$

Example 3 **Solve by Using Division**

Solve $-3y = 1.5$. Check your solution.

$$-3y = 1.5 \qquad \text{Write the equation.}$$

$$\frac{-3y}{-3} = \frac{1.5}{-3} \qquad \text{Divide each side by } -3.$$

$$y = -0.5 \qquad \text{Simplify.}$$

CHECK

$$-3y = 1.5 \qquad \text{Write the original equation.}$$

$$-3(-0.5) \overset{?}{=} 1.5 \qquad \text{Replace } y \text{ with } -0.5.$$

$$1.5 = 1.5 \checkmark \qquad \text{Simplify.}$$

Example 4 **Solve by Using Multiplication**

a. Solve $5 = \frac{1}{4}y$. Check your solution.

$$5 = \frac{1}{4}y \qquad \text{Write the equation.}$$

$$4(5) = 4\left(\frac{1}{4}y\right) \qquad \text{Multiply each side by 4.}$$

$$20 = y \qquad \text{Simplify.}$$

CHECK $\quad 5 = \frac{1}{4}y \qquad \text{Write the original equation.}$

$$5 \overset{?}{=} \frac{1}{4}(20) \qquad \text{Replace } y \text{ with 20.}$$

$$5 = 5 \checkmark \qquad \text{Simplify.}$$

b. Solve $\frac{2}{3}x = 7$. Check your solution.

$$\frac{2}{3}x = 7 \qquad \text{Write the equation.}$$

$$\frac{3}{2}\left(\frac{2}{3}x\right) = \frac{3}{2}(7) \qquad \text{Multiply each side by } \frac{3}{2}.$$

$$x = \frac{21}{2} \qquad \text{Simplify.}$$

$$x = 10\frac{1}{2} \qquad \text{Simplify. Check the solution.}$$

Concept Check What is the first step in solving $\frac{1}{8}r = \frac{1}{4}$?
Multiply each side by 8.

www.pre-alg.com/extra_examples/ny

DAILY
INTERVENTION

Differentiated Instruction

- **Logical** Make a series of cards with equations (one equation per card). Put each solution on a separate card. Scramble the cards and lay them face down on a table. Have groups of students play a memory-type game. Each student turns over two cards; if they match, the student collects the cards and plays again. If the cards don't match, the turn goes to the next player. The game ends when all the cards are revealed. The winner has the most equation/solution matches.

---

2 Teach

SOLVE ADDITION AND SUBTRACTION EQUATIONS

In-Class Examples Power Point®

1 Solve $y - \frac{3}{8} = \frac{3}{4}$. Check your solution. $\frac{9}{8}$ or $1\frac{1}{8}$

2 Solve $m + 8.6 = 11.2$. Check your solution. **2.6**

SOLVE MULTIPLICATION AND DIVISION EQUATIONS

In-Class Examples Power Point®

3 Solve $9a = 3.6$. Check your solution. **0.4**

4 **a.** Solve $8 = \frac{1}{6}x$. Check your solution. **48**

b. Solve $\frac{3}{5}t = -6$. Check your solution. **−10**

Teaching Tip In Example 4a in the text, when multiplying both sides of an equation by 4, some students may need to write 4 as $\frac{4}{1}$ initially.

Skills Check

Solving Equations What needs to be added or subtracted from each side of the equation to solve it?

a. $y + \frac{3}{4} = 3$ subtract $\frac{3}{4}$

b. $x - 5.5 = 2.4$ add 5.5

What needs to be multiplied or divided to solve each equation?

a. $3m = 8.3$ divide by 3

b. $\frac{2}{5}n = 8$ multiply by $\frac{5}{2}$

Study Notebook

Have students—
- record Examples 1–4 to illustrate solving equations using each operation.
- include any other item(s) that they find helpful in mastering the skills in this lesson.

DAILY
INTERVENTION FIND THE ERROR
Have students review Example 3 on page 245. Remind them that the goal is to end up with the variable alone on one side of the equation. When there are decimals in the equation, they need to pay particular attention not to overlook decimal points. 3 is not the same as 0.3.

About the Exercises . . .
Organization by Objective
- **Solve Addition and Subtraction Equations:** 14–27, 37–40
- **Solve Multiplication and Division Equations:** 28–36

Odd/Even Assignments
Exercises 14–40 are structured so that students practice the same concepts whether they are assigned odd or even problems.

Assignment Guide
Basic: 15–43 odd, 46–70
Average: 15–45 odd, 46–70
Advanced: 14–44 even, 45–64 (Optional: 65–70)
All: Practice Quiz 2 (1–10)

Check for Understanding

Concept Check

1. Subtraction Property of Equality

1. **Name** the property of equality that you would use to solve $2 = \frac{3}{4} + x$.

2. **OPEN ENDED** Write an equation that can be solved by multiplying each side by 6. **Sample answer:** $\frac{1}{6}x = 2$

3. **FIND THE ERROR** Grace and Ling are solving $0.3x = 4.5$.

Grace	Ling
$0.3x = 4.5$	$0.3x = 4.5$
$\frac{0.3x}{3} = \frac{4.5}{3}$	$\frac{0.3x}{0.3} = \frac{4.5}{0.3}$
$x = 1.5$	$x = 15$

Who is correct? Explain your reasoning. **Ling; dividing 0.3 by 3 does not isolate the variable on one side.**

Guided Practice

Solve each equation. Check your solution.

GUIDED PRACTICE KEY

Exercises	Examples
4–9, 13	1, 2
10–12	3, 4

4. $y + 3.5 = 14.9$ **11.4**
5. $b - 5 = 13.7$ **18.7**
6. $\frac{3}{2} = w + \frac{3}{5}$ **$\frac{9}{10}$**
7. $c - \frac{3}{5} = \frac{5}{6}$ **$1\frac{13}{30}$**
8. $x + \frac{5}{8} = 7\frac{1}{2}$ **$6\frac{7}{8}$**
9. $4\frac{1}{6} = r + 6\frac{1}{4}$ **$-2\frac{1}{12}$**
10. $3.5a = 7$ **2**
11. $-\frac{1}{6}s = 15$ **−90**
12. $9 = \frac{3}{4}g$ **12**

Application

13. **METEOROLOGY** When a storm struck, the barometric pressure was 28.79 inches. Meteorologists said that the storm caused a 0.36-inch drop in pressure. What was the barometric pressure before the storm? **29.15 in.**

★ indicates increased difficulty

Practice and Apply

Homework Help

For Exercises	See Examples
14–27, 37–40	1, 2
28–36	3, 4

Extra Practice
See page 736.

Solve each equation. Check your solution. **18. −6.34**

14. $y + 7.2 = 21.9$ **14.7**
15. $4.7 = a + 7.1$ **−2.4**
16. $x - 5.3 = 8.1$ **13.4**
17. $n - 4.72 = 7.52$ **12.24**
18. $t + 3.17 = -3.17$
19. $a - 2.7 = 3.2$ **5.9**
20. $\frac{2}{3} = \frac{1}{8} + b$ **$\frac{13}{24}$**
21. $m + \frac{7}{12} = -\frac{5}{18}$ **$-\frac{31}{36}$**
22. $g + \frac{2}{3} = 2$ **$1\frac{1}{3}$**
23. $7 = \frac{2}{9} + k$ **$6\frac{7}{9}$**
24. $n - \frac{3}{8} = \frac{1}{6}$ **$\frac{13}{24}$**
25. $x - \frac{2}{5} = -\frac{8}{15}$ **$-\frac{2}{15}$**
26. $7\frac{1}{3} = c - \frac{4}{5}$ **$8\frac{2}{15}$**
27. $-2 = \frac{3}{10} + f$ **$-2\frac{3}{10}$**
28. $\frac{7}{9}k = -\frac{5}{12}$ **$-\frac{15}{28}$**
29. $4.1p = 16.4$ **4**
30. $8 = \frac{2}{3}d$ **12**
31. $0.4y = 2$ **5**
32. $\frac{1}{5}t = 9$ **45**
33. $4 = -\frac{1}{8}q$ **−32**
34. $\frac{1}{3}n = \frac{2}{9}$ **$\frac{2}{3}$**
35. $\frac{5}{8} = \frac{1}{2}r$ **$1\frac{1}{4}$**
36. $\frac{2}{3}a = 6$ **9**
37. $b - 1\frac{1}{2} = 4\frac{1}{4}$ **$5\frac{3}{4}$**
38. $7\frac{1}{2} = r - 5\frac{2}{3}$ **$13\frac{1}{6}$**
39. $3\frac{3}{4} + n = 6\frac{5}{8}$ **$2\frac{7}{8}$**
40. $y + 1\frac{1}{3} = 3\frac{1}{18}$ **$1\frac{13}{18}$**

41. **PUBLISHING** A newspaper is $12\frac{1}{4}$ inches wide and 22 inches long. This is $1\frac{1}{4}$ inches narrower and half an inch longer than the old edition. What were the previous dimensions of the newspaper? **$13\frac{1}{2}$ in. by $21\frac{1}{2}$ in.**

Answer (p.247)

47. Equations with fractions can be written to represent the number of vibrations per second for different notes. To solve, multiply each side of the equation by the reciprocal of the fraction. Answers should include the following.

- For example, if n vibrations per second produce middle C, then $\frac{5}{4}n$ vibrations per second produce the note E above middle C.

42. AIRPORTS The graph shows the world's busiest cargo airports. What is the difference in cargo handling between Memphis and Tokyo? **0.73 million or 730,000 metric tons**

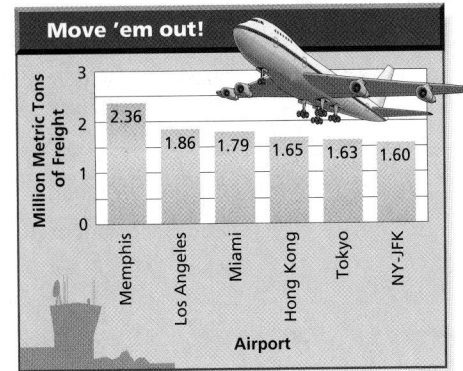

Move 'em out!

Memphis 2.36, Los Angeles 1.86, Miami 1.79, Hong Kong 1.65, Tokyo 1.63, NY-JFK 1.60

Million Metric Tons of Freight vs *Airport*

Source: Airports Council International

43. BUSINESS A store is going out of business. All of the items are marked $\frac{1}{3}$ off the ticketed price. How much would a shirt that was originally priced at $24.99 cost now? **$16.66**

44. COOKING Lucas made $2\frac{1}{2}$ batches of cookies for a bake sale and used $3\frac{3}{4}$ cups of sugar. How much sugar is needed for one batch of cookies? $1\frac{1}{2}$ **c**

★ **45. TRAINS** As a train begins to roll, the cars are "jerked" into motion. Slack is built into the couplings so that the engine does not have to move every car at once. If the slack built into each coupling is 3 inches, how many feet of slack is there between ten freight cars? (*Hint:* Do not include the coupling between the engine and the first car.) $2\frac{1}{4}$ **ft**

46. CRITICAL THINKING The denominator of a fraction is 4 more than the numerator. If both the numerator and denominator are increased by 1, the resulting fraction equals $\frac{1}{2}$. Find the original fraction. $\frac{3}{7}$

47. WRITING IN MATH Answer the question that was posed at the beginning of the lesson. **See margin.**

How are reciprocals used in solving problems involving music?

Include the following in your answer:
- an example of how fractions are used to compare musical notes, and
- an explanation of how reciprocals are useful in finding the number of vibrations per second needed to produce certain notes.

NEW YORK Test Practice

Standardized Test Practice

48. Find the value of z in $\frac{5}{6}z = \frac{3}{5}$. **A**

(A) $\frac{18}{25}$ (B) $\frac{15}{30}$ (C) $\frac{1}{2}$ (D) $1\frac{7}{18}$

49. The area A of the triangle is $33\frac{3}{4}$ square centimeters. Use the formula $A = \frac{1}{2}bh$ to find the height h of the triangle. **D**

(A) $3\frac{13}{18}$ cm   (B) $6\frac{1}{2}$ cm

(C) $18\frac{13}{18}$ cm   (D) $7\frac{1}{2}$ cm

9 cm, *h*

More About. . .

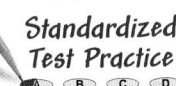

Airports •

In 1995, there were 580 million airline passengers. In 2005, there will be an estimated 823 million airline passengers.

Source: Department of Transportation

- The equation $\frac{5}{3}n = 440$ represents the number of vibrations per second to produce middle C. To solve, multiply each side by the reciprocal of $\frac{5}{3}$, $\frac{3}{5}$.

Open-Ended Assessment

Speaking Put students in groups of three. Give each group three equations to solve. After the groups solve the equations, have them present their work to the class. Each student must present one problem. The class and teacher may give feedback. Look for clarity of explanations, correctness of work, and a check of the solution.

Tips for New Teachers

Repetition Some students may require additional time and examples to fully understand solving equations with fractions. You may want to frequently refer to equations involving whole numbers as well as consider spending an extra day on this lesson. Use the Extra Practice on page 736. You can also use the Study Guide and Intervention masters or the Practice masters in the *Chapter 5 Resource Masters* to reinforce this concept.

Getting Ready for Lesson 5-10

PREREQUISITE SKILL Lesson 5-10 presents arithmetic and geometric sequences. Exercises 65–70 should be used to determine your students' familiarity with dividing integers. This skill will be used to find ratios of terms in sequences.

Assessment Options

Practice Quiz 2 The quiz provides students with a brief review of the concepts and skills in Lessons 5-6 through 5-9. Lesson numbers are given to the right of exercises or instruction lines so students can review concepts not yet mastered.

Maintain Your Skills

Mixed Review

Find the mean, median, and mode for each set of data. If necessary, round to the nearest tenth. *(Lesson 5-8)* **51. 13; 12; 11 and 12**

50. 2, 8, 5, 18, 3, 5, 6 **6.7; 5; 5**

51. 11, 12, 12, 14, 16, 11, 15

52. 0.9, 0.5, 0.7, 0.4, 0.3, 0.2 **0.5; 0.5; none**

53. 56, 77, 60, 60, 72, 100 **70.8; 66; 60**

Find each sum or difference. Write in simplest form. *(Lesson 5-7)*

54. $\frac{3}{5} + \frac{1}{3}$ **$\frac{14}{15}$**

55. $\frac{5}{6} - \frac{1}{8}$ **$\frac{17}{24}$**

56. $-4\frac{1}{4} - \frac{1}{6}$ **$-4\frac{5}{12}$**

57. $\frac{5}{9} + \left(-\frac{1}{12}\right)$ **$\frac{17}{36}$**

58. $-3\frac{3}{4} + \left(-2\frac{1}{8}\right)$ **$-5\frac{7}{8}$**

59. $8\frac{9}{10} - 1\frac{1}{6}$ **$7\frac{11}{15}$**

60. **ALGEBRA** Evaluate $a - b$ if $a = 9\frac{5}{6}$ and $b = 1\frac{1}{6}$. *(Lesson 5-5)* **$8\frac{2}{3}$**

61. **HEALTH** According to the National Sleep Foundation, teens should get approximately 9 hours of sleep each day. What fraction of the day is this? Write in simplest form. *(Lesson 4-5)* **$\frac{3}{8}$**

ALGEBRA Solve each equation. Check your solution. *(Lesson 3-5)*

62. $3t - 6 = 15$ **7**

63. $8 = \frac{k}{-2} + 5$ **-6**

64. $9n - 13n = 4$ **-1**

Getting Ready for the Next Lesson

PREREQUISITE SKILL Divide. If necessary, write as a fraction in simplest form. *(To review **dividing integers**, see Lesson 2-5.)*

65. $-18 \div 3$ **-6**

66. $24 \div (-2)$ **-12**

67. $-20 \div (-4)$ **5**

68. $-55 \div (-5)$ **11**

69. $-12 \div 36$ **$-\frac{1}{3}$**

70. $9 \div (-81)$ **$-\frac{1}{9}$**

Practice Quiz 2   *Lessons 5-6 through 5-9*

Find the least common multiple of each set of numbers. *(Lesson 5-6)*

1. 8, 9 **72**

2. 12, 30 **60**

3. 2, 10 **10**

4. 6, 8 **24**

Find each sum or difference. Write in simplest form. *(Lesson 5-7)*

5. $\frac{3}{4} + \frac{1}{16}$ **$\frac{13}{16}$**

6. $-\frac{3}{7} + \frac{5}{14}$ **$-\frac{1}{14}$**

7. $1\frac{1}{5} - \left(-\frac{7}{15}\right)$ **$1\frac{2}{3}$**

8. $6\frac{3}{4} - 2\frac{1}{6}$ **$4\frac{7}{12}$**

9. **WEATHER** The low temperatures on March 24 for twelve different cities are recorded at the right. Find the mean, median, and mode. If necessary, round to the nearest tenth. *(Lesson 5-8)* **32.4; 30.5; 29**

Low Temperatures (°F)			
31	29	30	22
45	35	29	30
40	29	31	38

10. **ALGEBRA** Solve $a - 1\frac{1}{3} = 4\frac{1}{6}$. *(Lesson 5-9)* **$5\frac{1}{2}$**

Arithmetic and Geometric Sequences

NEW YORK *Performance Indicator* **8.PS.4 Observe patterns and formulate generalizations**

What You'll Learn

- Find the terms of arithmetic sequences.
- Find the terms of geometric sequences.

Vocabulary

- sequence
- arithmetic sequence
- term
- common difference
- geometric sequence
- common ratio

How can sequences be used to make predictions?

The table shows the distance a car moves during the time it takes to apply the brakes and while braking.

a. What is the reaction distance for a car going 70 mph? **70 ft**

b. What is the braking distance for a car going 70 mph? **245 ft**

c. What is the difference in reaction distances for every 10-mph increase in speed? **10 ft**

d. Describe the braking distance as speed increases.

Speed (mph)	Reaction Distance (ft)	Braking Distance (ft)
20	20	20
30	30	45
40	40	80
50	50	125
60	60	180

d. Sample answer: The difference increases by 10 feet each time: 25, 35, 45, 55....

TEACHING TIP

Discuss the pronunciation of arithmetic (ar-ith-met'-ik) when it is used as an adjective rather than a noun.

ARITHMETIC SEQUENCES

A **sequence** is an ordered list of numbers. An **arithmetic sequence** is a sequence in which the difference between any two consecutive terms is the same. So, you can find the next term in the sequence by adding the same number to the previous term.

Each number is called a **term** of the sequence.

$20, \quad 30, \quad 40, \quad 50, \quad 60, \ldots$

$+10 \quad +10 \quad +10 \quad +10$

The difference is called the **common difference**.

Example 1 Identify an Arithmetic Sequence

State whether the sequence 8, 5, 2, −1, −4, … is arithmetic. If it is, state the common difference and write the next three terms.

$8, \quad 5, \quad 2, -1, -4$ Notice that $5 - 8 = -3$, $2 - 5 = -3$, and so on.

$-3 \quad -3 \quad -3 \quad -3$

The terms have a common difference of −3, so the sequence is arithmetic. Continue the pattern to find the next three terms.

$-4, -7, -10, -13$

$-3 \quad -3 \quad -3$

The next three terms of the sequence are −7, −10, and −13.

Lesson 5-10 Arithmetic and Geometric Sequences **249**

---

1 Focus

5-Minute Check Transparency 5-10 Use as a quiz or review of Lesson 5-9.

Mathematical Background notes are available for this lesson on page 198D.

How can sequences be used to make predictions?

The opening activity questions are repeated on page 273 of the *Chapter 5 Resource Masters.*

Reading to Learn Mathematics, p. 273 **ELL**

Pre-Activity How can sequences be used to make predictions?

Do the activity at the top of page 249 in your textbook. Write your answers below.

  a. What is the reaction distance for a car going 70 mph? **70 ft**

  b. What is the braking distance for a car going 70 mph? **245 ft**

  c. What is the difference in reaction distance for every 10-mph increase in speed? **10 ft**

  d. Describe the braking distance as speed increases.
  Sample answer: The difference increases by 10 feet each time: 25, 35, 45, 55, ...

Reading the Lesson 1–6. See students' work.

Write a definition and give an example of each new vocabulary word or phrase.

Vocabulary	Definition	Example
1. sequence		
2. arithmetic sequence		
3. term		
4. common difference		
5. geometric sequence		
6. common ratio		

7. What is the common difference in the sequence 8, 17, 26, 35, . . .? **9**

8. What is the common ratio in the sequence 1, −2, 4, −8, 16, . . .? **−2**

Helping You Remember

9. *Sequence* is a word that is used in everyday English.

  a. Find the definition of *sequence* in a dictionary. Write the definition. **act of following**

  b. Explain how the English definition can help you remember how *sequence* is used in mathematics. **Terms in arithmetic and geometric sequences follow based on a common difference or ratio**

Resource Manager

Workbooks and Reproducible Masters

Chapter 5 Resource Masters
- Study Guide and Intervention, p. 270
- Skills Practice, p. 271
- Practice, p. 272
- Reading to Learn Mathematics, p. 273
- Enrichment, p. 274
- Assessment, p. 290

Parent and Student Study Guide Workbook, p. 42
Prerequisite Skills Workbook, pp. 1–2, 45–48

 Transparencies

5-Minute Check Transparency 5-10
Answer Key Transparencies

Technology

Interactive Chalkboard
Pre-AlgePASS: Tutorial Plus, Lessons 10 and 11

2 Teach

ARITHMETIC SEQUENCES

1 State whether the sequence $-5, -1, 3, 7, 11, \ldots$ is arithmetic. If it is, state the common difference and write the next three terms. **arithmetic; 4; 15, 19, 23**

2 State whether the sequence $0, 2, 6, 12, 20, \ldots$ is arithmetic. If it is, state the common difference and write the next three terms. **not arithmetic**

Teaching Tip In-class Example 2 does have a pattern that allows you to determine the next three terms: 30, 42, and 56.

GEOMETRIC SEQUENCES

In-Class Example

3 a. State whether the sequence 2, 4, 4, 8, 8, 16, 16, . . . is geometric. If it is, state the common ratio and write the next three terms. **not geometric**

Teaching Tip Note that two ratios alternate throughout the sequence, but it does not meet the definition of geometric.

b. State whether the sequence $27, -9, 3, -1, \frac{1}{3}$, . . . is geometric. If it is, state the common ratio and write the next three terms. **geometric;** $-\frac{1}{3}; -\frac{1}{9}, \frac{1}{27}, -\frac{1}{81}$

Example 2 Identify an Arithmetic Sequence

State whether the sequence 1, 2, 4, 7, 11, … is arithmetic. If it is, write the next three terms of the sequence.

1, 2, 4, 7, 11
$+1 \ +2 \ +3 \ +4$
The terms do not have a common difference.

The sequence is not arithmetic. However, if the pattern continues, the next three differences will be 5, 6, and 7.

11, 16, 22, 29
$+5 \ +6 \ +7$
The next three terms are 16, 22, and 29.

GEOMETRIC SEQUENCES
A **geometric sequence** is a sequence in which the quotient of any two consecutive terms is the same. So, you can find the next term in the sequence by multiplying the previous term by the same number.

1, 4, 16, 64, 256, …
$\times 4 \ \times 4 \ \times 4 \ \times 4$
The quotient is called the **common ratio**.

TEACHING TIP
Point out that common differences and common ratios may be positive or negative numbers.

✓ **Concept Check** Name the common ratio in the sequence 10, 20, 40, 80, 160, … . **2**

Example 3 Identify Geometric Sequences

a. State whether the sequence $-2, 6, -18, 54, \ldots$ is geometric. If it is, state the common ratio and write the next three terms.

$-2, \ 6, \ -18, \ 54$ Notice that $6 \div (-2) = -3$, $-18 \div 6 = -3$, and
$\times(-3) \ \times(-3) \ \times(-3)$ $54 \div (-18) = -3$.

The common ratio is -3, so the sequence is geometric. Continue the pattern to find the next three terms.

$54, \ -162, \ 486, \ -1458$
$\times(-3) \ \times(-3) \ \times(-3)$ The next three terms are $-162, 486,$ and -1458.

b. State whether the sequence $20, 10, 5, \frac{5}{2}, \frac{5}{4}, \ldots$ is geometric. If it is, state the common ratio and write the next three terms.

$20, \ 10, \ 5, \ \frac{5}{2}, \ \frac{5}{4}$
$\times\frac{1}{2} \ \times\frac{1}{2} \ \times\frac{1}{2} \ \times\frac{1}{2}$

The common ratio is $\frac{1}{2}$ or 0.5, so the sequence is geometric. Continue the pattern to find the next three terms.

$\frac{5}{4}, \ \frac{5}{8}, \ \frac{5}{16}, \ \frac{5}{32}$
$\times\frac{1}{2} \ \times\frac{1}{2} \ \times\frac{1}{2}$ The next three terms are $\frac{5}{8}, \frac{5}{16},$ and $\frac{5}{32}$.

Study Tip

Alternative Method
Multiplying by $\frac{1}{2}$ is the same as dividing by 2, so the following is also true.

$20, \ 10, \ 5, \ \frac{5}{2}, \ \frac{5}{4}$
$\div 2 \ \div 2 \ \div 2 \ \div 2$

DAILY
INTERVENTION
Differentiated Instruction

- **Auditory/Musical** Students who relate to music should identify a musical scale and relate it to an arithmetic sequence. Skipping every other note on the scale can also represent an arithmetic sequence. Challenge the students to find a sequence of musical notes to represent a geometric sequence.

Check for Understanding

Concept Check

1. See margin.
2. The terms are decreasing; sample answer: 8, 4, 2, 1; 0.5.

1. **Compare and contrast** arithmetic and geometric sequences.

2. **OPEN ENDED** Describe the terms of a geometric sequence whose common ratio is a fraction or decimal between 0 and 1. Then write four terms of such a sequence and name the common ratio.

Guided Practice

GUIDED PRACTICE KEY

Exercises	Examples
3–9	1–3

State whether each sequence is *arithmetic*, *geometric*, or *neither*. If it is arithmetic or geometric, state the common difference or common ratio and write the next three terms of the sequence. **3–8. See margin.**

3. 3, 7, 11, 15, …

4. 1, 3, 9, 27, …

5. 6, 8, 12, 18, …

6. 13, 8, 3, −2, …

7. $3, \frac{8}{3}, \frac{7}{3}, 2, …$

8. $48, 12, 3, \frac{3}{4}, …$

Application

9. **CARS** A new car is worth only about 0.82 of its value from the previous year during the first three years. Approximately how much will a $20,000 car be worth in 3 years? **Source:** www.caprice.com **$11,027.36**

★ indicates increased difficulty

Practice and Apply

Homework Help

For Exercises	See Examples
10–29	1–3

Extra Practice
See page 736.

State whether each sequence is *arithmetic*, *geometric*, or *neither*. If it is arithmetic or geometric, state the common difference or common ratio and write the next three terms of the sequence. **10–27. See p. 261A.**

10. 2, 5, 8, 11, …

11. −6, 5, 16, 27, …

12. $\frac{1}{2}, 1, 2, 4, …$

13. 2, 6, 18, 54, …

14. 18, 11, 4, −3, …

15. 25, 22, 19, 16, …

16. $4, 1, \frac{1}{4}, \frac{1}{16}, …$

17. $-5, 1, -\frac{1}{5}, \frac{1}{25}, …$

18. $\frac{1}{2}, 1, \frac{3}{2}, 2, …$

19. $0, \frac{1}{6}, \frac{1}{3}, \frac{1}{2}, …$

20. 0.75, 1.5, 2.25, …

21. 4.5, 4.0, 3.5, 3.0, …

22. 11, 14, 19, 26, …

23. 17, 16, 14, 11, …

24. 24, 12, 6, 3, …

★ 25. $18, -6, 2, -\frac{2}{3}, …$

★ 26. 0.1, 0.3, 0.9, 2.7, …

★ 27. $\frac{1}{2}, \frac{1}{4}, \frac{1}{8}, \frac{1}{16}, …$

28. **PHYSICAL SCIENCE** A ball bounces back 0.75 of its height on every bounce. If a ball is dropped from 160 feet, how high does it bounce on the third bounce? **67.5 ft**

29. **TELEPHONE RATES** For an overseas call, WorldTel charges $6 for the first minute and then $3 for each additional minute. **a. See p. 261A.**

   a. Is the cost an arithmetic or geometric sequence? Explain.

   b. How much would a 15-minute call cost? **$48**

30. **CRITICAL THINKING** The sum of four numbers in an arithmetic sequence is 42. What could the numbers be? Give two different examples.
   Sample answer: 9, 10, 11, 12; 6, 9, 12, 15

31. **WRITING IN MATH** Answer the question that was posed at the beginning of the lesson. **See p. 261A.**

   How can sequences be used to make predictions?

   Include the following in your answer:

   • a discussion of common difference and common ratio, and

   • examples of sequences occurring in nature.

Practice/Apply

Study Notebook

Have students—

• complete the definitions/examples for the remaining terms on their Vocabulary Builder worksheets for Chapter 5.

• record examples of sequences that are geometric, arithmetic, and neither. Each example should have a brief explanation.

• include any other item(s) that they find helpful in mastering the skills in this lesson.

About the Exercises . . .

Odd/Even Assignments
Exercises 10–27 are structured so that students practice the same concepts whether they are assigned odd or even problems.

Assignment Guide

Basic: 11–23 odd, 29, 30–33, 36–49

Average: 11–29 odd, 30–33, 36–49 (Optional: 34–35)

Advanced: 10–28 even, 30–49

Answers

1. Arithmetic sequences have a common difference and the terms can be found by adding or subtracting. Geometric sequences have a common ratio and the terms can be found by multiplying or dividing.

3. A; 4; 19, 23, 27

4. G; 3; 81, 243, 729

5. neither

6. A; −5; −7, −12, −17

7. $A; -\frac{1}{3}; \frac{5}{3}, \frac{4}{3}, 1$

8. $G; \frac{1}{4}; \frac{3}{16}, \frac{3}{64}, \frac{3}{256}$

Study Guide and Intervention, p. 270

A sequence is an ordered list of numbers. An arithmetic sequence is a sequence in which the difference between any two consecutive terms, called the common difference, is the same. In the sequence 2, 9, 16, 23, 30, . . . , the common difference is 7.

A geometric sequence is a sequence in which the quotient of any two consecutive terms, called the common ratio, is the same. In the sequence 1, −4, 16, −64, 256, . . . , the common ratio is −4.

Example State whether the sequence is *arithmetic, geometric,* or *neither*. If it is arithmetic or geometric, state the common difference or common ratio and write the next three terms of the sequence.

a. 7, 14, 28, 56, 112, . . .

The common ratio is 2, so the sequence is geometric. The next three terms are
112 · 2 or 224, 224 · 2 or 448, and 448 · 2 or 896.

b. 8, 6, 4, 2, 0, −2, . . .

The common difference is −2, so the sequence is arithmetic. The next three terms are
−2 + (−2) or −4, −4 + (−2) or −6, and −6 + (−2) or −8.

Exercises

State whether each sequence is *arithmetic, geometric,* or *neither*. If it is arithmetic or geometric, state the common difference or common ratio and write the next three terms.

1. 10, 20, 40, 80, 160, . . .
   geometric; 2; 320, 640, 1280
2. 7, 17, 27, 37, 47, . . .
   arithmetic; 10; 57, 67, 77
3. 100, 50, 25, $\frac{25}{2}$, $\frac{25}{4}$, . . .
   geometric; $\frac{1}{2}$; $\frac{25}{8}$, $\frac{25}{16}$, $\frac{25}{32}$
4. 12, 9, 6, 3, 0, . . .
   arithmetic; −3; −3, −6, −9
5. 1, 2, 2, 3, 3, 3, . . .
   neither
6. 1, −1, 1, −1, 1, . . .
   geometric; −1; −1, 1, −1
7. 2, 3, 4.5, . . .
   geometric; 1.5; 6.75, 10.125, 15.1875
8. −21, −10, 1, 12, 23, . . .
   arithmetic; 11; 34, 45, 56
9. 1.6, 3.2, 4.8, . . .
   arithmetic; 1.6; 6.4, 8, 9.6
10. 4, 12, 36, . . .
   geometric; 3; 108, 324, 972

Skills Practice, p. 271 and Practice, p. 272 (shown)

State whether each sequence is *arithmetic, geometric,* or *neither*. If it is arithmetic or geometric, state the common difference or common ratio and write the next three terms.

1. 4, 12, 20, 28, 36, . . . arithmetic; 8; 44, 52, 60
2. 1, 1$\frac{1}{3}$, 1$\frac{2}{3}$, 2, 2$\frac{1}{3}$, . . . arithmetic; $\frac{1}{3}$; 2$\frac{2}{3}$, 3, 3$\frac{1}{3}$
3. 10, 11, 13, 16, 20, . . . neither
4. 3, −9, 27, −81, 243, . . . geometric; −3; −729, 2187, −6561
5. 1, 0.5, 0.25, 0.125, 0.0625, . . . geometric; 0.5; 0.03125, 0.015625, 0.0078125
6. 4, −1, −6, −11, −16, . . . arithmetic; −5; −21, −26, −31
7. 0.7, 1.4, 2.8, 5.6, 11.2, . . . geometric; 2; 22.4, 44.8, 89.6
8. 17, 10, 3, −4, −11, . . . arithmetic; −7; −18, −25, −32
9. 1, 0, 2, 0, 3, . . . neither
10. 2, 3$\frac{1}{2}$, 5, 6$\frac{1}{2}$, 8, . . . arithmetic; 1$\frac{1}{2}$; 9$\frac{1}{2}$, 11, 12$\frac{1}{2}$
11. 100, 20, 4, 0.8, 0.16, . . . geometric; 0.2; 0.032, 0.0064, 0.00128
12. 6, 2, $\frac{2}{3}$, $\frac{2}{9}$, $\frac{2}{27}$, . . . geometric; $\frac{1}{3}$; $\frac{2}{81}$, $\frac{2}{243}$, $\frac{2}{729}$
13. −23, −12, −1, 10, 21, . . . arithmetic; 11; 32, 43, 54

14. **DEPRECIATION** A new sport utility vehicle (SUV) costs $25,000. If it depreciates 20% of its value each year, find the value of the vehicle for each of the next five years. $20,000, $16,000, $12,800, $10,240, $8192

Enrichment, p. 274

Applications of Geometric Sequences

Populations often grow according to a geometric sequence. If the population of a city grows at the rate of 2% per year, then the common ratio, r, is 1.02. To find the population of a city of 100,000 after 5 years of 2% growth, use the formula ar^{n-1}, where r is the common ratio and n is the number of years.

$ar^{n-1} = 100,000 (1.02)^{5-1}$ $a = 100,000, r = 1.02, n = 5$
       $= 100,000 (1.02)^4$
       $\approx 108,243$ So, the city has a population of 108,243 people.

After a few years, a small change in the annual growth rate can cause enormous differences in the population.

Assume that the nation of Grogro had a population of one million in 2000. Using a calculator, find the population of the country in the years 2020, 2070, and 2120 at growth rates of 1%, 3%, and 5% per year. Record your results in the table below.

	Population of Grogro		
Growth Rate	Year		
	2020	2070	2120
1. 1%	1,208,109	1,986,894	3,267,710
2. 3%	1,753,506	7,687,206	33,699,988
3. 5%	2,526,950	28,977,548	332,297,129

Suppose we want to find the total upward distance a bouncing ball has moved. It bounces up 36 inches on the first bounce and $\frac{3}{4}$ times its height on each of five more consecutive bounces.

1st bounce   2nd bounce   3rd bounce
36 in.   27 in.   20$\frac{1}{4}$ in.

$\times\frac{3}{4}$ $\times\frac{3}{4}$

The distances form the terms of a geometric sequence. We want to find the sum of the distances, or the sum of the six terms in the sequence.

The sum of the terms of a geometric sequence is called a geometric series. The formula for the sum S_n of the first n terms of a geometric series is $S_n = \frac{a - ar^n}{1 - r}$, where a = the first term and r = the common ratio ($r \neq 1$).

$S_n = \frac{a - ar^n}{1 - r}$ Write the formula.

$= \frac{36 - 36\left(\frac{3}{4}\right)^6}{1 - \frac{3}{4}}$ $a = 36, r = \frac{3}{4}, n = 6$

≈ 118.4 So, the ball bounces upward approximately 118.4 inches.

Use the formula above to find each sum. Then check your answer by adding.
4. 5 + 10 + 20 + 40 + 80 155
5. 80 + 240 + 720 + 2160 + 6480 9680

252 Chapter 5 Rational Numbers

---

32. State the next term in the sequence 56, 48, 40, 32, ... **C**

Ⓐ 20   Ⓑ 22   Ⓒ 24   Ⓓ 28

33. Which statement is true as the side length of a square increases? **A**

Side Length	Perimeter	Area
1	4	1
2	8	4
3	12	9
4	16	16
5	20	25

Ⓐ The perimeter values form an arithmetic sequence.

Ⓑ The perimeter values form a geometric sequence.

Ⓒ The area values form an arithmetic sequence.

Ⓓ The area values form a geometric sequence.

Extending the Lesson In an arithmetic sequence, d represents the common difference, a_1 represents the first term, a_2 represents the second term, and so on. For example, in the sequence 6, 9, 12, 15, 18, 21, ..., $a_1 = 6$ and $d = 3$.

34. Use the information in the table to write an expression for finding the nth term of an arithmetic sequence. $a_1 + (n - 1)d$

Arithmetic Sequence	numbers	6	9	12	15	...	
	symbols	a_1	a_2	a_3	a_4	...	a_n
Expressed in Terms of d and the First Term	numbers	6 + 0(3)	6 + 1(3)	6 + 2(3)	6 + 3(3)	...	6 + (n − 1)(3)
	symbols	$a_1 + 0d$	$a_1 + 1d$	$a_1 + 2d$	$a_1 + 3d$	...	?

35. Use the expression you wrote in Exercise 34 to find the 9th term of an arithmetic sequence if $a_1 = 16$ and $d = 5$. **56**

Maintain Your Skills

Mixed Review **ALGEBRA** Solve each equation. Check your solution. *(Lesson 5-9)*

36. $\frac{7}{6} = y + \frac{5}{12}$ $\frac{3}{4}$

37. $k - 4.1 = -9.38$ **−5.28**

38. $40.3 = 6.2x$ **6.5**

39. $\frac{3}{4}b = 7\frac{1}{2}$ **10**

Find the mean, median, and mode for each set of data. If necessary, round to the nearest tenth. *(Lesson 5-8)*

40. 11, 45, 62, 12, 47, 8, 12, 35 **29; 23.5; 12**

41. 2.3, 3.6, 4.1, 3.6, 2.9, 3.0 **3.3; 3.3; 3.6**

42. **ALGEBRA** Find the LCD of $\frac{1}{6a^2}$ and $\frac{5}{9a^3}$. *(Lesson 5-6)* $18a^3$

43. **HOME REPAIR** Cole is installing shelves in his closet. Because of the shape of the closet, the three shelves measure $34\frac{3}{8}$ inches, $33\frac{7}{8}$ inches, and $34\frac{5}{8}$ inches. What length of lumber does he need to buy? *(Lesson 5-5)* $102\frac{7}{8}$ in.

Find each product or quotient. Express using exponents. *(Lesson 4-6)*

44. $3^4 \cdot 3^2$ **3^6**

45. $\frac{b^5}{b^2}$ **b^3**

46. $2x^3(5x^2)$ **$10x^5$**

Find the greatest common factor of each set of numbers. *(Lesson 4-4)*

47. 36, 42 **6**

48. 9, 24 **3**

49. 60, 45, 30 **15**

4 Assess

Open-Ended Assessment

Modeling Have students model different sequences using small blocks or number cubes. Include an arithmetic sequence, a geometric sequence, and a sequence that has a pattern other than these.

Assessment Options

Quiz (Lessons 5-9 and 5-10) is available on p. 290 of the *Chapter 5 Resource Masters.*

Algebra Activity

 NEW YORK *Performance Indicator* **8.PS.4 Observe patterns and formulate generalizations**

Fibonacci Sequence

A special sequence that is neither arithmetic nor geometric is called the **Fibonacci sequence**. Each term in the sequence is the sum of the previous two terms, beginning with 1.

1, 1, 2, 3, 5, 8, 13, ...
      +1 +1 +2 +3 +5

Collect the Data
- Examine an artichoke, a pineapple, a pinecone, or the seeds in the center of a sunflower.
- For each item, count the number of spiral rows and record your data in a table. If possible, count the rows that spiral up from left to right and count the rows that spiral up from right to left. *Note:* It may be helpful to use a marker to keep track of the rows as you are counting.

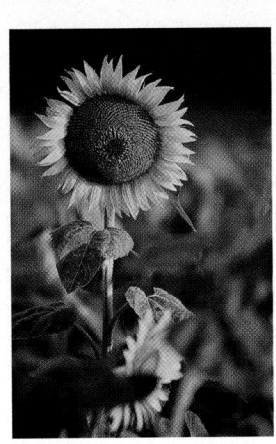

Analyze the Data 1–3. See p. 261A.
1. What do you notice about the number of rows in each item?
2. Compare your data with the data of the other students. How do they compare?

Make a Conjecture
3. Have a discussion with other students to determine the relationship between the number of rows in sunflowers, pinecones, pineapples, and artichokes and the Fibonacci sequence.

Extend the Activity 5. See p. 261A.
Numbers in an arithmetic sequence have a common difference, and numbers in a geometric sequence have a common ratio. The numbers in a Fibonacci sequence have a different kind of pattern. **4. 1, 1, 2, 3, 5, 8, 13, 21, 34, 55, 89, 144, 233, 377, 610**

4. Write the first fifteen terms in the Fibonacci sequence.
5. Use a calculator to divide each term by the previous term. Make a list of the quotients. If necessary, round to seven decimal places.
6. Describe the pattern in the quotients. **They get increasingly closer to 1.618.**
7. **RESEARCH** Find the definition of the **golden ratio**. What is the relationship between the numbers in the Fibonacci sequence and the golden ratio? **See p. 261A.**

Algebra Activity Fibonacci Sequence **253**

Algebra Activity

A Follow-Up of Lesson 5-10

Getting Started

Objective Become familiar with the Fibonacci sequence.

Materials
artichoke, pineapple, pinecone, or sunflower, markers

Teach

- Before starting this activity, have students describe the appearance of an artichoke, pineapple, pinecone, and/or sunflower. Have them compare features.
- Encourage students to research other connections to the Fibonacci sequence in nature.
- Direct students to notice some of the patterns of divisibility. For example, every third number is divisible by 2, every fourth by 3, every fifth by 5, every sixth by 8, every seventh by 13, and every eighth by 21.

Assess

In **Exercises 1–3**, students should recognize the number of rows as a number in the Fibonacci sequence.

In **Exercises 4–7**, students explore the connection between the Fibonacci sequence and the golden ratio.

Study Notebook

You may wish to have students summarize this activity and what they learned from it.

Resource Manager

📁 ***Teaching Pre-Algebra with Manipulatives***
- p. 79 (student recording sheet)

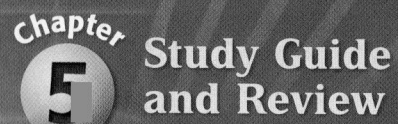
Vocabulary and Concept Check

- This alphabetical list of vocabulary terms in Chapter 5 includes a page reference where each term was introduced.
- **Assessment** A vocabulary review/test for Chapter 5 is available on p. 288 of the *Chapter 5 Resource Masters*.

Lesson-by-Lesson Review

For each lesson,
- the main ideas are summarized,
- additional examples review concepts, and
- practice exercises are provided.

Vocabulary PuzzleMaker

ELL The Vocabulary PuzzleMaker software improves students' mathematics vocabulary using four puzzle formats—crossword, scramble, word search using a word list, and word search using clues. Students can work on a computer screen or from a printed handout.

MindJogger Videoquizzes

ELL MindJogger Videoquizzes provide an alternative review of concepts presented in this chapter. Students work in teams in a game show format to gain points for correct answers. The questions are presented in three rounds.

Round 1 Concepts (5 questions)
Round 2 Skills (4 questions)
Round 3 Problem Solving (4 questions)

Study Guide and Review

Vocabulary and Concept Check

arithmetic sequence (p. 249)	least common denominator (LCD) (p. 227)	multiplicative inverse (p. 215)
bar notation (p. 201)	least common multiple (LCM) (p. 226)	period (p. 201)
common difference (p. 249)	mean (p. 238)	rational number (p. 205)
common multiples (p. 226)	measures of central tendency (p. 238)	reciprocals (p. 215)
common ratio (p. 250)	median (p. 238)	repeating decimal (p. 201)
dimensional analysis (p. 212)	mixed number (p. 200)	sequence (p. 249)
Fibonacci sequence (p. 253)	mode (p. 238)	term (p. 249)
geometric sequence (p. 250)	multiple (p. 226)	terminating decimal (p. 200)

Choose the correct term to complete each sentence.

1. A mixed number is an example of a (whole, <u>rational</u>) number.

2. The decimal 0.900 is a (<u>terminating</u>, repeating) decimal.

3. $\frac{x}{15}$ is an example of an (<u>algebraic fraction</u>, integer).

4. The numbers 12, 15, and 18 are (factors, <u>multiples</u>) of 3.

5. To add unlike fractions, rename the fractions using the (<u>LCD</u>, GCF).

6. The product of a number and its multiplicative inverse is (0, <u>1</u>).

7. To divide by a fraction, multiply the number by the (<u>reciprocal</u>, LCD) of the fraction.

8. The (median, <u>mode</u>) is the number that occurs most often in a set of data.

9. A common difference is found between terms in a(n) (<u>arithmetic</u>, geometric) sequence.

Lesson-by-Lesson Review

5-1 Writing Fractions as Decimals

See pages 200–204.

Concept Summary
- Any fraction or mixed number can be written as a terminating or repeating decimal.

Example Write $2\frac{7}{10}$ as a decimal.

$2\frac{7}{10} = 2 + \frac{7}{10}$ Write as the sum of an integer and a fraction.

$\quad\quad = 2 + 0.7$ or 2.7 Write $\frac{7}{10}$ as a decimal and add.

Exercises Write each fraction or mixed number as a decimal. Use a bar to show a repeating decimal. *See Examples 1–3 on pages 200 and 201.*

10. $\frac{7}{8}$ **0.875**   11. $\frac{9}{20}$ **0.45**   12. $\frac{2}{3}$ **$0.\overline{6}$**   13. $-\frac{7}{15}$ **$-0.4\overline{6}$**   14. $8\frac{3}{25}$ **8.12**   15. $6\frac{4}{11}$ **$6.\overline{36}$**

 www.pre-alg.com/vocabulary_review

FOLDABLES™ Study Organizer

For more information about Foldables, see *Teaching Mathematics with Foldables.*

Have students look through the chapter to make sure they have included notes and examples in their Foldables for each lesson of Chapter 5.

Encourage students to refer to their Foldable journals while completing the Study Guide and Review and to use them in preparing for the Chapter Test.

5-2 Rational Numbers

See pages 205–209.

Concept Summary

- Any number that can be written as a fraction is a rational number.
- Decimals that are terminating or repeating are rational numbers.

Example Write 0.16 as a fraction in simplest form.

$0.16 = \dfrac{16}{100}$ 0.16 is 16 hundredths.

$\quad\ = \dfrac{4}{25}$ Simplify. The GCF of 16 and 100 is 4.

Exercises Write each decimal as a fraction or mixed number in simplest form. *See Examples 2 and 3 on page 206.*

16. 0.23 $\dfrac{23}{100}$
17. 0.6 $\dfrac{3}{5}$
18. -0.05 $-\dfrac{1}{20}$
19. 0.125 $\dfrac{1}{8}$
20. 2.36 $2\dfrac{9}{25}$
21. 4.44 $4\dfrac{11}{25}$
22. -8.002 $-8\dfrac{1}{500}$
23. $0.555\ldots$ $\dfrac{5}{9}$
24. $0.\overline{3}$ $\dfrac{1}{3}$
25. $1.\overline{7}$ $1\dfrac{7}{9}$
26. $0.\overline{72}$ $\dfrac{8}{11}$
27. $3.\overline{36}$ $3\dfrac{4}{11}$

5-3 Multiplying Rational Numbers

See pages 210–214.

Concept Summary

- To multiply fractions, multiply the numerators and multiply the denominators.
- Dimensional analysis is a useful way to keep track of units while computing.

Example Find $\dfrac{4}{5} \cdot 3\dfrac{1}{3}$. Write the product in simplest form.

$\dfrac{4}{5} \cdot 3\dfrac{1}{3} = \dfrac{4}{5} \cdot \dfrac{10}{3}$ Rename $3\dfrac{1}{3}$ as an improper fraction.

$\qquad = \dfrac{4}{\overset{}{5}} \cdot \dfrac{\overset{2}{10}}{3}$ Divide by the GCF, 5.

$\qquad = \dfrac{8}{3} \text{ or } 2\dfrac{2}{3}$ Multiply and then simplify.

Exercises Find each product. Write in simplest form. *See Examples 1–5 on pages 210 and 211.*

28. $\dfrac{2}{3} \cdot \dfrac{1}{8}$ $\dfrac{1}{12}$
29. $-\dfrac{7}{15} \cdot \dfrac{5}{9}$ $-\dfrac{7}{27}$
30. $\dfrac{6}{11} \cdot \dfrac{2}{15}$ $\dfrac{4}{55}$
31. $8 \cdot \dfrac{4}{5}$ $6\dfrac{2}{5}$
32. $-1\dfrac{5}{6} \cdot 9$ $-16\dfrac{1}{2}$
33. $\dfrac{6}{7} \cdot \dfrac{14}{9}$ $1\dfrac{1}{3}$
34. $\dfrac{8}{9} \cdot \dfrac{5}{12}$ $\dfrac{10}{27}$
35. $2\dfrac{1}{4} \cdot \left(-\dfrac{4}{3}\right)$ -3
36. $\dfrac{14}{15} \cdot 3\dfrac{2}{7}$ $3\dfrac{1}{15}$
37. $2\dfrac{5}{6} \cdot 3\dfrac{1}{3}$ $9\dfrac{4}{9}$
38. $\dfrac{ab}{4} \cdot \dfrac{2}{bc}$ $\dfrac{a}{2c}$
39. $\dfrac{x^2}{r} \cdot \dfrac{r}{x}$ x

5-4 *Dividing Rational Numbers*

See pages 215–219.

Concept Summary

- The product of a number and its multiplicative inverse or reciprocal is 1.
- To divide by a fraction, multiply by its reciprocal.

Example Find $\frac{6}{7} \div \frac{3}{4}$. Write the quotient in simplest form.

$$\frac{6}{7} \div \frac{3}{4} = \frac{\overset{2}{\cancel{6}}}{7} \cdot \frac{4}{\underset{1}{\cancel{3}}} \qquad \text{Multiply by the reciprocal of } \frac{3}{4}, \frac{4}{3}.$$

$$= \frac{8}{7} \text{ or } 1\frac{1}{7} \qquad \text{Multiply and then simplify.}$$

Exercises Find each quotient. Write in simplest form.
See Examples 2–5 on pages 216 and 217.

40. $\frac{4}{9} \div \frac{1}{3}$ **$1\frac{1}{3}$** 　　41. $\frac{2}{5} \div \left(-\frac{1}{15}\right)$ **-6** 　42. $\frac{6}{13} \div \frac{8}{9}$ **$\frac{27}{52}$** 　　43. $5 \div \left(-1\frac{1}{3}\right)$ **$-3\frac{3}{4}$**

44. $\frac{11}{18} \div 4\frac{1}{2}$ **$\frac{11}{81}$** 　45. $-3\frac{3}{5} \div \frac{6}{7}$ **$-4\frac{1}{5}$** 　46. $\frac{n}{8} \div \frac{n}{32}$ **4** 　　47. $\frac{2}{7x} \div \frac{3}{2}$ **$\frac{4}{21x}$**

5-5 *Adding and Subtracting Like Fractions*

See pages 220–224.

Concept Summary

- To add like fractions, add the numerators and write the sum over the denominator.
- To subtract like fractions, subtract the numerators and write the sum over the denominator.

Example Find $3\frac{7}{8} + 9\frac{3}{8}$. Write the sum in simplest form.

Estimate: $4 + 9 = 13$

$$3\frac{7}{8} + 9\frac{3}{8} = (3 + 9) + \left(\frac{7}{8} + \frac{3}{8}\right) \qquad \text{Add the whole numbers and fractions separately.}$$

$$= 12 + \frac{7 + 3}{8} \qquad \text{The denominators are the same. Add the numerators.}$$

$$= 12\frac{10}{8} \qquad \text{Simplify.}$$

$$= 13\frac{2}{8} \text{ or } 13\frac{1}{4} \qquad \text{Simplify.}$$

Exercises Find each sum or difference. Write in simplest form.
See Examples 1–3 and 5 on pages 220 and 221.

48. $\frac{5}{18} + \frac{11}{18}$ **$\frac{8}{9}$** 　49. $\frac{7}{9} + \left(-\frac{2}{9}\right)$ **$\frac{5}{9}$** 　50. $\frac{19}{20} - \frac{17}{20}$ **$\frac{1}{10}$** 　51. $1\frac{16}{21} - \frac{9}{21}$ **$1\frac{1}{3}$**

52. $-\frac{12}{17} + \frac{10}{17}$ **$-\frac{2}{17}$** 　53. $8\frac{3}{10} - 5\frac{7}{10}$ **$2\frac{3}{5}$** 　54. $\frac{7t}{15} + \frac{t}{15}$ **$\frac{8t}{15}$** 　55. $\frac{5}{3x} - \frac{1}{3x}$ **$\frac{4}{3x}$**

5-6 Least Common Multiple

See pages 226–230.

Concept Summary

- The LCM of two numbers is the least nonzero multiple common to both numbers.
- To compare fractions with unlike denominators, write the fractions using the LCD and compare the numerators.

Example　Replace ● with <, >, or = to make $\frac{7}{15}$ ● $\frac{5}{9}$ a true statement.

The LCD is $3^2 \cdot 5$ or 45. Rewrite the fractions using the LCD.

$$\frac{7}{15} \cdot \frac{3}{3} = \frac{21}{45} \qquad\qquad \frac{5}{9} \cdot \frac{5}{5} = \frac{25}{45}$$

Since $21 < 25$, $\frac{21}{45} < \frac{25}{45}$. So, $\frac{7}{15} < \frac{5}{9}$.

Exercises　Find the least common multiple (LCM) of each pair of numbers or monomials.　*See Examples 1 and 2 on pages 226 and 227.*

56. 4, 18 **36**　　　**57.** 24, 20 **120**　　　**58.** $4a, 6a$ **12a**　　　**59.** $7c^2, 21c$ **21c^2**

Replace each ● with <, >, or = to make a true statement.
See Example 5 on page 228.

60. $\frac{3}{8}$ ● $\frac{5}{12}$ **<**　　**61.** $\frac{2}{9}$ ● $\frac{4}{15}$ **<**　　**62.** $\frac{5}{20}$ ● $\frac{1}{4}$ **=**　　**63.** $\frac{3}{7}$ ● $\frac{8}{21}$ **>**

5-7 Adding and Subtracting Unlike Fractions

See pages 232–236.

Concept Summary

- To add or subtract fractions with unlike denominators, rename the fractions with the LCD. Then add or subtract.

Example　Find $\frac{7}{9} - \frac{5}{12}$.

$$\frac{7}{9} - \frac{5}{12} = \frac{7}{9} \cdot \frac{4}{4} - \frac{5}{12} \cdot \frac{3}{3} \qquad \text{The LCD is } 3^2 \cdot 2^2 \text{ or 36.}$$

$$= \frac{28}{36} - \frac{15}{36} \qquad\qquad \text{Rename the fractions using the LCD.}$$

$$= \frac{13}{36} \qquad\qquad\qquad \text{Subtract the like fractions.}$$

Exercises　Find each sum or difference. Write in simplest form.
See Examples 2–5 on pages 233 and 234.

64. $\frac{1}{3} + \frac{5}{6}$ $1\frac{1}{6}$　　**65.** $\frac{11}{12} + \frac{3}{4}$ $1\frac{2}{3}$　　**66.** $\frac{7}{8} - \frac{5}{6}$ $\frac{1}{24}$　　**67.** $3\frac{7}{12} - \frac{3}{4}$ $2\frac{5}{6}$

68. $-\frac{3}{7} + \left(-\frac{11}{14}\right)$ $-1\frac{3}{14}$　　**69.** $1\frac{2}{5} - \left(-\frac{1}{3}\right)$ $1\frac{11}{15}$ **70.** $5\frac{1}{2} - 2\frac{2}{3}$ $2\frac{5}{6}$　　**71.** $-2\frac{1}{6} + 5\frac{1}{3}$ $3\frac{1}{6}$

Study Guide and Review

Chapter 5 For More ... • Extra Practice, see pages 733–736.
• Mixed Problem Solving, see page 762.

5-8 Measures of Central Tendency

See pages 238–242.

Concept Summary

• The mean, median, and mode can be used to describe sets of data.

Example Find the mean, median, and mode of 8, 4, 2, 2, and 10.

mean: $\dfrac{8 + 4 + 2 + 2 + 10}{5}$ or 5.2   median: 4   mode: 2

Exercises Find the mean, median, and mode for each set of data. If necessary, round to the nearest tenth. *See Example 1 on page 238.*

72. 4, 5, 7, 3, 9, 11, 23, 37 **12.4; 8; none** **73.** 3.6, 7.2, 9.0, 5.2, 7.2, 6.5, 3.6

6.0; 6.5; 3.6 and 7.2

5-9 Solving Equations with Rational Numbers

See pages 244–248.

Concept Summary

• To solve an equation, use inverse operations to isolate the variable.

Example Solve $1.6x = 8$. Check your solution.

$1.6x = 8$	Write the equation.	**CHECK** $1.6x = 8$ Write the equation.
$\dfrac{1.6x}{1.6} = \dfrac{8}{1.6}$	Divide each side by 1.6.	$1.6(5) \stackrel{?}{=} 8$ Replace x with 5.
$x = 5$	Simplify.	$8 = 8 \checkmark$ Simplify.

Exercises Solve each equation. Check your solution.
See Examples 1–4 on pages 244 and 245.

74. $\dfrac{1}{2} = a + \dfrac{3}{8}$ **$\dfrac{1}{8}$**   **75.** $x - 1.5 = 1.75$ **76.** $0.2t = 6$ **30**   **77.** $2 = -\dfrac{4}{5}n$ **$-2\dfrac{1}{2}$**

3.25

5-10 Arithmetic and Geometric Sequences

See pages 249–252.

Concept Summary

• In an arithmetic sequence, the terms have a common difference.
• In a geometric sequence, the terms have a common ratio.

Example State whether −8, −2, 4, 10, 16, ... is *arithmetic*, *geometric*, or *neither*. If it is arithmetic or geometric, write the next three terms.

−8, −2, 4, 10, 16   The common difference is 6, so the sequence is arithmetic.
+6 +6 +6 +6   The next three terms are 16 + 6 or 22, 22 + 6 or 28, and 28 + 6 or 34.

80. G; $\dfrac{1}{4}, \dfrac{1}{8}, \dfrac{1}{32}, \dfrac{1}{128}$

Exercises State whether each sequence is *arithmetic*, *geometric*, or *neither*. If it is arithmetic or geometric, state the common difference or common ratio and write the next three terms of the sequence. *See Examples 1–3 on pages 249 and 250.*

78. 4, 9, 14, 19, ... **79.** 1, 3, 9, 27, ...   **80.** 32, 8, 2, $\dfrac{1}{2}$, ...   **81.** −6, −5, −2, 3, ...
A; 5; 24, 29, 34   **G; 3; 81, 243, 729**   **neither**

Vocabulary and Concepts

1. **State** the difference between a terminating and a repeating decimal. **1–2. See p. 261A.**
2. **Describe** how to add fractions with unlike denominators.
3. **Define** *geometric sequence.* **a sequence in which the quotient of any two consecutive terms is the same**

Skills and Applications

Write each fraction or mixed number as a decimal. Use a bar to show a repeating decimal.

4. $\frac{9}{20}$ **0.45**

5. $-\frac{7}{8}$ **−0.875**

6. $4\frac{2}{9}$ **$4.\overline{2}$**

Write each decimal as a fraction or mixed number in simplest form.

7. 0.24 **$\frac{6}{25}$**

8. 5.06 **$5\frac{3}{50}$**

9. $-2.\overline{3}$ **$-2\frac{1}{3}$**

Replace each ● with <, >, or = to make a true sentence.

10. 0.6 ● $\frac{2}{3}$ **<**

11. $-1\frac{5}{8}$ ● -1.6 **<**

Find the least common denominator (LCD) of each pair of fractions.

12. $\frac{5}{6}, \frac{2}{9}$ **18**

13. $\frac{9}{4a^2}, \frac{2}{3ab}$ **$12a^2b$**

Find each product, quotient, sum, or difference. Write in simplest form.

14. $\frac{5}{8} \cdot \frac{6}{11}$ **$\frac{15}{44}$**

15. $\frac{5}{8} + \frac{1}{8}$ **$\frac{3}{4}$**

16. $\frac{7}{9} \div \frac{4}{15}$ **$2\frac{11}{12}$**

17. $3\frac{5}{6} + 1\frac{2}{9}$ **$5\frac{1}{18}$**

18. $\frac{ab}{9} \div \frac{b}{3}$ **$\frac{a}{3}$**

19. $\frac{11x}{3y} - \frac{8x}{3y}$ **$\frac{x}{y}$**

For Exercises 20 and 21, use the data set {20.5, 18.6, 16.3, 4.8, 19.1, 17.3, 20.5}.

20. Find the mean, median, and mode. If necessary, round to the nearest tenth. **16.7; 18.6; 20.5**
21. Identify an extreme value and describe how it affects the mean. **4.8; It decreases the mean by 2.**

Solve each equation. Check your solution.

22. $x + 4.3 = 9.8$ **5.5**

23. $12 = 0.75x$ **16**

24. $3.1m = 12.4$ **4**

25. $p - \frac{4}{5} = \frac{2}{3}$ **$1\frac{7}{15}$**

26. $-\frac{3}{8} = \frac{5}{3}a$ **$-\frac{9}{40}$**

27. $y - 2\frac{1}{4} = 1\frac{5}{6}$ **$4\frac{1}{12}$**

State whether each sequence is *arithmetic, geometric,* or *neither.* If it is arithmetic or geometric, state the common difference or common ratio and write the next three terms of the sequence. **28. G; 4; 512, 2048, 8192   29. A; −0.6; 3.1, 2.5, 1.9**

28. 2, 8, 32, 128, …

29. 5.5, 4.9, 4.3, 3.7, …

30. 1, 2, 4, 7, … **neither**

31. **TRAVEL** Max drives 6 hours at an average rate of 65 miles per hour. What is the distance Max travels? Use $d = rt$. **390 mi**

32. **SEWING** Allie needs $4\frac{2}{3}$ yards of lace to finish sewing the edges of a blanket. She only has $\frac{3}{4}$ of that amount. How much lace does Allie have? **$3\frac{1}{2}$ yd**

33. **STANDARDIZED TEST PRACTICE** Write the sum of $-6\frac{1}{4}$ and $-9\frac{3}{20}$. **A**

   Ⓐ $-15\frac{2}{5}$ Ⓑ $-15\frac{1}{4}$ Ⓒ $-16\frac{2}{5}$ Ⓓ $-3\frac{1}{5}$

ORK actice

www.pre-alg.com/chapter_test /ny

Assessment Options

Vocabulary Test A vocabulary review/test for Chapter 5 can be found on p. 288 of the *Chapter 5 Resource Masters.*

Chapter Tests There are six Chapter 5 Tests and an Open-Ended Assessment task available in the *Chapter 5 Resource Masters.*

Chapter 5 Tests			
Form	Type	Level	Pages
1	MC	basic	275–276
2A	MC	average	277–278
2B	MC	average	279–280
2C	FR	average	281–282
2D	FR	average	283–284
3	FR	advanced	285–286

MC = multiple-choice questions
FR = free-response questions

Open-Ended Assessment Performance tasks for Chapter 5 can be found on p. 287 of the *Chapter 5 Resource Masters*, along with a sample scoring rubric for these tasks on p. A32.

First Semester Test A test for Chapters 1–5 can be found on pp. 295–298 of the *Chapter 5 Resource Masters.*

ExamView® Pro

Use the networkable ExamView® Pro to:

- Create **multiple versions** of tests.
- Create **modified** tests for *Inclusion* students.
- **Edit** existing questions and **add** your own questions.
- Use built-in **state curriculum correlations** to create tests aligned with state standards.
- Change **English** tests to **Spanish** and vice versa.

Portfolio Suggestion

Introduction In Chapter 5, students converted numbers to different forms, solved equations, performed computations, found measures of central tendency, and examined sequences. This chapter opened up a variety of application problems based on utilizing rational numbers.

Ask Students to write three ways that rational numbers help them relate to the world. For example, data in the newspaper help them become more informed citizens or better consumers.

These two pages contain practice questions in the various formats that can be found on the most frequently given standardized tests.

A practice answer sheet for these two pages can be found on page A1 of the *Chapter 5 Resource Masters.*

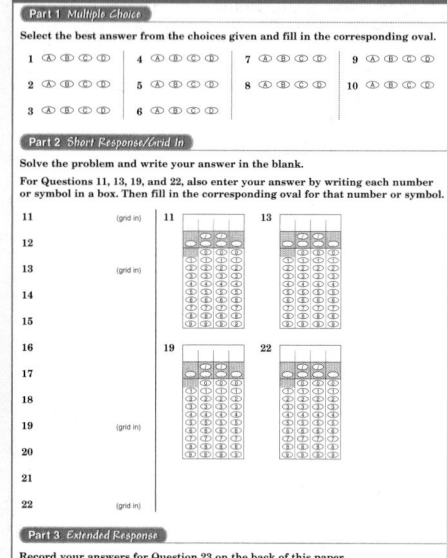

Additional Practice

See pp. 293–294 of the *Chapter 5 Resource Masters* for additional standardized test practice.

See pp. 293–294 of the *Chapter 5 Resource Masters* for additional standardized test practice.

NEW YORK
Test Practice

Part 1 Multiple Choice

Record your answers on the answer sheet provided by your teacher or on a sheet of paper.

1. Kenzie paid for a CD with a $20 bill. She received 3 dollars, 3 dimes, and 2 pennies in change. How much did she pay for the CD? (Prerequisite Skill, p. 707) **A**

   (A) $16.68   (B) $16.88

   (C) $17.68   (D) $17.88

2. A survey of 110 people asked which country they would most like to visit. The bar graph shows the data. How many people chose Canada, England, or Australia as the country they would most like to visit? (Prerequisite Skill, pp. 722–723) **B**

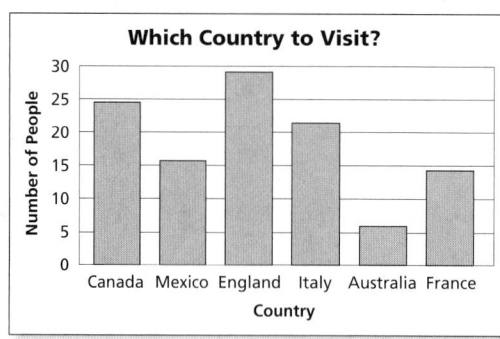

Which Country to Visit?

   (A) 52   (B) 58

   (C) 68   (D) 74

Test-Taking Tip

Question 2
When an item includes a graph, scan the graph to see what kind of information it includes and how the information is organized. Don't try to memorize the information. Read each answer choice and compare it with the graph to see if the information in the answer choice is correct. Eliminate any wrong answer choices.

260   **Chapter 5**   Rational Numbers

3. The low temperature overnight was $-1°F$. Each night for the next four nights, the low temperature was 7° lower than the previous night. What was the low temperature during the last night? (Lesson 2-4) **A**

   (A) $-29°$ (B) $-27°$ (C) $-22°$ (D) $-8°$

4. Write $\frac{6t^4}{18ts}$ in simplest form. (Lesson 4-5) **C**

   (A) $\frac{1}{3}t^3s$ (B) $3t^5s$

   (C) $\frac{t^3}{3s}$ (D) $\frac{t^5}{3s}$

5. What is 8×10^{-2} in standard notation? (Lesson 4-8) **B**

   (A) 0.008   (B) 0.08

   (C) 0.8   (D) 800

6. Add $\frac{2}{3} + \frac{1}{4} + \frac{5}{6}$. (Lesson 5-7) **C**

   (A) $\frac{2}{3}$ (B) $\frac{5}{4}$

   (C) $\frac{7}{4}$ (D) $\frac{11}{6}$

7. Evaluate $\frac{1}{4}(2 - x) - x$ if $x = \frac{1}{2}$. (Lesson 5-7) **B**

   (A) $-\frac{1}{2}$ (B) $-\frac{1}{8}$ (C) $\frac{1}{8}$ (D) $\frac{1}{2}$

8. Antonia read four books that had the following number of pages: 324, 375, 420, 397. What is the mean number of pages in these books? (Lesson 5-8) **B**

   (A) 375   (B) 379

   (C) 380   (D) 386

9. Which sequence is a geometric sequence with a common ratio of 2? (Lesson 5-10) **D**

   (A) $2, -4, 8, -16, \ldots$ (B) $2, 4, 6, 8, 10, \ldots$

   (C) $3, 5, 7, 9, 11, \ldots$ (D) $3, 6, 12, 24, \ldots$

10. State the next three terms in the sequence $128, 32, 8, 2, \ldots$ (Lesson 5-10) **A**

   (A) $\frac{1}{2}, \frac{1}{8}, \frac{1}{32}$ (B) $\frac{1}{2}, \frac{1}{16}, \frac{1}{32}$

   (C) $\frac{1}{4}, \frac{1}{8}, \frac{1}{16}$ (D) $\frac{1}{4}, \frac{1}{6}, \frac{1}{8}$

ExamView® Pro

Special banks of standardized test questions similar to those on the SAT, ACT, TIMSS 8, NAEP 8, and Pre-Algebra End-of-Course tests can be found on this CD-ROM.

Part 2 | Short Response/Grid In

Record your answers on the answer sheet provided by your teacher or on a sheet of paper.

11. Nate is cutting shelves from a board that is 15 feet long. Each shelf is 3 feet 4 inches long. What is the greatest number of shelves he can make from the board? (Prerequisite Skill, pp. 720–721) **4**

12. Write the ordered pair that names point *L*. (Lesson 2-6) **(4, −3)**

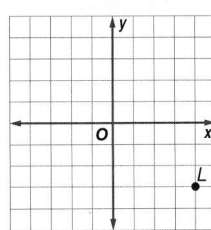

13. Find *x* if $3x + 4 = 28$. (Lesson 3-5) **8**

14. Write an equation to represent the total number of Calories *t* in one box of snack crackers. The box of crackers contains 8 servings. Each serving has 125 Calories. (Lesson 3-6) $t = 8 \cdot 125$

15. On Saturday, Juan plans to drive 275 miles at a rate of 55 miles per hour. How many hours will his trip take? Use the formula $d = rt$, where *d* represents the distance, *r* represents rate, and *t* represents the time. (Lesson 3-7) **5 h**

16. Write $4^2 \times 5^3$ as a product of prime factors without using exponents. (Lesson 4-3) $2 \cdot 2 \cdot 2 \cdot 2 \cdot 5 \cdot 5 \cdot 5$

17. The average American worker spends 44 minutes traveling to and from work each day. What fraction of the day is this? (Lesson 4-5) $\frac{11}{360}$

18. The Saturn V rocket that took the Apollo astronauts to the moon weighed 6.526×10^6 pounds at lift-off. Write its weight in standard notation. (Lesson 4-8) **6,526,000 lb**

19. Write a decimal to represent the shaded portion of the figure below. (Lesson 5-1) **.375**

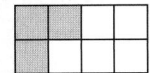

20. One elevator in a 40-story building is programmed to stop at every third floor. Another is programmed to stop at every fourth floor. Which floors in the building are served by both elevators? (Lesson 5-6) **floor 12, floor 24, floor 36**

21. Beth has $\frac{3}{4}$ cup of grated cheese. She needs $2\frac{1}{2}$ cups of grated cheese for making pizzas. How many more cups does she need? (Lesson 5-7) $1\frac{3}{4}$

22. The number of tickets sold for each performance of the Spring Music Fest are 352, 417, 307, 367, 433, and 419. What is the median number of tickets sold per performance? (Lesson 5-8) **392**

Part 3 | Extended Response

Record your answers on a sheet of paper. Show your work. 23a–d. See margin.

23. During seven regular season games, the Hawks basketball team scored the points shown in the table below. (Lesson 5-8)

Game	1	2	3	4	5	6	7
Points	68	60	73	74	64	78	73

a. Find the mean, median, and mode of these seven scores.

b. During the first playoff game after the regular season, the Hawks scored only 40 points. Find the mean, median, and mode of all eight scores.

c. Which of these three measures of central tendency—mean, median, or mode—changed the most as a result of the playoff score? Explain your answer.

d. Does the mean score or the median score best represent the team's scores for all eight games? Explain your answer.

Evaluating Extended Response Questions

Extended Response questions are graded by using a multilevel rubric that guides you in assessing a student's knowledge of a particular concept.

Goal: Review the measures of central tendency.

Sample Scoring Rubric: The following rubric is a sample scoring device. You may wish to add more detail to this sample to meet your individual scoring needs.

Score	Criteria
4	A correct solution that is supported by well-developed, accurate explanations
3	A generally correct solution, but may contain minor flaws in reasoning or computation
2	A partially correct interpretation and/or solution to the problem
1	A correct solution with no supporting evidence or explanation
0	An incorrect solution indicating no mathematical understanding of the concept or task, or no solution is given

23d. The median best represents the team's eight scores, because it is less affected by the playoff game score, which is much lower than the other scores.

Answers

23a. mean $= \frac{60 + 64 + 68 + 73 + 73 + 74 + 78}{7} = \frac{490}{7}$ or **70**

median = 73, mode = 73

23b. mean $= \frac{490 + 40}{8} = \frac{530}{8}$ or **66.25**

median $= \frac{68 + 73}{2}$ or 70.5; mode = 73

23c. The mean changed the most. To find the difference, subtract the mean for the 8 scores from the mean for the 7 scores. Do the same for the medians and the modes.

	7 scores	8 scores	Change
mean	70	66.25	70 − 66.25 = 3.75
median	73	70.5	73 − 70.5 = 2.5
mode	73	73	73 − 73 = 0

Page 251, Lesson 5-10

10. A; 3; 14, 17, 20,

11. A; 11; 38, 49, 60

12. G; 2; 8, 16, 32

13. G; 3; 162, 486, 1458

14. A; −7; −10, −17, −24

15. A; −3; 13, 10, 7

16. G; $\frac{1}{4}$; $\frac{1}{64}$, $\frac{1}{256}$, $\frac{1}{1024}$

17. G; $-\frac{1}{5}$; $-\frac{1}{125}$, $\frac{1}{625}$, $-\frac{1}{3125}$

18. A; $\frac{1}{2}$, $\frac{5}{2}$, 3, $\frac{7}{2}$

19. A; $\frac{1}{6}$, $\frac{2}{3}$, $\frac{5}{6}$, 1

20. A; 0.75; 3, 3.75, 4.5

21. A; −0.5, 2.5, 2, 1.5

22. neither

23. neither

24. G; $\frac{1}{2}$; $\frac{3}{2}$, $\frac{3}{4}$, $\frac{3}{8}$

25. G; $-\frac{1}{3}$; $\frac{2}{9}$, $-\frac{2}{27}$, $\frac{2}{81}$

26. G; 3; 8.1, 24.3, 72.9

27. G; $\frac{1}{2}$; $\frac{1}{32}$, $\frac{1}{64}$, $\frac{1}{128}$

29a. Arithmetic; the common difference is $3.

31. Find the pattern, continue the sequence, and use the new values to make predictions. Answers should include the following.

- The difference between any two consecutive terms in an arithmetic sequence is the common difference. To find the next value in such a sequence, add the common difference to the last term. The ratio of any two consecutive terms in a geometric sequence is the common ratio. So, to find the next value in such a sequence, multiply the last term by the common ratio.

- Sequences occurring in nature include geysers spouting every few minutes, the arrangement of geese in migration patterns, and ocean tides.

Page 253, Algebra Activity

1. Sample answer: Most of them should be terms of the Fibonacci sequence.

2. Sample answer: Most of them should be terms of the Fibonacci sequence. Some groups may have different numbers based on the size of their object.

3. Sample answer: The number of rows is a term of the Fibonacci sequence.

5. 1, 2, 1.5, 1.6666667, 1.6, 1.625, 1.6153846, 1.6190476, 1.6176471, 1.6181818, 1.6179775, 1.6180556, 1.6180258, 1.6180371

7. The golden ratio is approxiamately 1:1.618. After the first few terms, the ratio of successive numbers in the Fibonacci sequence is the golden ratio.

Page 259, Practice Test

1. The digits of a terminating decimal end and the digits of a repeating decimal continue repeating.

2. Rename the fractions with a common denominator. Then add and simplify.

Notes

Chapter 6

Ratio, Proportion, and Percent
Chapter Overview and Pacing

 An electronic version of this chapter is available on **StudentWorks™**. *This backpack solution CD-ROM allows students instant access to the Student Edition, lesson worksheet pages, and web resources.*

Year-long pacing: pages T20–T21.

LESSON OBJECTIVES

	PACING (days)			
	Regular		**Block**	
	Basic/Average	Advanced	Basic/Average	Advanced
6-1 Ratios and Rates (pp. 264–268) • Write ratios as fractions in simplest form. • Determine unit rates.	1	1	0.5	0.5
6-2 Using Proportions (pp. 270–275) • Solve proportions. • Use proportions to solve real-world problems. *Follow-Up:* Use proportions with the capture-recapture method of counting.	2 (with 6-2 Follow-Up)	2 (with 6-2 Follow-Up)	1	1.5 (with 6-2 Follow-Up)
6-3 Scale Drawings and Models (pp. 276–280) • Use scale drawings. • Construct scale drawings.	1	1	0.5	0.5
6-4 Fractions, Decimals, and Percents (pp. 281–285) • Express percents as fractions and vice versa. • Express percents as decimals and vice versa.	1	1	0.5	0.5
6-5 Using the Percent Proportion (pp. 286–292) *Preview:* Use a percent model to find a percent or a part. • Use the percent proportion to solve problem	2 (with 6-5 Preview)	1	1	0.5
6-6 Finding Percents Mentally (pp. 293–297) • Compute mentally with percents. • Estimate with percents.	1	1	0.5	0.5
6-7 Using Percent Equations (pp. 298–303) • Solve percent problems using percent equations. • Solve real-life problems involving discount and interest. *Follow-Up:* Find compound interest.	1	2 (with 6-7 Follow-Up)	0.5	1 (with 6-7 Follow-Up)
6-8 Percent of Change (pp. 304–308) • Find percent of increase. • Find percent of decrease.	1	1	0.5	0.5
6-9 Probability and Predictions (pp. 309–315) *Preview:* Take a survey. • Find the probability of simple events. • Use a sample to predict the actions of a larger group. *Follow-Up:* Describe how the graphing calculator generates random numbers.	2 (with 6-9 Preview)	1	1	0.5
Study Guide and **Practice Test** (pp. 316–321) **Standardized Test Practice** (pp. 322–323)	1	1	0.5	0.5
Chapter Assessment	1	1	0.5	0.5
TOTAL	14	13	7	7

Chapter Resource Manager

Timesaving Tools™
TeacherWorks™
All-In-One Planner and Resource Center
See pages T5 and T21.

CHAPTER 6 RESOURCE MASTERS

Study Guide and Intervention	Practice (Skills and Average)	Reading to Learn Mathematics	Enrichment	Assessment	Prerequisite Skills Workbook	Applications*	Parent and Student Study Guide Workbook	5-Minute Check Transparencies	Interactive Chalkboard	Pre-AlgePASS: Tutorial Plus (lessons)	Materials
299	300–301	302	303		39–40		44	6-1	6-1	12, 13	
304	305–306	307	308		37–40	SC 11	45	6-2	6-2	14	*Follow-Up:* bag of dried beans, paper bag, permanent marker
309	310–311	312	313	359		GCS 30	46	6-3	6-3		
314	315–316	317	318		15–18		47	6-4	6-4	15	
319	320–321	322	323	359, 361		SM 18	48	6-5	6-5		*Preview:* grid paper
324	325–326	327	328		39–40		49	6-6	6-6		
329	330–331	332	333	360			50	6-7	6-7	16, 17	*Follow-Up:* spreadsheet software
334	335–336	337	338			SC 12 GCS 29	51	6-8	6-8		
339	340–341	342	343	360			52	6-9	6-9	18	*Follow-Up:* graphing calculator
				345–358 362–364 365–366							

* *Key to Abbreviations:* GCS = Graphing Calculator and Spreadsheet Masters, SC = School-to-Career Masters, SM = Science and Mathematics Lab Manual

 ELL Study Guide and Intervention, Skills Practice, Practice, and Parent and Student Study Guide Workbooks are also available in Spanish.

Chapter 6 Mathematical Connections and Background

Continuity of Instruction

Prior Knowledge

In Chapter 5, students learned to multiply and divide rational numbers. They also converted fractions to decimals and added and subtracted fractions. They factored numbers and determined least common multiple. They also used measures of central tendency to analyze data. Students solved equations with rational numbers and identified sequences.

This Chapter

Students will examine ratios and rates and use cross products to determine whether two rates form a proportion. They will use ratios and proportions to solve problems, including scale drawings and models. Students will extend their study of ratios to include percent and the conversion of fractions and decimals to percents. Students will also find simple probability.

Future Connections

Ratios, rates, proportions, and percents all relate to the world of business. Ratios and scale drawings and models are used extensively in architecture and engineering. Probability is frequently used in chemistry and physics to predict the orbits of electrons.

6-1 Ratios and Rates

A ratio is a comparison of two numbers by division. If a basketball player makes 8 out of 10 free throws, the ratio would be written as 8 to 10, 8:10, and $\frac{8}{10}$. Ratios are usually written in simplest form. In simplest form, the ratio 8 out of 10 is written as 4 to 5, 4:5, or $\frac{4}{5}$.

A rate is a ratio of two measurements having different kinds of units. When a rate is simplified so that it has a denominator of 1, it is called a unit rate. An example of a unit rate is 9 miles per hour.

6-2 Using Proportions

A proportion is an equation stating that two ratios are equal. For example, $\frac{3}{18} = \frac{13}{78}$ is an example of a proportion. Every proportion has two cross products. In the proportion, $\frac{3}{18} = \frac{13}{78}$, the cross products are $3 \cdot 78$ and $18 \cdot 13$. The cross products of a proportion are equal.

6-3 Scale Drawings and Models

A scale drawing or a scale model is used to represent an object that is too large or too small to be drawn or built at actual size. The ratio of length on a scale drawing or model corresponds to the length of the real object. This ratio is called the scale factor. The lengths and widths of objects of a scale drawing or model are proportional to those of the actual object.

6-4 Fractions, Decimals, and Percents

A percent is a ratio that compares a number to 100. To write a percent as a fraction, express the ratio as a fraction with a denominator of 100. Then simplify, if possible. For example, $76\% = \frac{76}{100}$ or $\frac{19}{25}$. To write a fraction as a percent, write an equivalent fraction with a denominator of 100. For example, $\frac{3}{4} = \frac{75}{100}$ or 75%.

A fraction can be expressed as a percent by first expressing the fraction as a decimal, by dividing the numerator by the denominator, and then converting the decimal to a percent by moving the decimal point two places to the right.

6-5 Using the Percent Proportion

In the percent proportion $\frac{\text{part}}{\text{base}} = \frac{\text{percent}}{100}$, one of the numbers, called the part, is being compared to the whole quantity, called the base. The other ratio is the percent, written as a fraction, whose base is 100. The percent proportion can be used to find a missing part or base.

6-6 Finding Percents Mentally

When working with common percents like 10%, 25%, 40%, and 50%, it may be helpful to use the fraction form of the percent. Percent-fraction equivalents can be useful in solving real-world problems, particularly when dealing with sale prices. To find the percent of each number mentally, convert the percent to its fractional equivalent and then calculate. For example, to find 25% of 40, change 25% to $\frac{1}{4}$; and $\frac{1}{4}$ of 40 is 10.

6-7 Using Percent Equations

The percent equation is an equivalent form of the percent proportion in which the percent is written as a decimal. The percent equation is written as Part = Percent · Base. You can use this equation to find the missing part, percent, or base. The percent equation can also be used to solve problems involving discount and interest. Discount is the amount by which the regular price of an item is reduced. Simple interest is the amount of money paid or earned for the use of money.

6-8 Percent of Change

A percent of change tells the percent an amount has increased or decreased in relation to the original amount. To find the percent of change, write a ratio that compares the amount of change to the original measurement. That is, percent of change = $\frac{\text{amount of change}}{\text{original measurement}}$. Express the ratio as a percent. When an amount increases, the percent of change is a percent of increase. When an amount decreases, the percent of change is a percent of decrease. Percent of change is particularly useful in solving real-world, money-related problems.

6-9 Probability and Predictions

Probability is a ratio that compares the number of favorable outcomes to the number of possible outcomes. Probability is expressed as the ratio $\frac{\text{number of favorable outcomes}}{\text{number of possible outcomes}}$. The probability of an event is always between 0 and 1, inclusive. The closer a probability is to 1, the more likely it is to occur. The set of all possible outcomes is called the sample space. For a number cube, the sample space is {1, 2, 3, 4, 5, 6}, for a coin it is {heads, tails}. There are two types of probabilities. Theoretical probability is what should occur. Experimental probability is what actually occurs when conducting a probability experiment.

Quick Review Math Handbook

Hot Words includes a glossary of terms while Hot Topics consists of explanations of key mathematical concepts with exercises to test comprehension. This valuable resource can be used as a reference in the classroom or for home study.

Lesson	Hot Topics Section	Lesson	Hot Topics Section
GS 6	2.1, 2.6, 8.2	6-5	2.4, 2.9
6-1	6.4, 6.5	6-6	2.8, 6.4
6-2	6.5, 8.2	6-7	2.6, 2.8, 2.9
6-2F	6.5	6-8	2.8, 2.9
6-3	2.1, 6.5	6-9P	4.6
6-4	2.1, 2.8	6-9	4.6
6-5P	2.9	6-9F	4.6

GS = Getting Started, P = Preview, F = Follow-Up

 Additional mathematical information and teaching notes are available at www.pre-alg.com/key_concepts.

DAILY
INTERVENTION and Assessment

Key to Abbreviations:
TWE = Teacher Wraparound Edition; CRM = Chapter Resource Masters

	Type	Student Edition	Teacher Resources	Technology/Internet
INTERVENTION	Ongoing	Prerequisite Skills, pp. 263, 268, 274, 280, 285, 292, 297, 302, 308 Practice Quiz 1, p. 292 Practice Quiz 2, p. 308	5-Minute Check Transparencies *Prerequisite Skills Workbook,* pp. 15–18, 37–40 Quizzes, *CRM,* pp. 359, 360 Mid-Chapter Test, *CRM,* p. 361 Study Guide and Intervention, *CRM,* pp. 299, 304, 309, 314, 319, 324, 329, 334, 339	Pre-AlgePASS: Tutorial Plus, Lessons 12, 13, 14, 15, 16, 17, and 18 www.pre-alg.com/self_check_quiz www.pre-alg.com/extra_examples
	Mixed Review	pp. 268, 274, 280, 285, 292, 297, 302, 308, 314	Cumulative Review, *CRM,* p. 362	
	Error Analysis	Find the Error, pp. 278, 291, 306	Find the Error, *TWE,* pp. 278, 290 Unlocking Misconceptions, *TWE,* pp. 267, 306	
ASSESSMENT	Standardized Test Practice	pp. 268, 274, 280, 285, 292, 297, 302, 305, 306, 308, 314, 322–323	*TWE,* pp. 322–323 Standardized Test Practice, *CRM,* pp. 363–364	Standardized Test Practice CD-ROM www.pre-alg.com/standardized_test
	Open-Ended Assessment	Writing in Math, pp. 268, 274, 280, 285, 292, 297, 302, 307, 314 Open Ended, pp. 266, 272, 278, 283, 291, 295, 300, 306, 312 Standardized Test, p. 323	Speaking: *TWE,* pp. 274, 285, 314 Writing: *TWE,* pp. 268, 292, 302 Modeling: *TWE,* pp. 280, 297, 308 Open-Ended Assessment, *CRM,* p. 357	
	Chapter Assessment	Study Guide, pp. 316–320 Practice Test, p. 321	Multiple-Choice Tests (Forms 1, 2A, 2B), *CRM,* pp. 345–350 Free-Response Tests (Forms 2C, 2D, 3), *CRM,* pp. 351–356 Vocabulary Test/Review, *CRM,* p. 358	ExamView® Pro (see below) MindJogger Videoquizzes www.pre-alg.com/vocabulary_review www.pre-alg.com/chapter_test

For more information on Yearly ProgressPro, see p. 144.

Pre-Algebra Lesson	Yearly ProgressPro Skill Lesson
6-1	Rates
6-2	Solve Proportions
6-3	Scale Models
6-4	Fraction/Decimal/Percent Conversions: Level 2
6-5	Ratios and Percent
6-6	Finding Percents Mentally
6-7	Percent Proportion and Equation
6-8	Percent of Change
6-9	Probability as Fractions: Level 2

ExamView® Pro

Use the networkable **ExamView® Pro** to:
- Create **multiple versions** of tests.
- Create **modified** tests for *Inclusion* students.
- **Edit** existing questions and **add** your own questions.
- Use built-in **state curriculum correlations** to create tests aligned with state standards.
- Change **English** tests to **Spanish** and vice versa.

For more information on Intervention and Assessment, see pp. T8–T11.

Reading and Writing in Mathematics

Glencoe Pre-Algebra provides numerous opportunities to incorporate reading and writing into the mathematics classroom.

Student Edition

- Foldables™ Study Organizer, p. 263
- Reading Mathematics, p. 269
- Concept Check questions require students to verbalize and write about what they have learned in the lesson. (pp. 265, 266, 270, 272, 276, 278, 283, 288, 291, 295, 300, 306, 310, 312)
- Writing in Math questions in every lesson, pp. 268, 274, 280, 285, 292, 297, 302, 307, 314
- Reading Math, pp. 281, 300, 311
- WebQuest, pp. 301, 314

Teacher Wraparound Edition

- Foldables™ Study Organizer, pp. 263, 316
- Study Notebook suggestions, pp. 266, 269, 272, 275, 278, 283, 287, 290, 295, 300, 303, 306, 309, 312
- Modeling activities, pp. 280, 297, 308
- Speaking activities, pp. 274, 285, 314
- Writing activities, pp. 268, 292, 302
- Differentiated Instruction (Verbal/Linguistic), pp. 294, 311
- **ELL** Resources, pp. 262, 264, 269, 270, 276, 281, 288, 293, 294, 298, 304, 310, 311, 316

Additional Resources

- Vocabulary Builder worksheets require students to define and give examples for key vocabulary terms as they progress through the chapter (*Chapter 6 Resource Masters*, pp. vii–viii)
- Reading to Learn Mathematics master for each lesson (*Chapter 6 Resource Masters*, pp. 302, 307, 312, 317, 322, 327, 332, 337, 342)
- *Vocabulary PuzzleMaker* software creates crossword, jumble, and word search puzzles using vocabulary lists that you can customize.
- *Teaching Mathematics with Foldables* provides suggestions for promoting cognition and language.
- *Reading and Writing in the Mathematics Classroom*
- *WebQuest and Project Resources*

For more information on Reading and Writing in Mathematics, see pp. T6–T7.

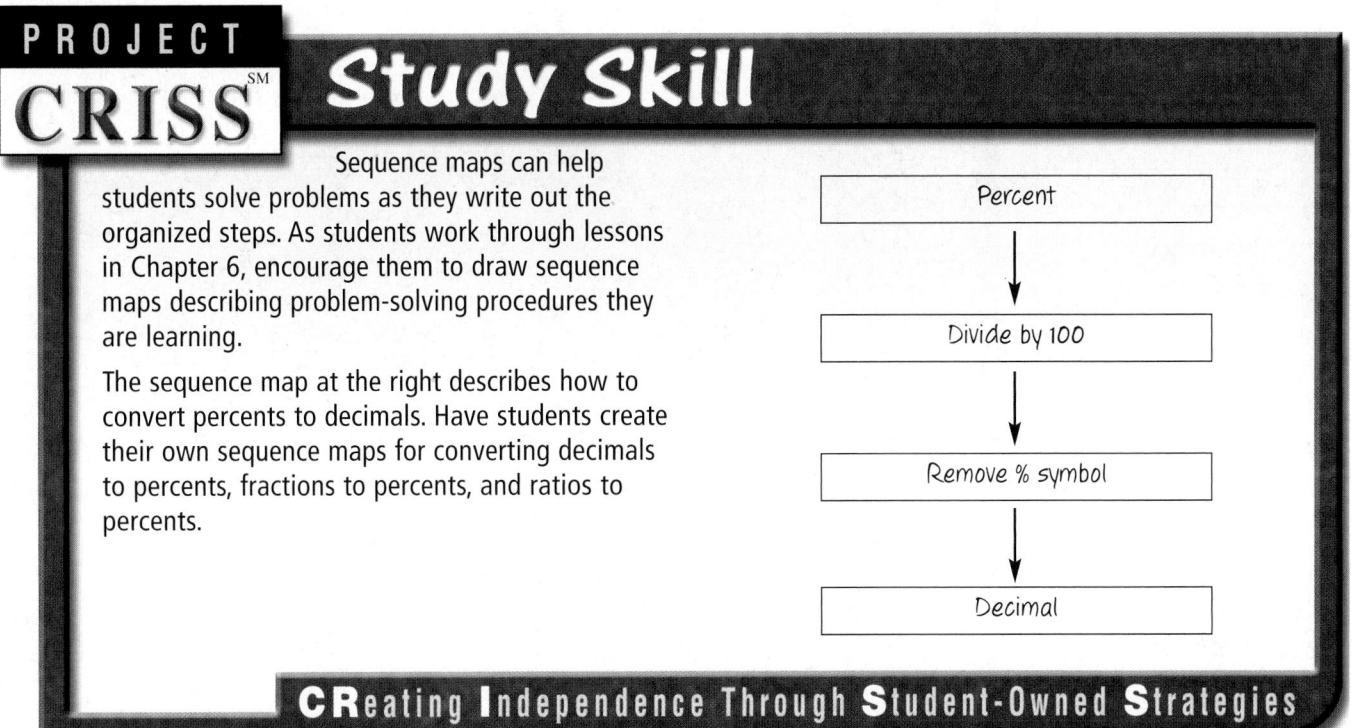

PROJECT CRISS℠ Study Skill

Sequence maps can help students solve problems as they write out the organized steps. As students work through lessons in Chapter 6, encourage them to draw sequence maps describing problem-solving procedures they are learning.

The sequence map at the right describes how to convert percents to decimals. Have students create their own sequence maps for converting decimals to percents, fractions to percents, and ratios to percents.

Percent → Divide by 100 → Remove % symbol → Decimal

CReating **I**ndependence **T**hrough **S**tudent-**O**wned **S**trategies

What You'll Learn

Have students read over the list of objectives and make a list of any words with which they are not familiar.

Why It's Important

Point out to students that this is only one of many reasons why each objective is important. Others are provided in the introduction to each lesson.

What You'll Learn

- **Lesson 6-1** Write ratios as fractions and find unit rates.
- **Lessons 6-2 and 6-3** Use ratios and proportions to solve problems, including scale drawings.
- **Lesson 6-4** Write decimals and fractions as percents and vice versa.
- **Lessons 6-5, 6-6, 6-7, and 6-8** Estimate and compute with percents.
- **Lesson 6-9** Find simple probability.

Key Vocabulary
- ratio (p. 264)
- rate (p. 265)
- proportion (p. 270)
- percent (p. 281)
- probability (p. 310)

Why It's Important

The concept of proportionality is the foundation of many branches of mathematics, including geometry, statistics, and business math. Proportions can be used to solve real-world problems dealing with scale drawings, indirect measurement, predictions, and money. *You will solve a problem about currency exchange rates in Lesson 6-2.*

262 Chapter 6 Ratio, Proportion, and Percent

Lesson	NCTM Standards	Local Objectives
6-1	1, 2, 4, 9, 10	
6-2	1, 2, 4, 6, 9, 10	
6-2 Follow-Up	1,2,4,5,6,8,9,10	
6-3	1, 2, 4, 6, 9, 10	
6-4	1, 9, 10	
6-5 Preview	1, 3, 4, 7, 9, 10	
6-5	1, 2, 6, 7, 8, 9, 10	
6-6	1, 6, 8, 9	
6-7	1, 2, 6, 9, 10	
6-7 Follow-Up	1, 5, 6, 8, 9, 10	
6-8	1, 2, 3, 6, 9, 10	
6-9 Preview	1, 2, 5, 6, 8, 9, 10	
6-9	1, 2, 5, 9, 10	
6-9 Follow-Up	1, 2, 5, 9, 10	

Key to NCTM Standards:

1=Number & Operations, 2=Algebra, 3=Geometry, 4=Measurement, 5=Data Analysis & Probability, 6=Problem Solving, 7=Reasoning & Proof, 8=Communication, 9=Connections, 10=Representation

Vocabulary Builder

(ELL)

The Key Vocabulary list introduces students to some of the main vocabulary terms included in this chapter. For a more thorough vocabulary list with pronunciations of new words, give students the Vocabulary Builder worksheets found on pages vii and viii of the *Chapter 6 Resource Masters*. Encourage them to complete the definition of each term as they progress through the chapter. You may suggest that they add these sheets to their study notebooks for future reference when studying for the Chapter 6 test.

Getting Started

▶ **Prerequisite Skills** To be successful in this chapter, you'll need to master these skills and be able to apply them in problem-solving situations. Review these skills before beginning Chapter 6.

For Lesson 6-1   **Convert Measurements**

Complete each sentence. *(For review, see pages 718–721.)*

1. 2 ft = _?_ in. **24**   **2.** 4 yd = _?_ ft **12**   **3.** 2 mi = _?_ ft **10,560**

4. 3 h = _?_ min **180**   **5.** 8 min = _?_ s **480**   **6.** 4 lb = _?_ oz **64**

7. 2 T = _?_ lb **4000**   **8.** 5 gal = _?_ qt **20**   **9.** 3 pt = _?_ c **6**

10. 3 m = _?_ cm **300**   **11.** 5.8 m = _?_ cm **580**   **12.** 2 km = _?_ m **2000**

13. 5 cm = _?_ mm **50**   **14.** 2.3 L = _?_ mL **2300**   **15.** 15 kg = _?_ g **15,000**

For Lessons 6-2 and 6-3   **Multiply Decimals**

Find each product. *(For review, see page 715.)*

16. 7(3.4) **23.8**   **17.** 6.1(8) **48.8**   **18.** 2.8×5.9 **16.52**   **19.** 1.6×8.4 **13.44**

20. 0.8×9.3 **7.44**   **21.** 0.6(0.3) **0.18**   **22.** 12.4(3.8) **47.12**   **23.** 15.2×0.2 **3.04**

For Lesson 6-9   **Write Fractions in Simplest Form**

Simplify each fraction. If the fraction is already in simplest form, write *simplified*.

(For review, see Lesson 4-5.)

24. $\frac{4}{8}$ **$\frac{1}{2}$**   **25.** $\frac{5}{15}$ **$\frac{1}{3}$**   **26.** $\frac{6}{10}$ **$\frac{3}{5}$**   **27.** $\frac{12}{25}$ **simplified**

28. $\frac{22}{20}$ **$\frac{11}{10}$**   **29.** $\frac{15}{16}$ **simplified**   **30.** $\frac{36}{42}$ **$\frac{6}{7}$**   **31.** $\frac{36}{48}$ **$\frac{3}{4}$**

FOLDABLES™ Study Organizer

Fractions, Decimals, and Percents Make this Foldable to help you organize your notes. Begin with a piece of notebook paper.

Step 1   **Fold in Thirds**

Fold in thirds lengthwise.

Step 2   **Label**

Draw lines along folds and label as shown.

Fraction	Decimal	Percent

Reading and Writing As you read and study the chapter, complete the table with the commonly-used fraction, decimal, and percent equivalents.

This section provides a review of the basic concepts needed before beginning Chapter 6. Page references are included for additional student help.

Additional review is provided in the *Prerequisite Skills Workbook*, pages 15–18 and 37–40.

Prerequisite Skills in the Getting Ready for the Next Lesson section at the end of each lesson reviews a skill needed in the next lesson.

For Lesson	Prerequisite Skill
6-2	Solving Equations (p. 268)
6-3	Converting Measurements (p. 274)
6-4	Simplest Form (p. 280)
6-5	Proportions (p. 285)
6-6	Multiplying Fractions (p. 292)
6-7	Solving Equations (p. 297)
6-8	Writing Decimals as Percents (p. 302)
6-9	Writing Fractions as Percents (p. 308)

FOLDABLES™ Study Organizer

For more information about Foldables, see *Teaching Mathematics with Foldables.*

Using Charts to Compare and Contrast Students can use their Foldables to take notes, define terms, and record concepts about fractions, decimals, and percentages. Encourage students to record daily examples of how they use fractions, decimals, and percent, such as telling time, making change, eating a whole sandwich, and walking a quarter of a mile. Use the back of the Foldable if necessary.

1 Focus

5-Minute Check Transparency 6-1 Use as a quiz or review of Chapter 5.

Mathematical Background notes are available for this lesson on page 262C.

How are ratios used in paint mixtures?

The opening activity questions are repeated on page 302 of the *Chapter 6 Resource Masters*.

Reading to Learn Mathematics, p. 302 **ELL**

Pre-Activity *How are ratios used in paint mixtures?*

Do the activity at the top of page 264 in your textbook. Write your answers below.

a. Which combination of paint would you use to make a smaller amount of the same shade of paint? Explain. **Combination B; It has the same ratio as the original mixture but in a smaller amount.**

b. Suppose you want to make the same shade of paint as the original mixture. How many parts of yellow paint should you use for each part of blue paint? **For each part of blue paint, 2 parts yellow paint should be used.**

Reading the Lesson 1–3. See students' work.

Write a definition and give an example of each new vocabulary word or phrase.

Vocabulary	Definition	Example
1. ratio		
2. rate		
3. unit rate		

4. What is the difference between a ratio that compares measurements and a rate? **The units of measure in a ratio that compares two measurements must have the same unit of measure. A rate is a comparison of two measurements having different kinds of units.**

Helping You Remember

5. The word *rate* is part of the term *unit rate*. Explain how a rate can be written as a unit rate. **Simplify the rate so it has a denominator of 1.**

Teaching Tip Students can use two-color counters to model ratios in this lesson.

 NEW YORK *Performance Indicator* **Reinforcement of 6.N.8** Distinguish the difference between rate and ratio

What You'll Learn

- Write ratios as fractions in simplest form.
- Determine unit rates.

Vocabulary
- ratio
- rate
- unit rate

a. Combination B; It has the same ratio as the original mixture but in a smaller amount.

b. For each part of blue paint, 2 parts yellow paint should be used.

How are ratios used in paint mixtures?

The diagram shows a gallon of paint that is made using 2 parts blue paint and 4 parts yellow paint.

a. Which combination of paint would you use to make a smaller amount of the same shade of paint? Explain.

Combination A   Combination B

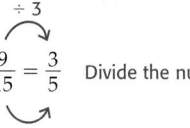

b. Suppose you want to make the same shade of paint as the original mixture? How many parts of yellow paint should you use for each part of blue paint?

WRITE RATIOS AS FRACTIONS IN SIMPLEST FORM

A **ratio** is a comparison of two numbers by division. If a gallon of paint contains 2 parts blue paint and 4 parts yellow paint, then the ratio comparing the blue paint to the yellow paint can be written as follows.

$$2 \text{ to } 4 \qquad\qquad 2{:}4 \qquad\qquad \frac{2}{4}$$

Recall that a fraction bar represents division. When the first number being compared is less than the second, the ratio is usually written as a fraction in simplest form.

The GCF of 2 and 4 is 2. → $\dfrac{2}{4} = \dfrac{1}{2}$ ← The simplest form of $\frac{2}{4}$ is $\frac{1}{2}$.

Study Tip

Look Back

To review how to write a fraction in **simplest form**, see Lesson 4-5.

Example 1 Write Ratios as Fractions

Express the ratio *9 goldfish out of 15 fish* as a fraction in simplest form.

$$\frac{9}{15} = \frac{3}{5}$$ Divide the numerator and denominator by the GCF, 3.

The ratio of goldfish to fish is 3 to 5. This means that for every 5 fish, 3 of them are goldfish.

Resource Manager

📂 Workbooks and Reproducible Masters

Chapter 6 Resource Masters
- Study Guide and Intervention, p. 299
- Skills Practice, p. 300
- Practice, p. 301
- Reading to Learn Mathematics, p. 302
- Enrichment, p. 303

Parent and Student Study Guide Workbook, p. 44
Prerequisite Skills Workbook, pp. 39–40

📺 Transparencies
5-Minute Check Transparency 6-1
Answer Key Transparencies

💿 Technology
Interactive Chalkboard
Pre-AlgePASS: Tutorial Plus, Lessons 12 and 13

When writing a ratio involving measurements, both quantities should have the same unit of measure.

Example 2 *Write Ratios as Fractions*

Express the ratio *3 feet to 16 inches* **as a fraction in simplest form.**

3 ft

16 in.

$$\frac{3 \text{ feet}}{16 \text{ inches}} = \frac{36 \text{ inches}}{16 \text{ inches}} \quad \text{Convert 3 feet to inches.}$$

$$= \frac{9 \text{ inches}}{4 \text{ inches}} \quad \text{Divide the numerator and denominator by the GCF, 4.}$$

Written in simplest form, the ratio is 9 to 4.

✓ **Concept Check** Give an example of a ratio in simplest form.
Sample answer: 2 to 3

FIND UNIT RATES A **rate** is a ratio of two measurements having different kinds of units. Here are two examples of rates.

Miles and hours are different kinds of units.	Dollars and pounds are different kinds of units.

65 miles in 3 hours $16 for 2 pounds

When a rate is simplified so that it has a denominator of 1, it is called a **unit rate**. An example of a unit rate is $5 per pound, which means $5 per 1 pound.

Example 3 *Find Unit Rate*

SHOPPING A package of 20 recordable CDs costs $18, and a package of 30 recordable CDs costs $28. Which package has the lower cost per CD?

Find and compare the unit rates of the packages.

$$\frac{18 \text{ dollars}}{20 \text{ CDs}} = \frac{0.9 \text{ dollars}}{1 \text{ CD}} \quad \text{Divide the numerator and denominator by 20 to get a denominator of 1.}$$

For the 20-pack, the unit rate is $0.90 per CD.

$$\frac{28 \text{ dollars}}{30 \text{ CDs}} = \frac{0.9\overline{3} \text{ dollars}}{1 \text{ CD}} \quad \text{Divide the numerator and denominator by 30 to get a denominator of 1.}$$

For the 30-pack, the unit rate is $0.93 per CD.

So, the package that contains 20 CDs has the lower cost per CD.

✓ **Concept Check** Is $50 in 3 days a rate or a unit rate? Explain.

www.pre-alg.com/extra_examples/ny

Lesson 6-1 Ratios and Rates **265**

Concept Check: Since the ratio does not have a denominator of 1, it is a rate.

---

2 Teach

WRITE RATIOS AS FRACTIONS IN SIMPLEST FORM

In-Class Examples Power Point®

1 Express the ratio *10 roses out of 12 flowers* as a fraction in simplest form. $\frac{5}{6}$

2 Express the ratio *21 inches to 2 yards* as a fraction in simplest form. $\frac{7}{24}$

Teaching Tip Watch for students who use subtraction instead of division to simplify ratios.

✓ **Skills Check**

Write Ratios as Fractions in Simplest Form A class consists of 12 girls and 16 boys. Express the ratio of boys to total students as a fraction in simplest form. $\frac{4}{7}$

FIND UNIT RATES

In-Class Example Power Point®

3 **SHOPPING** A 12-oz bottle of cleaner costs $4.50. A 16-oz bottle of cleaner costs $6.56. Which costs less per ounce? **12-oz bottle. $ 0.38; 16-oz bottle: $ 0.41; The 12-oz bottle costs less.**

Teaching Tip Suggest that students use dimensional analysis to keep them from switching the divisor and dividend when finding unit prices.

Interactive Chalkboard
PowerPoint® Presentations

This CD-ROM is a customizable Microsoft® Power-Point® presentation that includes:
• Step-by-step, dynamic solutions of each In-Class Example from the Teacher Wraparound Edition
• Additional, Your Turn exercises for each example
• The 5-Minute Check Transparencies
• Hot links to Glencoe Online Study Tools

4 ANIMALS A snail moved 30 feet in 2 hours. How many inches per minute did the snail move? **3 in./min**

Study Tip

Look Back
To review **dimensional analysis,** see Lesson 5-3.

3 Practice/Apply

Study Notebook

Have students—

• add the definitions/examples of the vocabulary terms to their Vocabulary Builder worksheets for Chapter 6.

• write a paragraph describing a situation in which using a unit price would be helpful to them.

• include any other item(s) that they find helpful in mastering the skills in this lesson.

About the Exercises . . .

Organization by Objective
• **Write Ratios as Fractions in Simplest Form:** 16–27
• **Find Unit Rates:** 28–37, 46–48

Odd/Even Assignments
Exercises 16–45 are structured so that students practice the same concepts whether they are assigned odd or even problems.

Alert! Exercise 46 involves research on the Internet or other reference materials.

Assignment Guide

Basic: 17–23 odd, 29–33 odd, 37–43 odd, 47–52, 54–70

Average: 17–45 odd, 47–52, 54–70 (Optional: 53)

Advanced: 16–44 even, 47–64 (Optional: 65–70)

To convert a rate such as miles per hour to a rate such as feet per second, you can use dimensional analysis. Recall that this is the process of carrying units throughout a computation.

Example 4 *Convert Rates*

ANIMALS A grizzly bear can run 30 miles in 1 hour. How many feet is this per second?

You need to convert $\frac{30 \text{ mi}}{1 \text{ h}}$ to $\frac{\blacksquare \text{ ft}}{1 \text{ s}}$. There are 5280 feet in 1 mile and 3600 seconds in 1 hour. Write 30 miles per hour as $\frac{30 \text{ mi}}{1 \text{ h}}$.

$$\frac{30 \text{ mi}}{1 \text{ h}} = \frac{30 \text{ mi}}{1 \text{ h}} \cdot \frac{5280 \text{ ft}}{1 \text{ mi}} \div \frac{3600 \text{ s}}{1 \text{ h}}$$ Convert miles to feet and hours to seconds.

$$= \frac{30 \text{ mi}}{1 \text{ h}} \cdot \frac{5280 \text{ ft}}{1 \text{ mi}} \cdot \frac{1 \text{ h}}{3600 \text{ s}}$$ The reciprocal of $\frac{3600 \text{ s}}{1 \text{ h}}$ is $\frac{1 \text{ h}}{3600 \text{ s}}$.

$$= \frac{\overset{1}{\cancel{30 \text{ mi}}}}{1 \cancel{\text{ h}}} \cdot \frac{\overset{44}{\cancel{5280 \text{ ft}}}}{1 \cancel{\text{ mi}}} \cdot \frac{1 \cancel{\text{ h}}}{\underset{120}{\cancel{3600 \text{ s}}}}$$ Divide the common factors and units.

$$= \frac{44 \text{ ft}}{\text{s}}$$ Simplify.

So, 30 miles per hour is equivalent to 44 feet per second.

Check for Understanding

Concept Check

1. **Draw** a diagram in which the ratio of circles to squares is 2:3.

2. **Explain** the difference between ratio and rate. **1–3. See pp. 323A–323B.**

3. **OPEN ENDED** Give an example of a unit rate.

Guided Practice

Express each ratio as a fraction in simplest form. **4–11. See pp. 323A–323B.**

4. 4 goals in 10 attempts
5. 15 dimes out of 24 coins
6. 10 inches to 3 feet
7. 5 feet to 5 yards

GUIDED PRACTICE KEY

Exercises	Examples
4–7	1, 2
8–11	3
12, 13	4
14, 15	2

Express each ratio as a unit rate. Round to the nearest tenth, if necessary.

8. $183 for 4 concert tickets
9. 9 inches of snow in 12 hours
10. 100 feet in 14.5 seconds
11. 254.1 miles on 10.5 gallons

Convert each rate using dimensional analysis.

12. 20 mi/h = ■ ft/min **1760**
13. 16 cm/s = ■ m/h **576**

Application

GEOMETRY For Exercises 14 and 15, refer to the figure below.

14. Express the ratio of width to length as a fraction in simplest form. $\frac{3}{5}$

15. Suppose the width and length are each increased by 2 centimeters. Will the ratio of the width to length be the same as the ratio of the width to length of the original rectangle? Explain. **No; the ratio will be 2 to 3.**

6 cm

10 cm

DAILY
INTERVENTION **Differentiated Instruction**

• **Visual/Spatial** Have students bring advertisements and coupons from newspapers and magazines. Ask them to explain the different ways ratios are used in the ads or coupons. Then have them work together to make a collage of the ads or coupons. Encourage them to highlight the ratios and to include some math problems based on the ratios.

★ indicates increased difficulty
Practice and Apply

Homework Help

For Exercises	See Examples
16–27	1, 2
28–37	3
38–45	4
46, 47	3

Extra Practice
See page 736.

Express each ratio as a fraction in simplest form. 16–35. See pp. 323A–323B.

16. 6 ladybugs out of 27 insects

17. 14 girls to 35 boys

18. 18 cups to 45 cups

19. 12 roses out of 28 flowers

20. 7 cups to 9 pints

21. 9 pounds to 16 tons

22. 11 gallons to 11 quarts

23. 18 miles to 18 yards

★ 24. 15 dollars out of 123 dollars

★ 25. 17 rubies out of 118 gems

★ 26. 155 apples to 75 oranges

★ 27. 321 articles in 107 magazines

Express each ratio as a unit rate. Round to the nearest tenth, if necessary.

28. $3 for 6 cans of tuna

29. $0.99 for 10 pencils

30. 140 miles on 6 gallons

31. 68 meters in 15 seconds

32. 19 yards in 2.5 minutes

33. 25 feet in 3.2 hours

★ 34. 236.7 miles in 4.5 days

★ 35. 331.5 pages in 8.5 weeks

36. **MAGAZINES** Which costs more per issue, an 18-issue subscription for $40.50 or a 12-issue subscription for $33.60? Explain.
36–37. See pp. 323A–323B.

37. **SHOPPING** Determine which is less expensive per can, a 6-pack of soda for $2.20 or a 12-pack of soda for $4.25. Explain.

Convert each rate using dimensional analysis.

38. 45 mi/h = ■ ft/s **66**

39. 18 mi/h = ■ ft/s **26.4**

40. 26 cm/s = ■ m/min **15.6**

41. 32 cm/s = ■ m/min **19.2**

42. 2.5 qt/min = ■ gal/h **37.5**

43. 4.8 qt/min = ■ gal/h **72**

★ 44. 4 c/min = ■ qt/h **60**

★ 45. 7 c/min = ■ qt/h **105**

46. **POPULATION** Population density is a unit rate that gives the number of people per square mile. Find the population density for each state listed in the table at the right. Round to the nearest whole number. **See pp. 323A–323B.**

State	Population (2000)	Area (sq mi)
Alaska	626,932	570,374
New York	18,976,457	47,224
Rhode Island	1,048,319	1045
Texas	20,851,820	261,914
Wyoming	493,782	97,105

Source: U.S. Census Bureau

 Online Research Data Update How has the population density of the states in the table changed since 2000? Visit www.pre-alg.com/data_update to learn more.

More About...

Population
In 2000, the population density of the United States was about 79.6 people per square mile.
Source: The World Almanac

TRAVEL For Exercises 47 and 48, use the following information.
An airplane flew from Boston to Chicago to Denver. The distance from Boston to Chicago was 1015 miles and the distance from Chicago to Denver was 1011 miles. The plane traveled for 3.5 hours and carried 285 passengers.

47. About how fast did the airplane travel? **about 579 mi/h**

★ 48. Suppose it costs $5685 per hour to operate the airplane. Find the cost per person per hour for the flight. **$19.95/per hour**

DAILY INTERVENTION

Unlocking Misconceptions

- **Write Ratios as Fractions** Ratios can be part:whole, whole:part, or part:part. For example, if there are 4 red marbles and 1 blue marble, ratios of color can be (a) 1:5 (ratio of blue to all) or 4:5 (ratio of red to all), (b) 5:1 (ratio of all to blue) or 5:4 (ratio of all to red), or (c) 1:4 (ratio of blue to red) or 4:1 (ratio of red to blue).

Study Guide and Intervention, p. 299

Ratios written as 7 to 12, 7:12, and $\frac{7}{12}$ are different ways to write the same ratio. Ratios should be written in simplest form.

Example 1 Express the ratio *6 feet to 15 inches* as a fraction in simplest form.

$\frac{6 \text{ feet}}{15 \text{ inches}}$ Write the ratio as a fraction.

$= \frac{72 \text{ inches}}{15 \text{ inches}}$ Convert feet to inches.

$= \frac{\overset{24}{72} \text{ inches}}{\underset{5}{15} \text{ inches}}$ Divide the numerator and denominator by the GCF, 3.

$= \frac{24}{5}$

Written as a fraction in simplest form, the ratio is 24 to 5.

Example 2 Express the ratio *$10 for 8 fish* as a unit rate. Round to the nearest tenth, if necessary.

$\frac{10 \text{ dollars}}{8 \text{ fish}}$ Write the ratio as a fraction.

$\frac{10 \text{ dollars}}{8 \text{ fish}} = \frac{1.25 \text{ dollars}}{1 \text{ fish}}$ Divide the numerator and denominator by 8 to get a denominator of 1.

The unit rate is $1.25 per fish.

Exercises

Express each ratio as a fraction in simplest form.

1. 4 weeks to plan 2 events $\frac{2}{1}$

2. 9 inches to 2 feet $\frac{3}{8}$

3. 8 teaspoons to 12 forks $\frac{2}{3}$

4. 16 cups to 10 servings $\frac{8}{5}$

5. 7 shelves to 84 books $\frac{1}{12}$

6. 6 teachers to 165 students $\frac{2}{55}$

Express each ratio as a unit rate. Round to the nearest tenth, if necessary.

7. $58 for 5 tickets   **$11.60 per 1 ticket**

8. $4.19 for 4 cans of soup   **$1.05 per can**

9. $274.90 for 6 people   **$45.82 per person**

10. 565 miles in 12 hours   **47.1 miles per hour**

Skills Practice, p. 300 and Practice, p. 301 (shown)

Express each ratio as a fraction in simplest form.

1. 56 pencils out of 64 erasers $\frac{7}{8}$

2. 25 calculators to 20 students $\frac{5}{4}$

3. 36 cassettes to 60 CDs $\frac{3}{5}$

4. 18 minnows to 27 fish $\frac{2}{3}$

5. 6 pounds to 256 ounces $\frac{3}{8}$

6. 5 hours to 720 minutes $\frac{5}{12}$

7. 9 gallons to 48 quarts $\frac{3}{4}$

8. 24 feet to 30 yards $\frac{4}{15}$

Express each ratio as a unit rate. Round to the nearest tenth, if necessary.

9. $4.60 for 5 cans of soup $0.92 per can

10. $51 for a box of 75 tiles $0.68 per tile

11. 652 miles in 9 days   72.4 miles per day

12. 116 meters in 12 seconds   9.7 meters per second

13. 176 new employees in 22 years   8 new employees per year

14. 34 yards for 6 costumes   5.7 yards per costume

15. 55 pages in 25 minutes   2.2 pages per minute

16. $3015 from 36 people $83.75 per person

Convert each rate using dimensional analysis.

17. 18 m/min = _?_ cm/s   30

18. 5.7 gal/h = _?_ c/min   1.52

19. 264 yd/s = _?_ mi/h   540

20. 2 qt/min = _?_ gal/h   30

21. 99 in./s = _?_ mi/day (1 day = 24 h)   135

22. 154 mi/h = _?_ in./s   2710.4

23. **TRACK AND FIELD** Rita sprinted 77 feet in 10 seconds. How many miles per hour is this?   5.25 miles per hour

---

Enrichment, p. 303

Comparison Shopping

Rates are useful and meaningful when expressed as a unit rate. For example, which is the better buy—one orange for $0.50 or 8 oranges for $3.49?

To find the unit rate for 8 oranges, divide $3.49 by 8. The result is $0.44 per orange. If a shopper needs to buy at least 8 oranges, then 8 oranges for $3.49 is the better buy.

For each exercise below, rates are given in Column A and Column B. In the blank next to each exercise number, write the letter of the column that contains the better buy.

		Column A	Column B
A	1.	1 apple for $0.19	3 apples for $0.59
A	2.	20 pounds of pet food for $14.99	50 pounds of pet food for $37.99
B	3.	A car that travels 308 miles on 11 gallons of gasoline	A car that travels 406 miles on 14 gallons of gasoline
B	4.	10 floppy discs for $8.99	25 floppy discs for $19.75
B	5.	1-gallon can of paint for $13.99	5-gallon can of paint for $67.45
A	6.	84 ounces of liquid detergent for $10.64	48 ounces of liquid detergent for $6.19
A	7.	5000 square feet of lawn food for $11.99	12,500 square feet of lawn food for $29.99
A	8.	2 compact discs for $26.50	3 compact discs for $40.00
A	9.	8 pencils for $0.99	12 pencils for $1.49
B	10.	1000 sheets of computer paper for $8.95	5000 sheets of computer paper for $41.99

Open-Ended Assessment

Writing Have students express the ratio of toes to elbows in simplest form and explain whether the ratio is a unit ratio.

Tips for New Teachers

Motivating Students Have students look around the room for ratios, such as desks per student, windows to doors, and so forth. Display the representations in the room for the remainder of the chapter.

Getting Ready for Lesson 6-2

PREREQUISITE SKILL Lesson 6-2 presents solving proportions, which requires students to solve equations using the Division Property of Equality. Exercises 65–70 should be used to determine your students' familiarity with solving equations.

Answers

50. Ratios are used in paint mixtures to achieve a desired color by using two or more different colors. Answers should include the following.
   - If you want a darker shade of green, use a ratio in which there is a greater amount of blue paint compared to yellow paint. An example is 3 blue to 4 yellow.
   - If you want a lighter shade of green, use a ratio in which there is a greater amount of yellow paint compared to blue paint. An example is 5 yellow to 2 blue.

---

49. **CRITICAL THINKING** Marty and Spencer each saved money earned from shoveling snow. The ratio of Marty's money to Spencer's money is 3:1. If Marty gives Spencer $3, their ratio will be 1:1. How much money did Marty earn? **$9**

50. **WRITING IN MATH** Answer the question that was posed at the beginning of the lesson. **See margin.**

   How are ratios used in paint mixtures?

   Include the following in your answer:
   - an example of a ratio of blue to yellow paint that would result in a darker shade of green, and
   - an example of a ratio of blue to yellow paint that would result in a lighter shade of green.

NEW YORK Test Practice

Standardized Test Practice
Ⓐ Ⓑ Ⓒ Ⓓ

51. Which ratio represents the same relationship as *for every 4 apples, 3 of them are green*? **C**
   - Ⓐ 9:16
   - Ⓑ 3:4
   - Ⓒ 12:9
   - Ⓓ 6:8

52. Joe paid $2.79 for a gallon of milk. Find the cost per quart of milk. **A**
   - Ⓐ $0.70
   - Ⓑ $1.40
   - Ⓒ $0.93
   - Ⓓ $0.55

Extending the Lesson

53. Many objects such as credit cards or phone cards are shaped like golden rectangles. **a–c. See margin.**

   a. Find three different objects that are close to a golden rectangle. Make a table to display the dimensions and the ratio found in each object.

   b. Describe how each ratio compares to the golden ratio.

   c. **RESEARCH** Use the Internet or another source to find three places where the golden rectangle is used in architecture.

> A *golden rectangle* is a rectangle in which the ratio of the length to the width is approximately 1.618 to 1. This ratio is called the **golden ratio**.

Maintain Your Skills

Mixed Review

State whether each sequence is *arithmetic*, *geometric*, or *neither*. Then state the common difference or common ratio and write the next three terms of the sequence. *(Lesson 5-10)* **54–55. See margin.**

54. $-3, 6, -12, 24, \ldots$

55. $12.1, 12.4, 12.7, 13, \ldots$

ALGEBRA Solve each equation. *(Lesson 5-9)*

56. $3.6 = x - 7.1$ **10.7**

57. $y + \frac{3}{4} = \frac{2}{3} - \frac{1}{12}$ **58.** $-4.8 = 6z$ **−0.8**

59. $\frac{3}{8}w = 5$ **$13\frac{1}{3}$**

60. Find the quotient of $1\frac{1}{7}$ and $-\frac{4}{7}$. *(Lesson 5-4)* **−2**

Write each number in scientific notation. *(Lesson 4-8)*

61. 52,000,000 **5.2×10^7**

62. 42,240 **4.224×10^4**

63. 0.038 **3.8×10^{-2}**

64. Write $8 \cdot (k + 3) \cdot (k + 3)$ using exponents. *(Lesson 4-2)* **$8(k + 3)^2$**

Getting Ready for the Next Lesson

PREREQUISITE SKILL Solve each equation.
*(To review **solving equations**, see Lesson 3-4.)*

65. $10x = 300$ **30**

66. $25m = 225$ **9**

67. $8k = 320$ **40**

68. $192 = 4t$ **48**

69. $195 = 15w$ **13**

70. $231 = 33n$ **7**

---

53. a. Answers will vary.

   b. The ratios should be close in value.

   c. Sample answer: Pyramid of Khufu in Giza, Egypt; The Taj Mahal in India; The Lincoln Memorial in Washington, D.C.

54. geometric; −2; −48, 96, −192

55. arithmetic; Each term increases by 0.3; 13.3, 13.6, 13.9

Reading Mathematics

Making Comparisons

In mathematics, there are many different ways to compare numbers. Consider the information in the table.

Zoo	Size (acres)	Animals	Species
San Diego	100	4000	800
Houston	55	5000	700
Oakland	100	400	100
Columbus	400	11,000	700

The following types of comparison statements can be used to describe this information.

Difference Comparisons

• The Houston Zoo has 1000 more animals than the San Diego Zoo.
• The Columbus Zoo is 345 acres larger than the Houston Zoo.
• The Oakland Zoo has 700 less species of animals than the San Diego Zoo.

Ratio Comparisons

• The ratio of the size of the San Diego Zoo to the size of the Columbus Zoo is 1:4. So, the San Diego Zoo is one-fourth the size of the Columbus Zoo.
• The ratio of the number of animals at the San Diego Zoo to the number of animals at the Oakland Zoo is 4000:400 or 10:1. So, San Diego Zoo has ten times as many animals as the Oakland Zoo.

Reading to Learn 1–4. See margin.

1. Refer to the zoo information above. Write a difference comparison and a ratio comparison statement that describes the information.

Refer to the information below. Identify each statement as a difference comparison or a ratio comparison.

Florida
The Sunshine State
Total area: 59,928 sq mi
Land area: 53,937 sq mi
Land forested: 26,478.4 sq mi

Ohio
The Buckeye State
Total area: 44,828 sq mi
Land area: 40,953 sq mi
Land forested: 12,580.8 sq mi

Source: *The World Almanac*

2. The area of Florida is about 15,000 square miles greater than the area of Ohio.

3. The ratio of the amount of land forested in Ohio to the amount forested in Florida is about 1 to 2.

4. More than one-fourth of the land in Ohio is forested.

Reading Mathematics Making Comparisons **269**

Answers

1. Sample answer: difference comparison: The Houston Zoo has 6000 fewer animals than the Columbus Zoo; ratio comparison: The ratio of the size of the San Diego Zoo to the Houston Zoo is 100:55 or 20:11. The San Diego Zoo is about twice the size of the Houston Zoo.

2. difference comparison

3. ratio comparison

4. ratio comparison

1 Focus

What You'll Learn

- Solve proportions.
- Use proportions to solve real-world problems.

5-Minute Check Transparency 6-2 Use as a quiz or review of Lesson 6-1.

Mathematical Background notes are available for this lesson on page 262C.

How are proportions used in recipes?

The opening activity questions are repeated on page 307 of the *Chapter 6 Resource Masters.*

Vocabulary

- proportion
- cross products

a. lemonade: $\frac{1}{7}$;

grape juice: $\frac{1}{7}$;

orange juice: $\frac{1}{7}$;

lemon-lime soda: $\frac{10}{21}$

b. same as part a

c. Yes; each part was multiplied by the same number.

How are proportions used in recipes?

For many years, Phyllis Norman was famous in her neighborhood for making her flavorful fruit punch.

a. For each of the first four ingredients, write a ratio that compares the number of ounces of each ingredient to the number of ounces of water.

b. Double the recipe. Write a ratio for the ounces of each of the first four ingredients to the ounces of water as a fraction in simplest form.

c. Are the ratios in parts **a** and **b** the same? Why or why not?

Fruit Punch

12 oz frozen lemonade concentrate
12 oz frozen grape juice concentrate
12 oz frozen orange juice concentrate
40 oz lemon-lime soda
84 oz water
Yields: 160 oz of punch

PROPORTIONS To solve problems that relate to ratios, you can use a proportion. A **proportion** is a statement of equality of two ratios.

Key Concept   Proportion

- **Words**   A proportion is an equation stating that two ratios are equal.
- **Symbols** $\frac{a}{b} = \frac{c}{d}$ **Example** $\frac{2}{3} = \frac{6}{9}$

Consider the following proportion.

$$\frac{a}{b} = \frac{c}{d}$$

$$\frac{a}{b} \cdot bd = \frac{c}{d} \cdot bd \quad \text{Multiply each side by } bd \text{ to eliminate the fractions.}$$

$$ad = cb \qquad \text{Simplify.}$$

The products ad and cb are called the **cross products** of a proportion. Every proportion has two cross products.

Reading to Learn Mathematics, p. 307   ELL

Pre-Activity *How are proportions used in recipes?*

Do the activity at the top of page 270 in your textbook. Write your answers below.

a. For each of the first four ingredients, write a ratio that compares the number of ounces of each ingredient to the number of ounces of water.
lemonade: $\frac{1}{7}$; grape juice: $\frac{1}{7}$; orange juice: $\frac{1}{7}$; lemon-lime soda: $\frac{10}{21}$

b. Double the recipe. (*Hint:* Multiply each number of ounces by 2.) Then write a ratio for the ounces of each of the first four ingredients to the ounces of water in simplest form.
lemonade: $\frac{1}{7}$; grape juice: $\frac{1}{7}$; orange juice: $\frac{1}{7}$; lemon-lime soda: $\frac{10}{21}$

c. Are the ratios in parts **a** and **b** the same? Why or why not?
Yes; each part was multiplied by the same number.

Reading the Lesson   1–2. See students' work.

Write a definition and give an example of each new vocabulary word or phrase.

Vocabulary	Definition	Example
1. proportion		
2. cross products		

3. Do $\frac{3}{5}$ and $\frac{12}{20}$ form a proportion? Explain.   Yes; both cross products are 60.

4. Write a ratio that forms a proportion with $\frac{3}{4}$. Sample answer: $\frac{9}{12}$

Helping You Remember

5. *Proportion* is a common word in the English language.

a. Write its definition.   relation of parts to each other or to the whole

b. How does this definition relate to the one given on page 270 of your textbook?
A proportion is an equation that states how two ratios relate to each other.

c. Explain how cross products are used to solve a proportion.   First find the cross products and write an equation to show that they are equal. Then solve the equation.

Study Tip

Properties
When you multiply each side of an equation by bd, you are using the Multiplication Property of Equality.

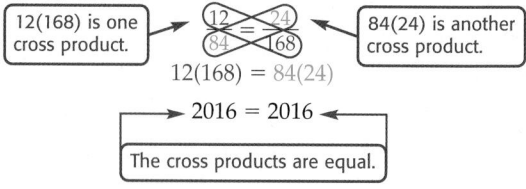

12(168) is one cross product.

$\frac{12}{84} = \frac{24}{168}$

84(24) is another cross product.

$12(168) = 84(24)$

$2016 = 2016$

The cross products are equal.

Teaching Tip Emphasize that adding or subtracting the same number to the numerator and denominator of a fraction changes the ratio.

✓ **Concept Check** Write a proportion whose cross products are equal to 18.
Sample answer: $\frac{2}{6}$ and $\frac{3}{9}$

Resource Manager

Workbooks and Reproducible Masters

Chapter 6 Resource Masters
- Study Guide and Intervention, p. 304
- Skills Practice, p. 305
- Practice, p. 306
- Reading to Learn Mathematics, p. 307
- Enrichment, p. 308

Parent and Student Study Guide Workbook, p. 45
Prerequisite Skills Workbook, pp. 37–40
School-to-Career Masters, p. 11

Transparencies
5–Minute Check Transparency 6-2
Answer Key Transparencies

 Technology
Interactive Chalkboard
Pre-AlgePASS: Tutorial Plus, Lesson 14

Cross products can be used to determine whether two ratios form a proportion.

Example 1   *Identify Proportions*

Determine whether each pair of ratios forms a proportion.

a. $\frac{1}{3}, \frac{3}{9}$

$\quad \frac{1}{3} \overset{?}{=} \frac{3}{9}$ Write a proportion.

$\quad 1 \cdot 9 \overset{?}{=} 3 \cdot 3$ Cross products

$\quad\quad 9 = 9$ Simplify.

So, $\frac{1}{3} = \frac{3}{9}$.

b. $\frac{1.2}{4.0}, \frac{2}{5}$

$\quad \frac{1.2}{4.0} \overset{?}{=} \frac{2}{5}$ Write a proportion.

$\quad 1.2 \cdot 5 \overset{?}{=} 4.0 \cdot 2$ Cross products

$\quad\quad 6 \neq 8$ Simplify.

So, $\frac{1.2}{4.0} \neq \frac{2}{5}$.

Example 2   *Solve Proportions*

Solve each proportion.

a. $\frac{a}{25} = \frac{52}{100}$

$\quad \frac{a}{25} = \frac{52}{100}$

$\quad a \cdot 100 = 25 \cdot 52$ Cross products

$\quad 100a = 1300$ Multiply.

$\quad \frac{100a}{100} = \frac{1300}{100}$ Divide.

$\quad a = 13$

The solution is 13.

b. $\frac{12.5}{m} = \frac{15}{7.5}$

$\quad \frac{12.5}{m} = \frac{15}{7.5}$

$\quad 12.5 \cdot 7.5 = m \cdot 15$ Cross products

$\quad 93.75 = 15m$ Multiply.

$\quad \frac{93.75}{15} = \frac{15m}{15}$ Divide.

$\quad 6.25 = m$

The solution is 6.25.

> **Study Tip**
>
> **Cross Products**
> When you find cross products, you are *cross multiplying*.

USE PROPORTIONS TO SOLVE REAL-WORLD PROBLEMS   When you solve a problem using a proportion, be sure to compare the quantities in the same order.

Example 3   *Use a Proportion to Solve a Problem*

FOOD   Refer to the recipe at the beginning of the lesson. How much soda should be used if 16 ounces of each type of juice are used?

Explore   You know how much soda to use for 12 ounces of each type of juice. You need to find how much soda to use for 16 ounces of each type of juice.

Plan   Write and solve a proportion using ratios that compare juice to soda. Let *s* represent the amount of soda to use in the new recipe.

(continued on the next page)

 www.pre-alg.com/extra_examples/ny   **Lesson 6-2** Using Proportions   **271**

---

2 Teach

PROPORTIONS

In-Class Examples Power Point®

1 Determine whether each pair of ratios forms a proportion.

a. $\frac{2}{3}, \frac{12}{20}$ $\frac{2}{3} \neq \frac{12}{20}$

b. $\frac{0.8}{3.2}, \frac{2}{8}$ $\frac{0.8}{3.2} = \frac{2}{8}$

2 Solve each proportion.

a. $\frac{c}{36} = \frac{9}{15}$ $c = 21.6$

b. $\frac{16}{v} = \frac{4.8}{1.5}$ $v = 5$

Teaching Tip Frequently remind students to check their answer by substituting it into the original proportion.

✓ Skills Check

Solve Proportions Ask students how they know which number to divide by after they have written the cross products. **Divide by the coefficient of the variable.**

USE PROPORTIONS TO SOLVE REAL-WORLD PROBLEMS

In-Class Example Power Point®

3 **ARCHITECTURE** An architect builds a model of a building before the actual building is built. The model is 8 inches tall and the actual building will be 22 feet tall. The model is 20 inches wide. Find the width of the actual building. **55 ft**

Teacher to Teacher

Barbara Cain   Thomas Jefferson M.S., Merritt Island, FL

"When we multiply a decimal by another number using a multiplication dot in my classroom, we usually put the decimal number in parentheses. This helps to avoid confusion in a handwritten problem with two different uses of the dot."

In-Class Example ··· Power Point®

4 **ATTRACTIONS** The Circleville Pumpkin Show in Circleville, Ohio, boasts the world's largest pumpkin pie. The pie weighs 350 pounds and is 5 feet in diameter. Find the diameter of the pie in centimeters if 1 ft = 30.48 cm. **152.4 cm**

3 Practice/Apply

Study Notebook

Have students—

• add the definitions/examples of the vocabulary terms to their Vocabulary Builder worksheets for Chapter 6.

• include any other item(s) that they find helpful in mastering the skills in this lesson.

About the Exercises . . .

Organization by Objective
• **Proportions:** 9–31
• **Use Proportions to Solve Real-World Problems:** 32–42, 45

Odd/Even Assignments
Exercises 9–35 are structured so that students practice the same concepts whether they are assigned odd or even problems.

Assignment Guide

Basic: 9–25 odd, 33, 35–37, 39, 41, 43–55

Average: 9–35 odd, 36–37, 39, 41, 43–55

Advanced: 10–34 even, 38–51 (Optional: 52–55)

TEACHING TIP

You can also solve the problem by comparing soda to juice.

$$\frac{\text{soda in original}}{\text{juice in original}} = \frac{\text{soda in new}}{\text{juice in new}}$$

More About. . .

Attractions

The world's largest baseball bat is located in Louisville, Kentucky. It is 120 feet long, has a diameter from 3.5 to 9 feet, and weighs 68,000 pounds.

Source: World's Largest Roadside Attractions

Solve $\dfrac{\text{juice in original recipe}}{\text{soda in original recipe}} = \dfrac{\text{juice in new recipe}}{\text{soda in new recipe}}$

$\dfrac{12}{40} = \dfrac{16}{s}$ Write a proportion.

$12 \cdot s = 40 \cdot 16$ Cross products

$12s = 640$ Multiply.

$\dfrac{12s}{12} = \dfrac{640}{12}$ Divide.

$s = 53\frac{1}{3}$ Simplify.

$53\frac{1}{3}$ ounces of soda should be used.

Examine Check the cross products. Since $12 \cdot 53\frac{1}{3} = 640$ and $40 \cdot 16 = 640$, the answer is correct.

Proportions can also be used in measurement problems.

Example **4** **Convert Measurements**

ATTRACTIONS Louisville, Kentucky, is home to the world's largest baseball glove. The glove is 4 feet high, 10 feet long, 9 feet wide, and weighs 15 tons. Find the height of the glove in centimeters if 1 ft = 30.48 cm.

Let x represent the height in centimeters.

customary measurement → $\dfrac{1 \text{ ft}}{30.48 \text{ cm}} = \dfrac{4 \text{ ft}}{x \text{ cm}}$ ← customary measurement
metric measurement →   ← metric measurement

$1 \cdot x = 30.48 \cdot 4$ Cross products

$x = 121.92$ Simplify.

The height of the glove is 121.92 centimeters.

Check for Understanding

Concept Check 1. **Define** *proportion.* **1–2. See margin.**

2. **OPEN ENDED** Find two counterexamples for the statement *Two ratios always form a proportion.*

Guided Practice

GUIDED PRACTICE KEY	
Exercises	Examples
3, 4	1
5–7	2
8	3, 4

Determine whether each pair of ratios forms a proportion.

3. $\dfrac{1}{4}, \dfrac{4}{16}$ **yes**

4. $\dfrac{2.1}{3.5}, \dfrac{3}{7}$ **no**

ALGEBRA Solve each proportion.

5. $\dfrac{k}{35} = \dfrac{3}{7}$ **15**

6. $\dfrac{3}{t} = \dfrac{18}{24}$ **4**

7. $\dfrac{10}{8.4} = \dfrac{5}{m}$ **4.2**

Application 8. **PHOTOGRAPHY** A 3″ × 5″ photo is enlarged so that the length of the new photo is 7 inches. Find the width of the new photo. $4\frac{1}{5}$ **in.**

272   Chapter 6   Ratio, Proportion, and Percent

Answers

1. A statement of equality of two ratios.

2. Sample answer: $\dfrac{2}{3} = \dfrac{3}{4}$; $\dfrac{1}{2} = \dfrac{1}{4}$

Practice and Apply

Homework Help

For Exercises	See Examples
9–14	1
15–31	2
32–35, 36–42	3, 4

Extra Practice
See page 737.

Determine whether each pair of ratios forms a proportion.

9. $\dfrac{2}{3}, \dfrac{8}{12}$ **yes**

10. $\dfrac{4}{2}, \dfrac{16}{5}$ **no**

11. $\dfrac{1.5}{5.0}, \dfrac{3}{9}$ **no**

12. $\dfrac{18}{2.4}, \dfrac{15}{2}$ **yes**

13. $\dfrac{3.4}{1.6}, \dfrac{5.1}{2.4}$ **yes**

14. $\dfrac{5.3}{15.9}, \dfrac{2.7}{8.1}$ **yes**

ALGEBRA Solve each proportion.

15. $\dfrac{p}{6} = \dfrac{24}{36}$ **4**

16. $\dfrac{w}{11} = \dfrac{14}{22}$ **7**

17. $\dfrac{4}{10} = \dfrac{8}{a}$ **20**

18. $\dfrac{18}{12} = \dfrac{24}{q}$ **16**

19. $\dfrac{5}{h} = \dfrac{10}{30}$ **15**

20. $\dfrac{51}{z} = \dfrac{17}{7}$ **21**

21. $\dfrac{7}{45} = \dfrac{x}{9}$ **1.4**

22. $\dfrac{2}{15} = \dfrac{c}{72}$ **9.6**

23. $\dfrac{7}{5} = \dfrac{10.5}{b}$ **7.5**

24. $\dfrac{16}{7} = \dfrac{4.8}{h}$ **2.1**

25. $\dfrac{2}{9.4} = \dfrac{0.2}{v}$ **0.94**

26. $\dfrac{9}{7.2} = \dfrac{3.5}{k}$ **2.8**

★ 27. $\dfrac{a}{0.28} = \dfrac{4}{1.4}$ **0.8**

★ 28. $\dfrac{3}{14} = \dfrac{15}{m-3}$ **73**

★ 29. $\dfrac{16}{x+5} = \dfrac{4}{5}$ **15**

★ 30. Find the value of d that makes $\dfrac{5.1}{1.7} = \dfrac{7.5}{d}$ a proportion. **2.5**

★ 31. What value of m makes $\dfrac{6.5}{1.3} = \dfrac{m}{5.2}$ a proportion? **26**

Write a proportion that could be used to solve for each variable. Then solve.

33. $\dfrac{12}{3} = \dfrac{72}{m}$; **18**

32. 8 pencils in 2 boxes
20 pencils in x boxes $\dfrac{8}{2} = \dfrac{20}{x}$; **5**

33. 12 glasses in 3 crates
72 glasses in m crates

34. y dollars for 5.4 gallons
14 dollars for 3 gallons
$\dfrac{y}{5.4} = \dfrac{14}{3}$; **$25.20**

35. 5 quarts for $6.25
d quarts for $8.75 $\dfrac{5}{6.25} = \dfrac{d}{8.75}$; **7**

OLYMPICS For Exercises 36 and 37, use the following information.
There are approximately 3.28 feet in 1 meter.

36. Write a proportion that could be used to find the distance in feet of the 110-meter dash. $\dfrac{1\text{ m}}{3.28\text{ ft}} = \dfrac{110\text{ m}}{x\text{ ft}}$

37. What is the distance in feet of the 110-meter dash? **about 360.8 ft**

38. **PHOTOGRAPHY** Suppose an 8″ × 10″ photo is reduced so that the width of the new photo is 4.5 inches. What is the length of the new photo? **$5\dfrac{5}{8}$ in.**

CURRENCY For Exercises 39 and 40, use the following information and the table shown.
The table shows the exchange rates for certain countries compared to the U.S. dollar on a given day.

Country	Rate
United Kingdom	0.667
Egypt	3.481
Australia	1.712
China	8.280

39. What is the cost of an item in U.S. dollars if it costs 14.99 in British pounds? **$22.47**

40. Find the cost of an item in U.S. dollars if it costs 12.50 in Egyptian pounds. **$3.59**

Study Guide and Intervention, p. 304

A **proportion** is an equation stating that two ratios are equal. You can use cross products to solve a proportion.

Example Solve the proportion $\dfrac{14.1}{c} = \dfrac{3}{4}$.

$\dfrac{14.1}{c} = \dfrac{3}{4}$

$14.1 \cdot 4 = c \cdot 3$ Cross products.

$56.4 = 3c$ Multiply.

$\dfrac{56.4}{3} = \dfrac{3c}{3}$ Divide.

$18.8 = c$

The solution is 18.8.

Exercises

ALGEBRA Solve each proportion.

1. $\dfrac{x}{9} = \dfrac{16}{12}$ 12
2. $\dfrac{32}{28} = \dfrac{w}{7}$ 8
3. $\dfrac{5}{u} = \dfrac{60}{132}$ 11
4. $\dfrac{36}{21} = \dfrac{24}{s}$ 14
5. $\dfrac{a}{64} = \dfrac{225}{480}$ 30
6. $\dfrac{42}{w} = \dfrac{56}{8}$ 6
7. $\dfrac{1}{10} = \dfrac{m}{12}$ 1.2
8. $\dfrac{5}{3} = \dfrac{85}{h}$ 51
9. $\dfrac{24}{g} = \dfrac{2}{30}$ 360
10. $\dfrac{f}{21} = \dfrac{57}{63}$ 19
11. $\dfrac{22}{z} = \dfrac{121}{16.5}$ 3
12. $\dfrac{2}{3} = \dfrac{k}{12.6}$ 8.4
13. $\dfrac{r}{9} = \dfrac{5}{20}$ 2.25
14. $\dfrac{d}{21} = \dfrac{1.5}{3.5}$ 9
15. $\dfrac{46}{57.5} = \dfrac{360}{q}$ 450
16. $\dfrac{4.2}{4.8} = \dfrac{d}{80}$ 70
17. $\dfrac{1}{c} = \dfrac{4.5}{11.7}$ 2.6
18. $\dfrac{0.3}{n} = \dfrac{4.75}{14.25}$ 0.9
19. $\dfrac{9.1}{14.7} = \dfrac{1.3}{p}$ 2.1
20. $\dfrac{0.4}{3} = \dfrac{y}{98.25}$ 13.1
21. $\dfrac{v}{33.44} = \dfrac{1}{3.2}$ 10.45

Skills Practice, p. 305 and Practice, p. 306 (shown)

Determine whether each pair of ratios forms a proportion.

1. $\dfrac{5}{8}, \dfrac{20}{32}$ yes
2. $\dfrac{12}{28}, \dfrac{27}{63}$ yes
3. $\dfrac{8}{50}, \dfrac{1}{43}$ no
4. $\dfrac{40}{48}, \dfrac{56}{42}$ no
5. $\dfrac{6.4}{16}, \dfrac{32}{80}$ yes
6. $\dfrac{12}{18}, \dfrac{90}{135}$ yes
7. $\dfrac{21}{24}, \dfrac{56}{64}$ yes
8. $\dfrac{9}{16}, \dfrac{3}{4}$ no
9. $\dfrac{12}{32}, \dfrac{8}{3}$ no
10. $\dfrac{2.6}{4}, \dfrac{4.6}{8}$ no
11. $\dfrac{5.1}{1.7}, \dfrac{7.5}{2.5}$ yes
12. $\dfrac{8.5}{25}, \dfrac{17}{50}$ yes

ALGEBRA Solve each proportion.

13. $\dfrac{n}{12} = \dfrac{6}{18}$ 4
14. $\dfrac{8}{v} = \dfrac{56}{105}$ 15
15. $\dfrac{15}{35} = \dfrac{s}{7}$ 3
16. $\dfrac{24}{30} = \dfrac{8}{w}$ 10
17. $\dfrac{c}{28} = \dfrac{5}{7}$ 20
18. $\dfrac{3}{r} = \dfrac{39}{65}$ 5
19. $\dfrac{9}{15} = \dfrac{m}{25}$ 15
20. $\dfrac{7.5}{6.0} = \dfrac{3.6}{x}$ 2.88
21. $\dfrac{12}{25} = \dfrac{u}{40}$ 19.2
22. $\dfrac{1}{a} = \dfrac{33}{132}$ 4
23. $\dfrac{f}{5} = \dfrac{16}{40}$ 2
24. $\dfrac{r}{6.5} = \dfrac{0.2}{1.3}$ 1
25. $\dfrac{30}{14} = \dfrac{k}{1.54}$ 3.3
26. $\dfrac{3.5}{7.2} = \dfrac{k}{57.6}$ 28
27. $\dfrac{2.1}{42} = \dfrac{7}{t}$ 140

28. **FOOD** Gayle is making fruit punch that consists of 2 quarts of juice and 1 quart of soda water. How much soda water does she need if she has 5 quarts of juice? **2.5 quarts**

Enrichment, p. 308

Cross Products Proof

Recall the Cross Products Property: If $\dfrac{a}{b} = \dfrac{c}{d}$, then $ad = bc$. Use the statements below to justify this property.

Write the reason for each statement.
1. Prove: $ad = bc$

Statement	Reason
$\dfrac{a}{b} = \dfrac{c}{d}$	a. Given
$bd \cdot \dfrac{a}{b} = bd \cdot \dfrac{c}{d}$	b. Mult. Prop. Equality
$bd \cdot \left(a \cdot \dfrac{1}{b}\right) = bd \cdot \left(c \cdot \dfrac{1}{d}\right)$	c. Rewrite division as multiplication.
$\left(b \cdot \dfrac{1}{b}\right)ad = \left(d \cdot \dfrac{1}{d}\right)cb$	d. Comm. Prop. Mult.
$1ad = 1cb$	e. Inverse Prop. Mult.
$ad = bc$	f. Mult. Identity Prop.

Solve each proportion problem.

2. **AGE** The ratio of Brandi's age to Jason's age is 4:5. In eight years the ratio will be 6:7. How old are Brandi and Jason now? **16 and 20**

3. **AGE** The ratio of Drew's age to Stacey's age is 3:4. Four years ago the ratio was 2:3. How old were Drew and Stacey four years ago? **8 and 12**

DAILY INTERVENTION

Differentiated Instruction

- **Interpersonal** Write ratios on several index cards. Write equivalent ratios on the same number of other index cards. Give one card to each student. Have them look for the equivalent ratio held by another student. Encourage discussion by the students, and ask them to stand in pairs to display their equivalent ratios.

Open-Ended Assessment

Speaking Have students explain to the class how to write and solve a proportion. Be sure they use specific examples.

Tips for New Teachers

Cooperative Learning Allow students to work in pairs or small groups to work the word problems together. Assign roles for students, such as reader, recorder, planner, and presenter.

Getting Ready for Lesson 6-3

PREREQUISITE SKILL Lesson 6-3 uses proportion to solve problems involving scale drawings and models. Exercises 52–55 should be used to determine your students' familiarity with converting measurements.

Answer

44. Proportions can be used in recipes to determine the amount of ingredients needed when increasing or decreasing a recipe. Answers should include the following.

- If you want to increase or decrease a recipe, you can use proportions to find the amounts needed so that the ratios remain the same.

- Adding 10 ounces to each ingredient in the punch recipe will not result in the same flavor because the ingredients are in proportion to each other. By adding the same amount to each ingredient, the ingredients are no longer proportional and the flavor is changed.

---

41. SNACKS The Skyway Snack Company makes a snack mix that contains raisins, peanuts, and chocolate pieces. The ingredients are shown at the right. Suppose the company wants to sell a larger-sized bag that contains 6 cups of raisins. How many cups of chocolate pieces and peanuts should be added? **chocolate pieces: 3 c; peanuts: $1\frac{1}{2}$ c**

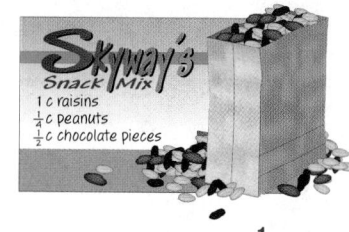

Skyway's Snack Mix
1 c raisins
$\frac{1}{4}$ c peanuts
$\frac{1}{2}$ c chocolate pieces

★ **42. PAINT** If 1 pint of paint is needed to paint a square that is 5 feet on each side, how many pints must be purchased in order to paint a square that is 9 feet 6 inches on each side? **4 pints**

43. CRITICAL THINKING The Property of Proportions states that if $\frac{a}{b} = \frac{c}{d}$, then $ad = bc$. Write two proportions in which the cross products are ad and bc. $\frac{a}{c} = \frac{b}{d}$, $\frac{b}{a} = \frac{d}{c}$, or $\frac{c}{a} = \frac{d}{b}$

44. **WRITING IN MATH** Answer the question that was posed at the beginning of the lesson. **See margin.**

How are proportions used in recipes?

Include the following in your answer:

- an explanation telling how proportions can be used to increase or decrease the amount of ingredients needed, and

- an explanation of why adding 10 ounces to each ingredient in the punch recipe will not result in the same flavor of punch.

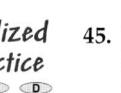

NEW YORK Test Practice

Standardized Test Practice Ⓐ Ⓑ Ⓒ Ⓓ

45. Jack is standing next to a flagpole as shown at the right. Jack is 6 feet tall. Which proportion could you use to find the height of the flagpole? **C**

Ⓐ $\frac{3}{6} = \frac{x}{12}$ Ⓑ $\frac{x}{6} = \frac{3}{12}$

Ⓒ $\frac{6}{3} = \frac{x}{12}$ Ⓓ $\frac{3}{x} = \frac{12}{6}$

3 ft

12 ft

Maintain Your Skills

Mixed Review Express each ratio as a unit rate. Round to the nearest tenth, if necessary. *(Lesson 6-1)*

46. $5 for 4 loaves of bread **$1.25/loaf** **47.** 183.4 miles in 3.2 hours **57.3 mph**

48. Find the next three numbers in the sequence 2, 5, 8, 11, 14, ... *(Lesson 5-10)* **17, 20, 23**

ALGEBRA Find each quotient. *(Lesson 5-4)*

49. $\frac{x}{5} \div \frac{x}{20}$ **4** **50.** $\frac{3y}{4} \div \frac{5y}{8}$ **$\frac{6}{5}$** **51.** $\frac{4z}{w} \div \frac{7yz}{w}$ **$\frac{4}{7y}$**

Getting Ready for the Next Lesson **PREREQUISITE SKILL** Complete each sentence. *(To review **converting measurements**, see pages 720 and 721.)*

52. 5 feet = ■ inches **60** **53.** 8.5 feet = ■ inches **102**

54. 36 inches = ■ feet **3** **55.** 78 inches = ■ feet **6.5**

Algebra Activity

A Follow-Up of Lesson 6-2

NEW YORK *Performance Indicator* **8.PS.10 Use proportionality to model problems**

Capture-Recapture

Scientists often determine the number of fish in a pond, lake, or other body of water by using the *capture-recapture* method. A number of fish are captured, counted, carefully tagged, and returned to their habitat. The tagged fish are counted again and proportions are used to estimate the entire population. In this activity, you will model this estimation technique.

Collect the Data

Step 1 Copy the table below onto a sheet of paper.

Original Number Captured:		
Sample	**Recaptured**	**Tagged**
1		
2		
3		
4		
⋮		
10		
Total		

Step 2 Empty a bag of dried beans into a paper bag.

Step 3 Remove a handful of beans. Using a permanent marker, place an X on each side of each bean. These beans will represent the tagged fish. Record this number at the top of your table as the original number captured. Return the beans to the bag and mix.

Step 4 Remove a second handful of beans without looking. This represents the first sample of recaptured fish. Record the number of beans. Then count and record the number of beans that are tagged. Return the beans to the bag and mix.

Step 5 Repeat Step 4 for samples 2 through 10. Then use the results to find the total number of recaptured fish and the total number of tagged fish.

Analyze the Data

1. Use the following proportion to estimate the number of beans in the bag.

$$\frac{\text{original number captured}}{\text{total number in bag}} = \frac{\text{total number tagged}}{\text{total number recaptured}}$$

2. Count the number of beans in the bag. Compare the estimate to the actual number.
   1–2. Answers will vary. The estimate should be close to the actual number.

Make a Conjecture

3. Why is it a good idea to base a prediction on several samples instead of one sample? **Sample answer: More samples leads to an accurate estimate.**

4. Why does this method work?

4. Sample answer: The ratio of tagged fish to actual fish should be approximately the same as the ratio of tagged fish to total recaptured fish in the samples.

Algebra Activity Capture-Recapture **275**

Algebra Activity

Getting Started

Objective Use proportions with the capture-recapture method of counting.

Materials
bag of dried beans
paper bag
permanent marker

Teach

- Have two students simultaneously use the beans to demonstrate the capture-recapture method to the class. Then have the class compare their results.
- Have two groups of students collect the data in Steps 1–5.
- Divide each group into smaller groups to answer the questions.
- When students get to Exercise 2, have students count the total beans from each original bag of beans.

Assess

In **Exercise 3**, students should explain why several samples give a more accurate result than one sample.

Study Notebook

Ask students to write a paragraph explaining the capture-recapture method. Have them record their results of the activity with the explanation.

Resource Manager

📁 *Teaching Pre-Algebra with Manipulatives*
• p. 86 (student recording sheet)

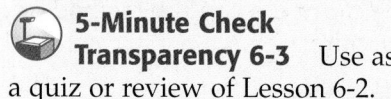

6-3 Lesson Notes

1 Focus

5-Minute Check Transparency 6-3 Use as a quiz or review of Lesson 6-2.

Mathematical Background notes are available for this lesson on page 262C.

How are scale drawings used in everyday life?

The opening activity questions are repeated on page 312 of the *Chapter 6 Resource Masters*.

Reading to Learn Mathematics, p. 312 ELL

Pre-Activity How are scale drawings used in everyday life?

Do the activity at the top of page 276 in your textbook. Write your answers below.

a. Suppose the landscape plans are drawn on graph paper and the side of each square on the paper represents 2 feet. What is the actual width of a rose garden if its width on the drawing is 4 squares long? **8 ft**

b. All maps have a scale. How can the scale help you estimate the distance between cities? **Sample answer: Suppose a map has a scale of 0.25 inch = 10 miles, and two towns are 1 inch apart. Since 1 inch is equivalent to four times 0.25 inch, and each of the 0.25 inch equals 10 miles, this tells you that the actual distance is 4 × 10 or 40 miles. Use a proportion.** $\frac{0.25}{10} = \frac{1.0}{x}$

Reading the Lesson 1–4. See students' work.

Write a definition and give an example of each new vocabulary word or phrase.

Vocabulary	Definition	Example
1. scale drawing		
2. scale model		
3. scale		
4. scale factor		

Helping You Remember

5. How is a scale different from a scale factor? **A scale gives a relationship that can contain different units of measure, while a scale factor is a ratio that uses the same units of measure.**

Teaching Tip Show students a map of your state and a map of your town. Compare the scales. Ask students why the scales are different.

Resource Manager

📁 Workbooks and Reproducible Masters

Chapter 6 Resource Masters
- Study Guide and Intervention, p. 309
- Skills Practice, p. 310
- Practice, p. 311
- Reading to Learn Mathematics, p. 312
- Enrichment, p. 313
- Assessment, p. 359

Graphing Calculator and Spreadsheet Masters, p. 30
Parent and Student Study Guide Workbook, p. 46

🖥 Transparencies
5-Minute Check Transparency 6-3
Answer Key Transparencies

💿 Technology
Interactive Chalkboard

6-3 Scale Drawings and Models

What You'll Learn

- Use scale drawings.
- Construct scale drawings.

Vocabulary
- scale drawing
- scale model
- scale
- scale factor

NEW YORK
Performance Indicator
8.R.9 Use mathematics to show and understand physical phenomena (e.g., make and interpret scale drawings of figures or scale models of objects)

How are scale drawings used in everyday life?

A set of landscape plans and a map are shown.

> Designers use blueprints when planning landscapes.

> Maps are used to find actual distances between cities.

a. Suppose the landscape plans are drawn on graph paper and the side of each square on the paper represents 2 feet. What is the actual width of a rose garden if its width on the drawing is 4 squares long? **8 ft**

b. All maps have a scale. How can the scale help you estimate the distance between cities? **See margin.**

USE SCALE DRAWINGS AND MODELS A **scale drawing** or a **scale model** is used to represent an object that is too large or too small to be drawn or built at actual size. A few examples are maps, blueprints, model cars, and model airplanes.

> Model cars are replicas of actual cars.

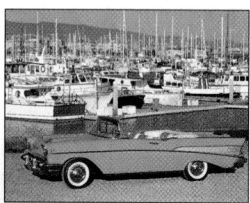

Concept Check: to represent an object that is too large or too small to be drawn or built at actual size

✓ Concept Check Why are scale drawings or scale models used?

The **scale** gives the relationship between the measurements on the drawing or model and the measurements of the real object. Consider the following scales.

1 inch = 3 feet

> 1 inch represents an actual distance of 3 feet.

1:24

> 1 unit represents an actual distance of 24 units.

Study Tip

Scale Factor
When finding the scale factor, be sure to use the same units of measure.

The ratio of a length on a scale drawing or model to the corresponding length on the real object is called the **scale factor**. Suppose a scale model has a scale of 2 inches = 16 inches. The scale factor is $\frac{2}{16}$ or $\frac{1}{8}$.

The lengths and widths of objects of a scale drawing or model are proportional to the lengths and widths of the actual object.

Example 1 Find Actual Measurements

DESIGN A set of landscape plans shows a flower bed that is 6.5 inches wide. The scale on the plans is 1 inch = 4 feet.

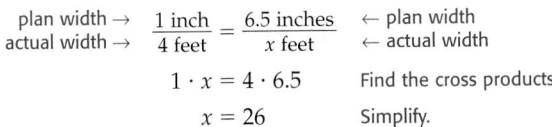
— 6.5 in. —

a. What is the width of the actual flower bed?

Let x represent the actual width of the flower bed. Write and solve a proportion.

plan width → $\dfrac{1 \text{ inch}}{4 \text{ feet}} = \dfrac{6.5 \text{ inches}}{x \text{ feet}}$ ← plan width
actual width →   ← actual width

$1 \cdot x = 4 \cdot 6.5$ Find the cross products.

$x = 26$ Simplify.

The actual width of the flower bed is 26 feet.

b. What is the scale factor?

To find the scale factor, write the ratio of 1 inch to 4 feet in simplest form.

$\dfrac{1 \text{ inch}}{4 \text{ feet}} = \dfrac{1 \text{ inch}}{48 \text{ inches}}$ Convert 4 feet to inches.

The scale factor is $\frac{1}{48}$. That is, each measurement on the plan is $\frac{1}{48}$ the actual measurement.

More About . . .

Architecture
The exterior of the Lincoln Memorial features 36 columns that represent the states in the Union when Lincoln died in 1865. Each column is 44 feet high.
Source: www.infoplease.com

Example 2 Determine the Scale

ARCHITECTURE The inside of the Lincoln Memorial contains three chambers. The central chamber, which features a marble statue of Abraham Lincoln, has a height of 60 feet. Suppose a scale model of the chamber has a height of 4 inches. What is the scale of the model?

Write the ratio of the height of the model to the actual height of the statue. Then solve a proportion in which the height of the model is 1 inch and the actual height is x feet.

model height → $\dfrac{4 \text{ inches}}{60 \text{ feet}} = \dfrac{1 \text{ inch}}{x \text{ feet}}$ ← model height
actual height →   ← actual height

$4 \cdot x = 60 \cdot 1$ Find the cross products.

$4x = 60$ Simplify.

$\dfrac{4x}{4} = \dfrac{60}{4}$ Divide each side by 4.

$x = 15$ Simplify.

So, the scale is 1 inch = 15 feet.

USE SCALE DRAWINGS AND MODELS

In-Class Examples Power Point®

1 MAP A map has a scale of 1 inch = 8 miles. Two towns are 3.25 inches apart on the map.

a. What is the actual distance between the two towns? **26 miles**

b. What is the scale factor?
$\dfrac{1}{506{,}880}$

2 MODEL CAR A model car is 4 inches long. The actual car is 12 feet long. What is the scale of the model?
1 inch = 3 feet

Teaching Tip Ask students to compare scale factor and scale in Examples 1 and 2.

CONSTRUCT SCALE DRAWINGS

In-Class Example Power Point®

Teaching Tip For Example 3, ask students if the drawing would become larger or smaller if the scale were changed from 0.25 inches = 4 feet to 0.25 inches = 2 feet. **larger**

3 PATIO DESIGN Sheila is designing a patio that is 16 feet long and 14 feet wide. Make a scale drawing of the patio. Use a scale of 0.5 inches = 4 feet. **Check students' drawings. The length should be 2 inches and the width should be 1.75 inches.**

✓ Skills Check

Use Scale Drawings and Models Ask students if they can invert the ratios on both sides of the equations and get the same answer. **yes** Ask if it works consistently. **yes** Ask why it works. **The cross products are the same.** Ask if they can invert one ratio and not the other. **no**

DAILY
INTERVENTION **FIND THE ERROR**
If students are having difficulty determining the correct scale, have them find 1 inch and 2 feet on a yardstick. Using the yardstick, they can see how many inches are in 2 feet.

About the Exercises . . .
Organization by Objective
• Use Scale Drawings and Models: 8–19
• Construct Scale Drawings: 20

Odd/Even Assignments
Exercises 8–19 are structured so that students practice the same concepts whether they are assigned odd or even problems.

Assignment Guide
Basic: 9–21 odd, 22–24, 26–44
Average: 9–19 odd, 21–24, 26–44 (Optional: 25)
Advanced: 8–18 even, 20–36 (Optional: 37–44)

Answers

1. ☐ 1 unit   ☐ 3 units

2. Luisa; Since there are 24 inches in 2 feet, the ratio 1:24 is correct.

278   Chapter 6 Ratio, Proportion, and Percent

CONSTRUCT SCALE DRAWINGS   To construct a scale drawing of an object, use the actual measurements of the object and the scale to which the object is to be drawn.

Example 3 *Construct a Scale Drawing*

INTERIOR DESIGN   Antonio is designing a room that is 20 feet long and 12 feet wide. Make a scale drawing of the room. Use a scale of 0.25 inch = 4 feet.

Step 1 Find the measure of the room's length on the drawing. Let x represent the length.

drawing length → $\dfrac{0.25 \text{ inch}}{4 \text{ feet}} = \dfrac{x \text{ inches}}{20 \text{ feet}}$ ← drawing length
actual length →   ← actual length

$0.25 \cdot 20 = 4 \cdot x$ Find the cross products.
$5 = 4x$ Simplify.
$1.25 = x$ Divide each side by 4.

On the drawing, the length is 1.25 or $1\frac{1}{4}$ inches.

Step 2 Find the measure of the room's width on the drawing. Let w represent the width.

drawing length → $\dfrac{0.25 \text{ inch}}{4 \text{ feet}} = \dfrac{w \text{ inches}}{12 \text{ feet}}$ ← drawing length
actual length →   ← actual length

$0.25 \cdot 12 = 4 \cdot w$ Find the cross products.
$3 = 4w$ Simplify.
$\dfrac{3}{4} = \dfrac{4w}{4}$ Divide each side by 4.
$0.75 = w$ Simplify.

On the drawing, the width is 0.75 or $\frac{3}{4}$ inch.

Step 3 Make the scale drawing. Use $\frac{1}{4}$-inch grid paper. Since $1\frac{1}{4}$ inches = 5 squares and $\frac{3}{4}$ inch = 3 squares, draw a rectangle that is 5 squares by 3 squares.

Career Choices

Interior Designer

Interior designers plan the space and furnish the interiors of places such as homes, offices, restaurants, hotels, hospitals, and even theaters. Creativity and knowledge of computer-aided design software is essential.

📖 **Online Research**
For information about a career as an interior designer, visit: www.pre-alg.com/careers

---

Check for Understanding

Concept Check
1–2. See margin.

1. **OPEN ENDED**   Draw two squares in which the ratio of the sides of the first square to the sides of the second square is 1:3.

2. **FIND THE ERROR**   Montega and Luisa are rewriting the scale 1 inch = 2 feet in a:b form.

Montega	Luisa
1:36	1:24

Who is correct? Explain your reasoning.

278   Chapter 6 Ratio, Proportion, and Percent

DAILY
INTERVENTION   **Differentiated Instruction**

• **Intrapersonal**   Have students find a magazine photo, then have them tape a 0.25-inch grid transparency on top of the picture. Ask students to systematically copy the contents of each grid onto centimeter grid paper. Their drawing will be an enlargement of the original. Encourage them to include both the photo and their drawing in their Math Journals, and ask them whether it helped their understanding of scale and proportions.

Guided Practice

GUIDED PRACTICE KEY

Exercises	Examples
3, 4	1
5, 6	1, 2
7	3

On a map of Pennsylvania, the scale is 1 inch = 20 miles. Find the actual distance for each map distance.

	From	To	Map Distance	
3.	Pittsburgh	Perryopolis	2 inches	**40 mi**
4.	Johnston	Homer City	$1\frac{3}{4}$ inches	**35 mi**

Applications

STATUES For Exercises 5 and 6, use the following information.
The Statue of Zeus at Olympia is one of the Seven Wonders of the World. On a scale model of the statue, the height of Zeus is 8 inches. **5. 1 in. = 5 ft**

5. If the actual height of Zeus is 40 feet, what is the scale of the statue?

6. What is the scale factor? $\frac{1}{60}$

7. **DESIGN** An architect is designing a room that is 15 feet long and 10 feet wide. Construct a scale drawing of the room. Use a scale of 0.5 in. = 10 ft. **See margin.**

Practice and Apply

Homework Help

For Exercises	See Examples
8–17	1
18, 19	1, 2
20	3

Extra Practice
See page 737.

On a set of architectural drawings for an office building, the scale is $\frac{1}{2}$ inch = 3 feet. Find the actual length of each room.

	Room	Drawing Distance	
8.	Conference Room	7 inches	**42 ft**
9.	Lobby	2 inches	**12 ft**
10.	Mail Room	2.3 inches	**13.8 ft**
11.	Library	4.1 inches	**24.6 ft**
12.	Copy Room	2.2 inches	**13.2 ft**
13.	Storage	1.9 inches	**11.4 ft**
14.	Exercise Room	$3\frac{3}{4}$ inches	**$22\frac{1}{2}$ ft**
15.	Cafeteria	$8\frac{1}{4}$ inches	**$49\frac{1}{2}$ ft**

16. Refer to Exercises 8–15. What is the scale factor? $\frac{1}{72}$

17. What is the scale factor if the scale is 8 inches = 1 foot? $\frac{2}{3}$

18. **ROLLER COASTERS** In a scale model of a roller coaster, the highest hill has a height of 6 inches. If the actual height of the hill is 210 feet, what is the scale of the model? **1 in. = 35 ft**

19. **INSECTS** In an illustration of a honeybee, the length of the bee is 4.8 centimeters. The actual size of the honeybee is 1.2 centimeters. What is the scale of the drawing? **1 cm = 0.25 cm**

4.8 cm

20. **GARDENS** A garden is 8 feet wide by 16 feet long. Make a scale drawing of the garden that has a scale of $\frac{1}{4}$ in. = 2 ft. **See margin.**

Answers

7. |← 15 ft →| 10 ft

20. |← 16 ft →| 8 ft

Study Guide and Intervention, p. 309

A **scale** gives the relationship between the measurements on the drawing or model and the measurements of the real object.

Example A map shows a scale of 1 inch = 6 miles. The distance between two places on the map is 4.25 inches. What is the actual distance?

Let x represent the actual distance. Write and solve a proportion.

$$\frac{\text{map width} \rightarrow}{\text{actual width} \rightarrow} \frac{1 \text{ inch}}{6 \text{ miles}} = \frac{4.25 \text{ inches}}{x \text{ miles}} \begin{array}{l} \leftarrow \text{map width} \\ \leftarrow \text{actual width} \end{array}$$

$1 \cdot x = 6 \cdot 4.25$ Find the cross products.

$x = 25.5$ Simplify.

The actual distance is 25.5 miles.

Exercises

On a set of architectural drawings for an office building, the scale is 0.25 inch = 5 feet. Find the actual length of each room.

	Room	Drawing Distance	Actual Distance
1.	Lobby	1.6 inches	32 feet
2.	CEO Office	1.35 inches	27 feet
3.	Copy Room	0.55 inch	11 feet
4.	CEO Secretary's Office	0.6 inch	12 feet
5.	Vice President's Office	0.9 inch	18 feet
6.	Library	1.525 inches	30.5 feet
7.	Storage Area	2.1125 inches	42.25 feet
8.	Personal Manager's Office	1.7375 inches	34.75 feet
9.	Manager's Office	0.625 inch	12.5 feet
10.	Mail Room	2.2625 inches	45.25 feet
11.	Boiler Room	3.725 inches	74.5 feet
12.	Conference Room A	2.62 inches	52.4 feet
13.	Conference Room B	0.925 inch	18.5 feet
14.	Cafeteria	2.3 inches	46 feet
15.	Kitchen	2 inches	40 feet

Skills Practice, p. 310 and Practice, p. 311 (shown)

On a map, the scale is 5 centimeters = 2 kilometers. Find the missing distances.

	Location	Map Distance	Actual Distance
1.	Town A to Town B	10 cm	4 km
2.	Town A to Town C	25 cm	10 km
3.	Town A to Town D	14 cm	5.6 km
4.	Town A to Town E	2 cm	0.8 km
5.	Town A to Town F	0.5 cm	0.2 km
6.	Town A to Town G	8 cm	3.2 km
7.	Town A to Town H	0.25 cm	0.1 km
8.	Town A to Town I	6 cm	2.4 km
9.	Town A to Town J	0.1 cm	0.04 km
10.	Town A to Town K	1 cm	0.4 km
11.	Town A to Town L	2.5 cm	1 km
12.	Town A to Town M	1.2 cm	0.48 km

13. Refer to Exercises 1–12. What is the scale factor?
$\frac{5}{200,000}$ or $\frac{1}{40,000}$

14. What is the scale factor if the scale is 15 inches = 1 yard?
$\frac{15}{36}$ or $\frac{5}{12}$

15. **STRUCTURES** A barn is 50 feet wide by 80 feet long. Make a scale drawing of the barn that has a scale of $\frac{1}{2}$ inch = 10 feet. **Check students' drawings. The width is 2.5 inches and the length is 4 inches.**

16. **PHOTOGRAPHY** A man in a photograph is 1.5 inches in height. If the man is 6 feet tall, what is the scale? **1 inch = 4 feet**

Enrichment, p. 313

Direct Variation

If the relationship between two quantities is such that when one quantity increases, the other increases, or when one quantity decreases, the other decreases, the quantities are said to **vary directly**.

Example **MONEY** If 2 loaves of bread cost $1.60, how much will 3 loaves of the same type of bread cost?

The number of loaves and the cost vary directly; that is, as the number of loaves increases, so does the cost.

$$\frac{2 \text{ loaves}}{\$1.60} = \frac{3 \text{ loaves}}{x}$$ For direct variations, place like quantities directly across from each other in a proportion.

$2x = 4.80$

$x = 2.40$

The cost for 3 loaves of bread is $2.40.

Write a proportion to represent each situation. Then solve.

1. **MONEY** Three gallons of gasoline cost $3.36. How much do 5 gallons cost?
$\frac{3}{3.36} = \frac{5}{x}$; $x = 5.6$; $5.60

2. **DISTANCE** At a rate of 50 mph, a car travels a distance of 600 miles. How far will the car travel at a rate of 40 mph if it is driven the same amount of time?
$\frac{50}{600} = \frac{40}{x}$; $x = 480$; 480 miles

3. **MONEY** If the rent for two weeks is $500, how much rent is paid for 5 weeks?
$\frac{2}{500} = \frac{5}{x}$; $x = 1250$; $1250

4. **MONEY** If 8 newspapers cost $3.20, how much will 6 newspapers cost?
$\frac{8}{3.20} = \frac{6}{x}$; $x = 2.40$; $2.40

5. **WEIGHT** If 9 fully loaded trucks carry a total of 140,400 pounds, how many pounds can 3 trucks carry?
$\frac{9}{140,400} = \frac{3}{x}$; $x = 46,800$;
46,800 pounds

6. **TECHNOLOGY** Twelve floppy disks can hold 16.8 million bytes of data. How many bytes will 20 floppy disks hold?
$\frac{12}{16,800,000} = \frac{20}{x}$; $x = 28,000,000$;
28 million bytes

7. **TECHNOLOGY** If 12 floppy disks hold 16.8 million bytes of data, how many floppy disks are needed to hold 10 million bytes of data?
$\frac{12}{16,800,000} = \frac{x}{10,000,000}$; $x \approx 7.14$;
8 disks are needed.

8. **HEALTH** There are a total of 2100 Calories in 5 candy bars (all the same kind). How many total Calories are there in 3 dozen of these candy bars?
$\frac{5}{2100} = \frac{36}{x}$; $x = 15,120$;
15,120 Calories

Lesson 6-3 Scale Drawings and Models   **279**

Open-Ended Assessment

Modeling Have students draw a 9-by-15 rectangle on grid paper. Then have them draw a similar rectangle so that the scale factor of the original rectangle to the new rectangle is 3:1. Have them explain how the new rectangle would differ if the scale factor were 1:3. **The new rectangle would be larger.**

Getting Ready for Lesson 6-4

PREREQUISITE SKILL In Lesson 6-4, students will express percents as fractions. Exercises 37–44 should be used to determine your students' familiarity with writing fractions in simplest form.

Assessment Options

Quiz (Lessons 6-1 through 6-3) is available on p. 359 of the *Chapter 6 Resource Masters*.

Answers

21. A scale factor less than 1 means that the drawing or model is drawn smaller than actual size. A scale factor of 1 means that the drawing or model is drawn actual size. A scale factor greater than 1 means the drawing or model is drawn larger than actual size.

22. In everyday life, scale drawings or models are used to represent objects that are too large or too small to be drawn or built at actual size. Answers should include the following.
    • Sample answer: a model airplane, a globe, and a set of blueprints
    • Sample answer: A scale drawing such as a map can help you find actual distance and a scale model such as a replica of a dinosaur can help to see the actual image of a dinosaur.

---

21. **CRITICAL THINKING** What does it mean if the scale factor of a scale drawing or model is less than 1? greater than 1? equal to 1? **See margin.**

22. 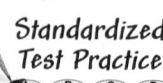 Answer the question that was posed at the beginning of the lesson. **See margin.**

    How are scale drawings used in everyday life?
    Include the following in your answer:
    • an example of three kinds of scale drawings or models, and
    • an explanation of how you use scale drawings in your life.

NEW YORK Test Practice

Standardized Test Practice A B C D

23. Which scale has a scale factor of $\frac{1}{18}$? **B**
    A 3 in. = 6 ft   B 6 in. = 9 ft   C 3 in. = 54 ft   D 6 in. = 6 ft

24. A model airplane is built using a 1:16 scale. On the model, the length of the wing span is 5.8 feet. What is the actual length of the wing? **C**
    A 84.8 ft   B 91.6 ft   C 92.8 ft   D 89.8 ft

Extending the Lesson

25. Two rectangles are shown. The ratio comparing their sides is 1:2.

    a. Write the ratio that compares their perimeters. $\frac{1}{2}$
    b. Write the ratio that compares their areas. $\frac{1}{4}$
    c. Find the perimeter and area of a 3-inch by 5-inch rectangle. Then make a conjecture about the perimeter and area of a 6-inch by 10-inch rectangle. Check by finding the actual perimeter and area. **See margin.**

Maintain Your Skills

Mixed Review Solve each proportion. *(Lesson 6-2)*

26. $\frac{n}{20} = \frac{15}{50}$ **6**   27. $\frac{14}{32} = \frac{x}{8}$ **3.5**   28. $\frac{3}{2.2} = \frac{7.5}{y}$ **5.5**

Convert each rate using dimensional analysis. *(Lesson 6-1)*

29. 36 cm/s = ■ m/min **21.6**   30. 66 gal/h = ■ qt/min **4.4**

31. Find $1\frac{1}{4} + 4\frac{5}{6}$. Write the answer in simplest form. *(Lesson 5-7)* $6\frac{1}{12}$

ALGEBRA Find each product or quotient. Express in exponential form. *(Lesson 4-6)*

32. $4^3 \cdot 4^5$ **4^8**   33. $3t^4 \cdot 6t$ **$18t^5$**   34. $7^{14} \div 7^8$ **7^6**   35. $\frac{24m^5}{18m^2}$ **$\frac{4m^3}{3}$**

36. **ALGEBRA** Find the greatest common factor of $14x^2y$ and $35xy^3$. *(Lesson 4-4)* **$7xy$**

Getting Ready for the Next Lesson **PREREQUISITE SKILL** Simplify each fraction.
(To review simplest form, see Lesson 4-5.)

37. $\frac{5}{100}$ $\frac{1}{20}$ 38. $\frac{25}{100}$ $\frac{1}{4}$ 39. $\frac{40}{100}$ $\frac{2}{5}$ 40. $\frac{52}{100}$ $\frac{13}{25}$

41. $\frac{78}{100}$ $\frac{39}{50}$ 42. $\frac{75}{100}$ $\frac{3}{4}$ 43. $\frac{82}{100}$ $\frac{41}{50}$ 44. $\frac{95}{100}$ $\frac{19}{20}$

25c. The perimeter of a 3-inch by 5-inch rectangle is 16 inches. The area is 15 square inches. For a 6-inch by 10-inch rectangle, the perimeter should be double the 3-inch by 5-inch rectangle. That is, 16 × 2 or 32 inches. The area should be 4 times the area of the 3-inch by 5-inch rectangle. That is, 4 × 15 or 60 square inches. Since the perimeter of the 6-inch by 10-inch rectangle is 32 and its area is 60, the conjecture is true.

Fractions, Decimals, and Percents

NEW YORK *Performance Indicator* 8.N.3 Read, write, and identify percents less than 1% and greater than 100%

What You'll Learn

- Express percents as fractions and vice versa.
- Express percents as decimals and vice versa.

Vocabulary

- percent

How are percents related to fractions and decimals?

A portion of each figure is shaded.

  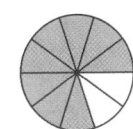

a. Write a ratio that compares the shaded region of each figure to its total region as a fraction in simplest form.

b. Rewrite each fraction using a denominator of 100. $\frac{75}{100}; \frac{60}{100}; \frac{80}{100}$

c. Which figure has the greatest part of its area shaded? **circle**

d. Was it easier to compare the fractions in part **a** or part **b**? Explain.

a. $\frac{3}{4}, \frac{3}{5}, \frac{4}{5}$

d. Part b; the fractions have a common denominator.

Reading Math

Percent

Root Word: Cent

There are 100 *cents* in one dollar. *Percent* means *per hundred* or *hundredths*.

PERCENTS AND FRACTIONS
A **percent** is a ratio that compares a number to 100. The meaning of 75% is shown at the right. In the figure, 75 out of 100 squares are shaded.

To write a percent as a fraction, express the ratio as a fraction with a denominator of 100. Then simplify if possible. Notice that a percent can be greater than 100% or less than 1%.

Example 1 Percents as Fractions

Express each percent as a fraction in simplest form.

a. 45%

$$45\% = \frac{45}{100}$$
$$= \frac{9}{20}$$

b. 120%

$$120\% = \frac{120}{100}$$
$$= \frac{6}{5} \text{ or } 1\frac{1}{5}$$

c. 0.5%

$$0.5\% = \frac{0.5}{100}$$
$$= \frac{0.5}{100} \cdot \frac{10}{10}$$
$$= \frac{5}{1000} \text{ or } \frac{1}{200}$$

> Multiply by $\frac{10}{10}$ to eliminate the decimal in the numerator.

d. $83\frac{1}{3}\%$

$$83\frac{1}{3}\% = \frac{83\frac{1}{3}}{100}$$
$$= 83\frac{1}{3} \div 100$$
$$= \frac{\overset{5}{\cancel{250}}}{3} \cdot \frac{1}{\underset{2}{\cancel{100}}} \text{ or } \frac{5}{6}$$

> The fraction bar indicates division.

---

1 Focus

5-Minute Check Transparency 6-4 Use as a quiz or review of Lesson 6-3.

Mathematical Background notes are available for this lesson on page 262C.

How are percents related to fractions and decimals?

The opening activity questions are repeated on page 317 of the *Chapter 6 Resource Masters*.

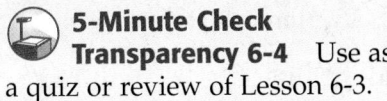

Reading to Learn Mathematics, p. 317 **ELL**

Pre-Activity *How are percents related to fractions and decimals?*

Do the activity at the top of page 281 in your textbook. Write your answers below.

a. Write a ratio that compares the shaded region of each figure to its total region as a fraction in simplest form. $\frac{3}{4}, \frac{3}{5}, \frac{4}{5}$

b. Rewrite each fraction using a denominator of 100. $\frac{75}{100}; \frac{60}{100}; \frac{80}{100}$

c. Which figure has the greatest part of its area shaded? circle

d. Was it easier to compare the fractions in part a or part b? Explain. Part b; the fractions have a common denominator.

Reading the Lesson

Write a definition and give an example of the new vocabulary word.

	Vocabulary	Definition	Example
1.	percent	See students' work.	

2. Shade 50% of each grid below, using three different ways. Be creative. Sample answers are given.

Helping You Remember

3. Percents can be expressed as fractions or decimals and vice versa. Fill in each box with an example of the process described. Answers will vary.

% → fraction	% → decimal
fraction → %	decimal → %

Resource Manager

Workbooks and Reproducible Masters

Chapter 6 Resource Masters
- Study Guide and Intervention, p. 314
- Skills Practice, p. 315
- Practice, p. 316
- Reading to Learn Mathematics, p. 317
- Enrichment, p. 318

Parent and Student Study Guide Workbook, p. 47

Prerequisite Skills Workbook, pp. 15–18

Transparencies

5-Minute Check Transparency 6-4
Answer Key Transparencies

Technology

Interactive Chalkboard
Pre-AlgePASS: Tutorial Plus, Lesson 15

PERCENTS AND FRACTIONS

In-Class Examples

1 Express each percent as a fraction in simplest form.

a. 60%　$\dfrac{3}{5}$

b. 104%　$1\dfrac{1}{25}$

c. 0.3%　$\dfrac{3}{1000}$

d. $56\dfrac{1}{4}\%$　$\dfrac{9}{16}$

2 Express each fraction as a percent.

a. $\dfrac{19}{20}$　**95%**

b. $\dfrac{8}{5}$　**160%**

Teaching Tip To express a fraction as a percent, divide 100 by the denominator. Then multiply that number by the numerator to find the percent.

PERCENTS AND DECIMALS

In-Class Examples

3 Express each percent as a decimal.

a. 60%　**0.6**

b. 2%　**0.02**

c. 658%　**6.58**

d. 0.4%　**0.004**

4 Express each decimal as a percent.

a. 0.4　**40%**

b. 0.05　**5%**

c. 0.0008　**0.08%**

d. 7.3　**730%**

To write a fraction as a percent, write an equivalent fraction with a denominator of 100.

Example 2 *Fractions as Percents*

Express each fraction as a percent.

a. $\dfrac{4}{5}$

$$\dfrac{4}{5} = \dfrac{80}{100} \text{ or } 80\%$$

b. $\dfrac{9}{4}$

$$\dfrac{9}{4} = \dfrac{225}{100} \text{ or } 225\%$$

PERCENTS AND DECIMALS　Remember that *percent* means *per hundred.* In the previous examples, you wrote percents as fractions with 100 in the denominator. Similarly, you can write percents as decimals by dividing by 100.

> **Key Concept**　　　*Percents and Decimals*
> - To write a percent as a decimal, divide by 100 and remove the percent symbol.
> - To write a decimal as a percent, multiply by 100 and add the percent symbol.

Example 3 *Percents as Decimals*

Express each percent as a decimal.

a. 28%

$28\% = 28\%$　Divide by 100 and
$= 0.28$　remove the %.

b. 8%

$8\% = 08\%$　Divide by 100 and
$= 0.08$　remove the %.

c. 375%

$375\% = 375\%$　Divide by 100 and
$= 3.75$　remove the %.

d. 0.5%

$0.5\% = 00.5\%$　Divide by 100 and
$= 0.005$　remove the %.

Example 4 *Decimals as Percents*

Express each decimal as a percent.

a. 0.35

$0.35 = 0.35$　Multiply by 100
$= 35\%$　and add the %.

b. 0.09

$0.09 = 0.09$　Multiply by 100
$= 9\%$　and add the %.

c. 0.007

$0.007 = 0.007$　Multiply by 100
$= 0.7\%$　and add the %.

d. 1.49

$1.49 = 1.49$　Multiply by 100
$= 149\%$　and add the %.

You have expressed fractions as decimals and decimals as percents. Fractions, decimals, and percents are all different names that represent the same number.

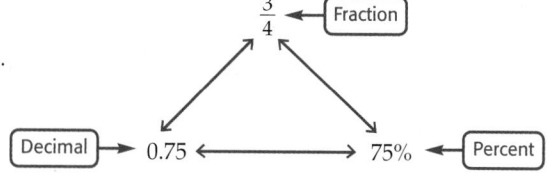

282　**Chapter 6**　Ratio, Proportion, and Percent

DAILY
INTERVENTION　　**Differentiated Instruction**

- **Logical** Have students make a display or poster showing the following ratios expressed as fractions, decimals, and percents: 1:8, 1:4, 3:8, 1:3, 1:2, 5:8, 2:3, 3:4, 7:8, and 8:8.

You can also express a fraction as a percent by first expressing the fraction as a decimal and then expressing the decimal as a percent.

Example 5 *Fractions as Percents*

Express each fraction as a percent. Round to the nearest tenth percent, if necessary.

a. $\frac{7}{8}$

$\frac{7}{8} = 0.875$

$= 87.5\%$

b. $\frac{2}{3}$

$\frac{2}{3} = 0.6666666\ldots$

$\approx 66.7\%$

c. $\frac{3}{500}$

$\frac{3}{500} = 0.006$

$= 0.6\%$

d. $\frac{15}{7}$

$\frac{15}{7} \approx 2.1428571$

$\approx 214.3\%$

Example 6 *Compare Numbers*

SHOES In a survey, one-fifth of parents said that they buy shoes for their children every 4–5 months while 27% of parents said that they buy shoes twice a year. Which of these groups is larger?

Write one-fifth as a percent. Then compare.

$\frac{1}{5} = 0.20$ or 20%

Since 27% is greater than 20%, the group that said they buy shoes twice a year is larger.

Check for Understanding

Concept Check
1–2. See margin.

1. **Describe** two ways to express a fraction as a percent. Then tell how you know whether a fraction is greater than 100% or less than 1%.

2. **OPEN ENDED** Explain the method you would use to express $64\frac{1}{2}\%$ as a decimal.

Guided Practice

Express each percent as a fraction or mixed number in simplest form and as a decimal.

GUIDED PRACTICE KEY	
Exercises	Examples
3–8	1, 3
9–14	2, 4, 5
15	6

3. 30% $\frac{3}{10}$, 0.3
4. $12\frac{1}{2}\%$ $\frac{1}{8}$, 0.125
5. 125% $1\frac{1}{4}$, 1.25
6. 65% $\frac{13}{20}$, 0.65
7. 135% $1\frac{7}{20}$, 1.35
8. 0.2% $\frac{1}{500}$, 0.002

Express each decimal or fraction as a percent. Round to the nearest tenth percent, if necessary.

9. 0.45 **45%**
10. 1.3 **130%**
11. 0.008 **0.8%**
12. $\frac{1}{4}$ **25%**
13. $\frac{12}{9}$ **133.3%**
14. $\frac{3}{600}$ **0.5%**

Application 15. **MEDIA** In a survey, 55% of those surveyed said that they get the news from their local television station while three-fifths said that they get the news from a daily newspaper. From which source do more people get their news? **daily newspaper**

 www.pre-alg.com/extra_examples/ny

Lesson 6-4 Fractions, Decimals, and Percents **283**

5 Express each fraction as a percent. Round to the nearest tenth percent, if necessary.

a. $\frac{5}{8}$ **62.5%**
b. $\frac{1}{3}$ **33.3%**
c. $\frac{9}{1000}$ **0.9%**
d. $\frac{23}{14}$ **164.3%**

6 **BAKERY** A baker says that 25% of his customers buy only bread and $\frac{2}{5}$ of his customers buy only cookies. Which group is larger?

$\frac{2}{5} = 40\%$ and 40% > 25%. So, the group buying cookies is larger.

3 Practice/Apply

Study Notebook

Have students—
• add the definition/example of the vocabulary term to their Vocabulary Builder worksheets for Chapter 6.
• include any other item(s) that they find helpful in mastering the skills in this lesson.

About the Exercises . . .

Organization by Objective
• **Percents and Fractions:** 16–27, 34–39
• **Percents and Decimals:** 28–33

Odd/Even Assignments
Exercises 16–48 are structured so that students practice the same concepts whether they are assigned odd or even problems.

Assignment Guide
Basic: 17–47 odd, 51–71
Average: 17–49 odd, 51–71
Advanced: 16–48 even, 49–65 (Optional: 66–71)

Answers

1. Sample answer: Write an equivalent fraction with a denominator of 100 or express the fraction as a decimal and then express the decimal as a percent. A fraction is greater than 100% if it is greater than 1. It is less than 1% if it is less than $\frac{1}{100}$.

2. Sample answer: Change $64\frac{1}{2}\%$ to 64.5% and then move the decimal point two places to the left and drop the percent sign.

★ **indicates increased difficulty**

Practice and Apply

Express each percent as a fraction or mixed number in simplest form and as a decimal. 16–27. See margin.

16. 42%
17. 88%
18. $16\dfrac{2}{3}\%$
19. 87.5%
20. 150%
21. 350%
22. 18%
23. 61%
24. 117%
25. 223%
26. 0.8%
27. 0.53%

Express each decimal or fraction as a percent. Round to the nearest tenth percent, if necessary.

28. 0.51 **51%**
29. 0.09 **9%**
30. 3.21 **321%**
31. 2.7 **270%**
32. 0.0042 **0.42%**
33. 0.0006 **0.06%**
34. $\dfrac{7}{25}$ **28%**
35. $\dfrac{9}{40}$ **22.5%**
36. $\dfrac{10}{3}$ **333.3%**
37. $\dfrac{14}{8}$ **175%**
38. $\dfrac{15}{2500}$ **0.6%**
39. $\dfrac{20}{1200}$ **1.7%**

40. **GEOGRAPHY** Forty-six percent of the world's water is in the Pacific Ocean. What fraction is this? $\dfrac{23}{50}$

41. **GEOGRAPHY** The Arctic Ocean contains 3.7% of the world's water. What fraction is this? $\dfrac{37}{1000}$

42. **FOOD** According to a survey, 22% of people said that mustard is their favorite condiment while two-fifths of people said that they prefer ketchup. Which group is larger? Explain. **See pp. 323A–323B.**

Choose the greatest number in each set.

43. $\left\{\dfrac{2}{5},\ \underline{0.45},\ 35\%,\ 3 \text{ out of } 8\right\}$

44. $\left\{\dfrac{3}{4},\ 0.70,\ 78\%,\ \underline{4 \text{ out of } 5}\right\}$

45. $\left\{\underline{19\%},\ \dfrac{3}{16},\ 0.155,\ 2 \text{ to } 15\right\}$

46. $\left\{89\%,\ \dfrac{10}{11},\ 0.884,\ 12 \text{ to } 14\right\}$

Write each list of numbers in order from least to greatest.

47. $\dfrac{2}{3}$, 61%, 0.69 **61%, $\dfrac{2}{3}$, 0.69**

48. $\dfrac{2}{7}$, 0.027, 27% **0.027, 27%, $\dfrac{2}{7}$**

★ **GEOMETRY** For Exercises 49 and 50, use the information and the figure shown. Suppose that two fifths of the rectangle is shaded.

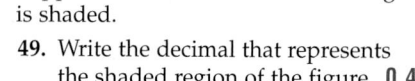

15 units · 25 units

49. Write the decimal that represents the shaded region of the figure. **0.4**

50. What is the area of the shaded region? **150 square units**

51. **CRITICAL THINKING** Find a fraction that satisfies the conditions below. Then write a sentence explaining why you think your fraction is or is not the only solution that satisfies the conditions. **See pp. 323A–323B.**

- The fraction can be written as a percent greater than 1%.
- The fraction can be written as a percent less than 50%.
- The decimal equivalent of the fraction is a terminating decimal.
- The value of the denominator minus the value of the numerator is 3.

Answers

16. $\dfrac{21}{50}$, 0.42
17. $\dfrac{22}{25}$, 0.88
18. $\dfrac{1}{6}$, 0.16$\overline{6}$
19. $\dfrac{7}{8}$, 0.875
20. $1\dfrac{1}{2}$, 1.5
21. $3\dfrac{1}{2}$, 3.5
22. $\dfrac{9}{50}$, 0.18
23. $\dfrac{61}{100}$, 0.61
24. $1\dfrac{17}{100}$, 1.17
25. $2\dfrac{23}{100}$, 2.23
26. $\dfrac{1}{125}$, 0.008
27. $\dfrac{53}{1000}$, 0.0053

52. CRITICAL THINKING Explain why percents are rational numbers.
See margin

53. WRITING IN MATH Answer the question that was posed at the beginning of the lesson. **See margin.**

How are percents related to fractions and decimals?

Include the following in your answer:
- examples of figures in which 25%, 30%, 40%, and 65% of the area is shaded, and
- an explanation of why each percent represents the shaded area.

Standardized Test Practice
Ⓐ Ⓑ Ⓒ Ⓓ

54. Assuming that the regions in each figure are equal, which figure has the greatest part of its area shaded? **D**

Ⓐ   Ⓑ

Ⓒ   Ⓓ

55. According to a survey, 85% of people eat a salad at least once a week. Which ratio represents this portion? **A**

Ⓐ 17 to 20   Ⓑ 13 to 20   Ⓒ 9 to 10   Ⓓ 4 to 5

Maintain Your Skills

Mixed Review Write the scale factor of each scale. *(Lesson 6-3)*

56. 3 inches = 18 inches $\frac{1}{6}$ **57.** 2 inches = 2 feet $\frac{1}{12}$

58. ALGEBRA Find the solution of $\frac{x}{54} = \frac{2}{3}$. *(Lesson 6-2)* **36**

Find each product. Write in simplest form. *(Lesson 5-3)*

59. $\frac{4}{7} \cdot \frac{11}{12}$ $\frac{11}{21}$ **60.** $-\frac{3}{5} \cdot \frac{10}{18}$ $-\frac{1}{3}$ **61.** $4 \cdot \frac{16}{52}$ $1\frac{3}{13}$

62. Write 5.6×10^{-4} in standard form. *(Lesson 4-8)* **0.00056**

Determine whether each number is *prime* or *composite*. *(Lesson 4-3)*

63. 21 **composite**   **64.** 47 **prime**   **65.** 57 **composite**

Getting Ready for the Next Lesson **PREREQUISITE SKILL** Solve each proportion.
(To review **proportions***, see Lesson 6-2.)*

66. $\frac{25}{4} = \frac{x}{100}$ **625**   **67.** $\frac{56}{7} = \frac{y}{100}$ **800**

68. $\frac{75}{8} = \frac{n}{100}$ **937.5**   **69.** $\frac{m}{10} = \frac{9.4}{100}$ **0.94**

70. $\frac{h}{350} = \frac{46}{100}$ **161**   **71.** $\frac{86.4}{k} = \frac{27}{100}$ **320**

Answers

52. Because they can be expressed in the form $\frac{a}{b}$ where a and b are integers and $b \neq 0$

53. Percents are related to fractions and decimals because they can be expressed as them. Answers should include the following.

 $25\% = \frac{1}{4} = 0.25$

25%

 $30\% = \frac{3}{10} = 0.3$

30%

 $40\% = \frac{2}{5} = 0.4$

40%

 $65\% = \frac{13}{20} = 0.65$

65%

Lesson 6-4 Fractions, Decimals, and Percents. **285**

---

4 Assess

Open-Ended Assessment

Speaking Have students explain how they can compare a percent to a decimal or a fraction to determine which is greater.

Tips for New Teachers

Intervention
Many students seek simplified ways to relate fractions, decimals, and percents. For example, students may write $\frac{2}{5}$ as 2.5 or 0.25 instead of 0.4. Use models to show the multiple representations of $2 \div 5$.

Getting Ready for Lesson 6-5

PREREQUISITE SKILL In Lesson 6-5, students use the percent proportion to solve percent problems. Exercises 66–71 should be used to determine your students' familiarity with solving proportions.

Objective Use a percent model to find a percent or a part.

Materials
grid paper

Activity 1

- Ask one student to demonstrate Exercise 1 on the board. Encourage students to discuss any questions they may have concerning this model.
- Have students draw the percent model on the far right-hand side of the page. Then they can reuse the model by folding the grid paper over the left-hand numbers.
- Have students complete the rest of the page individually or in small groups.

Algebra Activity

A Preview of Lesson 6-5

NEW YORK *Performance Indicator* **8.N.5 Estimate a percent of quantity, given an application**

Using a Percent Model

Activity 1

When you see advertisements on television or in magazines, you are often bombarded with many claims. For example, you might hear that four out of five use a certain long-distance phone service. What percent does this represent?

You can find the percent by using a model.

Finding a Percent		
Step 1	**Step 2**	**Step 3**
Draw a 10-unit by 1-unit rectangle on grid paper. Label the units on the right from 0 to 100, because percent is a ratio that compares a number to 100.	On the left side, mark equal units from 0 to 5, because 5 represents the whole quantity. Locate 4 on this scale.	Draw a horizontal line from 4 on the left side to the right side of the model. The number on the right side is the percent. Label the model as shown.

Using the model, you can see that the ratio *4 out of 5* is the same as 80%. So, according to this claim, 80% of people prefer the certain long-distance phone service.

Model 1–10. Exact answers are given. For models, see pp. 323A–323B.
Draw a model and find the percent that is represented by each ratio.
If it is not possible to find the exact percent using the model, estimate.

1. 6 out of 10 **60%**

2. 9 out of 10 **90%**

3. 2 out of 5 **40%**

4. 3 out of 4 **75%**

5. 9 out of 20 **45%**

6. 8 out of 50 **16%**

7. 2 out of 8 **25%**

8. 3 out of 8 **37.5%**

9. 2 out of 3 $66\frac{2}{3}$%

10. 5 out of 9 $55\frac{5}{9}$%

Resource Manager

 Teaching Pre-Algebra with Manipulatives

- p. 1 (master for grid paper)
- p. 89 (student recording sheet)

Activity 2

Suppose a store advertises a sale in which all merchandise is 20% off the original price. If the original price of a pair of shoes is $50, how much will you save?

In this case, you know the percent. You need to find what part of the original price you'll save.

You can find the part by using a similar model.

Finding a Part		
Step 1	**Step 2**	**Step 3**
Draw a 10-unit by 1-unit rectangle on grid paper. Label the units on the right from 0 to 100 because percent is a ratio that compares a number to 100.	On the left side, mark equal units from 0 to 50, because 50 represents the whole quantity.	Draw a horizontal line from 20% on the right side to the left side of the model. The number on the left side is the part. Label the model as shown.

Using the model, you can see that 20% of 50 is 10. So, you will save $10 if you buy the shoes.

Model **11–20. Exact answers are given. For models, see pp. 323A–323B.**
Draw a model and find the part that is represented. If it is not possible to find an exact answer from the model, estimate.

11. 10% of 50 **5**

12. 60% of 20 **12**

13. 90% of 40 **36**

14. 30% of 10 **3**

15. 25% of 20 **5**

16. 75% of 40 **30**

17. 5% of 200 **10**

18. 85% of 500 **425**

19. $33\frac{1}{3}$% of 12 **4**

20. 37.5% of 16 **6**

Activity 2

- Ask one student to demonstrate Exercise 1 on the board. Encourage students to discuss any questions they may have concerning this model.
- Have students complete the rest of the page individually or in pairs.

Assess

In **Exercises 1–10**, students should use a model to write the ratio of two numbers as a percent.

In **Exercises 11–20**, students should use a model to find the part that is represented by a percent.

Study Notebook

Have students record a model for finding the percent represented by the ratio 4 out of 12. Then have students record a model for finding 35% of 80.

1 Focus

Mathematical Background notes are available for this lesson on page 262D.

Why are percents important in real-world situations?

The opening activity questions are repeated on page 322 of the *Chapter 6 Resource Masters*.

Reading to Learn Mathematics, p. 322 **ELL**

Pre-Activity *Why are percents important in real-world situations?*

Do the activity at the top of page 288 in your textbook. Write your answers below.

a. Write a ratio that compares the amount of copper to the total amount of metal in the outer layer. **3 to 4**

b. Write the ratio as a fraction and as a percent. $\frac{3}{4}$, **75%**

Reading the Lesson 1–3. See students' work.

Write a definition and give an example of each new vocabulary word or phrase.

Vocabulary	Definition	Example
1. percent proportion		
2. part		
3. base		

4. In a percent proportion, the percent is always written as a fraction whose denominator is **100**.

5. What can percent proportions be used to do? **solve problems that involve percents**

Helping You Remember

6. Fill in the blanks to identify the base, the part, and the percent in the following percent proportion.

$\frac{\text{Part}}{\text{Base}}$ $\frac{13}{20} = \frac{65}{100}$ Percent

What letter do both numerators begin with? **p**

NEW YORK *Performance Indicator* **8.PS.10 Use proportionality to model problems**

What You'll Learn

• Use the percent proportion to solve problems.

Why are percents important in real-world situations?

Have you collected any of the new state quarters?

The quarters are made of a pure copper core and an outer layer that is an alloy of 3 parts copper and 1 part nickel.

a. Write a ratio that compares the amount of copper to the total amount of metal in the outer layer. **3 to 4**

b. Write the ratio as a fraction and as a percent. $\frac{3}{4}$, **75%**

USE THE PERCENT PROPORTION In a **percent proportion**, one of the numbers, called the **part**, is being compared to the whole quantity, called the **base**. The other ratio is the percent, written as a fraction, whose base is 100.

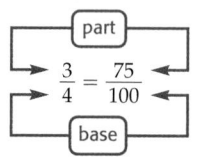

$$\frac{3}{4} = \frac{75}{100}$$

part · base

Vocabulary

• percent proportion
• part
• base

Key Concept *Percent Proportion*

• **Words** $\dfrac{\text{part}}{\text{base}} = \dfrac{\text{percent}}{100}$

• **Symbols** $\dfrac{a}{b} = \dfrac{p}{100}$, where a is the part, b is the base, and p is the percent.

Example 1 *Find the Percent*

Five is what percent of 8?

Five is being compared to 8. So, 5 is the part and 8 is the base. Let p represent the percent.

$\dfrac{a}{b} = \dfrac{p}{100} \rightarrow \dfrac{5}{8} = \dfrac{p}{100}$ Replace a with 5 and b with 8.

$5 \cdot 100 = 8 \cdot p$ Find the cross products.

$500 = 8p$ Simplify.

$\dfrac{500}{8} = \dfrac{8p}{8}$ Divide each side by 8.

$62.5 = p$ So, 5 is 62.5% of 8.

Study Tip

Estimation
Five is a little more than one-half of eight. So, the answer should be a little more than 50%.

✓ **Concept Check** In the percent proportion $\frac{15}{20} = \frac{75}{100}$, which number is the base? **20**

Resource Manager

📂 Workbooks and Reproducible Masters

Chapter 6 Resource Masters
• Study Guide and Intervention, p. 319
• Skills Practice, p. 320
• Practice, p. 321
• Reading to Learn Mathematics, p. 322
• Enrichment, p. 323
• Assessment, pp. 359, 361

Parent and Student Study Guide Workbook, p. 48
Science and Mathematics Lab Manual, pp. 83–86

📖 Transparencies
5-Minute Check Transparency 6-5
Answer Key Transparencies

💿 Technology
Interactive Chalkboard

Example 2 *Find the Percent*

What percent of 4 is 7?

Seven is being compared to 4. So, 7 is the part and 4 is the base. Let p represent the percent.

$$\frac{a}{b} = \frac{p}{100} \rightarrow \frac{7}{4} = \frac{p}{100}$$ Replace a with 7 and b with 4.

$$7 \cdot 100 = 4 \cdot p$$ Find the cross products.

$$700 = 4p$$ Simplify.

$$\frac{700}{4} = \frac{4p}{4}$$ Divide each side by 4.

$$175 = p$$ So, 175% of 4 is 7.

Example 3 *Apply the Percent Proportion*

ENVIRONMENT The graphic shows the number of threatened species in the United States. What percent of the total number of threatened species are mammals?

Compare the number of species of mammals, 37, to the total number of threatened species, 443. Let a represent the part, 37, and let b represent the base, 443, in the percent proportion. Let p represent the percent.

USA TODAY Snapshots®

Number of threatened species in USA

Plants 168	Reptiles 27	Birds 55
	Amphibians 25	Mammals 37
	Fish 131	

Source: The International Union for Conservation of Nature and Natural Resources

By Hilary Wasson and Alejandro Gonzalez, USA TODAY

$$\frac{a}{b} = \frac{p}{100} \rightarrow \frac{37}{443} = \frac{p}{100}$$

$$37 \cdot 100 = 443 \cdot p$$

$$3700 = 443p$$ Simplify.

$$\frac{3700}{443} = \frac{443p}{443}$$ Divide each side by 443.

$$8.4 \approx p$$ Simplify.

So, about 8.4% of the total number of threatened species are mammals.

You can also use the percent proportion to find a missing part or base.

Concept Summary		*Types of Percent Problems*
Type	**Example**	**Proportion**
Find the Percent	3 is <u>what percent</u> of 4?	$\frac{3}{4} = \frac{p}{100}$
Find the Part	<u>What number</u> is 75% of 4?	$\frac{a}{4} = \frac{75}{100}$
Find the Base	3 is 75% of <u>what number</u>?	$\frac{3}{b} = \frac{75}{100}$

Study Notebook

Have students—
• add the definitions/examples of the vocabulary terms to their Vocabulary Builder worksheets for Chapter 6.
• include any other item(s) that they find helpful in mastering the skills in this lesson.

DAILY INTERVENTION **FIND THE ERROR** If students are having difficulty with determining the correct proportion, have them make and fill in a table like the following.

	actual numbers	percent numbers
parts	(unknown)	35
whole	21	100

Then encourage them to notice that Judie's proportion is the one that resembles the table.

About the Exercises . . .

Odd/Even Assignments
Exercises 9–22 are structured so that students practice the same concepts whether they are assigned odd or even problems.

Alert! Exercise 24 involves research on the Internet or other reference materials.

Assignment Guide
Basic: 9–15 odd, 21, 23, 25–41
Average: 9–23 odd, 25–41
Advanced: 10–26 even, 27–35 (Optional: 36–41)
All: Practice Quiz 1 (1–5)

Example 4 **Find the Part**

What number is 5.5% of 650?

The percent is 5.5, and the base is 650. Let *a* represent the part.

$$\frac{a}{b} = \frac{p}{100} \rightarrow \frac{a}{650} = \frac{5.5}{100}$$ Replace *b* with 650 and *p* with 5.5.

$$a \cdot 100 = 650 \cdot 5.5$$ Find the cross products.

$$100a = 3575$$ Simplify.

$$a = 35.75$$ Mentally divide each side by 100.

So, 5.5% of 650 is 35.75.

Log on for:
• Updated data
• More activities on using the percent proportion.
www.pre-alg.com/usa_today

Example 5 **Apply the Percent Proportion**

CHORES Use the graphic to determine how many of the 1074 youths surveyed do not clean their room because there is not enough time.

The total number of youths is 1074. So, 1074 is the base. The percent is 29%.

To find 29% of 1074, let *b* represent the base, 1074, and let *p* represent the percent, 29%, in the percent proportion. Let *a* represent the part.

$$\frac{a}{b} = \frac{p}{100} \rightarrow \frac{a}{1074} = \frac{29}{100}$$

$$a \cdot 100 = 1074 \cdot 29$$

$$100a = 31146$$ Simplify.

$$a = 311.46$$ Mentally divide each side by 100.

So, about 311 youths do not clean their room because there is not enough time.

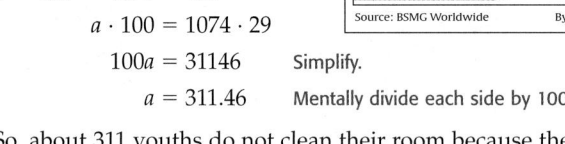

USA TODAY Snapshots®

Kids don't enjoy cleaning their rooms
When 1,074 youths 19 and under were asked why they don't clean their room more often, these were their responses[1]:

I don't like to — 66%
Not enough time — 29%
I'm too lazy — 28%
The rest of the house is dirty — 6%
No reply — 2%

1 — More than one response allowed

Source: BSMG Worldwide   By Lori Joseph and Sam Ward, USA TODAY

Example 6 **Find the Base**

Fifty-two is 40% of what number?

The percent is 40% and the part is 52. Let *b* represent the base.

$$\frac{a}{b} = \frac{p}{100} \rightarrow \frac{52}{b} = \frac{40}{100}$$ Replace *a* with 52 and *p* with 40.

$$52 \cdot 100 = b \cdot 40$$ Find the cross products.

$$5200 = 40b$$ Simplify.

$$\frac{5200}{40} = \frac{40b}{40}$$ Divide each side by 40.

$$130 = b$$ Simplify.

So, 52 is 40% of 130.

DAILY INTERVENTION **Differentiated Instruction**

• **Visual/Spatial** Have students make and fill in a table to aid them in writing a proportion. For example, to find 90% of 15, the table would look like this:

	actual numbers	percent numbers
parts	(unknown)	90
whole	15	100

Check for Understanding

Concept Check

1. OPEN ENDED Write a proportion that can be used to find the percent scored on an exam that has 50 questions.

1–2. See margin.

2. FIND THE ERROR Judie and Pennie are using a proportion to find what number is 35% of 21. Who is correct? Explain your reasoning.

Judie	Pennie
$\dfrac{n}{21} = \dfrac{35}{100}$	$\dfrac{21}{n} = \dfrac{35}{100}$

GUIDED PRACTICE KEY

Exercises	Examples
3–6	1, 2, 4, 6
7	3
8	5

Guided Practice **Use the percent proportion to solve each problem.**

3. 16 is what percent of 40? **40%**

4. 21 is 30% of what number? **70**

5. What is 80% of 130? **104**

6. What percent of 5 is 14? **280%**

Applications

7. BOOKS Fifty-four of the 90 books on a shelf are history books. What percent of the books are history books? **60%**

8. CHORES Refer to Example 5 on page 290. How many of the 1074 youths surveyed do not clean their room because they do not like to clean? **about 709**

★ indicates increased difficulty

Practice and Apply

Homework Help

For Exercises	See Examples
9–20	1, 2, 4, 6
21, 23, 24	3
22, 25	5

Extra Practice
See page 738.

Use the percent proportion to solve each problem. Round to the nearest tenth. 9–20. See margin.

9. 72 is what percent of 160?

10. 17 is what percent of 85?

11. 36 is 72% of what number?

12. 27 is 90% of what number?

13. What is 44% of 175?

14. What is 84% of 150?

15. 52.2 is what percent of 145?

16. 19.8 is what percent of 36?

★ 17. 14 is $12\frac{1}{2}$% of what number?

★ 18. 36 is $8\frac{3}{4}$% of what number?

★ 19. 7 is what percent of 3500?

★ 20. What is 0.3% of 750?

21. BIRDS If 12 of the 75 animals in a pet store are parakeets, what percent are parakeets? **16%**

22. FISH Of the fish in an aquarium, 26% are angelfish. If the aquarium contains 50 fish, how many are angelfish? **13**

SCIENCE For Exercises 23 and 24, use the information in the table.

23. What percent of the world's fresh water does the Antarctic Icecap contain? **about 70%**

24. The total volume of the world's fresh and salt water is 326,038,400 mi³. The Antarctic Icecap contains about 2% of the world's total water supply.

24. **RESEARCH** Use the Internet or another source to find the total volume of the world's fresh and salt water. What percent of the world's total water supply does the Antarctic Icecap contain?

World's Fresh Water Supply	
Source	**Volume (mi³)**
Freshwater Lakes	30,000
All Rivers	300
Antarctic Icecap	6,300,000
Arctic Icecap and Glaciers	680,000
Water in the Atmosphere	3100
Ground Water	1,000,000
Deep-lying Ground Water	1,000,000
Total	**9,013,400**

Source: *Time Almanac*

www.pre-alg.com/self_check_quiz/ny

Lesson 6-5 Using the Percent Proportion 291

Answers

1. $\dfrac{\text{number correct}}{50} = \dfrac{\%}{100}$

2. Judie; In the sentence *what number is 35% of 21*, *what number* is the part, 21 is the base, and 35% is the percent. So, to solve the problem, you would use the proportion $\dfrac{n}{21} = \dfrac{35}{100}$.

9. 45%
10. 20%
11. 50
12. 30
13. 77
14. 126

15. 36%
16. 55%
17. 112
18. 411.4
19. 0.2%
20. 2.25

Lesson 6-5 Using the Percent Proportion 291

Open-Ended Assessment

Writing Have students write their own percent problems based on what they see in their own classroom. For example, if 4 out of 20 students are wearing red today, what percent of the students are wearing red? Have them solve their problems, and then trade with another student to solve.

Getting Ready for Lesson 6-6

PREREQUISITE SKILL Lesson 6-6 presents finding percents mentally. It is helpful to use the fraction form of a percent. Exercises 36–41 should be used to determine your students' familiarity with finding products involving fractions.

Assessment Options

Practice Quiz 1 The quiz provides students with a brief review of the concepts and skills in Lessons 6-1 through 6-5. Lesson numbers are given to the right of exercises or instruction lines so students can review concepts not yet mastered.

Quiz (Lessons 6-4 and 6-5) is available on p. 359 of the *Chapter 6 Resource Masters*.

Mid-Chapter Test (Lessons 6-1 through 6-5) is available on p. 361 of the *Chapter 6 Resource Masters*.

Answers

26. Since n is 25% of some number a, and 35% of some number b, we can write $\frac{n}{a} = \frac{25}{100}$ and $\frac{n}{b} = \frac{35}{100}$. By solving for n, we find that $n = \frac{25a}{100}$ and $n = \frac{35b}{100}$. Since $n = n$, we can write $\frac{25a}{100} = \frac{35b}{100}$. Solving for a, $a = \frac{35b}{25} = \frac{7b}{5} = \frac{7}{5}b = 1.4b$ results. So, $a > b$.

---

25. **LIFE SCIENCE** Carbon constitutes 18.5% of the human body by weight. Determine the amount of carbon contained in a person who weighs 145 pounds. **26.8 lb**

26. **CRITICAL THINKING** A number n is 25% of some number a and 35% of a number b. Tell the relationship between a and b. Is $a < b$, $a > b$, or is it impossible to determine the relationship? Explain. **See margin.**

27. **WRITING IN MATH** Answer the question that was posed at the beginning of the lesson. **See margin.**

   Why are percents important in real-world situations?

   Include the following in your answer:
   • an example of a real-world situation where percents are used, and
   • an explanation of the meaning of the percent in the situation.

NEW YORK Test Practice
Standardized Test Practice
A B C D

28. The table shows the number of people in each section of the school chorale. Which section makes up exactly 25% of the chorale? **B**

   (A) Tenor   (B) Alto
   (C) Soprano (D) Bass

School Chorale	
Section	Number
Soprano	16
Alto	15
Tenor	12
Bass	17

Maintain Your Skills

Mixed Review Write each percent as a fraction in simplest form. *(Lesson 6-4)*

29. 42% $\frac{21}{50}$ 30. 56% $\frac{14}{25}$ 31. 120% $1\frac{1}{5}$

32. **MAPS** On a map of a state park, the scale is 0.5 inch = 1.5 miles. Find the actual distance from the ranger's station to the beach if the distance on the map is 1.75 inches. *(Lesson 6-3)* **5.25 mi**

Find each sum or difference. Write in simplest form. *(Lesson 5-5)*

33. $\frac{2}{9} + \frac{5}{9}$ $\frac{7}{9}$ 34. $\frac{11}{12} - \frac{3}{12}$ $\frac{2}{3}$ 35. $2\frac{5}{8} + \frac{7}{8}$ $3\frac{1}{2}$

Getting Ready for the Next Lesson

PREREQUISITE SKILL Find each product.
(To review multiplying fractions, see Lesson 5-3.)

36. $\frac{1}{2} \times 14$ **7**   37. $\frac{1}{4} \times 32$ **8**   38. $\frac{1}{5} \times 15$ **3**

39. $\frac{2}{3} \times 9$ **6**   40. $\frac{3}{4} \times 16$ **12**   41. $\frac{5}{6} \times 30$ **25**

Practice Quiz 1 — Lessons 6-1 through 6-5

1. Express $3.29 for 24 cans of soda as a unit rate. *(Lesson 6-1)* **$0.14 per can**

2. What value of x makes $\frac{3}{4} = \frac{x}{68}$ a proportion? *(Lesson 6-2)* **51**

3. **SCIENCE** A scale model of a volcano is 4 feet tall. If the actual height of the volcano is 12,276 feet, what is the scale of the model? *(Lesson 6-3)* **1 ft = 3069 ft**

4. Express 352% as a decimal. *(Lesson 6-4)* **3.52**

5. Use the percent proportion to find 32.5% of 60. *(Lesson 6-5)* **19.5**

---

27. In real-world situations, percents are important because they show how something compares to the whole. Answers should include the following.

   • Sample answer: The outer layer of the new state quarters is an alloy of 3 parts copper to 1 part nickel.

   • There are 4 parts to the outer layer (copper, copper, copper, nickel). The outer layer is $\frac{3}{4}$ or 75% copper and $\frac{1}{4}$ or 25% nickel.

Finding Percents Mentally

NEW YORK *Performance Indicator* **8.N.5** Estimate a percent of quantity, given an application, **8.N.6** Justify the reasonableness of answers using estimation

 What You'll Learn

- Compute mentally with percents.
- Estimate with percents.

How is estimation used when determining sale prices?

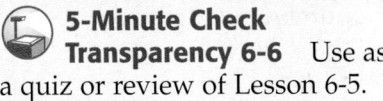

A sporting goods store is having a sale in which all merchandise is on sale at half off. A few regularly priced items are shown at the right.

a. What is the sale price of each item?

b. What percent represents half off? **50%**

c. Suppose the items are on sale for 25% off. Explain how you would determine the sale price.

a. tennis racquet: $34; baseball hat: $7.50; baseball glove: $18.50; football: $22
c. Sample answer: Divide the regular price by 4 and then subtract the result from the original price.

FIND PERCENTS OF A NUMBER MENTALLY When working with common percents like 10%, 25%, 40%, and 50%, it may be helpful to use the fraction form of the percent. A few percent-fraction equivalents are shown.

0% $12\frac{1}{2}$% 25% 40% 50% $66\frac{2}{3}$% 75% $87\frac{1}{2}$% 100%

0 $\frac{1}{8}$ $\frac{1}{4}$ $\frac{2}{5}$ $\frac{1}{2}$ $\frac{2}{3}$ $\frac{3}{4}$ $\frac{7}{8}$ 1

Some percents are used more frequently than others. So, it is a good idea to be familiar with these percents and their equivalent fractions.

Concept Summary			Percent–Fraction Equivalents	
$20\% = \frac{1}{5}$	$10\% = \frac{1}{10}$	$25\% = \frac{1}{4}$	$12\frac{1}{2}\% = \frac{1}{8}$	$16\frac{2}{3}\% = \frac{1}{6}$
$40\% = \frac{2}{5}$	$30\% = \frac{3}{10}$	$50\% = \frac{1}{2}$	$37\frac{1}{2}\% = \frac{3}{8}$	$33\frac{1}{3}\% = \frac{1}{3}$
$60\% = \frac{3}{5}$	$70\% = \frac{7}{10}$	$75\% = \frac{3}{4}$	$62\frac{1}{2}\% = \frac{5}{8}$	$66\frac{2}{3}\% = \frac{2}{3}$
$80\% = \frac{4}{5}$	$90\% = \frac{9}{10}$		$87\frac{1}{2}\% = \frac{7}{8}$	$83\frac{1}{3}\% = \frac{5}{6}$

Example 1 Find Percent of a Number Mentally

Find the percent of each number mentally.

a. **50% of 32**

50% of $32 = \frac{1}{2}$ of 32 — Think: $50\% = \frac{1}{2}$.

$= 16$ — Think: $\frac{1}{2}$ of 32 is 16.

So, 50% of 32 is 16.

Study Tip

Look Back
To review **multiplying fractions**, see Lesson 5-3.

 6-6 **Lesson Notes**

1 Focus

5-Minute Check Transparency 6-6 Use as a quiz or review of Lesson 6-5.

Mathematical Background notes are available for this lesson on page 262D.

How is estimation used when determining sale prices?

The opening activity questions are repeated on page 327 of the *Chapter 6 Resource Masters*.

Reading to Learn Mathematics, p. 327 **ELL**

Pre-Activity *How is estimation used when determining sale prices?*

Do the activity at the top of page 293 in your textbook. Write your answers below.

a. What is the sale price of each item? Tennis racquet: $34; baseball hat: $7.50; baseball glove: $18.50; football: $22

b. What percent represents half off? 50%

c. Suppose the items are on sale for 25% off. Explain how you would determine the sale price. Sample answer: Divide the regular price by 4 and then subtract the result from the original price.

Reading the Lesson

1. Give an example of a real-life situation in which you can estimate with percents. Sample answer: determining the amount of a tip

2. When can you find the percent of a number mentally? when working with common percents like 10%, 25%, 40%, and 50%

Helping You Remember

3. Name the three methods that can be used to estimate with percents. Give an example of each. Examples will vary. See students' work.

Method	Example
Fraction	
1%	
Meaning of Percent	

Teaching Tip Ask students what percent they pay if an item is marked 50% off. **50%** Also ask what percent they pay if an item is marked 25% off. **75%**

Resource Manager

 Transparencies

5-Minute Check Transparency 6-6
Answer Key Transparencies

Technology

Interactive Chalkboard

Workbooks and Reproducible Masters

Chapter 6 Resource Masters
- Study Guide and Intervention, p. 324
- Skills Practice, p. 325
- Practice, p. 326
- Reading to Learn Mathematics, p. 327
- Enrichment, p. 328

Parent and Student Study Guide Workbook, p. 49
Prerequisite Skills Workbook, pp. 39–40

FIND PERCENTS OF A NUMBER MENTALLY

In-Class Example Power Point®

1 Find the percent of each number mentally.

a. 50% of 46   **23**

b. 25% of 88   **22**

c. 70% of 110   **77**

Teaching Tip Encourage students to solve problems mentally by having them work in small groups of similar capabilities. Provide problems one at a time and have students see if they can solve them faster than others in their group.

ESTIMATE WITH PERCENTS

In-Class Examples Power Point®

2 **a.** Estimate 22% of 494.   **100**

b. Estimate 63% of 788.   **480**

c. Estimate $\frac{1}{4}$% of 1,219.   **3**

d. Estimate 155% of 38.   **60**

Teaching Tip To help students develop number sense for percents, have them check their estimates by finding the actual amount.

3 **MONEY** A restaurant bill totals $21.35. You want to leave a 15% tip. What is a reasonable amount for the tip?   **$3**

Teaching Tip Depending upon whether both the percent and the number are rounded up or down, the estimate will be too high or too low. Recommend that students round one up and one down whenever possible to find a more reliable estimate.

Find the percent of each number mentally.

b. 25% of 48

$25\% \text{ of } 48 = \frac{1}{4} \text{ of } 48$ Think: $25\% = \frac{1}{4}$.

$= 12$ Think: $\frac{1}{4}$ of 48 is 12.

So, 25% of 48 is 12.

c. 40% of 45

$40\% \text{ of } 45 = \frac{2}{5} \text{ of } 45$ Think: $40\% = \frac{2}{5}$.

$= 18$ Think: $\frac{1}{5}$ of 45 is 9. So, $\frac{2}{5}$ of 45 is 18.

So, 40% of 45 is 18.

ESTIMATE WITH PERCENTS   Sometimes, an exact answer is not needed. In these cases, you can estimate. Consider the following model.

- 14 of the 30 circles are shaded.

- $\frac{14}{30}$ is about $\frac{15}{30}$ or $\frac{1}{2}$.

- $\frac{1}{2} = 50\%$. So, about 50% of the model is shaded.

The table below shows three methods you can use to estimate with percents. For example, let's estimate 22% of 237.

Method	Estimate 22% of 237.
Fraction	22% is a bit more than 20% or $\frac{1}{5}$. 237 is a bit less than 240. So, 22% of 237 is about $\frac{1}{5}$ of 240 or 48. Estimate: 48
1%	22% = 22 × 1% 1% of 237 = 2.37 or about 2. So, 22% of 237 is about 22 × 2 or 44. Estimate: 44
Meaning of Percent	22% means about 20 for every 100 or about 2 for every 10. 237 has 2 hundreds and about 4 tens. (20 × 2) + (2 × 4) = 40 + 8 or 48 Estimate: 48

You can use these methods to estimate the percent of a number.

Example 2 *Estimate Percents*

a. Estimate 13% of 120.

13% is about 12.5% or $\frac{1}{8}$.

$\frac{1}{8}$ of 120 is 15.

So, 13% of 120 is about 15.

b. Estimate 80% of 296.

80% is equal to $\frac{4}{5}$.

296 is about 300.

$\frac{4}{5}$ of 300 is 240.

So, 80% of 296 is about 240.

Study Tip

Percents
To find 1% of any number, move the decimal point two places to the left.

DAILY INTERVENTION   **Differentiated Instruction**   **ELL**

- **Verbal/Linguistic** Give students one estimate problem at a time. Have them speak their answer as soon as they get it. When students have different estimates, encourage them to compare their strategies and then to explain to the class why the estimates did not match.

c. Estimate $\frac{1}{3}\%$ of 598.

$\frac{1}{3}\% = \frac{1}{3} \times 1\%$. 598 is almost 600.

1% of 600 is 6.

So, $\frac{1}{3}\%$ of 598 is about $\frac{1}{3} \times 6$ or 2.

d. Estimate 118% of 56.

118% means about 120 for every 100 or about 12 for every 10.

56 has about 6 tens.

$12 \times 6 = 72$

So, 118% of 56 is about 72.

Estimating percents is a useful skill in real-life situations.

Example 3 *Use Estimation to Solve a Problem*

MONEY Amelia takes a taxi from the airport to a hotel. The fare is $31.50. Suppose she wants to tip the driver 15%. What would be a reasonable amount of tip for the driver?

$31.50 is about $32.

$15\% = 10\% + 5\%$

10% of $32 is $3.20.   Move the decimal point 1 place to the left.

5% of $32 is $1.60.   5% is one half of 10%.

So, 15% is about $3.20 + $1.60 or $4.80.

A reasonable amount for the tip would be $5.

Study Tip

Finding Percents
To find 10% of a number, move the decimal point one place to the left.

Check for Understanding

Concept Check

1. Explain how to estimate 18% of 216 using the fraction method.

2. Estimate the percent of the figure that is shaded. **1–2. See margin.**

3. OPEN ENDED Tell which method of estimating a percent you prefer. Explain your decision.
See students' work.

Guided Practice Find the percent of each number mentally. **4–12. See margin.**

GUIDED PRACTICE KEY	
Exercises	Examples
4–7	1
8–11	2
12	3

4. 75% of 64

5. 25% of 52

6. $33\frac{1}{3}\%$ of 27

7. 90% of 80

Estimate. Explain which method you used to estimate.

8. 20% of 61

9. 34% of 24

10. $\frac{1}{2}\%$ of 396

11. 152% of 14

Application **12. MONEY** Lu Chan wants to leave a tip of 20% on a dinner check of $52.48. About how much should he leave?

 www.pre-alg.com/extra_examples/ny

3 Practice/Apply

Study Notebook

Have students—
• copy the Percent-Fraction Table from page 293.
• copy Exercise 5 in Check for Understanding and explain how to find the percent mentally.
• explain how to estimate 32% of 62.
• include any other item(s) that they find helpful in mastering the skills in this lesson.

About the Exercises . . .

Organization by Objective
• **Find Percents of a Number Mentally:** 13–26
• **Estimate with Percents:** 27–42

Odd/Even Assignments
Exercises 13–35 and 39–42 are structured so that students practice the same concepts whether they are assigned odd or even problems.

Assignment Guide
Basic: 13–35 odd, 39, 43–66
Average: 13–41 odd, 43–66
Advanced: 14–34 even, 36–38, 40, 42, 43–60 (Optional: 61–66)

Answers

1. 18% is about 20% or $\frac{1}{5}$. 216 is about 220. $\frac{1}{5}$ of 220 is 44. So, 18% of 216 is about 44.

2. about 10%

4–12. Sample answers are given.

4. 48

5. 13

6. 9

7. 72

8. 12; fraction method: $\frac{1}{5} \times 60$ or 12

9. 8; fraction method: $\frac{1}{3} \times 24$ or 8

10. 2; 1% method: Since 1% of 396 is about 4, $\frac{1}{2}\%$ of 396 is about $\frac{1}{2}$ of 4 or 2.

11. 21; meaning of percent method: 152% means about 150 for every 100 or about 15 for every 10. 14 has 1 tens. $1 \times 15 = 15$. So, 152% of 14 is about 21.

12. $\frac{1}{5} \times \$50$ or $10

Study Guide and Intervention, p. 324

When working with common percents like 10%, 25%, 40%, and 50%, it may be helpful to use the fraction form of the percent.

Percent-Fraction Equivalents

$20\% = \frac{1}{5}$	$10\% = \frac{1}{10}$	$25\% = \frac{1}{4}$	$12\frac{1}{2}\% = \frac{1}{8}$	$16\frac{2}{3}\% = \frac{1}{6}$	
$40\% = \frac{2}{5}$	$30\% = \frac{3}{10}$	$50\% = \frac{1}{2}$	$37\frac{1}{2}\% = \frac{3}{8}$	$33\frac{1}{3}\% = \frac{1}{3}$	
$60\% = \frac{3}{5}$	$70\% = \frac{7}{10}$	$75\% = \frac{3}{4}$	$62\frac{1}{2}\% = \frac{5}{8}$	$66\frac{2}{3}\% = \frac{2}{3}$	
$80\% = \frac{4}{5}$	$90\% = \frac{9}{10}$	$100\% = 1$	$87\frac{1}{2}\% = \frac{7}{8}$	$83\frac{1}{3}\% = \frac{5}{6}$	

Example Find 20% of 35 mentally.

20% of $35 = \frac{1}{5}$ of 35 Think: $20\% = \frac{1}{5}$

$= 7$ Think: $\frac{1}{5}$ of 35 is 7. So, 20% of 35 is 7.

Exercises

Find the percent of each number mentally.

1. 50% of 6 3
2. 25% of 100 25
3. 60% of 25 15
4. 75% of 28 21
5. $66\frac{2}{3}\%$ of 33 22
6. 150% of 2 3
7. 125% of 4 5
8. 175% of 4 7
9. 10% of 110 11
10. 80% of 20 16
11. 20% of 80 16
12. 20% of 800 160
13. 90% of 600 540
14. 25% of 240 60
15. 50% of 7 3.5
16. 30% of 250 75
17. 60% of 250 150
18. 75% of 1000 750
19. 10% of 900 90
20. 20% of 900 180
21. 40% of 900 360
22. 25% of 360 90
23. 50% of 360 180
24. 75% of 360 270
25. 25% of 56 14
26. $33\frac{1}{3}\%$ of 363 121
27. $16\frac{2}{3}\%$ of 66 11
28. $62\frac{1}{2}\%$ of 32 20
29. $37\frac{1}{2}\%$ of 32 12
30. 200% of 21 42
31. $66\frac{2}{3}\%$ of 54 36
32. 150% of 2222 3333
33. $12\frac{1}{2}\%$ of 720 90
34. 30% of 30 9
35. $66\frac{2}{3}\%$ of 150 100
36. 80% of 1500 1200

Skills Practice, p. 325 and Practice, p. 326 (shown)

Find the percent of each number mentally.

1. 10% of 812 81.2
2. 50% of 1044 522
3. 40% of 25 10
4. 20% of 45 9
5. $62\frac{1}{2}\%$ of 80 50
6. 80% of 15 12
7. 30% of 400 120
8. 75% of 880 660
9. $16\frac{2}{3}\%$ of 72 12
10. $33\frac{1}{3}\%$ of 150 50
11. 60% of 2500 1500
12. $37\frac{1}{2}\%$ of 48 18
13. 25% of 244 61
14. 900% of 3 27
15. 150% of 260 390

Estimate. 16–33. Sample answers are given.

16. 31% of 62
$\frac{3}{10}$ of 60; 18
17. 65% of 83
$\frac{2}{3}$ of 81; 54
18. 87% of 850
$\frac{7}{8}$ of 800; 700
19. 32% of 26
$\frac{1}{3}$ of 27; 9
20. 47% of 213
$\frac{1}{2}$ of 200; 100
21. 22% of 536
$\frac{1}{5}$ of 500; 100
22. 68% of 12
$\frac{2}{3}$ of 12; 8
23. 11% of 29
$\frac{1}{10}$ of 30; 3
24. 78% of 4
$\frac{3}{4}$ of 4; 3
25. 21% of 18
$\frac{1}{5}$ of 20; 4
26. 73% of 91
$\frac{3}{4}$ of 88; 66
27. 8% of 1008
$\frac{1}{10}$ of 1000; 100
28. $\frac{1}{8}\%$ of 381
$\frac{1}{8}$ of 4; 2
29. $\frac{1}{6}\%$ of 567
$\frac{1}{6}$ of 6; 1
30. $\frac{2}{5}\%$ of 856
$\frac{2}{5}$ of 9; 6
31. 210% of 425
2×400; 800
32. 153% of 801
$800 + 400$; 1200
33. 689% of 2981
7×3000; 21,000

34. **MONEY** Last week a waitress made $204 in tips. This week she made 135% of that. How much did she make this week? $275.40

Enrichment, p. 328

Finding the Percent One Number Is of Another

Solve. Use the circle graph.

1. How much money did Eric spend on all the camera equipment? $520

2. What percent of the total cost of the equipment did Eric spend on the camera? 47%

3. What percent of the total cost was spent on the camera case? 6%

4. What percent of the total cost was spent on the flash? 11%

5. What percent of the total cost was spent on the wide-angle lens? 27%

6. What percent of the total cost was spent on the tripod? 9%

7. What percent of the total cost was spent on the camera case, tripod, and flash? 26%

8. The salesperson who sold Eric the equipment earned a $6\frac{1}{2}\%$ commission on the sale. How much was the commission? $33.80

Cost of Eric's Camera Equipment

Camera $244.40
Camera Case $31.20
Tripod $46.80
Flash $57.20
Wide-Angle Lens $140.40

★ indicates increased difficulty

Practice and Apply

Homework Help

For Exercises	See Examples
13–26	1
27–35	2
39, 40	3

Extra Practice
See page 738.

Find the percent of each number mentally. 13–24. See margin.

13. 50% of 28
14. 75% of 16
15. 60% of 55
16. 20% of 105
17. $87\frac{1}{2}\%$ of 56
18. $16\frac{2}{3}\%$ of 42
19. $12\frac{1}{2}\%$ of 32
20. $66\frac{2}{3}\%$ of $24
21. 200% of 45
22. 150% of 54
23. 125% of 300
24. 175% of 200

MONEY For Exercises 25 and 26, use the following information.
In a recent year, the number of $1 bills in circulation in the United States was about 7 billion. **25–26. See margin.**

25. Suppose the number of $5 bills in circulation was 25% of the number of $1 bills. About how many $5 bills were in circulation?

26. If the number of $10 bills was 20% of the number of $1 bills, about how many $10 bills were in circulation?

Estimate. Explain which method you used to estimate. 27–34. See margin.

27. 30% of 89
28. 25% of 162
29. 38% of 88
30. 81% of 25
31. $\frac{1}{4}\%$ of 806
32. $\frac{1}{5}\%$ of 40
33. 127% of 64
34. 140% of 95
35. 295% of 145
35. See pp. 323A–323B.

SPACE For Exercises 36–38, refer to the information in the table.

36. Which planet has a radius that measures about 50% of the radius of Mercury? **Pluto**

37. Sample answer: **Pluto and Mars, or Neptune and Jupiter**

★ 37. Name two planets such that the radius of one planet is about one-third the radius of the other planet.

★ 38. Name two planets such that the mass of one planet is about 330% the mass of the other. **Sample answer: Jupiter and Saturn**

Radius and Mass of Each Planet

Planet	Radius (mi)	Mass
Mercury	1516	0.0553
Venus	3761	0.815
Earth	3960	1.000
Mars	2107	0.107
Jupiter	43,450	317.830
Saturn	36,191	95.160
Uranus	15,763	14.540
Neptune	15,304	17.150
Pluto	707	0.0021

Source: The World Almanac

39. **GEOGRAPHY** The United States has 88,633 miles of shoreline. Of the total amount, 35% is located in Alaska. About how many miles of shoreline are located in Alaska? **See pp. 323A–323B.**

40. **GEOGRAPHY** About 8.5% of the total Pacific coastline is located in California. Use the information at the left to estimate the number of miles of coastline located in California. **See pp. 323A–323B.**

★ 41. **FOOD** A serving of shrimp contains 90 Calories and 7 of those Calories are from fat. About what percent of the Calories are from fat? **about 10%**

★ 42. **FOOD** Fifty-six percent of the Calories in corn chips are from fat. Estimate the number of Calories from fat in a serving of corn chips if one serving contains 160 Calories. **about 80**

More About...

Geography •·········

There are four U.S. coastlines. They are the Atlantic, Gulf, Pacific, and Arctic coasts. Most of the coastline is located on the Pacific Ocean. It contains 40,298 miles.

Source: The World Almanac

Answers

13–24.	Sample answers are given.	17. 49	23. 375

13. 14
14. 12
15. 33
16. 21
17. 49
18. 7
19. 4
20. 16
21. 90
22. 81
23. 375
24. 350
25. $\frac{1}{4} \times 8$ or 2 billion
26. $\frac{1}{5} \times 10$ or 2 billion

43. CRITICAL THINKING In an election, 40% of the Democrats and 92.5% of the Republicans voted "yes". Of all of the Democrats and Republicans, 68% voted "yes". Find the ratio of Democrats to Republicans. **7 to 8**

44. **WRITING IN MATH** Answer the question that was posed at the beginning of the lesson. **See margin.**

How is estimation used when determining sale prices?

Include the following in your answer:
- an example of a situation in which you used estimation to determine the sale price of an item, and
- an example of a real-life situation other than shopping in which you would use estimation with percents.

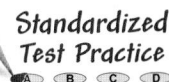

NEW YORK Test Practice

Standardized Test Practice
Ⓐ Ⓑ Ⓒ Ⓓ

45. Which percent is greater than $\frac{3}{5}$ but less than $\frac{2}{3}$? **C**

　Ⓐ 68%　　　Ⓑ 54%　　　Ⓒ 64%　　　Ⓓ 38%

46. Choose the best estimate for 26% of 362. **A**

　Ⓐ 91　　　Ⓑ 72　　　Ⓒ 108　　　Ⓓ 85

Maintain Your Skills

Mixed Review **Use the percent proportion to solve each problem.** *(Lesson 6-5)*

47. What is 28% of 75? **21**

48. 37.8 is what percent of 84? **45%**

49. FORESTRY The five states with the largest portion of land covered by forests are shown in the graphic. For each state, how many square miles of land are covered by forests? **See margin.**

State	Percent of land covered by forests	Area of state (square miles)
Maine	89.9%	35,387
New Hampshire	88.1%	9351
West Virginia	77.5%	24,231
Vermont	75.7%	9615
Alabama	66.9%	52,423

Source: The Learning Kingdom, Inc.

Express each decimal as a percent. *(Lesson 6-4)*

50. 0.27 **27%**　　　**51.** 1.6 **160%**　　　**52.** 0.008 **0.8%**

Express each percent as a decimal. *(Lesson 6-4)*

53. 77% **0.77**　　**54.** 8% **0.08**　　**55.** 421% **4.21**　　**56.** 3.56% **0.0356**

ALGEBRA **Solve each equation. Check your solution.** *(Lesson 5-9)*

57. $n + 4.7 = 13.6$ **8.9**　　**58.** $x + \frac{5}{6} = 2\frac{3}{8}$ $1\frac{13}{24}$　　**59.** $\frac{3}{7}r = -9$ **−21**

60. GEOMETRY The perimeter of a rectangle is 22 feet. Its length is 7 feet. Find its width. *(Lesson 3-7)* **4 ft**

Getting Ready for the Next Lesson **PREREQUISITE SKILL** **Solve each equation. Check your solution.**
*(To review **solving equations**, see Lesson 3-4.)*

61. $10a = 5$ **0.5**　　　　　　**62.** $20m = 4$ **0.2**

63. $60h = 15$ **0.25**　　　　　**64.** $28g = 1.4$ **0.05**

65. $80w = 5.6$ **0.07**　　　　　**66.** $125n = 15$ **0.12**

4 Assess

Open-Ended Assessment

Modeling Make two sets of cards, one with various percents on them and the other with various numbers on them. Shuffle each deck separately. Have students choose a card from each deck and mentally estimate the product of the amounts on the two cards.

Getting Ready for Lesson 6-7

PREREQUISITE SKILL Lesson 6-7 presents using percent equations to solve percent problems. Exercises 61–66 should be used to determine your students' familiarity with solving equations.

Answers

44. By estimating the cost of an item and estimating the percent of the discount, the sale price can be determined. Answers should include the following.
- Sample answer: Estimating the cost of a book that was on sale for 25% off.
- Sample answer: Estimating the amount of paint needed to paint a room.

49. Maine: 31,813 sq mi; New Hampshire: 8238 sq mi; West Virginia: 18,779 sq mi; Vermont: 7279 sq mi; Alabama: 35,071 sq mi

Answers

27. 27; fraction method: $\frac{3}{10} \times 90$ or 27

28. 40; fraction method: $\frac{1}{4} \times 160$ or 40

29. 36; fraction method: $\frac{2}{5} \times 90$ or 36

30. 20; fraction method: $\frac{4}{5} \times 25$ or 20

31. 2; 1% method: Since 1% of 806 is about 8, $\frac{1}{4}$% of 806 is about $\frac{1}{4}$ of 8 or 2.

32. 0.08; 1% method: Since 1% of 40 is 0.4, $\frac{1}{5}$% of 40 is $\frac{1}{5}$ of 0.4 or 0.08.

33. 78; meaning of percent: 127% means about 130 for every 100 or about 13 for every 10. 64 has 6 tens. 6 × 13 = 78. So, 127% of 64 is about 78.

34. 140; meaning of percent: 140% means about 140 for every 100 or about 14 for every 10. 95 has about one 100. 1 × 140 = 140. So, 140% of 95 is about 140.

NEW YORK *Performance Indicator* **8.N.4 Apply percents to:** tax, percent increase/decrease, **simple interest, sale price,** commission, interest rates, gratuities

1 Focus

5-Minute Check Transparency 6-7 Use as a quiz or review of Lesson 6-6.

Mathematical Background notes are available for this lesson on page 262D.

How is the percent proportion related to an equation?

The opening activity questions are repeated on page 332 of the *Chapter 6 Resource Masters*.

Reading to Learn Mathematics, p. 332 **ELL**

Pre-Activity *How is the percent proportion related to an equation?*

Do the activity at the top of page 298 in your textbook. Write your answers below.

a. Use the percent proportion to find the amount of tax on a $35 purchase for each state. **AL: $1.40; CT: $2.10; NM: $1.75; TX: $2.19**

b. Express each tax rate as a decimal. **AL: 0.04; CT: 0.06; NM: 0.05; TX: 0.0625**

c. Multiply the decimal form of the tax rate by $35 to find the amount of tax on the $35 purchase for each state. **AL: $1.40; CT: $2.10; NM: $1.75; TX: $2.19**

d. How are the amounts of tax in parts **a** and **c** related? **They are the same.**

Reading the Lesson 1–3. See students' work.

Write a definition and give an example of each new vocabulary word or phrase.

Vocabulary	Definition	Example
1. percent equation		
2. discount		
3. simple interest		

Helping You Remember

4. The label above each oval represents what is missing from a percent equation. In each oval, write and solve a percent equation to find that missing information. **Sample answers are given.**

Missing Base
$54 = 0.72(n)$
$n = 75$

Missing Part
$n = 0.36(80)$
$n = 28.8$

Missing Percent
$45 = n(125)$
$n = 36\%$

What You'll Learn

* Solve percent problems using percent equations.
* Solve real-life problems involving discount and interest.

Vocabulary
* percent equation
* discount
* simple interest

How is the percent proportion related to an equation?

As of July 1, 1999, 45 of the 50 U.S. states had a sales tax. The table shows the tax rate for four U.S. states.

a. Use the percent proportion to find the amount of tax on a $35 purchase for each state. **a–c. See margin.**

b. Express each tax rate as a decimal.

c. Multiply the decimal form of the tax rate by $35 to find the amount of tax on the $35 purchase for each state.

d. How are the amounts of tax in parts **a** and **c** related? **They are the same.**

State	Tax Rate (percent)
Alabama	4%
Connecticut	6%
New Mexico	5%
Texas	6.25%

Source: www.taxadmin.org

PERCENT EQUATIONS The **percent equation** is an equivalent form of the percent proportion in which the percent is written as a decimal.

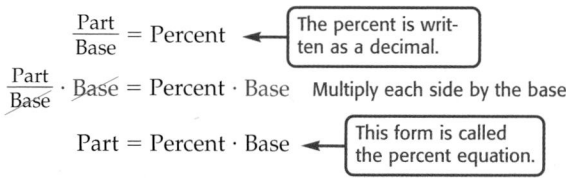

$$\frac{\text{Part}}{\text{Base}} = \text{Percent}$$ ← The percent is written as a decimal.

$$\frac{\text{Part}}{\text{Base}} \cdot \text{Base} = \text{Percent} \cdot \text{Base}$$ Multiply each side by the base.

$$\text{Part} = \text{Percent} \cdot \text{Base}$$ ← This form is called the percent equation.

Concept Summary *The Percent Equation*

Type	Example	Equation
Missing Part	What number is 75% of 4?	$n = 0.75(4)$
Missing Percent	3 is what percent of 4?	$3 = n(4)$
Missing Base	3 is 75% of what number?	$3 = 0.75n$

Study Tip

Estimation
To determine whether your answer is reasonable, estimate before finding the exact answer.

Example 1 Find the Part

Find 52% of 85. **Estimate:** $\frac{1}{2}$ of 90 is 45.

You know that the base is 85 and the percent is 52%. Let n represent the part.

$n = 0.52(85)$ Write 52% as the decimal 0.52.
$n = 44.2$ Simplify.

So, 52% of 85 is 44.2.

Resource Manager

 Workbooks and Reproducible Masters

Chapter 6 Resource Masters
* Study Guide and Intervention, p. 329
* Skills Practice, p. 330
* Practice, p. 331
* Reading to Learn Mathematics, p. 332
* Enrichment, p. 333
* Assessment, p. 360

Parent and Student Study Guide Workbook, p. 50

Transparencies
5-Minute Check Transparency 6-7
Answer Key Transparencies

 Technology

Interactive Chalkboard
Pre-AlgePASS: Tutorial Plus, Lessons 16 and 17

Example 2 Find the Percent

28 is what percent of 70? **Estimate:** $\frac{28}{70} \approx \frac{25}{75}$ or $\frac{1}{3}$, which is $33\frac{1}{3}\%$.

You know that the base is 70 and the part is 28.
Let n represent the percent.

$28 = n(70)$

$\frac{28}{70} = n$ Divide each side by 70.

$0.4 = n$ Simplify.

So, 28 is 40% of 70.   The answer makes sense compared to the estimate.

Example 3 Find the Base

18 is 45% of what number? **Estimate:** 18 is 50% of 36.

You know that the part is 18 and the percent is 45.
Let n represent the base.

$18 = 0.45n$ Write 45% as the decimal 0.45.

$\frac{18}{0.45} = \frac{0.45n}{0.45}$ Divide each side by 0.45.

$40 = n$ Simplify.

So, 18 is 45% of 40.   The answer is reasonable since it is close to the estimate.

DISCOUNT AND INTEREST   The percent equation can also be used to solve problems involving discount and interest. **Discount** is the amount by which the regular price of an item is reduced.

Example 4 Find Discount

• **SKATEBOARDS**   Mateo wants to buy a skateboard. The regular price of the skateboard is $135. Suppose it is on sale at a 25% discount. Find the sale price of the skateboard.

Method 1

First, use the percent equation to find 25% of 135.   **Estimate:** $\frac{1}{4}$ of 140 = 35

Let d represent the discount.

$d = 0.25(135)$ The base is 135 and the percent is 25%.

$d = 33.75$ Simplify.

Then, find the sale price.

$135 - 33.75 = 101.25$ Subtract the discount from the original price.

Method 2

A discount of 25% means the item will cost 100% − 25% or 75% of the original price. Use the percent equation to find 75% of 135.

Let s represent the sale price.

$s = 0.75(135)$ The base is 135 and the percent is 75%.

$s = 101.25$ Simplify.

The sale price of the skateboard will be $101.25.

---

2 Teach

PERCENT EQUATIONS

Teaching Tip Discuss how to write an equation for "find 36% of 120." Explain that it helps to rewrite the sentence as "36% of 120 is what?" Then write the equation: $0.36(120) = n$.

In-Class Examples Power Point

Teaching Tip Review changing percents to decimals.

1 Find 38% of 22.   **8.36**

2 19 is what percent of 25? **76%**

3 84 is 16% of what number? **525**

DISCOUNT AND INTEREST

In-Class Examples Power Point

4 **JEWELRY** The regular price of a ring is $495. It is on sale at a 20% discount. What is the sale price of the ring? **$396**

Teaching Tip Have students work each problem using both methods until they understand each method. Then have them choose the method they prefer.

5 **BANKING** Suppose you invest $2000 at an annual interest rate of 4.5%. How long will it take for it to earn $495? **5.5 years**

✓ Skills Check

a. Sandrine invests $500 at 5.5% interest. In two years, how much interest will she earn? **$55**

b. Ricardo borrows $250 at 9% interest. In six months, how much interest will he pay? **$11.25**

DAILY
INTERVENTION   **Differentiated Instruction**

• **Kinesthetic** Have students play "rock, paper, scissors" by having them randomly make a fist (rock), flatten their hand (paper), or creating cutting scissors with the index and middle fingers. Count the rocks and determine what percent of the students in the class made rocks. Continue playing several rounds, randomly choosing which item should be counted.

Study Notebook

Have students—

• add the definitions/examples of the vocabulary terms to their Vocabulary Builder worksheets for Chapter 6.

• copy three different exercises from their homework that represent each of the three different types of percent problems. Have them explain how to write an equation for each.

• include any other item(s) that they find helpful in mastering the skills in this lesson.

About the Exercises . . .

Organization by Objective
• **Percent Equations:** 12–27
• **Discount and Interest:** 28–38

Odd/Even Assignments
Exercises 12–41 are structured so that students practice the same concepts whether they are assigned odd or even problems.

Assignment Guide

Basic: 13–23 odd, 29–39 odd, 42–61

Average: 13–41 odd, 42–61

Advanced: 12–40 even, 42–55 (Optional: 56–61)

Tips for New Teachers

Introducing Algebra
Encourage students to write the equations, even if they can work the problems mentally. Emphasize that using equations will become easier with practice and that some problems must be solved by using equations.

Reading Math

Formulas
The formula $I = prt$ is read *Interest is equal to principal times rate times time.*

Simple interest is the amount of money paid or earned for the use of money. For a savings account, interest is earned. For a credit card, interest is paid. To solve problems involving interest, use the following formula.

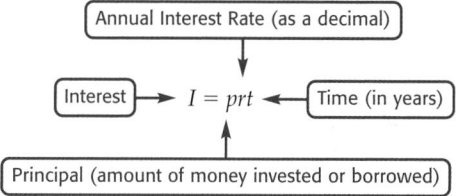

☑ **Concept Check** Name a situation where interest is earned and a situation where interest is paid. **Sample answers: checking account; home loan**

Example 5 Apply Simple Interest Formula

BANKING Suppose Miguel invests $1200 at an annual rate of 6.5%. How long will it take until Miguel earns $195?

$I = prt$	Write the simple interest formula.
$195 = 1200(0.065)t$	Replace I with 195, p with 1200, and r with 0.065.
$195 = 78t$	Simplify.
$\dfrac{195}{78} = \dfrac{78t}{78}$	Divide each side by 78.
$2.5 = t$	Simplify.

Miguel will earn $195 in interest in 2.5 years.

Check for Understanding

Concept Check
1. **OPEN ENDED** Give an example of a situation in which using the percent equation would be easier than using the percent proportion.

2. Define *discount*. **1–3. See margin.**

3. **Explain** what I, p, r, and t represent in the simple interest formula.

Guided Practice

GUIDED PRACTICE KEY	
Exercises	Examples
4–7	1–3
8, 10	4
9, 11	5

Solve each problem using the percent equation.

4. 15 is what percent of 60? **25%**   5. 30 is 60% of what number? **50**

6. What is 20% of 110? **22**   7. 12 is what percent of 400? **3%**

8. Find the discount for a $268 DVD player that is on sale at 20% off. **$53.60**

9. What is the interest on $8000 that is invested at 6% for $3\frac{1}{2}$ years? Round to the nearest cent. **$1680**

Applications
10. **SHOPPING** A jacket that normally sells for $180 is on sale at a 35% discount. What is the sale price of the jacket? **$117**

11. **BANKING** How long will it take to earn $252 in interest if $2400 is invested at a 7% annual interest rate? **1.5 years**

Answers

1. Use the percent equation in any situation where the rate and base are known.

2. Discount is the amount by which the regular price of an item is reduced.

3. I = interest; p = principal; r = annual interest rate; t = time in years

★ indicates increased difficulty

Practice and Apply

For Exercises	See Examples
12–27, 39	1–3
28–33	4
34–38	5

Extra Practice
See page 738.

Solve each problem using the percent equation. 12–27. See margin.

12. 9 is what percent of 25?

13. 38 is what percent of 40?

14. 48 is 64% of what number?

15. 27 is 54% of what number?

16. Find 12% of 72.

17. Find 42% of 150.

18. 39.2 is what percent of 112?

19. 49.5 is what percent of 132?

20. What is 37.5% of 89?

21. What is 24.2% of 60?

22. 37.5 is what percent of 30?

23. 43.6 is what percent of 20?

★ **24.** 1.6 is what percent of 400?

★ **25.** 1.35 is what percent of 150?

★ **26.** 83.5 is 125% of what number?

★ **27.** 17.6 is $133\frac{1}{3}$% of what number?

28. FOOD A frozen pizza is on sale at a 25% discount. Find the sale price of the pizza if it normally sells for $4.85. **$3.64**

29. CALCULATORS Suppose a calculator is on sale at a 15% discount. If it normally sells for $29.99, what is the sale price? **$25.49**

Find the discount to the nearest cent.

30. **SALE! 25% off** Original Price: $65 **$16.25**

31. $85 cordless phone, 20% off **$17**

32. $489 stereo, 15% off **$73.35**

33. 25% off a $74 baseball glove **$18.50**

Find the interest to the nearest cent. 34. $1010.35

34.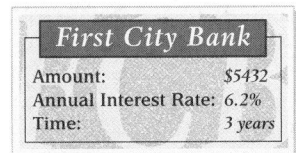
First City Bank
Amount: $5432
Annual Interest Rate: 6.2%
Time: 3 years

35. $4500 at 5.5% for $4\frac{1}{2}$ years **$1113.75**

36. $3680 at 6.75% for $2\frac{1}{4}$ years **$558.90**

37. 5.5% for $1\frac{3}{4}$ years on $2543 **$244.76**

38. BANKING What is the annual interest rate if $1600 is invested for 6 years and $456 in interest is earned? **4.75%**

39. SPORTS One season, a football team had 7 losses. This was 43.75% of the total games they played. How many games did they play? **16**

★ **40. REAL ESTATE** A **commission** is a fee paid to a salesperson based on a percent of sales. Suppose a real estate agent earns a 3% commission. What commission would be earned for selling the house shown?

New Listing! Two-story home with 4 bedrooms and 2 bathrooms. Price: $130,000

★ **41. BUSINESS** To make a profit, stores try to sell an item for more than it paid for the item. The increase in price is called the **markup**. Suppose a store purchases paint brushes for $8 each. Find the markup if the brushes are sold for 15% over the price paid for them. **$1.20**

WebQuest

The percent equation can help you analyze the nutritional value of food. Visit www.pre-alg.com/webquest to continue work on your WebQuest project.

40. $3900

www.pre-alg.com/self_check_quiz/ny

Lesson 6-7 Using Percent Equations **301**

Answers

12. 36%	18. 35%	24. 0.4%
13. 95%	19. 37.5%	25. 0.9%
14. 75	20. 33.375	26. 66.8
15. 50	21. 14.52	27. 13.2
16. 8.64	22. 125%	
17. 63	23. 218%	

Study Guide and Intervention, p. 329

The **percent equation** is an equivalent form of the percent proportion. In the percent equation, the percent is written as a decimal.

Example Solve each problem using the percent equation.
a. Find 22% of 95.
   $n = 0.22(95)$
   $n = 20.9$
   So, 22% of 95 is 20.9.
b. 15 is what percent of 75?
   $15 = n(75)$
   $0.2 = n$
   So, 15 is 20% of 75.
c. 90 is 20% of what number?
   $90 = 0.2n$
   $450 = n$
   So, 90 is 20% of 450.

Exercises
Solve each problem using the percent equation.
1. Find 76% of 25. 19
2. Find 9% of 410. 36.9
3. Find 40% of 7. 2.8
4. Find 26% of 505. 131.3
5. Find 3.5% of 280. 9.8
6. Find 18.5% of 60. 11.1
7. Find 107% of 1080. 1155.6
8. 256 is what percent of 800? 32%
9. 36 is what percent of 240? 15%
10. 2089.5 is what percent of 2100? 99.5%
11. 15.4 is what percent of 55? 28%
12. 7 is what percent of 350? 2%
13. 13.2 is what percent of 80? 16.5%
14. 14.4 is what percent of 120? 12%
15. 36 is 9% of what number? 400
16. 2925 is 39% of what number? 7500
17. 576 is 90% of what number? 640
18. 24.2 is 55% of what number? 44
19. 25 is 125% of what number? 20
20. 0.6 is 7.5% of what number? 8

Skills Practice, p. 330 and Practice, p. 331 (shown)

Solve each problem using the percent equation.
1. What is 5% of 224? 11.2
2. What is 18% of 65? 11.7
3. What is 63% of 300? 189
4. What is 40% of 980? 392
5. What is 18% of 650? 117
6. Find 2% of 820. 16.4
7. Find 75% of 312. 234
8. Find 312% of 75. 234
9. Find 5.6% of 1050. 58.8
10. Find 21.4% of 855. 182.97
11. 52.3 is what percent of 1046? 5%
12. 48 is what percent of 75? 64%
13. 100 is what percent of 250? 40%
14. 96 is what percent of 400? 24%
15. 10 is what percent of 625? 1.6%
16. 49.8 is what percent of 415? 12%
17. 0.4 is what percent of 5? 8%
18. 157 is what percent of 2512? 6.25%
19. 1206 is what percent of 8040? 15%
20. 63 is what percent of 60? 105%
21. 13 is 50% of what number? 26
22. 121 is 22% of what number? 550
23. 11 is 4% of what number? 275
24. 438 is 24% of what number? 1825
25. 612 is 25% of what number? 2448
26. 960 is 30% of what number? 3200
27. 3570 is 42% of what number? 8500
28. 8 is 1% of what number? 800
29. SHOPPING A jacket is on sale at 15% off the original price of $68.00. What is the sale price? $57.80

Enrichment, p. 333

Compound Interest
Interest may be paid, or compounded, annually (each year), semiannually (twice per year), quarterly (four times per year), monthly (once per month), or daily.

Example FINANCE George had $100 in an account for $1\frac{1}{2}$ years that paid 8% interest compounded semiannually. What was the total amount in his account at the end of $1\frac{1}{2}$ years?

At the end of $\frac{1}{2}$ year: Interest: $100 × 0.08 × $\frac{1}{2}$ = $4.00
                        New Principal: $100 + $4 = $104

At the end of 1 year: Interest: $104 × 0.08 × $\frac{1}{2}$ = $4.16
                        New Principal: $104 + $4.16 = $108.16

At the end of $1\frac{1}{2}$ years: Interest: $108.16 × 0.08 × $\frac{1}{2}$ = $4.33
                        New Principal: $108.16 + $4.33 = $112.49

Find the total amount for each of the following.

	Principal	Rate	Time	Compounded	Total Amount
1.	$200	6%	$1\frac{1}{2}$ years	semiannually	$218.55
2.	$300	5%	2 years	semiannually	$331.14
3.	$100	6%	1 year	quarterly	$106.14
4.	$500	8%	$\frac{3}{4}$ year	quarterly	$530.60
5.	$500	10%	4 months	monthly	$516.88
6.	$800	8%	$\frac{1}{4}$ year	monthly	$816.10
7.	$1000	8%	4 years	annually	$1360.49
8.	$700	6%	$1\frac{1}{2}$ years	semiannually	$764.91

Lesson 6-7 Using Percent Equations **301**

Open-Ended Assessment

Writing Have students work in pairs. Each student should write three percent problems, including at least one interest problem and one discount problem. Have them trade problems and check each others' work.

Getting Ready for Lesson 6-8

PREREQUISITE SKILL Lesson 6-8 presents percent of change. Students will need to express decimals as percents. Exercises 56–61 should be used to determine your students' familiarity with writing decimals as percents.

Assessment Options

Quiz (Lessons 6-6 and 6-7) is available on p. 360 of the *Chapter 6 Resource Masters*.

Answers

42. Yes; $n\%$ of $m = \dfrac{n}{100} \cdot m$ or $\dfrac{mn}{100}$ and $m\%$ of $n = \dfrac{m}{100} \cdot n$ or $\dfrac{mn}{100}$.

43. If you know two of the three values, you can use the percent proportion to solve for the missing value. Answers should include the following.

• To find the amount of tax on an item, you can use the percent proportion or the percent equation.

• For example, the following methods can be used to find 6% tax on $24.99.

Method 1: Percent Proportion
$$\dfrac{x}{24.99} = \dfrac{6}{100}$$

Method 2: Percent Equation
$$n = 0.06(24.99)$$

Using either method, $x = 1.50$. The amount of tax is $1.50.

46–48. Sample answers are given.

46. 40; fraction method: $\dfrac{1}{2} \times 80$ or 40

---

42. **CRITICAL THINKING**   Determine whether $n\%$ of m is always equal to $m\%$ of n. Give examples to support your answer. **See margin.**

43. **WRITING IN MATH**   Answer the question that was posed at the beginning of the lesson. **See margin.**

How is the percent proportion related to an equation?

Include the following in your answer:
• an explanation describing two methods for finding the amount of tax on an item, and
• an example of using both methods to find the amount of sales tax on an item.

NEW YORK Test Practice

Standardized Test Practice
Ⓐ Ⓑ Ⓒ Ⓓ

44. What percent of 320 is 19.2? **C**
    Ⓐ 0.6%   Ⓑ 60%   Ⓒ 6%   Ⓓ 0.06%

45. Ryan wants to buy a tent that costs $150 for his camping trip. The tent is on sale at a 30% discount. What will be the sale price of the tent? **B**
    Ⓐ 95   Ⓑ 105   Ⓒ 45   Ⓓ 110

Maintain Your Skills

Mixed Review
46–48. See margin.

Estimate. Explain which method you used to estimate. *(Lesson 6-6)*

46. 47% of 84   47. 126% of 198   48. 9% of 514

Use the percent proportion to solve each problem. *(Lesson 6-5)*

49. What is 55% of 220? **121**   50. 50.88 is what percent of 96? **53%**

51. **POPULATION**   The graphic shows the number of stories of certain buildings in Tulsa, Oklahoma. What is the mean of the data? *(Lesson 5-8)* **41**

Building	Stories
Williams Center	52
Cityplex Central Tower	60
First National Bank	41
Mid-Continent Tower	36
Fourth National Bank	33
National Bank of Tulsa	24

Source: *The World Almanac*

52. List all the factors of 30. *(Lesson 4-1)* **1, 2, 3, 5, 6, 10, 15, 30**

GEOMETRY   Find the perimeter of each rectangle. *(Lesson 3-7)*

53.   13 cm 6 cm **38 cm**   54. 25 in. 11 in. **72 in.**

55. **ALGEBRA**   Use the Distributive Property to rewrite $(w - 3)8$. *(Lesson 3-1)* **$8w - 24$**

Getting Ready for the Next Lesson

PREREQUISITE SKILL   Write each decimal as a percent.
*(To review **writing decimals as percents**, see Lesson 6-4.)*

56. 0.58 **58%**   57. 0.89 **89%**   58. 0.125 **12.5%**
59. 1.56 **156%**   60. 2.04 **204%**   61. 0.224 **22.4%**

302 Chapter 6 Ratio, Proportion, and Percent

---

47. 250; meaning of percent method: 126% means about 125 for every 100 and 12.5 for every 10. 198 has about 2 one-hundreds. 125 × 2 = 250. So, 126% of 198 is about 250.

48. 45; 1% method: Since 1% of 514 is about 5, 9% of 514 is 9 × 5 or about 45.

NEW YORK *Performance Indicator* **8.N.4 Apply percents to:** tax, percent increase/decrease, simple interest, sale price, commission, **interest rates,** gratuities

Compound Interest

Simple interest, which you studied in the previous lesson, is paid only on the initial principal of a savings account or a loan. **Compound interest** is paid on the initial principal and on interest earned in the past. You can use a spreadsheet to investigate the impact of compound interest.

SAVINGS Find the value of a $1000 savings account after five years if the account pays 6% interest compounded semiannually.

6% interest compounded semiannually means that the interest is paid twice a year, or every 6 months. The interest rate is 6% ÷ 2 or 3%.

The rate is entered as a decimal. →

The spreadsheet evaluates the formula A4 × B1. →

The interest is added to the principal every 6 months. The spreadsheet evaluates the formula A4 + B4. →

Compound Interest

	A	B	C	D
1	RATE	0.03		
2				
3	PRINCIPAL	INTEREST	NEW PRINCIPAL	TIME (YR)
4	1000.00	30.00	1030.00	0.5
5	1030.00	30.90	1060.90	1.0
6	1060.90	31.83	1092.73	1.5
7	1092.73	32.78	1125.51	2.0
8	1125.51	33.77	1159.27	2.5
9	1159.27	34.78	1194.05	3.0
10	1194.05	35.82	1229.87	3.5
11	1229.87	36.90	1266.77	4.0
12	1266.77	38.00	1304.77	4.5
13	1304.77	39.14	1343.92	5.0

Sheet1 / Sheet2 / Sh

Edit

The value of the savings account after five years is $1343.92.

1. The simple interest, $300, is $43.92 less than the compound interest.

Model and Analyze

1. Suppose you invest $1000 for five years at 6% simple interest. How does the simple interest compare to the compound interest shown above?

2. Use a spreadsheet to find the amount of money in a savings account if $1000 is invested for five years at 6% interest compounded quarterly. **$1346.86**

3. Suppose you leave $100 in each of three bank accounts paying 5% interest per year. One account pays simple interest, one pays interest compounded semiannually, and one pays interest compounded quarterly. Use a spreadsheet to find the amount of money in each account after three years.
$115.00, $115.97, $116.08

Make a Conjecture

4. How does the amount of interest change if the compounding occurs more frequently? **The amount of interest increases.**

Spreadsheet Investigation   Compound Interest   **303**

Getting Started

Objective Find compound interest.

Materials
spreadsheet software

Teaching Tip Have students work the first two or three rows by hand or with a calculator so they can see how the added interest also earns interest.

Teach

- Have students use the simple interest formula $I = prt$ to help them estimate the compounded interest.

In **Exercises 1–3,** students should:

- use a spreadsheet to compare simple interest to compound interest.
- use a spreadsheet to determine the amount of growth of an account earning compound interest.
- compare different intervals of compound interest.

In **Exercise 4,** students make a conjecture based on different time intervals for the same interest rate and principal.

Assess

- After students have worked Exercises 1–3, ask them how long it would take for an account with an initial amount $75 at 10% compounded semiannually to exceed that of one with $100 at 5% interest compounded semiannually.   **6 years**

Study Notebook

Have student print out one of their spreadsheets to keep in their journal. Have them circle and label the interest rate, principal, and elapsed time.

NEW YORK *Performance Indicator* **8.N.4 Apply percents to:** tax, **percent increase/decrease,** simple interest, sale price, commission, interest rates, gratuities

1 Focus

5-Minute Check Transparency 6-8 Use as a quiz or review of Lesson 6-7.

Mathematical Background
notes are available for this lesson on page 262D.

How can percents help to describe a change in area?

The opening activity questions are repeated on page 337 of the *Chapter 6 Resource Masters.*

Reading to Learn Mathematics, p. 337 ELL

Pre-Activity *How can percents help to describe a change in area?*

Do the activity at the top of page 304 in your textbook. Write your answers below.

Draw each pair of rectangles. Then compare the rectangles. Express the increase as a fraction and as a percent.

a. X: 2 units by 3 units
Y: 2 units by 4 units
$\frac{1}{3}$ or $33\frac{1}{3}$%

b. G: 2 units by 5 units
H: 2 units by 6 units
$\frac{1}{5}$ or 20%

c. J: 2 units by 4 units
K: 2 units by 5 units
$\frac{1}{4}$ or 25%

d. P: 2 units by 6 units
Q: 2 units by 7 units
$\frac{1}{6}$ or $16\frac{2}{3}$%

e. For each pair of rectangles, the change in area is 2 square units. Explain why the percent of change is different. The percent of change is different because the area of each original rectangle is different.

Reading the Lesson 1–3. See students' work.

Write a definition and give an example of each new vocabulary phrase.

Vocabulary	Definition	Example
1. percent of change		
2. percent of increase		
3. percent of decrease		

Helping You Remember

4. For a percent of increase, is the percent of change always positive or negative? Why? Positive; The smaller amount is always subtracted from the larger amount.

5. For a percent of decrease, is the percent of change always positive or negative? Why? Negative; The larger amount is always subtracted from the smaller amount.

Vocabulary
- percent of change
- percent of increase
- percent of decrease

a. $\frac{1}{3}$ or $33\frac{1}{3}$%

b. $\frac{1}{5}$ or 20%

c. $\frac{1}{4}$ or 25%

d. $\frac{1}{6}$ or $16\frac{2}{3}$%

e. The percent of change is different because the area of each original rectangle is different.

What You'll Learn
- Find percent of increase.
- Find percent of decrease.

How can percents help to describe a change in area?

Suppose the length of rectangle A is increased from 4 units to 5 units.

Rectangle A

4 units   5 units

Rectangle A had an initial area of 8 square units. It increased to 10 square units. This is a change in area of 2 square units. The following ratio shows this relationship.

$$\frac{\text{change in area}}{\text{original area}} = \frac{2}{8} = \frac{1}{4} \text{ or } 25\%$$

This means that, compared to the original area, the new area increased by 25%.

Draw each pair of rectangles. Then compare the rectangles. Express the increase as a fraction and as a percent.

a. X: 2 units by 3 units
Y: 2 units by 4 units

b. G: 2 units by 5 units
H: 2 units by 6 units

c. J: 2 units by 4 units
K: 2 units by 5 units

d. P: 2 units by 6 units
Q: 2 units by 7 units

e. For each pair of rectangles, the change in area is 2 square units. Explain why the percent of change is different.

FIND PERCENT OF INCREASE A **percent of change** tells the percent an amount has increased or decreased in relation to the original amount.

Example 1 Find Percent of Change

Find the percent of change from 56 inches to 63 inches.

Step 1 Subtract to find the amount of change.

$$63 - 56 = 7 \quad \text{new measurement} - \text{original measurement}$$

Step 2 Write a ratio that compares the amount of change to the original measurement. Express the ratio as a percent.

$$\text{percent of change} = \frac{\text{amount of change}}{\text{original measurement}}$$

$$= \frac{7}{56} \qquad \text{Substitution.}$$

$$= 0.125 \text{ or } 12.5\% \quad \text{Write the decimal as a percent.}$$

The percent of change from 56 inches to 63 inches is 12.5%.

Resource Manager

📁 Workbooks and Reproducible Masters

Chapter 6 Resource Masters
- Study Guide and Intervention, p. 334
- Skills Practice, p. 335
- Practice, p. 336
- Reading to Learn Mathematics, p. 337
- Enrichment, p. 338

Graphing Calculator and Spreadsheet Masters, p. 29
Parent and Student Study Guide Workbook, p. 51
School-to-Career Masters, p. 12

💡 Transparencies
5-Minute Check Transparency 6-8
Real-World Transparency 6
Answer Key Transparencies

💿 Technology
Interactive Chalkboard

When an amount increases, as in Example 1, the percent of change is a **percent of increase**.

Example 2 *Find Percent of Increase*

FUEL In 1975, the average price per gallon of gasoline was $0.57. In 2000, the average price per gallon was $1.47. Find the percent of change.

Source: *The World Almanac*

Step 1 Subtract to find the amount of change.

$1.47 - 0.57 = 0.9$ new price − original price

Step 2 Write a ratio that compares the amount of change to the original price. Express the ratio as a percent.

$$\text{percent of change} = \frac{\text{amount of change}}{\text{original price}}$$

$$= \frac{0.9}{0.57} \qquad \text{Substitution.}$$

$$\approx 1.58 \text{ or } 158\% \qquad \text{Write the decimal as a percent.}$$

The percent of change is about 158%. In this case, the percent of change is a percent of increase.

NEW YORK
Test Practice

Standardized Test Practice
Ⓐ Ⓑ Ⓒ Ⓓ

Example 3 *Find Percent of Increase*

Multiple-Choice Test Item

Refer to the table shown. Which county had the greatest percent of increase in population from 1990 to 2000?

Ⓐ Breckinridge   Ⓑ Bracken
Ⓒ Calloway   Ⓓ Fulton

County	1990	2000
Breckinridge	16,312	18,648
Bracken	7766	8279
Calloway	30,735	34,177
Fulton	8271	7752

Read the Test Item

Percent of increase tells how much the population has increased in relation to 1990.

Solve the Test Item

Use a ratio to find each percent of increase. Then compare the percents.

- **Breckinridge**

  $$\frac{18,648 - 16,312}{16,312} = \frac{2336}{16,312}$$
  $$\approx 0.1432 \text{ or } 14.3\%$$

- **Bracken**

  $$\frac{8279 - 7766}{7766} = \frac{513}{7766}$$
  $$\approx 0.0661 \text{ or } 6.6\%$$

- **Calloway**

  $$\frac{34,177 - 30,735}{30,735} = \frac{3442}{30,735}$$
  $$\approx 0.112 \text{ or } 11.2\%$$

- **Fulton**

  Eliminate this choice because the population decreased.

Breckinridge County had the greatest percent of increase in population from 1990 to 2000. The answer is A.

Test-Taking Tip
If you are unsure of the correct answer, eliminate the choices you know are incorrect. Then consider the remaining choices.

D A I L Y
INTERVENTION   **Differentiated Instruction**

- **Kinesthetic** Provide students with one-inch grid paper. Have them cut out a rectangle with a maximum area of 20 square inches. Then have students cut out a larger rectangle. Have them count the squares in each rectangle and find the percent of increase in size.

---

2 Teach

FIND PERCENT OF INCREASE

In-Class Examples   Power Point®

Teaching Tip Have students work several problems using both methods to assure that they understand both before they choose which they prefer.

1 Find the percent of change from 325 to 390.   **20%**

Teaching Tip Have students identify the original amount before computing.

2 **TUITION** In 1965, when John entered college, the tuition per year was $7500. In 2000, when his daughter went to the same school, the tuition was $25,500. Find the percent of change.   **240%**

3 **Multiple-Choice Test Item** In Example 3, which county had the least percent of increase in population from 1990 to 2000?   **B**
  A Breckinridge B Bracken
  C Calloway D Fulton

PERCENT OF DECREASE

In-Class Example   Power Point®

4 **CLOTHING** A $110 sweater is on sale for $88. What is the percent of change?   **−20%**

Standardized Test Practice
Ⓐ Ⓑ Ⓒ Ⓓ

Example 3 Point out to students that Fulton can be eliminated immediately, since its population decreased rather than increased. The other choices can be quickly determined by rounding each of the numbers to the nearest thousand before computing. Any two that come too close to determine can then be calculated accurately.

About the Exercises . . .
Organization by Objective
• **Percent of Increase:** 10–11, 16–17, 19, 20, 23
• **Percent of Decrease:** 12–15, 18, 21, 22

Odd/Even Assignments
Exercises 9–25 are structured so that students practice the same concepts whether they are assigned odd or even problems.

Alert! Exercise 26 involves research on the Internet or other reference materials.

Assignment Guide
Basic: 11–19 odd, 24–42
Average: 11–23 odd, 24–42
Advanced: 10–22 even, 24–37 (Optional: 38–42)
All: Practice Quiz 2 (1–5)

Answers

1. If the amount increases, it is a percent of increase. If the amount decreases, it is a percent of decrease.

2. Sample answer: a temperature change from 65°F to 50°F.

3. Mark is correct because he divided the difference of the new amount and the original amount by the original amount.

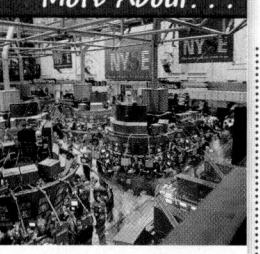

More About . . .

Stock Market •⋯⋯
About 20 years ago, only 12.2% of Americans had money invested in the stock market. Today, more than 44% of Americans invest in the stock market.
Source: www.infoplease.com

PERCENT OF DECREASE When the amount decreases, the percent of change is negative. You can state a negative percent of change as a **percent of decrease**.

Example 4 *Find Percent of Decrease*

• **STOCK MARKET** One of the largest stock market drops on Wall Street occurred on October 19, 1987. On this day, the stock market opened at 2246.74 points and closed at 1738.42 points. What was the percent of change?

Step 1 Subtract to find the amount of change.

$1738.42 - 2246.74 = -508.32$ closing points − opening points

Step 2 Compare the amount of change to the opening points.

$$\text{percent of change} = \frac{\text{amount of change}}{\text{opening points}}$$
$$= \frac{-508.32}{2246.74} \qquad \text{Substitution.}$$
$$\approx -0.226 \text{ or } -22.6\% \qquad \text{Write the decimal as a percent.}$$

The percent of change is -22.6%. In this case, the percent of change is a percent of decrease.

Check for Understanding

Concept Check
1. **Explain** how you know whether a percent of change is a percent of increase or a percent of decrease. **1–2. See margin.**

2. **OPEN ENDED** Give an example of a percent of decrease.

3. **FIND THE ERROR** Scott and Mark are finding the percent of change when a shirt that costs $15 is on sale for $10.

Scott	Mark
$\frac{10-15}{10} = \frac{-5}{10}$ or -50%	$\frac{10-15}{15} = \frac{-5}{15}$ or $-33\frac{1}{3}\%$

Who is correct? Explain your reasoning. **See margin.**

Guided Practice

GUIDED PRACTICE KEY

Exercises	Examples
4–8	1, 2, 4
9	3

NEW YORK
Test Practice

Standardized Test Practice
Ⓐ Ⓑ Ⓒ Ⓓ

Find the percent of change. Round to the nearest tenth, if necessary. Then state whether the percent of change is a *percent of increase* or a *percent of decrease*.

4. from $50 to $67 **34%; I**

5. from 45 in. to 18 in. **−60%; D**

6. from 80 cm to 55 cm **−31.3%; D**

7. from $228 to $251 **10.1%; I**

8. **ANIMALS** In 2000, there were 356 endangered species in the U.S. One year later, 367 species were considered endangered. What was the percent of change? **3.1%**

9. Refer to Example 3 on page 305. Suppose in 10 years, the population of Calloway is 36,851. What will be the percent of change from 1990? **A**
   Ⓐ 19.9%   Ⓑ 9.8%   Ⓒ 10.7%   Ⓓ 15.3%

DAILY INTERVENTION
Unlocking Misconceptions

• **Percent Change** Watch for students who systematically want to divide the greater number into the lesser number. Tell them to always first ask themselves what the original measurement was.

• **Undoing Increases** Students may think that a 20% decrease will "undo" a 20% increase. Have them find a 20% increase of $100. **$120** Then show them that from $120 to $100 is not a 20% change. The change is about **−16.7%.**

★ indicates increased difficulty

Practice and Apply

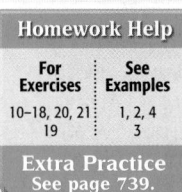

Homework Help

For Exercises	See Examples
10–18, 20, 21 19	1, 2, 4 3

Extra Practice
See page 739.

Find the percent of change. Round to the nearest tenth, if necessary. Then state whether the percent of change is a *percent of increase* or a *percent of decrease.*

10. from 25 cm to 36 cm **44%; I**

11. from $10 to $27 **170%; I**

12. from 68 min to 51 min **−25%; D**

13. from 50 lb to 44 lb **−12%; D**

14. from $135 to $120 **−11.1%; D**

15. from 257 m to 243 m **−5.4%; D**

16. from 365 ft to 421 ft **15.3%; I**

17. from $289 to $762 **164%; I**

18. **WEATHER** Seattle, Washington, receives an average of 6.0 inches of precipitation in December. In March, the average precipitation is 3.8 inches. What is the percent of change in precipitation from December to March? **−36.7%**

19. **POPULATION** In 1990, the population of Alabama was 4,040,587. In 2000, the population was 4,447,100. Find the percent of change from 1990 to 2000. **10.1%**

★ 20. Suppose 36 videos are added to a video collection that has 24 videos. What is the percent of change? **150%**

★ 21. A biology class has 28 students. Four of the students transferred out of the class to take chemistry. Find the percent of change in the number of students in the biology class. **−14.3%**

★ 22. **BUSINESS** A restaurant manager wants to reduce spending on supplies 10% in January and an additional 15% in February. In January, the expenses were $2875. How much should the expenses be at the end of February? **$2199.38**

★ 23. **SCHOOL** Jiliana is using a copy machine to increase the size of a 2-inch by 3-inch picture of a spider. The enlarged picture needs to measure 3 inches by 4.5 inches. **150%**

What enlargement setting on the copy machine should she use?

24. **CRITICAL THINKING** Explain why a 10% increase followed by a 10% decrease is less than the original amount if the original amount was positive. **See margin.**

25. **WRITING IN MATH** Answer the question that was posed at the beginning of the lesson. **See margin.**

How can percents help to describe a change in area?

Include the following in your answer:
- an explanation describing how you can tell whether the percent of increase will be greater than 100%, and
- an example of a model that shows an increase less than 100% and one that shows an increase greater than 100%.

Answer

24. Suppose *x* represents the original amount. After the increase, it is 1.1*x*. After the decrease, it is 0.9(1.1*x*) or 0.99*x*. Since when *x* is positive, 0.99*x* < *x*, the final amount is less than the original.

25. See p. 308.

Lesson 6-8 Percent of Change **307**

4 Assess

Open-Ended Assessment

Modeling Have students bring to class advertisements from newspapers or magazines that show reduced prices for items. Post some of the ads and have students figure out the percent of change for the prices of the items. Discuss the steps involved, and post the percent changes with the ads.

Getting Ready for Lesson 6-9

PREREQUISITE SKILL In Lesson 6-9, students will use what they have learned about percents and ratios to solve probability problems. Exercises 38–42 should be used to determine your students' familiarity with writing fractions as percents.

Assessment Options

Practice Quiz 2 The quiz provides students with a brief review of the concepts and skills in Lessons 6-6 through 6-8. Lesson numbers are given to the right of exercises or instruction lines so students can review concepts not yet mastered.

Answer (p. 307)

25. The amount by which a rectangle is increased or decreased can be represented by a percent. Answers should include the following.
   - If the size of the new rectangle is greater than the size of the original rectangle, the percent of increase is greater than 100%.

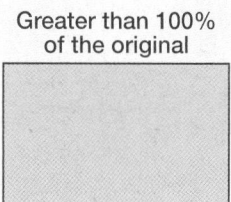

Original Rectangle

Greater than 100% of the original

Less than 100% of the original

NEW YORK
Test Practice

Standardized Test Practice
Ⓐ Ⓑ Ⓒ Ⓓ

26. **RESEARCH** Use the Internet or another source to find the population of your town now and ten years ago. What is the percent of change? **See students' work.**

For Exercises 27 and 28, refer to the information in the table.

27. What percent represents the percent of change in the number of beagles from 1998 to 1999? **D**

   Ⓐ −8.1%   Ⓑ −7.5%
   Ⓒ −9.7%   Ⓓ −8.0%

Kennel Club Registrations

Breed	1998	1999
Labrador Retriever	157,936	157,897
Beagle	53,322	49,080
Maltese	18,013	16,358
Golden Retriever	65,681	62,652
Shih Tzu	38,468	34,576
Cocker Spaniel	34,632	29,958
Siberian Husky	21,078	18,106

28. Which breed had the largest percent of decrease? **A**

   Ⓐ Siberian Husky   Ⓑ Cocker Spaniel
   Ⓒ Golden Retriever   Ⓓ Labrador Retriever

Maintain Your Skills

Mixed Review

29. Find the discount to the nearest cent for a television that costs $999 and is on sale at 15% off. *(Lesson 6-7)* **$149.85**

30. Find the interest on $1590 that is invested at 8% for 3 years. Round to the nearest cent. *(Lesson 6-7)* **$381.60**

31. A calendar is on sale at a 10% discount. What is the sale price if it normally sells for $14.95? *(Lesson 6-7)* **$13.46**

Estimate. Explain which method you used to estimate. *(Lesson 6-6)*

32–34. Sample answers are given. See pp. 323A–323B for explanations.

32. 60% of 134 **81**   33. 88% of 72 **63**   34. 123% of 32 **36**

Identify all of the sets to which each number belongs. *(Lesson 5-2)*

35. −8 **integer, rational**   36. $1\frac{1}{4}$ **rational**   37. −5.63 **rational**

Getting Ready for the Next Lesson

PREREQUISITE SKILL Write each fraction as a percent.
*(To review **writing fractions as percents**, see Lesson 6-4.)*

38. $\frac{3}{4}$ **75%**   39. $\frac{1}{5}$ **20%**   40. $\frac{2}{3}$ **$66\frac{2}{3}$%**   41. $\frac{5}{6}$ **$83\frac{1}{3}$%**   42. $\frac{3}{8}$ **$37\frac{1}{2}$%**

Practice Quiz 2   *Lessons 6-6 through 6-8*

Estimate. Explain which method you used to estimate. *(Lesson 6-6)*

1. 42% of 68   2. $66\frac{2}{3}$% of 34 **1–2. See margin.**

3. Find the discount to the nearest cent on a backpack that costs $58 and is on sale at 25% off. *(Lesson 6-7)* **$14.50**

4. Find the interest to the nearest cent on $2500 that is invested at 4% for 2.5 years. *(Lesson 6-7)* **$250**

5. Find the percent of change from $0.95 to $2.45. *(Lesson 6-8)* **158%**

Answers (Practice Quiz 2)

For Exercises 1 and 2, sample answers are given.

1. 28; fraction method: $\frac{2}{5} \times 70$ or 28

2. 22; fraction method: $\frac{2}{3} \times 33$ or 22

Algebra Activity

NEW YORK *Performance Indicator* **8.PS.11 Work in collaboration with others to solve problems, 8.PS.15 Choose methods for obtaining required information**

Taking a Survey

The graph shows the results of a survey about what types of stores people in the United States shop at the most. Since it would be impossible to survey everyone in the country, a sample was used. A **sample** is a subgroup or subset of the population.

It is important to obtain a sample that is unbiased. An **unbiased** sample is a sample that is:

• representative of the larger population,
• selected at **random** or without preference, and
• large enough to provide accurate data.

WHERE WE SHOP MOST

62.4% Discount stores

15.6% National chains

22.0% Conventional stores

Source: International Mass Retail Association

To insure an unbiased sample, the following sampling methods may be used.

• **Random**   The sample is selected at random.
• **Systematic** The sample is selected by using every nth member of the population.
• **Stratified**   The sample is selected by dividing the population into groups.

Model and Analyze 1–6. See pp. 323A–323B.

Tell whether or not each of the following is a random sample. Then provide an explanation describing the strengths and weaknesses of each sample.

Type of Survey	Location of Survey
1. travel preference	mall
2. time spent reading	library
3. favorite football player	Miami Dolphins football game

4. Brad conducted a survey to find out which food people in his community prefer. He surveyed every second person that walked into a certain fast-food restaurant. Identify this type of sampling. Explain how the survey may be biased.

5. Suppose a study shows that teenagers who eat breakfast each day earn higher grades than teenagers who skip breakfast. Tell how you can use the stratified sampling technique to test this claim in your school.

6. Suppose you want to determine where students in your school shop the most.
   a. Formulate a hypothesis about where students shop the most.
   b. Design and conduct a survey using one of the sampling techniques described above.
   c. Organize and display the results of your survey in a chart or graph.
   d. Evaluate your hypothesis by drawing a conclusion based on the survey.

Algebra Activity Taking a Survey **309**

Getting Started

Objective Take a survey.

Teach

• Personalize this lesson by asking one student what he or she thinks is the favorite song of most students. Ask the class why they should or should not assume that person's choice is correct. Ask what a better sample would be.
• Discuss Exercises 1–3 with the class. Have students explain their answers and suggest alternative locations.
• Have students work in small groups to answer Exercises 4–6.

Assess

In **Exercises 1–5,** students should
• correctly identify an appropriate location for each type of survey.
• understand how surveys can be biased.
• describe an unbiased survey for a particular situation.

In **Exercise 6,** students conduct a survey from its hypothesis to its conclusion. Be sure students use an appropriate sampling technique and use it correctly.

Study Notebook

Have students start a journal page entitled *Taking a Survey.* They should copy the tables *Criteria for an Unbiased Sample* and *Sampling Techniques.* Ask them to summarize the survey they performed, including an evaluation of its strengths and weaknesses.

Resource Manager

📁 **Teaching Pre-Algebra with Manipulatives**

• p. 94 (student recording sheet)

6-9 Probability and Predictions

NEW YORK *Performance Indicator* **Reinforcement of 7.S.8 Interpret data to provide the basis for predictions and to establish experimental probabilities**

1 Focus

5-Minute Check Transparency 6-9 Use as a quiz or review of Lesson 6-8.

Mathematical Background notes are available for this lesson on page 262D.

How can probability help you make predictions?

The opening activity questions are repeated on page 342 of the *Chapter 6 Resource Masters.*

Vocabulary

- outcomes
- simple event
- probability
- sample space
- theoretical probability
- experimental probability

Study Tip

Probability

Each of the outcomes must be equally likely to happen.

What You'll Learn

- Find the probability of simple events.
- Use a sample to predict the actions of a larger group.

How can probability help you make predictions?

A popular word game is played using 100 letter tiles. The object of the game is to use the tiles to spell words scoring as many points as possible. The table shows the distribution of the tiles.

Letter	Number of Tiles
E	12
A, I	9
O	8
N, R, T	6
D, L, S, U	4
G	3
B, C, F, H, M, P, V, W, Y, blank	2
J, K, Q, X, Z	1

a. Write the ratio that compares the number of tiles labeled E to the total number of tiles. $\frac{12}{100}$

b. What percent of the tiles are labeled E? **12%**

c. What fraction of tiles is this? $\frac{3}{25}$

d. Suppose a player chooses a tile. Is there a better chance of choosing a D or an N? Explain.

d. There is a better chance of choosing an N because there are more of them.

PROBABILITY OF SIMPLE EVENTS In the activity above, there are 27 possible tiles. These results are called **outcomes**. A **simple event** is one outcome or a collection of outcomes. For example, choosing a tile labeled E is a simple event.

You can measure the chances of an event happening with **probability**.

Key Concept — Probability

- **Words** The probability of an event is a ratio that compares the number of favorable outcomes to the number of possible outcomes.

- **Symbols** $P(\text{event}) = \dfrac{\text{number of favorable outcomes}}{\text{number of possible outcomes}}$

The probability of an event is always between 0 and 1, inclusive. The closer a probability is to 1, the more likely it is to occur.

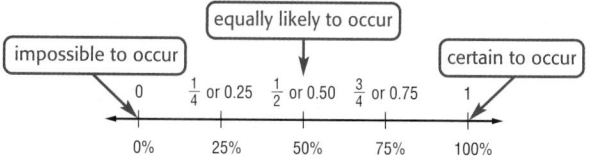

impossible to occur		equally likely to occur		certain to occur
0	$\frac{1}{4}$ or 0.25	$\frac{1}{2}$ or 0.50	$\frac{3}{4}$ or 0.75	1
0%	25%	50%	75%	100%

✓ Concept Check Suppose there is a 45% chance that an event occurs. How likely is it that the event will occur? **about equally likely**

Resource Manager

📁 Workbooks and Reproducible Masters

Chapter 6 Resource Masters
- Study Guide and Intervention, p. 339
- Skills Practice, p. 340
- Practice, p. 341
- Reading to Learn Mathematics, p. 342
- Enrichment, p. 343
- Assessment, p. 360

Parent and Student Study Guide Workbook, p. 52

📺 Transparencies
5-Minute Check Transparency 6-9
Answer Key Transparencies

Technology
Interactive Chalkboard
Pre-AlgePASS: Tutorial Plus, Lesson 18
Multimedia Applications

Example 1 Find Probability

Suppose a number cube is rolled. What is the probability of rolling a prime number?

There are 3 prime numbers on a number cube: 2, 3, and 5.

There are 6 possible outcomes: 1, 2, 3, 4, 5, and 6.

$$P(\text{prime}) = \frac{\text{number of favorable outcomes}}{\text{number of possible outcomes}}$$

$$= \frac{3}{6} \text{ or } \frac{1}{2}$$

So, the probability of rolling a prime number is $\frac{1}{2}$ or 50%.

Reading Math

P(prime)

P(prime) is read as *the probability of rolling a prime number.*

The set of all possible outcomes is called the **sample space**. For Example 1, the sample space was {1, 2, 3, 4, 5, 6}. When you toss a coin, the sample space is {heads, tails}.

Example 2 Find Probability

Suppose two number cubes are rolled. Find the probability of rolling an even sum.

Make a table showing the sample space when rolling two number cubes.

	1	2	3	4	5	6
1	(1, 1)	(1, 2)	(1, 3)	(1, 4)	(1, 5)	(1, 6)
2	(2, 1)	(2, 2)	(2, 3)	(2, 4)	(2, 5)	(2, 6)
3	(3, 1)	(3, 2)	(3, 3)	(3, 4)	(3, 5)	(3, 6)
4	(4, 1)	(4, 2)	(4, 3)	(4, 4)	(4, 5)	(4, 6)
5	(5, 1)	(5, 2)	(5, 3)	(5, 4)	(5, 5)	(5, 6)
6	(6, 1)	(6, 2)	(6, 3)	(6, 4)	(6, 5)	(6, 6)

There are 18 outcomes in which the sum is even.

So, $P(\text{even sum}) = \frac{18}{36}$ or $\frac{1}{2}$.

This means there is a 50% chance of rolling an even sum.

The probabilities in Examples 1 and 2 are called theoretical probabilities. **Theoretical probability** is what *should* occur. **Experimental probability** is what *actually* occurs when conducting a probability experiment.

Example 3 Find Experimental Probability

The table shows the results of an experiment in which a coin was tossed. Find the experimental probability of tossing a coin and getting tails for this experiment.

Outcome	Tally	Frequency
Heads	�illll �illll llll	14
Tails	�illll �illll l	11

$$\frac{\text{number of times tails occur}}{\text{number of possible outcomes}} = \frac{11}{14 + 11} \text{ or } \frac{11}{25}$$

The experimental probability of getting tails in this case is $\frac{11}{25}$ or 44%.

Building on Prior Knowledge

In Lesson 4-5, students learned how to simplify fractions. This is a necessary skill when solving problems of probability.

PROBABILITY OF SIMPLE EVENTS

In-Class Examples

1 Suppose a number cube is rolled. What is the probability of rolling a 4 or a 5? $\frac{1}{3}$ or $33\frac{1}{3}$%

2 Suppose two number cubes are rolled. Find the probability of rolling two identical numbers. $\frac{1}{6}$ or $16\frac{2}{3}$%

Teaching Tip Many students require help in organizing information in a table. Draw students' attention to how various tables are organized.

3 Use the table in Example 3 to determine the experimental probability of landing on heads for this experiment. $\frac{14}{25}$ or 56%

USE A SAMPLE TO MAKE PREDICTIONS

In-Class Example

4 **SPORTS** Miss Newman surveyed her class to see which sports they preferred watching. 44% preferred football, 28% basketball, 20% soccer, and 8% tennis. Out of 560 students in the entire school, how many would you expect to say they preferred watching basketball? **about 157 students**

INTERVENTION   **Differentiated Instruction**   **ELL**

- **Verbal/Linguistic** Have students work in small groups and look over Exercises 21 to 26 on page 313. Ask them to discuss how to find the opposite probabilities—P(not blue), P(not yellow), P(green), P(not purple), P(neither red nor blue), P(neither blue nor yellow). Ask them how they might find the opposite probability if they already know the probability. **Subtract it from 100%.**

Study Notebook

Have students—

• complete the definitions/examples for the remaining terms on the Vocabulary Builder worksheets for Chapter 6.

• copy Exercise 11 and write a paragraph explaining how to make the prediction.

• include any other item(s) that they find helpful in mastering the skills in this lesson.

About the Exercises . . .

Organization by Objective
• **Probability of Simple Events:** 12–36
• **Use a Sample to Make Predictions:** 35–37

Odd/Even Assignments
Exercises 12–36 are structured so that students practice the same concepts whether they are assigned odd or even problems.

Assignment Guide
Basic: 13–17 odd, 21–25 odd, 29–37 odd, 38–47

Average: 13–37 odd, 38–47

Advanced: 12–34 even, 35, 36, 38–47

Answers

2. Theoretical probability is what should occur. Experimental probability is what actually occurs.

3. Sample answer: Spinning the spinner as shown and having it land on 4.

USE A SAMPLE TO MAKE PREDICTIONS You can use an athlete's past performance to predict whether she will get a hit or make a basket. You can also use the results of a survey to predict the actions of a larger group.

Log on for:
• Updated data
• More activities on Making Predictions

www.pre-alg.com/usa_today

Example 4 Make a Prediction

FOOD The graph shows the results of a survey. Out of a group of 450 people, how many would you expect to say that they prefer thin mint cookies?

The total number of people is 450. So, 450 is the base. The percent is 26%.

To find 26% of 450, let b represent the base, 450, and let p represent the percent, 26%, in the percent proportion. Let a represent the part.

part →
base → $\dfrac{a}{450} = \dfrac{26}{100}$ ← percent

$$100 \cdot a = 26 \cdot 450$$
$$100a = 11700 \qquad \text{Simplify.}$$
$$a = 117 \qquad \text{Mentally divide each side by 100.}$$

You can expect 117 people to say that they prefer thin mint cookies.

USA TODAY Snapshots®

Monster cookies

Girl Scout cookie sales are an annual tradition from January to March in most of the USA. Last year's best-selling cookies in sales share:

- 26% Thin Mints
- 19% Samoas/Caramel deLites[1]
- 13% Tagalongs/Peanut Butter
- 12% Do-Si-Dos/Peanut Butter Sandwich[1]
- 11% Trefoils/Shortbread

1 – Same cookie with different name depending on baker
Source: Girl Scouts of the U.S.A.

By Anne R. Carey and Quin Tian, USA TODAY

Check for Understanding

Concept Check

1. **Tell** what a probability of 0 means. **The event will not happen.**

2. **Compare and contrast** theoretical and experimental probability.

3. **OPEN ENDED** Give an example of a situation in which the probability of the event is 25%. **2–3. See margin.**

Guided Practice

GUIDED PRACTICE KEY	
Exercises	Examples
4–7	1
8, 9	2
10	3
11	4

8–9. See pp. 323A–323B.

Ten cards are numbered 1 through 10, and one card is chosen at random. Determine the probability of each outcome. Express each probability as a fraction and as a percent. **4–7. See pp. 323A–323B.**

4. $P(5)$

5. $P(\text{odd})$

6. $P(\text{less than 3})$

7. $P(\text{greater than 6})$

For Exercises 8 and 9, refer to the table in Example 2 on page 311. Determine each probability. Express each probability as a fraction and as a percent.

8. $P(\text{sum of 2 or 6})$

9. $P(\text{even or odd sum})$

10. Refer to Example 3 on page 311. Find the experimental probability of getting heads for the experiment. $\dfrac{14}{25}$ or 56%

Application

11. **FOOD** Maresha took a sample from a package of jellybeans and found that 30% of the beans were red. Suppose there are 250 jellybeans in the package. How many can she expect to be red? **75**

Online Lesson Plans

USA TODAY's Education Online site offers resources and interactive features connected to each day's newspaper. *Experience TODAY*, USA TODAY's daily lesson plan, is available on the site and delivered daily to subscribers. This plan provides instruction for integrating USA TODAY graphics and key editorial features into your mathematics classroom. Log on to **www.education.usatoday.com**

★ indicates increased difficulty

Practice and Apply

Homework Help

For Exercises	See Examples
12–34, 35, 36	1, 2
	3
37	4

Extra Practice
See page 739.

A spinner like the one shown is used in a game. Determine the probability of each outcome if the spinner is equally likely to land on each section. Express each probability as a fraction and as a percent. **12–28. See margin.**

12. $P(8)$

13. $P(\text{red})$

14. $P(\text{even})$

15. $P(\text{prime})$

16. $P(\text{greater than 5})$

17. $P(\text{less than 2})$

★ **18.** $P(\text{blue or 11})$

★ **19.** $P(\text{not yellow})$

20. $P(\text{not red})$

There are 2 red marbles, 4 blue marbles, 7 green marbles, and 5 yellow marbles in a bag. Suppose one marble is selected at random. Find the probability of each outcome. Express each probability as a fraction and as a percent.

21. $P(\text{blue})$

22. $P(\text{yellow})$

23. $P(\text{not green})$

24. $P(\text{purple})$

25. $P(\text{red or blue})$

26. $P(\text{blue or yellow})$

★ **27.** $P(\text{not orange})$

★ **28.** $P(\text{not blue or not red})$

29. What is the probability that a calendar is randomly turned to the month of January or April? $\frac{1}{6}$

30. Find the probability that today is November 31. **0**

Suppose two spinners like the ones shown are spun. Find the probability of each outcome. (*Hint*: Make a table to show the sample space as in Example 2 on page 311.)

31. $P(2, 7)$ $\frac{1}{16}$

32. $P(\text{even, even})$ $\frac{1}{4}$

33. $P(\text{sum of 9})$ $\frac{1}{4}$

34. $P(2, \text{greater than 5})$ $\frac{3}{16}$

DRIVING For Exercises 35 and 36, use the following information and the table shown.
The table shows the approximate number of licensed automobile drivers in the United States in a certain year. An automobile company is conducting a telephone survey using a list of licensed drivers.

35. Find the probability that a driver will be 19 years old or younger. Express the answer as a decimal rounded to the nearest hundredth and as a percent. **0.05; 5%**

36. What is the probability that a randomly chosen driver will be 40–49 years old? Write the answer as a decimal rounded to the nearest hundredth and as a percent. **0.21; 21%**

Age	Drivers (millions)
19 and under	9
20–29	34
30–39	41
40–49	37
50–59	24
60–69	18
70 and over	17
Total	**180**

Source: U.S. Department of Transportation

www.pre-alg.com/self_check_quiz/ny

Lesson 6-9 Probability and Predictions **313**

Study Guide and Intervention, p. 339

Probability is the chance some event will happen.

$$P(\text{event}) = \frac{\text{(number of favorable outcomes)}}{\text{(number of possible outcomes)}}$$

Example A bag contains 6 red marbles, 1 blue marble, and 3 yellow marbles. One marble is selected at random. Find the probability of each outcome.

a. $P(\text{yellow})$
$P(\text{event}) = \frac{\text{(number of favorable outcomes)}}{\text{(number of possible outcomes)}}$
$= \frac{3}{10}$ or 30%
There is a 30% chance of choosing a yellow marble.

b. $P(\text{blue or yellow})$
$P(\text{event}) = \frac{\text{(number of favorable outcomes)}}{\text{(number of possible outcomes)}}$
$= \frac{(1+3)}{10} = \frac{4}{10}$ or 40%
There is a 40% chance of choosing a blue or yellow marble.

c. $P(\text{red, blue, or yellow})$
$P(\text{event}) = \frac{\text{(number of favorable outcomes)}}{\text{(number of possible outcomes)}}$
$= \frac{(6+1+3)}{10} = \frac{10}{10}$ or 100%
There is a 100% chance of choosing a red, blue, or yellow marble.

d. $P(\text{black})$
$P(\text{event}) = \frac{\text{(number of favorable outcomes)}}{\text{(number of possible outcomes)}}$
$= \frac{0}{10}$ or 0%
There is a 0% chance of choosing a black marble.

Exercises

A bag contains 5 red marbles, 5 blue marbles, 6 green marbles, 8 purple marbles, and 1 white marble. One is selected at random. Find the probability of each outcome. Express each probability as a fraction and as a percent.

1. $P(\text{white})$ $\frac{1}{25}$, 4%

2. $P(\text{red})$ $\frac{1}{5}$, 20%

3. $P(\text{green})$ $\frac{6}{25}$, 24%

4. $P(\text{purple})$ $\frac{8}{25}$, 32%

5. $P(\text{white, blue, green})$ $\frac{12}{25}$, 48%

6. $P(\text{red or blue})$ $\frac{2}{5}$, 40%

7. $P(\text{red or purple})$ $\frac{13}{25}$, 52%

8. $P(\text{green or purple})$ $\frac{14}{25}$, 56%

9. $P(\text{green, purple, or white})$ $\frac{3}{5}$, 60%

10. $P(\text{red, blue, green, purple, or white})$ $\frac{1}{1}$, 100%

11. $P(\text{red, blue, or purple})$ $\frac{18}{25}$, 72%

Skills Practice, p. 340 and Practice, p. 341 (shown)

A spinner like the one shown is used in a game. Determine the probability of each outcome if the spinner is equally likely to land on each section. Express each probability as a fraction and as a percent.

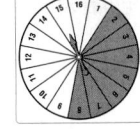

1. $P(15)$ $\frac{1}{16}$, 6.25%

2. $P(\text{even})$ $\frac{1}{2}$, 50%

3. $P(\text{greater than 10})$ $\frac{3}{8}$, 37.5

4. $P(\text{perfect square})$ $\frac{1}{4}$, 25%

5. $P(1 \text{ or } 2)$ $\frac{1}{8}$, 12.5%

6. $P(\text{less than 9})$ $\frac{1}{2}$, 50%

7. $P(\text{not shaded})$ $\frac{9}{16}$, 56.25%

8. $P(\text{shaded})$ $\frac{7}{16}$, 43.75%

There are 8 red marbles, 5 blue marbles, 11 green marbles, and 1 yellow marble in a bag. Suppose one marble is selected at random. Find the probability of each outcome. Express each probability as a fraction and as a percent.

9. $P(\text{red})$ $\frac{8}{25}$, 32%

10. $P(\text{blue})$ $\frac{1}{5}$, 20%

11. $P(\text{yellow})$ $\frac{1}{25}$, 4%

12. $P(\text{red or blue})$ $\frac{13}{25}$, 52%

13. $P(\text{black})$ $\frac{0}{1}$, 0%

14. $P(\text{red, blue, or green})$ $\frac{24}{25}$, 96%

Suppose two 1–6 number cubes are rolled. Find the probability of each outcome. Express each probability as a fraction and as a percent. (*Hint:* Make a table to show the sample space as in Example 2.) Round to the nearest tenth if necessary.

15. $P(1 \text{ or } 5)$ $\frac{5}{9}$, 55.6%

16. $P(\text{both odd})$ $\frac{1}{4}$, 25%

17. $P(\text{red product})$ $\frac{3}{4}$, 75%

18. $P(\text{sum more than 8})$ $\frac{5}{18}$, 27.8%

19. $P(\text{both different})$ $\frac{5}{6}$, 83.3%

20. $P(\text{sum is a square})$ $\frac{7}{36}$, 19.4%

21. To the nearest tenth of a percent, what is the probability that today is a weekday? 71.4%

Enrichment, p. 343

Probability and Tables

SCHOOL In Rockville High School there are

400 freshmen—60 have A averages and 90 have B averages.
300 sophomores—40 have A averages and 60 have B averages.
200 juniors—10 have A averages and 30 have B averages.
100 seniors—20 have A averages and 60 have B averages.

1. Use the information above to complete the table below. Then use the table to answer Exercises 2–11.

Class \ Grade	A	B	Below B	Total
Freshmen	60	90	250	400
Sophomores	40	60	200	300
Juniors	10	30	160	200
Seniors	20	60	20	100
Total	130	240	630	1000

Suppose a student is selected at random from Rockville High School. Find the probability of selecting each of the following.

2. a freshman $\frac{2}{5}$ or 40%

3. a senior $\frac{1}{10}$ or 10%

4. an A student $\frac{13}{100}$ or 13%

5. a student whose grade is below B $\frac{63}{100}$ or 63%

6. a sophomore B student $\frac{3}{50}$ or 6%

7. a junior A student or a senior A student $\frac{3}{100}$ or 3%

8. a student who is neither a junior A student nor a senior A student $\frac{97}{100}$ or 97%

9. a B student who is *not* a junior $\frac{21}{100}$ or 21%

10. If selecting only from the juniors, what is the probability of picking an A student? $\frac{1}{20}$ or 5%

11. If selecting only from the students who are neither A nor B students, what is the probability of picking a senior? $\frac{2}{63}$ or about 3.2%

Answers

12. $\frac{1}{8}$; $12\frac{1}{2}\%$

13. $\frac{1}{4}$; 25%

14. $\frac{1}{2}$; 50%

15. $\frac{1}{2}$; 50%

16. $\frac{5}{8}$; $62\frac{1}{2}\%$

17. 0; 0%

18. $\frac{1}{2}$; 50%

19. $\frac{7}{8}$; 87.5%

20. $\frac{3}{4}$; 75%

21. $\frac{2}{9}$; 22.2%

22. $\frac{5}{18}$; 27.8%

23. $\frac{11}{18}$; 61.1%

24. 0; 0%

25. $\frac{1}{3}$; $33\frac{1}{3}\%$

26. $\frac{1}{2}$; 50%

27. 1; 100%

28. $\frac{2}{3}$; $66\frac{2}{3}\%$

Lesson 6-9 Probability and Predictions **313**

Open-Ended Assessment

Speaking Have students explain what each of the following phrases means.

a. 0% chance of rain

b. 50% chance of rain

c. 100% chance of rain

d. 25% chance of guessing a correct answer

e. 80% of guessing incorrectly

Assessment Options

Quiz (Lessons 6-8 and 6-9) is available on p. 360 of the *Chapter 6 Resource Masters*.

Answers

38. No; many of the common two-letter words like *at*, *in*, *of*, and *on* do not contain the letter E.

39. Once the probability or likeliness of something happening is known, then you can use the probability to make a prediction. For example, in football, if you know the number of field goals a player has made in the past, you can use the information to predict the number of field goals he/she will make in upcoming games. Answers should include the following.

- E: $\frac{12}{100}$ or 12%; A, I: $\frac{9}{100}$ or
  9%; O: $\frac{8}{100}$ or 8%; N, R, T:
  $\frac{6}{100}$ or 6%; D, L, S, U: $\frac{4}{100}$ or
  4%; G: $\frac{3}{100}$ or 3%; B, C, F, H,
  M, P, V, W, Y, blank: $\frac{2}{100}$ or
  2%; J, K, Q, X, Z: $\frac{1}{100}$ or 1%
- See students' work.

---

37. FOOD Refer to the graph. Out of 1200 people, how many would you expect to say they crave chocolate after dinner? **444**

38. See margin.

38. CRITICAL THINKING In the English language, 13% of the letters used are E's. Suppose you are guessing the letters in a two-letter word of a puzzle. Would you guess an E? Explain.

39. WRITING IN MATH Answer the question that was posed at the beginning of the lesson.

How can probability help you make predictions?

Include the following in your answer: **See margin.**

- an explanation telling the probability of choosing each letter tile, and
- an example of how you can use probability to make predictions.

NEW YORK
Test Practice

Standardized Test Practice
Ⓐ Ⓑ Ⓒ Ⓓ

40. What is the probability of spinning an even number on the spinner shown? **D**

Ⓐ $\frac{1}{2}$ Ⓑ $\frac{1}{4}$ Ⓒ $\frac{2}{3}$ Ⓓ $\frac{3}{4}$

USA TODAY Snapshots®

Chocolate cravings
Time of day that adults say they crave chocolate:

Midafternoon **47%**
Evening **42%**
After dinner **37%**
Lunch **21%**
Before bed **18%**
Midmorning **17%**
Middle of the night **10%**
Breakfast **9%**

Source: Yankelovich Partners for the American Boxed Chocolate Manufacturers

By Cindy Hall and Alejandro Gonzalez, USA TODAY

Maintain Your Skills

Mixed Review

41. Find the percent of change from 32 feet to 79 feet. Round to the nearest tenth, if necessary. Then state whether the percent of change is a *percent of increase* or a *percent of decrease*. *(Lesson 6-8)* **146.9%; I**

Solve each problem using an equation. Round to the nearest tenth. *(Lesson 6-7)*

42. 7 is what percent of 32? **21.9%**   **43.** What is 28.5% of 84? **23.9**

ALGEBRA Find each product or quotient. Express your answer in exponential form. *(Lesson 4-6)*

44. $7^2 \cdot 7^3$ **7^5**   **45.** $x^4 \cdot 2x$ **$2x^5$**   **46.** $\frac{8^{12}}{8^8}$ **8^4**   **47.** $\frac{36n^4}{14n^2}$ **$\frac{18n^2}{7}$**

 Internet Project

Kids Gobbling Empty Calories
It is time to complete your project. Use the information and data you have gathered to prepare a brochure or Web page about the nutritional value of fast-food meals. Include the total Calories, grams of fat, and amount of sodium for five meals that a typical student would order from at least three fast-food restaurants.

www.pre-alg.com/webquest

Graphing Calculator Investigation

A Follow-Up of Lesson 6-9

NEW YORK *Performance Indicator* Reinforcement of 7.S.11 Design and conduct an experiment to test predictions, Reinforcement of 7.S.12 Compare actual results to predicted results

Probability Simulation
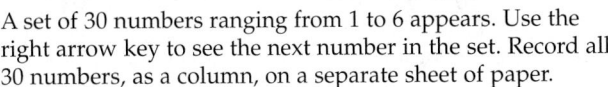

A random number generator can simulate a probability experiment. From the simulation, you can calculate experimental probabilities. Repeating a simulation may result in different probabilities since the numbers generated are different each time.

Example   **Generate 30 random numbers from 1 to 6, simulating 30 rolls of a number cube.**

* Access the random number generator.
* Enter 1 as a lower bound and 6 as an upper bound for 30 trials.

KEYSTROKES: MATH ◄ 5 1 , 6 , 30) ENTER

A set of 30 numbers ranging from 1 to 6 appears. Use the right arrow key to see the next number in the set. Record all 30 numbers, as a column, on a separate sheet of paper.

Exercises **1–4. See margin.**

1. Record how often each number on the number cube appeared.
   a. Find the experimental probability of each number.
   b. Compare the experimental probabilities with the theoretical probabilities.

2. Repeat the simulation of rolling a number cube 30 times. Record this second set of numbers in a column next to the first set of numbers. Each pair of 30 numbers represents a roll of two number cubes. Find the sum for each of the 30 pairs of rolls.
   a. Find the experimental probability of each sum.
   b. Compare the experimental probability with the theoretical probabilities.

3. Design an experiment to simulate 30 spins of a spinner that has equal sections colored red, white, and blue.
   a. Find the experimental probability of each color.
   b. Compare the experimental probabilities with the theoretical probabilities.

4. Suppose you play a game where there are three containers, each with ten balls numbered 0 to 9. Pick three numbers and then use the random number generator to simulate the game. Score 2 points if one number matches, 16 points if two numbers match, and 32 points if all three numbers match. Note: numbers can appear more than once.
   a. Play the game if the order of your numbers *does not* matter. Total your score for 10 simulations.
   b. Now play the game if the order of the numbers *does* matter. Total your score for 10 simulations.
   c. With which game rules did you score more points?

Answers

1–2. See students' answers.

3–4. To use the random number generator, let red = 1, let white = 2, and let blue = 3. See students' answers.

Graphing Calculator Investigation

A Follow-Up of Lesson 6-9

Getting Started

Know Your Calculator The graphing calculator has the capability of generating random numbers when given an upper limit, a lower limit, and the quantity of numbers to generate.

Teaching Tip To clarify Exercises 4a and 4b, point out to students that in 4a, if you choose the numbers 446 and the simulation shows 564, you score 16 points for picking one 4 and one 6. In 4b, where order does matter, 446 and 564 would be a score of 0 points.

Teach

* Have students duplicate the keystrokes given in the example.
* If students need to review entering numbers in a list, see page 45.

Assess

* Ask students how the graphing calculator helps make simulating a probability an easier task.   **Many numbers can be quickly generated.**
* Ask students why different numbers are generated each time.   **Because the numbers are generated randomly.**

Chapter 6 Study Guide and Review

Vocabulary and Concept Check

- This alphabetical list of vocabulary terms in Chapter 6 includes a page reference where each term was introduced.

- **Assessment** A vocabulary review/test for Chapter 6 is available on p. 358 of the *Chapter 6 Resource Masters*

Lesson-by-Lesson Review

For each lesson,

- the main ideas are summarized,
- additional examples review concepts, and
- practice exercises are provided.

Vocabulary PuzzleMaker

ELL The Vocabulary PuzzleMaker software improves students' mathematics vocabulary using four puzzle formats—crossword, scramble, word search using a word list, and word search using clues. Students can work on a computer screen or from a printed handout.

MindJogger Videoquizzes

ELL MindJogger Videoquizzes provide an alternative review of concepts presented in this chapter. Students work in teams in a game show format to gain points for correct answers. The questions are presented in three rounds.

Round 1 Concepts (5 questions)
Round 2 Skills (4 questions)
Round 3 Problem Solving (4 questions)

Vocabulary and Concept Check

base (p. 288)	percent of decrease (p. 306)	scale (p. 276)
compound interest (p. 303)	percent of increase (p. 305)	scale drawing (p. 276)
cross products (p. 270)	percent proportion (p. 288)	scale factor (p. 277)
discount (p. 299)	probability (p. 310)	scale model (p. 276)
experimental probability (p. 311)	proportion (p. 270)	simple event (p. 310)
outcome (p. 310)	random (p. 309)	simple interest (p. 300)
part (p. 288)	rate (p. 265)	theoretical probability (p. 311)
percent (p. 281)	ratio (p. 264)	unbiased (p. 309)
percent equation (p. 298)	sample (p. 309)	unit rate (p. 265)
percent of change (p. 304)	sample space (p. 311)	

Complete each sentence with the correct term.

1. A statement of equality of two ratios is called a(n) __proportion__ .
2. A(n) __percent__ is a ratio that compares a number to 100.
3. The ratio of a length on a scale drawing to the corresponding length on the real object is called the __scale factor__ .
4. The set of all possible outcomes is the __sample space__ .
5. _____ is what actually occurs when conducting a probability experiment. __Experimental probability__

Lesson-by-Lesson Review

6-1 *Ratios and Rates*

See pages 264–268.

Concept Summary

- A ratio is a comparison of two numbers by division.
- A rate is a ratio of two measurements having different units of measure.
- A rate that is simplified so that it has a denominator of 1 is called a unit rate.

Example Express the ratio *2 meters to 35 centimeters* as a fraction in simplest form.

$$\frac{2 \text{ meters}}{35 \text{ centimeters}} = \frac{200 \text{ centimeters}}{35 \text{ centimeters}}$$ Convert 2 meters to centimeters.

$$= \frac{40 \text{ centimeters}}{7 \text{ centimeters}} \text{ or } \frac{40}{7}$$ Divide the numerator and denominator by the GCF, 5.

Exercises Express each ratio as a fraction in simplest form.
See Examples 1 and 2 on pages 264 and 265.

6. 9 students out of 33 students $\frac{3}{11}$
7. 12 hits out of 16 times at bat $\frac{3}{4}$
8. 30 hours to 18 hours $\frac{5}{3}$
9. 5 quarts to 5 gallons $\frac{1}{4}$
10. 10 inches to 4 feet $\frac{5}{24}$
11. 2 tons to 1800 pounds $\frac{20}{9}$

 www.pre-alg.com/vocabulary_review

FOLDABLES™ Study Organizer

For more information about Foldables, see *Teaching Mathematics with Foldables.*

Have students reexamine their Foldables to make sure all their equivalents are correct. Have them refer to their Foldables if needed when working through the Study Guide and Review or preparing for the Chapter Test.

6-2 Using Proportions

See pages
270–274.

Concept Summary

- A proportion is an equation stating two ratios are equal.
- If $\frac{a}{b} = \frac{c}{d}$, then $ad = bc$.

Example   Solve $\frac{3}{7} = \frac{15}{x}$.

$\frac{3}{7} = \frac{15}{x}$ Write the proportion.

$3 \cdot x = 7 \cdot 15$ Cross products

$3x = 105$ Multiply.

$\frac{3x}{3} = \frac{105}{3}$ Divide each side by 3.

$x = 35$ The solution is 35.

Exercises   Solve each proportion.   *See Example 2 on page 271.*

12. $\frac{n}{12} = \frac{4}{3}$ **16**   **13.** $\frac{21}{x} = \frac{84}{120}$ **30**   **14.** $\frac{9}{7} = \frac{22.5}{y}$ **17.5**   **15.** $\frac{5}{7.5} = \frac{0.6}{k}$ **0.9**

6-3 Scale Drawings and Models

See pages
276–280.

Concept Summary

- A scale drawing or a scale model represents an object that is too large or too small to be drawn or built at actual size.
- The ratio of a length on a scale drawing or model to the corresponding length on the real object is called the scale factor.

Example   A scale drawing shows a pond that is 1.75 inches long. The scale on the drawing is 0.25 inch = 1 foot. What is the length of the actual pond?

drawing length → $\quad \frac{0.25 \text{ in.}}{1 \text{ ft}} = \frac{1.75 \text{ in.}}{x \text{ ft}}$ ← drawing length
actual length → $\qquad\qquad\qquad\qquad$ ← actual length

$0.25 \cdot x = 1 \cdot 1.75$ Find the cross products.

$0.25x = 1.75$ Simplify.

$x = 7$ Divide each side by 0.25.

The actual length of the pond is 7 feet.

Exercises   On the model of a ship, the scale is 1 inch = 12 feet. Find the actual length of each room.   *See Example 1 on page 277.*

	Room	Model Length	
16.	Stateroom	0.9 in.	10.8 ft
17.	Galley	3.8 in.	45.6 ft
18.	Gym	6.0 in.	72 ft

6-4 Fractions, Decimals, and Percents

See pages 281–285.

Concept Summary

- A percent is a ratio that compares a number to 100.
- Fractions, decimals, and percents are all different ways to represent the same number.

Examples

1 Express 60% as a fraction in simplest form and as a decimal.

$60\% = \frac{60}{100}$ or $\frac{3}{5}$ $60\% = 60\%$ or 0.6

2 Express 0.38 as a percent.

0.38 = 0.38 or 38%

3 Express $\frac{5}{8}$ as a percent.

$\frac{5}{8} = 0.625$ or 62.5%

Exercises Express each percent as a fraction or mixed number in simplest form and as a decimal.   *See Examples 1 and 3 on pages 281 and 282.*

19. 35% $\frac{7}{20}$; **0.35** **20.** 42% $\frac{21}{50}$; **0.42** **21.** 8% $\frac{2}{25}$; **0.08** **22.** 19% $\frac{19}{100}$; **0.19**
23. 120% $1\frac{1}{5}$; **1.2** **24.** 250% $2\frac{1}{2}$; **2.5** **25.** 62.5% $\frac{5}{8}$; **0.625** **26.** 8.8% $\frac{11}{125}$; **0.088**

Express each decimal or fraction as a percent. Round to the nearest tenth percent, if necessary.   *See Examples 2, 4, and 5 on pages 282 and 283.*

27. 0.24 **24%**   **28.** 0.03 **3%**   **29.** 0.452 **45.2%**   **30.** 1.9 **190%**
31. $\frac{2}{5}$ **40%**   **32.** $\frac{13}{22}$ **59.1%**   **33.** $\frac{6}{80}$ **7.5%**   **34.** $\frac{77}{225}$ **34.2%**

6-5 Using the Percent Proportion

See pages 288–292.

Concept Summary

- If a is the part, b is the base, and p is the percent, then $\frac{a}{b} = \frac{p}{100}$.

Example Forty-eight is 32% of what number?

$\frac{a}{b} = \frac{p}{100} \rightarrow \frac{48}{b} = \frac{32}{100}$ Replace a with 48 and p with 32.

$48 \cdot 100 = b \cdot 32$ Find the cross products.

$4800 = 32b$ Simplify.

$150 = b$ Divide each side by 32.

So, 48 is 32% of 150.

Exercises Use the percent proportion to solve each problem.
See Examples 1–6 on pages 288–290.

35. 18 is what percent of 45? **40%**   **36.** What percent of 60 is 39? **65%**
37. 23 is 92% of what number? **25**   **38.** What is 74% of 110? **81.4**
39. What is 80% of 62.5? **50**   **40.** 36 is 15% of what number? **240**

6-6 Finding Percents Mentally

See pages 293–297.

Concept Summary

- When working with common percents like 10%, 20%, 25%, and 50%, it is helpful to use the fraction form of the percent.

Examples

1 **Find 20% of $45 mentally.**

20% of $45 = \frac{1}{5}$ of 45 Think: $20\% = \frac{1}{5}$.

   $= 9$ Think: $\frac{1}{5}$ of 45 is 9.

So, 20% of $45 is $9.

2 **Estimate 32% of 150.**

32% is about $33\frac{1}{3}\%$ or $\frac{1}{3}$.

$\frac{1}{3}$ of 150 is 50.

So, 32% of 150 is about 50.

Exercises   Find the percent of each number mentally.
See Example 1 on pages 293 and 294.

41. 50% of 86 **43**
42. 20% of 55 **11**
43. 25% of 36 **9**
44. 40% of 75 **30**
45. $33\frac{1}{3}\%$ of 24 **8**
46. 90% of 60 **54**

Estimate. Explain which method you used to estimate.
See Example 2 on pages 294 and 295. **47–52. See margin.**

47. 48% of 32
48. 67% of 30
49. 20% of 51
50. 25% of 27
51. $\frac{1}{3}\%$ of 304
52. 147% of 200

Answers

For Exercises 47–52, sample answers are given.

47. 16; fraction method: $\frac{1}{2} \times 32$ or 16

48. 20; fraction method: $\frac{2}{3} \times 30$ or 20

49. 10; fraction method: $\frac{1}{5} \times 50$ or 10

50. 7; fraction method: $\frac{1}{4} \times 28$ or 7

51. 1; 1% method: Since 1% of 304 is about 3, $\frac{1}{3}\%$ of 304 is about $\frac{1}{3}$ of 3 or 1.

52. 300; meaning of percent: 147% means about 150 for every 100. 200 has two 100. $150 \times 2 = 300$

6-7 Using Percent Equations

See pages 298–302.

Concept Summary

- The percent equation is an equivalent form of the percent proportion in which the percent is written as a decimal.
- Part = Percent · Base, where percent is in decimal form.

Example

119 is 85% of what number?
The part is 119, and the percent is 85%. Let n represent the base.

$119 = 0.85n$ Write 85% as the decimal 0.85.

$\dfrac{119}{0.85} = \dfrac{0.85n}{0.85}$ Divide each side by 0.85.

$140 = n$ So, 119 is 85% of 140.

Exercises   Solve each problem using the percent equation.
See Examples 1–3 on pages 298 and 299.

53. 24 is what percent of 50? **48%**
54. 70 is 40% of what number? **175**
55. What is 90% of 105? **94.5**
56. What is 12.5% of 68? **8.5**
57. 56 is 28% of what number? **200**
58. 35.7 is what percent of 17? **210%**

6-8 Percent of Change

See pages 304–308.

Concept Summary

- A percent of increase tells how much an amount has increased in relation to the original amount. (The percent will be positive.)
- A percent of decrease tells how much an amount has decreased in relation to the original amount. (The percent will be negative.)

Example Find the percent of change from 36 pounds to 14 pounds.

$$\text{percent of change} = \frac{\text{new weight} - \text{original weight}}{\text{original weight}} \quad \text{Write the ratio.}$$

$$= \frac{14 - 36}{36} \quad \text{Substitution}$$

$$= \frac{-22}{36} \quad \text{Subtraction}$$

$$\approx -0.611 \text{ or } -61.1\% \quad \text{Simplify.}$$

The percent of decrease is about 61.1%.

Exercises Find the percent of change. Round to the nearest tenth, if necessary. Then state whether each change is a *percent of increase* or a *percent of decrease*. *See Examples 1, 2, and 4 on pages 304–306.*

59. from 40 ft to 12 ft **D; −70%**   **60.** from 80 cm to 96 cm **I; 20%**

61. from 29 min to 54 min **I; 86.2%**   **62.** from 80 lb to 77 lb **D; −3.8%**

6-9 Probability and Predictions

See pages 310–314.

Concept Summary

- The probability of an event is a ratio that compares the number of favorable outcomes to the number of possible outcomes.

Example Suppose a number cube is rolled. Find the probability of rolling a 5 or 6.

Favorable outcomes: 5 and 6.

Possible outcomes: 1, 2, 3, 4, 5, and 6.

$$P(5 \text{ or } 6) = \frac{\text{number of favorable outcomes}}{\text{number of possible outcomes}}$$

$$= \frac{2}{6} \text{ or } \frac{1}{3} \quad \text{So, the probability of rolling a 5 or 6 is } \frac{1}{3} \text{ or } 33\frac{1}{3}\%$$

Exercises There are 2 blue marbles, 5 red marbles, and 8 green marbles in a bag. One marble is selected at random. Find the probability of each outcome. *See Examples 1 and 2 on page 311.*

63. $P(\text{red})$ $\frac{1}{3}$ **64.** $P(\text{green})$ $\frac{8}{15}$ **65.** $P(\text{blue or green})$ $\frac{2}{3}$

66. $P(\text{not blue})$ $\frac{13}{15}$ **67.** $P(\text{yellow})$ **0**   **68.** $P(\text{green, red, or blue})$ **1**

320 Chapter 6 Ratio, Proportion, and Percent

Answers (p. 321)

1. A ratio is a comparison of two numbers by division. A rate is a ratio of two measurements having different kinds of units. For example, 2 inches to 24 inches is a ratio, and 2 inches in 3 hours is a rate.

2. To write a fraction as a percent, first write the fraction as a decimal. Then write the decimal as a percent by moving the decimal 2 places to the right and adding the percent symbol.

Vocabulary and Concepts

1. **Explain** the difference between a ratio and a rate. **1–2. See margin.**
2. **Describe** how to express a fraction as a percent.

Skills and Applications

Express each ratio as a fraction in simplest form.

3. 15 girls out of 40 students $\frac{3}{8}$

4. 6 feet to 3 yards $\frac{2}{3}$

Express each ratio as a unit rate. Round to the nearest tenth or cent.

5. 145 miles in 3 hours **48.3 mi/h**

6. $245 for 9 tickets **$27.22 per ticket**

7. Convert 15 miles per hour to x feet per minute. **1320 feet per minute**

8. What value of y makes $\frac{8.4}{y} = \frac{1.2}{1.1}$ a proportion? **7.7**

Express each percent as a fraction or mixed number in simplest form and as a decimal.

9. 36% $\frac{9}{25}$; **0.36**

10. 52% $\frac{13}{25}$; **0.52**

11. 225% $2\frac{1}{4}$; **2.25**

12. 315% $3\frac{3}{20}$; **3.15**

13. 0.6% $\frac{3}{500}$; **0.006**

14. 0.4% $\frac{1}{250}$; **0.004**

Express each decimal or fraction as a percent. Round to the nearest tenth percent, if necessary.

15. 0.47 **47%**

16. 0.025 **2.5%**

17. 5.38 **538%**

18. $\frac{7}{20}$ **35%**

19. $\frac{30}{22}$ **136.4%**

20. $\frac{18}{4000}$ **0.45%**

Use the percent proportion to solve each problem.

21. 36 is what percent of 80? **45%**

22. 35.28 is 63% of what number? **56**

Estimate.

23. 25% of 82 **20**

24. 63% of 77 **48**

25. Find the interest on $2700 that is invested at 4% for $2\frac{1}{2}$ years. **$270**

26. Find the discount for a $135 coat that is on sale at 15% off. **$20.25**

27. Find the percent of change from 175 pounds to 140 pounds. Round to the nearest tenth. **−20%**

28. There are 3 purple balls, 5 orange balls, and 8 yellow balls in a bowl. Suppose one ball is selected at random. Find $P(\text{orange})$. $\frac{5}{16}$

29. **DESIGN** A builder is designing a swimming pool that is 8.5 inches in length on the scale drawing. The scale of the drawing is 1 inch = 6 feet. What is the length of the actual swimming pool? **51 feet**

30. **STANDARDIZED TEST PRACTICE** The table lists the reasons shoppers use online customer service. Out of 350 shoppers who own a computer, how many would you expect to say they use online customer service to track packages? **A**

Reasons	Percent
Track Delivery	54
Product Information	24
Verify Shipping Charges	17
Transaction Help	16

Ⓐ 189   Ⓑ 84   Ⓒ 19   Ⓓ 154

 www.pre-alg.com/chapter_test/ny

Assessment Options

Vocabulary Test A vocabulary review/test for Chapter 6 can be found on p. 358 of the *Chapter 6 Resource Masters*.

Chapter Tests There are six Chapter 6 Tests and an Open-Ended Assessment task available in the *Chapter 6 Resource Masters*.

Chapter 6 Tests			
Form	Type	Level	Pages
1	MC	basic	345–346
2A	MC	average	347–348
2B	MC	average	349–350
2C	FR	average	351–352
2D	FR	average	353–354
3	FR	advanced	355–356

MC = multiple-choice questions
FR = free-response questions

Open-Ended Assessment
Performance tasks for Chapter 6 can be found on p. 357 of the *Chapter 6 Resource Masters*, along with a sample scoring rubric for these tasks on p. A30.

Unit 2 Test A unit test/review can be found on pp. 365–366 of the *Chapter 6 Resource Masters*.

 ExamView® Pro

Use the networkable **ExamView® Pro** to:

- Create **multiple versions** of tests.
- Create **modified** tests for *Inclusion* students.
- **Edit** existing questions and **add** your own questions.
- Use built-in **state curriculum correlations** to create tests aligned with state standards.
- Change **English** tests to **Spanish** and vice versa.

Portfolio Suggestion

Introduction Equations are used to solve many different types of problems. Sometimes special types of equations called formulas are used.

Ask Students to find a problem from their work in this chapter and explain how they used an equation or formula to solve it.

These two pages contain practice questions in the various formats that can be found on the most frequently given standardized tests.

A practice answer sheet for these two pages can be found on page A1 of the *Chapter 6 Resource Masters.*

Standardized Test Practice
Student Recording Sheet, p. A1

Part 1 Multiple Choice

Select the best answer from the choices given and fill in the corresponding oval.

1 Ⓐ Ⓑ Ⓒ Ⓓ   4 Ⓐ Ⓑ Ⓒ Ⓓ   7 Ⓐ Ⓑ Ⓒ Ⓓ

2 Ⓐ Ⓑ Ⓒ Ⓓ   5 Ⓐ Ⓑ Ⓒ Ⓓ   8 Ⓐ Ⓑ Ⓒ Ⓓ

3 Ⓐ Ⓑ Ⓒ Ⓓ   6 Ⓐ Ⓑ Ⓒ Ⓓ   9 Ⓐ Ⓑ Ⓒ Ⓓ

Part 2 Short Response/Grid In

Solve the problem and write your answer in the blank.

For Questions 12, 13, 15, and 17, also enter your answer by writing each number or symbol in a box. Then fill in the corresponding oval for that number or symbol.

10 ___   12   13

11 ___

12 ___ (grid in)

13 ___ (grid in)

14 ___

15 ___ (grid in)   15   17

16 ___

17 ___ (grid in)

Part 3 Extended Response

Record your answers for Questions 18–19 on the back of this paper.

Additional Practice

Additional Standardized Test Practice is available on pp. 363–364 of the *Chapter 6 Resource Masters.*

 NEW YORK Test Practice

Part 1 Multiple Choice

Record your answers on the answer sheet provided by your teacher or on a sheet of paper.

1. Evaluate $x - y + z$ if $x = -6$, $y = 9$, and $z = -3$.   (Lesson 2-3) **C**
   - Ⓐ 0
   - Ⓑ −6
   - Ⓒ −18
   - Ⓓ 15

2. Which figure has an area of 192 cm²? (Lesson 3-7) **D**

  Ⓐ 18 cm, 12 cm

  Ⓑ 11 cm, 11 cm

  Ⓒ 9 cm, 12 cm

  Ⓓ 16 cm, 12 cm

3. Which expression is *not* a monomial? (Lesson 4-1) **C**
   - Ⓐ $5(-y)$
   - Ⓑ $8k$
   - Ⓒ $m - n$
   - Ⓓ $2x(-3y)$

4. Which fraction represents the ratio *8 apples to 36 pieces of fruit* in simplest form? (Lesson 6-1) **C**
   - Ⓐ $\frac{1}{4}$
   - Ⓑ $\frac{4}{9}$
   - Ⓒ $\frac{2}{9}$
   - Ⓓ $\frac{1}{6}$

5. The ratio of girls to boys in a class is 5 to 4. Suppose there are 27 students in the class. How many of the students are girls? (Lesson 6-2) **B**
   - Ⓐ 40
   - Ⓑ 15
   - Ⓒ 12
   - Ⓓ 9

6. A scale model of an airplane has a width of 13.5 inches. The scale of the model is 1 inch = 8 feet. What is the width of the actual airplane?   (Lesson 6-3) **B**
   - Ⓐ 110 ft
   - Ⓑ 108 ft
   - Ⓒ 104 ft
   - Ⓓ 115 ft

---

7. Randy, Eduardo, and Kelli took a quiz. For every 50 questions on the quiz, Randy answered 47 correctly. Eduardo answered 91% of the questions correctly. For every 10 questions on the quiz, Kelli answered 9 correctly. Who had the highest score? **A**
   - Ⓐ Randy
   - Ⓑ Eduardo
   - Ⓒ Kelli
   - Ⓓ all the same

8. The graph shows the amount of canned food collected by the 9th grade classes at Hilltop High School.

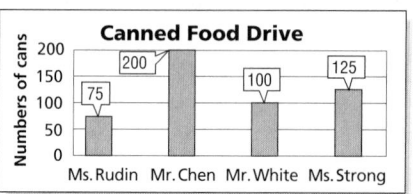

Canned Food Drive — Numbers of cans: Ms. Rudin 75, Mr. Chen 200, Mr. White 100, Ms. Strong 125

Of the total amount of cans collected, what percent did Mr. Chen's class collect? (Lesson 6-4) **C**
   - Ⓐ 25%
   - Ⓑ 33%
   - Ⓒ 40%
   - Ⓓ 50%

9. The table shows the average salaries in each of the four major sports for the 1990–91 and 2000–01 seasons.   (Lesson 6-8)

Sport	1990−91	2000−01
Hockey	$271,000	$1,400,000
Basketball	823,000	3,530,000
Football	430,000	1,200,000
Baseball	597,537	2,260,000

Source: *USA TODAY*

Which sport had a percent of increase in average salary of about 325%? **B**
   - Ⓐ Hockey
   - Ⓑ Basketball
   - Ⓒ Football
   - Ⓓ Baseball

Test-Taking Tip Ⓐ Ⓑ Ⓒ Ⓓ

Question 8

To find what percent of the cans a class collected, you will first need to find the total number of cans collected by all of the 9th grade classes.

💿 **ExamView® Pro**

Special banks of standardized test questions similar to those on the SAT, ACT, TIMSS 8, NAEP 8, and Pre-Algebra End-of-Course tests can be found on this CD-ROM.

Part 2 | Short Response/Grid In

Record your answers on the answer sheet provided by your teacher or on a sheet of paper.

10. Ana earns $6.80 per hour when she works on weekdays. She earns twice that amount per hour when she works on weekends. If Ana worked 4 hours on Tuesday, 4 hours on Thursday, and 5 hours on Saturday, then how much did she earn? (Prerequisite Skill, p. 713) **$122.40**

11. Juan and Julia decided to eat lunch at The Sub Shop. Juan ordered a veggie sub, lemonade, and a cookie. Julia ordered a ham sub, milk, and a cookie. What was the total cost of Juan and Julia's lunch? (Prerequisite Skill, p. 713) **$11.15**

Item	Cost
Veggie Sub	$3.89
Turkey Sub	$3.79
Ham Sub	$3.49
Soda	$1.25
Lemonade	$1.00
Milk	$0.79
Cookie	$0.99

12. What number should replace X in this pattern? (Lesson 4-2) **256**

$$4^0 = 1$$
$$4^1 = 4$$
$$4^2 = 16$$
$$4^3 = 64$$
$$4^4 = X$$

13. Find the value of m in $\frac{3}{8}m = \frac{1}{4}$. (Lesson 5-9) **2/3**

14. Nakayla purchased a package of 8 hamburger buns for $1.49. What is the ratio of the cost per hamburger bun? Round to the nearest penny. (Lesson 6-1) **$0.19 per hamburger bun**

15. What is 40% of 70? (Lesson 6-5) **28**

16. Cameron purchased the portable stereo shown. About how much money did he save? (Lesson 6-7) **$21**

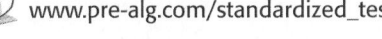

$69.99 before sale
30% off SALE!

17. If you spin the spinner shown at the right, what is the probability that the arrow will stop at an even number? (Lesson 6-9) **3/8**

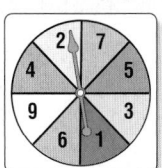

Part 3 | Extended Response

Record your answers on a sheet of paper. Show your work.

18. An electronics store is having a sale on certain models of televisions. Mr. Castillo would like to buy a television that is on sale. This television normally costs $679. (Lesson 6-7) **c. $271.60**

Last Year's Models
40% off
Wednesday Only
Take an additional
10% off
Television Sale!

a. What price, not including tax, will Mr. Castillo pay if he buys the television on Saturday? **$407.40**

b. What price, not including tax, will Mr. Castillo pay if he buys the television on Wednesday? **$339.50**

c. How much money will Mr. Castillo save if he buys the television on a Saturday?

19. The graph shows the number of domain registrations for the years 1997–2000.

Number of domain registrations

Registrations (millions)

1997: 1.54
1998: 3.36
1999: 9
2000: 28.2

Year

Source: Network Solutions (VeriSign)

Write a few sentences describing the percent of change in the number of domain registrations from one year to the next. (Lesson 6-8) **See margin.**

Evaluating Extended Response Questions

Extended Response questions are graded by using a multilevel rubric that guides you in assessing a student's knowledge of a particular concept.

Goal: Review ratios, proportions, and percents.

Sample Scoring Rubric: The following rubric is a sample scoring device. You may wish to add more detail to this sample to meet your individual scoring needs.

Score	Criteria
4	A correct solution that is supported by well-developed, accurate explanations
3	A generally correct solution, but may contain minor flaws in reasoning or computation
2	A partially correct interpretation and/or solution to the problem
1	A correct solution with no supporting evidence or explanation
0	An incorrect solution indicating no mathematical understanding of the concept or task, or no solution is given

Answer

19. From 1997 to 1998, the percent of change was 118%, from 1998 to 1999, the percent of change was 168%, and from 1999 to 2000, the percent of change was 213%.

Page 266, Lesson 6-1

1.

2. A ratio is a comparison of two numbers by division. A rate is a ratio of two measurements having different units of measure.

3. Sample answer: $12 per person

4. $\frac{2}{5}$ 5. $\frac{5}{8}$ 6. $\frac{5}{18}$ 7. $\frac{1}{3}$

8. $45.75/ticket

9. 0.75 inches/hour

10. 6.9 feet/second

11. 24.2 miles/gallon

Page 267, Lesson 6-1

16. $\frac{2}{9}$ 17. $\frac{2}{5}$ 18. $\frac{2}{5}$ 19. $\frac{3}{7}$

20. $\frac{7}{18}$ 21. $\frac{9}{32,000}$ 22. $\frac{4}{1}$ 23. $\frac{1760}{1}$

24. $\frac{5}{41}$ 25. $\frac{17}{118}$ 26. $\frac{31}{15}$ 27. $\frac{3}{1}$

28. $0.50/can

29. 0.10 cents/pencil

30. 23.3 mi/gal

31. 4.5 m/sec

32. 7.6 yd/min

33. 7.8 ft/h

34. 52.6 mi/day

35. 39 pages/week

36. Since the 12-issue subscription costs $2.80 per issue, and the 18-issue subscription costs $2.25 per issue, the 12-issue subscription costs more per issue.

37. The 6-pack of soda costs $0.37 per can. The 12-pack of soda costs $0.35 per can. So, the 12-pack is less expensive.

46. Alaska: 1 person/sq mi; New York: 402/people/sq mi; Rhode Island: 1003 people/sq mi; Texas: 80 people/sq mi; Wyoming: 5 people/sq mi

Page 284, Lesson 6-4

42. Since $\frac{2}{5} = 40\%$, and 40% is greater than 22%, the group that said they prefer ketchup is larger.

51. There are only two possibilities that satisfy the conditions, $\frac{1}{4}$ and $\frac{2}{5}$. See students' explanations.

Pages 286–287, Algebra Activity

1.

2.

3.

4.

5.

6.

7.

8.

9.

10.

11.

12.

13.
0	0
4	10
8	20
12	30
16	40
20	50
24	60
28	70
32	80
36	90
40	100

14.
0	0
1	10
2	20
3	30
4	40
5	50
6	60
7	70
8	80
9	90
10	100

15.
0	0
2	10
4	20
6	30
8	40
10	50
12	60
14	70
16	80
18	90
20	100

16.
0	0
4	10
8	20
12	30
16	40
20	50
24	60
28	70
32	80
36	90
40	100

17.
0	0
20	10
40	20
60	30
80	40
100	50
120	60
140	70
160	80
180	90
200	100

18.
0	0
50	10
100	20
150	30
200	40
250	50
300	60
350	70
400	80
450	90
500	100

19.
0	0
1	10
2	20
3	30
4	40
5	50
6	60
7	70
8	80
9	90
10	100
11	
12	

20.
0	0
1	10
2	20
3	30
4	
5	
6	40
7	
8	50
9	60
10	
11	70
12	
13	80
14	
15	90
16	100

Page 296, Lesson 6-6

35. 450; meaning of percent: 295% means about 300 for every 100 or about 30 for every 10. 145 has one 100 and about 5 tens. $(300 \times 1) + (30 \times 5) = 300 + 150$ or 450.

39. Sample answer: $\frac{1}{3} \times 90{,}000$ or 30,000 miles

40. Sample answer: $\frac{1}{10} \times 40{,}000$ or 4000 miles

Page 308, Lesson 6-8

32. Sample answer: 81; fraction method: $\frac{3}{5} \times 135$ or 81

33. Sample answer: 63; fraction method: $\frac{9}{10} \times 70$ or 63

34. Sample answer: 36; meaning of percent: 123% means about 123 for every 100 or about 12 for every 10. 32 has 3 tens. $3 \times 12 = 36$. So, 123% of 32 is about 36.

Page 309, Algebra Activity

1. Yes; strength: large enough population

2. no; weakness: the people in a library may read more often than others.

3. no; weakness: many of the fans may be Dolphin fans

4. systematic; people may prefer the restaurant

5. Find the percent of students in each grade that eat breakfast.

6a–d. See students' work.

Page 312, Lesson 6-9

4. $\frac{1}{10}$; 10%

5. $\frac{1}{2}$; 50%

6. $\frac{1}{5}$; 20%

7. $\frac{2}{5}$; 40%

8. $\frac{1}{6}$; $16\frac{2}{3}$%

9. 1; 100%

Linear Equations, Inequalities, and Functions

Introduction

In this unit, students will learn about linear equations, inequalities, functions, and graphing. They will analyze data to discover whether a linear relationship exists. They will learn that inequalities can help describe relationships between mathematical expressions.

Students will analyze how equations and graphs are used to describe mathematical relationships. They will expand their knowledge in the use of x- and y-intercepts, slope, and rate of change.

Assessment Options

 Unit 3 Test Pages 487–488 of the *Chapter 8 Resource Masters* may be used as a test or review for Unit 3. This assessment contains both multiple-choice and short answer items.

ExamView® Pro

This CD-ROM can be used to create additional unit tests and review worksheets.

Progress Yearly Pro

An online, research-based instructional, assessment, and intervention tool that provides specific feedback on student mastery of state and national standards, instant remediation, and a data management system to track performance. For more information, contact mhdigitallearning.com.

Your study of algebra includes more than just solving equations. Many real-world situations can be modeled by equations and their graphs. In this unit, you will learn about functions and graphs.

Chapter 7
Equations and Inequalities

Chapter 8
Functions and Graphing

What's MATH Got To Do With It?

Real-Life Math Videos

What's Math Got to Do With It? Real-Life Math Videos engage students showing them how math is used in everyday situations. Use Video 2 with this unit.

WebQuest Internet Project

Just for Fun

What do you like to do in your spare time—shop at the mall, attend a baseball or football game, go to the movies, ride the rides at an amusement park, or hike in the great outdoors?

In this project, you will be exploring how equations, functions, and graphs can help you examine how people spend their leisure time.

 Log on to www.pre-alg.com/webquest. Begin your WebQuest by reading the Task.

Then continue working on your WebQuest as you study Unit 3.

Lesson	7-1	8-8
Page	333	412

USA TODAY Snapshots®

What fans pay after ticket

An average fan at a Major League Baseball game spends $15.40 on parking, food, drinks and souvenirs in addition to the $15 ticket price.

MLB $15.40   NBA $18.20   NHL $18.25   NFL $19.00

Source: American Demographics, Team Marketing Report

By Anne R. Carey and Marcy E. Mullins, USA TODAY

Unit 3 Linear Equations, Inequalities, and Functions **325**

WebQuest Internet Project

Problem-Based Learning A WebQuest is an online project in which students do research on the Internet, gather data, and make presentations using word processing, graphing, page-making, or presentation software. In each chapter, students advance to the next step in their WebQuest. At the end of Chapter 8, the project culminates with a presentation of their findings.

Teaching suggestions and sample answers are available in the *WebQuest and Project Resources.*

Equations and Inequalities
Chapter Overview and Pacing

Year-long pacing: pages T20–T21.

LESSON OBJECTIVES

	PACING (days)			
	Regular		**Block**	
	Basic/ Average	Advanced	Basic/ Average	Advanced
7-1 Solving Equations with Variables on Each Side (pp. 328–333) *Preview:* Use algebra tiles and an equation mat to solve equations with variables on each side. • Solve equations with variables on each side.	3 (with 7-1 Preview)	2	1.5 (with 7-1 Preview)	1
7-2 Solving Equations with Grouping Symbols (pp. 334–338) • Solve equations that involve grouping symbols. • Identify equations that have no solution or an infinite number of solutions.	2	1	1	0.5
7-3 Inequalities (pp. 340–344) • Write inequalities. • Graph inequalities.	1	1	0.5	0.5
7-4 Solving Inequalities by Adding or Subtracting (pp. 345–349) • Solve inequalities by using the Addition and Subtraction Properties of Inequality.	1	1	0.5	0.5
7-5 Solving Inequalities by Multiplying or Dividing (pp. 350–354) • Solve inequalities by multiplying or dividing by a positive number. • Solve inequalities by multiplying or dividing by a negative number.	2	2	1	1
7-6 Solving Multi-Step Inequalities (pp. 355–359) • Solve inequalities that involve more than one operation.	1	1	0.5	0.5
Study Guide and **Practice Test** (pp. 360–363) **Standardized Test Practice** (pp. 364–365)	1	1	0.5	0.5
Chapter Assessment	1	1	0.5	0.5
TOTAL	12	10	6	5

*An electronic version of this chapter is available on **StudentWorks**™. This backpack solution CD-ROM allows students instant access to the Student Edition, lesson worksheet pages, and web resources.*

Chapter Resource Manager

| CHAPTER 7 RESOURCE MASTERS | | | | | | | | | | | Materials |
Study Guide and Intervention	Practice (Skills and Average)	Reading to Learn Mathematics	Enrichment	Assessment	Prerequisite Skills Workbook	Applications*	Parent and Student Study Guide Workbook	5-Minute Check Transparencies	Interactive Chalkboard	Pre-AlgePASS: Tutorial Plus (lessons)	
367	368–369	370	371				54	7-1	7-1		
372	373–374	375	376	411			55	7-2	7-2	19	
377	378–379	380	381	411, 413	1–2	GCS 32	56	7-3	7-3	20	
382	383–384	385	386		1–2, 21–24, 55–62	SC 13	57	7-4	7-4		
387	388–389	390	391	412	1–2, 27–28, 31–32, 47–54		58	7-5	7-5		
392	393–394	395	396	412	1–2	SC 14 GCS 31	59	7-6	7-6	21	
				397–410 414–416							

* *Key to Abbreviations:* GCS = Graphing Calculator and Spreadsheet Masters
SC = School-to-Career Masters
SM = Science and Mathematics Lab Manual

ELL Study Guide and Intervention, Skills Practice, Practice, and Parent and Student Study Guide Workbooks are also available in Spanish.

Chapter 7

Mathematical Connections and Background

Continuity of Instruction

Prior Knowledge

Students solved basic one- and two-step equations in Chapter 3. In Chapter 4, students learned about rational numbers, including fractions, decimals, and integers. In Chapter 5, students learned about adding, subtracting, multiplying, and dividing rational numbers. In Chapter 6, students learned to solve proportions.

This Chapter

Students expand their skill in solving equations to solving equations with variables on each side. They solve equations involving grouping symbols by using the Distributive Property. Students write and graph inequalities and learn to solve inequalities by using properties of inequality. Finally, they solve inequalities involving more than one operation.

Future Connections

Students will solve systems of linear equations and linear inequalities in Chapter 8. In Chapter 9, they will solve equations by finding square roots and will find dimensions of triangles by solving equations involving the Pythagorean Theorem, proportions, and trigonometric ratios. In Chapters 10 and 11, students will solve equations to find missing values in two- and three-dimensional figures.

7-1 Solving Equations with Variables on Each Side

To solve equations with variables on each side, use the Addition or Subtraction Property of Equality, which was introduced in Lesson 3-3, to write an equivalent equation with the variables on one side of the equation. Then solve the equation. For example, to solve $3x - 8 = 5x$, subtract $3x$ from each side to get $-8 = 2x$, then divide each side by 2 to find that $x = -4$.

7-2 Solving Equations with Grouping Symbols

Equations often contain grouping symbols such as parentheses or brackets. The first step in solving these equations is to use the Distributive Property to remove the grouping symbols.

Some equations have no solution. That is, there is no value of the variable that results in a true sentence. For such an equation, the solution set is called the null or empty set, and is represented by the symbol $\varnothing$ or {}. Other equations may have every number as the solution. An equation that is true for every value of the variable is called an identity.

7-3 Inequalities

A mathematical sentence that contains the symbols < (less than), > (greater than), ≤ (less than or equal to), or ≥ (greater than or equal to) is called an inequality. For example, the statement that it is legal to drive 55 miles per hour or slower on a stretch of highway can be shown by the sentence $s \leq 55$. Inequalities with variables are called open sentences. When a variable is replaced with a number, the inequality may be true or false.

The solutions of inequalities can be graphed on a number line. For example, if the solution of an inequality is $x < 5$, start an arrow at 5 on the number line and continue the arrow left to show all values less than 5 as the solution. Put an open circle at 5 to show that the point 5 is *not* included in the graph. Use a closed circle when graphing solutions that are greater than or equal to, or less than or equal to, a number.

7-4 Solving Inequalities by Adding or Subtracting

Solving an inequality means finding values for the variable that make the inequality true. Some inequalities can be solved by using the Addition and Subtraction Properties of Inequalities. These properties say that when you add or subtract the same number from each side of an inequality, the inequality remains true. For example, if you add 5 to each side of the inequality $3 < 6$, the resulting inequality $8 < 11$ is also true. Adding or subtracting the same number from each side of an inequality does not affect the inequality sign. Since the solutions to an inequality include all rational numbers satisfying it, inequalities have an infinite number of solutions.

7-5 Solving Inequalities by Multiplying or Dividing

Some inequalities can be solved by using the Multiplication and Division Properties of Inequalities. These properties say that when multiplying or dividing each side of an inequality by the same positive number, the inequality remains true. In such cases, the inequality symbol does not change. When multiplying or dividing each side of an inequality by a negative number, the inequality symbol must be reversed. For example, when dividing each side of the inequality $-4 \geq -8$ by -2, the inequality sign must be changed to $\leq$ for the resulting inequality, $2 \leq 4$, to be true.

7-6 Solving Multi-Step Inequalities

When solving inequalities that involve more than one operation, work backward to undo the operations, just as when solving multi-step equations. Remember to reverse the inequality symbol if you multiply or divide each side of an inequality by a negative number. Use the Distributive Property to begin simplifying inequalities that contain grouping symbols.

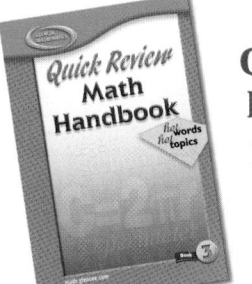

Quick Review Math Handbook

Hot Words includes a glossary of terms while Hot Topics consists of explanations of key mathematical concepts with exercises to test comprehension. This valuable resource can be used as a reference in the classroom or for home study.

Lesson	Hot Topics Section	Lesson	Hot Topics Section
GS 7	1.5, 6.4	7-4	6.4, 6.6
7-1	6.2, 6.4	7-5	6.4, 6.6
7-2	6.3, 6.4	7-6	6.6
7-3	6.4, 6.6		

GS = Getting Started

 Additional mathematical information and teaching notes are available at www.pre-alg.com/key_concepts.

DAILY INTERVENTION and Assessment

Key to Abbreviations:
TWE = Teacher Wraparound Edition; CRM = Chapter Resource Masters

	Type	Student Edition	Teacher Resources	Technology/Internet
INTERVENTION	Ongoing	Prerequisite Skills, pp. 327, 333, 338, 344, 349, 354 Practice Quiz 1, p. 338 Practice Quiz 2, p. 354	5-Minute Check Transparencies *Prerequisite Skills Workbook*, pp. 1–2, 21–24, 27–28, 31–32, 47–62 Quizzes, *CRM*, pp. 411, 412 Mid-Chapter Test, *CRM*, p. 413 Study Guide and Intervention, *CRM*, p. 367, 372, 377, 382, 387, 392	Pre-AlgePASS: Tutorial Plus, Lessons 19, 20, and 21 www.pre-alg.com/self_check_quiz www.pre-alg.com/extra_examples
	Mixed Review	pp. 333, 338, 344, 349, 354, 359	Cumulative Review, *CRM*, p. 414	
	Error Analysis	Find the Error, pp. 347, 353, 357	Find the Error, *TWE*, pp. 353, 357 Unlocking Misconceptions, *TWE*, pp. 335, 357	
	Standardized Test Practice	pp. 333, 338, 344, 349, 351, 353, 354, 359, 364–365	*TWE*, pp. 364–365 Standardized Test Practice, *CRM*, pp. 415–416	Standardized Test Practice CD-ROM www.pre-alg.com/standardized_test
ASSESSMENT	Open-Ended Assessment	Writing in Math, pp. 333, 338, 344, 349, 354, 359 Open Ended, pp. 332, 336, 342, 347, 353, 357 Standardized Test, p. 365	Speaking: *TWE*, pp. 354, 359 Writing: *TWE*, pp. 344, 349 Modeling: *TWE*, pp. 332, 338 Open-Ended Assessment, *CRM*, p. 409	
	Chapter Assessment	Study Guide, pp. 360–362 Practice Test, p. 363	Multiple-Choice Tests (Forms 1, 2A, 2B), *CRM*, pp. 397–402 Free-Response Tests (Forms 2C, 2D, 3), *CRM*, pp. 403–408 Vocabulary Test/Review, *CRM*, p. 410	ExamView® Pro (see below) MindJogger Videoquizzes www.pre-alg.com/vocabulary_review www.pre-alg.com/chapter_test

For more information on Yearly ProgressPro, see p. 324.

Pre-Algebra Lesson	Yearly ProgressPro Skill Lesson
7-1	Solving Equations with Variables on Each Side
7-2	Solving Equations with Variables on Each Side
7-3	Inequalities
7-4	Solve Simple Inequalities
7-5	Solve Simple Inequalities
7-6	Problem Solving with Inequalities

ExamView® Pro

Use the networkable **ExamView® Pro** to:
- Create **multiple versions** of tests.
- Create **modified** tests for *Inclusion* students.
- **Edit** existing questions and **add** your own questions.
- Use built-in **state curriculum correlations** to create tests aligned with state standards.
- Change **English** tests to **Spanish** and vice versa.

For more information on Intervention and Assessment, see pp. T8–T11.

Reading and Writing in Mathematics

Glencoe Pre-Algebra provides numerous opportunities to incorporate reading and writing into the mathematics classroom.

Student Edition

- Foldables™ Study Organizer, p. 327
- Reading Mathematics, p. 339
- Concept Check questions require students to verbalize and write about what they have learned in the lesson. (pp. 330, 332, 335, 336, 342, 345, 346, 347, 352, 353, 356, 357)
- Writing in Math questions in every lesson, pp. 333, 338, 344, 349, 354, 359
- Reading Math, p. 341
- WebQuest, p. 333

Teacher Wraparound Edition

- Foldables™ Study Organizer, pp. 327, 360
- Study Notebook suggestions, pp. 329, 332, 336, 339, 342, 347, 352, 357
- Modeling activities, pp. 332, 338
- Speaking activities, pp. 354, 359
- Writing activities, pp. 344, 349
- Differentiated Instruction (Verbal/Linguistic), p. 331
- **ELL** Resources, pp. 326, 330, 331, 334, 339, 340, 345, 350, 355, 360

Additional Resources

- Vocabulary Builder worksheets require students to define and give examples for key vocabulary terms as they progress through the chapter (*Chapter 7 Resource Masters*, pp. vii–viii)
- Reading to Learn Mathematics master for each lesson (*Chapter 7 Resource Masters*, pp. 370, 375, 380, 385, 390, 395)
- *Vocabulary PuzzleMaker* software creates crossword, jumble, and word search puzzles using vocabulary lists that you can customize.
- *Teaching Mathematics with Foldables* provides suggestions for promoting cognition and language.
- *Reading and Writing in the Mathematics Classroom*
- *WebQuest and Project Resources*

For more information on Reading and Writing in Mathematics, see pp. T6–T7.

PROJECT CRISS℠ Study Skill

Before beginning this chapter, demonstrate how students can use two-column notes like those for solving equations shown at the right. Explain that the left column should contain each of the topics presented in the chapter. The right column should include short summaries of the steps needed to solve the problems.

Students may also wish to include other notes about the topics that they feel are helpful.

Topic	Notes
Solving equations with variables on each side	1. combine like terms
	2. can use the Distributive Property
	3. place all variable terms on one side
	4. solve for unknown

CReating **I**ndependence **T**hrough **S**tudent-Owned **S**trategies

What You'll Learn

Have students read over the list of objectives and make a list of any words with which they are not familiar.

Why It's Important

Point out to students that this is only one of many reasons why each objective is important. Others are provided in the introduction to each lesson.

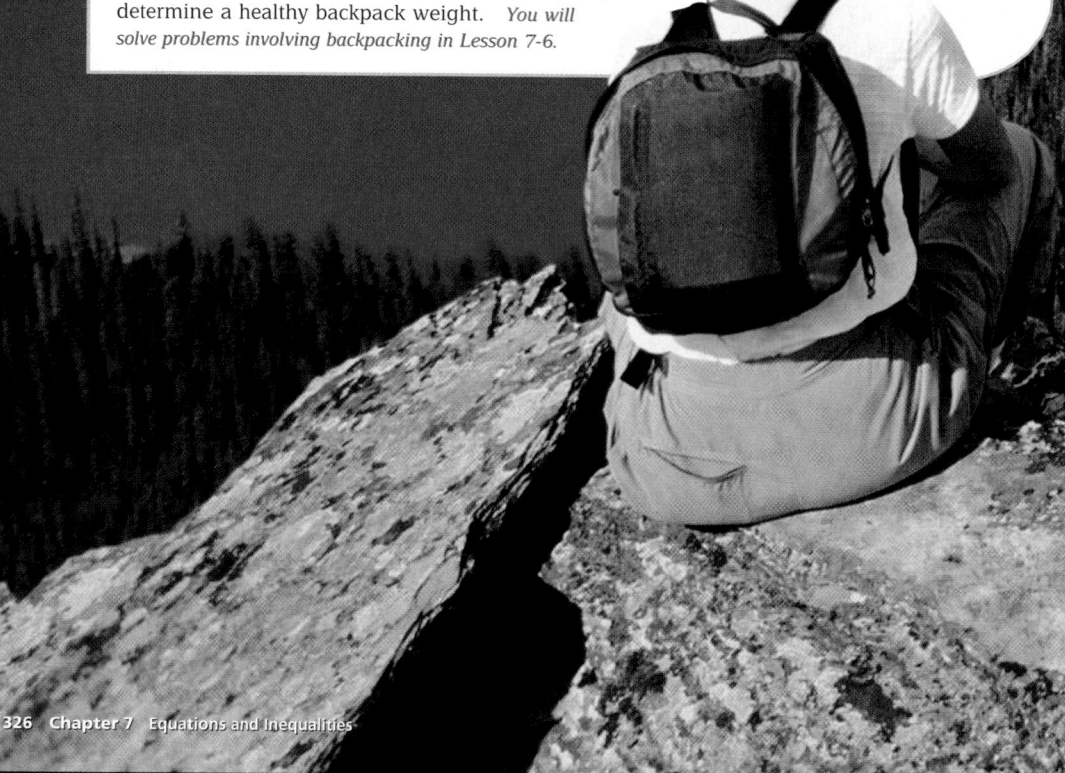

What You'll Learn

- **Lessons 7-1 and 7-2** Solve equations with variables on each side and with grouping symbols.
- **Lesson 7-3** Write and graph inequalities.
- **Lessons 7-4 and 7-5** Solve inequalities using the Properties of Inequalities.
- **Lesson 7-6** Solve multi-step inequalities.

Key Vocabulary

- null or empty set (p. 336)
- identity (p. 336)
- inequality (p. 340)

Why It's Important

An equation is a statement that two expressions are equal. Sometimes, you want to know when one expression is greater or less than another. This kind of statement is an inequality. For example, you can solve an inequality to determine a healthy backpack weight. *You will solve problems involving backpacking in Lesson 7-6.*

326 Chapter 7 Equations and Inequalities

Lesson	NCTM Standards	Local Objectives
7-1 Preview	2, 10	
7-1	2, 6	
7-2	2, 3, 6	
7-3	1, 2, 8	
7-4	1, 2, 6, 8	
7-5	1, 2, 6	
7-6	1, 2, 6, 9	

Key to NCTM Standards:

1=Number & Operations, 2=Algebra, 3=Geometry, 4=Measurement, 5=Data Analysis & Probability, 6=Problem Solving, 7=Reasoning & Proof, 8=Communication, 9=Connections, 10=Representation

Vocabulary Builder

ELL

The Key Vocabulary list introduces students to some of the main vocabulary terms included in this chapter. For a more thorough vocabulary list with pronunciations of new words, give students the Vocabulary Builder worksheets found on pages vii and viii of the *Chapter 7 Resource Masters*. Encourage them to complete the definition of each term as they progress through the chapter. You may suggest that they add these sheets to their study notebooks for future reference when studying for the Chapter 7 test.

▶ **Prerequisite Skills** To be successful in this chapter, you'll need to master these skills and be able to apply them in problem-solving situations. Review these skills before beginning Chapter 7.

For Lesson 7-1   Solve Two-Step Equations

Solve each equation. Check your solution.   *(For review, see Lesson 3-5.)*

1. $2x + 5 = 13$ **4**   **2.** $4n - 3 = 5$ **2**   **3.** $16 = 8 + \frac{d}{3}$ **24**   **4.** $\frac{c}{-4} + 3 = -9$ **48**

For Lesson 7-4   Add and Subtract Integers

Find each sum or difference.   *(For review, see Lessons 2-2 and 2-3.)*

5. $-28 + (-16)$ **−44**   **6.** $17 + (-25)$ **−8**   **7.** $-13 + 24$ **11**

8. $36 + (-18)$ **18**   **9.** $31 - 48$ **−17**   **10.** $-16 - 7$ **−23**

11. $4 - (-12)$ **16**   **12.** $-23 - (-29)$ **6**   **13.** $-19 - (-5)$ **−14**

For Lesson 7-5   Multiply and Divide Integers

Find each product or quotient.   *(For review, see Lessons 2-4 and 2-5.)*

14. $-6(8)$ **−48**   **15.** $-3 \cdot 5$ **−15**   **16.** $-6(-25)$ **150**

17. $2(-4)(-9)$ **72**   **18.** $64 \div (-32)$ **−2**   **19.** $-15 \div 3$ **−5**

20. $-12 \div (-3)$ **4**   **21.** $-6 \div (-6)$ **1**   **22.** $24 \div (-2)$ **−12**

Equations and Inequalities Make this Foldable to help you organize your notes. Begin with a plain sheet of $8\frac{1}{2}$" by 11" paper.

Step 1 **Fold in Half**

Fold in half lengthwise.

Step 2 **Fold in Sixths**

Fold in thirds and then fold each third in half.

Step 3 **Cut**

Open. Cut one side along the folds to make tabs.

Step 4 **Label**

Label each tab with a lesson number as shown.

| 7-1 |
| 7-2 |
| 7-3 |
| 7-4 |
| 7-5 |
| 7-6 |

Reading and Writing As you read and study the chapter, write notes and examples under each tab.

Getting Started

This section provides a review of the basic concepts needed before beginning Chapter 7. Page references are included for additional student help.

Additional review is provided in the *Prerequisite Skills Workbook*, pages 1–2, 21–24, 27–28, 31–32, and 47–62.

Prerequisite Skills in the Getting Ready for the Next Lesson section at the end of each lesson reviews a skill needed in the next lesson.

For Lesson	Prerequisite Skill
7-2	Using the Distributive Property (p. 333)
7-3	Evaluating Expressions (p. 338)
7-4	Solving Equations (p. 344)
7-5	Solving Equations (p. 349)
7-6	Solving Two-Step Equations (p. 354)

Questioning Skills Before beginning each lesson, ask students to look through the lesson and write one question that they have about what they have seen. Write the question on the front of the corresponding lesson tab. As students study the lesson, have them record the answer to their question under the tab and other questions that arise. Self-questioning is a strategy that helps students stay focused during reading, writing, and skills practice.

For more information about Foldables, see *Teaching Mathematics with Foldables.*

Getting Started

Objective Use algebra tiles and an equation mat to solve equations with variables on each side.

Materials
algebra tiles
equation mat

Teaching Tip Model Activity 1 on an overhead with an equation mat and algebra tiles.

Teach

- Show students how algebra tiles are both added or both removed to maintain balance on each side of the equation.
- Also show students examples where they don't end up with just one *x*-tile on the side.

Answers

1.

2.

3.

4.

Algebra Activity

NEW YORK *Performance Indicator* **8.A.5 Use physical models to perform operations with polynomials**

Equations with Variables on Each Side

In Chapter 3, you used algebra tiles and an equation mat to solve equations in which the variable was on only one side of the equation. You can use algebra tiles and an equation mat to solve equations with variables on each side of the equation.

Activity 1

The following example shows how to solve $x + 3 = 2x + 1$ using algebra tiles.

Model the equation.

$x + 3 \quad = \quad 2x + 1$

Remove the same number of *x*-tiles from each side of the mat until there is an *x*-tile by itself on one side.

$x - x + 3 \quad = \quad 2x - x + 1$

Remove the same number of 1-tiles from each side of the mat until the *x*-tile is by itself on one side.

$2 \quad = \quad x$

There are two 1-tiles on the left side of the mat and one *x*-tile on the right side. Therefore, $x = 2$. Since $2 + 3 = 2(2) + 1$, the solution is correct.

Model

Use algebra tiles to model and solve each equation. 1–6. See margin for models.

1. $2x + 3 = x + 5$ **2**
2. $3x + 4 = 2x + 8$ **4**
3. $3x = x + 6$ **3**
4. $6 + x = 4x$ **2**
5. $2x - 4 = x - 6$ **−2**
6. $5x - 1 = 4x - 5$ **−4**

Analyze 8. The value of *x* is the same on each side of the mat.

7. Which property of equality allows you to remove a 1-tile from each side of the mat? **subtraction**

8. Explain why you can remove an *x*-tile from each side of the mat.

Resource Manager

📁 *Teaching Pre-Algebra with Manipulatives*
- pp. 7–8 (masters for algebra tiles)
- p. 13 (master for equation mat)
- p. 99 (student recording sheet)

Glencoe Mathematics Classroom Manipulative Kit
- algebra tiles
- equation mat

Activity 2

Some equations are solved by using zero pairs. Remember, you may add or subtract a zero pair from either side of an equation mat without changing its value. The following example shows how to solve $2x + 1 = x - 5$.

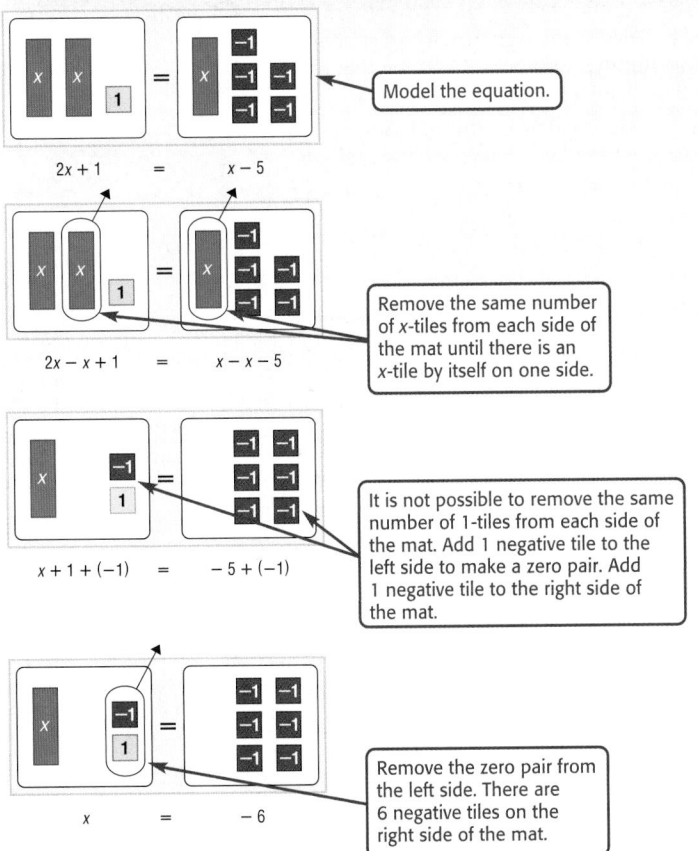

$2x + 1 = x - 5$

Model the equation.

$2x - x + 1 = x - x - 5$

Remove the same number of x-tiles from each side of the mat until there is an x-tile by itself on one side.

$x + 1 + (-1) = -5 + (-1)$

It is not possible to remove the same number of 1-tiles from each side of the mat. Add 1 negative tile to the left side to make a zero pair. Add 1 negative tile to the right side of the mat.

$x = -6$

Remove the zero pair from the left side. There are 6 negative tiles on the right side of the mat.

Therefore, $x = -6$. Since $2(-6) + 1 = -6 - 5$, the solution is correct.

Model

Use algebra tiles to model and solve each equation. 9–14. See pp. 365A–365B for models.

9. $2x + 3 = x - 5$ **−8**   10. $3x - 2 = x + 6$ **4**   11. $x - 1 = 3x + 7$ **−4**

12. $x + 6 = 2x - 3$ **9**   13. $2x + 4 = 3x - 2$ **6**   14. $4x - 1 = 2x + 5$ **3**

Analyze

15. Does it matter whether you remove x-tiles or 1-tiles first? Explain. **See margin.**

16. Explain how you could use models to solve $-2x + 5 = -x - 2$. **See margin.**

Algebra Activity Equations with Variables on Each Side **329**

Answers

5.

6.

15. You can remove either tile first. But it is a good idea to remove the 1-tile first, because you are using the work backward strategy.

16. Add two 1-tiles to each side. Then add 2 x-tiles to each side. So, $x = 7$.

7-1 Solving Equations with Variables on Each Side

1 Focus

5-Minute Check Transparency 7-1 Use as a quiz or review of Chapter 6.

Mathematical Background notes are available for this lesson on page 326C.

How is solving equations with variables on each side like solving equations with variables on one side?

The opening activity questions are repeated on page 370 of the *Chapter 7 Resource Masters*.

What You'll Learn

- Solve equations with variables on each side.

How is solving equations with variables on each side like solving equations with variables on one side?

On the balance at the right, each bag contains the same number of blocks. (Assume that the paper bag weighs nothing.)

a. The two sides balance. Without looking in a bag, how can you determine the number of blocks in each bag?

b. Explain why your method works.

c. Suppose x represents the number of blocks in the bag. Write an equation that is modeled by the balance. **2x + 3 = x + 5**

d. Explain how you could solve the equation.

a. Sample answer: Remove one bag from each side. Then remove 3 blocks from each side. There must be 2 blocks in each bag.
b. Removing the same thing from each side keeps the scale in balance.

d. Subtract *x* from each side. Then subtract 3 from each side.

EQUATIONS WITH VARIABLES ON EACH SIDE To solve equations with variables on each side, use the Addition or Subtraction Property of Equality to write an equivalent equation with the variables on one side. Then solve the equation.

Example 1 — Equations with Variables on Each Side

Solve $2x + 3 = 3x$. Check your solution.

$$2x + 3 = 3x \quad \text{Write the equation.}$$
$$2x - 2x + 3 = 3x - 2x \quad \text{Subtract 2x from each side.}$$
$$3 = x \quad \text{Simplify.}$$

Subtract 2x from the left side of the equation to isolate the variable.

Subtract 2x from the right side of the equation to keep it balanced.

To check your solution, replace x with 3 in the original equation.

CHECK $2x + 3 = 3x$ Write the equation.
$2(3) + 3 \stackrel{?}{=} 3(3)$ Replace x with 3.
$6 + 3 \stackrel{?}{=} 9$ Check to see whether this statement is true.
$9 = 9 \checkmark$ The statement is true.

The solution is 3.

✓ Concept Check What property allows you to add the same quantity to each side of an equation? **Addition Property of Equality**

Resource Manager

📁 Workbooks and Reproducible Masters

Chapter 7 Resource Masters
- Study Guide and Intervention, p. 367
- Skills Practice, p. 368
- Practice, p. 369
- Reading to Learn Mathematics, p. 370
- Enrichment, p. 371

Parent and Student Study Guide Workbook, p. 54

📺 Transparencies
5-Minute Check Transparency 7-1
Answer Key Transparencies

💿 Technology
Interactive Chalkboard
Multimedia Applications

Example 2 Equations with Variables on Each Side

a. Solve $5x + 4 = 3x - 2$. Check your solution.

$5x + 4 = 3x - 2$	Write the equation.
$5x - 3x + 4 = 3x - 3x - 2$	Subtract $3x$ from each side.
$2x + 4 = -2$	Simplify.
$2x + 4 - 4 = -2 - 4$	Subtract 4 from each side.
$2x = -6$	Simplify.
$x = -3$	Mentally divide each side by 2.

TEACHING TIP

Point out that this step eliminates the variable on the right side.

This step eliminates the constant term on the left side.

CHECK

$5x + 4 = 3x - 2$	Write the equation.
$5(-3) + 4 \stackrel{?}{=} 3(-3) - 2$	Is this statement true?
$-11 = -11 \checkmark$	The solution checks.

The solution is -3.

b. Solve $2.4 + a = 2.5a - 4.5$.

$2.4 + a = 2.5a - 4.5$	Write the equation.
$2.4 + a - a = 2.5a - a - 4.5$	Subtract a from each side.
$2.4 = 1.5a - 4.5$	Simplify.
$2.4 + 4.5 = 1.5a - 4.5 + 4.5$	Add 4.5 to each side.
$6.9 = 1.5a$	Simplify.
$\dfrac{6.9}{1.5} = \dfrac{1.5a}{1.5}$	Divide each side by 1.5.
$4.6 = a$	Check your solution.

The solution is 4.6.

You can use equations with variables on each side to solve problems.

Example 3 Use an Equation to Solve a Problem

VIDEOS A video store has two membership plans. Under plan A, a yearly membership costs $30 plus $1.50 for each rental. Under plan B, the yearly membership costs $12 plus $3 for each rental. What number of rentals results in the same yearly cost?

Let v represent the number of videos rented.

Words	$30 plus $1.50 for each video	$12 plus $3 for each video
Variables	$30 + 1.50v$	$12 + 3v$

Equation	$30 + 1.50v = 12 + 3v$	Write an equation.
	$30 + 1.5v - 1.5v = 12 + 3v - 1.5v$	Subtract $1.5v$ from each side.
	$30 = 12 + 1.5v$	Simplify.
	$30 - 12 = 12 - 12 + 1.5v$	Subtract 12 from each side.
	$18 = 1.5v$	Simplify.
	$\dfrac{18}{1.5} = \dfrac{1.5v}{1.5}$	Divide each side by 1.5.
	$12 = v$	Simplify.

The yearly cost is the same for 12 rentals.

More About...

Videos

In 1980, only 1% of American households owned a VCR. Today, more than 80% do.

Source: Statistical Abstracts

---

2 Teach

Building on Prior Knowledge

In Chapter 3, students learned to solve two-step equations. In this lesson, students learn to solve more complex equations with variables on each side.

EQUATIONS WITH VARIABLES ON EACH SIDE

In-Class Examples

1 Solve $5x + 12 = 2x$. Check your solution. -4

2 a. Solve $7x + 3 = 2x + 23$. **4**

   b. Solve $1.7 + a = 2.5a - 4.9$. **4.4**

Teaching Tip You can show the solutions for the Example problems by using a graphing calculator. Graph each side of a problem as separate equations in y_1 and y_2. The x-coordinate of their intersection point is the solution to the problem.

3 **CAR RENTAL** A car rental agency has two plans. Under plan A, a car rents for $80 plus $20 each day. Under plan B, a car rents for $120 plus $15 each day. What number of days results in the same cost? **The cost is the same for 8 days.**

Teaching Tip You may want to investigate the scenario of Example 3 by having students observe the patterns of renting 1 day, renting 2 days, renting 3 days, etc.

Study Notebook

Have students—

• write out a simple equation with variables on both sides and list the steps to solve the equation.

• include any other item(s) that they find helpful in mastering the skills in this lesson.

About the Exercises . . .

Odd/Even Assignments

Exercises 10–35 are structured so that students practice the same concepts whether they are assigned odd or even problems.

Assignment Guide

Basic: 11–29 odd, 35, 37–40, 42–53

Average: 11–35 odd, 37–40, 42–53 (Optional: 41)

Advanced: 10–36 even, 37–47 (Optional: 48–53)

4 Assess

Open-Ended Assessment

Modeling Have students create balances and use blocks and paper bags to develop problems similar to the one at the beginning of the lesson.

Getting Ready for Lesson 7-2

PREREQUISITE SKILL Lesson 7-2 presents solving equations with grouping symbols. Exercises 48–53 should be used to determine your students' familiarity with using the Distributive Property to rewrite algebraic expressions.

Check for Understanding

Concept Check

GUIDED PRACTICE KEY	
Exercises	Examples
3–8	1, 2
9	3

1. **Name** the property of equality that allows you to subtract the same quantity from each side of an equation. **Subt. Prop. of Equality**

2. **OPEN ENDED** Write an example of an equation with variables on each side. State the steps you would use to isolate the variable. **See margin.**

Guided Practice

Solve each equation. Check your solution.

3. $4x - 8 = 5x$ **−8**
4. $12x = 2x + 40$ **4**
5. $4x - 1 = 3x + 2$ **3**
6. $4k + 24 = 6k - 10$ **17**
7. $n + 0.4 = -n + 1$ **0.3**
8. $3.1w + 5 = 0.8 + w$ **−2**

Application

9. **CAR RENTAL** Suppose you can rent a car from ABC Auto for either $25 a day plus $0.45 a mile or for $40 a day plus $0.25 a mile. What number of miles results in the same cost for one day? **75 miles**

★ indicates increased difficulty

Practice and Apply

Homework Help

For Exercises	See Examples
10–27, 30–33, 28, 29, 34–36	1, 2 3

Extra Practice See page 739.

Solve each equation. Check your solution.

10. $4x + 9 = 7x$ **3**
11. $6a = 26 + 4a$ **13**
12. $3y + 16 = 5y$ **8**
13. $n - 14 = 3n$ **−7**
14. $8 - 3c = 2c - 2$ **2**
15. $3 - 4b = 10b + 10$ **−0.5**
16. $7d - 13 = 3d + 7$ **5**
17. $2f - 6 = 7f + 24$ **−6**
18. $-s + 4 = 7s - 3$ **0.875**
19. $4a - 2 = 7a - 6$ **$\frac{4}{3}$**
20. $12n - 24 = -14n + 28$ **2**
21. $13y - 18 = -5y + 36$ **3**
22. $12 + 1.5a = 3a$ **8**
23. $12.6 - x = 2x$ **4.2**
24. $2b + 6.2 = 13.2 - 8b$ **0.7**
25. $3c + 4.5 = 7.2 - 6c$ **0.3**
26. $12.4y + 14 = 6y - 2$ **−2.5**
27. $4.3n - 1.6 = 2.3n + 5.2$ **3.4**

Define a variable and write an equation to find each number. Then solve.

28. Twice a number is 220 less than six times the number. What is the number? **$2x = 6x - 220$; 55**

29. Fourteen less than three times a number equals the number. What is the number? **$3y - 14 = y$; 7**

Solve each equation. Check your solution.

★ 30. $\frac{4}{5}y - 8 = \frac{2}{5}y + 16$ **60**
★ 31. $\frac{3}{4}k + 16 = 2 - \frac{1}{8}k$ **−16**
★ 32. $\frac{x}{0.4} = 2x + 1.2$ **2.4**
★ 33. $\frac{1}{3}b + 8 = \frac{1}{2}b - 4$ **72**

34. **GEOGRAPHY** The coastline of California is 46 miles longer than twice the length of Louisiana's coastline. It is also 443 miles longer than Louisiana's coastline. Find the lengths of the coastlines of California and Louisiana. **CA: 840 mi; LA: 397 mi**

35. **CELLULAR PHONES** One cellular phone carrier charges $29.75 a month plus $0.15 a minute for local calls. Another carrier charges $19.95 a month and $0.29 a minute for local calls. For how many minutes is the cost of the plans the same? **70 min**

Answers

2. Sample answer: $3x + 4 = 2x - 8$; subtract $2x$ from each side, subtract 4 from each side.

38. In both cases, the goal is to isolate the variable. Answers should include the following.
 • Sample equations: variables on both sides: $-2x - 8 = 4x - 2$, variables

on one side: $3x + 2 = 8$

 • They are alike because the goal is to isolate the variable. However, in equations with variables on both sides, you have to add or subtract variables from each side as well as constant terms.

★ **36.** An empty bucket is put under two faucets. If one faucet is turned on alone, the bucket fills in 6 minutes. If the other faucet is turned on alone, the bucket fills in 4 minutes. If both are turned on, how many seconds will it take to fill the bucket? **144 s**

37. CRITICAL THINKING Three times the quantity $y + 7$ equals four times the quantity $y - 2$. What value of y makes the sentence true? **29**

38. WRITING IN MATH Answer the question that was posed at the beginning of the lesson. **See margin.**

How is solving equations with variables on each side like solving equations with variables on one side?

Include the following in your answer:

- examples of an equation with variables on each side and an equation with the variable on one side, and
- an explanation of how they are alike and how they are different.

Standardized Test Practice

Ⓐ Ⓑ Ⓒ Ⓓ

39. Shoe World offers Olivia a temporary job during her spring break. The manager gives her a choice as to how she wants to be paid, but she must decide before she starts working. The choices are shown below.

	Pay per Hour	Pay for Each Dollar of Shoe Sales
Plan 1	$3	15¢
Plan 2	$4	10¢

Which equation shows what Olivia's sales would need to be in one hour to earn the same amount under either plan? **A**

Ⓐ $3 + 0.15s = 4 + 0.10s$
Ⓑ $3s + 0.15 = 4s + 0.10$
Ⓒ $3 + 0.10s = 4 + 0.15s$
Ⓓ $3(s + 0.15) = 4(s + 0.10)$

40. What is the solution of $3x - 1 = x + 3$? **B**

Ⓐ 1 Ⓑ 2 Ⓒ 3 Ⓓ 4

Extending the Lesson

★ **41. WEATHER** The formula $F = \frac{9}{5}C + 32$ is used for finding the Fahrenheit temperature when a Celsius temperature is known. Find the temperature where the Celsius and Fahrenheit scales are the same. **−40°**

Maintain Your Skills

Mixed Review

42. PROBABILITY What is the probability of randomly choosing the letter T from the letters in PITTSBURGH? *(Lesson 6-9)* **20%**

43. Find the percent of increase from $80 to $90. *(Lesson 6-8)* **12.5%**

ALGEBRA Solve each problem using an equation. *(Lesson 6-7)*

44. 14 is what percent of 20? **70%**
45. Find 36% of 18. **6.48**
46. 1.5 is 30% of what number? **5**
47. Find 140% of 50. **70**

Getting Ready for the Next Lesson

PREREQUISITE SKILL Use the Distributive Property to rewrite each expression as an equivalent algebraic expression.
(To review the Distributive Property, see Lesson 3-1.) **52. −32k + 18.4**

48. $4(x - 8)$ **4x − 32**
49. $3(2a + 9)$ **6a + 27**
50. $5(12 - x)$ **60 − 5x**
51. $2(1.2c + 14)$ **2.4c + 28**
52. $8(-4k + 2.3)$
53. $\frac{1}{2}(n - 9)$ **$\frac{1}{2}n - \frac{9}{2}$**

Teacher to Teacher

Jack F. Rose, Jr. John Winthrop M.S., Deep River, CT

"I like to use a graphing calculator to show how to solve equations with variables on each side. For an equation like 30 + 1.50v = 12 + 3v, enter the expression 30 + 1.50X = 12 + 3X in the Y= list. The equals sign can be found in the TEST menu. Use the TABLE feature to observe the values for X and Y1. A Y1 value of 1 identifies the values of x for which the equation is true."

Study Guide and Intervention, p. 367

To solve equations with variables on each side, use the Addition or Subtraction Property of Equality to write an equivalent equation with the variable on one side. Then solve the equation.

Example Solve the equation $12x - 3 = 4x + 13$. Then check your solution.

$12x - 3 = 4x + 13$ Write the equation.
$12x - 4x - 3 = 4x - 4x + 13$ Subtract 4x from each side.
$8x - 3 = 13$ Simplify.
$8x - 3 + 3 = 13 + 3$ Add 3 to each side.
$8x = 16$ Simplify.
$x = 2$ Mentally divide each side by 8.

To check your solution, replace x with 2 in the original equation.

CHECK

$12x - 3 = 4x + 13$ Write the equation.
$12(2) - 3 \stackrel{?}{=} 4(2) + 13$ Replace x with 2.
$24 - 3 \stackrel{?}{=} 8 + 13$ Check to see whether the statement is true.
$21 = 21$ The statement is true.

Exercises

Solve each equation. Check your solution.

1. $2x + 1 = x + 11$ $x = 10$
2. $a + 2 = 5 + 4a$ $a = -1$
3. $7y + 25 = 2y$ $y = -5$
4. $n + 11 = 2n$ $n = 11$
5. $7 - 4c = 3c - 7$ $c = 2$
6. $4 - 3b = 6b - 5$ $b = 1$
7. $9d - 9 = 3d - 3$ $d = 1$
8. $f - 4 = 6f + 26$ $f = -6$
9. $-2s + 3 = 5s + 24$ $s = -3$
10. $5a - 3 = 8a + 6$ $a = -3$
11. $8n - 12 = -12n + 8$ $n = 1$
12. $7y + 8 = -2y - 64$ $y = -8$
13. $1 + 3x = 7x - 7$ $x = 2$
14. $6a - 3 = 4 + 7a$ $a = -7$
15. $3b - 1 = 14 + 2b$ $b = 15$
16. $12c + 18 = 4 + 5c$ $c = -2$
17. $9y + 3 = 5y - 13$ $y = -4$
18. $3n - 2 = 5n + 12$ $n = -7$

Skills Practice, p. 368 and Practice, p. 369 (shown)

Solve each equation. Check your solution.

1. $3g - 12 = 9g$ -2
2. $14m = 18 + 12m$ 9
3. $7c - 7 = 4c + 17$ 8
4. $-11t = 15 - 6t$ -3
5. $20s + 4 = 13s - 10$ -2
6. $-2h - 16 = 3h - 6$ -2
7. $27j - 6 = 14j + 7$ 1
8. $-1 + 19w = 11w + 23$ 3
9. $8 - p = -12 - 3p$ -10
10. $9k - 26 = 6k - 8$ 6
11. $28 - 4d = 5d - 17$ 5
12. $2y + 7 = y$ -7
13. $11.7 - 2x = x$ 3.9
14. $3b + 4.4 = 2.6 - 6b$ -0.2
15. $\frac{3}{4}y - 6 = \frac{1}{4}y + 10$ 32
16. $2c + 7.5 = 6.2 - 3c$ -0.26
17. $5d - 11 = 2d + 2$ $\frac{13}{3}$ or $4\frac{1}{3}$
18. $6a - 10 = 2a - 7$ $\frac{3}{4}$
19. $8n - 6 = -9n + 11$ 1
20. $2f - 9 = 14f + 1$ $-\frac{5}{6}$

Define a variable and write an equation to find each number. Then solve.

21. Twice a number is 60 more than five times the number. What is the number? $2x = 60 + 5x; -20$
22. Four times a number is 21 more than the number. What is the number? $4x = 21 + x; 7$
23. Eight less than three times a number equals the number. What is the number? $3x - 8 = x; 4$
24. A number equals six less than four times a number. What is the number? $x = 4x - 6; 2$
25. **TENNIS** The area of a tennis court is 2808 ft², or 8 square feet more than 3.5 times the size of the area of a racquetball court. What is the area of a racquetball court? **800 ft²**
26. **CELLULAR PHONES** One cellular phone carrier charges $26.50 a month plus $0.15 a minute for local calls. Another carrier charges $14.50 a month and $0.25 a minute for local calls. For how many minutes is the cost of the plans the same? **120 minutes**

Enrichment, p. 371

Fractional Equations

To solve equations containing fractions, multiply both sides by the least common denominator. Then solve as usual.

Example Solve $\frac{2x}{5} - \frac{x}{10} = 6$.

$\frac{2x}{5} - \frac{x}{10} = 6$ The least common denominator is 10.
$10\left(\frac{2x}{5} - \frac{x}{10}\right) = 10(6)$
$10\left(\frac{2x}{5}\right) - 10\left(\frac{x}{10}\right) = 10(6)$
$4x - x = 10(6)$
$3x = 60$
$\frac{3x}{3} = \frac{60}{3}$
$x = 20$

Solve each equation.

1. $\frac{3x}{2} - x = 1$ 2
2. $\frac{3x}{8} = \frac{x}{3} + \frac{4}{3}$ 32
3. $\frac{y}{6} - \frac{y}{4} = 5$ -60
4. $2a + \frac{a}{3} = \frac{a}{3} + 5$ $\frac{12}{5}$
5. $\frac{x-2}{3} = \frac{x+1}{4}$ 11
6. $\frac{x-1}{2} + \frac{x-2}{3} = 1$ $\frac{13}{5}$
7. $\frac{x-3}{5} - \frac{x+2}{15} + \frac{2}{3} = 0$ $\frac{1}{2}$
8. $\frac{x+4}{3} - 4 = \frac{x-11}{4}$ -1
9. $\frac{-d}{4} + d = \frac{1}{8}$ $\frac{1}{6}$
10. $\frac{x-7}{5} + 2 = \frac{x+8}{10}$ 2
11. $z + \frac{z}{4} = 14 - \frac{z}{2}$ 8
12. $\frac{y+3}{16} - \frac{y-4}{6} = \frac{1}{3}$ 5

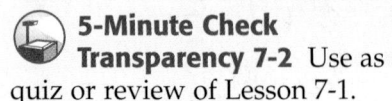

1 Focus

5-Minute Check
Transparency 7-2 Use as a quiz or review of Lesson 7-1.

Mathematical Background
notes are available for this lesson on page 326C.

Why is the Distributive Property important in solving equations?

The opening activity questions are repeated on page 375 of the *Chapter 7 Resource Masters*.

Reading to Learn Mathematics, p. 375 **ELL**

Pre-Activity *Why is the Distributive Property important in solving equations?*
Do the activity at the top of page 334 in your textbook. Write your answers below.

a. What does *t* represent? the time Josh travels

b. Why is Maria's time shown as *t* − 1?
She left 1 h later than Josh.

c. Write an equation that represents the time when Maria catches up to Josh. (*Hint:* They will have traveled the same distance.)
2*t* = 10(*t* − 1)

Reading the Lesson 1–2. See students' work.
Write a definition and give an example of each new vocabulary word or phrase.

Vocabulary	Definition	Example
1. null or empty set		
2. identity		

3. If an equation results in a sentence that is never true, the solution set is the null or empty set .

4. When an equation results in an identity, the solution set is all numbers .

5. To solve an equation containing grouping symbols, you must first use the Distributive Property .

6. For a rectangle, two times the length plus two times the width equals the perimeter .

Helping You Remember

7. Explain in a paragraph why solving a geometry problem, like that in Example 2 in your text, requires the use of the Distributive Property. You may wish to sketch a figure and assign values to the sides to aid your explanation. **Sample answer:** To find the perimeter, you must add together two times the width and two times the length. Since the length is given as an expression, such as 3*x* + 2, you must multiply the expression by 2, 2(3*x* + 2), therefore requiring the use of the Distributive Property.

What You'll Learn

- Solve equations that involve grouping symbols.
- Identify equations that have no solution or an infinite number of solutions.

Vocabulary
- null or empty set
- identity

Why is the Distributive Property important in solving equations?

Josh starts walking at a rate of 2 mph. One hour later, his sister Maria starts on the same path on her bike, riding at 10 mph.

The table shows expressions for the distance each has traveled after a given time.

	Rate (mph)	Time (hours)	Distance (miles)
Josh	2	*t*	2*t*
Maria	10	*t* − 1	10(*t* − 1)

a. What does *t* represent?

> a. the time Josh travels

b. Why is Maria's time shown as *t* − 1? **She left 1 h later than Josh.**

c. Write an equation that represents the time when Maria catches up to Josh. (*Hint*: They will have traveled the same distance.) **2*t* = 10(*t* − 1)**

NEW YORK—
Performance Indicator
Reinforcement of 7.A.4
Solve multi-step equations by combining like terms, using the distributive property, or moving variables to one side of the equation

Study Tip

Look Back
To review the **Distributive Property**, see Lesson 3-1.

SOLVE EQUATIONS WITH GROUPING SYMBOLS To find how many hours it takes Maria to catch up to Josh, you can solve the equation $2t = 10(t - 1)$. First, use the Distributive Property to remove the grouping symbols.

Example 1 *Solve Equations with Parentheses*

a. Solve the equation $2t = 10(t - 1)$. Check your solution.

$2t = 10(t - 1)$	Write the equation.
$2t = 10(t) - 10(1)$	Use the Distributive Property.
$2t = 10t - 10$	Simplify.
$2t - 10t = 10t - 10t - 10$	Subtract 10*t* from each side.
$-8t = -10$	Simplify.
$\dfrac{-8t}{-8} = \dfrac{-10}{-8}$	Divide each side by −8.
$t = \dfrac{5}{4} \text{ or } 1\dfrac{1}{4}$	Simplify.

CHECK Josh traveled $\dfrac{2 \text{ miles}}{\text{hour}} \cdot \dfrac{5 \text{ hour}}{4}$ or $2\dfrac{1}{2}$ miles.

Maria traveled one hour less than Josh. She traveled $\dfrac{10 \text{ miles}}{\text{hour}} \cdot \dfrac{1 \text{ hour}}{4}$ or $2\dfrac{1}{2}$ miles.

Therefore, Maria caught up to Josh in $\dfrac{1}{4}$ hour, or 15 minutes.

Resource Manager

📁 Workbooks and Reproducible Masters

Chapter 7 Resource Masters
- Study Guide and Intervention, p. 372
- Skills Practice, p. 373
- Practice, p. 374
- Reading to Learn Mathematics, p. 375
- Enrichment, p. 376
- Assessment, p. 411

Parent and Student Study Guide Workbook, p. 55

🖼 Transparencies
5-Minute Check Transparency 7-2
Real-World Transparency 7
Answer Key Transparencies

💿 Technology
Interactive Chalkboard
Pre-AlgePASS: Tutorial Plus, Lesson 19

b. Solve $5(a - 4) = 3(a + 1.5)$.

$5(a - 4) = 3(a + 1.5)$	Write the equation.
$5a - 20 = 3a + 4.5$	Use the Distributive Property.
$5a - 20 + 20 = 3a + 4.5 + 20$	Add 20 to each side.
$5a = 3a + 24.5$	Simplify.
$5a - 3a = 3a - 3a + 24.5$	Subtract 3a from each side.
$2a = 24.5$	Simplify.
$\dfrac{2a}{2} = \dfrac{24.5}{2}$	Divide each side by 2.
$a = 12.25$	Simplify.

The solution is 12.25. Check your solution.

Study Tip

Alternative Method
You can also solve the equation by subtracting 3a from each side first, then adding 20 to each side.

✓ **Concept Check** What property do you use to remove the grouping symbols from the equation $2(8 - a) = 4(a + 9)$? **Distributive Property**

Sometimes a geometric figure is described in terms of only one of its dimensions. To find the dimensions, you may have to solve an equation that contains grouping symbols.

Example 2 *Use an Equation to Solve a Problem*

GEOMETRY The perimeter of a rectangle is 46 inches. Find the dimensions if the length is 5 inches greater than twice the width.

Words The length is 5 inches greater than twice the width.
The perimeter is 46 inches.

Variables Let w = the width.
Let $2w + 5$ = the length.

w · · · · $2w + 5$

Study Tip

Look Back
To review **perimeter of a rectangle**, see Lesson 3-7.

$$\underbrace{2 \text{ times length}}_{2(2w + 5)} + \underbrace{2 \text{ times width}}_{2w} = \underbrace{\text{perimeter}}_{46}$$

Equation

Solve $2(2w + 5) + 2w = 46$.

$2(2w + 5) + 2w = 46$	Write the equation.
$4w + 10 + 2w = 46$	Use the Distributive Property.
$6w + 10 = 46$	Simplify.
$6w + 10 - 10 = 46 - 10$	Subtract 10 from each side.
$6w = 36$	Simplify.
$w = 6$	Mentally divide each side by 6.

Evaluate $2w + 5$ to find the length.

$2(6) + 5 = 12 + 5$ or 17   Replace w with 6.

CHECK Add the lengths of the four sides.
$6 + 17 + 6 + 17 = 46 \checkmark$

The width is 6 inches. The length is 17 inches.

www.pre-alg.com/extra_examples/ny

---

2 Teach

SOLVE EQUATIONS WITH GROUPING SYMBOLS

In-Class Examples

1 **a.** Solve the equation $3h = 5(h - 2)$. Check your solution. $h = 5$

b. Solve $6(b - 2) = 3(b + 8.5)$. $b = 12.5$

2 **GEOMETRY** The perimeter of a rectangle is 36 inches. Find the dimensions if the length is 2 inches greater than three times the width. $w = 4$ in., $\ell = 14$ in.

Teaching Tip Have students make drawings whenever they do problems related to geometric figures.

✓ **Skills Check**

Solve Equations with Grouping Symbols The perimeter of a rectangle is 74 mm. Find the dimensions if the length is 2 mm greater than six times the width. $w = 5$ mm, $\ell = 32$ mm

Interactive Chalkboard
PowerPoint® Presentations

This CD-ROM is a customizable Microsoft® Power-Point® presentation that includes:

- Step-by-step, dynamic solutions of each In-Class Example from the Teacher Wraparound Edition
- Additional, Your Turn exercises for each example
- The 5-Minute Check Transparencies
- Hot links to Glencoe Online Study Tools

DAILY

INTERVENTION **Unlocking Misconceptions**

- **No Solution** When the variable term drops out of an equation, students may assume there is no solution. Remind them to evaluate the statement that remains. If it is not a true statement, then there is no solution. There will never be a variable in the final step of an equation with no solution. However, if the statement is true, the equation has an infinite number of solutions.

3 Solve $4x - 0.3 = 4x + 0.9$. The solution set is $\varnothing$.

4 Solve $3(4x - 2) + 15 = 12x + 9$. The solution set is all numbers.

3 Practice/Apply

Study Notebook

Have students—
- add the definitions/examples of the vocabulary terms to their Vocabulary Builder worksheets for Chapter 7.
- copy the rectangle from Example 2 and write notes on how to solve for its dimensions.
- include any other item(s) that they find helpful in mastering the skills in this lesson.

About the Exercises . . .
Organization by Objective
- **Solve Equations that Involve Grouping Symbols:** 10–29
- **Identify Equations that Have No Solution or an Infinite Number of Solutions:** 20–23, 26–27

Odd/Even Assignments
Exercises 10–33 are structured so that students practice the same concepts whether they are assigned odd or even problems.

Assignment Guide
Basic: 11–25 odd, 31–35 odd, 38–56

Average: 11–37 odd, 38–56

Advanced: 10–36 even, 37–50 (Optional: 51–56)

All: Practice Quiz 1 (1–5)

NO SOLUTION OR ALL NUMBERS AS SOLUTIONS Some equations have *no* solution. That is, no value of the variable results in a true sentence. The solution set is the **null** or **empty set**, shown by the symbol $\varnothing$ or $\{\}$.

Example 3 **No Solution**

Solve $3x + \frac{1}{3} = 3x - \frac{1}{2}$.

$$3x + \frac{1}{3} = 3x - \frac{1}{2} \qquad \text{Write the equation.}$$

$$3x - 3x + \frac{1}{3} = 3x - 3x - \frac{1}{2} \qquad \text{Subtract } 3x \text{ from each side.}$$

$$\frac{1}{3} = -\frac{1}{2} \qquad \text{Simplify.}$$

The sentence $\frac{1}{3} = -\frac{1}{2}$ is *never* true. So, the solution set is $\varnothing$.

Other equations may have every number as the solution. An equation that is true for every value of the variable is called an **identity**.

Example 4 **All Numbers as Solutions**

Solve $2(2x - 1) + 6 = 4x + 4$.

$$2(2x - 1) + 6 = 4x + 4 \qquad \text{Write the equation.}$$

$$4x - 2 + 6 = 4x + 4 \qquad \text{Use the Distributive Property.}$$

$$4x + 4 = 4x + 4 \qquad \text{Simplify.}$$

$$4x + 4 - 4 = 4x + 4 - 4 \qquad \text{Subtract 4 from each side.}$$

$$4x = 4x \qquad \text{Simplify.}$$

$$x = x \qquad \text{Mentally divide each side by 4.}$$

The sentence $x = x$ is *always* true. The solution set is all numbers.

Check for Understanding

Concept Check

1. **List** the steps you would take to solve the equation $2x + 3 = 4(x - 1)$. See margin.
2. **OPEN ENDED** Give an example of an equation that has no solution and an equation that is an identity. **Sample answer: $3x + 2 = 3x + 1$ has no solution; $2x + 4 = 2(x + 2)$ is an identity.**

Guided Practice

Solve each equation. Check your solution.

GUIDED PRACTICE KEY

Exercises	Examples
3–6	1
7, 8	3, 4
9	2

3. $3(a - 5) = 18$ **11**
4. $32 = 4(x + 9)$ **−1**
5. $2(d + 6) = 3d - 1$ **13**
6. $6(n - 3) = 4(n + 2.1)$ **13.2**
7. $12 - h = -h + 3$ $\varnothing$
8. $3(2g + 4) = 6(g + 2)$ **all numbers**

Application

9. **GEOMETRY** The perimeter of a rectangle is 20 feet. The width is 4 feet less than the length. Find the dimensions of the rectangle. Then find its area. $\ell = 7$ ft; $w = 3$ ft; $A = 21$ ft^2

DAILY
INTERVENTION

Differentiated Instruction

- **Logical** Have students write equations that are identities by working in reverse order. Students should begin with $x = x$, then multiply or divide the variable by a number, followed by several more operations until a complete equation is achieved. A grouping symbol (parentheses) that requires the use of the Distributive Property should be included.

★ indicates increased difficulty

Practice and Apply

Homework Help

For Exercises	See Examples
10–19, 24, 25, 28, 29	1
20–23, 26, 27	3, 4
30–33	2

Extra Practice
See page 740.

Solve each equation. Check your solution.

10. $3(g - 3) = 6$ **5**

11. $3(x + 1) = 21$ **6**

12. $5(2c + 7) = 80$ **4.5**

13. $6(3d + 5) = 75$ **2.5**

14. $3(a - 3) = 2(a + 4)$ **17**

15. $3(s + 22) = 4(s + 12)$ **18**

16. $4(x - 2) = 3(1.5 + x)$ **12.5**

17. $3(a - 1) = 4(a - 1.5)$ **3**

18. $2(3.5n + 6) = 2.5n - 2$ **$-3.\overline{1}$**

19. $4.2x - 9 = 3(1.2x + 4)$ **35**

20. $4(f + 3) + 5 = 17 + 4f$ **all numbers**

21. $3n + 4 = 5(n + 2) - 2n$ **∅**

22. $8y - 3 = 5(y - 1) + 3y$ **∅**

23. $2(x - 5) = 4x - 2(x + 5)$

23. all numbers

24. $\frac{1}{2}(2n - 5) = 4n - 1$ **-0.5**

25. $y - 2 = \frac{1}{3}(y + 6)$ **6**

26. all numbers

★ 26. $-3(4b - 10) = \frac{1}{2}(-24b + 60)$

★ 27. $\frac{3}{4}a + 4 = \frac{1}{4}(3a + 16)$ **all numbers**

★ 28. $\frac{d}{0.4} = 2d + 1.24$ **2.48**

★ 29. $\frac{a - 6}{12} = \frac{a - 2}{4}$ **0**

Find the dimensions of each rectangle. The perimeter is given.

30. $P = 460$ ft

w

$w + 30$

100 ft by 130 ft

31. $P = 440$ yd

w

$3w - 60$

70 yd by 150 yd

32. $P = 11$ m

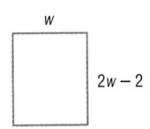

w

$2w - 2$

2.5 m by 3 m

33. **GEOMETRY** The perimeter of a rectangle is 32 feet. Find the dimensions if the length is 4 feet longer than three times the width. Then find the area of the rectangle. **w: 3 ft; ℓ: 13 ft; A: 39 ft²**

34. **NUMBER THEORY** Three times the sum of three consecutive integers is 72. What are the integers? **7, 8, 9**

35. **GEOMETRY** The triangle and the rectangle have the same perimeter. Find the dimensions of each figure. Then find the perimeter. **triangle: 7, 8, 9; rectangle, 4, 8; perimeter: 24**

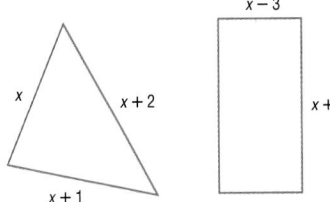

x $x + 2$ $x + 1$ $x - 3$ $x + 1$

More About. . .

Decorating •

A gallon of paint covers about 350 square feet. Estimate the square footage by multiplying the combined wall lengths by wall height and subtracting 15 square feet for each window and door.

Source: *The Family Handyman Magazine Presents Handy Hints for Home, Yard, and Workshop*

36. **BASKETBALL** Camilla has three times as many points as Lynn. Lynn has five more points than Kim. Camilla, Lynn, and Kim combined have twice as many points as Jasmine. If Jasmine has 25 points, how many points does each of the other three girls have? **Kim: 6, Lynn: 11, Camilla: 33**

★ 37. **DECORATING** Suppose a rectangular room measures 15 feet long by 12 feet wide by 7 feet high and has two windows and two doors. Use the information at the left to find how many gallons of paint are needed to paint the room using two coats of paint. **2 gal**

Answer (p. 336)

1. Multiply 4 times $(x - 1)$. Subtract $2x$ from each side. Add 4 to each side. Divide each side by 2.

---

38. CRITICAL THINKING An apple costs the same as 2 oranges. Together, an orange and a banana cost 10¢ more than an apple. Two oranges cost 15¢ more than a banana. What is the cost for one of each fruit? **apple: 50¢, banana: 35¢; orange: 25¢**

39. WRITING IN MATH Answer the question that was posed at the beginning of the lesson. **See margin.**

Why is the Distributive Property important in solving equations?

Include the following in your answer:
- a definition of the Distributive Property, and
- a description of its use in solving equations.

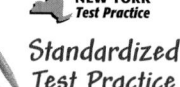

Standardized Test Practice
Ⓐ Ⓑ Ⓒ Ⓓ

40. Which equation is equivalent to $2(3x - 1) = 10 + 2x$? **C**

Ⓐ $8x - 2 = 10$ Ⓑ $6x = 11 + 2x$

Ⓒ $4x - 2 = 10$ Ⓓ $6x - 1 = 10 + 2x$

41. Car X leaves Northtown traveling at a steady rate of 55 mph. Car Y leaves 1 hour later following Car X, traveling at a steady rate of 60 mph. Which equation can be used to determine how long after Car X leaves Car Y will catch up? **D**

Ⓐ $55x = 60x - 1$ Ⓑ $55x = 60x$

Ⓒ $60x = 55(x - 1)$ Ⓓ $55x = 60(x - 1)$

Maintain Your Skills

Mixed Review   **ALGEBRA** Solve each equation. Check your solution. *(Lesson 7-1)*

42. $4x = 2x + 5$ **2.5**   **43.** $3x + 5 = 7 - 2x$ **0.4**   **44.** $1.5x + 9 = 3x - 3$ **8**

45. PROBABILITY Find the probability of choosing a girl's name at random from 20 girls' names and 30 boys' names. *(Lesson 6-9)* **40%**

Write each fraction as a decimal. Use a bar to show a repeating decimal. *(Lesson 5-1)*

46. $\frac{4}{10}$ **0.4**   **47.** $\frac{3}{8}$ **0.375**   **48.** $-\frac{1}{3}$ **$-0.\overline{3}$**   **49.** $3\frac{6}{25}$ **3.24**   **50.** $4\frac{5}{11}$ **$4.\overline{45}$**

Getting Ready for the Next Lesson   **PREREQUISITE SKILL** Evaluate each expression.
*(To review **evaluating expressions**, see Lesson 1-3.)*

51. $x - 12, x = 5$ **-7**   **52.** $b + 11, b = -15$ **-4**   **53.** $4a, a = -6$ **-24**

54. $2t + 8, t = -3$ **2**   **55.** $\frac{24}{c}, c = -3$ **-8**   **56.** $\frac{3x}{4} + 2, x = 6$ **6.5**

Practice Quiz 1   Lessons 7-1 and 7-2

Define a variable and write an equation. Then solve. *(Lesson 7-1)*

1. Twice a number is 150 less than 5 times the number. What is the number? **$2x = 5x - 150$; 50**

Solve each equation. Check your solution. *(Lessons 7-1 and 7-2)*

2. $6y + 42 = 4y$ **-21**

3. $7m - 12 = 2.5m + 2$ **$3.\overline{1}$**

4. $8(p - 4) = 2(2p + 1)$ **8.5**

5. $b + 2(b + 5) = 3(b - 1) + 13$ **all numbers**

Answer

39. Sample answer: Many equations include grouping symbols. You must use the Distributive Property to correctly solve the equation. Answers should include the following.

- The Distributive Property states that $a(b + c) = ab + ac$.

- You use the Distributive Property to remove the grouping symbols when you are solving equations.

Reading Mathematics

Meanings of At Most and At Least

The phrases *at most* and *at least* are used in mathematics. In order to use them correctly, you need to understand their meanings.

Phrase	Meaning	Mathematical Symbol
at most	• no more than • less than or equal to	$\leq$
at least	• no less than • greater than or equal to	$\geq$

Here is an example of one common use of each phrase, its meaning, and a mathematical expression for the situation.

Verbal Expression	You can spend *at most* $20.
Meaning	You can spend $20 or any amount less than $20.
Mathematical Expression	$s \leq 20$, where s represents the amount you spend.

Verbal Expression	A person must be *at least* 18 to vote.
Meaning	A person who is 18 years old or any age older than 18 may vote.
Mathematical Expression	$a \geq 18$, where a represents age.

Notice that the word *or* is part of the meaning in each case.

Reading to Learn

1. Write your own rule for remembering the meanings of *at most* and *at least*.
Sample answer: at most—no more than; at least—no less than

For each expression, write the meaning. Then write a mathematical expression using $\leq$ or $\geq$. **2–5. See margin for meanings.**

2. You need to earn at least $50 to help pay for a class trip. $e \geq 50$

3. The sum of two numbers is at most 6. $a + b \leq 6$

4. You want to drive at least 250 miles each day. $m \geq 250$

5. You want to hike 4 hours each day at most. $h \leq 4$

Sample Answers

2. You must earn $50 or more than $50.

3. The sum is 6 or less than 6.

4. You drive 250 miles or more.

5. You will hike 4 hours or less than 4 hours.

1 Focus

 5-Minute Check Transparency 7-3 Use as a quiz or review of Lesson 7-2.

Mathematical Background notes are available for this lesson on page 326C.

How can inequalities help you describe relationships?

The opening activity questions are repeated on page 380 of the *Chapter 7 Resource Masters.*

Reading to Learn Mathematics, p. 380 **ELL**

Pre-Activity *How can inequalities help you describe relationships?*

Do the activity at the top of page 340 in your textbook. Write your answers below.

a. Name three ages of children who can eat free at the restaurant. Does a child who is 6 years old eat free? **Sample ages: 3, 4, 5; no**

b. Name three heights of children who can ride the ride at the amusement park. Can a child who is 40 inches tall ride? **Sample heights: 42 in., 43 in., 44 in., no**

c. Name three speeds that are legal. Is a driver who is traveling at 35 mph driving at a legal speed? **Sample speeds: 25 mph, 30 mph, 35 mph; yes**

Reading the Lesson

Write a definition and give an example of the new vocabulary word.

Vocabulary	Definition	Example
1. inequality	See students' work.	

For each of the following phrases, write in the blank the corresponding inequality symbol. Use <, >, ≤, or ≥.

2. is greater than $>$ 3. is less than or equal to $\leq$

4. is at least $\geq$ 5. is no less than $\geq$

6. exceeds $>$ 7. is less than $<$

8. is more than $>$ 9. is at most $\leq$

Helping You Remember

10. The word *inequality* is composed of the prefix *in-* and the base word *equality.*

a. Find the definitions of *in-* and *equality* in a dictionary. Write their definitions. **not, without; of the same size or value**

b. Explain how the definitions can help you remember how *inequality* is used in mathematics. **Since *in-* means "not" and *equality* means "same size," *inequality* means not the same size, or not equal in value.**

Teaching Tip Have students make their own poster or sign and write an inequality to match it.

NEW YORK *Performance Indicator* **8.A.1** Translate verbal sentences into algebraic inequalities, **8.G.19** Graph the solution set of an inequality on a number line

What You'll Learn

- Write inequalities.
- Graph inequalities.

Vocabulary
- inequality

How can inequalities help you describe relationships?

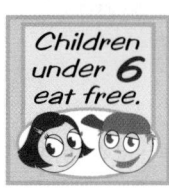

Children under 6 eat free.

If your age is *less than* 6, you eat free.

MUST BE OVER 40 INCHES TALL TO RIDE.

If your height is *more than 40 inches,* you can ride.

Speed Limit 35

A speed of *35 or less* is legal.

a. Name three ages of children who can eat free at the restaurant. Does a child who is 6 years old eat free? **Sample ages: 3, 4, 5; no**

b. Name three heights of children who can ride the ride at the amusement park. Can a child who is 40 inches tall ride?

c. Name three speeds that are legal. Is a driver who is traveling at 35 mph driving at a legal speed? **Sample speeds: 25 mph, 30 mph, 35 mph; yes**

b. Sample heights: 42 in., 43 in., 44 in.; no

WRITE INEQUALITIES A mathematical sentence that contains < or > is called an **inequality**.

Example 1 Write Inequalities with < or >

Write an inequality for each sentence.

a. Your age is less than 6 years.

Variable Let a represent age.

Inequality $a < 6$

b. Your height is greater than 40 inches.

Variable Let h represent height.

Inequality $h > 40$

Some inequalities contain ≤ or ≥ symbols.

Example 2 Write Inequalities with ≤ or ≥

Write an inequality for each sentence.

a. Your speed is less than or equal to 35 miles per hour.

Variable Let s represent speed.

Inequality $s \leq 35$

Resource Manager

Workbooks and Reproducible Masters

Chapter 7 Resource Masters
- Study Guide and Intervention, p. 377
- Skills Practice, p. 378
- Practice, p. 379
- Reading to Learn Mathematics, p. 380
- Enrichment, p. 381
- Assessment, pp. 411, 413

Graphing Calculator and Spreadsheet Masters, p. 32
Parent and Student Study Guide Workbook, p. 56
Prerequisite Skills Workbook, pp. 1–2

Transparencies

5-Minute Check Transparency 7-3
Answer Key Transparencies

Technology

Interactive Chalkboard
Pre-AlgePASS: Tutorial Plus, Lesson 20

b. Your speed is greater than or equal to 55 miles per hour.

Variable   Let *s* represent speed.

Inequality $s \geq 55$

The table below shows some common verbal phrases and the corresponding mathematical inequalities.

2 Teach

WRITE INEQUALITIES

In-Class Examples   Power Point®

Study Tip

Inequalities
Notice that ≤ and ≥ combine the symbol < or > with part of the symbol for equals, =.

Concept Summary			Inequalities
<	>	≤	≥
• is less than • is fewer than	• is greater than • is more than • exceeds	• is less than or equal to • is no more than • is at most	• is greater than or equal to • is no less than • is at least

Example 3   Use an Inequality

NUTRITION   A food can be labeled low fat only if it has no more than 3 grams of fat per serving. Write an inequality to describe low fat foods.

Words   Grams of fat per serving is no more than 3.

Variable   Let *f* = number of grams of fat per serving.

Inequality   *f*   ≤   3

The inequality is $f \leq 3$.

Inequalities with variables are open sentences. When the variable in an open sentence is replaced with a number, the inequality may be true or false.

Example 4   Determine Truth of an Inequality

For the given value, state whether each inequality is *true* or *false*.

a. $s - 7 < 5,\ s = 14$

$\quad s - 7 < 5$ Write the inequality.

$\quad 14 - 7 \overset{?}{<} 5$ Replace *s* with 14.

$\quad\quad 7 \not< 5$ Simplify.

This sentence is false.

Reading Math

Symbols
Read the symbol ≮ as *is not less than*.

b. $12 \geq \frac{a}{2} + 2,\ a = 20$

$\quad 12 \geq \frac{a}{2} + 2$ Write the inequality.

$\quad 12 \overset{?}{\geq} \frac{20}{2} + 2$ Replace *a* with 20.

$\quad 12 \overset{?}{\geq} 10 + 2$ Simplify.

$\quad 12 \geq 12$ Simplify.

Although the inequality $12 > 12$ is false, the equation $12 = 12$ is true.

Therefore, this sentence is true.

www.pre-alg.com/extra_examples/ny

1 Write an inequality for each sentence.

a. Your age is less than 19 years. $a < 19$

b. Your height is greater than 52 inches. $h > 52$

2 Write an inequality for each sentence.

a. Your speed is less than or equal to 62. $s \leq 62$

b. Your speed is greater than or equal to 42. $s \geq 42$

Teaching Tip   Students may still confuse the < and > symbols. Remind them that the symbol always points to the lesser value. You may also use the elementary reminder that the symbol is like an open mouth and always opens toward the greater value.

3 **AIR POLLUTION**   To meet a certain air quality standard, an automobile must have a fuel efficiency of not less than 27.5 miles per gallon. Write an inequality to describe this situation. $e \geq 27.5$

Teaching Tip   Remind students that "2 is greater than *x*" and "*x* is less than 2" are equivalent statements. The variable can be on either side of the equation—the direction of the inequality simply changes.

4 For the given value, state whether each inequality is *true* or *false*.

a. $s - 9 < 4,\ s = 6$
This sentence is true.

b. $14 \leq \frac{a}{3} + 1,\ a = 36$
This sentence is false.

DAILY
INTERVENTION

Differentiated Instruction

• **Naturalist**   Have students take nature walks to record examples of relationships among natural elements that can be described using inequalities. For example, students may note that the size of a crow is greater than the size of a sparrow. They might also compare leaves from different tree species. Encourage students to research the organisms they observe.

GRAPH INEQUALITIES

5 Graph each inequality.

a. $x > 10$

b. $x \geq 10$

c. $x < 10$

d. $x \leq 10$

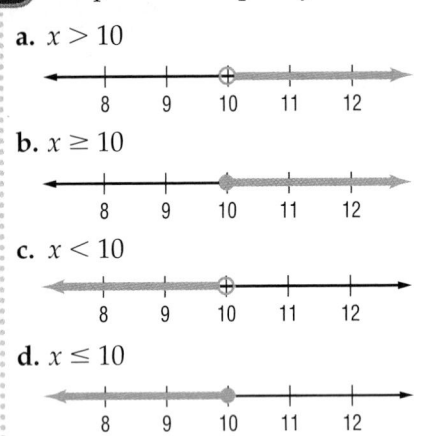

6 Write the inequality for the graph. $x \geq -38$

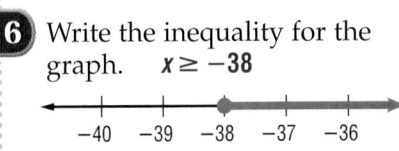

3 Practice/Apply

About the Exercises . . .

Organization by Objective
• Write Inequalities: 13–22
• Graph Inequalities: 23–40

Odd/Even Assignments
Exercises 13–42 are structured so that students practice the same concepts whether they are assigned odd or even problems.

Assignment Guide
Basic: 13–43 odd, 45–48, 50–62
Average: 13–43 odd, 45–48, 50–62 (Optional: 49)
Advanced: 14–44 even, 45–56 (Optional: 57–62)

GRAPH INEQUALITIES Inequalities can be graphed on a number line. The graph helps you visualize the values that make the inequality true.

Example 5 Graph Inequalities

Graph each inequality on a number line.

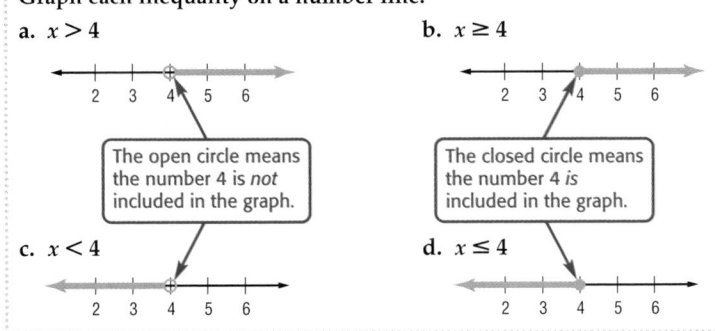

a. $x > 4$

b. $x \geq 4$

The open circle means the number 4 is *not* included in the graph.

The closed circle means the number 4 *is* included in the graph.

c. $x < 4$

d. $x \leq 4$

Example 6 Write an Inequality

Write the inequality for the graph.

An open circle is on 10, so the point 10 is *not* included in the graph. The arrow points to the right, so the graph includes all numbers greater than 10. The inequality is $x > 10$.

✓ **Concept Check**   What symbols are used to write inequalities and what does each symbol mean? $<$ (less than), $>$ (greater than), $\leq$ (less than or equal to), $\geq$ (greater than or equal to)

Check for Understanding

Concept Check
1. **Explain** why a number line graph is a good way to represent an inequality. **1–2. pp. 365A–365B.**

2. **OPEN ENDED** Write four examples of inequalities using each of the symbols $<$, $>$, $\leq$, and $\geq$. Tell the meaning of each inequality.

Guided Practice

GUIDED PRACTICE KEY	
Exercises	Examples
3, 4	1, 2
5, 6	4
7–9	5
10, 11	6
12	3

Write an inequality for each sentence.
3. A number increased by 14 is at least 25. $n + 14 \geq 25$
4. Five times some number is less than 65. $5n < 65$

ALGEBRA For the given value, state whether the inequality is *true* or *false*.
5. $n + 4 > 6, n = 12$ **true**
6. $34 \leq 4r, r = 8$ **false**

Graph each inequality on a number line. **7–9. See pp. 365A–365B.**
7. $n > 3$ 8. $p \leq 5$ 9. $x < 7$

Write the inequality for each graph. **10.** $x < 11$ **11.** $x \geq -20$
10.   11.

Study Notebook

Have students—
• add the definition/example of the vocabulary term to their Vocabulary Builder worksheets for Chapter 7.
• include any other item(s) that they find helpful in mastering the skills in this lesson.

Application 12. **SAFETY** The elevators in an office building have been approved for a maximum load of 3600 pounds. Write an inequality to describe a safe load. $m \leq 3600$

★ indicates increased difficulty

Practice and Apply

Homework Help

For Exercises	See Examples
13–16	1, 2
17–22	4
23–34	5
35–40	6
41–43	3

Extra Practice
See page 740.

Write an inequality for each sentence.

13. More than 18,000 fans attended the Kings' opening hockey game at the Staples Center in Los Angeles. $f > 18{,}000$

14. Kyle's earnings at $15 per hour were no more than $60. $15h \leq 60$

15. The 10-km race time of 86 minutes was at least twice as long as the winner's time. $86 \geq 2w$

16. A savings account decreased by $75 is now less than $500. $s - 75 < 500$

ALGEBRA For the given value, state whether each inequality is *true* or *false*.

17. $18 - x > 4, x = 12$ **true**   18. $14 + n < 23, n = 8$ **true**

19. $5k > 35, k = 7$ **false**   20. $16 \leq 3c, c = 8$ **true**

21. $\frac{x}{3} \geq 2, x = 9$ **true**   22. $\frac{14}{c} < 7, c = 2$ **false**

Graph each inequality on a number line. 23–34. See pp. 365A–365D.

23. $a > 4$ 24. $x > 6$ 25. $n < 11$ 26. $x < 5$

27. $t \geq 9$ 28. $b \geq 8$ 29. $d \leq 5$ 30. $w \leq 8$

31. $x > -4$ 32. $n \geq -3$ 33. $x \leq -5$ 34. $x < -2$

Write the inequality for each graph. 35. $x > 13$ 36. $x \geq -8$ 37. $x \leq -3$

35.

36.

38. $x < 0$

37.

38.

39. $x \geq -32$
40. $x < 11$

39.

40.

HOMEWORK For Exercises 41 and 42, use the graphic.

41. Inali spends at least an hour more than the average time spent by boys on homework each week. Write an inequality for Inali's homework time. $m \geq 6.4$

42. Anna usually spends no more than the average time spent by girls on homework each week. Write an inequality to represent Anna's homework time. $j \leq 6.8$

USA TODAY Snapshots®

High school homework time
Students ages 14-18 say they spent a weekly average 6.1 hours on homework last school year, down from 6.6 in 1996-97. Weekly average hours reported by these groups:

Male	Female	Public school student	Private school student	Caucasian	African-American	Other race/ethnicity
5.4	6.8	5.5	10.2	5.8	6.9	8.3

Source: The State of Our Nation's Youth 1998-1999, Horatio Alger Association
By Cindy Hall and Sam Ward, USA TODAY

 www.pre-alg.com/self_check_quiz/ny

Online Lesson Plans

USA TODAY Education's Online site offers resources and interactive features connected to each day's newspaper. *Experience TODAY*, USA TODAY's daily lesson plan, is available on the site and delivered daily to subscribers. This plan provides instruction for integrating USA TODAY graphics and key editorial features into your mathematics classroom. Log on to **www.education.usatoday.com**

Writing Have students search newspapers or magazines for graphs that can be used to write inequality statements. They can exchange graphs and inequalities with other students to check.

Getting Ready
for Lesson 7-4

PREREQUISITE SKILL Lesson 7-4 presents solving inequalities by adding or subtracting. Exercises 57–62 should be used to determine your students' familiarity with solving equations by adding or subtracting.

Assessment Options

Quiz (Lesson 7-3) is available on p. 411 of the *Chapter 7 Resource Masters.*

Mid-Chapter Test (Lessons 7-1 through 7-3) is available on p. 413 of the *Chapter 7 Resource Masters.*

Answers

45. **Symmetric: If** $a < b$, **then** $b < a$; **not true. Sample counterexample:** $4 < 5$, **but** $5 \not< 4$. **Transitive: If** $a < b$ **and** $b < c$, **then** $a < c$; **true.**

46. **Inequalities describe numbers that are greater than or less than a given number. Answers should include the following.**
    • **Sample answer: My brother's age is less than** $(<)$ **my age. My age is less than or equal to** $(\leq)$ **the ages of the other students in my class. My house is more than 2 miles** $(>)$ **from school. I drink at least 2** $(\geq)$ **glasses of milk each day.**
    • **Sample answer: My brother is younger than I am. The other students are my age or older. I live farther than 2 miles from school. I drink 2 or more glasses of milk each day.**

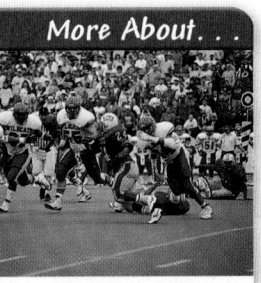

More About . . .

Sports •·······

Almost twice as many boys play high school football as basketball, but basketball is offered at more high schools.

Source: National Association of State High School Associations

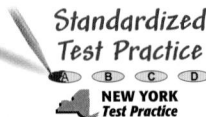

Standardized Test Practice

Ⓐ Ⓑ Ⓒ Ⓓ

NEW YORK
Test Practice

Extending ★
the Lesson

•··• 43. **SPORTS** There are more than 30,000 high school basketball and track programs in the United States. If there are 14,600 track programs, write and solve an inequality to determine the number of basketball programs. $b + 14{,}600 > 30{,}000;\ b > 15{,}400$

★ 44. Find a value for x that satisfies the inequality $0.6 < x < 0.75$.
Sample answer: 0.7

45. **CRITICAL THINKING** In Chapter 1, you studied the Symmetric and Transitive Properties of Equality. Restate these properties using inequalities. Are the properties true for inequalities? If a property is not true, give a counterexample. **See margin.**

46. WRITING IN MATH   Answer the question that was posed at the beginning of the lesson. **See margin.**

   How can inequalities help you describe relationships?
   Include the following in your answer:
   • real-life examples using the four inequality symbols, and
   • an explanation of the relationships described by each inequality.

47. Which inequality represents *a number decreased by 2 is at most 8*? **B**
   Ⓐ $n - 2$ Ⓑ $n - 2 \leq 8$
   Ⓒ $n - 2 \geq 8$ Ⓓ $n - 2 > 8$

48. Which of the following is an inequality? **A**
   Ⓐ $4 \leq x + 2$ Ⓑ $x + 4 = 3$
   Ⓒ $x + 5 + y$ Ⓓ $x - y$

★ 49. Graph the solutions for each compound inequality. **See margin.**
   a. $y < -2$ or $y > 3$. (*Hint:* In a sentence, *or* means either part is true.)
   b. $y \geq 0$ and $y \leq 5$ (*Hint:* In a sentence, *and* means both parts must be true.)

Mixed Review   **ALGEBRA   Solve each equation. Check your solution.** *(Lesson 7-2)*
   50. $2(3 + x) = 14$ **4**   51. $63 = 9(2y - 3)$ **5**   52. $3(n - 1) = 1.5(n + 2)$ **4**

53. **ALGEBRA** Four times a number minus 6 is equal to the sum of 3 times the number and 2. Define a variable and write an equation to find the number. *(Lesson 7-1)* $4n - 6 = 3n + 2;\ 8$

State whether each sequence is *arithmetic, geometric,* **or** *neither.* **Then write the next three terms of each sequence.** *(Lesson 5-10)*
   54. $-4, -1, 2, 5, \ldots$ 55. $-1, 2, -4, 8, \ldots$ 56. $1, 2, 4, 7, \ldots$
       A: 8, 11, 14   **G: −16, 32, −64**   **N: 11, 16, 22**

Getting Ready for   **PREREQUISITE SKILL   Solve each equation.**
the Next Lesson   *(To review* **solving equations,** *see Lesson 3-3.)*
   57. $x + 19 = 32$ **13**   58. $a + 7 = -3$ **−10**   59. $26 + c = 19$ **−7**
   60. $44 - c = 26$ **18**   61. $y - 9.7 = 10.1$ **19.8**   62. $r - 1.6 = -0.6$ **1**

49. a.

b.

Solving Inequalities by Adding or Subtracting

What You'll Learn

* Solve inequalities by using the Addition and Subtraction Properties of Inequality.

NEW YORK
Performance Indicator

8.A.14 Solve linear inequalities by combining like terms, using the distributive property, or moving variables to one side of the inequality (include multiplication or division of inequalities by a negative number)

8.G.19 Graph the solution set of an inequality on a number line

How is solving an inequality similar to solving an equation?

On the balance at the right, the paper bag may contain some blocks.

The blocks and bag on the scale model an inequality because the two sides are not equal.

$x + 2 < 5$

The model shows the inequality $x + 2 < 5$. The side with the bag and 2 blocks weighs less than the side with 5 blocks.

a. How many blocks would be in the bag if the left side balanced the right side? (Assume that the paper bag weighs nothing.) **3**

b. Explain how you determined your answer to part **a**.

c. What numbers of blocks can be in the bag to make the left side weigh *less than* the right side? **0, 1, or 2**

d. Write an inequality to represent your answer to part c. $x < 3$

b. Sample answer: Remove 2 blocks from each side. There are 3 blocks remaining on the right, so there must be 3 blocks in the bag.

SOLVE INEQUALITIES BY ADDING OR SUBTRACTING Solving an inequality means finding values for the variable that make the inequality true. In the example above, any number less than 3 is a solution. The solution is written as the inequality $x < 3$.

You can solve inequalities by using the Addition and Subtraction Properties of Inequalities.

1 Focus

 5-Minute Check Transparency 7-4 Use as a quiz or review of Lesson 7-3.

Mathematical Background notes are available for this lesson on page 326D.

How is solving an inequality similar to solving an equation?

The opening activity questions are repeated on page 385 of the *Chapter 7 Resource Masters*.

Reading to Learn Mathematics, p. 385 **ELL**

Pre-Activity **How is solving an inequality similar to solving an equation?**

Do the activity at the top of page 345 in your textbook. Write your answers below.

a. How many blocks would be in the bag if the left side balanced the right side? (Assume that the paper bag weighs nothing.) 3

b. Explain how you determined your answer to part a. Sample answer: Remove 2 blocks from each side. There are 3 blocks remaining on the right, so there must be 3 blocks in the bag.

c. What numbers of blocks can be in the bag to make the left side weigh *less than* the right side? 0, 1, or 2

d. Write an inequality to represent your answer to part c. $x < 3$

Reading the Lesson

1. Describe the Addition Property of Inequality and give an example of a problem that requires its use. When you add the same number to each side of an inequality, the inequality remains true. Students' examples will vary.

2. Describe the Subtraction Property of Inequality and give an example of a problem that requires its use. When you subtract the same number from each side of an inequality, the inequality remains true. Students' examples will vary.

3. Is 6 a solution for the inequality $17 + x > 23$? Explain. No; the solution is $x > 6$, so 6 will not work.

Helping You Remember

4. In each box below, write three inequalities that can be solved by using the given property. Include at least one negative integer in each box. Sample answers are given.

Addition Property of Inequality	Subtraction Property of Inequality
$x - 4 > 10$	$x + 1 < 2$
$y - 2 \leq -3$	$y + 5 \geq 10$
$z - 8 \geq 2$	$z + 2 > -4$

Key Concept — Addition and Subtraction Properties

* **Words**: When you add or subtract the same number from each side of an inequality, the inequality remains true.

* **Symbols**: For all numbers a, b, and c,
  1. if $a > b$, then $a + c > b + c$ and $a - c > b - c$.
  2. if $a < b$, then $a + c < b + c$ and $a - c < b - c$.

* **Examples**:

  $2 < 4$ $6 > 3$
  $2 + 3 < 4 + 3$ $6 - 4 > 3 - 4$
  $5 < 7$ $2 > -1$

These properties are also true for $a \geq b$ and $a \leq b$.

Study Tip

Inequalities
When you add or subtract any number from each side of an inequality, the inequality symbol remains the same.

Concept Check answer appears on next page.

✓ **Concept Check** How are these properties similar to the Properties of Equality? **See margin.**

Resource Manager

Workbooks and Reproducible Masters

Chapter 7 Resource Masters
* Study Guide and Intervention, p. 382
* Skills Practice, p. 383
* Practice, p. 384
* Reading to Learn Mathematics, p. 385
* Enrichment, p. 386

Parent and Student Study Guide Workbook, p. 57
Prerequisite Skills Workbook, pp. 1–2, 21–24, 55–62
School-to-Career Masters, p. 13

 Transparencies
5-Minute Check Transparency 7-4
Answer Key Transparencies

Technology
Interactive Chalkboard

Building on Prior Knowledge

In Chapter 2, students reviewed adding and subtracting integers. In this lesson, they will use addition and subtraction to solve inequalities.

SOLVE INEQUALITIES BY ADDING OR SUBTRACTING

In-Class Examples

1 Solve $y + 5 > 11$. Check your solution. $y > 6$

Teaching Tip Another way to check the solution is to see whether 7 is a solution of the equation $x + 3 = 10$. Then try a number greater than 7 and compare the sum to the original equation to determine whether the solution is greater than or less than 7.

2 Solve $-21 \geq d - 8$. Check your solution. $-13 \geq d$ or $d \leq -13$

3 Solve $h - 1\frac{1}{2} < 5$. Graph the solution on a number line.
$h < 6\frac{1}{2}$

✓ Skills Check

Solve Inequalities by Adding or Subtracting Solve $f + 3\frac{1}{2} > 3$. Graph the solution on a number line. $f > -\frac{1}{2}$

Study Tip

Checking Solutions
Try a number less than 7 to show that it is *not* a solution.

TEACHING TIP
Ask students whether 7 is included in the solution.

TEACHING TIP
Remind students that an open circle means the number is not included in the solution.

Example 1 Solve an Inequality Using Subtraction

Solve $x + 3 > 10$. Check your solution.

$x + 3 > 10$	Write the inequality.
$x + 3 - 3 > 10 - 3$	Subtract 3 from each side.
$x > 7$	Simplify.

To check your solution, try any number greater than 7.

CHECK

$x + 3 > 10$	Write the inequality.
$8 + 3 \overset{?}{>} 10$	Replace x with 8.
$11 > 10$ ✓	This statement is true.

Any number greater than 7 will make the statement true. Therefore, the solution is $x > 7$.

Example 2 Solve an Inequality Using Addition

Solve $-6 \geq n - 5$. Check your solution.

$-6 \geq n - 5$	Write the inequality.
$-6 + 5 \geq n - 5 + 5$	Add 5 to each side.
$-1 \geq n$	Simplify.

CHECK You can check your result by replacing n in the original inequality with a number less than or equal to -1.

The solution is $-1 \geq n$ or $n \leq -1$.

Example 3 Graph Solutions of Inequalities

Solve $a + \frac{1}{2} < 2$. Graph the solution on a number line.

$a + \frac{1}{2} < 2$	Write the inequality.
$a + \frac{1}{2} - \frac{1}{2} < 2 - \frac{1}{2}$	Subtract $\frac{1}{2}$ from each side.
$a < \frac{4}{2} - \frac{1}{2}$	Rename 2 as a fraction with a denominator of 2.
$a < \frac{3}{2}$ or $1\frac{1}{2}$	Simplify.

The solution is $a < 1\frac{1}{2}$. Check your solution.

Graph the solution.

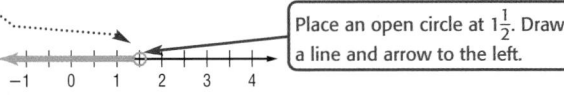

Place an open circle at $1\frac{1}{2}$. Draw a line and arrow to the left.

✓ **Concept Check** Does an inequality have only one solution? Explain.
No; there are infinite solutions.

Answer (Concept Check, p. 345)

Sample answer: For both equalities and inequalities, adding or subtracting the same number from each side does not change the truth of the statement.

Example 4 *Use an Inequality to Solve a Problem*

STATE FAIRS Antonio has $18 to ride go-carts and play games at the State Fair. If the go-carts cost $5.50, what is the most he can spend on games?

Explore   We need to find the greatest amount of money Antonio can spend on games.

Plan   Let x represent the amount Antonio can spend on games. Write an inequality to represent the problem. Recall that *at most* means *less than or equal to.*

Cost of go-cart	plus	cost of games	must be less than or equal to	total amount.
5.50	+	x	≤	18

Solve
$$5.5 + x \le 18 \qquad \text{Write the inequality. } (5.50 = 5.5)$$
$$5.5 - 5.5 + x \le 18 - 5.5 \qquad \text{Subtract 5.5 from each side.}$$
$$x \le 12.5 \qquad \text{Simplify.}$$

Examine   Check by choosing an amount less than or equal to $12.50, say, $10. Then Antonio would spend $5.50 + $10 or $15.50 in all. Since $15.50 < $18, the answer is reasonable.

So, the most Antonio can spend on games is $12.50.

In-Class Example   Power Point

4 **BOWLING** Katya has $12 to take to the bowling alley. If the shoe rental costs $3.75, what is the most she can spend on games and snacks? **Katya can spend no more than $8.25 on games and snacks.**

Teaching Tip Remind students that the expression "no more than" means less than or equal to, which is symbolized by ≤.

Check for Understanding

Concept Check

1. Use addition to undo subtraction; use subtraction to undo addition.

1. **Explain** when you would use addition and when you would use subtraction to solve an inequality.

2. **FIND THE ERROR** Dylan and Jada are using the statement *a minus three is greater than or equal to 15* to find values of *a*. **See margin.**

Dylan
$$a - 3 \ge 15$$
$$a - 3 + 3 \ge 15 + 3$$
$$a \ge 18$$

Jada
$$a - 3 = 15$$
$$a - 3 + 3 = 15 + 3$$
$$a = 18$$

Who is correct? Explain your reasoning.

3. **OPEN ENDED** Make up a problem whose solution is graphed below. **See margin.**

[number line graph marked 16, 18, 20, 22, 24 with open circle at 23]

Guided Practice

GUIDED PRACTICE KEY	
Exercises	Examples
4–6	1
7–9	2
10, 11	3
12	4

Solve each inequality. Check your solution.

4. $x + 3 < 8$ $x < 5$ 5. $14 + y \ge 7$ $y \ge -7$ 6. $-13 \ge 9 + b$ $b \le -22$

7. $a - 5 > 6$ $a > 11$ 8. $c - (-2) \le 3$ $c \le 1$ 9. $-5 < t - 2$ $t > -3$

Solve each inequality. Then graph the solution on a number line.

10. $h + 4 > 4$ $h > 0$ 11. $x - 6 \le 4$ $x \le 10$
10–11. See pp. 365A–365D for graphs.

Application

12. **SAVINGS** Chris is saving money for a ski trip. He has $62.50, but his goal is to save at least $100. What is the least amount Chris needs to save to reach his goal? **$37.50**

More About...

State Fairs
More than three million fairgoers are greeted each year by Big Tex, the symbol of the State Fair of Texas.
Source: www.bigtex.com

---

3 Practice/Apply

Study Notebook

Have students—
• write an example of an inequality and list the steps needed to solve the inequality by adding or subtracting.
• include any other item(s) that they find helpful in mastering the skills in this lesson.

About the Exercises . . .

Odd/Even Assignments
Exercises 13–46 are structured so that students practice the same concepts whether they are assigned odd or even problems.

Alert! A follow-up activity for Exercise 44 involves research on the Internet or other reference materials.

Assignment Guide
Basic: 13–45 odd, 47–70
Average: 13–45 odd, 47–70
Advanced: 14–46 even, 47–64 (Optional: 65–70)

Answers

2. Sample answer: Dylan; both solutions include 18, but the solution to the inequality also includes numbers greater than 18.

3. Sample answer: Joanna works part-time at a clothing store. Part-time workers must work fewer than 30 hours a week. If Joanna has already worked 8 hours this week, how many hours can she still work?

Study Guide and Intervention, p. 382

Use the Addition and Subtraction Properties of Inequalities to solve inequalities. When you add or subtract a number from each side of an inequality, the inequality remains true.

Example Solve $12 + y > 20$. Check your solution.

$12 + y > 20$ Write the inequality.
$12 - 12 + y > 20 - 12$ Subtract 12 from each side.
$y > 8$ Simplify.

To check your solution, try any number greater than 8.

CHECK
$12 + y \overset{?}{>} 20$ Write the inequality.
$12 + 9 \overset{?}{>} 20$ Replace y with 9.
$21 > 20$ This statement is true.

Any number greater than 8 will make the statement true. Therefore, the solution is $y > 8$.

Exercises

Solve each inequality. Check your solution.

1. $-12 < 8 + b$ $b > -20$
2. $t - 5 > -4$ $t > 1$
3. $p + 5 < -13$ $p < -18$
4. $5 > 6 + y$ $y < 11$
5. $21 < n - (-18)$ $n > 3$
6. $s - 4 \le 3$ $s \le 7$
7. $14 > w + (-2)$ $w < 16$
8. $j + 6 \ge -4$ $j \ge -10$
9. $z + (-4) < -2.5$ $z < 1.5$
10. $b - \frac{1}{4} < 2\frac{1}{4}$ $b < 2\frac{1}{2}$
11. $g - 2\frac{1}{3} \ge 3\frac{1}{6}$ $g \le 5\frac{1}{2}$
12. $-2 + z < 5$ $z < 7$
13. $-10 \le x - 5$ $x \ge -5$
14. $-23 \ge a + (-6)$ $a \le -17$
15. $20 < m - 6$ $m > 26$
16. $1\frac{1}{2} + b > 7$ $b > 5\frac{1}{2}$
17. $k + 5 \ge -7$ $k \ge -12$
18. $-\frac{2}{3} \le w - 2$ $w \ge 1\frac{1}{3}$

Skills Practice, p. 383 and Practice, p. 384 (shown)

Solve each inequality. Check your solution.

1. $h + 1 < 7$ $h < 6$
2. $c + 3 > -4$ $c > -7$
3. $22 \le m - 9$ $m \ge 31$
4. $-6 \ge g + 4$ $g \le -10$
5. $15 + d > 10$ $d > -5$
6. $p + (-8) \le -12$ $p \ge -4$
7. $-13 < k - (-16)$ $k > -29$
8. $-1 + s \le 5$ $s \le 6$
9. $12 > w - (-0.3)$ $w < 11.7$
10. $-1\frac{7}{8} < d + (-2)$ $d > \frac{1}{8}$
11. $z - 0.9 > -4.8$ $z > -3.9$
12. $b - \frac{1}{5} < 3\frac{1}{10}$ $b < 3\frac{3}{10}$

Solve each inequality. Then graph the solution on a number line.

13. $5 + a > 16$ $a > 11$
14. $c + 12 \le 14$ $c \le 2$
15. $-20 > h - 3$ $h < -17$
16. $16 \ge k + (-17)$ $k \le 33$
17. $p - (-2) \ge -4\frac{1}{2}$ $p \ge -6\frac{1}{2}$
18. $-2 + z < 3\frac{3}{4}$ $z < 5\frac{3}{4}$

19. **TRANSPORTATION** A certain minivan has a maximum carrying capacity of 1200 pounds. If the luggage weighs 150 pounds, what is the maximum weight allowable for passengers? **1050 lb**

20. **DRINKS** A large punch bowl holds 12 gallons of liquids. If five gallons of ginger ale have already been poured into the bowl, what is the most fruit juice that can be added? $5 + f \le 12$, $f \le 7$

21. **FUND-RAISING** A neighborhood association wants to replace the playground equipment at a park. The playground equipment they would like to buy starts at $4500. If they have already raised $2700, what is the least they must still collect? $p + 2700 \ge 4500$; $p \ge \$1800$

Enrichment, p. 386

Solving Inequalities Using Addition and Subtraction

Inequalities can be written many different ways in English.

English Phrase	Mathematical Phrase
at most x	$\le x$
at least x	$\ge x$
5 less than x	$x - 5$
5 more than x	$x + 5$
5 is less than x	$5 < x$
x is between 4 and 6	$4 < x < 6$ or $x > 4$ and $x < 6$

1. Write a mathematical phrase for each of the following English phrases.
   a. 8 more than x. $x + 8$
   b. x is at least 3. $x \ge 3$
   c. x is between 6 and 12. $6 < x < 12$ or $x > 6$ and $x < 12$
   d. x cannot exceed -5. $x \le -5$

2. For what values of x, if any, is the mathematical phrase $5 > x > 7$ true? **none**

To solve compound inequalities, you must perform the same operation on each of the three parts of the inequality.

Example Solve the compound inequality $3 < x - 2 < 5$.

$3 < x - 2 < 5$
$3 + 2 < x - 2 + 2 < 5 + 2$ To get x by itself, add 2 to each part.
$5 < x < 7$

Thus, x is all numbers between 5 and 7.

Solve each compound inequality.

3. $-2 < x + 1 < 4$ $-3 < x < 3$
4. $-4 \le x - 1 \le 0$ $-3 \le x \le 1$
5. $3 < 15 + x < 10$ $-12 < x < -5$
6. $-12 < x - 3 \le 1$ $-9 < x \le 4$

Practice and Apply

Homework Help

For Exercises	See Examples
13–18, 25–28	1
19–24, 29, 30	2
31–42	3
43–46	4

Extra Practice
See page 740.

Solve each inequality. Check your solution.   18. $n > 37$ 24. $d \ge -25$

13. $p + 7 < 9$ $p < 2$
14. $t + 6 > -3$ $t > -9$
15. $-14 \ge 8 + b$ $b \le -22$
16. $16 > -11 + k$ $k < 27$
17. $3 \ge -2 + y$ $y \le 5$
18. $25 < n + (-12)$
19. $r - 5 \le 2$ $r \le 7$
20. $a - 6 < 13$ $a < 19$
21. $j - 8 \le -12$ $j \le -4$
22. $-8 > h - 1$ $h < -7$
23. $22 > w - (-16)$ $w < 6$
24. $-30 \le d + (-5)$
25. $1 + y \le 2.4$ $y \le 1.4$
26. $2.9 < c + 7$ $c > -4.1$
27. $f + (-4) \ge 1.4$ $f \ge 5.4$
28. $z + (-2) > -3.8$ $z > -1.8$
29. $b - \frac{3}{4} < 2\frac{1}{2}$ $b < 3\frac{1}{4}$
30. $g - 1\frac{2}{3} > 2\frac{1}{6}$ $g > 3\frac{5}{6}$

Solve each inequality. Then graph the solution on a number line.   36. $a \le -27$

31. $n + 4 < 9$ $n < 5$
32. $t + 7 > 12$ $t > 5$
33. $p + (-5) > -3$ $p > 2$
34. $-3 + z > 2$ $z > 5$
35. $-13 \ge x - 8$ $x \le -5$
36. $-32 \ge a + (-5)$
37. $33 \le m - (-6)$
38. $k + 9 \ge -21$ $k \ge -30$
39. $1\frac{1}{4} + b < 3$ $b < 1\frac{3}{4}$
40. $3 \le \frac{1}{2} + a$ $a \ge 2\frac{1}{2}$
41. $4 \ge s - \frac{2}{3}$ $s \le 4\frac{2}{3}$
42. $-\frac{3}{4} < w - 1$ $w > \frac{1}{4}$

31–42. See pp. 365A–365D for graphs.

37. $m \ge 27$

43. **TRANSPORTATION** A certain minivan has a maximum carrying capacity of 1100 pounds. If the luggage weighs 120 pounds, what is the maximum weight allowable for passengers? **980 lb**

44. **BIOLOGY** Female killer whales usually weigh more than 3000 pounds and are up to 19 feet long. Suppose a female whale is 12 feet long. Write and solve an inequality to find how much longer the whale could grow.
Source: www.seaworld.org $12 + y \le 19$; the whale could grow as much as 7 feet.

 Online Research Data Update Are there any whales in the world that are heavier or longer than the killer whale? Visit www.pre-alg.com/data_update to learn more.

WEATHER For Exercises 45 and 46, use the diagram below.

Types of Storms
Depression   Tropical Storm   Hurricane
39   74
Wind Speed of Storm (mph)

45. A hurricane has winds that are at least 74 miles per hour. Suppose a tropical storm has winds that are 42 miles per hour. Write and solve an inequality to find how much the winds must increase before the storm becomes a hurricane. $42 + x \ge 74$; $x \ge 32$; at least 32 mph

46. A *major storm* has wind speeds that are at least 110 miles per hour. Write and solve an inequality that describes how much greater these wind speeds are than the slowest hurricane. $74 + y \ge 110$; $y \ge 36$; at least 36 mph

47. **CRITICAL THINKING** Is it *always*, *sometimes*, or *never* true that $x - 1 < x$? Explain your answer. **Always; subtracting x gives $-1 < 0$, which is always true.**

Career Choices

Marine Biologist

Marine biologists study the behavior, diseases, and life processes of salt-water organisms.

Online Research
For information about a career as a marine biologist, visit:
www.pre-alg.com/careers

348   Chapter 7   Equations and Inequalities

48. **WRITING IN MATH** Answer the question that was posed at the beginning of the lesson. **See margin.**

How is solving an inequality similar to solving an equation?

Include the following in your answer:

- a description of what would happen if 3 blocks were removed from each side of the scale modeled at the right, and,

- a sentence that compares removing 3 blocks from each side of a scale and subtracting 3 from each side of an inequality.

$x + 3 > 5$

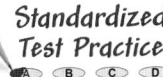
Standardized
Test Practice
Ⓐ Ⓑ Ⓒ Ⓓ

49. Which inequality represents a temperature that is equal to or less than 42°? **C**

Ⓐ $t \geq 42$ Ⓑ $t > 42$ Ⓒ $t \leq 42$ Ⓓ $t < 42$

50. Trevor has $25 to spend on a T-shirt and shorts for gym class. The shorts cost $14. Based on the inequality $14 + t \leq 25$, where t represents the cost of the T-shirt, what is the most Trevor can spend on the T-shirt? **C**

Ⓐ $9   Ⓑ $10.99   Ⓒ $11   Ⓓ $11.50

Maintain Your Skills

Mixed Review **ALGEBRA** **For the given value, state whether each inequality is *true* or *false*.**
(Lesson 7-3)

51. $x - 5 > 4, x = 9$ **F**   **52.** $9 + a \leq 3, a = -7$ **T**

53. $\frac{x}{2} \geq 8, x = 4$ **F**   **54.** $6n < -4, n = -1$ **T**

55. **GEOMETRY** The perimeter of a rectangle is 24 centimeters. Find the dimensions if the length is 3 more than twice the width. *(Lesson 7-2)*
3 cm, 9 cm

56. **GEOMETRY** Find the perimeter and area of the rectangle at the right.
(Lesson 3-7) **P = 54 cm; A = 152 cm²**

19 cm

8 cm

ALGEBRA **Use the Distributive Property to rewrite each expression.**
(Lesson 3-1)

57. $4(2 + 8)$ **8 + 32**   **58.** $-2(n + 6)$ **−2n − 12**

59. $5(x - 3.5)$ **5x − 17.5**   **60.** $(9 - d)(-3c)$ **−27c + 3cd**

Find each difference. *(Lesson 2-3)*

61. $-15 - (-12)$ **−3**   **62.** $8 - (-5)$ **13**

63. $-9 - 6$ **−15**   **64.** $27 - 45$ **−18**

Getting Ready for the Next Lesson **PREREQUISITE SKILL** **Solve each equation.**
(To review solving equations, see Lesson 3-4.)

65. $-7x = 14$ **−2**   **66.** $-3y = -27$ **9**

67. $5x = -20$ **−4**   **68.** $\frac{d}{-3} = -6$ **18**

69. $\frac{c}{-4} = 12$ **−48**   **70.** $\frac{a}{2} = -8$ **−16**

---

4 Assess

Open-Ended Assessment

Writing Have students write a number of inequalities that must be solved by adding or subtracting and graph the solutions on number lines. Students should then recopy their inequalities without the inequality signs. They should present the number lines and the incomplete inequalities to a partner. Partners must fill in the correct inequality signs.

Getting Ready for Lesson 7-5

PREREQUISITE SKILL Lesson 7-5 presents solving inequalities by multiplying or dividing. Exercises 65–70 should be used to determine your students' familiarity with solving equations using multiplication and division.

Answer

48. Solving an inequality is similar to solving an equation because when you add or subtract the same thing on each side, the inequality remains true. Sample answers should include the following.

- If you subtract 3 blocks from each side, the balance will stay the same.

- Subtracting 3 blocks from each side of the scale is like subtracting 3 from each side of an inequality—the inequality remains true.

7-5 Solving Inequalities by Multiplying or Dividing

1 Focus

5-Minute Check Transparency 7-5 Use as a quiz or review of Lesson 7-4.

Mathematical Background notes are available for this lesson on page 326D.

How are inequalities used in studying space?

The opening activity questions are repeated on page 390 of the *Chapter 7 Resource Masters.*

Reading to Learn Mathematics, p. 390 **ELL**

Pre-Activity *How are inequalities used in studying space?*

Do the activity at the top of page 350 in your textbook. Write your answers below.

a. Divide each side of the inequality 300 > 50 by 2. Is the inequality still true? Explain by using an inequality. **yes; 150 > 25**

b. Would the weight of 5 astronauts be greater on Pluto or on Earth? Explain by using an inequality. **Earth; 300 > 67, so 5(300) > 5(67).**

Reading the Lesson

1. Describe the Multiplication Property of Inequality for both positive and negative numbers and give an example of a problem for each type of number. **When you multiply each side of an inequality by the same positive number, the inequality remains true. When you multiply each side of an inequality by the same negative number, the inequality sign must be reversed for the inequality to remain true. Students' examples will vary.**

2. Describe the Division Property of Inequality for both positive and negative numbers and give an example of a problem for each type of number. **When you divide each side of an inequality by the same positive number, the inequality remains true. When you divide each side of an inequality by the same negative number, the inequality sign must be reversed for the inequality to remain true. Students' examples will vary.**

Helping You Remember

3. In the boxes below, write examples of inequalities in which the sign does and does not reverse. Write at least three examples in each box. **Sample answers are given.**

Inequalities in Which the Sign Does Not Reverse	Inequalities in Which the Sign Reverses
$\frac{x}{4} \le 5$	$9 < -3x$
$3y \ge 3$	$25 \le \frac{y}{-9}$
$\frac{z}{2} < -4$	$-3z \ge -4$

NEW YORK — *Performance Indicator*

8.A.14 Solve linear inequalities by combining like terms, using the distributive property, or moving variables to one side of the inequality (include multiplication or division of inequalities by a negative number)

8.G.19 Graph the solution set of an inequality on a number line

Study Tip

Positive Number
The inequality $c > 0$ means that c is a positive number.

7-5 Solving Inequalities by Multiplying or Dividing

What You'll Learn

- Solve inequalities by multiplying or dividing by a positive number.
- Solve inequalities by multiplying or dividing by a negative number.

How are inequalities used in studying space?

An astronaut in a space suit weighs about 300 pounds on Earth, but only 50 pounds on the moon because of weaker gravity.

$$\underset{\text{weight on Earth}}{300} > \underset{\text{weight on moon}}{50}$$

If the astronaut and space suit each weighed half as much, would the inequality still be true? That is, would the astronaut's weight still be greater on Earth?

Location	Weight of Astronaut (lb)
Earth	300
Moon	50
Pluto	67
Mars	113
Neptune	407
Jupiter	796

a. Divide each side of the inequality 300 > 50 by 2. Is the inequality still true? Explain by using an inequality. **yes; 150 > 25**

b. Would the weight of 5 astronauts be greater on Pluto or on Earth? Explain by using an inequality. **Earth; 300 > 67, so 5(300) > 5(67).**

MULTIPLY OR DIVIDE BY A POSITIVE NUMBER The application above demonstrates how you can solve inequalities by using the Multiplication and Division Properties of Inequalities.

Key Concept — Multiplication and Division Properties

- **Words**   When you multiply or divide each side of an inequality by the same positive number, the inequality remains true.

- **Symbols**   For all numbers a, b, and c, where $c > 0$,

  1. if $a > b$, then $ac > bc$ and $\frac{a}{c} > \frac{b}{c}$.

  2. if $a < b$, then $ac < bc$ and $\frac{a}{c} < \frac{b}{c}$.

- **Examples**

$2 < 6$	$3 > -9$
$4(2) < 4(6)$	$\frac{3}{3} > \frac{-9}{3}$
$8 < 24$	$1 > -3$

These properties are also true for $a \ge b$ and $a \le b$.

Resource Manager

📂 Workbooks and Reproducible Masters

Chapter 7 Resource Masters
- Study Guide and Intervention, p. 387
- Skills Practice, p. 388
- Practice, p. 389
- Reading to Learn Mathematics, p. 390
- Enrichment, p. 391
- Assessment, p. 412

Parent and Student Study Guide Workbook, p. 58
Prerequisite Skills Workbook, pp. 1–2, 27–28, 31–32, 47–54

 Transparencies
5-Minute Check Transparency 7-5
Answer Key Transparencies

 Technology
Interactive Chalkboard

Example 1 *Multiply or Divide by a Positive Number*

a. Solve $8x \leq 40$. **Check your solution.**

$8x \leq 40$ Write the inequality.

$\dfrac{8x}{8} \leq \dfrac{40}{8}$ Divide each side by 8.

$x \leq 5$ Simplify.

The solution is $x \leq 5$. You can check this solution by substituting 5 or a number less than 5 into the inequality.

b. Solve $\dfrac{d}{2} > 7$. **Check your solution.**

$\dfrac{d}{2} > 7$ Write the inequality.

$2\left(\dfrac{d}{2}\right) > 2(7)$ Multiply each side by 2.

$d > 14$ Simplify.

The solution is $d > 14$. You can check this solution by substituting a number greater than 14 into the inequality.

NEW YORK
Test Practice

Standardized Test Practice
Ⓐ Ⓑ Ⓒ Ⓓ

Example 2 *Write an Inequality*

Multiple-Choice Test Item

> Ling earns \$8 per hour in the summer working at the zoo. Which inequality can be used to find how many hours he must work in a week to earn at least \$120?
>
> Ⓐ $8x < 120$ Ⓑ $8x \leq 120$ Ⓒ $8x > 120$ Ⓓ $8x \geq 120$

Read the Test Item

You are to write an inequality to represent a real-world problem.

Test-Taking Tip
Before taking a standardized test, review the meanings of phrases like *at least* and *at most*.

Solve the Test Item

Let x represent the number of hours worked.

Amount earned per hour	times	number of hours	is at least	amount earned each week.
8	·	x	$\geq$	120

The answer is D.

MULTIPLY OR DIVIDE BY A NEGATIVE NUMBER What happens when each side of an inequality is multiplied or divided by a negative number?

$-6 < 11$

$-1(-6) \overset{?}{<} -1(11)$ Multiply each side by -1.

$6 \overset{?}{<} -11$ This inequality is false.

$10 > 5$

$\dfrac{10}{-5} \overset{?}{>} \dfrac{5}{-5}$ Divide each side by -5.

$-2 \overset{?}{>} -1$ This inequality is false.

Standardized Test Practice
Ⓐ Ⓑ Ⓒ Ⓓ

Example 2 Point out to students that *at least* and *at most* are common phrases that appear on standardized tests. Having a good understanding of these phrases will help students more quickly recognize the type of inequality sign required for the problem.

---

2 Teach

Building on Prior Knowledge

In Chapter 2, students reviewed multiplying and dividing integers. In this lesson, students will solve inequalities using multiplication and division.

MULTIPLY OR DIVIDE BY A POSITIVE NUMBER

In-Class Examples   Power Point®

1   **a.** Solve $9x \leq 54$. Check your solution. $x \leq 6$

     b. Solve $\dfrac{d}{9} > 4$. Check your solution. $d > 36$

2   **Multiple-Choice Test Item**
Martha earns \$9 per hour working for a fast food restaurant. Which inequality can be used to find how many hours she must work in a week to earn at least \$243?

   A $9x < 243$

   B $9x \geq 243$

   C $9x > 243$

   D $9x \leq 243$ **B**

MULTIPLY OR DIVIDE BY A NEGATIVE NUMBER

In-Class Example   Power Point®

3   Solve each inequality and check your solution. Then graph the solution on a number line.

a. $\dfrac{x}{-5} \geq 7$ $x \leq -35$

b. $-9x < -27$ $x > 3$

Study Notebook

Have students—

• make a chart with four examples of inequalities demonstrating using both multiplication and division with positive and negative numbers to solve the inequalities.

• include any other item(s) that they find helpful in mastering the skills in this lesson.

About the Exercises . . .

Organization by Objective
• Solve Inequalities by Multiplying or Dividing by a Positive Number: 14–21, 32–33, 38–39
• Solve Inequalities by Multiplying or Dividing by a Negative Number: 22–31, 34–37

Odd/Even Assignments
Exercises 14–39 are structured so that students practice the same concepts whether they are assigned odd or even problems.

Assignment Guide

Basic: 15–39 odd, 40–57
Average: 15–39 odd, 40–57
Advanced: 14–38 even, 40–51 (Optional: 52–57)
All: Practice Quiz 2 (1–10)

The inequalities $6 < -11$ and $-2 > -1$ are both false. However, they would both be true if the inequality symbols were reversed. That is, change $<$ to $>$ and change $>$ to $<$.

$$6 > -11 \quad \text{true} \qquad -2 < -1 \quad \text{true}$$

This investigation suggests the following properties.

Key Concept — Multiplication and Division Properties

• **Words**   When you multiply or divide each side of an inequality by the same negative number, the inequality symbol must be reversed for the inequality to remain true.

• **Symbols**   For all numbers a, b, and c, where $c < 0$,
  1. if $a > b$, then $ac < bc$ and $\dfrac{a}{c} < \dfrac{b}{c}$.
  2. if $a < b$, then $ac > bc$ and $\dfrac{a}{c} > \dfrac{b}{c}$.

• **Examples**
$$7 > 1 \qquad\qquad -4 < 16$$
$$-2(7) < -2(1) \quad \text{Reverse the symbols.} \qquad \frac{-4}{-4} > \frac{16}{-4}$$
$$-14 < -2 \qquad\qquad 1 > -4$$

These properties are also true for $a \geq b$ and $a \leq b$.

✓ **Concept Check**   Explain why it is necessary to reverse the symbol when you multiply each side of an inequality by a negative number. **The inequality symbol must be reversed to keep the inequality true.**

Example 3 *Multiply or Divide by a Negative Number*

Solve each inequality and check your solution. Then graph the solution on a number line.

a. $\dfrac{x}{-3} \leq 4$

$$\frac{x}{-3} \leq 4 \qquad \text{Write the inequality.}$$
$$-3\left(\frac{x}{-3}\right) \geq -3(4) \qquad \text{Multiply each side by } -3 \text{ and reverse the symbol.}$$
$$x \geq -12 \qquad \text{Check this result.}$$

CHECK   You can check your result by replacing x in the original inequality with a number greater than -12.

Graph the solution, $x \geq -12$.

b. $-7x > -56$

$$-7x > -56 \qquad \text{Write the inequality.}$$
$$\frac{-7x}{-7} < \frac{-56}{-7} \qquad \text{Divide each side by } -7 \text{ and reverse the symbol.}$$
$$x < 8 \qquad \text{Check this result.}$$

Graph the solution, $x < 8$.

• **Kinesthetic** Using cardboard, glue, toothpicks or wire, scissors, and any other necessary materials, have students create a board with a flipping (reversing) inequality sign to which numbers/terms can be attached to model various inequalities. As students carry out the operations necessary to solve an inequality, they can replace the numbers/terms to show each step and flip the inequality sign to face the correct way.

Concept Check

1. **List** the steps you would use to solve $\dfrac{y}{-12} < 6$. **See margin.**

2. **OPEN ENDED** Write an inequality that can be solved using the Division Property of Inequality, where the inequality symbol is *not* reversed. **Sample answer:** $3x < 24$

3. **FIND THE ERROR** Brittany and Tamika each solved $-45 \geq 9k$.

Brittany	Tamika
$-45 \geq 9k$	$-45 \geq 9k$
$\dfrac{-45}{9} \leq \dfrac{9k}{9}$	$\dfrac{-45}{9} \geq \dfrac{9k}{9}$
$-5 \leq k$	$-5 \geq k$

Who is correct? Explain your reasoning. **See margin.**

Guided Practice

Solve each inequality and check your solution. Then graph the solution on a number line. **4–12. See pp. 365A–365D for graphs.**

GUIDED PRACTICE KEY	
Exercises	Examples
4, 5, 7	1
6, 8–12	3
13	2

4. $2x < 8$ $x < 4$
5. $3x \geq -6$ $x \geq -2$
6. $-4t > -20$ $t < 5$

7. $\dfrac{a}{5} > 10$ $a > 50$
8. $-8 > \dfrac{k}{-0.4}$ $k > 3.2$
9. $\dfrac{m}{-7} \leq 1.2$ $m \geq -8.4$

10. $-\dfrac{s}{3} \leq -3.5$ $s \geq 10.5$
11. $36 \geq -\dfrac{1}{2}y$ $y \geq -72$
12. $-273 \geq -13z$ $z \geq 21$

Standardized Test Practice

Ⓐ Ⓑ Ⓒ Ⓓ

NEW YORK Test Practice

13. **EARNINGS** Julia delivers pizzas on weekends. Her average tip is $1.50 for each pizza that she delivers. How many pizzas must she deliver to earn at least $20 in tips? **C**

Ⓐ 10 Ⓑ 13 Ⓒ 14 Ⓓ 20

Homework Help	
For Exercises	See Examples
14–21, 32, 33	1
22–31, 34–37	3
42, 43	2

Extra Practice
See page 741.

Solve each inequality and check your solution. Then graph the solution on a number line. **14–37. See pp. 365A–365D for graphs.**

14. $4x < 4$ $x < 1$
15. $7y > 63$ $y > 9$
16. $13a \geq -26$ $a \geq -2$

17. $-15 \leq 5b$ $b \geq -3$
18. $144 < 12d$ $d > 12$
19. $15 \geq 3t$ $t \leq 5$

20. $\dfrac{p}{6} > 5$ $p > 30$
21. $7 \geq \dfrac{h}{14}$ $h \leq 98$
22. $-3m > -33$ $m < 11$

23. $-8z \leq -24$ $z \geq 3$
24. $18 > -2g$ $g > -9$
25. $-8 \leq -4w$ $w \leq 2$

26. $6 > \dfrac{x}{-7}$ $x > -42$
27. $\dfrac{r}{-2} < -2$ $r > 4$
28. $\dfrac{y}{-3} < -7$ $y > 21$

29. $\dfrac{k}{-2} < 9$ $k > -18$
30. $-6a > -78$ $a < 13$
31. $-25t \leq 400$ $t \geq -16$

32. $\dfrac{y}{4} \geq 2.4$ $y \geq 9.6$
33. $\dfrac{n}{5} \leq 0.8$ $n \leq 4$
34. $-5 \leq \dfrac{c}{-4.5}$ $c \leq 22.5$

35. $-19 > \dfrac{y}{-0.3}$ $y > 5.7$
36. $-\dfrac{1}{3}x \geq -9$ $x \leq 27$
37. $-36 < -\dfrac{1}{2}b$ $b < 72$

38. **SOCCER** Tomás wants to spend less than $100 for a new soccer ball and shoes. The ball costs $24. **a.** $24 + s < 100$

a. Write an inequality to represent the amount left for shoes.

b. What amount can he spend on shoes? **less than $76**

Answers

1. Multiply each side by -12 and reverse the inequality symbol.

3. Tamika is correct. She divided each side of the inequality by 9. Since 9 is a positive number, she did not reverse the inequality symbol.

DAILY INTERVENTION FIND THE ERROR

Students may incorrectly assume that the inequality sign must be reversed whenever an inequality contains a negative number.

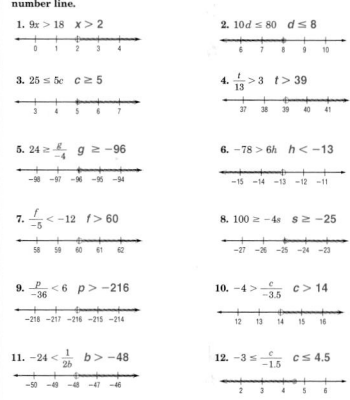

Use the Multiplication and Division Properties of Inequalities to solve inequalities. When you multiply or divide each side of an inequality by a positive number, the inequality remains true. The direction of the inequality sign does not change.

Example 1 Solve $8x \geq 72$. Check your solution.

$8x \geq 72$ Write the inequality.

$\dfrac{8x}{8} \geq \dfrac{72}{8}$ Divide each side by 8.

$x \geq 9$ Simplify.

The solution is $x \geq 9$. You can check this solution by substituting 9 or a number greater than 9 into the inequality.

For an inequality to remain true when multiplying or dividing each side of the inequality by a negative number, however, you must reverse the direction of the inequality symbol.

Example 2 Solve $\dfrac{y}{-12} < 4$ and check your solution. Then graph the solution on a number line.

$\dfrac{y}{-12} < 4$ Write the inequality.

$-12\left(\dfrac{y}{-12}\right) > -12(4)$ Multiply each side by -12 and reverse the symbol.

$y > -48$ Check the result.

Graph the solution, $y > -48$.

Exercises

Solve each inequality and check your solution. Then graph the solution on a number line.

1. $81 < 9d$ $d > 9$
2. $\dfrac{p}{3} < -12$ $p > -36$
3. $\dfrac{h}{-4} \geq 3$ $h \leq -12$

4. $-20c \leq 100$ $t \geq -5$
5. $\dfrac{-2}{3x} > 12$ $x < -18$
6. $-16 \leq -\dfrac{1}{4}b$ $b \leq 64$

7. $-8 < \dfrac{c}{-2.5}$ $c < 20$
8. $\dfrac{n}{3} > 0.5$ $n > 1.5$

Solve each inequality and check your solution. Then graph the solution on a number line.

1. $9x > 18$ $x > 2$
2. $10d \leq 80$ $d \leq 8$

3. $25 \leq 5c$ $c \geq 5$
4. $\dfrac{t}{13} > 3$ $t > 39$

5. $24 \geq \dfrac{g}{-4}$ $g \geq -96$
6. $-78 > 6h$ $h < -13$

7. $\dfrac{f}{-5} < -12$ $f > 60$
8. $100 > -4s$ $s \geq -25$

9. $\dfrac{p}{-36} < 6$ $p > -216$
10. $-4 > \dfrac{c}{-3.5}$ $c > 14$

11. $-24 < \dfrac{1}{2b}$ $b > -48$
12. $-3 \leq \dfrac{c}{-1.5}$ $c \leq 4.5$

13. **DISCOUNTS** To qualify for a store discount, Jorge's soccer team must spend at least $560 for new jerseys. The team needs 20 jerseys.
   a. Write an inequality to represent how much the team should spend on each jersey to qualify for the discount. $20p \geq 560$
   b. How much should the team spend for each jersey? $p \geq 28

14. **POLITICS** Mi-Ling wants to mail at least 850 fliers encouraging voters to vote for the upcoming school levy. She has five days to get them all in the mail.
   a. Write an inequality to represent how many fliers Mi-Ling must mail every day. $5f \geq 850$
   b. How many fliers should Mi-Ling mail each day? $f \geq 170$

Hidden Word

In each group of five inequalities, only two have the same solution set. For each group, write the solution of each inequality and then circle the letters of the two inequalities having the same solution set. After completing all four groups, use the circled letters to form a one-word answer to the question at the bottom of the page.

GROUP 1
Ⓔ. $3x < 30$ B. $-3x < -30$ F. $-30 > 3x$ Ⓓ. $-30 < -3x$ D. $-3x < 30$
$x < 10$ $x > 10$ $-10 > x$ $10 > x$ $x > -10$

GROUP 2
M. $\dfrac{x}{5} \leq -2$ N. $\dfrac{-x}{5} \leq 2$ Ⓦ. $\dfrac{-x}{5} \leq -2$ Ⓡ. $\dfrac{-x}{2} \leq -5$ R. $\dfrac{-x}{5} < -2$
$x \leq -10$ $x \geq -10$ $x \geq 10$ $x \geq 10$ $x > 10$

GROUP 3
Q. $\dfrac{3x}{2} < 0$ K. $0 \leq -12x$ L. $\dfrac{-1}{x} \leq 0$ Ⓛ. $0.73x \geq 0$ Ⓐ. $0 \geq -912x$
$x < 0$ $0 \geq x$ $x > 0$ $x \geq 0$ $0 \leq x$

GROUP 4
L. $200 > 0.05x$ Ⓐ. $0.05x < 20$ D. $\dfrac{1}{5}x > 20$ E. $200 > 5x$ Ⓔ. $\dfrac{x}{0.1} < 4000$
$4000 > x$ $x < 400$ $x > 100$ $40 > x$ $x < 400$

Unscramble the circled letters to find the name of the first of the original 13 colonies to ratify the U.S. Constitution. Delaware

Open-Ended Assessment

Speaking Have students describe what should happen to an inequality symbol when the inequality is multiplied or divided by a positive and a negative number.

Tips for New Teachers

Intervention If there is any doubt whether your students thoroughly understand multiplying or dividing inequalities by negative numbers, consider spending an extra day on this lesson. Use the Extra Practice on pp. 388 and 389. You can also use the Study Guide and Intervention masters or the Practice masters in the *Chapter 7 Resource Masters* to reinforce this concept.

Getting Ready for Lesson 7-6

PREREQUISITE SKILL Lesson 7-6 presents solving multi-step inequalities. Exercises 52–57 should be used to determine your students' familiarity with solving two-step equations.

Assessment Options

Practice Quiz 2 The quiz provides students with a brief review of the concepts and skills in Lessons 7-3 through 7-5. Lesson numbers are given to the right of exercises or instruction lines so students can review concepts not yet mastered.

Quiz (Lessons 7-4 and 7-5) is available on p. 412 of the *Chapter 7 Resource Masters*.

---

39. **SWIMMING** Nicole swims 40 meters per minute, and she wants to swim at least 2000 meters this morning. **a. $40m \geq 2000$**
    a. Write an inequality to represent how long she should swim.
    b. How many minutes should she swim? **at least 50 min**

40. **CRITICAL THINKING** The product of an integer and -7 is less than -84. Find the least integer that meets this condition. **13**

41. Answer the following question that was posed at the beginning of the lesson. **See margin.**

    How are inequalities used in studying space?

    Include the following in your answer:
    • inequalities comparing the weight of two astronauts on Mars and on the moon, and
    • an explanation of how the Multiplication and Division Properties of Inequality can be used to compare planets' gravities.

NEW YORK Test Practice

Standardized Test Practice
Ⓐ Ⓑ Ⓒ Ⓓ

42. Which number is *not* a possible length of the rectangle if the area is less than 36 square inches? **D**
    Ⓐ 6   Ⓑ 7
    Ⓒ 8   Ⓓ 9

43. **GRID IN** Jessica is putting water into a 20-gallon fish tank using a 2-quart pitcher. How many pitchers of water will she need to fill the tank? **40**

Maintain Your Skills

Mixed Review **ALGEBRA** Solve each inequality. Check your solution. *(Lesson 7-4)*

44. $-4 + x > 23$ **$x > 27$**   45. $c + 18 \leq -2$ **$c \leq -20$** 46. $6 > n - 10$ **$n < 16$**

47. Write an inequality for *2 times a number is at most 14.* *(Lesson 7-3)* **$2n \leq 14$**

Find each product. Write in simplest form. *(Lesson 5-3)*

48. $\frac{1}{8} \cdot \frac{3}{4}$ **$\frac{3}{32}$**   49. $-\frac{3}{7} \cdot \frac{5}{9}$ **$-\frac{5}{21}$**   50. $2\frac{1}{2} \cdot \left(-\frac{5}{6}\right)$ **$-2\frac{1}{12}$** 51. $\frac{ab}{2} \cdot \frac{4}{bc}$ **$\frac{2a}{c}$**

Getting Ready for the Next Lesson **PREREQUISITE SKILL** **ALGEBRA** Solve each equation.
(To review **two-step equations**, see Lesson 3-5.)

52. $2x + 3 = 9$ **3**   53. $5a - 6 = 14$ **4**   54. $3n - 8 = -26$ **-6**
55. $\frac{t}{3} + 5 = 2$ **-9**   56. $\frac{c}{4} - 1 = 4$ **20**   57. $\frac{d}{2} + 3 = 19$ **32**

Practice Quiz 2   Lessons 7-3 through 7-5

Graph each inequality on a number line. *(Lesson 7-3)* **1–2. See margin.**

1. $x < -3$ 2. $y \geq 5$

Solve each inequality. Check your solution. *(Lessons 7-4 and 7-5)*

3. $a - 26 \leq 14$ **$a \leq 40$**   4. $46 + k > -8$ **$k > -54$** 5. $115 \leq -9 + n$ **$n \geq 124$** 6. $2.5 > 5r$ **$r < 0.5$**
7. $\frac{r}{5} < -45$ **$r < -225$**   8. $-\frac{s}{8} < -80$ **$s > 640$**   9. $-12g \geq -84$ **$g \leq 7$**   10. $5w \geq -2$ **$w \geq -0.4$**

Answer

41. Inequalities can be used to compare the weights of objects on different planets. Answers should include the following.
    • Comparing the weight of an astronaut in a space suit on Mars to the same astronaut on the moon: $113 > 50$.
    • If you multiply or divide the astronaut's weight by the same number, the inequality comparing the weights on different planets would still be true.

Answers (Practice Quiz 2)

1.

2.

Solving Multi-Step Inequalities

NEW YORK *Performance Indicator* **8.A.13** Solve multi-step inequalities and graph the solution set on a number line

What You'll Learn

- Solve inequalities that involve more than one operation.

How are multi-step inequalities used in backpacking?

Nearly 10 million Americans go backpacking each year. According to a fitness magazine, to avoid injury, three times the weight of your backpack and its contents should be less than your body weight.

a. Write an inequality that represents the relationship between body weight and a safe total backpack and contents weight. $3(p + c) < b$

b. Suppose you weigh 120 pounds and your empty backpack weighs 5 pounds. Write an inequality that represents the maximum weight you can safely carry in the backpack. $3(5 + c) < 120$

INEQUALITIES WITH MORE THAN ONE OPERATION Some inequalities involve more than one operation. To solve the inequality, work backward to undo the operations, just as you did in solving multi-step equations.

Example 1 Solve a Two-Step Inequality

Solve $6x + 15 > 9$ and check your solution. Graph the solution on a number line.

$6x + 15 > 9$	Write the inequality.
$6x + 15 - 15 > 9 - 15$	Subtract 15 from each side.
$6x > -6$	Simplify.
$x > -1$	Mentally divide each side by 6.

To check your solution, try 0, a number greater than -1.

CHECK	$6x + 15 > 9$	Write the inequality.
	$6(0) + 15 > 9$	Replace x with 0.
	$0 + 15 > 9$	Simplify.
	$15 > 9$ ✓	The solution checks.

Graph the solution, $x > -1$.

Number line from -5 to 5 with open circle at -1 and arrow pointing right.

$$-5 \quad -4 \quad -3 \quad -2 \quad -1 \quad 0 \quad 1 \quad 2 \quad 3 \quad 4 \quad 5$$

Study Tip

Common Misconception
Do not reverse the inequality sign just because there is a negative sign in the inequality. Only reverse the sign when you multiply or divide by a negative number.

---

1 Focus

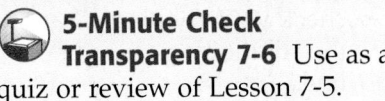

5-Minute Check Transparency 7-6 Use as a quiz or review of Lesson 7-5.

Mathematical Background notes are available for this lesson on page 326D.

How are multi-step inequalities used in backpacking?

The opening activity questions are repeated on page 395 of the *Chapter 7 Resource Masters*.

Reading to Learn Mathematics, p. 395 — ELL

Pre-Activity *How are multi-step inequalities used in backpacking?*

Do the activity at the top of page 355 in your textbook. Write your answers below.

a. Write an inequality that represents the relationship between body weight and a safe total backpack and contents weight. $3(p + c) < b$

b. Suppose you weigh 120 pounds and your empty backpack weighs 5 pounds. Write an inequality that represents the maximum weight you can safely carry in the backpack. $3(5 + c) < 120$

Reading the Lesson

Fill in the blank with the term or phrase that best completes each statement.

1. Solving multi-step inequalities is much like solving multi-step __equations__ .

2. To solve a multi-step inequality, you should work __backward__ to undo the operations.

3. The first step in solving an inequality that contains parentheses is to __use the Distributive Property__ .

4. Remember to __reverse__ the inequality symbol when multiplying or dividing both sides of the inequality by a negative number.

5. To check the solution $x > 14$, you should try a number __greater__ than 14 in the original inequality.

Helping You Remember

6. Fill in the flow chart for solving an inequality such as $-4(d + 2) \geq -8d - 32$ using the steps listed below. Write the letter of the correct step in the appropriate box on the flow chart.
   a. Multiply or divide both sides by the coefficient of the variable
   b. Use the Distributive Property
   c. Add or subtract a term with the variable from both sides
   d. Reverse the inequality sign if necessary
   e. Add or subtract a constant term from both sides

Flow chart boxes: b, c, Simplify, e, Simplify, a, d, Simplify

---

Resource Manager

Workbooks and Reproducible Masters

Chapter 7 Resource Masters
- Study Guide and Intervention, p. 392
- Skills Practice, p. 393
- Practice, p. 394
- Reading to Learn Mathematics, p. 395
- Enrichment, p. 396
- Assessment, p. 412

Graphing Calculator and Spreadsheet Masters, p. 31
Parent and Student Study Guide Workbook, p. 59
Prerequisite Skills Workbook, pp. 1–2
School-to-Career Masters, p. 14

Transparencies
5-Minute Check Transparency 7-6
Answer Key Transparencies

Technology
Interactive Chalkboard
Pre-AlgePASS: Tutorial Plus, Lesson 21

2 Teach

INEQUALITIES WITH MORE THAN ONE OPERATION

In-Class Examples   Power Point®

1 Solve $5x + 13 > 83$ and check your solution. Graph the solution on a number line. $x > 14$

$$\begin{array}{ccccc} \xleftarrow{\hspace{0.5cm}} & | & | & \oplus & | & | & \xrightarrow{\hspace{0.5cm}} \\ & 12 & 13 & 14 & 15 & 16 \end{array}$$

2 Solve $7 - 4a \le 23 - 2a$ and check your solution. Graph the solution on a number line. $a \ge -8$

$$\begin{array}{ccccc} \xleftarrow{\hspace{0.5cm}} & \bullet\!\!-\!\!-\!\!-\!\!- & \xrightarrow{\hspace{0.5cm}} \\ -10 & -9 & -8 & -7 & -6 \end{array}$$

3 A person weighing 213 pounds has a 10-pound backpack. Refer to the application at the beginning of page 355 in the student text. What is the maximum weight for the contents of the pack? **The weight of the contents should be less than 61 pounds.**

Teaching Tip Remind students that $4 > a$ is the same as $a < 4$.

✓ Skills Check

Inequalities with More than One Operation Solve $-4(h - 3) \le 32$ and check your solution. $h \ge -5$

Remember that you must reverse the inequality symbol if you multiply or divide each side of an inequality by a negative number.

Example 2   *Reverse the Inequality Symbol*

Solve $10 - 3a \le 25 + 2a$ and check your solution. Graph the solution on a number line.

$$\begin{array}{ll} 10 - 3a \le 25 + 2a & \text{Write the inequality.} \\ 10 - 3a - 2a \le 25 + 2a - 2a & \text{Subtract } 2a \text{ from each side.} \\ 10 - 5a \le 25 & \text{Simplify.} \\ 10 - 10 - 5a \le 25 - 10 & \text{Subtract 10 from each side.} \\ -5a \le 15 & \text{Simplify.} \\ \dfrac{-5a}{-5} \ge \dfrac{15}{-5} & \text{Divide each side by } -5 \text{ and change} \le \text{to} \ge \\ a \ge -3 & \text{Simplify.} \end{array}$$

[Reverse the inequality in this step.] →

CHECK
$$\begin{array}{ll} 10 - 3a \le 25 + 2a & \text{Try } -2, \text{ a number greater than } -3. \\ 10 - 3(-2) \overset{?}{\le} 25 + 2(-2) & \text{Replace } a \text{ with } -2. \\ 10 + 6 \overset{?}{\le} 25 - 4 & \text{Simplify.} \\ 16 \le 21 \checkmark & \text{The solution checks.} \end{array}$$

Graph the solution, $a \ge -3$.

$$\begin{array}{c} \xleftarrow{\hspace{0.3cm}} | \;\bullet\!\!-\!\!-\!\!-\!\!-\!\!-\!\!-\!\!-\!\!-\!\!-\!\!- \xrightarrow{\hspace{0.3cm}} \\ -5\,-4\,-3\,-2\,-1\;\;0\;\;1\;\;2\;\;3\;\;4\;\;5 \end{array}$$

When inequalities contain grouping symbols, you can use the Distributive Property to begin simplifying the inequality.

Example 3   *Inequalities with Grouping Symbols*

BACKPACKING A person weighing 126 pounds has a 6-pound backpack. Refer to the application at the beginning of page 355. What is the maximum weight for the contents of the pack?

Let c represent the weight of the contents of the pack.

Words	3	times	weight of pack and contents	should be less than	body weight.
Inequality	3	·	$(6 + c)$	$<$	126

Solve the inequality.

$$\begin{array}{ll} 3(6 + c) < 126 & \text{Write the inequality.} \\ 18 + 3c < 126 & \text{Use the Distributive Property.} \\ 18 + 3c - 18 < 126 - 18 & \text{Subtract 18 from each side.} \\ 3c < 108 & \text{Simplify.} \\ \dfrac{3c}{3} < \dfrac{108}{3} & \text{Divide each side by 3.} \\ c < 36 & \text{Simplify.} \end{array}$$

The weight of the contents should be less than 36 pounds.

✓ **Concept Check**   Undo the operations in reverse order.   How do you solve an inequality with more than one operation?

Backpacking
One of the most popular treks for backpackers is Yosemite National Park in California's High Sierra. It is possible to hike there for two weeks and never see a road!
Source: www.gorp.com

DAILY
INTERVENTION   **Differentiated Instruction**

- **Intrapersonal** Have students make a journal entry that includes the steps in solving a multi-step inequality, what they find most difficult about solving such problems, any hints they have learned to aid them, and what they need to do or practice to become more proficient at solving such inequalities.

Check for Understanding

Concept Check
. See margin.

1. **OPEN ENDED**   Explain how to check the solution of an inequality.

2. **Write** an inequality for the model at the right. Then solve the inequality.
$2x + 3 < 7; x < 2$

3. **FIND THE ERROR**   Jerome and Ryan are beginning to solve $2(2y + 3) > y + 1$.

Jerome	Ryan
$2(2y + 3) > y + 1$	$2(2y + 3) > y + 1$
$4y + 6 > y + 1$	$4y + 3 > y + 1$

Who is correct? Explain your reasoning. **See margin.**

Guided Practice

Solve each inequality and check your solution. Then graph the solution on a number line. **4–11. See pp. 365A–365D for graphs.**

GUIDED PRACTICE KEY	
Exercises	Examples
4–6, 12	1
7–9	2
10, 11	3

4. $3x + 4 \le 31$ $x \le 9$

5. $2n + 5 > 11 - n$ $n > 2$

6. $y + 1 \ge 4y + 4$ $y \le -1$

7. $16 - 2c < 14$ $c > 1$

8. $-6.1n \ge 3.9n + 5$ $n \le -0.5$

9. $-4 \le \frac{x}{4} - 6$ $x \ge 8$

10. $-3(b - 1) > 18$ $b < -5$

11. $\frac{1}{2}(2d + 3) < -8$ $d < -9\frac{1}{2}$

Application

12. **MONEY**   Dante's telephone company charges $10 a month plus $0.05 for every minute or part of a minute. Dante wants his monthly bill to be under $30. What is the greatest number of minutes he can talk? **399 min**

★ indicates increased difficulty

Practice and Apply

Homework Help	
For Exercises	See Examples
13–18, 25, 26	1
19, 20, 27, 28	2
21–24, 29, 30, 33–36	3

Extra Practice
See page 741.

Solve each inequality and check your solution. Then graph the solution on a number line. **13–28. See pp. 365A–365D for graphs.**

13. $2x + 8 > 24$ $x > 8$

14. $3y - 1 \le 5$ $y \le 2$

15. $3 + 4c > -13$ $c > -4$

16. $9 + 2p \le 15$ $p \le 3$

17. $3x - 2 > 10 - x$ $x > 3$

18. $c - 1 < 3c + 5$ $c > -3$

19. $4 - 3k \le 19$ $k \ge -5$

20. $16 - 4n > 20$ $n < -1$

21. $2(n + 3) < -4$ $n < -5$

22. $2(d + 1) > 16$ $d > 7$

23. $8 + 3b \le 2(9 - b)$ $b \le 2$

24. $\frac{m}{2} + 9 \ge 5$ $m \ge -8$

25. $2 + 0.3y \ge 11$ $y \ge 30$

26. $0.5a - 1.4 \le 2.1$ $a \le 7$

27. $\frac{1}{2}(6 - c) > 5$ $c < -4$

28. $\frac{2}{3}(9 - x) < 3$ $x > 4.5$

29. Four times a number less 6 is greater than two times the same number plus 8. For what number or numbers is this true? $n > 7$

30. One-half of the sum of a number and 6 is less than 25. What is the number? $n < 44$

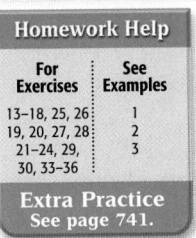

Study Notebook

Have students—
• write out several examples of inequalities that require two steps to solve and label each step with the operation being undone.
• include any other item(s) that they find helpful in mastering the skills in this lesson.

DAILY
INTERVENTION **FIND THE ERROR**
   If students are having difficulty with solving inequalities that contain grouping symbols, discuss and practice using the Distributive Property.

About the Exercises . . .
Odd/Even Assignments
Exercises 13–40 are structured so that students practice the same concepts whether they are assigned odd or even problems.

Assignment Guide
Basic: 13–33 odd, 37, 39, 43, 45–48, 50–63

Average: 13–43 odd, 45–48, 50–63 (Optional: 49)

Advanced: 14–44 even, 45–63

Answers

1. Check the solution by replacing the variable with a number in the solution. If the inequality is true, the solution checks.

3. Jerome is correct. By the Distributive Property $2(2y + 3) = 4y + 6$ not $4y + 3$.

DAILY
INTERVENTION   **Unlocking Misconceptions**

• **Solving Inequalities with Fractions**   When solving inequalities with fractions, it is common for students to take only one approach to problem solving. Have students solve problems like those in Exercises 35 and 36 by finding least common denominators, by multiplying each side of the equation by the least common denominator, and by cross multiplication.

Solve each inequality and check your solution. Graph the solution on a number line. 31–36. See margin for graphs.

31. $1.3n + 6.7 \ge 3.1n - 1.4$ $n \le 4.5$
32. $-5a + 3 > 3a + 23$ $a < -2.5$
33. $-5(t + 4) \ge 3(t - 4)$ $t \le -1$
34. $8x - (x - 5) > x + 17$ $x > 2$
★35. $\frac{c + 8}{4} < \frac{5 - c}{9}$ $c < -4$
★36. $\frac{2(n + 1)}{7} \ge \frac{n + 4}{5}$ $n \ge 6$

For Exercises 37–40, write and solve an inequality.

37. **CANDY** You buy some candy bars at $0.55 each and one newspaper for $0.35. How many candy bars can you buy with $2?
$0.55c + 0.35 \le 2$; 3 candy bars

38. **SCHOOL** Nate has scores of 85, 91, 89, and 93 on four tests. What is the least number of points he can get on the fifth test to have an average of at least 90? $(85 + 91 + 89 + 93 + p) \div 5 \ge 90$; 92 points

39. **SALES** You earn $2.00 for every magazine subscription you sell plus a salary of $10 each week. How many subscriptions do you need to sell each week to earn at least $40 each week? $2s + 10 \ge 40$, 15 subscriptions

40. **REAL ESTATE** A real estate agent receives a monthly salary of $1500 plus a 4% commission on every home sold. For what amount of monthly sales will the agent earn at least $5000? $1500 + 0.04s \ge 5000$; $87,500

★41. **CAR RENTAL** The costs for renting a car from Able Car Rental and from Baker Car Rental are shown in the table. For what mileage does Baker have the better deal? Use the inequality $30 + 0.05x > 20 + 0.10x$. Explain why this inequality works.
$x < 200$; See margin for explanation.

Rental Car Costs		
	Cost per Day	Cost per Mile
Able Car Rental	$30	$0.05
Baker Car Rental	$20	$0.10

42. **HIKING** You hike along the Appalachian Trail at 3 miles per hour. You stop for one hour for lunch. You want to walk at least 18 miles. How many hours should you expect to spend on the trail? **at least 7 h**

43. **PHONE SERVICES** Miko was asked by FoneCom to sign up for their service at $15 per month plus $0.10 per minute. Miko currently has BestPhone service at $20 per month plus $0.05 per minute. Miko figures that her monthly bill would be more with FoneCom. For how many minutes per month does she use the phone? **more than 100 minutes**

★44. **FUND-RAISERS** The Booster Club sells football programs for $1 each. The costs to make the programs are $60 for page layout plus $0.20 for printing each program. If they print 400 programs, how many programs must the Club sell to make at least $200 profit? **at least 340**

45. **CRITICAL THINKING** Assume that k is an integer. Solve the inequality $10 - 2|k| > 4$. $k < 3$ and $k > -3$, or $k = \{-2, -1, 0, 1, 2\}$

Career Choices

Real Estate Agent

Real estate agents help people with one of the most important financial decisions of their lives—buying and selling a home. All states require prospective agents to pass a written test, which usually contains a section on mathematics.

Online Research
For information about a career as a real estate agent, visit: www.pre-alg.com/careers

Answers

31.
32.
33.
34.
35.
36.

46. WRITING IN MATH Answer the question that was posed at the beginning of the lesson. **See margin.**

How are multi-step inequalities used in backpacking?

Include the following in your answer:
- an explanation of what multi-step inequalities are, and
- a solution of the inequality you wrote for part **b** on page 355.

NEW YORK
Test Practice

*Standardized
Test Practice*
Ⓐ Ⓑ Ⓒ Ⓓ

47. Which inequality represents *five more than twice a number is less than ten*? **D**

Ⓐ $(5 + 2)n < 10$ Ⓑ $2n - 5 < 10$

Ⓒ $10 < 2n + 5$ Ⓓ $5 + 2n < 10$

48. Enola's scores on the first five science tests are shown in the table. Which inequality represents the score she must receive on the sixth test to have an average score of more than 88? **D**

Test	Score
1	85
2	84
3	90
4	95
5	88

Ⓐ $s \geq 86$ Ⓑ $s \leq 88$

Ⓒ $s < 88$ Ⓓ $s > 86$

Extending ★ the Lesson
49. The sum of three times a number and 5 lies between –10 and 8. Solve the *compound inequality* $-10 < 3x + 5 < 8$ to find the solution(s). (*Hint:* Any operation must be done to all three parts of the inequality.)
$-5 < x < 1$

Maintain Your Skills

Mixed Review **ALGEBRA Solve each inequality. Check your solution.** *(Lessons 7-4 and 7-5)*

50. $20 < -9 + k$ **$k > 29$**   **51.** $22 \leq -15 + y$ **$y \geq 37$**

52. $6x < -27$ **$x < -4.5$**   **53.** $-5n \geq -25$ **$n \leq 5$**

54. $\frac{n}{-4} \leq -11$ **$n \geq 44$**   **55.** $\frac{a}{-3} > 6.2$ **$a < -18.6$**

56. If 12 of the 20 students in a class are boys, what percent are boys? *(Lesson 6-5)* **60%**

57. Write $\frac{1}{200}$ as a percent. *(Lesson 6-4)* **0.5%**

Express each ratio as a unit rate. *(Lesson 6-1)*

58. $5 for 2 loaves of bread **$2.50 a loaf**   **59.** 200 miles on 12 gallons **$16.\overline{6}$ mpg**

60. 24 meters in 4 seconds
    6 meters per second
    61. 9 monthly issues for $11.25
    $1.25 an issue

GEOMETRY Find the missing dimension in each rectangle. *(Lesson 3-7)*

62.   **6.4 ft**   **63.**   **6 m**

18.4 ft

w

Perimeter = 49.6 ft

ℓ

5.1 m | Area = 30.6 m²

Open-Ended Assessment
Speaking Have students describe the similarities and differences between solving multi-step equations and inequalities.

Assessment Options
Quiz (Lesson 7-6) is available on p. 412 of the *Chapter 7 Resource Masters.*

Answers

41. Sample explanation: The inequality finds at what mileage Able's charge is greater than Baker's charge.

46. Multi-step inequalities are used to find the amount of weight a certain person can carry in proportion to that person's body weight. Answers should include the following.
- Multi-step inequalities are inequalities that involve more than one operation.
- $c < 35$

Vocabulary and Concept Check

- This alphabetical list of vocabulary terms in Chapter 7 includes a page reference where each term was introduced.

- **Assessment** A vocabulary review/test for Chapter 7 is available on p. 410 of the *Chapter 7 Resource Masters*.

Lesson-by-Lesson Review

For each lesson,

- the main ideas are summarized,
- additional examples review concepts, and
- practice exercises are provided.

Vocabulary PuzzleMaker

ELL The Vocabulary PuzzleMaker software improves students' mathematics vocabulary using four puzzle formats—crossword, scramble, word search using a word list, and word search using clues. Students can work on a computer screen or from a printed handout.

MindJogger Videoquizzes

ELL MindJogger Videoquizzes provide an alternative review of concepts presented in this chapter. Students work in teams in a game show format to gain points for correct answers. The questions are presented in three rounds.

Round 1 Concepts (5 questions)
Round 2 Skills (4 questions)
Round 3 Problem Solving (4 questions)

Chapter 7 Study Guide and Review

Vocabulary and Concept Check

identity (p. 336)   inequality (p. 340)   null or empty set (p. 336)

Determine whether each statement is *true* or *false*. If false, replace the underlined word or number to make a true statement. 3. false; identity 4. false; Multiplication

1. When an equation has no solution, the solution set is the <u>null set</u>. **true**

2. The inequality $n + 8 - 8 \geq 14 - 8$ demonstrates the <u>Subtraction</u> Property of Inequality. **true**

3. An equation that is true for every value of the variable is called an <u>inequality</u>.

4. The inequality $\frac{x}{4}(4) < 7(4)$ demonstrates the <u>Division</u> Property of Inequality.

5. A mathematical sentence that contains $<$ or $>$ is called an <u>empty set</u>. **false; inequality**

6. When the final result in solving an equation is $5 = -8$, the solution set is the <u>null set</u>. **true**

7. When the final result in solving an equation is $x = x$, the solution set is <u>all numbers</u>. **true**

8. To solve $3(x + 5) = 10$, use the <u>Distributive Property</u> to remove the parentheses. **true**

9. The symbol $\geq$ means <u>is less than or equal to</u>. **false; is greater than or equal to**

10. A closed circle on a number line indicates that the point <u>is included</u> in the solution set for the inequality. **true**

Lesson-by-Lesson Review

7-1 Solving Equations with Variables on Each Side

See pages 330–333.

Concept Summary

- Use the Addition or Subtraction Property of Equality to isolate the variables on one side of an equation.

Example **Solve $7x = 3x - 12$.**

$7x = 3x - 12$	Write the equation.
$7x - 3x = 3x - 3x - 12$	Subtract 3x from each side.
$4x = -12$	Simplify.
$x = -3$	Mentally divide each side by 4.

Exercises Solve each equation. Check your solution.
See Example 1 on page 330. **17. −1**

11. $2a + 9 = 5a$ **3**	12. $x - 4 = 3x$ **−2**	13. $3y - 8 = y$ **4**
14. $19t = 26 + 6t$ **2**	15. $2 + 7n = 8 + n$ **1**	16. $5 + 6t = 10t - 7$ **3**
17. $-r + 4.2 = 8.8r + 14$	18. $12 + 1.5x = 9x$ **1.6**	19. $5b - 1 = 2.5b - 4$ **−1.2**

 www.pre-alg.com/vocabulary_review

FOLDABLES™
Study Organizer

For more information about Foldables, see *Teaching Mathematics with Foldables.*

Have students review their Foldables and reexamine the questions they wrote for each lesson. They should also reexamine the answers they recorded under each lesson's tab. Have them refer to their Foldables as they prepare for the Chapter Test.

7-2 Solving Equations with Grouping Symbols

See pages 334–338.

Concept Summary

- Use the Distributive Property to remove the grouping symbols.

Example Solve $2(x + 3) = 15$.

$2(x + 3) = 15$ Write the equation.

$2x + 6 = 15$ Use the Distributive Property.

$2x = 9$ Subtract 6 from each side and simplify.

$x = 4.5$ Divide each side by 2 and simplify.

Exercises Solve each equation. *See Examples 1–4 on pages 334–336.* **25. all numbers**

20. $4(k + 1) = 16$ **3**   **21.** $2(n - 5) = 8$ **9**   **22.** $11 + 2q = 2(q + 4)$ **Ø**

23. $\frac{1}{2}(t + 8) = \frac{3}{4}t$ **16**   **24.** $4(x + 2.5) = 3(7 + x)$ **11** **25.** $3(x + 1) - 5 = 3x - 2$

7-3 Inequalities

See pages 340–344.

Concept Summary

- An inequality is a mathematical sentence that contains $<, >, \leq$, or $\geq$.

Example State whether $n + 11 < 14$ is *true* or *false* for $n = 5$.

$n + 11 < 14$ Write the inequality.

$5 + 11 \overset{?}{<} 14$ Replace n with 5.

$16 \not< 14$ Simplify.   The sentence is false.

Exercises For the given value, state whether each inequality is *true* or *false*.
See Example 4 on page 341.

26. $x + 4 > 9, x = 12$ **true** **27.** $15 \leq 5n, n = 3$ **true**   **28.** $3n + 1 \geq 14, n = 4$ **false**

7-4 Solving Inequalities by Adding or Subtracting

See pages 345–349.

Concept Summary

- Solving an inequality means finding values for the variable that make the inequality true.

Example Solve $x - 7 < 3$. Graph the solution on a number line.

$x - 7 < 3$ Write the inequality.

$x - 7 + 7 < 3 + 7$ Add 7 to each side.

$x < 10$ Simplify.

Exercises Solve each inequality. Graph the solution on a number line.
See Examples 1 and 2 on page 346. **29–31. See margin for graphs.**

29. $b - 9 \geq 8$ $b \geq 17$ **30.** $x + 4.8 \leq 2$ $x \leq -2.8$ **31.** $t + \frac{1}{2} < 4$ $t < 3\frac{1}{2}$

Answers

29.

14 16 18 20 22 24

30.

-3 -2.6 -2.2 -1.8 -1.4 -1

31.

0 1 2 3 4 5

Study Guide and Review

Chapter 7 For More ...
- Extra Practice, see pages 739–741.
- Mixed Problem Solving, see page 764.

Answers

32.
20 22 24 26 28

33.
−1 0 1 2 3 4 5 6 7 8 9

34.
2   4   6   8   10   12

35.
−12 −10 −8 −6 −4

36.
−40 −38 −36 −34 −32

37.
−4 −2 0 2 4 6

Answers (p. 363)

1. An open circle is used when the inequality symbol is $<$ or $>$; a closed circle is used when the inequality symbol is $\leq$ or $\geq$.

2. When an inequality is multiplied or divided by a negative number, the direction of the inequality symbol is reversed.

18.
−4 −3 −2 −1 0 1 2 3 4

19.
1 2 3 4 5 6 7 8 9

20.
10   30   50   70   90

21.
−10 −8 −6 −4 −2

22.
−4 −3 −2 −1 0 1 2 3 4

23.
−20 −18 −16 −14 −12

7-5 Solving Inequalities by Multiplying or Dividing

See pages 350–354.

Concept Summary

- When you multiply or divide each side of an inequality by a positive number, the inequality symbol remains the same.
- When you multiply or divide each side of an inequality by a negative number, the inequality symbol must be reversed.

Examples 1 Solve $\frac{a}{3} > 2$. Graph the solution on a number line.

$\frac{a}{3} > 2$	Write the inequality.
$3\left(\frac{a}{3}\right) > 3(2)$	Multiply each side by 3.
$a > 6$	Simplify.

2   4   6   8   10

The solution is $a > 6$.

2 Solve $-2n \geq 26$. Graph the solution on a number line.

$-2n \geq 26$	Write the inequality.
$\frac{-2n}{-2} \leq \frac{26}{-2}$	Divide each side by -2 and reverse the symbol.
$n \leq -13$	Simplify.

−18 −16 −14 −12 −10

The solution is $n \leq -13$.

Exercises Solve each inequality. Graph the solution on a number line. *See Examples 1 and 3 on pages 351 and 352.* **32–37. See margin for graphs.**

32. $\frac{n}{4} < 6$ **$n < 24$**   **33.** $\frac{k}{1.7} \leq 3$ **$k \leq 5.1$**   **34.** $0.5x > 3.2$ **$x > 6.4$**

35. $-56 \geq 8y$ **$y \leq -7$**   **36.** $9 > \frac{x}{-4}$ **$x > -36$**   **37.** $-\frac{5}{6}a \leq 2$ **$a \geq -2\frac{2}{5}$**

7-6 Solving Multi-Step Inequalities

See pages 355–359.

Concept Summary

- To solve an inequality that involves more than one operation, work backward to undo the operations.

Example Solve $4t + 7 < -5$.

$4t + 7 < -5$	Write the inequality.
$4t + 7 - 7 < -5 - 7$	Subtract 7 from each side.
$4t < -12$	Simplify.
$t < -3$	Mentally divide each side by 4.

The solution is $t < -3$.

Exercises Solve each inequality. *See Examples 1 and 2 on pages 355 and 356.*

38. $2x - 3 > 19$ **$x > 11$**   **39.** $5n + 4 \leq 24$ **$n \leq 4$**   **40.** $6 \geq \frac{r}{7} + 1$ **$r \leq 35$**

41. $\frac{t}{-2} + 15 < 21$ **$t > -12$** **42.** $3(a + 8.4) > 30$ **$a > 1.6$** **43.** $\frac{1}{4} + 2b < 13 + 5b$ **$b > -4\frac{1}{4}$**

Vocabulary and Concepts

1. **State** when to use an open circle and a closed circle in graphing an inequality. **See margin.**
2. **Describe** what happens to an inequality when each side is multiplied or divided by a negative number. **See margin.**

Skills and Applications

Solve each equation. Check your solution.

3. $7x - 3 = 10x$ **−1**
4. $p - 9 = 4p$ **−3**
5. $2.3n - 8 = 1.2n + 3$ **10**
6. $\frac{3}{8}y - 5 = \frac{5}{8}y - 3$ **−8**
7. $6 + 2(x - 4) = 2(x - 1)$ **all numbers**
8. $2(6 - 5d) = 8$ **0.4**
9. $8(2x - 9) = 4(5 + 4x)$ **∅**
10. $4(a + 3) = 20$ **2**
11. $\frac{1}{3}(9b + 1) = b - 1$ **$-\frac{2}{3}$**

Define a variable and write an equation to find each number. Then solve.

12. Eight more than three times a number equals four less than the number. **$3x + 8 = x - 4$; −6**
13. The product of a number and five is twelve more than the number. **$5x = x + 12$; 3**

14. **GEOMETRY** The perimeter of the rectangle is 22 feet. Find the dimensions of the rectangle. **2.5 ft by 8.5 ft**

w
$2w + 3.5$

15. **SHOPPING** The cost of purchasing four shirts is at least $120. Write an inequality to describe this situation. **$4s \geq 120$**

Write the inequality for each graph.

16. $x > 4$
   −2 0 2 4 6

17. $x \leq -1$
   −6 −4 −2 0 2 4

Solve each inequality and check your solution. Then graph the solution on a number line. 18–23. See margin for graphs.

18. $-4 \geq p - 2$ **$p \leq -2$**
19. $3x \geq 15$ **$x \geq 5$**
20. $-42 < -0.6x$ **$x < 70$**
21. $c - 3 \leq 4c + 9$ **$c \geq -4$**
22. $7(3 - 2b) > 5b + 2$ **$b < 1$**
23. $\frac{1}{2}(a + 4) > \frac{1}{4}(a - 8)$ **$a > -16$**

24. **SALES** The Cookie Factory has a fixed cost of $300 per month plus $0.45 for each cookie sold. Each cookie sells for $0.95. How many cookies must be sold during one month for the profit to be at least $100? **at least 800 cookies**

25. **STANDARDIZED TEST PRACTICE** Danny earns $6.50 per hour working at a movie theater. Which inequality can be used to find how many hours he must work each week to earn at least $100 a week? **D**

ORK
actice

   (A) $6.50h < 100$
   (B) $6.50h > 100$
   (C) $6.50h \leq 100$
   (D) $6.50h \geq 100$

Portfolio Suggestion

Introduction The ability to translate words into equations or inequalities is an important skill that applies mathematics to real-life situations. This chapter featured word problems that required increasingly more complex equations/inequalities to solve.

Ask Students to choose their favorite word problem from the chapter and place it in their portfolio. They should attach a note explaining why it is their favorite.

Assessment Options

Vocabulary Test A vocabulary review/test for Chapter 7 can be found on p. 410 of the *Chapter 7 Resource Masters.*

Chapter Tests There are six Chapter 7 Tests and an Open-Ended Assessment task available in the *Chapter 7 Resource Masters.*

Chapter 7 Tests			
Form	Type	Level	Pages
1	MC	basic	397–398
2A	MC	average	399–400
2B	MC	average	401–402
2C	FR	average	403–404
2D	FR	average	405–406
3	FR	advanced	407–408

MC = multiple-choice questions
FR = free-response questions

Open-Ended Assessment
Performance tasks for Chapter 7 can be found on p. 409 of the *Chapter 7 Resource Masters.* A sample scoring rubric for these tasks appears on p. A22.

ExamView® Pro

Use the networkable **ExamView® Pro** to:

- Create **multiple versions** of tests.
- Create **modified** tests for *Inclusion* students.
- **Edit** existing questions and **add** your own questions.
- Use built-in **state curriculum correlations** to create tests aligned with state standards.
- Change **English** tests to **Spanish** and vice versa.

These two pages contain practice questions in the various formats that can be found on the most frequently given standardized tests.

A practice answer sheet for these two pages can be found on page A1 of the *Chapter 7 Resource Masters*.

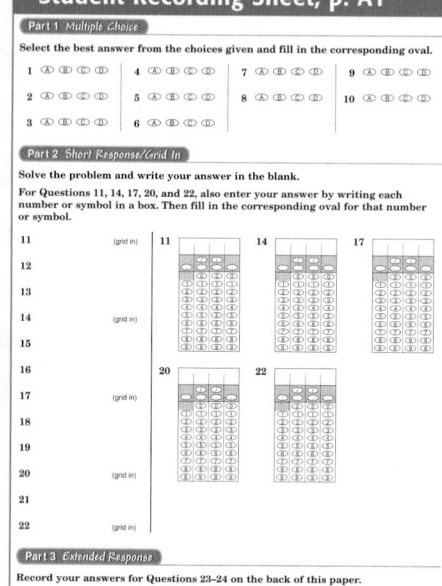

Additional Practice

See pp. 415–416 of the *Chapter 7 Resource Masters* for additional standardized test practice.

 NEW YORK
Test Practice

Part 1 Multiple Choice

Record your answers on the answer sheet provided by your teacher or on a sheet of paper.

1. A delivery service calculates the cost c of shipping a package with the equation $c = 0.30w + 6$, where w is the weight of the package in pounds. Your package weighs at least 8 pounds. What is the lowest possible cost to ship your package?   (Lesson 3-7) **B**
   - (A) $6.30
   - (B) $8.40
   - (C) $14.30
   - (D) $30.00

2. The school band traveled on two buses with 36 students on each bus. At a lunch stop, two-thirds of the students on the first bus ate at Hamburger Haven, and the others ate at Taco Time. Three-fourths of the students on the second bus ate at Hamburger Haven. How many students in all ate at Hamburger Haven?   (Lesson 5-3) **C**
   - (A) 24
   - (B) 48
   - (C) 51
   - (D) 102

3. Shanté earned $360 last summer. She spent $\frac{5}{9}$ of her earnings. How much money did she have left?   (Lesson 5-3) **B**
   - (A) $40
   - (B) $160
   - (C) $200
   - (D) $320

4. While exercising, Luke's heart is beating at 170 beats per minute. If he maintains this rate, about how many times will his heart beat in one hour?   (Lesson 6-1) **C**
   - (A) 1000
   - (B) 5000
   - (C) 10,000
   - (D) 100,000

Test-Taking Tip   (A) (B) (C) (D)
Questions 9 and 10
When an item requires you to solve an equation or inequality, plug in your solution to the original problem in order to check your answer.

5. Which of the circles has approximately the same fractional part shaded as that of the rectangle below?   (Lesson 6-4) **C**

   - (A)
   - (B)
   - (C)
   - (D)

6. Which of the following statements is true?   (Lesson 6-4) **D**
   - (A) $0.4 > 40\%$
   - (B) $0.04 = 40\%$
   - (C) $40\% \leq 0.04$
   - (D) $40\% > 0.04$

7. A survey at the MegaMall showed that 15% of visitors attend a movie while at the mall. If 8700 people are at the mall, how many of these visitors are likely to attend a movie there?   (Lesson 6-7) **C**
   - (A) 580
   - (B) 870
   - (C) 1305
   - (D) 5800

8. Last year there were 1536 students at Cortéz Middle School. This year there are 5% more students. *About* how many students attend Cortéz this year?   (Lesson 6-9) **B**
   - (A) 1550
   - (B) 1600
   - (C) 1650
   - (D) 1700

9. If $5(x + 2) = 40$, what is the value of x?   (Lesson 7-2) **B**
   - (A) 4
   - (B) 6
   - (C) 8
   - (D) 10

10. Which of the following inequalities is equivalent to $\frac{x}{3} < 5$?   (Lesson 7-5) **D**
    - (A) $x < \frac{5}{3}$
    - (B) $x < 2$
    - (C) $x > 2$
    - (D) $x < 15$

ExamView® Pro

Special banks of standardized test questions similar to those on the SAT, ACT, TIMSS 8, NAEP 8, and Pre-Algebra End-of-Course tests can be found on this CD-ROM.

Part 2 | Short Response/Grid In

Record your answers on the answer sheet provided by your teacher or on a sheet of paper.

11. What is the value of $16 + 18 \div 2 \times 3$? (Lesson 1-2) **43**

12. In 5 days, the stock market fell 25 points. What integer expresses the average change in the stock market per day? (Lesson 2-5) **−5**

13. Write $\dfrac{1}{5 \times 5 \times 5 \times 5}$ using a negative exponent. (Lesson 4-7) **5^{-4}**

14. Find $\dfrac{5}{12} - \dfrac{3}{8}$. (Lesson 5-4) **1/24**

15. The high temperatures for five days in April are shown in the table below. What was the median high temperature? (Lesson 5-8) **53°**

High Temperatures	
Monday	45°
Tuesday	62°
Wednesday	57°
Thursday	41°
Friday	53°

16. To mix a certain color of paint, Alexis combines 5 liters of white paint, 2 liters of red paint, and 1 liter of blue paint. What is the ratio of white paint to the total amount of paint? (Lesson 6-1) **5:8**

17. A box contains 42 pencils. Some are yellow, some are red, some are white, and some are black. If the probability of randomly selecting a red pencil is $\dfrac{3}{7}$, how many red pencils are in the box? (Lesson 6-2) **18**

18. A city received a federal grant of $350 million to build a light-rail system which actually cost $625 million. What percent of the total cost was paid for with the Federal grant? Round to the nearest percent. (Lesson 6-7) **56%**

19. A leather jacket is on sale for 40% off the original price. The sale price is $64 less than the original price. What was the original price of the jacket? (Lesson 6-8) **$160**

20. Find x if $8x - 12 = 5x + 6$. (Lesson 7-1) **6**

21. Find the width w of the rectangle below if its perimeter is 88 meters. (Lesson 7-2) **8 m**

$5w - 4$

w

22. Dakota earns $8 per hour working at a landscaping company and wants to earn at least $1200 this summer. What is the minimum number of hours he will have to work? (Lesson 7-5) **150**

Part 3 | Extended Response

Record your answers on a sheet of paper. Show your work.

23. At a post office, a customer bought an equal number of the following stamps: 1¢, 22¢, and 34¢. She also mailed a package that required $2.80 in postage. The total bill was $14. (Lesson 3-6) **a–d. See margin.**
    a. Write an equation that describes this situation.
    b. What does the variable in your equation represent?
    c. Solve the equation. Show your work.
    d. Write a sentence describing what the solution represents.

24. A magazine publisher collected data on subscription renewals and found that each year 3 out of 50 subscribers do *not* renew. The magazine currently has 24,000 subscribers. (Lesson 6-6)
    a. What percent of subscribers do *not* renew their subscriptions? **6%**
    b. What percent of subscribers per year do renew their subscriptions? **94%**
    c. How many subscribers will likely renew their subscriptions this year? **22,560**

Evaluating Extended Response Questions

Extended Response questions are graded by using a multilevel rubric that guides you in assessing a student's knowledge of a particular concept.

Goal: Solve problems using equations/percentages.

Sample Scoring Rubric: The following rubric is a sample scoring device. You may wish to add more detail to this sample to meet your individual scoring needs.

Score	Criteria
4	A correct solution that is supported by well-developed, accurate explanations
3	A generally correct solution, but may contain minor flaws in reasoning or computation
2	A partially correct interpretation and/or solution to the problem
1	A correct solution with no supporting evidence or explanation
0	An incorrect solution indicating no mathematical understanding of the concept or task, or no solution is given

Answer

23a. $0.01x + 0.22x + 0.34x + 2.80 = 14$

23b. the number of each kind of stamp

23c.
$$0.01x + 0.22x + 0.34x + 2.80 = 14.20$$
$$(0.01 + 0.22 + 0.34)x + 2.80 = 14.20$$
$$0.57x + 2.80 = 14.20$$
$$0.57x + 2.80 - 2.80 = 14.20 - 2.80$$
$$0.57x = 11.40$$
$$\frac{0.57x}{0.57} = \frac{11.40}{0.57}$$
$$x = 20$$

23d. The customer bought 20 of each kind of stamp.

Page 329, Algebra Activity

9.

10.

11.

12.

13.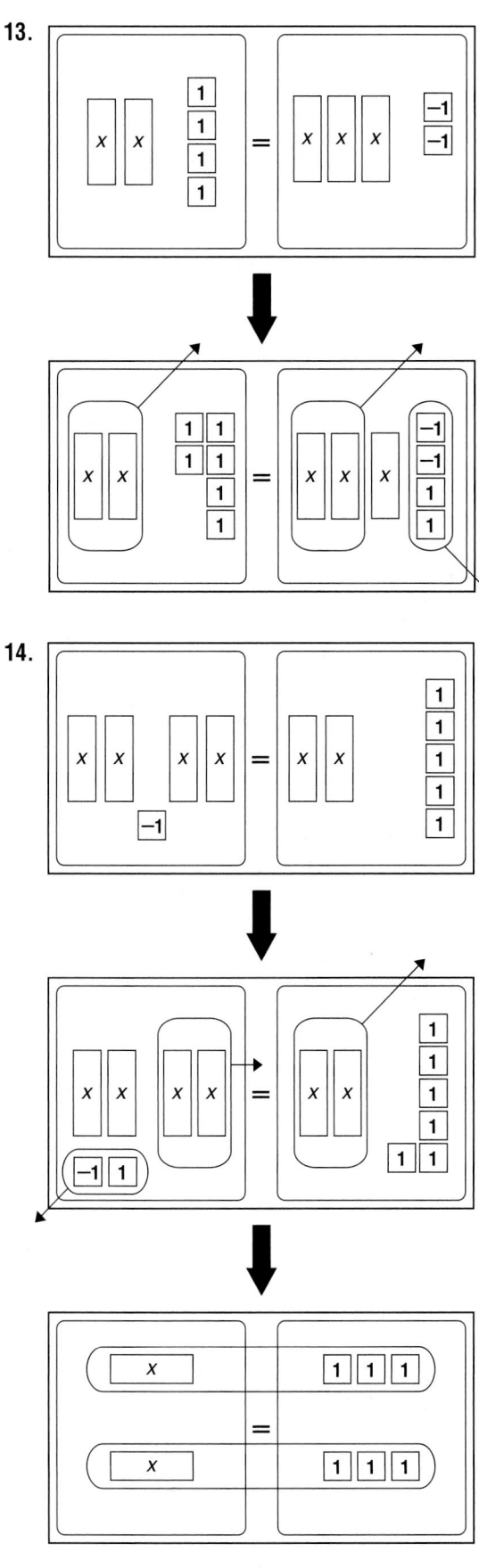

14.

Page 342, Lesson 7-3

1. A number line graph can represent all numbers greater or less than a given number.

2. Sample answer: $x < 9$ means that the value of x is less than 9; $x > 9$ means that the value of x is greater than 9; $x \leq 9$ means that the value of x is 9 or less; $x \geq 9$ means that the value of x is 9 or greater.

7.
```
←+—+—+—+—+—⊕━━━+→
  −2 −1  0  1  2  3  4  5  6
```

8.
```
←━━━━━━━━━━●—+—+→
  −2 −1  0  1  2  3  4  5  6
```

9.
```
←━━━━━━━⊕—+—+→
   1  2  3  4  5  6  7  8  9
```

Page 343, Lesson 7-3

23.
```
←+—+—+—+—⊕━━━+→
  −1  0  1  2  3  4  5  6  7
```

24.
```
←+—+—⊕━━━━━━━→
   3  4  5  6  7  8  9 10 11
```

25.
```
←━━━━━━━⊕—+—+→
   4  5  6  7  8  9 10 11 12
```

26.
```
←━━━━━━━━━⊕—+→
  −2 −1  0  1  2  3  4  5  6
```

27.
```
←+—+—+—●━━━━━━━→
   6  7  8  9 10 11 12 13 14
```

28.
```
←+—+—●━━━━━━━━→
   6  7  8  9 10 11 12 13 14
```

29.
```
←━━━━━━━━━●—+→
  −2 −1  0  1  2  3  4  5  6
```

30.
```
←━━━━━━━━━●—+—+→
   2  3  4  5  6  7  8  9 10
```

31.
```
←+—⊕━━━━━━━━→
  −6 −5 −4 −3 −2 −1  0  1  2
```

32.
```
←+—+—●━━━━━━━→
  −6 −5 −4 −3 −2 −1  0  1  2
```

33.
```
←━━━━●—+—+—+—+→
  −8 −7 −6 −5 −4 −3 −2 −1  0
```

34.
```
←━━━━⊕—+—+—+→
  −6 −5 −4 −3 −2 −1  0  1  2
```

Page 347, Lesson 7-4

10.
```
←+—+—+—+—⊕━━━+→
  −4 −3 −2 −1  0  1  2  3  4
```

11.
```
←+—+—+—●━━━━━━→
   7  8  9 10 11 12 13 14 15
```

Page 348, Lesson 7-4

31. 1 2 3 4 5 6 7 8 9

32. 1 2 3 4 5 6 7 8 9

33. 1 2 3 4 5 6 7 8 9

34. 1 2 3 4 5 6 7 8 9

35. −7 −6 −5 −4 −3 −2 −1 0 1

36. −30 −28 −26 −24 −22

37. 23 25 27 29 31

38. −31 −29 −27 −25 −23

39. 0 $\frac{1}{2}$ 1 $1\frac{1}{2}$ 2

40. 0 1 2 3 4

41. 3 4 5

42. 0 $\frac{1}{2}$ 1 $1\frac{1}{2}$ 2

Page 353, Lesson 7-5

4. 1 2 3 4 5 6 7 8 9

5. −4 −3 −2 −1 0 1 2 3 4

6. 1 2 3 4 5 6 7 8 9

7. 10 30 50 70 90

8. 3 3.2 3.4 3.6 3.8

9. −9 −8.6 −8.2 −7.8 −7.4

10. 9 10 11 12 13

11. −80 −76 −72 −68 −64

12. 20 22 24 26 28

14. −4 −3 −2 −1 0 1 2 3 4

15. 5 6 7 8 9 10 11 12 13

16. −4 −3 −2 −1 0 1 2 3 4

17. −4 −3 −2 −1 0 1 2 3 4

18. 0 4 8 12 16

19. 1 2 3 4 5 6 7 8 9

20. 10 30 50 70 90

21. 90 94 98 102 106

22. 10 12 14 16 18

23. 1 2 3 4 5 6 7 8 9

24. −10 −8 −6 −4 −2

25. −4 −3 −2 −1 0 1 2 3 4

26. −50 −46 −42 −38 −34

27. 1 2 3 4 5 6 7 8 9

28. 16 18 20 22 24

29. −20 −18 −16 −14 −12

30. 10 12 14 16 18

31. −20 −18 −16 −14 −12

32. 9.0 9.2 9.4 9.6 9.8

33. 1 2 3 4 5 6 7 8 9

34.
21 22 23 24 25

35.
5 5.2 5.4 5.6 5.8

36.
25 27 29 31 33

37.
70 74 78 82 86

Page 357, Lesson 7-6

4.
5 6 7 8 9 10 11 12 13

5.
1 2 3 4 5 6 7 8 9

6.
−4 −3 −2 −1 0 1 2 3 4

7.
−4 −3 −2 −1 0 1 2 3 4

8.
−1 0 1 2 3

9.
1 2 3 4 5 6 7 8 9

10.
−7 −6 −5 −4 −3 −2 −1 0 1

11.
−10 −9 −8 −7 −6

13.
1 2 3 4 5 6 7 8 9

14.
−4 −3 −2 −1 0 1 2 3 4

15.
−4 −3 −2 −1 0 1 2 3 4

16.
−4 −3 −2 −1 0 1 2 3 4

17.
−4 −3 −2 −1 0 1 2 3 4

18.
−4 −3 −2 −1 0 1 2 3 4

19.
−7 −6 −5 −4 −3 −2 −1 0 1

20.
−4 −3 −2 −1 0 1 2 3 4

21.
−7 −6 −5 −4 −3 −2 −1 0 1

22.
1 2 3 4 5 6 7 8 9

23.
−4 −3 −2 −1 0 1 2 3 4

24.
−10 −8 −6 −4 −2

25.
10 30 50 70 90

26.
1 2 3 4 5 6 7 8 9

27.
−10 −8 −6 −4 −2

28.
1 2 3 4 5 6 7 8 9

*An electronic version of this chapter is available on **StudentWorks™**. This backpack solution CD-ROM allows students instant access to the Student Edition, lesson worksheet pages, and web resources.*

Year-long pacing: pages T20–T21.

LESSON OBJECTIVES	PACING (days)			
	Regular		Block	
	Basic/ Average	Advanced	Basic/ Average	Advanced
8-1 Functions *(pp. 368–373)* ***Preview:*** Explore the relationship between sets of numbers by making a function machine. • Determine whether relations are functions. • Use functions to describe relationships between two quantities.	2 (with 8-1 Preview)	1	1 (with 8-1 Preview)	0.5
8-2 Linear Equations in Two Variables *(pp. 374–379)* ***Preview:*** Demonstrate an understanding of the relationship between domain and range. • Solve linear equations with two variables. • Graph linear equations using ordered pairs.	2 (with 8-2 Preview)	1	1 (with 8-2 Preview)	0.5
8-3 Graphing Linear Equations Using Intercepts *(pp. 381–385)* • Find the *x*- and *y*-intercepts of graphs. • Graph linear equations using the *x*- and *y*-intercepts.	1	1	0.5	0.5
8-4 Slope *(pp. 386–391)* ***Preview:*** Explore slope by examining how fast an object rolls down various hills. • Find the slope of a line.	2 (with 8-4 Preview)	1	1 (with 8-4 Preview)	0.5
8-5 Rate of Change *(pp. 392–397)* ***Preview:*** Explore the relationship between slope and rate of change by comparing heights of water levels in a glass. • Find rates of change. • Solve problems involving direct variation.	2 (with 8-5 Preview)	1	1 (with 8-5 Preview)	0.5
8-6 Slope-Intercept Form *(pp. 398–403)* • Determine slopes and *y*-intercepts of lines. • Graph linear equations using the slope and *y*-intercept. ***Follow-Up:*** Use a graphing calculator to investigate families of graphs.	2	2 (with 8-6 Follow-Up)	1	1 (with 8-6 Follow-Up)
8-7 Writing Linear Equations *(pp. 404–408)* • Write equations given the slope and *y*-intercept, a graph, a table, or two points.	1	1	0.5	0.5
8-8 Best-Fit Lines *(pp. 409–413)* • Draw best-fit lines for sets of data. • Use best-fit lines to make predictions about data.	2	1	1	0.5
8-9 Solving Systems of Equations *(pp. 414–418)* • Solve systems of linear equations by graphing. • Solve systems of linear equations by substitution.	2	2	1.5	1
8-10 Graphing Inequalities *(pp. 419–423)* • Graph linear inequalities. • Describe solutions of linear inequalities. ***Follow-Up:*** Use a graphing calculator to investigate graphs of inequalities.	1	2 (with 8-10 Follow-Up)	0.5	1.5 (with 8-10 Follow-Up)
Study Guide and **Practice Test** *(pp. 424–429)* **Standardized Test Practice** *(pp. 430–431)*	1	1	0.5	0.5
Chapter Assessment	1	1	0.5	0.5
TOTAL	19	15	10	8

Chapter Resource Manager

Timesaving Tools

TeacherWorks™
All-In-One Planner and Resource Center
See pages T5 and T21.

CHAPTER 8 RESOURCE MASTERS

Study Guide and Intervention	Practice (Skills and Average)	Reading to Learn Mathematics	Enrichment	Assessment	Prerequisite Skills Workbook	Applications*	Parent and Student Study Guide Workbook	5-Minute Check Transparencies	Interactive Chalkboard	Pre-AlgePASS: Tutorial Plus (lessons)	Materials
417	418–419	420	421				61	8-1	8-1	22	*Preview:* 3 x 5 index cards, scissors
422	423–424	425	426				62	8-2	8-2		
427	428–429	430	431	481		SM 4	63	8-3	8-3		
432	433–434	435	436				64	8-4	8-4	23	*Preview:* posterboard, tape, book, ruler, toy car
437	438–439	440	441	481, 483		GCS 34 SC 15	65	8-5	8-5		*Preview:* grid paper, water, beaker, metric ruler, tablespoon, $\frac{1}{8}$-cup measuring cup
442	443–444	445	446				66	8-6	8-6	24	*Follow-Up:* graphing calculator
447	448–449	450	451				67	8-7	8-7		
452	453–454	455	456	482			68	8-8	8-8		
457	458–459	460	461			GCS 33	69	8-9	8-9		
462	463–464	465	466	482	1–2	SC 16	70	8-10	8-10	25	*Follow-Up:* graphing calculator
				467–480, 484–488							

* *Key to Abbreviations:* GCS = Graphing Calculator and Spreadsheet Masters, SC = School-to-Career Masters, SM = Science and Mathematics Lab Manual

ELL Study Guide and Intervention, Skills Practice, Practice, and Parent and Student Study Guide Workbooks are also available in Spanish.

Mathematical Connections and Background

Continuity of Instruction

Prior Knowledge

Students studied relations in Chapter 1, including ordered pairs and how to determine the domain and range of a relation. Then in Chapter 2 they learned about the Cartesian coordinate system and how to locate points on a coordinate plane. In Chapter 7, students learned to write, solve, and graph inequalities.

This Chapter

Students will learn that a function is a special type of relation and that a linear equation is one of many ways to represent a function. They will learn to write linear equations and use them to solve real-world problems such as those involving rate of change. Students also will learn to graph linear equations and inequalities. They will use best-fit lines to predict data.

Future Connections

Students will study functions further in Chapter 13, examining linear and nonlinear functions. In particular, they will learn to graph quadratic and cubic functions on a coordinate plane. Graphing functions and inequalities is a skill that students will use in future mathematics courses and in engineering fields.

8-1 Functions

A function is a special relation in which each member of the domain is paired with exactly one member in the range. Functions may be represented using ordered pairs, tables, or graphs. One way to determine whether a relation is a function is to use the vertical line test. Using an object to represent a vertical line, move the object from left to right across the graph. If, for each value of x in the domain, the object passes through no more than one point on the graph, then the graph represents a function.

8-2 Linear Equations in Two Variables

In a linear equation in two variables, such as $y = x - 3$, the variables appear in separate terms and neither variable contains an exponent other than 1. The graphs of all linear equations are straight lines. All points on a line are solutions of the equation that is graphed.

8-3 Graphing Linear Equations Using Intercepts

Sets of data can be either discrete or continuous. Discrete data have a finite number of possible values, such as books or people. Continuous data usually are associated with physical measurements. In mathematics, an intercept is the point where a line crosses a coordinate axis. In graphing a linear equation, you can find, plot, and connect the points where the graph crosses the x- and y-axes.

8-4 Slope

Slope is the ratio of the rise, or vertical change, to the run, or horizontal change of a line: slope $= \frac{\text{rise}}{\text{run}}$. Slope ($m$) is the same for any two points on a straight line and can be found by using the coordinates of any two points on a line: $m = \frac{y_2 - y_1}{x_2 - x_1}$, where $x_2 \neq x_1$.

8-5 Rate of Change

A change in one quantity with respect to another quantity is called the rate of change. Rates of change can be described using slope:

$$\text{slope} = \frac{\text{change in } y}{\text{change in } x}.$$

You can find rates of change from an equation, a table of values, or a graph.

A special type of linear equation that describes rate of change is called a direct variation. The graph of a direct variation always passes through the origin and represents a proportional situation. In the equation $y = kx$, k is called the constant of variation. It is the slope, or rate of change. As x increases in value, y increases or decreases at a constant rate k, or y varies directly with x. Another way to say this is that y is directly proportional to x. The direct variation $y = kx$ also can be written as $k = \frac{y}{x}$. In this form, you can see that the ratio of y to x is the same for any corresponding values of y and x.

8-6 Slope-Intercept Form

Equations written as $y = mx + b$, where m is the slope and b is the y-intercept, are linear equations in slope-intercept form. For example, the graph of $y = 5x - 6$ is a line that has a slope of 5 and crosses the y-axis at $(0, -6)$. Sometimes you must first write an equation in slope-intercept form before finding the slope and y-intercept. For example, the equation $2x + 3y = 15$ can be expressed in slope-intercept form by subtracting $2x$ from each side and then dividing by 3: $y = -\frac{2}{3}x + 5$, revealing a slope of $-\frac{2}{3}$ and a y-intercept of 5.

8-7 Writing Linear Equations

If you know the slope and y-intercept, you can write the equation of a line by substituting these values in $y = mx + b$. For example, if a line has a slope of 2 and a y-intercept of 3, its equation can be expressed as $y = 2x + 3$. You can also use the graph of a line to write an equation. Locate the y-intercept and choose another point on the line. Find the slope between the two points. Then write the equation for the line.

You also can write an equation for a line if you know the coordinates of two points on the line by using the definition of slope: $m = \frac{y_2 - y_1}{x_2 - x_1}$.

8-8 Best-Fit Lines

When real-life data are collected, the points graphed usually do not form a straight line, but they may approximate a linear relationship. A best-fit line is a line that lies very close to most of the data points. It can be used to predict data. You also can use the equation of the best-fit line to make predictions.

8-9 Solving Systems of Equations

Two equations together are called a system of equations. The solution of a system is the ordered pair that is a solution of both equations. The system of equations can have one solution, no solution, or infinitely many solutions. One method for solving is to graph the equations on the same coordinate plane. The coordinates of the point where the graphs intersect is the solution. A more accurate way to solve a system of equations is by using a method called substitution. Write both equations in terms of y. Replace y in the first equation with the right side of the second equation.

8-10 Graphing Inequalities

To graph an inequality, first graph the related equation, which is the boundary. All points in the shaded region are solutions of the inequality. If an inequality contains the symbol $\leq$ or $\geq$, then use a solid line to indicate that the boundary is included in the graph. If an inequality contains the symbol $<$ or $>$, then use a dashed line to indicate that the boundary is not included in the graph.

Quick Review Math Handbook

Hot Words includes a glossary of terms while Hot Topics consists of explanations of key mathematical concepts with exercises to test comprehension. This valuable resource can be used as a reference in the classroom or for home study.

Lesson	Hot Topics Section	Lesson	Hot Topics Section
GS 8	6.4, 6.6, 6.7	8-5	6.4, 6.8
8-1	6.3, 6.8	8-6	1.3, 6.2, 6.8
8-2	6.7, 6.8	8-7	4.3, 6.7, 6.8
8-3	1.5, 2.3, 2.6, 6.8	8-8	4.3, 6.4
8-4	6.4, 6.8	8-10	6.6

GS = Getting Started

 Additional mathematical information and teaching notes are available at www.pre-alg.com/key_concepts.

DAILY INTERVENTION and Assessment

Key to Abbreviations:
TWE = Teacher Wraparound Edition; CRM = Chapter Resource Masters

	Type	Student Edition	Teacher Resources	Technology/Internet
INTERVENTION	Ongoing	Prerequisite Skills, pp. 367, 373, 379, 385, 391, 397, 401, 408, 413, 418 Practice Quiz 1, p. 397 Practice Quiz 2, p. 418	5-Minute Check Transparencies *Prerequisite Skills Workbook,* pp. 1–2 Quizzes, *CRM,* pp. 481, 482 Mid-Chapter Test, *CRM,* p. 483 Study Guide and Intervention, *CRM,* pp. 417, 422, 427, 432, 437, 442, 447, 452, 457, 462	Pre-AlgePASS: Tutorial Plus, Lessons 22, 23, 24, and 25 www.pre-alg.com/ self_check_quiz www.pre-alg.com/ extra_examples
	Mixed Review	pp. 373, 379, 385, 391, 397, 401, 408, 413, 418, 422	Cumulative Review, *CRM,* p. 484	
	Error Analysis	Find the Error, pp. 389, 395, 400	Find the Error, *TWE,* pp. 389, 395 Unlocking Misconceptions, *TWE,* p. 371, 394, 399, 406 Tips for New Teachers, *TWE,* p. 408	
	Standardized Test Practice	pp. 373, 379, 385, 389, 390, 391, 397, 401, 408, 413, 418, 422, 430–431	*TWE,* pp. 430–431 Standardized Test Practice, *CRM,* pp. 485–486	Standardized Test Practice CD-ROM www.pre-alg.com/ standardized_test
ASSESSMENT	Open-Ended Assessment	Writing in Math, pp. 373, 379, 385, 391, 397, 401, 408, 412, 418, 422 Open Ended, pp. 371, 377, 384, 389, 395, 400, 407, 410, 416, 421 Standardized Test, p. 431	Speaking: *TWE,* pp. 373, 413, 422 Writing: *TWE,* pp. 379, 401, 408 Modeling: *TWE,* pp. 385, 391, 397, 418 Open-Ended Assessment, *CRM,* p. 479	
	Chapter Assessment	Study Guide, pp. 424–428 Practice Test, p. 429	Multiple-Choice Tests (Forms 1, 2A, 2B), *CRM,* pp. 467–472 Free-Response Tests (Forms 2C, 2D, 3), *CRM,* pp. 473–478 Vocabulary Test/Review, *CRM,* p. 480	ExamView® Pro (see below) MindJogger Videoquizzes www.pre-alg.com/ vocabulary_review www.pre-alg.com/chapter_test

For more information on Yearly ProgressPro, see p. 324.

Pre-Algebra Lesson(s)	Yearly ProgressPro Skill Lesson
8-1	Functions
8-2	Functions and Equations
8-3	Graphing Linear Equations
8-4	Slope: Level 1
8-5	Rate of Change
8-6, 8-7	Slope-Intercept Form
8-8	Scatter Plots
8-9	Graphing Systems of Equations
8-10	Graphing Inequalities

ExamView® Pro

Use the networkable **ExamView® Pro** to:
- Create **multiple versions** of tests.
- Create **modified** tests for *Inclusion* students.
- **Edit** existing questions and **add** your own questions.
- Use built-in **state curriculum correlations** to create tests aligned with state standards.
- Change **English** tests to **Spanish** and vice versa.

For more information on Intervention and Assessment, see pp. T8–T11.

Reading and Writing in Mathematics

Glencoe Pre-Algebra provides numerous opportunities to incorporate reading and writing into the mathematics classroom.

Student Edition

- Foldables™ Study Organizer, p. 367
- Reading Mathematics, p. 380
- Concept Check questions require students to verbalize and write about what they have learned in the lesson. (pp. 370, 371, 376, 377, 381, 384, 387, 389, 395, 398, 400, 407, 410, 414, 416, 420, 421)
- Writing in Math questions in every lesson, pp. 373, 379, 385, 391, 397, 401, 408, 412, 418, 422
- Reading Math, pp. 370, 381, 383
- WebQuest, pp. 411, 422

Teacher Wraparound Edition

- Foldables™ Study Organizer, pp. 367, 424
- Study Notebook suggestions, pp. 368, 371, 378, 380, 384, 386, 389, 392, 395, 401, 406, 411, 416, 420
- Modeling activities, pp. 385, 391, 397, 418
- Speaking activities, pp. 373, 413, 422
- Writing activities, pp. 379, 401, 408
- Differentiated Instruction (Verbal/Linguistic), pp. 412, 415
- **ELL** Resources, pp. 366, 369, 375, 380, 381, 387, 393, 398, 404, 409, 412, 415, 419, 424

Additional Resources

- Vocabulary Builder worksheets require students to define and give examples for key vocabulary terms as they progress through the chapter (*Chapter 8 Resource Masters,* pp. vii–viii)
- Reading to Learn Mathematics master for each lesson (*Chapter 8 Resource Masters*, pp. 420, 425, 430, 435, 440, 445, 450, 455, 460, 465)
- *Vocabulary PuzzleMaker* software creates crossword, jumble, and word search puzzles using vocabulary lists that you can customize.
- *Teaching Mathematics with Foldables* provides suggestions for promoting cognition and language.
- *Reading and Writing in the Mathematics Classroom*
- *WebQuest and Project Resources*

For more information on Reading and Writing in Mathematics, see pp. T6–T7.

 ENGLISH LANGUAGE LEARNERS

Lesson 8-1
Building on Prior Knowledge

Give students an example of evaluating an expression. For example, $3x - 6$, where $x = 5$.

$$3x - 6 = 3(5) - 6$$
$$= 15 - 6$$
$$= 9$$

Then show students the concept of evaluating a function for a specified value. Have the students note the similarities in the procedures.

Lesson 8-4
Using Technology

Have pairs of students use a graphing calculator. Show the students how to input ordered pairs using the list function of the calculator. Once the calculator has graphed the data, ask students what they noticed about the points. Use the connected graph feature to see what is formed when the points on the graph are connected. Ask students to write the linear equation and tell the slope and y-intercept of the equation.

Lesson 8-8
Using Multisensory Activities

To determine a line of best fit, bring in a box of spaghetti. Have students graph a set of data and use the spaghetti to model the line of best fit. Using the spaghetti helps students determine a positive or negative relationship for the given values. Once they have agreed on a best line for a set of data, the group can find the slope and y-intercept for the line.

What You'll Learn

Have students read over the list of objectives and make a list of any words with which they are not familiar.

Why It's Important

Point out to students that this is only one of many reasons why each objective is important. Others are provided in the introduction to each lesson.

Lesson	NCTM Standards	Local Objectives
8-1 Preview	2, 7, 10	
8-1	2, 6	
8-2 Preview	2, 6, 10	
8-2	2, 6, 10	
8-3	2, 6, 10	
8-4 Preview	2, 4, 7	
8-4	2, 6, 10	
8-5 Preview	4, 7, 9, 10	
8-5	2, 3, 6, 9, 10	
8-6	2, 6, 10	
8-6 Follow-Up	2, 7, 9, 10	
8-7	2, 6, 8, 10	
8-8	2, 5, 6, 10	
8-9	2, 6, 10	
8-10	2, 6, 10	
8-10 Follow-Up	2, 10	

Key to NCTM Standards:

1=Number & Operations, 2=Algebra,
3=Geometry, 4=Measurement,
5=Data Analysis & Probability, 6=Problem
Solving, 7=Reasoning & Proof,
8=Communication, 9=Connections,
10=Representation

What You'll Learn

- **Lesson 8-1** Use functions to describe relationships between two quantities.
- **Lessons 8-2, 8-3, 8-6, and 8-7** Graph and write linear equations using ordered pairs, the *x*- and *y*-intercepts, and slope and *y*-intercept.
- **Lessons 8-4 and 8-5** Find slopes of lines and use slope to describe rates of change.
- **Lesson 8-8** Draw and use best-fit lines to make predictions about data.
- **Lessons 8-9 and 8-10** Solve systems of linear equations and linear inequalities.

Key Vocabulary

- function (p. 369)
- linear equation (p. 375)
- slope (p. 387)
- rate of change (p. 393)
- system of equations (p. 414)

Why It's Important

You can often use functions to represent real-world data. For example, the winning times in Olympic swimming events can be shown in a scatter plot. You can then use the data points to write an equation representing the relationship between the year and the winning times. *You will use a function in Lesson 8-8 to predict the winning time in the women's 800-meter freestyle event for the 2008 Olympics.*

Vocabulary Builder   ELL

The Key Vocabulary list introduces students to some of the main vocabulary terms included in this chapter. For a more thorough vocabulary list with pronunciations of new words, give students the Vocabulary Builder worksheets found on pages vii and viii of the *Chapter 8 Resource Masters*. Encourage them to complete the definition of each term as they progress through the chapter. You may suggest that they add these sheets to their study notebooks for future reference when studying for the Chapter 8 test.

Getting Started

Getting Started

Prerequisite Skills To be successful in this chapter, you'll need to master these skills and be able to apply them in problem-solving situations. Review these skills before beginning Chapter 8.

For Lesson 8-1   Relations

Express each relation as a table. Then determine the domain and range.
(For review, see Lesson 1-6.) **1–5. See pp. 431A–431H.**

1. $\{(0, 4), (-3, 3)\}$
2. $\{(-5, 11), (2, 1)\}$
3. $\{(6, 8), (7, 10), (8, 12)\}$
4. $\{(1, -9), (5, 12), (-3, -10)\}$
5. $\{(-8, 5), (7, -1), (6, 1), (1, -2)\}$

For Lesson 8-3   The Coordinate System

Use the coordinate grid to name the point for each ordered pair. *(For review, see Lesson 2-6.)*

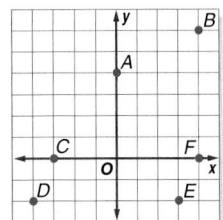

6. $(-3, 0)$ *C*
7. $(3, -2)$ *E*
8. $(-4, -2)$ *D*
9. $(0, 4)$ *A*
10. $(4, 6)$ *B*
11. $(4, 0)$ *F*

For Lesson 8-10   Inequalities

For the given value, state whether the inequality is *true* or *false*. *(For review, see Lesson 7-3.)*

12. $8y \geq 25, y = 4$ **true**
13. $18 < t + 12, t = 10$ **true**
14. $n - 15 > 7, n = 20$ **false**
15. $5 \geq 2x + 3, x = 1$ **true**
16. $12 \leq \frac{2}{3}n, n = 9$ **false**
17. $\frac{1}{2}x - 5 < 0, x = 8$ **true**

Functions Make this Foldable to help you organize your notes. Begin with an 11" × 17" sheet of paper.

Step 1 Fold

Fold the short sides so they meet in the middle.

Step 2 Fold Again

Fold the top to the bottom.

Step 3 Cut

Open. Cut along the second fold to make four tabs. Staple a sheet of grid paper inside.

Step 4 Label

Add axes as shown. Label the quadrants on the tabs.

Reading and Writing As you read and study the chapter, draw examples of functions on the grid paper and write notes under the tabs.

This section provides a review of the basic concepts needed before beginning Chapter 8. Page references are included for additional student help.

Additional review is provided in the *Prerequisite Skills Workbook*, pages 1–2.

Prerequisite Skills in the Getting Ready for the Next Lesson section at the end of each lesson reviews a skill needed in the next lesson.

For Lesson	Prerequisite Skill
8-2	Evaluate Expressions (p. 373)
8-3	Substitution (p. 379)
8-4	Subtract Integers (p. 385)
8-5	Substitution (p. 391)
8-6	Solve Equations for a Variable (p. 397)
8-7	Order of Operations (p. 401)
8-8	Scatter Plots (p. 408)
8-9	Substitution (p. 413)
8-10	Inequalities (p. 418)

Study Organizer

For more information about Foldables, see *Teaching Mathematics with Foldables*.

Note Taking and Organizing Data Note taking is a skill that is based upon listening or reading for main ideas and then recording those ideas for future reference. Under the tabs of their Foldables, have students take notes about what they need to know about functions and graphs. Encourage students to apply these concepts by drawing examples of functions on the front of each tab, and writing about them under the tabs.

Algebra Activity

A Preview of Lesson 8-

Getting Started

Objective Explore the relationship between sets of numbers by making a function machine.

Materials
3-by-5-inch index cards
scissors

Teaching Tip The concept of a function machine can be observed using a graphing calculator. Enter the rule into the Y= list letting X represent any number. Use TABLE to view the results.

Teach

- Have a sample function machine on hand to show students who might have difficulty visualizing the final product.
- Some students may wish to glue the sides of another index card to the back of the front card and cut the inside card slightly narrower. This will make it possible to hold the function machine up with one hand while using the other hand to write.

Assess

In **Exercises 1–5**, students should come to understand clearly how data entered into the function become output.

In **Exercise 6,** students should demonstrate an ease with using function machines.

Study Notebook

You may wish to have students summarize this activity and what they learned from it.

NEW YORK *Performance Indicator* **8.A.17 Define and use correct terminology when referring to function (domain and range)**

Input and Output

In a *function*, there is a relationship between two quantities or sets of numbers. You start with an input value, apply a function rule of one or more operations, and get an output value. In this way, each input is assigned exactly one output.

Collect the Data

Step 1 To make a *function machine*, draw three squares in the middle of a 3-by-5-inch index card, shown here in blue.

Step 2 Cut out the square on the left and the square on the right. Label the left "window" INPUT and the right "window" OUTPUT.

Step 3 Write a rule such as "× 2 + 3" in the center square.

Step 4 On another index card, list the integers from −5 to 4 in a column close to the left edge.

	Input	Rule	Output
−5	−5	×2+3	−7
−4			
−3			
−2			
−1			
0			
1			
2			
3			
4			1
			2
			3
			4

Step 5 Place the function machine over the number column so that −5 is in the left window.

Step 6 Apply the rule to the input number. The output is −5 × 2 + 3, or −7. Write −7 in the right window.
1. −5, −3, −1, 1, 3, 5, 7, 9, 11

Make a Conjecture

1. Slide the function machine down so that the input is −4. Find the output and write the number in the right window. Continue this process for the remaining inputs.

2. Suppose x represents the input and y represents the output. Write an algebraic equation that represents what the function machine does. $y = 2x + 3$

3. Explain how you could find the input if you are given a rule and the corresponding output. **Write an equation and work backward to solve for the input value.**

4. Determine whether the following statement is *true* or *false*. Explain.

   The input values depend on the output values.

5. Write an equation that describes the relationship between the input value x and output value y in each table.

Input	Output
−1	−2
0	0
1	2
3	6

$y = 2x$

Input	Output
−2	2
−1	3
0	4
1	5

$y = x + 4$

Extend the Activity

6. Write your own rule and use it to make a table of inputs and outputs. Exchange your table of values with another student. Use the table to determine each other's rule. **See pp. 431A–431H.**   4. False; the output values depend on the input values

368 Chapter 8 Functions and Graphing

Resource Manager

📁 **Teaching Pre-Algebra with Manipulatives**
- p. 105 (student recording sheet)

Glencoe Mathematics Classroom Manipulative Kit
- scissors

8-1 Functions

NEW YORK *Performance Indicator* **8.A.15** Understand that numerical information can be represented in multiple ways: arithmetically, algebraically, and graphically

What You'll Learn

- Determine whether relations are functions.
- Use functions to describe relationships between two quantities.

Vocabulary

- function
- vertical line test

a–c. See margin.

NEW YORK
Performance Indicator
8.A.17 Define and use correct terminology when referring to function (domain and range)

8.A.18 Determine if a relation is a function

How can the relationship between actual temperatures and windchill temperatures be a function?

The table compares actual temperatures and windchill temperatures when the wind is blowing at 10 miles per hour.

a. On grid paper, graph the temperatures as ordered pairs (actual, windchill).

b. Describe the relationship between the two temperature scales.

c. When the actual temperature is −20°F, which is the best estimate for the windchill temperature: −46°F, −28°F, or 0°F? Explain.

Actual Temperature (°F)	Windchill Temperature (°F)
−10	−34
0	−22
10	−9
20	3

Source: *The World Almanac*

RELATIONS AND FUNCTIONS

Recall that a relation is a set of ordered pairs. A **function** is a special relation in which each member of the domain is paired with *exactly* one member in the range.

Study Tip

Look Back
To review **relations**, **domain**, and **range**, see Lesson 1-6.

Relation	Diagram	Is the Relation a Function?
{(−10, −34), (0, −22), (10, −9), (20, 3)}	domain (x) range (y) −10 → −34 0 → −22 10 → −9 20 → 3	Yes, because each domain value is paired with exactly one range value.
{(−10, −34), (−10, −22), (10, −9), (20, 3)}	domain (x) range (y) −10 → −34 ↘ −22 10 → −9 20 → 3	No, because −10 in the domain is paired with two range values, −34 and −22.

Since functions are relations, they can be represented using ordered pairs, tables, or graphs.

Example 1 Ordered Pairs and Tables as Functions

Determine whether each relation is a function. Explain.

a. {(−3, 1), (−2, 4), (−1, 7), (0, 10), (1, 13)}

This relation is a function because each element of the domain is paired with exactly one element of the range.

b.
x	5	3	2	0	−4	−6
y	1	3	1	3	−2	2

This is a function because for each element of the domain, there is only one corresponding element in the range.

TEACHING TIP

Note that it does not matter if two elements in the domain are paired with the same element in the range.

8-1 Lesson Notes

1 *Focus*

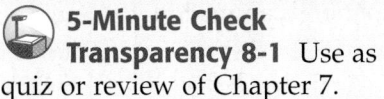

5-Minute Check Transparency 8-1 Use as a quiz or review of Chapter 7.

Mathematical Background notes are available for this lesson on page 366C.

How can the relationship between actual temperatures and windchill temperatures be a function?

The opening activity questions are repeated on page 420 of the *Chapter 8 Resource Masters*.

Reading to Learn Mathematics, p. 420   **ELL**

Pre-Activity How can the relationship between actual temperatures and windchill temperatures be a function?

Do the activity at the top of page 369 in your textbook. Write your answers below.

a. On grid paper, graph the temperatures as ordered pairs (actual, windchill).

b. Describe the relationship between the two temperature scales. **Sample answer:** As the actual temperature increases, the windchill temperature also increases.

c. When the actual temperature is −20°F, which is the best estimate for the windchill: −46°F, −28°F, or 0°F? Explain. −46°F; when the actual temperature decreases, the windchill temperature also decreases.

Reading the Lesson 1–2. See students' work.

Write a definition and give an example of each new vocabulary word or phrase.

Vocabulary	Definition	Example
1. function		
2. vertical line test		

3. For a relation to be a function, each element in the   domain   must have only one corresponding element in the   range   .

4. Explain what is meant by the phrase "distance is a function of time." **Sample answer:** How far something travels depends on how much time elapses.

Helping You Remember

5. You have learned various ways to determine whether a relation is a function. Choose which method is the easiest for you to use, then write a few sentences explaining how that method relates to the other methods. **Sample answer:** Placing the range values in a table with their corresponding domain values makes it easy to see whether an element in the domain is paired with only one element in the range. By graphing and connecting the points, the vertical line test can be applied to arrive at the same answer.

Resource Manager

Workbooks and Reproducible Masters

Chapter 8 Resource Masters
- Study Guide and Intervention, p. 417
- Skills Practice, p. 418
- Practice, p. 419
- Reading to Learn Mathematics, p. 420
- Enrichment, p. 421

Parent and Student Study Guide Workbook, p. 61

Transparencies

5-Minute Check Transparency 8-1
Answer Key Transparencies

Technology

Interactive Chalkboard
Pre-AlgePASS: Tutorial Plus, Lesson 22

RELATIONS AND FUNCTIONS

In-Class Examples Power Point®

1 Determine whether each relation is a function. Explain.

a. {(−3, −3), (−1, −1), (0, 0), (−1, 1), (3, 3)}   **No; −1 in the domain is paired with −1 and 1 in the range.**

b.

x	7	6	5	2	−3	−6
y	2	4	6	4	2	−2

Yes; each x value is paired with only one y value.

2 Determine whether the graph is a function. Explain.

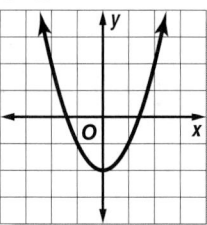

Yes; it passes the vertical line test.

DESCRIBE RELATIONSHIPS

In-Class Example Power Point®

3 **BUSINESS** The table shows the number of boxes made.

Number of Hours	Number of Boxes
0	0
10	3000
20	6000
30	9000

a. Do these data represent a function? Explain.   **Yes; for each 10 hours, only one amount of boxes is made.**

b. Describe how box production is related to hours of operation.   **As hours increase, the number of boxes produced increases.**

Reading Math

Function

Everyday Meaning: a relationship in which one quality or trait depends on another. Height is a function of age.

Math Meaning: a relationship in which a range value depends on a domain value. y is a function of x.

More About. . .

Scuba Diving

To prevent decompression sickness, or the "bends," it is recommended that divers ascend to the surface no faster than 30 feet per minute.
Source: www.mtsinai.org

Another way to determine whether a relation is a function is to use the **vertical line test**. Use a pencil or straightedge to represent a vertical line.

Place the pencil at the left of the graph. Move it to the right across the graph. If, for each value of x in the domain, it passes through no more than one point on the graph, then the graph represents a function.

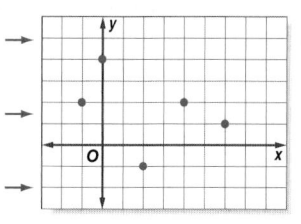

Example 2 Use a Graph to Identify Functions

Determine whether the graph at the right is a function. Explain your answer.

The graph represents a relation that is *not* a function because it does not pass the vertical line test. By examining the graph, you can see that when x = 2, there are three different y values.

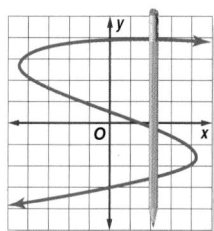

DESCRIBE RELATIONSHIPS   A function describes the relationship between two quantities such as time and distance. For example, the distance you travel on a bike depends on how long you ride the bike. In other words, *distance is a function of time.*

Example 3 Use a Function to Describe Data

SCUBA DIVING   The table shows the water pressure as a scuba diver descends.

a. Do these data represent a function? Explain.

This relation is a function because at each depth, there is only one measure of pressure.

b. Describe how water pressure is related to depth.

Water pressure depends on the depth. As the depth increases, the pressure increases.

Depth (ft)	Water Pressure (lb/ft³)
0	0
1	62.4
2	124.8
3	187.2
4	249.6
5	312.0

Source: www.infoplease.com

✓ **Concept Check**   In Example 3, what is the domain and what is the range? **The depth values are the domain, the water pressure values are the range.**

 Interactive Chalkboard
PowerPoint® Presentations

This CD-ROM is a customizable Microsoft® Power-Point® presentation that includes:

- Step-by-step, dynamic solutions of each In-Class Example from the Teacher Wraparound Edition
- Additional, Your Turn exercises for each example
- The 5-Minute Check Transparencies
- Hot links to Glencoe Online Study Tools

Check for Understanding

Concept Check
1. **Describe** three ways to represent a function. Show an example of each.
2. **Describe** two methods for determining whether a relation is a function.
3. **OPEN ENDED** Draw the graph of a relation that is not a function. Explain why it is not a function.
   1–3. See pp. 431A–431H.

Guided Practice

Determine whether each relation is a function. Explain.

GUIDED PRACTICE KEY

Exercises	Examples
4–7	1
8, 9	2
10, 11	3

4. {(13, 5), (−4, 12), (6, 0), (13, 10)} **No; 13 is paired with 5 and 10.**
5. {(9.2, 7), (9.4, 11), (9.5, 9.5), (9.8, 8)}

5. Yes; each x value is paired with only one y value.

6.
Domain	Range
−3	3
−1	−2
0	5
1	−4
2	3

7.
x	y
5	4
2	8
−7	9
2	12
5	14

No; 5 is paired with 4 and 14.

6. Yes; each domain value is paired with only one range value.

8.

9.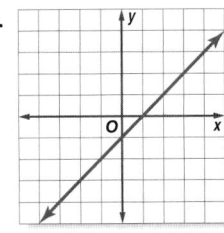

8. No; a vertical line passes through more than one point.

9. Yes; any vertical line passes through no more than one point of the graph.

Application

WEATHER For Exercises 10 and 11, use the table that shows how various wind speeds affect the actual temperature of 30°F.

Wind Speed (mph)	Windchill Temperature (°F)
0	30
10	16
20	4
30	−2
40	−5

Source: *The World Almanac*

10. Do the data represent a function? Explain.
11. Describe how windchill temperatures are related to wind speed.
    As wind speed increases, the windchill temperature decreases.

10. Yes; each wind speed is paired with only one windchill temperature.

Practice and Apply

Homework Help

For Exercises	See Examples
12–19	1
20–23	2
24–27	3

Extra Practice
See page 741.

Determine whether each relation is a function. Explain. **12–17. See margin.**

12. {(−1, 6), (4, 2), (2, 36), (1, 6)}
13. {(−2, 3), (4, 7), (24, −6), (5, 4)}
14. {(9, 18), (0, 36), (6, 21), (6, 22)}
15. {(5, −4), (−2, 3), (5, −1), (2, 3)}

16.
Domain	Range
−4	−2
−2	1
0	2
3	1

17.
Domain	Range
−1	5
−2	5
−2	1
−6	1

DAILY INTERVENTION

Unlocking Misconceptions

- **Relations and Functions**
  Students may mistakenly think that each value in the domain *and* range must be paired with only one value. Stress that only the values in the domain of a function must have unique range values. It might be helpful to show students a table such as the one above.

x	1	2	3	−1	−2	−3
y	1	4	9	1	4	9

About the Exercises . . .

Organization by Objective
- **Relations and Functions:** 12–24, 26, 28, 30–31
- **Describe Relationships:** 25, 27, 29

Odd/Even Assignments
Exercises 12–31 are structured so that students practice the same concepts whether they are assigned odd or even problems.

Assignment Guide

Basic: 13–23 odd, 24–29, 31–52
Average: 13–23 odd, 24–29, 31–52
Advanced: 12–22 even, 24–29, 30–46 (Optional: 47–52)

Answers

12. Yes; each x value is paired with only one y value.
13. Yes; each x value is paired with only one y value.
14. No; 6 in the domain is paired with 21 and 22 in the range.
15. No; 5 in the domain is paired with −4 and −1 in the range.
16. Yes; each domain value is paired with only one range value.
17. No; −2 in the domain is paired with 5 and 1 in the range.

Study Notebook

Have students—
- add the definitions/examples of the vocabulary terms to their Vocabulary Builder worksheets for Chapter 8.
- include a graph of a function and a graph that is not a function with accompanying explanations of the vertical line test.
- include any other item(s) that they find helpful in mastering the skills in this lesson.

Study Guide and Intervention, p. 417

Function	A special relation in which each member of the domain is paired with exactly one member in the range.
Vertical Line Test	Move a pencil or straightedge from left to right across the graph of a relation. • If it passes through no more than one point on the graph, the graph represents a function. • If it passes through more than one point on the graph, the graph does not represent a function.

Since functions are relations, they can be represented using ordered pairs, tables, or graphs.

Example Determine whether each relation is a function. Explain.

a. {(−10, −34), (0, −22), (10, −9), (20, 3)}

Domain (x) Range (y)

Because each element in the domain is paired with only one value in the range, this is a function.

b.

x	−10	−10	10	20
y	−34	−22	−9	3

Domain (x) Range (y)

Because −10 in the domain is paired with −34 and −22 in the range, this is not a function.

Exercises

Determine whether each relation is a function. Explain.

1. {(−5, 2), (3, −3), (1, 7), (3, 0)}
No; 3 in the domain is paired with −3 and 0 in the range.

2. {(2, 7), (−5, 20), (−10, 20), (−2, 10), (1, 20)}
Yes; each x value is paired with only one y value.

3.
x	1	−3	8	−8	20
y	2	6	6	5	11
Yes; each x value is paired with only one y value.

4.
x	8	1	−5	1	−10
y	−2	3	7	7	13
No; 1 in the domain is paired with 3 and 7 in the range.

Skills Practice, p. 418 and Practice, p. 419 (shown)

Determine whether each relation is a function. Explain.

1. {(4, −5), (0, −9), (1, 0), (7, 0)}
Yes; each x value is paired with only one y value.

2. {(5, −12), (−1, −2), (8, −5), (4, −2), (3, −5)}
Yes; each x value is paired with only one y value.

3. {(−2, −3), (6, −8), (4, 2), (6, −5), (2, −5)}
No; 6 in the domain is paired with −8 and −5 in the range.

4. {(−7, 15), (1, 5), (4, 15), (−7, 2)}
No; −7 in the domain is paired with 15 and 2 in the range.

5.
x	4	−5	11	−5	23
y	−3	1	1	0	6
No; −5 in the domain is paired with 1 and 0 in the range.

6.
x	7	14	11	−10	−1
y	−3	−9	−4	−3	15
Yes; each x value is paired with only one y value.

7.
x	−3.0	3.5	4.1	−3.0	3.4
y	4.2	3.7	−3.8	3.7	4.0
No; −3.0 in the domain is paired with 4.2 and 3.7 in the range.

8.
x	11	4	−2	4	−7
y	−7	−2	2	2	6
No; 4 in the domain is paired with −2 and 2 in the range.

EMPLOYMENT For Exercises 9–12, use the table, which shows the percent of employed men and women in the U.S. labor force every five years from 1980 to 2000.

Employed Members of Labor Force

Year	Men (% of male population)	Women (% of female population)
1980	77.4	51.5
1985	76.3	54.5
1990	76.4	57.5
1995	75.0	58.9
2000	78.9	67.3

Source: U.S. Census Bureau

9. Is the relation (year, percent of men) a function? Explain. **Yes; each year is paired with only one value for the percent of employed men.**

10. Describe how the percent of employed men is related to the year. **The number of employed men varies each year, but is around 76 percent of the male population.**

11. Is the relation (year, percent of women) a function? Explain. **Yes; each year is paired with only one value for the percent of employed women.**

12. Describe how the percent of employed women is related to the year. **As the years progress, the percent of employed women increases.**

Enrichment, p. 421

Emmy Noether

Emmy Noether (1882–1935) was a German mathematician and a leading figure in modern abstract algebra. Her contributions helped change the role of women in German universities and advanced the mathematical progress of the time. Noether fought and overcame rules that once prevented her from becoming a faculty member. Her most notable work pertains to linear transformations of non-commutative algebras and their structures.

A linear equation is an example of a **transformation**, unless it is the equation for a vertical line. In a transformation, a given rule transforms each number in one set, the **domain**, into one and only one number in another set, the **range**. In graphing linear equations, the domain is usually the set of real numbers and the range is either the set of real numbers or a subset of the real numbers. Each value of x is transformed into some value of y.

Transformation f is shown in the diagram below. The transformation takes each element of the domain {1, 2, 3} and adds 1 to produce the corresponding value in the range. Functional notation is used to show the rule f(x) = x + 1.

f(x) = x + 1

Use functional notation to write the rule for each transformation.

1.
g(x) = 2x + 1

2.
h(x) = 5

3. What do you think is a **non-commutative** algebra?
a + b ≠ b + a for some a, b ∈ R

4. Explain whether the diagram below shows a transformation.

No, the number 4 corresponds to more than one value in the range.

Determine whether each relation is a function. Explain.

18–23. See margin.

18.

x	y
−7	2
0	4
11	6
11	8
0	10

19.

x	y
14	5
15	10
16	15
17	20
18	25

20.

21.

22.

23.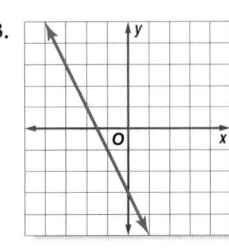

Study Tip

Trends

There may be general trends in sets of data. However, not every data point may follow the trend exactly.

FARMING For Exercises 24–27, use the table that shows the number and size of farms in the United States every decade from 1950 to 2000. **24–26. See margin.**

24. Is the relation (year, number of farms) a function? Explain.

25. Describe how the number of farms is related to the year.

26. Is the relation (year, average size of farms) a function? Explain.

27. Describe how the average size of farms is related to the year. **Generally, as the years progress, the size of farms increases. An exception is in the year 2000.**

Farms in the United States

Year	Number (millions)	Average Size (acres)
1950	5.6	213
1960	4.0	297
1970	2.9	374
1980	2.4	426
1990	2.1	460
2000	2.2	434

Source: The Wall Street Journal Almanac

MEASUREMENTS For Exercises 28 and 29, use the data in the table.

28. No; 24 in the domain is paired with 163 and 168 in the range.

28. Do the data represent a function? Explain.

29. Is there any relation between foot length and height? **Generally, as foot length increases, height increases.**

Tell whether each statement is *always*, *sometimes*, or *never* true. Explain.

30. A function is a relation.

31. A relation is a function. **30–31. See margin.**

Name	Foot Length (cm)	Height (cm)
Rosa	24	163
Tanner	28	182
Enrico	25	163
Jahad	24	168
Abbi	22	150
Cory	26	172

372 Chapter 8 Functions and Graphing

Answers

18. No; the x value 0 is paired with y values 4 and 10; the x value 11 is paired with y values 6 and 8.

19. Yes; each x value is paired with only one y value.

20. Yes; any vertical line passes through no more than one point of the graph.

21. No; a vertical line passes through more than one point.

22. Yes; any vertical line passes through no more than one point of the graph.

23. Yes; any vertical line passes through no more than one point of the graph.

32b. Sometimes; the inverse of {(1, 5), (2, 10)} is also a function, but the inverse of {(1, 5), (2, 5)} is not a function.

32. CRITICAL THINKING The *inverse* of any relation is obtained by switching the coordinates in each ordered pair of the relation.

  a. Determine whether the inverse of the relation {(4, 0), (5, 1), (6, 2), (6, 3)} is a function. **yes**

  b. Is the inverse of a function *always*, *sometimes*, or *never* a function? Give an example to explain your reasoning.

33. WRITING IN MATH   Answer the question that was posed at the beginning of the lesson. **See pp. 431A–431H.**

How can the relationship between actual temperatures and windchill temperatures be a function?

Include the following in your answer:
- an explanation of how actual temperatures and windchill temperatures are related for a given wind speed, and
- a discussion about whether an actual temperature can ever have two corresponding windchill temperatures when the wind speed remains the same.

NEW YORK
Test Practice

Standardized Test Practice
A B C D

34. The relation {(2, 11), (−9, 8), (14, 1), (5, 5)} is *not* a function when which ordered pair is added to the set? **D**

  Ⓐ (8, −9)   Ⓑ (6, 11)   Ⓒ (0, 0)   Ⓓ (2, 18)

35. Which statement is true about the data in the table? **A**

  Ⓐ The data represent a function.

  Ⓑ The data do not represent a function.

  Ⓒ As the value of *x* increases, the value of *y* increases.

  Ⓓ A graph of the data would not pass the vertical line test.

x	y
−4	−4
2	16
5	8
10	−4
12	15

Maintain Your Skills

Mixed Review **Solve each inequality. Check your solution.**   *(Lessons 7-5 and 7-6)*

36. $4y > 24$ **y > 6**   **37.** $\frac{a}{3} < -7$ **a < −21**   **38.** $18 \geq -2k$ **k ≥ −9**

39. $2x + 5 < 17$ **x < 6**   **40.** $2t - 3 \geq 1.4t + 6$ **t ≥ 15**   **41.** $12r - 4 > 7 + 12r$ **Ø**

Solve each problem by using the percent equation.   *(Lesson 6-7)*

42. 10 is what percent of 50? **20%**   **43.** What is 15% of 120? **18**

44. Find 95% of 256. **243.2**   **45.** 46.5 is 62% of what number? **75**

46. State whether the sequence 120, 100, 80, 60, … is *arithmetic*, *geometric*, or *neither*. Then write the next three terms of the sequence.   *(Lesson 5-10)* **arithmetic; 40, 20, 0**

Getting Ready for the Next Lesson **PREREQUISITE SKILL** Evaluate each expression if $x = 4$ and $y = -1$.
*(To review **evaluating expressions**, see Lesson 1-3.)*

47. $3x + 1$ **13**   **48.** $2y$ **−2**   **49.** $y + 6$ **5**

50. $-5x$ **−20**   **51.** $2x - 8$ **0**   **52.** $3y - 4$ **−7**

---

4 Assess

Open-Ended Assessment

Speaking Have students explain how to determine whether a function is a relation.

Tips for New Teachers

Connections
Show students how functions are like many everyday machines by choosing one or a few such items to bring to class. For example, a toaster receives bread as input and produces toast as output. Other machines include a label maker, a shredder, and a laminator.

Getting Ready for Lesson 8-2

PREREQUISITE SKILL Lesson 8-2 presents linear equations in two variables for which they will choose a value for *x* and find the corresponding value for *y*. Exercises 47–52 should be used to determine your students' familiarity with evaluating expressions.

Answers (p. 372)

24. Yes; each year is only paired with one value for the number of farms.

25. Generally, as the years progress, the number of farms decreases. An exception is in the year 2000.

26. Yes; each year is paired with only one value for the average size of farms.

30. Always; every function can be written as a set of ordered pairs.

31. Sometimes; a relation that has a member of the domain paired with more than one member in the range is not a function.

Getting Started

Know Your Calculator If after pressing [Y=] you see something other than a Y= list, the calculator is set for a different mode. To change the mode to graph functions, press [MODE] and use the arrow keys to highlight FUNC in the fourth row. Press [ENTER] and try entering values into the Y= list again.

Table Setup Because you will be entering all values for the domain, you do not need to adjust the values after TblStart= and ΔTbl=.

Teach

- The far right column in the table is for Y2 values. Ask students what would be true if the X values resulted in Y1 and Y2 values. **The equation in the Y= list would not be a function.**
- Have students complete Exercises 1–3.

Assess

Students should demonstrate an understanding of the relationship between the domain and the range.

Teaching Tip If graphing calculators are unavailable, have students work this activity later in the chapter by computing the range values by hand.

Graphing Calculator Investigation

A Preview of Lesson 8-2

NEW YORK *Performance Indicator* **8.A.19** Interpret multiple representations **using equation, table of values,** and graph

Function Tables

8.R.1 Use physical objects, drawings, charts, **tables,** graphs, symbols, equations, **and objects created using technology as representations**

You can use a TI-83 Plus graphing calculator to create function tables. By entering a function and the domain values, you can find the corresponding range values.

> **Use a function table to find the range of $y = 3n + 1$ if the domain is $\{-5, -2, 0, 0.5, 4\}$.**
>
> **Step 1** *Enter the function.*
> - The graphing calculator uses X for the domain values and Y for the range values. So, $Y = 3X + 1$ represents $y = 3n + 1$.
> - Enter $Y = 3X + 1$ in the Y= list.
> **KEYSTROKES:** [Y=] 3 [X,T,θ,n] [+] 1
>
> **Step 2** *Format the table.*
> - Use TBLSET to select *Ask* for the independent variable and *Auto* for the dependent variable. Then you can enter any value for the domain.
> **KEYSTROKES:** [2nd] [TBLSET] [▼] [▼] [►] [ENTER] [▼] [ENTER]
>
> **Step 3** *Find the range by entering the domain values.*
> - Access the table.
> **KEYSTROKES:** [2nd] [TABLE]
> - Enter the domain values.
> **KEYSTROKES:** −5 [ENTER] −2 [ENTER] ... 4 [ENTER]
>
>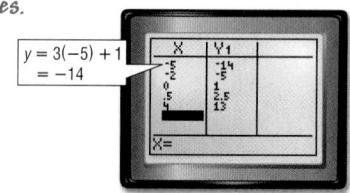
>
> The range is $\{-14, -5, 1, 2.5, 13\}$.

Exercises **1b. As X increases by 1 unit, Y decreases by 2 units.**

Use the TABLE option on a graphing calculator to complete each exercise.

1. Consider the function $f(x) = -2x + 4$ and the domain values $\{-2, -1, 0, 1, 2\}$.
   a. Use a function table to find the range values. **{8, 6, 4, 2, 0}**
   b. Describe the relationship between the X and Y values.
   c. If X is less than −2, would the value for Y be greater or less than 8? Explain. **See pp. 431A–431H.**

2. Suppose you are using the formula $d = rt$ to find the distance d a car travels for the times t in hours given by $\{0, 1, 3.5, 10\}$.
   a. If the rate is 60 miles per hour, what function should be entered in the Y= list? **Y = 60X**
   b. Make a function table for the given domain. **See pp. 431A–431H.**
   c. Between which two times in the domain does the car travel 150 miles? **1 h and 3.5 h**
   d. Describe how a function table can be used to better estimate the time it takes to drive 150 miles. **See pp. 431A–431H.**

3. Serena is buying one packet of pencils for $1.50 and a number of fancy folders x for $0.40 each. The total cost y is given by $y = 1.50 + 0.40x$.
   a. Use a function table to find the total cost if Serena buys 1, 2, 3, 4, and 12 folders. **$1.90, $2.30, $2.70, $3.10, $6.30**
   b. Suppose plain folders cost $0.25 each. Enter $y = 1.50 + 0.25x$ in the Y= list as Y2. How much does Serena save if she buys pencils and 12 plain folders rather than pencils and 12 fancy folders? **$1.80**

 www.pre-alg.com/other_calculator_keystrokes

Tips for New Teachers

Independence Discourage students from becoming totally dependent on their calculators. Many values can be easily calculated mentally. Calculators should be used only when hand calculation is too tedious or is unfeasible.

Linear Equations in Two Variables

What You'll Learn

- Solve linear equations with two variables.
- Graph linear equations using ordered pairs.

Vocabulary

- linear equation

NEW YORK
Performance Indicator

8.A.4 Create a graph given a description or an expression for a situation involving a linear or nonlinear relationship

8.G.15 Graph a line using a table of values

How can linear equations represent a function?

Peaches cost $1.50 per can.

a. Complete the table to find the cost of 2, 3, and 4 cans of peaches.

b. On grid paper, graph the ordered pairs (number, cost). Then draw a line through the points. **See margin.**

c. Write an equation representing the relationship between number of cans x and cost y. $y = 1.5x$ or $1.50x$

Number of Cans (x)	$1.50x$	Cost (y)
1	1.50(1)	1.50
2	1.50(2)	3.00
3	1.50(3)	4.50
4	1.50(4)	6.00

Study Tip

Input and Output
The variable for the input is called the **independent variable** because it can be any number. The variable for the output is called the **dependent variable** because it *depends* on the input value.

TEACHING TIP

Be sure students understand that any rational numbers may be chosen for x, but integers are usually most convenient.

SOLUTIONS OF EQUATIONS Functions can be represented in words, in a table, as ordered pairs, with a graph, and with an equation.

An equation such as $y = 1.50x$ is called a linear equation. A **linear equation** in two variables is an equation in which the variables appear in separate terms and neither variable contains an exponent other than 1.

Solutions of a linear equation are ordered pairs that make the equation true. One way to find solutions is to make a table. Consider the equation $y = -x + 8$.

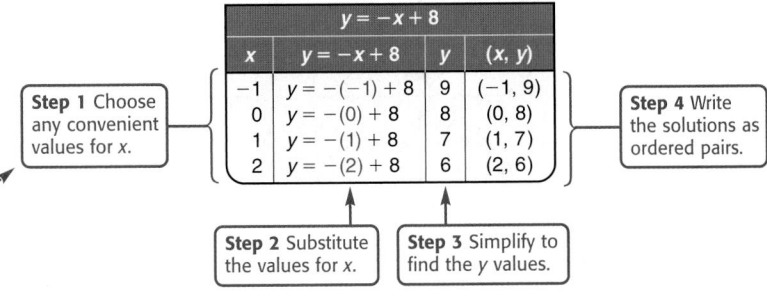

	$y = -x + 8$		
x	$y = -x + 8$	y	(x, y)
-1	$y = -(-1) + 8$	9	$(-1, 9)$
0	$y = -(0) + 8$	8	$(0, 8)$
1	$y = -(1) + 8$	7	$(1, 7)$
2	$y = -(2) + 8$	6	$(2, 6)$

Step 1 Choose any convenient values for x.

Step 2 Substitute the values for x.

Step 3 Simplify to find the y values.

Step 4 Write the solutions as ordered pairs.

So, four solutions of $y = -x + 8$ are $(-1, 9)$, $(0, 8)$, $(1, 7)$, and $(2, 6)$.

Example 1 Find Solutions

Find four solutions of $y = 2x - 1$.

Choose four values for x. Then substitute each value into the equation and solve for y.

Four solutions are $(0, -1)$, $(1, 1)$, $(2, 3)$, and $(3, 5)$.

x	$y = 2x - 1$	y	(x, y)
0	$y = 2(0) - 1$	-1	$(0, -1)$
1	$y = 2(1) - 1$	1	$(1, 1)$
2	$y = 2(2) - 1$	3	$(2, 3)$
3	$y = 2(3) - 1$	5	$(3, 5)$

1 Focus

5-Minute Check Transparency 8-2 Use as a quiz or review of Lesson 8-1.

Mathematical Background notes are available for this lesson on page 366C.

How can linear equations represent a function?

The opening activity questions are repeated on page 425 of the *Chapter 8 Resource Masters*.

Reading to Learn Mathematics, p. 425   **ELL**

Pre-Activity *How can linear equations represent a function?*

Do the activity at the top of page 375 in your textbook. Write your answers below.

a. Complete the table to find the cost of 2, 3, and 4 cans of peaches.

b. On grid paper, graph the ordered pairs (number, cost). Then draw a line through the points.

Number of Cans (x)	$1.50x$	Cost (y)
1	1.50(1)	1.50
2	1.50(2)	3.00
3	1.50(3)	4.50
4	1.50(4)	6.00

c. Write an equation representing the relationship between number of cans x and cost y. $y = 1.5x$ or $1.50x$

Reading the Lesson

Write a definition and give an example of the new vocabulary phrase.

	Vocabulary	Definition	Example
1.	linear equation	See students' work.	

2. Determine whether each equation below is linear or nonlinear and explain why.
   a. $y = x + 1$ Linear; the variables appear in separate terms, and neither variable contains an exponent other than 1.
   b. $y = x^2 + 1$ Nonlinear; the variable x has an exponent of 2.
   c. $xy = 4$ Nonlinear; the variables appear in the same term.

3. Solutions of a linear equation are ___ordered pairs___ that make the equation true.

Helping You Remember

4. Work with one of your classmates translating linear equations into English. First, each of you should write a linear equation. Then trade equations and take turns reading the equations in everyday words. Second, each of you should describe a line in terms of its x and y values. Trade sentences and translate them into linear equations. **Sample answer:** $x - y = 10$; The value of y subtracted from the value of x is 10.

Resource Manager

Workbooks and Reproducible Masters

Chapter 8 Resource Masters
- Study Guide and Intervention, p. 422
- Skills Practice, p. 423
- Practice, p. 424
- Reading to Learn Mathematics, p. 425
- Enrichment, p. 426

Parent and Student Study Guide Workbook, p. 62

Transparencies
5-Minute Check Transparency 8-2
Answer Key Transparencies

Technology
Interactive Chalkboard
Multimedia Applications

SOLUTIONS OF EQUATIONS

In-Class Examples Power Point®

1 Find four solutions of $y = 4x + 3$. **Sample answer: (0, 3), (1, 7), (2, 11), and (3, 15)**

Teaching Tip Because Example 2 asks for a number of real items, positive integers should be chosen for sample x values.

2 **BUSINESS** At a local software company, Level 1 employees x earn $48,000, and level 2 employees y earn $24,000. Find four solutions of $48,000x + 24,000y = 216,000$ to determine how many employees at each level the company can hire for $216,000. **Sample answer: (0, 9), (1, 7), (2, 5), (3, 3) 0 Level 1, 9 Level 2 1 Level 1, 7 Level 2 2 Level 1, 5 Level 2 3 Level 1, 3 Level 2**

GRAPH LINEAR EQUATIONS

In-Class Example Power Point®

3 Graph $y = x - 3$ by plotting ordered pairs.

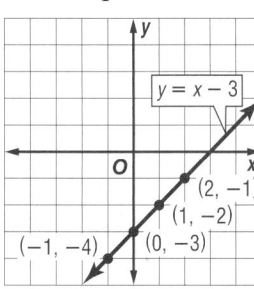

Sometimes it is necessary to first rewrite an equation by solving for y.

Example 2 **Solve an Equation for y**

SHOPPING Fancy goldfish x cost $3, and regular goldfish y cost $1. Find four solutions of $3x + y = 8$ to determine how many of each type of fish Tyler can buy for $8.

First, rewrite the equation by solving for y.

$3x + y = 8$	Write the equation.
$3x + y - 3x = 8 - 3x$	Subtract $3x$ from each side.
$y = 8 - 3x$	Simplify.

Choose four x values and substitute them into $y = 8 - 3x$. Four solutions are $(0, 8)$, $(1, 5)$, $(2, 2)$, and $(3, -1)$.

x	$y = 8 - 3x$	y	(x, y)
0	$y = 8 - 3(0)$	8	$(0, 8)$
1	$y = 8 - 3(1)$	5	$(1, 5)$
2	$y = 8 - 3(2)$	2	$(2, 2)$
3	$y = 8 - 3(3)$	-1	$(3, -1)$

$(0, 8)$ — He can buy 0 fancy goldfish and 8 regular goldfish.

$(1, 5)$ — He can buy 1 fancy goldfish and 5 regular goldfish.

$(2, 2)$ — He can buy 2 fancy goldfish and 2 regular goldfish.

$(3, -1)$ — This solution does not make sense, because there cannot be a negative number of goldfish.

Study Tip

Choosing x Values
It is often convenient to choose 0 as an x value to find a value for y.

✓ **Concept Check** Write the solution of $3x + y = 10$ if $x = 2$. **(2, 4)**

GRAPH LINEAR EQUATIONS A linear equation can also be represented by a graph. Study the graphs shown below.

Linear Equations

$y = x + 1$

$y = -2x$

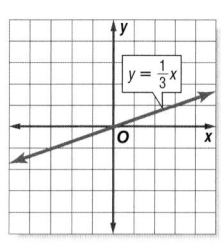
$y = \frac{1}{3}x$

Nonlinear Equations

$y = x^2 + 1$

$y = -2x^3$

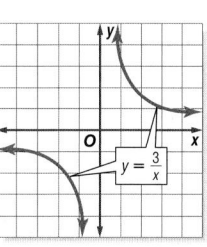
$y = \frac{3}{x}$

Notice that graphs of the linear equations are straight lines. This is true for all linear equations and is the reason they are called "linear." The coordinates of all points on a line are solutions to the equation.

DAILY INTERVENTION **Differentiated Instruction**

- **Auditory/Musical** Bring several passages of sheet music to class. Include scales, melodic strings of notes, and passages with chords. Have students tell which passages are similar to functions and which ones are dissimilar. **Sample answer: scales resemble linear functions; melodic passages have one unique y value for each beat, x. Passages with chords do not resemble functions because for each beat, x, there is more than one note, y.**

To graph a linear equation, find ordered pair solutions, plot the corresponding points, and draw a line through them. It is best to find at least three points.

Example 3 Graph a Linear Equation

Graph $y = x + 1$ by plotting ordered pairs.

First, find ordered pair solutions. Four solutions are $(-1, 0)$, $(0, 1)$, $(1, 2)$, and $(2, 3)$.

x	y = x + 1	y	(x, y)
−1	y = −1 + 1	0	(−1, 0)
0	y = 0 + 1	1	(0, 1)
1	y = 1 + 1	2	(1, 2)
2	y = 2 + 1	3	(2, 3)

Plot these ordered pairs and draw a line through them. Note that the ordered pair for any point on this line is a solution of $y = x + 1$. The line is a complete graph of the function.

CHECK It appears from the graph that $(-2, -1)$ is also a solution. Check this by substitution.

$y = x + 1$ Write the equation.

$-1 \stackrel{?}{=} -2 + 1$ Replace x with −2 and y with −1.

$-1 = -1 \checkmark$ Simplify.

A linear equation is one of many ways to represent a function.

Concept Summary — Representing Functions

- **Words** The value of y is 3 less than the corresponding value of x.

- **Table**

x	y
0	−3
1	−2
2	−1
3	0

- **Graph**

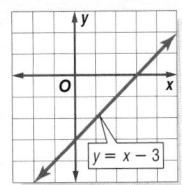

- **Ordered Pairs** $(0, -3)$, $(1, -2)$, $(2, -1)$, $(3, 0)$

- **Equation** $y = x - 3$

Check for Understanding

Concept Check
1. **Explain** why a linear equation has infinitely many solutions. **See margin.**

2. Sample answer:
$y = x + 6$

Guided Practice
2. **OPEN ENDED** Write a linear equation that has $(-2, 4)$ as a solution.

3. Copy and complete the table. Use the results to write four solutions of $y = x + 5$. Write the solutions as ordered pairs. $(-3, 2)$, $(-1, 4)$, $(0, 5)$, $(1, 6)$

x	x + 5	y
−3	−3 + 5	2
−1	−1 + 5	4
0	0 + 5	5
1	1 + 5	6

Answer

1. Sample answer: Infinitely many values can be substituted for x, or the domain.

Answers (p. 378)

4. Sample answer: $(-1, 7)$, $(0, 8)$, $(1, 9)$, $(2, 10)$

5. Sample answer: $(-1, -4)$, $(0, 0)$, $(1, 4)$, $(2, 8)$

6. Sample answer: $(-1, -9)$, $(0, -7)$, $(1, -5)$, $(2, -3)$

7. Sample answer: $(-1, 1)$, $(0, 6)$, $(1, 11)$, $(2, 16)$

About the Exercises . . .

Organization by Objective
• **Solutions of Equations:** 12–25
• **Graph Linear Equations:** 30–41

Odd/Even Assignments
Exercises 12–41 and 45–50 are structured so that students practice the same concepts whether they are assigned odd or even problems.

Alert! Exercises 8–10, 30–41, and 43 require graph paper.

Assignment Guide

Basic: 13–23 odd, 27, 31–37 odd, 42–51 odd, 52–65

Average: 13–41 odd, 42–44, 45–51 odd, 52–65

Advanced: 12–42 even, 43, 44–50 even, 51–61 (Optional: 62–65)

GUIDED PRACTICE KEY	
Exercises	Examples
4–7	1
8–10	3
11	2

Find four solutions of each equation. Write the solutions as ordered pairs.

4. $y = x + 8$ **5.** $y = 4x$ **6.** $y = 2x - 7$ **7.** $-5x + y = 6$
4–7. See p. 377 margin.
Graph each equation by plotting ordered pairs. **8–10. See margin.**

8. $y = x + 3$ **9.** $y = 2x - 1$ **10.** $x + y = 5$

Application   **11. SCIENCE**   The distance y in miles that light travels in x seconds is given by $y = 186,000x$. Find two solutions of this equation and describe what they mean. **See margin.**

★ indicates increased difficulty

Practice and Apply

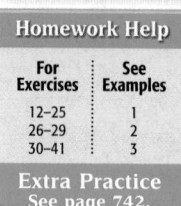

Homework Help	
For Exercises	See Examples
12–25	1
26–29	2
30–41	3

Extra Practice
See page 742.

Copy and complete each table. Use the results to write four solutions of the given equation. Write the solutions as ordered pairs.

12. $y = x - 9$

x	x − 9	y
−1	−1 − 9	−10
0	0 − 9	−9
4	4 − 9	−5
7	7 − 9	−2

$(-1, -10), (0, -9), (4, -5), (7, -2)$

13. $y = 2x + 6$

x	2x + 6	y
−4	2(−4) + 6	−2
0	2(0) + 6	6
2	2(2) + 6	10
4	2(4) + 6	14

$(-4, -2), (0, 6), (2, 10), (4, 14)$

Find four solutions of each equation. Write the solutions as ordered pairs.

14. $y = x + 2$ **15.** $y = x - 7$ **16.** $y = 3x$ **17.** $y = -5x$

18. $y = 2x - 3$ **19.** $y = 3x + 1$ **20.** $x + y = 9$ **21.** $x + y = -6$

22. $4x + y = 2$ **23.** $3x - y = 10$ ★**24.** $y = 8$ ★**25.** $x = -1$
14–25. See margin.

MEASUREMENT   The equation $y = 0.62x$ describes the approximate number of miles y in x kilometers.

26. Describe what the solution (8, 4.96) means. **8 km ≈ 4.96 mi**

27. About how many miles is a 10-kilometer race? **6.2 mi**

HEALTH   During a workout, a target heart rate y in beats per minute is represented by $y = 0.7(220 - x)$, where x is a person's age.

★**28.** Compare target heart rates of people 20 years old and 50 years old.

★**29.** In which quadrant(s) would the graph of $y = 0.7(220 - x)$ make sense? Explain your reasoning. **28–29. See margin.**

Graph each equation by plotting ordered pairs. **30–41. See pp. 431A–431H.**

30. $y = x + 2$ **31.** $y = x + 5$ **32.** $y = x - 4$ **33.** $y = -x - 6$

34. $y = -2x + 2$ **35.** $y = 3x - 4$ **36.** $x + y = 1$ **37.** $x - y = 6$

38. $2x + y = 5$ ★**39.** $3x - y = 7$ ★**40.** $x = 2$ ★**41.** $y = -3$

GEOMETRY   For Exercises 42–44, use the following information.
The formula for the perimeter of a square with sides s units long is $P = 4s$.

42. Find three ordered pairs that satisfy this condition.   **42–44. See margin.**

43. Draw the graph that contains these points.

44. Why do negative values of s make no sense?

Answers

8.

9.

10.

11. Sample answer: (1, 186,000) means that light travels 186,000 miles in 1 second. (2, 372,000) means that light travels 372,000 miles in 2 seconds.

45. Yes; the points lie on a straight line.

46. No; the points do not lie on a straight line.

47. Yes; the points lie on a straight line.

48. Yes; the graph is a line.

49. No; the exponent of *x* is not 1.

50. Yes; the graph is a horizontal line.

Determine whether each relation or equation is linear. Explain.

45.

x	y
−1	−2
0	0
1	2
2	4

46.

x	y
−1	1
0	0
1	1
2	4

47.

x	y
−1	−1
0	−1
1	−1
2	−1

48. $3x + y = 20$

49. $y = x^2$

50. $y = 5$

51. CRITICAL THINKING Compare and contrast the functions shown in the tables. (*Hint:* Compare the change in values for each column.) **See pp. 431A–431H.**

x	y
−1	−2
0	0
1	2
2	4

x	y
−1	1
0	0
1	1
2	4

52. WRITING IN MATH Answer the question that was posed at the beginning of the lesson. **See pp. 431A–431H.**

How can linear equations represent a function?

Include the following in your answer:
- a description of four ways that you can represent a function, and
- an example of a linear equation that could be used to determine the cost of *x* pounds of bananas that are $0.49 per pound.

NEW YORK
Test Practice

Standardized Test Practice
Ⓐ Ⓑ Ⓒ Ⓓ

53. Identify the equation that represents the data in the table. **B**

x	y
−2	11
0	5
1	2
3	−4

Ⓐ $y = x + 5$　　Ⓑ $y = -3x + 5$
Ⓒ $y = -5x + 1$　　Ⓓ $y = x + 13$

54. The graph of $2x - y = 4$ goes through which pair of points? **C**

Ⓐ $P(-2, -3), Q(0, 2)$　　Ⓑ $P(-2, -1), Q(2, -3)$
Ⓒ $P(1, -2), Q(3, 2)$　　Ⓓ $P(-3, 2), Q(0, -4)$

Maintain Your Skills

Mixed Review
55–58. See pp. 431A–431H.

Determine whether each relation is a function. Explain.　*(Lesson 8-1)*

55. {(2, 3), (3, 4), (4, 5), (5, 6)}

56. {(0, 6), (−3, 9), (4, 9), (−2, 1)}

57. {(11, 8), (13, −2), (11, 21)}

58. {(−0.1, 5), (0, 10), (−0.1, −5)}

Solve each inequality and check your solution. Graph the solution on a number line. *(Lesson 7-6)* **59–60.** See pp. 431A–431H for graphs.

59. $3x + 4 < 16$　$x < 4$

60. $9 - 2d \leq 23$　$d \geq -7$

61. Evaluate $a \div b$ if $a = \frac{4}{7}$ and $b = \frac{2}{3}$. *(Lesson 5-4)* $\frac{6}{7}$

Getting Ready for the Next Lesson

PREREQUISITE SKILL In each equation, find the value of *y* when $x = 0$.
(To review substitution, see Lesson 1-5.)

62. $y = 5x - 3$ **−3**

63. $-x + y = 3$ **3**

64. $x + 2y = 12$ **6**

65. $4x - 5y = -20$ **4**

Lesson 8-2　Linear Equations in Two Variables　379

Open-Ended Assessment

Writing Have students write a definition of *linear equation* in their own words and illustrate the definition with an example.

Getting Ready for Lesson 8-3

PREREQUISITE SKILL Lesson 8-3 presents finding intercepts from equations, in which they substitute zero for *x* or *y* when solving for the other variable. Exercises 62–65 should be used to determine your students' familiarity with substitution.

Answers (p. 378)

28. 140 beats per minute; 119 beats per minute

29. Quadrant I; a person cannot have a negative age or heart rate.

42. Sample answer: (1, 4), (2, 8), (3, 12)

43.

44. Length cannot have a negative value.

14–25. Sample answers are given.

14. (−1, 1), (0, 2), (1, 3), (2, 4)

15. (−1, −8), (0, −7), (1, −6), (2, −5)

16. (−1, −3), (0, 0), (1, 3), (2, 6)

17. (−1, 5), (0, 0), (1, −5), (2, −10)

18. (−1, −5), (0, −3), (1, −1), (2, 1)

19. (−1, −2), (0, 1), (1, 4), (2, 7)

20. (−1, 10), (0, 9), (1, 8), (2, 7)

21. (−1, −5), (0, −6), (1, −7), (2, −8)

22. (−1, 6), (0, 2), (1, −2), (2, −6)

23. (−1, −13), (0, −10), (1, −7), (2, −4)

24. (−1, 8), (0, 8), (1, 8), (2, 8)

25. (−1, 0), (−1, 1), (−1, 2), (−1, 3)

Getting Started

Remind students of the function machines they made at the beginning of the chapter. Have them think of the middle box of the function machine as the function *f*. The input *x* goes into the function *f* as shown by *x* being enclosed by parentheses. The output then comes out as $f(x)$.

Teach

Functional Notation Point out that when functions are graphed, the functional notation for the range is used to designate the *y*-axis. For example, when graphing $f(x) = x + 2$, the *y*-axis is marked on the graph as $f(x)$ instead of as *y*.

Assess

Study Notebook

Have students write a paragraph explaining in their own words the meaning of the notation $f(x) = 2x - 3$.

ELL English Language Learners may benefit from writing key concepts from this activity in their Study Notebooks in their native language and then in English.

Language of Functions

Equations that are functions can be written in a form called *functional notation*, as shown below.

equation	functional notation
$y = 4x + 10$	$f(x) = 4x + 10$

Read $f(x)$ as f of x.

TEACHING TIP
Explain that $f(x)$ can also be read as f at x. This makes the concept of functions easier for students to understand.

So, $f(x)$ is simply another name for *y*. Letters other than *f* are also used for names of functions. For example, $g(x) = 2x$ and $h(x) = -x + 6$ are also written in functional notation.

In a function, *x* represents the domain values, and $f(x)$ represents the range values.

$$\underset{f(x)}{} = 4x + 10$$
range   domain

$f(3)$ represents the element in the range that corresponds to the element 3 in the domain. To find $f(3)$, substitute 3 for *x* in the function and simplify.

Read $f(3)$ as f of 3.

$f(x) = 4x + 10$ Write the function.
$f(3) = 4(3) + 10$ Replace x with 3.
$f(3) = 12 + 10$ or 22   Simplify.

So, the functional value of *f* for $x = 3$ is 22.

Reading to Learn

1. **RESEARCH** Use the Internet or a dictionary to find the everyday meaning of the word *function*. Write a sentence describing how the everyday meaning relates to the mathematical meaning. **See margin.**

2. Write your own rule for remembering how the domain and the range are represented using functional notation. **Sample answer: *x* represents the domain; *y* represents the range.**

3. Copy and complete the table below.

x	f(x) = 3x + 5	f(x)
0	$f(0) = 3(0) + 5$	5
1	$f(1) = 3(1) + 5$	8
2	$f(2) = 3(2) + 5$	11
3	$f(3) = 3(3) + 5$	14

4. If $f(x) = 4x - 1$, find each value.
   a. $f(2)$ **7**   b. $f(-3)$ **−13**   c. $f\left(\frac{1}{2}\right)$ **1**

5. Find the value of *x* if $f(x) = -2x + 5$ and the value of $f(x)$ is −7. **6**

Answer

1. Sample answer: One meaning of the word *function* is purpose. In mathematics, the purpose of a function is to assign each value of the domain exactly one range value.

Graphing Linear Equations Using Intercepts

What You'll Learn

- Find the *x*- and *y*-intercepts of graphs.
- Graph linear equations using the *x*- and *y*-intercepts.

Vocabulary

- *x*-intercept
- *y*-intercept

How can intercepts be used to represent real-life information?

The relationship between the temperature in degrees Fahrenheit F and the temperature in degrees Celsius C is given by the equation $F = \frac{9}{5}C + 32$. This equation is graphed at the right.

a. Write the ordered pair for the point where the graph intersects the *y*-axis. What does this point represent?

b. Write the ordered pair for the point where the graph intersects the *x*-axis. What does this point represent?

a. (0, 32); a temperature of 0°C equals 32°F.

b. (−18, 0); a temperature of approximately −18°C equals 0°F.

Reading Math

Intercept

Everyday Meaning: to interrupt or cut off

Math Meaning: the point where a coordinate axis crosses a line

---

NEW YORK
Performance Indicator

8.G.14 Determine the y-intercept of a line from a graph and be able to explain the y-intercept

FIND INTERCEPTS

The **x-intercept** is the *x*-coordinate of a point where a graph crosses the *x*-axis. The *y*-coordinate of this point is 0.

The **y-intercept** is the *y*-coordinate of a point where a graph crosses the *y*-axis. The *x*-coordinate of this point is 0.

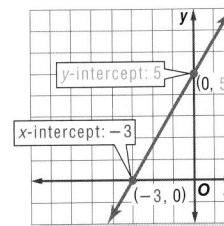

Example 1 Find Intercepts From Graphs

State the *x*-intercept and the *y*-intercept of each line.

a.

b.

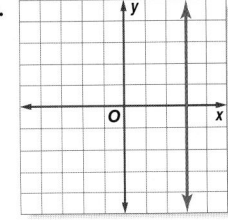

The graph crosses the *x*-axis at (4, 0). The *x*-intercept is 4. The graph crosses the *y*-axis at (0, −2). The *y*-intercept is −2.

The graph crosses the *x*-axis at (3, 0). The *x*-intercept is 3. The graph does not cross the *y*-axis. There is no *y*-intercept.

✓ **Concept Check** A graph passes through a point at (0, −10). Is −10 an *x*-intercept or a *y*-intercept? **y-intercept**

---

1 Focus

 5-Minute Check Transparency 8-3 Use as a quiz or review of Lesson 8-2.

Mathematical Background notes are available for this lesson on page 366C.

How can intercepts be used to represent real-life information?

The opening activity questions are repeated on page 430 of the *Chapter 8 Resource Masters.*

Reading to Learn Mathematics, p. 430 **ELL**

Pre-Activity How can intercepts be used to represent real-life information?
Do the activity at the top of page 381 in your textbook. Write your answers below.

a. Write the ordered pair for the point where the graph intersects the *y*-axis. What does this point represent? (0, 32); a temperature of 0°C equals 32°F.

b. Write the ordered pair for the point where the graph intersects the *x*-axis. What does this point represent? (−18, 0); a temperature of approximately −18°C equals 0°F.

Reading the Lesson 1–2. See students' work.
Write a definition and give an example of each new vocabulary word.

Vocabulary	Definition	Example
1. *x*-intercept		
2. *y*-intercept		

3. The **y-coordinate** of the *x*-intercept is 0.
The **x-coordinate** of the *y*-intercept is 0.

4. Draw a model on the coordinate grid that shows how to graph a line using the *x*-intercept and the *y*-intercept of a line. Explain your model.

 Sample answer: The *x*-intercept is 5, which means that one point of the graph is at (5, 0). The *y*-intercept is 3, which means that another point of the graph is at (0, 3). Graph both points on the grid and draw a line through them.

5. Is a line with no *x*-intercept vertical or horizontal? Explain. **Horizontal;** if a line has no *x*-intercept, the line will never cross the *x*-axis. Therefore, the line must be parallel to the *x*-axis.

Helping You Remember

6. The word *intercept* has many synonyms in English. Look up intercept in a thesaurus and find one or two synonyms that help you remember the mathematical meaning of the word. Explain your selection. **Sample answer:** cut off; The *y*-intercept is where the *y*-axis cuts off the line; the *x*-intercept is where the *x*-axis cuts off the line.

---

2 Teach

FIND INTERCEPTS

 In-Class Examples 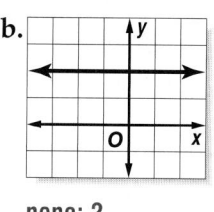 Power Point®

1 State the x-intercept and the y-intercept of each line.

a.

b.

−2; −2   none; 2

2 Find the x-intercept and the y-intercept for the graph of $x + 2y = 4$.   4; 2

GRAPH EQUATIONS

 In-Class Examples 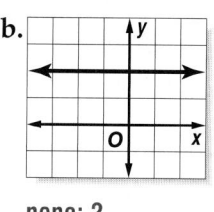 Power Point®

3 Graph $y = 3x - 6$ using the x- and y-intercepts.

4 HOME REPAIR Renata Jones has $300 for home repairs. A plumber charges her $50 an hour. The equation $y = -50x + 300$ represents the amount of money left in her budget after x number of plumbing hours.

a. Use the intercepts to graph the equation.

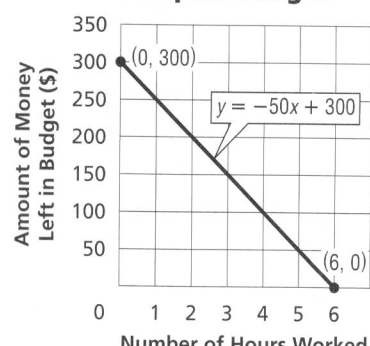

Home Repair Budget

You can also find the x-intercept and the y-intercept from an equation of a line.

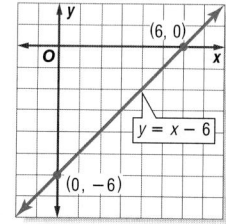

> **Key Concept** **Intercepts of Lines**
>
> - To find the x-intercept, let $y = 0$ in the equation and solve for x.
> - To find the y-intercept, let $x = 0$ in the equation and solve for y.

Example 2 Find Intercepts from Equations

Find the x-intercept and the y-intercept for the graph of $y = x - 6$.

To find the x-intercept, let $y = 0$.

$y = x - 6$	Write the equation.
$0 = x - 6$	Replace y with 0.
$6 = x$	Simplify.

The x-intercept is 6.   So, the graph crosses the x-axis at $(6, 0)$.

To find the y-intercept, let $x = 0$.

$y = x - 6$	Write the equation.
$y = 0 - 6$	Replace x with 0.
$y = -6$	Simplify.

The y-intercept is -6.   So, the graph crosses the y-axis at $(0, -6)$.

GRAPH EQUATIONS   You can use the x- and y-intercepts to graph equations of lines.

In Example 2, we determined that the graph of $y = x - 6$ passes through $(6, 0)$ and $(0, -6)$. To draw the graph, plot these points and draw a line through them.

Example 3 Use Intercepts to Graph Equations

Graph $x + 2y = 4$ using the x- and y-intercepts.

Step 1
Find the x-intercept.

$x + 2y = 4$	Write the equation.
$x + 2(0) = 4$	Let $y = 0$.
$x = 4$	Simplify.

The x-intercept is 4, so the graph passes through $(4, 0)$.

Step 2
Find the y-intercept.

$x + 2y = 4$	Write the equation.
$0 + 2y = 4$	Let $x = 0$.
$y = 2$	Divide each side by 2.

The y-intercept is 2, so the graph passes through $(0, 2)$.

Step 3
Graph the points at $(4, 0)$ and $(0, 2)$ and draw a line through them.

CHECK   Choose some other point on the line and determine whether its ordered pair is a solution of $x + 2y = 4$.

 Study Tip

Graphing Shortcuts
The ordered pairs of any two solutions can be used to graph a linear equation. However, it is often easiest to find the intercepts.

b. Describe what the intercepts mean.   **The y-intercept shows how much money Renata has in her budget before any work is done. The x-intercept means that she can afford only 6 hours of plumbing repair.**

More About. . .

Earth Science •········
The temperature of the air is about 3°F cooler for every 1000 feet increase in altitude.

Source: www.hot-air-balloons.com

Example 4 *Intercepts of Real-World Data*

•**EARTH SCIENCE** Suppose you take a hot-air balloon ride on a day when the temperature is 24°C at sea level. The equation $y = -6.6x + 24$ represents the temperature at x kilometers above sea level.

a. Use the intercepts to graph the equation.

Step 1 Find the x-intercept.

$y = -6.6x + 24$	Write the equation.
$0 = -6.6x + 24$	Replace y with 0.
$0 - 24 = -6.6x + 24 - 24$	Subtract 24 from each side.
$\dfrac{-24}{-6.6} = \dfrac{-6.6x}{-6.6}$	Divide each side by -6.6.
$3.6 \approx x$	The x-intercept is approximately 3.6.

Step 2 Find the y-intercept.

$y = -6.6x + 24$	Write the equation.
$y = -6.6(0) + 24$	Replace x with 0.
$y = 24$	The y-intercept is 24.

Step 3 Plot the points with coordinates (3.6, 0) and (0, 24). Then draw a line through the points.

Temperature Above Sea Level

b. Describe what the intercepts mean.

The x-intercept 3.6 means that when the hot-air balloon is 3.6 kilometers above sea level, the temperature is 0°C. The y-intercept 24 means that the temperature at sea level is 24°C.

TEACHING TIP
Point out to students that when real-life data are represented by a linear function, the intercepts of the graph of the function often reveal useful information.

Some linear equations have just one variable. Their graphs are horizontal or vertical lines.

Example 5 *Horizontal and Vertical Lines*

Graph each equation using the x- and y-intercepts.

Reading Math

• $y = 3$ can be read for all x, $y = 3$.
• $x = -2$ can be read for all y, $x = -2$.

a. $y = 3$

Note that $y = 3$ is the same as $0x + y = 3$. The y-intercept is 3, and there is no x-intercept.

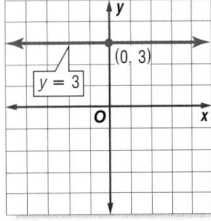

b. $x = -2$

Note that $x = -2$ is the same as $x + 0y = -2$. The x-intercept is -2, and there is no y-intercept.

---

 www.pre-alg.com/extra_examples/ny   **Lesson 8-3** Graphing Linear Equations Using Intercepts **383**

---

5 Graph each equation using the x- and y-intercepts.

a. $y = -4$

b. $x = 5$

Study Guide and Intervention, p. 427

Finding Intercepts	
The x-intercept is the x-coordinate of a point where a graph crosses the x-axis. The y-coordinate of this point is 0.	To find the x-intercept, let $y = 0$ in the equation and solve for x.
The y-intercept is the y-coordinate of a point where a graph crosses the y-axis. The x-coordinate of this point is 0.	To find the y-intercept, let $x = 0$ in the equation and solve for y.

Example 1 Find the x-intercept and the y-intercept for the graph of $2x + 5y = 10$.

To find the x-intercept, let $y = 0$.
$2x + 5y = 10$	Write the equation.
$2x + 5(0) = 10$	Replace y with 0.
$x = 5$	Simplify.

To find the y-intercept, let $x = 0$.
$2x + 5y = 10$	Write the equation.
$2(0) + 5y = 10$	Replace x with 0.
$y = 2$	Simplify.

Example 2 Graph $2x + 5y = 10$.

Exercises

Find the x-intercept and the y-intercept for the graph of each equation.

1. $y = x - 5$ 2. $y - 1 = 0$ 3. $3x - 2y = 12$
   5; -5 none; 1   4; -6

Graph each equation using the x- and y-intercepts.

4. $y = -3x - 3$ 5. $y = x + 5$ 6. $y = -x + 9$

Skills Practice, p. 428 and Practice, p. 429 (shown)

Find the x-intercept and the y-intercept for the graph of each equation.

1. $y = 2x - 2$ 2. $y + 4 = 0$ 3. $y = 3x + 9$
   1, -2 none, -4 -3, 9
4. $6x + 12y = 24$ 5. $5x - 3y = 15$ 6. $-x - 7 = 0$
   4, 2   3, -5 -7, none

Graph each equation using the x- and y-intercepts.

7. $y = x - 7$ 8. $y = -x + 5$ 9. $y = 2x - 4$

10. $y = -\frac{1}{4}x - 1$ 11. $5x + 2y = 10$ 12. $x = 2$

13. **SAVINGS** Rashid's grandparents started a savings account for him, contributing $1000. He deposits $430 each month into the account. The equation $y = 430x + 1000$ represents how much money is in the savings account after x number of months. Graph the equation and explain what the y-intercept means.
The y-intercept 1000 shows how much money was in the savings account before Rashid made any deposits.

Enrichment, p. 431

Curves

Step 1	Make a table of ordered pairs that satisfy the equation.	If you know the graph is going to be a straight line, then you only need two points (a third one as a check). But if the graph is going to be a curved line, then you need enough points to be able to sketch a nice smooth curve. This may be 5 or more points.
Step 2	Graph each point.	
Step 3	Draw a smooth curve connecting the points.	

Sketch a smooth curve through the points shown. The right side of the first curve has been done for you.

1.   2.   3.

Graph each equation.

4. $y = 2x^2$ 5. $y = x^2 + 2$ 6. $y = x^2 - 1$

x	-2	-1.5	-1	0	1	1.5	2
y	8	4.5	2	0	2	4.5	8

x	-3	-2	-1	0	1	2	3
y	8	3	0	-1	0	3	8

x	-3	-2	-1	0	1	2	3
y	11	6	3	2	3	6	11

Lesson 8-3 Graphing Linear Equations Using Intercepts **383**

Study Notebook

Have students—
- add the definitions/examples of the vocabulary terms to their Vocabulary Builder worksheets for Chapter 8.
- copy the Key Concept box and add a graph for each item.
- include any other item(s) that they find helpful in mastering the skills in this lesson.

About the Exercises . . .

Organization by Objective
- Find Intercepts: 12–24, 36
- Graph Equations: 25–35

Odd/Even Assignments
Exercises 12–35 are structured so that students practice the same concepts whether they are assigned odd or even problems.

Alert! Exercises 8–11, 25–35, 37, and 38 require graph paper.

Assignment Guide

Basic: 13–31 odd, 35, 37–53
Average: 13–37 odd, 38–53
Advanced: 12–36 even, 37–49
(Optional: 50–53)

Answers

1. To find the *x*-intercept, let $y = 0$ and solve for *x*. To find the *y*-intercept, let $x = 0$ and solve for *y*.

2. Sample answer:

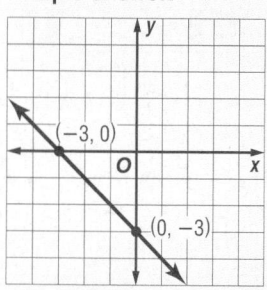

Check for Understanding

Concept Check
1–2. See margin.

1. **Explain** how to find the *x*- and *y*-intercepts of a line given its equation.

2. **OPEN ENDED** Sketch the graph of a function whose *x*- and *y*-intercepts are both negative. Label the intercepts.

Guided Practice

State the *x*-intercept and the *y*-intercept of each line.

GUIDED PRACTICE KEY	
Exercises	Examples
3, 4	1
5–7	2
8–10	3, 5
11	4

3.   −1; −3

4.   5; none

Find the *x*-intercept and the *y*-intercept for the graph of each equation.

5. $y = x + 4$ **−4; 4**
6. $y = 7$ **none; 7**
7. $2x + 3y = 6$ **3; 2**

Graph each equation using the *x*- and *y*-intercepts. **8–10. See margin.**

8. $y = x + 1$
9. $x - 2y = 6$
10. $x = -1$

Application

11. **BUSINESS** A lawn mowing service charges a base fee of $3, plus $6 per hour for labor. This can be represented by $y = 6x + 3$, where *y* is the total cost and *x* is the number of hours. Graph this equation and explain what the *y*-intercept represents. **See pp. 431A–431H.**

★ indicates increased difficulty

Practice and Apply

Homework Help

For Exercises	See Examples
12–15	1
16–24	2
25–33	3, 5
34, 35	4

Extra Practice
See page 742.

State the *x*-intercept and the *y*-intercept of each line.

12.   −3; 2

13.   1; 1

14.   −4; −6

15. 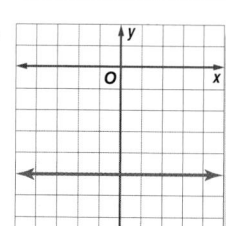   none; −5

Find the *x*-intercept and the *y*-intercept for the graph of each equation.

16. $y = x - 1$ **1; −1**
17. $y = x + 5$ **−5; 5**
18. $x = 9$ **9; none**
19. $y + 4 = 0$ **none; −4**
20. $y = 2x + 10$ **−5; 10**
21. $x - 2y = 8$ **8; −4**
22. $y = -3x - 12$ **−4; −12**
23. $4x + 5y = 20$ **5; 4**
★ 24. $6x + 7y = 12$ **2; $\frac{12}{7}$**

Answers

8.

9.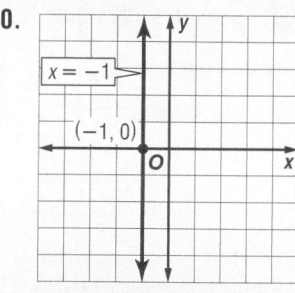

10.

25–33. See pp. 431A–431H.

Graph each equation using the x- and y-intercepts.

25. $y = x + 2$ 26. $y = x - 3$ 27. $x + y = 4$

28. $y = 5x + 5$ 29. $y = -2x + 4$ 30. $x + 2y = -6$

31. $y = -2$ 32. $x - 3 = 0$ ★33. $3x + 6y = 18$

TEACHING TIP
Discuss the difference between continuous and discrete sets of data. For example, temperature is continuous; books and people are discrete.

34. **CATERING** For a luncheon, a caterer charges $8 per person, plus a setup fee of $24. The total cost of the luncheon y can be represented by $y = 8x + 24$, where x is the number of people. Graph the equation and explain what the y-intercept represents. **See margin.**

35. **MONEY** Jasmine has $18 to buy books at the library used book sale. Paperback books cost $3 each. The equation $y = 18 - 3x$ represents the amount of money she has left over if she buys x paperback books. Graph the equation and describe what the intercepts represent. **See margin.**

36. 25; 25; They represent one dimension when the other dimension is 0, which is impossible for a rectangle.

★36. **GEOMETRY** The perimeter of a rectangle is 50 centimeters. This can be given by the equation $50 = 2\ell + 2w$, where ℓ is the length and w is the width. Name the x- and y-intercepts of the equation and explain what they mean.

37. **CRITICAL THINKING** Explain why you cannot graph $y = 2x$ by using intercepts only. Then draw the graph. **See pp. 431A–431H.**

38. WRITING IN MATH   Answer the question that was posed at the beginning of the lesson. **See pp. 431A–431H.**

How can intercepts be used to represent real-life information?

Include the following in your answer:

• a graph showing a decrease in temperature, with the x-axis representing time and the y-axis representing temperature, and

• an explanation of what the intercepts mean.

NEW YORK
Test Practice

Standardized Test Practice
Ⓐ Ⓑ Ⓒ Ⓓ

39. What is the x-intercept of the graph of $y = 8x - 32$? **B**
   Ⓐ −4   Ⓑ 4   Ⓒ −32   Ⓓ 32

40. The graph of which equation does *not* have a y-intercept of 3? **C**
   Ⓐ $2x + 3y = 9$ Ⓑ $4x + y = 3$ Ⓒ $x + 3y = 6$ Ⓓ $x - 2y = -6$

Maintain Your Skills

Mixed Review
41–43. See margin for sample answers.

Find four solutions of each equation. *(Lesson 8-2)*

41. $y = 2x + 7$ 42. $y = -3x + 1$ 43. $4x - y = -5$

Determine whether each relation is a function. *(Lesson 8-1)*

44. $\{(2, 12), (4, -5), (-3, -4), (11, 0)\}$ **yes**

45. $\{(-4.2, 17), (-4.3, 16), (-4.3, 15), (-4.3, 14)\}$ **no**

Solve each inequality. *(Lesson 7-4)*

46. $y + 3 < 5$ **y < 2**   47. $-2 + n > 10$ **n > 12**   48. $7 \le x + 8$ **x ≥ −1**

49. Express 0.028 as a percent. *(Lesson 6-4)* **2.8%**

Getting Ready for the Next Lesson   **PREREQUISITE SKILL** Subtract. *(To review subtracting integers, see Lesson 2-3.)*

50. $-11 - 13$ **−24**   51. $15 - 31$ **−16**   52. $-26 - (-26)$ **0**   53. $9 - (-16)$ **25**

DAILY INTERVENTION   **Differentiated Instruction**

• **Visual/Spatial** Bring in weather reports clipped from the newspaper showing temperatures in both Fahrenheit and Celsius degrees. A page of temperatures in different cities around the world would work well. Make a large graph on the chalkboard similar to the one in the opening activity. Have each student plot a city's Fahrenheit and Celsius temperatures on the graph. After all the points have been plotted, ask the class what the graph looks like. **a straight line; a function**

4 Assess

Open-Ended Assessment
Modeling Have students list the steps necessary to graph a linear equation using the x- and y-intercepts.

Getting Ready for Lesson 8-4

PREREQUISITE SKILL In Lesson 8-4, students will subtract x and y values to find slope. Exercises 50–53 should be used to determine your students' familiarity with subtracting integers.

Assessment Options

Quiz (Lessons 8-1 through 8-3) is available on p. 481 of the *Chapter 8 Resource Masters.*

Answers

34.

The y-intercept 24 represents the setup fee.

35.

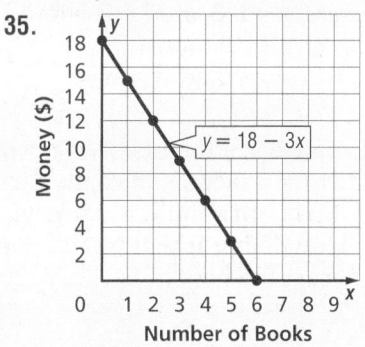

The x-intercept 6 represents the number of books she can buy with no money left over. The y-intercept 18 represents the money she has before she buys any books.

41. $(-1, 5)$, $(0, 7)$, $(1, 9)$, $(2, 11)$

42. $(-1, 4)$, $(0, 1)$, $(1, -2)$, $(2, -5)$

43. $(-1, 1)$, $(0, 5)$, $(1, 9)$, $(2, 13)$

Algebra Activity

A Preview of Lesson 8-4

Getting Started

Objective Explore slope by examining how fast an object rolls down various hills.

Materials
posterboard or wooden board
tape
books
ruler
toy car

Teach

- Use smaller toy cars that are not carried beyond the length of the room by their weight. Also, be sure that students do not push the cars when releasing them down the hill.
- Watch for students who need reassurance while calculating slope.
- Point out that slope is expressed as an integer or an improper fraction, and never as a mixed number.

Assess

In **Exercises 1–3,** students should discover the relationship between slope and distance traveled.

In **Exercise 4,** students need not predict the exact distance the car will travel but should accurately predict whether it will travel farther on the new hill.

Study Notebook

You may wish to have students summarize this activity and what they learned from it.

NEW YORK *Performance Indicator* **8.G.13 Determine the slope of a line from a graph and explain the meaning of slope as a constant rate of change**

It's All Downhill

The steepness, or *slope*, of a hill can be described by a ratio.

$$\text{slope} = \frac{\text{vertical change}}{\text{horizontal change}} \begin{array}{l} \leftarrow \text{height} \\ \leftarrow \text{length} \end{array}$$

Collect the Data

Step 1 Use posterboard or a wooden board, tape, and three or more books to make a "hill."

Step 2 Measure the height y and length x of the hill to the nearest $\frac{1}{2}$ inch or $\frac{1}{4}$ inch. Record the measurements in a table like the one below.

Hill	Height y (in.)	Length x (in.)	Car Distance (in.)	Slope $\frac{y}{x}$
1				
2				
3				

Step 3 Place a toy car at the top of the hill and let it roll down. Measure the distance from the bottom of the ramp to the back of the car when it stops. Record the distance in the table.

Step 4 For the second hill, increase the height by adding one or two more books. Roll the car down and measure the distance it rolls. Record the dimensions of the hill and the distance in the table.

Step 5 Take away two or three books so that hill 3 has the least height. Roll the car down and measure the distance it rolls. Record the dimensions of the hill and the distance in the table.

Step 6 Find the slopes of hills 1, 2, and 3 and record the values in the table.

Analyze the Data   1. slope increased   2. slope decreased

1. How did the slope change when the height increased and the length decreased?

2. How did the slope change when the height decreased and the length increased?

3. **MAKE A CONJECTURE**   On which hill would a toy car roll the farthest—a hill with slope $\frac{18}{25}$ or $\frac{25}{18}$? Explain by describing the relationship between slope and distance traveled. $\frac{25}{18}$ because it is greater than $\frac{18}{25}$; the greater the slope, the farther the toy car traveled.

Extend the Activity

4. Make a fourth hill. Find its slope and predict the distance a toy car will go when it rolls down the hill. Test your prediction by rolling a car down the hill.

4. The car will travel farther if the slope is greater than the other slopes and less far if the slope is less than the other slopes.

Resource Manager

📁 **Teaching Pre-Algebra with Manipulatives**
- p. 22 (master for rulers)
- p. 106 (student recording sheet)

Glencoe Mathematics Classroom Manipulative Kit
- rulers

8-4 # Slope

NEW YORK *Performance Indicator* **8.G.13 Determine the slope of a line from a graph and explain the meaning of slope as a constant rate of change**

What You'll Learn

- Find the slope of a line.

How is slope used to describe roller coasters?

Some roller coasters can make you feel heavier than a shuttle astronaut feels on liftoff. This is because the speed and steepness of the hills increase the effects of gravity.

56 ft

42 ft

Vocabulary
- slope

a. Use the roller coaster to write the ratio $\frac{\text{height}}{\text{length}}$ in simplest form. $\frac{4}{3}$

b. Find the ratio of a hill that has the same length but is 14 feet higher than the hill above. Is this hill steeper or less steep than the original? $\frac{5}{3}$; steeper

---

TEACHING TIP

Encourage students to orally relate the *x* value, or domain, with a move to the right or left and the *y* value, or range, with a move up or down.

SLOPE **Slope** describes the steepness of a line. It is the ratio of the *rise*, or the vertical change, to the *run*, or the horizontal change.

$$\text{slope} = \frac{\text{rise}}{\text{run}} \quad \leftarrow \text{vertical change} \\ \leftarrow \text{horizontal change}$$

$$= \frac{4}{3}$$

Note that the slope is the same for any two points on a straight line.

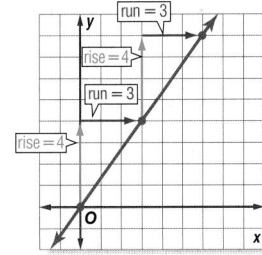

run = 3
rise = 4
run = 3
rise = 4

Example 1 Use Rise and Run to Find Slope

Find the slope of a road that rises 25 feet for every horizontal change of 80 feet.

$$\text{slope} = \frac{\text{rise}}{\text{run}} \qquad \text{Write the formula.}$$

$$= \frac{25 \text{ ft}}{80 \text{ ft}} \qquad \text{rise} = 25 \text{ ft, run} = 80 \text{ ft}$$

$$= \frac{5}{16} \qquad \text{Simplify.}$$

The slope of the road is $\frac{5}{16}$ or 0.3125.

25 ft

80 ft

✓ **Concept Check** What is the slope of a ramp that rises 2 inches for every horizontal change of 24 inches? $\frac{1}{12}$

Lesson 8-4 Slope **387**

8-4 # Lesson Notes

1 Focus

 5-Minute Check Transparency 8-4 Use as a quiz or review of Lesson 8-3.

Mathematical Background notes are available for this lesson on page 366C.

How is slope used to describe roller coasters?

The opening activity questions are repeated on page 435 of the *Chapter 8 Resource Masters.*

Reading to Learn Mathematics, p. 435 — ELL

Pre-Activity *How is slope used to describe roller coasters?*

Do the activity at the top of page 387 in your textbook. Write your answers below.

a. Use the roller coaster to write the ratio $\frac{\text{height}}{\text{length}}$ in simplest form. $\frac{4}{3}$

b. Find the ratio of a hill that has the same length but is 14 feet higher than the hill on page 387. Is this hill steeper or less steep than the original? $\frac{5}{3}$; steeper

Reading the Lesson

Write a definition and give an example of the new vocabulary word.

Vocabulary	Definition	Example
1. slope	See students' work.	

Complete each sentence.

2. Slope is _the same_ for any two points on the line.

3. A line that slopes downward from left to right has a _negative_ slope.

4. A line that slopes upward from left to right has a _positive_ slope.

5. A horizontal line has a _zero_ slope.

6. The slope of a vertical line is _undefined_.

Helping You Remember

7. For each graph, draw a line with the given slope.

a. Positive   b. Negative   c. Zero   d. Undefined

See students' graphs.

Resource Manager

📁 Workbooks and Reproducible Masters

Chapter 8 Resource Masters
- Study Guide and Intervention, p. 432
- Skills Practice, p. 433
- Practice, p. 434
- Reading to Learn Mathematics, p. 435
- Enrichment, p. 436

Parent and Student Study Guide Workbook, p. 64

Transparencies

5-Minute Check Transparency 8-4
Answer Key Transparencies

💿 Technology

Interactive Chalkboard
Pre-AlgePASS: Tutorial Plus, Lesson 23

2 Teach

SLOPE

In-Class Examples ... Power Point®

1 Find the slope of a hill that rises 30 feet for every horizontal change of 150 feet. $\frac{1}{5}$

2 Find the slope of the line.

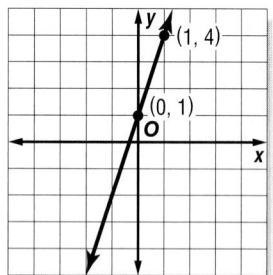

3

3 Find the slope of the line.

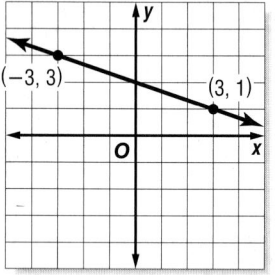

$-\frac{1}{3}$

Teaching Tip Point out that mental math should be sufficient to find the answer to Example 4.

4 Find the slope of the line.

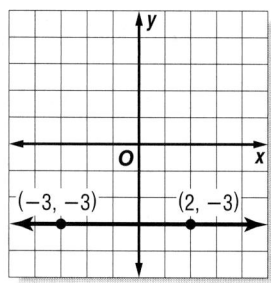

0

You can also find the slope by using the coordinates of any two points on a line.

Key Concept — **Slope**

- **Words**   The slope m of a line passing through points at (x_1, y_1) and (x_2, y_2) is the ratio of the difference in y-coordinates to the corresponding difference in x-coordinates.

- **Model**

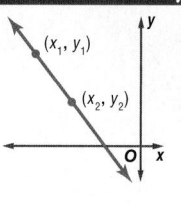

- **Symbols** $m = \dfrac{y_2 - y_1}{x_2 - x_1}$, where $x_2 \neq x_1$

The slope of a line may be positive, negative, zero, or undefined.

Study Tip

Choosing Points
- Any two points on a line can be chosen as (x_1, y_1) and (x_2, y_2).
- The coordinates of both points must be used in the same order.

Check: In Example 2, let $(x_1, y_1) = (5, 3)$ and let $(x_2, y_2) = (2, 2)$, then find the slope.

Example 2   *Positive Slope*

Find the slope of the line.

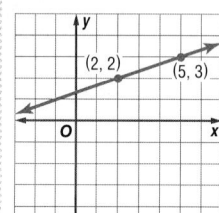

$m = \dfrac{y_2 - y_1}{x_2 - x_1}$ Definition of slope

$m = \dfrac{3 - 2}{5 - 2}$ $(x_1, y_1) = (2, 2)$, $(x_2, y_2) = (5, 3)$

$m = \dfrac{1}{3}$

The slope is $\dfrac{1}{3}$.

Example 3   *Negative Slope*

Find the slope of the line.

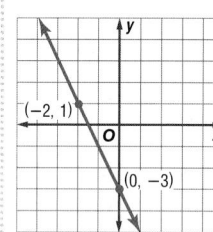

$m = \dfrac{y_2 - y_1}{x_2 - x_1}$ Definition of slope

$m = \dfrac{-3 - 1}{0 - (-2)}$ $(x_1, y_1) = (-2, 1)$, $(x_2, y_2) = (0, -3)$

$m = \dfrac{-4}{2}$ or -2

The slope is -2.

Example 4   *Zero Slope*

Find the slope of the line.

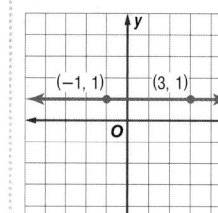

$m = \dfrac{y_2 - y_1}{x_2 - x_1}$ Definition of slope

$m = \dfrac{1 - 1}{3 - (-1)}$ $(x_1, y_1) = (-1, 1)$, $(x_2, y_2) = (3, 1)$

$m = \dfrac{0}{4}$ or 0

The slope is 0.

388   **Chapter 8**   Functions and Graphing

DAILY INTERVENTION

Differentiated Instruction

- **Naturalist** Have students collect data on the slant of several tree branches. They should consider the point where a branch connects with the trunk to be the origin. Then they should measure the rise and the run. They can number the branches and organize the data in a chart. Then, back in the classroom, they can graph the branches and label them on the graph.

Example 5 **Undefined Slope**

Find the slope of the line.

$$m = \frac{y_2 - y_1}{x_2 - x_1} \quad \text{Definition of slope}$$

$$m = \frac{0 - 6}{-5 - (-5)} \quad \begin{array}{l}(x_1, y_1) = (-5, 6),\\ (x_2, y_2) = (-5, 0)\end{array}$$

$$m = \frac{-6}{0}$$

Division by 0 is undefined. So, the slope is undefined.

The steepness of real-world inclines can be compared by using slope.

Example 6 **Compare Slopes**

Multiple-Choice Test Item

There are two major hills on a hiking trail. The first hill rises 6 feet vertically for every 42-foot run. The second hill rises 10 feet vertically for every 98-foot run. Which statement is true?

Ⓐ The first hill is steeper than the second hill.

Ⓑ The second hill is steeper than the first hill.

Ⓒ Both hills have the same steepness.

Ⓓ You cannot determine which hill is steeper.

Read the Test Item To compare steepness of the hills, find the slopes.

Solve the Test Item

first hill

$$\text{slope} = \frac{\text{rise}}{\text{run}}$$

$$= \frac{6 \text{ ft}}{42 \text{ ft}} \quad \text{rise = 6 ft, run = 42 ft}$$

$$= \frac{1}{7} \text{ or about 0.14}$$

second hill

$$\text{slope} = \frac{\text{rise}}{\text{run}}$$

$$= \frac{10 \text{ ft}}{98 \text{ ft}} \quad \text{rise = 10 ft, run = 98 ft}$$

$$= \frac{5}{49} \text{ or about 0.10}$$

$0.14 > 0.10$, so the first hill is steeper than the second. The answer is A.

Test-Taking Tip

Make a Drawing
Whenever possible, make a drawing that displays the given information. Then use the drawing to estimate the answer.

Check for Understanding

Concept Check
1. **Describe** your own method for remembering whether a horizontal line has 0 slope or an undefined slope.

2. **OPEN ENDED** Draw a line whose slope is $-\frac{1}{4}$. **See margin.**

3. **FIND THE ERROR** Mike and Chloe are finding the slope of the line that passes through $Q(-2, 8)$ and $R(11, 7)$.

1. Sample answer: horizontals do not rise, so slope $= \frac{\text{rise}}{\text{run}} = \frac{0}{\text{run}}$ or 0.

3. Mike; Chloe should have subtracted -2 from 11 in the denominator.

Mike
$$m = \frac{8 - 7}{-2 - 11}$$

Chloe
$$m = \frac{7 - 8}{11 - 2}$$

Who is correct? Explain your reasoning.

 www.pre-alg.com/extra_examples/ny

Lesson 8-4 Slope **389**

Answer

2. Sample answer:

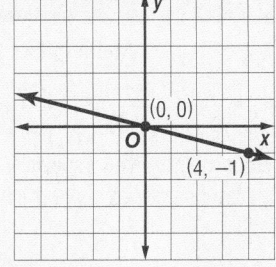

5 Find the slope of the line.

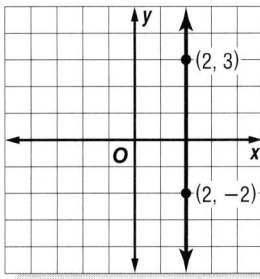

undefined

6 **Multiple-Choice Test Item**
Two highway routes connect City A and City B. The first route rises 4 yards vertically for every 30-mile stretch. The second route rises 8 yards vertically for every 70-mile stretch. Which statement is true? **A**

A The first route is steeper than the second route.

B The second route is steeper than the first route.

C Both routes have the same steepness.

D You cannot determine which route is steeper.

3 Practice/Apply

Study Notebook

Have students—
• add the definition/example of the vocabulary term to their Vocabulary Builder worksheets for Chapter 8.
• include a sample equation, graph, and slope for each of the following: positive slope, negative slope, zero slope, and undefined slope.
• include any other item(s) that they find helpful in mastering the skills in this lesson.

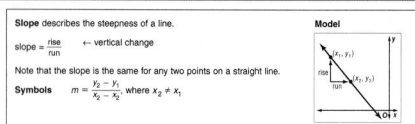

Study Guide and Intervention, p. 432

Slope describes the steepness of a line.

slope = $\frac{rise}{run}$ ← vertical change

Note that the slope is the same for any two points on a straight line.

Model

Symbols $m = \frac{y_2 - y_1}{x_2 - x_1}$, where $x_2 \neq x_1$

Example Find the slope of the line.

$m = \frac{y_2 - y_1}{x_2 - x_1}$ Definition of slope

$m = \frac{4 - 1}{9 - 5}$ $(x_1, y_1) = (5, 1)$
            $(x_2, y_2) = (9, 4)$

$m = \frac{3}{4}$

The slope is $\frac{3}{4}$.

Exercises

Find the slope of each line.

1.   2.   3.

$-\frac{1}{4}$ 3 $-\frac{4}{5}$

Find the slope of the line that passes through each pair of points.

4. $A(2, 2), B(-5, 4)$ 5. $L(5, 5), M(4, 2)$ 6. $R(7, -4), S(7, 3)$
$-\frac{2}{7}$ 3   undefined

Skills Practice, p. 433 and Practice, p. 434 (shown)

Find the slope of each line.

1.   2.   3.

4      $\frac{2}{3}$ -5

Find the slope of the line that passes through each pair of points.

4. $A(-10, 6), B(-5, 8)$ 5. $C(7, -3), D(11, -4)$ 6. $E(5, 2), F(12, -3)$
$\frac{2}{5}$ $-\frac{1}{4}$ $-\frac{5}{7}$

7. $G(-15, 7), H(-10, 6)$ 8. $J(13, 0), K(-3, -12)$ 9. $L(-5, 3), M(-4, 9)$
$-\frac{1}{5}$ $\frac{3}{4}$ 6

10. $P(12, 2), Q(18, -2)$ 11. $R(-2, -3), S(-2, -5)$ 12. $T(-13, 8), U(21, 8)$
$-\frac{2}{3}$ undefined   0

13. **CAKES** A wedding cake measures 2 feet high in the center and the diameter of the bottom tier is 12 inches. What is the slope of the cake? 4

14. **INSECTS** One particularly large ant hill found in 1997 measured 40 inches wide at the base and 18 inches high. What was the slope of the ant hill? $\frac{9}{10}$

15. **ARCHAEOLOGY** Today, the Great Pyramid at Giza near Cairo, Egypt, stands 137 meters tall, coming to a point. Its base is a square with each side measuring 230 meters wide. What is the slope of the pyramid? $\frac{137}{115}$

16. **BUSINESS** One warehouse uses 8-foot long ramps to load its forklifts onto the flat beds of trucks for hauling. If the bed of a truck is 2 feet above the ground and the ramp is secured to the truck at its end, what is the slope of the ramp while in operation? $\frac{1}{4}$

Enrichment, p. 436

Investments

The graph below represents two different investments. Line A represents an initial investment of $30,000 at a bank paying passbook-savings interest. Line B represents an initial investment of $5000 in a profitable mutual fund with dividends reinvested and capital gains accepted in shares. By deriving the equation, $y = mx + b$, for A and B, a projection of the future can be made.

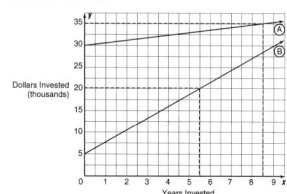

Solve.

1. The y-intercept, b, is the initial investment. Find b for each of the following.
   a. line A   30,000   b. line B   5000

2. The slope of the line, m, is the rate of return. Find m for each of the following.
   a. line A $\frac{35,000 - 30,000}{8.5 - 0} \approx 588$ b. line B $\frac{20,000 - 5000}{5.5 - 0} = 2727$

3. What are the equations of each of the following lines?
   a. line A $y = 588x + 30,000$ b. line B $y = 2727x + 5000$

Answer each of the following, assuming that the growth of each investment continues in the same pattern.

4. What will be the value of the mutual fund after the 11th year?
   $y = 2727(11) + 5000 = \$34,997$

5. What will be the value of the bank account after the 11th year?
   $y = 588(11) + 30,000 = \$36,468$

6. When will the mutual fund and the bank account be of equal value?
   $588x + 30,000 = 2727x + 5000 \rightarrow x \approx 11.7$ years

7. In the long term, which investment has the greater payoff?   mutual fund

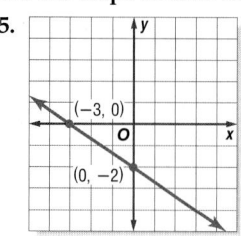

Guided Practice

GUIDED PRACTICE KEY

Exercises	Examples
4	1
5–10	2–5
11	6

4. Find the slope of a line that decreases 24 centimeters vertically for every 30-centimeter horizontal increase. $-\frac{4}{5}$

Find the slope of each line.

5. $-\frac{2}{3}$ 6.   0

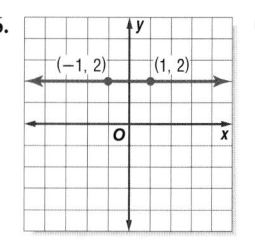

Find the slope of the line that passes through each pair of points.

7. $A(3, 4), B(4, 6)$ 2   8. $J(-8, 0), K(-8, 10)$ undefined

9. $P(7, -1), Q(9, -1)$ 0   10. $C(-6, -4), D(-8, -3)$ $-\frac{1}{2}$

NEW YORK Test Practice

Standardized Test Practice
Ⓐ Ⓑ Ⓒ Ⓓ

11. Which bike ramp is the steepest?   B
   Ⓐ 1
   Ⓑ 2
   Ⓒ 3
   Ⓓ 4

Bike Ramp	Height (ft)	Length (ft)
1	6	8
2	10	4
3	5	3
4	8	4

★ indicates increased difficulty

Practice and Apply

Homework Help

For Exercises	See Examples
12, 13	1
14–25	2–5
26, 27	6

Extra Practice
See page 742.

12. **CARPENTRY** In a stairway, the slope of the handrail is the ratio of the riser to the tread. If the tread is 12 inches long and the riser is 8 inches long, find the slope. $\frac{2}{3}$

13. **HOME REPAIR** The bottom of a ladder is placed 4 feet away from a house and it reaches a height of 16 feet on the side of the house. What is the slope of the ladder? 4

Find the slope of each line.

14.   1   15. $-\frac{3}{4}$

16.   undefined   17.   0

Teacher to Teacher

Rhonda Bailey   Mathematics Consultant, Richardson, TX

"I like for my students to use 1-inch grid paper and a game piece to allow students to 'move-out' a slope. Have them move toward the right and toward the left to understand what slope means. The experience of moving in the direction of the slope really becomes concrete when experienced in this manner."

Find the slope of the line that passes through each pair of points. 20. $-\dfrac{5}{8}$

23. undefined

18. $A(1, -3)$, $B(5, 4)$ $\dfrac{7}{4}$ 19. $Y(4, -3)$, $Z(5, -2)$ **1**   20. $D(5, -1)$, $E(-3, 4)$

21. $J(-3, 6)$, $K(-5, 9)$ $-\dfrac{3}{2}$ 22. $N(2, 6)$, $P(-1, 6)$ **0**   23. $S(-9, -4)$, $T(-9, 8)$

★ 24. $F(0, 1.6)$, $G(0.5, 2.1)$ **1**   ★ 25. $W\left(3\dfrac{1}{2}, 5\dfrac{1}{4}\right)$, $X\left(2\dfrac{1}{2}, 6\right)$ $-\dfrac{3}{4}$

ENTERTAINMENT For Exercises 26 and 27, use the graph.

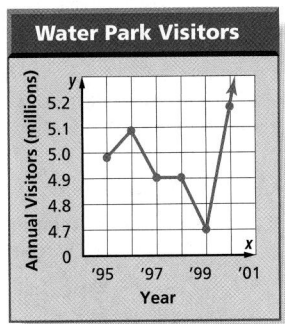

Water Park Visitors

Source: *Amusement Business*

★ 26. Which section of the graph shows the greatest increase in attendance? Describe the slope. **'99–'00; steep positive slope**

27. It decreased; negative slope.

★ 27. What happened to the attendance at the water park from 1996–1997? Describe the slope of this part of the graph.

28. $\dfrac{b}{a}$; the slope is the y-coordinate of C divided by the x-coordinate of C.

28. **CRITICAL THINKING** The graph of a line goes through the origin $(0, 0)$ and $C(a, b)$. State the slope of this line and explain how it relates to the coordinates of point C.

29. **WRITING IN MATH** Answer the question that was posed at the beginning of the lesson. **See margin.**

How is slope used to describe roller coasters?

Include the following in your answer:
- a description of slope, and
- an explanation of how changes in rise or run affect the steepness of a roller coaster.

NEW YORK Test Practice

Standardized Test Practice
Ⓐ Ⓑ Ⓒ Ⓓ

30. Identify the graph that has a positive slope. **D**

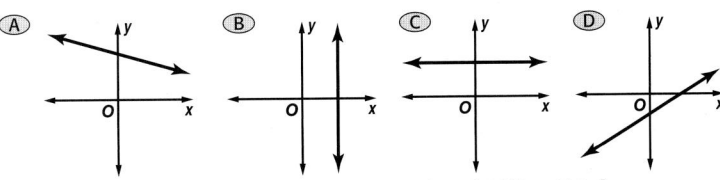

Ⓐ   Ⓑ   Ⓒ   Ⓓ

31. What is the slope of line LM given $L(9, -2)$ and $M(3, -5)$? **A**

Ⓐ $\dfrac{1}{2}$ Ⓑ $-\dfrac{1}{2}$ Ⓒ 5 Ⓓ $-\dfrac{1}{3}$

Maintain Your Skills

Mixed Review **Find the x-intercept and the y-intercept for the graph of each equation.**
(Lesson 8-3)

32. $y = x + 8$ **−8; 8**   33. $y = -3x + 6$ **2; 6**   34. $4x - y = 12$ **3; −12**

36. $(-1, 3)$, $(0, 0)$, $(1, -3)$, $(2, -6)$

37. $(-1, 8)$, $(0, 7)$, $(1, 6)$, $(2, 5)$

Find four solutions of each equation. Write the solutions as ordered pairs.
(Lesson 8-2) 35. $(-1, 3)$, $(0, 5)$, $(1, 7)$, $(2, 9)$ **35–37. Sample answers are given.**

35. $y = 2x + 5$ 36. $y = -3x$ 37. $x + y = 7$

Getting Ready for the Next Lesson **PREREQUISITE SKILL** Rewrite $y = kx$ by replacing k with each given value.
*(To review **substitution**, see Lesson 1-3.)*

38. $k = 5$ $y = 5x$ 39. $k = -2$ 40. $k = 0.25$ 41. $k = \dfrac{1}{3}$ $y = \dfrac{1}{3}x$
     $y = -2x$ $y = 0.25x$

Answer

29. Slope can be used to describe the steepness of roller coaster hills. Answers should include the following.

- Slope is the steepness of a line or incline. It is the ratio of the rise to the run.

- An increase in rise with no change in run makes a roller coaster hill steeper. An increase in run with no change in rise makes a roller coaster less steep.

---

4 Assess

Open-Ended Assessment
Modeling Have students work in pairs using a length of string or yarn to model slope. Each student should hold one end of the string to the forehead while his or her partner tapes the other end to a spot on the floor. Each pair should then measure rise and run and calculate the slope of the string.

Tips for New Teachers

Cooperative Learning This lesson presents a good opportunity for students to work cooperatively. Set up flash cards with the coordinates of a point written on each. Have students work in two teams to calculate slopes quickly and accurately. Two members of a team draw a card each and find the slope. Make sure all students get a fair number of turns.

Getting Ready for Lesson 8-5

PREREQUISITE SKILL Lesson 8-5 presents rates of change, in which they must explore values for x and y. Exercises 38–41 should be used to determine your students' familiarity with substituting for variables.

Getting Started

Objective Explore the relationship between slope and rate of change by comparing heights of water levels in a glass.

Materials
grid paper
water
beaker
metric ruler
tablespoon
$\frac{1}{8}$-cup measuring cup

Teach

- Use narrow beakers so that removing a tablespoon of water will cause a noticeable drop in water level.
- Have students use different colors for tablespoons as for cups in the table and on the graph.

Assess

In **Exercises 1–7,** students should make the connection between steepness of slope and rate of change.

In **Exercise 8,** students should demonstrate a clear understanding of rate of change. While **a** has a constant rate of change, **b's** rate of change increases gradually, and **c** experiences an abrupt shift from a constant rate of change to a gradually increasing rate of change.

Study Notebook

You may wish to have students summarize this activity and what they learned from it.

NEW YORK *Performance Indicator* **8.G.13** Determine the slope of a line from a graph and explain the meaning of slope as a constant rate of change

Slope and Rate of Change

In this activity, you will investigate the relationship between slope and rate of change.

Collect the Data

Step 1 On grid paper, make a coordinate grid of the first quadrant. Label the *x*-axis *Number of Measures* and label the *y*-axis *Height of Water (cm)*.

Step 2 Pour water into a drinking glass or a beaker so that it is more than half full.

Step 3 Use a ruler to find the initial height of the water and record the measurement in a table.

Step 4 Remove a tablespoon of water from the glass or beaker and record the new height in your table.

Step 5 Repeat Step 4 so that you have six measures.

Step 6 Fill the glass or beaker again so that it has the same initial height as in Step 3.

Step 7 Repeat Steps 4 and 5, using a $\frac{1}{8}$-cup measuring cup.

Analyze the Data 2. Line 2 has a steeper negative slope.

1. On the coordinate grid, graph the ordered pairs (number of measures, height of water) for each set of data. Draw a line through each set of points. Label the lines 1 and 2, respectively. **See students' work.**

2. Compare the steepness of the two graphs. Which has a steeper slope?

3. What does the height of the water depend on? **number of measures removed**

4. What happens as the number of measures increases?   **The height of water decreases.**

5. Did you empty the glass at a faster rate using a tablespoon or a $\frac{1}{8}$-cup? Explain.
   See pp. 431A–431H.

Make a Conjecture

6. Describe the relationship between slope and the rate at which the glass was emptied. **The steeper the slope, the faster the rate.**

7. What would a graph look like if you emptied a glass using a teaspoon? a $\frac{1}{4}$ cup? Explain. **See pp. 431A–431H.**

Extend the Activity

8. Water is emptied at a constant rate from containers shaped like the ones shown below. Draw a graph of the water level in each of the containers as a function of time. **a–c. See pp. 431A–431H.**

   a.   b.   c.

Resource Manager

📁 *Teaching Pre-Algebra with Manipulatives*
- p. 1 (master for grid paper)
- p. 22 (master for rulers)
- p. 108 (student recording sheet)

Glencoe Mathematics Classroom Manipulative Kit
- rulers
- measuring cups

Rate of Change

NEW YORK *Performance Indicator* **8.G.13** Determine the slope of a line from a graph and explain the meaning of slope as a constant rate of change

What You'll Learn

- Find rates of change.
- Solve problems involving direct variation.

Vocabulary
- rate of change
- direct variation
- constant of variation

How are slope and speed related?

A car traveling 55 miles per hour goes 110 miles in 2 hours, 165 miles in 3 hours, and 220 miles in 4 hours, as shown.

a. For every 1-hour increase in time, what is the change in distance? **55 mi**

b. Find the slope of the line. **55**

c. Slope is equal to the speed of the car.

c. **Make a conjecture** about the relationship between slope of the line and speed of the car.

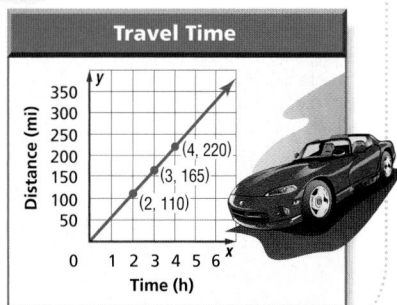
Travel Time
(4, 220)
(3, 165)
(2, 110)
Distance (mi) / Time (h)

RATE OF CHANGE A change in one quantity with respect to another quantity is called the **rate of change**. Rates of change can be described using slope.

$$\text{slope} = \frac{\text{change in } y}{\text{change in } x}$$

$$= \frac{55 \text{ mi}}{1 \text{ h}} \text{ or } 55 \text{ mi/h}$$

Time (h)	Distance (mi)
x	**y**
2	110
3	165
4	220
5	275

+1 (+55
+1 (+55
+1 (+55

Each time *x* increases by 1, *y* increases by 55.

The slope of the line is the speed of the car.

You can find rates of change from an equation, a table of values, or a graph.

Example 1 Find a Rate of Change

TECHNOLOGY The graph shows the expected growth of subscribers to satellite radio for the first five years that it is introduced. Find the expected rate of change from Year 2 to Year 5.

rate of change = slope

$$= \frac{y_2 - y_1}{x_2 - x_1} \quad \text{Definition of slope}$$

$$= \frac{21.0 - 3.4}{5 - 2} \quad \begin{array}{l} \leftarrow \text{change in subscribers} \\ \leftarrow \text{change in time} \end{array}$$

$$\approx 5.9 \quad \text{Simplify.}$$

Satellite Radio
Total Subscribers (millions) / Year
15.2
21.0
3.4
0.8
9.2

Source: The Yankee Group

So, the expected rate of change in satellite radio subscribers is an increase of about 5.9 million people per year.

TEACHING TIP

Students can identify a rate of increase by stating "increase" or by using a positive number. In the same way, they can identify a rate of decrease by stating "decrease" or by using a negative number.

---

1 Focus

5-Minute Check Transparency 8-5 Use as a quiz or review of Lesson 8-4.

Mathematical Background notes are available for this lesson on page 366C.

How are slope and speed related?

The opening activity questions are repeated on page 440 of the *Chapter 8 Resource Masters.*

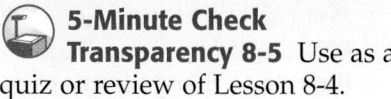

Reading to Learn Mathematics, p. 440 **ELL**

Pre-Activity **How are slope and speed related?**
Do the activity at the top of page 393 in your textbook. Write your answers below.

    a. For every 1-hour increase in time, what is the change in distance? 55 mi

    b. Find the slope of the line. 55

    c. Make a conjecture about the relationship between slope of the line and speed of the car. Slope is equal to the speed of the car.

Reading the Lesson 1–3. See students' work.
Write a definition and give an example of each new vocabulary phrase.

Vocabulary	Definition	Example
1. rate of change		
2. direct variation		
3. constant of variation		

Complete each sentence.

4. Rates of change can be described using _____slope_____.

5. Direct variation is a special type of __linear__ equation.

Helping You Remember

6. The word *ratio* comes from the Latin word meaning rate and can also mean proportion or relation. Direct variation is often called direct proportion. Look up *ratio* in the dictionary. Then use this information to explain the relationship between rate of change and direct variation. **Sample answers: The rate of change is the ratio of the change in one quantity to the change in another quantity. If the ratio is direct, or proportional, then both quantities vary at the same, or constant, rate. Either they both increase at the same rate or they both decrease at the same rate.**

Teaching Tip Students will need graph paper in this lesson.

Resource Manager

📁 Workbooks and Reproducible Masters

Chapter 8 Resource Masters
- Study Guide and Intervention, p. 437
- Skills Practice, p. 438
- Practice, p. 439
- Reading to Learn Mathematics, p. 440
- Enrichment, p. 441
- Assessment, pp. 481, 483

Graphing Calculator and Spreadsheet Masters, p. 34
Parent and Student Study Guide Workbook, p. 65
School-to-Career Masters, p. 15

Transparencies

5-Minute Check Transparency 8-5
Answer Key Transparencies

Technology

Interactive Chalkboard

RATE OF CHANGE

1 **SCHOOL** The graph shows Jadon's quiz scores for the first five weeks after he joined a study group. Find the rate of change from Week 2 to Week 5.

about 4.3 points per week

2 **INCOME** The table shows the yearly incomes of two families. Compare the rates of change.

Year	Income ($)	
	Millers	Joneses
2001	49,000	50,000
2002	51,000	52,000
2003	52,500	54,500
2004	55,000	57,000

The income of the Joneses increases at a faster rate than the income of the Millers.

DIRECT VARIATION

3 Suppose y varies directly with x and $y = 6$ when $x = 54$. Write an equation relating x and y. $y = \frac{1}{9}x$

The steepness of slopes is also important in describing rates of change.

Example 2 **Compare Rates of Change**

GEOMETRY The table shows how the perimeters of an equilateral triangle and a square change as side lengths increase. Compare the rates of change.

Side Length x	Perimeter y	
	Triangle	Square
0	0	0
2	6	8
4	12	16

triangle rate of change $= \dfrac{\text{change in } y}{\text{change in } x}$

$= \dfrac{6}{2}$ or 3   For each side length increase of 2, the perimeter increases by 6.

square rate of change $= \dfrac{\text{change in } y}{\text{change in } x}$

$= \dfrac{8}{2}$ or 4   For each side length increase of 2, the perimeter increases by 8.

The perimeter of a square increases at a faster rate than the perimeter of a triangle. A steeper slope on the graph indicates a greater rate of change for the square.

DIRECT VARIATION   A special type of linear equation that describes rate of change is called a **direct variation**. The graph of a direct variation always passes through the origin and represents a proportional situation.

Key Concept   *Direct Variation*

- **Words**   A direct variation is a relationship such that as x increases in value, y increases or decreases at a constant rate k.

- **Symbols** $y = kx$, where $k \neq 0$

- **Example** $y = 2x$

- **Model**

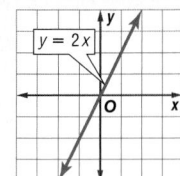

In the equation $y = kx$, k is called the **constant of variation**. It is the slope, or rate of change. We say that y *varies directly with* x.

Example 3 **Write a Direct Variation Equation**

Suppose y varies directly with x and $y = -6$ when $x = 2$. Write an equation relating x and y.

Step 1   Find the value of k.

$y = kx$ Direct variation

$-6 = k(2)$ Replace y with -6 and x with 2.

$-3 = k$ Simplify.

Step 2   Use k to write an equation.

$y = kx$ Direct variation

$y = -3x$ Replace k with -3.

So, a direct variation equation that relates x and y is $y = -3x$.

DAILY INTERVENTION   **Unlocking Misconceptions**

- **Slope** In Example 1, students might assume that the slope is the same for any two points. However, they should realize that a line graph is actually composed of many line segments, each with its own distinct slope.

- **Rates** Remind students that the denominator is always 1 with rates. They should write rates as decimals rather than fractions.

The direct variation $y = kx$ can be written as $k = \frac{y}{x}$. In this form, you can see that the ratio of y to x is the same for any corresponding values of y and x.

Example 4 Use Direct Variation to Solve Problems

POOLS The height of the water as a pool is being filled is recorded in the table below.

a. Write an equation that relates time and height.

Step 1 Find the ratio of y to x for each recorded time. These are shown in the third column of the table. The ratios are approximately equal to 0.4.

Time (min)	Height (in.)	$k = \frac{y}{x}$
x	**y**	
5	2.0	0.40
10	3.75	0.38
15	5.5	0.37
20	7.5	0.38

To the nearest tenth, $k \approx 0.4$.

Step 2 Write an equation.

$y = kx$ Direct variation
$y = 0.4x$ Replace k with 0.4.

So, a direct variation equation that relates the time x and the height of the water y is $y = 0.4x$.

b. Predict how long it will take to fill the pool to a height of 48 inches.

$y = 0.4x$ Write the direct variation equation.
$48 = 0.4x$ Replace y with 48.
$120 = x$ Divide each side by 0.4.

It will take about 120 minutes, or 2 hours to fill the pool.

Check for Understanding

Concept Check

1. **Describe** how slope, rate of change, and constant of variation are related by using $y = 60x$ as a model. **See margin.**

2. **OPEN ENDED** Draw a line that shows a 2-unit increase in y for every 1-unit increase in x. State the rate of change.

3. **FIND THE ERROR** Justin and Carlos are determining how to find rate of change from the equation $y = 4x + 5$.

2. See pp. 431A–431H for graph; rate of change = 2.

3. Justin; any linear function, including direct variations, has a rate of change.

> **Justin**
> The rate of change is the slope of its graph.

> **Carlos**
> There is no rate of change because the equation is not a direct variation.

Who is correct? Explain your reasoning.

Guided Practice

Find the rate of change for each linear function. 5. increase of $12 per hour

GUIDED PRACTICE KEY	
Exercises	Examples
4, 5	1, 2
6, 7	3
8	4

4.

decrease of 5 gal/min

5.

Time (h)	Wage ($)
x	**y**
0	0
1	12
2	24
3	36

www.pre-alg.com/extra_examples/ny

Lesson 8-5 Rate of Change **395**

4. **LANDSCAPING** The depth of a wide hole for a backyard pond as it is being dug is recorded in the table.

Time (min)	Hole Depth (in.)
x	**y**
10	8
20	15
30	24
40	31

a. Write an equation that relates time and hole depth.
   $y = 0.8x$

b. Predict how long it will take to dig to a depth of 36 inches. **45 min**

3 Practice/Apply

Study Notebook

Have students—
• add the definitions/examples of the vocabulary terms to their Vocabulary Builder worksheets for Chapter 8.
• include their answers to Exercise 1.
• include any other item(s) that they find helpful in mastering the skills in this lesson.

Answer

1. The slope is 60, the rate of change is 60 units for every 1 unit, and the constant of variation is 60.

Rate of Change	A change in one quantity with respect to another quantity	slope = $\frac{\text{change in } y}{\text{change in } x}$
Direct Variation	A special type of linear equation that describes rate of change	$y = kx$, where $k \neq 0$
	x and y both increase or both decrease at the same rate—y varies directly with x.	
	Slope, or rate of change, k, is called the **constant of variation.**	

Example 1 Find the rate of change for the linear function represented in the table.

rate of change = slope
$= \frac{\text{change in } y}{\text{change in } x}$
$= \frac{2}{1}$ or 2   For each time increase of 1h, the temperature increases by 2°C.

Time (h)	x	0	1	2	3
Temperature (°C)	y	0	2	4	6

Example 2 Write an equation relating x and y from Example 1.

Step 1 Find the value of k.
$y = kx$ Direct variation
$2 = k(1)$ Replace y with 2 and x with 1.
$2 = k$ Simplify.

Step 2 Use k to write an equation.
$y = kx$ Direct variation
$y = 2x$ Replace k with 2.

Exercises

1. Find the rate of change for the linear function.   **increase of 500 mph**

Time (h)	x	0	2	4	6
Distance Flown (mi)	y	0	1000	2000	3000

Suppose y varies directly with x. Write an equation relating x and y.

2. $y = 14$ when $x = 7$
$y = 2x$

3. $y = 3$ when $x = 5$
$y = \frac{3}{5}x$

4. $y = 2$ when $x = -4$
$y = -\frac{1}{2}x$

Find the rate of change for each linear function.

1.

2.
Time (h)	Distance (km)
x	y
0	0
5	510
10	1020
15	1530

decrease of 2 psi/min   **increase of 102 km/h**

Suppose y varies directly with x. Write an equation relating x and y.

3. $y = -6$ when $x = -2$
$y = 3x$

4. $y = -27$ when $x = 9$
$y = -3x$

5. $y = 4$ when $x = 16$
$y = \frac{1}{4}x$

6. $y = 10$ when $x = 2$
$y = 5x$

7. $y = -42$ when $x = 7$
$y = -6x$

8. $y = 3$ when $x = 36$
$y = \frac{1}{12}x$

9. $y = 4.5$ when $x = -9$
$y = -0.5x$

10. $y = 11$ when $x = 33$
$y = \frac{1}{3}x$

11. $y = 25$ when $x = -5$
$y = -5x$

12. $y = 63$ when $x = 7$
$y = 9x$

13. $y = 48$ when $x = -4$
$y = -12x$

14. $y = 26$ when $x = 13$
$y = 2x$

TRAFFIC MANAGEMENT   For Exercises 15 and 16, use the following information.

San Diego reserves express lanes on the freeways for the use of carpoolers. In order to increase traffic flow during rush hours, other drivers may use the express lanes for a fee. The toll varies directly with the number of cars on the road. The table shows a sample of possible tolls.

Toll ($)	Traffic Volume (vehicles/h)
1.00	521
2.00	1042
3.00	1563
4.00	2084

15. Write an equation that relates the toll x and traffic volume y.
$y = 521x$

16. Predict the number of vehicles at a peak time if the toll increases to $6.00.   **3126 vehicles/h**

17. **OFFICE SUPPLIES** The cost of paper varies directly with the number of reams of paper purchased. If 2 reams cost $9.60, find the cost of 41 reams.   **$196.80**

Fibonacci Sequence
The first fifteen terms of the **Fibonacci sequence** are shown below.
1, 1, 2, 3, 5, 8, 13, 21, 34, 55, 89, 144, 233, 377, 610
In addition to the fact that each term is the sum of the two previous terms, there are other interesting relationships.

Complete.
1. Find the sum of the first four terms.   **7**
2. Find the sum of the first five terms.   **12**
3. Find the sum of the first six terms.   **20**
4. What is the relationship between the sums and terms in the sequence?   **The sum is one less than the Fibonacci number after the next Fibonacci number.**
5. Use your answer from Exercise 4 above to predict the sum of the first 10 terms, and of the first 12 terms. Check your answers by finding the sums.   **143, 376**
6. Divide each of the first 15 terms by 4. Make a list of the remainders. What pattern do you see in the remainder sequence?   **1, 1, 2, 3, 1, 0, 1, 1, 2, 3, 1, 0, 1, 1, 2; The six digits 1, 1, 2, 3, 1, 0 repeat.**
7. The sums of the squares of consecutive terms of the Fibonacci sequence are shown below. Complete the next three lines of this pattern.
$1^2 + 1^2 = 1 \times 2$
$1^2 + 1^2 + 2^2 = 2 \times 3$
$1^2 + 1^2 + 2^2 + 3^2 = 3 \times 5$
$1^2 + 1^2 + 2^2 + 3^2 + 5^2 = 5 \times 8$
$1^2 + 1^2 + 2^2 + 3^2 + 5^2 + 8^2 = 8 \times 13$
$1^2 + 1^2 + 2^2 + 3^2 + 5^2 + 8^2 + 13^2 = 13 \times 21$
$1^2 + 1^2 + 2^2 + 3^2 + 5^2 + 8^2 + 13^2 + 21^2 = 21 \times 34$

Suppose y varies directly with x. Write an equation relating x and y.

6. $y = 5$ when $x = -15$ $y = -\frac{1}{3}x$

7. $y = 24$ when $x = 4$ $y = 6x$

Application   8. **PHYSICAL SCIENCE** The length of a spring varies directly with the amount of weight attached to it. When a 25-gram weight is attached, a spring stretches to 8 centimeters.   **a. $y = 0.32x$ b. 19.2 cm**

a. Write a direct variation equation relating the weight x and the length y.

b. Estimate the length of a spring that has a 60-gram weight attached.

★ indicates increased difficulty

Practice and Apply

Homework Help

For Exercises	See Examples
9–12	1
13	2
14, 15	3
16, 17	4

Extra Practice See page 743.

Find the rate of change for each linear function.

9. 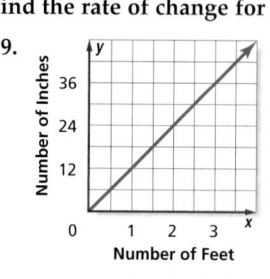   **increase of 12 in./ft**

10.   **decrease of $\frac{1}{100}$ °C/m or 0.01 °C/m**

11.
Time (min)	Temperature (°F)
x	y
0	58
1	56
2	54
3	52

decrease of 2°F/min

12.
Time (h)	Distance (mi)
x	y
0.0	0
0.5	25
1.5	75
3.0	150

increase of 50 mi/h

★ 13. **ENDANGERED SPECIES** The graph shows the populations of California condors in the wild and in captivity.   **See margin.**

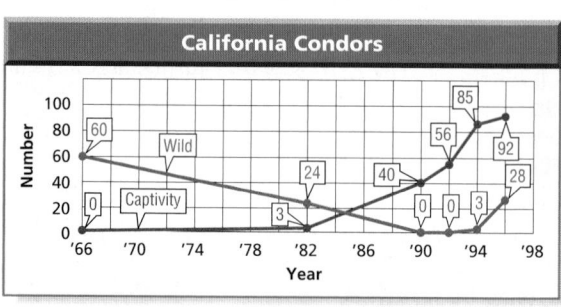

Source: Los Angeles Zoo

Write several sentences that describe how the populations have changed since 1966. Include the rate of change for several key intervals.

 Online Research Data Update What has happened to the condor population since 1996? Visit www.pre-alg.com/data_update to learn more.

Suppose y varies directly with x. Write an equation relating x and y.

14. $y = 8$ when $x = 4$ $y = 2x$

15. $y = -30$ when $x = 6$ $y = -5x$

16. $y = 9$ when $x = 24$ $y = \frac{3}{8}x$

17. $y = 7.5$ when $x = 10$ $y = 0.75x$

Answer

13. Sample answer: The population of wild condors decreased from 1966 to 1990. Then the population increased from 1990 to 1996. The population of condors in captivity increased slowly from 1966 to 1982, then increased more rapidly from 1982 to 1996.

	Rate of Change (number per year)	
Interval	Condors in the Wild	Condors in Captivity
1966–1982	−2.25	0.1875
1982–1990	−3	4.625
1990–1992	0	8
1992–1994	1.5	14.5
1994–1996	12.5	3.5

18. $14.70

18. **FOOD COSTS** The cost of cheese varies directly with the number of pounds bought. If 2 pounds cost $8.40, find the cost of 3.5 pounds.

19. **CONVERTING MEASUREMENTS** The number of centimeters in a measure varies directly as the number of inches. Write a direct variation equation that could be used to convert inches to centimeters. $y = 2.54x$

Measure in Inches x	Measure in Centimeters y
1	2.54
2	5.08
3	7.62

20. **CRITICAL THINKING** Describe the rate of change for a graph that is a horizontal line and a graph that is a vertical line. **See pp. 431A–431H.**

21. [WRITING IN MATH] Answer the question that was posed at the beginning of the lesson. **See pp. 431A–431H.**

How are slope and speed related?

Include the following in your answer:
- a drawing of a graph showing distance versus time, and
- an explanation of how slope changes when speed changes.

Standardized Test Practice
Ⓐ Ⓑ Ⓒ Ⓓ

22. A graph showing an increase in sales over time would have a(n) **A**
   Ⓐ positive slope.　　　　　Ⓑ negative slope.
   Ⓒ undefined slope.　　　　Ⓓ slope of 0.

23. Choose an equation that does *not* represent a direct variation. **B**
   Ⓐ $y = x$　　Ⓑ $y = 1$　　Ⓒ $y = -5x$　　Ⓓ $y = 0.9x$

Maintain Your Skills

Mixed Review　Find the slope of the line that passes through each pair of points. *(Lesson 8-4)*

24. $Q(-4, 4)$, $R(3, 5)$　$\frac{1}{7}$　　　　25. $A(2, 6)$, $B(-1, 0)$　**2**

Graph each equation using the x- and y-intercepts. *(Lesson 8-3)*

26–28. See pp. 431A–431H.

26. $y = x + 5$　　　27. $y = -x + 1$　　　28. $2x + y = 4$

29. Estimate 20% of 72. *(Lesson 6-6)* **14**

Getting Ready for the Next Lesson　**PREREQUISITE SKILL** Solve each equation for y.
(To review solving equations for a variable, see Lesson 8-2.)　**32.** $y = 2 + \frac{1}{5}x$

30. $x + y = 6$　$y = 6 - x$　　31. $3x + y = 1$　$y = 1 - 3x$　32. $-x + 5y = 10$

Practice Quiz 1　　　　　　　　　　　　　　**Lessons 8-1 through 8-5**

Determine whether each relation is a function. Explain. *(Lesson 8-1)*

1. $\{(0, 5), (1, 2), (1, -3), (2, 4)\}$
   No; 1 is paired with 2 and −3.
2. $\{(-6, 3.5), (-3, 4.0), (0, 4.5), (3, 5.0)\}$
   Yes; each x value is paired with only one y value.

Graph each equation using ordered pairs. *(Lesson 8-2)*

3. $y = x - 4$　　　　　　　　　4. $y = 2x + 3$　**3–4. See margin.**

Find the x-intercept and the y-intercept for the graph of each equation. *(Lesson 8-3)*

5. $y = x + 9$　$-9; 9$　　　6. $x + 2y = 12$　**12; 6**　　　7. $4x - 5y = 20$　**5; −4**

Find the slope of the line that passes through each pair of points. *(Lessons 8-4 and 8-5)*

8. $(1, 4), (0, 0)$　**4**　　　9. $(-2, 4), (3, -6)$　**−2**　　　10. $(0, 2), (5, 2)$　**0**

Answers (Practice Quiz 1)

3.

4.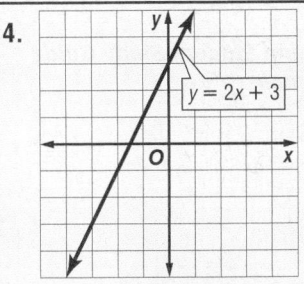

4 Assess

Open-Ended Assessment

Modeling Have students measure the outside temperature during class every day for a week. Ask them to find the rate of change in temperatures.

Getting Ready for Lesson 8-6

PREREQUISITE SKILL In Lesson 8-6 students rewrite equations in slope-intercept form ($y = mx + b$). Exercises 30–32 should be used to determine your students' familiarity with solving equations for a given variable.

Assessment Options

Practice Quiz 1 The quiz provides students with a brief review of the concepts and skills in Lessons 8-1 through 8-5. Lesson numbers are given to the right of exercises or instruction lines so students can review concepts not yet mastered.

Quiz (Lessons 8-4 and 8-5) is available on p. 481 of the *Chapter 8 Resource Masters*.

Mid-Chapter Test (Lessons 8-1 through 8-5) is available on p. 483 of the *Chapter 8 Resource Masters*.

About the Exercises . . .

Organization by Objective
- **Rate of Change:** 9–13
- **Direct Variation:** 14–19

Odd/Even Assignments
Exercises 9–12 and 14–19 are structured so that students practice the same concepts whether they are assigned odd or even problems.

Assignment Guide
Basic: 9, 11, 15–19 odd, 20–32
Average: 9–19 odd, 20–32
Advanced: 10–18 even, 20–29 (Optional: 30–32)
All: Practice Quiz 1 (1–10)

NEW YORK *Performance Indicator* **8.G.17 Graph a line from an equation in slope-intercept form ($y = mx + b$)**

What You'll Learn

- Determine slopes and y-intercepts of lines.
- Graph linear equations using the slope and y-intercept.

Vocabulary
- slope-intercept form

How can knowing the slope and y-intercept help you graph an equation?

Copy the table.

a. On the same coordinate plane, use ordered pairs or intercepts to graph each equation in a different color. **See margin.**

b. Find the slope and the y-intercept of each line. Complete the table.

c. The slope is the coefficient of x; the y-intercept is the constant.

c. Compare each equation with the value of its slope and y-intercept. What do you notice?

Equation	Slope	y-intercept
$y = 2x + 1$	2	1
$y = \frac{1}{3}x - 3$	$\frac{1}{3}$	−3
$y = -2x + 1$	−2	1

SLOPE AND y-INTERCEPT

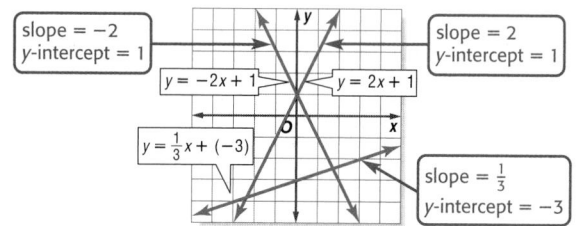

slope = −2
y-intercept = 1

slope = 2
y-intercept = 1

$y = -2x + 1$ $y = 2x + 1$

$y = \frac{1}{3}x + (-3)$

slope = $\frac{1}{3}$
y-intercept = −3

All the equations above are written in the form $y = mx + b$, where m is the slope and b is the y-intercept. This is called **slope-intercept form**.

$$y = mx + b$$

slope ⟍   ⟋ y-intercept

Study Tip

Different Forms
Both equations below are written in slope-intercept form.
$y = x + (-2)$
$y = x - 2$

Example 1 Find the Slope and y-Intercept

State the slope and the y-intercept of the graph of $y = \frac{3}{5}x - 7$.

$y = \frac{3}{5}x - 7$ Write the original equation.

$y = \frac{3}{5}x + (-7)$ Write the equation in the form $y = mx + b$.

↑   ↑

$y = mx + b$ $m = \frac{3}{5}, b = -7$

The slope of the graph is $\frac{3}{5}$, and the y-intercept is −7.

✓ **Concept Check** What is the slope of $y = 8x + 6$? **8**

---

1 Focus

5-Minute Check Transparency 8-6 Use as a quiz or review of Lesson 8-5.

Mathematical Background notes are available for this lesson on page 366D.

How can knowing the slope and y-intercept help you graph an equation?

The opening activity questions are repeated on page 445 of the *Chapter 8 Resource Masters.*

Reading to Learn Mathematics, p. 445   **ELL**

Pre-Activity *How can knowing the slope and y-intercept help you graph an equation?*

Do the activity at the top of page 398 in your textbook. Write your answers below.

a. On the same coordinate plane, use ordered pairs or intercepts to graph each equation in a different color.

b. Find the slope and the y-intercept of each line. Complete the table.

Equation	Slope	y-intercept
$y = 2x + 1$	2	1
$y = \frac{1}{3}x - 3$	$\frac{1}{3}$	−3
$y = -2x + 1$	−2	1

c. Compare each equation with the value of its slope and y-intercept. What do you notice? **The slope is the coefficient of x, the y-intercept is the constant.**

Reading the Lesson

Write a definition and give an example of the new vocabulary phrase.

Vocabulary	Definition	Example
1. slope-intercept form	See students' work.	

2. Sometimes you must solve an equation for __y__ before you can write the equation in slope-intercept form.

3. Explain why $y = mx + b$ is called the slope-intercept form. The form $y = mx + b$ describes a line according to its slope, m, and its y-intercept, b.

Helping You Remember

4. Mathematicians debate the origin of the slope-intercept form of a line, particularly the use of m to represent slope. Make up a mnemonic phrase to help you remember the slope-intercept form. Sample answer: y is the m(ountain slope) times x plus the b(all intercepted on the y-yardline).

Resource Manager

📁 Workbooks and Reproducible Masters

Chapter 8 Resource Masters
- Study Guide and Intervention, p. 442
- Skills Practice, p. 443
- Practice, p. 444
- Reading to Learn Mathematics, p. 445
- Enrichment, p. 446

Parent and Student Study Guide Workbook, p. 66

Transparencies
5-Minute Check Transparency 8-6
Answer Key Transparencies

Technology
Interactive Chalkboard
Pre-AlgePASS: Tutorial Plus, Lesson 24

Sometimes you must first write an equation in slope-intercept form before finding the slope and y-intercept.

Example 2 Write an Equation in Slope-Intercept Form

State the slope and the y-intercept of the graph of $5x + y = 3$.

$$5x + y = 3 \qquad \text{Write the original equation.}$$
$$5x + y - 5x = 3 - 5x \qquad \text{Subtract } 5x \text{ from each side.}$$
$$y = -5x + 3 \qquad \text{Write the equation in slope-intercept form.}$$
$$y = mx + b \quad m = -5, b = 3$$

The slope of the graph is -5, and the y-intercept is 3.

TEACHING TIP
Explain to students that there are two ways to interpret a negative slope. Both give the same result.
- $\frac{-1}{2}$ means go down 1 unit and right 2 units.
- $\frac{1}{-2}$ means go up 1 unit and left 2 units.

GRAPH EQUATIONS   You can use the slope-intercept form of an equation to easily graph a line.

Example 3 Graph an Equation

Graph $y = -\frac{1}{2}x - 4$ using the slope and y-intercept.

Step 1 Find the slope and y-intercept.

$$\text{slope} = -\frac{1}{2} \qquad y\text{-intercept} = -4$$

Step 2 Graph the y-intercept point at $(0, -4)$.

Step 3 Write the slope $-\frac{1}{2}$ as $\frac{-1}{2}$. Use it to locate a second point on the line.

$$m = \frac{-1}{2} \quad \begin{array}{l} \leftarrow \text{change in } y\text{: down 1 unit} \\ \leftarrow \text{change in } x\text{: right 2 units} \end{array}$$

Another point on the line is at $(2, -5)$.

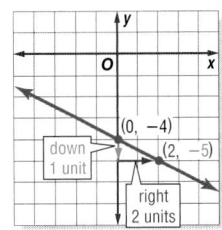

down 1 unit — right 2 units — $(0, -4)$ — $(2, -5)$

Step 4 Draw a line through the two points.

Example 4 Graph an Equation to Solve a Problem

BUSINESS   A T-shirt company charges a design fee of $24 for a pattern and then sells the shirts for $12 each. The total cost y can be represented by the equation $y = 12x + 24$, where x represents the number of T-shirts.

a. Graph the equation.

First, find the slope and the y-intercept.

slope $= 12$

y-intercept $= 24$

Plot the point at $(0, 24)$. Then go up 12 and right 1. Connect these points.

Cost ($) / Number of T-Shirts — $(0, 24)$

b. Describe what the y-intercept and the slope represent.

The y-intercept 24 represents the design fee. The slope 12 represents the cost per T-shirt, which is the rate of change.

Career Choices

Business Owner
Business owners must understand the factors that affect cost and profit. Graphs are a useful way for them to display this information.

Online Research
For information about a career as a business owner, visit: www.pre-alg.com/careers

www.pre-alg.com/extra_examples/ny
Lesson 8-6 Slope-Intercept Form   **399**

DAILY INTERVENTION

Unlocking Misconceptions

- **Discrete Solutions** Students might assume that every point on the graph in Example 4 is a solution for the problem. Emphasize that the equation represents a set of points in which the solutions to the real-world problem exist. A true graph of the real-world situation would only have points where x is a whole number.

2 Teach

SLOPE AND Y-INTERCEPT

In-Class Examples Power Point®

1 State the slope and the y-intercept of the graph of $y = \frac{1}{2}x + 3$. $\frac{1}{2}$; 3

2 State the slope and the y-intercept of the graph of $-4x + 5y = -10$. $\frac{4}{5}$; -2

GRAPH EQUATIONS

In-Class Examples Power Point®

3 Graph $3x + y = 9$ using the slope and y-intercept.

$(0, 9)$ — $3x + y = 9$ — $(3, 0)$

4 **BAKING** A school group making cookies for a bake sale spends $75 on ingredients and then sells the cookies for $5 a dozen. The amount earned y can be represented by the equation $y = 5x - 75$, where x equals the number of dozens sold.

a. Graph the equation.

Amount Earned ($) / Number of Dozens Sold — $(0, -75)$

b. Describe what the y-intercept and the slope represent. The y-intercept -75 represents the cost of the ingredients. Slope 5 represents the dollars earned per dozen cookies.

Lesson 8-6 Slope-Intercept Form   **399**

Study Guide and Intervention, p. 442

The **slope-intercept form** of a line makes it easy to graph the line:
$y = mx + b$ **Example:** $y = 3x + 2$
slope = m slope = 3
y-intercept = b y-intercept = 2

Example   Graph $y = -4x - 3$ using the slope and y-intercept.

Step 1   Find the slope and y-intercept.
slope = -4 y-intercept = -3

Step 2   Graph the y-intercept point at $(0, -3)$.

Step 3   Write the slope -4 as $\frac{-4}{1}$. Use the slope to locate a second point on the line.
$m = \frac{-4}{1}$ change in y: down 4 units / change in x: right 1 unit

Step 4   Draw a line through the two points.

Step 5   Check by locating another point on the line and substituting the coordinates into the original equation.

Exercises

Given the slope and y-intercept, graph each line.

1. slope = 4,   2. slope = 6,   3. slope = $-\frac{1}{4}$,
y-intercept = -1 y-intercept = 4 y-intercept = 5

Graph each equation using the slope and y-intercept.

4. $y = 3x - 2$ 5. $y = \frac{2}{3}x + 3$ 6. $y = 5x - 3$

Skills Practice, p. 443 and Practice, p. 444 (shown)

Given the slope and y-intercept, graph each line.

1. slope = $\frac{3}{4}$,   2. slope = $\frac{5}{6}$,   3. slope = 1,
y-intercept = -3 y-intercept = 1 y-intercept = 5

Graph each equation using the slope and y-intercept.

4. $y = -\frac{1}{2}x - 4$ 5. $y = x - 4$ 6. $y = -6x + 3$

EXERCISE For Exercises 7 and 8, use the following information.
A person weighing 150 pounds burns about 320 Calories per hour walking at a moderate pace. Suppose that the same person burns an average of 1500 Calories per day through basic activities. The total Calories y burned by that person can be represented by the equation $y = 320x + 1500$, where x represents the number of hours spent walking.

7. Graph the equation using the slope and y-intercept.

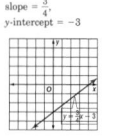

8. State the slope and y-intercept of the graph of the equation and describe what they represent. **The y-intercept 1500 represents the number of Calories burned without exercising. The slope 320 represents the number of Calories burned per hour when walking.**

Enrichment, p. 446

Translations and Reflections

The lines on graph paper can help you draw slide images of figures.

1. Graph $\triangle ABC$ with vertices $A(1, 1)$, $B(-3, 4)$, and $C(-3, -4)$. Draw $\triangle A'B'C'$, the translation image of $\triangle ABC$, where the slide is 3 units to the right. Name the coordinates of the image of each vertex.
$A'(4, 1)$, $B'(0, 4)$, $C'(0, -4)$

2. Draw $\triangle JKL$ with vertices $J(-4, 3)$, $K(0, 2)$, and $L(-2, 0)$. Let $\triangle J'K'L'$ be the image of $\triangle JKL$ under a slide of 4 units to the right and then a slide of 3 units up. Graph $\triangle J'K'L'$. Name the coordinates of the vertices of $\triangle J'K'L'$.
$J'(0, 6)$, $K'(4, 5)$, $L'(2, 3)$

3. Draw $\overline{A'B'}$, the image formed by reflecting $\overline{AB}$ over the x-axis. Then draw $\overline{A''B''}$, the image formed by reflecting $\overline{A'B'}$ over the x-axis. What are the coordinates of A'' and B''? What is the relationship between the coordinates of the endpoints of $\overline{AB}$ and those of $\overline{A''B''}$?

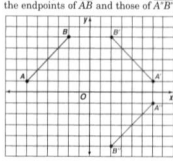

$A''(6, -1)$, $B''(2, -5)$; The coordinates of A'' and B'' have the opposite signs of A and B.

4. Draw $\overline{P'Q'}$, the reflection image of $\overline{PQ}$ over the y-axis. Draw $\overline{P''Q''}$, the reflection image of $\overline{P'Q'}$ over the x-axis. Find the slopes of $\overline{PQ}$, $\overline{P'Q'}$, and $\overline{P''Q''}$. What is the relationship between the slopes of $\overline{PQ}$ and $\overline{P''Q''}$?

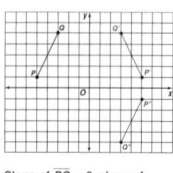

Slope of $\overline{PQ} = 2$; slope of $\overline{P'Q'} = -2$; slope of $\overline{P''Q''} = 2$; They are the same.

Check for Understanding

Concept Check

1. **State** the value that tells you how many units to go up or down from the y-intercept if the slope of a line is $\frac{a}{b}$. **a**

2. **OPEN ENDED** Draw the graph of a line that has a y-intercept but no x-intercept. What is the slope of the line? **See pp. 431A–431H for graph; slope = 0.**

3. **FIND THE ERROR** Carmen and Alex are finding the slope and y-intercept of $x + 2y = 8$. **Alex; the equation in slope-intercept form is $y = -\frac{1}{2}x + 4$.**

> **Carmen**
> slope = 2
> y-intercept = 8

> **Alex**
> slope = $-\frac{1}{2}$
> y-intercept = 4

Who is correct? Explain your reasoning.

Guided Practice

State the slope and the y-intercept for the graph of each equation.

4. $y = x + 8$ **1; 8**   5. $x + y = 0$ **−1; 0**   6. $x + 3y = 6$ **$-\frac{1}{3}$; 2**

GUIDED PRACTICE KEY	
Exercises	Examples
4–6	1, 2
7–9	3
10, 11	4

Graph each equation using the slope and y-intercept. **7–9. See pp. 431A–431H.**

7. $y = \frac{1}{4}x + 1$ 8. $3x + y = 2$ 9. $x - 2y = 4$

Application

BUSINESS Mrs. Allison charges \$25 for a basic cake that serves 12 people. A larger cake costs an additional \$1.50 per serving. The total cost can be given by $y = 1.5x + 25$, where x represents the number of additional slices.

10. Graph the equation. **See pp. 431A–431H.**

11. Explain what the y-intercept and the slope represent.
The y-intercept 25 represents the charge for a basic cake. Slope 1.5 represents the cost per additional slice.

★ indicates increased difficulty

Practice and Apply

Homework Help

For Exercises	See Examples
12–17	1, 2
18–31	3
32–34	4

Extra Practice
See page 743.

State the slope and the y-intercept for the graph of each equation.

12. $y = x + 2$ **1; 2**   13. $y = 2x - 4$ **2; −4**

14. $x + y = -3$ **−1; −3**   15. $2x + y = -3$ **−2; −3**

16. $5x + 4y = 20$ **$-\frac{5}{4}$; 5**   17. $y = 4$ **0; 4**

Graph each line with the given slope and y-intercept.

18. slope = 3, y-intercept = 1   19. slope = $-\frac{3}{2}$, y-intercept = -1
18–19. See pp. 431A–431H.

Graph each equation using the slope and y-intercept.

20–31. See pp. 431A–431H.

20. $y = x + 5$ 21. $y = -x + 6$

22. $y = 2x - 3$ 23. $y = \frac{3}{4}x + 2$

24. $x + y = -3$ 25. $x + y = 0$

26. $-2x + y = -1$ 27. $5x + y = -3$

★ 28. $x - 3y = -6$ ★ 29. $2x + 3y = 12$

★ 30. $3x + 4y = 12$ ★ 31. $y = -3$

DAILY INTERVENTION
Differentiated Instruction

- **Logical** Remind students that it is important to work with a proper sequence when graphing an equation. It might be helpful for students to first put an equation in slope-intercept form before graphing the equation, even if the equation is not very complex.

•••**HANG GLIDING**   For Exercises 32–34, use the following information.
The altitude in feet y of a hang glider who is slowly landing can be given by $y = 300 - 50x$, where x represents the time in minutes.

★ **32.** Graph the equation using the slope and y-intercept. **See pp.431A–431H.**

★ **33.** State the slope and y-intercept of the graph of the equation and describe what they represent. **See margin.**

★ **34.** Name the x-intercept and describe what it represents.
6; the time in minutes that it takes the glider to land

35. CRITICAL THINKING   What is the x-intercept of the graph of $y = mx + b$? Explain how you know. $-\dfrac{b}{m}$. **Replace y with 0 in $y = mx + b$ and solve for x.**

36. **WRITING IN MATH**   Answer the question that was posed at the beginning of the lesson. **See margin.**

How can knowing the slope and y-intercept help you graph an equation?

Include the following in your answer:
- a description of how the slope-intercept form of an equation gives information, and
- an explanation of how you could write an equation for a line if you know the slope and y-intercept.

37. Which is $2x + 3y = 6$ written in slope-intercept form? **B**

ⓐ $y = -\dfrac{2}{3}x - 2$ ⓑ $y = -\dfrac{2}{3}x + 2$

ⓒ $y = -\dfrac{3}{2}x + 2$ ⓓ $y = \dfrac{3}{2}x - 2$

38. What is the slope and y-intercept of the graph of $-x + 2y = 6$? **D**

ⓐ $-\dfrac{1}{2}, 1$ ⓑ $1, 6$

ⓒ $1, 3$ ⓓ $\dfrac{1}{2}, 3$

Maintain Your Skills

Mixed Review   Suppose y varies directly with x. Write an equation relating x and y for each pair of values.   *(Lesson 8-5)*

39. $y = -36$ when $x = 9$ $y = -4x$ **40.** $y = 5$ when $x = 25$ $y = \dfrac{1}{5}x$

Find the slope of the line that passes through each pair of points.
(Lesson 8-4)

41. $A(3, 1), B(6, 7)$ **2**   **42.** $J(-2, 5), K(8, 5)$ **0**   **43.** $Q(2, 4), R(0, -4)$ **4**

44. Solve $4(r - 3) = 8$.   *(Lesson 7-2)* **5**

45. Six times a number is 28 more than twice the number. Write an equation and find the number.   *(Lesson 7-1)* **6x = 2x + 28; 7**

Getting Ready for the Next Lesson   **PREREQUISITE SKILL**   **Simplify.**   *(To review order of operations, see Lesson 1-2.)*

46. $2(18) - 1$ **35**   **47.** $(-2 - 4) \div 10$ $-\dfrac{3}{5}$

48. $-1(6) + 8$ **2**   **49.** $5 - 8(-3)$ **29**

50. $(9 + 6) \div 3$ **5**   **51.** $3 - (-2)(4)$ **11**

Answers

33. slope = −50, the descent in feet per minute; y-intercept = 300, initial altitude

36. Graph the y-intercept point. Then use the slope to locate a second point on the line. Draw a line through the two points. Answers should include the following.

- When an equation is written in slope-intercept form $y = mx + b$, the slope is m and the y-intercept is b.

- To write an equation of a line, substitute the known values for m and b in $y = mx + b$.

A Follow-Up of Lesson 8-6

Getting Started

Know Your Calculator The graphing calculator has the ability to make the graphs appear differently on screen. The symbol before each **Y=** entry shows how the line will appear. Use the arrow keys to highlight a symbol repeatedly until a thin slanted line appears.

Standard Viewing Window
Pressing ZOOM 6 selects the standard viewing window.

Entering Multiple Functions To enter a new function while keeping the previously entered function, be sure to use the down arrow to enter the new function on a different line.

Teach

• If students find that TRACE shows r and θ values instead of x and y values, have them enter 2nd [Format] and highlight RectGC in the first line.

• Have students complete Exercises 1–13.

NEW YORK *Performance Indicator* **8.G.17 Graph a line from an equation in slope-intercept form ($y = mx + b$)**

Families of Graphs

A graphing calculator is a valuable tool when investigating characteristics of linear functions. Before graphing, you must create a viewing window that shows both the x- and y-intercepts of the graph of a function.

You can use the standard viewing window $[-10, 10]$ scl: 1 by $[-10, 10]$ scl: 1 or set your own minimum and maximum values for the axes and the scale factor by using the WINDOW option.

You can use a TI-83 Plus graphing calculator to enter several functions and graph them at the same time on the same screen. This is useful when studying a **family of graphs**. A family of linear graphs is related by having the same slope or the same y-intercept.

> The tick marks on the x scale and on the y scale are 1 unit apart.

$[-10, 10]$ scl: 1 by $[-10, 10]$ scl: 1

> The x-axis goes from -10 to 10.

> The y-axis goes from -10 to 10.

Graph $y = 3x - 2$ and $y = 3x + 4$ in the standard viewing window and describe how the graphs are related.

Step 1 *Graph $y = 3x + 4$ in the standard viewing window.*

• Clear any existing equations from the **Y=** list.
  KEYSTROKES: Y= CLEAR

• Enter the equation and graph.
  KEYSTROKES: Y= 3 X,T,θ,n + 4 ZOOM 6

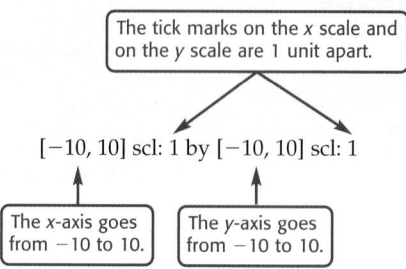

$y = 3x + 4$

Step 2 *Graph $y = 3x - 2$.*

• Enter the function $y = 3x - 2$ as **Y2** with $y = 3x + 4$ already existing as **Y1**.
  KEYSTROKES: Y= 3 X,T,θ,n − 2

• Graph both functions in the standard viewing window.
  KEYSTROKES: ZOOM 6

The first function graphed is **Y1** or $y = 3x + 4$. The second function graphed is **Y2** or $y = 3x - 2$. Press TRACE . Move along each function using the right and left arrow keys. Move from one function to another using the up and down arrow keys. The graphs have the same slope, 3, but different y-intercepts at 4 and -2.

 www.pre-alg.com/other_calculator_keystrokes

Exercises

Graph $y = 2x - 5$, $y = 2x - 1$, and $y = 2x + 7$.

1. Compare and contrast the graphs. **They all have the same slope, different y-intercepts.**

2. How does adding or subtracting a constant c from a linear function affect its graph? **It shifts the graph vertically c units.**

3. Write an equation of a line whose graph is parallel to $y = 3x - 5$, but is shifted up 7 units. **$y = 3x + 2$**

4. Write an equation of the line that is parallel to $y = 3x - 5$ and passes through the origin. **$y = 3x$**

5. Four functions with a slope of 1 are graphed in the standard viewing window, as shown at the right. Write an equation for each, beginning with the left-most graph.
   $y = x + 6$, $y = x$, $y = x - 4$, $y = x - 7$

Clear all functions from the Y= menu and graph $y = \frac{1}{3}x$, $y = \frac{3}{4}x$, $y = x$, and $y = 4x$ in the standard viewing window. 6. See margin.

6. How does the steepness of a line change as the coefficient for x increases?

7. Without graphing, determine whether the graph of $y = 0.4x$ or the graph of $y = 1.4x$ has a steeper slope. Explain. **$y = 1.4x$, because $1.4 > 0.4$**

Clear all functions from the Y= menu and graph $y = -4x$ and $y = 4x$.

8. How are these two graphs different? **8–11. See margin.**

9. How does the sign of the coefficient of x affect the slope of a line?

10. Clear Y2. Then with $y = -4x$ as Y1, enter $y = -x$ as Y2 and $y = -\frac{1}{2}x$ as Y3.

    Graph the functions and draw the three graphs on grid paper. How does the steepness of the line change as the absolute value of the coefficient of x increases?

11. The graphs of $y = 3x + 1$, $y = \frac{1}{2}x + 1$, and $y = -x + 1$ are shown at the right. Draw the graphs on the same coordinate grid and label each graph with its equation.

12. Describe the similarities and differences between the graph of $y = 2x - 3$ and the graph of each equation listed below.
    a. $y = 2x + 3$ **a–c. See margin.**
    b. $y = -2x - 3$
    c. $y = 0.5x + 3$

13. Write an equation of a line whose graph lies between the graphs of $y = -3x$ and $y = -6x$. **Sample answer: $y = -4x$**

Assess

Have students work individually using their graphing calculators to answer Exercises 12 and 13. Students should be able to operate the calculator with enough ease to be able to concentrate on the concept of families of functions.

Answers

11.

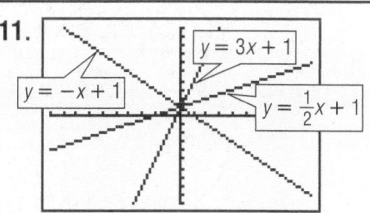

12a. same slope, different y-intercepts

12b. Same y-intercepts, opposite slopes; $y = 2x - 3$ slopes up from left to right and $y = -2x - 3$ slopes down from left to right.

12c. The graph of $y = 0.5x + 3$ is less steep and has a different y-intercept.

Answers

6. As the coefficient of x increases, the line becomes steeper.

8. The graphs have opposite slopes; the graph of $y = -4x$ falls from left to right and the graph of $y = 4x$ rises from left to right.

9. If the coefficient is negative, the graph has a negative slope. If the coefficient is positive, the graph has a positive slope.

10. As the absolute value of the coefficient of x increases, the line becomes steeper.

NEW YORK *Performance Indicator* 8.G.16 Determine the equation of a line given the slope and the y-intercept

1 Focus

5-Minute Check Transparency 8-7 Use as a quiz or review of Lesson 8-6.

Mathematical Background notes are available for this lesson on page 366D.

How can you model data with a linear equation?

The opening activity questions are repeated on page 450 of the *Chapter 8 Resource Masters.*

Reading to Learn Mathematics, p. 450 **ELL**

Pre-Activity | How can you model data with a linear equation?

Do the activity at the top of page 404 in your textbook. Write your answers below.

a. Graph the ordered pairs (chirps, temperature). Draw a line through the points.

b. Find the slope and the y-intercept of the line. What do these values represent? **Slope = 1 represents the rate of change, 1 degree for every 1 chirp; y-intercept = 40 represents the temperature at which the crickets are not chirping.**

c. Write an equation in the form y = mx + b for the line then translate the equation into a sentence. **y = x + 40; The temperature equals the number of chirps in 15 seconds plus 40.**

Reading the Lesson

1. Explain how you can use the following information to write the slope-intercept form of a line.
   a. graph of a line **Find the y-intercept. From that point, count how many units up or down and how many units left or right to another point. The slope is the ratio of the rise over the run. Then substitute the slope and the y-intercept into the slope-intercept form.**
   b. two points on a line **Substitute the coordinates of two points on the line into the definition of slope. Then use the slope and one of the points to find the y-intercept. Substitute the slope and the point's coordinates into slope-intercept form. Then substitute the slope and the y-intercept into the slope-intercept form.**
   c. a table of values **Use the table to identify the coordinates of two points on the line. Then substitute the coordinates of the two points into the definition of slope. Then use the slope and one of the points to find the y-intercept. Substitute the slope and the point's coordinates into slope-intercept form. Then substitute the slope and the y-intercept into the slope-intercept form.**

What You'll Learn

• Write equations given the slope and y-intercept, a graph, a table, or two points.

How can you model data with a linear equation?

You can determine the approximate outside temperature by counting the chirps of crickets, as shown in the table.

Number of Chirps in 15 Seconds	Temperature (°F)
0	40
5	45
10	50
15	55
20	60

a. Graph the ordered pairs (chirps, temperature). Draw a line through the points.

b. Find the slope and the y-intercept of the line. What do these values represent?

c. Write an equation in the form $y = mx + b$ for the line. Then translate the equation into a sentence.

a–b. See margin.

c. $y = x + 40$; The temperature equals the number of chirps in 15 seconds plus 40.

WRITE EQUATIONS There are many different methods for writing linear equations. If you know the slope and y-intercept, you can write the equation of a line by substituting these values in $y = mx + b$.

Example 1 Write Equations From Slope and y-Intercept

Write an equation in slope-intercept form for each line.

a. slope = 4, y-intercept = −8

$y = mx + b$ Slope-intercept form
$y = 4x + (-8)$ Replace m with 4 and b with −8.
$y = 4x - 8$ Simplify.

b. slope = 0, y-intercept = 5

$y = mx + b$ Slope-intercept form
$y = 0x + 5$ Replace m with 0 and b with 5.
$y = 5$ Simplify.

c. slope = $-\frac{1}{2}$, y-intercept = 0

$y = mx + b$ Slope-intercept form
$y = -\frac{1}{2}x + 0$ Replace m with $-\frac{1}{2}$ and b with 0.
$y = -\frac{1}{2}x$ Simplify.

Resource Manager

 Workbooks and Reproducible Masters

Chapter 8 Resource Masters
• Study Guide and Intervention, p. 447
• Skills Practice, p. 448
• Practice, p. 449
• Reading to Learn Mathematics, p. 450
• Enrichment, p. 451

Parent and Student Study Guide Workbook, p. 67

Transparencies
5-Minute Check Transparency 8-7
Answer Key Transparencies

 Technology
Interactive Chalkboard

You can also write equations from a graph.

Example 2 Write an Equation From a Graph

Write an equation in slope-intercept form for the line graphed.

The y-intercept is 1. From (0, 1), you can go down 3 units and right 1 unit to another point on the line. So, the slope is $\frac{-3}{1}$, or -3.

$y = mx + b$ Slope-intercept form
$y = -3x + 1$ Replace m with -3 and b with 1.

In Lesson 8-3, you explored the relationship between altitude and temperature. You can write an equation for this relationship and use it to make predictions.

Example 3 Write an Equation to Solve a Problem

EARTH SCIENCE On a summer day, the temperature at altitude 0, or sea level, is 30°C. The temperature decreases 2°C for every 305 meters increase in altitude.

a. Write an equation to show the relationship between altitude x and temperature y.

Words   Temperature decreases 2°C for every 305 meters increase in altitude.

Variables   Let $x =$ the altitude and let $y =$ the temperature.

Equations   Use $m = \frac{\text{change in } y}{\text{change in } x}$ and $y = mx + b$.

Step 1
Find the slope m.

$m = \dfrac{\text{change in } y}{\text{change in } x}$ ← change in temperature / change in altitude

$= \dfrac{-2}{305}$ ← decrease of -2°C / increase of 305 m

≈ -0.007 Simplify.

Step 2
Find the y-intercept b.

$(x, y) = $ (altitude, temperature)
$\qquad = (0, b)$

When the altitude is 0, or sea level, the temperature is 30°C. So, the y-intercept is 30.

Step 3
Write the equation.

$y = mx + b$ Slope-intercept form
$y = -0.007x + 30$ Replace m with -0.007 and b with 30.

So, the equation that represents this situation is $y = -0.007x + 30$.

b. Predict the temperature for an altitude of 2000 meters.

$y = -0.007x + 30$ Write the equation.
$y = -0.007(2000) + 30$ Replace x with 2000.
$y \approx 16$ Simplify.

So, at an altitude of 2000 meters, the temperature is about 16°C.

2 Teach

WRITE EQUATIONS

In-Class Examples

1 Write an equation in slope-intercept form for each line.

a. slope $= -\frac{1}{4}$, y-intercept $= 7$
$y = -\frac{1}{4}x + 7$

b. slope $= 0$, y-intercept $= -3$
$y = -3$

c. slope $= 2$, y-intercept $= 0$
$y = 2x$

2 Write an equation in slope-intercept form for the line graphed.

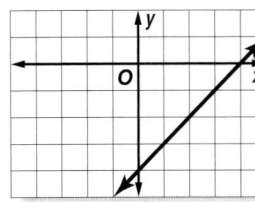

$y = x + (-4)$ or $y = x - 4$

3 **BUSINESS** The owners of the Good Times Eatery surveyed their customers to find out where they lived. They learned that for each 5-mile radius from their restaurant, 30 fewer people visited them. They had 150 patrons in the area immediately surrounding the diner.

a. Write an equation to show the relationship between miles x and customers y.
$y = -6x + 150$

b. Predict the number of customers who lived 20 miles away.   30

---

4 Write an equation for the line that passes through $(7, 0)$ and $(6, 3)$.
$y = -3x + 21$

5 Use the table of values to write an equation in slope-intercept form.
$y = -6x + 4$

x	y
−2	16
−1	10
0	4
1	−2

3 Practice/Apply

Study Notebook

Have students—

• copy Example 4 into their notebooks and illustrate the equation with a graph.

• include any other item(s) that they find helpful in mastering the skills in this lesson.

About the Exercises . . .

Odd/Even Assignments

Exercises 11–30 are structured so that students practice the same concepts whether they are assigned odd or even problems.

Assignment Guide

Basic: 11–29 odd, 33–41

Average: 11–33 odd, 34–41

Advanced: 12–32 even, 33–40
(Optional: 41)

You can also write an equation for a line if you know the coordinates of two points on a line.

Example 4 Write an Equation Given Two Points

Write an equation for the line that passes through $(-2, 5)$ and $(2, 1)$.

Step 1 Find the slope m.

$$m = \frac{y_2 - y_1}{x_2 - x_1} \qquad \text{Definition of slope}$$

$$m = \frac{5 - 1}{-2 - 2} \text{ or } -1 \qquad \begin{array}{l}(x_1, y_1) = (-2, 5), \\ (x_2, y_2) = (2, 1)\end{array}$$

Step 2 Find the y-intercept b. Use the slope and the coordinates of either point.

$$y = mx + b \qquad \text{Slope-intercept form}$$
$$5 = -1(-2) + b \qquad \text{Replace } (x, y) \text{ with } (-2, 5) \text{ and } m \text{ with } -1.$$
$$3 = b \qquad \text{Simplify.}$$

Step 3 Substitute the slope and y-intercept.

$$y = mx + b \qquad \text{Slope-intercept form}$$
$$y = -1x + 3 \qquad \text{Replace } m \text{ with } -1 \text{ and } b \text{ with 3.}$$
$$y = -x + 3 \qquad \text{Simplify.}$$

Example 5 Write an Equation From a Table

Use the table of values to write an equation in slope-intercept form.

x	y
−5	6
5	−2
10	−6
15	−10

Step 1 Find the slope m. Use the coordinates of any two points.

$$m = \frac{y_2 - y_1}{x_2 - x_1} \qquad \text{Definition of slope}$$

$$m = \frac{-2 - 6}{5 - (-5)} \text{ or } -\frac{4}{5} \qquad \begin{array}{l}(x_1, y_1) = (-5, 6), \\ (x_2, y_2) = (5, -2)\end{array}$$

Study Tip

Alternate Strategy
If a table includes the y-intercept, simply use this value and the slope to write an equation.

x	y
−5	6
0	2

y-intercept = 2

Step 2 Find the y-intercept b. Use the slope and the coordinates of any point.

$$y = mx + b \qquad \text{Slope-intercept form}$$
$$6 = -\frac{4}{5}(-5) + b \qquad \text{Replace } (x, y) \text{ with } (-5, 6) \text{ and } m \text{ with } -\frac{4}{5}.$$
$$2 = b \qquad \text{Simplify.}$$

Step 3 Substitute the slope and y-intercept.

$$y = mx + b \qquad \text{Slope-intercept form}$$
$$y = -\frac{4}{5}x + 2 \qquad \text{Replace } m \text{ with } -\frac{4}{5} \text{ and } b \text{ with 2.}$$

CHECK
$$y = -\frac{4}{5}x + 2 \qquad \text{Write the equation.}$$
$$-10 \overset{?}{=} -\frac{4}{5}(15) + 2 \qquad \begin{array}{l}\text{Replace } (x, y) \text{ with the coordinates} \\ \text{of another point, } (15, -10).\end{array}$$
$$-10 = -10 \checkmark \qquad \text{Simplify.}$$

DAILY INTERVENTION

Unlocking Misconceptions

• **Use Two Points on the Line** Some students may mistakenly believe that they must choose points in a particular order, such as left to right, or such that the smaller number is subtracted from the larger number. Demonstrate that any arrangement of any two points on the line will result in the same equation in slope-intercept form. Switch the position of the points in Example 4 and find the equation.

Check for Understanding

Concept Check
–2. See margin.

1. **Explain** how to write the equation of a line if you are given a graph.

2. **OPEN ENDED** Choose a slope and y-intercept. Then graph the line.

Guided Practice

Write an equation in slope-intercept form for each line. **4.** $y = -7$

GUIDED PRACTICE KEY	
Exercises	Examples
3, 4	1
5, 6	2
7, 8	4
9	5
10	3

3. slope $= \frac{1}{2}$, y-intercept $= 1$ $y = \frac{1}{2}x + 1$ **4.** slope $= 0$, y-intercept $= -7$

5. $y = -2x + 3$

6. 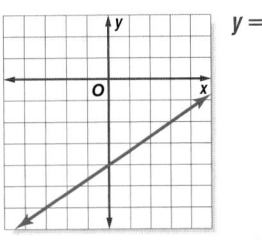 $y = \frac{2}{3}x - 4$

Write an equation in slope-intercept form for the line passing through each pair of points.

7. $(2, 2)$ and $(4, 3)$ $y = \frac{1}{2}x + 1$

8. $(3, -4)$ and $(-1, 4)$ $y = -2x + 2$

9. $y = \frac{3}{4}x - 1$

9. Write an equation in slope-intercept form to represent the table of values.

x	-4	0	4	8
y	-4	-1	2	5

Application

10. **PICNICS** It costs $50 plus $10 per hour to rent a park pavilion.
   a. Write an equation in slope-intercept form that shows the cost y for renting the pavilion for x hours. $y = 10x + 50$
   b. Find the cost of renting the pavilion for 8 hours. **$130**

★ indicates increased difficulty

Practice and Apply

Homework Help	
For Exercises	See Examples
11–16	1
17–22	2
23–28	4
29, 30	5
31–33	3

Extra Practice
See page 743.

Write an equation in slope-intercept form for each line. **12.** $y = -4x + 1$

11. slope $= 2$, y-intercept $= 6$ $y = 2x + 6$ **12.** slope $= -4$, y-intercept $= 1$

13. slope $= 0$, y-intercept $= 5$ $y = 5$

14. slope $= 1$, y-intercept $= -2$

15. slope $= -\frac{1}{3}$, y-intercept $= 8$

16. slope $= \frac{2}{5}$, y-intercept $= 0$ $y = \frac{2}{5}x$

14. $y = x - 2$
15. $y = -\frac{1}{3}x + 8$
17. $y = 2x + 3$
18. $y = -x + 6$
19. $y = -2.5$
20. $y = 4x - 5$
21. $y = -\frac{1}{2}x$
22. $y = \frac{1}{4}x + 2$

17.
18.
19.
20.
21.
22.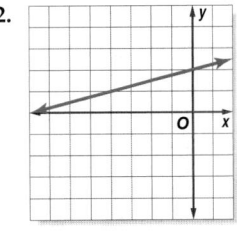

Study Guide and Intervention, p. 447

If you know the slope and y-intercept, you can write the equation of a line by substituting these values in $y = mx + b$.

Example 1
Write an equation in slope-intercept form for each line.
a. slope $= -\frac{1}{4}$, y-intercept $= -3$
$y = mx + b$ Slope-intercept form
$y = -\frac{1}{4}x + (-3)$ Replace m with $-\frac{1}{4}$ and b with -3.
$y = -\frac{1}{4}x - 3$ Simplify.

b. slope $= 0$, y-intercept $= -9$
$y = mx + b$ Slope-intercept form
$y = 0x + (-9)$ Replace m with 0 and b with -9.
$y = -9$ Simplify.

Example 2
Write an equation in slope-intercept form for the line passing through (–4, 4) and (2, 7).
Step 1 Find the slope m.
$m = \frac{y_2 - y_1}{x_2 - x_1}$ Definition of slope
$m = \frac{7 - 4}{2 - (-4)}$ or $\frac{1}{2}$ $(x_1, y_1) = (-4, 4)$. $(x_2, y_2) = (2, 7)$

Step 2 Find the y-intercept b. Use the slope and the coordinates of either point.
$y = mx + b$ Slope-intercept form
$4 = \frac{1}{2}(-4) + b$ Replace (x, y) with (-4, 4) and m with $\frac{1}{2}$.
$6 = b$ Simplify.
An equation is $y = \frac{1}{2}x + 6$.

Exercises
Write an equation in slope-intercept form for each line.
1. slope $= 1$, y-intercept $= 2$ $y = x + 2$
2. slope $= -\frac{3}{4}$, y-intercept $= -5$ $y = -\frac{3}{4}x - 5$
3. slope $= 0$, y-intercept $= -3$ $y = -3$

Write an equation in slope-intercept form for the line passing through each pair of points.
4. (6, 2) and (3, 1) $y = \frac{1}{3}x$
5. (8, 8) and (-4, 6) $y = \frac{1}{6}x + 6$
6. (7, -3) and (-5, -3) $y = -3$

Skills Practice, p. 448 and Practice, p. 449 (shown)

Write an equation in slope-intercept form for each line.
1. slope $= 3$, y-intercept $= -2$ $y = 3x - 2$
2. slope $= 0$, y-intercept $= 7$ $y = 7$
3. $y = -\frac{4}{3}x + 3$
4. $y = 3x$

Write an equation in slope-intercept form for the line passing through each pair of points.
5. (9, 0) and (6, -1) $y = \frac{1}{3}x - 3$
6. (8, 6) and (-8, 2) $y = \frac{1}{4}x + 4$
7. (7, -5) and (-4, -5) $y = -5$
8. (2, 7) and (-1, 4) $y = x + 5$
9. (4, 4) and (-8, 10) $y = -\frac{1}{2}x + 6$
10. (0, 2) and (-3, 14) $y = -4x + 2$

BUSINESS For Exercises 11 and 12, use the following information.
Flourishing Flowers charges $125 plus $60 for each standard floral arrangement to deliver and set up flowers for a banquet.
11. Write an equation in slope-intercept form that shows the cost y for flowers for x number of arrangements. $y = 60x + 125$
12. Find the cost of providing 20 floral arrangements.   **$1325**

INSULATION For Exercises 13 and 14, use the following information.
Renata González wants to increase the energy efficiency of her house by adding to the insulation previously installed. The better a material protects against heat loss, the higher its R-value, or resistance to heat flow. The table shows the R-value of fiberglass blanket insulation per inch of thickness. The existing insulation in Renata's attic has an R-value of 10.

R-value	Thickness (in.)
0.0	0
3.2	1
6.4	2
9.6	3

Source: Oak Ridge National Laboratory

13. Write an equation in slope-intercept form that shows the total R-value y in the attic if she adds x number of inches of additional insulation. $y = 3.2x + 10$
14. Estimate the total R-value in the attic if she adds 6 inches of insulation.   **29.2**

Enrichment, p. 451

Problem Solving: Gathering Data
When investors decide to buy or sell stock, they usually base their decisions on data. They read stock market reports, investigate companies they are interested in, and look at economic trends. This activity focuses on reading stock market reports.

To read a stock market report, you need to become familiar with the terms that are used, the facts and figures that are published in the newspaper, and the methods used to keep track of the stocks.

Many newspapers print stock reports such as the New York Stock Exchange (NYSE) report. The final entry for each stock is a fraction or mixed number that is positive (indicating a gain in value) or negative (indicating a loss).

Find the New York Stock Exchange (NYSE) report in the business section of your local Sunday newspaper. Using just those stocks that begin with A, B, or C, tally the number of stocks that had each of the gains and losses listed below.

+2 points or more		+1.00		-.12		-1.12	
+1.87		+.87		-.25		-1.25	
+1.75		+.75		-.37		-1.37	
+1.62		+.62		-.50		-1.50	
+1.50		+.50		-.62		-1.62	
+1.37		+.37		-.75		-1.75	
+1.25		+.25		-.87		-1.87	
+1.12		+.12		-1.00		-2 points or more	
		No change					

1–5. Answers will vary.
1. Did more stocks gain in value or lose value?
2. How did the market do as a whole?
3. How did the newspapers describe the trading this week?
4. Make a scatterplot that shows how two specific stocks change over the period of one week. Use their daily closing prices.
5. Is there any relationship between the two stocks you chose? Explain why or why not.

Answers

1. Sample answer: Find the y-intercept b and another point on the line. Use the points to determine the slope m. Then substitute these values in $y = mx + b$ and write the equation.

2. Sample answer: State the slope and y-intercept. Include a graph whose y-intercept point and another point on the line are both labeled. Show how the slope was used to graph the line.

Open-Ended Assessment

Writing Have students write a paragraph comparing the methods for writing linear functions shown in Example 2 and Example 4. Suggest that they use the same pair of points with both methods. **Students should note that both methods use two points and the concept of rise over run.**

Tips for New Teachers

Intervention If there is any doubt whether your students thoroughly understand writing linear functions, consider spending an extra day on this lesson. Use the Extra Practice on p. 743. You can also use the Study Guide and Intervention masters or the Practice masters in the *Chapter 8 Resource Masters* to reinforce this concept.

Getting Ready for Lesson 8-8

PREREQUISITE SKILL Lesson 8-8 presents best-fit lines drawn on scatter plots. Exercise 41 should be used to determine your students' familiarity with scatter plots.

Answers

31. $y = 1088x$; The speed of sound is 1088 feet per second.

34. Write the data as ordered pairs and graph the points. Then draw a line through the points. Find the slope and y-intercept of the line and substitute the values in $y = mx + b$. Answers should include the following.

- The y-intercept is the y value in the table when the corresponding x value is 0. Use two pairs of x- and y-coordinates in the table to find the slope.

---

23. $y = x + 1$
24. $y = -\frac{1}{2}x + 1$
25. $y = -x$
26. $y = \frac{3}{2}x - 4$

More About . . .

Sound Coyotes communicate by using different barks and howls. Because of the way in which sound travels, a coyote is usually not in the area from which the sound seems to be coming.

Source: www.livingdesert.org

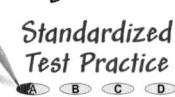

NEW YORK Test Practice

Standardized Test Practice

Write an equation in slope-intercept form for the line passing through each pair of points.

23. $(-2, -1)$ and $(1, 2)$ **24.** $(-4, 3)$ and $(4, -1)$ **25.** $(0, 0)$ and $(-1, 1)$

26. $(4, 2)$ and $(-8, -16)$ **27.** $(8, 7)$ and $(-9, 7)$ $\quad y = 7$ **28.** $(5, -6)$ and $(3, 2)$ $\quad y = -4x + 14$

Write an equation in slope-intercept form for each table of values.

29.

x	−1	0	1	2
y	−7	−3	1	5

$y = 4x - 3$

30.

x	−3	−1	1	3
y	7	5	3	1

$y = -x + 4$

SOUND For Exercises 31 and 32, use the table that shows the distance that sound travels through dry air at 0°C.

Time(s) x	Distance (ft) y
0	0
1	1088
2	2176
3	3264

31. See margin.

★ **31.** Write an equation in slope-intercept form to represent the data in the table. Describe what the slope means.

★ **32.** Estimate the number of miles that sound travels through dry air in one minute. **12.4 mi**

33. CRITICAL THINKING A CD player has a pre-sale price of $c. Kim buys it at a 30% discount and pays 6% sales tax. After a few months, she sells it for $d, which was 50% of what she paid originally.
  a. Express d as a function of c. $d = 0.5(0.7c \times 1.06)$ or $d = 0.371c$
  b. How much did Kim sell it for if the pre-sale price was $50? **$18.55**

34. **WRITING IN MATH** Answer the question that was posed at the beginning of the lesson. **See margin.**

How can you model data with a linear equation?

Include the following in your answer:
- an explanation of how to find the y-intercept and slope by using a table.

35. Which equation is of a line that passes through $(2, -2)$ and $(0, 2)$? **C**
  (A) $y = -3x$ (B) $y = -2x + 3$ (C) $y = -2x + 2$ (D) $y = -3x + 2$

36. Which equation represents the table of values? **C**

x	−4	−8	−12	−16
y	6	8	10	12

  (A) $y = -2x + 4$ (B) $y = 2x + 6$
  (C) $y = -\frac{1}{2}x + 4$ (D) $y = -x - 6$

Maintain Your Skills

Mixed Review State the slope and the y-intercept for the graph of each equation. *(Lesson 8-6)*

37. $y = 6x + 7$ **6; 7**   **38.** $y = -x + 4$ **−1; 4**   **39.** $-3x + y = -2$ **3; −2**

40. Suppose y varies directly as x and $y = 14$ when $x = 35$. Write an equation relating x and y. *(Lesson 8-5)* $y = \frac{2}{5}x$

Getting Ready for the Next Lesson

PREREQUISITE SKILL *(To review scatter plots, see Lesson 1-7.)*

41. State whether a scatter plot containing the following set of points would show a *positive*, *negative*, or *no* relationship.
  $(0, 15), (2, 20), (4, 36), (5, 44), (4, 32), (3, 30), (6, 50)$ **positive**

What You'll Learn

- Draw best-fit lines for sets of data.
- Use best-fit lines to make predictions about data.

Vocabulary
- best-fit line

How can a line be used to predict life expectancy for future generations?

The scatter plot shows the number of years people in the United States are expected to live, according to the year they were born.

a. Use the line drawn through the points to predict the life expectancy of a person born in 2010. **83**

b. What are some limitations in using a line to predict life expectancy? **See margin.**

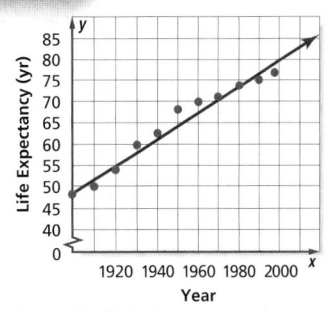

Source: *The World Almanac*

Study Tip

Estimation
Drawing a best-fit line using the method in this lesson is an estimation. Therefore, it is possible to draw different lines to approximate the same data.

TEACHING TIP
Explain to students that lines of best fit can be calculated using sophisticated statistical methods, rather than the visual estimations used in this lesson.

BEST-FIT LINES When real-life data are collected, the points graphed usually do not form a straight line, but may approximate a linear relationship. A best-fit line can be used to show such a relationship. A **best-fit line** is a line that is very close to most of the data points.

Example 1 Make Predictions from a Best-Fit Line

MONEY The table shows the changes in the minimum wage since 1980.

a. Make a scatter plot and draw a best-fit line for the data.

Draw a line that best fits the data.

Year	Wage ($/h)
1980	3.10
1981	3.35
1990	3.80
1996	4.25
1997	4.75
2000	5.15

b. Use the best-fit line to predict the minimum wage for the year 2010.

Extend the line so that you can find the y value for an x value of 2010. The y value for 2010 is about 6.4. So, a prediction for the minimum wage in 2010 is approximately $6.40.

---

1 Focus

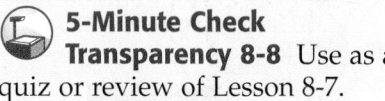

5-Minute Check Transparency 8-8 Use as a quiz or review of Lesson 8-7.

Mathematical Background notes are available for this lesson on page 366D.

How can a line be used to predict life expectancy for future generations?

The opening activity questions are repeated on page 455 of the *Chapter 8 Resource Masters.*

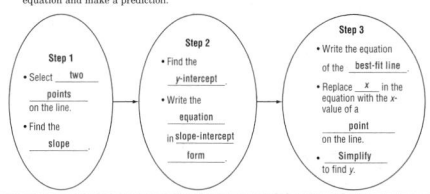

Reading to Learn Mathematics, p. 455 **ELL**

Pre-Activity *How can a line be used to predict life expectancy for future generations?*

Do the activity at the top of page 409 in your textbook. Write your answers below.

a. Use the line drawn through the points to predict the life expectancy of a person born in 2010. **83**

b. What are some limitations in using a line to predict life expectancy? **Sample answer: Medical improvements could change the accuracy of the model. Also, the line continues to go up, but people's ages will not increase forever.**

Reading the Lesson

Write a definition and give an example of the new vocabulary phrase.

	Vocabulary	Definition	Example
1.	slope intercept form	See students' work.	

2. A best-fit line can be used when the data points approximate a **linear** relationship.

3. Explain what a prediction equation is. **A prediction equation is an equation of a best-fit line used to tell what course the data will likely take in the future.**

Helping You Remember

4. Complete the following concept map showing the steps needed to find a prediction equation and make a prediction.

Resource Manager

Workbooks and Reproducible Masters

Chapter 8 Resource Masters
- Study Guide and Intervention, p. 452
- Skills Practice, p. 453
- Practice, p. 454
- Reading to Learn Mathematics, p. 455
- Enrichment, p. 456
- Assessment, p. 482

Parent and Student Study Guide Workbook, p. 68

Transparencies

5-Minute Check Transparency 8-8
Real-World Transparency 8
Answer Key Transparencies

Technology

Interactive Chalkboard

BEST-FIT LINES

1 **AGRICULTURE** The table shows the amount of land in U. S. farms from 1980 to 2000.

Year	Land (million acres)
1980	1039
1985	1012
1990	986
1995	963
2000	943

Source: U.S. Department of Agriculture

a. Make a scatter plot and draw a best-fit line for the data.

b. Use the best-fit line to predict the amount of land in the year 2010. **about 892 million acres**

PREDICTION EQUATIONS

2 **AGRICULTURE** The scatter plot shows the number of milk cow operations in New Mexico from 1975 to 1995.

Source: U.S. Department of Agriculture

a. Write an equation in slope-intercept form for the best-fit line.
$y = -48x + 1920$

b. Predict the number of milk cow operations in the year 2005. **about 480**

PREDICTION EQUATIONS You can also make predictions from the equation of a best-fit line.

TEACHING TIP
If you extend the best-fit line, it will cross the x-axis, making the winning time 0 seconds. This is not possible and shows one limitation of using a model to predict real-world situations.

Example 2 **Make Predictions from an Equation**

SWIMMING The scatter plot shows the winning Olympic times in the women's 800-meter freestyle event from 1968 through 2000.

a. Write an equation in slope-intercept form for the best-fit line.

Women's 800-Meter Freestyle Event

Step 1

First, select two points on the line and find the slope. Notice that the two points on the best-fit line are not original data points. We have chosen (1980, 525) and (1992, 500).

$$m = \frac{y_2 - y_1}{x_2 - x_1} \quad \text{Definition of slope}$$

$$= \frac{525 - 500}{1980 - 1992} \quad (x_1, y_1) = (1992, 500), (x_2, y_2) = (1980, 525)$$

$$\approx -2.1 \quad \text{Simplify.}$$

Step 2

Next, find the y-intercept.

$$y = mx + b \quad \text{Slope-intercept form}$$
$$525 = -2.1(1980) + b \quad \text{Replace } (x, y) \text{ with } (1980, 525) \text{ and } m \text{ with } -2.1.$$
$$4683 \approx b \quad \text{Simplify.}$$

Step 3

Write the equation.

$$y = mx + b \quad \text{Slope-intercept form}$$
$$y = -2.1x + 4683 \quad \text{Replace } m \text{ with } -2.1 \text{ and } b \text{ with } 4683.$$

b. Predict the winning time in the women's 800-meter freestyle event in the year 2008.

$$y = -2.1x + 4683 \quad \text{Write the equation of the best-fit line.}$$
$$y = -2.1(2008) + 4683 \quad \text{Replace } x \text{ with } 2008.$$
$$y \approx 466.2 \quad \text{Simplify.}$$

A prediction for the winning time in the year 2008 is approximately 466.2 seconds or 7 minutes, 46.2 seconds.

Check for Understanding

Concept Check **1. Explain** how to use a best-fit line to make a prediction.

1–2. See margin.

2. OPEN ENDED Make a scatter plot with at least ten points that appear to be somewhat linear. Draw two different lines that could approximate the data.

Guided Practice

TECHNOLOGY For Exercises 3 and 4, use the table that shows the number of U.S. households with Internet access. **3. See margin.**

3. Make a scatter plot and draw a best-fit line.

4. Use the best-fit line to predict the number of U.S. households that will have Internet access in 2005. **Sample answer: 65 million**

Year	Number of Households (millions)
1995	9.4
1996	14.7
1997	21.3
1998	27.3
1999	32.7
2000	36.0

Source: *Wall Street Journal Almanac*

Application

SPENDING For Exercises 5 and 6, use the best-fit line that shows the billions of dollars spent by travelers in the United States.

5. Write an equation in slope-intercept form for the best-fit line. $y = 20x + 320$

6. Use the equation to predict how much money travelers will spend in 2008. **$620 billion**

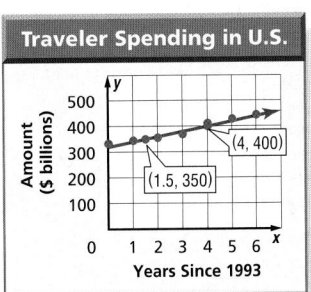

Traveler Spending in U.S.

Study Notebook

Have students—
- add the definition/example of the vocabulary term to their Vocabulary Builder worksheets for Chapter 8.
- copy Exercises 3 and 4, including the answers, into their notebooks.
- include any other item(s) that they find helpful in mastering the skills in this lesson.

★ indicates increased difficulty

Practice and Apply

ENTERTAINMENT For Exercises 7 and 8, use the table that shows movie attendance in the United States. **7. See pp. 431A–431H.**

7. Make a scatter plot and draw a best-fit line.

8. Use the best-fit line to predict movie attendance in 2005.
Sample answer: 1700 million

Year	Attendance (millions)
1993	1244
1994	1292
1995	1263
1996	1339
1997	1388
1998	1475
1999	1460

Source: *Wall Street Journal Almanac*

10. Sample answer: $y = -0.0006x + 27$; -9; this is not reasonable because barometric pressure cannot be negative.

11. No, the equation gives a negative value for barometric pressure, which is not possible. Also, the data in the scatter plot do not appear to be linear.

PRESSURE For Exercises 9–11, use the table that shows the approximate barometric pressure at various altitudes.

9. Make a scatter plot of the data and draw a best-fit line. **See pp. 431A–431H.**

★10. Write an equation for the best-fit line and use it to estimate the barometric pressure at 60,000 feet. Is the estimation reasonable? Explain.

★11. Do you think that a line is the best model for this data? Explain.

Altitude (ft)	Barometric Pressure (in. mercury)
0	30
5000	25
10,000	21
20,000	14
30,000	9
40,000	6
50,000	3

Source: *New York Public Library Science Desk Reference*

www.pre-alg.com/self_check_quiz/ny

Lesson 8-8 Best-Fit Lines **411**

About the Exercises . . .

Organization by Objective
- **Best-Fit Lines:** 7, 9, 12, 14
- **Prediction Equations:** 8, 10–11, 13, 15–17

Odd/Even Assignments
Exercises 7–10 and 12–17 are structured so that students practice the same concepts whether they are assigned odd or even problems.

Alert! Exercises 2, 3, 7, 9, 12, and 14 require graph paper.

Assignment Guide
Basic: 7, 9, 12, 13, 15, 17–42
Average: 7–11 odd, 12, 13, 15, 17–42
Advanced: 8–12 even, 13, 14–18 even, 20–36 (Optional: 37–42)

Answer
3. Sample answer:

Answers (p. 410)

1. Sample answer: Use a ruler to extend the line so that it passes through the x value for which you want to predict. Locate the x value on the line and determine the corresponding y value. Or, write an equation for the best-fit line and substitute the desired value of x to find the corresponding value of y.

2. Sample answer:

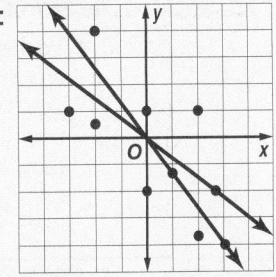

Study Guide and Intervention, p. 452

A best-fit line is a line that is very close to most of the data points. You can use best-fit lines to make predictions from real-world data.

Example 1 Make a scatter plot and draw a best-fit line for the data in the table.

Year	Percent of Population	Year	Percent of Population
1970	60.4	1995	66.6
1980	63.8	1997	67.1
1985	64.8	1998	67.1
1990	66.5	1999	67.1

Source: U.S. Census Bureau

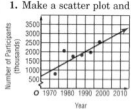

U.S. Civilian Labor Force

Source: U.S. Census Bureau

Example 2 Use the best-fit line in example 1 to predict the percent of the population in the U.S. labor force in 2010.

Use the extended line to find the y value for an x value of 2010—about 70. A prediction for the percent of the U.S. population in the labor force in 2010 is approximately 70 percent.

Exercises

Use the table that shows the number of girls who participated in high school athletic programs from 1973 to 1998.

1. Make a scatter plot and draw a best-fit line.

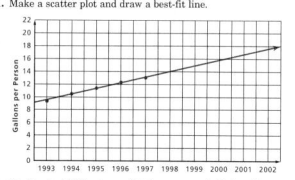

Year	1973	1978	1983	1988	1993	1998
Number of Participants (thousands)	817	2083	1780	1850	1997	2570

Source: U.S. Census Bureau

2. Use the best-fit line to predict the number of female participants in 2008. **Sample answer: about 3,000,000 female participants**

Skills Practice, p. 453 and Practice, p. 454 (shown)

BEVERAGES For Exercises 1 and 2, use the table that shows the amount of whole milk consumed per person in the United States from 1993 to 1997.

Year	Gallons per Person
1993	9.4
1994	10.7
1995	11.6
1996	12.5
1997	13.1

Source: U.S. Census Bureau

1. Make a scatter plot and draw a best-fit line.

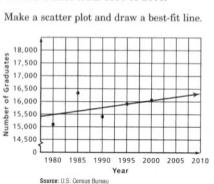

2. Use the best-fit line to predict the amount of whole milk consumed per person in 2002.

Sample answer: about 18 gallons of whole milk per person

EDUCATION For Exercises 3 and 4, use the table that shows the number of students graduating from medical school in the United States from 1980 to 2000.

Year	Graduates
1980	15,113
1985	16,318
1990	15,398
1995	15,888
2000	16,112

Source: U.S. Census Bureau

3. Make a scatter plot and draw a best-fit line.

4. Write an equation for the best-fit line and use it to predict the number of medical school graduates in 2010. **Sample answer: y = 44.8x − 73,488; approximately 16,560 medical school graduates**

Enrichment, p. 456

Line of Best Fit

Each point on the graph shows the relation between the number of people attending the Roxy Cinema and the number of cars in the parking lot.

A line is drawn that appears to lie close to most of the points. This is called the *line of best fit*. Here is how to find the equation of this line.

The line passes through (100, 40) and (300, 120). Use the slope intercept form.

Attendance and Parking

$m = \dfrac{y_2 - y_1}{x_2 - x_1}$ Definition of slope $y = mx + b$ Slope-intercept form

$m = \dfrac{120 - 40}{300 - 100}$ $(x_1, y_1) = (100, 40)$ $40 = \dfrac{2}{5}(100) + b$ Replace (x, y) with (100, 40) and m with $\frac{2}{5}$
   $(x_2, y_2) = (300, 120)$

$= \dfrac{80}{200}$ or $\dfrac{2}{5}$ Simplify. $0 = b$ Simplify.

So an equation for the line is $y = \dfrac{2}{5}x + 0$ or $y = \dfrac{2}{5}x$.

Solve each problem.

1. Suppose the owner of the Roxy decides to increase the seating capacity of the theater to 1000. How many cars should the parking lot be prepared to accommodate? **400 cars**

2. The points (240, 60) and (340, 120) lie on the scatter plot. Write an equation for the line through these points. $y = \dfrac{3}{5}x - 84$

3. Do you think the equation in Exercise 2 is a good representation of the relationship in this problem? Explain. **No; The graph of the equation does not appear to go through the center of the data points.**

4. Suppose the equation for the relationship between attendance at the theater and cars in the parking lot is $y = 2x + 20$. What might you suspect about the users of the parking lot? **Many people are parking in the lot who are not going to the Roxy.**

Middle / Right column

More About...

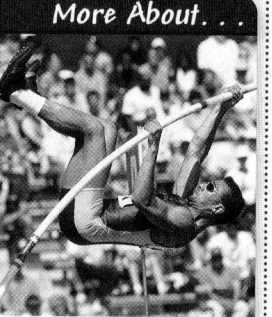

Pole Vaulting

In 1964, thirteen competitors broke or equaled the previous Olympic pole vault record a total of 36 times. This was due to the new fiberglass pole.

Source: *Chance*

• **POLE VAULTING** For Exercises 12 and 13, use the table that shows the men's winning Olympic pole vault heights to the nearest inch.

Year	Height (in.)
1976	217
1980	228
1984	226
1988	232
1992	228
1996	233
2000	232

Source: *The World Almanac*

12. Make a scatter plot and draw a best-fit line. **See pp. 431A–431H.**

13. Use the best-fit line to predict the winning pole vault height in the 2008 Olympics. **Sample answer: 238 in.**

EARTH SCIENCE For Exercises 14–17, use the table that shows the latitude and the average temperature in July for five cities in the United States.

City	Latitude (°N)	Average July High Temperature (°F)
Chicago, IL	41	73
Dallas, TX	32	85
Denver, CO	39	74
New York, NY	40	77
Duluth, MN	46	66

Source: *The World Almanac*

14. Make a scatter plot of the data and draw a best-fit line. **See pp. 431A–431H.**

15. Describe the relationship between latitude and temperature shown by the graph. **As latitude increases, temperature decreases.**

16. Sample answer: $y = -1.33x + 127.8$

★ 16. Write an equation for the best-fit line you drew in Exercise 14.

17. Use your equation to estimate the average July temperature for a location with latitude 50° north. **Sample answer: 61.3°F**

18. **CRITICAL THINKING** The table at the right shows the percent of public schools in the United States with Internet access. Suppose you use (Year, Percent of Schools) to write a linear equation describing the data. Then you use (Years Since 1996, Percent of Schools) to write an equation. Is the slope or y-intercept of the graphs of the equations the same? Explain. **See margin.**

Year	Years Since 1996	Percent of Schools
1996	0	65
1997	1	78
1998	2	89
1999	3	95
2000	4	98

Source: National Center for Education Statistics

WebQuest

Best-fit lines can help make predictions about recreational activities. Visit www.pre-alg.com/webquest to continue work on your WebQuest project.

19. **WRITING IN MATH** Answer the question that was posed at the beginning of the lesson. **See margin.**

How can a line be used to predict life expectancy for future generations?

Include the following in your answer:

- a description of a best-fit line, and
- an explanation of how lines can represent sets of data that are not exactly linear.

412 Chapter 8 Functions and Graphing

DAILY INTERVENTION

Differentiated Instruction   **ELL**

- **Verbal/Linguistic** Have the class interview students in the school on an age-related topic, such as how much students earn on average per age. Have students construct a scatter plot of the data, including a best-fit line. Then have them explain the data and describe how much they would expect students to earn by age 17. Have each student write a few sentences hypothesizing reasons for the prediction. Then have students briefly discuss their answers. **See students' work.**

20. Use the best-fit line at the right to predict the value of y when $x = 7$. **B**

Ⓐ 4   Ⓑ 6

Ⓒ 0   Ⓓ 7

21. Choose the correct statement about best-fit lines. **A**

Ⓐ A best-fit line is close to most of the data points.

Ⓑ A best-fit line describes the exact coordinates of each point in the data set.

Ⓒ A best-fit line always has a positive slope.

Ⓓ A best-fit line must go through at least two of the data points.

Maintain Your Skills

Mixed Review   Write an equation in slope-intercept form for each line.   *(Lesson 8-7)*

22. $y = 3x + 5$

23. $y = -2x + 2$

22. slope = 3, y-intercept = 5   **23.** slope = -2, y-intercept = 2

24.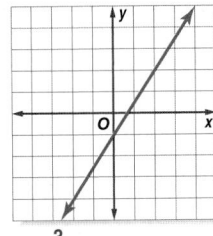

$y = \frac{3}{2}x - 1$

25.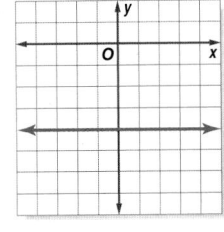

$y = -4$

Graph each equation using the slope and y-intercept.   *(Lesson 8-6)*

26. $y = x - 2$ **27.** $y = -x + 3$ **28.** $y = \frac{1}{2}x$

26–28. See margin.

Solve each inequality and check your solution.   *(Lesson 7-6)*   **31.** $d > -\frac{3}{2}$

29. $3n - 11 \le 10$ **30.** $8(x + 1) < 16$ **31.** $5d + 2 > d - 4$

$n \le 7$ $x < 1$

32. SCHOOL   Zach has no more than twelve days to complete his science project. Write an inequality to represent this sentence.   *(Lesson 7-3)* $d \le 12$

Solve each proportion.   *(Lesson 6-2)*

33. $\frac{a}{3} = \frac{16}{24}$ **2**   **34.** $\frac{5}{10} = \frac{15}{x}$ **30**   **35.** $\frac{2}{16} = \frac{n}{36}$ **4.5**

36. Evaluate xy if $x = \frac{8}{9}$ and $y = \frac{12}{30}$. Write in simplest form.   *(Lesson 5-3)* $\frac{16}{45}$

Getting Ready for the Next Lesson   **PREREQUISITE SKILL**   Find the value of y in each equation by substituting the given value of x.   *(To review **substitution**, see Lesson 1-2.)*

37. $y = x + 1; x = 2$ **3**   **38.** $y = x + 5; x = -1$ **4**

39. $y = x - 4; x = 3$ **−1**   **40.** $x + y = 2; x = 0$ **2**

41. $x + y = -1; x = 1$ **−2**   **42.** $x + y = 0; x = 4$ **−4**

Lesson 8-8   Best-Fit Lines   **413**

Answers

26.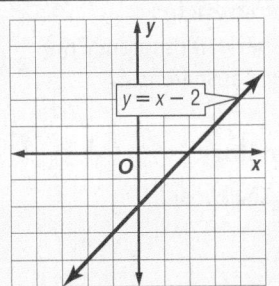

$y = x - 2$

27.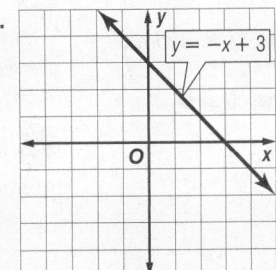

$y = -x + 3$

28.

$y = \frac{1}{2}x$

---

4 **Assess**

Open-Ended Assessment

Speaking Ask students to explain the use of best-fit lines and their equations in making predictions from real-world data.

Getting Ready for Lesson 8-9

PREREQUISITE SKILL Lesson 8-9 presents solving systems of equations by substitution. Exercises 37–42 should be used to determine your students' familiarity with substituting given values for variables in an equation.

Assessment Options

Quiz (Lessons 8-6 through 8-8) is available on p. 482 of the *Chapter 8 Resource Masters*.

Answers (p. 412)

18. Sample answer: The slopes are the same because the rate of change in the percent of schools is the same per year whether you use the year or the number of years since 1996. The y-intercepts are different, depending on which scale you use.

19. The data describing the life expectancy for past generations can be displayed using a scatter plot. Then a line is drawn as close to as many of the points as possible. Then the line can be extended and used to predict the life expectancy for future generations. Answers should include the following.

- A best-fit line is a line drawn as close to as many of the data points as possible.
- Although the points may not be exactly linear, a best-fit line can be used to approximate the data set.

8-9 **Solving Systems of Equations**

NEW YORK *Performance Indicator* **8.G.18 Solve systems of equations graphically (only linear, integral solutions, $y = mx + b$ format, no vertical/horizontal lines)**

1 Focus

5-Minute Check Transparency 8-9 Use as a quiz or review of Lesson 8-8.

Mathematical Background notes are available for this lesson on page 366D.

How can a system of equations be used to compare data?

The opening activity questions are repeated on page 460 of the *Chapter 8 Resource Masters*.

Reading to Learn Mathematics, p. 460   ELL

Pre-Activity *How can a system of equations be used to compare data?*

Do the activity at the top of page 414 in your textbook. Write your answers below.

a. Write an equation to represent the income from each job. Let *y* equal the salary and let *x* equal the number of hours worked. (*Hint:* Income = hourly rate · number of hours worked + bonus.)
$y = 10x + 50$ and $y = 15x$

b. Graph both equations on the same coordinate plane.

c. What are the coordinates of the point where the two lines meet? What does this point represent? (10, 150); In 10 hours, the salary will be the same for both jobs, $150.

Reading the Lesson 1–2. See students' work.

Write a definition and give an example of each new vocabulary word or phrase.

Vocabulary	Definition	Example
1. system of equations		
2. substitution		

3. The __solution__ of a system of equations is the coordinates of the point where the graphs of the equations __intersect__.

4. If two equations have the same graph, there are __infinitely many__ solutions to that system of equations.

Helping You Remember

5. Review the Study Tip on page 415 in your textbook. Complete each section of the chart with the number of solutions and an explanation, model, or logical proof for the situation. Sample answers are given.

Different Slopes	Same Slope, Different y-Intercepts	Same Slope, Same y-Intercept
Exactly one solution: if two lines have different slopes, they will meet at one point even if that point is far beyond the scope of the graph. Because both lines are straight, they will only meet once.	No solution: if two lines have the same slope but different y-intercepts, they are parallel lines. By definition, the two lines will never meet.	Infinitely many solutions: if two lines have the same slope and the same y-intercept, then they have the same graph. Any point on the graph satisfies both equations.

Vocabulary
* system of equations
* substitution

Study Tip

Matrices
Another way to organize the data displayed in this table is with a *matrix*. To learn more about matrices, see page 705.

c. (10, 150); For 10 hours worked, the salary is the same for both jobs, $150.

What You'll Learn

* Solve systems of linear equations by graphing.
* Solve systems of linear equations by substitution.

How can a system of equations be used to compare data?

Yolanda is offered two summer jobs, as shown in the table.

a. Write an equation to represent the income from each job. Let *y* equal the salary and let *x* equal the number of hours worked. (*Hint:* Income = hourly rate · number of hours worked + bonus.) $y = 10x + 50$ and $y = 15x$

b. Graph both equations on the same coordinate plane. **See margin.**

c. What are the coordinates of the point where the two lines meet? What does this point represent?

Job	Hourly Rate	Bonus
A	$10	$50
B	$15	$0

SOLVE SYSTEMS BY GRAPHING The equations $y = 10x + 50$ and $y = 15x$ together are called a **system of equations**. The solution of this system is the ordered pair that is a solution of both equations, (10, 150).

$$y = 10x + 50$$
$$150 \stackrel{?}{=} 10(10) + 50$$
$$150 = 150 \checkmark$$

Replace (x, y) with (10, 150).

$$y = 15x$$
$$150 \stackrel{?}{=} 15(10)$$
$$150 = 150 \checkmark$$

One method for solving a system of equations is to graph the equations on the same coordinate plane. The coordinates of the point where the graphs intersect is the solution of the system of equations.

Example 1 Solve by Graphing

Solve the system of equations by graphing.

$$y = -x$$
$$y = x + 2$$

The graphs appear to intersect at $(-1, 1)$. Check this estimate by substituting the coordinates into each equation.

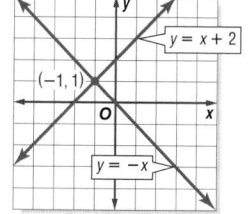

CHECK
$$y = -x \qquad\qquad y = x + 2$$
$$1 \stackrel{?}{=} -(-1) \qquad 1 \stackrel{?}{=} -1 + 2$$
$$1 = 1 \checkmark \qquad\qquad 1 = 1 \checkmark$$

The solution of the system of equations is $(-1, 1)$.

✓ **Concept Check** Is (0, 0) a solution of the system of equations in Example 1? Explain. **No; (0, 0) is a solution of the first equation, but not the second.**

Resource Manager

📁 Workbooks and Reproducible Masters

Chapter 8 Resource Masters
* Study Guide and Intervention, p. 457
* Skills Practice, p. 458
* Practice, p. 459
* Reading to Learn Mathematics, p. 460
* Enrichment, p. 461

Graphing Calculator and Spreadsheet Masters, p. 33
Parent and Student Study Guide Workbook, p. 69

💻 Transparencies

5-Minute Check Transparency 8-9
Answer Key Transparencies

💿 Technology

Interactive Chalkboard

Example 2 *One Solution*

ENTERTAINMENT Video Planet offers two rental plans.

Plan	Rental Fee Per Video	Annual Fee
A	$4.00	$0
B	$1.50	$20

a. How many videos would Walt need to rent in a year for the plans to cost the same?

Explore You know the rental fee per video and the annual fee.

Plan Write an equation to represent each plan, and then graph the equations to find the solution.

Solve Let x = number of videos rented and let y = the total cost.

	total cost		rental fee times number of videos		annual fee
Plan A	y	=	$4x$	+	0
Plan B	y	=	$1.50x$	+	20

The graph of the system shows the solution is (8, 32). This means that if Walt rents 8 videos in a year, the plans cost the same, $32.

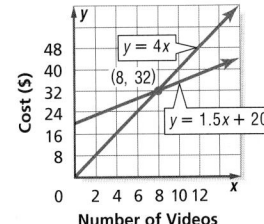

Examine Check by substituting (8, 32) into both equations in the system.

b. Which plan would cost less if Walt rents 12 videos in a year?

For $x = 12$, the line representing Plan B has a smaller y value. So, Plan B would cost less.

Example 3 *No Solution*

Solve the system of equations by graphing.

$y = 2x + 4$

$y = 2x - 1$

The graphs appear to be parallel lines. Since there is no coordinate pair that is a solution to both equations, there is no solution of this system of equations.

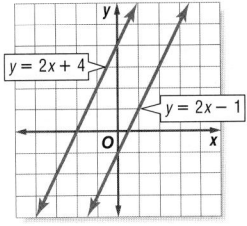

Example 4 *Infinitely Many Solutions*

Solve the system of equations by graphing.

$2y = x + 6$

$y = \frac{1}{2}x + 3$

Both equations have the same graph. Any ordered pair on the graph will satisfy both equations. Therefore, there are infinitely many solutions of this system of equations.

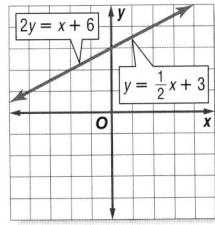

www.pre-alg.com/extra_examples/ny

Lesson 8-9 Solving Systems of Equations **415**

Study Tip

Slopes/Intercepts
When the graphs of a system of equations have:
- different slopes, there is exactly one solution,
- the same slope and different y-intercepts, there is no solution,
- the same slope and the same y-intercept, there are infinitely many solutions.

---

2 Teach

SOLVE SYSTEMS BY GRAPHING

In-Class Examples Power Point®

1 Solve the system of equations by graphing.

$y = x - 1$ **(1, 0)**

$y = 2x - 2$

2 **ENTERTAINMENT** One CD club, A, charges members a $25.00 annual fee. After that, CDs cost $5.00 each. Another CD club, B, has no annual fee and sells its members CDs for $7.50 each.

a. How many CDs would you need to buy in a year for the clubs to cost the same? **10**

b. Which club would be a better deal for a customer buying 20 CDs in a year? **Club A**

Teaching Tip Ask students whether it is safe to say that any two equations with the same slopes will never meet. **No; they must also have different y-intercepts in order to never meet.**

3 Solve the system of equations by graphing.

$y = \frac{1}{3}x - 5$ **no solution**

$y = \frac{1}{3}x + 2$

4 Solve the system of equations by graphing.

$y = \frac{3}{4}x + 6$

$4y - 3x = 24$

infinitely many solutions

DAILY

INTERVENTION

Differentiated Instruction   **ELL**

- **Verbal/Linguistic** Point out that systems of linear equations often are used in business to maximize profits. In such situations, the point at which two lines intersect is called a *break-even point*. At this point, the money invested is returned; after this point, everything is profit. For example, a book publisher may find that it must sell 120,000 copies of a novel before it will show a profit. Have students write a paragraph relating what they have learned in this lesson to this concept.

In-Class Example

Power
Point®

5 Solve the system of equations by substitution.

$y = 3x - 4$ **(2, 2)**

$y = 2$

3 Practice/Apply

Study Notebook

Have students—

• add the definitions/examples of the vocabulary terms to their Vocabulary Builder worksheets for Chapter 8.

• copy the Study Tip from p. 415 into their notebooks.

• include any other item(s) that they find helpful in mastering the skills in this lesson.

About the Exercises . . .

Organization by Objective
• Solve Systems by Graphing: 9–17
• Solve Systems by Substitution: 18–26

Odd/Even Assignments
Exercises 9–10 and 12–26 are structured so that students practice the same concepts whether they are assigned odd or even problems.

Alert! Exercises 2, 4, 5, and 12–17 require graph paper.

Assignment Guide

Basic: 9–21 odd, 24–40
Average: 9–23 odd, 24–40
Advanced: 10–24 even, 25–34 (Optional: 35–40)
All: Practice Quiz 2 (1–10)

Concept Summary   *Solutions to Systems of Equations*

One Solution	No Solution	Infinitely Many Solutions
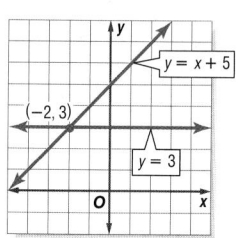		
Intersecting Lines	**Parallel Lines**	**Same Line**

SOLVE SYSTEMS BY SUBSTITUTION   A more accurate way to solve a system of equations is by using a method called **substitution**.

Example 5   *Solve by Substitution*

Solve the system of equations by substitution.

$y = x + 5$

$y = 3$

Since y must have the same value in both equations, you can replace y with 3 in the first equation.

$y = x + 5$ Write the first equation.

$3 = x + 5$ Replace y with 3.

$-2 = x$ Solve for x.

The solution of this system of equations is $(-2, 3)$. You can check the solution by graphing. The graphs appear to intersect at $(-2, 3)$, so the solution is correct.

Check for Understanding

Concept Check

1. See margin.

Guided Practice

GUIDED PRACTICE KEY	
Exercises	Examples
3–5	1, 3, 4
6, 7	5
8	2

1. **Explain** what is meant by a system of equations and describe its solution.

2. **OPEN ENDED** Draw a graph of a system of equations that has one solution, a system that has no solution, and a system that has infinitely many solutions. **See margin.**

3. State the solution of the system of equations graphed at the right. **(−5, −4)**

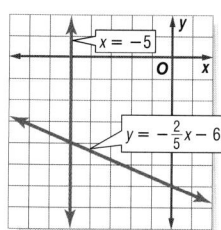

4–5. See pp. 431A–431H for graphs.
Solve each system of equations by graphing.

4. $y = 2x + 1$ **(0, 1)**   **5.** $x + y = 4$ **no**
   $y = -x + 1$ $x + y = 2$ **solution**

Solve each system of equations by substitution.

6. $y = 3x - 4$ **(0, −4)**   **7.** $x + y = 8$ **(2, 6)**
   $x = 0$ $y = 6$

Answers

1. Sample answer: A group of two or more equations form a system of equations. The solution is the ordered pair that satisfies all the equations in the system. If the equations are graphed, the solution is the coordinates of the point where the graphs intersect. The system has infinitely many solutions if the equations are the same and the graphs coincide.

2. Sample answers are shown at the right.

Application

8. GEOMETRY The perimeter of a garden is 40 feet. If the width y equals 7 feet, write and solve a system of equations to find the length of the garden.

8. $2x + 2y = 40$ and $y = 7$; 13 ft

★ indicates increased difficulty

Practice and Apply

Homework Help

For Exercises	See Examples
9–17	1, 3, 4
18–23	5
24–26	2

Extra Practice
See page 744.

State the solution of each system of equations.

9.

(3, −2)

10.

no solution

11.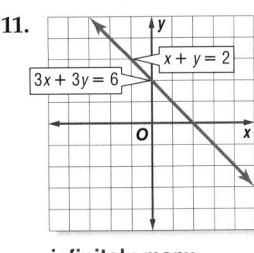

infinitely many

12–17. See pp. 431A–431H for graphs.

Solve each system of equations by graphing.

12. $y = -x$ **(−1, 1)**
$y = x + 2$

13. $x + y = 6$ **(3, 3)**
$y = x$

14. $2x + y = 1$
$y = -2x + 5$ **no solution**

15. $y = \frac{2}{3}x$ **infinitely many**
$2x - 3y = 0$

16. $x + y = -4$ **(−4, 0)**
$x - y = -4$

17. $y = -\frac{1}{2}x + 3$
$y = -2x$ **(−2, 4)**

Solve each system of equations by substitution.

18. $y = x + 1$ **(3, 4)**
$x = 3$

19. $y = x + 2$ **(−2, 0)**
$y = 0$

20. $y = 2x + 7$ **(−6, −5)**
$y = -5$

21. $x + y = 6$ **(−4, 10)**
$x = -4$

★ 22. $2x + 3y = 5$ **(1, 1)**
$y = x$

★ 23. $x + y = 9$ **(3, 6)**
$y = 2x$

More About. . .

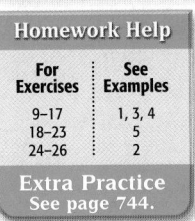

Snowboards ....

In 1998, snowboarding became an Olympic event in Nagano, Japan, with a giant slalom and halfpipe competition.

Source: www.snowboarding.about.com

SNOWBOARDS For Exercises 24–26, use the following information and the table. Two Internet sites sell a snowboard for the same price, but have different shipping charges. **24. $y = 5 + x$ and $y = 2 + 1.5x$**

Shipping Charges		
Internet Site	Base Fee	Charge per Pound
A	$5.00	$1.00
B	$2.00	$1.50

24. Write a system of equations that represents the shipping charges y for x pounds. (*Hint*: Shipping charge = base fee + charge per pound · number of pounds.)

25. Solve the system of equations. Explain what the solution means.

26. If the snowboard weighs 8 pounds, which Internet site would be less expensive? Explain. **site A; $13.00 < $14.00**

25. **(6, 11)**; an order of 6 pounds will cost the same, $11.00, for both sites.

27. **CRITICAL THINKING** Two runners A and B are 50 meters apart and running at the same rate along the same path. **a–b. See pp. 431A–431H.**

a. If their rates continue, will the second runner ever catch up to the first? Draw a graph to explain why or why not.

b. Draw a graph that represents the second runner catching up to the first. What is different about the two graphs that you drew?

one solution

no solution

infinitely many solutions

Open-Ended Assessment

Modeling Have students use a geoboard and rubber bands to model the three situations shown in the Concept Summary box on p. 416.

Getting Ready for Lesson 8-10

PREREQUISITE SKILL The concept of graphing inequalities is presented in Lesson 8-10. Exercises 35–40 should be used to determine your students' familiarity with solving inequalities.

Assessment Options

Practice Quiz 2 The quiz provides students with a brief review of the concepts and skills in Lessons 8-6 through 8-9. Lesson numbers are given to the right of exercises or instruction lines so students can review concepts not yet mastered.

Answer

28. Each set of data can be represented by an equation. All the equations in the system can be graphed and analyzed to compare the data. Answers should include the following.
- Equations can be used to represent incomes of different employees, where y represents income, m is the hourly rate, x is the number hours, and b is the bonus.
- A solution (x, y) represents a situation in which the number of hours worked and the income is the same for all the employees.

---

28. **WRITING IN MATH** Answer the question that was posed at the beginning of the lesson. **See margin.**

How can a system of equations be used to compare data?

Include the following in your answer:
- a situation that can be modeled by a system of equations, and
- an explanation of what a solution to such a system of equations means.

29. Which system of equations represents the following verbal description? **C**
The sum of two numbers is 6. The second number is three times greater than the first number.

Ⓐ $x + y = 6$ Ⓑ $y = x + 6$ Ⓒ $x + y = 6$ Ⓓ $x - y = 6$
     $x = 3 + y$ $y = x + 3$ $y = 3x$ $y = -3x$

30. Which equation, together with $x + y = 1$, forms a system that has a solution of $(-3, 4)$? **C**

Ⓐ $y = x$ Ⓑ $x - y = 1$ Ⓒ $y = x + 7$ Ⓓ $-3x + 4y = 1$

Maintain Your Skills

Mixed Review

31. **SALES** Ice cream sales increase as the temperature outside increases. Describe the slope of a best-fit line that represents this situation. *(Lesson 8-8)*
positive slope

Write an equation in slope-intercept form for the line passing through each pair of points. *(Lesson 8-7)*

34. $y = \frac{1}{4}x - 2$

32. $(0, 1)$ and $(3, 7)$ 33. $(-2, 6)$ and $(1, -3)$ 34. $(8, 0)$ and $(-8, -4)$
     $y = 2x + 1$ $y = -3x$

Getting Ready for the Next Lesson

PREREQUISITE SKILL State whether each number is a solution of the given inequality. *(To review inequalities, see Lesson 7-3.)*

35. $1 < x + 3$; 0 **yes**   36. $9 > t - 5$; 1 **yes**   37. $2y \geq 2$; -1 **no**

38. $14 < 6 - n$; 0 **no**   39. $35 > 12 + k$; 12 **yes**   40. $5n + 1 \leq 0$; -2 **yes**

Practice Quiz 2   *Lessons 8-6 through 8-9*

State the slope and the y-intercept for the graph of each equation. *(Lesson 8-6)*

1. $y = -x + 8$ **-1; 8**   2. $y = 3x - 5$ **3; -5**   3. $x + 2y = 6$ **$-\frac{1}{2}$; 3**

Write an equation in slope-intercept form for each line. *(Lesson 8-7)*

4. slope = 6 **$y = 6x - 7$**
   y-intercept = -7

5. slope = 0 **$y = 1$**
   y-intercept = 1

6. slope = 1 **$y = x$**
   y-intercept = 0

7. **STATISTICS** The table shows the average age of the Women's U.S. Olympic track and field team. Make a scatter plot of the data and draw a best-fit line. *(Lesson 8-8)* **See margin.**

Year	1984	1988	1992	1996	2000
Average Age	24.6	25.0	27.3	28.7	29.2

Source: *Sports Illustrated*

Solve each system of equations by substitution. *(Lesson 8-9)*

8. $y = x - 1$ **(3, 2)**
   $y = 2$

9. $y = x + 5$ **(0, 5)**
   $x = 0$

10. $y = 2x + 4$ **$(-4, -4)$**
    $y = -4$

Answer (Practice Quiz 2)

7. Sample answer:

Graphing Inequalities

NEW YORK *Performance Indicator* **8.G.19 Graph the solution set of an inequality** on a number line

What You'll Learn

- Graph linear inequalities.
- Describe solutions of linear inequalities.

Vocabulary
- boundary
- half plane

How can shaded regions on a graph model inequalities?

Refer to the graph at the right.

a. Substitute $(-4, 2)$ and $(3, 1)$ in $y > 2x + 1$. Which ordered pair makes the inequality true? **(−4, 2)**

b. Substitute $(-4, 2)$ and $(3, 1)$ in $y < 2x + 1$. Which ordered pair makes the inequality true? **(3, 1)**

c. Which area represents the solution of $y < 2x + 1$? **shaded area**

GRAPH INEQUALITIES To graph an inequality such as $y > 2x - 3$, first graph the related equation $y = 2x - 3$. This is the **boundary**.

- If the inequality contains the symbol $\leq$ or $\geq$, then use a solid line to indicate that the boundary is included in the graph.
- If the inequality contains the symbol $<$ or $>$, then use a dashed line to indicate that the boundary is not included in the graph.

Next, test any point above or below the line to determine which region is the solution. It is easy to test $(0, 0)$.

$y > 2x - 3$ Write the inequality.
$0 \overset{?}{>} 2(0) - 3$ Replace x with 0 and y with 0.
$0 > -3 \checkmark$ Simplify.

Since $0 > -3$ is true, $(0, 0)$ is a solution of $y > 2x - 3$. Shade the region that contains the solution. This region is called a **half plane**. All points in this region are solutions of the inequality.

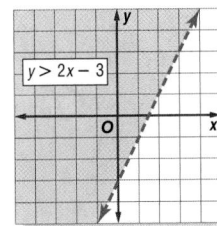

Example 1 Graph Inequalities

a. Graph $y < -x + 1$.

Graph $y = -x + 1$. Draw a dashed line since the boundary is not part of the graph.

Test $(0, 0)$: $y \overset{?}{<} -x + 1$
            $0 \overset{?}{<} -0 + 1$ Replace (x, y) with $(0, 0)$.
            $0 < 1 \checkmark$

Thus, the graph is all points in the region below the boundary.

 www.pre-alg.com/extra_examples/ny

Lesson Notes

1 *Focus*

5-Minute Check Transparency 8-10 Use as a quiz or review of Lesson 8-9.

Mathematical Background notes are available for this lesson on page 366D.

How can shaded regions on a graph model inequalities?

The opening activity questions are repeated on page 465 of the *Chapter 8 Resource Masters*.

Resource Manager

Workbooks and Reproducible Masters

Chapter 8 Resource Masters
- Study Guide and Intervention, p. 462
- Skills Practice, p. 463
- Practice, p. 464
- Reading to Learn Mathematics, p. 465
- Enrichment, p. 466
- Assessment, p. 482

Parent and Student Study Guide Workbook, p. 70
Prerequisite Skills Workbook, pp. 1–2
School-to-Career Masters, p. 16

Transparencies
5-Minute Check Transparency 8-10
Answer Key Transparencies

Technology
Interactive Chalkboard
Pre-AlgePASS: Tutorial Plus, Lesson 25

GRAPH INEQUALITIES

In-Class Example

1 **a.** Graph $y > 3x - 3$.

$y > 3x - 3$

b. Graph $y \leq -\frac{1}{4}x$.

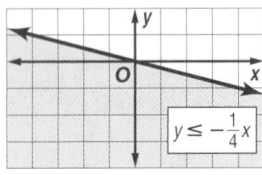

$y \leq -\frac{1}{4}x$

FIND SOLUTIONS

In-Class Example

2 **BAKING** Terrence needs 3 cups of flour to make a batch of cookies and 5 cups to make a loaf of bread. He has 30 cups of flour. How many batches of cookies and loaves of bread can he bake?
Sample answer:
0 batches of cookies, 6 loaves
4 batches of cookies, 3 loaves
5 batches of cookies, 3 loaves
7 batches of cookies, 1 loaf

3 Practice/Apply

Study Notebook

Have students—
• complete the definitions/examples for the remaining terms on the Vocabulary Builder worksheets for Chapter 8.
• include any other item(s) that they find helpful in mastering the skills in this lesson.

b. Graph $y \geq 2x + 2$.

Graph $y = 2x + 2$. Draw a solid line since the boundary is part of the graph.

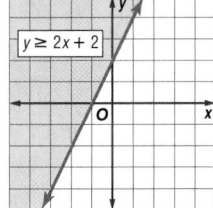

$y \geq 2x + 2$

Test (0, 0): $y \geq 2x + 2$
$0 \overset{?}{\geq} 2(0) + 2$ Replace (x, y) with (0, 0).
$0 \geq 2$ not true

(0, 0) is not a solution, so shade the other half plane.

CHECK   Test an ordered pair in the other half plane.

☑ **Concept Check**   Is (0, 2) a solution of $y \geq 2x + 2$? Explain.
Yes; (0, 2) lies on the boundary, which is included in the solution.

FIND SOLUTIONS   You can write and graph inequalities to solve real-world problems. In some cases, you may have to solve the inequality for y first and then graph the inequality.

Example 2 **Write and Graph an Inequality to Solve a Problem**

SCHOOL   Nathan has at most 30 minutes to complete his math and science homework. How much time can he spend on each?

Step 1   Write an inequality.

Let x represent the time spent doing math homework and let y represent the time spent doing science homework.

Minutes doing math	plus	minutes doing science	is at most	30 minutes.
x	$+$	y	$\leq$	30

Step 2   Graph the inequality.

To graph the inequality, first solve for y.

$x + y \leq 30$ Write the inequality.
$y \leq -x + 30$ Subtract x from each side.

Graph $y \leq -x + 30$ as a solid line since the boundary is part of the graph. The origin is part of the graph since $0 \leq -0 + 30$. Thus, the coordinates of all points in the shaded region are possible solutions.

(10, 20) = 10 minutes on math, 20 minutes on science

(15, 15) = 15 minutes on math, 15 minutes on science

(10, 15) = 10 minutes on math, 15 minutes on science

(30, 0) = 30 minutes on math, 0 minutes on science

Note that the solutions are only in the first quadrant because negative values of time do not make sense.

Study Tip

Common Misconception
You may think that only whole number solutions are possible. Points in the shaded region such as (10.5, 18.5) are also solutions.

420 **Chapter 8** Functions and Graphing

DAILY INTERVENTION   **Differentiated Instruction**

• **Visual/Spatial**   Scott sells tapes for $6 and CDs for $12. How many of each can he sell and still collect at least $144? Let tapes = x and CDs = y. Graph $6x + 12y = 144$. Have each student graph a point that produces an answer greater than or equal to 144 on the same grid on the chalkboard or with stickers on poster board. Ask students what the graph would look like if infinitely many solution points were graphed. **a solid line with a shaded plane above and to the right of the line**

Check for Understanding

Concept Check

1. **Write** an inequality that describes the graph at the right. $y < -x + 3$

2. **Explain** how to determine which side of the boundary line to shade when graphing an inequality. **See margin.**

3a–b. Sample answers are given.
3a. (0, −1), (1, 0), (2, 1)
3b. (0, 0), (1, 1), (2, 2)

3. **List** three solutions of each inequality.
   a. $y < x$
   b. $y \geq x - 3$

4. **OPEN ENDED** Write an inequality that has (1, 4) as a solution. **Sample answer:** $x + y < 6$

Guided Practice

Graph each inequality. 5–7. **See pp. 431A–431H.**

5. $y > x - 1$
6. $y \leq 2$
7. $y \geq -3x + 2$

Application

GUIDED PRACTICE KEY	
Exercises	Examples
5–7	1
8, 9	2

ENTERTAINMENT For Exercises 8 and 9, use the following information.
Adult passes for World Waterpark are $25, and children's passes are $15. A company is buying tickets for its employees and wants to spend no more than $630.

8. Write an inequality to represent this situation. $25x + 15y \leq 630$

9. Graph the inequality and use the graph to determine three possible combinations of tickets that the company could buy. **See pp. 431A–431H.**

Practice and Apply

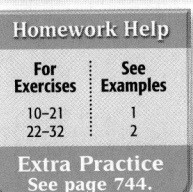

Homework Help

For Exercises	See Examples
10–21	1
22–32	2

Extra Practice
See page 744.

Graph each inequality. 10–21. **See pp. 431A–431H.**

10. $y \geq x$
11. $y < x$
12. $y < 1$
13. $y \geq -3$
14. $y > x - 1$
15. $y \leq x + 4$
16. $y \leq -x$
17. $y \geq 0$
18. $y > 2x + 3$
19. $y < 2x - 4$
20. $y < \frac{1}{2}x + 2$
21. $y \geq -\frac{1}{3}x - 1$

BUSINESS For Exercises 22–26, use the following information.
For a certain business to be successful, its monthly sales y must be at least $3000 greater than its monthly costs x.

22. Write an inequality to represent this situation. $y \geq x + 3000$

23. Graph the inequality. **See margin.**

24. Above the line; (1000, 5000) is a solution of $y \geq x + 3000$.

24. Do points above or below the boundary line indicate a successful business? Explain how you know.

25. Would negative numbers make sense in this problem? Explain.

25. No; the number of sales and the costs cannot be negative.

26. List two solutions. **Sample answer:** (1000, 5000), (4000, 7000)

Study Tip

Solutions
In Exercise 29, only whole-number solutions make sense since there cannot be parts of baskets.

CRAFTS For Exercises 27–29, use the following information.
Celia can make a small basket in 10 minutes and a large basket in 25 minutes. This month, she has no more than 24 hours to make these baskets for an upcoming craft fair.

27. Write an inequality to represent this situation. $10x + 25y \leq 1440$

28. Graph the inequality. **See margin.**

29. Use the graph to determine how many of each type of basket that she could make this month. List three possibilities. **See margin.**

 www.pre-alg.com/self_check_quiz/ny Lesson 8-10 Graphing Inequalities **421**

Answer

2. **Sample answer:** Choose a test point not on the boundary line and substitute its coordinates in the inequality. If the result is true, shade that side of the boundary. If the result is false, shade the other side of the boundary.

23, 28, 29. See p. 422.

Reading Tip To help students read inequality symbols correctly, suggest that they think of the < and > symbols as microscopes. Each symbol takes what is on the small, pointed end and magnifies it, moving it to the open end. The symbols ≤ and ≥ are similar, but include the bottom part of the equal sign, to mean *less than or equal to* and *greater than or equal to.*

Lesson 8-10 Graphing Inequalities **421**

About the Exercises . . .

Organization by Objective
- **Graph Solutions:** 10–23
- **Find Solutions:** 24–32

Odd/Even Assignments
Exercises 10–25 and 27–32 are structured so that students practice the same concepts whether they are assigned odd or even problems.

Alert! Exercises 5–7, 9–21, 23, and 28 require graph paper.

Assignment Guide
Basic: 11–21 odd, 22–43
Average: 11–21 odd, 22–43
Advanced: 10–20 even, 22–43

4 Assess

Open-Ended Assessment

Speaking Have one student write an inequality, another student translate it into words, and the two work together to graph it.

Assessment Options

Quiz (Lessons 8-9 and 8-10) is available on p. 482 of the *Chapter 8 Resource Masters*.

Answers (pp. 421–422)

23.

28.

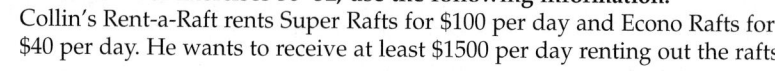

More About. . .

Rafting •·················
More than 25 whitewater rafting companies are located on the American River in California. A typical fee is $125 per person per day.
Source: www.rafting-whitewater.com

NEW YORK Test Practice

Standardized Test Practice
Ⓐ Ⓑ Ⓒ Ⓓ

•· **RAFTING**   For Exercises 30–32, use the following information.
Collin's Rent-a-Raft rents Super Rafts for $100 per day and Econo Rafts for $40 per day. He wants to receive at least $1500 per day renting out the rafts.

30. Write an inequality to represent this situation. $100x + 40y \geq 1500$

31. Graph the inequality. **See pp. 431A–431H.**

32. Determine how many of each type of raft that Collin could rent out each day in order to receive at least $1500. List three possibilities. **See margin.**

33. CRITICAL THINKING   The solution of a *system of inequalities* is the set of all ordered pairs that satisfies *both* inequalities.

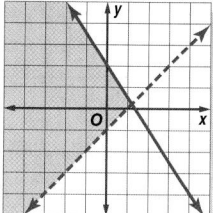

  a. Write a system of inequalities for the graph at the right. $y > x - 1, y \leq -\dfrac{3}{2}x + 2$
  b. List three solutions of the system.
    Sample answers: (0, 2), (−1, 2), (−3, −2)

34. WRITING IN MATH   Answer the question that was posed at the beginning of the lesson. **See margin.**

  How can shaded regions on a graph model inequalities?
  Include the following in your answer:
  - a description of which points in the graph are solutions of the inequality.

35. Determine which ordered pair is a solution of $y - 8 > x$. **C**
  Ⓐ (0, 2)   Ⓑ (2, 5)   Ⓒ (−9, 0)   Ⓓ (1, 4)

36. Which inequality does *not* have the boundary included in its graph? **A**
  Ⓐ $y > x$ Ⓑ $y \leq 1$ Ⓒ $y \geq x + 5$ Ⓓ $y \geq 0$

Maintain Your Skills

Mixed Review

37–39. See pp. 431A–431H for graphs.

40. Sample answer: Make a scatter plot of the data and draw a best-fit line. Then use the line to make a prediction.

Solve each system of equations by graphing. *(Lesson 8-9)*

37. $y = x + 3$ **(0, 3)**
    $x = 0$

38. $y = -x + 2$ **(−1, 3)**
    $y = x + 4$

39. $y = -2x - 1$ **(2, −5)**
    $y = -x - 3$

40. Explain how you can make predictions from a set of ordered-pair data. *(Lesson 8-8)*

Write each fraction or mixed number as a decimal. Use a bar to show a repeating decimal. *(Lesson 5-1)*

41. $\dfrac{2}{5}$ **0.4**

42. $3\dfrac{7}{10}$ **3.7**

43. $-\dfrac{5}{9}$ **$-0.\overline{5}$**

Web Quest Internet Project

Just for Fun
It is time to complete your project. Use the information and data you have gathered about recreational activities to prepare a Web page or poster. Be sure to include a scatter plot and a prediction for each activity.

www.pre-alg.com/webquest

---

29. Sample answer: 25 small, 45 large; 50 small, 30 large; 100 small, 10 large

32. Sample answer: 5 Super, 30 Econo; 10 Super, 15 Econo; 15 Super, 5 Econo

34. To model an inequality, graph the related equation and choose a point not on the line. If the inequality is true when the coordinates of the point are substituted, then that region is shaded.

If the inequality is false, then the region on the other side of the line is shaded. Answers should include the following.

- Any point in the shaded region is a solution of the inequality.

Graphing Inequalities

You can use a TI-83 Plus graphing calculator to investigate the graphs of inequalities. Since the graphing calculator only shades between two functions, enter a lower boundary as well as an upper boundary for each inequality.

A Follow-Up of Lesson 8-10

Getting Started

Know Your Calculator The DRAW menu on the graphing calculator has many interesting capabilities that students may wish to experiment with. Before beginning this Investigation, students should clear existing drawings by pressing `2nd` [DRAW] 1 `ENTER`. Before using ClrDraw, drawings can be stored with StorePic in the **DRAW STO** menu.

Graph two different inequalities on your graphing calculator.

Step 1 *Graph* $y \leq -x + 4$.

• Clear all functions from the Y= list.
  KEYSTROKES: `Y` `CLEAR`

• Graph $y \leq -x + 4$ in the standard window.
  KEYSTROKES: `2nd` [DRAW] 7 `(−)` 10 `,`
  `(−)` `X,T,θ,n` `+` 4 `)`
  `ENTER`

Ymin or −10 is used as the lower boundary and $y = -x + 4$ as the upper boundary. All ordered pairs in the shaded region satisfy the inequality $y \leq -x + 4$.

Step 2 *Graph* $y \geq -x + 4$.

• Clear the current drawing displayed.
  KEYSTROKES: `2nd` [DRAW] `ENTER`

• Graph $y \geq -x + 4$ in the standard window.
  KEYSTROKES: `2nd` [DRAW] 7 `(−)`
  `X,T,θ,n` `+` 4 `,` 10 `)`
  `ENTER`

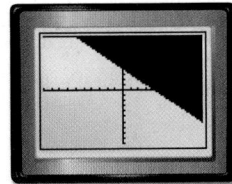

In this case, the lower boundary is $y = -x + 4$. The upper boundary is **Ymax** or 10. All ordered pairs in the shaded region satisfy the inequality $y \geq -x + 4$.

Teach

• Point out that students must have in mind where the shading should fall before graphing an inequality. You may wish to write several inequalities on the chalkboard and have the class call out where the shading should go.
• Have students complete Exercises 1–10.

Assess

Ask students to name several solutions that satisfy the inequalities in Exercises 3–10.

Exercises **2b. lower bound:** $-2x - 6$; **upper bound: Ymax or 10**

1. Compare and contrast the two graphs shown above. **See margin.**

2. a. Graph $y \geq -2x - 6$ in the standard viewing window. Draw the graph on grid paper. **See margin.**

   b. What functions do you enter as the lower and upper boundaries?

   c. Use the graph to name four solutions of the inequality.
      Sample answer: (0, 0), (1, 5), (−1, 4), (−2, 2)

Use a graphing calculator to graph each inequality. Draw each graph on grid paper. 3–10. See pp. 431A–431H.

3. $y \leq x - 3$ **4.** $y \leq -1$ **5.** $x + y \geq 6$ **6.** $y \geq 3x$

7. $y \leq 0$ **8.** $y + 3 \leq -x$ **9.** $x + y \leq 5$ **10.** $2y - x \geq 2$

Answers

1. The graphs have the same boundary line, but opposite sides of the line are shaded.

2a.

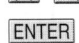

$y \geq -2x - 6$

Chapter 8 Study Guide and Review

Vocabulary and Concept Check

- This alphabetical list of vocabulary terms in Chapter 8 includes a page reference where each term was introduced.

- **Assessment** A vocabulary review/test for Chapter 8 is available on p. 480 of the *Chapter 8 Resource Masters*.

Lesson-by-Lesson Review

For each lesson,
- the main ideas are summarized,
- additional examples review concepts, and
- practice exercises are provided.

Vocabulary PuzzleMaker

ELL The Vocabulary PuzzleMaker software improves students' mathematics vocabulary using four puzzle formats—crossword, scramble, word search using a word list, and word search using clues. Students can work on a computer screen or from a printed handout.

MindJogger Videoquizzes

ELL MindJogger Videoquizzes provide an alternative review of concepts presented in this chapter. Students work in teams in a game show format to gain points for correct answers. The questions are presented in three rounds.

Round 1 Concepts (5 questions)
Round 2 Skills (4 questions)
Round 3 Problem Solving (4 questions)

Vocabulary and Concept Check

best-fit line (p. 409)	half plane (p. 419)	system of equations (p. 414)
boundary (p. 419)	linear equation (p. 375)	vertical line test (p. 370)
constant of variation (p. 394)	rate of change (p. 393)	x-intercept (p. 381)
direct variation (p. 394)	slope (p. 387)	y-intercept (p. 381)
family of graphs (p. 402)	slope-intercept form (p. 398)	
function (p. 369)	substitution (p. 416)	

Choose the letter of the term that best matches each statement or phrase.

1. a relation in which each member of the domain is paired with exactly one member of the range **d**
2. in a graph of an inequality, the line of the related equation **b**
3. a value that describes the steepness of a line **h**
4. a group of two or more equations **j**
5. can be drawn through data points to approximate a linear relationship **a**
6. a change in one quantity with respect to another quantity **g**
7. a graph of this is a straight line **f**
8. one type of method for solving systems of equations **i**
9. a linear equation that describes rate of change **c**
10. in the graph of an inequality, the region that contains all solutions **e**

a.	best-fit line
b.	boundary
c.	direct variation
d.	function
e.	half plane
f.	linear equation
g.	rate of change
h.	slope
i.	substitution
j.	system of equations

Lesson-by-Lesson Review

8-1 Functions

See pages 369–373.

Concept Summary

- In a function, each member in the domain is paired with exactly one member in the range.

Example Determine whether $\{(-9, 2), (1, 5), (1, 10)\}$ is a function. Explain.

domain (x)   range (y)

$-9 \longrightarrow 2$ This relation is not a function
$1 \longrightarrow 5$ because 1 in the domain is paired
$\quad \longrightarrow 10$ with two range values, 5 and 10.

Exercises Determine whether each relation is a function. Explain.
See Example 1 on page 369. **11–14. See margin for explanations.**

11. $\{(1, 12), (-4, 3), (6, 36), (10, 6)\}$ **yes** 12. $\{(11.8, -9), (10.4, -2), (11.8, 3.8)\}$ **no**
13. $\{(0, 0), (2, 2), (3, 3), (4, 4)\}$ **yes** 14. $\{(-0.5, 1.2), (3, 1.2), (2, 36)\}$ **yes**

 www.pre-alg.com/vocabulary_review

FOLDABLES™ Study Organizer

For more information about Foldables, see *Teaching Mathematics with Foldables.*

Have students review the notes they have taken under the tabs of their Foldables, as well as any examples they have drawn. If any of the notes are hard for them to understand, they should review the lessons covering those topics and revise their notes.

Encourage students to refer to their Foldables while completing the Study Guide and Review and to use them in preparing for the Chapter Test.

8-2 Linear Equations in Two Variables

See pages 375–379.

Concept Summary

- A solution of a linear equation is an ordered pair that makes the equation true.
- To graph a linear equation, plot points and draw a line through them.

Example Graph $y = -x + 2$ by plotting ordered pairs.

Find ordered pair solutions. Then plot and connect the points.

x	$-x + 2$	y	(x, y)
0	$-0 + 2$	2	$(0, 2)$
1	$-1 + 2$	1	$(1, 1)$
2	$-2 + 2$	0	$(2, 0)$
3	$-3 + 2$	-1	$(3, -1)$

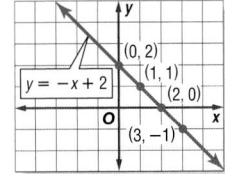

Exercises Graph each equation by plotting ordered pairs.
See Example 3 on page 377. **15–22. See margin.**

15. $y = x + 4$ **16.** $y = x - 2$ **17.** $y = -x$ **18.** $y = 2x$

19. $y = 3x + 2$ **20.** $y = -2x - 4$ **21.** $x + y = 4$ **22.** $x - y = -3$

8-3 Graphing Linear Equations Using Intercepts

See pages 381–385.

Concept Summary

- To graph a linear equation, you can find and plot the points where the graph crosses the x-axis and the y-axis. Then connect the points.

Example Graph $-3x + y = 3$ using the x- and y-intercepts.

$-3x + y = 3$

$-3x + 0 = 3$

$x = -1$ The x-intercept is -1.

$-3x + y = 3$

$-3(0) + y = 3$

$y = 3$ The y-intercept is 3.

Graph the points at $(-1, 0)$ and $(0, 3)$ and draw a line through them.

Exercises Graph each equation using the x- and y-intercepts.
See Example 3 on page 382. **23–30. See pp. 426–427.**

23. $y = x + 2$ **24.** $y = x + 6$ **25.** $y = -x - 3$ **26.** $y = x - 1$

27. $x = -4$ **28.** $y = 5$ **29.** $x + y = -2$ **30.** $3x + y = 6$

Answers

16.

17.

18.

19.

20.
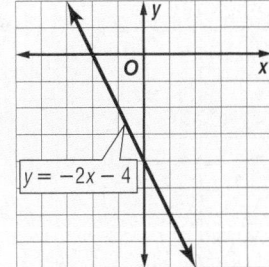

(continued on the next page)

Answers (pp. 424–425)

11. Yes; each x value is paired with only one y value.

12. No; 11.8 in the domain is paired with -9 and 3.8 in the range.

13. Yes; each x value is paired with only one y value.

14. Yes; each x value is paired with only one y value.

15.
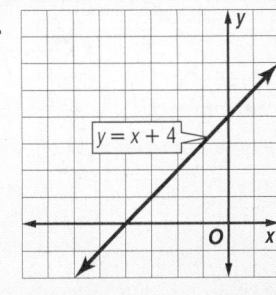

Answers (p. 425)

21.

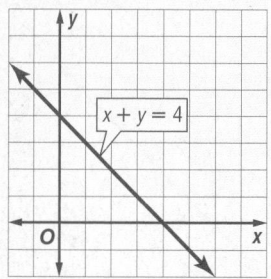

$x + y = 4$

22.

$x - y = -3$

23.

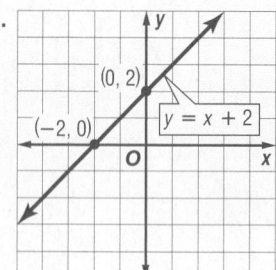

$(0, 2)$
$(-2, 0)$
$y = x + 2$

24.

$(0, 6)$
$y = x + 6$
$(-6, 0)$

25.

$(-3, 0)$
$y = -x - 3$
$(0, -3)$

8-4 Slope

See pages 387–391.

Concept Summary

- Slope is the ratio of the *rise*, or the vertical change, to the *run*, or the horizontal change.

Example   Find the slope of the line that passes through $A(0, 6)$, $B(4, -2)$.

$m = \dfrac{y_2 - y_1}{x_2 - x_1}$ Definition of slope

$m = \dfrac{-2 - 6}{4 - 0}$ $(x_1, y_1) = (0, 6),$
$(x_2, y_2) = (4, -2)$

$m = \dfrac{-8}{4}$ or -2 The slope is -2.

Exercises   Find the slope of the line that passes through each pair of points.
See Examples 2–5 on pages 388 and 389.

31. $J(3, 4)$, $K(4, 5)$ **1**   **32.** $C(2, 8)$, $D(6, 7)$ $-\dfrac{1}{4}$ **33.** $R(7, 3)$, $B(-1, -4)$ $\dfrac{7}{8}$

34. $Q(2, 10)$, $B(4, 6)$ **−2**   **35.** $X(-1, 5)$, $Y(-1, 9)$ **36.** $S(0, 8)$, $T(-3, 8)$ **0**

undefined

8-5 Rate of Change

See pages 393–397.

Concept Summary

- A change in one quantity with respect to another quantity is called the rate of change.
- Slope can be used to describe rates of change.

Example   Find the rate of change in population from 1990 to 2000 for Oakland, California, using the graph.

Year	Population (1000s)
x	*y*
1990	372
2000	400

rate of change $= \dfrac{y_2 - y_1}{x_2 - x_1}$ Definition of slope

$= \dfrac{400 - 372}{2000 - 1990}$ ← change in population
← change in time

$= 2.8$ Simplify.

So, the rate of change in population was an increase of about 2.8 thousand, or 2800 people per year.

Exercises   Find the rate of change for the linear function represented in each table.   *See Example 1 on page 393.* **37. inc. of 8 m/s   38. dec. of 2°F/h**

37.

Time (s)	Distance (m)
x	*y*
0	0
1	8
2	16

38.

Time (h)	Temperature (°F)
x	*y*
1	45
2	43
3	41

26.

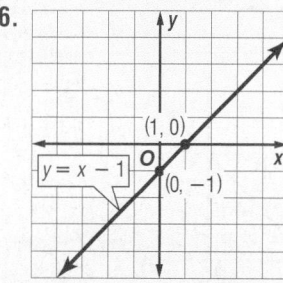

$(1, 0)$
$y = x - 1$
$(0, -1)$

27.

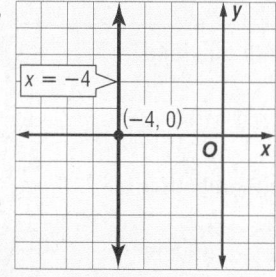

$x = -4$
$(-4, 0)$

28.

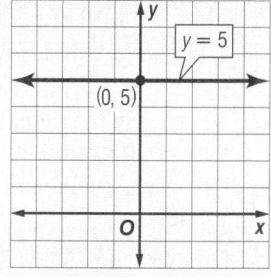

$y = 5$
$(0, 5)$

8-6 Slope-Intercept Form

See pages 398–401.

Concept Summary

- In the slope-intercept form $y = mx + b$, m is the slope and b is the y-intercept.

Example　State the slope and the y-intercept of the graph of $y = -2x + 3$.

The slope of the graph is -2, and the y-intercept is 3.

Exercises　Graph each equation using the slope and y-intercept.
See Example 3 on page 399. **39–42. See margin.**

39. $y = x + 4$　　**40.** $y = -2x + 1$　　**41.** $y = \frac{1}{3}x - 2$　　**42.** $x + y = -5$

8-7 Writing Linear Equations

See pages 404–408.

Concept Summary

- You can write a linear equation by using the slope and y-intercept, two points on a line, a graph, a table, or a verbal description.

Example　Write an equation in slope-intercept form for the line having slope 4 and y-intercept -2.

$y = mx + b$　　Slope-intercept form
$y = 4x + (-2)$　　Replace m with 4 and b with -2.
$y = 4x - 2$　　Simplify.

Exercises　Write an equation in slope-intercept form for each line.
See Example 1 on page 404. **43.** $y = -x + 3$

43. slope $= -1$, y-intercept $= 3$　　**44.** slope $= 6$, y-intercept $= -3$　$y = 6x - 3$

8-8 Best-Fit Lines

See pages 409–413.

Concept Summary

- A best-fit line can be used to approximate data.

Example　Draw a best-fit line through the scatter plot.

Draw a line that is close to as many data points as possible.

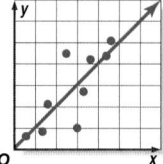

Exercises　The table shows the attendance for an annual art festival.　*See Example 1 on page 409.*

45. Make a scatter plot and draw a best-fit line. **See margin.**

46. Use the best-fit line to predict art festival attendance in 2008. **Sample answer: 3600**

Year	Attendance
2000	2500
2001	2650
2002	2910
2003	3050

29.

30.

Answers

39.

40.

41.

42.

45. Sample answer:

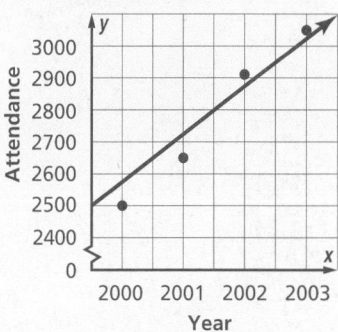

Study Guide and Review

Chapter **8** For More ...
- Extra Practice, see pages 741–744.
- Mixed Problem Solving, see page 765.

Answers

47.

48.

49.

53.

54.

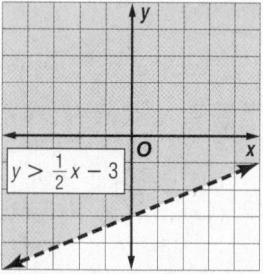

8-9 Solving Systems of Equations

See pages 414–418.

Concept Summary

- The solution of a system of equations is the ordered pair that satisfies all equations in the system.

Examples

1 Solve the system of equations by graphing.

$y = x$
$y = -x + 2$

The graphs appear to intersect at (1, 1). The solution of the system of equations is (1, 1).

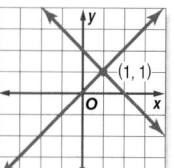

2 Solve the system $y = x - 1$ and $y = 3$ by substitution.

$y = x - 1$ Write the first equation.
$3 = x - 1$ Replace y with 3.
$4 = x$ Solve for x.

The solution of this system of equations is (4, 3).   Check by graphing.

Exercises   Solve each system of equations by graphing.

See Examples 1–4 on pages 414 and 415.   **47–49. See margin for graphs.**

47. $y = x$ **(3, 3)**
$y = 3$

48. $y = 2x + 4$ **(−2, 0)**
$x + y = -2$

49. $3x + y = 1$ **no solution**
$y = -3x + 5$

Solve each system of equations by substitution.   See Example 5 on page 416.

50. $y = x + 6$ **(−7, −1)**
$y = -1$

51. $y = x$ **(4, 4)**
$x = 4$

52. $y = 2x - 3$ $\left(\dfrac{3}{2}, 0\right)$
$y = 0$

8-10 Graphing Inequalities

See pages 419–422.

Concept Summary

- To graph an inequality, first graph the related equation, which is the boundary.
- All points in the shaded region are solutions of the inequality.

Example   Graph $y < x + 2$.

Graph $y = x + 2$. Draw a dashed line since the boundary is not part of the graph. Test a point in the original inequality and shade the appropriate region.   **53–56. See margin.**

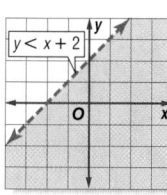

Exercises   Graph each inequality.   See Example 1 on pages 419 and 420.

53. $y \leq 3x - 1$
54. $y > \dfrac{1}{2}x - 3$
55. $y \geq -x + 4$
56. $y < -2x$

55.

56.

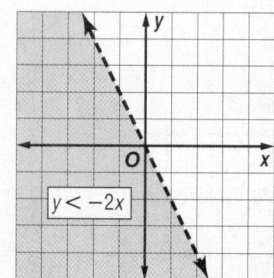

Practice Test

Vocabulary and Concepts

1. **Describe** how to find the x-intercept and the y-intercept of a linear equation. **1–2. See pp. 431A–431H.**
2. **State** how to choose which half plane to shade when graphing an inequality.
3. **OPEN ENDED** Write a system of equations and explain what the solution is.
   Sample answer: $y = x$ and $y = -x + 2$; the solution $(1, 1)$ is a solution of both equations.

Skills and Applications

Determine whether each relation is a function. Explain. **4–5. See pp. 431A–431H for explanations.**

4. $\{(-3, 4), (2, 9), (4, -1), (-3, 6)\}$ **no**
5. $\{(1, 2), (4, -6), (-3, 5), (6, 2)\}$ **yes**

Graph each equation by plotting ordered pairs. **6–7. See pp. 431A–431H.**

6. $y = 2x + 1$
7. $3x + y = 4$

Find the x-intercept and y-intercept for the graph of each equation.
Then, graph the equation using the x- and y-intercepts. **8–9. See pp. 431A–431H for graphs.**

8. $y = x + 3$ **$-3; 3$**
9. $2x - y = 4$ **$2; -4$**

Find the slope of the line that passes through each pair of points.

10. $A(2, 5)$, $B(4, 11)$ **3**
11. $C(-4, 5)$, $D(6, -3)$ $-\dfrac{4}{5}$

12. Find the rate of change for the linear
    function represented in the table.
    increase $5.50/h

Hours Worked	1	2	3	4
Money Earned ($)	5.50	11.00	16.50	22.00

State the slope and y-intercept for the graph of each equation. Then,
graph each equation using the slope and y-intercept. **13–14. See pp. 431A–431H for graphs.**

13. $y = \dfrac{2}{3}x - 4$ $\dfrac{2}{3}; -4$
14. $2x + 4y = 12$ $-\dfrac{1}{2}; 3$

15. Write an equation in slope-intercept form for the line with a slope of $\dfrac{3}{8}$ and
    y-intercept $= -2$. $y = \dfrac{3}{8}x - 2$

16. Solve the system of equations $2x - y = 4$ and $4x + y = 2$. **$(1, -2)$**

17. Graph $y > 2x - 1$. **See pp. 431A–431H.**

GARDENING For Exercises 18 and 19, use the table at the right and
the information below.
The full-grown height of a tomato plant and the number of tomatoes it
bears are recorded for five tomato plants. **18. See pp. 431A–431H.**

18. Make a scatter plot of the data and draw a best-fit line.

19. Use the best-fit line to predict the number of tomatoes a
    43-inch tomato plant will bear. **Sample answer: 20**

Height (in.)	Number of Tomatoes
27	12
33	18
19	9
40	16
31	15

20. **STANDARDIZED TEST PRACTICE** Which is a solution of $y \geq -2x + 5$? **D**
    Ⓐ $(1, -7)$ Ⓑ $(1, -3)$ Ⓒ $(-1, 3)$ Ⓓ $(-1, 7)$

Portfolio Suggestion

Introduction Linear equations and their graphs often can be used to
solve real-world problems. Being able to recognize the various ways in
which lines can be represented will help you solve many problems more
quickly.

Ask Students to choose a line to represent in their portfolios. Show its
equation in slope-intercept form, its x- and y-intercepts, a table of values
showing selected points on the line, and a graph of the line.

Assessment Options

Vocabulary Test A vocabulary
review/test for Chapter 8 can be
found on p. 480 of the *Chapter 8
Resource Masters.*

Chapter Tests There are six
Chapter 8 Tests and an Open-
Ended Assessment task available
in the *Chapter 8 Resource Masters.*

Chapter 8 Tests			
Form	Type	Level	Pages
1	MC	basic	467–468
2A	MC	average	469–470
2B	MC	average	471–472
2C	FR	average	473–474
2D	FR	average	475–476
3	FR	advanced	477–478

MC = multiple-choice questions
FR = free-response questions

Open-Ended Assessment
Performance tasks for Chapter 8
can be found on p. 479 of the
Chapter 8 Resource Masters. A
sample scoring rubric for these
tasks appears on p. A32.

Unit Test for Unit 3 is available
on pp. 487–488 of the *Chapter 8
Resource Masters.*

 ExamView® Pro

Use the networkable
ExamView® Pro to:

- Create **multiple versions** of
  tests.
- Create **modified** tests for
  Inclusion students.
- **Edit** existing questions and
  add your own questions.
- Use built-in **state curriculum
  correlations** to create tests
  aligned with state standards.
- Change **English** tests to
  Spanish and vice versa.

These two pages contain practice questions in the various formats that can be found on the most frequently given standardized tests.

A practice answer sheet for these two pages can be found on page A1 of the *Chapter 8 Resource Masters*.

Additional Practice

See pp. 485–486 of the *Chapter 8 Resource Masters* for additional standardized test practice.

NEW YORK Test Practice

Part 1 Multiple Choice

Record your answers on the answer sheet provided by your teacher or on a sheet of paper.

1. A wooden rod is 5.5 feet long. If you cut the rod into 10 equal pieces, how many inches long will each piece be? (Prerequisite Skill, p. 715) **C**
   (A) 0.55 in.   (B) 5.5 in.
   (C) 6.6 in.   (D) 66 in.

2. Which of the following is a true statement? (Lesson 2-1) **D**
   (A) $\frac{9}{3} < \frac{3}{9}$ (B) $-\frac{3}{9} < -\frac{9}{3}$
   (C) $-\frac{9}{3} > \frac{3}{9}$ (D) $-\frac{3}{9} > -\frac{9}{3}$

3. You roll a cube that has 2 blue sides, 2 yellow sides, and 2 red sides. What is the probability that a yellow side will face upwards when the cube stops rolling? (Lesson 6-9) **B**
   (A) $\frac{1}{6}$ (B) $\frac{1}{3}$
   (C) $\frac{1}{2}$ (D) $\frac{2}{3}$

4. Luis used 3 quarts of paint to cover 175 square feet of wall. He now wants to paint 700 square feet in another room. Which proportion could he use to calculate how many quarts of paint he should buy? (Lesson 6-3) **D**
   (A) $\frac{175}{700} = \frac{x}{3}$ (B) $\frac{3}{700} = \frac{175}{x}$
   (C) $\frac{700}{3} = \frac{175}{x}$ (D) $\frac{3}{175} = \frac{x}{700}$

Test-Taking Tip (A) (B) (C) (D)
Question 1
Pay attention to units of measurement, such as inches, feet, grams, and kilograms. A problem may require you to convert units; for example, you may be told the length of an object in feet and need to find the length of that object in inches.

5. A shampoo maker offered a special bottle with 30% more shampoo than the original bottle. If the original bottle held 12 ounces of shampoo, how many ounces did the special bottle hold? (Lesson 6-7) **C**
   (A) 3.6   (B) 12.3   (C) 15.6   (D) 16

6. The graph shows the materials in a town's garbage collection. If the week's garbage collection totals 6000 pounds, how many pounds of garbage are *not* paper? (Lesson 6-7) **B**

   Garbage Contents
   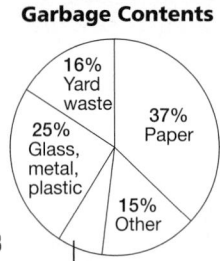
   7% Food waste

   (A) 2220   (B) 3780   (C) 5630   (D) 5963

7. The sum of an integer and the next greater integer is more than 51. Which of these could be the integer? (Lesson 7-6) **D**
   (A) 23   (B) 24   (C) 25   (D) 26

8. The table represents a function between x and y. What is the missing number in the table? (Lesson 8-1) **B**

x	y
1	3
2	■
4	9
6	13

   (A) 4   (B) 5
   (C) 6   (D) 7

9. Which equation is represented by the graph? (Lesson 8-7) **B**
   (A) $y = 2x - 4$
   (B) $y = 2x + 8$
   (C) $y = \frac{1}{2}x - 8$
   (D) $y = \frac{1}{2}x + 4$

10. Which ordered pair is the solution of this system of equations? (Lesson 8-9) **C**
    $$2x + 3y = 7$$
    $$3x - 3y = 18$$
    (A) (25, 1)   (B) (2, 1)
    (C) (5, −1)   (D) (7, 1)

ExamView® Pro

Special banks of standardized test questions similar to those on the SAT, ACT, TIMSS 8, NAEP 8, and Pre-Algebra End-of-Course tests can be found on this CD-ROM.

Part 2 Short Response/Grid In

Record your answers on the answer sheet provided by your teacher or on a sheet of paper.

11. The graph shows the shipping charges per order, based on the number of items shipped in the order. What is the shipping charge for an order with 4 items? (Prerequisite Skill, pp. 722–723) **$13**

Number of Items

12. The length of a rectangle is 8 centimeters, and its perimeter is 24 centimeters. What is the area of the rectangle in square centimeters? (Lesson 3-5) **32**

13. Write the statement *y is 5 more than one half the value of x* as an equation. (Lesson 3-6)
$$y = \frac{1}{2}x + 5$$

14. Write the number 0.09357 in scientific notation. Round your answer to two decimal places. (Lesson 4-8) 9.36×10^{-2}

15. If $y = -\frac{3}{2}$, what is the value of x in $y = 4x - 3$? (Lesson 5-8) **3/8**

16. Write $\frac{3}{5}$ as a percent. (Lesson 6-4) **60%**

17. In a diving competition, the diver in first place has a total score of 345.4. Ming has scored 68.2, 68.9, 67.5, and 71.7 for her first four dives and has one more dive remaining. Write an inequality to show the score x that Ming must receive on her fifth dive in order to overtake the diver in first place. (Lesson 7-4) $x > 69.1$

 www.pre-alg.com/standardized_test/ny

18. Ms. Vang drove at 30 mph for 30 minutes and at 56 mph for one hour and fifteen minutes. How far did she travel? (Lesson 8-5) **85 miles**

19. What is the slope of the line that contains (0, 4) and (2, 5)? (Lesson 8-6) **1/2**

20. Find the solution of the system of equations graphed below. (Lesson 8-9) **(4, 5)**

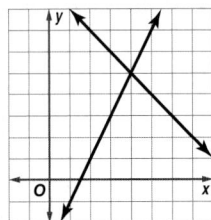

Part 3 Extended Response

Record your answers on a sheet of paper. Show your work. **21a, b, d. See margin.**

21. Krishnan is considering three plans for cellular phone service. The plans each offer the same services for different monthly fees and different costs per minute. (Lesson 8-6)

Plan	Monthly Fee	Cost per Minute
X	$0	$0.24
Y	$15.95	$0.08
Z	$25.95	$0.04

a. For each plan, write an equation that shows the total monthly cost c for m minutes of calls.

b. What is the cost of each plan if Krishnan uses 100 minutes per month?

c. Which plan costs the least if Krishnan uses 100 minutes per month? **Plan Y**

d. What is the cost of each plan if Krishnan uses 300 minutes per month?

e. Which plan costs the least if Krishnan uses 300 minutes per month? **Plan Z**

Chapter 8 Standardized Test Practice **431**

Answer

21a. X: $c = 0 + 0.24m$
     Y: $c = 15.95 + 0.08m$
     Z: $c = 25.95 + 0.04m$

21b. X: $c = 0.24(100) = \$24.00$
     Y: $c = 15.95 + 0.08(100) = \$23.95$
     Z: $c = 25.95 + 0.04(100) = \$29.95$

21d. X: $c = 0.24(300) = \$72.00$
     Y: $c = 15.95 + 0.08(300) = \$39.95$
     Z: $c = 25.95 + 0.04(300) = \$37.95$

Page 367, Getting Started

1.

x	y
0	4
-3	3

domain = {0, -3};
range = {4, 3}

2.

x	y
-5	11
2	1

domain = {-5, 2};
range = {11, 1}

3.

x	y
6	8
7	10
8	12

domain = {6, 7, 8};
range = {8, 10, 12}

4.

x	y
1	-9
5	12
-3	-10

domain = {1, 5, -3};
range = {-9, 12, -10}

5.

x	y
-8	5
7	-1
6	1
1	-2

domain = {-8, 7, 6, 1};
range = {5, -1, 1, -2}

Page 368, Algebra Activity

6. Sample answer:

Input	Output
-5	-9
-4	-7
-3	-5
-2	-3
-1	-1
0	1
1	3
2	5
3	7
4	9

rule: $\times 2 + 1$

Page 371, Lesson 8-1

1. Sample answer: a set of ordered pairs: {(1, 2), (4, 3), (-2, -1), (-3, 3)}

x	y
1	2
4	3
-2	-1
-3	3

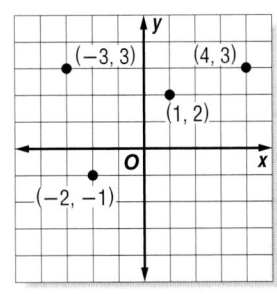

2. Sample answer: Check that each domain value is paired with only one range value or use the vertical line test.

3. Sample answer: This graph does not represent a function because when x equals 1, there are two y values, 0 and 2.

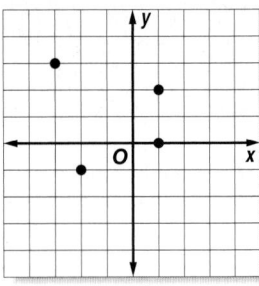

Page 373, Lesson 8-1

33. For a given wind speed, there is only one windchill temperature for each actual temperature. So, the relationship between actual temperatures and windchill temperatures is a function. Answers should include the following.

- For a given wind speed, as the actual temperature increases, the windchill temperature increases.
- Since the relationship between actual temperatures and windchill temperatures is a function, there cannot be two different windchill temperatures for the same actual temperature when the wind speed remains the same.

Page 374, Graphing Calculator Investigation

1c. Greater than 8; the pattern of the range values indicates that if the domain value decreases by 1, then the range value increases by 2.

2b.

Time	Distance
x	y
0	0
1	60
3.5	210
10	600

2d. Sample answer: Input X values between 1 and 3.5 until you get a Y value closer to 150.

Page 378, Lesson 8-2

30.

31.

32.

33.

34.

35.

36.

37.

38.

39.

40.

41.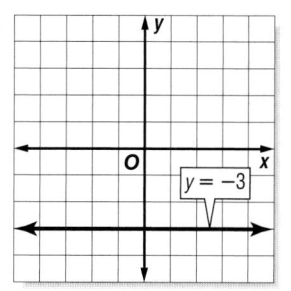

Page 379, Lesson 8-2

51. Sample answer: In the first table, as the *x* values increase by 1, the *y* values increase by 2. In the second table, as the *x* values increase by 1, the *y* values do not change by a constant amount.

52. Linear equations use variables to show the relationship between the domain values and the range values of a function. Answers should include the following.
   - Functions can be represented using a table, a graph, a verbal description, or an equation.
   - The equation $y = 0.49x$ represents the cost of *x* pounds of bananas at $0.49 per pound.

55. Yes; each *x* value is paired with only one *y* value.

56. Yes; each *x* value is paired with only one *y* value.

57. No; 11 in the domain is paired with 8 and 21 in the range.

58. No; −0.1 in the domain is paired with 5 and −5 in the range.

59.

60.

Page 384, Lesson 8-3

11.

The *y*-intercept 3 represents the base fee of $3.

Page 385, Lesson 8-3

25.

26.

27.

28.

29.

30.

31.

32.

33.

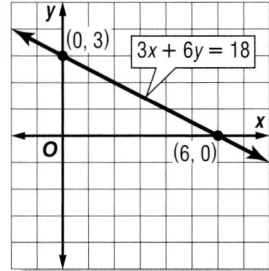

(0, 3)
$3x + 6y = 18$
(6, 0)

37. The *x*- and *y*-intercept are both 0. Therefore, the line passes through the origin. Since two points are needed to graph a line, $y = 2x$ cannot be graphed using only the intercepts.

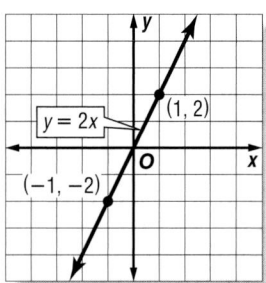

$y = 2x$
(1, 2)
(−1, −2)

38. The intercepts can be used to show values at time 0, temperature 0, and so on. Answers should include the following.
- Sample graph:
- The *x*-intercept 5 means that after 5 hours the temperature is 0°F. The *y*-intercept 30 means that at time 0, the temperature was 30°F.

(0, 30)
(5, 0)
Temperature (°F)
Time (h)

Page 392, Algebra Activity

5. Using a $\frac{1}{8}$ cup; the cup is larger than the tablespoon, so it emptied the glass at a faster rate.

7. Sample answer: teaspoon: slope is less steep than the other graphs because the rate of emptying the glass is slower; $\frac{1}{4}$ cup: steeper slope than the other graphs because the rate of emptying the glass is faster.

8a.   **8b.**   **8c.**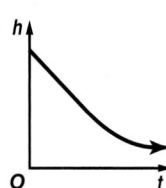

Page 395, Lesson 8-5

2. Sample answer:

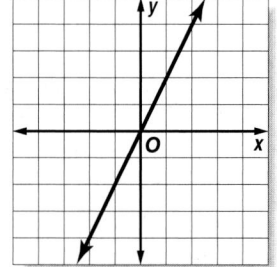

Page 397, Lesson 8-5

20. A horizontal line represents a zero rate of change because there is no change in *y*. A vertical line represents no passage of time, so a rate of change does not make sense.

21. A line representing the relationship between time and distance has a slope that is equal to the speed. Answers should include the following.
- Sample drawing:

Distance (mi)
300
200
100
0 1 2 3 4 5 6
Time (h)

- As speed increases, the slope of the graph becomes steeper.

26.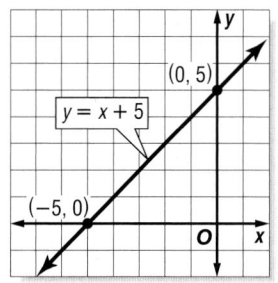

(0, 5)
$y = x + 5$
(−5, 0)

27.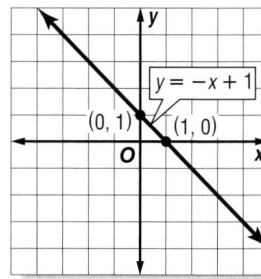

$y = -x + 1$
(0, 1)
(1, 0)

28.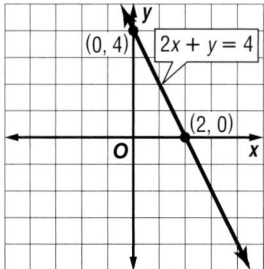

(0, 4)
$2x + y = 4$
(2, 0)

Page 400, Lesson 8-6

2. Sample answer:

7.

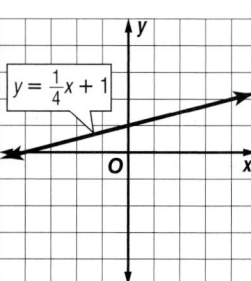

$y = \frac{1}{4}x + 1$

8.

$3x + y = 2$

9.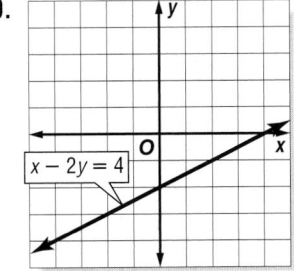

$x - 2y = 4$

10.

$y = 1.5x + 25$

Cost ($)

Additional Slices

18.

19.

20.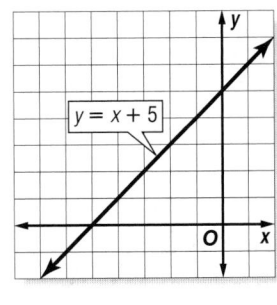

$y = x + 5$

21.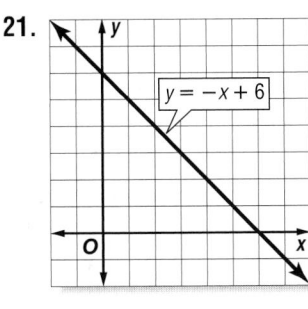

$y = -x + 6$

22.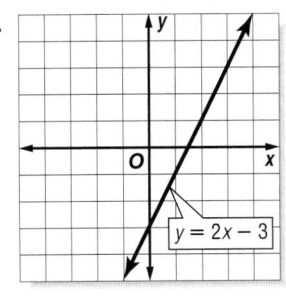

$y = 2x - 3$

23.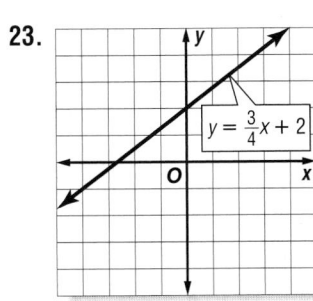

$y = \frac{3}{4}x + 2$

24.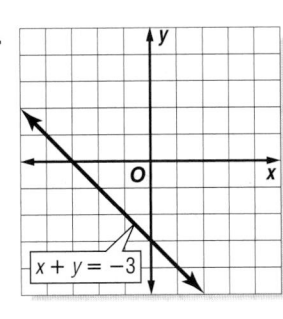

$x + y = -3$

25.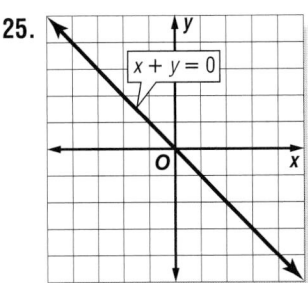

$x + y = 0$

26.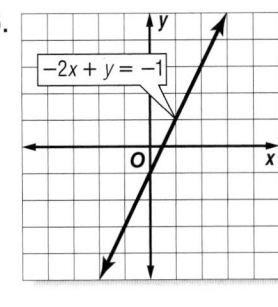

$-2x + y = -1$

27.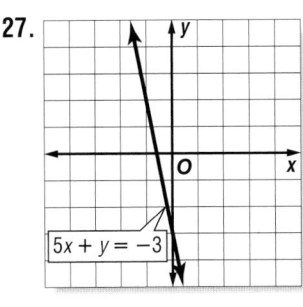

$5x + y = -3$

28.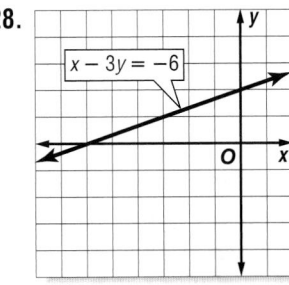

$x - 3y = -6$

29.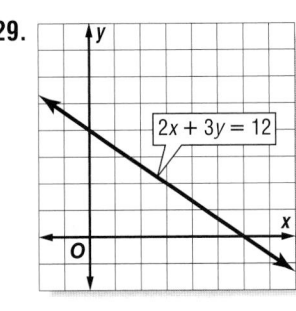

$2x + 3y = 12$

30.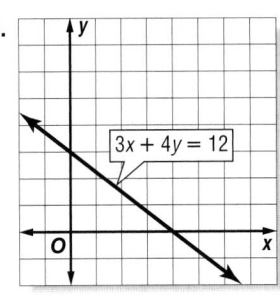

$3x + 4y = 12$

31.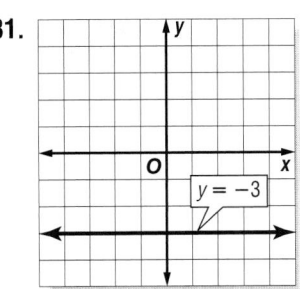

$y = -3$

Page 401, Lesson 8-6

32.

$y = 300 - 50x$

Altitude (ft)

Time (min)

Page 411, Lesson 8-8

7.

9.

Page 412, Lesson 8-8

12. Sample answer:

14.

Page 416, Lesson 8-9

4.

5.

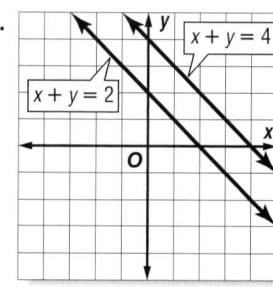

Page 417, Lesson 8-9

12.

13.

14.

15.

16.

17.

27a. Sample answer:

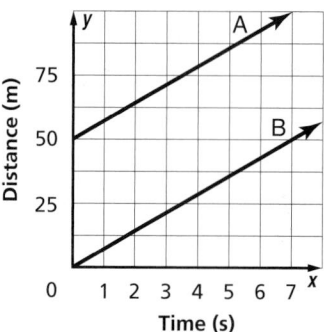

No; since slope represents rate, the slopes of the graphs are the same. Therefore, the runners will never meet.

27b. Sample answer:

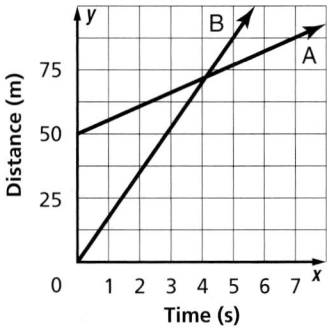

The line representing runner B has a steeper slope than the line representing runner A. The intersection point represents the time and distance at which runner B catches up to runner A.

Page 421, Lesson 8-10

5.

$y > x - 1$

6.

$y \leq 2$

7.
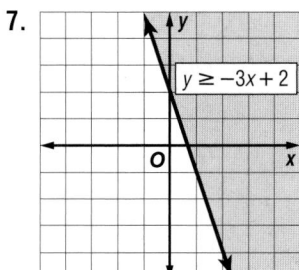
$y \geq -3x + 2$

9.

$25x + 15y \leq 630$

Sample answer: 5 adults, 30 children; 10 adults, 22 children; 15 adults, 15 children

10.

$y \geq x$

11.

$y < x$

12.

$y < 1$

13.

$y \geq -3$

14.
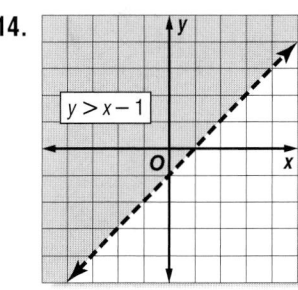
$y > x - 1$

15.
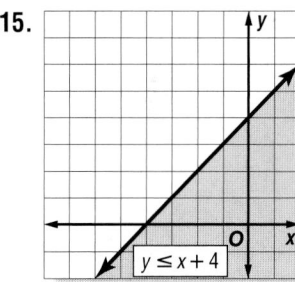
$y \leq x + 4$

16.

$y \leq -x$

17.

$y \geq 0$

18.
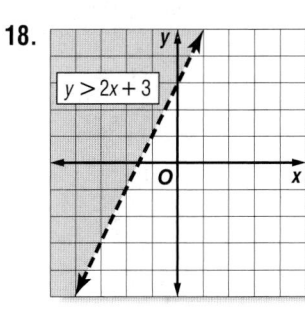
$y > 2x + 3$

19.
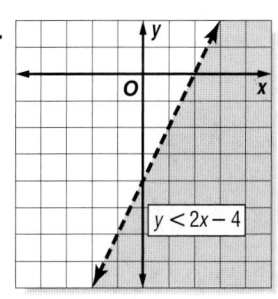
$y < 2x - 4$

20.
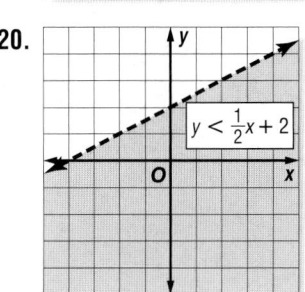
$y < \frac{1}{2}x + 2$

21.
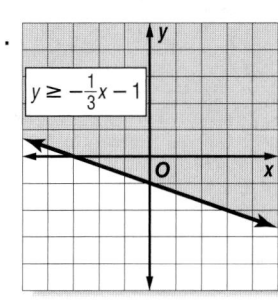
$y \geq -\frac{1}{3}x - 1$

Page 422, Lesson 8-10

31.

$$100x + 40y \geq 1500$$

Econo Rafts / Super Rafts

37.

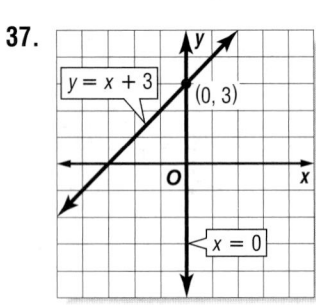

$y = x + 3$ (0, 3) $x = 0$

38.

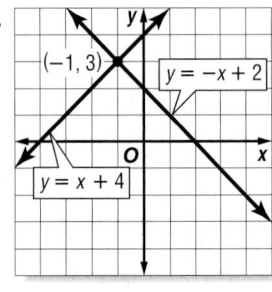

(−1, 3) $y = -x + 2$ $y = x + 4$

39.

$y = -2x - 1$ $y = -x - 3$ (2, −5)

Page 423, Graphing Calculator Investigation

3.

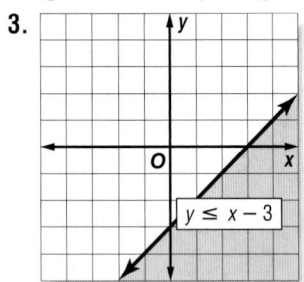

$y \leq x - 3$

4.

$y \leq -1$

5.

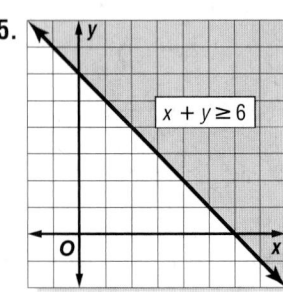

$x + y \geq 6$

6.

$y \geq 3x$

7.

$y \leq 0$

8.

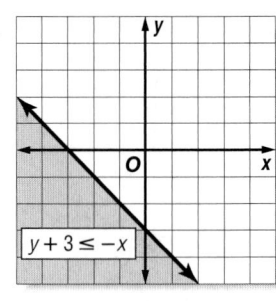

$y + 3 \leq -x$

9.

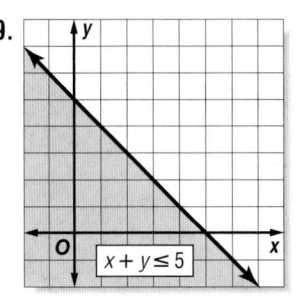

$x + y \leq 5$

10.

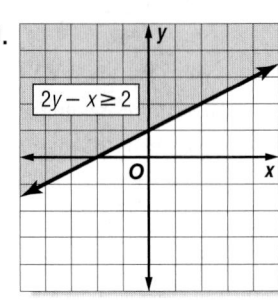

$2y - x \geq 2$

Page 429, Practice Test

1. To find the x-intercept, let $y = 0$ in the equation and solve for x. To find the y-intercept, let $x = 0$ in the equation and solve for y.

2. Choose a point above or below the boundary line and substitute its coordinates in the inequality. If the result is true, shade that side of the boundary. If the result is false, shade the other side of the boundary.

4. −3 in the domain is paired with 4 and 6 in the range.

5. Each x value is paired with only one y value.

6.

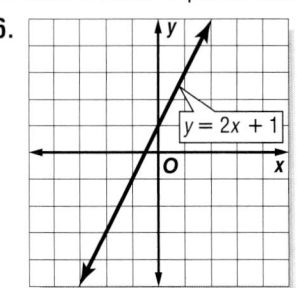

$y = 2x + 1$

7.

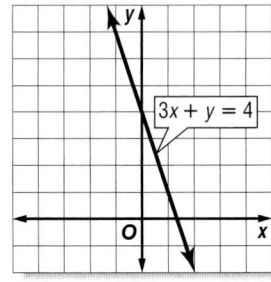

$3x + y = 4$

8.

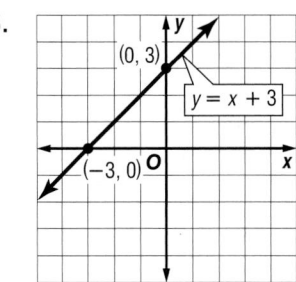

(0, 3) $y = x + 3$ (−3, 0)

9.

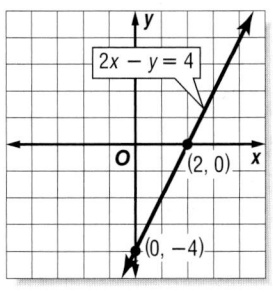

$2x - y = 4$ (2, 0) (0, −4)

13.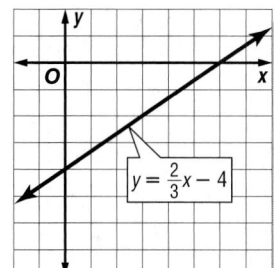

$y = \frac{2}{3}x - 4$

14.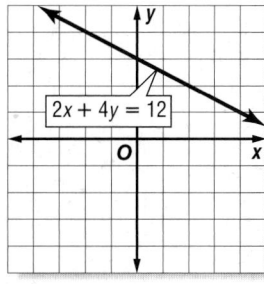

$2x + 4y = 12$

17.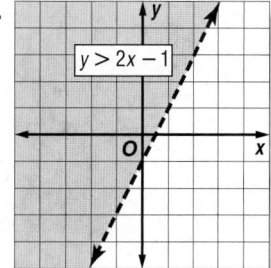

$y > 2x - 1$

18.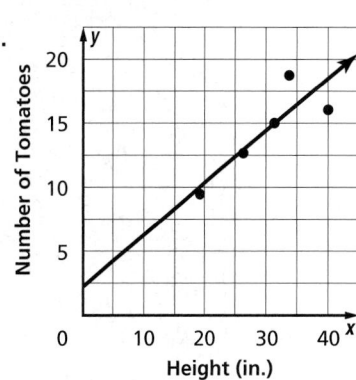

UNIT 4

Applying Algebra to Geometry

Introduction

In this unit, students will examine square roots, and the real number system. They will classify angles and triangles, and explore the Pythagorean Theorem, the Distance Formula, Midpoint Formula, and the properties of similar figures. Students will also use trigonometric ratios to solve problems. In addition, students will classify, find the angle measures, and find the area of various polygons. Students will examine the circumference and area of circles. Additionally, they will find the volume and surface area of three-dimensional objects, and use precision and significant digits to describe measurements.

Assessment Options

 Unit 4 Test Pages 665–666 of the *Chapter 11 Resource Masters* may be used as a test or review for Unit 4. This assessment contains both multiple-choice and short answer items.

ExamView® Pro
This CD-ROM can be used to create additional unit tests and review worksheets.

An online, research-based instructional, assessment, and intervention tool that provides specific feedback on student mastery of state and national standards, instant remediation, and a data management system to track performance. For more information, contact mhdigitallearning.com.

UNIT 4

Although they may seem like different subjects, algebra and geometry are closely related. In this unit, you will use algebra to solve geometry problems.

Chapter 9
Real Numbers and Right Triangles

Chapter 10
Two-Dimensional Figures

Chapter 11
Three-Dimensional Figures

Real-Life Math Videos

What's Math Got to Do With It? Real-Life Math Videos engage students showing them how math is used in everyday situations. Use Video 3 with this unit.

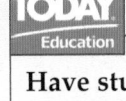
WebQuest Internet Project

Able to Leap Tall Buildings

The building with the tallest rooftop is the Sears Tower in Chicago, with a height of 1450 feet. However, the tallest building is the Petronas Twin Towers in Kuala Lumpur, Malaysia, whose architectural spires rise to 1483 feet.

In this project, you will be exploring how geometry and algebra can help you describe unusual or large structures of the world.

 Log on to www.pre-alg.com/webquest. Begin your WebQuest by reading the Task.

Then continue working on your WebQuest as you study Unit 4.

Lesson	9-8	10-8	11-3
Page	481	543	571

USA TODAY Snapshots®

World's tallest buildings

The ranking of the tallest skyscrapers is based on measuring the building from the sidewalk level of the main entrance to the structural top of the building. That includes spires, but not antennas or flagpoles.

1,483' — **1** Petronas Twin Towers — Kuala Lumpur, Malaysia

1,450' — **2** Sears Tower — Chicago

1,380' — **3** Jin Mao Building — Shanghai

Source: Council on Tall Buildings and Urban Habitat

USA TODAY

Unit 4 Applying Algebra to Geometry 433

WebQuest Internet Project

Problem-Based Learning A WebQuest is an online project in which students do research on the Internet, gather data, and make presentations using word processing, graphing, page-making, or presentation software. In each chapter, students advance to the next step in their WebQuest. At the end of Chapter 11, the project culminates with a presentation of their findings.

Teaching suggestions and sample answers are available in the *WebQuest and Project Resources*.

Chapter 9

Real Numbers and Right Triangles
Chapter Overview and Pacing

Year-long pacing: pages T20–T21.

LESSON OBJECTIVES	PACING (days)			
	Regular		Block	
	Basic/ Average	Advanced	Basic/ Average	Advanced
9-1 Squares and Square Roots *(pp. 436–440)* • Find squares and square roots. • Estimate square roots.	1	1	0.5	0.5
9-2 The Real Number System *(pp. 441–442)* • Identify and compare numbers in the real number system. • Solve equations by finding square roots.	1	1	0.5	0.5
9-3 Angles *(pp. 447–452)* • Measure and draw angles. • Classify angles as acute, right, obtuse, or straight. *Follow-Up:* Graph the results of a probability experiment in a circle graph.	1	2 (with 9-3 Follow-Up)	0.5	0.5 (with 9-3 Follow-Up)
9-4 Triangles *(pp. 453–457)* • Find the missing angle measure of a triangle. • Classify triangles by angles and by sides.	1	1	0.5	0.5
9-5 The Pythagorean Theorem *(pp. 458–465)* *Preview:* Find the area of figures using rectangular dot paper. • Use the Pythagorean Theorem to find the length of a side of a right triangle. • Use the converse of the Pythagorean Theorem to determine whether a triangle is a right triangle. *Follow-Up:* Graph irrational numbers on a number line.	3 (with 9-5 Preview)	2 (with 9-5 Follow-Up)	1	1 (with 9-5 Follow-Up)
9-6 The Distance and Midpoint Formulas *(pp. 466–470)* • Use the Distance Formula to determine lengths on a coordinate plane. • Use the Midpoint Formula to find the midpoint of a line segment on the coordinate plane.	2	2	1	1
9-7 Similar Triangles and Indirect Measurement *(pp. 471–475)* • Identify corresponding parts and find missing measures of similar triangles. • Solve problems involving indirect measurement using similar triangles.	1	1	0.5	0.5
9-8 Sine, Cosine, and Tangent Ratios *(pp. 476–482)* *Preview:* Discover the special relationship among right triangles and their sides. • Find sine, cosine, and tangent ratios. • Solve problems by using the trigonometric ratios. *Follow-Up:* Use a graphing calculator to find angle measures in a right triangle	3 (with 9-8 Preview)	3 (with 9-8 Follow-Up)	1.5 (with 9-8 Preview)	1.5 (with 9-8 Follow-Up)
Study Guide and **Practice Test** *(pp. 483–487)* **Standardized Test Practice** *(pp. 488–489)*	1	1	0.5	0.5
Chapter Assessment	1	1	0.5	0.5
TOTAL	15	15	7	7

*An electronic version of this chapter is available on **StudentWorks™**. This backpack solution CD-ROM allows students instant access to the Student Edition, lesson worksheet pages, and web resources.*

Chapter Resource Manager

CHAPTER 9 RESOURCE MASTERS

Study Guide and Intervention	Practice (Skills and Average)	Reading to Learn Mathematics	Enrichment	Assessment	Prerequisite Skills Workbook	Applications*	Parent and Student Study Guide Workbook	5-Minute Check Transparencies	Interactive Chalkboard	Pre-AlgePASS: Tutorial Plus (lessons)	Materials
489	490–491	492	493				72	9-1	9-1	26	
494	495–496	497	498	543		GCS 35	73	9-2	9-2		
499	500–501	502	503				74	9-3	9-3		*Follow-Up:* spreadsheet software
504	505–506	507	508	543, 545			75	9-4	9-4		
509	510–511	512	513			SC 17	76	9-5	9-5	27, 28	*Preview:* rectangular dot paper *Follow-Up:* grid paper, compass
514	515–516	517	518	544			77	9-6	9-6		
519	520–521	522	523			SC 18	78	9-7	9-7	29	
524	525–526	527	528	544		GCS 36	79	9-8	9-8	30	*Preview:* metric ruler, protractor, calculator *Follow-Up:* graphing calculator
				529–542, 546–548							

* *Key to Abbreviations:* GCS = Graphing Calculator and Spreadsheet Masters, SC = School-to-Career Masters, SM = Science and Mathematics Lab Manual

ELL Study Guide and Intervention, Skills Practice, Practice, and Parent and Student Study Guide Workbooks are also available in Spanish.

Mathematical Connections and Background

Continuity of Instruction

Prior Knowledge

In Chapter 7, students learned to solve equations with variables on each side of the equation. They also learned to write and graph inequalities, and to solve multi–step inequalities. In Chapter 8, students wrote and graphed equations, found slopes of lines, and used slope to describe rates of change. Students also learned to use best–fit lines to make predictions.

This Chapter

Students learn to use squares and square roots, classify angles and triangles, and find missing angle measurements in triangles. They use the Pythagorean Theorem to explore right triangles, and study the Distance and Midpoint Formulas. Students also identify and use properties of similar figures. In addition, they learn to use trigonometric ratios to solve problems.

Future Connections

The properties of right triangles are the basis for the study of trigonometry, which is related to geometry. Trigonometry was developed to calculate distances and angles in various fields such as cartography, astronomy, and surveying. The Distance Formula and Midpoint Formula will be used in Calculus.

9-1 Squares and Square Roots

The square root of a number is one of two equal factors of a number. Every positive number has a positive and a negative square root. For example, since $8 \cdot 8 = 64$, 8 is a square root of 64. Since $(-8) \cdot (-8) = 64$, -8 is a square root of 64. The notation $\sqrt{}$ indicates the positive square root, $-\sqrt{}$ indicates the negative square root, and $\pm\sqrt{}$ indicates both square roots. For example, $\sqrt{81} = 9$, $-\sqrt{49} = -7$, and $\pm\sqrt{4} = \pm 2$. A negative number has no real square root because the square root of a number is never negative. That is, $\sqrt{-32}$ is not possible.

9-2 The Real Number System

The real number system is made up of the sets of rational and irrational numbers. Rational numbers are numbers that can be written in the form $\frac{a}{b}$ where a and b are integers and $b \neq 0$. Examples are 0.45, $\frac{1}{4}$, and $\sqrt{0.36}$. Irrational numbers are non–repeating or non–terminating decimals. Examples are $\sqrt{71}$, π, and 0.020020002....

9-3 Angles

Two rays that have the same endpoint form an angle. The common endpoint is called the vertex, and the two rays that make up the angle are called the sides of the angle. The most common unit of measure for angles is the degree. Protractors can be used to measure angles or to draw an angle of a given measure.

Angles can be classified by their degree measure. Acute angles have measures less than 90° but greater than 0°. Obtuse angles have measures greater than 90° but less than 180°. Right angles have measures of 90°.

9-4 Triangles

A triangle is a figure formed by three line segments that intersect only at their endpoints. The sum of the measures of the angles of a triangle is 180°.

Triangles can be classified by their angles. An acute triangle contains all acute angles. An obtuse triangle has one obtuse angle. A right triangle has one right angle.

Triangles also can be classified by their sides. A scalene triangle has no congruent sides. An isosceles triangle has at least two sides congruent. An equilateral triangle has all sides congruent.

9-5 The Pythagorean Theorem

In a right triangle, the sides that are adjacent to the right angle are called the legs. The side opposite the right angle is the hypotenuse.

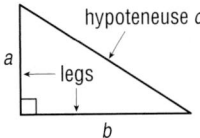

The Pythagorean Theorem describes the relationship between the lengths of the legs and the hypotenuse c. It states that if a triangle is a right triangle, then the square of the length of the hypotenuse is equal to the sum of the squares of the lengths of the legs. In symbols, $c^2 = a^2 + b^2$.

9-6 The Distance and Midpoint Formulas

The Distance Formula can be used to find the length of a segment on a coordinate plane. It states that the distance d between two points with coordinates (x_1, y_1) and (x_2, y_2) is given by
$$d = \sqrt{(x_2 - x_1)^2 + (y_2 - y_1)^2}.$$
On a line segment, the point that is halfway between the endpoints is called the midpoint. To find the midpoint of a segment on a coordinate plane, you can use the Midpoint Formula. This formula states that on a coordinate plane, the coordinates of the midpoint of a segment whose endpoints have coordinates at (x_1, y_1) and (x_2, y_2) are given by $\left(\dfrac{x_1 + x_2}{2}, \dfrac{y_1 + y_2}{2} \right)$.

9-7 Similar Triangles and Indirect Measurement

Triangles that have the same shape but not necessarily the same dimensions are similar triangles. Similar triangles have corresponding angles and sides. Arcs are used to show congruent angles.

If two triangles are similar, then the corresponding angles have the same measure, and the corresponding sides are proportional. Therefore, to determine the measures of the sides of similar triangles when some measures are known, proportions can be used.

9-8 Sine, Cosine, and Tangent Ratios

Trigonometry is the study of the properties of triangles. A trigonometric ratio is a ratio of the lengths of two sides of a right triangle. The most common trigonometric ratios are the sine, cosine, and tangent ratios. These ratios are abbreviated as sin, cos, and tan, respectively. Consider the right triangle shown.

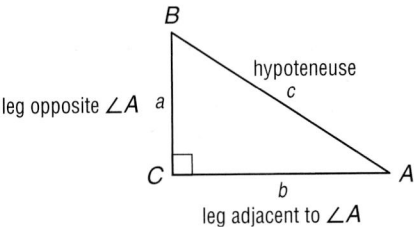

If $\angle A$ is an acute angle of a right triangle, then

$$\sin \angle A = \frac{\text{measure of leg opposite } \angle A}{\text{measure of hypotenuse}},$$

$$\cos \angle A = \frac{\text{measure of leg adjacent to } \angle A}{\text{measure of hypotenuse}}, \text{ and}$$

$$\tan \angle A = \frac{\text{measure of leg opposite } \angle A}{\text{measure of leg adjacent to } \angle A}.$$

Quick Review Math Handbook

Hot Words includes a glossary of terms while Hot Topics consists of explanations of key mathematical concepts with exercises to test comprehension. This valuable resource can be used as a reference in the classroom or for home study.

Lesson	Hot Topics Section	Lesson	Hot Topics Section
9-1	3.1, 3.2	9-6	6.5
9-3	6.4, 7.1, 7.2	9-7	8.6
9-4	3.1, 3.4, 6.2, 7.1	9-8	7.10
9-5	3.1, 3.4, 6.2, 7.9		

 Additional mathematical information and teaching notes are available at www.pre-alg.com/key_concepts.

Type		Student Edition	Teacher Resources	Technology/Internet
INTERVENTION	Ongoing	Prerequisite Skills, p. 435, 440, 445, 451, 457, 464, 470, 475 Practice Quiz 1, p. 451 Practice Quiz 2, p. 470	5-Minute Check Transparencies Quizzes, *CRM*, pp. 543, 544 Mid-Chapter Test, *CRM*, p. 545 Study Guide and Intervention, *CRM*, pp. 489, 494, 499, 504, 509, 514, 519, 524	Pre-AlgePASS: Tutorial Plus, Lessons 26, 27, 28, 29, and 30 www.pre-alg.com/self_check_quiz www.pre-alg.com/extra_examples
	Mixed Review	pp. 440, 445, 451, 457, 464, 470, 475, 481	Cumulative Review, *CRM*, p. 546	
	Error Analysis	Find the Error, pp. 462, 479	Find the Error, *TWE*, pp. 462, 479 Unlocking Misconceptions, *TWE*, pp. 437, 448, 455, 472, 478 Tips for New Teachers, *TWE*, pp. 451, 464	
	Standardized Test Practice	pp. 440, 445, 451, 457, 461, 462, 464, 470, 475, 481, 488–489	*TWE*, pp. 488–489 Standardized Test Practice, *CRM*, pp. 547–548	Standardized Test Practice CD-ROM www.pre-alg.com/standardized_test
ASSESSMENT	Open-Ended Assessment	Writing in Math, pp. 440, 445, 451, 457, 464, 469, 475, 481 Open Ended, pp. 438, 443, 449, 455, 462, 468, 473, 479 Standardized Test, p. 489	Speaking: *TWE*, pp. 440, 464 Writing: *TWE*, pp. 445, 475, 481 Modeling: *TWE*, pp. 451, 457, 470 Open-Ended Assessment, *CRM*, p. 479	
	Chapter Assessment	Study Guide, pp. 483–486 Practice Test, p. 487	Multiple Choice Tests (Forms 1, 2A, 2B), *CRM*, pp. 529–534 Free-Response Tests (Forms 2C, 2D, 3), *CRM*, pp. 535–540 Vocabulary Test/Review, *CRM*, p. 542	ExamView® Pro (see below) MindJogger Videoquizzes www.pre-alg.com/vocabulary_review www.pre-alg.com/chapter_test

For more information on Yearly ProgressPro, see p. 432.

Pre-Algebra Lesson	Yearly ProgressPro Skill Lesson(s)
9-1	Square Roots
9-2	Classify Real Numbers
9-3	Types of Angles: Level 2
9-4	Types of Triangles
9-5	Pythagorean Theorem
9-6	Distance on the Coordinate Plane
9-7	Similar Figures Indirect measurement
9-8	Trigonometric Ratios

ExamView® Pro

Use the networkable **ExamView® Pro** to:
- Create **multiple versions** of tests.
- Create **modified** tests for *Inclusion* students.
- **Edit** existing questions and **add** your own questions.
- Use built-in **state curriculum correlations** to create tests aligned with state standards.
- Change **English** tests to **Spanish** and vice versa.

For more information on Intervention and Assessment, see pp. T8–T11.

Reading and Writing in Mathematics

Glencoe Pre-Algebra provides numerous opportunities to incorporate reading and writing into the mathematics classroom.

Student Edition

- Foldables™ Study Organizer, p. 435
- Reading Mathematics, p. 446
- Concept Check questions require students to verbalize and write about what they have learned in the lesson. (pp. 437, 438, 441, 443, 449, 455, 461, 462, 466, 468, 472, 473, 479)
- Writing in Math questions in every lesson, pp. 440, 445, 451, 457, 464, 469, 475, 481
- Reading Math, pp. 437, 448, 453, 471, 472, 477
- WebQuest, p. 481

Teacher Wraparound Edition

- Foldables™ Study Organizer, pp. 435, 483
- Study Notebook suggestions, pp. 438, 443, 446, 449, 452, 455, 459, 462, 465, 468, 473, 476, 479
- Modeling activities, pp. 451, 457, 470
- Speaking activities, pp. 440, 464
- Writing activities, pp. 445, 475, 481
- Differentiated Instruction (Verbal/Linguistic), p. 442
- **ELL** Resources, pp. 434, 436, 441, 442, 446, 447, 453, 460, 466, 471, 477, 483

Additional Resources

- Vocabulary Builder worksheets require students to define and give examples for key vocabulary terms as they progress through the chapter (*Chapter 9 Resource Masters,* pp. vii–viii)
- Reading to Learn Mathematics master for each lesson (*Chapter 9 Resource Masters*, pp. 492, 497, 502, 507, 512, 517, 522, 527)
- *Vocabulary PuzzleMaker* software creates crossword, jumble, and word search puzzles using vocabulary lists that you can customize.
- *Teaching Mathematics with Foldables* provides suggestions for promoting cognition and language.
- *Reading and Writing in the Mathematics Classroom*
- *WebQuest and Project Resources*

For more information on Reading and Writing in Mathematics, see pp. T6–T7.

PROJECT CRISS^{SM} Study Skill

Producing an accurate, detailed written summary can help students' understanding of new material. Demonstrate the summarization process using the example at the right for Lesson 9-1. Begin by having students notice lesson titles, boldface words, and illustrations. Next, have them read the lesson. Then summarize it on the chalkboard as shown. Finally, students should write a summary, in their own words, based on the notes.

Have students work through this process individually or in cooperative groups for the remaining lessons in Chapter 9.

Lesson 9-1
- The square of a number is the product of the number and itself.
  Example: $3^2 = 9$
- Perfect squares are squares of whole numbers.
  Example: 25 is a perfect square with factors 5, 5
- Square roots are the factors multiplied to form perfect squares.
- A radical sign indicates the positive square root of a number.

CReating **I**ndependence **T**hrough **S**tudent-**O**wned **S**trategies

Have students read over the list of objectives and make a list of any words with which they are not familiar.

Why It's Important

Point out to students that this is only one of many reasons why each objective is important. Others are provided in the introduction to each lesson.

Lesson	NCTM Standards	Local Objectives
9-1	1, 4, 6, 8	
9-2	1, 2	
9-3	3, 4, 6	
9-3 Follow-Up	3,4,6	
9-4	1, 2, 3, 4, 6, 8, 9	
9-5 Preview	1, 2, 3, 4, 6, 7, 8	
9-5	1, 2, 3, 4, 6, 7, 8	
9-5 Follow-Up	1, 2, 3, 4, 6, 8	
9-6	1, 2, 3, 4, 6, 8	
9-7	1, 2, 3, 4, 6, 8, 9, 10	
9-8 Preview	1, 2, 3, 4, 6, 8, 9, 10	
9-8	1, 2, 3, 4, 6, 8, 9, 10	
9-8 Follow-Up	1, 2, 3, 4, 6, 9	

Key to NCTM Standards:

1=Number & Operations, 2=Algebra,
3=Geometry, 4=Measurement,
5=Data Analysis & Probability, 6=Problem Solving, 7=Reasoning & Proof,
8=Communication, 9=Connections,
10=Representation

Chapter 9 Real Numbers and Right Triangles

What You'll Learn

- **Lessons 9-1 and 9-2** Find and use squares and square roots and identify numbers in the real number system.
- **Lessons 9-3 and 9-4** Classify angles and triangles and find the missing angle measure of a triangle.
- **Lessons 9-5 and 9-6** Use the Pythagorean Theorem, the Distance Formula, and the Midpoint Formula.
- **Lesson 9-7** Identify and use properties of similar figures.
- **Lesson 9-8** Use trigonometric ratios to solve problems.

Key Vocabulary

- angle (p. 447)
- triangle (p. 453)
- Pythagorean Theorem (p. 460)
- similar triangles (p. 471)
- trigonometric ratios (p. 477)

Why It's Important

All of the numbers we use on a daily basis are real numbers. Formulas that contain real numbers can be used to solve real-world problems dealing with distance. For example, if you know the height of a lighthouse, you can use a formula to determine how far you can see from the top of the lighthouse. *You will solve a problem about lighthouses in Lesson 9-1.*

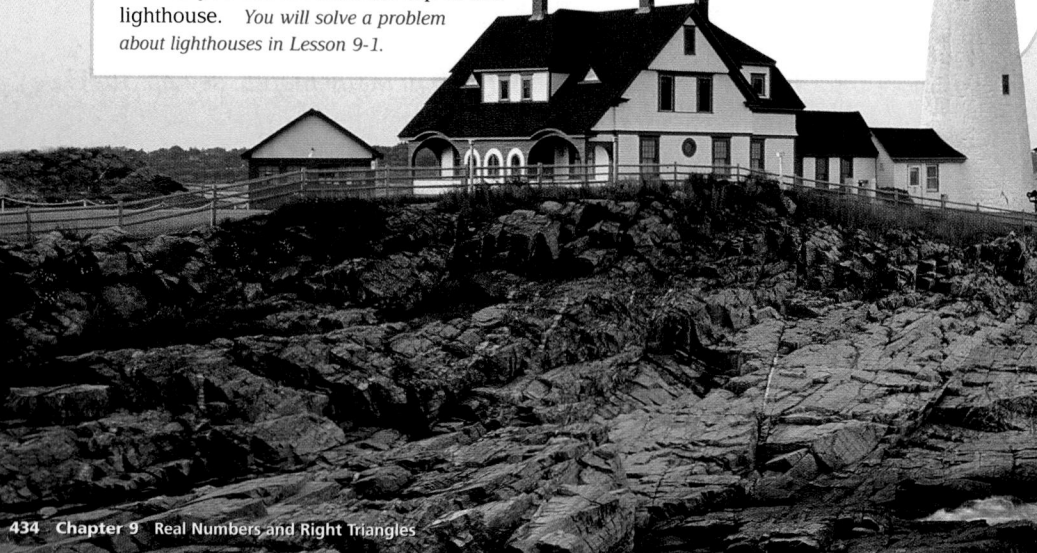

Vocabulary Builder ⬭ELL

The Key Vocabulary list introduces students to some of the main vocabulary terms included in this chapter. For a more thorough vocabulary list with pronunciations of new words, give students the Vocabulary Builder worksheets found on pages vii and viii of the *Chapter 9 Resource Masters*. Encourage them to complete the definition of each term as they progress through the chapter. You may suggest that they add these sheets to their study notebooks for future reference when studying for the Chapter 9 test.

▶ **Prerequisite Skills** To be successful in this chapter, you'll need to master these skills and be able to apply them in problem-solving situations. Review these skills before beginning Chapter 9.

For Lesson 9-2   Compare Decimals

Replace each ● with <, >, or = to make a true statement. *(For review, see page 710.)*

1. 3.2 ● 3.5 **<**   **2.** 7.8 ● 7.7 **>**   **3.** 5.13 ● 5.16 **<**   **4.** 4.92 ● 4.89 **>**

5. 2.62 ● 2.6 **>**   **6.** 3.4 ● 3.41 **<**   **7.** 0.07 ● 0.7 **<**   **8.** 1.16 ● 1.06 **>**

For Lessons 9-4 and 9-7   Solve Equations by Dividing

ALGEBRA Solve each equation. *(For review, see Lesson 3-4.)*

9. $3x = 24$ **8**   **10.** $7y = 49$ **7**   **11.** $120 = 2n$ **60**   **12.** $54 = 6a$ **9**

13. $90 = 10m$ **9**   **14.** $144 = 12m$ **12**   **15.** $15d = 165$ **11**   **16.** $182 = 14w$ **13**

For Lesson 9-6   Exponents

Find the value of each expression. *(For review, see Lesson 4-2.)*

17. $(3 - 1)^2 + (4 - 2)^2$ **8**   **18.** $(5 - 2)^2 + (6 - 3)^2$ **18**   **19.** $(4 - 7)^2 + (3 - 8)^2$ **34**

20. $(8 - 2)^2 + (3 - 9)^2$ **72**   **21.** $(2 - 6)^2 + [(-8) - 1]^2$ **97** **22.** $(-7 - 2)^2 + [3 - (-4)]^2$
130

FOLDABLES™
Study Organizer

Right Triangles Make this Foldable to help you organize your notes. Begin with three plain sheets of $8\frac{1}{2}$" by 11" paper.

Step 1 **Fold**

Fold to make a triangle. Cut off the extra paper.

Step 2 **Repeat**

Repeat Step 1 twice. You have three squares.

Step 3 **Stack and Staple**

Stack the three squares and staple along the fold.

Step 4 **Label**

Label each section with a lesson number.

Right Triangles

Reading and Writing As you read and study the chapter, fill the pages with examples, diagrams, and formulas.

This section provides a review of the basic concepts needed before beginning Chapter 9. Page references are included for additional student help.

Prerequisite Skills in the Getting Ready for the Next Lesson section at the end of each lesson reviews a skill needed in the next lesson.

For Lesson	Prerequisite Skill
9-2	Rational Numbers (p. 440)
9-3	Drawing Angles (p. 445)
9-4	Solving Two-Step Equations (p. 451)
9-5	Exponents (p. 457)
9-6	Order of Operations/Exponents (p. 464)
9-7	Proportions (p. 470)
9-8	Writing Fractions as Decimals (p. 475)

FOLDABLES™
Study Organizer

For more information about Foldables, see *Teaching Mathematics with Foldables.*

Use of Visuals, Captions, and Labels On the pages of their Foldable journals, students take notes, define terms, sketch diagrams, and write formulas. Have students design one or more visuals (graph, diagram, picture, chart) per lesson that present the information introduced in a concise, easy-to-study format. Encourage students to clearly label their visuals and write captions when needed.

1 Focus

5-Minute Check Transparency 9-1 Use as a quiz or review of Chapter 8.

Mathematical Background notes are available for this lesson on page 434C.

How are square roots related to factors?

The opening activity questions are repeated on page 492 of the *Chapter 9 Resource Masters*.

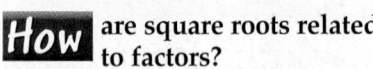

Reading to Learn Mathematics, p. 492 **ELL**

Pre-Activity *How are square roots related to factors?*

Do the activity at the top of page 436 in your textbook. Write your answers below.

a. Describe the difference between the first four and the last four values of *x*.
The first four are whole numbers and the last four are not.

b. Explain how you found an exact answer for the first four values of *x*.
To find an exact answer, determine what number times itself is equal to each value of *x*.

c. How did you find an estimate for the last four values of *x*? Choose a decimal value that, when multiplied by itself, is approximately equal to the value of *x*.

Reading the Lesson 1–3. See students' work.

Write a definition and give an example of each new vocabulary word or phrase.

Vocabulary	Definition	Example
1. perfect square		
2. square root		
3. radical sign		

Helping You Remember

4. For each number in the table, tell whether it has a real square root and explain why or why not. Then indicate if the number is a perfect square and explain.

	Real Square Root ?	Perfect Square ?
26	Yes; positive number	No; not the square of a whole number
−81	No; negative number	
256	Yes; positive number	Yes; square of 16
1444	Yes; positive number	Yes; square of 38
−5	No; negative number	

Teaching Tip The positive or nonnegative square root is also called the principal square root. The symbol $\sqrt{x}$ indicates the principal square root of *x*.

9-1 Squares and Square Roots

NEW YORK *Performance Indicator* **Reinforcement of 7.N.15** Recognize and state the value of the square root of a perfect square (up to 225), **Reinforcement of 7.N.16** Determine the square root of non-perfect squares using a calculator

What You'll Learn

- Find squares and square roots.
- Estimate square roots.

Vocabulary

- perfect square
- square root
- radical sign

a. The first four are whole numbers and the last four are not.
b. To find an exact answer, determine what number times itself is equal to each value of *x*.
c. Choose a decimal value that, when multiplied by itself, is approximately equal to the value of *x*.

How are square roots related to factors?

Values of x^2 are shown in the second column in the table. Guess and check to find the value of *x* that corresponds to x^2. If you cannot find an exact answer, estimate with decimals to the nearest tenth to find an approximate answer.

x	x^2
5	25
7	49
13	169
15	225
2.8	8
3.5	12
8.1	65
10.5	110

a. Describe the difference between the first four and the last four values of *x*.

b. Explain how you found an exact answer for the first four values of *x*.

c. How did you find an estimate for the last four values of *x*?

SQUARES AND SQUARE ROOTS Numbers like 25, 49, 169, and 225 are **perfect squares** because they are squares of whole numbers.

$$5 \times 5 \text{ or } 5^2 \qquad 7 \times 7 \text{ or } 7^2 \qquad 13 \times 13 \text{ or } 13^2 \qquad 15 \times 15 \text{ or } 15^2$$
$$\downarrow \qquad\qquad \downarrow \qquad\qquad \downarrow \qquad\qquad \downarrow$$
$$25 \qquad\qquad 49 \qquad\qquad 169 \qquad\qquad 225$$

A **square root** of a number is one of two equal factors of the number. Every positive number has a positive square root and a negative square root. A negative number like -9 has no real square root because the square of a number is never negative.

Key Concept **Square Root**

- **Words** A square root of a number is one of its two equal factors.
- **Symbols** If $x^2 = y$, then *x* is a square root of *y*.
- **Examples** Since $5 \cdot 5$ or $5^2 = 25$, 5 is a square root of 25.
  Since $(-5) \cdot (-5)$ or $(-5)^2 = 25$, -5 is a square root of 25.

A **radical sign**, , is used to indicate the square root.

Example 1 *Find Square Roots*

Find each square root.

a. $\sqrt{36}$ $\sqrt{36}$ indicates the *positive* square root of 36.
Since $6^2 = 36$, $\sqrt{36} = 6$.

Resource Manager

📂 Workbooks and Reproducible Masters

Chapter 9 Resource Masters
- Study Guide and Intervention, p. 489
- Skills Practice, p. 490
- Practice, p. 491
- Reading to Learn Mathematics, p. 492
- Enrichment, p. 493

Parent and Student Study Guide Workbook, p. 72

🖥 Transparencies

5-Minute Check Transparency 9-1
Answer Key Transparencies

⚙ Technology

Interactive Chalkboard
Pre-AlgePASS: Tutorial Plus, Lesson 26

b. $-\sqrt{81}$ $-\sqrt{81}$ indicates the *negative* square root of 81.

Since $9^2 = 81$, $-\sqrt{81} = -9$.

c. $\pm\sqrt{9}$ $\pm\sqrt{9}$ indicates *both* square roots of 9.

Since $3^2 = 9$, $\sqrt{9} = 3$ and $-\sqrt{9} = -3$.

✓ **Concept Check** What does the radical sign indicate? **the square root**

You can use a calculator to find an approximate square root of a number that is not a perfect square. The decimal portion of these square roots goes on forever.

Example 2 Calculate Square Roots

Use a calculator to find each square root to the nearest tenth.

a. $\sqrt{10}$

2nd [$\sqrt{}$] 10 ENTER 3.16227766   Use a calculator.

$\sqrt{10} \approx 3.2$ Round to the nearest tenth.

CHECK Since $(3)^2 = 9$, the answer is reasonable. ✓

b. $-\sqrt{27}$

2nd [$\sqrt{}$] 27 ENTER 5.19615242   Use a calculator.

$-\sqrt{27} \approx -5.2$ Round to the nearest tenth.

CHECK Since $(-5)^2 = 25$, the answer is reasonable. ✓

ESTIMATE SQUARE ROOTS You can also estimate square roots without using a calculator.

Example 3 Estimate Square Roots

Estimate each square root to the nearest whole number.

a. $\sqrt{38}$

Find the two perfect squares closest to 38. To do this, list some perfect squares.

1, 4, 9, 16, 25, 36, 49, …

└─ 36 and 49 are closest to 38.

$36 < 38 < 49$ 38 is between 36 and 49.
$\sqrt{36} < \sqrt{38} < \sqrt{49}$ $\sqrt{38}$ is between $\sqrt{36}$ and $\sqrt{49}$.
$6 < \sqrt{38} < 7$ $\sqrt{36} = 6$ and $\sqrt{49} = 7$.

Since 38 is closer to 36 than 49, the best whole number estimate for $\sqrt{38}$ is 6.

www.pre-alg.com/extra_examples/ny

DAILY

INTERVENTION

Unlocking Misconceptions

- **Squares and Square Roots** Students may confuse $-\sqrt{16}$ and $\sqrt{-16}$ and believe the answer for both to be -4. Explain the difference and demonstrate why the square root of a negative number does not exist.

---

2 Teach

SQUARES AND SQUARE ROOTS

In-Class Examples   Power Point®

1 Find each square root.

a. $\sqrt{64}$ **8**

b. $-\sqrt{121}$ **−11**

c. $\pm\sqrt{4}$ **+2 and −2**

Teaching Tip Remind students to check the sign of their answer.

Teaching Tip Discuss with students why the square of a number is never negative.

2 Use a calculator to find each square root to the nearest tenth.

a. $\sqrt{23}$ **4.8**

b. $-\sqrt{46}$ **−6.8**

ESTIMATE SQUARE ROOTS

In-Class Example   Power Point®

3 Estimate each square root to the nearest whole number.

a. $\sqrt{22}$ **5**

b. $-\sqrt{319}$ **−18**

Interactive Chalkboard
PowerPoint® Presentations

This CD-ROM is a customizable Microsoft® Power-Point® presentation that includes:

- Step-by-step, dynamic solutions of each In-Class Example from the Teacher Wraparound Edition
- Additional, Your Turn exercises for each example
- The 5-Minute Check Transparencies
- Hot links to Glencoe Online Study Tools

4 **LANDMARKS** The observation deck at the Seattle Space Needle is 520 feet above the ground. On a clear day, about how far could a tourist on the deck see? Round to the nearest tenth. **27.8 mi**

3 Practice/Apply

Study Notebook

Have students—

• add the definitions/examples of the vocabulary terms to their Vocabulary Builder worksheets for Chapter 9.

• include any other item(s) that they find helpful in mastering the skills in this lesson.

About the Exercises . . .

Organization by Objective
• **Squares and Square Roots:** 12–33
• **Estimate Square Roots:** 34–46

Odd/Even Assignments
Exercises 12–33, 35–48, 49–50, and 52–55 are structured so that students practice the same concepts whether they are assigned odd or even problems.

Assignment Guide

Basic: 13–19 odd, 25–31 odd, 35–41 odd, 47–51 odd, 57–60, 64–80

Average: 13–55 odd, 57–60, 64–80 (Optional: 61–63)

Advanced: 12–56 even, 57–74 (Optional: 75–80)

More About. . .

Science •
To estimate how far you can see from a point above the horizon, you can use the formula $D = 1.22 \times \sqrt{A}$ where D is the distance in miles and A is the altitude, or height, in feet.

---

b. $-\sqrt{175}$

Find the two perfect squares closest to 175. List some perfect squares.

$$\ldots, 100, 121, 144, 169, 196, \ldots$$

169 and 196 are closest to 175.

$-196 < -175 < -169$ -175 is between -196 and -169.

$-\sqrt{196} < -\sqrt{175} < -\sqrt{169}$ $-\sqrt{175}$ is between $-\sqrt{196}$ and $-\sqrt{169}$.

$-14 < -\sqrt{175} < -13$ $-\sqrt{196} = -14$ and $-\sqrt{169} = -13$.

Since -175 is closer to -169 than -196, the best whole number estimate for $-\sqrt{175}$ is -13. **CHECK** $-\sqrt{175} \approx -13.2$ ✓

Many formulas used in real-world applications involve square roots.

Example 4 *Use Square Roots to Solve a Problem*

SCIENCE Use the information at the left. The light on Cape Hatteras Lighthouse in North Carolina is 208 feet high. On a clear day, from about what distance on the ocean is the light visible? Round to the nearest tenth.

$D = 1.22 \times \sqrt{A}$ Write the formula.

$= 1.22 \times \sqrt{208}$ Replace A with 208.

$\approx 1.22 \times 14.42$ Evaluate the square root first.

≈ 17.5924 Multiply.

On a clear day, the light will be visible from about 17.6 miles.

Check for Understanding

Concept Check
1–3. See margin.

1. **Explain** why every positive number has two square roots.
2. **List** three numbers between 200 and 325 that are perfect squares.
3. **OPEN ENDED** Write a problem in which the negative square root is not an integer. Then graph the square root.

Guided Practice

GUIDED PRACTICE KEY	
Exercises	Examples
4–6	1
7, 8	2
9, 10	3
11	4

Find each square root, if possible.

4. $\sqrt{49}$ **7**   5. $-\sqrt{64}$ **−8**   6. $\sqrt{-36}$ **not possible**

Use a calculator to find each square root to the nearest tenth.

7. $\sqrt{15}$ **3.9**   8. $-\sqrt{32}$ **−5.7**

Estimate each square root to the nearest whole number. Do not use a calculator.

9. $\sqrt{66}$ **8**   10. $-\sqrt{103}$ **−10**

Application 11. **SKYSCRAPERS** Refer to Example 4. Ryan is standing in the observation area of the Sears Tower in Chicago. About how far can he see on a clear day if the deck is 1353 feet above the ground? **44.9 mi**

DAILY
INTERVENTION

Differentiated Instruction

• **Intrapersonal** Have students write in their journals some examples of when and why squares and square roots are used. Have them ask their science teacher how squares are used in science and include the answer in their entries.

★ indicates increased difficulty

Practice and Apply

Homework Help

For Exercises	See Examples
12–23	1
24–33	2
34–46	3
47, 48	4

Extra Practice
See page 745.

Find each square root, if possible. **16, 17. not possible**

12. $\sqrt{16}$ **4**   **13.** $\sqrt{36}$ **6**   **14.** $-\sqrt{1}$ **−1**   **15.** $-\sqrt{25}$ **−5**

16. $\sqrt{-4}$ **17.** $\sqrt{-49}$ **18.** $\sqrt{100}$ **10**   **19.** $\sqrt{196}$ **14**

★ **20.** $\pm\sqrt{256}$ **16, −16**   ★ **21.** $\pm\sqrt{324}$ **18, −18**   ★ **22.** $\sqrt{0.81}$ **0.9**   ★ **23.** $\sqrt{2.25}$ **1.5**

Use a calculator to find each square root to the nearest tenth. **31. −1.7**

24. $\sqrt{15}$ **3.9**   **25.** $\sqrt{56}$ **7.5**   **26.** $-\sqrt{43}$ **−6.6**   **27.** $-\sqrt{86}$ **−9.3**

28. $\sqrt{180}$ **13.4**   **29.** $\sqrt{250}$ **15.8**   **30.** $-\sqrt{0.75}$ **−0.9**   **31.** $-\sqrt{3.05}$

★ **32.** Find the negative square root of 1000 to the nearest tenth. **−31.6**

★ **33.** If $x = \sqrt{5000}$, what is the value of x to the nearest tenth? **70.7**

34. The number $\sqrt{54}$ lies between which two consecutive whole numbers? Do not use a calculator. **7 and 8**

Estimate each square root to the nearest whole number. Do not use a calculator.

35. $\sqrt{79}$ **9**   **36.** $\sqrt{95}$ **10**   **37.** $-\sqrt{54}$ **−7**   **38.** $-\sqrt{125}$ **−11**

39. $\sqrt{200}$ **14**   **40.** $\sqrt{396}$ **20**   **41.** $-\sqrt{280}$ **−17**   **42.** $-\sqrt{490}$ **−22**

★ **43.** $-\sqrt{5.25}$ **−2**   ★ **44.** $-\sqrt{17.3}$ **−4**   ★ **45.** $\sqrt{38.75}$ **6**   ★ **46.** $\sqrt{140.57}$ **12**

ROLLER COASTERS   For Exercises 47–48, use the table shown and refer to Example 4 on page 438.

47. On a clear day, how far can a person see from the top hill of the Vortex? **14.8 mi**

48. How far can a person see on a clear day from the top hill of the Titan? **19.5 mi**

Coaster	Maximum Height (ft)
Double Loop	95
The Villain	120
Mean Streak	161
Raptor	137
The Beast	110
Vortex	148
Titan	255
Shockwave	116

Source: Roller Coaster Database

 Online Research Data Update
How far can you see from the top of the tallest roller coaster in the United States? Visit www.pre-alg.com/data_update to learn more.

Complete Exercises 49 and 50 without the help of a calculator.

49–50. See margin for explanations.

49. Which is greater, $\sqrt{65}$ or 9? Explain your reasoning. **9**

50. Which is less, 11 or $\sqrt{120}$? Explain your reasoning. $\sqrt{120}$

51. GEOMETRY   The area of each square is given. Estimate the length of a side of each square to the nearest tenth. Then find its approximate perimeter.

a. 109 in²   **10.4 in.; 41.6 in.**

b. 203 cm²   **14.2 cm; 56.8 cm**

c. 70 m²   **8.4 m; 33.6 m**

Simplify.

★ **52.** $2 + \sqrt{81} \times 3$ **29**   ★ **53.** $\sqrt{256} \div 8 \times 5$ **10**

★ **54.** $(9 - \sqrt{36}) + (16 - \sqrt{100})$ **9**   ★ **55.** $(\sqrt{1} + 7) \div (\sqrt{121} - 7)$ **2**

Answers

1. A positive number squared results in a positive number, and a negative number squared results in a positive number.

2. Sample answer: 225, 256, 324

3. Sample answer: $-\sqrt{1.69}$

49. 9; Since $64 < 65 < 81$, $\sqrt{64} < \sqrt{65} < \sqrt{81}$. Thus, it follows that $8 < \sqrt{65} < 9$. So, 9 is greater than $\sqrt{65}$.

50. $\sqrt{120}$; Since $100 < 120 < 121$, $\sqrt{100} < \sqrt{120} < \sqrt{121}$. Thus, it follows that $10 < \sqrt{120} < 11$. So, $\sqrt{120}$ is less than 11.

Study Guide and Intervention, p. 489

Squares and Square Roots
- A **perfect square** is the square of a whole number.
- A **square root** of a number is one of two equal factors of the number.
- Every positive number has a positive square root and a negative square root.
- The square root of a negative number such as −25, is not real because the square of a number is never negative.

Example 1 Find each square root.
a. $\sqrt{144}$ $\sqrt{144}$ indicates the positive square root of 144.
Since $12^2 = 144$, $\sqrt{144} = 12$
b. $-\sqrt{121}$ $-\sqrt{121}$ indicates the negative square root of 121.
Since $11^2 = 121$, $-\sqrt{121} = -11$
c. $\pm\sqrt{4}$ $\pm\sqrt{4}$ indicates both square roots of 4.
Since $2^2 = 4$, $\sqrt{4} = 2$ and $-\sqrt{4} = -2$

Example 2 Use a calculator to find $\sqrt{34}$ to the nearest tenth.
[2nd] [√] 34 [ENTER] 5.830951895 Use a calculator.
$\sqrt{34} \approx 5.8$ Round to the nearest tenth.

Exercises
Find each square root.

1. $-\sqrt{100}$ −10   **2.** $\sqrt{256}$ 16   **3.** $\sqrt{4}$ 2
4. $\sqrt{-4}$ not poss.   **5.** $-\sqrt{144}$ −12   **6.** $-\sqrt{225}$ −15
7. $\pm\sqrt{289}$ ± 17   **8.** $-\sqrt{16}$ −4   **9.** $\sqrt{484}$ 22
10. $\sqrt{-25}$ not poss.   **11.** $\pm\sqrt{361}$ ±19   **12.** $\sqrt{1521}$ 39

Use a calculator to find each square root to the nearest tenth.

13. $\sqrt{11}$ 3.3   **14.** $\sqrt{19}$ 4.4   **15.** $-\sqrt{47}$ −6.9
16. $\sqrt{57}$ −7.5   **17.** $\sqrt{172}$ 13.1   **18.** $\sqrt{521}$ 22.8
19. $\sqrt{427}$ 20.7   **20.** $-\sqrt{310}$ −17.6   **21.** $-\sqrt{490}$ −22.1

Skills Practice, p. 490 and Practice, p. 491 (shown)

Find each square root, if possible.

1. $\sqrt{100}$ 10   **2.** $\sqrt{144}$ 12   **3.** $\sqrt{-36}$ not possible
4. $\sqrt{121}$ 11   **5.** $\sqrt{-148}$ not possible   **6.** $-\sqrt{4}$ −2
7. $-\sqrt{9}$ −3   **8.** $-\sqrt{49}$ −7   **9.** $\sqrt{256}$ 16
10. $\sqrt{529}$ 23   **11.** $\sqrt{361}$ 19   **12.** $-\sqrt{196}$ −14

Use a calculator to find each square root to the nearest tenth.

13. $-\sqrt{2.25}$ −1.5   **14.** $\sqrt{38}$ 6.2   **15.** $\sqrt{249}$ 15.8
16. $\sqrt{131}$ 11.4   **17.** $\sqrt{7}$ 2.6   **18.** $\sqrt{52}$ 7.2
19. $\sqrt{168}$ 13.0   **20.** $\sqrt{499}$ 22.3   **21.** $-\sqrt{217}$ −14.7
22. $\pm\sqrt{218}$ ±14.8   **23.** $\pm\sqrt{42}$ ±6.5   **24.** $\pm\sqrt{94}$ ±9.7
25. $\pm\sqrt{50}$ ±7.1   **26.** $\pm\sqrt{137}$ ±11.7   **27.** $\pm\sqrt{208}$ ±14.4

28. Find the negative square root of 840 to the nearest tenth. −29.0

29. If $x^2 = 476$, what is the value of x to the nearest tenth? 21.8

30. The number $\sqrt{22}$ lies between which two consecutive whole numbers? Do not use a calculator. 4 and 5

Estimate each square root to the nearest whole number. Do not use a calculator.

31. $\sqrt{76}$ 9   **32.** $\sqrt{123}$ 11   **33.** $\sqrt{300}$ 17
34. $\sqrt{90}$ 9   **35.** $\sqrt{19}$ 4   **36.** $\sqrt{248}$ 16

37. GEOMETRY A square tarpaulin covering a softball field has an area of 441 m². What is the length of one side of the tarpaulin? 21 m

38. MONUMENTS Refer to Example 4 on page 438 of your textbook. The highest observation deck on the Eiffel Tower in Paris is about 899 feet above the ground. About how far could a visitor see on a clear day? about 36.6 mi

---

Enrichment, p. 493

Roots
The symbol $\sqrt{\ }$ indicates a square root. By placing a number in the upper left, the symbol can be changed to indicate higher roots.
$\sqrt[3]{8} = 2$ because $2^3 = 8$
$\sqrt[4]{81} = 3$ because $3^4 = 81$
$\sqrt[5]{100,000} = 10$ because $10^5 = 100,000$

Find each of the following.

1. $\sqrt[3]{125}$ 5   **2.** $\sqrt[4]{16}$ 2   **3.** $\sqrt[9]{1}$ 1
4. $\sqrt[3]{27}$ 3   **5.** $\sqrt[5]{32}$ 2   **6.** $\sqrt[3]{64}$ 4
7. $\sqrt[3]{1000}$ 10   **8.** $\sqrt[3]{216}$ 6   **9.** $\sqrt[6]{1,000,000}$ 10
10. $\sqrt[3]{1,000,000}$ 100   **11.** $\sqrt[4]{256}$ 4   **12.** $\sqrt[3]{729}$ 9
13. $\sqrt[6]{64}$ 2   **14.** $\sqrt[4]{625}$ 5   **15.** $\sqrt[5]{243}$ 3

Open-Ended Assessment

Speaking Write all the perfect squares between 1 and 400 on the chalkboard. Then have students take turns explaining how to estimate square roots of numbers provided by you or other students.

Tips for New Teachers

Assessment When having students estimate, make sure they are not using their calculators. You may wish to have students work in pairs so they can discuss developing estimates and check each other's work.

Getting Ready for Lesson 9-2

PREREQUISITE SKILL Lesson 9-2 presents the real number system. The real number system is composed of rational and irrational numbers. Exercises 75–80 should be used to determine your students' familiarity with rational numbers.

Answers

57. Sample answer: A number that has a rational square root will have an ending digit of 0, 1, 4, 5, 6, or 9. The last digit is the ending digit in one of the squares from 1–100. There are just six ending digits.

58. Square roots are related to factors in that if a number is a perfect square, the square root of the number is a factor of the number. Answers should include the following.
• Sample answer: 121
• Sample answer: 120

---

56. GEOMETRY Find the perimeter of a square that has an area of $\sqrt{2080}$ square meters. Round to the nearest tenth. **about 182.4 m**

57. CRITICAL THINKING What are the possibilities for the ending digit of a number that has a whole number square root? Explain your reasoning. **See margin.**

58. WRITING IN MATH Answer the question that was posed at the beginning of the lesson. **See margin.**

How are square roots related to factors?

Include the following in your answer:
• an example of a number between 100 and 200 whose square root is a whole number, and
• an example of a number between 100 and 200 whose square root is a decimal that does not terminate.

NEW YORK Test Practice

Standardized Test Practice
Ⓐ Ⓑ Ⓒ Ⓓ

59. Which statement is *not* true? **D**
Ⓐ $6 < \sqrt{39} < 7$ Ⓑ $9 < \sqrt{89} < 10$
Ⓒ $-7 > -\sqrt{56} > -8$ Ⓓ $-4 < -\sqrt{17} < -5$

60. Choose the expression that is a rational number. **A**
Ⓐ $-\sqrt{361}$ Ⓑ $\sqrt{125}$ Ⓒ $\sqrt{200}$ Ⓓ $\sqrt{325}$

Extending the Lesson

61. Sample answer: addition and subtraction

61. Squaring a number and finding the square root of a number are *inverse operations*. That is, one operation undoes the other operation. Name another pair of inverse operations.

62. Use inverse operations to evaluate each expression.
  a. $(\sqrt{64})^2$ **64**   b. $(\sqrt{100})^2$ **100**   c. $(\sqrt{169})^2$ **169**

63. Use the pattern from Exercise 62 to find $(\sqrt{a})^2$. **a**

Maintain Your Skills

Mixed Review **ALGEBRA** Graph each inequality. *(Lesson 8-10)* **64–66. See pp. 489A–489B.**

64. $y > x - 2$ **65.** $y < -4$ **66.** $y \geq 2x + 3$

ALGEBRA Solve each system of equations by substitution. *(Lesson 8-9)*

67. $y = x + 2$ **68.** $y = x + 3$ **69.** $y = 2x + 5$
$x = 5$ **(5, 7)** $y = 0$ **(-3, 0)** $y = -3$ **(-4, -3)**

70. Determine whether the relation $(4, -1)$, $(3, 5)$, $(-4, 1)$, $(4, 2)$ is a function. Explain. *(Lesson 8-1)* **No, because 4 is paired with -1 and 2.**

71. Suppose a number cube is rolled. What is the probability of rolling a 4 or a prime number? *(Lesson 6-9)* $\frac{2}{3}$

Solve each proportion. *(Lesson 6-2)*

72. $\frac{n}{9} = \frac{15}{27}$ **5**   **73.** $\frac{4}{b} = \frac{16}{36}$ **9**   **74.** $\frac{7}{8.4} = \frac{0.5}{x}$ **0.6**

Getting Ready for the Next Lesson **PREREQUISITE SKILL** Explain why each number is a rational number. *(To review **rational numbers**, see Lesson 5-2.)* **75–80. See margin.**

75. $\frac{10}{2}$ **76.** $1\frac{1}{2}$ **77.** 0.75

78. $0.\overline{8}$ **79.** 6   **80.** -7

75. It can be written as a fraction.

76. It can be written as $\frac{3}{2}$.

77. It can be written as $\frac{3}{4}$.

78. It can be written as $\frac{8}{9}$.

79. It can be written as $\frac{6}{1}$.

80. It can be written as $-\frac{7}{1}$.

The Real Number System

What You'll Learn

- Identify and compare numbers in the real number system.
- Solve equations by finding square roots.

Vocabulary

- irrational numbers
- real numbers

a. $\frac{1}{2}$ units^2

c. 2 square units

NEW YORK
Performance Indicator

Reinforcement of 7.N.1 Distinguish between the various subsets of real numbers (counting/ natural numbers, whole numbers, integers, rational numbers, and irrational numbers)

Reinforcement of 7.N.2 Recognize the difference between rational and irrational numbers (e.g., explore different approximations of π)

How can squares have lengths that are not rational numbers?

In this activity, you will find the length of a side of a square that has an area of 2 square units.

a. The small square at the right has an area of 1 square unit. Find the area of the shaded triangle.

b. Suppose eight triangles are arranged as shown. What shape is formed by the shaded triangles? **square**

c. Find the total area of the four shaded triangles.

d. What number represents the length of the side of the shaded square? $\sqrt{2}$

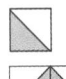

IDENTIFY AND COMPARE REAL NUMBERS

In Lesson 5-2, you learned that *rational numbers* can be written as fractions. A few examples of rational numbers are listed below.

$$-6 \qquad 8\frac{2}{5} \qquad 0.05 \qquad -2.6 \qquad 5.\overline{3} \qquad -8.12121212\ldots \qquad \sqrt{16}$$

Not all numbers are rational numbers. A few examples of numbers that are *not* rational are shown below. These numbers are not repeating or terminating decimals. They are called **irrational numbers**.

$$0.101001000100001\ldots \qquad \sqrt{2} = 1.414213562\ldots \qquad \pi = 3.14159\ldots$$

Key Concept — Irrational Number

An irrational number is a number that cannot be expressed as $\frac{a}{b}$, where a and b are integers and b does not equal 0.

✓ **Concept Check** *True* or *False*? All square roots are irrational numbers. **False**

The set of rational numbers and the set of irrational numbers together make up the set of **real numbers**. The Venn diagram at the right shows the relationship among the real numbers.

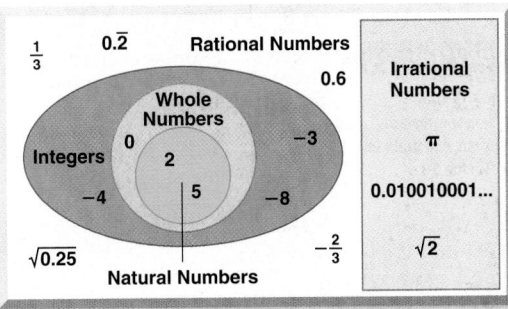

Real Numbers

$\frac{1}{3}$ $\quad 0.\overline{2}$ **Rational Numbers**

0.6

Irrational Numbers

Whole Numbers

0 $\quad -3$

Integers $\quad 2$ $\qquad \pi$

$-4 \qquad 5 \qquad -8$ $\qquad 0.010010001\ldots$

$\sqrt{0.25}$ $\qquad\qquad -\frac{2}{3} \qquad \sqrt{2}$

Natural Numbers

---

1 Focus

5-Minute Check Transparency 9-2 Use as a quiz or review of Lesson 9-1.

Mathematical Background notes are available for this lesson on page 434C.

How can squares have lengths that are not rational numbers?

The opening activity questions are repeated on page 497 of the *Chapter 9 Resource Masters*.

Reading to Learn Mathematics, p. 497 **ELL**

Pre-Activity *How can squares have lengths that are not rational numbers?*
Do the activity at the top of page 441 in your textbook. Write your answers below.

a. The small square at the right has an area of 1 square unit. Find the area of the shaded triangle. $\frac{1}{2}$ units^2

b. Suppose eight triangles are arranged as shown. What shape is formed by the shaded triangles? **square**

c. Find the total area of the four shaded triangles. **2 square units**

d. What number represents the length of the side of the shaded square? $\sqrt{2}$

Reading the Lesson 1–2. See students' work.
Write a definition and give an example of each new vocabulary word or phrase.

Vocabulary	Definition	Example
1. irrational numbers		
2. real numbers		

Choose the correct term to complete each sentence.

3. Numbers with decimals that are not repeating or terminating (are, are not) irrational numbers.

4. All square roots (are, are not) irrational numbers.

5. Irrational numbers (are, are not) real numbers.

Helping You Remember

6. Fill in the missing terms on the following diagram. Then fill in the remaining blanks with examples of each type of number. Use numbers different than those in your textbook. Sample examples are given.

Teaching Tip Review repeating decimals and terminating decimals with students.

Resource Manager

Workbooks and Reproducible Masters

Chapter 9 Resource Masters
- Study Guide and Intervention, p. 494
- Skills Practice, p. 495
- Practice, p. 496
- Reading to Learn Mathematics, p. 497
- Enrichment, p. 498
- Assessment, p. 543

Graphing Calculator and Spreadsheet Masters, p. 35
Parent and Student Study Guide Workbook, p. 73

Transparencies
5-Minute Check Transparency 9-2
Answer Key Transparencies

Technology
Interactive Chalkboard

IDENTIFY AND COMPARE REAL NUMBERS

In-Class Examples Power Point®

1 Name all of the sets of numbers to which each real number belongs.

a. 17   natural number, whole number, integer, rational number

b. $-\dfrac{72}{6}$ integer, rational number

c. $\sqrt{225}$ natural number, whole number, integer, rational number

d. $0.2\overline{46}$ rational number

e. $\sqrt{52}$ irrational number

Teaching Tip In Example 2, make sure students rewrite each number into the same format before comparing.

2 a. Replace ● with $<$, $>$, or $=$ to make $\sqrt{125}$ ● $11\dfrac{7}{8}$ a true statement. $<$

b. Order $6\dfrac{1}{4}$, $\sqrt{38}$, $6.\overline{5}$, and $\sqrt{36}$ from least to greatest.
$\sqrt{36}$, $\sqrt{38}$, $6\dfrac{1}{4}$, $6.\overline{5}$

Example 1 *Classify Real Numbers*

Name all of the sets of numbers to which each real number belongs.

a. 9   This number is a natural number, a whole number, an integer, and a rational number.

b. $0.\overline{3}$ This repeating decimal is a rational number because it is equivalent to $\dfrac{1}{3}$. $1 \div 3 = 0.33333...$

c. $\sqrt{67}$ $\sqrt{67} = 8.185352772...$ It is not the square root of a perfect square so it is irrational.

d. $-\dfrac{28}{4}$ Since $-\dfrac{28}{4} = -7$, this number is an integer and a rational number.

e. $-\sqrt{121}$ Since $-\sqrt{121} = -11$, this number is an integer and a rational number.

Concept Summary   **Classification of Numbers**

Example	Natural	Whole	Integer	Rational	Irrational	Real
0		✓	✓	✓		✓
4	✓	✓	✓	✓		✓
−7			✓	✓		✓
$\sqrt{25}$	✓	✓	✓	✓		✓
$\sqrt{41}$					✓	✓
$\dfrac{3}{4}$				✓		✓
0.121212...				✓		✓
0.010110111...					✓	✓

Example 2 *Compare Real Numbers on a Number Line*

a. **Replace ● with $<$, $>$, or $=$ to make $\sqrt{34}$ ● $5\dfrac{3}{8}$ a true statement.**

Express each number as a decimal. Then graph the numbers.

$\sqrt{34} = 5.830951895...$

$5\dfrac{3}{8} = 5.375$

Since $\sqrt{34}$ is to the right of $5\dfrac{3}{8}$, $\sqrt{34} > 5\dfrac{3}{8}$.

b. **Order $4\dfrac{1}{2}$, $\sqrt{17}$, $4.\overline{4}$, and $\sqrt{16}$ from least to greatest.**

Express each number as a decimal. Then compare the decimals.

$4\dfrac{1}{2} = 4.5$

$\sqrt{17} = 4.123105626...$

$4.\overline{4} = 4.444444444...$

$\sqrt{16} = 4$

From least to greatest, the order is $\sqrt{16}$, $\sqrt{17}$, $4.\overline{4}$, $4\dfrac{1}{2}$.

Study Tip

Look Back
To review **comparing fractions and decimals,** see Lesson 5-1.

442   Chapter 9   Real Numbers and Right Triangles

DAILY
INTERVENTION   **Differentiated Instruction**   **ELL**

- **Verbal/Linguistic** Have teams of students find real-world examples for each type of number in the real number system. Then have students present their findings to the rest of the class. Encourage students to find unique examples. For example, the bus has four tires. Four is a natural number.

ALGEBRA CONNECTION

SOLVE EQUATIONS BY FINDING SQUARE ROOTS Some equations have irrational number solutions. You can solve some of these equations by taking the square root of each side.

Example 3 *Solve Equations*

Solve each equation. Round to the nearest tenth, if necessary.

a. $x^2 = 64$

$$x^2 = 64$$ Write the equation.

$$\sqrt{x^2} = \sqrt{64}$$ Take the square root of each side.

$$x = \sqrt{64} \text{ or } x = -\sqrt{64}$$ Find the positive and negative square root.

$$x = 8 \text{ or } x = -8$$

The solutions are 8 and −8.

b. $n^2 = 85$

$$n^2 = 85$$ Write the equation.

$$\sqrt{n^2} = \sqrt{85}$$ Take the square root of each side.

$$n = \sqrt{85} \text{ or } n = -\sqrt{85}$$ Find the positive and negative square root.

$$n \approx 9.2 \text{ or } n \approx -9.2$$ Use a calculator.

The solutions are 9.2 and −9.2.

Study Tip

Check Your Work
Check the reasonableness of the results by evaluating 9^2 and $(-9)^2$.
$9^2 = 81$
$(-9)^2 = 81$
Since 81 is close to 85, the solutions are reasonable.

Check for Understanding

Concept Check
1. **Explain** the difference between a rational and irrational number. **See margin.**
2. **OPEN ENDED** Give an example of a number that is an integer and a rational number. **Sample answer:** $-\sqrt{25}$

Guided Practice
Name all of the sets of numbers to which each real number belongs. Let N = natural numbers, W = whole numbers, Z = integers, Q = rational numbers, and I = irrational numbers.

3. 7 **N, W, Z, Q**
4. 0.5555… **Q**
5. $-\frac{3}{4}$ **Q**
6. $\sqrt{12}$ **I**

GUIDED PRACTICE KEY	
Exercises	Examples
3–6	1
7–9	2
10–12	3

Replace each ● with <, >, or = to make a true statement.

7. $6\frac{4}{5}$ ● $\sqrt{48}$ **<**
8. $-\sqrt{74}$ ● $-8.\overline{4}$ **<**

9. Order $3.\overline{7}, 3\frac{3}{5}, \sqrt{13}, \frac{10}{3}$ from least to greatest. $\frac{10}{3}, 3\frac{3}{5}, \sqrt{13}, 3.\overline{7}$

ALGEBRA Solve each equation. Round to the nearest tenth, if necessary.

10. $y^2 = 25$ **5, −5**
11. $m^2 = 74$ **8.6, −8.6**

Application
12. **GEOMETRY** To find the radius r of a circle, you can use the formula $r = \sqrt{\frac{A}{\pi}}$ where A is the area of the circle. To the nearest tenth, find the radius of a circle that has an area of 40 square feet. **3.6 ft**

 www.pre-alg.com/extra_examples/ny   **Lesson 9-2** The Real Number System **443**

Answer

1. Whereas rational numbers can be expressed in the form $\frac{a}{b}$, where a and b are integers and b does not equal 0, irrational numbers cannot.

SOLVE EQUATIONS BY FINDING SQUARE ROOTS

In-Class Example Power Point®

3 Solve each equation. Round to the nearest tenth, if necessary.

a. $w^2 = 169$ **w = 13 or w = −13**

b. $r^2 = 50$ **r ≈ 7.1 or r ≈ −7.1**

3 Practice/Apply

Study Notebook

Have students—
• add the definitions/examples of the vocabulary terms to their Vocabulary Builder worksheets for Chapter 9.
• include any other item(s) that they find helpful in mastering the skills in this lesson.

About the Exercises . . .

Organization by Objective
• **Identify and Compare Real Numbers :** 13–44
• **Solve Equations by Finding Square Roots:** 45–61

Odd/Even Assignments
Exercises 13–58 and 60–61 are structured so that students practice the same concepts whether they are assigned odd or even problems.

Assignment Guide

Basic: 13–55 odd, 61, 62–65, 69–84

Average: 13–61 odd, 62–65, 69–84 (Optional: 66–68)

Advanced: 14–60 even, 62–78 (Optional: 79–84)

★ indicates increased difficulty

Practice and Apply

Name all of the sets of numbers to which each real number belongs. Let N = natural numbers, W = whole numbers, Z = integers, Q = rational numbers, and I = irrational numbers.

13. 8 N, W, Z, Q
14. 4 N, W, Z, Q
15. $\frac{2}{5}$ Q
16. $\frac{1}{2}$ Q
17. $0.\overline{2}$ Q
18. 0.131313… Q
19. $\sqrt{10}$ I
20. $\sqrt{32}$ I
21. 1.247896… I
22. 6.182576… I
23. $-\frac{24}{8}$ Z, Q
24. $-\frac{56}{8}$ Z, Q
25. 2.8 Q
26. 7.6 Q
27. $-\sqrt{64}$ Z, Q
28. $-\sqrt{100}$ Z, Q

Determine whether each statement is *sometimes, always,* or *never* true.

29. A whole number is an integer. **always**
30. An irrational number is a negative integer. **never**
31. A repeating decimal is a real number. **always**
32. An integer is a whole number. **sometimes**

Replace each ● with <, >, or = to make a true statement.

33. $5\frac{1}{4}$ ● $\sqrt{26}$ >
34. $\sqrt{80}$ ● 9.2 <
35. -3.3 ● $-\sqrt{10}$ <
36. $-\sqrt{18}$ ● $-4\frac{3}{8}$ >
37. $1\frac{1}{2}$ ● $\sqrt{2.25}$ =
38. $-\sqrt{6.25}$ ● $-\frac{5}{2}$ =

Order each set of numbers from least to greatest. 39–42. See margin.

39. $5\frac{1}{4}$, $2.\overline{1}$, $\sqrt{4}$, $\frac{6}{5}$
40. $4.\overline{23}$, $4\frac{2}{3}$, $\sqrt{18}$, $\sqrt{16}$
41. -10, -1.05, $-\sqrt{105}$, $-10\frac{1}{2}$
42. $-\sqrt{14}$, $-4\frac{1}{10}$, -3.8, $-\frac{17}{4}$

Give a counterexample for each statement.

43. All square roots are irrational numbers. **Sample answer:** $\sqrt{4}$ and $\sqrt{49}$
44. All rational numbers are integers. **Sample answer:** $\frac{1}{2}$ and -4.5

45–56. See margin.
ALGEBRA Solve each equation. Round to the nearest tenth, if necessary.

45. $a^2 = 49$
46. $d^2 = 81$
47. $y^2 = 22$
48. $p^2 = 63$
49. $144 = w^2$
50. $289 = m^2$
51. $127 = b^2$
52. $300 = h^2$
53. $x^2 = 1.69$
54. $0.0016 = q^2$
55. $n^2 = 3.56$
56. $0.0058 = k^2$

★ 57. If $(-a)^2 = 144$, what is the value of a? **12 or –12**

★ 58. What is the value of x to the nearest tenth if $x^2 - 4^2 = \sqrt{15^2}$? **5.6 or –5.6**

★ 59. Find the value of m if $\sqrt{256} = m^2$. **4 or –4**

•••• 60. WEATHER Use the information at the left. Suppose a thunderstorm is 7 miles wide. How long will the storm last? **about 1.3 h**

61. FLOORING A square room has an area of 324 square feet. The homeowners plan to cover the floor with 6-inch square tiles. How many tiles will be in each row on the floor? **36**

More About…

Weather •·············
To find the time t in hours that a thunderstorm will last, meteorologists can use the formula $t^2 = \frac{d^3}{216}$ where d is the distance across the storm in miles.

Answers

39. $\frac{6}{5}$, $\sqrt{4}$, $2.\overline{1}$, $5\frac{1}{4}$
40. $\sqrt{16}$, $4.\overline{23}$, $\sqrt{18}$, $4\frac{2}{3}$
41. $-10\frac{1}{2}$, $-\sqrt{105}$, -10, -1.05
42. $-\frac{17}{4}$, $-4\frac{1}{10}$, -3.8, $-\sqrt{14}$
45. 7, –7
46. 9, –9
47. 4.7, –4.7
48. 7.9, –7.9
49. 12, –12
50. 17, –17
51. 11.3, –11.3
52. 17.3, –17.3
53. 1.3, –1.3
54. 0.04, –0.04
55. 1.9, –1.9
56. 0.1, –0.1

62. CRITICAL THINKING Tell whether the product of a rational number like 8 and an irrational number like 0.101001000… is rational or irrational. Explain your reasoning. **Irrational; see students' explanations.**

63. WRITING IN MATH   Answer the question that was posed at the beginning of the lesson. **See margin.**

How can squares have lengths that are not rational numbers?

Include the following in your answer:
- an example of a square whose side length is irrational, and
- an example of a square that has a rational side length.

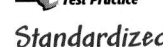
Standardized Test Practice
A B C D

64. Which number can *only* be classified as a rational number? **A**

Ⓐ $\frac{1}{2}$ Ⓑ $\sqrt{2}$ Ⓒ -2 Ⓓ 2

65. Which statement is *not* true? **B**

Ⓐ All integers are rational numbers.

Ⓑ Every whole number is a natural number.

Ⓒ All natural numbers are integers.

Ⓓ Every real number is either a rational or irrational number.

Extending the Lesson

66. Heron's formula states that if the measures of the sides of a triangle are a, b, and c, the area $A = \sqrt{s(s-a)(s-b)(s-c)}$, where s is one-half the perimeter. Find the area of the triangle at the right. Round to the nearest tenth, if necessary. **14.5 m²**

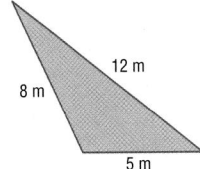

12 m
8 m
5 m

67. Find the area of a triangle whose sides measure 65 feet, 82 feet, and 95 feet. **2621.2 ft²**

68. Make a Conjecture Is the area of any triangle always a rational number? Support your answer with an example. **See margin.**

Maintain Your Skills

Mixed Review   **Estimate each square root to the nearest whole number.** *(Lesson 9-1)*

69. $\sqrt{54}$ **7**   **70.** $-\sqrt{126}$ **−11**   **71.** $\sqrt{8.67}$ **3**

ALGEBRA   List three solutions of each inequality. *(Lesson 8-10)*

72. $y < -x$ **73.** $y \geq x + 5$ **74.** $y \leq x - 3$

ALGEBRA   Solve each inequality. *(Lesson 7-6)*

75. $3x + 2 > 17$ **x > 5**   **76.** $-2y + 9 \leq 3$ **y ≥ 3**

Express each ratio as a unit rate. Round to the nearest tenth, if necessary. *(Lesson 6-1)*

77. $8 for 15 cupcakes **$0.53/cupcake**   **78.** 120 miles on 4.3 gallons **27.9 mi/gal**

72. Sample answer: (0, −2), (1, −3), (2, −4)
73. Sample answer: (0, 5), (1, 6), (−6, 2)
74. Sample answer: (0, −3), (1, −2), (2, −3)

Getting Ready for the Next Lesson

BASIC SKILL   Use a ruler or straightedge to draw a diagram that shows how the hands on a clock appear at each time. 79–84. See margin.

79. 3:00   **80.** 9:15   **81.** 10:00

82. 2:30   **83.** 7:45   **84.** 8:05

---

63. If a square has an area that is not a perfect square, the lengths of the sides will be irrational. Answers should include the following.

Area = 56 in²

Area = 64 in²

68. No, because triangles can have dimensions that are irrational numbers. Thus, the area will be irrational. For example, a triangle with a base of 2 inches and a height of $\sqrt{3}$ inches has an area of $\frac{1}{2} \cdot 2 \cdot \sqrt{3}$ or $\sqrt{3}$ square inches.

---

4 Assess

Open-Ended Assessment

Writing Have students write a paragraph explaining how to compare and order a group of numbers that are in different formats.

Getting Ready for Lesson 9-3

BASIC SKILL Lesson 9-3 presents angles. Students will need to be able to draw angles of various degrees. Exercises 79–84 should be used to determine your students' familiarity with drawing angles.

Quiz (Lessons 9-1 and 9-2) is available on p. 543 of the *Chapter 9 Resource Masters.*

Answers

79. 3:00   **80.** 9:15

81. 10:00   **82.** 2:30

83. 7:45   **84.** 8:05

Lesson 9-2 Squares and Square Roots   **445**

Getting Started

Ask students what the word *line* can mean. Besides its geometrical definition, they may mention "policy," "business," or "a series of objects." Then have students read the meanings of *ray*. Discuss how a ray and a line are related.

Teach

Discuss how a point, rays, and degrees are combined to make angles. Make sure students understand that the arrowhead on a ray represents that the ray continues on into infinity.

Alert! Exercises 2 and 3 involve research on the Internet or other reference materials.

Assess

Study Notebook

Ask students to describe how the everyday meaning of one of the terms relates to its mathematical meaning.

ELL English Language Learners may benefit from writing key concepts from this activity in their Study Notebooks in their native language and then in English.

Learning Geometry Vocabulary

Many of the words used in geometry are commonly used in everyday language. The everyday meanings of these words can be used to understand their mathematical meaning better.

The table below shows the meanings of some geometry terms you will use throughout this chapter.

Term	Everyday Meaning	Mathematical Meaning
ray	any of the thin lines, or beams, of light that appear to come from a bright source • a *ray* of light	a part of a line that extends from a point indefinitely in one direction
degree	extent, amount, or relative intensity • third *degree* burns	a common unit of measure for angles
acute	characterized by sharpness or severity • an *acute* pain	an angle with a measure that is greater than 0° and less than 90°
obtuse	not producing a sharp impression • an *obtuse* statement	an angle with a measure that is greater than 90° but less than 180°

Source: Merriam Webster's Collegiate Dictionary

Reading to Learn

1. Write a sentence using each term listed above. Be sure to use the everyday meaning of the term. **See margin.**

2. **RESEARCH** Use the Internet or a dictionary to find the everyday meaning of each term listed below. Compare them to their mathematical meaning. Note any similarities and/or differences. **See students' work.**

   a. midpoint **b.** converse **c.** indirect

3. **RESEARCH** Use the Internet or dictionary to determine which of the following words are used only in mathematics. **equilateral, scalene, isosceles**

   vertex   equilateral   similar   scalene   side   isosceles

446 Chapter 9 Real Numbers and Right Triangles

Answer

1. Sample answer: *ray*: A ray of sunshine appeared through a cloud. *degree*: Today's temperature is 10 degrees colder than yesterday's temperature. *acute*: Neena is experiencing acute stomach pains. *obtuse*: His answer to the question was vague and obtuse.

9-3 Angles

NEW YORK *Performance Indicator* Reinforcement of 5.M.8 Measure and draw angles using a protractor

What You'll Learn

- Measure and draw angles.
- Classify angles as acute, right, obtuse, or straight.

Vocabulary

- point
- ray
- line
- angle
- vertex
- side
- degree
- protractor
- acute angle
- right angle
- obtuse angle
- straight angle

How are angles used in circle graphs?

The graph shows how voters prefer to vote.

a. Which method did half of the voters prefer? **in booths**

b. Suppose 100 voters were surveyed. How many more voters preferred to vote in booths than on the Internet? **26**

c. Each section of the graph shows an *angle*. A *straight angle* resembles a line. Which section shows a straight angle? **in booths**

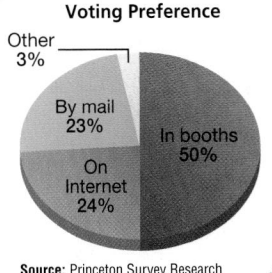

Voting Preference

Other 3%
By mail 23%
On Internet 24%
In booths 50%

Source: Princeton Survey Research

MEASURE AND DRAW ANGLES

The center of a circle represents a **point**. A point is a specific location in space with no size or shape.

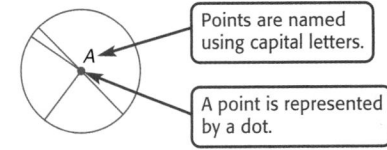

Points are named using capital letters.

A point is represented by a dot.

In the circle below, notice how the sides of each section begin at the center and extend in one direction. These are examples of **rays**. A **line** is a never-ending straight path extending in two directions.

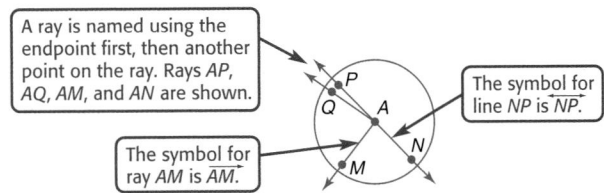

A ray is named using the endpoint first, then another point on the ray. Rays *AP*, *AQ*, *AM*, and *AN* are shown.

The symbol for line *NP* is $\overleftrightarrow{NP}$.

The symbol for ray *AM* is $\overrightarrow{AM}$.

Two rays that have the same endpoint form an **angle**. The common endpoint is called the **vertex**, and the two rays that make up the angle are called the **sides** of the angle.

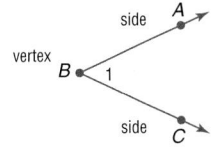

side A
vertex B 1
side C

The symbol ∠ represents angle. There are several ways to name the angle shown above.

- Use the vertex and a point from each side.   ∠*ABC* or ∠*CBA*
  The vertex is always the middle letter.

- Use the vertex only.   ∠*B*

- Use a number.   ∠1

9-3 Lesson Notes

1 Focus

5-Minute Check

Transparency 9-3 Use as a quiz or review of Lesson 9-2.

Mathematical Background notes are available for this lesson on page 434C.

How are angles used in circle graphs?

The opening activity questions are repeated on page 502 of the *Chapter 9 Resource Masters*.

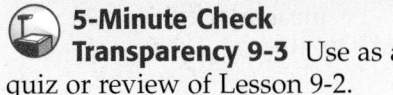

Reading to Learn Mathematics, p. 502   ELL

Pre-Activity   *How are angles used in circle graphs?*

Do the activity at the top of page 447 in your textbook. Write your answers below.

a. Which method did half of the voters prefer?   **in booths**

b. Suppose 100 voters were surveyed. How many more voters preferred to vote in booths than on the Internet?   **26**

c. Each section of the graph shows an angle. A straight angle resembles a line. Which section shows a straight angle?   **in booths**

Reading the Lesson   1–12. See students' work.

Write a definition and give an example of each new vocabulary word or phrase.

Vocabulary	Definition	Example
1. point		
2. ray		
3. line		
4. angle		
5. vertex		
6. side		
7. degree		
8. protractor		
9. acute angle		
10. right angle		
11. obtuse angle		
12. straight angle		

Helping You Remember

13. Label the parts of the angles below and classify each as *acute, right, obtuse,* or *straight*.

side, obtuse angle, vertex, side, 100°

ray AB, acute angle, point C

Teaching Tip You may want students to copy ∠*QAP*, ∠*QAM*, ∠*MAP*, ∠*PAN*, ∠*QAN*, and ∠*MAN* separately so they can visualize each angle without distractions.

Resource Manager

Transparencies

5-Minute Check Transparency 9-3
Answer Key Transparencies

Technology

Interactive Chalkboard

2 Teach

MEASURE AND DRAW ANGLES

In-Class Examples 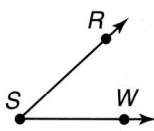 Power Point®

1 **a.** Use a protractor to measure ∠*RSW*. **42°**

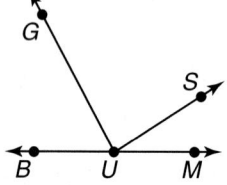

b. Find the measures of ∠*GUM*, ∠*SUM*, and ∠*BUG*.

m∠*GUM* = 120° *m*∠*SUM* = 32°
m∠*BUG* = 60°

2 Draw ∠*R* having a measure of 145°.

Teaching Tip Make sure students understand why the numbers on a protractor go in two directions.

CLASSIFY ANGLES

In-Class Example Power Point®

3 Classify each angle as *acute*, *obtuse*, *right*, or *straight*.

a.

acute

b.

straight

c.

obtuse

The most common unit of measure for angles is the **degree**. A circle can be separated into 360 arcs of the same length. An angle has a measurement of one degree if its vertex is at the center of the circle and the sides contain the endpoints of one of the 360 equal arcs.

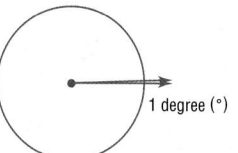

1 degree (°)

You can use a **protractor** to measure angles.

Example 1 **Measure Angles**

a. Use a protractor to measure ∠*CDE*.

Step 1 Place the center point of the protractor's base on vertex *D*. Align the straight side with side $\overrightarrow{DE}$ so that the marker for 0° is on the ray.

Step 2 Use the scale that begins with 0° at $\overrightarrow{DE}$. Read where the other side of the angle, $\overrightarrow{DC}$, crosses this scale.

The measure of angle *CDE* is 120°. Using symbols, *m*∠*CDE* = 120°.

b. Find the measures of ∠*KXN*, ∠*MXN*, and ∠*JXK*.

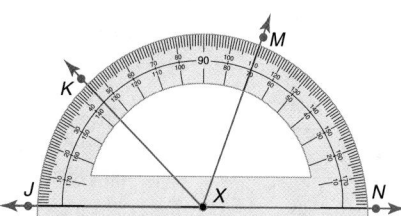

m∠*KXN* = 135°
$\overrightarrow{XN}$ is at 0° on the right.

m∠*MXN* = 70°
$\overrightarrow{XN}$ is at 0° on the right.

m∠*JXK* = 45°
$\overrightarrow{XJ}$ is at 0° on the left.

> **Reading Math**
>
> **Angle Measure**
> Read *m*∠*CDE* = 120° as *the measure of angle CDE is 120 degrees.*

Protractors can also be used to draw an angle of a given measure.

Example 2 **Draw Angles**

Draw ∠*X* having a measure of 85°.

Step 1 Draw a ray with endpoint *X*.

Step 2 Place the center point of the protractor on *X*. Align the mark labeled 0 with the ray.

Step 3 Use the scale that begins with 0. Locate the mark labeled 85. Then draw the other side of the angle.

448 Chapter 9 Real Numbers and Right Triangles

DAILY

INTERVENTION **Unlocking Misconceptions**

• **Measure and Draw Angles** Students may see angles in which neither of the rays is set at 0° and misjudge the measure of the angle, not recognizing a right angle or believing the measure to be greater than it is. If students are having trouble measuring an angle, encourage them to rotate the illustration clockwise until a ray lines up at 0°.

CLASSIFY ANGLES Angles can be classified by their degree measure.

Key Concept   *Types of Angles*

Acute Angle	Right Angle	Obtuse Angle	Straight Angle

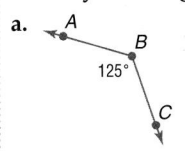

This symbol is used to indicate a right angle.

$0° < m\angle A < 90°$ $m\angle A = 90°$ $90° < m\angle A < 180°$ $m\angle A = 180°$

Example 3 *Classify Angles*

Classify each angle as *acute, obtuse, right,* or *straight.*

a.

$m\angle ABC > 90°$.
So, $\angle ABC$ is obtuse.

b.

$m\angle DEF = 90°$.
So, $\angle DEF$ is right.

c.

$m\angle GHJ < 90°$.
So, $\angle GHJ$ is acute.

Example 4 *Use Angles to Solve a Problem*

RACING The diagram shows the angle of the track at a corner of the Texas Motor Speedway in Fort Worth, Texas. Classify this angle.

Since 24° is greater than 0° and less than 90°, the angle is acute.

Check for Understanding

Concept Check

1. **Name** the vertex and sides of the angle shown. Then name the angle in four ways. **1–2. See pp. 489A–489B.**

2. **OPEN ENDED** Draw an obtuse angle.

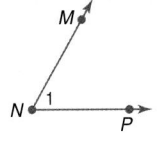

Guided Practice

Use a protractor to find the measure of each angle. Then classify each angle as *acute, obtuse, right,* or *straight.*

GUIDED PRACTICE KEY	
Exercises	Examples
3–6	1, 3
7, 8	2, 3
9	4

3. $\angle CED$ **20°; acute** 4. $\angle BED$ **90°; right**

5. $\angle CEB$ **70°; acute** 6. $\angle AED$ **125°; obtuse**

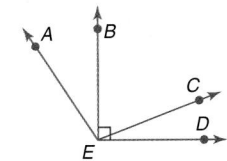

Use a protractor to draw an angle having each measurement. Then classify each angle as *acute, obtuse, right,* or *straight.* **7–8. See pp. 489A–489B for graphs.**

7. 55° **acute**   8. 140° **obtuse**

Application

9. **TIME** What type of angle is formed by the hands on a clock at 6:00?
straight angle

www.pre-alg.com/extra_examples/ny   *Lesson 9-3 Angles* 449

---

3 **Practice/Apply**

Study Notebook

Have students—
• add the definitions/examples of the vocabulary terms to their Vocabulary Builder worksheets for Chapter 9.
• draw and label examples of each type of angle.
• include any other item(s) that they find helpful in mastering the skills in this lesson.

★ indicates increased difficulty

Practice and Apply

Homework Help

For Exercises	See Examples
10–20	1, 3
21–30	2, 3
31, 32	4

Extra Practice
See page 745.

Use a protractor to find the measure of each angle. Then classify each angle as *acute, obtuse, right,* or *straight.*

10. ∠XZY
11. ∠SZT
12. ∠SZY
13. ∠UZX
14. ∠TZW
15. ∠XZT
16. ∠UZV
17. ∠WZU

10. 30°; acute
11. 15°; acute
12. 180°; straight
13. 85°; acute
14. 105°; obtuse
15. 135°; obtuse
16. 25°; acute
17. 60°; acute

Use a protractor to find the measure of each angle.

18.   45°
19.   90°
20.   60°

Use a protractor to draw an angle having each measurement. Then classify each angle as *acute, obtuse, right,* or *straight.* 21–23. See margin.

21. 40°
22. 70°
23. 65°
24. 85°
25. 95°
26. 110°
27. 155°
28. 140°
★ 29. 38°
★ 30. 127°

24–30. See pp. 489A–489B.

31. **BASEBALL** If you swing the bat too early or too late, the ball will probably go foul. The best way to hit the ball is at a right angle. Classify each angle shown.

a.
Incoming Path
Angle > 90°
obtuse

b.
Angle = 90°
right

c.
Angle < 90°
acute

FITNESS For Exercises 32–34, use the graphic.

32. Classify each angle in the circle graph as *acute, obtuse, right,* or *straight.*

33. Find the measure of each angle of the circle graph.

34. Suppose 500 adults were surveyed. How many would you expect to exercise moderately? **145**

32–33. See pp. 489A–489B.

35. **CRITICAL THINKING** In twelve hours, how many times do the hands of a clock form a right angle? **24**

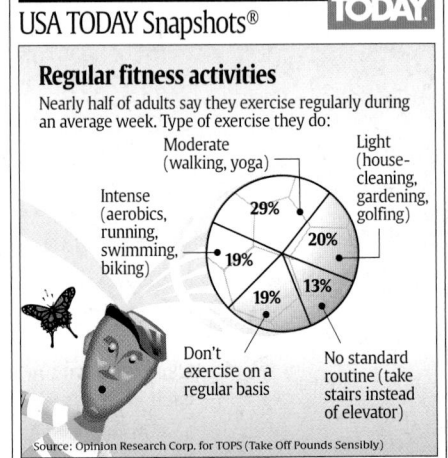

Regular fitness activities

Nearly half of adults say they exercise regularly during an average week. Type of exercise they do:

Moderate (walking, yoga) 29%
Light (house-cleaning, gardening, golfing) 20%
Intense (aerobics, running, swimming, biking) 19%
No standard routine (take stairs instead of elevator) 13%
Don't exercise on a regular basis 19%

Source: Opinion Research Corp. for TOPS (Take Off Pounds Sensibly)

By Cindy Hall and Dave Merrill, USA TODAY

Online Lesson Plans

USA TODAY Education's Online site offers resources and interactive features connected to each day's newspaper. *Experience TODAY,* USA TODAY's daily lesson plan, is available on the site and delivered daily to subscribers. This plan provides instruction for integrating USA TODAY graphics and key editorial features into your mathematics classroom. Log on to www.education.usatoday.com

36. WRITING IN MATH   Answer the question that was posed at the beginning of the lesson. **See margin.**

How are angles used in circle graphs?

Include the following in your answer:
- a classification of the angles in each section of the circle graph shown at the beginning of the lesson, and
- a range of percents that can be represented by an acute angle and an obtuse angle.

NEW YORK Test Practice

Standardized Test Practice
Ⓐ Ⓑ Ⓒ Ⓓ

37. Which angle is an obtuse angle? **C**

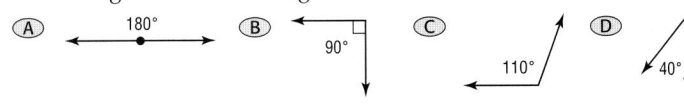

38. Which of the following is closest to the measure of ∠XYZ? **A**

Ⓐ 45°
Ⓑ 55°
Ⓒ 135°
Ⓓ 145°

Maintain Your Skills

Mixed Review   Name all of the sets of numbers to which each real number belongs. Let N = natural numbers, W = whole numbers, Z = integers, Q = rational numbers, and I = irrational numbers.   *(Lesson 9-2)*

39. −5 **Z, Q**   **40.** $0.\overline{4}$ **Q**   **41.** $\sqrt{63}$ **I**   **42.** 7.4 **Q**

Estimate each square root to the nearest whole number.   *(Lesson 9-1)*

43. $\sqrt{18}$ **4**   **44.** $\sqrt{79}$ **9**

45. Translate the sentence *A number decreased by seven is at least twenty-two.*   *(Lesson 7-3)* $x - 7 \geq 22$

Getting Ready for the Next Lesson   **PREREQUISITE SKILL**   Solve each equation.
(To review solving two-step equations, see Lesson 3-5.)

46. $18 + 57 + x = 180$ **105**   **47.** $x + 27 + 54 = 180$ **99**   **48.** $85 + x + 24 = 180$ **71**

49. $x + x + x = 180$ **60**   **50.** $2x + 3x + 4x = 180$ **20**   **51.** $2x + 3x + 5x = 180$ **18**

Practice Quiz 1   Lessons 9-1 through 9-3

Find each square root, if possible.   *(Lesson 9-1)*
1. $\sqrt{36}$ **6**   **2.** $-\sqrt{169}$ **−13**

3. ALGEBRA   Solve $m^2 = 68$ to the nearest tenth.   *(Lesson 9-2)*   **8.2, −8.2**

Classify each angle measure as *acute, obtuse, right,* or *straight*.   *(Lesson 9-3)*
4. 83° **acute**   **5.** 115° **obtuse**

Answers (p. 450)

21.

40°
acute

22.

70°
acute

23.

65°
acute

Spreadsheet Investigation

A Follow-Up of Lesson 9-3

A Follow-Up of Lesson 9-3

Getting Started

Objective Graph the results of a probability experiment in a circle graph.

Materials
spreadsheet software

Teaching Tip After reading the example, ask students what different methods are used for keeping track of frequency data. Discuss why a spreadsheet would be an easy way to organize frequency data.

Teach

- Remind students that the sum of their totals for each color should equal the number of spins performed.
- Be careful that only the totals are used when selecting the data to be included in the graph. The totals are at the top of the spreadsheet so that trials can be added without inserting rows.

Assess

For Exercise 4, discuss with students why the experimental number must be high to match the theoretical number. Make sure they understand that using a spreadsheet simplifies the work because it makes it easier to add more data and create a new circle graph.

Study Notebook

Have students print their graph to keep in their journal. Have them include a paragraph describing the experiment as they carried it out.

NEW YORK *Performance Indicator* **8.R.1 Use** physical objects, drawings, **charts**, tables, **graphs**, symbols, equations, **and objects created using technology as representation**

Circle Graphs and Spreadsheets

In the following example, you will learn how to use a computer spreadsheet program to graph the results of a probability experiment in a circle graph.

Example

The spinner like the one shown at the right was spun 20 times each for two trials. The data are shown below. Use a spreadsheet to make a circle graph of the results.

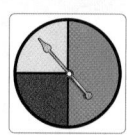

Step 1   Enter the data in a spreadsheet as shown.

The spreadsheet evaluates the formula =SUM(D3:D14) to find the total.

Step 2   Select the data to be included in your graph. Then use the graph tool to create the graph. The spreadsheet will allow you to add titles, change colors, and so on.

Exercises

1. Describe the results you would theoretically expect for one trial of 20 spins. Explain your reasoning. **See margin.**

2. Make a spinner like the one shown above. Collect data for five trials of 20 spins each. Use a spreadsheet program to create a circle graph of the data. **See students' work.**

3. A **central angle** is an angle whose vertex is the center of a circle and whose sides intersect the circle. After 100 spins, what kind of central angle would you theoretically expect for each section of the circle graph? Explain. **See margin.**

4. Predict how many trials of the experiment are required to match the theoretical results. Test your prediction. **See students' work.**

5. When the theoretical results match the experimental results, what is true about the circle graph and the spinner? **They look the same.**

452 Chapter 9 Real Numbers and Right Triangles

Answers

1. $P(\text{Blue}) = \frac{1}{2}$, so you would expect $\frac{1}{2}$ of 20 or 10 Blue. $P(\text{Yellow}) = \frac{1}{4}$, so you would expect $\frac{1}{4}$ of 20 or 5 Yellow. Similarly, you would expect 5 Red.

3. The central angle for the Blue section should be a straight angle because $\frac{1}{2}$ of 360° is 180°. The central angle for the Red or Yellow section should be a right angle because $\frac{1}{4}$ of 360° is 90°.

9-4 Triangles

NEW YORK *Performance Indicator* Reinforcement of 5.G.6 Classify triangles by properties of their angles and sides, Reinforcement of 5.G.7 Know that the sum of the interior angles of a triangle is 180 degrees, Reinforcement of 5.G.8 Find a missing angle when given two angles of a triangle

What You'll Learn

- Find the missing angle measure of a triangle.
- Classify triangles by angles and by sides.

Vocabulary

- line segment
- triangle
- vertex
- acute triangle
- obtuse triangle
- right triangle
- congruent
- scalene triangle
- isosceles triangle
- equilateral triangle

How do the angles of a triangle relate to each other?

There is a relationship among the measures of the angles of a triangle.

a. Use a straightedge to draw a triangle on a piece of paper. Then cut out the triangle and label the vertices X, Y, and Z. **a–d. See students' work.**

b. Fold the triangle as shown so that point Z lies on side XY as shown. Label ∠Z as ∠2.

c. Fold again so point X meets the vertex of ∠2. Label ∠X as ∠1.

d. Fold so point Y meets the vertex of ∠2. Label ∠Y as ∠3.

Step 1

Step 2

Step 3
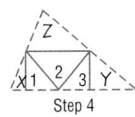
Step 4

e. **Make a Conjecture** about the sum of the measures of ∠1, ∠2, and ∠3. Explain your reasoning. **The sum of the measures is 180°.**

ANGLE MEASURES OF A TRIANGLE

A **line segment** is part of a line containing two endpoints and all of the points between them. A **triangle** is a figure formed by three line segments that intersect only at their endpoints.

Each pair of segments forms an angle of the triangle.

The **vertex** of each angle is a vertex of the triangle. Vertices is the plural of vertex.

Reading Math

Line Segment
The symbol for line segment XY is $\overline{XY}$.

Triangles are named by the letters at their vertices. Triangle XYZ, written △XYZ, is shown.

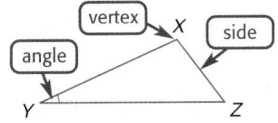

The sides are $\overline{XY}$, $\overline{YZ}$, and $\overline{XZ}$.
The vertices are X, Y, and Z.
The angles are ∠X, ∠Y, and ∠Z.

The activity above suggests the following relationship about the angles of any triangle.

Key Concept — Angles of a Triangle

- **Words** The sum of the measures of the angles of a triangle is 180°.

- **Model**

- **Symbols** $x + y + z = 180$

Lesson 9-4 Triangles **453**

Workbooks and Reproducible Masters

Chapter 9 Resource Masters
- Study Guide and Intervention, p. 504
- Skills Practice, p. 505
- Practice, p. 506
- Reading to Learn Mathematics, p. 507
- Enrichment, p. 508
- Assessment, pp. 543, 545

Parent and Student Study Guide Workbook, p. 75

9-4 Lesson Notes

1 Focus

5-Minute Check Transparency 9-4 Use as a quiz or review of Lesson 9-3.

Mathematical Background notes are available for this lesson on page 434C.

How do the angles of a triangle relate to each other?

The opening activity questions are repeated on page 507 of the *Chapter 9 Resource Masters.*

Reading to Learn Mathematics, p. 507 **ELL**

Pre-Activity How do the angles of a triangle relate to each other?

Do the activity at the top of page 453 in your textbook. Write your answers below. a–d. See students' work.

a. Use a straightedge to draw a triangle on a piece of paper. Then cut out the triangle and label the vertices X, Y, and Z.

b. Fold the triangle as shown so that point Z lies on side XY as shown. Label ∠Z as ∠2.

c. Fold again so point X meets the vertex of ∠2. Label ∠X as ∠1.

d. Fold so point Y meets the vertex of ∠2. Label ∠Y as ∠3.

e. Make a conjecture about the sum of the measures of ∠1, ∠2, and ∠3. Explain your reasoning. The sum of the measures is 180°.

Reading the Lesson 1–10. See students' work.

Write a definition and give an example of each new vocabulary word or phrase.

Vocabulary	Definition	Example
1. line segment		
2. vertex		
3. acute triangle		
4. obtuse triangle		
5. right triangle		
6. congruent		
7. scalene triangle		
8. isosceles triangle		
9. equilateral triangle		

Helping You Remember

10. Describe an obtuse, scalene triangle. a triangle with one obtuse angle and no congruent sides

11. Describe an equilateral triangle. all angles and sides are congruent

Teaching Tip Remind students that in step **b** of the opening activity, the fold should be parallel to the bottom of the figure.

Resource Manager

 Transparencies
5-Minute Check Transparency 9-4
Answer Key Transparencies

 Technology
Interactive Chalkboard

Building on Prior Knowledge

In Lesson 3-4, students solved equations by dividing. In this lesson, they will need to divide when using ratios to solve for angle measures.

ANGLE MEASURES OF A TRIANGLE

 In-Class Examples — Power Point®

1 Find the value of x in $\triangle DEF$.

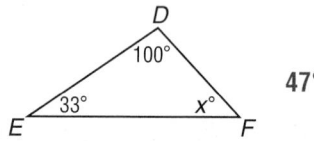
47°

2 ALGEBRA The measures of the angles of a certain triangle are in the ratio 2:3:5. What are the measures of the angles?
36°, 54°, 90°

Teaching Tip Tell students it is important that the sum of their three answers is 180. For example, 10, 40, and 70 are three numbers in the ratio 1:4:7. However, they don't add to 180, so they can't represent the measures of the angles of one triangle.

CLASSIFY TRIANGLES

 In-Class Example — Power Point®

3 Classify each triangle by its angles and by its sides.

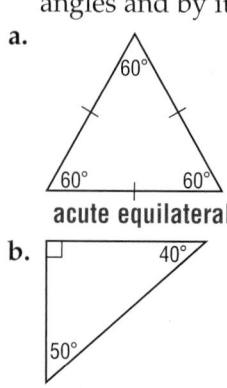
a. 60° 60° 60°
acute equilateral
b. 40° 50°
right scalene

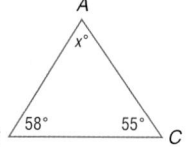 **Example 1** *Find Angle Measures*

Find the value of x in $\triangle ABC$.

A
$x°$
B 58°   55° C

$m\angle A + m\angle B + m\angle C = 180$	The sum of the measures is 180.
$x + 58 + 55 = 180$	Replace $m\angle B$ with 58 and $m\angle C$ with 55.
$x + 113 = 180$	Simplify.
$x + 113 - 113 = 180 - 113$	Subtract 113 from each side.
$x = 67$	

The measure of $\angle A$ is 67°.

The relationships of the angles in a triangle can be represented using algebra.

Example 2 *Use Ratios to Find Angle Measures*

ALGEBRA The measures of the angles of a certain triangle are in the ratio 1:4:7. What are the measures of the angles?

Words The measures of the angles are in the ratio 1:4:7.

Variables Let x represent the measure of one angle, $4x$ the measure of a second angle, and $7x$ the measure of the third angle.

Equation

$x + 4x + 7x = 180$	The sum of the measures is 180.
$12x = 180$	Combine like terms.
$\dfrac{12x}{12} = \dfrac{180}{12}$	Divide each side by 12.
$x = 15$	Simplify.

Since $x = 15$, $4x = 4(15)$ or 60, and $7x = 7(15)$ or 105. The measures of the angles are 15°, 60°, and 105°.
CHECK $15 + 60 + 105 = 180$. So, the answer is correct. ✓

CLASSIFY TRIANGLES Triangles can be classified by their angles. All triangles have at least two acute angles. The third angle is either acute, obtuse, or right.

Study Tip

Equiangular
In an *equiangular* triangle, all angles have the same measure, 60°.

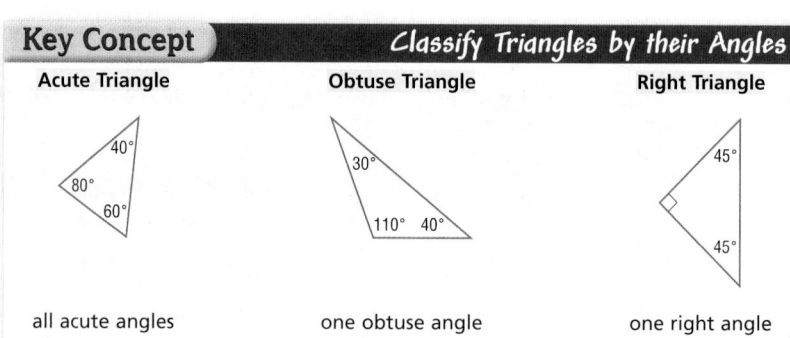

Key Concept	Classify Triangles by their Angles

Acute Triangle — 40° 80° 60° — all acute angles

Obtuse Triangle — 30° 110° 40° — one obtuse angle

Right Triangle — 45° 45° — one right angle

DAILY INTERVENTION   **Differentiated Instruction**

• **Visual/Spatial** Have students cut out a triangle and color each of its three corners, putting a heavy dot near each vertex. Then have students cut or tear the triangle into three pieces so that each vertex is on a separate piece. Tell students to arrange the pieces so that the vertices are all on the same location and so that the sides of the angles create adjacent angles. Ask what figure is formed by the outer sides of the outer two angles. **a straight line** What kind of angle is formed by all three pieces and what is its measure? **a straight angle; 180°**

Triangles can also be classified by their sides. **Congruent** sides have the same length.

Key Concept — Classify Triangles by their Sides

Scalene Triangle	Isosceles Triangle	Equilateral Triangle
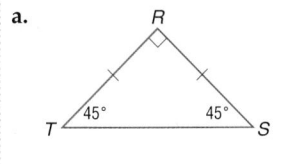		
no congruent sides	at least two sides congruent	all sides congruent

Example 3 — Classify Triangles

Classify each triangle by its angles and by its sides.

a.

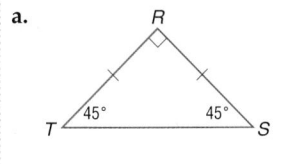

Angles
△RST has a right angle.

Sides
△RST has two congruent sides.
So, △RST is a right isosceles triangle.

b.

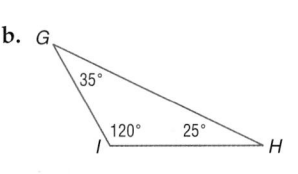

Angles
△GHI has one obtuse angle.

Sides
△GHI has no two sides that are congruent.
So, △GHI is an obtuse scalene triangle.

Check for Understanding

Concept Check

1. **Compare** an isosceles triangle and an equilateral triangle. **See margin.**

2. **Sample answer: yield sign**

2. **Name** a real-world object that is an equilateral triangle.

3. **OPEN ENDED** Draw an obtuse isosceles triangle. **See margin.**

Guided Practice

Find the value of *x* in each triangle. Then classify each triangle as *acute, right,* or *obtuse.*

GUIDED PRACTICE KEY	
Exercises	Examples
4–6	1
7–9	3
10	2

4. **25; acute**

5. **90; right**

6. **105; obtuse**

7. **right isosceles**
8. **obtuse scalene**
9. **acute isosceles**

Classify each indicated triangle by its angles and by its sides.

7.

8.

9.

Application

10. **ALGEBRA** Triangle *EFG* has angles whose measures are in the ratio 2:4:9. What are the measures of the angles? **24°, 48°, 108°**

Study Notebook

Have students—
• add the definitions/examples of the vocabulary terms to their Vocabulary Builder worksheets for Chapter 9.
• create a chart, including examples, explaining the classifications of triangles.
• include any other item(s) that they find helpful in mastering the skills in this lesson.

Answers

1. Whereas an isosceles triangle has at least two sides congruent, an equilateral triangle has three sides congruent.

3. Sample answer:

About the Exercises . . .

Organization by Objective
• **Angle Measures of a Triangle:** 11–18, 34–36
• **Classify Triangles:** 19–33

Odd/Even Assignments
Exercises 11–26, and 30–33 are structured so that students practice the same concepts whether they are assigned odd or even problems.

Assignment Guide

Basic: 11–29 odd, 37–54
Average: 11–35 odd, 37–54
Advanced: 12–36 even, 37–48 (Optional: 49–54)

★ indicates increased difficulty

Practice and Apply

Find the value of *x* in each triangle. Then classify each triangle as *acute, right,* or *obtuse.*

11. 27; right
12. 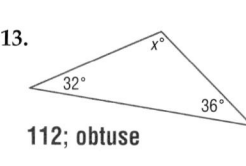 55; acute
13. 32° 36° *x*° 112; obtuse
14. 45° 33° *x*° 102; obtuse
15. 28° 62° *x*° 90; right
16. 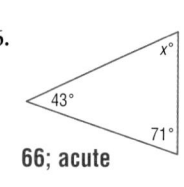 43° 71° *x*° 66; acute

17. **ALGEBRA** The measures of the angles of a triangle are in the ratio 1:3:5. What is the measure of each angle? 20°, 60°, 100°

18. **ALGEBRA** Determine the measures of the angles of △ABC if the measures of the angles are in the ratio 7:7:22. 35°, 35°, 110°

19–24. See margin.

Classify each indicated triangle by its angles and by its sides.

19.
20.
21.
22.
23.
24.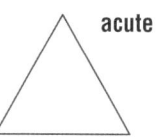

Determine whether each statement is *sometimes, always,* or *never* true.

25. Equilateral triangles are isosceles triangles. **always**

26. Isosceles triangles are equilateral triangles. **sometimes**

Estimate the measure of the angles in each triangle. Then classify each triangle as *acute, right,* or *obtuse.*

27. obtuse 28. right 29. acute

Sketch each triangle. If it is not possible to sketch the triangle, write *not possible.* 30–33. See margin.

★ 30. acute scalene
★ 31. right equilateral
★ 32. obtuse and *not* scalene
★ 33. obtuse equilateral

Answers

19. acute equilateral
20. obtuse isosceles
21. right scalene
22. acute isosceles
23. acute scalene
24. obtuse isosceles

30. 89° 39° 52°

31. not possible

32. 96° 42° 42°

33. not possible

ALGEBRA Find the measures of the angles in each triangle.

★34.
20°; 60°; 100°

★35.
45°; 50°; 85°

★36. 30°; 45°; 105°

37. **CRITICAL THINKING** Numbers that can be represented by a triangular arrangement of dots are called *triangular numbers*. The first three triangular numbers are 1, 3, and 6. Find the next three triangular numbers. **10, 15, 21**

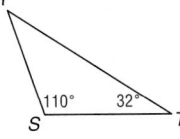

38. **WRITING IN MATH** Answer the question that was posed at the beginning of the lesson. **See margin.**

How do the angles of a triangle relate to each other?

Include the following in your answer:
- an explanation telling why the sum of the angles is 180°, and
- drawings of two triangles with their angles labeled.

NEW YORK
Test Practice

Standardized Test Practice
(A) (B) (C) (D)

39. Refer to the figure shown. What is the measure of ∠R? **B**
   (A) 28°   (B) 38°
   (C) 48°   (D) 180°

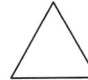

40. The measures of the angles of a triangle are 30°, 90°, and 60°. Which triangle most likely has these angle measures? **C**
   (A)   (B)   (C)   (D)

  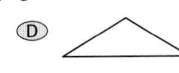

Maintain Your Skills

Mixed Review   Use a protractor to find the measure of each angle. Then classify each angle as *acute, obtuse, right,* or *straight*.
(Lesson 9-3) **41. 180°; straight**

41. ∠ADC   42. ∠ADE **35°; acute**
43. ∠CDE   44. ∠EDF
   145°; obtuse   **85°; acute**

ALGEBRA Solve each equation. Round to the nearest tenth, if necessary.
(Lesson 9-2)
45. $m^2 = 81$ **9, −9**   46. $196 = y^2$ **14, −14**   47. $84 = p^2$ **9.2, −9.2**

48. Twenty-six is 25% of what number? *(Lesson 6-5)* **104**

Getting Ready for the Next Lesson   **PREREQUISITE SKILL** Find the value of each expression.
(To review exponents, see Lesson 4-2.)
49. 12^2 **144**   50. 15^2 **225**   51. 18^2 **324**
52. 24^2 **576**   53. 27^2 **729**   54. 31^2 **961**

www.pre-alg.com/self_check_quiz/ny

Open-Ended Assessment

Modeling Give students state maps, tacks, and string and have them find groups of three towns that, when connected with straight lines, form acute triangles, obtuse triangles, and if possible, right triangles.

Getting Ready for Lesson 9-5

PREREQUISITE SKILL Lesson 9-5 presents the Pythagorean Theorem, which requires the use of squares and square roots. Exercises 49–54 should be used to determine your students' familiarity with squaring numbers.

Quiz (Lessons 9-3 and 9-4) is available on p. 543 of the *Chapter 9 Resource Masters.*

Mid-Chapter Test (Lessons 9-1 through 9-4) is available on p. 545 of the *Chapter 9 Resource Masters.*

Answer

38. The angles of a triangle have a sum of 180°. Answers should include the following.
   - The angles of a triangle can be folded to form a straight angle. Since the measure of a straight angle is 180°, the sum of the angles of a triangle is 180°.
   - Sample answer:

Getting Started

Objective Find the area of figures using rectangular dot paper.

Materials
rectangular dot paper

Teach

Activity 1
- You may need to review formulas for area.
- Students may use colored pencils to organize the smaller regions.
- Students could carefully cut the figures out and then cut the figures into smaller regions. They could then reassemble the pieces onto dot paper to determine the total area.

Activity 2
- Explain to students that the hypotenuse is always designated as side "c."

Algebra Activity

A Preview of Lesson 9-5

NEW YORK *Performance Indicator* Reinforcement of 7.G.6 Explore the relationship between the lengths of the three sides of a right triangle to develop the Pythagorean Theorem

The Pythagorean Theorem

Activity 1

To find the area of certain geometric figures, dot paper can be used. Consider the following examples.

Find the area of each shaded region if each square represents one square unit.

$A = \frac{1}{2}(1)$ or $\frac{1}{2}$ unit^2 $A = \frac{1}{2}(2)$ or 1 unit^2 $A = \frac{1}{2}(4)$ or 2 units^2

The area of other figures can be found by first separating the figure into smaller regions and then finding the sum of the areas of the smaller regions.

$A = 2$ units^2 $A = 5$ units^2 $A = 4$ units^2

Model
Find the area of each figure.

1. **8 units^2**

2. **6 units^2**

3. **10 units^2**

4. 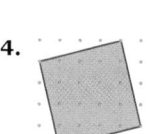 **17 units^2**

458   Chapter 9   Real Numbers and Right Triangles

Resource Manager

 Teaching Pre-Algebra with Manipulatives
- p. 15 (rectangular dot paper)
- p. 115 (student recording sheet)

Glencoe Mathematics Classroom Manipulative Kit
- rectangular dot paper

Activity 2

Let's investigate the relationship that exists among the sides of a right triangle. In each diagram shown, notice how a square is attached to each side of a right triangle.

Triangle 1

Triangle 2

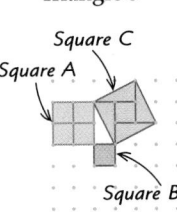

Triangle 3

Triangle 4

Triangle 5

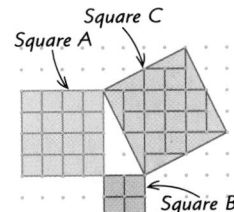

Copy the table. Then find the area of each square that is attached to the triangle. Record the results in your table.

Triangle	Area of Square A (units²)	Area of Square B (units²)	Area of Square C (units²)
1	1	1	2
2	4	4	8
3	4	1	5
4	1	9	10
5	16	4	20

Exercises   **5. The sum of the areas of squares A and B is equal to the area of square C.**

5. Refer to your table. How does the sum of the areas of square A and square B compare to the area of square C?

6. Refer to the diagram shown at the right. If the lengths of the sides of a right triangle are whole numbers such that $a^2 + b^2 = c^2$, the numbers a, b, and c are called a **Pythagorean Triple**. Tell whether each set of numbers is a Pythagorean Triple. Explain why or why not. **See margin for explanations.**

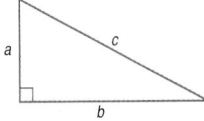

a. 3, 4, 5 **yes**   **b.** 5, 7, 9 **no**   **c.** 6, 9, 12 **no**   **d.** 7, 24, 25 **yes**

7. Write two different sets of numbers that are a Pythagorean Triple.
Sample answer: 10, 24, 26 and 12, 16, 20

Algebra Activity The Pythagorean Theorem **459**

Assess

In **Exercises 1–4**, students should
- break the figure into smaller regions.
- determine the area for each region.
- add the areas of the smaller regions to get the total area.

In **Exercises 5–7**, remind students to square the numbers, then add the smaller two.

Study Notebook

Have students write a definition for Pythagorean Triple and include several examples. Have them also include a triangle with sides labeled a, b, and c.

Answer

6a. $3^2 + 4^2 = 5^2$

6b. $5^2 + 7^2 \neq 9^2$

6c. $6^2 + 9^2 \neq 12^2$

6d. $7^2 + 24^2 = 25^2$

9-5 The Pythagorean Theorem

1 Focus

5-Minute Check
Transparency 9-5 Use as a quiz or review of Lesson 9-4.

Mathematical Background notes are available for this lesson on page 434D.

How do the sides of a right triangle relate to each other?

The opening activity questions are repeated on page 512 of the *Chapter 9 Resource Masters*.

Reading to Learn Mathematics, p. 512 — ELL

Pre-Activity *How do the sides of a right triangle relate to each other?*

Do the activity at the top of page 460 in your textbook. Write your answers below.

a. Find the area of each square. 9 units²; 16 units²; 25 units²

b. What relationship exists among the areas of the squares? The area of the large square is equal to the sum of the areas of the two smaller squares.

c. Draw three squares with sides 5, 12, and 13 units so that they form a right triangle. What relationship exists among the areas of these squares? The area of the large square is equal to the sum of the areas of the two smaller squares.

Reading the Lesson 1–5. See students' work.

Write a definition and give an example of the new vocabulary word or phrase.

Vocabulary	Definition	Example
1. legs		
2. hypotenuse		
3. Pythagorean Theorem		
4. solving a right triangle		
5. converse		

Helping You Remember

6. Write out in words the steps for solving the right triangle shown.

$c^2 = a^2 + b^2$	Pythagorean Theorem
$22^2 = a^2 + 20^2$	Replace c with 22 and b with 20.
$484 = a^2 + 400$	Evaluate 22^2 and 20^2.
$484 - 400 = a^2 + 400 - 400$	Subtract 400 from each side.
$84 = a^2$	Simplify.
$\sqrt{84} = \sqrt{a^2}$	Take the square root of each side.
$a \approx 9.2$	The length of the leg is about 9.2 units.

Vocabulary
- legs
- hypotenuse
- Pythagorean Theorem
- solving a right triangle
- converse

a. 9 units², 16 units², 25 units²
b. The area of the large square is equal to the sum of the areas of the two smaller squares.

Study Tip

Hypotenuse
The hypotenuse is the longest side of a triangle.

NEW YORK — Performance Indicator

Reinforcement of 7.G.8 Use the Pythagorean Theorem to determine the unknown length of a side of a right triangle

Reinforcement of 7.G.9 Determine whether a given triangle is a right triangle by applying the Pythagorean Theorem and using a calculator

What You'll Learn

- Use the Pythagorean Theorem to find the length of a side of a right triangle.
- Use the converse of the Pythagorean Theorem to determine whether a triangle is a right triangle.

How do the sides of a right triangle relate to each other?

In the diagram, three squares with sides 3, 4, and 5 units are used to form a right triangle.

a. Find the area of each square.
b. What relationship exists among the areas of the squares?
c. Draw three squares with sides 5, 12, and 13 units so that they form a right triangle. What relationship exists among the areas of these squares?

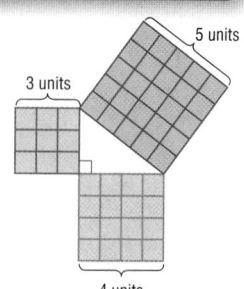

c. The area of the large square is equal to the sum of the areas of the two smaller squares.

THE PYTHAGOREAN THEOREM In a right triangle, the sides that are adjacent to the right angle are called the **legs**. The side opposite the right angle is the **hypotenuse**.

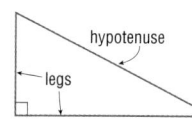

The **Pythagorean Theorem** describes the relationship between the lengths of the legs and the hypotenuse. This theorem is true for *any* right triangle.

Key Concept — Pythagorean Theorem

- **Words** If a triangle is a right triangle, then the square of the length of the hypotenuse is equal to the sum of the squares of the lengths of the legs.

- **Model**
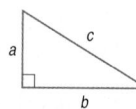

- **Symbols** $c^2 = a^2 + b^2$

- **Example** $5^2 = 3^2 + 4^2$
  $25 = 9 + 16$
  $25 = 25$

Example 1 Find the Length of the Hypotenuse

Find the length of the hypotenuse of the right triangle.

$c^2 = a^2 + b^2$	Pythagorean Theorem
$c^2 = 12^2 + 16^2$	Replace a with 12 and b with 16.
$c^2 = 144 + 256$	Evaluate 12^2 and 16^2.
$c^2 = 400$	Add 144 and 256.
$\sqrt{c^2} = \sqrt{400}$	Take the square root of each side.
$c = 20$	The length of the hypotenuse is 20 feet.

Resource Manager

📁 Workbooks and Reproducible Masters

Chapter 9 Resource Masters
- Study Guide and Intervention, p. 509
- Skills Practice, p. 510
- Practice, p. 511
- Reading to Learn Mathematics, p. 512
- Enrichment, p. 513

Parent and Student Study Guide Workbook, p. 76
School-to-Career Masters, p. 17

📠 Transparencies
5-Minute Check Transparency 9-5
Real-World Transparency 9
Answer Key Transparencies

💿 Technology
Interactive Chalkboard
Pre-AlgePASS: Tutorial Plus, Lessons 27, 28
Multimedia Applications

Concept Check Which side of a right triangle is the hypotenuse?
The side across from the right angle.

If you know the lengths of two sides of a right triangle, you can use the Pythagorean Theorem to find the length of the third side. This is called **solving a right triangle**.

Example 2 *Solve a Right Triangle*

Find the length of the leg of the right triangle.

$c^2 = a^2 + b^2$	Pythagorean Theorem
$14^2 = a^2 + 10^2$	Replace c with 14 and b with 10.
$196 = a^2 + 100$	Evaluate 14^2 and 10^2.
$196 - 100 = a^2 + 100 - 100$	Subtract 100 from each side.
$96 = a^2$	Simplify.
$\sqrt{96} = \sqrt{a^2}$	Take the square root of each side.

2nd [√] 96 ENTER 9.797958971

The length of the leg is about 9.8 centimeters.

Standardized tests often contain questions involving the Pythagorean Theorem.

Example 3 *Use the Pythagorean Theorem*

Multiple-Choice Test Item

> A painter positions a 20-foot ladder against a house so that the base of the ladder is 4 feet from the house. About how high does the ladder reach on the side of the house?
>
> Ⓐ 17.9 ft   Ⓑ 18.0 ft   Ⓒ 19.6 ft   Ⓓ 20.4 ft

Read the Test Item

Make a drawing to illustrate the problem. The ladder, ground, and side of the house form a right triangle.

Solve the Test Item

Use the Pythagorean Theorem to find how high the ladder reaches on the side of the house.

$c^2 = a^2 + b^2$	Pythagorean Theorem
$20^2 = 4^2 + b^2$	Replace c with 20 and a with 4.
$400 = 16 + b^2$	Evaluate 20^2 and 4^2.
$400 - 16 = 16 + b^2 - 16$	Subtract 16 from each side.
$384 = b^2$	Simplify.
$\sqrt{384} = \sqrt{b^2}$	Take the square root of each side.
$19.6 \approx b$	Round to the nearest tenth.

The ladder reaches about 19.6 feet on the side of the house. The answer is C.

---

2 Teach

THE PYTHAGOREAN THEOREM

In-Class Examples Power Point®

1 Find the length of the hypotenuse of the right triangle.   **29 ft**

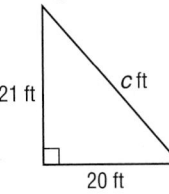

2 Find the length of the leg of the right triangle.   **≈7.5 m**

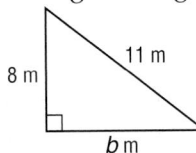

Teaching Tip Make sure students recognize that a and b always represent the legs, and c always represents the hypotenuse when solving a triangle with the Pythagorean Theorem.

3 **Multiple-Choice Test Item** A building is 10 feet tall. A ladder is positioned against the building so that the base of the ladder is 3 feet from the building. How long is the ladder? **B**

A 12.4 ft   **B** 10.4 ft

C 10.0 ft   **D** 14.9 ft

Standardized Test Practice
Ⓐ Ⓑ Ⓒ Ⓓ

Example 3 Point out to students that they should draw a simple picture and label the triangle, including the right angle, for such test items. Then solve for the missing side.

CONVERSE OF THE PYTHAGOREAN THEOREM

In-Class Example

Power Point®

4 The measures of three sides of a triangle are given. Determine whether each triangle is a right triangle.

a. 48 ft, 60 ft, 78 ft   **no**

b. 24 cm, 70 cm, 74 cm   **yes**

---

3 Practice/Apply

Study Notebook

Have students—

• add the definitions/examples of the vocabulary terms to their Vocabulary Builder worksheets for Chapter 9.

• draw a right triangle, label the parts, and show how the Pythagorean Theorem applies to the triangle.

• include any other item(s) that they find helpful in mastering the skills in this lesson.

About the Exercises . . .

Organization by Objective
• **The Pythagorean Theorem:** 10–27
• **Converse of the Pythagorean Theorem:** 28–33

Odd/Even Assignments
Exercises 10–33 are structured so that students practice the same concepts whether they are assigned odd or even problems.

Assignment Guide

Basic: 11, 13, 17–21 odd, 27–31 odd, 37–40, 44–52

Average: 11–33 odd, 34, 35, 37–40, 44–52 (Optional: 41–43)

Advanced: 10–32 even, 34–49 (Optional: 50–52)

CONVERSE OF THE PYTHAGOREAN THEOREM   The Pythagorean Theorem is written in *if-then* form. If you reverse the statements after *if* and *then*, you have formed the **converse** of the Pythagorean Theorem.

Pythagorean Theorem   If a triangle is a right triangle, then $c^2 = a^2 + b^2$.

Converse   If $c^2 = a^2 + b^2$, then a triangle is a right triangle.

You can use the converse to determine whether a triangle is a right triangle.

Example 4   Identify a Right Triangle

The measures of three sides of a triangle are given. Determine whether each triangle is a right triangle.

a. 9 m, 12 m, 15 m

$$c^2 = a^2 + b^2$$
$$15^2 \stackrel{?}{=} 9^2 + 12^2$$
$$225 \stackrel{?}{=} 81 + 144$$
$$225 = 225$$

The triangle is a right triangle.

b. 6 in., 7 in., 12 in.

$$c^2 = a^2 + b^2$$
$$12^2 \stackrel{?}{=} 6^2 + 7^2$$
$$144 \stackrel{?}{=} 36 + 49$$
$$144 \neq 85$$

The triangle is *not* a right triangle.

Check for Understanding

Concept Check

1. **OPEN ENDED**   State the measures of three sides that could form a right triangle. **Sample answer: 8, 15, 17**

2. See margin.

2. **FIND THE ERROR**   Marcus and Allyson are finding the missing measure of the right triangle shown. Who is correct? Explain your reasoning.

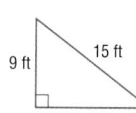

Marcus
$$c^2 = a^2 + b^2$$
$$15^2 = 9^2 + b^2$$
$$12 = b$$

Allyson
$$c^2 = a^2 + b^2$$
$$c^2 = 9^2 + 15^2$$
$$c \approx 17.5$$

Guided Practice

GUIDED PRACTICE KEY	
Exercises	Examples
3, 4	1
5, 6	2
7, 8	4
9	3

Find the length of the hypotenuse in each right triangle. Round to the nearest tenth, if necessary.

3. **25**

4. **13.4**

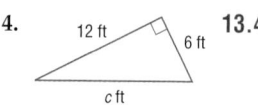

If *c* is the measure of the hypotenuse, find each missing measure. Round to the nearest tenth, if necessary.

5. $a = 8$, $b = ?$, $c = 17$ **15**

6. $a = ?$, $b = 24$, $c = 25$ **7**

The lengths of three sides of a triangle are given. Determine whether each triangle is a right triangle.

7. 5 cm, 7 cm, 8 cm   **no**

8. 10 ft, 24 ft, 26 ft   **yes**

NEW YORK Test Practice

Standardized Test Practice

Ⓐ Ⓑ Ⓒ Ⓓ

9. Kendra is flying a kite. The length of the kite string is 55 feet and she is positioned 40 feet away from beneath the kite. About how high is the kite? **B**

Ⓐ 33.1 ft   Ⓑ 37.7 ft   Ⓒ 56.2 ft   Ⓓ 68.0 ft

DAILY INTERVENTION   FIND THE ERROR

If students are having difficulty with determining which side of the triangle is *a*, *b*, or *c*, have them draw a few right triangles using a ruler. Remind them that *c* is always the longest side.

Answer

2. Marcus; Allyson incorrectly substitutes 15 for *b* in the equation. Since the side measuring 15 units is opposite the right angle, it is a hypotenuse. So, 15 should be substituted for *c* in the equation.

Practice and Apply

Find the length of the hypotenuse in each right triangle. Round to the nearest tenth, if necessary.

10. [triangle: 6 m, 8 m, *c* m] **10**

11. [triangle: 24 in., 10 in., *c* in.] **26**

12. [triangle: *c* yd, 5 yd, 9 yd] **10.3**

13. [triangle: 6 ft, 11 ft, *c* ft] **12.5**

★ 14. [triangle: 7.2 cm, 2.7 cm, *c* cm] **7.7**

★ 15. [triangle: 12.8 m, 13.9 m, *c* m] **18.9**

16. **GYMNASTICS** The floor exercise mat measures 40 feet by 40 feet. Find the measure of the diagonal. **about 56.6 ft**

17. **TELEVISION** The size of a television set is determined by the length of the diagonal of the screen. If a 35-inch television screen is 26 inches long, what is its height to the nearest inch? **23 in.**

If *c* is the measure of the hypotenuse, find each missing measure. Round to the nearest tenth, if necessary.

18. $a = 9, b = ?, c = 41$ **40**

19. $a = ?, b = 35, c = 37$ **12**

20. $a = ?, b = 12, c = 19$ **14.7**

21. $a = 7, b = ?, c = 14$ **12.1**

★ 22. $a = 27, b = ?, c = 61$ **54.7**

★ 23. $a = ?, b = 73, c = 82$ **37.3**

★ 24. $a = ?, b = \sqrt{123}, c = 22$ **19**

★ 25. $a = \sqrt{177}, b = ?, c = 31$ **28**

Find each missing measure to the nearest tenth.

26. [triangle: 17 m, 28 m, *x* m] **22.2**

27. [triangle: *x* ft, 45 ft, 30 ft] **33.5**

The lengths of three sides of a triangle are given. Determine whether each triangle is a right triangle.

28. $a = 5, b = 8, c = 9$ **no**

29. $a = 16, b = 30, c = 34$ **yes**

30. $a = 18, b = 24, c = 30$ **yes**

31. $a = 24, b = 28, c = 32$ **no**

★ 32. $a = \sqrt{21}, b = 6, c = \sqrt{57}$ **yes**

★ 33. $a = 11, b = \sqrt{55}, c = \sqrt{177}$ **no**

ART For Exercises 34 and 35, use the plasterwork design shown.

34. If the sides of the square measures 6 inches, what is the length of $\overline{AB}$? **about 8.5 in.**

★ 35. What is the perimeter of the design if $\overline{AB}$ measures $\sqrt{128}$? (*Hint:* Use the guess-and-check strategy.) **32 in.**

Open-Ended Assessment

Speaking Have students take turns giving one another problems to solve on the chalkboard. Problems could be finding a hypotenuse or leg or determining whether three measures indicate a right triangle. The student at the chalkboard should draw a sketch and explain the steps for solving.

Getting Ready for Lesson 9-6

PREREQUISITE SKILL Lesson 9-6 presents the distance and midpoint formulas. The order of operations must be followed to successfully use these formulas. Exercises 50–52 should be used to determine your students' familiarity with order of operations and exponents.

Answer

37. There is enough information to find the lengths of the legs. Since the right triangle is an isosceles right triangle, we know that the lengths of the legs are equal. So, in the Pythagorean Theorem, we can say that $a = b$. In addition, we know that $c = 8$.

$c^2 = a^2 + b^2$	Pythagorean Theorem
$8^2 = a^2 + a^2$	$a = b$ and $c = 8$
$8^2 = 2a^2$	Add a^2 and a^2.
$64 = 2a^2$	Evaluate 8^2.
$\dfrac{64}{2} = \dfrac{2a^2}{2}$	Divide each side by 2.
$32 = a^2$	Simplify.
$\sqrt{32} = a$	Take the square root of each side.

So, if a triangle is an isosceles right triangle and the hypotenuse is 8 inches, the length of each leg is $\sqrt{32}$ inches or about 5.7 inches.

36. GEOMETRY All angles *inscribed* in a semicircle are right angles. In the figure at the right, $\angle ACB$ is an inscribed right angle. If the length of $\overline{AB}$ is 17 and the length of $\overline{AC}$ is 8, find the length of $\overline{BC}$. **15**

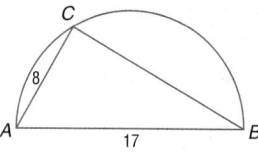

37. CRITICAL THINKING The hypotenuse of an isosceles right triangle is 8 inches. Is there enough information to find the length of the legs? If so, find the length of the legs. If not, explain why not. **See margin.**

38. WRITING IN MATH   Answer the question that was posed at the beginning of the lesson. **See pp. 489A–489B.**

How do the sides of a right triangle relate to each other?

Include the following in your answer:
- a right triangle with the legs and hypotenuse labeled, and
- an example of a set of numbers that represents the measures of the lengths of the legs and hypotenuse of a right triangle.

NEW YORK Test Practice

Standardized Test Practice

39. Which numbers represent the measures of the sides of a right triangle? **D**
- Ⓐ 3, 3, 6
- Ⓑ 3, 4, 7
- Ⓒ 5, 7, 12
- Ⓓ 6, 8, 10

40. Which is the best estimate for the value of x? **B**
- Ⓐ 5.0
- Ⓑ 7.9
- Ⓒ 8.3
- Ⓓ 16.0

Extending the Lesson **GEOMETRY** In the *rectangular prism* shown, $\overline{BD}$ is the diagonal of the base, and $\overline{FD}$ is the diagonal of the prism. **41. 17 units**

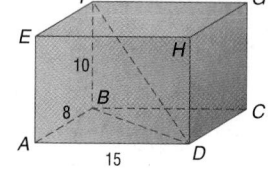

41. Find the measure of the diagonal of the base.

42. What is the measure of the diagonal of the prism to the nearest tenth? **19.7 units**

43. MODELING Measure the dimensions of a shoebox and use the dimensions to calculate the length of the diagonal of the box. Then use a piece of string and a ruler to check your calculation. **See students' work.**

Maintain Your Skills

Mixed Review **Find the value of x in each triangle. Then classify each triangle as *acute*, *right*, or *obtuse*.** *(Lesson 9-4)*

44. **101; obtuse**

45. **90; right**

46. **78; acute**

47. Use a protractor to draw an angle having a measure of 115°. *(Lesson 9-3)* **See students' work.**

ALGEBRA Solve each inequality. *(Lesson 7-4)*

48. $x + 4 < 12$ $x < 8$

49. $-15 \le n - 6$ $n \ge -9$

Getting Ready for the Next Lesson **PREREQUISITE SKILL** Simplify each expression.
*(To review **order of operations** and **exponents**, see Lessons 1-2 and 4-2.)*

50. $(2 + 6)^2 + (-5 + 6)^2$ **65** **51.** $(-4 + 3)^2 + (0 - 2)^2$ **5** **52.** $[3 + (-1)]^2 + (8 - 4)^2$ **20**

Tips for New Teachers

Intervention You may want to have students complete Exercises 1–9 in pairs. Check for questions before having them complete the assignment independently.

Algebra Activity

 NEW YORK *Performance Indicator* **8.CN.5 Understand how concepts, procedures, and mathematical results in one area of mathematics can be used to solve problems in other areas of mathematics**

Graphing Irrational Numbers

In Lesson 2-1, you learned to graph integers on a number line. Irrational numbers can also be graphed on a number line. Consider the irrational number $\sqrt{53}$. To graph $\sqrt{53}$, construct a right triangle whose hypotenuse measures $\sqrt{53}$ units.

Step 1 Find two numbers whose squares have a sum of 53. Since $53 = 49 + 4$ or $7^2 + 2^2$, one pair that will work is 7 and 2. These numbers will be the lengths of the legs of the right triangle.

Step 2 Draw the right triangle
- First, draw a number line on grid paper.

- Next, draw a right triangle whose legs measure 7 units and 2 units. Notice that this triangle can be drawn in two ways. Either way is correct.

Step 3 Graph $\sqrt{53}$.
- Open your compass to the length of the hypotenuse.
- With the tip of the compass at 0, draw an arc that intersects the number line at point B.

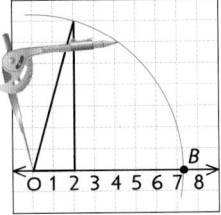

- The distance from 0 to B is $\sqrt{53}$ units. From the graph, $\sqrt{53} \approx 7.3$.

Model and Analyze

Use a compass and grid paper to graph each irrational number on a number line. 1–6. See pp. 489A–489B.

1. $\sqrt{5}$ **2.** $\sqrt{20}$ **3.** $\sqrt{45}$ **4.** $\sqrt{97}$

5. Describe two different ways to graph $\sqrt{34}$.

6. Explain how the graph of $\sqrt{2}$ can be used to locate the graph of $\sqrt{3}$.

Algebra Activity   Graphing Irrational Numbers   **465**

Algebra Activity

A Follow-Up of Lesson 9-5

Getting Started

Objective Graph irrational numbers on a number line.

Materials
grid paper
compass

Teach

- This method is an alternative means of finding the square root of a number.
- Discuss with students why the orientation of the triangle is not important.

Assess

In **Exercises 1–4**, students should:
- check their answers with a calculator.
- compare their work to see if they chose the same triangles to work the problems.

For **Exercises 5–6**, have students work in small groups. Discuss as a class how groups arrived at their answers.

Study Notebook

Have students summarize the procedure in this activity and provide another example.

Resource Manager

📁 Teaching Pre-Algebra with Manipulatives
- p. 1 (master for grid paper)
- p. 117 (student recording sheet)

Glencoe Mathematics Classroom Manipulative Kit
- compass

9-6 The Distance and Midpoint Formulas

NEW YORK
Performance Indicator
Reinforcement of 7.A.6
Evaluate formulas for given input values
(surface area, rate, and density problems)

1 Focus

5-Minute Check
Transparency 9-6 Use as a quiz or review of Lesson 9-5.

Mathematical Background
notes are available for this lesson on page 434D.

How is the Distance Formula related to the Pythagorean Theorem?

The opening activity questions are repeated on page 517 of the *Chapter 9 Resource Masters*.

Vocabulary
- Distance Formula
- midpoint
- Midpoint Formula

e. Pythagorean Theorem

Study Tip

Look Back
To review the notation (x_1, y_1) and (x_2, y_2), see Lesson 8-4.

What You'll Learn

- Use the Distance Formula to determine lengths on a coordinate plane.
- Use the Midpoint Formula to find the midpoint of a line segment on the coordinate plane.

How is the Distance Formula related to the Pythagorean Theorem?

The graph of points $N(3, 0)$ and $M(-4, 3)$ is shown. A horizontal segment is drawn from *M*, and a vertical segment is drawn from *N*. The intersection is labeled *P*.

a. Name the coordinates of *P*. **(3, 3)**

b. Find the distance between *M* and *P*. **7 units**

c. Find the distance between *N* and *P*. **3 units**

d. Classify △*MNP*. **right**

e. What theorem can be used to find the distance between *M* and *N*?

f. Find the distance between *M* and *N*. **√58 units**

THE DISTANCE FORMULA Recall that a line segment is a part of a line. It contains two endpoints and all of the points between the endpoints.

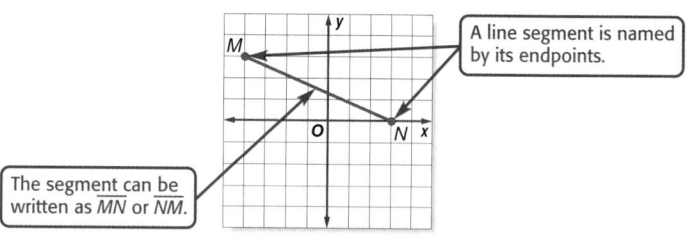

A line segment is named by its endpoints.

The segment can be written as $\overline{MN}$ or $\overline{NM}$.

To find the length of a segment on a coordinate plane, you can use the **Distance Formula**, which is based on the Pythagorean Theorem.

Key Concept *Distance Formula*

- **Words** The distance d between two points with coordinates (x_1, y_1) and (x_2, y_2), is given by $d = \sqrt{(x_2 - x_1)^2 + (y_2 - y_1)^2}$.

- **Model**

✓ **Concept Check** How is a line segment named? **by its endpoints**

Resource Manager

📂 Workbooks and Reproducible Masters

Chapter 9 Resource Masters
- Study Guide and Intervention, p. 514
- Skills Practice, p. 515
- Practice, p. 516
- Reading to Learn Mathematics, p. 517
- Enrichment, p. 518
- Assessment, p. 544

Parent and Student Study Guide Workbook, p. 77

🖥 Transparencies
5-Minute Check Transparency 9-6
Answer Key Transparencies

💿 Technology
Interactive Chalkboard

Example 1 Use the Distance Formula

Find the distance between $G(-3, 1)$ and $H(2, -4)$. Round to the nearest tenth, if necessary.

Use the Distance Formula.

$$d = \sqrt{(x_2 - x_1)^2 + (y_2 - y_1)^2}$$ Distance Formula

$$GH = \sqrt{[2 - (-3)]^2 + (-4 - 1)^2}$$ $(x_1, y_1) = (-3, 1), (x_2, y_2) = (2, -4)$

$$GH = \sqrt{(5)^2 + (-5)^2}$$ Simplify.

$$GH = \sqrt{25 + 25}$$ Evaluate 5^2 and $(-5)^2$.

$$GH = \sqrt{50}$$ Add 25 and 25.

$$GH \approx 7.1$$ Take the square root.

The distance between points G and H is about 7.1 units.

Study Tip

Substitution
You can use either point as (x_1, y_1). The distance will be the same.

The Distance Formula can be used to solve geometry problems.

Example 2 Use the Distance Formula to Solve a Problem

GEOMETRY   Find the perimeter of $\triangle ABC$ to the nearest tenth.

First, use the Distance Formula to find the length of each side of the triangle.

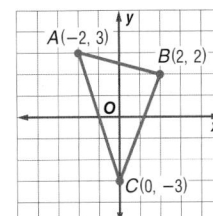

Side $\overline{AB}$: $A(-2, 3)$, $B(2, 2)$

$$d = \sqrt{(x_2 - x_1)^2 + (y_2 - y_1)^2}$$
$$AB = \sqrt{[2 - (-2)]^2 + (2 - 3)^2}$$
$$AB = \sqrt{(4)^2 + (-1)^2}$$
$$AB = \sqrt{16 + 1}$$
$$AB = \sqrt{17}$$

Side $\overline{BC}$: $B(2, 2)$, $C(0, -3)$

$$d = \sqrt{(x_2 - x_1)^2 + (y_2 - y_1)^2}$$
$$BC = \sqrt{[0 - 2]^2 + (-3 - 2)^2}$$
$$BC = \sqrt{(-2)^2 + (-5)^2}$$
$$BC = \sqrt{4 + 25}$$
$$BC = \sqrt{29}$$

Side $\overline{CA}$: $C(0, -3)$, $A(-2, 3)$

$$d = \sqrt{(x_2 - x_1)^2 + (y_2 - y_1)^2}$$
$$CA = \sqrt{[-2 - 0]^2 + (3 - (-3))^2}$$
$$CA = \sqrt{(-2)^2 + (6)^2}$$
$$CA = \sqrt{4 + 36}$$
$$CA = \sqrt{40}$$

Study Tip

Common Misconception
To find the sum of square roots, do *not* add the numbers inside the square root symbols.
$$\sqrt{17} + \sqrt{29} + \sqrt{40} \neq \sqrt{86}$$

Then add the lengths of the sides to find the perimeter.

$$\sqrt{17} + \sqrt{29} + \sqrt{40} \approx 4.123 + 5.385 + 6.325$$
$$\approx 15.833$$

The perimeter is about 15.8 units.

www.pre-alg.com/extra_examples/ny
   Lesson 9-6   The Distance and Midpoint Formulas   **467**

---

2 Teach

Building on Prior Knowledge

In Lesson 4-2, students studied exponents. In this lesson, students must use exponents when using the Distance Formula.

THE DISTANCE FORMULA

In-Class Examples

1 Find the distance between $M(8, 4)$ and $N(-6, -2)$. Round to the nearest tenth, if necessary. **15.2**

Teaching Tip   Point out to students that, given two points, it is always possible to make them the endpoints of the hypotenuse of a right triangle.

2 GEOMETRY   Find the perimeter of $\triangle XYZ$ to the nearest tenth. **15.8**

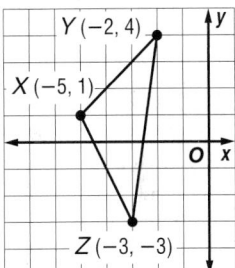

Teaching Tip   You may need to remind students that they must find the distance for all three line segments to determine perimeter.

DAILY INTERVENTION

Differentiated Instruction

- **Kinesthetic**   Using masking tape, lay out a grid on the floor in the gymnasium or classroom. Mark the origin and axes with different colored tape. Have each student choose a spot on the grid and determine its coordinates. Then have students find the distance between themselves and three other classmates. Use ropes marked off in grid units to check the answers.

In-Class Example

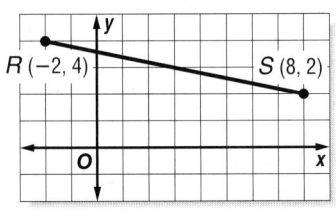
Power Point®

3 Find the coordinates of the midpoint of $\overline{RS}$. **(3, 3)**

R(−2, 4)   S(8, 2)

3 Practice/Apply

Study Notebook

Have students—

• add the definitions/examples of the vocabulary terms to their Vocabulary Builder worksheets for Chapter 9.

• draw examples demonstrating the Distance Formula and the Midpoint Formula.

• include any other item(s) that they find helpful in mastering the skills in this lesson.

About the Exercises . . .

Organization by Objective
• **The Distance Formula:** 9–18, 29–30
• **The Midpoint Formula:** 19–28

Odd/Even Assignments

Exercises 9–30 are structured so that students practice the same concepts whether they are assigned odd or even problems.

Assignment Guide

Basic: 9–13 odd, 17–25 odd, 29, 31–48

Average: 9–29 odd, 31–48

Advanced: 10–30 even, 31–42 (Optional: 43–48)

All: Practice Quiz 2 (1–5)

Average
The *x*-coordinate of the midpoint is the *average* of the *x*-coordinates of the endpoints. The *y*-coordinate of the midpoint is the *average* of the *y*-coordinates of the endpoints.

THE MIDPOINT FORMULA   On a line segment, the point that is halfway between the endpoints is called the **midpoint**.

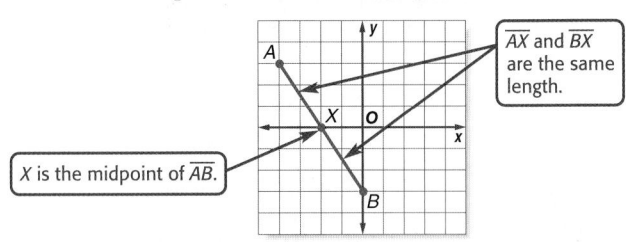

$\overline{AX}$ and $\overline{BX}$ are the same length.

X is the midpoint of $\overline{AB}$.

To find the midpoint of a segment on a coordinate plane, you can use the **Midpoint Formula**.

Key Concept   Midpoint Formula

• **Words** On a coordinate plane, the coordinates of the midpoint of a segment whose endpoints have coordinates at (x_1, y_1) and (x_2, y_2) are given by $\left(\dfrac{x_1 + x_2}{2}, \dfrac{y_1 + y_2}{2}\right)$.

• **Model**

Example 3 Use the Midpoint Formula

Find the coordinates of the midpoint of $\overline{CD}$.

$\text{midpoint} = \left(\dfrac{x_1 + x_2}{2}, \dfrac{y_1 + y_2}{2}\right)$ Midpoint Formula

$= \left(\dfrac{-2 + 4}{2}, \dfrac{-3 + 3}{2}\right)$ Substitution

$= (1, 0)$ Simplify.

The coordinates of the midpoint of $\overline{CD}$ are (1, 0).

D(4, 3)

C(−2, −3)

Check for Understanding

Concept Check   1. Define *midpoint*. **the point halfway between two endpoints**

2. **Explain** the Distance Formula in your own words. **2–3. See margin.**

3. **OPEN ENDED**   Draw any line segment on a coordinate system. Then find the midpoint of the segment.

Guided Practice   Find the distance between each pair of points. Round to the nearest tenth, if necessary.

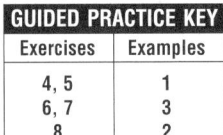

GUIDED PRACTICE KEY	
Exercises	Examples
4, 5	1
6, 7	3
8	2

4. $A(-1, 3)$, $B(8, -6)$ **12.7**   5. $M(4, -2)$, $N(-6, -7)$ **11.2**

The coordinates of the endpoints of a segment are given. Find the coordinates of the midpoint of each segment.

6. $B(4, 1)$, $C(-2, 5)$ **(1, 3)**   7. $R(3, -6)$, $S(1, -4)$ **(2, −5)**

Application   8. **GEOMETRY**   Triangle *EFG* has vertices $E(1, 4)$, $F(-3, 0)$, and $G(4, -1)$. Find the perimeter of $\triangle EFG$ to the nearest tenth. **18.6**

Answers

2. **Sample answer:** To find the distance between any two points with coordinates (x_1, y_1) and (x_2, y_2), first find the difference between x_2 and x_1, and the difference between y_2 and y_1. Then square each difference and take the square root of the sum of the squares.

3. **Sample answer:** The coordinates of the midpoint of $\overline{AB}$ are $\left(-\dfrac{1}{2}, 0\right)$.

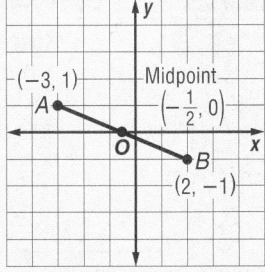

(−3, 1)   Midpoint $\left(-\dfrac{1}{2}, 0\right)$

A

B (2, −1)

Practice and Apply

Homework Help

For Exercises	See Examples
9–16	1
17, 18	2
19–28	3

Extra Practice
See page 746.

Find the distance between each pair of points. Round to the nearest tenth, if necessary.

9. $J(5, -4)$, $K(-1, 3)$ **9.2**

10. $C(-7, 2)$, $D(6, -4)$ **14.3**

11. $E(-1, -2)$, $F(9, -4)$ **10.2**

12. $V(8, -5)$, $W(-3, -5)$ **11**

13. $S(-9, 0)$, $T(6, -7)$ **16.6**

14. $M(0, 0)$, $N(-7, -8)$ **10.6**

★15. $Q\left(5\frac{1}{4}, 3\right)$, $R\left(2, 6\frac{1}{2}\right)$ **4.8**

★16. $A\left(-2\frac{1}{2}, 0\right)$, $B\left(-8\frac{3}{4}, -6\frac{1}{4}\right)$ **8.8**

GEOMETRY Find the perimeter of each figure.

17. **19.2**

18. **20.6**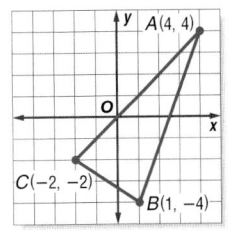

The coordinates of the endpoints of a segment are given. Find the coordinates of the midpoint of each segment.

19. $(1, 3)$

20. $\left(1, \frac{1}{2}\right)$

21. $A(6, 1)$, $B(2, -5)$ $(4, -2)$

22. $J(-3, 5)$, $K(7, 9)$ $(2, 7)$

23. $M(-1, -3)$, $N(5, 7)$ $(2, 2)$

24. $C(-4, 9)$, $D(6, -5)$ $(1, 2)$

25. $T(10, -3)$, $U(-4, -5)$ $(3, -4)$

26. $P(6, 11)$, $Q(-4, -3)$ $(1, 4)$

★27. $F(15, -4)$, $G(8, -6)$ $\left(11\frac{1}{2}, -5\right)$

★28. $E(-12, -5)$, $F(-3, -4)$

28. $\left(-7\frac{1}{2}, -4\frac{1}{2}\right)$

29. Yes; $\overline{PM}$ and $\overline{MN}$ have equal measures.

29. **GEOMETRY** Determine whether $\triangle MNP$ with vertices $M(3, -1)$, $N(-3, 2)$, and $P(6, 5)$ is isosceles. Explain your reasoning.

30. Yes; none of the measures of the sides are equal.

30. **GEOMETRY** Is $\triangle ABC$ with vertices $A(8, 4)$, $B(-2, 7)$, and $C(0, 9)$ a scalene triangle? Explain.

31. **CRITICAL THINKING** Suppose $C(8, -9)$ is the midpoint of $\overline{AB}$ and the coordinates of B are $(18, -21)$. What are the coordinates of A? $(-2, 3)$

32. **WRITING IN MATH** Answer the question that was posed at the beginning of the lesson. **See p. 470 margin.**

How is the Distance Formula related to the Pythagorean Theorem?

Include the following in your answer:

- a drawing showing how to use the Pythagorean Theorem to find the distance between two points on the coordinate system, and
- a comparison of the expressions $(x_2 - x_1)$ and $(y_2 - y_1)$ with the length of the legs of a right triangle.

 www.pre-alg.com/self_check_quiz/ny

Lesson 9-6 The Distance and Midpoint Formulas **469**

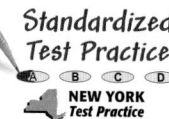

4 Assess

Open-Ended Assessment

Modeling Have students mark a piece of paper in units equal to the size of their grid paper. Have them use this paper to check their distance and midpoint answers.

Getting Ready for Lesson 9-7

PREREQUISITE SKILL Lesson 9-7 presents similar triangles and indirect measurement. Proportions are used to find missing measurements. Exercises 43–48 should be used to determine your students' familiarity with proportions.

Assessment Options

Practice Quiz 2 The quiz provides students with a brief review of the concepts and skills in Lessons 9-4 through 9-6. Lesson numbers are given to the right of exercises or instruction lines so students can review concepts not yet mastered.

Quiz (Lessons 9-5 and 9-6) is available on p. 544 of the *Chapter 9 Resource Masters*.

Answer (p. 469)

32. **Both the Distance Formula and the Pythagorean Theorem can be used to find the distance between any two points on the coordinate system. Answers should include the following.**

• **First, use the two points. Draw vertical and horizontal lines so that a right triangle is formed. Then determine the lengths of the legs. Replace the lengths of the legs in the Pythagorean Theorem to determine the length of the hypotenuse.**

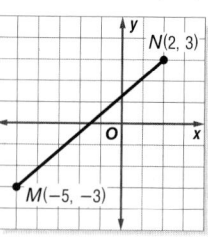

Standardized Test Practice
Ⓐ Ⓑ Ⓒ Ⓓ
NEW YORK Test Practice

33. What are the coordinates of the midpoint of the line segment with endpoints $H(-2, 0)$ and $G(8, 6)$? **C**
   Ⓐ $(-1, 7)$ Ⓑ $(5, 3)$ Ⓒ $(3, 3)$ Ⓓ $(2, 2)$

34. Which expression shows how to find the distance between points $M(-5, -3)$ and $N(2, 3)$? **B**

   Ⓐ $\sqrt{(2-5)^2 + (3-3)^2}$

   Ⓑ $\sqrt{[2-(-5)]^2 + [3-(-3)]^2}$

   Ⓒ $\sqrt{[2-(-5)]^2 + (3-3)^2}$

   Ⓓ $\sqrt{(3-2)^2 + [-3-(-5)]^2}$

Maintain Your Skills

Mixed Review   Find the length of the hypotenuse in each right triangle. Round to the nearest tenth, if necessary. *(Lesson 9-5)*

35. **9.2**   6 ft, c ft, 7 ft

36. **25.6**   24 yd, c yd, 9 yd

37. **35.1**   12 km, 33 km, c km

38. The measures of the angles of a triangle are in the ratio 1:4:5. Find the measure of each angle. *(Lesson 9-4)* **18°, 72°, 90°**

ALGEBRA   State the slope and the y-intercept for the graph of each equation. *(Lesson 8-6)*

39. $y = 2x + 1$ **2, 1**   40. $x + y = -4$ **−1, −4**   41. $4x + y = -6$ **−4, −6**

42. What number is 56% of 85? *(Lesson 6-7)* **47.6**

Getting Ready for the Next Lesson   **PREREQUISITE SKILL**   Solve each proportion. *(To review **proportions**, see Lesson 6-2.)*

43. $\dfrac{4}{16} = \dfrac{7}{x}$ **28**   44. $\dfrac{a}{15} = \dfrac{12}{60}$ **3**   45. $\dfrac{84}{m} = \dfrac{52}{13}$ **21**

46. $\dfrac{2.8}{h} = \dfrac{4.2}{12}$ **8**   47. $\dfrac{3.4}{85} = \dfrac{2.36}{n}$ **59**   48. $\dfrac{k}{5.5} = \dfrac{111}{15}$ **40.7**

Practice Quiz 2   *Lessons 9-4 through 9-6*

Classify each triangle by its angles and by its sides. *(Lesson 9-4)*

1. 96°, 42°, 42°   **obtuse isosceles**   2. 53°, 37°   **right scalene**

3. The lengths of three sides of a triangle are 34 meters, 30 meters, and 16 meters. Is the triangle a right triangle? Explain. *(Lesson 9-5)* **Yes; $34^2 = 30^2 + 16^2$**

4. Find the distance between $A(-4, -1)$ and $B(7, -9)$ to the nearest tenth. *(Lesson 9-6)* **13.6**

5. The coordinates of the endpoints of $\overline{MN}$ are $M(-2, 3)$ and $N(0, 7)$. What are the coordinates of the midpoint of $\overline{MN}$? *(Lesson 9-6)* **(−1, 5)**

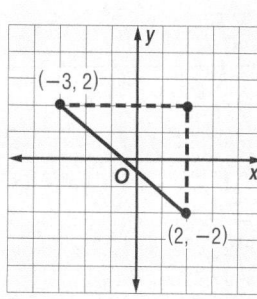

Pythagorean Theorem
$$c^2 = a^2 + b^2$$
$$c^2 = 5^2 + 4^2$$
$$c^2 = 25 + 16$$
$$c^2 = 41$$
$$c \approx 6.4$$

• **The value of $(x_2 - x_1)$ and $(y_2 - y_1)$ equals the lengths of a right triangle.**

Similar Triangles and Indirect Measurement

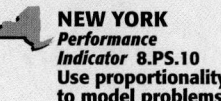

NEW YORK
Performance Indicator 8.PS.10
Use proportionality to model problems

What You'll Learn

- Identify corresponding parts and find missing measures of similar triangles.
- Solve problems involving indirect measurement using similar triangles.

Vocabulary
- similar triangles
- indirect measurement

How can similar triangles be used to create patterns?

The triangle at the right is called *Sierpinski's triangle.* The triangle is made up of various equilateral triangles. The following activity investigates patterns similar to the ones in Sierpinski's triangle.

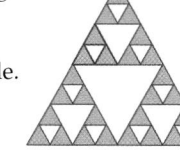

Step 1 On dot paper, draw a right triangle whose legs measures 8 and 16 units. Find the measure of each angle.

Step 2 Count to find the midpoint of each side of the triangle. Then connect the midpoints of each side.

Step 3 Shade the middle triangle.

Step 4 Repeat this process with each non-shaded triangle. Your triangles will resemble those shown below.

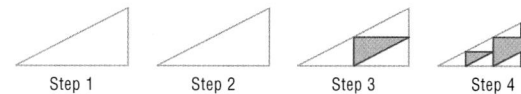

Step 1   Step 2   Step 3   Step 4

a. Compare the measures of the angles of each non-shaded triangle to the original triangle. **They are the same.**

b. They are shorter.

b. How do the lengths of the legs of the triangles compare?

CORRESPONDING PARTS Triangles that have the same shape but not necessarily the same size are called **similar triangles**. In the figure below, △ABC is similar to △XYZ. This is written as △ABC ~ △XYZ.

Reading Math

Similar Symbol
The symbol ~ is read
is similar to.

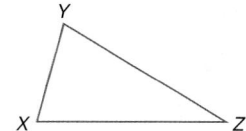

Similar triangles have corresponding angles and corresponding sides. Arcs are used to show congruent angles.

Corresponding Angles
∠A ↔ ∠X   ∠B ↔ ∠Y   ∠C ↔ ∠Z

Corresponding Sides
$\overline{AB}$ ↔ $\overline{XY}$ $\overline{BC}$ ↔ $\overline{YZ}$ $\overline{AC}$ ↔ $\overline{XZ}$

Lesson 9-7 Similar Triangles and Indirect Measurement **471**

---

1 Focus

5-Minute Check Transparency 9-7 Use as a quiz or review of Lesson 9-6.

Mathematical Background notes are available for this lesson on page 434D.

How can similar triangles be used to create patterns?

The opening activity questions are repeated on page 522 of the *Chapter 9 Resource Masters.*

Reading to Learn Mathematics, p. 522 **ELL**

Pre-Activity How can similar triangles be used to create patterns?
Do the activity at the top of page 471 in your textbook. Write your answers below.

    a. Compare the measures of the angles of each non-shaded triangle to the original triangle. **They are the same.**

    b. How do the lengths of the legs of the triangles compare?
    They are shorter.

Reading the Lesson 1–2. See students' work.
Write a definition and give an example of each new vocabulary word or phrase.

Vocabulary	Definition	Example
1. similar triangles		
2. indirect measurement		

3. The symbol ~ means (is uneven, is similar to).

4. Indirect measurement uses the properties of (similar triangles, midpoints) to find measurements that are difficult to measure directly.

Helping You Remember

5. *Similar* is a word that is used in everyday English.
    a. Find the definition of *similar* in a dictionary. Write the definition.   **related in appearance or nature; alike though not identical**
    b. Explain how the definition can help you remember how *similar* is used in mathematics.
    Similar triangles have angles that are the same and sides that, though not identical, are proportional.

Teaching Tip Explain to students that if a triangle were enlarged or reduced on a copier, similar triangles would be created.

Resource Manager

Workbooks and Reproducible Masters

Chapter 9 Resource Masters
- Study Guide and Intervention, p. 519
- Skills Practice, p. 520
- Practice, p. 521
- Reading to Learn Mathematics, p. 522
- Enrichment, p. 523

Parent and Student Study Guide Workbook, p. 78
School-to-Career Masters, p. 18

 Transparencies
5-Minute Check Transparency 9-7
Answer Key Transparencies

 Technology
Interactive Chalkboard
Pre-AlgePASS: Tutorial Plus, Lesson 29

CORRESPONDING PARTS

1 If $\triangle RUN \sim \triangle CAB$, what is the value of x? **20**

INDIRECT MEASUREMENT

2 **MAPS** A surveyor wants to find the distance RS across the lake. He constructs $\triangle PQT$ similar to $\triangle PRS$ and measures the distances as shown. What is the distance across the lake? **28.8 m**

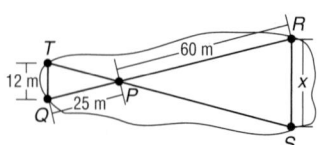

Teaching Tip Discuss with students when this type of measurement may be useful. Ask for examples from your neighborhood or area when indirect measurement might be used.

Concept Check Triangles that have the same shape but not necessarily the same size.

Reading Math

Segment Measure
The symbol *AB* means *the measure of segment AB.*

☑ **Concept Check** Define similar triangles.

The following properties are true for similar triangles.

Key Concept — *Corresponding Parts of Similar Triangles*

* **Words**   If two triangles are similar, then
  * the corresponding angles have the same measure, and
  * the corresponding sides are proportional.

* **Model**

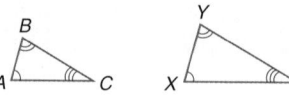

* **Symbols** $\angle A \cong \angle X$, $\angle B \cong \angle Y$, $\angle C \cong \angle Z$ and $\dfrac{AB}{XY} = \dfrac{BC}{YZ} = \dfrac{AC}{XZ}$

You can use proportions to determine the measures of the sides of similar triangles when some measures are known.

Example 1 *Find Measures of Similar Triangles*

If $\triangle JKM \sim \triangle RST$, what is the value of x?

The corresponding sides are proportional.

$\dfrac{JM}{RT} = \dfrac{KM}{ST}$ Write a proportion.

$\dfrac{3}{9} = \dfrac{5}{x}$ Replace *JM* with 3, *RT* with 9, *KM* with 5, and *ST* with *x*.

$3 \cdot x = 9 \cdot 5$ Find the cross products.

$3x = 45$ Simplify.

$x = 15$ Mentally divide each side by 3.

The value of x is 15.

INDIRECT MEASUREMENT The properties of similar triangles can be used to find measurements that are difficult to measure directly. This kind of measurement is called **indirect measurement**.

Career Choices

Cartographer •·······
A cartographer gathers geographic, political, and cultural information and then uses this information to create graphic or digital maps of areas.

📖 **Online Research**
For information about a career as a cartographer, visit:
www.pre-alg.com/careers

Example 2 *Use Indirect Measurement*

•**MAPS** In the figure, $\triangle ABE \sim \triangle DCE$. Find the distance across the lake.

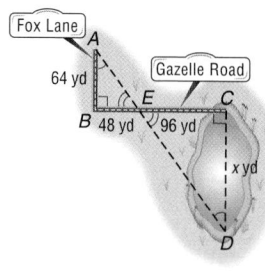

$\dfrac{EC}{EB} = \dfrac{CD}{BA}$ Write a proportion.

$\dfrac{96}{48} = \dfrac{x}{64}$ Replace *EC* with 96, *EB* with 48, *CD* with *x*, and *BA* with 64.

$96 \cdot 64 = 48 \cdot x$ Find the cross products.

$6144 = 48x$ Multiply.

$128 = x$ Divide each side by 48.

The distance across the lake is 128 yards.

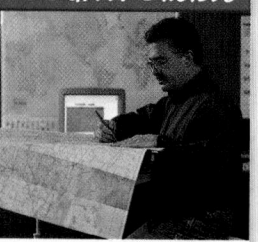

D A I L Y
INTERVENTION   **Unlocking Misconceptions**

* **Indirect Measurement** When looking at an illustration like that in Example 2 in the text, students may not recognize the similar triangles because of their orientation. If students are having difficulty, encourage them to copy the illustration, then cut the triangles apart and rotate them until the corresponding angles align. This should allow students to recognize the corresponding sides and set up a correct proportion.

The properties of similar triangles can be used to determine missing measures in shadow problems. This is called *shadow reckoning*.

Example 3 Use Shadow Reckoning

LANDMARKS Suppose the Space Needle in Seattle, Washington, casts a 220-foot shadow at the same time a nearby tourist casts a 2-foot shadow. If the tourist is 5.5 feet tall, how tall is the Space Needle?

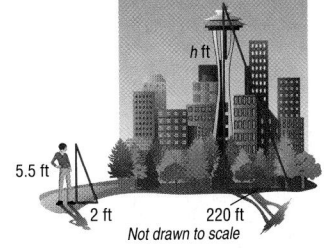

5.5 ft
2 ft   220 ft
Not drawn to scale

Explore You know the lengths of the shadows and the height of the tourist. You need to find the Space Needle's height.

Plan Write and solve a proportion.

Solve

tourist's height → $\dfrac{5.5}{h} = \dfrac{2}{220}$ ← tourist's shadow
Space Needle's height →   ← Space Needle's shadow

$5.5 \cdot 220 = h \cdot 2$ Find the cross products.
$1210 = 2h$ Multiply.
$605 = h$ Mentally divide each side by 2.

The height of the Space Needle is 605 feet.

Examine The tourist's height is a little less than 3 times the length of his or her shadow. The space needle should be a little less than 3 times its shadow, or $3 \cdot 220$, which is 660 feet. So, 605 is reasonable.

Check for Understanding

Concept Check

1. **OPEN ENDED** Draw two similar triangles and label the vertices. Then write a proportion that compares the corresponding sides. **1–2. See pp. 489A–489B.**

2. **Explain** indirect measurement in your own words.

Guided Practice

In Exercises 3 and 4, the triangles are similar. Write a proportion to find each missing measure. Then find the value of *x*. **3–4. See pp. 489A–489B.**

GUIDED PRACTICE KEY	
Exercises	**Examples**
3, 4	1
5	2
6	3

3.

4.

Applications

5. **MAPS** In the figure, $\triangle ABC \sim \triangle EDC$. Find the distance from Austintown to North Jackson. **6 km**

North Jackson   Austintown
D   x km   E
2 km
Deerfield
C
6 km
Ellsworth
A   18 km   B

6. **SHADOWS** At the same time a 10-foot flagpole casts an 8-foot shadow, a nearby tree casts a 40-foot shadow. How tall is the tree? **50 ft**

 www.pre-alg.com/extra_examples/ny   **Lesson 9-7** Similar Triangles and Indirect Measurement **473**

In-Class Example

3. **LANDMARKS** Suppose the John Hancock Center in Chicago, Illinois, casts a 257.5 foot shadow at the same time a nearby tourist casts a 1.5 foot shadow. If the tourist is 6 feet tall, how tall is the John Hancock Center? **1030 ft**

3 Practice/Apply

Study Notebook

Have students—
• add the definitions/examples of the vocabulary terms to their Vocabulary Builder worksheets for Chapter 9.
• draw and label a pair of similar triangles, then write out in symbols the relationships between the angles and sides.
• include any other item(s) that they find helpful in mastering the skills in this lesson.

About the Exercises . . .

Organization by Objective
• **Corresponding Parts:** 7–12
• **Indirect Measurement:** 15–18

Odd/Even Assignments
Exercises 7–18 are structured so that students practice the same concepts whether they are assigned odd or even problems.

Assignment Guide

Basic: 7, 9, 13–17 odd, 19–35
Average: 7–17 odd, 19–35
Advanced: 8–18 even, 19–31 (Optional: 32–35)

DAILY INTERVENTION

Differentiated Instruction

• **Naturalist** Have students work in pairs to use shadow reckoning to measure trees, bushes, or other natural objects in the area. Each pair should use a measuring tape to measure each other's height, their shadows' lengths, and the lengths of the objects' shadows. Have students do their measurements three times in one day—in the morning, at noon, and in the afternoon. Discuss whether their calculations for the objects' heights at the three different times remained equal. Discuss why the lengths of the shadows changed during the day.

★ indicates increased difficulty

Practice and Apply

In Exercises 7–12, the triangles are similar. Write a proportion to find each missing measure. Then find the value of x. **7–12. See margin.**

7.

8.

9.

10.

★11.

★12.

Determine whether each statement is *sometimes*, *always*, or *never* true.

13. always

13. The measures of corresponding angles in similar triangles are the same.

14. Similar triangles have the same shape and the same size. **sometimes**

In Exercises 15 and 16, the triangles are similar.

15. **PARKS** How far is the pavilion from the log cabin? **68 yd**

16. **ZOO** How far are the gorillas from the cheetahs? **105 m**

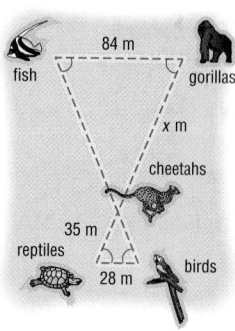

For Exercises 17 and 18, write a proportion. Then determine the missing measure.

••17. **ANIMALS** At the same time a baby giraffe casts a 3.2-foot shadow, a 15-foot adult giraffe casts an 8-foot shadow. How tall is the baby giraffe? **6 ft**

Answers

7. $\frac{x}{4} = \frac{10}{5}$; 8

8. $\frac{x}{6} = \frac{12}{8}$; 9

9. $\frac{x}{18} = \frac{20}{15}$; 24

10. $\frac{x}{9} = \frac{9}{6}$; 13.5

11. $\frac{x}{3} = \frac{7}{4.2}$; 5

12. $\frac{x}{9} = \frac{2}{7.5}$; 2.4

18. RIDES Suppose a roller coaster casts a shadow of 31.5 feet. At the same time, a nearby Ferris wheel casts a 19-foot shadow. If the roller coaster is 126 feet tall, how tall is the Ferris wheel? **76 ft**

19. No; triangles *ABC* and *DEF* are not similar since corresponding sides are not proportional.

19. CRITICAL THINKING Triangle *ABC* has side lengths 3 cm, 5 cm, and 6 cm. Triangle *DEF* has side lengths 4 cm, 6 cm, and 8 cm. Determine whether $\triangle ABC \sim \triangle DEF$. Explain.

20. WRITING IN MATH   Answer the question that was posed at the beginning of the lesson. **See margin.**

How can similar triangles be used to create patterns?

Include the following in your answer:
• an explanation telling how Sierpinski's triangle relates to similarity, and
• an example of the pattern formed when Steps 1–4 are performed on an acute scalene triangle.

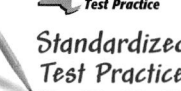

Standardized Test Practice
Ⓐ Ⓑ Ⓒ Ⓓ

21. The triangles shown are similar. Find the length of $\overline{JM}$ to the nearest tenth. **A**

Ⓐ 3.7   Ⓑ 3.9
Ⓒ 4.1   Ⓓ 8.3

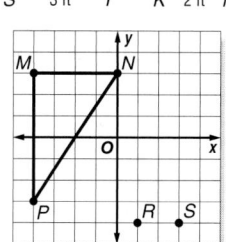

22. On the coordinate system, $\triangle MNP$ and two coordinates for $\triangle RST$ are shown. Which coordinate for point *T* will make $\triangle MNP$ and $\triangle RST$ similar triangles? **B**

Ⓐ $T(3, 1)$ Ⓑ $T(1, -1)$
Ⓒ $T(1, 2)$ Ⓓ $T(1, 1)$

Maintain Your Skills

Mixed Review   **Find the distance between each pair of points. Round to the nearest tenth, if necessary.** *(Lesson 9-6)*

23. $S(2, 3), T(0, 6)$ **3.6**   **24.** $E(-1, 1), F(3, -2)$ **5**   **25.** $W(4, -6), V(-3, -5)$ **7.1**

If *c* is the measure of the hypotenuse, find each missing measure. Round to the nearest tenth, if necessary. *(Lesson 9-5)*

26. $a = 8, b = ?, c = 34$ **33.0**   **27.** $a = ?, b = 27, c = 82$ **77.4**

28. ALGEBRA Write an equation for the line that passes through points at $(1, -1)$ and $(-2, 11)$. *(Lesson 8-7)* $y = -4x + 3$

Write each percent as a fraction in simplest form. *(Lesson 6-4)*

29. 25% $\frac{1}{4}$ **30.** $87\frac{1}{2}\%$ $\frac{7}{8}$ **31.** 150% $1\frac{1}{2}$

Getting Ready for the Next Lesson   **PREREQUISITE SKILL** Express each fraction as a decimal. Round to four decimal places, if necessary. *(To review writing fractions as decimals, see Lesson 5-1.)*

32. $\frac{12}{16}$ **0.75**   **33.** $\frac{10}{14}$ **0.7143**   **34.** $\frac{20}{25}$ **0.8**   **35.** $\frac{9}{40}$ **0.225**

---

4 Assess

Open-Ended Assessment
Writing Have students write instructions for finding height or length using similar triangles. Their example can involve shadow reckoning or another type of similar triangles problem.

Getting Ready for Lesson 9-8

PREREQUISITE SKILL Lesson 9-8 presents trigonometric ratios. Ratios involving the sides of triangles are used to find a trigonometric value. Exercises 32–35 should be used to determine your students' familiarity with expressing fractions as decimals.

Answer

20. By increasing or decreasing the size of similar triangles, patterns can be formed. Answers should include the following.

• All of the triangles used in Sierpinski's triangle are similar.

• Sample answer:

Teacher to Teacher

Andrea L. Ellyson   Great Bridge M.S., Chesapeake, VA

"My students often have trouble identifying corresponding parts when working with proportions. Have students use patty paper or tracing paper to trace each pair of similar triangles. Cut them apart and rotate or flip them so that the corresponding angles and sides are more easily identified. This visualization really helps students set up the proportions correctly."

Algebra Activity

Getting Started

Objective Discover the special relationship among right triangles and their sides.

Materials
metric ruler

protractor

calculator

Teach

- Make sure students measure their angles accurately.
- You may want to have students work in pairs and check each other's work.

Assess

In **Exercises 1–3**, students should
- make a new table for each triangle drawn.
- test their conjecture.

Study Notebook

You may wish to have students summarize this activity and what they learned from it.

Answers

1. See students' work.

2. The ratios of the sides of any 30°-60°-90° triangle are about 0.50, 0.875, and 1.75.

3. See students' work. The ratios of the sides of any 45°-45°-90° triangle are about 0.71, 0.71, and 1.00.

Algebra Activity

NEW YORK *Performance Indicator* **Reinforcement of 7.G.6 Explore the relationship between the lengths of the three sides of a right triangle** to develop the Pythagorean Theorem

Ratios in Right Triangles

In the following activity, you will discover the special relationship among right triangles and their sides.

In any right triangle, the side **opposite** an angle is the side that is not part of the angle. In the triangle shown,
- side a is opposite $\angle A$,
- side b is opposite $\angle B$, and
- side c is opposite $\angle C$.

The side that is not opposite an angle and not the hypotenuse is called the **adjacent** side. In $\triangle ABC$,
- side b is adjacent to $\angle A$,
- side a is adjacent to $\angle B$, and
- sides a and b are adjacent to $\angle C$.

Step 1 Copy the table shown.

Step 2 Draw right triangle XYZ in which $m\angle X = 30°$, $m\angle Y = 60°$, and $m\angle Z = 90°$.

Step 3 Find the length to the nearest millimeter of the leg opposite the angle that measures 30°. Record the length.

Step 4 Find the length of the leg adjacent to the 30° angle. Record the length.

	30° angle	60° angle
Length (mm) of opposite leg		
Length (mm) of adjacent leg		
Length (mm) of hypotenuse		
Ratio 1		
Ratio 2		
Ratio 3		

Step 5 Find the length of the hypotenuse. Record the length.

Step 6 Using the measurements and a calculator, find each of the following ratios to the nearest hundredth. Record the results.

$$\text{Ratio 1} = \frac{\text{opposite leg}}{\text{hypotenuse}} \quad \text{Ratio 2} = \frac{\text{adjacent leg}}{\text{hypotenuse}} \quad \text{Ratio 3} = \frac{\text{opposite leg}}{\text{adjacent leg}}$$

Step 7 Repeat the procedure for the 60° angle. Record the results.

Model and Analyze 1–3. See margin.

1. Draw another 30°-60°-90° triangle with side lengths that are different than the one drawn in the activity. Then find the ratios for the 30°angle and the 60° angle.

2. **Make a conjecture** about the ratio of the sides of any 30°-60°-90° triangle.

3. Repeat the activity with a triangle whose angles measure 45°, 45°, and 90°.

476 Chapter 9 Real Numbers and Right Triangles

Resource Manager

 Teaching Pre-Algebra with Manipulatives

- p. 21 (master for protractors)
- p. 22 (master for rulers)
- p. 120 (student recording sheet)

Glencoe Mathematics Classroom Manipulative Kit

- metric ruler
- protractor

Sine, Cosine, and Tangent Ratios

NEW YORK *Performance Indicator*
Reinforcement of 7.G.6 Explore the relationship between the lengths of the three sides of a right triangle to develop the Pythagorean Theorem.

What You'll Learn

- Find sine, cosine, and tangent ratios.
- Solve problems by using the trigonometric ratios.

Vocabulary

- trigonometry
- trigonometric ratio
- sine
- cosine
- tangent

How are ratios in right triangles used in the real world?

In parasailing, a towrope is used to attach the parachute to the boat.

a. What type of triangle do the towrope, water, and height of the person above the water form? **right**

b. Name the hypotenuse of the triangle. $\overline{AC}$

c. What type of angle do the towrope and the water form? **acute**

d. Which side is opposite this angle? $\overline{AB}$

e. Other than the hypotenuse, name the side adjacent to this angle. $\overline{BC}$

FIND TRIGONOMETRIC RATIOS

Trigonometry is the study of the properties of triangles. The word trigonometry means *angle measure*. A **trigonometric ratio** is a ratio of the lengths of two sides of a right triangle.

The most common trigonometric ratios are the **sine**, **cosine**, and **tangent** ratios. These ratios are abbreviated as *sin*, *cos*, and *tan*, respectively.

Key Concept — Trigonometric Ratios

- **Words** If $\angle A$ is an acute angle of a right triangle,

$$\sin \angle A = \frac{\text{measure of leg opposite } \angle A}{\text{measure of hypotenuse}},$$

$$\cos \angle A = \frac{\text{measure of leg adjacent to } \angle A}{\text{measure of hypotenuse}}, \text{ and}$$

$$\tan \angle A = \frac{\text{measure of leg opposite } \angle A}{\text{measure of leg adjacent to } \angle A}.$$

- **Model**

  leg opposite $\angle A$ — a
  hypotenuse — c
  leg adjacent to $\angle A$ — b

- **Symbols**

$$\sin A = \frac{a}{c}$$

$$\cos A = \frac{b}{c}$$

$$\tan A = \frac{a}{b}$$

Reading Math

Trigonometry Terms

The notation sin *A* is read *the sine of angle A*. The notation cos *A* is read *the cosine of angle A*. The notation tan *A* is read *the tangent of angle A*.

All right triangles that have the same measure for $\angle A$ are similar. So, the value of the trigonometric ratio depends only on the measure of $\angle A$, not the size of the triangle. The trigonometric ratios are the same for angle A no matter what the size of the triangle.

---

1 Focus

5-Minute Check Transparency 9-8 Use as a quiz or review of Lesson 9-7.

Mathematical Background notes are available for this lesson on page 434D.

How are ratios in right triangles used in the real world?

The opening activity questions are repeated on page 527 of the *Chapter 9 Resource Masters.*

Reading to Learn Mathematics, p. 527 — ELL

Pre-Activity *How are ratios in right triangles used in the real world?*

Do the activity at the top of page 477 in your textbook. Write your answers below.

a. What type of triangle do the towrope, water, and height of the person above the water form? right

b. Name the hypotenuse of the triangle. $\overline{AC}$

c. What type of angle do the towrope and the water form? acute

d. Which side is opposite this angle? $\overline{AB}$

e. Other than the hypotenuse, name the side adjacent to this angle. $\overline{BC}$

Reading the Lesson 1–5. See students' work.

Write a definition and give an example of each new vocabulary word or phrase.

Vocabulary	Definition	Example
1. trigonometry		
2. trigonometric ratio		
3. sine		
4. cosine		
5. tangent		

Decide whether each statement is true or false.

6. Trigonometric ratios can be used with acute and obtuse angles. false

7. The value of the trigonometric ratio does not depend on the size of the triangle. true

8. To determine tangent, you must know the measure of the hypotenuse. false

Helping You Remember

9. Develop a rhyme, abbreviation, or other memory device to help you remember the trigonometric ratios. Sample answer: SOH-CAH-TOA

Resource Manager

Workbooks and Reproducible Masters

Chapter 9 Resource Masters
- Study Guide and Intervention, p. 524
- Skills Practice, p. 525
- Practice, p. 526
- Reading to Learn Mathematics, p. 527
- Enrichment, p. 528
- Assessment, p. 544

Graphing Calculator and Spreadsheet Masters, p. 36
Parent and Student Study Guide Workbook, p. 79

  Transparencies

5-Minute Check Transparency 9-8
Answer Key Transparencies

  Technology

Interactive Chalkboard
Pre-AlgePASS: Tutorial Plus, Lesson 30

2 Teach

FIND TRIGONOMETRIC RATIOS

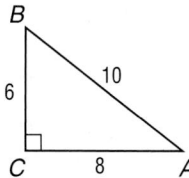
1 Find sin A, cos A, and tan A.

Triangle with B at top, C at bottom-left (right angle), A at bottom-right. Side $BC = 6$, side $CA = 8$, hypotenuse $BA = 10$.

sin A = 0.6; cos A = 0.8;
tan A = 0.75

2 Find each value to the nearest ten thousandth.

a. sin 19° **0.3256**

b. cos 51° **0.6293**

c. tan 24° **0.4452**

Teaching Tip Show students a table of trigonometric ratios and discuss how it is used.

APPLY TRIGONOMETRIC RATIOS

3 Find the missing measure. Round to the nearest tenth.
36.9

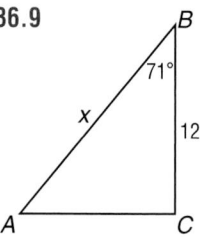

Triangle with B at top-right, angle 71° at B, side $BC = 12$, side x on left, A at bottom-left, C at bottom-right (right angle).

4 **ARCHITECTURE** A tourist visiting the Petronas Towers in Kuala Lumpur, Malaysia, stands 261 feet away from their base. She looks at the top at an angle of 80° with the ground. How tall are the Towers? **1480.2 ft**

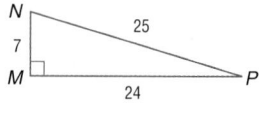

Example 1 Find Trigonometric Ratios

Find sin P, cos P, and tan P.

Triangle N, M, P with right angle at M. $NM = 7$, $NP = 25$, $MP = 24$.

$$\sin P = \frac{\text{measure of leg opposite } \angle P}{\text{measure of hypotenuse}}$$

$$= \frac{7}{25} \text{ or } 0.28$$

$$\cos P = \frac{\text{measure of leg adjacent to } \angle P}{\text{measure of hypotenuse}}$$

$$= \frac{24}{25} \text{ or } 0.96$$

$$\tan P = \frac{\text{measure of leg opposite } \angle P}{\text{measure of leg adjacent to } \angle P}$$

$$= \frac{7}{24} \text{ or } 0.2917$$

You can use a calculator or a table of trigonometric ratios to find the sine, cosine, or tangent ratio for an angle with a given degree measure. Be sure that your calculator is in *degree* mode.

Example 2 Use a Calculator to Find Trigonometric Ratios

Find each value to the nearest ten thousandth.

a. sin 42°

[SIN] 42 [ENTER] 0.669130606

So, sin 42° is about 0.6691.

b. cos 65°

[COS] 65 [ENTER] 0.422618262

So, cos 65° is about 0.4226.

c. tan 78°

[TAN] 78 [ENTER] 4.704630109

So, tan 78° is about 4.7046.

APPLY TRIGONOMETRIC RATIOS Trigonometric ratios can be used to find missing measures in a right triangle if the measure of an acute angle and the length of one side of the triangle are known.

Example 3 Use Trigonometric Ratios

Find the missing measure. Round to the nearest tenth.

Triangle with A at top, right angle at B (bottom-left), C at bottom-right. $AC = 21$ ft, side $x = AB$, angle at $C = 36°$.

The measures of an acute angle and the hypotenuse are known. You need to find the measure of the side opposite the angle. Use the sine ratio.

$$\sin \angle C = \frac{\text{measure of leg opposite to } \angle C}{\text{measure of hypotenuse}}$$ Write the sine ratio.

$$\sin 36° = \frac{x}{21}$$ Substitution

$$21(\sin 36°) = 21 \cdot \frac{x}{21}$$ Multiply each side by 21.

21 [×] [SIN] 36 [ENTER] 12.3434903

$$12.3 \approx x$$ Simplify.

The measure of the side opposite the acute angle is about 12.3 feet.

DAILY INTERVENTION

Unlocking Misconceptions

- **Find Trigonometric Ratios** Students may invert or confuse the ratios associated with sine, cosine, and tangent. Have students make study cards for each ratio, including the name, the ratio, and a sketch. These study cards can be used as students complete the exercises.

Example 4 Use Trigonometric Ratios to Solve a Problem

ARCHITECTURE The Leaning Tower of Pisa in Pisa, Italy, tilts about 5.2° from vertical. If the tower is 55 meters tall, how far has its top shifted from its original position?

Use the tangent ratio.

$\tan \angle A = \dfrac{\text{measure of leg opposite } \angle A}{\text{measure of leg adjacent to } \angle A}$ Write the tangent ratio.

$\tan 5.2° = \dfrac{x}{55}$ Substitution

$55(\tan 5.2°) = 55 \cdot \dfrac{x}{55}$ Multiply each side by 55.

55 ☒ TAN 5.2 ENTER   5.00539211

$5.0 \approx x$ Simplify.

The top of the tower has shifted about 5.0 meters from its original position.

Check for Understanding

Concept Check
1–2. See margin.

1. **OPEN ENDED** Compare and contrast the sine, cosine, and tangent ratios.

2. **FIND THE ERROR** Susan and Tadeo are finding the height of the hill.

Susan
$\sin 15° = \dfrac{x}{580}$
$580(\sin 15°) = x$
$150 \approx x$

Tadeo
$\sin 15° = \dfrac{x}{560}$
$560(\sin 15°) = x$
$145 \approx x$

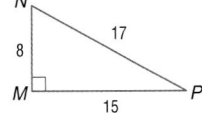

Who is correct? Explain your reasoning.

Guided Practice

GUIDED PRACTICE KEY	
Exercises	Examples
3–5	1
6–8	2
9–11	3
12	4

Find each sine, cosine, or tangent. Round to four decimal places, if necessary.

3. sin N **0.8824**

4. cos N **0.4706**

5. tan N **1.875**

Use a calculator to find each value to the nearest ten thousandth.

6. sin 52° **0.7880**   7. cos 19° **0.9455**   8. tan 76° **4.0108**

For each triangle, find each missing measure to the nearest tenth.

9. **25.6**   10. **26.2**   11. **7.8**

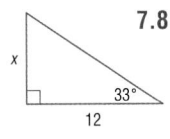

Application 12. **RECREATION** Miranda is flying a kite on a 50-yard string, which makes a 50° angle with the ground. How high above the ground is the kite? **38.3 yd**

www.pre-alg.com/extra_examples /ny   Lesson 9-8 Sine, Cosine, and Tangent Ratios   479

Answers

1. The sine ratio compares the measure of the leg opposite the angle to the measure of the hypotenuse. The cosine ratio compares the measure of the leg adjacent to the angle to the measure of the hypotenuse. The tangent ratio compares the measure of the leg opposite the angle to the measure of the leg adjacent to the angle.

2. Susan; The sine ratio is the ratio of the opposite side to the hypotenuse. The length of the side opposite the 15° angle is x m. The length of the hypotenuse is 580 m.
So, $\sin 15° = \dfrac{x}{580}$.

---

3 Practice/Apply

Study Notebook

Have students—
• complete the definitions/examples for the remaining terms on the Vocabulary Builder worksheets for Chapter 9.
• draw a right triangle, label its sides and angles, and write out in symbols the formulas for sine, cosine, and tangent for one of the angles.
• include any other item(s) that they find helpful in mastering the skills in this lesson.

About the Exercises . . .

Organization by Objective
• **Find Trigonometric Ratios:** 13–26
• **Apply Trigonometric Ratios:** 27–32, 33–36, 37–39

Odd/Even Assignments
Exercises 13–32 are structured so that students practice the same concepts whether they are assigned odd or even problems.

Assignment Guide

Basic: 13–17 odd, 21–35 odd, 40–52

Average: 13–39 odd, 40–52

Advanced: 14–38 even, 40–52

DAILY INTERVENTION FIND THE ERROR
If students are having difficulty recognizing which side is the hypotenuse when setting up trigonometric ratios, remind them that the hypotenuse is always the longest side of the triangle. Tell them to carefully observe the triangle when substituting values in the sine and cosine formulas.

★ indicates increased difficulty

Practice and Apply

Find each sine, cosine, or tangent. Round to four decimal places, if necessary.

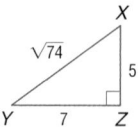

13. sin N **0.9231**   14. sin K **0.3846**
15. cos C **0.7241**   16. cos A **0.6897**
17. tan N **2.4**   18. tan C **0.9524**

★ 19. Triangle RST is shown. Find sin R, cos R, and tan R. **0.8944; 0.4472; 2.0**

★ 20. For △XYZ, what is the value of sin X, cos X, and tan X? **0.8137; 0.5812; 1.4**

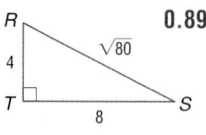

Use a calculator to find each value to the nearest ten thousandth.

21. sin 6° **0.1045**   22. sin 51° **0.7771**   23. cos 31° **0.8572**
24. cos 87° **0.0523**   25. tan 12° **0.2126**   26. tan 66° **2.2460**

For each triangle, find each missing measure to the nearest tenth.

27. **6.8**   28. **3.4**   29. **24.9**

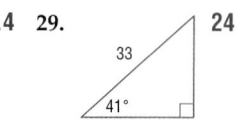

30. **4.7**   31. **97.6**   32. **24.4**

33. **SHADOWS** An *angle of elevation* is formed by a horizontal line and a line of sight above it. A flagpole casts a shadow 25 meters long when the angle of elevation of the Sun is 40°. How tall is the flagpole? **about 21 m**

34. **SAFETY** The angle that a wheelchair ramp forms with the ground should not exceed 6°. What is the height of the ramp if it is 20 feet long? Round to the nearest tenth. **2.1 ft**

35. **BUILDINGS** Refer to the diagram shown. What is the height of the building? **about 44 m**

36. **CIVIL ENGINEERING** An exit ramp makes a 17° angle with the highway. Suppose the length of the ramp is 210 yards. What is the length of the base of the ramp? Round to the nearest tenth. **200.8 yd**

DAILY INTERVENTION

Differentiated Instruction

• **Logical** Ask students to draw a right triangle, where $m\angle A = 42°$ and $m\angle B = 48°$. Have them find the sine, cosine, and tangent for each angle and present their answers in a chart. Discuss the relationship between the sine and cosine for the two angles. **sin A = cos B, cos A = sin B** Ask students if a relationship between the tangent measures exists. **tan A · tan B = 1** Discuss how knowing these relationships can help students check their work on problems dealing with the ratios.

Find each measure. Round to the nearest tenth.

★ 37. 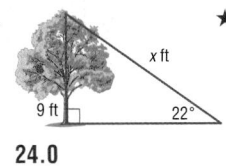 x ft, 9 ft, 22°

24.0

★ 38. 30°, x ft, 8 ft **13.9**

★ 39. 42°, 30 ft, x ft **40.4**

Trigonometric ratios are used to solve problems about the height of structures. Visit www.pre-alg.com/webquest to continue work on your WebQuest project.

CRITICAL THINKING
For Exercises 40–42, refer to the 45°-45°-90° and 30°-60°-90° triangles shown.

 45°, √2, 1, 45°, 1

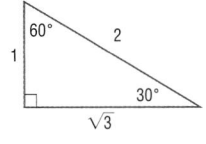 60°, 2, 1, 30°, √3

40. Complete the table shown. Round to four decimal places, if necessary.

x	30°	45°	60°
sin x	0.5	0.7071	0.866
cos x	0.866	0.7071	0.5
tan x	0.5774	1	1.7321

41. Write a few sentences describing the similarities among the resulting sine and cosine values. **See margin.**

42. Which angle measure has the same sine and cosine ratio? **45°**

43. WRITING IN MATH Answer the question that was posed at the beginning of the lesson. **See margin.**

How are ratios in right triangles used in the real world?

Include the following in your answer:
- an explanation of two different methods for finding the measures of the lengths of the sides of a right triangle, and
- a drawing of a real-world situation that involves the sine ratio, with the calculations and solution included.

44. If the measure of the hypotenuse of a right triangle is 5 feet and $m\angle B = 58°$, what is the measure of the leg adjacent to $\angle B$? **D**

Ⓐ 4.2402 Ⓑ 8.0017 Ⓒ 0.1060 Ⓓ 2.6496

45. Find the value of tan P to the nearest tenth. **C**

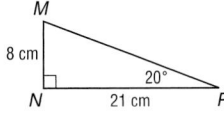 M, 8 cm, 20°, N, 21 cm, P

Ⓐ 2.6 Ⓑ 0.5 Ⓒ 0.4 Ⓓ 0.1

Maintain Your Skills

Mixed Review **46.** At the same time a 40-foot silo casts a 22-foot shadow, a fence casts a 3.3-foot shadow. Find the height of the fence. *(Lesson 9-7)* **6 ft**

The coordinates of the endpoints of a segment are given. Find the coordinates of the midpoint of each segment. *(Lesson 9-6)*

47. $\left(1\frac{1}{2}, \frac{1}{2}\right)$

47. A(3, −4), C(0, 5) **48.** M(−2, 1), N(6, −9) **49.** R(−3, 0), S(−3, −8)

48. (2, −4)
49. (−3, −4)

ALGEBRA Solve each inequality. *(Lesson 7-5)*

50. $5m < 5$ $m < 1$ **51.** $\frac{a}{-2} > 3$ $a < -6$ **52.** $-4x \geq -16$ $x \leq 4$

4 Assess

Open-Ended Assessment
Writing Have students write a paragraph explaining how knowing the angle between an observer on the ground and the top of a flagpole and the distance between the observer and flagpole will allow them to find the flagpole's height.

 Tips for New Teachers

Small-Group Management If you are having students work in groups of three to four, make sure each student has an assigned task or part of a problem. Students should have specific responsibilities to keep them involved and on-task.

Assessment Options
Quiz (Lessons 9-7 and 9-8) is available on p. 544 of the *Chapter 9 Resource Masters.*

Answers

41. sin 45° = cos 45°; sin 60° = cos 30°; sin 30° = cos 60°

43. To find heights of buildings. Answers should include the following.
- If two of the three measures of the sides of a right triangle are known, you can use the Pythagorean Theorem to find the measure of the third side. If the measure of an acute angle and the length of one side of a right triangle are known, trigonometric ratios can be used to find the missing measures.

 6°, 19 ft, x ft

$$\sin 6° = \frac{x}{19}$$

$19(\sin 6°) = x$ $2.0 \approx x$

The height of the ramp is about 2 feet.

Lesson 9-8 Sine, Cosine, and Tangent Ratios **481**

Getting Started

Know Your Calculator The graphing calculator has two functions assigned to each key. The additional function is accessed by pressing **2nd** first. The flashing up arrow icon will appear on your screen. This method must be used to solve for angles in a right triangle when only measures of the sides are provided.

Teach

- Have students write out each ratio before solving. As students work the exercises, their calculators should be in the degree, not radian, mode.
- Remind students that they can check their answers by adding the angle measures. The sum of the two acute angles should equal 90.
- Remind students that $\sin^{-1}$ means the inverse sine function, not the value of sine raised to the negative one power.
- Have students complete Exercises 1–3.

Assess

- Have students make up a problem and exchange with another student. Make sure they check their answers.
- Ask students what ratio they would use to solve a problem if the measures of the two sides and not the hypotenuse were given. **tangent**

NEW YORK *Performance Indicator* Reinforcement of 7.G.6 **Explore the relationship between the lengths of the three sides of a right triangle** to develop the Pythagorean Theorem

Finding Angles of a Right Triangle

A calculator can be used to find the measure of an acute angle of a right triangle if you know the measures of two sides of the triangle.

Example

The end of an exit ramp from an interstate highway is 22 feet higher than the highway. If the ramp is 630 feet long, what angle does it make with the highway?

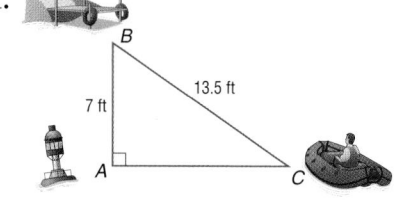

Step 1 Determine which trigonometric ratio is needed to solve the problem. Since you know the measure of the leg opposite $\angle A$ and the hypotenuse, use the sine ratio.

Step 2 Write the ratio.

$\sin \angle A = \dfrac{\text{opposite}}{\text{hypotenuse}}$ Sine Ratio

$\sin \angle A = \dfrac{22}{630}$ Substitution

Step 3 Use a calculator to find the measure of $\angle A$. The SIN^{-1} function will find the angle measure, given the value of its sine.

[2nd] [SIN⁻¹] 22 [÷] 630 [ENTER] 2.001211869

To the nearest degree, the measure of $\angle A$ is 2°.

Exercises

Use a calculator to find the measure of each acute angle. Round to the nearest degree.

1.

7 ft, 13.5 ft

$m\angle B \approx 59°$; $m\angle C \approx 31°$

2.

17 m, 39 m

$m\angle F \approx 26°$; $m\angle D \approx 64°$

3. A flower garden is located 46 meters due west of an elm tree. A fountain is located 19 meters due south of the same elm tree. What are the measures of the angles formed by these three park features? **22°, 68°, 90°**

 www.pre-alg.com/other_calculator_keystrokes

Study Guide and Review

Vocabulary and Concept Check

acute angle (p. 449)
acute triangle (p. 454)
angle (p. 447)
congruent (p. 455)
converse (p. 462)
cosine (p. 477)
degree (p. 448)
Distance Formula (p. 466)
equilateral triangle (p. 455)
hypotenuse (p. 460)
indirect measurement (p. 472)
irrational numbers (p. 441)
isosceles triangle (p. 455)
legs (p. 460)

line (p. 447)
line segment (p. 453)
midpoint (p. 468)
Midpoint Formula (p. 468)
obtuse angle (p. 449)
obtuse triangle (p. 454)
perfect square (p. 436)
point (p. 447)
protractor (p. 448)
Pythagorean Theorem (p. 460)
radical sign (p. 436)
ray (p. 447)
real numbers (p. 441)
right angle (p. 449)

right triangle (p. 454)
scalene triangle (p. 455)
sides (p. 447)
similar triangles (p. 471)
sine (p. 477)
solving a right triangle (p. 461)
square root (p. 436)
straight angle (p. 449)
tangent (p. 477)
triangle (p. 453)
trigonometric ratio (p. 477)
trigonometry (p. 477)
vertex (pp. 447, 453)

Complete each sentence with the correct term. Choose from the list above.

1. The set of rational numbers and the set of irrational numbers make up the set of __?__. **real numbers**

2. A(n) __?__ measures between 0° and 90°. **acute angle**

3. A(n) __?__ triangle has one angle with a measurement greater than 90°. **obtuse**

4. A(n) __?__ has all sides congruent. **equilateral triangle**

5. In a right triangle, the side opposite the right angle is the __?__. **hypotenuse**

6. Triangles that have the same shape but not necessarily the same size are called __?__. **similar triangles**

7. A(n) __?__ is a ratio of the lengths of two sides of a right triangle. **trigonometric ratio**

8. A(n) __?__ is a part of a line that extends indefinitely in one direction. **ray**

Lesson-by-Lesson Review

9-1 Squares and Square Roots

See pages 436–440.

Concept Summary
- The square root of a number is one of two equal factors of the number.

 Example Find the square root of $-\sqrt{49}$.

$-\sqrt{49}$ indicates the *negative* square root of 49. Since $7^2 = 49$, $-\sqrt{49}, = -7$.

Exercises Find each square root, if possible. *See Example 1 on page 436.*

9. $\sqrt{36}$ **6**   10. $\sqrt{100}$ **10**   11. $-\sqrt{81}$ **−9**

12. $\pm\sqrt{121}$ **±11**   13. $\sqrt{-25}$ **not possible**   14. $-\sqrt{225}$ **−15**

 www.pre-alg.com/vocabulary_review

Study Guide and Review

Vocabulary and Concept Check

- This alphabetical list of vocabulary terms in Chapter 9 includes a page reference where each term was introduced.

- **Assessment** A vocabulary review/test for Chapter 9 is available on p. 542 of the *Chapter 9 Resource Masters*.

Lesson-by-Lesson Review

For each lesson,
- the main ideas are summarized,
- additional examples review concepts, and
- practice exercises are provided.

Vocabulary PuzzleMaker

ELL The Vocabulary PuzzleMaker software improves students' mathematics vocabulary using four puzzle formats—crossword, scramble, word search using a word list, and word search using clues. Students can work on a computer screen or from a printed handout.

MindJogger Videoquizzes

ELL MindJogger Videoquizzes provide an alternative review of concepts presented in this chapter. Students work in teams in a game show format to gain points for correct answers. The questions are presented in three rounds.

Round 1 Concepts (5 questions)
Round 2 Skills (4 questions)
Round 3 Problem Solving (4 questions)

FOLDABLES™
Study Organizer

For more information about Foldables, see *Teaching Mathematics with Foldables*.

Have students review their Foldables to be sure they have included visuals for every lesson in this chapter.

Encourage students to refer to their Foldables while completing the Study Guide and Review and to use them in preparing for the Chapter Test.

9-2 The Real Number System

See pages 441–445.

Concept Summary

- Numbers that cannot be written as terminating or repeating decimals are called irrational numbers.
- The set of rational numbers and the set of irrational numbers together make up the set of real numbers.

Example   Solve $x^2 = 72$. Round to the nearest tenth.

$$x^2 = 72$$ Write the equation.

$$\sqrt{x^2} = \sqrt{72}$$ Take the square root of each side.

$$x = \sqrt{72} \text{ or } x = -\sqrt{72}$$ Find the positive and negative square root.

$$x \approx 8.5 \text{ or } x \approx -8.5$$

Exercises   Solve each equation. Round to the nearest tenth, if necessary.

See Example 3 on page 443. **16. 6.2, −6.2   17. 1.2, −1.2**

15. $n^2 = 81$ **9, −9 16.** $t^2 = 38$ **17.** $y^2 = 1.44$ **18.** $7.5 = r^2$ **2.7, −2.7**

9-3 Angles

See pages 447–451.

Concept Summary

- An acute angle has a measure between 0° and 90°.
- A right angle measures 90°.
- An obtuse angle has a measure between 90° and 180°.
- A straight angle measures 180°.

Example   Use a protractor to find the measure of ∠ABC. Then classify the angle as *acute, obtuse, right,* or *straight.*

∠ABC appears to be acute. So, its measure should be between 0° and 90°.

$m\angle ABC = 65°$

Since $m\angle ABC < 90°$, ∠ABC is acute.

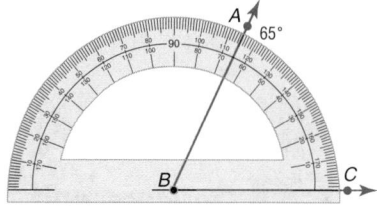

Exercises   Use a protractor to find the measure of each angle. Then classify each angle as *acute, obtuse, right,* or *straight.*

See Examples 1 and 3 on pages 448 and 449.

19. 90°; right   **20. 115°; obtuse**   **21.** **35°; acute**

9-4 Triangles

See pages
453–457.

Concept Summary

- Triangles can be classified by their angles as acute, obtuse, or right and by their sides as scalene, isosceles, or equilateral.

Example Classify the triangle by its angles and by its sides.
$\triangle HJK$ has all acute angles and two congruent sides.
So, $\triangle HJK$ is an acute isosceles triangle.

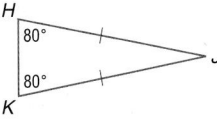

Exercises Classify each triangle by its angles and by its sides.
See Example 3 on page 455. **22. acute equilateral**

22.
23. 132° 24° 24° **obtuse isosceles**
24. 56° 34° **right scalene**

9-5 The Pythagorean Theorem

See pages
460–464.

Concept Summary

- Pythagorean Theorem: $c^2 = a^2 + b^2$

Example Find the missing measure of the right triangle.

$c^2 = a^2 + b^2$ Pythagorean Theorem
$22^2 = 9^2 + b^2$ Replace c with 22 and a with 9.
$403 = b^2$ Simplify; subtract 81 from each side.
$20.1 \approx b$ Take the square root of each side.

Exercises If c is the measure of the hypotenuse, find each missing measure. **Round to the nearest tenth, if necessary.** *See Example 2 on page 461.* **25. 13.7**

25. $a = 6, b = ?, c = 15$ **26.** $a = ?, b = 2, c = 7$ **6.7 27.** $a = 18, b = ?, c = 24$ **15.9**

9-6 The Distance and Midpoint Formulas

See pages
466–470.

Concept Summary

- Distance Formula: $d = \sqrt{(x_2 - x_1)^2 + (y_2 - y_1)^2}$
- Midpoint Formula: $\left(\dfrac{x_1 + x_2}{2}, \dfrac{y_1 + y_2}{2}\right)$

Example Find the distance between $A(-4, 0)$ and $B(2, 5)$.
$d = \sqrt{(x_2 - x_1)^2 + (y_2 - y_1)^2}$ Distance Formula
$d = \sqrt{[2 - (-4)]^2 + (5 - 0)^2}$ $(x_1, y_1) = (-4, 0), (x_2, y_2) = (2, 5)$.
$d \approx 7.8$ The distance between points A and B is about 7.8 units.

Study Guide and Review

Chapter
9 For More ...
• Extra Practice, see pages 745–747.
• Mixed Problem Solving, see page 766.

Exercises Find the distance between each pair of points. Round to the nearest tenth, if necessary. *See Example 1 on page 467.*

28. $J(0, 9)$, $K(2, 7)$ **2.8**   **29.** $A(-5, 1)$, $B(3, 6)$ **9.4**   **30.** $W(8, -4)$, $Y(3, 3)$ **8.6**

The coordinates of the endpoints of a segment are given. Find the coordinates of the midpoint of each segment. *See Example 3 on page 468.*

31. $M(8, 0)$, $N(-2, 10)$ **32.** $C(5, 9)$, $D(-7, 3)$ **33.** $Q(-6, 4)$, $R(6, -8)$

31. (3, 5)   **32.** (−1, 6)   **33.** (0, −2)

9-7 Similar Triangles and Indirect Measurement

See pages 471–475.

Concept Summary

• If two triangles are similar, then the corresponding angles have the same measure, and the corresponding sides are proportional.

Example If $\triangle ABC \sim \triangle KLM$, what is the value of x?

$\dfrac{AC}{KM} = \dfrac{BC}{LM}$ Write a proportion.

$\dfrac{x}{3} = \dfrac{2}{4}$ Substitution

$x = 1.5$ Find cross products and simplify.

Exercises In Exercises 34 and 35, the triangles are similar. Write a proportion to find each missing measure. Then find the value of x. *See Example 1 on page 472.*

34.

$\dfrac{LM}{TU} = \dfrac{MN}{UV}$; **7**

35.

$\dfrac{AB}{HJ} = \dfrac{BC}{JK}$; **10**

9-8 Sine, Cosine, and Tangent Ratios

See pages 477–481.

Concept Summary

• Trigonometric ratios compare the lengths of two sides of a right triangle.

Example Find cos S.

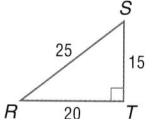

$\cos S = \dfrac{15}{25}$ or 0.6

Exercises Find each sine, cosine, or tangent in $\triangle RST$ above. Round to four decimal places, if necessary. *See Example 1 on page 478.*

36. $\sin R$ **0.6**   **37.** $\tan S$ **1.3333**   **38.** $\tan R$ **0.75**

Vocabulary and Concepts

1. **OPEN ENDED** Give an example of a whole number, a natural number, an irrational number, a rational number, and an integer. **Sample answer: 1; 5; $\sqrt{27}$; $\frac{5}{8}$; −6**

2. Explain how to classify a triangle by its angles and by its sides. **See margin.**

Skills and Applications

Find each square root, if possible.

3. $\sqrt{81}$ **9**
4. $-\sqrt{121}$ **−11**
5. $\pm\sqrt{49}$ **−7, 7**

6. Without using a calculator, estimate $-\sqrt{42}$ to the nearest integer. **−6**

ALGEBRA Solve each equation. Round to the nearest tenth, if necessary.

7. $x^2 = 100$ **10, −10**
8. $w^2 = 38$ **6.2, −6.2**

9. Use a protractor to measure $\angle CAB$. Then classify the angle as *acute, obtuse, right,* or *straight.* **65°; acute**

For Exercises 10 and 11, use the following information.
In $\triangle MNP$, $m\angle N = 87°$ and $m\angle P = 32°$.

10. Find the measure of $\angle M$. **61°**

11. Classify $\triangle MNP$ by its angles and by its sides. **acute scalene**

If c is the measure of the hypotenuse, find each missing measure. Round to the nearest tenth, if necessary.

12. $a = 6, b = 8, c = ?$ **10**
13. $a = 15, b = ?, c = 32$ **28.3**

14. **HIKING** Brandon hikes 7 miles south and 4 miles west. How far is he from the starting point of his hike? Round to the nearest tenth. **8.1 m**

15. Find the distance between $A(3, 8)$ and $B(-5, 2)$. Then find the coordinates of the midpoint of $\overline{AB}$. **10; (−1, 5)**

16. **PARKS** In the map of the park, the triangles are similar. Find the distance to the nearest tenth from the playground to the swimming pool. **62.5 ft**

Swimming Pool
45 ft
50 ft
36 ft
Playground
x ft

Find each sine, cosine, or tangent. Round to four decimal places, if necessary.

17. $\sin P$ **0.9231**
18. $\tan M$ **0.4167**
19. $\cos P$ **0.3846**

P
5
13
N
12
M

20. **STANDARDIZED TEST PRACTICE** Which statement is true? **C**

  Ⓐ $4 < \sqrt{10} < 3$
  Ⓑ $-6 > -\sqrt{28} > -5$
  Ⓒ $-7 > -\sqrt{59} > -8$
  Ⓓ $7 < \sqrt{47} < 6$

www.pre-alg.com/chapter_test/ny

Portfolio Suggestion

Introduction Trigonometric ratios can be used to find the measure of a side or an acute angle of a right triangle. The ratios are used with the sine, cosine, and tangent functions.

Ask Students to find examples of each trigonometric function in their homework. Students should write a description of how to use them to solve problems and include these descriptions in their portfolios.

Chapter 9 Practice Test

Chapter 9 Practice Test

Assessment Options

Vocabulary Test A vocabulary review/test for Chapter 9 can be found on p. 542 of the *Chapter 9 Resource Masters.*

Chapter Tests There are six Chapter 9 Tests and an Open-Ended Assessment task available in the *Chapter 9 Resource Masters.*

Chapter 9 Tests			
Form	Type	Level	Pages
1	MC	basic	529–530
2A	MC	average	531–532
2B	MC	average	533–534
2C	FR	average	535–536
2D	FR	average	537–538
3	FR	advanced	539–540

MC = multiple-choice questions
FR = free-response questions

Open-Ended Assessment
Performance tasks for Chapter 9 can be found on p. 541 of the *Chapter 9 Resource Masters,* along with a sample scoring rubric for these tasks on p. A27.

ExamView® Pro

Use the networkable **ExamView® Pro** to:

- Create **multiple versions** of tests.
- Create **modified** tests for *Inclusion* students.
- **Edit** existing questions and **add** your own questions.
- Use built-in **state curriculum correlations** to create tests aligned with state standards.
- Change **English** tests to **Spanish** and vice versa.

Answer

2. To classify a triangle by its angles and sides, first determine whether the triangle is acute, right, or obtuse. Then determine whether the triangle is scalene, isosceles, or equilateral.

These two pages contain practice questions in the various formats that can be found on the most frequently given standardized tests.

A practice answer sheet for these two pages can be found on page A1 of the *Chapter 9 Resource Masters*.

Standardized Test Practice Student Recording Sheet, p. A1

Part 1 Multiple Choice

Select the best answer from the choices given and fill in the corresponding oval.

1 Ⓐ Ⓑ Ⓒ Ⓓ   4 Ⓐ Ⓑ Ⓒ Ⓓ   7 Ⓐ Ⓑ Ⓒ Ⓓ   10 Ⓐ Ⓑ Ⓒ Ⓓ
2 Ⓐ Ⓑ Ⓒ Ⓓ   5 Ⓐ Ⓑ Ⓒ Ⓓ   8 Ⓐ Ⓑ Ⓒ Ⓓ   11 Ⓐ Ⓑ Ⓒ Ⓓ
3 Ⓐ Ⓑ Ⓒ Ⓓ   6 Ⓐ Ⓑ Ⓒ Ⓓ   9 Ⓐ Ⓑ Ⓒ Ⓓ

Part 2 Short Response/Grid In

Solve the problem and write your answer in the blank.

For Questions 12, 14, 16–17, and 20, also enter your answer by writing each number or symbol in a box. Then fill in the corresponding oval for that number or symbol.

Part 3 Extended Response

Record your answers for Question 24 on the back of this paper.

Additional Practice

See pp. 547–548 of the *Chapter 9 Resource Masters* for additional standardized test practice.

Part 1 Multiple Choice

Record your answers on the answer sheet provided by your teacher or on a sheet of paper.

1. When m and n are any two numbers, which of the following statements is true?   (Lesson 1-4) **D**

Ⓐ $m \cdot 0 = n$ Ⓑ $m \cdot n = n$
Ⓒ $n \cdot 1 = m$ Ⓓ $m + n = n + m$

2. How many units apart are the numbers -8 and 5 on a number line?   (Lesson 2-1) **A**

Ⓐ 13   Ⓑ 3
Ⓒ 14   Ⓓ 10

3. Find the length of a rectangle having a width of 9 feet and an area of 54 square feet. (Lesson 3-7) **B**

Ⓐ 9 ft   Ⓑ 6 ft
Ⓒ 10 ft   Ⓓ 18 ft

4. Which of the following results in a negative number?   (Lessons 4-2 and 4-7) **A**

Ⓐ $(-2)^5$ Ⓑ $(5)^{-3}$
Ⓒ $-5 \cdot (-2)^5$ Ⓓ $(-3)^{-2} \cdot 5$

5. What is the value of x if $\frac{1}{2} + x = \frac{5}{6}$? (Lesson 5-7) **D**

Ⓐ $\frac{1}{4}$ Ⓑ $\frac{2}{5}$
Ⓒ $\frac{2}{3}$ Ⓓ $\frac{1}{3}$

6. Elisa purchased two books that cost $15.95 and $6.95. The sales tax on the books was 6%. If she gave the sales clerk $25, then how much change did she receive?   (Lesson 6-9) **B**

Ⓐ $0.27   Ⓑ $0.73
Ⓒ $1.73   Ⓓ $2.10

7. What is the value of t in $2s - t = s + 3t$ if $s = \frac{1}{2}$?   (Lesson 7-1) **A**

Ⓐ $\frac{1}{8}$ Ⓑ $\frac{1}{4}$
Ⓒ $\frac{1}{2}$ Ⓓ $\frac{3}{8}$

488   Chapter 9   Real Numbers and Right Triangles

Test-Taking Tip   Ⓐ Ⓑ Ⓒ Ⓓ

Question 9
You can tell if a line has a negative or positive slope by looking at its graph. A line with a negative slope will slant down from left to right. A line with a positive slope will slant up from left to right.

8. The relation shown in the table is a function. Find the value of y when $x = 5$.   (Lesson 8-2) **C**

x	y
0	2
1	5
2	8
3	11

Ⓐ 13   Ⓑ 14
Ⓒ 17   Ⓓ 18

9. Which graph shows a line with a slope of –2?   (Lesson 8-6) **D**

10. Which point on the number line shown is closest to $\sqrt{7}$?   (Lesson 9-1) **B**

Ⓐ point P Ⓑ point Q
Ⓒ point R Ⓓ point S

11. Triangles ABC and DEF are similar triangles. What is the measure of side AB?   (Lesson 9-5)

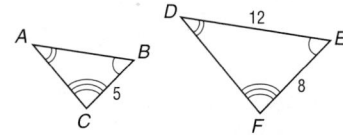

Ⓐ 3.33   Ⓑ 5.0   Ⓒ 6.5   Ⓓ 7.5

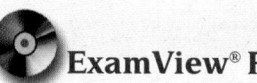

ExamView® Pro

Special banks of standardized test questions similar to those on the SAT, ACT, TIMSS 8, NAEP 8, and Pre-Algebra End-of-Course tests can be found on this CD-ROM.

Record your answers on the answer sheet provided by your teacher or on a sheet of paper.

12. When 8 is added to a number three times, the result is 27. Find the number. (Lesson 3-3) **3**

13. Order the numbers 1.4×10^{-5}, 4.0×10^2, and 1.04×10^{-2} from least to greatest. (Lesson 4-8) $\mathbf{1.4 \times 10^{-5}, 1.04 \times 10^{-2}, 4.0 \times 10^2}$

14. A conveyor belt moves at a rate of 6 miles in 4 hours. How many feet per minute does this conveyor belt move? (*Hint:* 1 mile = 5280 feet) (Lesson 6-1) **132**

15. Write $\frac{11}{14}$ as a percent, and round to the nearest tenth. (Lesson 6-4) **78.6%**

16. If you spin the arrow on the spinner below, what is the probability that the arrow will land on an even number? (Lesson 6-9) **1/2**

17. What is the least value of x in $y \leq 4x - 3$ if $y = 9$? (Lesson 7-6) **3**

18. Write *y is less than one-half the value of x* as a mathematical statement. (Lesson 7-7) $y < \frac{1}{2}x$

19. What is the slope of the line shown? (Lesson 8-4) $-\frac{2}{3}$

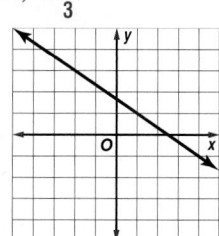

20. Find the positive square root of 196. (Lesson 9-1) **14**

21. What type of angle is formed by the minute hand and hour hand when the time on the clock is 3:35? (Lesson 9-3) **obtuse**

22. What is the measure of $\angle X$? (Lesson 9-4) **68°**

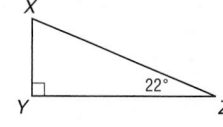

23. Find the distance between $A(-5, 4)$ and $B(6, -3)$ to the nearest tenth. (Lesson 9-6) **13.0 units**

Record your answers on a sheet of paper. Show your work.

24. The walls of a house usually meet to form a right angle. You can use string to determine whether two walls meet at a right angle.

   a. Copy the diagram shown below. Then illustrate the following situation. **See margin.**

   From a corner of the house, a 6-foot long piece of string is extended along one side of the wall, parallel to the floor. From the same corner, an 8-foot long piece of string is extended along the other wall, parallel to the floor.

   b. If the walls of the house meet at a right angle, then what is the distance between the ends of the two pieces of string? **10 feet**

   c. Draw an example of a situation where two walls of a house meet at an angle whose measure is greater than the measure of a right angle. **See margin.**

   d. Suppose the length of the walls in part c are the same length as the walls in part a, and that the 6-foot and 8-foot pieces of string are extended from the same corner. Do you think the distance between the two ends will be the same as in part **b**? Explain your reasoning. **See margin.**

Evaluating Extended Response Questions

Extended Response questions are graded by using a multilevel rubric that guides you in assessing a student's knowledge of a particular concept.

Goal: Form a right triangle given the lengths of the two sides.

Sample Scoring Rubric: The following rubric is a sample scoring device. You may wish to add more detail to this sample to meet your individual scoring needs.

Score	Criteria
4	A correct solution that is supported by well-developed, accurate explanations
3	A generally correct solution, but may contain minor flaws in reasoning or computation
2	A partially correct interpretation and/or solution to the problem
1	A correct solution with no supporting evidence or explanation
0	An incorrect solution indicating no mathematical understanding of the concept or task, or no solution is given

Answer

24a.

6 ft

8 ft

24c.

24d. No; If the measure of the angle between the walls is greater than 90°, then the length of the side opposite it will be greater than the side opposite the 90° angle.

Page 440, Lesson 9-1

64.

65.

66.
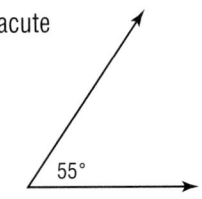

Page 449, Lesson 9-3

1. N; $\overrightarrow{NM}$, $\overrightarrow{NP}$; $\angle 1$, $\angle MNP$, $\angle PNM$, $\angle N$

2. Sample answer:

7. acute

8. obtuse

Page 450, Lesson 9-3

24. acute

25. obtuse

26. obtuse

27. obtuse

28. obtuse

29. acute

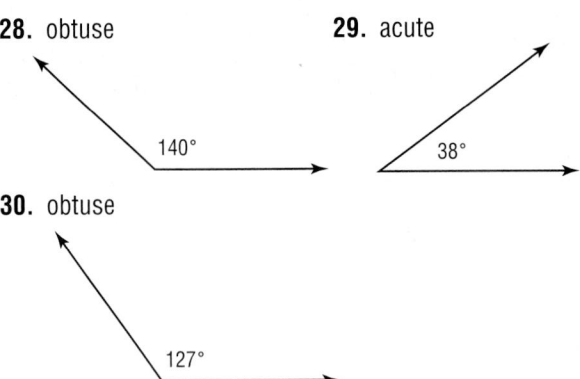

30. obtuse

32. Moderate: obtuse; all other angles: acute

33. Intense: about 68°; Moderate: about 104°; Light: 72°; No standard routine: about 47°; Don't exercise regularly: about 68°

Page 464, Lesson 9-5

38. The sum of the squares of the lengths of the legs is equal to the square of the length of the hypotenuse. Answers should include the following.

•
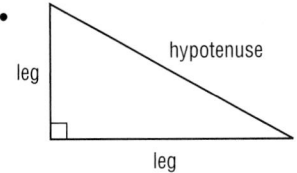

• An example of a set of numbers that represents the measures of the lengths of the legs and hypotenuse of a right triangle is 15, 20, 25.

Page 465, Algebra Activity

1.

2.

3.

4.

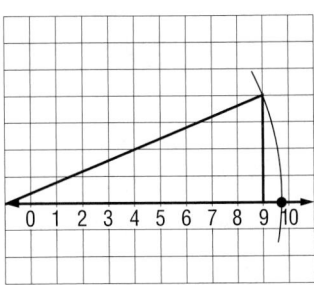

5. Sample answer: First, find two numbers whose square roots have a sum of 34. Since $3^2 + 5^2 = 34$, draw a right triangle with legs 3 units and 5 units long. Then, open the compass to the length of the hypotenuse. With the tip of the compass at 0, draw an arc that intersects the number line.

6. Sample answer: Since $(\sqrt{2})^2 + 1^2 = 3$, use $\sqrt{2}$ as one leg of a right triangle and 1 unit as the other leg. Then follow the procedure in the activity to locate the graph of $\sqrt{3}$.

Page 473, Lesson 9-7

1. Sample answer:

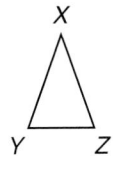

corresponding sides:
$$\frac{AB}{XY} = \frac{BC}{YZ} = \frac{AC}{XZ}$$

2. Sample answer: A method used to find measurements that are difficult to measure directly.

3. $\frac{x}{15} = \frac{6}{9}$; 10

4. $\frac{x}{6} = \frac{6}{2}$; 18

Two-Dimensional Figures

Chapter Overview and Pacing

Chapter 10

Year-long pacing: pages T20–T21.

LESSON OBJECTIVES	PACING (days)			
	Regular		Block	
	Basic/ Average	Advanced	Basic/ Average	Advanced
10-1 Line and Angle Relationships *(pp. 492–499)* • Identify the relationships of angles formed by two parallel lines and a transversal. • Identify the relationships of vertical, adjacent, complementary, and supplementary angles. *Follow-Up:* Construct congruent line segments and angles and perpendicular bisectors and angle bisectors.	2	2	1	1
10-2 Congruent Triangles *(pp. 500–504)* • Identify congruent triangles and corresponding parts of congruent triangles.	1	1	0.5	0.5
10-3 Transformations on the Coordinate Plane *(pp. 505–512)* *Preview:* Introduce three types of symmetry. • Draw translations, rotations, and reflections on a coordinate plane. *Follow-Up:* Investigate dilations, which alter the size of a figure.	3 (with 10-3 Preview)	2 (with 10-3 Follow-Up)	1.5 (with 10-3 Preview)	1.5 (with 10-3 Follow-Up)
10-4 Quadrilaterals *(pp. 513–517)* • Find the missing angles measures of a quadrilateral. • Classify quadrilaterals.	1	1	0.5	0.5
10-5 Area: Parallelograms, Triangles, and Trapezoids *(pp. 518–525)* *Preview:* Use geoboards to find the area of figures. • Find area of parallelograms. • Find the areas of triangles and trapezoids.	2	1	1	0.5
10-6 Polygons *(pp. 527–532)* • Classify polygons. • Determine the sum of the measures of the interior and exterior angles of a polygon. *Follow-Up:* Create tessellations using transformations.	1	2 (with 10-6 Follow-Up)	0.5	1 (with 10-6 Follow-Up)
10-7 Circumference and Area: Circles *(pp. 533–538)* • Find circumference of circles. • Find area of circles.	1	1	0.5	0.5
10-8 Area: Irregular Figures *(pp. 539–543)* • Find area of irregular figures.	1	1	0.5	0.5
Study Guide and **Practice Test** *(pp. 544–549)* **Standardized Test Practice** *(pp. 550–551)*	1	1	0.5	0.5
Chapter Assessment	1	1	0.5	0.5
TOTAL	14	13	7	7

*An electronic version of this chapter is available on **StudentWorks**™. This backpack solution CD-ROM allows students instant access to the Student Edition, lesson worksheet pages, and web resources.*

Chapter Resource Manager

Timesaving Tools

TeacherWorks™
All-In-One Planner and Resource Center
See pages T5 and T21.

CHAPTER 10 RESOURCE MASTERS

Study Guide and Intervention	Practice (Skills and Average)	Reading to Learn Mathematics	Enrichment	Assessment	Prerequisite Skills Workbook	Applications*	Parent and Student Study Guide Workbook	5-Minute Check Transparencies	Interactive Chalkboard	Pre-AlgePASS: Tutorial Plus (lessons)	Materials
549	550–551	552	553				81	10-1	10-1	31	*Follow-Up:* compass
554	555–556	557	558	603			82	10-2	10-2	32	
559	560–561	562	563			GCS 37	83	10-3	10-3	33	*Preview:* tracing paper (optional) *Follow-Up:* grid paper, protractor, ruler
564	565–566	567	568	603, 605			84	10-4	10-4		
569	570–571	572	573			SC 19 GCS 38	85	10-5	10-5		*Preview:* geoboards, geobands
574	575–576	577	578	604			86	10-6	10-6		*Follow-Up:* light cardboard (optional)
579	580–581	582	583			SC 20	87	10-7	10-7		
584	585–586	587	588	604		SM 5	88	10-8	10-8	34	
				589–602, 606–608							

Key to Abbreviations: GCS = Graphing Calculator and Spreadsheet Masters
SC = School-to-Career Masters
SM = Science and Mathematics Lab Manual

ELL Study Guide and Intervention, Skills Practice, Practice, and Parent and Student Study Guide Workbooks are also available in Spanish.

Mathematical Connections and Background

Continuity of Instruction

Prior Knowledge

In Chapter 9, students explored real numbers and right triangles, and classified angles and triangles. They used squares and square roots, and the Pythagorean Theorem to examine right triangles. Students also learned to use trigonometric ratios to find the missing measures of right triangles. In addition, the Distance and Midpoint Formulas were also examined.

This Chapter

Students will identify the relationships of parallel and intersecting lines, and the properties of congruent triangles. They will also identify and draw transformations, and classify and find angle measures of polygons. Students will also find the area of polygons and irregular figures. In addition, students will learn to find the circumference and area of circles.

Future Connections

Parallel and intersecting lines is a key concept that is also covered in algebra. The properties of triangles are the focus of geometry and trigonometry, as in the classification and measurement of angles. The area of polygons and circles will also be explored in geometry, and can be used in house design and landscaping.

10-1 Line and Angle Relationships

Two lines in a plane that never intersect are called parallel lines. When two parallel lines are intersected by a third line, called a transveral, eight angles are formed. Of these angles, corresponding angles are congruent, as are alternate interior angles and alternate exterior angles.

When two lines intersect, the form two pairs of opposite, congruent angles called vertical angles. When two angles have the same vertex and share a common side, they are adjacent angles. If the sum of the measures of two angles is 90°, the angles are complementary. If the sum of two angles is 180°, the angles are supplementary.

10-2 Congruent Triangles

Figures that have the same size and shape are congruent. The parts of congruent triangles that match are called corresponding parts. Congruence statements are used to identify corresponding parts of congruent triangles. When writing a congruence statement, the letters must be written so that corresponding vertices appear in the same order. Corresponding parts can be used to find the measures of angles and sides in a figure that is congruent to a figure with known measures.

10-3 Transformations on the Coordinate Plane

A transformation is a movement of a geometric figure. There are three types of transformations. In a translation, a figure is slid from one position to another without turning it. Every point of the original figure is moved the same distance and in the same direction. In a reflection, a figure is flipped over a line to form a mirror image. Every point of the original figure has a corresponding point on the other side of the line of symmetry. In a rotation, a figure is turned around a fixed point. A figure may be rotated 90° clockwise, 90° counterclockwise, or 180°.

10-4 Quadrilaterals

A quadrilateral is a closed figure with four sides and four vertices. The segments of a quadrilateral intersect only at their endpoints. Quadrilaterals can be separated into two triangles. Since the sum of the interior angles of all triangles totals 180°, the measures of the interior angles of a quadrilateral equal 360°. Quadrilaterals are classified according to their characteristics, and include trapezoids, parallelograms, rectangles, squares, and rhombuses.

10-5 Area: Parallelograms, Triangles, and Trapezoids

The area A of a parallelogram can be found by multiplying the measures of the base b and the height h. That is, $A = b \cdot h$.

The area of a triangle can be found by multiplying the measures of the base and height, and dividing the result by 2. In symbols, we write $A = \frac{1}{2}b \cdot h$. Any side of the triangle can be used as a base.

To find the area of a trapezoid, find the sum of the bases and then multiply the sum by one-half times the base. The formula can be written as $A = \frac{1}{2}h(a + b)$.

10-6 Polygons

A polygon is a simple, closed figure formed by three or more line segments. The line segments meet only at their endpoints. The points of intersection are called vertices, and the line segments are called sides. Polygons are classified by the number of sides they have.

The diagonals of a polygon divide the polygon into triangles. The number of triangles formed is two less than the number of sides. To find the sum of the measures of the interior angles of any polygon, multiply the number of triangles within a polygon by 180. That is, if n equals number of sides, then $(n - 2)$ 180 gives the sum of the measures of the polygon's interior angles.

10-7 Cirumference and Area: Circles

A circle is the set of all points in a plane that are the same distance from a given point. The distance across the circle through the center point is called the diameter. The distance from the center to any point on the circle is called the radius. The circumference is the distance around the circle. The ratio of the circumference of a circle to its diameter is always equal to 3.1415926. The Greek letter π (pi) represents this number. The circumference C of a circle is equal to its diameter d times π, or 2 times its radius times π. In symbols, this is written as $C = \pi d$, or $C = 2\pi r$. The area A of a circle is equal to π times the square of its radius. In symbols, this is written as $A = \pi r^2$.

10-8 Area: Irregular Figures

Irregular figures are figures that are composed of polygons of various shapes and sizes. To find the area of an irregular figure, separate the irregular figure into figures whose areas you do know how to find. The area of each polygon can then be determined. The sum of these areas provides the area of the irregular figure. Many real-world situations involve finding the area of an irregular figure.

Quick Review Math Handbook

Hot Words includes a glossary of terms while Hot Topics consists of explanations of key mathematical concepts with exercises to test comprehension. This valuable resource can be used as a reference in the classroom or for home study.

Lesson	Hot Topics Section	Lesson	Hot Topics Section
GS 10	2.3, 2.6, 6.4	10-4	2.6, 7.2
10-1	7.1, 9.3	10-5P	7.5
10-1F	7.1	10-5	1.3, 7.5
10-2	6.7, 7.1	10-6	7.2
10-3P	7.3	10-6F	7.3
10-3	6.4, 7.3	10-7	2.6, 7.8

GS = Getting Started, P = Preview, F = Follow-Up

 Additional mathematical information and teaching notes are available at www.pre-alg.com/key_concepts.

DAILY INTERVENTION and Assessment

Key to Abbreviations:
TWE = Teacher Wraparound Edition; CRM = Chapter Resource Masters

	Type	Student Edition	Teacher Resources	Technology/Internet
INTERVENTION	Ongoing	Prerequisite Skills, pp. 491, 497, 504, 511, 517, 525, 531, 538 Practice Quiz 1, p. 517 Practice Quiz 2, p. 538	5-Minute Check Transparencies Quizzes, *CRM*, pp. 603, 604 Mid-Chapter Test, *CRM*, p. 605 Study Guide and Intervention, *CRM*, pp. 549, 554, 559, 564, 574, 579, 584	Pre-AlgePASS: Tutorial Plus, Lessons 31, 32, 33, and 34 www.pre-alg.com/ self_check_quiz www.pre-alg.com/ extra_examples
	Mixed Review	pp. 497, 504, 511, 517, 525, 531, 538, 543	Cumulative Review, *CRM*, p. 606	
	Error Analysis	Find the Error, p. 536	Find the Error, *TWE*, p. 536 Unlocking Misconceptions, *TWE*, pp. 493, 501, 534 Tips for New Teachers, *TWE*, p. 511	
	Standardized Test Practice	pp. 494, 495, 497, 504, 511, 517, 525, 531, 537, 543, 550–551	*TWE*, pp. 550–551 Standardized Test Practice, *CRM*, pp. 607–608	Standardized Test Practice CD-ROM www.pre-alg.com/ standardized_test
ASSESSMENT	Open-Ended Assessment	Writing in Math, pp. 497, 504, 511, 517, 525, 531, 537, 543 Open Ended, pp. 495, 502, 509, 515, 523, 529, 535, 541 Standardized Test, p. 551	Speaking: *TWE*, pp. 504, 511 Writing: *TWE*, pp. 525, 538 Modeling: *TWE*, pp. 497, 517, 531, 543 Open-Ended Assessment, *CRM*, p. 601	
	Chapter Assessment	Study Guide, pp. 544–548 Practice Test, p. 549	Multiple-Choice Tests (Forms 1, 2A, 2B), *CRM*, pp. 589–594 Free-Response Tests (Forms 2C, 2D, 3), *CRM*, pp. 595–600 Vocabulary Test/Review, *CRM*, p. 602	ExamView® Pro (see below) MindJogger Videoquizzes www.pre-alg.com/ vocabulary_review www.pre-alg.com/chapter_test

 Yearly Progress Pro

For more information on Yearly ProgressPro, see p. 432.

Pre-Algebra Lesson	Yearly ProgressPro Skill Lesson(s)
10-1	Line and Angle Relationships
10-2	Congruent Polygons
10-3	Reflections; Translations; Rotations
10-4	Classifying Quadrilaterals
10-5	Area of Parallelograms Area of Triangles and Trapezoids
10-6	Congruent Polygons
10-7	Area of Circles Circumference of Circles
10-8	Area of Complex Figures

 ExamView® Pro

Use the networkable **ExamView® Pro** to:
- Create **multiple versions** of tests.
- Create **modified** tests for *Inclusion* students.
- **Edit** existing questions and **add** your own questions.
- Use built-in **state curriculum correlations** to create tests aligned with state standards.
- Change **English** tests to **Spanish** and vice versa.

For more information on Intervention and Assessment, see pp. T8–T11.

Reading and Writing in Mathematics

Glencoe Pre-Algebra provides numerous opportunities to incorporate reading and writing into the mathematics classroom.

Student Edition

- Foldables™ Study Organizer, p. 491
- Reading Mathematics, p. 526
- Concept Check questions require students to verbalize and write about what they have learned in the lesson. (pp. 493, 495, 500, 502, 509, 513, 515, 521, 523, 527, 529, 534, 535, 540, 541)
- Writing in Math questions in every lesson, pp. 497, 504, 511, 517, 525, 531, 537, 543
- Reading Math, pp. 493, 500, 508
- WebQuest, p. 542

Teacher Wraparound Edition

- Foldables™ Study Organizer, pp. 491, 544
- Study Notebook suggestions, pp. 495, 499, 502, 505, 509, 512, 515, 519, 523, 526, 529, 532, 535, 541
- Modeling activities, pp. 497, 517, 531, 543
- Speaking activities, pp. 504, 511
- Writing activities, pp. 525, 538
- Differentiated Instruction (Verbal/Linguistic), p. 508
- **ELL** Resources, pp. 490, 492, 500, 506, 508, 513, 520, 526, 527, 533, 539, 544

Additional Resources

- Vocabulary Builder worksheets require students to define and give examples for key vocabulary terms as they progress through the chapter (*Chapter 10 Resource Masters*, pp. vii–viii)
- Reading to Learn Mathematics master for each lesson (*Chapter 10 Resource Masters*, pp. 552, 557, 562, 567, 572, 577, 582, 587)
- *Vocabulary PuzzleMaker* software creates crossword, jumble, and word search puzzles using vocabulary lists that you can customize.
- *Teaching Mathematics with Foldables* provides suggestions for promoting cognition and language.
- *Reading and Writing in the Mathematics Classroom*
- *WebQuest and Project Resources*

For more information on Reading and Writing in Mathematics, see pp. T6–T7.

 ENGLISH LANGUAGE LEARNERS

Lesson 10-2	Lesson 10-3	Lesson 10-5
Using Manipulatives	**Language Experience Approach to Illustrations**	**Reading and Writing**
Give each group of students sets of shapes and have them categorize them as *similar* or *congruent*. It is important to emphasize that shapes that are congruent are also similar, but they may be similar and not congruent.	Write the words *transformation* and *translation* on the chalkboard. Ask students what these words have in common. Underline the prefix *trans* and have students look this up in a dictionary or on the Internet. They will find that trans means "across". This will help students to remember that they are moving an object or polygon across a plane.	Allow students time to work in pairs to do the Concept Check and Writing in Math exercises. This enables English Language Learners to express themselves in English and to express what they have learned. By allowing students to express themselves, you are permitting the opportunity to practice the language, writing skills, and understanding of the topic.

What You'll Learn

Have students read over the list of objectives and make a list of any words with which they are not familiar.

Why It's Important

Point out to students that this is only one of many reasons why each objective is important. Others are provided in the introduction to each lesson.

What You'll Learn

- **Lesson 10-1** Identify the relationships of parallel and intersecting lines.
- **Lesson 10-2** Identify properties of congruent triangles.
- **Lesson 10-3** Identify and draw transformations.
- **Lessons 10-4 and 10-6** Classify and find angle measures of polygons.
- **Lessons 10-5, 10-7, and 10-8** Find the area of polygons and irregular figures, and find the area and circumference of circles.

Key Vocabulary

- parallel lines (p. 492)
- transformation (p. 506)
- quadrilateral (p. 513)
- polygon (p. 527)
- circumference (p. 533)

Why It's Important

Two-dimensional shapes are usually found in many real-world objects. The properties of two-dimensional figures can be used to solve real-world problems dealing with snowflakes. For example, if you know the exact shape of a snowflake, you can find the measure of an interior angle in a snowflake. *You will solve a problem about snowflakes in Lesson 10-6.*

Lesson	NCTM Standards	Local Objectives
10-1	2, 3, 4, 6, 8, 9	
10-1 Follow-Up	3, 4	
10-2	2, 3, 4, 6, 8, 9	
10-3 Preview	3	
10-3	1, 3, 8, 9	
10-3 Follow-Up	3, 4, 8	
10-4	2, 3, 6, 8, 9	
10-5 Preview	3, 4	
10-5	1, 3, 4, 6, 7, 8, 9, 10	
10-6	1, 3, 4, 6, 8, 9, 10	
10-6 Follow-Up	3, 10	
10-7	1, 3, 4, 6, 7, 8, 9	
10-8	1, 3, 4, 6, 8, 9, 10	

Key to NCTM Standards:

1=Number & Operations, 2=Algebra, 3=Geometry, 4=Measurement, 5=Data Analysis & Probability, 6=Problem Solving, 7=Reasoning & Proof, 8=Communication, 9=Connections, 10=Representation

Vocabulary Builder

The Key Vocabulary list introduces students to some of the main vocabulary terms included in this chapter. For a more thorough vocabulary list with pronunciations of new words, give students the Vocabulary Builder worksheets found on pages vii and viii of the *Chapter 10 Resource Masters.* Encourage them to complete the definition of each term as they progress through the chapter. You may suggest that they add these sheets to their study notebooks for future reference when studying for the Chapter 10 test.

Getting Started

Getting Started

▶ **Prerequisite Skills** To be successful in this chapter, you'll need to master these skills and be able to apply them in problem-solving situations. Review these skills before beginning Chapter 10.

For Lessons 10-1 and 10-4   **Solve Equations**

Solve each equation. *(For review, see Lessons 3-3 and 3-5.)*

1. $x + 46 = 90$ **44**   **2.** $x + 35 = 180$ **145**   **3.** $2x - 12 = 90$ **51**   **4.** $3x - 24 = 180$ **68**

5. $2x + 34 = 90$ **28**   **6.** $4x + 44 = 180$ **34**   **7.** $5x + 165 = 360$ **39** **8.** $4x + 184 = 360$ **44**

For Lessons 10-5, 10-7, and 10-8   **Multiply Decimals**

Find each product. Round to the nearest tenth, if necessary. *(For review, see page 715.)*

9. $(5.5)(8)$ **44**   **10.** $(7.5)(3.4)$ **25.5**   **11.** $(6.3)(11.4)$ **71.8**   **12.** $\frac{1}{2}(8)(2.5)$ **10**

13. $\frac{1}{2}(4.3)(5.8)$ **12.5**   **14.** $(3.14)(7)$ **22.0**   **15.** $(2)(3.14)(1.7)$ **10.7** **16.** $2(3.1)(3.14)$ **19.5**

For Lesson 10-5   **Add Mixed Numbers**

Find each sum. *(For review, see Lesson 5-7.)*

17. $5\frac{1}{2} + 4\frac{2}{3}$ **$10\frac{1}{6}$**   **18.** $2\frac{1}{3} + 3\frac{3}{4}$ **$6\frac{1}{12}$**   **19.** $1\frac{3}{8} + 2\frac{1}{2}$ **$3\frac{7}{8}$**   **20.** $6\frac{1}{4} + 1\frac{5}{6}$ **$8\frac{1}{12}$**

21. $3\frac{5}{8} + 1\frac{3}{4}$ **$5\frac{3}{8}$**   **22.** $2\frac{3}{5} + 4\frac{7}{10}$ **$7\frac{3}{10}$**   **23.** $2\frac{2}{3} + 3\frac{5}{9}$ **$6\frac{2}{9}$**   **24.** $5\frac{2}{3} + 3\frac{4}{5}$ **$9\frac{7}{15}$**

Study Organizer

Polygons Make this Foldable to help you organize your notes. Begin with four plain sheets of $8\frac{1}{2}$" by 11" paper, eight index cards, and glue.

Step 1   **Fold**

Fold a sheet of paper in half widthwise.

Step 2   **Open and Fold Again**

Open and fold the bottom to form a pocket. Glue edges.

Step 3   **Repeat Steps 1 and 2**

Repeat three times. Then glue all four pieces together to form a booklet.

Step 4   **Label**

Label each pocket. Place an index card in each pocket

Reading and Writing As you read and study the chapter, write the name of a two-dimensional figure on each index card, draw a diagram, and write a definition or describe the characteristics of each figure.

This section provides a review of the basic concepts needed before beginning Chapter 10. Page references are included for additional student help.

Prerequisite Skills in the Getting Ready for the Next Lesson section at the end of each lesson reviews a skill needed in the next lesson.

For Lesson	Prerequisite Skill
10-2	Angles (p. 497)
10-3	The Coordinate System (p. 504)
10-4	Solving Equations (p. 511)
10-5	Multiplying Decimals (p. 517)
10-6	Order of Operations (p. 525)
10-7	Rounding Decimals (p. 531)
10-8	Adding Decimals (p. 538)

Tips for New Teachers

Visualizing Geometry is a visual form of mathematics. Make models or posters of concepts presented in this chapter to help students visualize what they are learning.

Study Organizer

For more information about Foldables, see *Teaching Mathematics with Foldables.*

Organization of Data Students will need 3" × 5" index cards or sheets of notebook paper cut into quarter sections. Each card can become a flashcard study tool. With each lesson, use the study cards to take notes, solve equations, record and define vocabulary words, and explain concepts. Use the cards to summarize concepts needed for the Chapter Test.

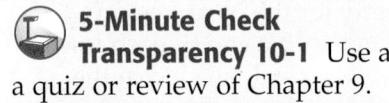

10-1 Lesson Notes

10-1 Line and Angle Relationships

NEW YORK *Performance Indicator* **8.A.12 Apply algebra to determine the measure of angles formed by or contained in parallel lines cut by a transversal and by intersecting lines**

1 Focus

5-Minute Check Transparency 10-1 Use as a quiz or review of Chapter 9.

Mathematical Background notes are available for this lesson on page 490C.

How are parallel lines and angles related?

The opening activity questions are repeated on page 552 of the *Chapter 10 Resource Masters*.

Reading to Learn Mathematics, p. 552 **ELL**

Pre-Activity *How are parallel lines and angles related?*

Do the activity at the top of page 492 in your textbook. Write your answers below.

a. Trace two of the horizontal lines on a sheet of notebook paper. Then draw another line that intersects the horizontal lines. **See students' work.**

b. Label the angles as shown. **See students' work.**

c. Find the measure of each angle. **Sample answer: $m\angle 1 = 110°$, $m\angle 2 = 70°$, $m\angle 3 = 110°$, $m\angle 4 = 70°$, $m\angle 5 = 110°$, $m\angle 6 = 70°$, $m\angle 7 = 110°$, $m\angle 8 = 70°$**

d. What do you notice about the measures of the angles? **There are just two different measures.**

e. Which angles have the same measure? **Sample answer: The angles across from each other; the angles in the same position on each of the horizontal lines; the angles on opposite sides inside the horizontal lines; the angles on opposite sides above and below the parallel lines**

f. What do you notice about the measures of the angles that share a side? **Their sum is 180°.**

Reading the Lesson 1–12. See students' work.

Write a definition and give an example of each new vocabulary word or phrase.

Vocabulary	Definition	Example
1. parallel lines		
2. transversal		
3. interior angles		
4. exterior angles		
5. alternate interior angles		
6. alternate exterior angles		
7. corresponding angles		
8. vertical angles		
9. adjacent angles		
10. complementary angles		
11. supplementary angles		
12. perpendicular lines		

Teaching Tip Help students find parallel lines in the classroom. For example, the opposite edges of a doorway are parallel.

Vocabulary

- parallel lines
- transversal
- interior angles
- exterior angles
- alternate interior angles
- alternate exterior angles
- corresponding angles
- vertical angles
- adjacent angles
- complementary angles
- supplementary angles
- perpendicular lines

Study Tip

Parallel Lines
Arrowheads are often used in figures to indicate parallel lines.

What You'll Learn

- Identify the relationships of angles formed by two parallel lines and a transversal.
- Identify the relationships of vertical, adjacent, complementary, and supplementary angles.

How are parallel lines and angles related?

Let's investigate what happens when two horizontal lines are intersected by a third line. **a–f. See margin.**

a. Trace two of the horizontal lines on a sheet of notebook paper. Then draw another line that intersects the horizontal lines.

b. Label the angles as shown.

c. Find the measure of each angle.

d. What do you notice about the measures of the angles?

e. Which angles have the same measure?

f. What do you notice about the measures of the angles that share a side?

PARALLEL LINES AND A TRANSVERSAL In geometry, two lines in a plane that never intersect are **parallel lines**.

Lines m and n are parallel. Using symbols, $m \parallel n$.		Parallel lines have no point of intersection.

When two parallel lines are intersected by a third line called a **transversal**, eight angles are formed.

Key Concept — *Names of Special Angles*

The eight angles formed by parallel lines and a transversal have special names.

- **Interior angles** lie inside the parallel lines.
  $\angle 3, \angle 4, \angle 5, \angle 6$

- **Exterior angles** lie outside the parallel lines.
  $\angle 1, \angle 2, \angle 7, \angle 8$

- **Alternate interior angles** are on opposite sides of the transversal and inside the parallel lines.
  $\angle 3$ and $\angle 5$, $\angle 4$ and $\angle 6$

- **Alternate exterior angles** are on opposite sides of the transversal and outside the parallel lines.
  $\angle 1$ and $\angle 7$, $\angle 2$ and $\angle 8$

- **Corresponding angles** are in the same position on the parallel lines in relation to the transversal.
  $\angle 1$ and $\angle 5$, $\angle 2$ and $\angle 6$, $\angle 3$ and $\angle 7$, $\angle 4$ and $\angle 8$

Resource Manager

Workbooks and Reproducible Masters

Chapter 10 Resource Masters
- Study Guide and Intervention, p. 549
- Skills Practice, p. 550
- Practice, p. 551
- Reading to Learn Mathematics, p. 552
- Enrichment, p. 553

Parent and Student Study Guide Workbook, p. 81

Transparencies

5-Minute Check Transparency 10-1
Answer Key Transparencies

Technology

Interactive Chalkboard
Pre-AlgePASS: Tutorial Plus, Lesson 31

In Lesson 9-4, you learned that line segments are congruent if they have the same measure. Similarly, angles are congruent if they have the same measure.

 Key Concept — **Parallel Lines Cut by a Transversal**

If two parallel lines are cut by a transversal, then the following pairs of angles are congruent.
- Corresponding angles are congruent.
- Alternate interior angles are congruent.
- Alternate exterior angles are congruent.

✓ **Concept Check** How many angles are formed when two parallel lines are intersected by a transversal? **8**

Example 1 *Find Measures of Angles*

In the figure at the right, $m \parallel n$ and t is a transversal. If $m\angle 1 = 68°$, find $m\angle 5$ and $m\angle 6$.

Since $\angle 1$ and $\angle 5$ are corresponding angles, they are congruent. So, $m\angle 5 = 68°$.

Since $\angle 1$ and $\angle 6$ are alternate exterior angles, they are congruent. So $m\angle 6 = 68°$.

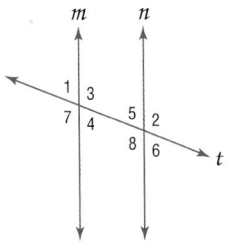

INTERSECTING LINES AND ANGLES Other pairs of angles have special relationships. When two lines intersect, they form two pairs of opposite angles called **vertical angles**. Vertical angles are congruent. The symbol for *is congruent to* is $\cong$.

$\angle 1$ and $\angle 2$ are vertical angles.
$\angle 1 \cong \angle 2$

 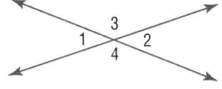

$\angle 3$ and $\angle 4$ are vertical angles.
$\angle 3 \cong \angle 4$

When two angles have the same vertex, share a common side, and do not overlap, they are **adjacent angles**.

$\angle 1$ and $\angle 2$ are adjacent angles.

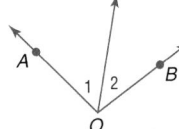

$m\angle AOB = m\angle 1 + m\angle 2$

If the sum of the measures of two angles is 90°, the angles are **complementary**.

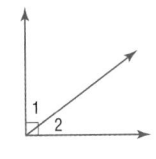

$m\angle 1 = 50°$, $m\angle 2 = 40°$
$m\angle 1 + m\angle 2 = 90°$

$m\angle 3 = 60°$, $m\angle 4 = 30°$
$m\angle 3 + m\angle 4 = 90°$

www.pre-alg.com/extra_examples/ny

Lesson 10-1 Line and Angle Relationships **493**

Lesson 10-1 Line and Angle Relationships **493**

INTERSECTING LINES AND ANGLES

2 **Multiple-Choice Test Item**
If $m\angle D = 53°$ and $\angle D$ and $\angle E$ are complementary, what is $m\angle E$? **B**

A 53°	**B** 37°
C 127°	**D** 7°

Teaching Tip In Example 3, make sure students realize that when they have found the value of x, this is not the answer to the problem. They must use that value to calculate the angle measures.

3 **ALGEBRA** Angles PQR and STU are supplementary. If $m\angle PQR = x - 15$ and $m\angle STU = x - 65$, find the measure of each angle. *$m\angle PQR = 115°$, $m\angle STU = 65°$*

4 **TRANSPORTATION** A road crosses railroad tracks at an angle as shown.

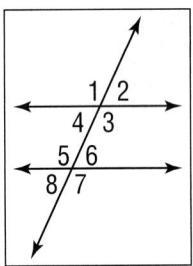

If $m\angle 1 = 131°$, find $m\angle 6$ and $m\angle 5$. *$m\angle 6 = 49°$ and $m\angle 5 = 131°$*

If the sum of the measures of two angles is 180°, the angles are **supplementary**.

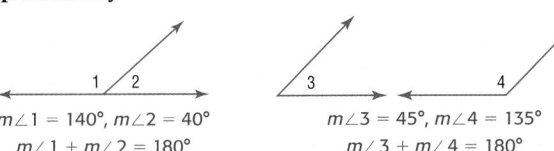

$m\angle 1 = 140°, m\angle 2 = 40°$ $m\angle 3 = 45°, m\angle 4 = 135°$
$m\angle 1 + m\angle 2 = 180°$ $m\angle 3 + m\angle 4 = 180°$

Lines that intersect to form a right angle are **perpendicular lines**.

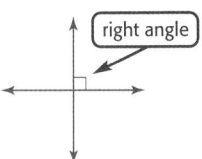

right angle

NEW YORK Test Practice

Standardized Test Practice A B C D

Example 2 Find a Missing Angle Measure

Multiple-Choice Test Item

If $m\angle B = 87°$ and $\angle A$ and $\angle B$ are supplementary, what is $m\angle A$?

(A) 3°   (B) 87°
(C) 93°   (D) 95°

87°
A B

Read the Test Item

Since $\angle A$ and $\angle B$ are supplementary, $m\angle A + m\angle B = 180°$.

Solve the Test Item

$m\angle A + m\angle B = 180°$	Supplementary angles
$m\angle A + 87° = 180°$	Replace $m\angle B$ with 87°.
$m\angle A + 87° - 87° = 180° - 87°$	Subtract 87 from each side.
$m\angle A = 93°$	

The answer is C.

Test-Taking Tip
It is a good idea to review definitions of key terms, such as supplementary, before taking the test.

Example 3 Find Measures of Angles

ALGEBRA Angles ABC and FGH are complementary. If $m\angle ABC = x + 8$ and $m\angle FGH = x - 10$, find the measure of each angle.

Step 1 Find the value of x.

$m\angle ABC + m\angle FGH = 90°$	Complementary angles
$(x + 8) + (x - 10) = 90°$	Substitution
$2x - 2 = 90°$	Combine like terms.
$2x = 92°$	Add 2 to each side.
$x = 46°$	Divide each side by 2.

Study Tip

Checking Reasonableness of Results
To check your answer, add to see if the sum of the measures of the angles is 90. Since 54 + 36 = 90, the answer is correct.

Step 2 Replace x with 46 to find the measure of each angle.

$m\angle ABC = x + 8$	$m\angle FGH = x - 10$
$= 46 + 8$ or 54	$= 46 - 10$ or 36

So, $m\angle ABC = 54°$ and $m\angle FGH = 36°$.

 Standardized Test Practice A B C D

Example 2 Point out to students that they must distinguish between supplementary, complementary, and congruent angles to answer this question. Answer choice A identifies a complementary angle, and choice B a congruent one. The diagram is very helpful in reminding students that the sum of the measures of supplementary angles is 180°. This will enable them to arrive at the correct answer, choice C.

Example 4 Apply Angle Relationships

SAFETY A lifeguard chair is shown.
If $m\angle 1 = 105°$, find $m\angle 4$ and $m\angle 6$.

Since $\angle 1$ and $\angle 4$ are vertical angles,
they are congruent. So, $m\angle 4 = 105°$.

Since $\angle 6$ and $\angle 1$ are supplementary,
the sum of their measures is 180°.

$180 - 105 = 75$. So, $m\angle 6 = 75°$.

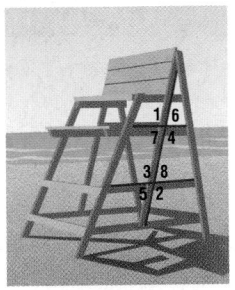

Concept Summary — Line and Angle Relationships

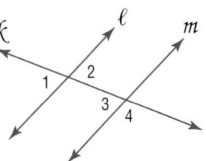

Parallel Lines	**Perpendicular Lines**	**Vertical Angles**
$a \parallel b$	$m \perp n$	$\angle 1 \cong \angle 3$ $\angle 2 \cong \angle 4$
Adjacent Angles	**Complementary Angles**	**Supplementary Angles**
$m\angle ABC = m\angle 1 + m\angle 2$	$m\angle 1 + m\angle 2 = 90°$	$m\angle 1 + m\angle 2 = 180°$

Check for Understanding

Concept Check

1. **Explain** the difference between complementary and supplementary angles.

1–2. See margin.

2. **OPEN ENDED** Draw a pair of adjacent, supplementary angles.

Guided Practice

In the figure at the right, $\ell \parallel m$ and k is a
transversal. If $m\angle 1 = 56°$, find the measure
of each angle.

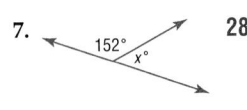

GUIDED PRACTICE KEY	
Exercises	Examples
3–5	1, 4
6, 7, 9	2
8	3

3. $\angle 2$ **56°**   **4.** $\angle 3$ **56°**   **5.** $\angle 4$ **124°**

Find the value of x in each figure.

6. **140**

7. **28**

8. **ALGEBRA** If $m\angle N = 3x$ and $m\angle M = 2x$ and $\angle M$ and $\angle N$ are
supplementary, what is the measure of each angle? **108°; 72°**

NEW YORK
Test Practice

Standardized
Test Practice
Ⓐ Ⓑ Ⓒ Ⓓ

9. If $m\angle B = 26°$ and $\angle A$ and $\angle B$ are complementary, what is $m\angle A$? **D**

Ⓐ 154°   Ⓑ 90°   Ⓒ 26°   Ⓓ 64°

Lesson 10-1 Line and Angle Relationships **495**

3 Practice/Apply

Study Notebook

Have students—
• add the definitions/examples of
  the vocabulary terms to their
  Vocabulary Builder worksheets for
  Chapter 10.
• draw and label examples of
  the various line and angle
  relationships.
• include any other item(s) that
  they find helpful in mastering the
  skills in this lesson.

About the Exercises . . .

Organization by Objective
• **Parallel Lines and a
  Transversal:** 10–15, 26–31
• **Intersecting Lines and
  Angles:** 16–25, 32

Odd/Even Assignments
Exercises 10–25 are structured
so that students practice the
same concepts whether they
are assigned odd or even
problems.

Alert! Exercises 40–42 require
a scientific calculator.

Assignment Guide

Basic: 11–19 odd, 23, 27–29,
31, 33–36, 40–50

Average: 10–25 odd, 27, 28,
29, 31, 33–36, 40–50 (Optional:
37–39)

Advanced: 10–26 even, 27, 28,
30, 32, 33–45 (Optional: 46–50)

Answers

1. Complementary angles have a
sum of 90° and supplementary
angles have a sum of 180°.

2. Sample answer:

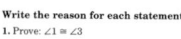
★ indicates increased difficulty

Practice and Apply

In the figure at the right, g‖h and t is a transversal. If m∠4 = 53°, find the measure of each angle.

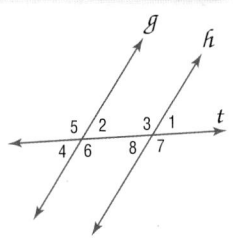

10. ∠1 **53°**   11. ∠5 **127°**
12. ∠7 **127°**   13. ∠8 **53°**
14. ∠2 **53°**   15. ∠3 **127°**

Find the value of x in each figure.

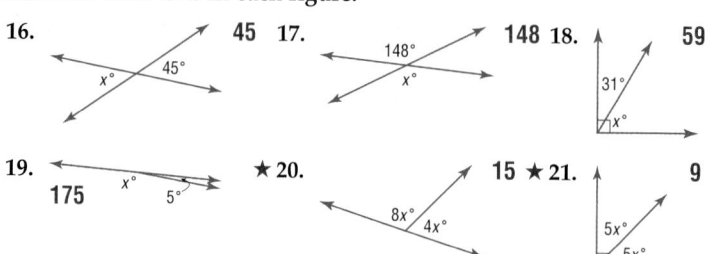

16. **45**   17. **148**   18. **59**

19. **175**   ★20.   15   ★21. **9**

22. Find m∠A if m∠B = 17° and ∠A and ∠B are complementary. **73°**

23. Angles P and Q are supplementary. Find m∠P if m∠Q = 139°. **41°**

24. **ALGEBRA** Angles J and K are complementary. If m∠J = x − 9 and m∠K = x + 5, what is the measure of each angle? **38°; 52°**

★ 25. **ALGEBRA** Find m∠E if ∠E and ∠F are supplementary, m∠E = 2x + 15, and m∠F = 5x − 38. **73°**

26. **SAFETY** Refer to Example 4 on page 495. Find the measure of angles ∠2, ∠3, ∠5, ∠7, and ∠8. **105°; 105°; 75°; 75°; 75°**

CONSTRUCTION For Exercises 27 and 28, use the following information and the diagram shown.
To measure the angle between a sloped ceiling and a wall, a carpenter uses a plumb line (a string with a weight attached).

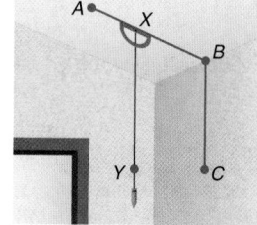

27. If m∠YXB = 68°, what is m∠XBC? **112°**

28. What type of angles are ∠YXB and ∠XBC? **supplementary angles**

ALGEBRA In the figure at the right, m‖ℓ and t is a transversal. Find the value of x for each of the following.

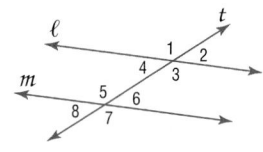

29. m∠2 = 2x + 3 and m∠4 = 4x − 7 **5**

30. m∠8 = 4x − 32 and m∠5 = 5x + 50 **18**

31. m∠7 = 10x + 15 and m∠3 = 7x + 42 **9**

★ 32. **ALGEBRA** The measure of the supplement of an angle is 15° less than four times the measure of the complement. Find the measure of the angle. **55°**

33. CRITICAL THINKING Suppose two parallel lines are cut by a transversal. How are the interior angles on the same side of the transversal related? **See margin.**

34. WRITING IN MATH Answer the question that was posed at the beginning of the lesson. **See margin.**

How are parallel lines and angles related?

Include the following in your answer:
- a drawing of parallel lines intersected by a transversal, and
- a list of the congruent and supplementary angles.

Standardized Test Practice
Ⓐ Ⓑ Ⓒ Ⓓ

For Exercises 35 and 36, use the diagram.

35. The upper rail is parallel to the lower rail. What is the measure of the angle formed by the upper rail and the first vertical post? **A**

Ⓐ 135°   Ⓑ 100°

Ⓒ 90°   Ⓓ 45°

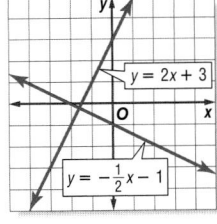

36. What is the measure of the angle formed by the second vertical post and the lower rail? **C**

Ⓐ 100°   Ⓑ 135°   Ⓒ 45°   Ⓓ 90°

Extending the Lesson

For Exercises 37–39, use the pairs of graphs shown at the right.

37–39. See margin.

37. How are each pair of graphs related?

38. What seems to be true about the slopes of the graphs?

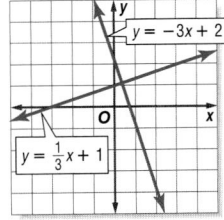

39. Make a conjecture about the slopes of the graphs of perpendicular lines.

Maintain Your Skills

Mixed Review **Use a calculator to find each value to the nearest ten thousandth.**
(Lesson 9-8)

40. cos 21° **0.9336**   **41.** sin 63° **0.8910**   **42.** tan 38° **0.7813**

43. If △ABC ~ △DEF, what is the value of x? *(Lesson 9-7)* **7.5**

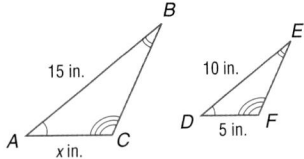

Simplify each expression. *(Lesson 3-2)*

44. $6a + (-18)a$ **−12a**

45. $-5m + (-4)m$ **−9m**

Getting Ready for the Next Lesson
PREREQUISITE SKILL Use a protractor to draw an angle having each measurement. *(To review angles, see Lesson 9-3.)* **46–50. See margin.**

46. 20°   **47.** 45°   **48.** 65°   **49.** 145°   **50.** 170°

Answers

46.
48.
49.

47.

50.

Open-Ended Assessment

Modeling Have students draw two parallel lines and a transversal on a piece of paper. Then give them one of the angle measures and have them fill in the measures of the other angles.

Getting Ready for Lesson 10-2

PREREQUISITE SKILL Lesson 10-2 presents congruent triangles. Congruent triangles have congruent corresponding angles. Exercises 46–50 should be used to determine your students' familiarity with drawing angles.

Answers

33. They are supplementary.

34. Angles and parallel lines are related in that when two parallel lines are cut by a transversal, angles are formed. Answers should include the following.

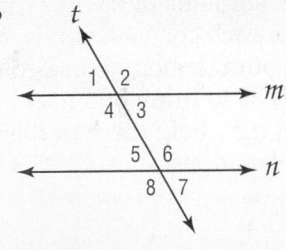

- congruent angles: ∠1, ∠3, ∠5, ∠7 and ∠2, ∠4, ∠6, ∠8

  supplementary angles: ∠1 and ∠2, ∠1 and ∠4, ∠3 and ∠4, ∠2 and ∠3, ∠5 and ∠6, ∠6 and ∠7, ∠8 and ∠7, ∠5 and ∠8, ∠1 and ∠6, ∠4 and ∠7, ∠2 and ∠5, ∠3 and ∠8, ∠3 and ∠6, ∠2 and ∠7, ∠4 and ∠5, ∠1 and ∠8

37. Sample answer: Both graphs intersect to form right angles.

38. They are negative reciprocals of each other.

39. Sample answer: The slopes of the graphs of perpendicular lines are negative reciprocals of each other.

Getting Started

Objective Construct congruent line segments and angles and perpendicular bisectors and angle bisectors.

Materials
compass

Teaching Tip Make sure students know how to use a compass.

Teach

- Students may benefit from taping their paper to a piece of cardboard. Have them poke the tip of the compass into the cardboard to keep it from slipping.
- Point out that the letters used in the copied figure are totally arbitrary.
- Ask students to try to explain why each construction is valid. Encourage them to use colored pencils to draw other segments that may help them in their explanations.

Algebra Activity

A Follow-Up of Lesson 10-1

NEW YORK *Performance Indicator* **8.G.0 Construct the following, using a straight edge and compass: segment congruent to a segment, angle congruent to an angle, perpendicular bisector, angle bisector**

Constructions

Activity 1   Construct a line segment congruent to a given line segment.

Step 1	**Step 2**	**Step 3**
Draw $\overline{AB}$. Then use a straightedge to draw $\overline{GH}$ so it is longer than $\overline{AB}$.	Place the tip of the compass at A and the pencil tip at B.	Using this setting, place the tip at G. Draw an arc to intersect $\overline{GH}$. Label the intersection J. $\overline{GJ} \cong \overline{AB}$.

Activity 2   Construct an angle congruent to a given angle.

Step 1	**Step 2**	**Step 3**
Draw $\angle DEF$. Then use a straightedge to draw $\overline{JK}$. 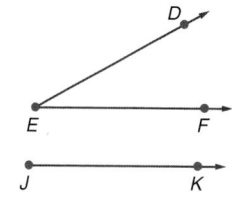	Place the tip of the compass at E. Draw an arc to intersect both sides of $\angle DEF$ to locate points X and Y. 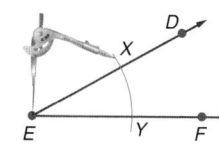	Using this setting, place the compass at point J. Draw an arc to intersect $\overline{JK}$. Label the intersection A. 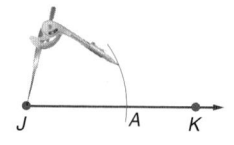
Step 4	**Step 5**	**Step 6**
Place the point of the compass on X and adjust so that the pencil tip is on Y. 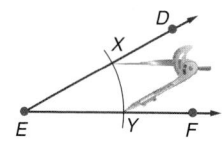	Using this setting, place the compass at A and draw an arc to intersect the arc drawn in Step 3. Label the intersection M. 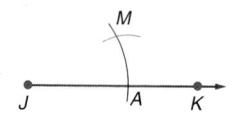	Draw $\overline{JM}$. $\angle MJK \cong \angle DEF$. 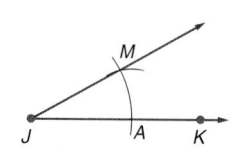

Model and Analyze   **1–2. See students' work.**

1. Draw a line segment. Construct a line segment congruent to the one drawn.

2. Draw an angle. Construct an angle congruent to the one drawn.

Resource Manager

 Teaching Pre-Algebra with Manipulatives

- p. 126 (student recording sheet)

Glencoe Mathematics Classroom Manipulative Kit

- compass

Activity 3   Construct the perpendicular bisector of a line segment.

Step 1

Draw $\overline{XY}$. Then place the compass at point X. Use a setting greater than one half of $\overline{XY}$. Draw an arc above and below $\overline{XY}$.

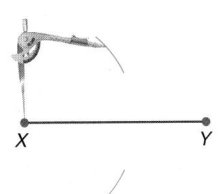

Step 2

Using this setting, place the compass at point Y. Draw an arc above and below $\overline{XY}$ as shown.

Step 3

Use a straightedge to align the two intersections. Draw a segment that intersects $\overline{XY}$. Label the intersection M.

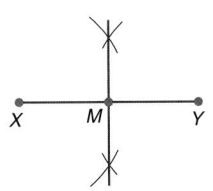

Activity 4   Construct the bisector of an angle.

Step 1

Draw $\angle MNP$. Then place the compass at point N and draw an arc that intersects both sides of the angle. Label the intersections X and Y.

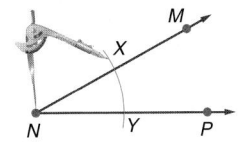

Step 2

With the compass at point X, draw an arc in the interior of $\angle N$. Using this setting, place the compass at point Y. Draw another arc. Label the intersection Q.

Step 3

Draw $\overrightarrow{NQ}$. $\overrightarrow{NQ}$ is the bisector of $\angle MNP$.

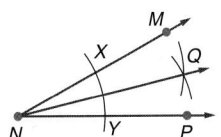

Model and Analyze

3. In Activity 3, use a ruler to measure $\overline{XM}$ and $\overline{MY}$. This construction *bisects* a segment. What do you think *bisects* means? **to divide into two equal parts**

4. Draw a line segment. Construct the perpendicular bisector of the segment. **See students' work.**

5. In Activity 4, what is true about the measures of $\angle MNQ$ and $\angle QNP$? **They are the same.**

6. Why do we say $\overrightarrow{NQ}$ is the bisector of $\angle MNP$? **$\overrightarrow{NQ}$ divides $\angle MNP$ into two equal angles.**

Tips for New Teachers

Safety Tip
There are safety compasses available that do not have sharp points. If using this type of compass, have students practice drawing arcs with them before attempting constructions.

Assess

In **Exercises 1–6**, students construct congruent line segments, congruent angles, perpendicular bisectors of line segments, and bisectors of angles. Ask them to conjecture how a landscape architect might use these skills.

Study Notebook

You may wish to have students summarize this activity and what they learned from it.

1 Focus

5-Minute Check Transparency 10-2 Use as a quiz or review of Lesson 10-1.

Mathematical Background notes are available for this lesson on page 490C.

Where are congruent triangles present in nature?

The opening activity questions are repeated on page 557 of the *Chapter 10 Resource Masters.*

Reading to Learn Mathematics, p. 557 **ELL**

Pre-Activity *Where are congruent triangles present in nature?*

Do the activity at the top of page 500 in your textbook. Write your answers below.

a. Trace the triangles shown in your textbook onto a sheet of paper. Then label the triangles. **See students' work.**

b. Measure and then compare the lengths of the sides of the triangles. **AB = DF, AC = DE, BC = FE**

c. Measure the angles of each triangle. How do the angles compare? **m∠A = m∠D, m∠B = m∠F, m∠C = m∠E**

d. Make a conjecture about the triangles. **Since the angles have the same measures and the sides have the same length, the triangles have the same size and shape.**

Reading the Lesson 1–2. See students' work.

Write a definition and give an example of each new vocabulary word or phrase.

Vocabulary	Definition	Example
1. congruent		
2. corresponding parts		

Helping You Remember

3. Below are two congruent triangles. Name the corresponding parts and complete the congruence statement.

△GHF ≅ ___?___ △MNL

Sample answer: ∠G ≅ ∠M, ∠H ≅ ∠N, ∠L ≅ ∠F, $\overline{FG} \cong \overline{ML}$, $\overline{FH} \cong \overline{LN}$, $\overline{HG} \cong \overline{NM}$

10-2 Congruent Triangles

NEW YORK *Performance Indicator* **Reinforcement of 5.G.9** Identify pairs of congruent triangles, **Reinforcement of 5.G.10** Identify corresponding parts of congruent triangles

What You'll Learn

• Identify congruent triangles and corresponding parts of congruent triangles.

Where are congruent triangles present in nature?

Ivy is a type of climbing plant. Most ivy leaves have five major veins. In the photo shown, the veins outlined form two triangles.

a. Trace the triangles shown at the right onto a sheet of paper. Then label the triangles.

b. Measure and then compare the lengths of the sides of the triangles.

c. Measure the angles of each triangle. How do the angles compare?

d. Make a conjecture about the triangles.

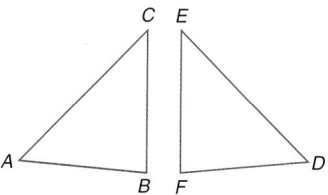

Vocabulary
• congruent
• corresponding parts

Reading Math

Corresponding
Everyday Meaning: *matching*
Math Meaning: *having the same position*

CONGRUENT TRIANGLES Figures that have the same size and shape are **congruent**. The parts of congruent triangles that "match" are **corresponding parts**.

Key Concept — Corresponding Parts of Congruent Triangles

• **Words** If two triangles are congruent, their corresponding sides are congruent and their corresponding angles are congruent.

• **Model**

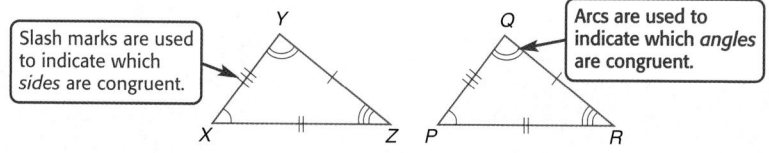

Slash marks are used to indicate which *sides* are congruent.

Arcs are used to indicate which *angles* are congruent.

• **Symbols** Congruent Angles: ∠X ≅ ∠P, ∠Y ≅ ∠Q, ∠Z ≅ ∠R
Congruent Sides: $\overline{XY} \cong \overline{PQ}$, $\overline{YZ} \cong \overline{QR}$, $\overline{XZ} \cong \overline{PR}$

 Concept Check What is true about the corresponding angles and sides of congruent triangles? **They are congruent.**

Resource Manager

📁 Workbooks and Reproducible Masters

Chapter 10 Resource Masters
• Study Guide and Intervention, p. 554
• Skills Practice, p. 555
• Practice, p. 556
• Reading to Learn Mathematics, p. 557
• Enrichment, p. 558
• Assessment, p. 603

Parent and Student Study Guide Workbook, p. 82

📖 Transparencies
5-Minute Check Transparency 10-2
Answer Key Transparencies

💿 Technology
Interactive Chalkboard
Pre-AlgePASS: Tutorial Plus, Lesson 32

When writing a congruence statement, the letters must be written so that corresponding vertices appear in the same order. For example, for the diagram below, write $\triangle FGH \cong \triangle JKM$.

Study Tip

Congruence Statements
You can also write a congruence statement as $\triangle GHF \cong \triangle KMJ$, $\triangle HFG \cong \triangle MJK$, $\triangle FHG \cong \triangle JMK$, $\triangle GFH \cong \triangle KJM$, and $\triangle HGF \cong \triangle MKJ$.

Vertex F corresponds to vertex J.
Vertex G corresponds to vertex K.
Vertex H corresponds to vertex M.

Example 1 *Name Corresponding Parts*

Name the corresponding parts in the congruent triangles shown. Then complete the congruence statement.

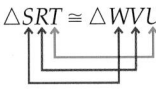

Corresponding Angles
$\angle A \cong \angle Z$, $\angle B \cong \angle Y$, $\angle C \cong \angle X$

Corresponding Sides
$\overline{AB} \cong \overline{ZY}$, $\overline{BC} \cong \overline{YX}$, $\overline{CA} \cong \overline{XZ}$

$\triangle ABC \cong \underline{\quad ? \quad}$

One congruence statement is $\triangle ABC \cong \triangle ZYX$.

Congruence statements can be used to identify corresponding parts of congruent triangles.

Example 2 *Use Congruence Statements*

If $\triangle SRT \cong \triangle WVU$, complete each congruence statement.

$\angle S \cong \underline{\ ?\ }$ $\angle U \cong \underline{\ ?\ }$ $\angle R \cong \underline{\ ?\ }$

$\overline{WV} \cong \underline{\ ?\ }$ $\overline{RT} \cong \underline{\ ?\ }$ $\overline{ST} \cong \underline{\ ?\ }$

Explore   You know the congruence statement. You need to find the corresponding parts.

Plan   Use the order of the vertices in $\triangle SRT \cong \triangle WVU$ to identify the corresponding parts.

Solve $\triangle SRT \cong \triangle WVU$ $\angle S$ corresponds to $\angle W$ so $\angle S \cong \angle W$.
                  $\angle R$ corresponds to $\angle V$ so $\angle R \cong \angle V$.
                  $\angle T$ corresponds to $\angle U$ so $\angle T \cong \angle U$.
   S corresponds to W, and R corresponds to V so $\overline{SR} \cong \overline{WV}$.
   R corresponds to V, and T corresponds to U so $\overline{RT} \cong \overline{VU}$.
   S corresponds to W, and T corresponds to U so $\overline{ST} \cong \overline{WU}$.

Examine   Draw the triangles, using arcs and slash marks to show the congruent angles and sides.

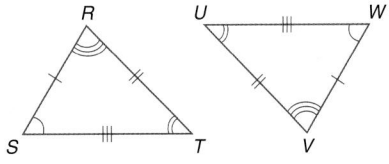

---

2 Teach

CONGRUENT TRIANGLES

Teaching Tip   Remind students that angles are congruent when their measures are equal, and line segments are congruent when their lengths are equal.

In-Class Examples

1 Name the corresponding parts in the congruent triangles shown. Then complete the congruence statement.

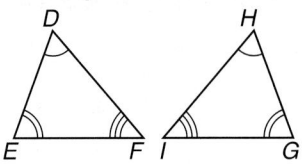

$\angle D \cong \angle H$, $\angle E \cong \angle G$, $\angle F \cong \angle I$; $\overline{DE} \cong \overline{HG}$, $\overline{DF} \cong \overline{HI}$, $\overline{EF} \cong \overline{GI}$; $\triangle HGI \cong \triangle DEF$

Teaching Tip   Have students write other triangle congruence statements so they recognize how to match up the vertices if the original triangle is not named in alphabetical order.

Teaching Tip   For Example 2, encourage students to draw the triangles and mark the congruent parts before completing the congruence statements.

2 If $\triangle MNO \cong \triangle QPR$, complete each congruence statement.

$\angle M \cong \underline{\ ?\ }$ $\angle P \cong \underline{\ ?\ }$ $\angle O \cong \underline{\ ?\ }$

$\overline{QP} \cong \underline{\ ?\ }$ $\overline{NO} \cong \underline{\ ?\ }$ $\overline{MO} \cong \underline{\ ?\ }$

$\angle M \cong \angle Q$, $\angle P \cong \angle N$, $\angle O \cong \angle R$; $\overline{QP} \cong \overline{MN}$, $\overline{NO} \cong \overline{PR}$, $\overline{MO} \cong \overline{QR}$

D A I L Y
INTERVENTION   **Unlocking Misconceptions**

- **Naming Triangles** Although triangles usually are named with the letters in alphabetical order, this practice is not required. The letters can be in any order and it still designates the same triangle. However, when writing congruence statements the order of the two sets of vertices must follow the order of the corresponding congruent angles.

3 **CONSTRUCTION** A brace is used to support a tabletop. In the figure, $\triangle ABC \cong \triangle DEF$.

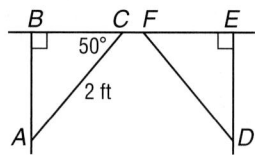

a. What is the measure of $\angle F$? **50°**

b. What is the length of $\overline{DF}$? **2 ft**

3 Practice/Apply

Study Notebook

Have students—

• add the definitions/examples of the vocabulary terms to their Vocabulary Builder worksheets for Chapter 10.

• draw a set of congruent triangles and write congruence statements for them.

• include any other item(s) that they find helpful in mastering the skills in this lesson.

About the Exercises . . .

Odd/Even Assignments

Exercises 10–15 and 18–28 are structured so that students practice the same concepts whether they are assigned odd or even problems.

Assignment Guide

Basic: 11–33 odd, 34–49

Average: 11–33 odd, 34–49

Advanced: 10–32 even, 34–43 (Optional: 44–49)

You can use corresponding parts to find the measures of angles and sides in a figure that is congruent to a figure with known measures.

Example 3 *Find Missing Measures*

LANDSCAPING A brace is used to support a tree and help it to grow straight. In the figure, $\triangle TRS \cong \triangle ERS$.

a. At what angle is the brace placed against the ground?

$\angle E$ and $\angle T$ are corresponding angles. So, they are congruent. Since $m\angle T = 65°$, $m\angle E = 65°$.

The brace is placed at a 65° angle with the ground.

b. What is the length of the brace?

$\overline{RE}$ corresponds to $\overline{RT}$. So, $\overline{RE}$ and $\overline{RT}$ are congruent. Since $RT = 8$ feet, $RE = 8$ feet.

The length of the brace is 8 feet.

Check for Understanding

Concept Check 1. **Explain** when two figures are congruent.

2. **OPEN ENDED** Draw and label a pair of congruent triangles. Be sure to mark the corresponding parts. **1–2. See pp. 551A–551B.**

Guided Practice For each pair of congruent triangles, name the corresponding parts. Then complete the congruence statement. **3–4. See pp. 551A–551B.**

GUIDED PRACTICE KEY	
Exercises	Examples
3, 4	1
5–8	2
9	3

3.

$\triangle KMJ \cong$ ___?___

4.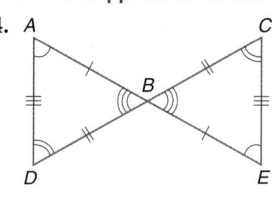

$\triangle CBE \cong$ ___?___

Complete each congruence statement if $\triangle DKJ \cong \triangle NAM$. **8. $\overline{KD}$**

5. $\angle J \cong$ ___?___ $\angle M$ 6. $\angle A \cong$ ___?___ $\angle K$ 7. $\overline{JD} \cong$ ___?___ $\overline{MN}$ 8. $\overline{AN} \cong$ ___?___

Application 9. **TOWERS** A tower that supports high voltage power lines is shown at the right. In the tower, $\triangle ETC \cong \triangle YRC$. What is the length of $\overline{RC}$ if $EC = 10$ feet and $TC = 15$ feet? **15 ft**

DAILY INTERVENTION

Differentiated Instruction

• **Visual/Spatial** Have students use compasses to create congruent triangles. Then have students cut out the triangles and lay one triangle on top of the other to verify that they match. Have students indicate the congruent sides and angles.

★ indicates increased difficulty

Practice and Apply

Homework Help

For Exercises	See Examples
10–13	1
16, 17, 27–29	3
18–26	2

Extra Practice
See page 748.

For each pair of congruent triangles, name the corresponding parts. Then complete the congruence statement. 10–13. See margin.

10.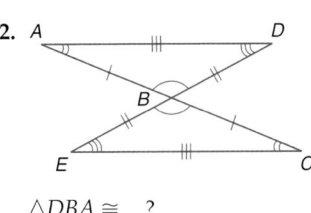

$\triangle DFE \cong$?

11.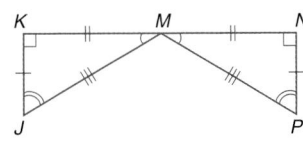

$\triangle KJM \cong$?

12.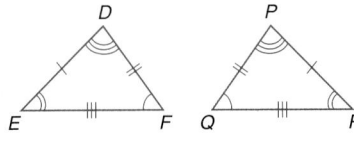

$\triangle DBA \cong$?

13.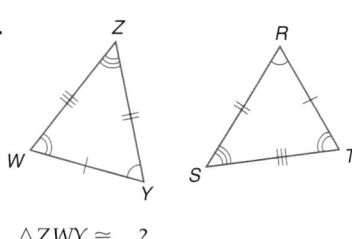

$\triangle ZWY \cong$?

Tell whether each statement is *sometimes*, *always*, or *never* true.

14. If two triangles are congruent, then the perimeters are equal. **always**

15. If the perimeters of two triangles are equal, then the triangles are congruent. **sometimes**

More About . . .

Architecture •·········

Trusses were used in the construction of the Eiffel Tower in Paris, France. The tower contains more than 15,000 pieces of steel and 2.5 million rivets.

Source: www.paris.org

ARCHITECTURE For Exercises 16 and 17, use the diagram of the roof truss at the right and the fact that $\triangle TRU \cong \triangle SRU$.

16. Find the distance from the left metal plate connector to the center web. **16 ft**

17. What is the measure of the angle formed by the top left chord and the bottom chord? **30°**

Complete each congruence statement if $\triangle FHG \cong \triangle CBD$ and $\triangle KMA \cong \triangle PRQ$.

18. $\angle G \cong$? $\angle D$

19. $\angle C \cong$? $\angle F$

20. $\angle M \cong \angle$? $\angle R$

21. $\angle Q \cong$? $\angle A$

22. $\overline{HG} \cong$? $\overline{BD}$

23. $\overline{BC} \cong$? $\overline{HF}$

24. $\overline{DC} \cong$? $\overline{GF}$

25. $\overline{GF} \cong$? $\overline{DC}$

★ 26. $\angle GFH \cong \angle$? $\angle DCB$

Find the value of x for each pair of congruent triangles.

27. **20**

28. **18**

 www.pre-alg.com/self_check_quiz/ny

Lesson 10-2 Congruent Triangles **503**

Answers

10. $\angle D \cong \angle P$, $\angle F \cong \angle Q$, $\angle E \cong \angle R$, $\overline{DF} \cong \overline{PQ}$, $\overline{FE} \cong \overline{QR}$, $\overline{DE} \cong \overline{PR}$; $\triangle PQR$

11. $\angle K \cong \angle N$, $\angle J \cong \angle P$, $\angle M \cong \angle M$, $\overline{KJ} \cong \overline{NP}$, $\overline{JM} \cong \overline{PM}$, $\overline{KM} \cong \overline{NM}$; $\triangle NPM$

12. $\angle D \cong \angle E$, $\angle B \cong \angle B$, $\angle A \cong \angle C$, $\overline{DB} \cong \overline{EB}$, $\overline{BA} \cong \overline{BC}$, $\overline{DA} \cong \overline{EC}$; $\triangle EBC$

13. $\angle Z \cong \angle S$, $\angle W \cong \angle T$, $\angle Y \cong \angle R$, $\overline{ZW} \cong \overline{ST}$, $\overline{WY} \cong \overline{TR}$, $\overline{ZY} \cong \overline{SR}$; $\triangle STR$

Study Guide and Intervention, p. 554

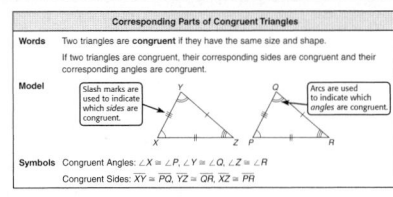

Corresponding Parts of Congruent Triangles

Skills Practice, p. 555 and Practice, p. 556 (shown)

Complete the congruence statement if $\triangle CMH \cong \triangle PLF$ and $\triangle DNO \cong \triangle AET$.

1. $\angle M \cong$? $\angle L$ 2. $\overline{MC} \cong$? $\overline{LP}$ 3. $\overline{DN} \cong$? $\overline{AE}$ 4. $\angle A \cong$? $\angle D$

5. $\overline{FL} \cong$? $\overline{HM}$ 6. $\angle C \cong$? $\angle P$ 7. $\overline{TE} \cong$? $\overline{ON}$ 8. $\angle O \cong$? $\angle T$

Find the value of x for each pair of congruent triangles.

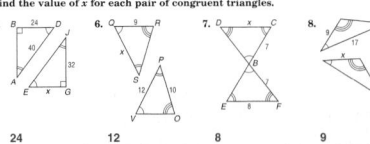

12. **ALGEBRA** If $\triangle DEC \cong \triangle PRM$, what is the value of x? **3**

13. **ALGEBRA** If $\triangle AHB \cong \triangle KJP$, what is the value of x? **2**

KALEIDOSCOPE For Exercises 14–19, use the kaleidoscope pattern at the right. Name a triangle that appears to be congruent to each triangle listed.

14. $\triangle GEH$ $\triangle GEF$ 15. $\triangle FCH$ $\triangle HAF$
16. $\triangle DEC$ $\triangle DEA$ 17. $\triangle ABD$ $\triangle CBD$
18. $\triangle HEF$ $\triangle HED$ 19. $\triangle CBE$ $\triangle ABE$
For Exercises 14–19, sample answers are given.

Enrichment, p. 558

Proofs of Triangle Congruence

One way to prove that two triangles are congruent is by using the *side-angle-side* (SAS) congruence postulate. By showing that two sides and the angle between the sides (*included angle*) of one triangle are congruent to two sides and the included angle of the other triangle, you can conclude that the triangles are congruent to one another. This is often faster than trying to show that all corresponding sides and all corresponding angles are congruent.

Write the reason for each statement.

1. Prove: $\triangle ABD \cong \triangle CDB$

Statement	Reason
a. $\overline{AB} \parallel \overline{CD}; \overline{AB} \cong \overline{CD}$	a. Given
b. $m\angle ABD \cong m\angle CDB$	b. Alternate Interior $\angle$s
c. $\overline{BD} \cong \overline{BD}$	c. Reflexive (Side shared)
d. $\triangle ABD \cong \triangle CDB$	d. SAS Congruence

2. Prove: $\angle Q \cong \angle S$

Statement	Reason
a. $\overline{QR} \parallel \overline{ST}; \overline{QT} \cong \overline{SR}$	a. Given
b. $\angle QRT \cong \angle STR$	b. Alternate Interior $\angle$s
c. $\overline{RT} \cong \overline{RT}$	c. Reflexive (Side shared)
d. $\triangle QRT \cong \triangle STR$	d. SAS Congruence
e. $\angle Q \cong \angle S$	e. CPCTC

Open-Ended Assessment

Speaking Divide students into groups of four. Have each student take a turn describing corresponding parts of congruent triangles. Students should also describe one real-world example of corresponding triangles.

Getting Ready for Lesson 10-3

PREREQUISITE SKILL Lesson 10-3 presents transformations on the coordinate plane. Exercises 44–49 should be used to determine your students' familiarity with graphing points on a coordinate plane.

Assessment Options

Quiz (Lessons 10-1 and 10-2) is available on p. 603 of the *Chapter 10 Resource Masters*.

---

29. ALGEBRA If $\triangle ABC \cong \triangle XYZ$, what is the value of x? **6**

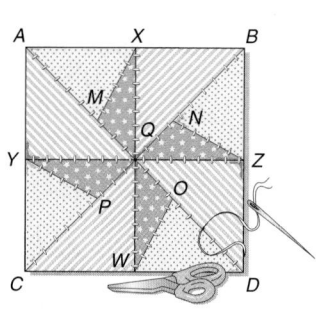

For Exercises 30–33, sample answers are given.

QUILTS For Exercises 30–33, use the quilt pattern shown at the left. Name a triangle that appears to be congruent to each triangle listed.

30. $\triangle XBQ$ △**WCQ** **31.** $\triangle YQP$ △**ZQN**
32. $\triangle DWO$ △**CYP** **33.** $\triangle ZQN$ △**WQO**

34. $\triangle ABH \cong \triangle IJG$; $\triangle ACG \cong \triangle IEF$

34. CRITICAL THINKING In the figure at the right, there are two pairs of congruent triangles. Write a congruence statement for each pair.

35. WRITING IN MATH Answer the question that was posed at the beginning of the lesson. **See margin.**

Where are congruent triangles present in nature?

Include the following in your answer:
• a definition of congruent triangles, and
• two examples of objects in nature that contain congruent triangles.

NEW YORK
Test Practice

Standardized Test Practice
Ⓐ Ⓑ Ⓒ Ⓓ

36. Which of the following must be true if $\triangle ACD \cong \triangle EHF$? **D**
Ⓐ $\angle C \cong \angle E$ Ⓑ $\overline{CA} \cong \overline{HF}$ Ⓒ $\overline{DC} \cong \overline{EF}$ Ⓓ $\angle CAD \cong \angle HEF$

37. Find the measure of $\overline{UY}$ if $\triangle XYZ \cong \triangle UYW$. **D**
Ⓐ 10 Ⓑ 20
Ⓒ 24 Ⓓ 26

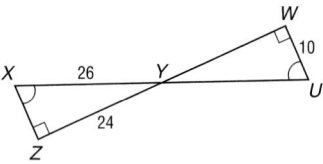

Maintain Your Skills

Mixed Review

38. 51°

38. Angles P and Q are supplementary. Find $m\angle P$ if $m\angle Q = 129°$. *(Lesson 10-1)*

Use a calculator to find each value to the nearest ten-thousandth. *(Lesson 9-8)*

39. $\cos 83°$ **0.1219** **40.** $\sin 39.7°$ **0.6388** **41.** $\tan 49.2°$ **1.1585**

42. Name the multiplicative inverse of $2\frac{1}{2}$. *(Lesson 5-4)* $\frac{2}{5}$

43. ALGEBRA Solve $-5a - 6 = 24$. *(Lesson 3-5)* **−6**

Getting Ready for the Next Lesson

PREREQUISITE SKILL Graph each point on a coordinate system. *(To review the coordinate system, see Lesson 2-6.)* **44–49. See margin.**

44. $A(2, 4)$ **45.** $J(-1, 3)$ **46.** $H(0, 5)$
47. $D(2, 0)$ **48.** $W(-2, -4)$ **49.** $T(-1, -3)$

Answers

35. Congruent triangles can be found on objects in nature like leaves and animals. Answers should include the following.

• Congruent triangles are triangles with the same angle measures and the same side lengths.

• Sample answer: A bird's wings when extended are an example of congruent angles. Another example of congruent angles would be the wings of a butterfly.

44–49.

Algebra Activity

A Preview of Lesson 10-3

Symmetry

Activity 1

Trace the outline of the butterfly shown. Then draw a line down the center of the butterfly. Notice how the two halves match. When this happens, a figure is said to have **line symmetry** and the line is called a *line of symmetry*. A figure that has line symmetry has **bilateral symmetry**.

Analyze

Determine whether each figure has line symmetry. If it does, trace the figure, and draw all lines of symmetry. If not, write *none*. 1, 3. See pp. 551A–551B.

1.

2. J none

3.

Activity 2

Copy the figure at the right. Then cut out the figure. Next, rotate the figure 90°, 180°, and 270°, about point *C*. What do you notice about the appearance of the figure in each rotation? **It looks exactly as it did in the original figure.**

Any figure that can be turned or rotated less than 360° about a fixed point so that the figure looks exactly as it does in its original position has **rotational** or **turn symmetry**.

Analyze 7. Sample answer: capital letter H, yield sign, square

Determine whether each figure has rotational symmetry. Write *yes* or *no*.

4. yes

5. yes

6. no

7. Name three objects that have both line symmetry and rotational symmetry.

Resource Manager

📁 *Teaching Pre-Algebra with Manipulatives*
• p. 128 (student recording sheet)

Algebra Activity

A Preview of Lesson 10-3

Getting Started

Objective Introduce three types of symmetry.

Materials
tracing paper (optional)

Teaching Tip Allow students to trace the figures onto paper and fold the paper to check for lines of symmetry. They may have to hold the paper up to the light to see through it.

Teach

• Line symmetry can also be introduced by using a mirror. Place the mirror on a figure so that the mirror is perpendicular to the page. If the image formed matches the original figure, the mirror is on a line of symmetry. For example, have students check the butterfly by placing the mirror along the middle of the body. The new image should match the original figure. Now check the starfish, the letter J, and the snowflake.

Assess

Ask students how symmetry might apply to the life sciences. Have them find pictures of animals that have bilateral symmetry and pictures of animals that have rotational symmetry.

Study Notebook

You may wish to have students summarize this activity and what they learned from it.

10-3 Transformations on the Coordinate Plane

1 Focus

5-Minute Check Transparency 10-3 Use as a quiz or review of Lesson 10-2.

Mathematical Background notes are available for this lesson on page 490C.

How are transformations involved in recreational activities?

The opening activity questions are repeated on page 562 of the *Chapter 10 Resource Masters*.

Reading to Learn Mathematics, p. 562 **ELL**

Pre-Activity *How are transformations involved in recreational activities?*

Do the activity at the top of page 506 in your textbook. Write your answers below.

a. Describe the motion involved in making a 180° turn on a skateboard.
   Sample answer: The skateboard lands in the opposite direction from where it started.

b. Describe the motion that is used when swinging on a swing.
   Sample answer: a back-and-forth motion

c. What type of motion does a scooter display when moving?
   Sample answer: A scooter moves from one position to another position.

Reading the Lesson 1–5. See students' work.

Write a definition and give an example of each new vocabulary word or phrase.

Vocabulary	Definition	Example
1. transformation		
2. translation		
3. reflection		
4. line of symmetry		
5. rotation		

Helping You Remember

6. Complete the diagrams below by filling in each blank with one of the vocabulary words or phrases.

A movement of a geometric figure is called a __transformation__.

What You'll Learn

- Draw translations, rotations, and reflections on a coordinate plane.

How are transformations involved in recreational activities?

The physical motions used in recreational activities such as skateboarding, swinging, or riding a scooter, are related to mathematics.

a. Describe the motion involved in making a 180° turn on a skateboard.
b. Describe the motion that is used when swinging on a swing.
c. What type of motion does a scooter display when moving?

TRANSFORMATIONS A movement of a geometric figure is a **transformation**. Three types of transformations are shown below.

- In a **translation**, you slide a figure from one position to another without turning it. Translations are also called *slides*.

Translation

- In a **reflection**, you flip a figure over a line. The figures are mirror images of each other. Reflections are also called *flips*. The line is called a **line of symmetry**.

Reflection

- In a **rotation**, you turn the figure around a fixed point. Rotations are also called *turns*.

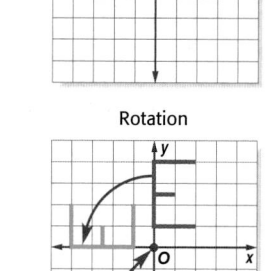

Rotation

Vocabulary
- transformation
- translation
- reflection
- line of symmetry
- rotation

Resource Manager

📁 Workbooks and Reproducible Masters

Chapter 10 Resource Masters
- Study Guide and Intervention, p. 559
- Skills Practice, p. 560
- Practice, p. 561
- Reading to Learn Mathematics, p. 562
- Enrichment, p. 563

Graphing Calculator and Spreadsheet Masters, p. 37
Parent and Student Study Guide Workbook, p. 83

🖥 Transparencies
5-Minute Check Transparency 10-3
Answer Key Transparencies

💿 Technology

Interactive Chalkboard
Pre-AlgePASS: Tutorial Plus, Lesson 33

When translating a figure, every point of the original figure is moved the same distance and in the same direction.

Translation 4 units left	Translation 5 units down	Translation 6 units right, 3 units up
	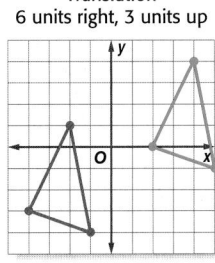	

The following steps can be used to translate a point in the coordinate plane.

Key Concept   *Translation*

Step 1   Describe the translation using an ordered pair.

Step 2   Add the coordinates of the ordered pair to the coordinates of the original point.

Example 1   Translation in a Coordinate Plane

The vertices of $\triangle MNP$ are $M(4, -2)$, $N(0, 2)$, and $P(5, 2)$. Graph the triangle and the image of $\triangle MNP$ after a translation 5 units left and 3 units up.

This translation can be written as the ordered pair $(-5, 3)$. To find the coordinates of the translated image, add -5 to each x-coordinate and add 3 to each y-coordinate.

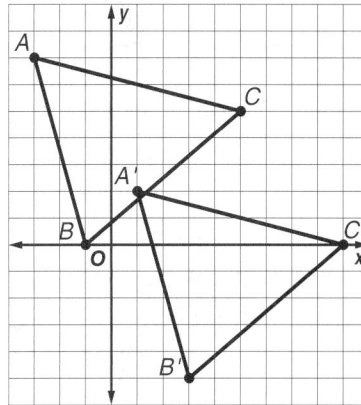

vertex		5 left, 3 up		translation
$M(4, -2)$	+	$(-5, 3)$	$\rightarrow$	$M'(-1, 1)$
$N(0, 2)$	+	$(-5, 3)$	$\rightarrow$	$N'(-5, 5)$
$P(5, 2)$	+	$(-5, 3)$	$\rightarrow$	$P'(0, 5)$

The coordinates of the vertices of $\triangle M'N'P'$ are $M'(-1, 1)$, $N'(-5, 5)$, and $P'(0, 5)$.

When reflecting a figure, every point of the original figure has a corresponding point on the other side of the line of symmetry.

Reflection over the *x*-axis	Reflection over the *y*-axis
	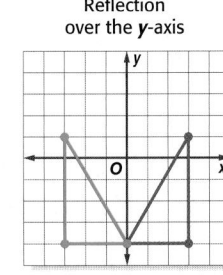

---

2 Teach

TRANSFORMATIONS

In-Class Example   Power Point®

1 The vertices of $\triangle ABC$ are $A(-3, 7)$, $B(-1, 0)$, and $C(5, 5)$. Graph the triangle and the image of $\triangle ABC$ after a translation 4 units right and 5 units down.

In-Class Example

2 The vertices of a figure are $M(-8, 6)$, $N(5, 9)$, $O(2, 1)$, and $P(-10, 3)$. Graph the figure and the image of the figure after a reflection over the y-axis.

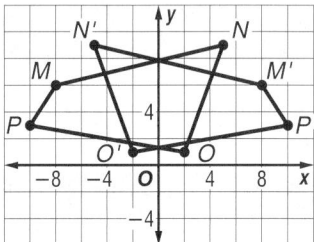

Teaching Tip Point out to students that a translation simply slides the figure to a new location and only requires addition to calculate the new vertices. Rotations and reflections change the way the figure is facing, and for these kinds of transformations, calculating the new vertices requires multiplication by -1.

Answers (p. 509)

1. The figure is moved 5 units to the right and 2 units down.

2. Sample answer:

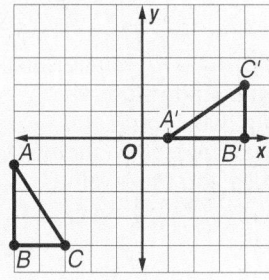

NEW YORK
Study Tip

Notice that when a figure is translated, reflected, or rotated, the lengths of the sides are preserved. The angle measures are also preserved. Thus, the two figures are congruent.

Reading Math

clockwise
The word clockwise refers to *the direction in which the hands of a clock rotate.*

counterclockwise
The word counterclockwise refers to *the direction opposite to that in which the hands of a clock rotate.*

The following rules can be used to reflect a point over the x- or y-axis.

Key Concept — Reflection

- To reflect a point over the x-axis, use the same x-coordinate and multiply the y-coordinate by -1.
- To reflect a point over the y-axis, use the same y-coordinate and multiply the x-coordinate by -1.

Example 2 — Reflection in a Coordinate Plane

The vertices of the figure below are $A(-2, 3)$, $B(0, 5)$, $C(3, 1)$, and $D(3, 3)$. Graph the figure and the image of the figure after a reflection over the x-axis.

To find the coordinates of the vertices of the image after a reflection over the x-axis, use the same x-coordinate and multiply the y-coordinate by -1.

vertex				reflection
$A(-2, 3)$	$\rightarrow$	$(-2, -1 \cdot 3)$	$\rightarrow$	$A'(-2, -3)$
$B(0, 5)$	$\rightarrow$	$(0, -1 \cdot 5)$	$\rightarrow$	$B'(0, -5)$
$C(3, 1)$	$\rightarrow$	$(3, -1 \cdot 1)$	$\rightarrow$	$C'(3, -1)$
$D(3, 3)$	$\rightarrow$	$(3, -1 \cdot 3)$	$\rightarrow$	$D'(3, -3)$

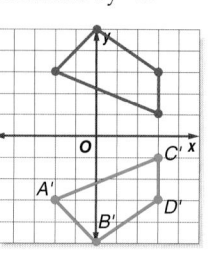

The coordinates of the vertices of the reflected figure are $A'(-2, -3)$, $B'(0, -5)$, $C'(3, -1)$, and $D'(3, -3)$.

The diagrams below show three of the ways a figure can be rotated.

Rotation of 90°
clockwise

Rotation of 90°
counterclockwise

Rotation of 180°

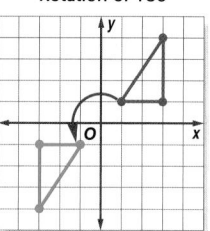

You can use these rules to rotate a figure 90° clockwise, 90° counterclockwise, or 180° about the origin.

Key Concept — Rotation

- To rotate a figure 90° clockwise about the origin, switch the coordinates of each point and then multiply the new second coordinate by -1.
- To rotate a figure 90° counterclockwise about the origin, switch the coordinates of each point and then multiply the new first coordinate by -1.
- To rotate a figure 180° about the origin, multiply both coordinates of each point by -1.

DAILY INTERVENTION — Differentiated Instruction — ELL

- **Verbal/Linguistic** Have students write descriptions of transformations in real-world situations. Encourage them to bring in pictures or models of what they are describing.

Example 3 Rotations in a Coordinate Plane

A figure has vertices $J(1, 1)$, $K(4, 1)$, $M(1, 2)$, $N(4, 2)$, and $P(3, 4)$. Graph the figure and the image of the figure after a rotation of 90° counterclockwise.

To rotate the figure, switch the coordinates of each vertex and multiply the first by -1.

$J(1, 1) \rightarrow J'(-1, 1)$ $N(4, 2) \rightarrow N'(-2, 4)$

$K(4, 1) \rightarrow K'(-1, 4)$ $P(3, 4) \rightarrow P'(-4, 3)$

$M(1, 2) \rightarrow M'(-2, 1)$

The coordinates of the vertices of the rotated figure are $J'(-1, 1)$, $K'(-1, 4)$, $M'(-2, 1)$, $N'(-2, 4)$, and $P'(-4, 3)$.

Check for Understanding

Concept Check

1–2. See margin.

Guided Practice

GUIDED PRACTICE KEY	
Exercises	Examples
3	1
4	2
5	3
6	1–3

Application

1. **Write** a sentence to describe a figure that is translated by (5, −2).

2. **OPEN ENDED** Draw a triangle on grid paper. Then draw the image of the triangle after it is moved 5 units right and then rotated counterclockwise 90°.

3. Rectangle *RSTU* is shown at the right. Graph the image of the rectangle after a translation 4 units right and 2 units down. **See margin.**

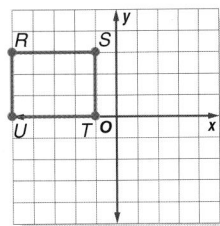

4. Suppose the figure graphed is reflected over the *y*-axis. Find the coordinates of the vertices after the reflection.
W′ **(4, 3)**, *X′* **(1, 5)**, *Y′* **(3, −1)**, *Z′* **(1, −2)**

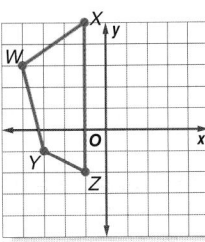

5. Triangle *ABC* is shown. Graph the image of △*ABC* after a rotation of 90° counterclockwise. **See margin.**

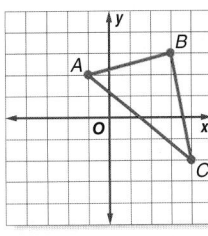

6. **ART** Identify the type of transformation that is shown below. **translation or reflection**

---

3. A figure has vertices $A(-4, 5)$, $B(-2, 4)$, $C(-1, 2)$, $D(-3, 1)$, and $E(-5, 3)$. Graph the figure and the image of the figure after a rotation of 180°.

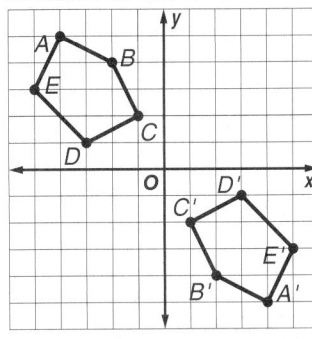

3 Practice/Apply

Study Notebook

Have students—

• add the definitions/examples of the vocabulary terms to their Vocabulary Builder worksheets for Chapter 10.

• include any other item(s) that they find helpful in mastering the skills in this lesson.

About the Exercises . . .

Odd/Even Assignments

Exercises 7–10, 11–14, 15, 17, and 25–56 are structured so that students practice the same concepts whether they are assigned odd or even problems.

Assignment Guide

Basic: 7, 11, 15–23 odd, 24–40

Average: 7–23 odd, 24–40

Advanced: 8–22 even, 24–34 (Optional: 35–40)

Answers

3.

5.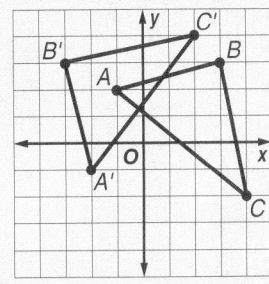

Study Guide and Intervention, p. 559

Transformation	Movement	How To's
Translation	You slide a figure from one position to another without turning it. Every point of the original figure is moved the same distance and in the same direction.	To describe the translation using an ordered pair, add the coordinates of the ordered pair to the coordinates of the original point.
Reflection	You flip a figure over a **line of symmetry**. The figures are mirror images of each other. Every point of the original figure has a corresponding point on the other side of the line of symmetry.	• To reflect a point over the x-axis, use the same x-coordinate and multiply the y-coordinate by −1. • To reflect a point over the y-axis, use the same y-coordinate and multiply the x-coordinate by −1.
Rotation	You turn the figure around a fixed point. You can turn the figure 90° clockwise, 90° counterclockwise, or 180° about the origin.	• To rotate a figure 90° clockwise, switch the coordinates of each point and multiply the new second coordinate by −1. • To rotate a figure 90° counterclockwise, switch the coordinates of each point and multiply the new first coordinate by −1. • To rotate a figure 180°, multiply both coordinates of each point by −1.

Example The vertices of figure PQRS are P(−2, 2), Q(−1, 2), R(−1, −2), and S(−3, −1). Graph the figure and its image after a reflection over the y-axis. Use the same y-coordinate and multiply the x-coordinate by −1.

vertex			reflection
P(−2, 2)	→	(−2 · −1, 2)	→ P'(2, 2)
Q(−1, 2)	→	(−1 · −1, 2)	→ Q'(1, 2)
R(−1, −2)	→	(−1 · −1, −2)	→ R'(1, −2)
S(−3, −1)	→	(−3 · −1, −1)	→ S'(3, −1)

Exercises

For Exercises 1–3, use the graph shown.

1. Graph the image of the figure after a rotation of 90° counterclockwise.
2. Graph the image of the figure after a rotation of 180°.
3. Find the vertices of the figure after a rotation of 90° clockwise. A(−1, 4), B(−1, 3), C(−2, 2), D(−1, 1), E(−3, 1), and F(−3, 4)

Skills Practice, p. 560 and Practice, p. 561 (shown)

Find the coordinates of the vertices of each figure after a reflection over the given axis. Then graph the reflection image.

1. y-axis
2. x-axis
3. x-axis

E'(−1, 1), G'(−2, 3), H'(−4, −1)
N'(−2, 2), T'(2, 1), R'(2, 3), P'(0, 4)
L'(−2, 0), M'(0, 1), N'(1, 0), P'(2, 4)

For Exercises 4–6, use the graph shown.

4. Graph the image of the figure after a rotation of 90° clockwise.
5. Find the coordinates of the vertices of the figure after a rotation of 180°. T'(4, 2), Z'(4, 3), W'(2, 5), V'(2, 1)
6. Graph the image of the figure after a rotation of 90° counterclockwise.

For Exercises 7–9, use the graph shown.

7. Graph the image of the figure after a rotation of 180°.
8. Graph the image of the figure after a rotation of 90° clockwise.
9. Find the vertices of the figure after a rotation of 90° counterclockwise. V'(−4, −1), J'(−1, −3), C'(−3,−3), B'(−3,−4)

Enrichment, p. 563

Using Coordinates

For Exercises 1–4, use the coordinate grid at the right.

1. Graph the points (1, 1), (4, 4), and (2, 4). Connect the dots. Name the figure formed. **triangle**
2. Multiply each y-coordinate in Exercise 1 by −1. Graph the points. How is this triangle related to the one in Exercise 1? **It is a reflection over the x-axis.**
3. Multiply each coordinate in Exercise 1 by −1. Graph the points.
4. What would you have to do to get the coordinates of a triangle in Quadrant II congruent to the ones in Exercises 1–3? **Multiply each x-coordinate in Exercise 1 by −1.**

For Exercises 5–10, use the coordinate grid at the right.

5. Graph the points (3, 1), (2, 3), (4, 6), and (5, 4). Connect the dots. The figure formed is called a parallelogram.
6. Add 2 to both coordinates of each point and graph the new figure formed. Name the figure formed. **parallelogram**
7. Add −4 to the x-coordinate of each point in Exercise 5 and graph the new coordinates. Is this figure also a parallelogram? **yes**
8. Graph the points (5, −2), (6, −3), (5, −5), and (3, −3) on the coordinate plane at the right. Name the figure formed. **trapezoid**
9. Multiply both coordinates of each point in Exercise 8 by 2 and graph the new coordinates. This is an enlargement.
10. Multiply both coordinates of each point in Exercise 8 by ½ and graph the new coordinates. This is a reduction.

★ indicates increased difficulty

Practice and Apply

Homework Help

For Exercises	See Examples
7–10	1
11–14	2
15–17	3
18–20	1–3

Extra Practice See page 748.

Find the coordinates of the vertices of each figure after the given translation. Then graph the translation image. **7–10. See margin.**

7. (2, 3)
8. (−4, 3)
★9. $\left(5, 2\frac{1}{2}\right)$

10. The vertices of a figure are D(1, 2), E(1, 4), F(−1, 2), G(−4, 4). Graph the image of the figure after a translation 4 units down.

Find the coordinates of the vertices of each figure after a reflection over the given axis. Then graph the reflection image. **11–14. See pp. 551A–551B.**

11. x-axis
12. y-axis
★13. x-axis

  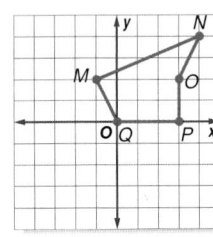

14. The vertices of a figure are W(−3, −3), X(0, −4), Y(4, −2), and Z(2, −1). Graph the image of its reflection over the y-axis.

For Exercises 15–17, use the graph shown.

15, 17. See pp. 551A–551B.

16. A'(−1, 1), B'(−3, 0), C'(−5, 2), D'(−3, 4), E'(−1, 4)

15. Graph the image of the figure after a rotation of 90° counterclockwise.
16. Find the coordinates of the vertices of the figure after a 180° rotation.
17. Graph the image of the figure after a rotation of 90° clockwise.

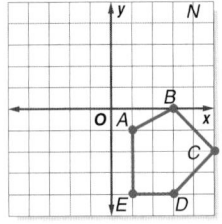

Identify each transformation as a *translation*, a *reflection*, or a *rotation*.

18. rotation
19. translation
20. reflection

18.
19.
20.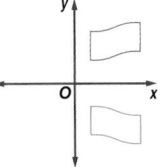

21. Give a counterexample for the following statement. *The image of a figure's reflection is never the same as the image of its translation.* **See pp. 551A–551B.**

510 Chapter 10 Two-Dimensional Figures

Answers

7. A'(−2, 5), B'(1, 3), C'(−2, 0)
8. H'(−4, 3), I'(0, 0), J'(0, 2), K'(−4, −1)

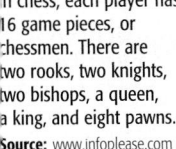
22. GAMES What type of transformation is used when moving a knight in a game of chess? **translation**

23. MIRRORS Which transformation exists when you look into a mirror? **reflection**

24. CRITICAL THINKING After a rotation of 90° counterclockwise, the coordinates of the vertices of the image of $\triangle ABC$ are $A'(3, 2)$, $B'(0, 4)$, and $C'(5, 5)$. What were the coordinates of the vertices before the rotation? **See margin.**

25. WRITING IN MATH Answer the question that was posed at the beginning of the lesson. **See margin.**

How are the transformations involved in recreational activities?

Include the following in your answer:

- an explanation describing each type of transformation, and
- an explanation telling the type of transformation each recreational activity represents.

Standardized
Test Practice
Ⓐ Ⓑ Ⓒ Ⓓ

For Exercises 26 and 27, suppose the figure shown is translated 4 units to the left and 3 units down.

26. Which point is *not* a vertex of the translated image? **B**

Ⓐ $(-2, -3)$ Ⓑ $(-4, -3)$

Ⓒ $(-3, -1)$ Ⓓ $(-2, 1)$

27. Which statement best describes this translation? **C**

Ⓐ $(x, y) \rightarrow (x + 4, y + 3)$ Ⓑ $(x, y) \rightarrow (x - 4, y + 3)$

Ⓒ $(x, y) \rightarrow (x - 4, y - 3)$ Ⓓ $(x, y) \rightarrow (x + 4, y - 3)$

Maintain Your Skills

Mixed Review Complete each congruence statement if $\triangle ABC \cong \triangle DEF$. *(Lesson 10-2)*

28. $\angle D \cong$ _?_ $\angle A$ **29.** $\overline{AC} \cong$ _?_ $\overline{DF}$ **30.** $\overline{DE} \cong$ _?_ $\overline{AB}$

Find the value of x in each figure. *(Lesson 10-1)*

31. **110°**

32. 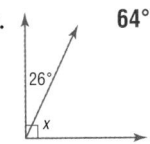 **64°**

33. ALGEBRA Solve $x - 3.4 \geq 6.2$. Graph the solution on a number line. *(Lesson 7-4)* $x \geq 9.6$; **See margin for graph.**

34. Evaluate $|-4| - |3|$. *(Lesson 2-1)* **1**

Getting Ready for
the Next Lesson

PREREQUISITE SKILL Solve each equation.
*(To review **solving two-step equations**, see Lesson 3-5.)*

35. $2x + 134 = 360$ **113**   **36.** $3x + 54 = 360$ **102**   **37.** $5x + 125 = 360$ **47**

38. $4x + 92 = 360$ **67**   **39.** $2x + 148 = 360$ **106**   **40.** $6x + 102 = 360$ **43**

9. $D'(1, 3\frac{1}{2})$,

$E'(3, 4\frac{1}{2})$,

$G'(1, -1\frac{1}{2})$,

$F'(3, -\frac{1}{2})$

10.

---

4 Assess

Open-Ended Assessment

Speaking Have pairs of students take turns talking each other through a transformation exercise.

Tips
for New
Teachers

Intervention If there is any doubt whether your students thoroughly understand transformations, consider spending an extra day on this lesson. Use the Extra Practice on p. 748. You can also use the Study Guide and Intervention masters or the Practice masters in the *Chapter 10 Resource Masters* to reinforce this concept.

Getting Ready
for Lesson 10-4

PREREQUISITE SKILL Lesson 10-4 presents quadrilaterals. Exercises 35–40 should be used to determine your students' familiarity with solving equations.

Answers

24. $A(2, -3)$, $B(4, 0)$, $C(5, -5)$

25. Since many of the movements used in recreational activities involve rotating, sliding, and flipping, they are examples of transformations. Answers should include the following.

- A translation is a slide, a reflection is a mirror-image, and a rotation is a turn.
- Sample answer: the swing represents a rotation, the scooter represents a translation, and the skateboard represents reflection.

33.

Algebra Activity

A Follow-Up of Lesson 10-3

Getting Started

Objective Investigate dilations, which alter the size of a figure.

Materials
grid paper, protractor, ruler

Teaching Tip Have students look up the definition of dilation in a dictionary, then predict what will happen to the figures.

Teach

• Review the term *scale factor*, presented in Chapter 6.
• Show students examples of figures enlarged on the copy machine. These are dilations.
• Compare dilations to the transformations in Lesson 10-3.
• Be sure students understand that a dilation can either enlarge (scale factor >1) or reduce (scale factor <1) the image.

Assess

In **Exercises 1–6**, students should recognize that the corresponding angles are equal, and that ratios of corresponding sides are equal. Ask students what relationship exists between *ABCD* and *A'B'C'D'*. **They are similar.**

In **Exercises 7–9**, students need to multiply both coordinates of each vertex by the given scale factor to find the dilation image.

Ask students what they think would happen if the scale factor were negative. **It would enlarge or reduce in the opposite direction.**

Study Notebook

You may wish to have students summarize this activity and what they learned from it.

Algebra Activity

A Follow-Up of Lesson 10-

NEW YORK *Performance Indicator* **8.G.11** Draw the image of a figure under a dilation, **8.G.12** Identify the properties preserved and not preserved under a reflection, rotation, translation, and dilation

Dilations

In this activity, you will investigate **dilations**, which alter the size of a figure.

Collect the Data

Step 1 Draw and label a polygon on a coordinate plane. Trapezoid *ABCD* is shown.

Step 2 Suppose the scale factor is 2. Multiply the coordinates of each vertex by 2.
$A(-1, 2) \rightarrow A'(-2, 4)$ $B(0, 3) \rightarrow B'(0, 6)$
$C(4, 1) \rightarrow C'(8, 2)$ $D(2, -1) \rightarrow D'(4, -2)$

Step 3 Draw the new trapezoid.

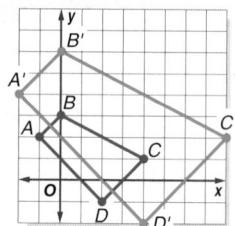

NEW YORK— Study Tip
Notice that when a figure is dilated, the angle measures are preserved but the lengths of the sides are not.

Analyze the Data   1–6. See pp. 551A–551B.

1. Use a protractor to measure the angles in each trapezoid. How do they compare?
2. Use a ruler to measure the sides of each trapezoid. How do they compare?
3. What ratio compares the measures of the corresponding sides?
4. Repeat the activity by multiplying the coordinates of trapezoid *ABCD* by $\frac{1}{2}$. Are the results the same? Explain.

Make a Conjecture

5. Explain how you know whether a dilation is a reduction or an enlargement.
6. Explain the difference between dilations and the other types of transformations.

Extend the Activity

Find the coordinates of the dilation image for the given scale factor, and graph the dilation image. 7–9. See pp. 551A–551B.

7. 3

8. $\frac{1}{4}$

9. $1\frac{1}{2}$
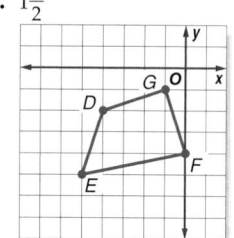

Identify each transformation as a *translation*, *rotation*, *reflection*, or *dilation*.

10.

11.

12.
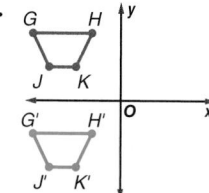

10. reflection
11. dilation
12. translation

512   **Chapter 10**   Two-Dimensional Figures

Resource Manager

📁 *Teaching Pre-Algebra with Manipulatives*
• p. 1 (master for grid paper)
• p. 21 (master for protractors)
• p. 22 (master for rulers)
• p. 129 (student recording sheet)

Glencoe Mathematics Classroom Manipulative Kit
• protractor
• ruler

Quadrilaterals

NEW YORK *Performance Indicator* **Reinforcement of 5.G.4** Classify quadrilaterals by properties of their angles and sides, **Reinforcement of 5.G.5** Know that the sum of the interior angles of a quadrilateral is 360 degrees

What You'll Learn

- Find the missing angle measures of a quadrilateral.
- Classify quadrilaterals.

How are quadrilaterals used in design?

Geometric figures are often used to create various designs. The design of a brick walkway is shown at the right. Notice how the walkway is formed using different-shaped bricks to create circles.

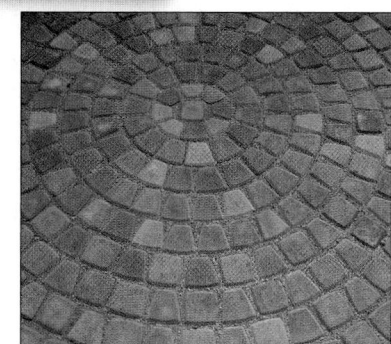

a. Describe the bricks that are used to create the smallest circles.

b. Describe how the shape of the bricks change as the circles get larger.

Vocabulary
- quadrilateral

a. squares, rectangles, trapezoids
b. Sample answer: The center of the circle is one square brick. The first row contains small trapezoids. The next four rows contain larger trapezoids. The next three rows contain trapezoids and squares that alternate.

QUADRILATERALS Squares, rectangles, and trapezoids are examples of quadrilaterals. A **quadrilateral** is a closed figure with four sides and four vertices. The segments that make up a quadrilateral intersect only at their endpoints.

Quadrilaterals	*Not* Quadrilaterals
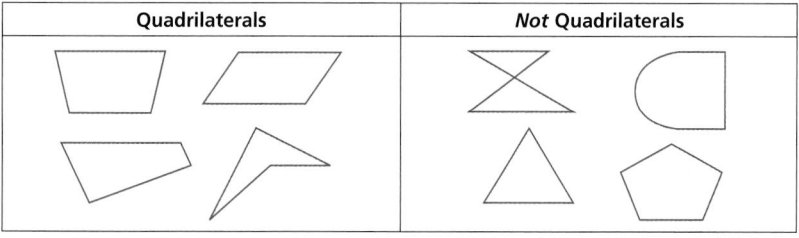	

As with triangles, a quadrilateral can be named by its vertices. The quadrilateral below can be named quadrilateral *ABCD*.

Study Tip

Naming Quadrilaterals
When you name a quadrilateral, you can begin at any vertex. However, it is important to name vertices in order.

| The vertices are *A*, *B*, *C*, and *D*. |
| The angles are ∠*A*, ∠*B*, ∠*C*, and ∠*D*. |
| The sides are $\overline{AB}$, $\overline{BC}$, $\overline{CD}$, and $\overline{DA}$. |

The quadrilateral shown above has many names. For example, it can also be named quadrilateral *BCDA*, quadrilateral *DABC*, or quadrilateral *CBAD*.

✓ **Concept Check** How many vertices does a quadrilateral have? **4**

Lesson Notes

1 *Focus*

5-Minute Check Transparency 10-4 Use as a quiz or review of Lesson 10-3.

Mathematical Background notes are available for this lesson on page 490C.

How are quadrilaterals used in design?

The opening activity questions are repeated on page 567 of the *Chapter 10 Resource Masters.*

Reading to Learn Mathematics, p. 567 **ELL**

Pre-Activity *How are quadrilaterals used in design?*

Do the activity at the top of page 513 in your textbook. Write your answers below.

a. Describe the bricks that are used to create the smallest circles.
squares, rectangles, trapezoids

b. Describe how the shape of the bricks changes as the circles get larger.
Sample answer: The center of the circle is one square brick. The first row contains small trapezoids. The next four rows contain larger trapezoids. The next three rows contain trapezoids and squares that alternate.

Reading the Lesson
Write a definition and give an example of the new vocabulary word.

	Vocabulary	Definition	Example
1.	quadrilateral	See students' work.	

After each description, write the correct word from the list.

trapezoid   rhombus   parallelogram   square   rectangle

2. a parallelogram with four right angles **rectangle**

3. a quadrilateral with both pairs of opposite sides parallel and congruent **parallelogram**

4. a quadrilateral with four congruent sides and four right angles **square**

5. a quadrilateral with one pair of opposite sides parallel **trapezoid**

6. a parallelogram with four congruent sides **rhombus**

Helping You Remember

7. The sum of the measures of the angles of a quadrilateral is 360°. Identify the quadrilaterals below and find the missing angle measure.

trapezoid; 110°   rhombus; 60°   parallelogram; 130°

Teaching Tip Point out to students that *quad* means four, so a *quadrilateral* must have four vertices and four sides.

Resource Manager

Workbooks and Reproducible Masters

Chapter 10 Resource Masters
- Study Guide and Intervention, p. 564
- Skills Practice, p. 565
- Practice, p. 566
- Reading to Learn Mathematics, p. 567
- Enrichment, p. 568
- Assessment, pp. 603, 605

Parent and Student Study Guide Workbook, p. 84

Transparencies

5-Minute Check Transparency 10-4
Answer Key Transparencies

Technology

Interactive Chalkboard

Building on Prior Knowledge

In Lessons 3-3 and 3-5, students learned to solve equations. In this lesson, students will solve equations to find missing angle measures.

 Teach

QUADRILATERALS

In-Class Example

Power Point®

1 ALGEBRA Find the value of *x*. Then find each missing angle measure.

R   *S*
4*x*°   110°
75°   *x*°
Q   *T*

$m\angle T = 35°$, $m\angle R = 140°$

Teaching Tip Instruct students not to use a protractor to find the measures of the angles. Pictures are not always accurate.

CLASSIFY QUADRILATERALS

In-Class Example

Power Point®

2 Classify each quadrilateral using the name that best describes it.

a.

trapezoid

b.
parallelogram

c.

square

Teaching Tip Ask students if a square is a rhombus. Is it a rectangle? **Yes to both.**

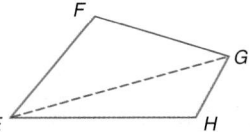

A quadrilateral can be separated into two triangles. Since the sum of the measures of the angles of a triangle is 180°, the sum of the measures of the angles of a quadrilateral is 2(180°) or 360°.

Key Concept   *Angles of a Quadrilateral*

The sum of the measures of the angles of a quadrilateral is 360°.

Example 1   *Find Angle Measures*

ALGEBRA Find the value of *x*. Then find each missing angle measure.

B 62°
2*x*°   *C*
A 88°   *x*° *D*

Words   The sum of the measures of the angles is 360°.

Variable   Let $m\angle A$, $m\angle B$, $m\angle C$, and $m\angle D$ represent the measures of the angles.

Equation

$m\angle A + m\angle B + m\angle C + m\angle D = 360$	Angles of a quadrilateral
$88 + 62 + 2x + x = 360$	Substitution
$3x + 150 = 360$	Combine like terms.
$3x + 150 - 150 = 360 - 150$	Subtract 150 from each side.
$3x = 210$	Simplify.
$x = 70$	

The value of *x* is 70. So, $m\angle D = 70°$ and $m\angle C = 2(70)$ or 140°.

CLASSIFY QUADRILATERALS The diagram below shows how quadrilaterals are related. Notice that it goes from the most general quadrilateral to the most specific.

Quadrilateral

Trapezoid
quadrilateral with one pair of opposite sides parallel

Parallelogram
quadrilateral with both pairs of opposite sides parallel and congruent

Rhombus
parallelogram with 4 congruent sides

Rectangle
parallelogram with 4 right angles

Square
parallelogram with 4 congruent sides and 4 right angles

The best description of a quadrilateral is the one that is the most specific.

Study Tip

Check Your Work
To check the answer, find the sum of the measures of the angles. Since $88° + 62° + 140° + 70° = 360°$, the answer is correct.

DAILY INTERVENTION   **Differentiated Instruction**

• **Auditory/Musical** Have students write raps, rhymes, or songs describing the various quadrilaterals. Students' work should explain how the various quadrilaterals relate to one another (a square is a form of parallelogram) and may include real-life examples of objects with the various shapes (the classroom window is a rectangle).

Example 2 *Classify Quadrilaterals*

Classify each quadrilateral using the name that best describes it.

a.

The quadrilateral has four congruent sides and four right angles. It is a square.

b.

The quadrilateral has opposite sides parallel and opposite sides congruent. It is a parallelogram.

c. **ART** Classify the quadrilaterals that are outlined in the painting at the right.

Each of the quadrilaterals has four right angles, but the four sides are not congruent. The quadrilaterals are rectangles.

Irene Rice Periera. *Untitled.* 1951

Check for Understanding

Concept Check

1. **OPEN ENDED** Give a real-world example of a quadrilateral, a parallelogram, a rhombus, and a square. **1–2. See margin.**

2. **Describe** the characteristics of a rectangle and draw an example of one.

Guided Practice

ALGEBRA Find the value of x. Then find the missing angle measures.

GUIDED PRACTICE KEY	
Exercises	Examples
3, 4	1
5–7	2

3. **110; 110°**

4. 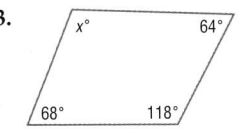 **45; 45°; 90°**

Classify each quadrilateral using the name that *best* describes it.

5. **rectangle**

6. 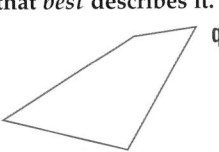 **quadrilateral**

Application

7. **SPORTS** Classify the quadrilaterals that are found on the scoring region of a shuffleboard court.
trapezoids, parallelograms

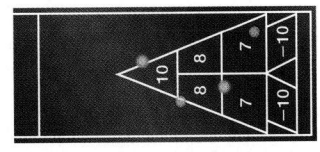

Answers

1. Sample answer: A textbook is an example of a quadrilateral; the tiles in a shuffleboard scoring region are examples of parallelograms; a "dead end" road sign is an example of a rhombus; and a floppy disk is an example of a square.

2. A rectangle has four sides, four right angles, opposite sides parallel, and opposite sides congruent.

★ indicates increased difficulty

Practice and Apply

ALGEBRA Find the value of *x*. Then find the missing angle measures.

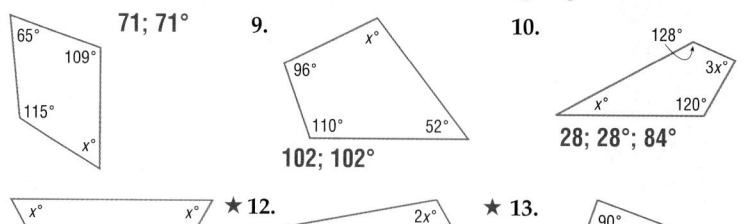

8. 65°, 109°, 115°, *x*°   **71; 71°**
9. 96°, *x*°, 110°, 52°   **102; 102°**
10. 128°, 3*x*°, *x*°, 120°   **28; 28°; 84°**

11. *x*°, *x*°, 2*x*°, 120°   **60; 60°; 60°; 120°**
12. 2*x*°, *x*°, 135°, (*x* + 5)°   **55; 55°; 60°; 110°**
13. 90°, (2*x* − 20)°, *x*°, (*x* + 10)°   **70; 70°; 80°; 120°**

11. 60; 60°; 60°; 120°
12. 55; 55°; 60°; 110°
13. 70; 70°; 80°; 120°

14. **COOKING** Name an item found in a kitchen that is rectangular in shape. Explain why the item is a rectangle. **14–15. See margin.**

15. **GAMES** Identify a board game that is played on a board that is shaped like a square. Explain why the board is a square.

Classify each quadrilateral using the name that *best* describes it.

16. rectangle
17. square
18. rectangle
19. parallelogram
20. quadrilateral
21. rhombus

22. **ART** The abstract painting is an example of how shape and color are used in art. Write a few sentences describing the geometric shapes used by the artist. **See margin.**

Elizabeth Murray. *Painter's Progress*, 1981

Tell whether each statement is *sometimes*, *always*, or *never* true.

23. A square is a rhombus. **always**
24. A parallelogram is a rectangle. **sometimes**
25. A rectangle is a square. **sometimes**
26. A parallelogram is a quadrilateral. **always**

Make a drawing of each quadrilateral. Then classify each quadrilateral using the name that *best* describes it. **27–28. See margin.**

★ 27. In quadrilateral *JKLM*, $m\angle J = 90°$, $m\angle K = 50°$, $m\angle L = 90°$, and $m\angle M = 130°$.

★ 28. In quadrilateral *CDEF*, $\overline{CD}$ and $\overline{EF}$ are parallel, and $\overline{CF}$ and $\overline{DE}$ are parallel. Angle *C* is not congruent to $\angle D$.

Answers

14. Sample answer: A baking sheet; it is a rectangle because it is a parallelogram with 4 right angles.

15. Sample answer: A chessboard; it is a square because it is a parallelogram with 4 congruent sides and 4 right angles.

22. Sample answer: The artist used triangles, quadrilaterals, and a few shapes having five and six sides. Some of the quadrilaterals are trapezoids.

27. See students' drawings; quadrilateral

28. See students' drawings; parallelogram

29. CRITICAL THINKING An *equilateral* figure is one in which all sides have the same measure. An *equiangular* figure is one in which all angles have the same measure. **a–b. See margin.**

a. Is it possible for a quadrilateral to be equilateral without being equiangular? If so, explain with a drawing.

b. Is it possible for a quadrilateral to be equiangular without being equilateral? If so, explain with a drawing.

30. WRITING IN MATH Answer the question that was posed at the beginning of the lesson. **See margin.**

How are quadrilaterals used in design?

Include the following in your answer:

• an example of a real-world design that contains quadrilaterals, and

• an explanation of the figures used in the design.

31. Which figure is a rhombus? **B**

Ⓐ Ⓑ Ⓒ Ⓓ

32. GRID IN Find the value of *x* in the figure at the right. **147**

Maintain Your Skills

Mixed Review

33. A figure has vertices $D(1, 2)$, $E(1, 4)$, $F(-4, 4)$, and $G(-2, 2)$. Graph the figure and its image after a translation 4 units down. *(Lesson 10-3)*
See margin.

Complete each congruence statement if $\triangle AKM \cong \triangle NDQ$. *(Lesson 10-2)*

34. $\angle K \cong \underline{\ ?\ }$ $\angle D$

35. $\overline{QN} \cong \underline{\ ?\ }$ $\overline{MA}$

36. Find the discount for a $45 shirt that is on sale for 20% off. *(Lesson 6-7)*
$9

Getting Ready for the Next Lesson

PREREQUISITE SKILL Find each product.
(To review multiplying decimals, see page 715.)

37. $(3)(4.8)$ **14.4** **38.** $(5.4)(6)$ **32.4** **39.** $(9.2)(3.1)$ **28.52** **40.** $(10.5)(5.7)$ **59.85**

Practice Quiz 1

Lessons 10-1 through 10-4

1. Angle A and $\angle B$ are complementary. Find $m\angle A$ if $m\angle B = 55°$. *(Lesson 10-1)* **35°**

2. Suppose $\triangle ABC \cong \triangle DEF$. Which angle is congruent to $\angle D$? *(Lesson 10-2)* **$\angle A$**

3. $\triangle QRS$ has vertices $Q(3, 3)$, $R(5, 6)$, and $S(7, 3)$. Find the coordinates for the vertices of the triangle after the figure is reflected over the x-axis. *(Lesson 10-3)*
$Q'(3, -3)$, $R'(5, -6)$, $S'(7, -3)$

ALGEBRA Find the value of x. Then find the missing angle measures. *(Lesson 10-4)*

4.   **65; 65°**

5.   **60; 60°; 120°**

Open-Ended Assessment

Modeling Have students use sticks or pipe cleaners to form different quadrilaterals. They can use pieces of yarn to mark any congruent angles or sides.

Getting Ready for Lesson 10-5

PREREQUISITE SKILL In Lesson 10-5, students find the areas of two-dimensional figures. This requires multiplying measures, some of which may be decimals. Exercises 37–40 should be used to determine your students' familiarity with multiplying decimals.

Assessment Options

Practice Quiz 1 The quiz provides students with a brief review of the concepts and skills in Lessons 10-1 through 10-4. Lesson numbers are given to the right of exercises or instruction lines so students can review concepts not yet mastered.

Quiz (Lessons 10-3 and 10-4) is available on p. 603 of the *Chapter 10 Resource Masters*.

Mid-Chapter Test (Lessons 10-1 through 10-4) is available on p. 605 of the *Chapter 10 Resource Masters*.

Answer

33.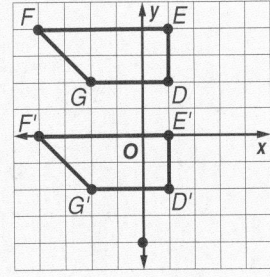

29a. Yes; a rhombus is equilateral but may not be equiangular.

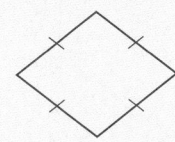

29b. Yes; a rectangle is equiangular but may not be equilateral.

30. Many designs contain patterns formed by using shapes such as quadrilaterals. Answers should include the following.

• Sample answer: Many quilt designs contain quadrilaterals. One such example is shown.

• The quadrilaterals used are trapezoids, squares, and parallelograms.

Algebra Activity

A Preview of Lesson 10-5

Getting Started

Objective Use geoboards to find the area of figures.

Materials
geoboards
geobands

Teaching Tip Have students practice making different-sized figures before starting the exercises.

Teach

- If you don't have geoboards, you can use dot paper or graph paper.
- Discuss with students if they can generalize from Activity 2 how to develop an equation for finding the area of a triangle.

 NEW YORK *Performance Indicator* Reinforcement of 6.G.3 Use a variety of strategies to find the area of regular and irregular polygons

Area and Geoboards

Activity 1

One square on a geoboard has an area of one square unit.

The area is about 5 square units.

The area is about 6 square units.

The area is 3.5 square units.

Model and Analyze **1.** 11 sq units **2.** about 4 sq units **3.** about 5.5 sq units

Find the area of each figure. Estimate, if necessary.

1. **2.** **3.**

4. Explain how you found the area of each figure in Exercises 1–3.

5. Make a figure on the geoboard. Ask a classmate to find the area of the figure. **See students' work.**
   4. Sample answer: count whole-squares and half-squares.

Activity 2

The following example shows how to find the area of a right triangle on a geoboard.

Step 1 First, make another triangle so that the two triangles form a rectangle.

Step 2 Then find the area of the rectangle.

Step 3 Next, divide by 2 to find the area of each triangle. The area of the rectangle is 6 square units. So, the area of each triangle is 3 square units.

Resource Manager

📁 ***Teaching Pre-Algebra with Manipulatives***
- p. 132 (student recording sheet)

Glencoe Mathematics Classroom Manipulative Kit
- geoboards
- geobands

Model and Analyze 9–10. See students' work.
Find the area of each triangle. 6. 3 sq units   7. 6 sq units   8. 4 sq units

6.   **7.**   **8.**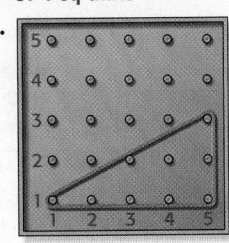

9. Make a right triangle on your geoboard. Find its area using this method.

10. Write a few sentences explaining how you found the area of the triangle.

Activity 3

Another way to find the area of a figure on a geoboard is to build a rectangle around the figure. Consider the following example.

Step 1 Make the triangle shown on a geoboard.

Step 2 Build a rectangle around the triangle.

Step 3 Subtract to find the area of the original triangle.

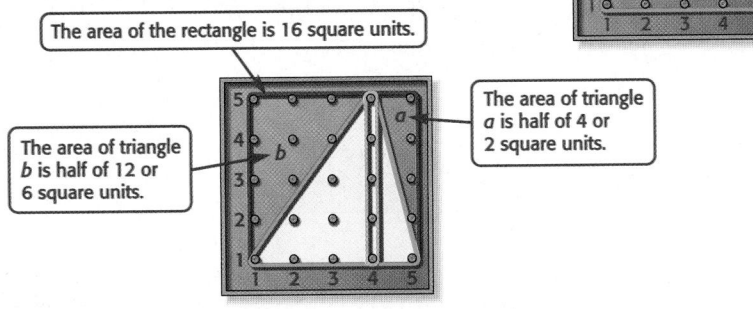

The area of the rectangle is 16 square units.

The area of triangle *a* is half of 4 or 2 square units.

The area of triangle *b* is half of 12 or 6 square units.

The area of the original triangle is 16 − 2 − 6 or 8 square units.

Model and Analyze 11. 4.5 sq units   12. 6 sq units   13. 4 sq units
Find the area of each figure by building a rectangle around the figure.

11.   **12.** 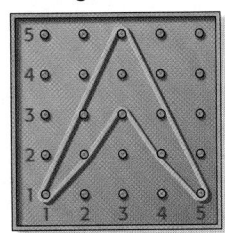   **13.**

14. Make a figure on your geoboard. Find the area using this method. **See students' work.**

Algebra Activity Area and Geoboards **519**

Assess

In **Exercises 1–5,** students should count squares to find the area of the figure.

In **Exercises 6–10,** students use a rectangle to find the area of a right triangle.

In **Exercises 11–14,** build a rectangle and subtract to find the area of the figure.

Study Notebook

You may wish to have students summarize this activity and what they learned from it.

1 Focus

5-Minute Check Transparency 10-5 Use as a quiz or review of Lesson 10-4.

Mathematical Background notes are available for this lesson on page 490D.

How is the area of a parallelogram related to the area of a rectangle?

The opening activity questions are repeated on page 572 of the *Chapter 10 Resource Masters*.

Reading to Learn Mathematics, p. 572 — ELL

Pre-Activity How is the area of a parallelogram related to the area of a rectangle?

Do the activity at the top of page 520 in your textbook. Write your answers below.

a. What figure is formed? **parallelogram**

b. Compare the area of the rectangle to the area of the parallelogram. **They are the same.**

c. What parts of a rectangle and parallelogram determine their area? **height and base**

Reading the Lesson 1–2. See students' work.

Write a definition and give an example of each new vocabulary word.

Vocabulary	Definition	Example
1. base		
2. altitude		

Helping You Remember

3. Below are three figures and three formulas for finding area. Match the formula with the correct figure and find its area.

$A = \frac{1}{2}h(a + b)$ $A = bh$ $A = \frac{1}{2}bh$

Formula: $A = \frac{1}{2}bh$ Formula: $A = bh$ Formula: $A = \frac{1}{2}h(a + b)$

Area: 52.5 cm²   Area: 48 in²   Area: 45.5 ft²

Teaching Tip Show students the similarities and differences between trapezoids and parallelograms.

Resource Manager

📂 Workbooks and Reproducible Masters

Chapter 10 Resource Masters
- Study Guide and Intervention, p. 569
- Skills Practice, p. 570
- Practice, p. 571
- Reading to Learn Mathematics, p. 572
- Enrichment, p. 573

Graphing Calculator and Spreadsheet Masters, p. 38
Parent and Student Study Guide Workbook, p. 85
School-to-Career Masters, p. 19

🖥 Transparencies
5-Minute Check Transparency 10-5
Answer Key Transparencies

💿 Technology
Interactive Chalkboard

What You'll Learn
- Find area of parallelograms.
- Find the areas of triangles and trapezoids.

Vocabulary
- base
- altitude

NEW YORK — Performance Indicator
Reinforcement of 6.G.2 Determine the area of triangles and quadrilaterals (squares, rectangles, rhombi, and trapezoids) and develop formulas

How is the area of a parallelogram related to the area of a rectangle?

The area of a rectangle can be found by multiplying the length and width. The rectangle shown below has an area of 3 × 6 or 18 square units.

Suppose a triangle is cut from one side of the rectangle and moved to the other side. **b. They are the same.**   **c. height and base**

a. What figure is formed? **parallelogram**

b. Compare the area of the rectangle to the area of the parallelogram.

c. What parts of a rectangle and parallelogram determine their area?

AREAS OF PARALLELOGRAMS The area of a parallelogram can be found by multiplying the measures of the base and the height.

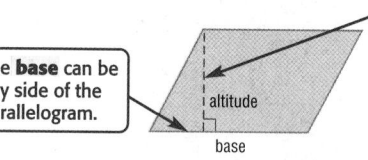

The **base** can be any side of the parallelogram.

The *height* is the length of an **altitude**, a line segment perpendicular to the bases with endpoints on the base and the side opposite the base.

Key Concept — Area of a Parallelogram

- **Words** If a parallelogram has a base of b units and a height of h units, then the area A is bh square units.
- **Symbols** $A = bh$
- **Model**

Example 1 Find Areas of Parallelograms

Find the area of each parallelogram.

a.

The base is 4 feet. The height is 2 feet.

$A = bh$ Area of a parallelogram
$A = 4 \cdot 2$ Replace b with 4 and h with 2.
$A = 8$ Multiply.

The area is 8 square feet.

b.

The base is 5.9 centimeters. The height is 7.5 centimeters.

$A = bh$ Area of a parallelogram

$A = (5.9)(7.5)$ Replace b with 5.9 and h with 7.5.

$A = 44.25$ Multiply.

The area is 44.25 square centimeters.

AREA OF TRIANGLES AND TRAPEZOIDS   A diagonal of a parallelogram separates the parallelogram into two congruent triangles. The area of each triangle is one-half the area of the parallelogram.

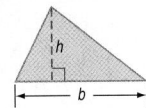

> The area of parallelogram *ABCD* is 7 · 4 or 28 square units.

> The area of triangle *ABD* is $\frac{1}{2}$ · 28 or 14 square units.

Using the formula for the area of a parallelogram, we can find the formula for the area of a triangle.

Key Concept   *Area of a Triangle*

- **Words**   If a triangle has a base of b units and a height of h units, then the area A is $\frac{1}{2}bh$ square units.

- **Symbols** $A = \frac{1}{2}bh$ • **Model**

✔ **Concept Check**   The area of a triangle is one half of the area of what figure with the same height and base? **parallelogram**

As with parallelograms, any side of a triangle can be used as a base. The height is the length of a corresponding altitude.

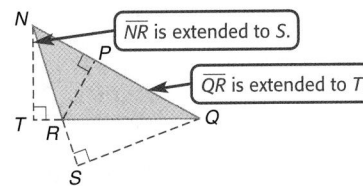

> $\overline{NR}$ is extended to S.

> $\overline{QR}$ is extended to T.

base	$\overline{AC}$	$\overline{AB}$	$\overline{BC}$
altitude	$\overline{BD}$	$\overline{CE}$	$\overline{AF}$

base	$\overline{NQ}$	$\overline{NR}$	$\overline{QR}$
altitude	$\overline{RP}$	$\overline{QS}$	$\overline{NT}$

✔ **Concept Check**   Which side of a triangle can be used as the base? **any side**

www.pre-alg.com/extra_examples/ny   Lesson 10-5   Area: Parallelograms, Triangles, and Trapezoids   **521**

Building on Prior Knowledge

In Lesson 5-7, students learned to add mixed numbers. In this lesson, students will add mixed numbers when calculating the area of a trapezoid.

2 Teach

AREAS OF PARALLELOGRAMS

In-Class Example

1 Find the area of each parallelogram.

a.

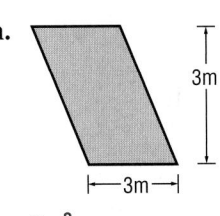

9m²

b.

26.66 in²

Teaching Tip   Make sure students include the correct units with their answers.

AREAS OF TRIANGLES AND TRAPEZOIDS

2 Find the area of each triangle.

a.

3 m · 4 m   **6m²**

b.

6.4 ft · 3.9 ft   **12.48 ft²**

3 Find the area of the trapezoid. **38¼ m²**

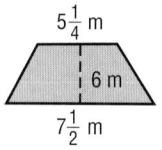

$5\frac{1}{4}$ m · 6 m · $7\frac{1}{2}$ m

4 **PAINTING** A wall that needs to be painted is 16 feet wide and 9 feet tall. There is a doorway that is 3 feet by 8 feet and a window that is 6 feet by $5\frac{1}{2}$ feet. What is the area to be painted?
87 ft²

Teaching Tip If students are having trouble understanding the formula for the area of a trapezoid, have them try the following exercise. Ask them to draw a trapezoid on a piece of paper and cut it out. They should then cut the trapezoid horizontally in half. Next, cut a right triangle from one end of the upper half of the trapezoid. Now, students should arrange the three pieces into a long rectangle whose area is $\frac{1}{2}h$ $(b_1 + b_2)$.

Example 2 Find Areas of Triangles

Find the area of each triangle.

a.

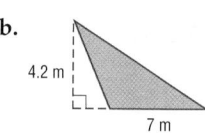

6 in. · 5 in.

The base is 5 inches. The height is 6 inches.

$A = \frac{1}{2}bh$	Area of a triangle
$A = \frac{1}{2}(5)(6)$	Replace b with 5 and h with 6.
$A = \frac{1}{2}(30)$	Multiply. $5 \times 6 = 30$
$A = 15$	The area of the triangle is 15 square inches.

b.

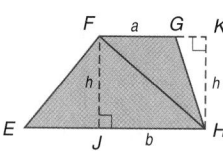

4.2 m · 7 m

The base is 7 meters. The height is 4.2 meters.

$A = \frac{1}{2}bh$	Area of a triangle
$A = \frac{1}{2}(7)(4.2)$	Replace b with 7 and h with 4.2.
$A = \frac{1}{2}(29.4)$	Multiply. $7 \times 4.2 = 29.4$
$A = 14.7$	The area of the triangle is 14.7 square meters.

A trapezoid has two bases. The height of a trapezoid is the distance between the bases. A trapezoid can be separated into two triangles.

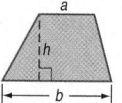

The triangles are $\triangle FGH$ and $\triangle EFH$.
The measure of a base of $\triangle FGH$ is a units.
The measure of a base of $\triangle EFH$ is b units.
The altitudes of the triangles, $\overline{FJ}$ and $\overline{HK}$, are congruent. Both are h units long.

area of trapezoid $EFGH$ = area of $\triangle FGH$ + area of $\triangle EFH$

$$= \frac{1}{2}ah + \frac{1}{2}bh$$

$$= \frac{1}{2}h(a + b) \quad \text{Distributive Property}$$

Key Concept — Area of a Trapezoid

- **Words** If a trapezoid has bases of a units and b units and a height of h units, then the area A of the trapezoid is $\frac{1}{2}h(a + b)$ square units.

- **Symbols** $A = \frac{1}{2}h(a + b)$

- **Model**

Example 3 Find Area of a Trapezoid

Find the area of the trapezoid.

The height is 4 inches.

The bases are $6\frac{1}{2}$ inches and $3\frac{1}{4}$ inches.

$A = \frac{1}{2}h(a + b)$ Area of a trapezoid

$A = \frac{1}{2} \cdot 4\left(6\frac{1}{2} + 3\frac{1}{4}\right)$ Replace h with 4, a with $6\frac{1}{2}$ and b with $3\frac{1}{4}$.

$A = \frac{1}{2} \cdot 4 \cdot 9\frac{3}{4}$ $6\frac{1}{2} + 3\frac{1}{4} = 9\frac{3}{4}$

$A = \frac{1}{2} \cdot \frac{\cancel{4}}{1} \cdot \frac{39}{\cancel{4}}$ Divide out the common factors.

$A = \frac{39}{2}$ or $19\frac{1}{2}$ The area of the trapezoid is $19\frac{1}{2}$ square inches.

Study Tip

Look Back
To review **multiplying fractions**, see Lesson 5-3.

Example 4 Use Area to Solve a Problem

FLAGS The signal flag shown represents the number five. Find the area of the blue region.

To find the area of the blue region, subtract the areas of the triangles from the area of the square.

Area of the square	Area of each triangle
$A = bh$	$A = \frac{1}{2}bh$
$A = 14 \cdot 14$	$A = \frac{1}{2} \cdot 10 \cdot 7$
$A = 196$	$A = 35$ $\frac{1}{2} \cdot 10 = 5, 5 \cdot 7 = 35$

The total area of the triangles is 4(35) or 140 square inches. So, the area of the blue region is $196 - 140$ or 56 square inches.

Check for Understanding

Concept Check

1. **OPEN ENDED** Draw and label a parallelogram that has an area of 24 square inches. **1–2. See margin.**

2. **Define** an *altitude* of a triangle and draw an example.

Guided Practice

Find the area of each figure.

GUIDED PRACTICE KEY	
Exercises	**Examples**
3–5	1–3
6	4

3.   **8 ft²**

4.   **8.1 cm²**   5.

Application

6. **FLAGS** The flag shown at the right is the international signal for the number three. Find the area of the red region. **48 in²**

Lesson 10-5 Area: Parallelograms, Triangles, and Trapezoids   523

3 Practice/Apply

Study Notebook

Have students—
- add the definitions/examples of the vocabulary terms to their Vocabulary Builder worksheets for Chapter 10.
- include an example of each figure and how to determine its area.
- include any other item(s) that they find helpful in mastering the skills in this lesson.

About the Exercises . . .

Organization by Objective
- **Areas of Parallelograms:** 7, 8, 15, 18, 19, 21, 23, 24, 26
- **Areas of Triangles and Trapezoids:** 9–14, 16–17, 20–24, 27–29

Odd/Even Assignments
Exercises 7–20 are structured so that students practice the same concepts whether they are assigned odd or even problems.

Alert! Exercise 36 requires graph paper.

Assignment Guide

Basic: 7–19 odd, 27, 30–43

Average: 7–23 odd, 24, 25, 27, 29, 30–43

Advanced: 8–22 even, 24–26, 28, 30–39 (Optional: 40–43)

Answers

1. Sample answer:

2. The altitude of a triangle is a line segment perpendicular to the base with endpoints on the base and the vertex opposite the base.

Lesson 10-5   Area: Parallelograms, Triangles, and Trapezoids   **523**

★ indicates increased difficulty

Practice and Apply

Find the area of each figure.

7. 11 m²
8. 25.9 in²
9. 90 cm²

10. 21.6 in²
11. 43.99 cm²
12. 156.4 ft²

Find the area of each figure described.

13. triangle: base, 8 in.; height, 7 in. **28 in²**
14. trapezoid: height, 2 cm; bases, 3 cm, 6 cm **9 cm²**
15. parallelogram: base, 3.8 yd; height, 6 yd **22.8 yd²**
16. triangle: base, 9 ft; height, 3.2 ft **14.4 ft²**
17. trapezoid: height, 3.5 m; bases, 10 m and 11 m **36.75 m²**
18. parallelogram: base, 5.6 km; height, 4.5 km **25.2 km²**

···• **GEOGRAPHY** For Exercises 19 and 20, use the approximate measurements to estimate the area of each state.

19. about 95,284 mi²
20. 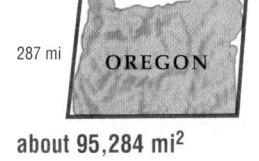 about 51,113 mi²

Find the area of each figure.

★ 21. 147 km²
★ 22. 48 m²
★ 23. 57 ft²

★ **LAWNCARE** For Exercises 24 and 25, use the diagram shown and the following information.
Mrs. Malone plans to fertilize her lawn. The fertilizer she will be using indicates that one bag fertilizes 2000 square feet.

24. Find the area of the lawn. **9270 ft²**
25. How many bags of fertilizer should she buy? **5 bags**

Answers (p. 525)

30. $A = \frac{1}{2}h(a + b)$; In a triangle, one "base" = 0, so $A = \frac{1}{2}h(0 + b)$, then $A = \frac{1}{2}hb$ or $A = \frac{1}{2}bh$. In a parallelogram, the bases are congruent so $a = b$. Thus, $A = \frac{1}{2}h(b + b)$ or $A = \frac{1}{2}h(2b)$, then $A = bh$.

31. The area of a parallelogram is found by multiplying the base and the height of the parallelogram. The area of a rectangle is found by multiplying the length and the width of the rectangle. Since in a parallelogram, the base is the length of the parallelogram, and the height is the width of the parallelogram, both

26. Find the base of a parallelogram with a height of 9.2 meters and an area of 36.8 square meters. **4 m**

27. Suppose a triangle has an area of 20 square inches and a base of 2.5 inches. What is the measure of the height? **16 in.**

28. A trapezoid has an area of 54 square feet. What is the measure of the height if the bases measure 16 feet and 8 feet? **4.5 ft**

★ 29. **REAL ESTATE** The McLaughlins plan to build a house on the lot shown. If an acre is 43,560 square feet, what percent of an acre is the land? **24.5%**

144.34 ft
57.62 ft
90.54 ft
147.08 ft

30. **CRITICAL THINKING** Explain how the formula for the area of a trapezoid can be used to find the formulas for the areas of parallelograms and triangles. **See margin.**

31. WRITING IN MATH Answer the question that was posed at the beginning of the lesson. **See margin.**

How is the area of a parallelogram related to the area of a rectangle?

Include the following in your answer:
- an explanation telling the similarities and differences between a rectangle and a parallelogram, and
- a diagram that shows how the area of a parallelogram is related to the area of a rectangle.

32. Which figure does *not* have an area of 48 square meters? **C**

Ⓐ 8 m
Ⓑ 8 m, 12 m
Ⓒ 3 m, 1.6 m
Ⓓ 12.8 m, 5 m, 6.4 m

6 m

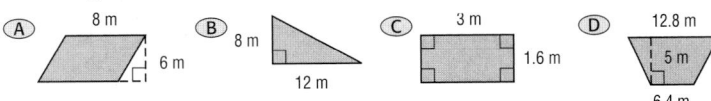

33. Square *X* has an area of 9 square feet. The sides of square *Y* are twice as long as the sides of square *X*. Find the area of square *Y*. **B**
Ⓐ 18 ft²   Ⓑ 36 ft²   Ⓒ 9 ft²   Ⓓ 6 ft²

Maintain Your Skills

Mixed Review   Find the value of *x*. Then find the missing angle measures. *(Lesson 10-4)*

34. *x*°, 60°, 60°, 120°   **120; 120°**

35. 130°, 110°, 4*x*°, *x*°   **24; 24°; 96°**

36. Triangle *MNP* has vertices *M*(−1, 1), *N*(5, 4), and *P*(4, 1). Graph the image of △*MNP* after a translation 3 units left and 4 units down. *(Lesson 10-3)* **See margin.**

Find the percent of each number mentally. *(Lesson 6-6)*
37. 25% of 120 **30**   38. 75% of 160 **120**   39. 40% of 65 **26**

Getting Ready for the Next Lesson   **PREREQUISITE SKILL** Simplify each expression.
*(To review **order of operations**, see Lesson 1-2).*
40. $(5 − 2)180$ **540**   41. $(7 − 2)180$ **900**   42. $(10 − 2)180$ **1440**   43. $(9 − 2)180$ **1260**

Open-Ended Assessment

Writing Have students write an exercise that has to be solved using area. They should then trade exercises with a partner and solve.

Getting Ready for Lesson 10-6

PREREQUISITE SKILL Lesson 10-6 presents polygons. To find the measure of the interior angles of a polygon requires evaluating a formula that involves multiple operations. Exercises 40–43 should be used to determine your students' familiarity with order of operations.

Answer

36.

---

areas are found by multiplying the length and the width. Answers should include the following.

- Parallelograms and rectangles are similar in that they are quadrilaterals with opposite sides parallel and opposite sides congruent. They are different in that rectangles always have 4 right angles.

Getting Started

Show students pictures of a bicycle, biped, tripod, quad-runner (four wheel bike), the Pentagon, and an octopus. Discuss where the names came from and how they describe the objects.

Teach

Word Origins Explain to students that you often can tell what a word means by breaking it down into parts. Use the word *equiangular* as an example. By dividing the word into *equi-* (equal) and *angular,* students can see that it refers to something with equal angles.

Assess

Study Notebook

Ask students to write a familiar word for each prefix that will help them remember what the prefix means.

ELL English Language Learners may benefit from writing key concepts from this activity in their Study Notebooks in their native language and then in English.

Learning Mathematics Prefixes

The table shows some of the prefixes that are used in mathematics. These prefixes are also used in everyday language. In order to use each prefix correctly, you need to understand its meaning.

Prefix	Meaning	Everyday Words	Meaning
quad-	four	quadrennial quadruple quadruplet quadriceps	happening every four years a sum four times as great as another one of four offspring born at one birth a muscle with four points of origin
pent-	five	Pentagon pentagram pentathlon pentad	headquarters of the Department of Defense a five-pointed star a five-event athletic contest a group of five
hex-	six	hexapod hexagonal hexastich hexangular	having six feet having six sides a poem of six lines having six angles
hept-	seven	heptad heptagonal heptarchy heptastich	a group of seven having seven sides a government by seven rulers a poem of seven lines
oct-	eight	octopus octet octan octennial	a type of mollusk having eight arms a musical composition for eight instruments occurring every eight days lasting eight years
dec-	ten	decade decameter decathlon decare	a period of ten years ten meters a ten-event athletic contest a metric unit of area equal to 10 acres

Reading to Learn 1. See margin.

1. Refer to the table above. For each prefix listed, choose one of the everyday words listed and write a sentence that contains the word.

2. **RESEARCH** Use the Internet, a dictionary, or another reference source to find a mathematical term that contains each of the prefixes listed. Write the definition of each term. **2–3. See pp. 551A–551B**

3. **RESEARCH** Use the Internet, a dictionary, or another reference source to find a different word that contains each prefix. Then define the term.

526 **Chapter 10** Two-Dimensional Figures

Answer

1. Sample answer: quad: A leap day is a quadrennial event.

   pent: Many military personnel work at the Pentagon.

   hex: An insect is an example of a hexapod.

   hept: Heptarchy was the name given to the seven kingdoms of England during the 7th and 8th centuries.

   oct: The giant octopus found in the Pacific Ocean may have a diameter greater than 30 feet.

   dec: Dan O'Brien is the current world record holder in the decathlon with 8891 points.

10-6 Polygons

NEW YORK *Performance Indicator* **Reinforcement of 7.A.9 Build a pattern to develop a rule for determining the sum of the interior angles of polygons**

What You'll Learn

- Classify polygons.
- Determine the sum of the measures of the interior and exterior angles of a polygon.

How are polygons used in tessellations?

The tiled patterns below are called *regular tessellations*. Notice how the figures repeat to form patterns that contain no gaps or overlaps.

  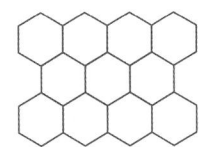

Vocabulary

- polygon
- diagonal
- interior angles
- regular polygon

a. square, triangle, hexagon

a. Which figure is used to create each tessellation?

b. Refer to the diagram at the right. What is the sum of the measures of the angles that surround the vertex? **360**

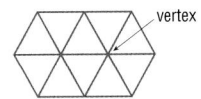
vertex

c. Yes; for each tessellation shown, the sum of the measures of the angles that surround a vertex is 360°.

c. Does the sum in part **b** hold true for the square tessellation? Explain.

d. Make a conjecture about the sum of the measures of the angles that surround a vertex in the hexagon tessellation. **The sum is 360°.**

CLASSIFY POLYGONS
A **polygon** is a simple, closed figure formed by three or more line segments. The figures below are examples of polygons.

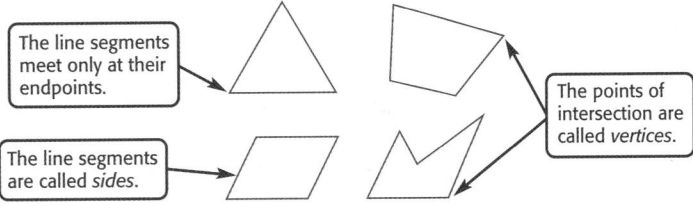

The line segments meet only at their endpoints.

The line segments are called *sides*.

The points of intersection are called *vertices*.

The following figures are *not* polygons.

**Concept Check:
Sample answer:**

This is not a polygon because it has a curved side.

This is not a polygon because it is an open figure.

This is not a polygon because the sides overlap.

✓ **Concept Check**   Sketch a different figure that is *not* a polygon.

10-6 Lesson Notes

1 Focus

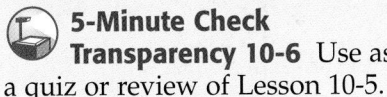

5-Minute Check Transparency 10-6 Use as a quiz or review of Lesson 10-5.

Mathematical Background notes are available for this lesson on page 490D.

How are polygons used in tessellations?

The opening activity questions are repeated on page 577 of the *Chapter 10 Resource Masters*.

Reading to Learn Mathematics, p. 577   **ELL**

Pre-Activity   *How are polygons used in testellations?*

Do the activity at the top of page 527 in your textbook. Write your answers below.

a. Which figure is used to create each tessellation?
   square, triangle, hexagon

b. Refer to the diagram in your textbook. What is the sum of the measures of the angles that surround the vertex? **360°**

c. Does the sum in part **b** hold true for the square tessellation? Explain.
   Yes; for each tessellation shown, the sum of the measures of the angles that surround a vertex is 360°.

d. Make a conjecture about the sum of the measures of the angles that surround a vertex in the hexagon tessellation. **The sum is 360°.**

Reading the Lesson   1–4. See students' work.

Write a definition and give an example of each new vocabulary word or phrase.

Vocabulary	Definition	Example
1. polygon		
2. diagonal		
3. interior angles		
4. regular polygon		

Helping You Remember

5. Complete the following concept map of how to find the sum of the measures of the interior angles of a regular polygon (all sides and angles are congruent) and how to find the measure of one interior angle.

Step 1
Count the polygon's **sides or vertices**

Step 2
Subtract 2 from this number and multiply by **180** to find sum of the measures of the **interior angles**

Step 3
Divide this sum by **the number of sides/vertices** to find the measure of one **interior angle**

Resource Manager

Workbooks and Reproducible Masters

Chapter 10 Resource Masters
- Study Guide and Intervention, p. 574
- Skills Practice, p. 575
- Practice, p. 576
- Reading to Learn Mathematics, p. 577
- Enrichment, p. 578
- Assessment, p. 604

Parent and Student Study Guide Workbook, p. 86

 Transparencies
5-Minute Check Transparency 10-6
Answer Key Transparencies

 Technology
Interactive Chalkboard

CLASSIFY POLYGONS

1 Classify each polygon.

a.

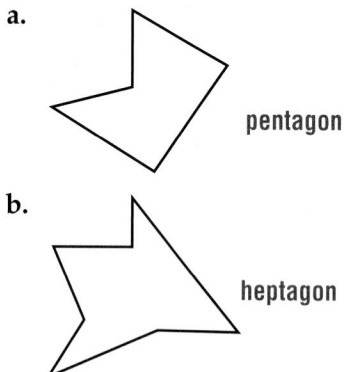

pentagon

b.

heptagon

MEASURES OF THE ANGLES OF A POLYGON

Teaching Tip You may want to give students copies of various polygons and ask them to determine the diagonals from one vertex and the number of triangles formed before presenting the information in the student text.

2 Find the sum of the measures of the interior angles of a quadrilateral. **360°**

Teaching Tip Remind students that the sum of the measures of the interior angles of a triangle is 180° (Chapter 9).

Study Tip

n-gon
A polygon with *n* sides is called an *n*-gon. For example, an octagon can also be called an 8-gon.

Polygons can be classified by the number of sides they have.

Number of Sides	Name of Polygon	Number of Sides	Name of Polygon
3	triangle	7	heptagon
4	quadrilateral	8	octagon
5	pentagon	9	nonagon
6	hexagon	10	decagon

Example 1 *Classify Polygons*

Classify each polygon.

a.

b.

The polygon has 8 sides. It is an octagon.

The polygon has 6 sides. It is a hexagon.

MEASURES OF THE ANGLES OF A POLYGON   A **diagonal** is a line segment in a polygon that joins two nonconsecutive vertices. In the diagram below, all possible diagonals from one vertex are shown.

quadrilateral   pentagon   hexagon   heptagon   octagon

   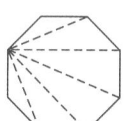

	Quadrilateral	Pentagon	Hexagon	Heptagon	Octagon
Sides	4	5	6	7	8
Diagonals	1	2	3	4	5
Triangles	2	3	4	5	6

Notice that the number of triangles is 2 less than the number of sides.

You can use the property of the sum of the measures of the angles of a triangle to find the sum of the measures of the interior angles of any polygon. An **interior angle** is an angle inside a polygon.

Key Concept ╱ *Interior Angles of a Polygon*

If a polygon has *n* sides, then $n - 2$ triangles are formed. The sum of the degree measures of the interior angles of the polygon is $(n - 2)180$.

Example 2 *Measures of Interior Angles*

Find the sum of the measures of the interior angles of a heptagon.

A heptagon has 7 sides. Therefore, $n = 7$.

$(n - 2)180 = (7 - 2)180$ Replace *n* with 7.
$= 5(180)$ or 900 Simplify.

The sum of the measures of the interior angles of a heptagon is 900°.

DAILY
INTERVENTION

Differentiated Instruction

- **Visual/Spatial** Have students design their own tessellations. Encourage them to use a variety of regular polygons. Then have them cut the shapes out of colored paper and adhere them to a backing to make a mosaic. Students should include descriptions of the polygons they used in their tessellations.

A **regular polygon** is a polygon that is *equilateral* (all sides are congruent) and *equiangular* (all angles are congruent). Since the angles of a regular polygon are congruent, their measures are equal.

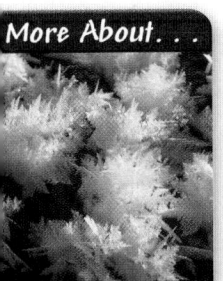
Example 3 *Find Angle Measure of a Regular Polygon*

• **SNOW** Snowflakes are some of the most beautiful objects in nature. Notice how they are regular and hexagonal in shape. What is the measure of one interior angle in a snowflake?

Step 1 Find the sum of the measures of the angles.

A hexagon has 6 sides. Therefore, $n = 6$.

$(n - 2)180 = (6 - 2)180$ Replace n with 6.

$= 4(180)$ or 720 Simplify.

The sum of the measures of the interior angles is 720°.

Step 2 Divide the sum by 6 to find the measure of one angle.

$720 \div 6 = 120$

So, the measure of one interior angle in a snowflake is 120°.

Check for Understanding

Concept Check

1–3. See margin.

1. **OPEN ENDED** Draw a polygon that is both equiangular and equilateral.

2. **Draw** examples of a pentagon, hexagon, heptagon, octagon, nonagon, and decagon.

3. **Explain** the relationship between the number of sides in a polygon and the number of triangles formed by each of the diagonals.

Guided Practice

Classify each polygon. Then determine whether it appears to be *regular* or *not regular*.

GUIDED PRACTICE KEY	
Exercises	Examples
4, 5, 8	1
6	2
7	3

4.

pentagon; not regular

5. octagon; regular

6. Find the sum of the measures of the interior angles of a nonagon. **1260°**

7. What is the measure of each interior angle of a regular heptagon? Round to the nearest tenth. **128.6°**

Application

8. **TESSELLATIONS** Identify the polygons that are used to create the tessellation shown at the right. **square, hexagon, 12-gon**

 www.pre-alg.com/extra_examples/ny

Lesson 10-6 Polygons **529**

Answers

1.

2. **Answers may vary. See students' work.**

3. **The number of triangles is 2 less than the number of sides.**

Study Guide and Intervention, p. 574

A **polygon** is a simple, closed figure formed by three or more line segments. The line segments, called *sides*, meet only at their endpoints. The points of intersection are called *vertices*. Polygons can be classified by the number of sides they have.

A **diagonal** is a line segment in a polygon that joins two nonconsecutive vertices, forming triangles. You can use the property of the sum of the measures of the angles of a triangle to find the sum of the measures of the interior angles of any polygon.

An **interior angle** is an angle inside a polygon.

Number of Sides	Name of Polygon
3	triangle
4	quadrilateral
5	pentagon
6	hexagon
7	heptagon
8	octagon
9	nonagon
10	decagon

If a polygon has n sides, then $n - 2$ triangles are formed. The sum of the degree measures of the interior angles of the polygon is $(n - 2)180$.

A **regular polygon** is a polygon that is *equilateral* (all sides are congruent) and *equiangular* (all angles are congruent). Since the angles of a regular polygon are congruent, their measures are equal.

Example Find the measure of one interior angle of a regular 20-gon.

Step 1 A 20-gon has 20 sides. Therefore, $n = 20$.
$(n - 2)180 = (20 - 2)180$ Replace n with 20.
$= 18(180)$ or 3240 Simplify

The sum of the measures of the interior angles is 3240°.

Step 2 Divide the sum by 20 to find the measure of one angle.
$3240 \div 20 = 162$

So, the measure of one interior angle in a regular 20-gon is 162°.

Exercises

Classify each polygon. Then determine whether it appears to be *regular* or *not regular*.

1. heptagon; not regular   2. octagon; not regular   3. quadrilateral; regular

Find the sum of the measures of the interior angles of each polygon.

4. quadrilateral 360°   5. nonagon 1260°   6. heptagon 900°   7. 12-gon 1800°

Skills Practice, p. 575 and Practice, p. 576 (shown)

Find the sum of the measures of the interior angles of each polygon.

1. quadrilateral 360°   2. decagon 1440°   3. 12-gon 1800°
4. heptagon 900°   5. pentagon 540°   6. hexagon 720°
7. 25-gon 4140°   8. 100-gon 17,640°

Find the measure of an interior angle of each polygon.

9. regular nonagon 140°   10. regular octagon 135°   11. regular hexagon 120°
12. regular 12-gon 150°   13. regular quadrilateral 90°   14. regular decagon 144°

TESSELLATIONS For Exercises 15 and 16, identify the polygons used to create each tessellation.

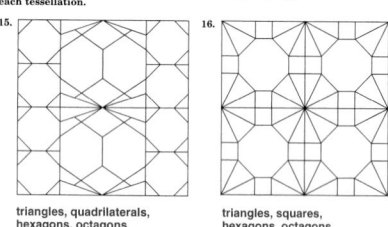

15. triangles, quadrilaterals, hexagons, octagons
16. triangles, squares, hexagons, octagons

17. Which figure best represents a regular polygon? D

A   B   C   D

Enrichment, p. 578

Polygons and Diagonals

A **diagonal** of a polygon is any segment that connects two nonconsecutive vertices of the polygon. In each of the following polygons, all possible diagonals are drawn.

Examples

In △ABC, no diagonals can be drawn. Why?   In quadrilateral DEFG, 2 diagonals can be drawn.   In pentagon HIJKL, 5 diagonals can be drawn.

Complete the chart below and try to find a pattern that will help you answer the questions that follow.

	Polygons	Number of Sides	Number of Diagonals From One Vertex	Total Number of Diagonals
	triangle	3	0	0
	quadrilateral	4	1	2
	pentagon	5	2	5
1.	hexagon	6	3	9
2.	heptagon	7	4	14
3.	octagon	8	5	20
4.	nonagon	9	6	27
5.	decagon	10	7	35

Find the total number of diagonals that can be drawn in a polygon with the given number of sides.

6. 6 9   7. 7 14   8. 8 20   9. 9 27
10. 10 35   11. 11 44   12. 12 54   13. 15 90
14. 20 170   15. 50 1175   16. 75 2700   17. n $\frac{n^2 - 3n}{2}$

★ indicates increased difficulty

Practice and Apply

Homework Help

For Exercises	See Examples
9–14, 21 29, 30	1
15–20	2
23–28	3

Extra Practice See page 749.

Classify each polygon. Then determine whether it appears to be *regular* or *not regular*. 9–14. See margin.

9.

10.

11.

12.

13.

14.

Find the sum of the measures of the interior angles of each polygon.

15. pentagon **540°**   16. octagon **1080°**   17. decagon **1440°**
18. hexagon **720°**   ★ 19. 18-gon **2880°**   ★ 20. 23-gon **3780°**

ART For Exercises 21 and 22, use the painting shown.

21. List five polygons used in the painting.

22. **RESEARCH** The title of the painting mentions the music symbol, *clef*. Use the Internet or another source to find a drawing of a clef. Is a clef a polygon? Explain.

Roy Lichtenstein. *Modern Painting with Clef.* 1967

21. Sample answer: hexagon, triangle, decagon, quadrilateral, and pentagon

22. No, it is not a polygon since it has curved sides.

Find the measure of an interior angle of each polygon.

23. regular nonagon **140°**   24. regular pentagon **108°**   25. regular octagon **135°**
26. regular decagon **144°**   ★ 27. regular 12-gon **150°**   ★ 28. regular 25-gon **165.6°**

TESSELLATIONS For Exercises 29 and 30, identify the polygons used to create each tessellation.

29.

octagons, squares

30.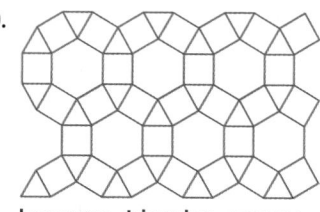

hexagons, triangles, squares

★ 31. **ART** Refer to Exercise 8 on page 529. The tessellation design contains regular polygons. Find the perimeter of the design if the measure of the sides of the 12-gon is 5 centimeters. **180 cm**

32. What is the perimeter of a regular pentagon with sides 4.2 feet long? **21 ft**

33. Find the perimeter of a regular nonagon having sides $6\frac{1}{2}$ inches long. **58.5 in.**

Answers

9. hexagon; regular

10. heptagon; not regular

11. nonagon; not regular

12. pentagon; regular

13. decagon; not regular

14. decagon; not regular

34. CRITICAL THINKING Copy the dot pattern shown at the right. Then without lifting your pencil from the paper, draw four line segments that connect all of the points. **See margin.**

35. `WRITING IN MATH` Answer the question that was posed at the beginning of the lesson. **See margin.**

How are polygons used in tessellations?

Include the following in your answer:
- an example of a tessellation in which the pattern is formed using only one type of polygon, and
- an example of a tessellation in which the pattern is formed using more than one polygon.

NEW YORK
Test Practice

Standardized Test Practice
Ⓐ Ⓑ Ⓒ Ⓓ
36. 60°

36. GRID IN The measure of one angle of a regular polygon with n sides is $\frac{180(n-2)}{n}$. What is the measure of an interior angle in a regular triangle?

37. Which figure best represents a regular polygon? **B**

Ⓐ   Ⓑ   Ⓒ   Ⓓ

Extending the Lesson **EXTERIOR ANGLES** When a side of a polygon is extended, an **exterior angle** is formed.

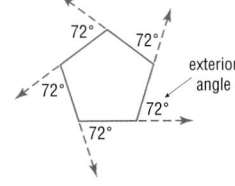
exterior angle

In any polygon, the sum of the measures of the exterior angles, one at each vertex, is 360.

Find the measure of each exterior angle of each regular polygon.

38. regular octagon **45°** **39.** regular triangle **120°** **40.** regular nonagon **40°**

41. regular hexagon **60°** **42.** regular decagon **36°** **43.** regular 12-gon **30°**

Maintain Your Skills

Mixed Review **Find the area of each figure described.** *(Lesson 10-5)*

44. triangle: base, 9 in.; height, 6 in. **27 in²**

45. trapezoid: height, 3 cm; bases, 4 cm, 8 cm **18 cm²**

Classify each quadrilateral using the name that *best* describes it.
(Lesson 10-4)

46. rhombus **47.** quadrilateral **48.**

rectangle

49. ALGEBRA Simplify $4.6x + 2.5x + 9.3x$. *(Lesson 3-2)* **16.4x**

Getting Ready for the Next Lesson **PREREQUISITE SKILL** Use a calculator to find each product. Round to the nearest tenth. *(To review **rounding decimals**, see page 711.)*

50. $\pi \cdot 4.3$ **13.5** **51.** $2 \cdot \pi \cdot 5.4$ **33.9** **52.** $\pi \cdot 4^2$ **50.3** **53.** $\pi(2.4)^2$ **18.1**

www.pre-alg.com/self_check_quiz/ny

Lesson 10-6 Polygons **531**

---

4 Assess

Open-Ended Assessment

Modeling Have students find examples of polygons in their homes. Have them bring pictures or sketches of the various objects to present to the class. Encourage students to be creative in recognizing polygons in common places.

Getting Ready for Lesson 10-7

PREREQUISITE SKILL Lesson 10-7 presents the formulas for circumference and area of a circle. These formulas involve π. Use Exercises 50–53 to determine your students' familiarity with evaluating expressions involving π.

Quiz (Lessons 10-5 and 10-6) is available on p. 604 of the *Chapter 10 Resource Masters*.

Sample Answers

34.
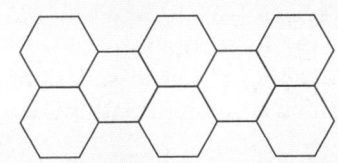

35. In tessellations, polygons are fit together to create a pattern such that there are no gaps or spaces. Answers should include the following.

A Follow-Up of Lesson 10-6

Getting Started

Objective Create tessellations using transformations.

Materials
While no special materials are needed for this activity, you may want students to use light cardboard to create each tessellation pattern unit for easier tracing.

Teaching Tip Students may want to cut figures out to make the tessellations. Have them cut out the section to be translated and tape it into position to create the pattern piece.

Teach

• Have students use colored pencils to keep track of the patterns.
• Show examples of artwork using tessellations, such as an Escher print.

Assess

In **Exercises 1–3**, students should practice making translations so that the tessellation has an even fit and discuss other pairs of figures that can be used to create tessellations.

In **Exercises 4–6**, students should make sure their rotations are done evenly so their tessellations maintain a consistent pattern.

Study Notebook

You may wish to have students summarize this activity and what they learned from it.

NEW YORK *Performance Indicator* **8.G.8 Draw the image of a figure under rotations of 90 and 180 degrees, 8.G.10 Draw the image of a figure under a translation**

 # Tessellations

A tessellation is a pattern of repeating figures that fit together with no overlapping or empty spaces. Tessellations can be formed using transformations.

Activity 1   **Create a tessellation using a translation.**

Step 1   Draw a square. Then draw a triangle inside the top of the square as shown.

Step 2   Translate or slide the triangle from the top to the bottom of the square.

Step 1   Step 2

Step 3   Repeat this pattern unit to create a tessellation.

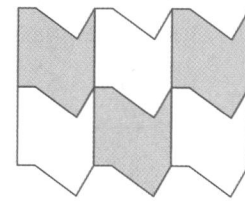

It is sometimes helpful to complete one pattern, cut it out, and trace it for the other pattern units.

Activity 2   **Create a tessellation using a rotation.**

Step 1   Draw an equilateral triangle. Then draw another triangle inside the left side of the triangle as shown below.

Step 2   Rotate the triangle so you can trace the change on the side as indicated.

Step 1   Step 2

Step 3   Repeat this pattern unit to create a tessellation.

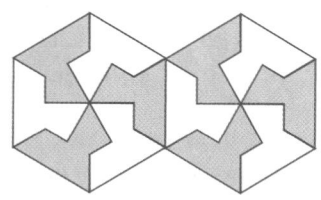

Model 1–6. See pp. 551A–551B.

Use a translation to create a tessellation for each pattern unit shown.

1.   **2.**   **3.**

Use a rotation to create a tessellation for each pattern unit shown.

4.   **5.**   **6.**

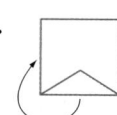

7. Make a tessellation that involves a translation, a rotation, or a combination of the two.
See students' work.

Resource Manager

 Teaching Pre-Algebra with Manipulatives
• p. 135 (student recording sheet)

Circumference and Area: Circles

NEW YORK *Performance Indicator*
Reinforcement of 6.G.7 Determine the area and circumference of a circle, using the appropriate formula

What You'll Learn

- Find circumference of circles.
- Find area of circles.

Vocabulary

- circle
- diameter
- center
- circumference
- radius
- π (pi)

**a–b. See students'
work.
c. The results are
about 3.**

How are circumference and diameter related?

Coins, paper plates, cookies, and CDs are all examples of objects that are circular in shape.

a. Collect three different-sized circular objects. Then copy the table shown.

b. Using a tape measure, measure each distance below to the nearest millimeter. Record your results.

- the distance across the circular object through its center (d)
- the distance around each circular object (C)

c. For each object, find the ratio $\frac{C}{d}$. Record the results in the table.

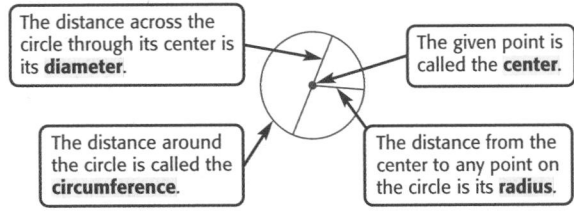

Object	d	C	$\frac{C}{d}$
1			
2			
3			

CIRCUMFERENCE OF CIRCLES A **circle** is the set of all points in a plane that are the same distance from a given point.

The distance across the circle through its center is its **diameter**.

The given point is called the **center**.

The distance around the circle is called the **circumference**.

The distance from the center to any point on the circle is its **radius**.

The relationship you discovered in the activity above is true for all circles. The ratio of the circumference of a circle to its diameter is always equal to 3.1415926… The Greek letter **π (pi)** stands for this number. Using this ratio, you can derive a formula for the circumference of a circle.

$\frac{C}{d} = \pi$ The ratio of the circumference to the diameter equals pi.

$\frac{C}{d} \cdot d = \pi \cdot d$ Multiply each side by d.

$C = \pi d$ Simplify.

Key Concept   *Circumference of a Circle*

- **Words**   The circumference of a circle is equal to its diameter times π, or 2 times its radius times π.

- **Model**

- **Symbols** $C = \pi d$ or $C = 2\pi r$

Workbooks and Reproducible Masters

Chapter 10 Resource Masters
- Study Guide and Intervention, p. 579
- Skills Practice, p. 580
- Practice, p. 581
- Reading to Learn Mathematics, p. 582
- Enrichment, p. 583

**Parent and Student Study Guide
Workbook,** p. 87
School-to-Career Masters, p. 20

---

1 Focus

5-Minute Check
Transparency 10-7 Use as a quiz or review of Lesson 10-6.

Mathematical Background notes are available for this lesson on page 490D.

How are circumference and diameter related?

The opening activity questions are repeated on page 582 of the *Chapter 10 Resource Masters*.

Reading to Learn Mathematics, p. 582   **ELL**

Pre-Activity   *How are circumference and diameter related?*

Do the activity at the top of page 533 in your textbook. Write your answers below.

   a. Collect three different-sized circular objects. Then copy the table shown. See students' work.

   b. Using a tape measure, measure each distance below to the nearest millimeter. Record your results.
     • the distance across the circular object through its center (d)
     • the distance around each circular object (C) See students' work.

   c. For each object, find the ratio $\frac{C}{d}$. Record the results in the table. The results are about 3.

Reading the Lesson   1–6. See students' work.
Write a definition and give an example of each new vocabulary word.

Vocabulary	Definition	Example
1. circle		
2. diameter		
3. center		
4. circumference		
5. radius		
6. π (pi)		

Helping You Remember

7. Study the circle at the right, label each part, then find the circle's circumference and area (round to the nearest tenth).

   formula for circumference: $C = \pi d$ or $2\pi r$
   formula for area: $A = \pi r^2$
   circumference: 15.7 cm
   area: 19.6 cm^2

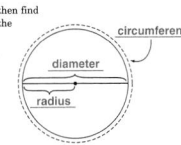

Teaching Tip Remind students that pi is a constant, not a variable. Also remind them to use π on their calculator and round the answer after calculating.

Resource Manager

 Transparencies

5-Minute Check Transparency 10-7
Answer Key Transparencies

 Technology

Interactive Chalkboard
Multimedia Applications

2 Teach

CIRCUMFERENCE OF CIRCLES

In-Class Examples — Power Point®

1 Find the circumference of each circle to the nearest tenth.

a.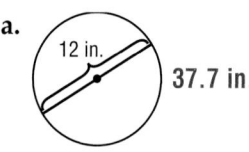
12 in. **37.7 in.**

b.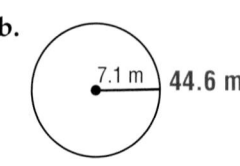
7.1 m **44.6 m**

2 LANDSCAPING A landscaper has a tree whose roots form a ball-shaped bulb with a circumference of about 110 inches. How wide will the landscaper have to dig the hole in order to plant the tree? **at least 35 in.**

Teaching Tip Make sure students keep track of whether they are using the radius or diameter.

Study Tip

Calculating with π
Unless otherwise specified, use a calculator to evaluate expressions involving π and then follow any instructions regarding rounding.

Study Tip

Estimation
To estimate the circumference of a circle, multiply the diameter by 3.

✓ **Concept Check** Which term describes the distance from the center of a circle to any point on the circle? **radius**

Example 1 *Find the Circumference of a Circle*

Find the circumference of each circle to the nearest tenth.

a.
5 cm

$C = \pi d$	Circumference of a circle
$C = \pi \cdot 5$	Replace d with 5.
$C = 5\pi$	Simplify. This is the *exact* circumference.

To estimate the circumference, use a calculator.

5 [×] [2nd] [π] [ENTER] 15.70796327

The circumference is about 15.7 centimeters.

b.
3.2 ft

$C = 2\pi r$	Circumference of a circle
$C = 2 \cdot \pi \cdot 3.2$	Replace r with 3.2.
$C \approx 20.1$	Simplify. Use a calculator.

The circumference is about 20.1 feet.

Many situations involve circumference and diameter of circles.

Example 2 *Use Circumference to Solve a Problem*

TREES A tree in Madison's yard was damaged in a storm. She wants to replace the tree with another whose trunk is the same size as the original tree. Suppose the circumference of the original tree was 14 inches. What should be the diameter of the replacement tree?

Explore You know the circumference of the original tree. You need to know the diameter of the new tree.

Plan Use the formula for the circumference of a circle to find the diameter.

Solve

$C = \pi d$	Circumference of a circle
$14 = \pi \cdot d$	Replace C with 14.
$\dfrac{14}{\pi} = d$	Divide each side by π.
$4.5 \approx d$	Simplify. Use a calculator.

The diameter of the tree should be about 4.5 inches.

Examine Check the reasonableness of the solution by replacing d with 4.5 in $C = \pi d$.

$C = \pi d$	Circumference of a circle
$C = \pi \cdot 4.5$	Replace d with 4.5.
$C \approx 14.1$	Simplify. Use a calculator.

The solution is reasonable.

534 Chapter 10 Two-Dimensional Figures

DAILY
INTERVENTION

Unlocking Misconceptions

- **Units of Measure** Students will often forget to write the units with their answers, but keeping the correct units in a problem can help students check their answers. Circumference is a linear measurement, and the answer is a unit to the first power. Area is a product of two linear measurements, and the answer is a unit squared. Volume is a product of three linear measurements, and the answer is a unit cubed.

AREAS OF CIRCLES A circle can be separated into parts as shown below. The parts can then be arranged to form a figure that resembles a parallelogram.

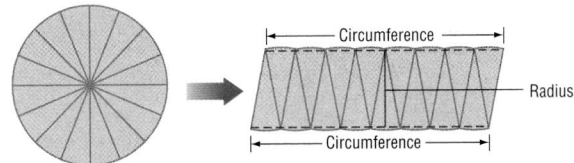

Since the circle has an area that is relatively close to the area of the figure, you can use the formula for the area of a parallelogram to find the area of a circle.

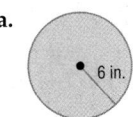

Study Tip

Look Back
To review **exponents**, see Lesson 4-2.

$A = bh$ Area of a parallelogram

$A = \left(\frac{1}{2} \times C\right) r$ The base of the parallelogram is one-half the circumference, and the radius is the height.

$A = \left(\frac{1}{2} \times 2\pi r\right) r$ Replace C with $2\pi r$.

$A = \pi \times r \times r$ Simplify.

$A = \pi r^2$ Replace $r \times r$ with r^2.

Key Concept   Area of a Circle

- **Words**   The area of a circle is equal to π times the square of its radius.
- **Model**
- **Symbols** $A = \pi r^2$

Study Tip

Estimation
To estimate the area of a circle, square the radius and then multiply by 3.

Example 3   Find Areas of Circles

Find the area of each circle. Round to the nearest tenth.

a.

6 in.

$A = \pi r^2$ Area of a circle
$A = \pi \cdot 6^2$ Replace r with 6.
$A = \pi \cdot 36$ Evaluate 6^2.
$A \approx 113.1$ Use a calculator.

The area is about 113.1 square inches.

b.

31 m

$A = \pi r^2$ Area of a circle
$A = \pi \cdot (15.5)^2$ Replace r with 15.5.
$A = \pi \cdot 240.25$ Evaluate $(15.5)^2$.
$A \approx 754.8$ Use a calculator.

The area is about 754.8 square meters.

Check for Understanding

Concept Check
1. **Tell** how to find the circumference of a circle if you know the measure of the radius. **Multiply 2 times π times the radius.**

2. **OPEN ENDED** Draw and label a circle that has an area between 5 and 8 square units. **See margin.**

In-Class Example Power Point®

Teaching Tip You may want students to actually do the development of the circumference as an activity.

3 Find the area of each circle. Round to the nearest tenth.

a.

11 ft   380.1 ft²

b.

8.3 cm   54.1 cm²

3 Practice/Apply

Study Notebook

Have students—
- add the definitions/examples of the vocabulary terms to their Vocabulary Builder worksheets for Chapter 10.
- include sketches depicting diameter and radius, along with the formulas for circumference and area of circles.
- include any other item(s) that they find helpful in mastering the skills in this lesson.

Answer

2. Sample answer:

1.5

Organization by Objective
• **Circumference of Circles:**
10–21, 24, 25, 27, 29, 34
• **Areas of Circles:** 10–19,
22–23, 26, 28, 30–33

Odd/Even Assignments
Exercises 10–29 are structured
so that students practice the
same concepts whether they
are assigned odd or even
problems.

Assignment Guide
Basic: 11, 13, 17, 19, 25–31
odd, 32, 33, 35–38, 48–56
Average: 11–31 odd, 32, 33,
35–38, 48–56 (Optional: 39–47)
Advanced: 10–32 even, 33–53
(Optional: 54–56)
All: Practice Quiz 2 (1–5)

DAILY
INTERVENTION **FIND THE ERROR**
If students are
having difficulty with
the problem, have them diagram
the circle. Ask them to label both
the diameter (d = 7 units) and
the radius (r = 3.5 units) of this
circle.

Answer

3. Mark; since the diameter of the
circle is 7 units, its radius is 3.5
units. Thus, the area of the circle
is π (3.5)² or 38.5 square units.

Answer (p. 537)

34.

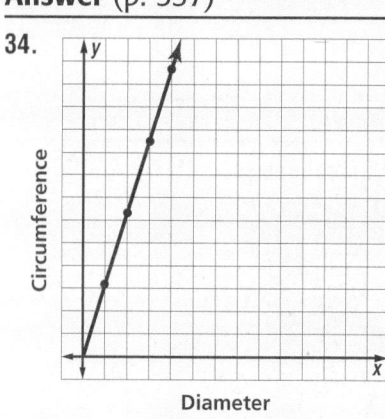

---

3. **FIND THE ERROR** Dario and Mark are finding the area of a circle with
diameter 7. **See margin.**

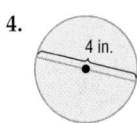
Dario
$A \approx 153.9$ units²

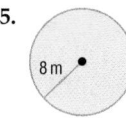
Mark
$A \approx 38.5$ units²

Who is correct? Explain your reasoning.

Guided Practice

GUIDED PRACTICE KEY

Exercises	Examples
4–9	1–3

Find the circumference and area of each circle. Round to the nearest tenth.

4. 4 in. — 12.6 in; 12.6 in²

5. 8 m — 50.3 m; 201.1 m²

6. 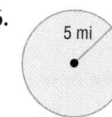 5 mi — 31.4 mi; 78.5 mi²

7. The radius is 1.3 kilometers.
8.2 km; 5.3 km²

8. The diameter is 6.1 centimeters.
19.2 cm; 29.2 cm²

Application

9. **MUSIC** During a football game, a marching band can be heard within a
radius of 1.7 miles. What is the area of the neighborhood that can hear
the band? **about 9.1 mi²**

★ indicates increased difficulty

Practice and Apply

Homework Help

For Exercises	See Examples
10–19, 24, 26–35	1, 3
20–23, 25	2

Extra Practice
See page 749.

Find the circumference and area of each circle. Round to the nearest tenth.

10. 6 cm — 18.8 cm; 28.3 cm²

11. 13 in. — 40.8 in.; 132.7 in²

12. 10 m — 62.8 m; 314.2 m²

13. 21 km — 131.9 km; 1385.4 km²

★ 14. $9\frac{1}{2}$ ft — 29.8 ft; 70.9 ft²

★ 15. 12.7 m — 79.8 m; 506.7 m²

16. 28.3 m; 63.6 m²
17. 22.9 cm; 41.9 cm²
18. 24.5 ft; 47.8 ft²
19. 96.6 in; 742.6 in²

16. The radius is 4.5 meters.

17. The diameter is 7.3 centimeters.

18. The diameter is $7\frac{4}{5}$ feet.

19. The radius is $15\frac{3}{8}$ inches.

★ 20. What is the diameter of a circle if its circumference is 25.8 inches? Round
to the nearest tenth. **8.2 in.**

★ 21. Find the radius of a circle if its circumference is 9.2 meters. Round to the
nearest tenth. **1.5 m**

★ 22. Find the radius of a circle if its area is 254.5 square inches. **9 in.**

★ 23. What is the diameter of a circle if its area is 132.7 square meters? **13 cm**

24. **BICYCLES** If a bicycle tire has a diameter of 27 inches, what is the
distance the bicycle will travel in 10 rotations of the tire? **848.2 in.**

25. **SCIENCE** The circumference of Earth is about
25,000 miles. What is the distance to the center
of Earth? **about 3979 mi**

25,000 mi

DAILY
INTERVENTION **Differentiated Instruction**

• **Intrapersonal** Ask students to choose a hobby or sport that they
enjoy. They should then find a circle related to that activity and determine the circumference, area, diameter, and radius of the circle. For
example, a basketball player might calculate the diameter of a basketball. He or she could then compare the diameter of the ball to the
diameter of the hoop. Ask students to record any insights into their
activity in their Math Journals.

More About...

History ·················

The Houston Astrodome opened on April 12, 1965. It is the first enclosed stadium built for baseball. The Houston Astrodome has a diameter of 216.4 meters.

Source: *Compton's Encyclopedia*

Match each circle described in the column on the left with its corresponding measurement in the column on the right.

26. radius: 4 units **c**
27. diameter: 7 units **d**
28. diameter: 3 units **b**
29. radius: 6 units **a**

a. circumference: 37.7 units
b. area: 7.1 units²
c. area: 50.3 units²
d. circumference: 22.0 units

30. **MONUMENTS** The Stonehenge monument in England is enclosed within a circular ditch that has a diameter of 300 feet. Find the area within the ditch to the nearest tenth. **70,685.8 ft²**

31. **HISTORY** The dome of the Roman Pantheon has a diameter of 42.7 meters. Use the information at the left to find about how many times more area the Astrodome covers than the Pantheon. **about 26 times**

FOOD For Exercises 32 and 33, use the following information and the graphic shown at the right.

Suppose the circle graph is redrawn onto a poster board so that the diameter of the graph is 9 inches.

32. How much space on the poster board will the circle graph cover? **63.6 in²**

33. How much of the total space will each section of the graph cover?
are safe: 25.4 in²;
are unsafe: 24.2 in²;
don't know: 14.0 in²

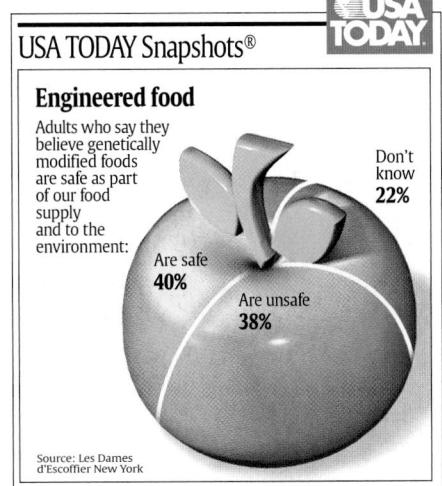

USA TODAY Snapshots®

Engineered food
Adults who say they believe genetically modified foods are safe as part of our food supply and to the environment:

Don't know **22%**
Are safe **40%**
Are unsafe **38%**

Source: Les Dames d'Escoffier New York

By Cindy Hall and Quin Tian, USA TODAY

★ 34. **FUNCTIONS** Graph the circumference of a circle as a function of the diameter. Use values of *d* like 1, 2, 3, 4, and so on. What is the slope of this graph? (*Hint:* To review **slope**, see Lesson 8-4.) **See margin for graph; π.**

35. **CRITICAL THINKING** The numerical value of the area of a circle is twice the numerical value of the circumference. What is the radius of the circle? (*Hint:* Use a chart of values for radius, circumference, and area.) **4**

36. **WRITING IN MATH** Answer the question that was posed at the beginning of the lesson. **See margin.**

How are circumference and diameter related?

Include the following in your answer:
• the ratio of the circumference to the diameter, and
• an explanation describing what happens to the circumference as the diameter increases or decreases.

37. The diameter of a circle is 8 units. What is the area of the circle if the diameter is doubled? **C**
Ⓐ 50.3 units² Ⓑ 100.5 units² Ⓒ 201.1 units² Ⓓ 804.2 units²

38. **GRID IN** The circumference of a circle is 18.8 meters. What is its area to the nearest tenth? **28.1 m²**

www.pre-alg.com/self_check_quiz/ny

Lesson 10-7 Circumference and Area: Circles **537**

Answer

36. **The circumference of a circle is about 3 times its diameter. Answers should include the following.**

• **Since the circumference is about 3 times the diameter, the ratio describing the relationship would be about 3 to 1.**

• **As the diameter increases, the circumference increases. As the diameter decreases, the circumference decreases.**

Study Guide and Intervention, p. 579

Circles		
A **circle** is the set of all points in a plane that are the same distance from a given point.	The **circumference** of a circle is equal to its diameter times π, or 2 times its radius times π.	C = πd or C = 2πr
	The **area** of a circle is equal to π times the square of its radius.	A = πr²

Example 1
Find the circumference of the circle to the nearest tenth.

a. 7 km

C = 2πr   Circumference of a circle
C = 2 · π · 7   Replace *r* with 7.
C ≈ 44.0   Simplify. Use a calculator.
The circumference is about 44.0 kilometers.

Example 2
Find the area of the circle. Round to the nearest tenth.

b. 30 in.

A = πr²   Area of a circle
A = π · (15)²   Replace *r* with 15.
A = π · 225   Evaluate (15)²
A ≈ 706.9   Use a calculator.
The area is about 706.9 square inches.

Exercises

Find the circumference and area of each circle. Round to the nearest tenth.

1. 10 m   2. 7 m   3. 8 cm   4. 12 ft
31.4 m; 78.5 m²   22.0 m; 38.5 m²   50.3 cm; 201.1 cm²   37.7 ft; 113.1 ft²

Match each circle described in the column on the left with its corresponding measurement in the column on the right.

5. radius: 5 units **c**   a. area: 63.6 units²
6. diameter: 9 units **a**   b. circumference: 50.3 units
7. diameter: 12 units **d**   c. circumference: 31.4 units
8. diameter: 16 units **b**   d. area: 113.1 units²

Skills Practice, p. 580 and Practice, p. 581 (shown)

Find the circumference and area of each circle. Round to the nearest tenth.

1. The diameter is 18 yards.
56.5 yd; 254.5 yd²
2. The radius is 4 meters.
25.1 m; 50.3 m²
3. The diameter is 4.2 meters.
13.2 m; 13.9 m²
4. The radius is 4.5 feet.
28.3 ft; 63.6 ft²
5. The radius is 9¾ miles.
61.3 mi; 298.6 mi²
6. The diameter is 6 kilometers.
18.8 km; 28.3 km²

Match each circle described in the column on the left with its corresponding measurement in the column on the right.

7. radius: 8.5 units **a**   a. circumference: 53.4 units
8. diameter: 9 units **c**   b. area: 33.2 units²
9. diameter: 6.5 units **b**   c. area: 63.6 units²
10. radius: 12 units **d**   d. circumference: 75.4 units

11. **SPORTS** A baseball has a radius of about 1.5 inches. Home plate is 16 inches wide. If a baseball were rolled across home plate, how many complete rotations would it take to cover the distance? **2 complete rotations**

12. **SPORTS** A soccer ball has a circumference of about 28 inches, while the goal is 24 feet wide. How many soccer balls would be needed to cover the distance between the goalposts? **33 soccer balls**

13. **HISTORY** Chariot races reached their peak in popularity in ancient Rome around the 1st and 2nd centuries A.D. A chariot wheel had a radius of about one foot. One lap around the track in the Circus Maximus was approximately 2,300 feet. How many chariot-wheel revolutions did it take to complete one lap? **about 366 revolutions**

14. **CULTURE** One of the artistic traditions of Tantric Buddhism is *dul-tson-kyil-khor*, which is the creation of intricately designed prayer circles (called mandalas) using colored sand. The sand is funneled through a hollow metal tube about 0.5 centimeter in diameter. If the prayer circle were a meter across, approximately how many funnel-tips of sand would be needed to cover its surface? **40,000 funnel-tips**

Enrichment, p. 583

Sector of a Circle
The sector of a circle is the region bounded by two radii and the arc of the circle. The area of a sector is a fractional part of the area of a circle.
A = n/360 × π × r² where n is the degree measure of the central angle.

Example 9 cm, 60°
Area of a sector ≈ 60/360 × 3.14 × 81
≈ 42.39 cm²

Find the area of each sector. Use 3.14 for π.

1. 12 cm, 45°   56.52 cm²
2. 12 cm, 30°   37.68 cm²
3. 12 cm, 60°   75.36 cm²
4. 6 cm, 90°   28.26 cm²
5. 6 cm, 60°   18.84 cm²
6. 9 cm, 120°   84.78 cm²

Open-Ended Assessment

Writing Have students write a paragraph explaining how to find the circumference and area of a circle when given the radius of the circle and when given the diameter of the circle.

Getting Ready for Lesson 10-8

PREREQUISITE SKILL In Lesson 10-8, students find the areas of irregular figures. This requires students to add and subtract areas that may be expressed as decimals. Use Exercises 54–56 to determine your students' familiarity with adding decimals.

Assessment Options

Practice Quiz 2 The quiz provides students with a brief review of the concepts and skills in Lessons 10-5 through 10-7. Lesson numbers are given to the right of exercises or instruction lines so students can review concepts not yet mastered.

Extending the Lesson

CENTRAL ANGLES A **central angle** is an angle whose vertex is the center of the circle. It separates a circle into a *major arc* and a *minor arc*. An **inscribed angle** has its vertex on the circle and sides that are chords. A **chord** is a segment of a circle whose endpoints are on the circle.

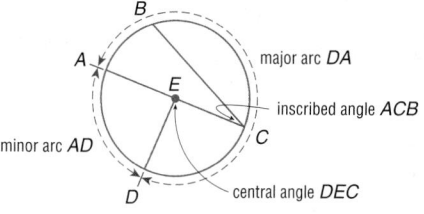

- The degree measure of a minor arc is the degree measure of the central angle.
- The measure of an inscribed angle equals one-half the measure of its intercepted arc.
- The degree measure of a major arc is 360 minus the degree measure of the central angle.

Refer to the diagram shown. Find the measures of the following angles and arcs.

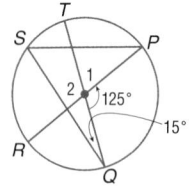

39. minor arc PQ **125°**   40. ∠1 **55°**
41. major arc QP **235°**   42. ∠2 **125°**
43. minor TR **125°**   44. minor RQ **55°**
45. ∠PSQ **62.5°**   ★ 46. minor SR **95°**

47. List three chords of the circle. **Sample answer: $\overline{SP}$, $\overline{SQ}$, $\overline{RP}$**

Maintain Your Skills

Mixed Review   Find the measure of an interior angle of each polygon. *(Lesson 10-6)*

48. regular hexagon **120°**   49. regular decagon **144°**   50. regular octagon **135°**

Find the area of each figure described. *(Lesson 10-5)*

51. trapezoid: height, 2 m; bases, 20 m and 18 m **38 m²**

52. parallelogram: base, 6 km; height, 8 km **48 km²**

53. **ALGEBRA**   Solve $2x - 7 > 5x + 14$. *(Lesson 7-6)* **$x < -7$**

Getting Ready for the Next Lesson   **PREREQUISITE SKILL**   Find each sum. *(To review **adding decimals**, see page 713.)*

54. 200 + 43.9 **243.9**   55. 23.6 + 126.9 **150.5**   56. 345.14 + 23.8 **368.94**

Practice Quiz 2   Lessons 10-5 through 10-7

Find the area of each figure. *(Lesson 10-5)*

1. **112.86 cm²**   2. **77 in²**   3. **32 m²**

4. Find the sum of the measures of the interior angles of a 15-gon. *(Lesson 10-6)* **2340°**

5. A circle has a radius of 4.7 inches. Find the circumference and area to the nearest tenth. *(Lesson 10-7)* **29.5 in.; 69.4 in²**

10-8 Area: Irregular Figures

NEW YORK *Performance Indicator* **Reinforcement of 6.G.3** Use a variety of strategies to find the area of regular and irregular polygons

What You'll Learn

• Find area of irregular figures.

How can polygons help to find the area of an irregular figure?

California is the most populous state in the United States. It ranks third among the U.S. states in area.
Source: www.infoplease.com

In the diagram, the area of California is separated into polygons.

a. Identify the polygons.

b. Explain how polygons can be used to estimate the total land area.

c. What is the area of each region?

d. What is the total area? **158,190 sq mi**

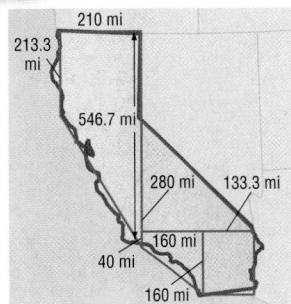

a. two trapezoids, a triangle, and a rectangle
b. Add the areas to find the total area.
c. large trapezoid: 79,800 sq mi; triangle: 41,062 sq mi; small trapezoid: 16,000 sq mi; rectangle: 21,328 sq mi

AREA OF IRREGULAR FIGURES
So far in this chapter, we have discussed the following area formulas.

Triangle	Trapezoid	Parallelogram	Circle
$A = \frac{1}{2}bh$	$A = \frac{1}{2}h(a + b)$	$A = bh$	$A = \pi r^2$

These formulas can be used to help you find the area of irregular figures. Some examples of irregular figures are shown.

To find the area of an irregular figure, separate the irregular figure into figures whose areas you know how to find.

Study Tip

Irregular Figures
There can be more than one way to separate an irregular figure. For example, another way to separate the first figure at the right is shown below.

parallelogram
trapezoid

half of a circle or semicircle
rectangle

triangle
IDAHO
rectangle

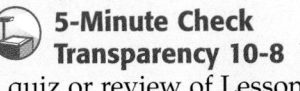

10-8 Lesson Notes

1 Focus

5-Minute Check Transparency 10-8 Use as a quiz or review of Lesson 10-7.

Mathematical Background notes are available for this lesson on page 490D.

How can polygons help to find the area of an irregular figure?

The opening activity questions are repeated on page 587 of the *Chapter 10 Resource Masters*.

Reading to Learn Mathematics, p. 587 **ELL**

Pre-Activity *How can polygons help to find the area of an irregular figure?*

Do the activity at the top of page 539 in your textbook. Write your answers below.

In the diagram, the area of California is separated into polygons.

a. Identify the polygons. two trapezoids, a triangle, and a rectangle

b. Explain how polygons can be used to estimate the total land area. Add the areas to find the total area.

c. What is the area of each region? large trapezoid: 79,800 sq mi; triangle: 41,062 sq mi; small trapezoid: 16,000 sq mi; rectangle: 21,328 sq mi

d. What is the total area? 158,190 sq mi

Reading the Lesson

Complete the following statements by filling in the blanks with the following words or symbols.

triangle	$A = \frac{1}{2}h(a + b)$	separating	formula	$A = bh$
trapezoid	$A = \pi r^2$	area	irregular figure	

1. The area of a(n) irregular figure can be determined by separating the figure into simple polygons.

2. Each separate polygon has a specific formula to determine its area. For a circle, it's $A = \pi r^2$, while a formula $A = \frac{1}{2}bh$ works for a triangle.

3. To find the area of a parallelogram, the formula $A = bh$ should be applied.

4. A(n) trapezoid, on the other hand, requires the formula $A = \frac{1}{2}h(a + b)$.

5. To find the area of the whole figure, the areas of the polygons are added together.

Helping You Remember

6. Study the figure below, identify the separate polygons, find the area of each polygon, and find the area of the entire figure. Round to the nearest tenth.

area of polygon 1: 9.8 in²   semicircle   16 in   6 in   triangle
area of polygon 2: 15 in²
area of polygon 3: 80 in²
total area of figure: 104.8 in²   rectangle

Teaching Tip Challenge students to find examples of both regular and irregular figures around the classroom.

Resource Manager

Workbooks and Reproducible Masters

Chapter 10 Resource Masters
• Study Guide and Intervention, p. 584
• Skills Practice, p. 585
• Practice, p. 586
• Reading to Learn Mathematics, p. 587
• Enrichment, p. 588
• Assessment, p. 604

Parent and Student Study Guide Workbook, p. 88
Science and Mathematics Lab Manual, pp. 21–26

Transparencies
5-Minute Check Transparency 10-8
Real-World Transparency 10
Answer Key Transparencies

Technology
Interactive Chalkboard
Pre-AlgePASS: Tutorial Plus, Lesson 34

2 Teach

AREA OF IRREGULAR FIGURES

1 Find the area of the figure to the nearest tenth.

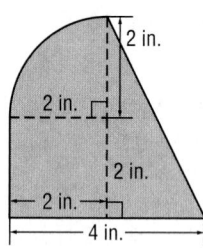

2 in.

2 in.

2 in.

2 in.

4 in.

11.1 in²

Teaching Tip Encourage students to look carefully at the irregular figure and separate it into the simplest possible areas before doing their calculations.

Answer (Concept Check)

Sample answer: triangle

$(A = \frac{1}{2} bh)$, parallelogram

$(A = bh)$, circle

$(A = \pi r^2)$

☑ Concept Check Name three area formulas that can be used to find the area of an irregular figure. **See margin.**

Example 1 *Find Area of Irregular Figures*

Find the area of the figure to the nearest tenth.

10 cm

12 cm

25 cm

Explore You know the dimensions of the figure. You need to find its area.

Plan Solve a simpler problem. First, separate the figure into a parallelogram and a semicircle. Then find the sum of the areas of the figures.

Estimate: The area of the entire figure should be a little greater than the area of the rectangle. One estimate is 10 × 25 or 250.

Solve Area of Parallelogram

$A = bh$ Area of a parallelogram

$A = 25 \cdot 12$ Replace *b* with 25 and *h* with 12.

$A = 300$ Simplify.

Area of Semicircle

$A = \frac{1}{2}\pi r^2$ Area of a semicircle

$A = \frac{1}{2} \cdot \pi \cdot 5^2$ Replace *r* with 5.

$A \approx 39.3$ Simplify.

The area of the figure is 300 + 39.3 or about 339.3 square centimeters.

Examine Check the reasonableness of the solution by solving the problem another way. Separate the figure into two rectangles and a semicircle.

15 cm

10 cm

12 cm

25 cm

The area of one rectangle is 10 · 12 or 120 square centimeters, the area of the other rectangle is 12 · 15 or 180 square centimeters, and the area of the semicircle remains 39.3 square centimeters.

120 + 180 + 39.3 = 339.3

So, the answer is correct.

DAILY

INTERVENTION   **Differentiated Instruction**

- **Interpersonal** Have students work in pairs or teams. Assign each team one of the fifty states or a Canadian province. Team members should decide what regular figures they might use to estimate the area for the state or province. If you have simple outline maps with scales, students can estimate the area and check against real totals. Have teams share their strategies with the class.

Many real-world situations involve finding the area of an irregular figure.

Example 2 Use Area of Irregular Figures

LANDSCAPE DESIGN Suppose one bag of mulch covers an area of about 9 square feet. How many bags of mulch will be needed to cover the flower garden?

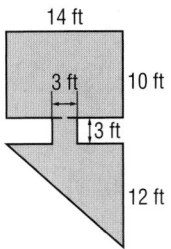

Step 1 Find the area of the flower garden.

Area of rectangle
$A = bh$ Area of a rectangle
$A = 24 \cdot 38$ Replace b with 24 and h with 38.
$A = 912$ Simplify.

Area of parallelogram
$A = bh$ Area of a parallelogram
$A = 28 \cdot 8$ Replace b with 28 and h with 8.
$A = 224$ Simplify.

The area of the garden is $912 + 224$ or 1136 square feet.

Step 2 Find the number of bags of mulch needed.

$1136 \div 9 \approx 126.2$

So, 127 bags of mulch will be needed.

In-Class Example

Power Point®

2 **CARPETING** Carpeting costs $2 per square foot. How much will it cost to carpet the area shown?

14 ft
3 ft
10 ft
3 ft
12 ft

$466

Teaching Tip Encourage students to look carefully at the irregular figure and separate it into the simplest possible areas before doing their calculations.

Check for Understanding

Concept Check 1. **OPEN ENDED** Draw two examples of irregular figures.

2. **Write** the steps you would use to find the area of the irregular figure shown at the right. **1–2. See margin.**

Guided Practice Find the area of each figure. Round to the nearest tenth.

GUIDED PRACTICE KEY	
Exercises	Examples
3, 4	1
5, 6	2

3.   3 yd 4 yd 9 yd   **49.5 yd²**

4.   5 in. 5 in.   **34.8 in²**

Application **HOME IMPROVEMENT** For Exercises 5 and 6, use the diagram shown and the following information.

The Slavens are planning to stain their wood deck. One gallon of stain costs $19.95 and covers approximately 200 square feet.

5. Suppose the Slavens need to apply only one coat of stain. How many gallons of stain will they need to buy? **2**

6. Find the total cost of the stain, not including tax. **$39.90**

www.pre-alg.com/extra_examples/ny   **Lesson 10-8** Area: Irregular Figures **541**

3 Practice/Apply

Study Notebook

Have students—
• identify an irregular figure and describe in a paragraph how they might find its area.
• include any other item(s) that they find helpful in mastering the skills in this lesson.

About the Exercises . . .

Odd/Even Assignments
Exercises 7–17 are structured so that students practice the same concepts whether they are assigned odd or even problems.

Alert! Exercise 23 involves research on the Internet or other reference materials.

Assignment Guide

Basic: 7, 9, 15, 19, 21–35
Average: 7–19 odd, 21–35
Advanced: 8–20 even, 21–35

Sample Answers

1.

2. **First, separate the figure into a rectangle and two triangles. Then find the area of each of the figures. Then find the sum of their areas.**

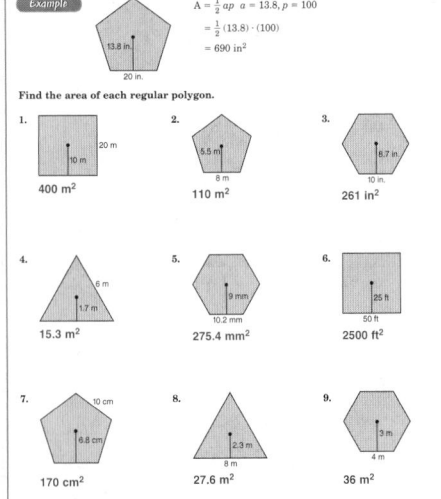
★ indicates increased difficulty

Practice and Apply

Find the area of each figure to the nearest tenth, if necessary.

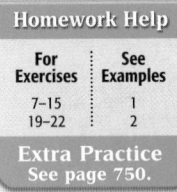

7. **72 ft²**

8. **27 m²**

9. **56.1 cm²**

10. **52.8 km²**

★ 11. **18.3 in²**

★ 12. **150 m²**

★ 13. **45 ft²**

14. What is the area of a figure that is formed using a square with sides 8 meters and a semicircle with a diameter of 5.6 meters? **76.3 m²**

15. Find the area of a figure formed using a rectangle with base 3.5 yards and height 2.8 yards and a semicircle with radius 7 yards. **86.8 yd²**

Find the area of each shaded region. Round to the nearest tenth, if necessary. (*Hint:* Find the total area and subtract the non-shaded area.)

★ 16. **167.9 units²**

★ 17. **85 units²**

★ 18. **331.1 units²**

19. **SPORTS** In the diagram shown, a track surrounds a football field. To the nearest tenth, what is the area of the grass region inside the track? **6963.5 yd²**

20. **WALKWAYS** A sidewalk forms a 3-foot wide border with the grass as shown. Find the area of the sidewalk. **108 ft²**

WebQuest

e formulas for area
d circumference of
cles are used in the
sign of various
ildings. Visit
ww.pre-alg.com/
ebquest to continue
ork on your
ebQuest project.

GEOGRAPHY For Exercises 21–23, use the diagram shown at the right.

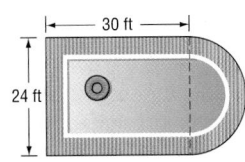

21. Tell how you would separate the irregular figure into polygons to find its area.

22. Use your method to find the total land area of Oklahoma.

23. **RESEARCH** Use the Internet or another source to find the actual total land area of Oklahoma. **21–23. See margin.**

Online Research **Data Update** How can you use irregular figures to estimate the total land area of your state? Visit www.pre-alg.com/data_update to learn more.

24. **CRITICAL THINKING** In the diagram, a patio that is 4 feet wide surrounds a swimming pool. What is the area of the patio? **429.7 ft²**

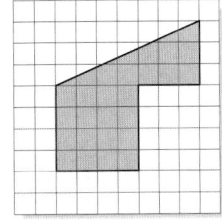

25. [**WRITING IN MATH**] Answer the question that was posed at the beginning of the lesson. **See margin.**

How can polygons help to find the area of an irregular figure?

Include the following in your answer:

• an example of an irregular figure, and

• an explanation as to how the figure can be separated to find its area.

NEW YORK
Test Practice

Standardized
Test Practice
Ⓐ Ⓑ Ⓒ Ⓓ

For Exercises 26 and 27, refer to the diagram shown. Suppose 1 square unit equals 5 square feet.

26. What is the area of the figure? **C**

  Ⓐ 26.5 ft² Ⓑ 34.5 ft²

  Ⓒ 132.5 ft² Ⓓ 185 ft²

27. What is the area of the nonshaded region? **C**

  Ⓐ 73.5 ft² Ⓑ 140.5 ft²

  Ⓒ 367.5 ft² Ⓓ 473.5 ft²

Maintain Your Skills

Mixed Review **Find the circumference and area of each circle. Round to the nearest tenth.**
(Lesson 10-7)

28. The wheel on a game show has a diameter of 8.5 feet. **26.7 ft, 56.7 ft²**

29. The radius is 7 centimeters. **44.0 cm, 153.9 cm²**

30. The diameter is 19 inches. **59.7 in., 283.5 in²**

Find the sum of the measures of the interior angles of each polygon.
(Lesson 10-6)

31. pentagon **540°** 32. quadrilateral **360°** 33. octagon **1080°**

34. Draw an angle that measures 35°. *(Lesson 9-3)* **See margin.**

35. Simplify $(4x)(-6y)$. *(Lesson 3-2)* **−24xy**

Open-Ended Assessment

Modeling Have students cut out an irregular figure. Then have them cut the figure into smaller figures for which they can find the area. Then use these areas to determine the area of the irregular figure.

Assessment Options

Quiz (Lessons 10-7 and 10-8) is available on p. 604 of the *Chapter 10 Resource Masters.*

Answers

21. **Sample answer:** Separate the area into a rectangle and a trapezoid.

22. **Sample answer: 62,500 mi²**

23. **68,679 mi²**

25. You can use polygons to find the area of an irregular figure by finding the area of each individual polygon and then finding the total area of the irregular figure. Answers should include the following.

  •

  • To find the area of the irregular figure shown above, the figure can be separated into two rectangles and a triangle.

34.

Vocabulary and Concept Check

Vocabulary and Concept Check

- This alphabetical list of vocabulary terms in Chapter 10 includes a page reference where each term was introduced.
- **Assessment** A vocabulary review/test for Chapter 10 is available on p. 602 of the *Chapter 10 Resource Masters*.

Lesson-by-Lesson Review

For each lesson,
- the main ideas are summarized,
- additional examples review concepts, and
- practice exercises are provided.

Vocabulary PuzzleMaker

ELL The Vocabulary PuzzleMaker software improves students' mathematics vocabulary using four puzzle formats—crossword, scramble, word search using a word list, and word search using clues. Students can work on a computer screen or from a printed handout.

MindJogger Videoquizzes

ELL MindJogger Videoquizzes provide an alternative review of concepts presented in this chapter. Students work in teams in a game show format to gain points for correct answers. The questions are presented in three rounds.

Round 1 Concepts (5 questions)
Round 2 Skills (4 questions)
Round 3 Problem Solving (4 questions)

adjacent angles (p. 493)	diameter (p. 533)	regular polygon (p. 529)
alternate exterior angles (p. 492)	dilation (p. 512)	rhombus (p. 514)
alternate interior angles (p. 492)	exterior angles (p. 492, 531)	rotation (p. 506)
altitude (p. 520)	interior angles (pp. 492, 528)	rotational symmetry (p. 505)
base (p. 520)	line symmetry (p. 505)	supplementary (p. 494)
bilateral symmetry (p. 505)	line of symmetry (pp. 505, 506)	tessellation (p. 532)
center (p. 533)	parallel lines (p. 492)	transformation (p. 506)
circle (p. 533)	parallelogram (p. 514)	translation (p. 506)
circumference (p. 533)	perpendicular lines (p. 494)	transversal (p. 492)
complementary (p. 493)	pi (p. 533)	trapezoid (p. 514)
congruent (p. 500)	polygon (p. 527)	turn symmetry (p. 505)
corresponding angles (p. 492)	quadrilateral (p. 513)	vertical angles (p. 493)
corresponding parts (p. 500)	radius (p. 533)	
diagonal (p. 528)	reflection (p. 506)	

Choose the correct term to complete each sentence.

1. Two angles are (complementary, <u>supplementary</u>) if the sum of their measures is 180°.
2. A (<u>rhombus</u>, trapezoid) has four congruent sides.
3. In congruent triangles, the (<u>corresponding angles</u>, adjacent angles) are congruent.
4. In a (<u>rotation</u>, translation), a figure is turned around a fixed point.
5. A polygon in which all sides are congruent is called (equiangular, <u>equilateral</u>).

Lesson-by-Lesson Review

10-1 Angle Relationships

See pages 492–497.

Concept Summary

- When two parallel lines are cut by a transversal, the corresponding angles, the alternate interior angles, and the alternate exterior angles are congruent.
- Two angles are complementary if the sum of their measures is 90°.
- Two angles are supplementary if the sum of their measures is 180°.

Example In the figure at the right, $\ell \parallel m$ and t is a transversal. If $m\angle 1 = 109°$, find $m\angle 7$.

Since $\angle 1$ and $\angle 7$ are alternate exterior angles, they are congruent. So, $m\angle 7 = 109°$.

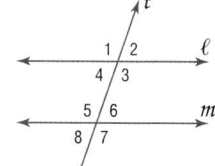

Exercises Use the figure shown to find the measure of each angle. *See Example 1 on page 493.*

6. $\angle 5$ **109°**   7. $\angle 3$ **109°**   8. $\angle 2$ **71°**   9. $\angle 6$ **71°**

FOLDABLES™ Study Organizer

For more information about Foldables, see *Teaching Mathematics with Foldables.*

Have students reexamine their Foldables to make sure all the information they have included about two-dimensional figures is correct. Suggest that they refer to their Foldables if needed when working through the Study Guide exercises.

10-2 *Congruent Triangles*

See pages
500–504.

Concept Summary

- Figures that have the same size and shape are congruent.
- The corresponding parts of congruent triangles are congruent.

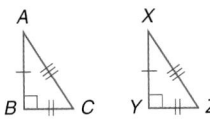

$\triangle ABC = \triangle XYZ$

Example Use $\triangle ABC$ and $\triangle XYZ$ above to complete each congruence statement.

$\angle B \cong$ ___?___ $\overline{YZ} \cong$ ___?___

B corresponds to Y, so $\angle B \cong \angle Y$.

$\overline{YZ}$ corresponds to $\overline{BC}$, so $\overline{YZ} \cong \overline{BC}$.

Exercises Complete each congruence statement if $\triangle FGH \cong \triangle QRS$.
See Example 2 on page 501.

10. $\angle F \cong$ ___?___ $\angle Q$ 11. $\angle S \cong$ ___?___ $\angle H$ 12. $\angle R \cong$ ___?___ $\angle G$

13. $\overline{GH} \cong$ ___?___ $\overline{RS}$ 14. $\overline{HF} \cong$ ___?___ $\overline{SQ}$ 15. $\overline{RQ} \cong$ ___?___ $\overline{GF}$

10-3 *Transformations on the Coordinate Plane*

See pages
506–511.

Concept Summary

- Three types of transformations are translations, reflections, and rotations.

Examples **1** The vertices of $\triangle JKL$ are $J(1, 2)$, $K(3, 2)$, and $L(1, -1)$. Graph the triangle and its image after a translation 3 units left and 2 units up.

This translation can be written as $(-3, 2)$.

vertex	3 left, 2 up	translation
$J(1, 2)$ +	$(-3, 2)$ →	$J'(-2, 4)$
$K(3, 2)$ +	$(-3, 2)$ →	$K'(0, 4)$
$L(1, -1)$ +	$(-3, 2)$ →	$L'(-2, 1)$

2 The vertices of figure $ABCD$ are $A(1, -3)$, $B(4, -3)$, $C(1, -1)$, and $D(-2, -1)$. Graph the figure and its image after a reflection over the x-axis.

Use the same x-coordinate and multiply the y-coordinate by -1.

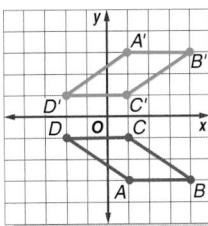

vertex		reflection
$A(1, -3)$ →	$(1, -3 \cdot -1)$ →	$A'(1, 3)$
$B(4, -3)$ →	$(4, -3 \cdot -1)$ →	$B'(4, 3)$
$C(1, -1)$ →	$(1, -1 \cdot -1)$ →	$C'(1, 1)$
$D(-2, -1)$ →	$(-2, -1 \cdot -1)$ →	$D'(-2, 1)$

Chapter 10 Study Guide and Review **545**

Answers

16.

17.

18.

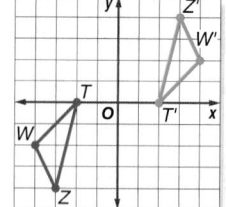

Example 3 A triangle has vertices $T(-2, 0)$, $W(-4, -2)$, and $Z(-3, -4)$. Graph the triangle and its image after a rotation of 180° about the origin.

Multiply both coordinates of each point by -1.

vertex		rotation
$T(-2, 0)$	$\rightarrow$	$T'(2, 0)$
$W(-4, -2)$	$\rightarrow$	$W'(4, 2)$
$Z(-3, -4)$	$\rightarrow$	$Z'(3, 4)$

Exercises   Graph each figure and its image.
See Examples 1–3 on pages 507–509. **16–18. See margin.**

16. The vertices of a rectangle are $C(0, 2)$, $D(2, 0)$, $F(-1, -3)$, and $G(-3, -1)$. The rectangle is translated 4 units right and two units down.

17. The vertices of a triangle are $H(-1, 4)$, $I(-4, -2)$, and $J(-2, -1)$. The triangle is reflected over the y-axis.

18. A triangle has vertices $N(1, 3)$, $P(3, 0)$, and $Q(1, -1)$. The triangle is rotated 90° clockwise.

10-4 Quadrilaterals

See pages 513–517.

Concept Summary

- The sum of the angle measures of a quadrilateral is 360°.
- A trapezoid, parallelogram, rhombus, square, and rectangle are examples of quadrilaterals.

Example   Find the value of x. Then find the missing angle measures.

$x + 2x + 96 + 87 = 360$ Angles of a quadrilateral
$3x + 183 = 360$ Combine like terms.
$3x = 177$ Simplify.
$x = 59$ Divide each side by 3.

The value of x is 59. So, the missing angle measures are 59° and 2(59) or 118°

Exercises   Find the value of x. Then find the missing angle measures.
See Example 1 on page 514. **20. 64; 64°; 128°**

19. 112; 112°   **20.**   **21.** 70; 70°; 70°

10-5 Area: Parallelograms, Triangles, and Trapezoids

See pages 520–525.

Concept Summary

- Area of a parallelogram: $A = bh$
- Area of a triangle: $A = \frac{1}{2}bh$
- Area of a trapezoid: $A = \frac{1}{2}h(a + b)$

Example Find the area of the trapezoid.

$A = \frac{1}{2}h(a + b)$ Area of a trapezoid

$A = \frac{1}{2}(1.8)(2 + 5)$ Substitution

$A = \frac{1}{2} \cdot 1.8 \cdot 7$ Add 2 and 5.

$A = 6.3$ The area of the trapezoid is 6.3 square centimeters.

Exercises Find the area of each figure. *See Examples 1–3 on pages 520–523.*

22. **117 in²**

23. **11 yd²**

24. **42.47 m²**

10-6 Polygons

See pages 527–531.

Concept Summary

- Polygons can be classified by the number of sides they have.
- If a polygon has n sides, then the sum of the degree measures of the interior angles of the polygon is $(n - 2)180$.

Example Classify the polygon. Then find the sum of the measures of the interior angles.

The polygon has 5 sides. It is a pentagon.

$(n - 2)180 = (5 - 2)180$ Replace n with 5.

$\quad\quad\quad\quad = 3(180)$ or 540   Simplify.

The sum of the measures of the angles is 540.

Exercises Classify each polygon. Then find the sum of the measures of the interior angles. *See Examples 1 and 2 on page 528.*

25. **hexagon; 720°**

26. **heptagon; 900°**

27. **decagon; 1440°**

Study Guide and Review

Chapter 10

For More ...
• Extra Practice, see pages 747–750.
• Mixed Problem Solving, see page 76

Answers (p. 549)

1a.

1b.

1c.
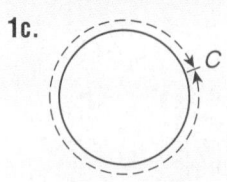

2. Whereas the sum of complementary angles is 90°, the sum of supplementary angles is 180°.

10.

D' (-1, 3); E' (-4, 4);
F' (-4, -2); G' (-1, -1)

11.

E' (-1, -2); F' (-1, -4);
G' (-3, -2); H' (-5, -4)

10-7 Circumference and Area: Circles

See pages 533–538.

Concept Summary
• The circumference C of a circle with radius r is given by $C = 2\pi r$.
• The area A of a circle with radius r is given by $A = \pi r^2$.

Example Find the circumference and area of the circle. Round to the nearest tenth.

15 m

$C = 2\pi r$ Circumference of a circle
$C = 2 \cdot \pi \cdot 7.5$ Replace r with 7.5.
$C \approx 47.1$ The circumference is about 47.1 inches.

$A = \pi r^2$ Area of a circle
$A = \pi \cdot 7.5^2$ Replace r with 7.5.
$A = \pi \cdot 56.25$ Evaluate 7.5^2.
$A \approx 176.7$ The area is about 176.7 square meters.

Exercises Find the circumference and area of each circle. Round to the nearest tenth. *See Examples 1 and 3 on pages 534 and 535.*

28. 5 cm — 31.4 cm; 78.5 cm²

29. 2.1 m — 13.2 m; 13.9 m²

30. 18 ft — 56.5 ft; 254.5 ft²

10-8 Area: Irregular Figures

See pages 539–543.

Concept Summary
• To find the area of an irregular figure, separate the irregular figure into figures whose areas you know how to find.

Example Find the area of the figure.

5 cm
3 cm
3 cm

Area of Parallelogram	Area of Square
$A = bh$	$A = s^2$
$A = 3(5)$ or 15	$A = 3^2$ or 9

The area of the figure is $15 + 9$ or 24 square centimeters.

Exercises Find the area of each figure. Round to the nearest tenth, if necessary. *See Example 1 on page 540.*

31. 7 in.; 7 in.; 6 in.; 16 in. — 118 in²

32. 11 m; 9.4 m; 5.2 m — 76.1 m²

33. 34 cm; 15 cm — 863.4 cm²

Vocabulary and Concepts

1. **Draw** and label a diagram that represents each of the following. **1–2. See margin.**
   a. congruent triangles   b. quadrilateral   c. circumference

2. **Compare** and **contrast** complementary and supplementary angles.

Skills and Applications

In the figure at the right, $a \parallel b$, and c is a transversal. If $m\angle 5 = 58°$, find the measure of each angle.

3. $\angle 6$ **58°**   4. $\angle 7$ **122°**   5. $\angle 4$ **58°**   6. $\angle 3$ **122°**

Complete each congruence statement if $\triangle MNO \cong \triangle PRS$.

7. $\angle P \cong$ __?__ $\angle M$ 8. $\overline{RS} \cong$ __?__ $\overline{NO}$ 9. $\angle MNO \cong$ __?__ $\angle PRS$

Find the coordinates of the vertices of each figure after the given transformation. Then graph the transformation image. 10–11. See margin.

10. reflection over the y-axis

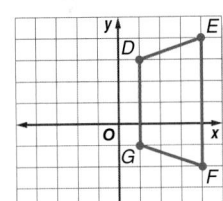

11. rotation of 90° clockwise

ALGEBRA   **Find the value of x. Then find the missing angle measure.**

12.   **106°**

13.   **83°; 72°; 165°**

Find the area of each figure described.

14. triangle: base, 21 ft.; height, 16 ft   **168 ft²**

15. parallelogram: base, 7 ft; height, 2.5 ft   **17.5 ft²**

Classify each polygon. Find the sum of the measures of the interior angles.

16.   **hexagon; 720°**

17.   **octagon; 1080°**

Find the area and circumference of each circle. Round to the nearest tenth.

18. The radius is 3 miles. **28.3 mi²; 18.8 mi**

19. The diameter is 10 inches. **78.5 in²; 31.4 in.**

20. **STANDARDIZED TEST PRACTICE**   What is the diameter of a circle if its circumference is 54.8 meters? Round to the nearest tenth. **C**

   (A) 8.7 m   (B) 15.6 m   (C) 17.4 m   (D) 34.9 m

Portfolio Suggestion

Introduction When finding the area of an irregular figure, there may be multiple ways to divide the figure.

Ask Students to pick an irregular figure from their work in this chapter and show at least two ways of subdividing it. Compare the ways based on number of formulas needed. Have them place their drawings and comparisons in their portfolios.

Assessment Options

Vocabulary Test A vocabulary review/test for Chapter 10 can be found on p. 602 of the *Chapter 10 Resource Masters.*

Chapter Tests There are six Chapter 10 Tests and an Open-Ended Assessment task available in the *Chapter 10 Resource Masters.*

Chapter 10 Tests			
Form	**Type**	**Level**	**Pages**
1	MC	basic	589–590
2A	MC	average	591–592
2B	MC	average	593–594
2C	FR	average	595–596
2D	FR	average	597–598
3	FR	advanced	599–600

MC = multiple-choice questions
FR = free-response questions

Open-Ended Assessment

Performance tasks for Chapter 10 can be found on p. 601 of the *Chapter 10 Resource Masters,* along with a sample scoring rubric for these tasks on p. A27.

ExamView® Pro

Use the networkable **ExamView® Pro** to:

- Create **multiple versions** of tests.
- Create **modified** tests for *Inclusion* students.
- **Edit** existing questions and **add** your own questions.
- Use built-in **state curriculum correlations** to create tests aligned with state standards.
- Change **English** tests to **Spanish** and vice versa.

These two pages contain practice questions in the various formats that can be found on the most frequently given standardized tests.

A practice answer sheet for these two pages can be found on page A1 of the *Chapter 10 Resource Masters*.

Standardized Test Practice
Student Recording Sheet, p. A1

Part 1 Multiple Choice

Select the best answer from the choices given and fill in the corresponding oval.

1 Ⓐ Ⓑ Ⓒ Ⓓ   4 Ⓐ Ⓑ Ⓒ Ⓓ   7 Ⓐ Ⓑ Ⓒ Ⓓ

2 Ⓐ Ⓑ Ⓒ Ⓓ   5 Ⓐ Ⓑ Ⓒ Ⓓ   8 Ⓐ Ⓑ Ⓒ Ⓓ

3 Ⓐ Ⓑ Ⓒ Ⓓ   6 Ⓐ Ⓑ Ⓒ Ⓓ   9 Ⓐ Ⓑ Ⓒ Ⓓ

Part 2 Short Response/Grid In

Solve the problem and write your answer in the blank.

For Questions 10, 12, and 17, also enter your answer by writing each number or symbol in a box. Then fill in the corresponding oval for that number or symbol.

10 _____ (grid in)

11 _____

12 _____ (grid in)

13 _____

14 _____

15 _____

16 _____

17 _____ (grid in)

18 _____

19 _____

Part 3 Extended Response

Record your answers for Question 20 on the back of this paper.

Additional Practice

See pp. 607–608 of the *Chapter 10 Resource Masters* for additional standardized test practice.

Part 1 Multiple Choice

Record your answers on the answer sheet provided by your teacher or on a sheet of paper.

1. Which expression is equivalent to $\frac{5^5}{5^3}$? (Lessons 4-2 and 4-7) **B**

Ⓐ 5^{-2} Ⓑ 5^2 Ⓒ 5^8 Ⓓ 5^{15}

2. The rectangles shown below are similar. Which proportion can be used to find x? (Lesson 6-2) **D**

Ⓐ $\frac{x}{3} = \frac{4}{16}$ Ⓑ $\frac{3}{16} = \frac{4}{x}$

Ⓒ $\frac{16}{3} = \frac{x}{4}$ Ⓓ $\frac{16}{4} = \frac{x}{3}$

3. Suppose 2% of the containers made by a manufacturer are defective. If 750 of the containers are inspected, how many can be expected *not* to be defective? (Lesson 6-9) **C**

Ⓐ 150   Ⓑ 730   Ⓒ 735   Ⓓ 748

4. Lawanda plans to paint each side of a cube either white or blue so that when the cube is tossed, the probability that the cube will land on a blue side is $\frac{1}{3}$. How many sides of the cube should she paint blue? (Lesson 6-9) **B**

Ⓐ 1   Ⓑ 2   Ⓒ 3   Ⓓ 4

5. In the spreadsheet below, a formula applied to the values in columns A and B results in the values in column C. What is the formula? (Lesson 8-1) **B**

Ⓐ $C = A - B$

Ⓑ $C = A - 2B$

Ⓒ $C = A + B$

Ⓓ $C = A + 2B$

	A	B	C
1	4	0	4
2	5	1	3
3	6	2	2
4	7	3	1

---

6. Triangle *ABC* is a right triangle. What is the length of the hypotenuse? (Lesson 9-5) **C**

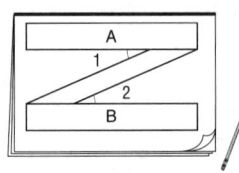

Ⓐ 12 units

Ⓑ 32 units

Ⓒ 60 units

Ⓓ 84 units

7. A graphic artist has designed the logo shown below. If rectangles A and B are parallel, then which statement is true? (Lesson 10-1) **A**

Ⓐ $m\angle 1 - m\angle 2 = 0°$

Ⓑ $m\angle 1 - m\angle 2 = 45°$

Ⓒ $m\angle 1 + m\angle 2 = 90°$

Ⓓ $m\angle 1 + m\angle 2 = 180°$

8. In quadrilateral *ABCD*, $m\angle A = 100°$, $m\angle B = 100°$, and $m\angle C = 90°$. Find $m\angle D$. (Lesson 10-4) **A**

Ⓐ 70°   Ⓑ 85°   Ⓒ 90°   Ⓓ 170°

9. Refer to the figure shown. What is the best estimate of the area of the circle inscribed in the square? (Lesson 10-7) **A**

Ⓐ 7 in²   Ⓑ 9 in²

Ⓒ 19 in²   Ⓓ 28 in²

3 in.

Test-Taking Tip Ⓐ Ⓑ Ⓒ Ⓓ

Question 9
Most standardized tests include any necessary formulas in the test booklet. It helps to be familiar with formulas such as the area of a rectangle and the circumference of a circle, but use any formulas that are given to you.

💿 **ExamView® Pro**

Special banks of standardized test questions similar to those on the SAT, ACT, TIMSS 8, NAEP 8, and Pre-Algebra End-of-Course tests can be found on this CD-ROM.

Preparing for Standardized Tests
For test-taking strategies and more
practice, see pages 771–788.

Part 2 Short Response/Grid In

Record your answers on the answer sheet
provided by your teacher or on a sheet of
paper.

10. If $x = 3$, what is the value of $\frac{14x + 6}{5x - 3}$?
(Lesson 1-2) **4**

11. Refer to the data set shown.

20 20 21 22 24 24 24 26

Which is greater, the median or the mode?
(Lesson 5-8) **mode**

12. A magazine asked 512 students who use
computers if they use e-mail. About 83%
of the students said that they use e-mail.
About how many of these students use
e-mail? (Lesson 6-9) **425**

13. Gracia is finding three consecutive whole
numbers whose sum is 78. She uses the
equation $n + (n + 1) + (n + 2) = 78$. What
expression represents the greatest of the
three numbers? (Lesson 7-2) **n + 2**

14. Solve $4x + 7 < 39$. (Lesson 7-6) **x < 8**

15. What is the slope of the line represented by
the equation $3x + y = 5$? (Lesson 8-4) **−3**

16. Find the coordinates of the vertices for
quadrilateral $WXYZ$ after a translation
of $(-2, -1)$. (Lesson 10-3) **See margin.**

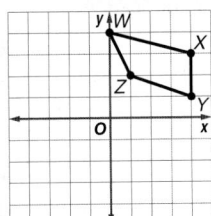

17. These two triangles are congruent. What is
the value of x? (Lesson 9-4) **40**

www.pre-alg.com/standardized_test/ny

18. What name *best* classifies
this quadrilateral?
(Lesson 10-4) **rhombus**

19. The diagram
shows a
kitchen
counter with
an area cut out
for a sink.
What is the
area of the
counter top?
(Lesson 10-8) **42 ft²**

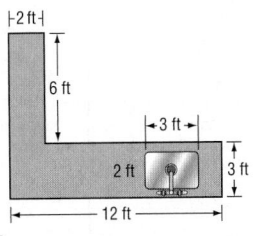

Part 3 Extended Response

Record your answers on a sheet of paper.
Show your work.

20. Triangle JKM
is shown.
(Lesson 10-3)

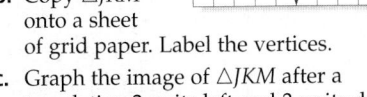

   a. What are the
coordinates
of the vertices
of $\triangle JKM$?

   b. Copy $\triangle JKM$
onto a sheet
of grid paper. Label the vertices.

   c. Graph the image of $\triangle JKM$ after a
translation 2 units left and 3 units down.
Label the translated image $\triangle J'K'M'$.

   d. Graph the image of $\triangle J'K'M'$ after a
reflection over the y-axis. Label the
reflection of $\triangle J'K'M'$ as $\triangle J''K''M''$.

   e. On another sheet of grid paper, graph
$\triangle JKM$. Then graph $\triangle JKM$ after a
reflection over the y-axis. Label the
reflection $\triangle J'K'M'$.

   f. Graph the image of the reflection in
part **e** after a translation 2 units right
and 3 units down. Label the translated
image $\triangle J''K''M''$.

   g. Tell whether the image of $\triangle J''K''M''$ in
part **d** is the same as the image of
$\triangle J''K''M''$ in part **e**. Explain why or why
not. **a–g. See margin.**

Chapter 10 Standardized Test Practice **551**

Evaluating Extended Response Questions

Extended Response questions
are graded by using a multilevel
rubric that guides you in assessing a student's knowledge of a
particular concept.

Goal: Identify the coordinates
and vertices of a triangle/Carry
out a series of translations and
reflections with a triangular
figure.

Sample Scoring Rubric: The following rubric is a sample scoring
device. You may wish to add
more detail to this sample to
meet your individual scoring
needs.

Score	Criteria
4	A correct solution that is supported by well-developed, accurate explanations
3	A generally correct solution, but may contain minor flaws in reasoning or computation
2	A partially correct interpretation and/or solution to the problem
1	A correct solution with no supporting evidence or explanation
0	An incorrect solution indicating no mathematical understanding of the concept or task, or no solution is given

Answers

16. $W'(-2, 3)$, $X'(2, 2)$, $Y'(2, 0)$,
$Z'(-1, 1)$

20a. $J(-3, 4)$, $K(-2, 1)$, $M(-1, 2)$

20b–d.

20e–f.

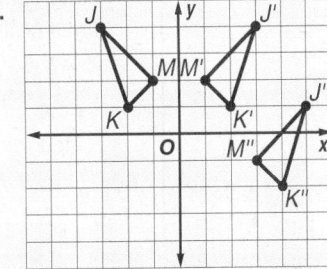

20g. The two images are the same
because the order in which these
operations are performed does not
matter. Thus, the result is the same.

Page 502, Lesson 10-2

1. They have the same size and shape.

2.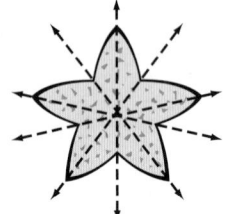

3. $\angle J \cong \angle C$, $\angle K \cong \angle B$, $\angle M \cong \angle G$, $\overline{KM} \cong \overline{BG}$, $\overline{MJ} \cong \overline{GC}$, $\overline{KJ} \cong \overline{BC}$; $\triangle BGC$

4. $\angle C \cong \angle D$, $\angle B \cong \angle B$, $\angle E \cong \angle A$, $\overline{CB} \cong \overline{DB}$, $\overline{BE} \cong \overline{BA}$, $\overline{CE} \cong \overline{DA}$; $\triangle DBA$

Page 505, Algebra Activity

1. **3.**

Page 510, Lesson 10-3

11. $R'(-4, -3)$, $S'(0, -3)$, $T'(-4, 1)$

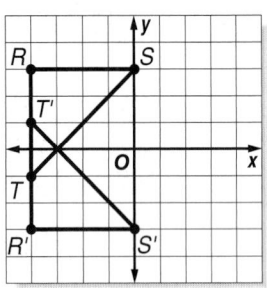

12. $A'(-1, 3)$, $B'(-4, 4)$, $C'(-4, 1)$, $D'(-2, -1)$

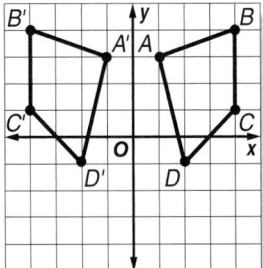

13. $M'(-1, -2)$, $N'(4, -4)$, $O'(3, -2)$, $P'(3, 0)$, $Q'(0, 0)$

14. **15.**

17.

21. Sample answer:

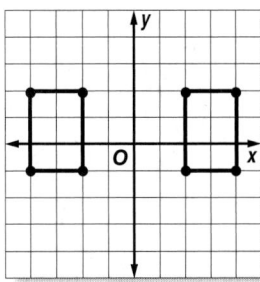

The image of the figure's reflection is the same as the image of its translation to the right 6 units.

Page 512, Algebra Activity

1. The corresponding angles have the same measure.

2. The lengths of the sides of the enlarged trapezoid are twice the length of the corresponding sides of the smaller trapezoid.

3. 2:1; The ratios are the same.

4. See students' work. The results are not the same. By multiplying the coordinates of trapezoid *ABCD* by a scale factor of one-half, the resulting figure is a trapezoid that has sides that are half the size of the original trapezoid.

5. If the scale factor is greater than 1, the image is an enlargement. If the scale factor is less than 1, the image is a reduction.

6. Whereas translations, reflections, and rotations produce congruent figures, dilations produce enlargements or reductions of the figure.

7. $M'(3, 6)$; $N'(6, 0)$

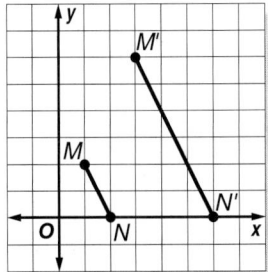

8. $A'(-1, 1)$; $B'(1, \frac{1}{2})$; $C'(1, 2)$

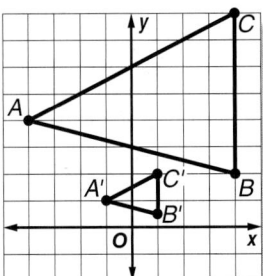

9. $D'(-6, -3)$; $E'(-7.5, -7.5)$; $F'(0, -6)$; $G'(-1.5, -1.5)$

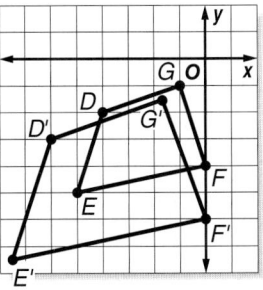

Page 526, Reading Mathematics

2. Sample answer: quad: quadrant— an arc of 90° that is one quarter of a circle.

pent: pentahedron— a three-dimensional solid with five faces.

hex: hexagram— a two-dimensional figure that has equilateral triangles on each side of a regular hexagon.

hept: heptagon— a two-dimensional, closed figure with seven sides.

oct: octal— a number system with a base of 8.

dec: decare— a metric unit of area equal to 0.2471 acre.

3. Sample answer: quad: quadricep— a muscle located on the front of the thigh that is divided into four parts.

pent: pentamerous— divided into or consisting of five parts.

hex: hexahydrate— a chemical compound with six molecules of water.

hept: heptameter— a line of verse consisting of seven metrical feet.

oct: octogenarian— a person whose age is in the eighties.

dec: decasyllabic— consisting of ten syllables or composed of verses of ten syllables.

Page 532, Algebra Activity

1.

2.

3.

4.

5.

6.

Three-Dimensional Figures
Chapter Overview and Pacing

Year-long pacing: pages T20–T21.

LESSON OBJECTIVES

	PACING (days)			
	Regular		**Block**	
	Basic/ Average	Advanced	Basic/ Average	Advanced
11-1 Three Dimensional Figures *(pp. 554–561)* *Preview:* Draw three-dimensional figures using different perspectives and create three-dimensional figures using nets. • Identify three-dimensional figures • Identify diagonals and skew lines.	2 (with 11-1 Preview)	1	1 (with 11-1 Preview)	0.5
11-2 Volume: Prisms and Cylinders *(pp. 562–567)* *Preview:* Investigate volume by creating and comparing containers of various shapes. • Find volumes of prisms. • Find volumes of circular cylinders.	2 (with 11-2 Preview)	1	1 (with 11-2 Preview)	0.5
11-3 Volume: Pyramids and Cones *(pp. 568–572)* • Find volumes of pyramids. • Find volumes of cones.	1	1	0.5	0.5
11-4 Surface Area: Prisms and Cylinders *(pp. 573–577)* • Find surface areas of prisms. • Find surface areas of cylinders.	1	1	0.5	0.5
11-5 Surface Area: Pyramids and Cones *(pp. 578–582)* • Find the surface areas of pyramids. • Find the surface areas of cones.	1	1	0.5	0.5
11-6 Similar Solids *(pp. 583–588)* *Preview:* Investigate similar solids using sugar cubes or centimeter cubes. • Identify similar solids. • Solve problems involving similar solids.	2 (with 11-6 Preview)	1	1 (with 11-6 Preview)	1
11-7 Precision and Significant Digits *(pp. 590–594)* • Describe measurements using precision and significant digits. • Apply precision and significant digits in problem-solving situations.	1	1	0.5	0.5
Study Guide and **Practice Test** *(pp. 595–599)* **Standardized Test Practice** *(pp. 600–601)*	1	1	0.5	0.5
Chapter Assessment	1	1	0.5	0.5
TOTAL	12	9	6	5

*An electronic version of this chapter is available on **StudentWorks**™. This backpack solution CD-ROM allows students instant access to the Student Edition, lesson worksheet pages, and web resources.*

Chapter Resource Manager

Timesaving Tools™

TeacherWorks™
All-In-One Planner and Resource Center
See pages T5 and T21.

CHAPTER 11 RESOURCE MASTERS

Study Guide and Intervention	Practice (Skills and Average)	Reading to Learn Mathematics	Enrichment	Assessment	Prerequisite Skills Workbook	Applications*	Parent and Student Study Guide Workbook	5-Minute Check Transparencies	Interactive Chalkboard	Pre-AlgePASS: Tutorial Plus (lessons)	Materials
609	610–611	612	613				90	11-1	11-1		*Preview:* centimeter cubes, isometric dot paper, unlined paper, scissors, tape
614	615–616	617	618	659		SC 21 GCS 39	91	11-2	11-2		*Preview:* 5 × 8 index cards, tape, rice
619	620–621	622	623				92	11-3	11-3	35	
624	625–626	627	628	659, 661		SC 22 GCS 40	93	11-4	11-4		
629	630–631	632	633				94	11-5	11-5		
634	635–636	637	638	660			95	11-6	11-6	36	*Preview:* sugar cubes, centimeter cubes
639	640–641	642	643	660			96	11-7	11-7		
				645–658, 662–666							

* *Key to Abbreviations:* GCS = Graphing Calculator and Spreadsheet Masters
SC = School-to-Career Masters
SM = Science and Mathematics Lab Manual

ELL Study Guide and Intervention, Skills Practice, Practice, and Parent and Student Study Guide Workbooks are also available in Spanish.

Mathematical Connections and Background

Continuity of Instruction

Prior Knowledge

In Chapter 10, students investigated intersecting lines and the relationships between the angles that are formed. Students identified properties of congruent triangles, drew transformations, and found angle measures of polygons. They learned to find the area of polygons and irregular figures. They explored properties of circles, including the relationships among diameter, circumference, area, and π.

This Chapter

Students will identify three-dimensional figures. They will find the surface area and volume of prisms, cylinders, pyramids, and cones. Students will also identify similar solids, noting that these figures have the same shape and their corresponding linear measures are proportional. Students will explore the concepts of precision and significant digits and apply precision and significant digits in problem-solving situations.

Future Connections

The study of three-dimensional figures, including surface area and volume, will be explored in analytical and solid geometry. Precision measurements and significant digits play important roles in engineering and the sciences.

11-1 Three-Dimensional Figures

A plane is a two-dimensional flat surface that extends in all directions. Intersecting planes can form the edges and vertices of three-dimensional figures or solids. A polyhedron is a solid with flat surfaces that are polygons. Polyhedrons are composed of faces, edges, and vertices and are differentiated by the shape and number of their bases. Skew lines are lines that lie in different planes. They are neither intersecting nor parallel.

11-2 Volume: Prisms and Cylinders

Volume is the measure of space occupied by a solid region. To find the volume of a prism, the area of the base is multiplied by the measure of the height, $V = Bh$. A solid containing several prisms can be broken down into its component prisms. Then the volume of each component can be found and the volumes added. The volume of a cylinder can be determined by finding the area of its circular base, πr^2, and then multiplying by the height of the cylinder.

11-3 Volume: Pyramids and Cones

A pyramid has one-third the volume of a prism with the same base and height. To find the volume of a pyramid, multiply the area of the base by the pyramid's height, and then divide by 3. Simply stated, the formula for the volume of a pyramid is $V = \frac{1}{3}bh$. A cone is a three-dimensional figure with one circular base and a curved surface connecting the base and the vertex. The volume of a cone is one-third the volume of a cylinder with the same base area and height. Like a pyramid, the formula for the volume of a cone is $V = \frac{1}{3}bh$. More specifically, the formula is $V = \frac{1}{3}\pi r^2 h$.

11-4 Surface Area: Prisms and Cylinders

The material needed to cover the surface of a figure is called its surface area. It can be calculated by finding the area of each face and adding them together. To find the surface area of a rectangular prism, for example, the formula $S = 2\ell w + 2\ell w + 2\ell w$ applies. A cylinder, on the other hand, may be unrolled to reveal two circles and a rectangle. Its surface area can be determined by finding the area of the two circles, $2\pi r^2$, and adding it to the area of the rectangle, $2\pi rh$ (the length of the rectangle is the circumference of one of the circles), or $S = 2\pi r^2 + 2\pi rh$.

11-5 Surface Area: Pyramids and Cones

The sides of a pyramid are triangles that intersect at the vertex. These sides are called lateral faces and the height of each is called the slant height. The sum of their areas is the lateral area of a pyramid. The surface area of a square pyramid is the lateral area $\frac{1}{2}bh$ (area of lateral face) times 4 (number of lateral faces), plus the area of the base. The surface area of a cone is the area of its circular base (πr^2) plus its lateral area ($\pi r \ell$, where ℓ is the slant height).

11-6 Similar Solids

Solid figures are considered to be similar if they have the same shape and their corresponding linear measures are proportional. Figures can be tested for similarity by comparing corresponding measures. If the compared ratios are proportional, then the figures are similar solids. Missing measures of similar solids can also be determined by using proportions. Proportional comparisons can be used to solve real-world problems involving relative size, scale models, and scale drawings.

11-7 Precision and Significant Digits

The precision of measurement is the exactness to which a measurement is made. Precision depends on the smallest unit of measure being used, or the precision unit. One way to record a measure is to estimate to the nearest precision unit. A more precise method is to include all of the digits that are actually measured, plus one estimated digit. The digits recorded, called significant digits, indicate the precision of the measurement. There are special rules for determining significant digits. If a number contains a decimal point, the number of significant digits is found by counting from left to right, starting with the first nonzero digit. If the number does not contain a decimal point, the number of significant digits is found by counting the digits from left to right, starting with the first digit and ending with the last nonzero digit.

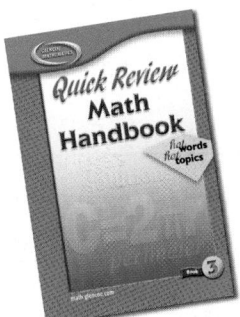

Quick Review Math Handbook

Hot Words includes a glossary of terms while Hot Topics consists of explanations of key mathematical concepts with exercises to test comprehension. This valuable resource can be used as a reference in the classroom or for home study.

Lesson	Hot Topics Section	Lesson	Hot Topics Section
GS 11	7.2, 7.4	11-3	7.7
11-1P	7.6, 7.7	11-4	2.4, 2.6, 7.6
11-1	7.5, 7.6, 7.7	11-5	6.5, 7.6
11-2P	7.7	11-6P, 11-6	8.6
11-2	1.5, 2.4, 7.7	11-7	8.1

GS = Getting Started, P = Preview

 Additional mathematical information and teaching notes are available at www.pre-alg.com/key_concepts.

D A I L Y
INTERVENTION and Assessment

Key to Abbreviations:
TWE = Teacher Wraparound Edition; CRM = Chapter Resource Masters

	Type	Student Edition	Teacher Resources	Technology/Internet
INTERVENTION	Ongoing	Prerequisite Skills, pp. 553, 561, 567, 572, 577, 582, 588 Practice Quiz 1, p. 572 Practice Quiz 2, p. 588	5-Minute Check Transparencies Quizzes, *CRM*, pp. 659–660 Mid-Chapter Test, *CRM*, p. 661 Study Guide and Intervention, *CRM*, pp. 609, 614, 619, 624, 629, 634, 639	Pre-AlgePASS: Tutorial Plus, Lessons 35 and 36 www.pre-alg.com/ self_check_quiz www.pre-alg.com/ extra_examples
	Mixed Review	pp. 561, 567, 572, 577, 582, 588, 594	Cumulative Review, *CRM*, p. 662	
	Error Analysis	Find the Error, pp. 565, 592	Find the Error, *TWE*, pp. 565, 592 Unlocking Misconceptions, *TWE*, pp. 557, 579, 591	
ASSESSMENT	Standardized Test Practice	pp. 561, 564, 566, 567, 572, 577, 582, 588, 594, 600–601	*TWE*, pp. 600–601 Standardized Test Practice, *CRM*, pp. 663–664	Standardized Test Practice CD-ROM www.pre-alg.com/ standardized_test
	Open-Ended Assessment	Writing in Math, pp. 561, 567, 571, 577, 582, 588, 594 Open Ended, pp. 559, 565, 570, 575, 580, 586, 592 Standardized Test, p. 601	Speaking: *TWE*, pp. 567, 576 Writing: *TWE*, pp. 572, 588 Modeling: *TWE*, pp. 561, 582, 594 Open-Ended Assessment, *CRM*, p. 657	
	Chapter Assessment	Study Guide, pp. 595–598 Practice Test, p. 599	Multiple-Choice Tests (Forms 1, 2A, 2B), *CRM*, pp. 645–650 Free-Response Tests (Forms 2C, 2D, 3), *CRM*, pp. 651–656 Vocabulary Test/Review, *CRM*, p. 658	ExamView® Pro (see below) MindJogger Videoquizzes www.pre-alg.com/ vocabulary_review www.pre-alg.com/chapter_test

For more information on Yearly ProgressPro, see p. 432.

For more information on Yearly ProgressPro, see p. 432.

Pre-Algebra Lesson	Yearly ProgressPro Skill Lesson
11-1	Three-Dimensional Figures
11-2	Volume of Triangular Prisms
11-3	Volume of Pyramids and Cones
11-4	Surface Area of Triangular Prisms
11-5	Surface Area of Pyramids and Cones
11-6	Similar Figures
11-7	Precision and Measurement

ExamView® Pro

Use the networkable **ExamView® Pro** to:
- Create **multiple versions** of tests.
- Create **modified** tests for *Inclusion* students.
- **Edit** existing questions and **add** your own questions.
- Use built-in **state curriculum correlations** to create tests aligned with state standards.
- Change **English** tests to **Spanish** and vice versa.

For more information on Intervention and Assessment, see pp. T8–T11.

Reading and Writing in Mathematics

Glencoe Pre-Algebra provides numerous opportunities to incorporate reading and writing into the mathematics classroom.

Student Edition

- Foldables™ Study Organizer, p. 553
- Reading Mathematics, p. 589
- Concept Check questions require students to verbalize and write about what they have learned in the lesson. (pp. 557, 559, 565, 569, 570, 575, 580, 586, 592)
- Writing in Math questions in every lesson, pp. 561, 567, 571, 577, 582, 588, 594
- Reading Math, pp. 565, 569
- WebQuest, pp. 571, 594

Teacher Wraparound Edition

- Foldables™ Study Organizer, pp. 553, 595
- Study Notebook suggestions, pp. 555, 559, 562, 565, 570, 575, 580, 583, 586, 589, 592
- Modeling activities, pp. 561, 582, 594
- Speaking activities, pp. 567, 576
- Writing activities, pp. 572, 588
- **ELL** Resources, pp. 552, 556, 563, 568, 573, 578, 584, 589, 590, 595

Additional Resources

- Vocabulary Builder worksheets require students to define and give examples for key vocabulary terms as they progress through the chapter (*Chapter 4 Resource Masters*, pp. vii–viii)
- Reading to Learn Mathematics master for each lesson (*Chapter 4 Resource Masters*, pp. 612, 617, 622, 627, 632, 637, 642)
- *Vocabulary PuzzleMaker* software creates crossword, jumble, and word search puzzles using vocabulary lists that you can customize.
- *Teaching Mathematics with Foldables* provides suggestions for promoting cognition and language.
- *Reading and Writing in the Mathematics Classroom*
- *WebQuest and Project Resources*

For more information on Reading and Writing in Mathematics, see pp. T6–T7.

PROJECT CRISS℠ Study Skill

A content frame can help students understand mathematical relationships, especially when a number of new formulas are being learned.

The frame at the right shows a comparison of the formulas for the volumes of rectangular prisms and the volumes of cylinders. From the sketches, students should note that the volumes could both be written as $V = Bh$, where B is the area of the base. Have students include additional figures and formulas in their frame as they read through Chapter 11. Then, allow time for a class discussion so students can compare formulas.

Figure	Sketch	Volume Formula
rectangular prism		$V = \ell \cdot w \cdot h$
cylinder		$V = \pi r^2 h$

CReating **I**ndependence **T**hrough **S**tudent-**O**wned **S**trategies

Chapter 11

Three-Dimensional Figures

What You'll Learn

Have students read over the list of objectives and make a list of any words with which they are not familiar.

Why It's Important

Point out to students that this is only one of many reasons why each objective is important. Others are provided in the introduction to each lesson.

Lesson	NCTM Standards	Local Objectives
11-1 Preview	3, 10	
11-1	3, 6, 8, 9, 10	
11-2 Preview	3, 4, 6, 7, 9	
11-2	1, 2, 3, 4, 6, 8, 9, 10	
11-3	1, 2, 3, 4, 6, 8, 9, 10	
11-4	1, 2, 3, 4, 6, 8, 9, 10	
11-5	1, 2, 3, 4, 6, 8, 9, 10	
11-6 Preview	3, 4, 5, 6, 7, 8, 10	
11-6	1, 2, 3, 4, 6, 8, 9, 10	
11-7	1, 3, 4, 6, 8, 9, 10	

Key to NCTM Standards:

1=Number & Operations, 2=Algebra, 3=Geometry, 4=Measurement, 5=Data Analysis & Probability, 6=Problem Solving, 7=Reasoning & Proof, 8=Communication, 9=Connections, 10=Representation

What You'll Learn

- **Lesson 11-1** Identify three-dimensional figures.
- **Lessons 11-2 and 11-3** Find volumes of prisms, cylinders, pyramids, and cones.
- **Lessons 11-4 and 11-5** Find surface areas of prisms, cylinders, pyramids, and cones.
- **Lesson 11-6** Identify similar solids.
- **Lesson 11-7** Use precision and significant digits to describe measurements.

Key Vocabulary

- polyhedron (p. 556)
- volume (p. 563)
- surface area (p. 573)
- similar solids (p. 584)
- precision (p. 590)

Why It's Important

Three-dimensional figures have special characteristics. These characteristics are important when architects are designing buildings and other three-dimensional structures. *You will investigate the characteristics of architectural structures in Lesson 11-1.*

552 Chapter 11 Three-Dimensional Figures

Vocabulary Builder ⟨ELL⟩

The Key Vocabulary list introduces students to some of the main vocabulary terms included in this chapter. For a more thorough vocabulary list with pronunciations of new words, give students the Vocabulary Builder worksheets found on pages vii and viii of the *Chapter 11 Resource Masters*. Encourage them to complete the definition of each term as they progress through the chapter. You may suggest that they add these sheets to their study notebooks for future reference when studying for the Chapter 11 test.

Getting Started

Getting Started

▶ **Prerequisite Skills** To be successful in this chapter, you'll need to master these skills and be able to apply them in problem-solving situations. Review these skills before beginning Chapter 11.

For Lesson 11-1   Polygons

Determine whether each figure is a polygon. If it is, classify the polygon.
(For review, see Lesson 10-6.) **4. yes; quadrilateral**

1. yes; triangle   **2.** no   **3.** no   **4.**

For Lessons 11-2 through 11-5   Multiplying Rational Numbers

Find each product. *(For review, see Lesson 5-3.)*

5. $8.5 \cdot 2$ **17**

6. $3.2(3.2)$ **10** **102.4**

7. $\frac{1}{2} \cdot 14$ **7**

8. $\frac{1}{2}(6.4)(5)$ **16**

9. $\frac{1}{3}(50)(9.3)$ **155**

10. $\frac{1}{3}\left(\frac{1}{2} \cdot 3 \cdot 8\right)$ **4**

For Lesson 11-6   Proportions

Determine whether each pair of ratios forms a proportion. *(For review, see Lesson 6-2.)*

11. $\frac{3}{8}, \frac{9}{24}$ **yes**

12. $\frac{7}{2}, \frac{14}{6}$ **no**

13. $\frac{18}{32}, \frac{9}{16}$ **yes**

14. $\frac{12}{15}, \frac{4}{5}$ **yes**

15. $\frac{1.2}{5}, \frac{6}{25}$ **yes**

16. $\frac{1.6}{2}, \frac{3.6}{6}$ **no**

FOLDABLES™ Study Organizer

Surface Area and Volume Make this Foldable to help you organize your notes. Begin with a plain piece of 11" × 17" paper.

Step 1 Fold
Fold the paper in thirds lengthwise.

Step 2 Open and Fold
Fold a 2" tab along the short side. Then fold the rest in fourths.

Step 3 Label
Draw lines along folds and label as shown.

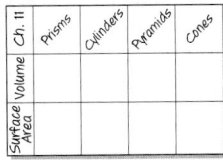

Reading and Writing As you read and study the chapter, write the formulas for surface area and volume and list the characteristics of each three-dimensional figure.

This section provides a review of the basic concepts needed before beginning Chapter 11. Page references are included for additional student help.

Prerequisite Skills in the Getting Ready for the Next Lesson section at the end of each lesson reviews a skill needed in the next lesson.

For Lesson	Prerequisite Skill
11-2	Areas of Triangles (p. 561)
11-3	Multiplying Fractions (p. 567)
11-4	Estimating Products (p. 572)
11-5	Multiplying Rational Numbers (p. 577)
11-6	Proportions (p. 582)
11-7	Rounding Decimals (p. 588)

FOLDABLES™ Study Organizer

For more information about Foldables, see *Teaching Mathematics with Foldables*.

Using Tables to Compare and Contrast In the grid of their table, students take notes, define terms, write formulas, and list characteristics of each three-dimensional figure. Use the data recorded to compare and contrast three-dimensional shapes. When making comparisons in mathematics, first determine what will be compared, then decide what standards will be used for comparison, and then use what is known to find similarities and differences.

A Preview of Lesson 11-1

Getting Started

Objective Draw three-dimensional figures using different perspectives and create three-dimensional figures using nets.

Materials
centimeter cubes, isometric dot paper, unlined paper, scissors, tape

Teaching Tip Use square building blocks to create a figure to demonstrate differing perspectives.

Teach

Activity 1
• Have students try to determine the number of blocks they need to build each figure before they begin. Discuss how they arrived at their answers.
• If students are having difficulty recognizing the different perspectives, encourage them to label their figures "top," "side," and "front."

Answers

1–3. Sample answers are given.

1.

2.

3.

Geometry Activity

A Preview of Lesson 11-1

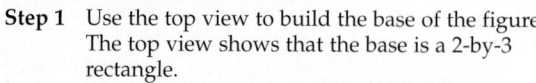
NEW YORK *Performance Indicator* Reinforcement of 7.G.3 Identify the two-dimensional shapes that make up the faces and bases of three-dimensional shapes (prisms, cylinders, cones, and pyramids)

Building Three-Dimensional Figures

Activity 1

Different views of a stack of cubes are shown at the right. A point of view is called a **perspective**. You can build or draw a three-dimensional figure using different perspectives.
When drawing figures, use isometric dot paper.

Step 1 Use the top view to build the base of the figure. The top view shows that the base is a 2-by-3 rectangle.

Step 2 Use the side view to complete the figure. The side view shows that the height of the first row is 1 unit, and the height of the second and third rows is 2 units.

Step 3 Use the front view to check the figure. The front view is a 2-by-2 square. This shows that the overall height and width of the figure is 2 units. So, the figure is correct.

Model 1–9. See margin.
The top view, a side view, and the front view of three-dimensional figures are shown. Use cubes to build each figure. Draw your model on isometric dot paper.

1. top   side   front

2. top   side   front

3. top   side   front

4. top   side   front

5. top   side   front

6. top   side   front

Draw and label the top view, a side view, and the front view for each figure.

7.

8.

9.

Resource Manager

📂 *Teaching Pre-Algebra with Manipulatives*
• p. 143 (student recording sheet)
• p. 16 (master for isometric paper)

Glencoe Mathematics Classroom Manipulative Kit
• isometric dot grid stamp
• centimeter cubes

Activity 2

Suppose you cut a cardboard box along its edges, open it up, and lay it flat. The result is a two-dimensional figure called a net. **Nets** are two-dimensional patterns for three-dimensional figures.

Nets can help you see the regions or *faces* that make up the surface of a figure. So, you can use a net to build a three-dimensional figure.

Step 1 Copy the net on a piece of paper, shading the base as shown.

Step 2 Use scissors to cut out the net.

Step 3 Fold on the dashed lines.

Step 4 Tape the sides together.

Different views of this figure are shown.

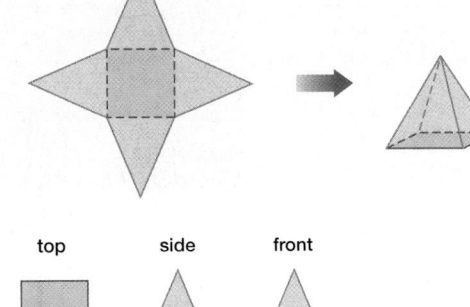

top   side   front

Model 10–15. See pp. 601A–601B.

Copy each net. Then cut out the net and fold on the dashed lines to make a 3-dimensional figure, using the purple areas as the bases. Sketch each figure, and draw and label the top view, a side view, and the front view.

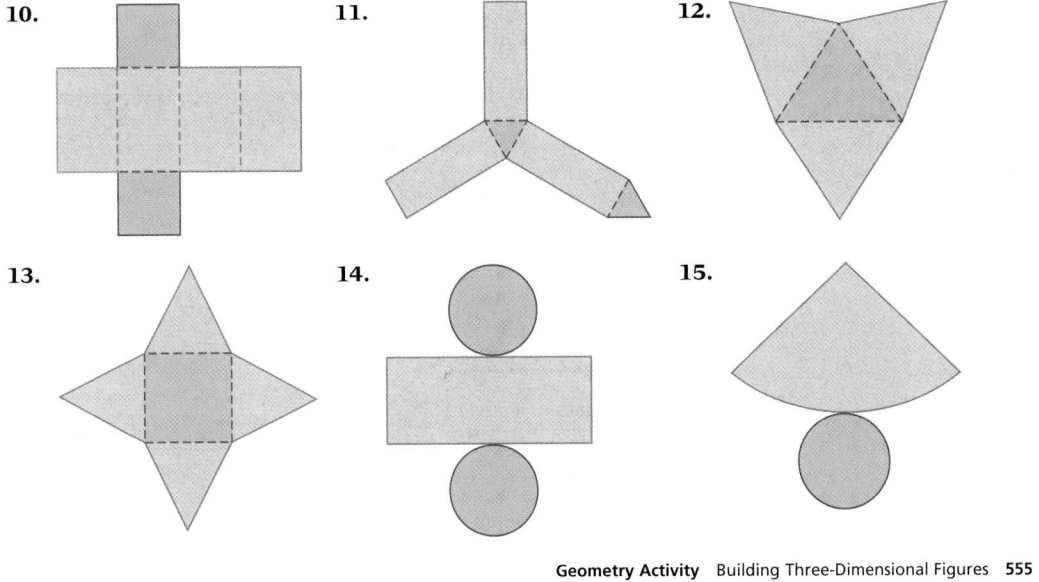

10.   11.   12.

13.   14.   15.

Geometry Activity   Building Three-Dimensional Figures   **555**

Activity 2

- Discuss with students how nets make the study of three-dimensional figures easier. Point out that nets allow for accurate measurements of the figure's faces, which cannot be done with the drawing of the entire figure.
- You may want to have advanced students attempt to make larger scale models of the figures in the exercises.

Assess

In **Exercises 1–9**, students should recognize and be able to build and draw various views of three-dimensional figures.

In **Exercises 10–15**, students should be able to construct three-dimensional figures from nets.

Study Notebook

Have students draw a three-dimensional figure, then draw and label its top, side, and front views in their notebooks.

7. top   side   front

8. top   side   front

9. top   side   front

Answers

4–9. Sample answers are given.

4.

5.   6.

NEW YORK *Performance Indicator* Reinforcement of 7.G.3 Identify the two-dimensional shapes that make up the faces and bases of three-dimensional shapes (prisms, cylinders, cones, and pyramids)

1 Focus

5-Minute Check Transparency 11-1 Use as a quiz or review of Chapter 10.

Mathematical Background notes are available for this lesson on page 552C.

How are 2-dimensional figures related to 3-dimensional figures?

The opening activity questions are repeated on page 612 of the *Chapter 11 Resource Masters*.

Reading to Learn Mathematics, p. 612 — ELL

Pre-Activity   *How are 2-dimensional figures related to 3-dimensional figures?*

Do the activity at the top of page 556 in your textbook. Write your answers below.

a. If you observed the Great Pyramid or the Inner Harbor and Trade Center from directly above, what geometric figure would you see?   square

b. If you stood directly in front of each structure, what geometric figure would you see?   Pyramid, triangle; Trade Center, rectangle

c. Explain how you can see different polygons when looking at the same 3-dimensional figure.   Sample answer: When a three-dimensional figure has faces that are different polygons, the polygon you see depends on your point of view.

Reading the Lesson   1–10. See students' work.

Write a definition and give an example of each new vocabulary word or phrase.

Vocabulary	Definition	Example
1. plane		
2. solid		
3. polyhedron		
4. edge		
5. vertex		
6. face		
7. prism		
8. base		
9. pyramid		
10. skew lines		

Vocabulary
- plane
- solid
- polyhedron
- edge
- vertex
- face
- prism
- base
- pyramid
- skew lines

c. Sample answer: When a three-dimensional figure has faces that are different polygons, the polygon you see depends on your point of view.

Study Tip

Dimensions
A two-dimensional figure has two dimensions, length and width. A three-dimensional figure has three dimensions, length, width, and depth (or height).

What You'll Learn
- Identify three-dimensional figures.
- Identify diagonals and skew lines.

How are 2-dimensional figures related to 3-dimensional figures?

Great Pyramid, Egypt

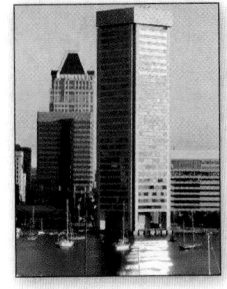
Inner Harbor & Trade Center, Baltimore

a. If you observed the Great Pyramid or the Inner Harbor & Trade Center from directly above, what geometric figure would you see?   **square**

b. If you stood directly in front of each structure, what geometric figure would you see?   **Pyramid, triangle; Trade Center, rectangle**

c. Explain how you can see different polygons when looking at a 3-dimensional figure.

IDENTIFY THREE-DIMENSIONAL FIGURES

A **plane** is a two-dimensional flat surface that extends in all directions. There are different ways that planes may be related in space.

Intersect in a Line   **Intersect in a Point**   **No Intersection**

These are called *parallel planes.*

Intersecting planes can also form three-dimensional figures or **solids**. A **polyhedron** is a solid with flat surfaces that are polygons.

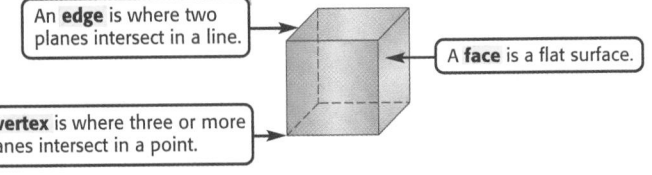

An **edge** is where two planes intersect in a line.

A **face** is a flat surface.

A **vertex** is where three or more planes intersect in a point.

Resource Manager

📁 Workbooks and Reproducible Masters

Chapter 11 Resource Masters
- Study Guide and Intervention, p. 609
- Skills Practice, p. 610
- Practice, p. 611
- Reading to Learn Mathematics, p. 612
- Enrichment, p. 613

Parent and Student Study Guide Workbook, p. 90

📄 Transparencies
5-Minute Check Transparency 11-1
Answer Key Transparencies

💿 Technology
Interactive Chalkboard

A **prism** is a polyhedron with two parallel, congruent faces called **bases**. A **pyramid** is a polyhedron with one base that is any polygon. Its other faces are triangles.

Prisms and pyramids are named by the shape of their bases.

prism
bases

pyramid
base

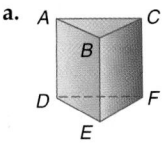
Study Tip

Common Misconception
In a rectangular prism, the bases do not have to be on the top and bottom. Any two parallel rectangles are bases. In a triangular pyramid, any face is a base.

Key Concept
Polyhedrons

Polyhedron	triangular prism	rectangular prism	triangular pyramid	rectangular pyramid
Number of Bases	2	2	1	1
Polygon Base	triangle	rectangle	triangle	rectangle
Figure				

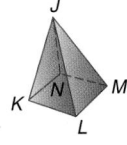
TEACHING TIP

Point out that if the base of a rectangular pyramid is a square, the figure can be called a square pyramid.

Use the labels on the vertices to name a base or a face of a solid.

Example 1 *Identify Prisms and Pyramids*

Identify each solid. Name the bases, faces, edges, and vertices.

a.

This figure has two parallel congruent bases that are triangles, *ABC* and *DEF*, so it is a triangular prism.

faces: *ABC, ADEB, BEFC, CFDA, DEF*

edges: $\overline{AB}, \overline{BC}, \overline{CA}, \overline{AD}, \overline{BE}, \overline{CF}, \overline{DE}, \overline{EF}, \overline{FD}$

vertices: *A, B, C, D, E, F*

b.

This figure has one rectangular base, *KLMN*, so it is a rectangular pyramid.

faces: *JKL, JLM, JMN, JNK, KLMN*

edges: $\overline{JK}, \overline{JL}, \overline{JM}, \overline{JN}, \overline{NK}, \overline{KL}, \overline{LM}, \overline{MN}$

vertices: *J, K, L, M, N*

✔ **Concept Check** How many faces does a cube have? 6

---

2 Teach

Building on Prior Knowledge

In Lesson 10-6, students studied and classified polygons. In this lesson they will use that knowledge to help identify various polyhedrons.

IDENTIFY THREE-DIMENSIONAL FIGURES

In-Class Example   Power Point®

1 Identify each solid. Name the bases, faces, edges, and vertices.

a.

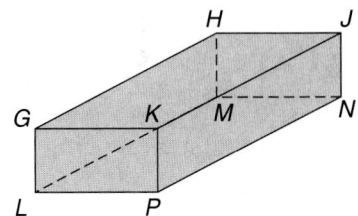

rectangular prism; bases: *GHJK, LMNP* or *GHML, KJNP* or *HJNM, GKPL*; faces: *GHJK, LMNP, GHML, HJNM, JKPN, GKPL*; edges: $\overline{GH}, \overline{HJ}, \overline{JK}, \overline{GK}, \overline{LM}, \overline{MN}, \overline{NP}, \overline{LP}, \overline{GL}, \overline{HM}, \overline{JN}, \overline{KP}$; vertices: *G, H, J, K, L, M, N, P*

b.

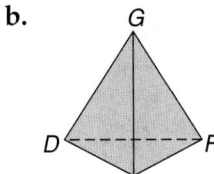

triangular pyramid; any one of the following faces can be a base: *DEF, DEG, DFG, EFG*; edges: $\overline{DE}, \overline{DF}, \overline{DG}, \overline{EF}, \overline{EG}, \overline{FG}$; vertices: *D, E, F, G*

Teaching Tip To help students who have trouble interpreting pictures of three-dimensional figures, use models that correspond to the pictures in the text.

D A I L Y
INTERVENTION

Unlocking Misconceptions

• **Identify Three-Dimensional Figures** Some students may think that parallel lines are skew lines because neither intersect. Point out that skew lines lie in different planes and parallel lines lie in the same plane.

2 Identify a diagonal and name all segments that are skew to it.

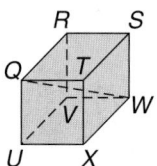

$\overline{QW}$; $\overline{UV}$, $\overline{UX}$, $\overline{RS}$, $\overline{ST}$, $\overline{TX}$, $\overline{RV}$

3 Refer to Example 3 to answer the following.

a. Find the area of the ground floor if each unit on the drawing represents 55 feet. **90,750 square feet**

b. How many floors are in the office building if each floor is 12 feet high? Assume each unit on the drawing represents 40 feet. **10 floors**

Teaching Tip Have students make a paper model of the figure, then draw the figure from the various angles.

This CD-ROM is a customizable Microsoft® Power-Point® presentation that includes:

- Step-by-step, dynamic solutions of each In-Class Example from the Teacher Wraparound Edition
- Additional, Your Turn exercises for each example
- The 5-Minute Check Transparencies
- Hot links to Glencoe Online Study Tools

DIAGONALS AND SKEW LINES **Skew lines** are lines that are neither intersecting nor parallel. They lie in different planes. Line ℓ along the bridge below and line m along the river beneath it are skew.

The river is not parallel to the bridge and it does not touch the top of the bridge.

We can use rectangular prisms to show skew lines. $\overline{EC}$ is a *diagonal* of the prism at the right because it joins two vertices that have no faces in common. $\overline{EC}$ is skew to $\overline{AD}$.

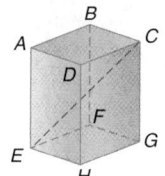

Example 2 *Identify Diagonals and Skew Lines*

Identify a diagonal and name all segments that are skew to it.

$\overline{MT}$ is a diagonal because vertex M and vertex T do not intersect any of the same faces.

$\overline{LP}$, $\overline{PN}$, $\overline{LQ}$, $\overline{NS}$, $\overline{QR}$, and $\overline{RS}$ are skew to $\overline{MT}$.

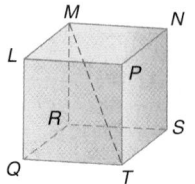

Example 3 *Analyze Real-World Drawings*

ARCHITECTURE An architect's sketch shows the plans for a new office building. Each unit on the drawing represents 40 feet.

a. Draw a top view and find the area of the ground floor.

The drawing is 6×5, so the actual dimensions are $6(40) \times 5(40)$ or 240 feet by 200 feet.

$A = \ell \cdot w$ Formula for area

$A = 240 \cdot 200$ or 48,000

The area of the ground floor is 48,000 square feet.

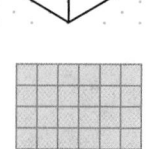

top view

b. How many floors are in the office building if each floor is 15 feet high?

You can see from the side view that the height of the building is 3 units.

total height: 3 units $\times$ 40 feet per unit = 120 feet

number of floors: 120 feet $\div$ 15 feet per floor = 8 floors

There are 8 floors in the office building.

side view

DAILY INTERVENTION **Differentiated Instruction**

- **Visual/Spatial** Provide students with scissors, cardboard or heavy paper, and tape. Have them make a rectangular prism, square pyramid, triangular prism, triangular pyramid, and intersecting planes. Have them assign letters to various points on the figures and identify skew lines.

Check for Understanding

Concept Check
1. **Describe** the number of planes that form a square pyramid and discuss how the planes form edges and vertices of the pyramid. **See margin.**

2. **OPEN ENDED** Choose a solid object from your home and give an example and a nonexample of edges that form skew lines. Include drawings of your example and nonexample. **See margin.**

Guided Practice

Identify each solid. Name the bases, faces, edges, and vertices.

GUIDED PRACTICE KEY	
Exercises	Examples
3, 4	1
5, 6	2
7, 8	3

3.

4.

3–4. See margin.

For Exercises 5 and 6, use the rectangular pyramid shown at the right.

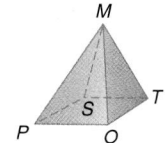

5. State whether $\overline{MP}$ and $\overline{TM}$ are *parallel, skew,* or *intersecting.* **intersecting**

6. Identify all lines skew to $\overline{PO}$. **$\overline{MS}, \overline{MT}$**

Application
BUILDING The sketch at the right shows the plans for porch steps.

7. Draw and label the top, front, and side views. **See pp. 601A–601B.**

8. If each unit on the drawing represents 4 inches, what is the height of the steps in feet? **$1\frac{1}{3}$ ft**

Practice and Apply

Homework Help	
For Exercises	See Examples
9–12, 19–21	1
13–16, 22–25	2
17, 18	3
Extra Practice See page 750.	

Identify each solid. Name the bases, faces, edges, and vertices.

9. 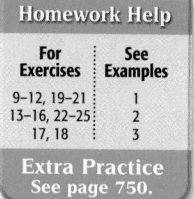 9–12. See pp. 601A–601B.

10.

11.

12.

Study Notebook

Have students—
• add the definitions/examples of the vocabulary terms to their Vocabulary Builder worksheets for Chapter 11.
• write a paragraph describing the differences between prisms and pyramids.
• include any other item(s) that they find helpful in mastering the skills in this lesson.

About the Exercises . . .
Organization by Objective
• Identify Three-Dimensional Figures: 9–12
• Diagonals and Skew Lines: 13–16

Odd/Even Assignments
Exercises 9–12 are structured so that students practice the same concepts whether they are assigned odd or even problems.

Alert! Exercise 18 requires the Internet or other reference materials.

Assignment Guide
Basic: 9–17 odd, 19, 23, 25, 26–44
Average: 9–25 odd, 26–44
Advanced: 10–22 even, 24, 26–40 (Optional: 41–44)

Answers

1. Five planes form a square pyramid because the solid has five faces. An edge is formed when two planes intersect; a vertex is formed when three or four planes intersect.

2. Sample answer: On a television, the top front edge and a bottom side edge form skew lines. The top and bottom front edges do not form skew lines because they are parallel. See students' drawings.

3. triangular pyramid; any one of the following faces can be considered a base: RST, QRS, QST, QRT; $\overline{QR}$, $\overline{QS}$, $\overline{QT}$, $\overline{RT}$, $\overline{RS}$, $\overline{ST}$; Q, R, S, T

4. rectangular prism; $ABCD$, $EHGF$ or $ABHE$, $DCGF$ or $ADFE$, $BCGH$; $ABCD$, $EHGF$, $ABHE$, $DCGF$, $ADFE$, $BCGH$; $\overline{AB}$, $\overline{BC}$, $\overline{CD}$, $\overline{DA}$, $\overline{EF}$, $\overline{FG}$, $\overline{GH}$, $\overline{HE}$, $\overline{AE}$, $\overline{BH}$, $\overline{CG}$, $\overline{DF}$; A, B, C, D, E, F, G, H

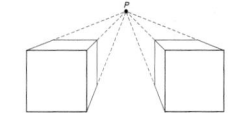
560 Chapter 11 Three-Dimensional Figures

For Exercises 13–16, use the rectangular prism.

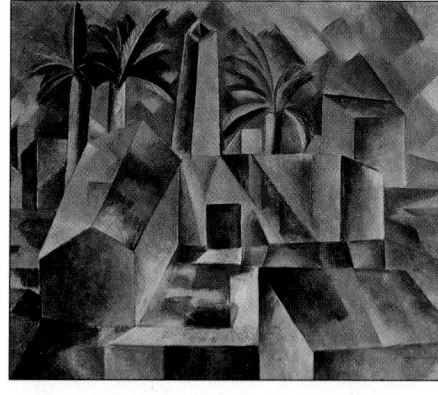

13. Identify a diagonal. $\overline{WR}$

14. Name four segments skew to $\overline{QR}$.

14. $\overline{WP}$, $\overline{ZS}$, $\overline{WX}$, $\overline{ZY}$

15. State whether $\overline{WR}$ and $\overline{XY}$ are parallel, skew, or intersecting. **skew**

16. Name a segment that does *not* intersect the plane that contains $WXYZ$. **Sample answer:** $\overline{PS}$

COMICS For Exercises 17 and 18, use the comic below.
SHOE

17. Which view of the Washington Monument is shown? **top**

18. **RESEARCH** Use the Internet or another source to find a photograph of the Washington Monument. Draw and label the top, side, and front views. **See pp. 601A–601B.**

ART For Exercises 19 and 20, refer to Picasso's painting *The Factory, Horta de Ebro* shown at the right.

19. Describe the polyhedrons shown in the painting.

19. rectangular and pentagonal prisms

20. Explain how the artist portrayed three-dimensional objects on a flat canvas. **See margin.**

21. **RESEARCH** Find other examples of art in which polyhedrons are shown. Describe the polyhedrons. **See students' work.**

Determine whether each statement is *sometimes*, *always*, or *never* true. Explain. 22–25. See margin for explanations.

22. Any two planes intersect in a line. **sometimes**

23. Two planes intersect in a single point. **never**

24. A pyramid contains a diagonal. **never**

25. Three planes do not intersect in a point. **sometimes**

26. **CRITICAL THINKING** Use isometric dot paper to draw a three-dimensional figure in which the front and top views have a line of symmetry but the side view does not. Then discuss whether the figure has bilateral symmetry or rotational symmetry. **See pp. 601A–601B.**

560 Chapter 11 Three-Dimensional Figures

More About . . .

Art

Pablo Picasso (1881–1973) was one of the developers of a movement in art called *Cubism*. Cubist paintings are characterized by their angular shapes and sharp edges.

Source: World Wide Arts Resources

Answers

20. Sample answer: using angles and shading to portray depth

22. Two planes may be parallel and not intersect at all.

23. Only three or more planes can intersect in a single point.

24. Every pair of vertices on a pyramid has a common edge.

25. Three planes may intersect in a line. Or, the planes may be parallel and not intersect at all.

27. WRITING IN MATH   Answer the question that was posed at the beginning of the lesson. **See margin.**

How are 2-dimensional figures related to 3-dimensional figures?

Include the following in your answer:
- an explanation of the difference between 2-dimensional figures and 3-dimensional figures, and
- a description of how 2-dimensional figures can form a 3-dimensional figure.

28. Determine the intersection of the three planes at the right. **A**
- Ⓐ point
- Ⓑ line
- Ⓒ plane
- Ⓓ no intersection

29. Which figure does *not* have the same dimensions as the other figures? **D**

Ⓐ   Ⓑ

Ⓒ   Ⓓ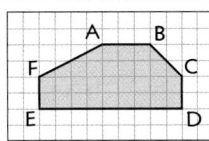

Maintain Your Skills

Mixed Review

30. Find the area of *ABCDEF* if each unit represents 1 square centimeter. *(Lesson 10-10)* **30 cm²**

31. Find the circumference and the area of a circle whose radius is 6 centimeters. Round to the nearest tenth. *(Lesson 10-9)* **37.7 cm; 113.1 cm²**

Use a calculator to find each ratio to the nearest ten thousandth. *(Lesson 9-7)*

32. sin 35° **0.5736**   **33.** sin 30° **0.5000**   **34.** cos 280° **0.1736**

Solve each inequality. Check your solution. *(Lesson 7-4)* **37.** $n > -11$

35. $c + 4 < 12$ **$c < 8$**   **36.** $7 \geq t - 2$ **$t \leq 9$**   **37.** $-26 < n + (-15)$

38. $k + (-4) \geq 3.8$ **$k \geq 7.8$** **39.** $y - \frac{1}{4} < 1\frac{1}{2}$ **$y < 1\frac{3}{4}$**   **40.** $3\frac{1}{5} > a - \frac{3}{10}$ **$a < 3\frac{1}{2}$**

Getting Ready for the Next Lesson

PREREQUISITE SKILL   Find the area of each triangle described.
*(To review **areas of triangles**, see Lesson 10-5.)*

41. base, 4 in.; height, 7 in. **14 in²**   **42.** base, 10 ft; height, 9 ft **45 ft²**

43. base, 6.5 cm; height, 2 cm **6.5 cm²**   **44.** base, 0.4 m; height, 1.3 m **0.26 m²**

Answer

27. Two-dimensional figures form three-dimensional figures. Answers should include the following.

- Two-dimensional figures have length and width and therefore lie in a single plane. Three-dimensional figures have length, width, and depth.

- Two-dimensional figures form the faces of three-dimensional figures.

Teaching Tip   For Exercise 26, explain to students that a three-dimensional figure has
- *bilateral symmetry* if a plane can divide the figure into matching halves, and
- *rotational symmetry* if the figure can be rotated less than 360° about a fixed axis and look exactly as it does in its original position.

4 Assess

Open-Ended Assessment

Modeling   Have students draw a line on each of two pieces of paper. Then have them hold the papers to represent parallel lines and skew lines.

Tips for New Teachers

Motivating Students   Demonstrate real-world uses of geometry by examining the shapes of objects created by humans, such as buildings, pencils, erasers, buses and other vehicles, walls, tiles, desks, elevators, and food containers.

Getting Ready for Lesson 11-2

PREREQUISITE SKILL   Lesson 11-2 presents finding the volumes of prisms and cylinders. Exercises 41–44 should be used to determine your students' familiarity with finding the areas of triangles, a necessary step in finding the volume of triangular prisms.

Geometry Activity

A Preview of Lesson 11-2

Getting Started

Objective Investigate volume by creating and comparing containers of various shapes.

Materials
5 in. × 8 in. index cards
tape
rice

Teaching Tip Discuss with students the types and shapes of large storage containers they have seen, such as water towers, oil storage tanks, and grain silos.

Teach

- After students have completed their containers, have them use additional index cards to make nets of the figures. Discuss whether the nets make comparing the figures any easier.

Assess

In **Exercises 1–6**, students should successfully compare the relative volumes of the three containers and recognize the relationship between base area and volume.

Study Notebook

Have students draw the three containers in their notebooks, labeling the dimensions and including their estimations of the base areas. Students should include notes on the relative volumes of the three containers.

NEW YORK *Performance Indicator* **8.CN.4 Model situations mathematically, using representations to draw conclusions, and formulate new situations**

Volume

In this activity, you will investigate volume by making containers of different shapes and comparing how much each container holds.

Activity

Collect the Data

Step 1 Use three 5-inch × 8-inch index cards to make three different containers, as shown below.

square base with   circular base with   triangular base
2-inch sides   8-inch circumference   with sides 2 inches,
                                                      3 inches, and 3 inches

Step 2 Tape one end of each container to another card as a bottom, but leave the top open, as shown at the right.

Step 3 Estimate which container would hold the most (have the greatest volume) and which would hold the least (have the least volume), or whether all the containers would hold the same amount.

Step 4 Use rice to fill the container that you believe holds the least amount. Then pour the rice from this container into another container. Does the rice fill the second container? Continue the process until you find out which container, if any, has the least volume and which has the greatest.

Analyze the Data **2. same height; 5 in.   4. circular: ≈ 5 in²; triangular: ≈ 3 in²; square: 4**

1. Which container holds the greatest amount of rice? Which holds the least amount? **cylinder; triangular prism**

2. How do the heights of the three containers compare? What is each height?

3. Compare the perimeters of the bases of each container. What is each base perimeter? **same; 8 in.**

4. Trace the base of each container onto grid paper. Estimate the area of each base.

5. Which container has the greatest base area? **cylinder**

6. Does there appear to be a relationship between the area of the bases and the volume of the containers when the heights remain unchanged? Explain.
Yes; the greater the base area, the greater the volume.

562 Chapter 11 Three-Dimensional Figures

Resource Manager

 Teaching Pre-Algebra with Manipulatives
- p. 144 (student recording sheet)

Volume: Prisms and Cylinders

11-2

NEW YORK *Performance Indicator* **Reinforcement of 7.G.2 Calculate the volume of prisms and cylinders, using a given formula and a calculator**

What You'll Learn

- Find volumes of prisms.
- Find volumes of circular cylinders.

Vocabulary
- volume
- cylinder

How is volume related to area?

The rectangular prism is built from 24 cubes.

a. Build three more rectangular prisms using 24 cubes. Enter the dimensions and base areas in a table.

Prism	Length (units)	Width (units)	Height (units)	Area of Base (units²)
1	6	1	4	6
2	6	2	2	12
3	4	3	2	12
4	8	1	3	8

Sample dimensions are given.

b. *Volume* equals the number of cubes that fill a prism. How is the volume of each prism related to the product of the length, width, and height?

b. Volume equals the product of the length, width, and height.

c. **Make a conjecture** about how the area of the base B and the height h are related to the volume V of a prism. $V = Bh$

Study Tip

Measures of Volume
A cubic centimeter (cm^3) is a cube whose edges measure 1 centimeter.

1 cm
1 cm
1 cm

VOLUMES OF PRISMS The prism above has a volume of 24 cubic centimeters. **Volume** is the measure of space occupied by a solid region.

To find the volume of a prism, you can use the area of the base and the height, as given by the following formula.

Key Concept — Volume of a Prism

- **Words** The volume V of a prism is the area of the base B times the height h.

- **Symbols** $V = Bh$

- **Models**

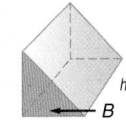

h
B
h
B

Example 1 — Volume of a Rectangular Prism

TEACHING TIP

An alternative method for finding the volume of a rectangular prism is by using the formula $V = \ell wh$.

Find the volume of the prism.

4 in.
2 in.
7.5 in.

$V = Bh$	Formula for volume of a prism
$V = (\ell \cdot w)h$	The base is a rectangle, so $B = \ell \cdot w$.
$V = (7.5 \cdot 2)4$	$\ell = 7.5$, $w = 2$, $h = 4$
$V = 60$	Simplify.

The volume is 60 cubic inches.

Lesson 11-2 Volume: Prisms and Cylinders **563**

11-2 **Lesson Notes**

1 Focus

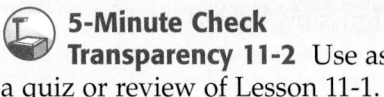

5-Minute Check Transparency 11-2 Use as a quiz or review of Lesson 11-1.

Mathematical Background notes are available for this lesson on page 552C.

How is volume related to area?

The opening activity questions are repeated on page 617 of the *Chapter 11 Resource Masters*.

Reading to Learn Mathematics, p. 617   **ELL**

Pre-Activity *How is volume related to area?*

Do the activity at the top of page 563 in your textbook. Write your answers below.

a. Build three more rectangular prisms using 24 cubes. Enter the dimensions and base areas in a table.

Sample dimensions are given.

Prism	Length (units)	Width (units)	Height (units)	Area of Base (units²)
1	6	1	4	6
2	6	2	2	12
3	4	3	2	12
4	8	1	3	8

b. *Volume* equals the number of cubes that fill a prism. How is the volume of each prism related to the product of the length, width, and height? Volume equals the product of the length, width, and height.

c. **Make a conjecture** about how the area of the base B and the height h are related to the volume V of a prism. $V = Bh$

Reading the Lesson 1–2. See students' work.

Write a definition and give an example of each new vocabulary word or phrase.

Vocabulary	Definition	Example
1. volume		
2. cylinder		

Helping You Remember

3. For each figure below, write out the longer version (showing how to determine the base area) of the formula for volume.

$V = \ell wh$ $V = \left(\frac{1}{2} \cdot b \cdot a\right)h$ $V = \pi r^2 h$

Resource Manager

Workbooks and Reproducible Masters

Chapter 11 Resource Masters
- Study Guide and Intervention, p. 614
- Skills Practice, p. 615
- Practice, p. 616
- Reading to Learn Mathematics, p. 617
- Enrichment, p. 618
- Assessment, p. 659

Graphing Calculator and Spreadsheet Masters, p. 39
Parent and Student Study Guide Workbook, p. 91
School-to-Career Masters, p. 21

Transparencies

5-Minute Check Transparency 11-2
Answer Key Transparencies

Technology

Interactive Chalkboard

Building on Prior Knowledge

In Lesson 5-3, students multiplied rational numbers. In this lesson, students will use multiplication to find the volume of prisms and cylinders.

VOLUMES OF PRISMS

 In-Class Examples Power Point®

1 Find the volume of the prism.

8 cm   25 cm
16 cm

3200 cm³

2 Find the volume of the triangular prism.

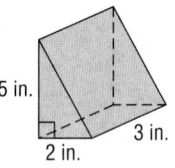

5 in.
2 in.   3 in.

15 in³

3 BAKING Cake batter is poured into a pan that is a rectangular prism whose base is an 8 inch square. If the cake batter occupies 192 cubic inches, what will be the height of the batter?
3 in.

4 Multiple-Choice Test Item
Find the volume of the solid.
D

9 m
9 m
12 m   9 m

A 262 m³   **B** 918 m³

C 972 m³   **D** 1458 m³

 Example 2 *Volume of a Triangular Prism*

Find the volume of the triangular prism.

6 cm   3 cm
4 cm

$V = Bh$	Formula for volume of a prism
$V = \left(\frac{1}{2} \cdot 4 \cdot 3\right)h$	B = area of base or $\frac{1}{2} \cdot 4 \cdot 3$
$V = \left(\frac{1}{2} \cdot 4 \cdot 3\right)6$	The height of the prism is 6 cm.
$V = 36$	Simplify.

The volume is 36 cubic centimeters.

Example 3 *Height of a Prism*

AQUARIUMS A wall is being constructed to enclose three sides of an aquarium that is a rectangular prism 8 feet long and 5 feet wide. If the aquarium is to contain 220 cubic feet of water, what is its height?

$V = Bh$	Formula for volume of a prism
$V = \ell \cdot w \cdot h$	Formula for volume of a rectangular prism
$220 = 8 \cdot 5 \cdot h$	Replace V with 220, ℓ with 8, and w with 5.
$220 = 40h$	Simplify.
$5.5 = h$	Divide each side by 40.

The height of the aquarium is 5.5 feet.

To find the volume of a solid with several prisms, break it into parts.

 NEW YORK Test Practice

Standardized Test Practice Ⓐ Ⓑ Ⓒ Ⓓ

Example 4 *Volume of a Complex Solid*

Multiple-Choice Test Item

Find the volume of the solid at the right.
Ⓐ 180 ft³
Ⓑ 1320 ft³
Ⓒ 960 ft³
Ⓓ 1140 ft³

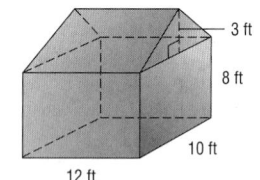

3 ft
8 ft
12 ft   10 ft

Read the Test Item

The solid is made up of a rectangular prism and a triangular prism. The *volume of the solid* is the sum of both volumes.

Solve the Test Item

Step 1 The volume of the rectangular prism is 12(10)(8) or 960 ft³.

Step 2 In the triangular prism, the area of the base is $\frac{1}{2}(10)(3)$, and the height is 12. Therefore, the volume is $\frac{1}{2}(10)(3)(12)$ or 180 ft³.

Step 3 Add the volumes.
960 ft³ + 180 ft³ = 1140 ft³

The answer is D.

Test-Taking Tip

Estimate You can eliminate A and C as answers because the volume of the rectangular prism is 960 ft³, so the volume of the whole solid must be greater.

 Standardized Test Practice Ⓐ Ⓑ Ⓒ Ⓓ

Example 4 Point out to students that another way to find the volume of the solid is to imagine the figure lying on a different base. For example, the figure could be lying on the right face. The height would then be 12. The area of that base is $(10)(8) + \frac{1}{2}(3)(10) = 80 + 15 = 95$. To find the volume, multiply that area by 12.

Reading Math

Cylinders

In this text, *cylinder* refers to a cylinder with a circular base.

VOLUMES OF CYLINDERS   A **cylinder** is a solid whose bases are congruent, parallel circles, connected with a curved side. Like prisms, the volume of a cylinder is the product of the base area and the height.

Key Concept   Volume of a Cylinder

- **Words**   The volume V of a cylinder with radius r is the area of the base B times the height h.

- **Model**

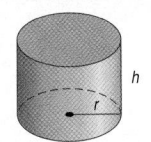

- **Symbols** $V = Bh$ or $V = \pi r^2 h$, where $B = \pi r^2$

VOLUMES OF CYLINDERS

In-Class Example Power Point®

5 Find the volume of each cylinder. Round to the nearest tenth.

a.
7 ft
14 ft

2155.1 ft³

b. diameter of base 10 m, height 2 m   **157.1 m³**

Teaching Tip   Have students measure various cereal boxes and cereal cylinders to see which dimensions have the greatest and least volume.

TEACHING TIP

Unless specified otherwise, encourage students to use ⌐2nd⌐ [π] on their calculators to evaluate expressions involving π. Then follow any instructions regarding rounding.

Example 5   *Volume of a Cylinder*

Find the volume of each cylinder. Round to the nearest tenth.

a.
5 ft
15 ft

$V = \pi r^2 h$ Formula for volume of a cylinder
$V = \pi \cdot 5^2 \cdot 15$ Replace r with 5 and h with 15.
$V \approx 1178.1$ Simplify.

The volume is about 1178.1 cubic feet.

b. diameter of base 16.4 mm, height 20 mm

Since the diameter is 16.4 mm, the radius is 8.2 mm.
$V = \pi r^2 h$ Formula for volume of a cylinder
$V = \pi \cdot 8.2^2 \cdot 20$ Replace r with 8.2 and h with 20.
$V \approx 4224.8$ Simplify.

The volume is about 4224.8 cubic millimeters.

Check for Understanding

Concept Check   **1. OPEN ENDED**   Describe a problem from an everyday situation in which you need to find the volume of a cylinder or a rectangular prism. Explain how to solve the problem. **See margin.**

2. FIND THE ERROR   Eric says that doubling the length of each side of a cube doubles the volume. Marissa says the volume is eight times greater. Who is correct? Explain your reasoning. **See margin.**

Guided Practice   Find the volume of each solid. If necessary, round to the nearest tenth.

GUIDED PRACTICE KEY	
Exercises	Examples
3, 6	1
4	2
5, 7	5
8, 9	3
10	4

3.   **183.6 cm³**
9 cm
5.1 cm
4 cm

4.
15 in.
8 in.
7 in.
420 in³

5.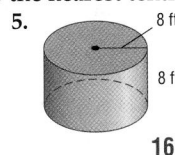
8 ft
8 ft
1608.5 ft³

6. rectangular prism: length 6 in., width 6 in., height 9 in. **324 in³**

7. cylinder: radius 3 yd, height 10 yd **282.7 yd³**

8. Find the height of a rectangular prism with a length of 3 meters, width of 1.5 meters, and a volume of 60.3 cubic meters. **13.4 m**

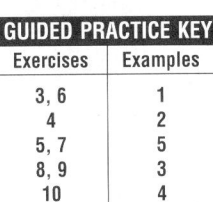

---

3 Practice/Apply

Study Notebook

Have students—
• add the definitions/examples of the vocabulary terms to their Vocabulary Builder worksheets for Chapter 11.
• write a paragraph that explains how to use the formula $V = Bh$ for both prisms and cylinders.
• include any other item(s) that they find helpful in mastering the skills in this lesson.

DAILY
INTERVENTION **FIND THE ERROR**
If students are having difficulty with change in volume, have them find the volume of a $3 \times 4 \times 5$ rectangular prism. **60** Then have them compare volumes after doubling only one dimension **120**, two original dimensions **240**, and all original dimensions **480**.

Answers

1. Sample answer: Finding how much sand is needed to fill a child's rectangular sandbox; measure the length, width, and height and then multiply to find the volume.

2. Marissa; a cube has three dimensions and when each dimension is multiplied by 2, the volume is multiplied by $2 \times 2 \times 2$ or 8.

Study Guide and Intervention, p. 614

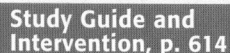

Volume of Prisms To find the volume V of a prism, use the formula V = Bh, where B is the area of the base, and h is the height of the solid.

Example 1 Find the volume of each prism.

a.
$V = Bh$
$V = (3 \cdot 6)4$
$V = 72$
The volume is 72 cm³.

b.
$V = Bh$
$V = \left(\frac{1}{2} \cdot 9.8 \cdot 5\right)4$
$V = 98$
The volume is 98 m³.

Volume of Cylinders The volume V of a cylinder with radius r is the area of the base, πr², times the height h, or V = πr²h.

Example 2 Find the volume of each cylinder.

$V = \pi r^2 h$
$V = \pi \cdot 2.2^2 \cdot 4.5$
$V \approx 68.4$
The volume is about 68.4 ft³.

Exercises

Find the volume of each solid. If necessary, round to the nearest tenth.

1. 15.6 in³
2. 114 mm³
3. 3600 ft³

4. rectangular prism: length 9 mm, width 8.2 mm, height 5 mm 369 mm³

5. triangular prism: base of triangle 5.8 ft, altitude of triangle 5.2 ft, height of prism 6 ft 90.5 ft³

Skills Practice, p. 615 and Practice, p. 616 (shown)

Find the volume of each solid shown or described. If necessary, round to the nearest tenth.

1. 360 cm³
2. 55 in³
3. 8685.9 ft³
4. 420 cm³
5. 1536 m³
6. 603.2 mm³
7. 5130 mm³
8. 63.6 in³
9. 3.5 cm³

10. rectangular prism: length 22.5 ft, width 12.5 ft, height 1.2 ft 337.5 ft³

11. triangular prism: base of triangle 17 cm, altitude of triangle 3 cm, height of prism 10.2 cm 260.1 cm³

12. Find the height of a rectangular prism with a length of 11 meters, a width of 0.5 meter, and a volume of 23.1 m³. 4.2 m

13. Find the height of a cylinder with a radius of 8.4 inches and a volume of 3546.7 in³. Round to the nearest tenth. 16.0 in.

14. A cube is 8 inches on each side. What is the height of a cylinder having the same volume, if its radius is 4 inches? Round to the nearest tenth. 10.2 in.

Enrichment, p. 618

Great Circles

The *great circle* on a sphere is the intersection of the sphere with a plane through the center. Both circles shown to the right are great circles. They are congruent and have circumferences that measure 2πr.

Volume of sphere: $V = \frac{4}{3}\pi r^3$

Surface area of a sphere: $S = 4\pi r^2$

Example

The area of the great circle is about 211.24 m².
The circumference of the great circle is about 51.52 m.
The surface area of the sphere is about 844.96 m².
The volume of the sphere is about 2309.56 m³.

Solve. Round answers to the nearest hundredth.

1. Find the volume of a sphere with a radius of 4 meters. 268.08 m³
2. Find the surface area of a sphere with a radius of 8 centimeters. 804.25 cm²
3. A hemispherical dome (half of a sphere) has a height of 32 meters.
   a. What is the volume of the dome? 68,629.14 m³
   b. What is the surface area? 6433.98 m²

4. Find the volume of the grain silo shown below. 1139.35 m³

5. A cold capsule is 12 millimeters long and 4 millimeters in diameter. Find the volume of medicine it can contain. 184.31 mm³

---

9. **ENGINEERING** A cylindrical storage tank is being manufactured to hold at least 1,000,000 cubic feet of natural gas and have a diameter of no more than 80 feet. What height should the tank be to the nearest tenth of a foot? **at least 198.9 ft**

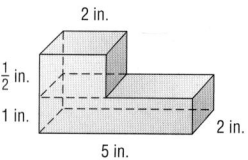

New York Test Practice

Standardized Test Practice
Ⓐ Ⓑ Ⓒ Ⓓ

10. Find the volume of the solid at the right. **D**
   Ⓐ 6 in³   Ⓑ 10 in³
   Ⓒ 13 in³   Ⓓ 16 in³

★ indicates increased difficulty

Practice and Apply

Homework Help

For Exercises	See Examples
11, 12, 17, 23–27	1
13, 14, 18	2
15, 16, 19, 28	5
21, 22	3

Extra Practice
See page 750.

Find the volume of each solid shown or described. If necessary, round to the nearest tenth.

11. 512 cm³
12. 81.9 m³
13. 748 in³

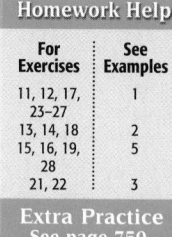

14. 600 in³
15. 88.0 ft³

16. 171.8 m³

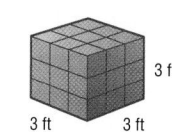

17. rectangular prism: length 3 mm, width 5 mm, height 15 mm **225 mm³**

18. triangular prism: base of triangle 8 in., altitude of triangle 15 in., height of prism $6\frac{1}{2}$ in. **390 in³**

19. cylinder: d = 2.6 m, h = 3.5 m **18.6 m³**

★ 20. octagonal prism: base area 25 m², height 1.5 m **37.5 m³**

21. Find the height of a rectangular prism with a length of 4.2 meters, width of 3.2 meters, and volume of 83.3 m³. **6.2 m**

22. Find the height of a cylinder with a radius of 2 feet and a volume of 28.3 ft³. **2.3 ft**

CONVERTING UNITS OF MEASURE

For Exercises 23–25, use the cubes at the right.
The volume of the left cube is 1 yd³. In the right cube, only the units have been changed. So, 1 yd³ = 3(3)(3) or 27 ft³. Use a similar process to convert each measurement.

23. 1 ft³ = ■ in³ **1728**   24. 1 cm³ = ■ mm³ **1000**   25. 1 m³ = ■ cm³ **1,000,000**

26. **METALS** The *density* of gold is 19.29 grams per cubic centimeter. Find the mass in grams of a gold bar that is 2 centimeters by 3 centimeters by 2 centimeters. **231.48 g**

DAILY INTERVENTION

Differentiated Instruction

- **Auditory/Musical** Let students experiment with five identical glass or ceramic cylinders to find how the volume of water in each cylinder affects its tone when struck. Identical coffee mugs will work for this. Students should be able to develop a partial musical scale based on the volume of water.

★ 27. MICROWAVES The inside of a microwave oven has a volume of 1.2 cubic feet and measures 18 inches wide and 10 inches long. To the nearest tenth, how deep is the inside of the microwave? (*Hint*: Convert 1.2 cubic feet to cubic inches.) **11.5 in.**

8. **D** 53.2 cm³;
25.5 cm³;
A 8.3 cm³;
AA 3.9 cm³

★ 28. BATTERIES The current of an alkaline battery corresponds to its volume. Find the volume of each cylinder-shaped battery shown in the table. Write each volume in cm³. (*Hint*: 1 cm³ = 1000 mm³)

Battery Size	Diameter (mm)	Height (mm)
D	33.3	61.1
C	25.5	50.0
AA	14.5	50.5
AAA	10.5	44.5

29. CRITICAL THINKING An $8\frac{1}{2}$-by-11-inch piece of paper is rolled to form a cylinder. Will the volume be greater if the height is $8\frac{1}{2}$ inches or 11 inches, or will the volumes be the same? Explain your reasoning. **See margin.**

30. WRITING IN MATH Answer the question that was posed at the beginning of the lesson. **See margin.**

How is volume related to area?

Include the following in your answer:

- an explanation of why area is given in square units and volume is given in cubic units, and
- a description of why the formula for volume includes area.

Standardized Test Practice
Ⓐ Ⓑ Ⓒ Ⓓ

31. Which is the best estimate for the volume of a cube whose sides measure 18.79 millimeters? **C**

Ⓐ 80 mm³   Ⓑ 800 mm³   Ⓒ 8000 mm³   Ⓓ 80,000 mm³

32. Find the volume of the figure at the right. **A**

Ⓐ 24.5 ft³   Ⓑ 20.5 ft³
Ⓒ 48 ft³   Ⓓ 49 ft³

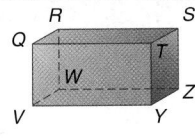

2.5 ft
10 ft

Maintain Your Skills

Mixed Review

33. Identify a pair of skew lines in the prism at the right. *(Lesson 11-1)*
Sample answer: $\overline{QT}$ and $\overline{YZ}$

R   S
Q   T
W
Z
V   Y

34. Estimate the area of the shaded figure to the nearest square unit. *(Lesson 10-8)*
Sample answer: 35 square units

Solve each inequality. Check your solution. *(Lesson 7-4)*

35. $x + 5 > -3$
$x > -8$

36. $k + (-9) \geq 1.8$
$k \geq 10.8$

Getting Ready for the Next Lesson

PREREQUISITE SKILL Find each product.
*(To review **multiplying fractions**, see Lesson 5-3.)*

37. $\frac{1}{3} \cdot 5 \cdot 15$ **25**

38. $\frac{1}{3} \cdot 4 \cdot 9$ **12**

39. $\frac{1}{3} \cdot 2 \cdot 2 \cdot 3$ **4**

40. $\frac{1}{3} \cdot 3 \cdot 4 \cdot 8$ **32**

41. $\frac{1}{3} \cdot 2^2 \cdot 21$ **28**

42. $\frac{1}{3} \cdot 3^2 \cdot 10$ **30**

---

4 Assess

Answers

29. The volume will be greater if the height is $8\frac{1}{2}$ inches. By using the formula for circumference, you can find the radius and volume of each cylinder. If the height is $8\frac{1}{2}$ inches, the volume is 86.5 in³; if the height is 11 inches, the volume is 67.7 in³.

30. Volume of a solid equals the area of the solid's base times its height. Answers should include the following.
- Area is a measure of figures on a flat plane having two dimensions, length and width. Volume is a measure of objects in space having three dimensions, length, width, and height.
- The dimensions that are used to find area are also used to find volume, so the formula for volume includes the formula for area.

1 Focus

Mathematical Background notes are available for this lesson on page 552C.

How is the volume of a pyramid related to the volume of a prism?

The opening activity questions are repeated on page 622 of the *Chapter 11 Resource Masters.*

Reading to Learn Mathematics, p. 622 **ELL**

Pre-Activity *How is the volume of a pyramid related to the volume of a prism?*

Do the activity at the top of page 568 in your textbook. Write your answers below.

a. Compare the base areas and compare the heights of the prism and the pyramid.   The areas of the bases and the heights of both solids are the same.

b. How many times greater is the volume of the prism than the volume of one pyramid? 3 times

c. What fraction of the prism volume does one pyramid fill? $\frac{1}{3}$

Reading the Lesson

Write a definition and give an example of the new vocabulary word.

	Vocabulary	Definition	Example
1.	cone	See students' work.	

2. What is the relationship between the volume of a pyramid and the volume of a prism if both figures have the same base areas and heights?   The volume of the pyramid is one-third that of the prism.

3. What is the relationship between the volume of a cone and the volume of a cylinder if both figures have the same base areas and heights?   The volume of the cone is one-third that of the cylinder.

Helping You Remember

4. Write out in words an explanation for each step in finding the volume of the pyramid at the right.

$V = \frac{1}{3}Bh$ Formula for volume of a pyramid

$V = \frac{1}{3}\left(\frac{1}{2} \cdot 5 \cdot 8\right)h$ The base is a triangle, so $B = \frac{1}{2} \cdot 5 \cdot 8$.

$V = \frac{1}{3}\left(\frac{1}{2} \cdot 5 \cdot 8\right)27$ The height of the pyramid is 27 yd.

$V = 180$ Simplify.

11-3 Volume: Pyramids and Cones

NEW YORK *Performance Indicator* Reinforcement of 7.A.6 Evaluate formulas for given input values (surface area, rate and density problems)

What You'll Learn

- Find volumes of pyramids.
- Find volumes of cones.

Vocabulary
- cone

How is the volume of a pyramid related to the volume of a prism?

You can see that the volume of the pyramid shown at the right is less than the volume of the prism in which it sits.

If the pyramid were made of sand, it would take three pyramids to fill a prism having the same base dimensions and height.

a. Compare the base areas and compare the heights of the prism and the pyramid.

b. How many times greater is the volume of the prism than the volume of one pyramid? **3 times**

c. What fraction of the prism volume does one pyramid fill? $\frac{1}{3}$

Study Tip

Height of Pyramid
The height of a pyramid is the distance from the vertex, perpendicular to the base.

VOLUMES OF PYRAMIDS A pyramid has one-third the volume of a prism with the same base area and height.

Key Concept — Volume of a Pyramid

- **Words** The volume V of a pyramid is one-third the area of the base B times the height h.
- **Symbols** $V = \frac{1}{3}Bh$
- **Model**

Example 1 Volumes of Pyramids

Find the volume of each pyramid. If necessary, round to the nearest tenth.

a.

$V = \frac{1}{3}Bh$ Formula for volume of a pyramid

$V = \frac{1}{3}\left(\frac{1}{2} \cdot 8 \cdot 6\right)h$ The base is a triangle, so $B = \frac{1}{2} \cdot 8 \cdot 6$.

$V = \frac{1}{3}\left(\frac{1}{2} \cdot 8 \cdot 6\right)20$ The height of the pyramid is 20 feet.

$V = 160$ Simplify.

The volume is 160 cubic feet.

Resource Manager

Workbooks and Reproducible Masters

Chapter 11 Resource Masters
- Study Guide and Intervention, p. 619
- Skills Practice, p. 620
- Practice, p. 621
- Reading to Learn Mathematics, p. 622
- Enrichment, p. 623

Parent and Student Study Guide Workbook, p. 92

Transparencies
5-Minute Check Transparency 11-3
Answer Key Transparencies

Technology
Interactive Chalkboard
Pre-AlgePASS: Tutorial Plus, Lesson 35

b. base area 125 cm², height 6.5 cm

$V = \frac{1}{3}Bh$ Formula for volume of a pyramid

$V = \frac{1}{3}(125)(6.5)$ Replace B with 125 and h with 6.5.

$V \approx 270.8$ Simplify.

The volume is about 270.8 cubic centimeters.

VOLUMES OF CONES   A **cone** is a three-dimensional figure with one circular base. A curved surface connects the base and the vertex.

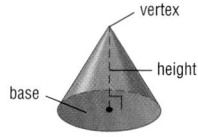

The volumes of a cone and a cylinder are related in the same way as the volumes of a pyramid and a prism are related.

The volume of a cone is $\frac{1}{3}$ the volume of a cylinder with the same base area and height.

Key Concept   Volume of a Cone

- **Words**   The volume V of a cone with radius r is one-third the area of the base B times the height h.

- **Model**

- **Symbols** $V = \frac{1}{3}Bh$ or $V = \frac{1}{3}\pi r^2 h$, where $B = \pi r^2$

Example 2   Volume of a Cone

Find the volume of the cone. Round to the nearest tenth.

$V = \frac{1}{3}\pi r^2 h$ Formula for volume of a cone

$V = \frac{1}{3} \cdot \pi \cdot 5^2 \cdot 12$ Replace r with 5 and h with 12.

$V \approx 314.2$ Simplify.

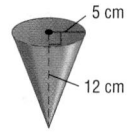

The volume is about 314.2 cubic centimeters.

✓ **Concept Check**   What is the volume of a cone whose base area is 86 meters squared and whose height is 3 meters? **86 m³**

 www.pre-alg.com/extra_examples/ny

Lesson 11-3   Volume: Pyramids and Cones   **569**

Lesson 11-3   Volume: Pyramids and Cones   **569**

3 **LANDSCAPING** When mulch was dumped from a truck, it formed a cone-shaped mound with a diameter of 15 feet and a height of 8 feet.

a. What is the volume of the mulch? **about 471 ft³**

b. How many square feet can be covered with this mulch if 1 cubic foot covers 4 square feet of ground? **1884 ft²**

3 Practice/Apply

Study Notebook

Have students—
- add the definition/example of the vocabulary term to their Vocabulary Builder worksheets for Chapter 11.
- include any other item(s) that they find helpful in mastering the skills in this lesson.

About the Exercises . . .
Organization by Objective
- **Volumes of Pyramids:** 10–13, 16, 17, 20, 25, 27
- **Volumes of Cones:** 14, 15, 18, 19, 21–24, 26, 28

Odd/Even Assignments
Exercises 10–22 are structured so that students practice the same concepts whether they are assigned odd or even problems.

Assignment Guide
Basic: 11, 15, 17, 19, 23, 25–28, 32–38

Average: 11–23 odd, 25–28, 32–38 (Optional: 29–31)

Advanced: 10–24 even, 25–35 (Optional: 36–38)

All: Practice Quiz 1 (1–5)

Example 3 *Use Volume to Solve Problems*

HIGHWAY MAINTENANCE Salt and sand mixtures are often used on icy roads. When the mixture is dumped from a truck into the staging area, it forms a cone-shaped mound with a diameter of 10 feet and a height of 6 feet.

a. What is the volume of the salt-sand mixture?

Estimate: $\frac{1}{3} \cdot 3 \cdot 5^2 \cdot 6 = 150$

$V = \frac{1}{3}\pi r^2 h$ Formula for volume of a cone

$V = \frac{1}{3} \cdot \pi \cdot 5^2 \cdot 6$ Since $d = 10$, replace r with 5. Replace h with 6.

$V \approx 157$

The volume of the mixture is about 157 cubic feet.

b. How many square feet of roadway can be salted using the mixture in part a if 500 square feet can be covered by 1 cubic foot of salt?

$\text{ft}^2 \text{ of roadway} = 157 \text{ ft}^3 \text{ mixture} \times \dfrac{500 \text{ ft}^2 \text{ of roadway}}{1 \text{ ft}^3 \text{ mixture}}$

$= 78{,}500 \text{ ft}^2 \text{ of roadway}$

So, 78,500 square feet of roadway can be salted.

Study Tip

Look Back
To review **dimensional analysis**, see Lesson 5-3.

Check for Understanding

Concept Check

2–3. See pp. 601A–601B

1. **Explain** why you can use πr^2 to find the area of the base of a cone. **The base is a circle.**
2. **List** the formulas for volume that you have learned so far in this chapter. Tell what the variables represent and explain how you can remember which formula goes with which solid.
3. **OPEN ENDED** Draw and label a cone whose volume is between 100 cm³ and 1000 cm³.

Guided Practice

GUIDED PRACTICE KEY	
Exercises	Examples
4–8	1, 2
9	3

Find the volume of each solid. If necessary, round to the nearest tenth.

4. **100 m³**

5.
37.7 cm³

6.
160 in³

7. rectangular pyramid: length 9 ft, width 7 ft, height 18 ft **378 ft³**
8. cone: radius 4 mm, height 6.5 mm **108.9 mm³**

Application

9. **HISTORY** The Great Pyramid of Khufu in Egypt was originally 481 feet high and had a square base 756 feet on a side. What was its volume? Use an estimate to check your answer. **91,636,272 ft³**

DAILY INTERVENTION

Differentiated Instruction

- **Kinesthetic** Have groups of students use modeling clay to make a cube and a cylinder. Have them measure and record the height and volume of each solid. Then, without adding or removing any clay, have them reform each cube into a square pyramid and each cylinder into a cone, maintaining the same base areas. Have students record the height and volume of their pyramids and cones. Compare the volumes and the changes that occurred in the models.

Practice and Apply

Homework Help

For Exercises	See Examples
10–22	1, 2
23–25	3

Extra Practice
See page 751.

Find the volume of each solid. If necessary, round to the nearest tenth.

10. **32 ft³**

11. **412 cm³**

12. **124.5 mm³**

★ 13. **150 in³**

14. **628.3 in³**

15. **78.5 m³**

16. square pyramid: length 5 in., height 6 in. **50 in³**

17. hexagonal pyramid: base area 125 cm², height 6.5 cm **270.8 cm³**

18. cone: radius 3 yd, height 14 yd **131.9 yd³**

19. cone: diameter 12 m, height 15 m **565.5 m³**

★ 20. **10,000 ft³**

★ 21. **44.0 m³**

★ 22. **733.0 cm³**

23. **GEOLOGY** A stalactite in the Endless Caverns in Virginia is cone-shaped. It is 4 feet long and has a diameter at its base of 1.5 feet.

   a. Find the volume of the stalactite to the nearest tenth. **2.4 ft³**

   b. The stalactite is made of calcium carbonate, which weighs 131 pounds per cubic foot. What is the weight of the stalactite? **314.4 lb**

★ 24. **SCIENCE** In science, a standard funnel is shaped like a cone, and a buchner funnel is shaped like a cone with a cylinder attached to the base. Which funnel has the greatest volume? **standard funnel**

standard   buchner

25. WRITING IN MATH Answer the question that was posed at the beginning of the lesson. **See margin.**

   How is the volume of a pyramid related to the volume of a prism?

   Include the following in your answer:
   • a discussion of the similarities between the dimensions and base area of the pyramid and prism shown at the beginning of the lesson, and
   • a description of how the formulas for the volume of a pyramid and the volume of a prism are similar.

Answer

25. The volume of a pyramid is one-third the volume of a prism with the same base and height. Answers should include the following.

   • The height of the pyramid and prism are equal. The bases of the pyramid and prism are squares with equal side lengths. Therefore, their base areas are equal.

   • The formula for the volume of a pyramid is one-third times the formula for the volume of a prism.

Tips for New Teachers

Rounding Answers Students should learn to save all rounding for the very last step in their solution. To avoid rounding π before using it in the formula, you may want to have students use a scientific calculator to compute volumes of cylinders.

4 Assess

Open-Ended Assessment

Writing Have students write problems that involve a number of different-shaped but similar-sized solids. Students can exchange problems with partners and solve to find which solids have the greatest and least volumes.

Getting Ready for Lesson 11-4

PREREQUISITE SKILL In Lesson 11-4, students will find the surface area of prisms and cylinders. Exercises 36–38 review estimating products, a useful skill when determining surface area.

Assessment Options

Practice Quiz 1 The quiz provides students with a brief review of the concepts and skills in Lessons 11-1 through 11-3. Lesson numbers are given to the right of exercises or instruction lines so students can review concepts not yet mastered.

Answer

26b. The volume quadruples. The radius is squared when you find the volume, so when the radius is doubled, 2r, the squared value is 4r^2. So, the volume is 4 times greater.

---

26. CRITICAL THINKING a. The volume doubles.
   a. If you double the height of a cone, how does the volume change?
   b. If you double the radius of the base of a cone, how does the volume change? Explain. **See margin.**

NEW YORK *Test Practice*
Standardized Test Practice
Ⓐ Ⓑ Ⓒ Ⓓ

27. Choose the best estimate for the volume of a rectangular pyramid 4.9 centimeters long, 3 centimeters wide, and 7 centimeters high. **B**
   Ⓐ 7 cm^3 Ⓑ 35 cm^3 Ⓒ 70 cm^3 Ⓓ 105 cm^3

28. The solids at the right have the same base area and height. If the cone is filled with water and poured into the cylinder, how much of the cylinder would be filled? **D**

   Ⓐ $\frac{3}{4}$ Ⓑ $\frac{1}{2}$ Ⓒ $\frac{2}{3}$ Ⓓ $\frac{1}{3}$

Extending the Lesson   The volume V of a sphere with radius r is given by the formula $V = \frac{4}{3}\pi r^3$. Find the volume of each sphere to the nearest tenth. **31. 107.5 mm^3**
   29. radius 6 cm **904.8 cm^3**   **30.** radius 1.4 in. **11.5 in^3**   **31.** diameter 5.9 mm

Maintain Your Skills

Mixed Review   Find the volume of each prism or cylinder. If necessary, round to the nearest tenth. *(Lesson 11-2)*

34. triangular pyramid; any one of the following faces is a base: *DCG*, *DGF*, *DFC*, *CGF*; $\overline{DC}$, $\overline{DG}$, $\overline{DF}$, $\overline{CG}$, $\overline{GF}$, $\overline{FC}$; *C, D, F, G*

   32. rectangular prism: length 4 cm, width 8 cm, height 2 cm **64 cm^3**
   33. cylinder: diameter 1.6 in., height 5 in. **10.1 in^3**
   34. Identify the solid at the right. Name the bases, faces, edges, and vertices. *(Lesson 11-1)*
   35. Find the distance between $A(3, 7)$ and $B(-2, 1)$. Round to the nearest tenth, if necessary. *(Lesson 9-6)*
   7.8

Getting Ready for the Next Lesson   **PREREQUISITE SKILL**   Estimate each product.
(To review estimating products, see page 714.) **36–38. Sample answers are given.**
   36. 4.9 · 5.1 · 3 **75**   **37.** 2 · 1.7 · 9 **36**   **38.** 2 · π · 6.8 **42**

Practice Quiz 1   *Lessons 11-1 through 11-3*

Identify each solid. *(Lesson 11-1)*

1. **triangular prism**   **2.**   **rectangular pyramid**

Find the volume of each solid. If necessary, round to the nearest tenth. *(Lesson 11-2)* **4. 756 ft^3**
3. cylinder: radius 2 cm, height 1 cm **12.6 cm^3**   **4.** hexagonal prism: base area 42 ft^2, height 18 ft
5. MINING   An open pit mine in the Elk mountain range is cone-shaped. The mine is 420 feet across and 250 feet deep. What volume of material was removed? *(Lesson 11-3)*
   ≈ 11,545,353 ft^3

Surface Area: Prisms and Cylinders

NEW YORK
Performance Indicator
Reinforcement of
7.G.4 Determine
the surface area of
prisms and
cylinders, using a
calculator and a
variety of methods

What You'll Learn

* Find surface areas of prisms.
* Find surface areas of cylinders.

How is the surface area of a solid different from its volume?

The sizes and prices of shipping boxes are shown in the table.

a. For each box, find the area of each face and the sum of the areas.

b. Find the volume of each box. Are these values the same as the values you found in part a? Explain.

Box	Size (in.)	Price ($)
A	8 × 8 × 8	$1.50
B	15 × 10 × 12	$2.25
C	20 × 14 × 10	$3.00

Vocabulary
surface area

. A, 384 in²;
. 900 in²; C, 1240 in²
. A, 512 in³;
, 1800 in³;
 2800 in³; No; for
ach box, the volume
s greater.

SURFACE AREAS OF PRISMS

If you open up a box or prism to form a net, you can see all the surfaces. The sum of the areas of these surfaces is called the **surface area** of the prism.

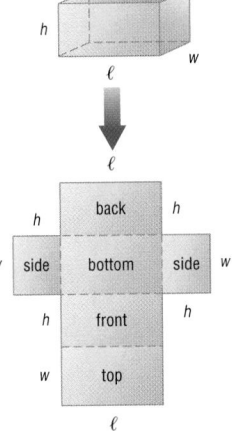

Faces	Area
top and bottom	$(\ell \cdot w) + (\ell \cdot w) = 2\ell w$
front and back	$(\ell \cdot h) + (\ell \cdot h) = 2\ell h$
two sides	$(w \cdot h) + (w \cdot h) = 2wh$
Sum of areas →	$2\ell w + 2\ell h + 2wh$ or $2(\ell w + \ell h + wh)$

Key Concept — Surface Area of Rectangular Prisms

* **Words** The surface area S of a rectangular prism with length ℓ, width w, and height h is the sum of the areas of the faces.

* **Model**

* **Symbols** $S = 2\ell w + 2\ell h + 2wh = 2(\ell w + \ell h + wh)$

Example 1 Surface Area of a Rectangular Prism

Find the surface area of the rectangular prism.

$S = 2\ell w + 2\ell h + 2wh$ Write the formula.

$S = 2(20)(14) + 2(20)(10) + 2(14)(10)$ Substitution

$S = 1240$ Simplify.

10 in.
20 in.
14 in.

The surface area of the prism is 1240 square inches.

---

1 Focus

5-Minute Check Transparency 11-4 Use as a quiz or review of Lesson 11-3.

Mathematical Background notes are available for this lesson on page 552C.

How is the surface area of a solid different than its volume?

The opening activity questions are repeated on page 627 of the *Chapter 11 Resource Masters*.

Resource Manager

Workbooks and Reproducible Masters

Chapter 11 Resource Masters
* Study Guide and Intervention, p. 624
* Skills Practice, p. 625
* Practice, p. 626
* Reading to Learn Mathematics, p. 627
* Enrichment, p. 628
* Assessment, pp. 659, 661

Graphing Calculator and Spreadsheet Masters, p. 40
Parent and Student Study Guide Workbook, p. 93
School-to-Career Masters, p. 22

Transparencies
5-Minute Check Transparency 11-4
Answer Key Transparencies

Technology
Interactive Chalkboard
Multimedia Applications

2 Teach

Teaching Tip Have a number of actual different-sized shipping boxes, along with their prices, available to share with students. You may also be able to find shipping containers in the shape of triangular prisms to share. Discuss the relationship between surface area, volume, and price of the containers.

SURFACE AREAS OF PRISMS

In-Class Examples

1 Find the surface area of the rectangular prism.

1868 cm²

2 Find the surface area of the triangular prism.

336 m²

Teaching Tip Have students use grid paper to create larger nets similar in shape to those on the student pages. Have students cut out and tape them together to form the solids. This will help them to see the surfaces that form the solids.

✓ Skills Check

Surface Areas of Prisms
A rectangular prism has a square base whose area is 25 ft². The height of the prism is 4 ft. Find the surface area. **130 ft²**

Example 2 Surface Area of a Triangular Prism

Find the surface area of the triangular prism.

One way to easily see all of the surfaces of the prism is to draw a net on grid paper and label the dimensions of each face.

Find the area of each face.

bottom $3 \cdot 6 = 18$
left side $4 \cdot 6 = 24$ $\Big\} A = \ell w$
right side $5 \cdot 6 = 30$
two bases $2\left(\frac{1}{2} \cdot 3 \cdot 4\right) = 12$ $A = \frac{1}{2}bh$

Add to find the total surface area.
$18 + 24 + 30 + 12 = 84$

The surface area of the triangular prism is 84 square centimeters.

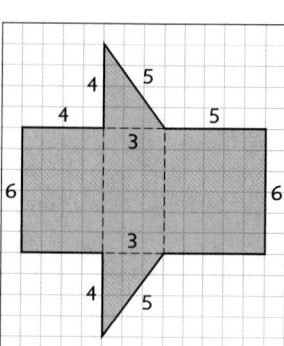

SURFACE AREAS OF CYLINDERS

You can also find surface areas of cylinders. If you unroll a cylinder, its net is a rectangle and two circles.

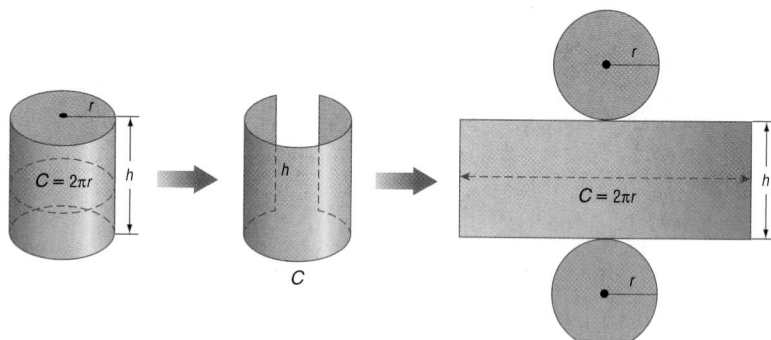

Study Tip

Circles and Rectangles
To see why $\ell = 2\pi r$, find the circumference of a soup can by using the formula $C = 2\pi r$. Then peel off its label and measure the length (minus the overlapping parts).

Model	Net
bases	congruent circles
curved surface	rectangle
height h	width of rectangle
circumference C	length of rectangle

The area of each circular base is πr^2. The area of the rectangular region is $\ell \cdot w$, or $2\pi r \cdot h$.

The surface area of a cylinder	equals	the area of two circular bases	plus	the area of the curved surface.
S	$=$	$2(\pi r^2)$	$+$	$2\pi rh$

DAILY INTERVENTION

Differentiated Instruction

- **Logical** Create the surface regions for a number of figures including rectangular prisms, triangular prisms, and cylinders. Cut apart or separate the surface regions for each figure, then shuffle all the pieces together. Have students, working alone or in groups, fit the pieces together again and either re-create the figures or make nets for the figures. Finally, have students find the surface areas for the figures they've put together.

Key Concept — Surface Area of Cylinders

- **Words** — The surface area S of a cylinder with height h and radius r is the area of the two bases plus the area of the curved surface.

- **Model**

- **Symbols** — $S = 2\pi r^2 + 2\pi rh$

Example 3 — Surface Area of a Cylinder

Find the surface area of the cylinder. Round to the nearest tenth.

$S = 2\pi r^2 + 2\pi rh$ Formula for surface area of a cylinder

$S = 2\pi(1)^2 + 2\pi(1)(3)$ Replace r with 1 and h with 3.

$S \approx 25.1$ Simplify.

The surface area is about 25.1 square meters.

You can compare surface areas of prisms and cylinders.

Example 4 — Compare Surface Areas

- **FRUIT DRINKS** Both containers hold about the same amount of pineapple juice. Does the box or the can have a greater surface area?

Surface area of box				Surface area of can	
top/bottom	sides	front/back		top/bottom	curved surface
$S = 2\ell w$	$+ \; 2\ell h$	$+ \; 2wh$		$S = 2\pi r^2$	$+ \; 2\pi rh$
$= 2(4 \cdot 7)$	$+ \; 2(4 \cdot 9)$	$+ \; 2(7 \cdot 9)$		$= 2\pi(3)^2$	$+ \; 2\pi(3)(9)$
$= 254$				≈ 226	

Since 254 cm^2 > 226 cm^2, the box has a greater surface area.

✓ **Concept Check**   Why might a company prefer to sell juice in cans?
Sample answer: less surface area to package, so less expensive to manufacture

---

Check for Understanding

Concept Check
1. **Explain** why surface area is given in square units rather than cubic units.
   See margin.
2. **OPEN ENDED** Find the surface areas of a rectangular prism and a cylinder found in your home. **Sample answer: find the surface area of a cedar chest and a cylinder-shaped potato chip container.**

 www.pre-alg.com/extra_examples/ny

Answer

1. Sample answer: The surface of a solid is two-dimensional. Its area is the sum of the face areas, which are given in square units.

In-Class Examples   Power Point®

Teaching Tip Some students may confuse the volume formula with the surface area formula. Use models to help students visualize the derivation of each formula.

3 Find the surface area of the cylinder. Round to the nearest tenth.

164.9 m^2

4 **CEREALS** A company packages its cereal in a rectangular prism that is 2.5 in. by 7 in. by 12 in. It is considering packaging it in a cylinder-shaped container having a 6-in. diameter and a height of 7.5 in. Which uses the least amount of packaging?
The cylinder has less packaging; 197.9 in^2 < 263 in^2.

---

3 Practice/Apply

Study Notebook

Have students—
- add the definition/example of the vocabulary term to their Vocabulary Builder worksheets for Chapter 11.
- write a paragraph describing the number of surface regions on a rectangular triangular prism, a triangular prism, and a cylinder.
- include any other item(s) that they find helpful in mastering the skills in this lesson.

About the Exercises . . .

Organization by Objective
- **Surface Areas of Prisms:**
  9–12, 15, 16, 20, 24, 26
- **Surface Areas of Cylinders:**
  13, 14, 17, 18, 21, 25

Odd/Even Assignments
Exercises 9–18 are structured so that students practice the same concepts whether they are assigned odd or even problems.

Assignment Guide

Basic: 9–17 odd, 23–26, 30–37

Average: 9–21 odd, 23–26, 30–37 (Optional: 27–29)

Advanced: 10–22 even, 23–31 (Optional: 32–37)

---

4 Assess

Open-Ended Assessment

Speaking Have students explain in their own words how to find the surface areas of a rectangular prism, a triangular prism, and a cylinder.

Getting Ready for Lesson 11-5

PREREQUISITE SKILL In Lesson 11-5 students find the surface areas of pyramids and cones. Exercises 32–37 review multiplying rational numbers, a necessary step when finding surface area.

Assessment Options

Quiz (Lessons 11-3 and 11-4) is available on p. 659 of the *Chapter 11 Resource Masters.*

Mid-Chapter Test (Lessons 11-1 through 11-4) is available on p. 661 of the *Chapter 11 Resource Masters.*

Guided Practice

Find the surface area of each solid shown or described. If necessary, round to the nearest tenth.

GUIDED PRACTICE KEY	
Exercises	Examples
3, 6	1
4	2
5, 7	3
8	4

3. **150 ft²**

4. **132 cm²**

5. **571.8 in**

6. rectangular prism: length 3 cm, width 2 cm, height 1 cm **22 cm²**

7. cylinder: radius 4 mm, height 1.6 mm **140.7 mm²**

Application

8. Box A;
166 in² > 145 in²

8. CRAFTS Brianna sews together pieces of plastic canvas to make tissue box covers. For which tissue box will she use more plastic canvas to cover the sides and the top? Explain.

Box	Length (in.)	Width (in.)	Height (in.)
A	9	4	5
B	5	5	6

★ **indicates increased difficulty**

Practice and Apply

Homework Help	
For Exercises	See Examples
9, 10, 15, 16	1
11, 12	2
13, 14, 17–19, 21, 22	3
20	4

Extra Practice
See page 751.

Find the surface area of each solid shown or described. If necessary, round to the nearest tenth. **11. 264 m²** **12. 211.2 cm²**

9.
282 in²

10.
220.5 m²

11.

12.

13.
1885.0 ft²

14.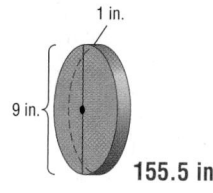
155.5 in²

15. cube: side length 7 ft **294 ft²**

16. rectangular prism: length 6.2 cm, width 4 cm, height 8.5 cm **223 cm²**

17. cylinder: radius 5 in., height 15 in. **628.3 in²**

18. cylinder: diameter 4 m, height 20 m **276.5 m²**

★ **19.** Find the surface area of the complex solid at the right. Use estimation to check the reasonableness of your answer. **264.0 in²**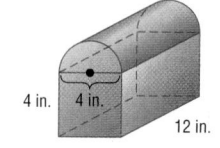

★ **20. AQUARIUMS** A standard 20-gallon aquarium tank is a rectangular prism that holds approximately 4600 cubic inches of water. The bottom glass needs to be 24 inches by 12 inches to fit on the stand. **b. 10 ft²**

a. Find the height of the aquarium to the nearest inch. **16 in.**

b. Find the total amount of glass needed in square feet for the five faces.

c. An aquarium with an octagonal base has sides that are 9 inches wide and 16 inches high. The area of the base is 392.4 square inches. Do the bottom and sides of this tank have a greater surface area than the rectangular tank? Explain. **Yes; see margin for explanation.**

576 Chapter 11 Three-Dimensional Figures

Answer

20c. The sides of both tanks have the same surface area, 1152 in². However, the area of the octagon base is 392.4 in² and the area of the rectangular base is 288 in². So, the total surface area of the octagon-shaped tank is greater.

POOLS Vinyl liners cover the inside walls and bottom of the swimming pools whose top views are shown below. Find the area of the vinyl liner for each pool if they are 4 feet deep. Round to the nearest square foot.

★ 21. **754 ft²**

★ 22. 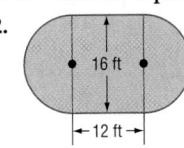 **690 ft²**

23. **CRITICAL THINKING** Suppose you double the length of the sides of a cube. How is the surface area affected? **The surface area is 4 times greater.**

24. **WRITING IN MATH** Answer the question that was posed at the beginning of the lesson. **See margin.**

How is the surface area of a solid different than its volume?

Include the following in your answer:
• a comparison of formulas for surface area and volume, and
• an explanation of the difference between surface area and volume.

Standardized Test Practice
Ⓐ Ⓑ Ⓒ Ⓓ

25. Find the surface area of a cylinder with a diameter of 15 centimeters and height of 2 centimeters. **D**
Ⓐ 30 cm² Ⓑ 117.8 cm² Ⓒ 353.4 cm² Ⓓ 447.7 cm²

26. How many 2-inch squares will completely cover a rectangular prism 10 inches long, 4 inches wide, and 6 inches high? **B**
Ⓐ 40 Ⓑ 62 Ⓒ 240 Ⓓ 248

Extending the Lesson If you make cuts in a solid, different 2-dimensional cross sections result, as shown at the right. Describe the cross section of each figure cut below.

rectangle

27.
square or rectangle

28.
circle

29.
rectangle

Maintain Your Skills

Mixed Review Find the volume of each solid. If necessary, round to the nearest tenth.
(Lessons 11-2 and 11-3)

30. rectangular pyramid: length 6 ft, width 5 ft, height 7 ft **70 ft³**

31. cylinder: diameter 6 in., height 20 in. **565.5 in³**

Getting Ready for the Next Lesson **PREREQUISITE SKILL** Find each product.
*(To review **multiplying rational numbers**, see Lesson 5-3.)*

32. 10.3(8) **82.4**
33. 3.9(3.9) **15.21**
34. 12.3(9.2)(6) **678.96**
35. $\frac{1}{2} \cdot 2.6$ **1.3**
36. $\frac{1}{2} \cdot 82 \cdot 90$ **3690**
37. $\frac{1}{2}\left(6\frac{1}{2}\right)$ **$3\frac{1}{4}$**

Lesson 11-4 Surface Area: Prisms and Cylinders **577**

Answer

24. Surface area is the boundary around a solid. Volume is the space inside a solid. Answers should include the following.

• The formula for surface area involves the product of two dimensions and is given in square units. The formula for volume involves the product of three dimensions and is given in cubic units.

• Surface area describes the size of the total surfaces of a solid. Volume describes the capacity or amount of space contained inside a solid.

Lesson 11-4 Surface Area: Prisms and Cylinders **577**

NEW YORK
Performance Indicator
Reinforcement of 7.A.6 Evaluate formulas for given input values (surface area, rate and density problems)

1 Focus

5-Minute Check Transparency 11-5 Use as a quiz or review of Lesson 11-4.

Mathematical Background notes are available for this lesson on page 552D.

How is surface area important in architecture?

The opening activity questions are repeated on page 632 of the *Chapter 11 Resource Masters*.

Reading to Learn Mathematics, p. 632 — ELL

Pre-Activity *How is surface area important in architecture?*

Do the activity at the top of page 578 in your textbook. Write your answers below.

    a. The front triangle has a base of about 230 feet and height of about 120 feet. What is the area? **13,800 ft²**

    b. How could you find the total amount of glass used in the pyramid? **Find the area of all the sides and add.**

Reading the Lesson   1–3. See students' work.

Write a definition and give an example of each new vocabulary phrase.

Vocabulary	Definition	Example
1. lateral face		
2. slant height		
3. lateral area		

4. How does the slant height of a pyramid differ from the height of the pyramid? Include a drawing to help explain your answer. **The slant height is the height of one of the lateral faces, while the height of the pyramid is the height from the vertex to the base.**

Helping You Remember

5. Prepare the script for a short presentation on how to find the surface areas of pyramids and cones. Be sure to include any necessary vocabulary terms in your explanation. You may wish to include diagrams with your presentation. **See students' work.**

What You'll Learn

- Find surface areas of pyramids.
- Find surface areas of cones.

Vocabulary
- lateral face
- slant height
- lateral area

How is surface area important in architecture?

The front of the Rock and Roll Hall of Fame in Cleveland, Ohio, is a glass pyramid.

a. The front triangle has a base of about 230 feet and height of about 120 feet. What is the area? **13,800 ft²**

b. How could you find the total amount of glass used in the pyramid?

b. Find the area of all the sides and add.

SURFACE AREAS OF PYRAMIDS

The sides of a pyramid are called **lateral faces**. They are triangles that intersect at the vertex. The altitude or height of each lateral face is called the **slant height**.

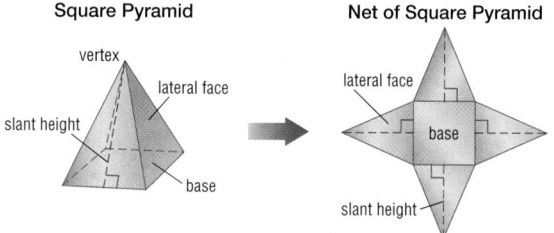

Square Pyramid   Net of Square Pyramid

The sum of the areas of the lateral faces is the **lateral area** of a pyramid. The surface area of a pyramid is the lateral area plus the area of the base.

Example 1   Surface Area of a Pyramid

Find the surface area of the square pyramid.

Find the lateral area and the base area.

8.2 m

6 m

Area of each lateral face

$$A = \frac{1}{2}bh \qquad \text{Area of a triangle}$$

$$A = \frac{1}{2}(6)(8.2) \qquad \text{Replace } b \text{ with 6 and } h \text{ with 8.2.}$$

$$A = 24.6 \qquad \text{Simplify.}$$

There are 4 faces, so the lateral area is 4(24.6) or 98.4 square meters.

Resource Manager

📂 Workbooks and Reproducible Masters

Chapter 11 Resource Masters
- Study Guide and Intervention, p. 629
- Skills Practice, p. 630
- Practice, p. 631
- Reading to Learn Mathematics, p. 632
- Enrichment, p. 633

Parent and Student Study Guide Workbook, p. 94

📺 Transparencies
5-Minute Check Transparency 11-5
Answer Key Transparencies

💿 Technology
Interactive Chalkboard

Area of base

$A = s^2$ Area of a square
$A = 6^2$ or 36   Replace *s* with 6 and simplify.

The surface area of a pyramid	equals	the lateral area	plus	the area of the base.
S	=	98.4	+	36

The surface area of the pyramid is 134.4 square meters.

Example 2   Use Surface Area to Solve a Problem

ARCHITECTURE   The Louvre museum in Paris has a huge square glass pyramid at the entrance with a slant height of about 92 feet. Its square base is 116 feet on each side. How much glass did it take to cover the pyramid?

Find the lateral area only, since the bottom of the pyramid is not covered in glass.

$A = \frac{1}{2}bh$ Formula for area of a triangle

$A = \frac{1}{2}(116)(92)$ Replace *b* with 116 and *h* with 92.

$A = 5336$ Simplify.

One lateral face has an area of 5336 square feet. There are 4 lateral faces, so the lateral area is 4 · 5336 or 21,344 square feet.

It took 21,344 square feet of glass to cover the pyramid.

SURFACE AREAS OF CONES   You can also find surface areas of cones. The net of a cone shows the regions that make up the cone.

Model of Cone

Net of Cone
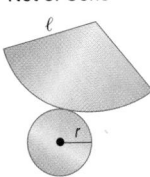

The lateral area of a cone with slant height ℓ is one-half the circumference of the base, $2\pi r$, times ℓ. So $A = \frac{1}{2} \cdot 2\pi r \cdot \ell$ or $A = \pi r \ell$. The base of the cone is a circle with area πr^2.

The surface area of a cone	equals	the lateral area	plus	the area of the base.
S	=	$\pi r \ell$	+	πr^2

Key Concept   **Surface Area of a Cone**

- **Words**   The surface area *S* of a cone with slant height ℓ and radius *r* is the lateral area plus the area of the base.

- **Model**

- **Symbols** $S = \pi r \ell + \pi r^2$

---

2 Teach

SURFACE AREAS OF PYRAMIDS

In-Class Examples   Power Point®

1 Find the surface area of the square pyramid.

8.9 ft

8 ft

206.4 ft²

2 **CANOPIES** A canopy is in the shape of a square pyramid that is 3.4 meters on each side. The slant height is 2 meters. How much canvas is used for the canopy?
13.6 m²

Teaching Tip Have students explain the difference between height and the slant height of a pyramid. If necessary, demonstrate with a model of a pyramid.

Career Choices

Architect
Architects must be able to combine geometric solids and understand their properties to form unified structures.

Online Research
For information about a career as an architect, visit: www.pre-alg.com/careers

---

D A I L Y
INTERVENTION   **Unlocking Misconceptions**

- **Surface Area of Pyramids and Cones** Students may mistakenly assume that different types of solid figures with similar measures will have equal surface areas. For example, students may believe that a pyramid with a slant height of 6 and a base length of 6 would have a surface area equal to that of a cone with a slant height of 6 and a diameter of 6. Have students work a number of problems with measurements like those just given and discuss their answers.

SURFACE AREAS OF CONES

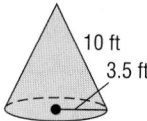

Example 3 Surface Area of a Cone

Find the surface area of the cone. Round to the nearest tenth.

$S = \pi r \ell + \pi r^2$ — Formula for surface area of a cone

$S = \pi(10.6)(15) + \pi(10.6)^2$ — Replace r with 10.6 and ℓ with 15.

$S \approx 852.5$ — Simplify.

The surface area of the cone is about 852.5 square meters.

15 m
10.6 m

✓ **Concept Check** What is the formula for the lateral area L of a cone? $L = \pi r \ell$

Check for Understanding

Concept Check
1. **Describe** the difference between slant height and height of a pyramid and a cone. **See margin.**

2. **Explain** how to find the lateral area of a pyramid. **See margin.**

3. **OPEN ENDED** Describe a situation in everyday life when a person might use the formulas for the surface area of a cone or a pyramid.
Sample answer: An architect might use the formulas to calculate the amount of materials needed for parts of a structure.

Guided Practice
Find the surface area of each solid. If necessary, round to the nearest tenth.

GUIDED PRACTICE KEY	
Exercises	Examples
4, 5	1
6	3
7	2

4. **66.4 ft²**
6.3 ft
4 ft   4 ft

5. **42.9 m²**
$A = 6.9 \, m^2$
6 m
4 m
4 m   4 m

6.
5 cm
13 cm
282.7 cm²

Application
7. **ARCHITECTURE** The small tower of a historic house is shaped like a regular hexagonal pyramid as shown at the right. How much roofing will be needed to cover this tower? (*Hint:* Do not include the base of the pyramid.) **336 ft²**

14 ft
8 ft

★ indicates increased difficulty

Practice and Apply

Find the surface area of each solid. If necessary, round to the nearest tenth.

8.
9 m
8 m   8 m
208 m²

9. **96.3 in²**
6 in.
$5\frac{1}{2}$ in.
$5\frac{1}{2}$ in.

10.
8 ft   6.9 ft
8 ft
8 ft
110.4 ft²

Find the surface area of each solid. If necessary, round to the nearest tenth.

11. 62.4 in^2
6 in.
5.2 in.
5.2 in.
6 in.
6 in.

12. 235.6 cm^2
10 cm
5 cm

13. ⟵ 10 in. ⟶
16.6 in.
339.3 in^2

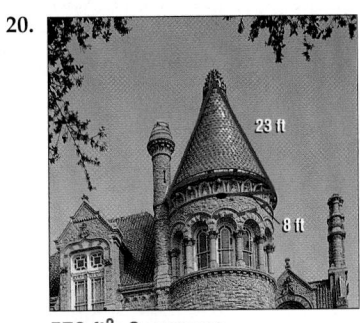

★ 14.
5 cm
15 cm
471.2 cm^2

★ 15.
$A = 48 \text{ m}^2$
10.6 m
8.3 m
311.9 m^2

★ 16.
5 in.
12.3 in.
15.2 in.
275 in^2

17. cone: radius 7.5 mm, slant height 14 mm 506.6 mm^2

18. square pyramid: base side length 9 yd, slant height 8 yd 225 yd^2

19. **FUND-RAISING** The cheerleaders are selling small megaphones decorated with the school mascot. There are two sizes, as shown at the right. What is the difference in the amount of plastic used in these two sizes? Round to the nearest square inch. (Note that a megaphone is open at the bottom.)
Style 8M has 29 in² more plastic.

8 in.
4 in.
Style 8M

6.5 in.
3.5 in.
Style 65M

ARCHITECTURE For Exercises 20 and 21, use the following information.
A roofing company is preparing bids on two special jobs involving cone-shaped roofs. Roofing material is usually sold in 100-square-foot squares. For each roof, find the lateral surface area to the nearest square foot. Then determine the squares of roofing materials that would be needed to cover each surface.

20.
23 ft
8 ft
578 ft^2; 6 squares

21.
12 ft
9 ft
339 ft^2; 4 squares

22. Sinkers: about 251 in², original bar: 82 in²; the surface area is about tripled.

22. **CRITICAL THINKING** A bar of lead in the shape of a rectangular prism 13 inches by 2 inches by 1 inch is melted and recast into 100 conical fishing sinkers. The sinkers have a diameter of 1 inch, a height of 1 inch, and a slant height of about 1.1 inches. Compare the total surface area of all the sinkers to the surface area of the original lead bar.

www.pre-alg.com/self_check_quiz/ny

Lesson 11-5 Surface Area: Pyramids and Cones **581**

Answers (p. 580)

1. Slant height is the altitude of a triangular face of a pyramid; it is the length from the vertex of a cone to the edge of its base. Height of a pyramid or cone is the altitude of the whole solid.

2. Use $A = \frac{1}{2}bh$ to find the area of each face. Then multiply by the number of faces.

Open-Ended Assessment

Modeling Have students make a net of a pyramid and a net of a cone out of heavy paper or cardboard. Have them label each face of the figures with the correct formula to determine its area, along with variables representing the needed measurements, such as slant height, base length, and radius. On a separate card, students should write the formula used to find the overall surface area of the solid and display the card with the net.

Getting Ready for Lesson 11-6

PREREQUISITE SKILL In Lesson 11-6, students will identify similar solids and solve problems involving similar solids. To determine whether solids are similar, a proportion comparing measurements of the solids must be written. Exercises 34–39 should be used to determine your students' familiarity with solving proportions.

---

23. **WRITING IN MATH** Answer the question that was posed at the beginning of the lesson. **See margin.**

How is surface area important in architecture?

Include the following in your answer:
- examples of how surface area is used in architecture, and
- an explanation of why building contractors and architects need to know surface areas.

NEW YORK
Test Practice

Standardized Test Practice
Ⓐ Ⓑ Ⓒ Ⓓ

24. Find the surface area of a cone with a radius of 7 centimeters and slant height of 11.4 centimeters. **D**
   Ⓐ 153.9 cm²   Ⓑ 250.7 cm²   Ⓒ 272.7 cm²   Ⓓ 404.6 cm²

25. What is the lateral area of the square pyramid at the right if the slant height is 7 inches? **C**
   Ⓐ 17.5 in²   Ⓑ 35 in²
   Ⓒ 70 in²   Ⓓ 95 in²

5 in.

Extending the Lesson The surface area S of a sphere with radius r is given by the formula $S = 4\pi r^2$. **Find the surface area of each sphere to the nearest tenth.**

26.

8 cm

804.2 cm²

27.

21 mm

5541.8 mm²

28.
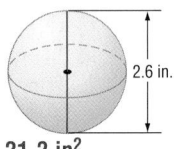
2.6 in.

21.2 in²

Maintain Your Skills

Mixed Review **Find the surface area of each solid. If necessary, round to the nearest tenth.**
(Lesson 11-4)

29. rectangular prism: length 2 ft, width 1 ft, height 0.5 ft **7 ft²**

30. cylinder: radius 4 cm, height 13.8 cm **447.4 cm²**

31. Find the volume of a cone that has a height of 6 inches and radius of 2 inches. Round to the nearest tenth. *(Lesson 11-3)* **25.1 in³**

State the solution of each system of equations. *(Lesson 8-9)*

32.
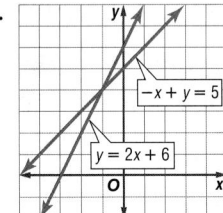
$-x + y = 5$
$y = 2x + 6$

(−1, 4)

33.
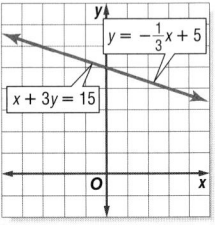
$y = -\frac{1}{3}x + 5$
$x + 3y = 15$

infinitely many solutions

Getting Ready for the Next Lesson **PREREQUISITE SKILL** Solve each proportion.
*(To review **proportions**, see Lesson 6-2.)*

34. $\frac{1}{6} = \frac{x}{24}$ **4**   35. $\frac{9}{15} = \frac{n}{5}$ **3**   36. $\frac{t}{7} = \frac{40}{56}$ **5**

37. $\frac{1.6}{y} = \frac{9.6}{18}$ **3**   38. $\frac{4}{3.2} = \frac{w}{20}$ **25**   39. $\frac{18}{21} = \frac{2.7}{n}$ **3.15**

582   Chapter 11   Three-Dimensional Figures

Answer

23. **Many building materials are priced and purchased by square footage. Architects use surface area when designing buildings. Answers should include the following.**
   - **Surface area is used in covering building exteriors and in designing interiors.**
   - **It is important to know surface areas so the amounts and costs of building materials can be estimated.**

NEW YORK *Performance Indicator* **8.PS.10 Use proportionality to model problems, 8.CN.2 Recognize connections between subsets of mathematical ideas**

Similar Solids

A model car is an exact replica of a real car, but much smaller. The dimensions of the model and the original are proportional. Therefore, these two objects are *similar solids*. The number of times that you increase or decrease the linear dimensions is called the scale factor.

You can use sugar cubes or centimeter blocks to investigate similar solids.

Activity 1
Collect the Data
- If each edge of a sugar cube is 1 unit long, then each face is 1 square unit and the volume of the cube is 1 cubic unit.
- Make a cube that has sides twice as long as the original cube.

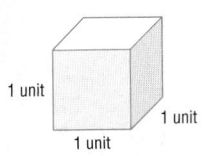

1 unit
1 unit
1 unit

Analyze the Data 3. 4 units²
1. How many small cubes did you use? **8**
2. What is the area of one face of the original cube? **1 unit²**
3. What is the area of one face of the cube that you built?
4. What is the volume of the original cube? **1 unit³**
5. What is the volume of the cube that you built? **8 units³**

Activity 2
Collect the Data
Build a cube that has sides three times longer than a sugar cube or centimeter block.

Analyze the Data 10. 4 times greater; 9 times greater
6. How many small cubes did you use? **27**
7. What is the area of one face of the cube? **9 units²**
8. What is the volume of the cube? **27 units³**
9. Complete the table at the right.
10. What happens to the area of a face when the length of a side is doubled? tripled?
11. Considering the unit cube, if the scale factor is x, what is the area of one face? the surface area? $x^2; 6x^2$

Scale Factor	Side Length	Area of a Face	Volume
1	1	1	1
2	2	4	8
3	3	9	27

12. What happens to the volume of a cube when **2³ or 8 times greater; 3³ or 27 times greater** the length of a side is doubled? tripled?
13. Considering the unit cube, let the scale factor be x. Write an expression for the cube's volume. x^3
14. **Make a conjecture** about the surface area and the volume of a cube if the sides are 4 times longer than the original cube. **96 units²; 64 units³**
15. **RESEARCH** the scale factor of a model car. Use the scale factor to estimate the surface area and volume of the actual car. **See students' work.**

Geometry Activity Similar Solids **583**

Resource Manager

📂 **Teaching Pre-Algebra with Manipulatives**
- p. 148 (student recording sheet)

Glencoe Mathematics Classroom Manipulative Kit
- centimeter cubes

Getting Started

Objective Investigate similar solids using sugar cubes or centimeter cubes.

Materials
sugar cubes
centimeter cubes

Teaching Tip Have four students with outstretched arms form a square. Ask what the area of the square is. 1 unit² Place another student on each side of the square and four students inside to complete the single unit squares. What is the area now? 4 units² Discuss how the two squares are similar.

Teach

- If the cubes being used are uniform in size, you may wish to have students measure the dimensions and determine true areas and volumes for the different figures to see if the relationships discussed can be verified.

Assess

In **Exercises 1–14**, students should be able to determine the relationship between scale factor and area and volume, thereby recognizing similar solids.

Study Notebook

Have students copy the scale factor table in their notebook for future reference. You may wish to have them complete the table for scale factors of 4, 5, or more.

1 Focus

 NEW YORK *Performance Indicator* **8.PS.10 Use proportionality to model problems**

5-Minute Check Transparency 11-6 Use as a quiz or review of Lesson 11-5.

Mathematical Background notes are available for this lesson on page 552D.

How can linear dimensions be used to identify similar solids?

The opening activity questions are repeated on page 637 of the *Chapter 11 Resource Masters*.

Reading to Learn Mathematics, p. 637 **ELL**

Pre-Activity *How can linear dimensions be used to identify similar solids?*

Do the activity at the top of page 584 in your textbook. Write your answers below.

a. The model boxcar is shaped like a rectangular prism. If it is 8.5 inches long and 1 inch wide, what are the length and width of the original train boxcar to the nearest hundredth of a foot? **61.63 ft long, 7.25 ft wide**

b. A model tank car is 7 inches long and is shaped like a cylinder. What is the length of the original tank car? **50.75 ft**

c. Make a conjecture about the radius of the original tank car compared to the model. **It is 87 times greater.**

Reading the Lesson

Write a definition and give an example of the new vocabulary word.

Vocabulary	Definition	Example
1. similar solids	See students' work.	

2. If two cylinders are similar, then their __radii__ and __heights__ are proportional.

3. If two cubes are similar, then their __edge lengths__ are proportional.

Helping You Remember

4. For each pair of solids listed in the table below, describe what measurements you would need to determine if the pair is similar.

Pair of Solids	Measurements Needed
Rectangular Prisms	base measures, length
Cylinders	radius or diameter, height
Square Pyramids	base length, height or slant height
Triangular Prisms	base measures, length
Cones	radius or diameter, height or slant height

Vocabulary
- similar solids

What You'll Learn
- Identify similar solids.
- Solve problems involving similar solids.

How can linear dimensions be used to identify similar solids?

The model train below is $\frac{1}{87}$ the size of the original train.

a. The model boxcar is shaped like a rectangular prism. If it is 8.5 inches long and 1 inch wide, what are the length and width of the original train boxcar to the nearest hundredth of a foot? **61.63 ft long, 7.25 ft wide**

b. A model tank car is 7 inches long and is shaped like a cylinder. What is the length of the original tank car? **50.75 ft**

c. **Make a conjecture** about the radius of the original tank car compared to the model. **It is 87 times greater.**

IDENTIFY SIMILAR SOLIDS The cubes below have the same shape. The ratio of their corresponding edge lengths is $\frac{6}{2}$ or 3. We say that 3 is the scale factor.

6 cm, 6 cm, 6 cm

2 cm, 2 cm, 2 cm

The cubes are **similar solids** because they have the same shape and their corresponding linear measures are proportional.

Study Tip

Look Back
To review **similar figures**, see Lesson 6-3.

TEACHING TIP

Point out that even though bases of cylinders have the same circular shape, if the corresponding lengths are not proportional, the cylinders are not similar.

Example 1 *Identify Similar Solids*

Determine whether each pair of solids is similar.

a.

32 cm, 1.25 cm, 40 cm, 1.0 cm

$\frac{32}{1} \overset{?}{=} \frac{40}{1.25}$ Write a proportion comparing radii and heights.

$32(1.25) \overset{?}{=} 1(40)$ Find the cross products.

$40 = 40 \checkmark$ Simplify.

The radii and heights are proportional, so the cylinders are similar.

Resource Manager

📁 **Workbooks and Reproducible Masters**

Chapter 11 Resource Masters
- Study Guide and Intervention, p. 634
- Skills Practice, p. 635
- Practice, p. 636
- Reading to Learn Mathematics, p. 637
- Enrichment, p. 638
- Assessment, p. 660

Parent and Student Study Guide Workbook, p. 95

📺 **Transparencies**
5-Minute Check Transparency 11-6
Real-World Transparency 11
Answer Key Transparencies

Technology
Interactive Chalkboard
Pre-AlgePASS: Tutorial Plus, Lesson 36

b.

$$\frac{14}{20} \stackrel{?}{=} \frac{7}{12}$$ Write a proportion comparing corresponding edge lengths.

$$14(12) \stackrel{?}{=} 20(7)$$ Find the cross products.

$$168 \neq 140$$ Simplify.

The corresponding measures are not proportional, so the pyramids are not similar.

USE SIMILAR SOLIDS   You can find missing measures if you know solids are similar.

Example 2   *Find Missing Measures*

The square pyramids at the right are similar. Find the height of pyramid B.

$$\frac{\text{base length of pyramid A}}{\text{base length of pyramid B}} = \frac{\text{height of pyramid A}}{\text{height of pyramid B}}$$

$$\frac{14}{28} = \frac{18}{h}$$ Substitute the known values.

$$14h = 28(18)$$ Find the cross products.

$$h = 36$$ Simplify.

The height of pyramid B is 36 meters.

The prisms at the right are similar with a scale factor of $\frac{3}{2}$.

Prism	Surface Area	Volume
X	90 m²	54 m³
Y	40 m²	16 m³

Prism X   Prism Y

Notice the pattern in the following ratios.

$$\frac{\text{surface area of prism X}}{\text{surface area of prism Y}} = \frac{90}{40} \text{ or } \frac{9}{4} \quad\Longrightarrow\quad \frac{9}{4} = \frac{3^2}{2^2}$$

$$\frac{\text{volume of prism X}}{\text{volume of prism Y}} = \frac{54}{16} \text{ or } \frac{27}{8} \quad\Longrightarrow\quad \frac{27}{8} = \frac{3^3}{2^3}$$

This and other similar examples suggest that the following ratios are true for similar solids.

Key Concept   *Ratios of Similar Solids*

- **Words**   If two solids are similar with a scale factor of $\frac{a}{b}$, then the surface areas have a ratio of $\frac{a^2}{b^2}$ and the volumes have a ratio of $\frac{a^3}{b^3}$.

- **Model**

Solid A   Solid B

Building on Prior Knowledge

In Lesson 6-2, students studied proportions. In this lesson, they will use proportions to determine whether various solids are similar.

2 Teach

IDENTIFY SIMILAR SOLIDS

In-Class Example   Power Point®

1 Determine whether each pair of solids is similar.

a.

no

b.

yes

Teaching Tip   Make sure students write proportions using a measure from the base as well as a lateral side or height.

USE SIMILAR SOLIDS

In-Class Example   Power Point®

Teaching Tip   Watch for students who erroneously invert one of the ratios. Have these students write out the proportion in words first and then substitute the known values.

2 The cylinders below are similar. Find the radius of cylinder A.

3 **DOLL HOUSES** Lita made a model of her fish tank for her doll house. The model is exactly $\frac{1}{25}$ the size of the original fish tank, whose dimensions are $120 \times 30 \times 38$ cm. What is the volume of the model? **8.8 cm³**

3 Practice/Apply

Study Notebook

Have students—

• add the definition/example of the vocabulary term to their Vocabulary Builder worksheets for Chapter 11.

• include any other item(s) that they find helpful in mastering the skills in this lesson.

About the Exercises . . .

Organization by Objective
• **Identify Similar Solids:** 10–13, 16–19, 23, 24
• **Use Similar Solids:** 14, 15, 20–22, 25

Odd/Even Assignments
Exercises 10–19 are structured so that students practice the same concepts whether they are assigned odd or even problems.

Assignment Guide

Basic: 11, 13, 17, 19, 22–38

Average: 11–19 odd, 21–38

Advanced: 10–18 even, 20–32 (Optional: 33–38)

All: Practice Quiz 2 (1–5)

More About. . .

Space ●··········

Engineers need to know the volume of the actual space capsules in order to estimate the air pressure.

Source: www.space.about.com

Example 3 *Use Similar Solids to Solve a Problem*

SPACE TRAVEL A scale model of the NASA space capsule is a combination of a truncated cone and cylinder. The small model built by engineers on a scale of 1 cm to 20 cm has a volume of 155 cm³. What is the volume of the actual space capsule?

Explore You know the scale factor $\frac{a}{b}$ is $\frac{1}{20}$ and the volume of the space capsule is 155 cm³.

Plan Since the volumes have a ratio of $\frac{a^3}{b^3}$ and $\frac{a}{b} = \frac{1}{20}$, replace a with 1 and b with 20 in $\frac{a^3}{b^3}$.

Solve

$$\frac{\text{volume of model}}{\text{volume of capsule}} = \frac{a^3}{b^3} \quad \text{Write the ratio of volumes.}$$

$$= \frac{1^3}{20^3} \quad \text{Replace } a \text{ with 1 and } b \text{ with 20.}$$

$$= \frac{1}{8000} \quad \text{Simplify.}$$

So, the volume of the capsule is 8000 times the volume of the model.

$8000 \cdot 155 \text{ cm}^3 = 1{,}240{,}000 \text{ cm}^3$

Examine Use estimation to check the reasonableness of this answer. $8000 \cdot 100 = 800{,}000$ and $8000 \cdot 200 = 1{,}600{,}000$, so the answer must be between 800,000 and 1,600,000. The answer 1,240,000 cm³ is reasonable.

Check for Understanding

Concept Check

1. **OPEN ENDED** Draw and label two cones that are similar. Explain why they are similar. **See pp. 601A–601B.**

2. **Explain** how you can find the surface area of a larger cylinder if you know the surface area of a smaller cylinder that is similar to it and the scale factor. **See margin.**

Guided Practice

GUIDED PRACTICE KEY	
Exercises	Examples
3, 4	1
5, 6	2
7–9	3

Determine whether each pair of solids is similar.

3. **no** 1 in. 1 in. 3 in. 4 in. 4 in. 8 in.

4. **yes** 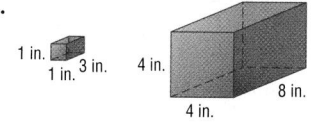 4 m 6 m 2 m 3 m

Find the missing measure for each pair of similar solids.

5. 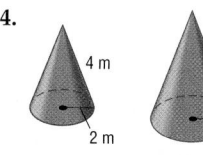 45 ft 6 ft 250 ft x $x = 33\frac{1}{3}$ ft

6. 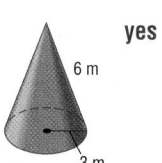 30 cm 45 cm 24 cm x 75 cm y $x = 50$ cm, $y = 36$ cm

---

DAILY
INTERVENTION   **Differentiated Instruction**

• **Interpersonal** Divide the class into small groups. Have each group draw a pair of similar solids with the appropriate dimensions labeled. The group should also determine the surface areas and volumes of their solids. Collect the groups' drawings, then present the dimensions of one of the pairs of similar solids to the class. Have the teams compete to see who can be the first to correctly give both the surface area and volume of each. Repeat several times.

Application **ARCHITECTURE** For Exercises 7–9, use the following information.
A model for an office building is 60 centimeters long, 42 centimeters wide, and 350 centimeters high. On the model, 1 centimeter represents 1.5 meters.

7. How tall is the actual building in meters? **525 m**

8. What is the scale factor between the model and the building? $\frac{1}{150}$

9. Determine the volume of the building in cubic meters. **2,976,750 m³**

★ indicates increased difficulty

Practice and Apply

Determine whether each pair of solids is similar.

10. **no**

11. **yes**

12. **no**

13. **yes**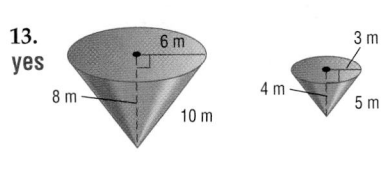

Find the missing measure for each pair of similar solids.

14. $x = 5.1$ ft

★ **15.** $x = 7$ m, $y = 18$ m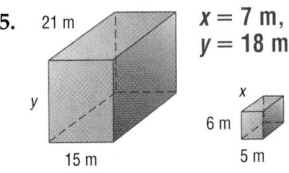

Determine whether each pair of solids is *sometimes, always,* or *never* similar. Explain. **16. always; same shape, lengths are proportional**

16. two cubes

17. two prisms

18. a cone and a cylinder
never; different shapes

19. two spheres

17. Sometimes; bases must be the same polygon and the corresponding side lengths must be proportional.

19. always; same shape, diameters or radii are proportional

HISTORY The *Mankaure* pyramid in Egypt has a square base that is 110 meters on each side, a height of 68.8 meters, and a slant height of 88.5 meters. Suppose you want to construct a scale model of the pyramid using a scale of 4 meters to 2 centimeters.

★ **20.** How much material will you need to use? **7892.5 cm²**

★ **21.** How much greater is the volume of the actual pyramid to the volume of the model? **200³ or 8,000,000 times greater**

 Online Research **Data Update** How have the dimensions of the Egyptian pyramids changed in thousands of years? Visit www.pre-alg.com/data_update to learn more.

22. CRITICAL THINKING The dimensions of a triangular prism are decreased so that the volume of the new prism is $\frac{1}{3}$ that of the original volume. Are the two prisms similar? Explain. **See margin.**

 www.pre-alg.com/self_check_quiz/ny

Answers

2. **Multiply the surface area of the smaller cylinder by the square of the scale factor.**

22. **Sample answer: The prisms are similar only if all the dimensions decreased proportionately.**

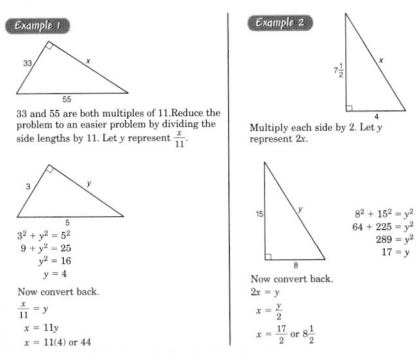

Teaching Tip Ask students to explain how they can use mental math to answer Exercise 24.

4 Assess

Open-Ended Assessment

Writing Have students describe in a short paragraph the use of proportions in identifying similar solids.

Getting Ready for Lesson 11-7

PREREQUISITE SKILL In Lesson 11-7, students will apply precision and significant digits to solving problems. Exercises 33–38 should be used to determine your students' familiarity with rounding decimals, which is an important step when determining significant digits.

Assessment Options

Practice Quiz 2 The quiz provides students with a brief review of the concepts and skills in Lessons 11-4 through 11-6. Lesson numbers are given to the right of exercises or instruction lines so students can review concepts not yet mastered.

Quiz (Lessons 11-5 and 11-6) is available on p. 660 of the *Chapter 11 Resource Masters*.

23. **WRITING IN MATH** Answer the question that was posed at the beginning of the lesson. **See margin.**

How can linear dimensions be used to identify similar solids?

Include the following in your answer:
- a description of the ratios needed for two solids to be similar, and
- an example of two solids that are *not* similar.

NEW YORK Test Practice

Standardized Test Practice
Ⓐ Ⓑ Ⓒ Ⓓ

24. Which prism shown in the table is *not* similar to the other three? **C**
Ⓐ prism A   Ⓑ prism B
Ⓒ prism C   Ⓓ prism D

Prism	Length	Width	Height
A	4	3	2
B	6	4.5	3
C	5	4	2
D	28	21	14

25. If the dimensions of a cone are doubled, the surface area **C**
Ⓐ stays the same.   Ⓑ is doubled.
Ⓒ is quadrupled.   Ⓓ is 8 times greater.

Maintain Your Skills

Mixed Review Find the surface area of each solid. If necessary, round to the nearest tenth. *(Lessons 11-4 and 11-5)* **28. 3166.7 m²**

26. 13 in. / 10 in.
282.7 in²

27. 5 ft / 4 ft / 10 ft / 6 ft
184 ft²

28. 22 m / 14 m

29. Angles J and K are complementary. Find $m\angle K$ if $m\angle J$ is 25°. *(Lesson 10-2)*
65°

Solve each equation. Check your solution. *(Lesson 5-9)*

30. $r - 3.5 = 8$ **11.5**   31. $\frac{2}{3} + y = \frac{1}{9}$ $-\frac{5}{9}$ 32. $\frac{1}{4}a = 6$ **24**

Getting Ready for the Next Lesson   PREREQUISITE SKILL   Find the value of each expression to the nearest tenth. *(To review rounding decimals, see page 711.)*

33. $13.28 + 6.05$ **19.3**   34. $8.99 - 1.2$ **7.8**   35. $2.4 \cdot 2.5$ **6.0**

36. $55 \div 3.8$ **14.5**   37. $6 + 1.9 + 1.45$ **9.4**   38. $6.7(0.3)(1.8)$ **3.6**

Practice Quiz 2
Lessons 11-4 through 11-6

Find the surface area of each solid. If necessary, round to the nearest tenth. *(Lessons 11-4 and 11-5)*

1. 5 mm / 4 mm / 7 mm
166 mm²

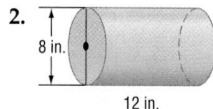
2. 8 in. / 12 in.
402.1 in²

3. **9.4 m²** / 2 m / 1 m

4. $8\frac{1}{4}$ in. / 10 in. / 10 in.
265 in²

5. Are the cylinders described in the table similar? Explain your reasoning. *(Lesson 11-6)*
Yes; their corresponding dimensions are proportional.

Cylinder	Diameter (mm)	Slant Height (mm)
A	24	21
B	16	14

Answer

23. If the ratios of corresponding linear dimensions are equal, the solids are similar. Answers should include the following.
- For example, if the ratio comparing the heights of two cylinders equals the ratio comparing their radii, then the cylinders are similar.
- A cone and a prism are not similar.

Precision and Accuracy

In everyday language, *precision* and *accuracy* are used to mean the same thing. When measurement is involved, these two terms have different meanings.

Term	Definition	Example
precision	the degree of exactness in which a measurement is made	A measure of 12.355 grams is more precise than a measure of 12 grams.
accuracy	the degree of conformity of a measurement with the true value	Suppose the actual mass of an object is 12.355 grams. Then a measure of 12 grams is more accurate than a measure of 18 grams.

Reading to Learn

1. Sample answer: Accuracy is how close a measurement is to the true value. Precision is how exact a measurement is.

1. Describe in your own words the difference between accuracy and precision.

2. **RESEARCH** Use the Internet or other resources to find an instrument used in science that gives very precise measurements. Describe the precision of the instrument. **Sample answer: A certain analytical balance is precise to the nearest 0.01 milligram.**

3. Use at least two different measuring instruments to measure the length, width, height, or weight of two objects in your home. Describe the measuring instruments that you used and explain which measurement was most precise. See students' work.

8. Sample answer: Accuracy, because it is more important to have approximately the correct amount of cement than it is to have a very precise amount.

Choose the correct term or terms to determine the degree of precision needed in each measurement situation.

4. In a travel brochure, the length of a cruise ship is described in (millimeters, meters).

5. The weight of a bag of apples in a grocery store is given to the nearest (tenth of a pound, tenth of an ounce).

6. In a science experiment, the mass of one drop of solution is found to the nearest 0.01 (gram, kilogram).

7. A person making a jacket measures the fabric to the nearest (inch, eighth of an inch).

8. **CONSTRUCTION** A construction company is ordering cement to complete all the sidewalks in a new neighborhood. Would the precision or accuracy be more important in the completion of their order? Explain.

Have students look up the words *precision* and *accuracy* in a dictionary and write two sentences, one for each word.

Teach

Provide students with a variety of instruments for measurement, for example, rulers, yardsticks, meter sticks, and tape measures with varying increments marked; thermometers; clocks, watches, and stopwatches; perhaps even a micrometer. Have students discuss which of the instruments are the most precise. Also discuss the accuracy of the instruments in a variety of situations.

Assess

Study Notebook

Have students pick a topic or field that interests them, such as sports or cooking, and discuss in several paragraphs how precision and accuracy relate to that topic. Students should provide several examples in their discussion.

ELL English Language Learners may benefit from writing key concepts from this activity in their Study Notebooks in their native language and then in English.

1 Focus

Mathematical Background notes are available for this lesson on page 552D.

Why are all measurements really approximations?

The opening activity questions are repeated on page 642 of the *Chapter 11 Resource Masters*.

Reading to Learn Mathematics, p. 642 **ELL**

Pre-Activity *Why are all measurements really approximations?*

Do the activity at the top of page 590 in your textbook. Write your answers below.

  a. Measure several objects (book widths, paper clips, pens…) using each ruler. Use a table to keep track of your measurements. **See students' work.**

  b. Analyze the measurements and determine which are most useful. Explain your reasoning. **Sample answer: The third ruler; it gives the most exact measurements.**

Reading the Lesson 1–2. See students' work.

Write a definition and give an example of each new vocabulary word or phrase.

Vocabulary	Definition	Example
1. precision		
2. significant digits		

3. When adding or subtracting measurements, the sum or difference should have the same precision as the least **precise measurement**.

4. When multiplying or dividing measurements, the product or quotient should have the same number of significant digits as the measurement with the least **number of significant digits**.

Helping You Remember

5. Provide two examples of each of the numbers described in the table below.

a. Write a number with four significant digits, two of which are zero.	b. Write a number with three significant digits, no decimal point, and three zeros.	c. Write a number with two significant digits, a decimal point, and two zeros.
70.02	325,000	0.068
0.053	987,000	0.10

11-7 Precision and Significant Digits

NEW YORK *Performance Indicator* Reinforcement of 7.M.9 Determine the tool and technique to measure with an appropriate level of precision: mass

What You'll Learn

- Describe measurements using precision and significant digits.
- Apply precision and significant digits in problem-solving situations.

Why are all measurements really approximations?

Vocabulary
- precision
- significant digits

Use cardboard to make three rulers 20 centimeters long, labeling the increments as shown at the right.

Ruler	Scale (cm)
1	0, 5, 10, 15, 20
2	0, 1, 2, 3, …, 18, 19, 20
3	0, 0.1, 0.2, 0.3, …, 19.8, 19.9, 20.0

  a. Measure several objects (book widths, paper clips, pens…) using each ruler. Use a table to keep track of your measurements. **See students' work.**

  b. Analyze the measurements and determine which are most useful. Explain your reasoning.

PRECISION AND SIGNIFICANT DIGITS

The **precision** of a measurement is the exactness to which a measurement is made. Precision depends on the smallest unit of measure being used, or the *precision unit*. You can expect a measurement to be accurate to the nearest precision unit.

The precision unit of this ruler is 1 centimeter.

Example 1 *Identify Precision Units*

Identify the precision unit of the ruler at the right.

The precision unit is one tenth of a centimeter, or 1 millimeter.

One way to record a measure is to estimate to the nearest precision unit. A more precise method is to include all of the digits that are actually measured, plus one *estimated* digit. The digits you record when you measure this way are called significant digits. **Significant digits** indicate the precision of the measurement.

estimated digit

17.7 cm ← 3 significant digits

digits known for certain

Study Tip

Precision
The precision unit of the measuring instrument determines the number of significant digits.

precision unit: 1 cm
actual measure: 17–18 cm
estimated measure: 17.7 cm

Resource Manager

Workbooks and Reproducible Masters

Chapter 11 Resource Masters
- Study Guide and Intervention, p. 639
- Skills Practice, p. 640
- Practice, p. 641
- Reading to Learn Mathematics, p. 642
- Enrichment, p. 643
- Assessment, p. 660

Parent and Student Study Guide Workbook, p. 96

Transparencies
5-Minute Check Transparency 11-7
Answer Key Transparencies

Technology
Interactive Chalkboard

estimated digit

17.<u>7</u>5 cm ← 4 significant digits

digits known for certain

precision unit: 0.1 cm
actual measure: 17.7–17.8 cm
estimated measure: 17.75 cm

There are special rules for determining significant digits in a given measurement. If a number contains a decimal point, the number of significant digits is found by counting the digits from left to right, starting with the first *nonzero* digit and ending with the last digit.

Number		Number of Significant Digits	
1.23	→	3	All nonzero digits are significant.
10.05	→	4	Zeros between two significant digits are significant.
0.072	→	2	Zeros used to show place value of the decimal are not significant.
50.00	→	4	In a number with a decimal point, all zeros to the right of a nonzero digit are significant.

If a number does *not* contain a decimal point, the number of significant digits is found by counting the digits from left to right, starting with the first digit and ending with the last *nonzero* digit. For example, 8400 contains 2 significant digits, 8 and 4.

Study Tip

Precision Units
Since 150 miles has only two significant digits, the measure is precise to the nearest 10 miles. Therefore, the precision unit is 10 miles, not 1 mile.

Example 2 *Identify Significant Digits*

Determine the number of significant digits in each measure.

a. 20.98 centimeters
   4 significant digits

b. 150 miles
   2 significant digits

c. 0.007 gram
   1 significant digit

d. 6.40 feet
   3 significant digits

COMPUTE USING SIGNIFICANT DIGITS When adding or subtracting measurements, the sum or difference should have the *same precision* as the least precise measurement.

Example 3 *Add Measurements*

The sides of a triangle measure 14.35 meters, 8.6 meters, and 9.125 meters. Use the correct number of significant digits to find the perimeter.

$$
\begin{array}{ll}
14.35 & \leftarrow \text{2 decimal places} \\
8.6 & \leftarrow \text{1 decimal place} \\
+\ 9.125 & \leftarrow \text{3 decimal places} \\
\hline
32.075 &
\end{array}
$$

The least precise measurement, 8.6 meters, has one decimal place. So, round 32.075 to one decimal place, 32.1. The perimeter of the triangle is about 32.1 meters.

Study Tip

Common Misconception
Calculators give answers with as many digits as the display can show. Be sure to use the correct number of significant digits in your answer.

www.pre-alg.com/extra_examples/ny

Lesson 11-7 Precision and Significant Digits **591**

2 Teach

PRECISION AND SIGNIFICANT DIGITS

In-Class Examples Power Point®

1 Identify the precision unit of the thermometer shown below. **5°F**

2 Determine the number of significant digits in each measure.

a. 1040 miles   **3**

b. 0.003 centimeter   **1**

c. 90.051 kilograms   **5**

d. 0.06300 liter   **4**

> **Teaching Tip** Ask students to describe measurements that require extreme precision and others that can be less precise. For example, a surgeon or dentist might require extremely precise measurements. A bulldozer operator's measurements would probably be less precise.

COMPUTE USING SIGNIFICANT DIGITS

In-Class Examples Power Point®

3 The sides of a quadrilateral measure 0.6 m, 0.044 m, 0.024 m, and 0.103 m. Use the correct number of significant digits to find the perimeter. **0.8 m**

4 Suppose the room in Example 4 was 12.25 ft wide and 14 ft long. What would be the area of the bedroom? **170 ft²**

DAILY INTERVENTION   Unlocking Misconceptions

- **Precision and Significant Digits** Students may automatically look to the number of digits beyond the decimal point when determining significant digits in a multiplication or division problem. Remind them that the number of decimal places in the numbers being multiplied may be irrelevant when determining significant digits in the product. The number with least amount of significant digits, both before and after the decimal point, determines significance in the product.

DAILY

INTERVENTION FIND THE ERROR
If students are having difficulty determining significant digits with zeros, make a two-column table with the heads *Significant Zeros* and *Insignificant Zeros*. List several examples for each. Have students choose the correct column for each number.

About the Exercises . . .

Organization by Objective
• **Precision and Significant Digits:** 13–22, 35–37, 40–43
• **Compute Using Significant Digits:** 23–34

Odd/Even Assignments
Exercises 13–34 are structured so that students practice the same concepts whether they are assigned odd or even problems.

Assignment Guide
Basic: 13–31 odd, 33, 35–37, 39–42, 44–47
Average: 13–33 odd, 35–37, 39–42, 44–47 (Optional: 43)
Advanced: 14–34 even, 35–47

When multiplying or dividing measurements, the product or quotient should have the *same number of significant digits* as the measurement with the least number of significant digits.

Example 4 Multiply Measurements

What is the area of the bedroom shown at the right?
To find the area, multiply the length and the width.

$$11.6 \leftarrow \text{3 significant digits}$$
$$\times\, 8.2 \leftarrow \text{2 significant digits}$$
$$95.12 \leftarrow \text{4 significant digits}$$

The answer cannot have more significant digits than the measurements of the length and width. So, round 95.12 ft² to 2 significant digits. The area of the bedroom is about 95 ft².

Check for Understanding

Concept Check

1. **FIND THE ERROR** A metal shelf is 0.0205 centimeter thick. Sierra says this measurement contains 2 significant digits. Josh says it contains 3 significant digits. Who is correct? Explain your reasoning. **See margin.**

2. **Choose** an instrument from the list at the right that is best for measuring each object.
   2b. surveyor's tools
   a. length of an envelope **cm ruler**
   b. distance between two stoplights
   c. width of a kitchen **12-ft tape measure**
   d. height of a small child **yardstick**

   > yardstick
   > centimeter ruler
   > surveyor's tools
   > 12-foot tape measure

3. **OPEN ENDED** Write a number that contains four digits, two of which are significant. **Sample answer: 0.012 or 2500**

Guided Practice

4. Identify the precision unit of the scale at the right. **1 oz**

GUIDED PRACTICE KEY	
Exercises	Examples
4	1
5–7	2
8–12	3, 4

Determine the number of significant digits in each measure.

5. 2.30 cm **3** 6. 50 yd **1** 7. 0.801 mm **3**

Calculate. Round to the correct number of significant digits.

8. 14.38 cm + 5.7 cm **20.1 cm**   9. 15.273 L − 8.2 L **7.1 L**

10. 3.147 mm · 1.8 mm **5.7 mm²**   11. 60.42 in. × 9.012 in. **544.5 in²**

Application

12. **MASONRY** A wall of bricks is 7.85 feet high and 13.0 feet wide. What is the area of the wall? Round to the correct number of significant digits.
102 ft²

Answers

1. Josh; the first two 0s are not significant because they are placeholders for the decimal point. The 0 between 2 and 5 is significant because it is between two significant digits and shows the actual value in the thousandths place.

33. b; The precision unit of ruler a is $\frac{1}{8}$ inch. The precision unit of ruler b is $\frac{1}{16}$ inch.

Answers for Excercises 35 and 39 are on page 594.

Practice and Apply

Identify the precision unit of each measuring tool.

13.
$\frac{1}{32}$ **in.**

14.
0.5 cm

Determine the number of significant digits in each measure.

15. 925 g **3**   **16.** 40 km **1**   **17.** 2200 ft **2**   **18.** 53.6 in. **3**

19. 0.01 mm **1**   **20.** 0.56 cm **2**   **21.** 18.50 m **4**   **22.** 4.0 L **2**

Calculate. Round to the correct number of significant digits. **27. 84.47 m**

23. 27 in. + 18.2 in. **45 in.**   **24.** 6.75 mm − 3.2 mm **3.6 mm**

25. 0.4 ft · 5.1 ft **2 ft²**   **26.** 7.30 yd × 1.61 yd **11.8 yd²**

27. 29.307 m + 4.23 m + 50.93 m   **28.** 127.2 g + 42.3 g − 5.7 g **163.8 g**

29. 50.2 cm − 0.75 cm **49.5 cm**   **30.** 18.160 L − 15 L **3 L**

31. 5.327 m · 4.8 m **26 m²**   ★ **32.** 4.397 cm · 2.01 cm **8.84 cm²**

33. MEASUREMENT Choose the best ruler for measuring an object to the nearest sixteenth of an inch. Explain your reasoning. **See margin.**

a.   **b.**

34. MEASUREMENT Order 0.40 mm, 40 mm, 0.4 mm, and 0.004 mm from most to least precise. **0.004 mm, 0.40 mm, 0.4 mm, 40 mm**

ORANGES For Exercises 35–37, refer to the graph at the right.

35. Are the numbers exact? Explain. **See margin.**

36. How many significant digits are used to describe orange production in 1992 and in 2001? **2; 3**

37. Write the number of tons of oranges produced in the United States in 2001 without using a decimal point. How many significant digits does this number have?
12,400,000; 3

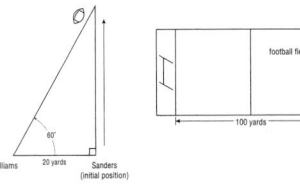

USA TODAY Snapshots®

Drought cuts orange crop

This year's U.S. orange production is expected to be down 5% from last year's 13-million-ton crop. Much of the drop is from reduced production in drought-stricken Florida. Annual U.S. orange production:

8.9 ... **12.4**

(in millions of tons)

1992 — 2001

Source: National Agricultural Statistics Service, April 2001 forecast

By Quin Tian, USA TODAY

38. MEASUREMENT ERROR Mrs. Hernandez is covering the top of a kitchen shelf that is $26\frac{3}{8}$ inches long and $15\frac{1}{2}$ inches wide. She incorrectly measures the length to be 25 inches long. How will this error affect her calculations?

39. CRITICAL THINKING The sizes of Allen hex wrenches are 2.0 mm, 3.0 mm, 4.0 mm, and so on. Will they work with hexagonal bolts that are marked 2 mm, 3 mm, 4 mm, and so on? Explain. **See margin.**

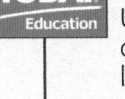 www.pre-alg.com/self_check_quiz/ny   **Lesson 11-7** Precision and Significant Digits **593**

Open-Ended Assessment

Modeling create a table showing the rules for determining significant digits when adding, subtracting, and multiplying and include an example for each.

Assessment Options

Quiz (Lesson 7) is available on p. 660 of the *Chapter 11 Resource Masters.*

Answers (p. 593)

35. No, the numbers are estimated to the nearest 0.1 million.

39. Not necessarily, because the actual size of the 2.0 mm wrench can range from 1.95 mm to 2.05 mm and the actual size of the 2 mm bolt can range from 1.5 mm to 2.5 mm. So, the bolts could be larger than the corresponding wrenches.

Answer

40. Measurements are accurate to the nearest precision unit. A smaller precision unit gives a more accurate measure. Answers should include the following.

   • The smallest unit of measure that is used determines the precision of a measurement.

   • For example, when a pharmacist is determining the amount of medicine to put in a prescription, an exact solution is needed. When a landscaper is determining how much mulch is needed for a client's yard, an approximate solution is sufficient.

40. **WRITING IN MATH** Answer the question that was posed at the beginning of the lesson. **See margin.**

   Why are all measurements really approximations?
   Include the following in your answer:
   • an explanation of what determines the precision of a measurement, and
   • an example of a real-life situation in which an exact solution is needed and a situation in which an approximate solution is sufficient.

NEW YORK Test Practice

Standardized Test Practice
Ⓐ Ⓑ Ⓒ Ⓓ

41. Choose the measurement that is most precise. **A**
   Ⓐ 12 mm Ⓑ 12 cm Ⓒ 1.2 m Ⓓ 12 m

42. Which solution contains the correct number of significant digits for the product 2.80 mm · 0.1 mm? **D**
   Ⓐ 0.28 mm² Ⓑ 0.280 mm² Ⓒ 0.30 mm² Ⓓ 0.3 mm²

Extending the Lesson

The **greatest possible error** is one-half the precision unit. It can be used to describe the actual measure. Refer to the paper clip in Example 1. It appears to be 4.9 centimeters long.

$$\text{greatest possible error} = \frac{1}{2} \cdot \text{precision unit}$$
$$= \frac{1}{2} \cdot 0.1 \text{ cm or } 0.05 \text{ cm}$$

The possible actual length of the paper clip is 0.05 centimeter less than or 0.05 centimeter greater than 4.9 centimeters, or between 4.85 and 4.95 centimeters.

★ 43. **TRAVEL** The odometer on a car shows 132.8 miles traveled. Find the greatest possible error of the measurement and use it to determine between which two values is the actual distance traveled.
   0.05 mi; between 132.75 mi and 132.85 mi

Maintain Your Skills

Mixed Review

44. Determine whether a cone with a height 14 centimeters and radius 8 centimeters is similar to a cone with a height of 12 centimeters and a radius of 6 centimeters. *(Lesson 11-6)* **no**

Find the surface area of each solid. If necessary, round to the nearest tenth.
(Lesson 11-5)

45.   1.3 cm
   5.2 cm
   26.5 cm²

46.   9 mm   **351.9 mm²**
   14 mm

47.   3.2 m   **14.8 m²**
   1.8 m   1.8 m

WebQuest Internet Project

Able to Leap Tall Buildings
It is time to complete your project. Use the information you have gathered about your building to prepare a report. Be sure to include information and facts about your building as well as a comparison of its size to some familiar item.

www.pre-alg.com/webquest

594 **Chapter 11** Three-Dimensional Figures

DAILY INTERVENTION

Differentiated Instruction

• **Logical** Ask students if, when determining significant digits, the answer to 3.28 × 4 would equal the answer to 3.28 + 3.28 + 3.28 + 3.28. Have them explain their answer. **No; the answer to 3.28 × 4 would need to be adjusted to one significant digit, therefore the answer would be 10. The answer to 3.28 + 3.28 + 3.28 + 3.28 would be adjusted to two decimal places, 13.12.**

Vocabulary and Concept Check

base (p. 557) plane (p. 556) skew lines (p. 558)
cone (p. 569) polyhedron (p. 556) slant height (p. 578)
cylinder (p. 565) precision (p. 590) solid (p. 556)
edge (p. 556) prism (p. 557) surface area (p. 573)
face (p. 556) pyramid (p. 557) vertex (p. 556)
lateral area (p. 578) significant digits (p. 590) volume (p. 563)
lateral face (p. 578) similar solids (p. 584)

Determine whether each statement is *true* or *false*. If false, replace the underlined word or number to make a true statement.

1. The <u>surface area</u> of a pyramid is the sum of the areas of its lateral faces. **false; lateral area**
2. <u>Volume</u> is the amount of space that a solid contains. **true**
3. The <u>edge</u> of a pyramid is the length of an altitude of one of its lateral faces. **false; slant height**
4. A triangular prism has two <u>bases</u>. **true**
5. A solid with two bases that are parallel circles is called a <u>cone</u>. **false; cylinder**
6. Prisms and pyramids are named by the shapes of their <u>bases</u>. **true**
7. Figures that have the same shape and corresponding linear measures that are proportional are called <u>similar solids</u>. **true**
8. Significant digits indicate the <u>precision</u> of a measurement. **true**

Lesson-by-Lesson Review

11-1 Three-Dimensional Figures

See pages 556–561.

Concept Summary

- Prisms and pyramids are three-dimensional figures.

Example **Identify the solid. Name the bases, faces, edges, and vertices.**
There is one triangular base, so the solid is a triangular pyramid.
faces: JKL, JLM, JMK
edges: $\overline{JK}$, $\overline{JL}$, $\overline{JM}$, $\overline{KL}$, $\overline{LM}$, $\overline{MK}$
vertices: J, K, L, M

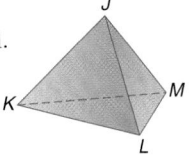

Exercises **Identify each solid. Name the bases, faces, edges, and vertices.**
See Example 1 on page 557. **9–11. See margin.**

9.
10.
11.

FOLDABLES
Study Organizer

For more information about Foldables, see *Teaching Mathematics with Foldables*.

Have students reexamine their Foldables to make sure the formulas and characteristics related to three-dimensional figures that they recorded are accurate.

Suggest that students refer to their Foldables if needed when working through the Study Guide exercises and studying for the chapter test.

Chapter
11 Study Guide and Review

Vocabulary and Concept Check

- This alphabetical list of vocabulary terms in Chapter 11 includes a page reference where each term was introduced.

- **Assessment** A vocabulary test/review for Chapter 11 is available on p. 658 of the *Chapter 11 Resource Masters*.

Lesson-by-Lesson Review

For each lesson,

- the main ideas are summarized,
- additional examples review concepts, and
- practice exercises are provided.

Vocabulary PuzzleMaker

ELL The Vocabulary PuzzleMaker software improves students' mathematics vocabulary using four puzzle formats—crossword, scramble, word search using a word list, and word search using clues. Students can work on a computer screen or from a printed handout.

MindJogger Videoquizzes

ELL MindJogger Videoquizzes provide an alternative review of concepts presented in this chapter. Students work in teams in a game show format to gain points for correct answers. The questions are presented in three rounds.

Round 1 Concepts (5 questions)
Round 2 Skills (4 questions)
Round 3 Problem Solving (4 questions)

Answers

See next page for Exercises 9–11.

Answers (p. 595)

9. rectangular prism; *QRST, UVWX* or *QTXU, RSWV* or *QRVU, TSWX*; *QRST, UVWX, QTXU, RSWV, QRVU, TSWX*; $\overline{QR}, \overline{RS}, \overline{ST}, \overline{TQ}, \overline{UV}, \overline{VW}, \overline{WX}, \overline{XU}, \overline{QU}, \overline{TX}, \overline{SW}, \overline{RV}$; *Q, R, S, T, U, V, W, X*

10. triangular prism; *GHJ, CDF*; *GHJ, CDF, CGJF, CGHD, FDHJ*; $\overline{CD}, \overline{DF}, \overline{FC}, \overline{GH}, \overline{HJ}, \overline{JG}, \overline{CG}, \overline{DH}, \overline{FJ}$; *C, D, F, G, H, J*

11. rectangular pyramid; *YNPZ*; *AYZ, AZP, ANP, ANY, YNPZ*; $\overline{AY}, \overline{AZ}, \overline{AP}, \overline{AN}, \overline{YZ}, \overline{ZP}, \overline{PN}, \overline{NY}$; *A, Y, Z, P, N*

11-2 Volume: Prisms and Cylinders

See pages 563–567.

Concept Summary

- Volume is the measure of space occupied by a solid region.
- The volume of a prism or a cylinder is the area of the base times the height.

Example   Find the volume of the cylinder. Round to the nearest tenth.

$V = \pi r^2 h$ Formula for volume of a cylinder
$V = \pi \cdot 2.3^2 \cdot 6.0$ Replace *r* with 2.3 and *h* with 6.0.
$V \approx 99.7$ Simplify.

The volume is about 99.7 cubic millimeters.

Exercises   Find the volume of each solid. If necessary, round to the nearest tenth.   *See Examples 1, 2, and 5 on pages 563–565.*

12.

217.9 m³

13.   **0.8 mm³**

14.   **192.5 cm³**

11-3 Volume: Pyramids and Cones

See pages 568–572.

Concept Summary

- The volume of a pyramid or a cone is one-third the area of the base times the height.

Example   Find the volume of the cone. Round to the nearest tenth.

$V = \frac{1}{3}\pi r^2 h$ Formula for volume of a cone

$V = \frac{1}{3} \cdot \pi \cdot 4^2 \cdot 8$ Replace *r* with 4 and *h* with 8.

$V \approx 134.0$ Simplify.

The volume is about 134.0 cubic inches.

Exercises   Find the volume of each solid. If necessary, round to the nearest tenth.   *See Examples 1 and 2 on pages 568 and 569.*

15.   **4 ft³**

16.

12.8 m³

17.   **1721.9 cm³**

11-4 Surface Area: Prisms and Cylinders

See pages 573–577.

Concept Summary

• The surface area of a prism is the sum of the areas of the faces.

• The surface area of a cylinder is the area of the two bases plus the product of the circumference and the height.

Example Find the surface area of the rectangular prism.

$S = 2\ell w + 2\ell h + 2wh$ Write the formula.

$S = 2(5)(4) + 2(5)(2) + 2(4)(2)$ Substitution

$S = 76$ Simplify.

The surface area is 76 square inches.

Exercises Find the surface area of each solid. If necessary, round to the nearest tenth. *See Examples 1–3 on pages 573–575.*

18.

190 in²

19. 13.1 mm

548.7 mm²

20.

466.5 cm²

11-5 Surface Area: Pyramids and Cones

See pages 578–582.

Concept Summary

• The surface area of a pyramid or a cone is the sum of the lateral area and the base area.

Example Find the surface area of the cone. Round to the nearest tenth.

$S = \pi r\ell + \pi r^2$ Write the formula.

$S = \pi(1.5)(4) + \pi(1.5)^2$ Replace r with 1.5 and ℓ with 4.

$S \approx 25.9$ Simplify.

The surface area is about 25.9 square meters.

Exercises Find the surface area of each solid. If necessary, round to the nearest tenth. *See Examples 1 and 3 on pages 578 and 580.*

21.   **45 in²**

22.

1411.8 cm²

23.   **37.1 in²**

Study Guide and Review

Chapter 11 For More ...
• Extra Practice, see pages 750–752.
• Mixed Problem Solving, see page 768.

11-6 Similar Solids

See pages 584–588.

Concept Summary

• Similar solids have the same shape and their corresponding linear measures are proportional.

Example Determine whether the solids are similar.

$\frac{12}{6} \stackrel{?}{=} \frac{8}{3}$ Write a proportion comparing radii and heights.

$12(3) \stackrel{?}{=} 6(8)$ Find the cross products.

$36 \neq 48$ Simplify.

The radii and heights are not proportional, so the cones are not similar.

Exercises Determine whether each pair of solids is similar.
See Example 1 on pages 584 and 585.

24.

no

25. **yes**

26. Find the missing measure for the pair of similar solids at the right.
See Example 2 on page 585. **x = 16.8 in.**

11-7 Precision and Significant Digits

See pages 590–594.

Concept Summary

• The precision of a measurement depends on the smallest unit of measure being used.

• Significant digits indicate the precision of a measurement.

Example Find 0.5 m + 0.75 m. Round to the correct number of significant digits.

$\begin{array}{r} 0.5 \quad \leftarrow \text{1 decimal place} \\ + 0.75 \quad \leftarrow \text{2 decimal places} \\ \hline 1.25 \end{array}$

The answer should have one decimal place. So, the sum is about 1.3 meters.

Calculate. Round to the correct number of significant digits.
See Examples 3 and 4 on pages 591 and 592. **27. 19.0 cm   28. 14.5 kg   30. 7.8 in²**

27. 10.3 cm + 8.7 cm   28. 25.71 kg − 11.2 kg   29. 0.04 m + 0.9 m **0.9 m**

30. 5.186 in. · 1.5 in.   31. 32.0 ft · 30.4 ft **973 ft²** 32. 80.51 g − 6.01 g **74.50 g**

Answers (p. 599)

1. A prism has two parallel congruent bases. A pyramid has one base.

2. Sample answer: Similar solids have the same shape and the corresponding linear measures are proportional.

4. rectangular prism; *ABCD*, *EFGH* or *ABFE*, *DCGH* or *ADHE*, *BCGF*; *ABCD*, *EFGH*, *ABFE*, *DCGH*, *ADHE*, *BCGF*; $\overline{AB}$, $\overline{BC}$, $\overline{CD}$, $\overline{DA}$, $\overline{EF}$, $\overline{FG}$, $\overline{GH}$, $\overline{HE}$, $\overline{AE}$, $\overline{BF}$, $\overline{CG}$, $\overline{DH}$; *A*, *B*, *C*, *D*, *E*, *F*, *G*, *H*

5. rectangular pyramid; *MNOP*; *LMN*, *LNO*, *LOP*, *LMP*, *MNOP*; $\overline{LM}$, $\overline{LN}$, $\overline{LO}$, $\overline{LP}$, $\overline{MN}$, $\overline{NO}$, $\overline{OP}$, $\overline{PM}$; *L*, *M*, *N*, *O*, *P*

Chapter 11 Practice Test

Vocabulary and Concepts

1. **Describe** the difference between a prism and a pyramid. **See margin.**
2. **Describe** the characteristics of similar solids. **See margin.**
3. **OPEN ENDED** Write a four-digit number that has three significant digits.
   Sample answer: **0.123 or 1230**

Skills and Applications

Identify each solid. Name the bases, faces, edges, and vertices. **4–5. See margin.**

4.

5.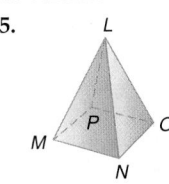

Find the volume of each solid. If necessary, round to the nearest tenth.

6. cylinder: radius 1.7 mm, height 8 mm **72.6 mm³**
7. rectangular pyramid: length 14 in., width 8 in., height 5 in. **186.7 in³**
8. cube: length 9.2 cm **778.7 cm³**
9. cone: diameter 26 ft, height 31 ft **5486.3 ft³**

Find the surface area of each solid. If necessary, round to the nearest tenth.

10. **3141.6 cm²**

11. **107 ft²**

12. **703.7 mm²**

13. Determine whether the given pair of solids is similar. Explain. **No; the corresponding measures are not proportional.**

Find the missing measure for each pair of similar solids.

14.   **x = 36 in.**

15.   **x = 14 m; y = 9 m**

Determine the number of significant digits in each measure.

16. 4500 mm **2**

17. 0.036 in. **2**

Calculate. Round to the correct number of significant digits.

18. 37.65 cm – 12.9 cm **24.8 cm**

19. 6.8 ft × 3.875 ft **26 ft²**

20. **STANDARDIZED TEST PRACTICE** A model of a new grocery store is 15 inches long, 9 inches wide, and 7 inches high. The scale is 50 feet to 3 inches. Find the length of the actual store. **C**

Ⓐ 45 ft   Ⓑ 150 ft   Ⓒ 250 ft   Ⓓ 750 ft

Assessment Options

Vocabulary Test A vocabulary test/review for Chapter 11 can be found on p. 658 of the *Chapter 11 Resource Masters*.

Chapter Tests There are six Chapter 11 Tests and an Open-Ended Assessment task available in the *Chapter 11 Resource Masters*.

Chapter 11 Tests			
Form	Type	Level	Pages
1	MC	basic	645–646
2A	MC	average	647–648
2B	MC	average	649–650
2C	FR	average	651–652
2D	FR	average	653–654
3	FR	advanced	655–656

MC = multiple-choice questions
FR = free-response questions

Open-Ended Assessment
Performance tasks for Chapter 11 can be found on p. 657 of the *Chapter 11 Resource Masters*, along with a sample scoring rubric for these tasks on p. A25.

Unit 4 Test A unit test/review can be found on pp. 665–666 of the *Chapter 11 Resource Masters*.

 ExamView® Pro

Use the networkable **ExamView® Pro** to:

- Create **multiple versions** of tests.
- Create **modified** tests for *Inclusion* students.
- **Edit** existing questions and **add** your own questions.
- Use built-in **state curriculum correlations** to create tests aligned with state standards.
- Change **English** tests to **Spanish** and vice versa.

Portfolio Suggestion

Introduction The study of three-dimensional figures and their properties is important for architects and others in design-related fields. It also serves as an introduction to a more detailed study of geometry in the future.

Ask Students to write a paragraph describing a number of real-life situations, such as architecture and packaging, in which the formulas for volume and surface area would be used.

These two pages contain practice questions in the various formats that can be found on the most frequently given standardized tests.

A practice answer sheet for these two pages can be found on page A1 of the *Chapter 11 Resource Masters*.

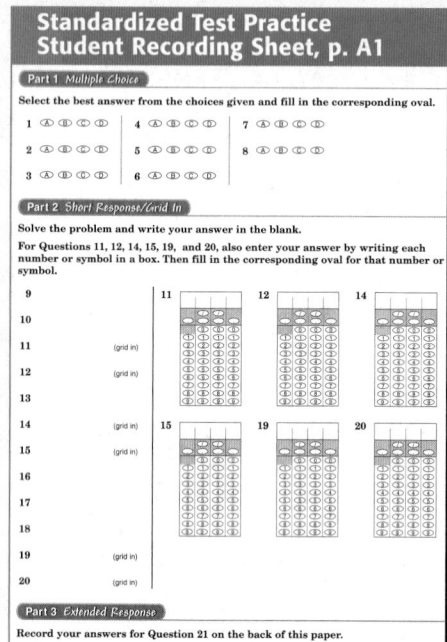

Additional Practice

See pp. 663–664 of the *Chapter 11 Resource Masters* for additional standardized test practice.

Part 1 Multiple Choice

Record your answers on the answer sheet provided by your teacher or on a sheet of paper.

1. If $-3x + 7 = -29$, then what is the value of x?   (Lesson 3-5) **D**
   (A) -12
   (B) -6
   (C) 6
   (D) 12

2. Austin wants to buy a fish tank so that his fish get as much oxygen as possible. The pet shop has four different fish tanks. The dimensions below represent the length and width of each fish tank. Which tank has the greatest surface area at the top?   (Lesson 3-7) **A**
   (A) 22 in. × 18 in.
   (B) 24 in. × 16 in.
   (C) 26 in. × 14 in.
   (D) 28 in. × 12 in.

3. The Hyde family's weekly food expenses for four consecutive weeks were $105.52, $98.26, $101.29, and $91.73. What is the mean of their weekly food expenses for those four weeks? (Lesson 5-7) **C**
   (A) $98.63
   (B) $98.75
   (C) $99.20
   (D) $99.78

4. Students taste-tested three brands of instant hot cereal and chose their favorite brand. Which of these statements is *not* supported by the data in the table?   (Lesson 6-1) **D**

Hot Cereal Brand			
	X	Y	Z
Girls	12	7	10
Boys	10	15	5

   (A) Twice as many girls as boys chose Brand Z.
   (B) The total number of students who chose Brand X is equal to the total number who chose Brand Y.
   (C) Three times as many boys chose Brand Y as Brand Z.
   (D) Half of the students who chose Brand Z were boys.

5. A sloppy-joe recipe for 12 servings calls for 2 pounds of ground beef. How many pounds of ground beef will be needed to make 30 servings?   (Lesson 6-3) **C**
   (A) 2.5 lb
   (B) 4.5 lb
   (C) 5 lb
   (D) 6 lb

6. Three-fourths of a county's population is registered to vote. Only 50% of the registered voters in the county actually voted in the election. What fractional part of the county's population voted?   (Lesson 6-4) **B**
   (A) $\frac{1}{2}$
   (B) $\frac{3}{8}$
   (C) $\frac{2}{3}$
   (D) $\frac{3}{4}$

7. Rod has $10 to spend at an arcade. Each bag of popcorn at the arcade costs $3.25, and each video game costs $1.00. Which expression represents the amount of money Rod will have left after he buys one bag of popcorn and plays n video games? (Lesson 7-2) **B**
   (A) $10.00 + 3.25 + 1.00n$
   (B) $10.00 - 3.25 - 1.00n$
   (C) $3.25 - 1.00n - 10.00$
   (D) $10.00 - 3.25n - 1.00n$

8. Cheyenne is 5 feet tall. She measures her shadow and a tree's shadow at the same time of day, as shown in the diagram below. How tall is the tree?   (Lesson 9-7) **B**

   (A) 20 ft
   (B) 22.5 ft
   (C) 40 ft
   (D) 57.6 f

Test-Taking Tip   (A) (B) (C) (D)

Pace yourself. Do not spend too much time on any one question. If you're having difficulty answering a question, mark it in your test booklet and go on to the next question. Make sure that you also skip the question on your answer sheet. At the end of the test, go back and answer the questions that you skipped.

ExamView® Pro

Special banks of standardized test questions similar to those on the SAT, ACT, TIMSS 8, NAEP 8, and Pre-Algebra End-of-Course tests can be found on this CD-ROM.

Record your answers on the answer sheet provided by your teacher or on a sheet of paper.

9. Determine the range of the relation shown in the graph. (Lesson 1-6) {1, 2, 8, 11}

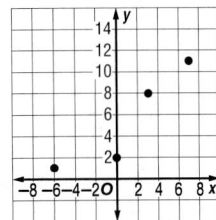

10. Simplify $-9s(4t)$. (Lesson 2-4) $-36st$

11. Thang is enclosing a rectangular area for his dog. He bought enough wire fencing to enclose 308 square feet of space. If he makes the length of the rectangle 22 feet, what is the width in feet? (Lesson 3-7) **14**

12. What is the value of x^{-2} for $x = 3$? (Lesson 4-7) **1/9**

13. Which number is greater, 3.45×10^3 or 5.87×10^2? (Lesson 4-8) $\mathbf{3.45 \times 10^3}$

14. Write the value of $\frac{5}{6} - \frac{1}{5} - \frac{1}{30}$ in simplest form. (Lesson 5-4) **3/5**

15. Mr. Vazquez budgeted $300 for his home's January heating bill. The actual bill was $240. What percent of the $300 was left after Mr. Vazquez paid the heating bill? (Lesson 6-4) **20**

16. What is the y-intercept of the graph of $y + 5 = 2x$? (Lesson 8-7) -5

17. Sarah is making a model house. The pitch of the roof is 35°. What is the measure, in degrees, of $\angle P$, the peak of the roof? (Lesson 10-3) **110**

18. What is the circumference of the circle? Use $\pi = 3.14$ and round to the nearest tenth, if necessary. (Lesson 10-9) **56.5 cm**

9 cm

19. A concrete worker is making six cement steps. Each step is 4 inches high, 7 inches deep, and 20 inches wide. What volume of cement, in cubic inches, will be needed to make these steps? (Lesson 11-2) **3360**

20. The prisms below are similar. Find the height of the larger prism in centimeters. If necessary, round to the nearest tenth. (Lesson 11-6) **60.3**

24.1 cm
18 cm
x
45 cm

Part 3 Extended Response

Record your answers on a sheet of paper. Show your work. 21c. 2560 cubic feet

21. A manufacturer ships its product in boxes that are 3 feet × 2 feet × 2 feet. The company needs to store some products in a warehouse space that is 32 feet long by 8 feet wide by 10 feet high. (Lesson 11-2)

a. What is the greatest number of boxes the company can store in this space? (All the boxes must be stored in the same position.) **200 boxes**

b. What is the total volume of the stored boxes? **2400 cubic feet**

c. What is the volume of the storage space?

d. How much storage space is *not* filled with boxes? **160 cubic feet**

Evaluating Extended Response Questions

Extended Response questions are graded by using a multilevel rubric that guides you in assessing a student's knowledge of a particular concept.

Goal: Identify three-dimensional figures and determine their volumes and surface areas.

Sample Scoring Rubric: The following rubric is a sample scoring device. You may wish to add more detail to this sample to meet your individual scoring needs.

Score	Criteria
4	A correct solution that is supported by well-developed, accurate explanations
3	A generally correct solution, but may contain minor flaws in reasoning or computation
2	A partially correct interpretation and/or solution to the problem
1	A correct solution with no supporting evidence or explanation
0	An incorrect solution indicating no mathematical understanding of the concept or task, or no solution is given

Page 555, Geometry Activity

10–15. Sample answers are given.

10. top side front

11. top side front

12. top side front

13. top side front

14. top side front

15. top side front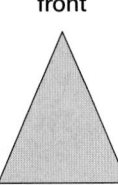

Pages 559–560, Lesson 11-1

7. top front side

  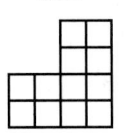

9. rectangular prism; *LMNP, QRST* or *LPTQ, MNSR* or *PNST, LMRQ*; *LMNP, QRST, LPTQ, MNSR, PNST, LMRQ*; $\overline{LM}$, $\overline{MN}$, $\overline{NP}$, $\overline{PL}$, $\overline{LQ}$, $\overline{MR}$, $\overline{NS}$, $\overline{PT}$, $\overline{QR}$, $\overline{RS}$, $\overline{ST}$, $\overline{TQ}$; *L, M, N, P, Q, R, S, T*

10. triangular prism; *FGH, IJK; FGH, IJK, HKIF, GHKJ, FGJI;* $\overline{FG}$, $\overline{GH}$, $\overline{HF}$, $\overline{IJ}$, $\overline{JK}$, $\overline{KI}$, $\overline{FI}$, $\overline{HK}$, $\overline{GJ}$; *F, G, H, I, J, K*

11. triangular pyramid; any one of the following faces can be considered a base: *WXY, WYZ, WZX, XYZ;* $\overline{WX}$, $\overline{WY}$, $\overline{WZ}$, $\overline{XZ}$, $\overline{XY}$, $\overline{YZ}$; *W, X, Y, Z*

12. rectangular pyramid; *BCDE; ABC, ACD, ADE, ABE, BCDE;* $\overline{AB}$, $\overline{AC}$, $\overline{AD}$, $\overline{AE}$, $\overline{BC}$, $\overline{CD}$, $\overline{DE}$, $\overline{EB}$; *A, B, C, D, E*

18. top side front

26. Sample answer:

The figure has bilateral symmetry because it can be divided into two matching halves. It does not have rotational symmetry because when rotated less than 360°, it never looks exactly as it does in its original position.

Page 570, Lesson 11-3

2. Prism $V = Bh$; cylinder $V = \pi r^2 h$; pyramid $V = \frac{1}{3}Bh$; cone $V = \frac{1}{3}\pi r^2 h$; B = area of base, h = height, r = radius; the formula for the volume of a pyramid and a cone is one-third times the formula for the volume of a prism and a cylinder, respectively.

3. Sample answer:

8 cm

4 cm

$V = 134.0$ cm^3

Page 586, Lesson 11-6

1. Sample answer:

The cones are similar because the ratios comparing their radii and slant heights are equal: $\frac{2}{3} = \frac{5}{7.5}$.

 5 m 2 m

 7.5 m 3 m

Notes

UNIT 5

Extending Algebra to Statistics and Polynomials

Introduction

In this unit, students will display and interpret data in various plots and graphs, and use measures of variation to compare data. Students also will count outcomes and use permutations and combinations. Probability will be extended to using simulations, finding experimental probability, and finding the probability of multiple events.

Students also will identify and classify polynomials and find the degree of a polynomial. They will learn to use operations involving manomials and poynomials. Students will finish the unit with an examination of linear and nonlinear functions, extending to the graphing of quadratic and cubic functions.

Assessment Options

 Unit 5 Test Pages 783–784 of the *Chapter 13 Resource Masters* may be used as a test or review for Unit 5. This assessment contains both multiple-choice and short answer items.

ExamView® Pro
This CD-ROM can be used to create additional unit tests and review worksheets.

Yearly Progress Pro
An online, research-based instructional, assessment, and intervention tool that provides specific feedback on student mastery of state and national standards, instant remediation, and a data management system to track performance. For more information, contact mhdigitallearning.com.

In Unit 3, you learned about real-world data that can be represented by linear functions. In this unit, you will learn about real-world data that can be represented by nonlinear functions.

Chapter 12
More Statistics and Probability

Chapter 13
Polynomials and Nonlinear Functions

What's MATH Got To Do With It?

Real-Life Math Videos

What's Math Got to Do With It? Real-Life Math Videos engage students showing them how math is used in everyday situations. Use Video 4 with this unit.

WebQuest Internet Project

Will Family Farms Die Like Mom, Pop Stores?

"Once upon a time, in little towns … across the USA, every business was family owned. Mom and Pop ran the grocery store. Also the butcher shop. Drugstore, Movie house. Gas station. Most of their customers were area farm families."

Source: *USA TODAY*, November 1, 2000

In this project, you will be using statistics and functions to analyze farming or ranching in America.

Log on to www.pre-alg.com/webquest. Begin your WebQuest by reading the Task.

Then continue working on your WebQuest as you study Unit 5.

Lesson	12-4	13-5
Page	626	690

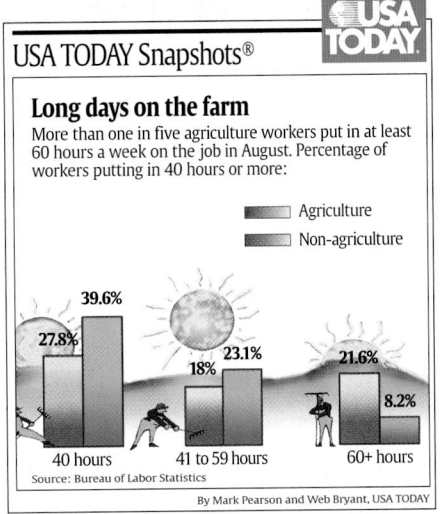

USA TODAY Snapshots®

Long days on the farm
More than one in five agriculture workers put in at least 60 hours a week on the job in August. Percentage of workers putting in 40 hours or more:

- Agriculture
- Non-agriculture

39.6%
27.8%
18% 23.1%
21.6%
8.2%

40 hours   41 to 59 hours   60+ hours

Source: Bureau of Labor Statistics

By Mark Pearson and Web Bryant, USA TODAY

Unit 5 Extending Algebra to Statistics and Polynomials **603**

WebQuest Internet Project

Problem-Based Learning A WebQuest is an online project in which students do research on the Internet, gather data, and make presentations using word processing, graphing, page-making, or presentation software. In each chapter, students advance to the next step in their WebQuest. At the end of Chapter 13, the project culminates with a presentation of their findings.

Teaching suggestions and sample answers are available in the *WebQuest and Project Resources*.

More Statistics and Probability
Chapter Overview and Pacing

Year-long pacing: pages T20–T21.

LESSON OBJECTIVES	PACING (days)			
	Regular		**Block**	
	Basic/ Average	Advanced	Basic/ Average	Advanced
12-1 Stem-and-Leaf Plots (pp. 606–611) • Display data in stem-and-leaf plots. • Interpret data in stem-and-leaf plots.	1	1	0.5	0.5
12-2 Measures of Variation (pp. 612–616) • Find measures of variation. • Use measures of variation to interpret and compare data.	1	1	0.5	0.5
12-3 Box-and-Whisker Plots (pp. 617–622) • Display data in a box-and-whisker plot. • Interpret data in a box-and-whisker plot. *Follow-Up:* Use a graphing calculator to create box-and-whisker plots.	1	2 (with 12-3 Follow-Up)	0.5	1 (with 12-3 Follow-Up)
12-4 Histograms (pp. 623–629) • Display data in a histogram. • Interpret data in a histogram. *Follow-Up:* Use a graphing calculator to make a histogram.	1	2 (with 12-4 Follow-Up)	0.5	1 (with 12-4 Follow-Up)
12-5 Misleading Statistics (pp. 630–633) • Recognize when statistics are misleading.	1	1	0.5	0.5
12-6 Counting Outcomes (pp. 635–640) • Use tree diagrams or the Fundamental Counting Principle to count outcomes. • Use the Fundamental Counting Principle to find the probability of an event. *Follow-Up:* Explore the relationship between tossing coins and Pascal's triangle.	1	2 (with 12-6 Follow-Up)	0.5	1 (with 12-6 Follow-Up)
12-7 Permutations and Combinations (pp. 641–645) • Use permutations. • Use combinations.	1	1	1	0.5
12-8 Odds (pp. 646–649) • Find the odds of a simple event.	1	1	0.5	0.5
12-9 Probability of Compound Events (pp. 650–657) • Find the probability of independent and dependent events. • Find the probability of mutually exclusive events. *Follow-Up:* Use simulations to examine outcomes.	1	2 (with 12-9 Follow-Up)	0.5	1.5 (with 12-9 Follow-Up)
Study Guide and **Practice Test** (pp. 658–663) **Standardized Test Practice** (pp. 664–665)	1	1	0.5	0.5
Chapter Assessment	1	1	1	0.5
TOTAL	11	15	6.5	8

*An electronic version of this chapter is available on **StudentWorks**™. This backpack solution CD-ROM allows students instant access to the Student Edition, lesson worksheet pages, and web resources.*

Chapter Resource Manager

CHAPTER 12 RESOURCE MASTERS						Prerequisite Skills Workbook	Applications*	Parent and Student Study Guide Workbook	5-Minute Check Transparencies	Interactive Chalkboard	Pre-AlgePASS: Tutorial Plus (lessons)	Materials
Study Guide and Intervention	Practice (Skills and Average)	Reading to Learn Mathematics	Enrichment		Assessment							
667	668–669	670	671			GCS 41	98	12-1	12-1			
672	673–674	675	676				99	12-2	12-2			
677	678–679	680	681	727		SM 22	100	12-3	12-3			*Follow-Up:* graphing calculator
682	683–684	685	686				101	12-4	12-4			*Follow-Up:* graphing calculator
687	688–689	690	691	727, 729			102	12-5	12-5	37		
692	693–694	695	696			SC 23	103	12-6	12-6			*Follow-Up:* penny, dime, nickel, quarter
697	698–699	700	701	728		SC 24	104	12-7	12-7			
702	703–704	705	706				105	12-8	12-8			
707	708–709	710	711	728		SM 6 GCS 42	106	12-9	12-9			*Follow-Up:* coin, number cube, red and white counters, blue and red marbles
				713–726, 730–732								

* *Key to Abbreviations:* GCS = Graphing Calculator and Spreadsheet Masters,
  SC = School-to-Career Masters,
  SM = Science and Mathematics Lab Manual

 ELL Study Guide and Intervention, Skills Practice, Practice, and Parent and Student Study Guide Workbooks are also available in Spanish.

Mathematical Connections and Background

Continuity of Instruction

Prior Knowledge

In Chapter 5, students learned how to find the mean, median, and mode, which are measures of central tendency. In Chapter 6, students discussed the difference between theoretical and experimental probability, learned how to calculate simple probabilities, and made predictions based on these calculations.

This Chapter

Students learn to display and interpret information in stem-and-leaf plots, box-and-whisker plots, and histograms. They also learn to recognize misleading displays and interpretations of data. Additionally, students calculate measures of variation for data sets. At the end of the chapter, students calculate more complex probabilities and odds, including probabilities of compound events.

Future Connections

This chapter forms a basis for further study in statistics, both in mathematics classes and applied in fields such as psychology and experimental science. Students' skill in understanding and interpreting data is vital in evaluating news broadcasts, advertisements, and political campaigns. An understanding of odds and probability will be useful in science and in interpreting weather data.

12-1 Stem-and-Leaf Plots

In a stem-and-leaf plot, numerical data are listed in ascending or descending order. The greatest place value of the data is used for the stems. The next greatest place value forms the leaves. For example, if the least number in a set of data is 32 and the greatest number is 56, draw a vertical line and write the stems from 3 to 5 to the left of the line. Write the leaves from 2 to 6 to the right of the line, with the corresponding stem. Next, rearrange the leaves so they are ordered from least to greatest. Then include a key or explanation, such as $3 \mid 2 = \$32$.

12-2 Measures of Variation

In statistics, measures of variation are used to describe how data are distributed. The range of a set of data is the difference between the greatest and the least values of the set. The quartiles are the values that divide the data into four equal parts. The median of a set of data separates the set in half. Similarly, the median of the lower half of a set of data is the lower quartile. The median of the upper half of a set of data is the upper quartile. The interquartile range is the difference between the upper quartile and the lower quartile.

12-3 Box-and-Whisker Plots

A box-and-whisker *plot* displays the measures of central tendency and variation. A box is drawn around the quartile values, and whiskers extend from each quartile to the extreme data points. To make a box-and-whisker plot for a set of data, draw a number line that covers the range of the data. Find the median, the extremes, and the upper and lower quartiles. Mark these points above the number line with bullets, then draw a box and the whiskers. The length of a whisker or box shows whether the values of the data in that part are concentrated or spread out.

12-4 Histograms

A histogram displays numerical data that have been organized into equal intervals with bars that have the same width and no space between them. While a histogram does not give exact data points, its shape shows the distribution of the data. Histograms also can be used to compare data.

12-5 Misleading Statistics

The way that statistics are displayed may sometimes be misleading. For example, expanding the vertical scale on a line graph can cause the line to flatten out, giving the appearance of slow, gradual change. Conversely, compressing the vertical scale emphasizes the variations, giving a more dramatic appearance. Similarly, breaking the vertical axis or not starting at zero changes the relative heights of the bars of a histogram. Other graph elements that may be misleading include the horizontal scale, the graph's title and labels, and the relative width of the bars in a bar graph.

12-6 Counting Outcomes

The Fundamental Counting Principle says that if event M can occur in m ways and is followed by event N that can occur in n ways, then the event M followed by N can occur in $m \cdot n$ ways. For example, if a shirt comes in 3 colors and 4 sizes, then there are $3 \cdot 4$ or 12 possible outcomes. If the number of possible outcomes is known, then the probability that an event will occur can be determined. For example, if 1 shirt is randomly selected from 12 shirts, the probability of randomly selecting a certain shirt is $\frac{1}{12}$.

12-7 Permutations and Combinations

An arrangement or listing in which order is important is called a permutation. The symbol $P(6, 3)$ represents the number of permutations of 6 things taken 3 at a time. For $P(6, 3)$, there are $6 \cdot 5 \cdot 4$ or 120 possible outcomes. An arrangement or listing where order is not important is called a combination. The symbol $C(10, 5)$ represents the number of combinations of 10 things taken 5 at a time. For $C(10, 5)$, there are

$$\frac{10 \cdot 9 \cdot 8 \cdot 7 \cdot 6}{5 \cdot 4 \cdot 3 \cdot 2 \cdot 1} \text{ or 252 possible outcomes.}$$

12-8 Odds

The odds in favor of an event is the ratio that compares the number of ways the event can occur to the ways that the event cannot occur. If the probability of an event occurring is $\frac{5}{7}$, then the odds of an event occurring are 5:2, or 5 to 2. The odds of the event *not* occurring are 2:5.

12-9 Probability of Compound Events

In independent events, the outcome of one event does *not* influence the outcome of a second. For example, if a bag contains 2 blue and 3 red marbles, then the probability of selecting a blue marble, replacing it, and then selecting a red marble is $P(A) \cdot P(B) = \frac{2}{5} \cdot \frac{3}{5}$ or $\frac{6}{25}$.

In dependent events, the outcome of one event affects the outcome of a second event. For example, if a bag contains 2 blue and 3 red marbles, then the probability of selecting a blue and then a red marble without replacing the first marble is $P(A) \cdot P(B \text{ following } A) = \frac{2}{5} \cdot \frac{3}{4}$ or $\frac{3}{10}$.

Two events that cannot happen at the same time are mutually exclusive. For example, when you roll two number cubes, you cannot roll a sum that is both 5 and even. So, $P(A \text{ or } B) = \frac{4}{36} + \frac{18}{36}$ or $\frac{11}{18}$.

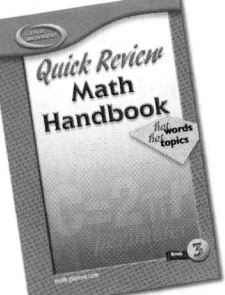

Quick Review Math Handbook

Hot Words includes a glossary of terms while Hot Topics consists of explanations of key mathematical concepts with exercises to test comprehension. This valuable resource can be used as a reference in the classroom or for home study.

Lesson	Hot Topics Section	Lesson	Hot Topics Section
GS 12	2.3, 2.4, 4.4, 4.6	12-5	4.1, 4.2
12-1	1.5, 4.2	12-6	2.1, 4.5
12-2	4.3, 4.4	12-6F	4.6
12-3	4.2	12-7	4.5, 6.5
12-3F	4.2	12-8	2.4, 4.5
12-4	4.2	12-9	4.6
12-4F	4.2	12-9F	4.6

GS = Getting Started, F = Follow-Up

 Additional mathematical information and teaching notes are available at www.pre-alg.com/key_concepts.

DAILY
INTERVENTION and Assessment

Key to Abbreviations:
TWE = Teacher Wraparound Edition; CRM = Chapter Resource Masters

	Type	Student Edition	Teacher Resources	Technology/Internet
INTERVENTION	Ongoing	Prerequisite Skills, pp. 605, 611, 616, 621, 628, 633, 639, 645, 649 Practice Quiz 1, p. 628 Practice Quiz 2, p. 645	5-Minute Check Transparencies Quizzes, *CRM*, pp. 727, 728 Mid-Chapter Test, *CRM*, p. 729 Study Guide and Intervention, *CRM*, pp. 667, 672, 677, 682, 687, 692, 697, 702, 707	Pre-Alge*pass*: Tutorial Plus, Lesson 37 www.pre-alg.com/self_check_quiz www.pre-alg.com/extra_examples
	Mixed Review	pp. 611, 616, 621, 628, 633, 639, 645, 649, 655	Cumulative Review, *CRM*, p. 730	
	Error Analysis	Find the Error, pp. 643, 648	Find the Error, *TWE*, pp. 643, 648 Unlocking Misconceptions, *TWE*, pp. 616, 652	
ASSESSMENT	Standardized Test Practice	pp. 611, 616, 621, 627, 633, 639, 645, 647, 648, 649, 655, 664–665	*TWE*, pp. 664–665 Standardized Test Practice, *CRM*, pp. 731–732	Standardized Test Practice CD-ROM www.pre-alg.com/standardized_test
	Open-Ended Assessment	Writing in Math, pp. 610, 616, 621, 627, 633, 639, 645, 649, 654 Open Ended, pp. 608, 614, 619, 625, 631, 637, 643, 648, 653 Standardized Test, p. 665	Modeling: *TWE*, pp. 616, 633, 645 Speaking: *TWE*, pp. 611, 621, 655 Writing: *TWE*, pp. 628, 639, 649 Open-Ended Assessment, *CRM*, p. 725	
	Chapter Assessment	Study Guide, pp. 658–662 Practice Test, p. 663	Multiple-Choice Tests (Forms 1, 2A, 2B), *CRM*, pp. 713–718 Free-Response Tests (Forms 2C, 2D, 3), *CRM*, pp. 719–724 Vocabulary Test/Review, *CRM*, p. 726	ExamView® Pro (see below) MindJogger Videoquizzes www.pre-alg.com/vocabulary_review www.pre-alg.com/chapter_test

For more information on Yearly ProgressPro, see p. 602.

Pre-Algebra Lesson	Yearly ProgressPro Skill Lesson
12-1	Stem-and-Leaf Plots
12-2	Measures of Variation
12-3	Box-and-Whisker Plots
12-4	Histograms: Level 1
12-5	Misleading Statistics
12-6	Tree Diagrams and the Fundamental Counting Principal
12-7	Permutations; Combinations
12-8	Probability as Fractions: Level 2
12-9	Probability of Compound Events

ExamView® Pro

Use the networkable **ExamView® Pro** to:
- Create **multiple versions** of tests.
- Create **modified** tests for *Inclusion* students.
- **Edit** existing questions and **add** your own questions.
- Use built-in **state curriculum correlations** to create tests aligned with state standards.
- Change **English** tests to **Spanish** and vice versa.

For more information on Intervention and Assessment, see pp. T8–T11.

Reading and Writing in Mathematics

Glencoe Pre-Algebra provides numerous opportunities to incorporate reading and writing into the mathematics classroom.

Student Edition

- Foldables™ Study Organizer, p. 605
- Reading Mathematics, p. 634
- Concept Check questions require students to verbalize and write about what they have learned in the lesson. (pp. 607, 608, 613, 614, 618, 619, 625, 631, 636, 637, 643, 646, 647, 648, 651, 652, 653)
- Writing in Math questions in every lesson, pp. 610, 616, 621, 627, 633, 639, 645, 649, 654
- Reading Math, pp. 624, 641, 642, 643, 647, 650
- WebQuest, p. 626

Teacher Wraparound Edition

- Foldables™ Study Organizer, pp. 605, 658
- Study Notebook suggestions, pp. 608, 614, 619, 626, 633, 634, 637, 640, 643, 647, 653, 657
- Modeling activities, pp. 616, 633, 645
- Speaking activities, pp. 611, 621, 655
- Writing activities, pp. 628, 639, 649
- Differentiated Instruction (Verbal/Linguistic), p. 632
- **ELL** Resources, pp. 604, 606, 612, 617, 623, 630, 632, 634, 635, 641, 646, 650, 658

For more information on Reading and Writing in Mathematics, see pp. T6–T7.

Additional Resources

- Vocabulary Builder worksheets require students to define and give examples for key vocabulary terms as they progress through the chapter (*Chapter 12 Resource Masters,* pp. vii–viii)
- Reading to Learn Mathematics master for each lesson (*Chapter 12 Resource Masters,* pp. 670, 675, 680, 685, 690, 695, 700, 705, 710)
- *Vocabulary PuzzleMaker* software creates crossword, jumble, and word search puzzles using vocabulary lists that you can customize.
- *Teaching Mathematics with Foldables* provides suggestions for promoting cognition and language.
- *Reading and Writing in the Mathematics Classroom*
- *WebQuest and Project Resources*

 ENGLISH LANGUAGE LEARNERS

Lesson 12-1
Using Models

Make a connection to real life by drawing a tree with its branches and leaves so that students can make a connection between real life and a stem-and-leaf plot. Next, show them how the plot is drawn and how the numbers in the data set are plotted. To extend the analogy, you may also wish to draw a stem with a leaf attached and place the digit in the tens place on the stem and the digit in the ones place on the leaf.

Lesson 12-4
Using Applications

Have students go around the class and ask as many students as possible what their favorite candy is. Then students can return to their desks. Show students how they would make a frequency table from the information they have collected. Explain the vocabulary *statistics, data,* and *frequency table* based on the activity.

Lesson 12-7
Building on Prior Knowledge

Ask students how they would define *combination.* Have students give real-life examples of how and when they use combinations. For instance cooking, clothing, arranging a wardrobe or packing for a trip. Then relate their applications to the mathematical definition of *combination.*

What You'll Learn

Have students read over the list of objectives and make a list of any words with which they are not familiar.

Why It's Important

Point out to students that this is only one of many reasons why each objective is important. Others are provided in the introduction to each lesson.

Lesson	NCTM Standards	Local Objectives
12-1	5, 6, 10	
12-2	5, 6, 9	
12-3	5, 6, 9, 10	
12-3 Follow-Up	5, 10	
12-4	5, 6, 10	
12-4 Follow-Up	5, 10	
12-5	5, 8, 10	
12-6	5, 6, 7, 10	
12-6 Follow-Up	5, 7, 10	
12-7	1, 5, 6, 9	
12-8	1, 5, 6, 9	
12-9	1, 5, 6, 7, 9	
12-9 Follow-Up	1, 5, 6, 7, 8, 9	

Key to NCTM Standards:

1=Number & Operations, 2=Algebra, 3=Geometry, 4=Measurement, 5=Data Analysis & Probability, 6=Problem Solving, 7=Reasoning & Proof, 8=Communication, 9=Connections, 10=Representation

Chapter 12 More Statistics and Probability

What You'll Learn

- **Lessons 12-1, 12-3, and 12-4** Display and interpret data in stem-and-leaf plots, box-and-whisker plots, and histograms.
- **Lesson 12-2** Find measures of variation.
- **Lesson 12-5** Recognize misleading statistics.
- **Lessons 12-6 and 12-7** Count outcomes using tree diagrams, the Fundamental Counting Principle, permutations, or combinations.
- **Lessons 12-8 and 12-9** Find probabilities and odds.

Key Vocabulary

- stem-and-leaf plot (p. 606)
- measures of variation (p. 612)
- box-and-whisker plot (p. 617)
- histogram (p. 623)
- odds (p. 646)

Why It's Important

Statistics is a branch of mathematics that involves the collection, presentation, and analysis of data. In statistics, graphs are usually used to present data. These graphs are important because they allow you to interpret the data easily. *You will display and interpret data about the United States government in Lesson 12-1.*

Vocabulary Builder

ELL

The Key Vocabulary list introduces students to some of the main vocabulary terms included in this chapter. For a more thorough vocabulary list with pronunciations of new words, give students the Vocabulary Builder worksheets found on pages vii and viii of the *Chapter 12 Resource Masters*. Encourage them to complete the definition of each term as they progress through the chapter. You may suggest that they add these sheets to their study notebooks for future reference when studying for the Chapter 12 test.

▶ **Prerequisite Skills**   To be successful in this chapter, you'll need to master these skills and be able to apply them in problem-solving situations. Review these skills before beginning Chapter 12.

For Lessons 12-1, 12-2, and 12-3   **Measures of Central Tendency**

Find the mean, median, and mode for each set of data. Round to the nearest tenth, if necessary.   *(For review, see Lesson 5-8.)* **4. 5.0, 5.1, 5.4**

 1. 10, 15, 23 **16; 15; none**   **2.** 21, 24, 24, 24, 42, 48 **30.5, 24, 24**

 3. 3.2, 5.1, 6.5, 6.5 **5.3, 5.8, 6.5**   **4.** 2.2, 4.3, 5.4, 3.2, 4.8, 5.4, 6.2, 8.1

For Lesson 12-9   **Simple Probability**

The spinner at the right is spun. Find each probability.
(For review, see Lesson 6-9.)

 5. $P(\text{green})$ $\frac{1}{3}$ **6.** $P(4)$ $\frac{1}{6}$ **7.** $P(\text{even})$ $\frac{1}{2}$

 8. $P(\text{not blue})$ $\frac{2}{3}$ **9.** $P(\text{prime})$ $\frac{1}{2}$ **10.** $P(\text{composite})$ $\frac{1}{3}$

For Lesson 12-9   **Compute with Fractions**

Find each product, sum, or difference.   *(For review, see Lessons 5-3 and 5-7.)*

 11. $\frac{1}{6} + \frac{1}{3}$ $\frac{1}{2}$ **12.** $\frac{2}{3} - \frac{4}{9}$ $\frac{2}{9}$ **13.** $\frac{3}{4} \times \frac{1}{6}$ $\frac{1}{8}$ **14.** $\frac{5}{8} \times \frac{3}{4}$ $\frac{15}{32}$

 15. $\frac{3}{8} \times \frac{4}{5} \times \frac{5}{9}$ $\frac{1}{6}$ **16.** $\frac{1}{2} \times \frac{5}{6} \times \frac{3}{4}$ $\frac{5}{16}$ **17.** $\frac{5}{12} + \frac{1}{12} - \frac{1}{3}$ $\frac{1}{6}$ **18.** $\frac{3}{8} + \frac{1}{2} - \frac{1}{4}$ $\frac{5}{8}$

FOLDABLES™
Study Organizer

Statistics and Probability Make this Foldable to help you organize your notes. Begin with a piece of notebook paper.

Step 1 Fold

Fold lengthwise to the holes.

Step 2 Cut

Cut along the top line and then cut 9 tabs.

Step 3 Label

Label lesson numbers and titles as shown.

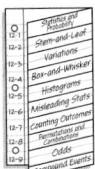

Reading and Writing As you read and study the chapter, you can write notes under the tabs.

This section provides a review of the basic concepts needed before beginning Chapter 12. Page references are included for additional student help.

Prerequisite Skills in the Getting Ready for the Next Lesson section at the end of each lesson reviews a skill needed in the next lesson.

For Lesson	Prerequisite Skill
12-2	Median (p. 611)
12-3	Ordering Decimals (p. 616)
12-4	Frequency Tables (p. 621)
12-5	Bar Graphs (p. 628)
12-6	Probability (p. 633)
12-7	Simplifying Fractions (p. 639)
12-8	Simplifying Ratios (p. 645)
12-9	Multiplying Fractions (p. 649)

FOLDABLES™
Study Organizer

For more information about Foldables, see *Teaching Mathematics with Foldables.*

Vocabulary and Writing Definitions This Foldable helps students better understand statistics and probability by organizing what they learn in their own words. Have students write concepts on the front of each tab and definitions on the back. Ask students to include their own statistical examples. Students can use this self-checking study guide to review as they proceed through the chapter.

NEW YORK *Performance Indicator* **8.R.1 Use** physical objects, drawings, **charts, tables,** graphs, symbols, equations, and objects created using technology **as representations**

1 Focus

5-Minute Check Transparency 12-1 Use as a quiz or review of Chapter 11.

Mathematical Background notes are available for this lesson on page 604C.

How can stem-and-leaf plots help you understand an election?

The opening activity questions are repeated on page 670 of the *Chapter 12 Resource Masters.*

Reading to Learn Mathematics, p. 670 **ELL**

Pre-Activity *How can stem-and-leaf plots help you understand an election?*

Do the activity at the top of page 606 in your textbook. Write your answers below.

a. Is there an equal number of electors in each group? Explain. Sample answer: Even though the intervals are the same, the data are not distributed evenly as the number of pieces of data in each interval are not the same.

b. Name an advantage of displaying the data in groups. Sample answer: You can see how the data are distributed.

Reading the Lesson 1–4. See students' work.

Write a definition and give an example of each new vocabulary word or phrase.

Vocabulary	Definition	Example
1. stem-and-leaf plot		
2. stems		
3. leaves		
4. back-to-back stem-and-leaf plot		

Helping You Remember

5. How will you remember which numbers of a stem-and-leaf plot represent the greater place value? Using the data at right, draw a back-to-back stem-and-leaf plot to look like actual leaves on stems. Then to read the data, start from the tree trunk and move outward.

Ages of Persons	
Apartment Building A	Apartment Building B
33, 16, 19, 26, 23, 11, 34, 24, 37, 17, 29	39, 21, 20, 1, 10, 21, 36, 37, 32, 22, 11, 2, 10, 1, 32, 38, 12, 36, 39

What You'll Learn

- Display data in stem-and-leaf plots.
- Interpret data in stem-and-leaf plots.

Vocabulary
- stem-and-leaf plot
- stems
- leaves
- back-to-back stem-and-leaf plot

a. Sample answer: Even though the intervals are the same, the data are not distributed evenly as the number of pieces of data in each interval are not the same.

b. Sample answer: You can see how the data are distributed.

How can stem-and-leaf plots help you understand an election?

The members of the Electoral College officially elect the President of the United States. These members are called electors. The number of electors for each state, including the District of Columbia, is shown.

Number of Electors								
AL: 9	DE: 3	IN: 12	MA: 12	NV: 4	OH: 21	TN: 11	WI: 11	
AK: 3	DC: 3	IA: 7	MI: 18	NH: 4	OK: 8	TX: 32	WY: 3	
AZ: 8	FL: 25	KS: 6	MN: 10	NJ: 15	OR: 7	UT: 5		
AR: 6	GA: 13	KY: 8	MS: 7	NM: 5	PA: 23	VT: 3		
CA: 54	HI: 4	LA: 9	MO: 11	NY: 33	RI: 4	VA: 13		
CO: 8	ID: 4	ME: 4	MT: 3	NC: 14	SC: 8	WA: 11		
CT: 8	IL: 22	MO: 10	NE: 5	ND: 3	SD: 3	WV: 5		

Source: *The World Almanac*

- Write each number on a self-stick note.
- Group the numbers: 0-9, 10-19, 20-29, 30-39, 40-49, 50-59.
- Organize the numbers in each group from least to greatest.

a. Is there an equal number of electors in each group? Explain.

b. Name an advantage of displaying the data in groups.

DISPLAY DATA   In a **stem-and-leaf plot**, numerical data are listed in ascending or descending order. The greatest place value of the data is used for the **stems**. The next greatest place value forms the **leaves**.

Example 1 Draw a Stem-and-Leaf Plot

ASTRONAUTS   Display the data shown at the right in a stem-and-leaf plot.

Step 1   Find the least and the greatest number. Then identify the greatest place value digit in each number. In this case, tens.

54 ⬆ The least number has 5 in the tens place.

77 ⬆ The greatest number has 7 in the tens place.

Oldest U.S. Astronauts	
Astronaut	**Age***
Roger K. Crouch	56
Don L. Lind	54
WIlliam G. Gregory	54
John H. Glenn	77
John E. Blaha	54
William E. Thornton	56
F. Story Musgrave	61
Karl G. Henize	58
Vance D. Brand	59
Henry W. Hartsfield	54

* At time of his last space shuttle flight

Source: *Top 10 of Everything*, 2001

Resource Manager

📂 Workbooks and Reproducible Masters

Chapter 12 Resource Masters
- Study Guide and Intervention, p. 667
- Skills Practice, p. 668
- Practice, p. 669
- Reading to Learn Mathematics, p. 670
- Enrichment, p. 671

Graphing Calculator and Spreadsheet Masters, p. 41
Parent and Student Study Guide Workbook, p. 98

Transparencies
5-Minute Check Transparency 12-1
Answer Key Transparencies

💿 Technology
Interactive Chalkboard

Step 2 Draw a vertical line and write the stems from 5 to 7 to the left of the line.

Stem
5
6
7

Step 3 Write the leaves to the right of the line, with the corresponding stem. For example, for 56, write 6 to the right of 5.

Stem	Leaf
5	6 4 4 4 6 8 9 4
6	1
7	7

Step 4 Rearrange the leaves so they are ordered from least to greatest. Then include a key or an explanation.

Stem	Leaf
5	4 4 4 4 6 6 8 9
6	1
7	7

> The key tells what the stems and leaves represent. → 5 | 6 = 56 years

☑ **Concept Check** Explain the difference between *stems* and *leaves*. See pp. 665A–665F.

INTERPRET STEM-AND-LEAF PLOTS It is often easier to interpret data when they are displayed in a stem-and-leaf plot instead of a table. You can "see" how the data are distributed.

Presidents •

The first President was George Washington. He was 57 years old at the time of his inauguration. He served as President from 1789 to 1797 and earned $25,000 per year.

Source: www.infoplease.com

Example 2 Interpret Data

PRESIDENTS The stem-and-leaf plot lists the ages of the U.S. Presidents at the time of their inauguration. **Source:** *The World Almanac*

Stem	Leaf
4	2 3 6 6 7 8 9 9
5	0 0 1 1 1 1 2 2 4 4 4 4 4 5 5 5 5 6 6 6 7 7 7 7 8
6	0 1 1 1 2 4 4 6 8 9

5 | 0 = 50 years

a. In which interval do most of the ages occur?

Most of the data occurs in the 50–59 interval.

b. What is the age difference between the youngest and oldest President?

The youngest age is 42. The oldest age is 69. The difference between these ages is 69 – 42 or 27.

c. What is the median age of a President at inauguration?

The median, or the number in the middle, is 55.

Study Tip

Look Back
To review **mean, median,** and **mode,** see Lesson 5-8.

Two sets of data can be compared using a **back-to-back stem-and-leaf plot**. The back-to-back stem-and-leaf plot below shows the scores of two basketball teams for the games in one season.

	Falcons		Cardinals	
The leaves for one set of data are on one side of the stem.	7 6 5 5 4 2 2 2	6	2 4	The leaves for the other set of data are on the other side of the stem.
	8 8 8 5 4	7	0 2 2 5 7 9	
	1 0 0	8	1 3 4 6 6 8 9 9	

1 | 8 = 81 points   8 | 6 = 86 points

DISPLAY DATA

In-Class Example Power Point®

1 **FOOD** Display the data in a stem-and-leaf plot.

Peanuts Harvested, 2001	
State	**Amount (lb)**
Alabama	2400
Florida	2800
Georgia	2800
New Mexico	2400
North Carolina	2900
Oklahoma	2200
South Carolina	2900
Texas	2600
Virginia	3000

Source: USDA

Stem	Leaf
2	2 4 4 6 8 8 9 9
3	0 2	4 = 2400 lb

INTERPRET STEM-AND-LEAF PLOTS

In-Class Example Power Point®

2 **VOTING** The stem-and-leaf plot lists the percent of voters in each state that voted for U.S. representatives in 1998. Source: U.S. Census Bureau

Stem	Leaf
1	1 0
2	2 5 5 8 8
3	0 0 0 2 2 2 3 3 3 4 4
3	5 5 6 6 7 7 7 8 8 9 9
4	0 0 0 1 1 3 3 3 4 4 4 4
4	5 6 7 9 9
5	0 1 4 9 3	4 = 34%

a. Which interval contains the most percentages? **in the 30–39 interval**

b. What is the greatest percent of voters that voted for U.S. representatives? **59%**

c. What is the median percent of voters that voted for U.S. representatives? **37.5%**

Interactive Chalkboard

PowerPoint® Presentations

This CD-ROM is a customizable Microsoft® Power-Point® presentation that includes:

- Step-by-step, dynamic solutions of each In-Class Example from the Teacher Wraparound Edition
- Additional, Your Turn exercises for each example
- The 5-Minute Check Transparencies
- Hot links to Glencoe Online Study Tools

Lesson 12-1 Stem-and-Leaf Plots **607**

3 **AGRICULTURE** The yearly production of honey in California and Florida is shown for the years 1993 to 1997, in millions of pounds. Source: USDA

California		Florida
	1	6 9
7 4	2	0 3 5
9 2	3	
5	4	

9 | 3 = 39   2 | 5 = 25

a. Which state produces more honey?   **California**

b. Which state has the most varied production? Explain. **California; the data are more spread out.**

---

3 Practice/Apply

Study Notebook

Have students—

- add the definitions/examples of the vocabulary terms to their Vocabulary Builder Worksheets for Chapter 12.

- copy one stem-and-leaf plot from their homework and use colored highlighters and a legend to explain what each part of the plot represents.

- include any other item(s) that they find helpful in mastering the skills in this lesson.

Example 3 **Compare Two Sets of Data**

WEATHER The average monthly temperatures for Helena, Montana, and Seattle, Washington, are shown.
Source: *The World Almanac*

Seattle, WA		Helena, MT
	2	0 1 6
	3	2 4
7 6 4 2 1	4	3 5
6 4 0	5	3 5
6 5 1 1	6	2 7 9

1 | 6 = 61°   4 | 5 = 45°

a. Which city has lower monthly temperatures? Explain.

Helena; it experiences temperatures in the 20's and 30's.

b. Which city has more varied temperatures? Explain.

The data for Helena are spread out from the 20's to the 60's. The data for Seattle are clustered from the 40's to the 60's. So, Helena has the most varied temperatures.

Check for Understanding

Concept Check

1. OPEN ENDED Write a statement describing how the data in Example 2 on page 607 are distributed. **See margin.**

2, 3, 4, 5, 6

2. Identify the stems for the data set {48, 52, 46, 62, 51, 39, 41, 57, 68}.

Guided Practice

Display each set of data in a stem-and-leaf plot. 3–4. See pp. 665A–665F.

GUIDED PRACTICE KEY	
Exercises	Examples
3, 4	1
5–7	2
8, 9	3

3.

Average Life Span					
Animal	**Years**	**Animal**	**Years**	**Animal**	**Years**
Asian Elephant	40	African Elephant	35	Lion	15
Horse	20	Red Fox	7	Chipmunk	6
Moose	12	Cow	15	Hippopotamus	41

Source: *The World Almanac*

4. **Summer Paralympic Games Participating Countries**

Year	'60	'64	'68	'72	'76	'80	'84	'88	'92	'96	'00
Countries	23	22	29	44	42	42	42	61	82	103	128

Source: www.paralympic.org

Applications

SCHOOL For Exercises 5–7, use the test score data shown at the right.

5. Find the lowest and highest scores. **50, 99**

6. What is the median score? **77.5**

7. Write a statement that describes the data. **See pp. 665A–665F.**

Pre-Algebra Test Scores

Stem	Leaf
5	0 9
6	4 5 7 8
7	0 4 4 5 5 6 7 8 8
8	2 3 3 5 7 8
9	0 1 5 5 9

5 | 9 = 59%

FOOD For Exercises 8 and 9, use the food data shown in the back-to-back stem-and-leaf plot.

8. What is the greatest number of fat grams in each sandwich? **20; 36**

9. In general, which type of sandwich has a lower amount of fat? Explain.

9. Chicken; whereas chicken sandwiches have 8–20 grams of fat, burgers have 10–36 grams of fat.

Fat (g) of Various Burgers and Chicken Sandwiches

Chicken		Burgers
8	0	
9 8 5 5 3 3	1	0 5 9
0	2	0 6
	3	0 3 6

8 | 0 = 8 g   2 | 6 = 26 g

Answer

1. Sample answer: The age of the youngest President at the time of his inauguration was 42 and the age of the oldest President to be inaugurated was 69. However, most of the Presidents were 50 to 59 years old at the time of their inauguration.

Practice and Apply

Display each set of data in a stem-and-leaf plot. **10–12. See margin.**

10.

State Representatives Northeast Region	
State	**Number**
Connecticut	6
Maine	2
Massachusetts	10
New Hampshire	2
Rhode Island	2
Vermont	1
New Jersey	13
New York	31
Pennsylvania	21

Source: *The World Almanac*

11.

Detroit Tigers Statistics, 2001	
Player	**Runs**
D. Cruz	39
Higginson	84
Encarnacion	52
Inge	13
Magee	26
T. Clark	67
Simon	28
Halter	53
Easley	77
Palmer	34
Macias	62
Fick	62
Cedeno	79

Source: *www.tigers.mlb.com*

12.

Percent of Young Adults (18–24) in U.S. Living at Home

Year	1960	1970	1980	1985	1990	1991	1992
Percent	52	54	54	60	58	60	60
Year	1993	1994	1995	1996	1997	1998	
Percent	59	60	58	59	60	59	

Source: *Bureau of the Census*

13–15. See pp. 665A–665F.

13.

Approximate Number of Students per Computer in U.S. Public Schools

Year	'85–'86	'86–'87	'87–'88	'88–'89	'89–'90	'90–'91	'91–'92
Number	50	37	32	25	22	20	18
Year	'92–'93	'93–'94	'94–'95	'95–'96	'96–'97	'97–'98	'98–'99
Number	16	14	11	10	8	6	6

Source: *The World Almanac*

TEACHING TIP
For Exercise 14, have students use stems from 46 to 57 to represent the whole number part of the data.

★ 14.

Olympic Men's 400-m Hurdles Time(s), 1900–2000

57.6	53.0	55.0	54.0	47.5	48.7
52.6	53.4	51.7	52.4	47.5	51.1
50.8	50.1	49.3	49.6	48.1	47.8
47.6	47.8	47.2	46.8		

Source: *The ESPN Sports Almanac*

★ 15.

Heights (ft) of Tallest Buildings in Miami, Florida

789	400	625	400	487	405
510	480	425	484	450	456
520	764				

Source: *The World Almanac*

Tell whether each statement is *sometimes, always,* or *never* true.

16. A back-to-back stem-and-leaf plot has two sets of data. **always**

17. A basic stem-and-leaf plot has two keys. **never**

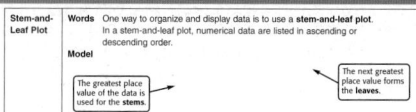

Study Guide and Intervention, p. 667

Stem-and-Leaf Plot	**Words** One way to organize and display data is to use a **stem-and-leaf plot**. In a stem-and-leaf plot, numerical data is listed in ascending or descending order.

Model

The greatest place value of the data is used for the **stems**.

The next greatest place value forms the **leaves**.

Example **ZOOS** Display the data shown at the right in a stem-and-leaf plot.

Step 1 The least and the greatest numbers are 55 and 95. The greatest place value digit in each number is in the tens. Draw a vertical line and write the stems from 5 to 9 to the left of the line.

Stem	Leaf
5	8 5
6	4
7	5
8	5 0 0
9	5 0 2

Step 2 Write the leaves to the right of the line, with the corresponding stem. For example, for 85, write 5 to the right of 8.

Step 3 Rearrange the leaves so they are ordered from least to greatest. Then include a key or an explanation.

Stem	Leaf
5	5 8
6	4
7	5
8	0 0 5
9	0 2 5

8 | 5 = 85 acres

Size of U. S. Zoos	
Zoo	**Size (acres)**
Audubon (New Orleans)	58
Cincinnati	85
Dallas	95
Denver	80
Houston	55
Los Angeles	80
Oregon	64
St. Louis	90
San Francisco	75
Woodland Park (Seattle)	92

Exercises

Display each set of data in a stem-and-leaf plot.

1. {27, 35, 39, 27, 24, 33, 18, 19}

Stem	Leaf
1	8 9
2	4 7 7
3	3 5 9

2 | 4 = 24

2. {94, 83, 88, 77, 95, 99, 88, 87}

Stem	Leaf
7	7
8	3 7 8 8
9	4 5 9

8 | 5 = 85

ROLLER COASTERS For Exercises 3 and 4, use the stem-and-leaf plot shown.

The Fastest Roller Coasters

Stem	Leaf
8	3 5
9	2 5
10	0

8 | 3 = 83 mph

3. What is the speed of the fastest roller coaster? The slowest? **100 mph; 83 mph**

4. What is the median speed? **92 mph**

Skills Practice, p. 668 and Practice, p. 669 (shown)

Display each set of data in a stem-and-leaf plot.

1. {68, 63, 70, 59, 78, 64, 68, 73, 61, 66, 70}

Stem	Leaf
5	9
6	1 3 4 6 8 8
7	0 0 3 8

6 | 4 = 64

2. {27, 32, 42, 31, 36, 37, 47, 23, 39, 31, 41, 38, 30, 34, 29, 42, 37}

Stem	Leaf
2	3 7 9
3	0 1 1 2 4 6 7 7 8 9
4	1 2 2 7

3 | 6 = 36

3.

Major League Baseball Leading Pitchers, 2000	
Player and Team	**Wins**
T. Glavine, Atlanta	21
T. Hudson, Oakland	20
R. Johnson, Arizona	19
D. Kile, St. Louis	20
G. Maddux, Atlanta	19
P. Martinez, Boston	18
C. Park, Los Angeles	18
A. Pettite, New York Y.	19
A. Sele, Seattle	17
D. Wells, Toronto	20

Source: World Almanac

Stem	Leaf
1	7 8 8 9 9 9
2	0 0 0 1

1 | 9 = 19

4.

Average Prices Received by U.S. Farmers, 1999	
Commodity	**Price (dollars per 100 pounds)**
Beef Cattle	63
Hogs	30
Lambs	75
Milk	15
Sheep	31
Veal Calves	88

Source: World Almanac

Stem	Leaf
1	5
2	
3	0 1
4	
5	
6	3
7	5
8	8

6 | 3 = $63 per 100 lbs

RECREATION For Exercises 5–7, use the information in the back-to-back stem-and-leaf plot shown at the right.

5. The category with the lowest total expenditure in 1992 was motion pictures. What was its total? **$5 billion**

6. What is the median total recreational spending for 1992? For 1998? **$17.5 billion; $26 billion**

7. Compare the total spending on recreation in 1992 with that in 1998. **In general, spending on recreation increases between 1992 and 1998.**

Total U.S. Spending on Personal Recreation (by Category)

1992		1998
7 5 5	0	7 8 9
8 7 2 0	1	5 7
7 2	2	4 8
4 0	3	2
	4	7
	5	6 8
	6	
	7	8
	8	
	9	3

7 | 2 = $27 billion   2 | 4 = $24 billion

Enrichment, p. 671

Statistical Graphs

Bar graphs and pictographs are used to compare quantities. Line graphs are used to show changes. Circle graphs compare parts to parts, or parts to the whole.

Solve. Use the pictograph.

Principal Languages of the World (to nearest fifty million)

English	
Hindi	
Arabic	
Portuguese	
Chinese	
Russian	
Spanish	
French	
Bengali	

= 100 million

1. How many people speak Portuguese? **150,000,000**

2. What is the ratio of people who speak Spanish to those who speak Russian? **1:1**

3. What three languages are each spoken by about 150 million people? **Arabic, Portuguese, Bengali**

4. How many fewer people speak Arabic than Hindi? **100,000,000**

Solve. Use the circle graph.

5. Which continent has the smallest population? **Australia**

6. How does the population of South America compare to that of Africa? **South America has about half as many people.**

7. What is the population of Australia if the world's population is about 6 billion? **about 18,000,000**

Population by Continent

Australia 0.3%
Europe 15.1%
North Am. 8.3%
South Am. 5.5%
Africa 10.9%
Asia 59.7%

Solve. Use the line graph.

Price Received by Farmers for One Dozen Eggs

8. During which ten-year period was the increase in the price of eggs greatest? **1940–1950**

9. What was the price of a dozen eggs in 1940? **16¢**

10. What was the percent of increase in the price of eggs from 1940 to 1950? **about 220–240%**

11. What was the increase in cents from 1930 to 1980? **about 32¢**

HEALTH For Exercises 18–21, use the graphic shown.

18. Display the data in a stem-and-leaf plot. **See margin.**

19. What is the greatest percent of people who exercise daily? **35%**

20. In how many of the cities do fewer than 30% of the people exercise daily? **5**

21. Write a sentence that describes the data. **See margin.**

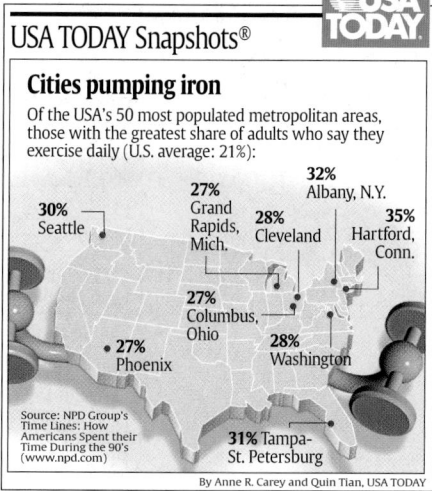

USA TODAY Snapshots®

Cities pumping iron

Of the USA's 50 most populated metropolitan areas, those with the greatest share of adults who say they exercise daily (U.S. average: 21%):

- 30% Seattle
- 27% Grand Rapids, Mich.
- 32% Albany, N.Y.
- 28% Cleveland
- 35% Hartford, Conn.
- 27% Columbus, Ohio
- 28% Washington
- 27% Phoenix
- 31% Tampa-St. Petersburg

Source: NPD Group's Time Lines: How Americans Spent their Time During the 90's (www.npd.com)

By Anne R. Carey and Quin Tian, USA TODAY

BASKETBALL For Exercises 22–25, use the information shown in the back-to-back stem-and-leaf plot. **Source:** USA TODAY

NCAA Woman's Basketball Statistics
Overall Games Won, 2000–2001

Big Ten Conference		Big East Conference
8 4	0	5 8 9 9
9 8 8 7 7 6 4 0	1	2 2 3 5 6 9 9
4	2	0 4 5

8 | 1 = 18 wins   1 | 5 = 15 wins

22. What is the greatest number of games won by a Big Ten Conference team? **24**

23. What is the least number of games won by a Big East Conference team? **5**

24. How many teams are in the Big East Conference? **14**

25. Compare the average number of games won by each conference. **See margin.**

RESEARCH For Exercises 26 and 27, use the Internet, a newspaper, or another reference source to gather data about a topic that interests you.

26. Make a stem-and-leaf plot of the data. **26–27. See students' work.**

27. Write a sentence that describes the data.

28. **WRITING IN MATH** Answer the question that was posed at the beginning of the lesson. **See pp. 665A–665F.**

How can stem-and-leaf plots help you understand an election?

Include the following in your answer:

- a stem-and-leaf plot that displays the number of electors for each state and the District of Columbia,
- a statement describing how the data in the stem-and-leaf plot are distributed, and
- an explanation telling how a presidential candidate might use the display.

610 Chapter 12 More Statistics and Probability

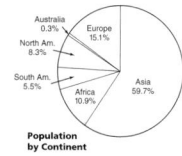

More About...

Basketball

The Louisiana Tech women's basketball team has the best-winning percentage in Division I. Over a 28-year period, the team has 793 wins and 133 losses.

Source: www.infoplease.com

Answers

18.

Stem	Leaf
2	7 7 7 8 8
3	0 1 2 5

3/1 = 31

21. Sample answer: In the most populated U.S. cities, about 27 to 35% of the people exercise daily.

25. The average number of games won by the teams in the Big East Conference is less than the average number of games won by the teams in the Big Ten Conference.

29. CRITICAL THINKING Suppose you have a table and a stem-and-leaf plot that display the same data. **See margin.**
  a. For which display is it easier to find the median? Explain.
  b. For which display is it easier to find the mean? Explain.
  c. For which display is it easier to find the mode? Explain.

30. What are the stems for the data {13, 34, 37, 25, 25, 35, 52, 28}? **B**
  Ⓐ {2, 3, 4, 5, 7, 8}   Ⓑ {1, 2, 3, 4, 5}
  Ⓒ {1, 2, 3, 5, 6}   Ⓓ {0, 1, 2, 3, 5}

31. The back-to-back stem-and-leaf plot shows the amount of protein in certain foods. Which of the following is a true statement? **C**

Amount of Protein (g)

Dairy Products		Legumes, Nuts, Seeds
9 8 8 7 7 5 2 2	0	5 6 9
0	1	4 5 8
6	2	
	3	9

6|2 = 26 grams   3|9 = 39 grams
Source: *The World Almanac*

  Ⓐ The median amount of protein in dairy products is 9 grams.
  Ⓑ The difference between the greatest and least amount of protein in dairy products is 28 grams.
  Ⓒ The average amount of protein in legumes, nuts, and seeds is more than the average amount in dairy products.
  Ⓓ The greatest amount of protein in legumes, nuts, and seeds is 93 grams.

Maintain Your Skills

Mixed Review   **32.** A triangle has sides that measure 12.38 inches, 7.5 inches, and 6.185 inches. Find the perimeter of the triangle using the correct number of significant digits. *(Lesson 11-7)* **26.1 in.**

Determine whether each pair of solids is similar. *(Lesson 11-6)*

33.
no   yes

35. Find the circumference and area of a circle with a radius of 10 feet. Round to the nearest tenth. *(Lesson 10-7)* **62.8 ft; 314.2 ft^2**

Express each decimal or fraction as a percent. Round to the nearest tenth percent, if necessary. *(Lesson 6-4)*

36. 0.36 **36%**   **37.** 2.47 **247%**   **38.** 0.019 **1.9%**   **39.** 0.0065 **0.65%**

40. $\frac{6}{25}$ **24%**   **41.** $\frac{4}{7}$ **57.1%**   **42.** $\frac{15}{8}$ **187.5%**   **43.** $\frac{24}{1500}$ **1.6%**

Getting Ready for the Next Lesson   **PREREQUISITE SKILL Find the median for each set of data. If necessary, round to the nearest tenth.** *(To review median, see Lesson 5-8.)* **47. 1.1**

44. 23, 45, 21, 35, 28 **28**   **45.** 18, 9, 2, 4, 6, 15, 13, 6, 1 **6**

46. 78, 54, 50, 64, 39, 45 **52**   **47.** 0.4, 1.3, 0.8, 2.6, 0.3, 1.8, 0.2, 2.1

Lesson 12-1   Stem-and-Leaf Plots   611

---

4 Assess

Open-Ended Assessment

Speaking Have students list the prices of various items sold in the school cafeteria. Ask them to describe what a stem-and-leaf plot of these data would look like and what the plot can tell them about cafeteria prices.

Getting Ready for Lesson 12-2

PREREQUISITE SKILL In Lesson 12-2, students will learn how to find the upper and lower quartiles of a set of data as well as the median. Use Exercises 44–47 to determine your students' familiarity with finding the median.

Answer

29a. Sample answer: It would be easier to find the median in a stem-and-leaf plot because the data are arranged in order from least to greatest.

29b. Sample answer: It would be easier to find the mean in a table because once you find the sum, it may be easier to count the number of items in a table.

29c. Sample answer: It would be easier to find the mode in a stem-and-leaf plot because the value or values that occur most often are grouped together.

DAILY
INTERVENTION   **Differentiated Instruction**

• **Visual/Spatial** Have each student find the average daily temperatures of a city, rounded to the nearest degree. Tell students to write the last digit of each temperature on one side of an index card and the first digit(s) on the other in a different color. Have students sort cards by stem and then write each stem on the board. Have students complete the stem-and-leaf plot by taping each leaf into place.

NEW YORK *Performance Indicator* Reinforcement of 7.S.4 Calculate the range for a given set of data

1 Focus

5-Minute Check Transparency 12-2 Use as a quiz or review of Lesson 12-1.

Mathematical Background notes are available for this lesson on page 604C.

Why are measures of varia-tion important in interpreting data?

The opening activity questions are repeated on page 675 of the *Chapter 12 Resource Masters.*

Reading to Learn Mathematics, p. 675 **ELL**

Pre-Activity *Why are measures of variation important in interpreting data?*

Do the activity at the top of page 612 in your textbook. Write your answers below.

a. What is the fastest speed? **173 mph**

b. What is the slowest speed? **142 mph**

c. Find the difference between these two speeds. **31 mph**

d. Write a sentence comparing the fastest winning average speed and the slowest winning average speed. **The fastest winning average speed and the slowest winning average speed are within 31 miles per hour of each other.**

Reading the Lesson 1–6. See students' work.

Write a definition and give an example of each new vocabulary word or phrase.

Vocabulary	Definition	Example
1. measures of variation		
2. range		
3. quartiles		
4. lower quartile		
5. upper quartile		
6. interquartile range		

Helping You Remember

7. Complete the following diagram by filling in the boxes with the appropriate vocabulary words.

Diagram Title: Measures of Variation

Vocabulary

- measures of variation
- range
- quartiles
- lower quartile
- upper quartile
- interquartile range

What You'll Learn

- Find measures of variation.
- Use measures of variation to interpret and compare data.

Why are measures of variation important in interpreting data?

The race that attracts the largest audience in auto racing is the Daytona 500. The average speed of each winning car from 1990 to 2001 is shown.

Car Driver	Speed (mph)	Car Driver	Speed (mph)
Derrike Cope	166	Dale Jarrett	154
Ernie Irvan	148	Jeff Gordon	148
Davey Allison	160	Dale Earnhardt	173
Dale Jarrett	155	Jeff Gordon	162
Sterling Marlin	157	Dale Jarrett	156
Sterling Marlin	142	Michael Waltrip	162

Source: *The World Almanac*

a. What is the fastest speed? **173 mph**

b. What is the slowest speed? **142 mph**

c. Find the difference between these two speeds. **31 mph**

d. Write a sentence comparing the fastest winning average speed and the slowest winning average speed.

d. The fastest winning average speed and the slowest winning average speed are within 31 miles per hour of each other.

MEASURES OF VARIATION

In statistics, **measures of variation** are used to describe the distribution of the data. One measure of variation is the range. The **range** of a set of data is the difference between the greatest and the least values of the set. It describes how a set of data varies.

Example 1 *Range*

Find the range of each set of data.

a. {5, 11, 16, 8, 4, 7, 15, 6}

The greatest value is 16, and the least value is 4.
So, the range is $16 - 4$ or 12.

b.

Stem	Leaf
5	4 4 4 4 6 6 8 9
6	1
7	7

$6 \mid 1 = 61$

The greatest value is 77, and the least value is 54.
So, the range is $77 - 54$ or 23.

Resource Manager

 Workbooks and Reproducible Masters

Chapter 12 Resource Masters
- Study Guide and Intervention, p. 672
- Skills Practice, p. 673
- Practice, p. 674
- Reading to Learn Mathematics, p. 675
- Enrichment, p. 676

Parent and Student Study Guide Workbook, p. 99

Transparencies
5-Minute Check Transparency 12-2
Answer Key Transparencies

 Technology
Interactive Chalkboard

In a set of data, the **quartiles** are the values that divide the data into four equal parts. Recall that the median of a set of data separates the set in half.

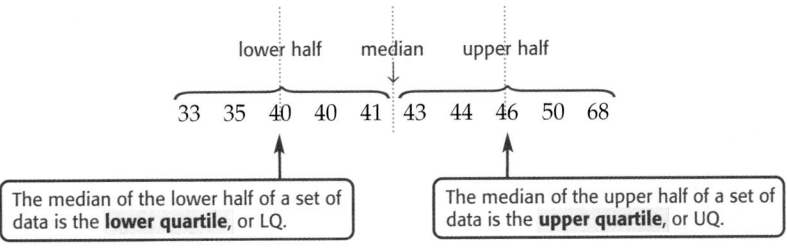

lower half   median   upper half

33 35 40 40 41 │ 43 44 46 50 68

The median of the lower half of a set of data is the **lower quartile**, or LQ.

The median of the upper half of a set of data is the **upper quartile**, or UQ.

✓ **Concept Check**   Into how many parts do the quartiles divide a set of data? **4**

The upper and lower quartiles can be used to find another measure of variation called the **interquartile range**.

Key Concept	Interquartile Range

- **Words**   The interquartile range is the range of the middle half of a set of data. It is the difference between the upper quartile and the lower quartile.

- **Symbols**   Interquartile range = UQ − LQ

Study Tip

Statistics

A small interquartile range means that the data in the middle of the set are close in value. A large interquartile range means that the data in the middle are spread out, or vary.

Example 2 **Interquartile Range**

Find the interquartile range for each set of data.

a. {27, 37, 21, 54, 47, 35}

Step 1 List the data from least to greatest. Then find the median.

21 27 35 37 47 54
↑
median = $\frac{35 + 37}{2}$ or 36

Step 2 Find the upper and lower quartiles.

The interquartile range is 47 − 27 or 20.

lower half   upper half

21 27 35 37 47 54
↑   ↑   ↑
LQ   median   UQ

b. {7, 12, 3, 2, 11, 9, 6, 4, 8}

Step 1 List the data from least to greatest. Then find the median.

2 3 4 6 7 8 9 11 12
↑
median

Step 2 Find the upper and lower quartiles.

The interquartile range is 10 − 3.5 or 6.5.

lower half   upper half

2 3 4 6 7 8 9 11 12
↑
median

LQ = $\frac{3 + 4}{2}$ or 3.5   UQ = $\frac{9 + 11}{2}$ or 10

---

2 Teach

MEASURES OF VARIATION

In-Class Examples   Power Point®

1 Find the range of each set of data.

a. {$79, $42, $38, $51, $63, $91}
$53

b.
Stem	Leaf	
3	3 3 5 7 7 8	**26**
4	0 3 3 4 9	
5	4 9	

$3 \mid 5 = 35$

2 Find the interquartile range for each set of data.

a. {38, 40, 32, 34, 36, 45, 33} **7**

b. {2, 27, 17, 14, 14, 22, 15, 32, 24, 25} **11**

Teaching Tip Point out that with an odd number of data, the median is the middle number and should be excluded from both halves. With an even number of data, the median falls between the two middle values and no data point is eliminated.

DAILY
INTERVENTION   **Differentiated Instruction**

- **Kinesthetic** Place 19 counters side-by-side in a row. Have a student locate the middle counter and slide it upward. Have two more students locate the middle counters of the two smaller groups and slide them downward. Explain that the interquartile range is the difference between the two lowered counters.

In-Class Example

Power Point®

3 **LAND USE** The urban land in certain western and eastern states is listed below as the percent of each state's total land, rounded to the nearest percent.

Western States		Eastern States
1 1 1 1 1 0 0	0	
3 2 2 2 1 1 1	0	3 3 4 5 6 6 8
5 4 4	0	8 9 9 9 9 9 9
	1	1 3 3 4 4 5
	2	3 6 7
$2 \mid 0 = 2\%$	3	5 $2 \mid 7 = 27\%$

Source: U.S. Census Bureau

a. What is the median percent of urban land use for each region?
western: 1%; eastern: 9%

b. Compare the range for each set of data.   **western: 5%; eastern: 32%; The percents of urban land use in the East vary more.**

3 Practice/Apply

Study Notebook

Have students—
• add the definitions/examples of the vocabulary terms to their Vocabulary Builder worksheets for Chapter 12.
• include any other item(s) that they find helpful in mastering the skills in this lesson.

More About. . .

SPEED LIMIT 75

Traffic Laws
In 1974, the national speed limit was 55 mph. Today, the speed limits for the 50 states range from 55 to 75 mph.
Source: www.infoplease.com

USE MEASURES OF VARIATION   You can use measures of variation to interpret and compare data.

Example 3   Interpret and Compare Data

TRAFFIC LAWS   The maximum allowable speed limits for certain western and eastern states are listed in the stem-and-leaf plot.

Western States		Eastern States
5	5	
5 5	6	5 5 5 5 5 5 5 5
5 5 5 5 5 5 5 0 0	7	0 0 0
$0 \mid 7 = 70$ mph		$6 \mid 5 = 65$ mph

Source: www.infoplease.com

a. What is the median speed limit for each region?
The median speed limit for the western states is 75.
The median speed limit for the eastern states is 65.

b. Compare the western states' range with the eastern states' range.
The range for the east is 70 − 65 or 5 mph, and the range for the west is 75 − 55 or 20 mph. So, the speed limits in the west vary more.

Check for Understanding

Concept Check
1. **Explain** how the range of a set of data differs from the interquartile range of a set of data. **1–3. See pp. 665A–665F.**

2. **Define** *upper quartile* and *lower quartile*.

3. **OPEN ENDED**   Write a list of at least 12 numbers that has an interquartile range of ten.

Guided Practice
Find the range and interquartile range for each set of data.

4. {26, 48, 12, 32, 41, 35} **36; 15**

5.
Stem	Leaf	**27; 6**
7	2 3 6 6 9	
8	0 0 1	
9	9	

GUIDED PRACTICE KEY

Exercises	Examples
4, 5	1, 2
6–8	3

Application
SCIENCE   For Exercises 6–8, use the information in the table.

6. Which planet's day length divides the data in half? **Earth**

7. What is the median length of day for the planets? **24 h**

8. Write a sentence describing how the lengths of days vary.
See pp. 665A–665F.

Planet	Length of Day* (Earth hours)
Mercury	1416
Venus	5832
Earth	24
Mars	25
Jupiter	10
Saturn	11
Uranus	17
Neptune	16
Pluto	154

*The lengths are approximate.
Source: *The World Almanac*

About the Exercises . . .

Organization by Objective
• **Measures of Variation:** 9–17, 19
• **Use Measures of Variation:** 17–20

Odd/Even Assignments
Exercises 9–16 are structured so that students practice the same concepts whether they are assigned odd or even problems.

Assignment Guide
Basic: 9–15 odd, 17, 18, 21–33
Average: 9–15 odd, 17–33
Advanced: 10–16 even, 17–29 (Optional: 30–33)

★ indicates increased difficulty

Practice and Apply

Homework Help

For Exercises	See Examples
9–16	1, 2
17–20	3

Extra Practice
See page 753.

Find the range and interquartile range for each set of data.

9. {65, 64, 73, 34, 15, 43, 92} **77; 39**   10. {9, 13, 25, 9, 1, 5, 6, 8} **24; 5.5**

11. {68°, 74°, 65°, 55°, 75°, 82°, 32°, 69°, 70°, 77°} **50; 10**

12. {$25, $21, $55, $43, $10, $89, $39, $91, $44, $76, $58} **81; 51**

13.

Stem	Leaf
0	1 2 2 5
1	3 4 7 8 9 9 9
2	6 6

2|6 = 26   **25; 15.5**

14.

Stem	Leaf
4	0
5	0 1 1 5 7 7 7 8
6	7 7 9

5|7 = 57   **29; 11.5**

15. Find the interquartile range for {213, 226, 204, 215, 210, 362, 119}. **22**

16. Determine the range of the middle half of the data set {30.2, 29.3, 35.3, 30.1, 28.5, 31.6, 27.5, 21.2}. **2.9**

WEATHER   For Exercises 17 and 18, use the data in the table.

Average Temperature (°F)				
City	Feb.	July	City	Feb.	July
Asheville, NC	39	73	Louisville, KY	36	77
Atlanta, GA	45	79	Oklahoma City, OK	41	82
Birmingham, AL	46	80	Portland, OR	44	68
Fresno, CA	51	82	Syracuse, NY	24	70
Houston, TX	54	83	Tampa, FL	62	82
Indianapolis, IN	30	75	Washington, DC	34	76
Little Rock, AR	44	82			

Source: The World Almanac

17. Find the interquartile range for each month's set of data. **Feb.: 13.5; July: 8**

18. Which month has more consistent temperatures? Justify your answer.
Sample answer: July; the temperatures are more tightly clustered around the median.

★ **BASEBALL**   For Exercises 19 and 20, use the data in the stem-and-leaf plot.

Home Runs Hit by League Leaders, 1960–2001

National League		American League
	2	2
9 9 8 8 8 7 7 7 6 6 6 5 1	3	2 2 2 2 3 6 6 7 9 9 9
4 4 4 3 1 0 0 0 0 0	4	0 0 0 0 1 2 3 3 4 4 4 4
9 9 9 8 8 8 7 7 7 6 6 5 5	4	5 5 6 6 7 8 8 9 9 9 9
2 2 0	5	0 1 2 2 6 6
5	6	1
3 0	7	

7|4 = 47 home runs   5|6 = 56 home runs
Source: The World Almanac

**19. National League:
42, 44, 48, 38, 10
American League: 39,
44, 49, 39, 10**

19. Find the range, median, upper quartile, lower quartile, and the interquartile range for each set of data.

20. Write a few sentences that compare the data. **See pp. 665A–665F.**

www.pre-alg.com/self_check_quiz/ny

Lesson 12-2 Measures of Variation **615**

Open-Ended Assessment

Modeling Have students make a list of 27 randomly selected numbers and write them in numerical order in a column on notebook paper, one number per line. They should cut out the strip that contains the numbers, fold the strip in half to find the median, and in half again to find the lower and upper quartiles. Have them compare these results with the computed results for the data.

Getting Ready for Lesson 12-3

PREREQUISITE SKILL Lesson 12-3 presents box-and-whisker plots, for which they must organize data, often in decimal form. Exercises 30–33 should be used to determine your students' familiarity with ordering decimals.

Answers

21a–c. Sample answers are given.

21a. {43, 49, 50, 50, 58, 60, 60, 66, 70, 70, 71, 78}

21b. {15, 18, 20, 20, 44, 60, 60, 64, 70, 70, 75, 79}

21c. The first set of data has a smaller interquartile range, thus the data in the first set are more tightly clustered around the median and the data in the second are more spread out over the range.

22. They allow us to see how the data are distributed. Answers should include the following.

• 156.5; 31; 11

• The average speed was 156.5 miles per hour. The speeds varied by 31 miles per hour. The speeds of the cars in the middle of the data set are close in value.

21a–c. See margin.

21. CRITICAL THINKING Write a set of data that satisfies each condition.

a. 12 pieces of data, a median of 60, an interquartile range of 20

b. 12 pieces of data, a median of 60, an interquartile range of 50

c. Compare the measures of variation for each set of data in parts **a** and **b**. What conclusions can be drawn about the sets of data?

22. **WRITING IN MATH** Answer the question that was posed at the beginning of the lesson. **See margin.**

Why are measures of variation important in interpreting data?

Include the following in your answer:

• the median, range, and interquartile range for the set of data, and

• an explanation telling what the median, range, and interquartile range convey about the speeds of the winning cars.

NEW YORK Test Practice

Standardized Test Practice
A B C D

23. Find the median for the set {43, 49, 91, 42, 94, 73, 93, 67, 55, 54, 78, 82}. **C**
    (A) 68   (B) 52   (C) 70   (D) 83

24. Which sentence best describes the data shown in the table? **B**

Height (ft) of Mountains in Alaska and Colorado

Colorado			Alaska		
14,238	14,433	14,309	14,163	14,410	20,320
14,083	14,264	14,197	16,550	14,530	14,831
14,269	14,196	14,150	17,400	16,237	14,070
14,165	14,420	14,246	15,885	14,573	16,390
14,286	14,265	14,361	15,638	14,730	16,286

Source: *The World Almanac*

(A) The heights of the mountains in Alaska vary by 6200 feet.

(B) The heights of the mountains in Colorado are clustered around the median height.

(C) The median height of a mountain in Alaska is 16,000 feet.

(D) The heights of the mountains in Colorado tend to be less consistent than the heights of the mountains in Alaska.

Maintain Your Skills

Mixed Review

25. Display the data set {$12, $15, $18, $21, $14, $37, $27, $9} in a stem-and-leaf plot. *(Lesson 12-1)* **See pp. 665A–665F.**

26. Calculate 27.08 mm + 6.5 mm. Round to the correct number of significant digits. *(Lesson 11-7)* **33.6 mm**

Find the volume of each cone described. Round to the nearest tenth. *(Lesson 11-3)* **28. 120.1 yd³**

27. radius 7 cm, height 9 cm **461.8 cm³**   28. diameter 8.4 yd, height 6.5 yd

29. The circumference of a circle is 9.82 feet. Find the radius of the circle to the nearest tenth. *(Lesson 10-7)* **1.6 ft**

Getting Ready for the Next Lesson

PREREQUISITE SKILL Order each set of decimals from least to greatest. *(To review **ordering decimals**, see page 710.)* **30–33. See pp. 665A–665F.**

30. 5.6, 5.3, 4.8, 4.3, 5.0, 4.9   31. 0.3, 1.4, 0.6, 1.5, 0.2, 0.8, 1.2

32. 45.2, 50.7, 46.0, 45.4, 40.6   33. 10.9, 11.4, 9.8, 10.5, 11.2, 9.9

D A I L Y INTERVENTION | **Unlocking Misconceptions**

• **Measures of Variation** Some students may mistakenly try to find the quartiles by dividing the range into four equal sections. Stress that *quartile* refers to quarters of the number of items, not quarters of the range.

Box-and-Whisker Plots

NEW YORK *Performance Indicator* **8.R.1 Use** physical objects, drawings, charts, **tables**, graphs, symbols, equations, **and objects created using technology as representations**

What You'll Learn

- Display data in a box-and-whisker plot.
- Interpret data in a box-and-whisker plot.

How can box-and-whisker plots help you interpret data?

The table shows the average monthly temperatures for two cities.

Vocabulary
- box-and-whisker plot

Average Monthly Temperatures (°F)

	J	F	M	A	M	J	J	A	S	O	N	D
Tampa, FL	60	62	67	71	77	81	82	82	81	75	68	62
Caribou, ME	9	12	25	38	51	61	66	63	54	43	31	15

a. Tampa: 60, 82, 73, 81, 64.5; Caribou: 9, 66, 40.5, 57.5, 20 b–d. See margin.

a. Find the low, high, and the median temperature, and the upper and lower quartile for each city.

b. Draw a number line extending from 0 to 85. Label every 5 units.

c. About one-half inch above the number line, plot the data found in part **a** for Tampa. About three-fourths inch above the number line, plot the data for Caribou.

d. Write a few sentences comparing the average monthly temperatures.

Study Tip

Common Misconception
You may think that the median always divides the box in half. However, the median may not divide the box in half because the data may be clustered toward one quartile.

DISPLAY DATA   A **box-and-whisker plot** divides a set of data into four parts using the median and quartiles. A *box* is drawn around the quartile values, and *whiskers* extend from each quartile to the extreme data points.

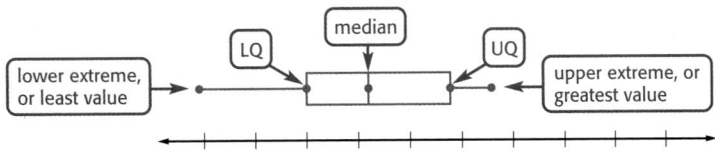

Example 1 Draw a Box-and-Whisker Plot

GEOGRAPHY   The amount of coastline for states along the Atlantic Coast is shown. Display the data in a box-and-whisker plot.

Atlantic Coast Coastline

State	Amount (mi)	State	Amount (mi)
Delaware	28	New Jersey	130
Florida	580	New York	127
Georgia	100	North Carolina	301
Maine	228	Rhode Island	40
Maryland	31	South Carolina	187
Massachusetts	192	Virginia	112
New Hampshire	13		

Source: www.infoplease.com

(continued on the next page)

Workbooks and Reproducible Masters

Chapter 12 Resource Masters
- Study Guide and Intervention, p. 677
- Skills Practice, p. 678
- Practice, p. 679
- Reading to Learn Mathematics, p. 680
- Enrichment, p. 681
- Assessment, p. 727

Parent and Student Study Guide Workbook, p. 100
Science and Mathematics Lab Manual, pp. 105–110

12-3 Lesson Notes

1 Focus

 5-Minute Check Transparency 12-3 Use as a quiz or review of Lesson 12-2.

Mathematical Background notes are available for this lesson on page 604C.

How can box-and-whisker plots help you interpret data?

The opening activity questions are repeated on page 680 of the *Chapter 12 Resource Masters*.

Reading to Learn Mathematics, p. 680   **ELL**

Pre-Activity   *How can box-and-whisker plots help you interpret data?*

Do the activity at the top of page 617 in your textbook. Write your answers below.

a. Find the low, high, and the median temperature, and the upper and lower quartile for each city.

	Low	LQ	Median	UQ	High
Tampa, FL	60	64.5	73	81	82
Caribou, ME	9	20	40.5	57.5	66

b. Draw a number line extending from 0 to 85. Label every 5 units.

c. About one-half inch above the number line, plot the data found in part a for Tampa. About three-fourths inch above the number line, plot the data for Caribou.

d. Write a few sentences comparing the average monthly temperatures. Sample answer: The average monthly temperatures vary greatly in Caribou, ME, whereas the average monthly temperatures in Tampa, FL, are more consistent.

Reading the Lesson

Write a definition and give an example for the new vocabulary phrase.

	Vocabulary	Definition	Example
1.	box-and-whisker plot	See students' work.	

Helping You Remember

2. Complete the following concept map of how to make a box-and-whisker plot.

Resource Manager

Transparencies
5-Minute Check Transparency 12-3
Answer Key Transparencies

Technology
Interactive Chalkboard

DISPLAY DATA

1 JOBS The projected number of employees in 2008 in the fastest-growing occupations is shown in the table in the bottom margin. Display the data in a box-and-whisker plot.

0 150 300 450 600 750 900 1050 1200

INTERPRET BOX-AND-WHISKER PLOTS

2 WEATHER The box-and-whisker plot below shows the average percent of sunny days per year for selected cities in each state.

20 30 40 50 60 70 80 90

a. What is the smallest percent of sunny days in any state?
23%

b. Half of the selected cities have an average of sunny days under what percent?
56%

c. What does the length of the box in the box-and-whisker plot tell about the data? **The length of the box in the box-and-whisker plot is short. This tells us that the values of the data are clustered together.**

Step 1 Find the least and greatest number. Then draw a number line that covers the range of the data.

0 50 100 150 200 250 300 350 400 450 500 550 600

Step 2 Find the median, the extremes, and the upper and lower quartiles. Mark these points above the number line.

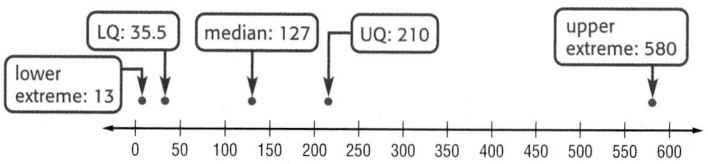

LQ: 35.5 | median: 127 | UQ: 210 | upper extreme: 580
lower extreme: 13

0 50 100 150 200 250 300 350 400 450 500 550 600

Step 3 Draw a box and the whiskers.

The box contains the UQ and the LQ. | The whiskers extend from each quartile to the extreme data points.

0 50 100 150 200 250 300 350 400 450 500 550 600

✓ **Concept Check** What are the extreme values of a set of data? **the highest and lowest values**

INTERPRET BOX-AND-WHISKER PLOTS Box-and-whisker plots separate data into four parts. Even though the parts may differ in length, each part contains 25% of the data.

25% of the data | 25% of the data | 25% of the data | 25% of the data

Data displayed in a box-and-whisker plot can be easily interpreted.

Example 2 *Interpret Data*

EDUCATION Refer to the information shown below.

50 52 54 56 58 60 62 64 66 68 70 72 74 76 78 80 82 84 86 88 90
Source: www.postsecondary.org

a. What is the smallest percent of students graduating in any state?
The smallest percent of students graduating in any state is 50%.

b. Half of the states have a graduation rate under what percent?
Half of the states have graduation rates under 72%.

c. What does the length of the box-and-whisker plot tell about the data?
The length of the box-and-whisker plot is long. This tells us that the values of the data are spread out.

Fastest-Growing Jobs			
Occupation	**Jobs (1000s)**	**Occupation**	**Jobs (1000s)**
Computer Engineer	622	Desktop Publishing	44
Computer Support	869	Paralegal/Legal Assistant	220
Systems Analyst	1194	Home Health Aide	1179
Database Administrator	155	Medical Assistant	398

Source: U.S. Census Bureau

Double box-and-whisker plots can be used to compare two sets of data. Notice that one number line is used to display both plots.

Example 3 *Compare Two Sets of Data*

ANIMALS The weight, in pounds, for Asiatic black bears and pandas is displayed below. How do the weights of Asiatic black bears compare to pandas?

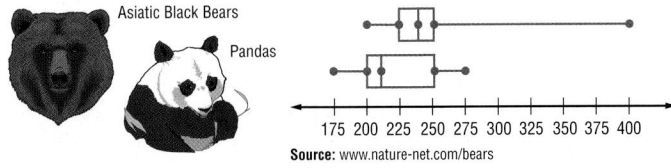

Asiatic Black Bears
Pandas

175 200 225 250 275 300 325 350 375 400

Source: www.nature-net.com/bears

Most Asiatic black bears weigh between 225 and 250 pounds. However, some weigh as much as 400 pounds. Most pandas weigh between 200 and 250 pounds. However, some weigh up to 275 pounds. Thus, the weights of the Asiatic black bears vary more than pandas.

Check for Understanding

Concept Check
1–3. See margin.

1. **Tell** which points the two whiskers of a box plot connect.

2. **Explain** how a box-and-whisker plot separates a set of data.

3. **OPEN ENDED** Write a set of data that, when displayed in a box-and-whisker plot, will result in a long box and short whiskers.

Guided Practice Draw a box-and-whisker plot for each set of data. 4–5. See margin.

4. 25, 30, 27, 35, 19, 23, 25, 22, 40, 34, 20

5. $15, $22, $29, $30, $32, $50, $26, $22, $36, $31

Applications

OLYMPICS For Exercises 6 and 7, use the data shown in the table.

GUIDED PRACTICE KEY	
Exercises	Examples
4–6	1
7	2
8, 9	3

Summer Olympic Games 1924–2000
Winning Times for Men's Marathon

Year	1924	1928	1932	1936	1948	1952	1956	1960	1964
Time (min)	161	153	152	149	155	143	145	135	132
Year	1968	1972	1976	1980	1984	1988	1992	1996	2000
Time (min)	140	132	130	131	129	131	133	133	130

Source: *The ESPN Sports Almanac*

6. Make a box-and-whisker plot for the data. 6–7. See pp. 665A–665F.

7. Write a sentence describing what the length of the box-and-whisker plot tells about the winning times for the men's marathon.

www.pre-alg.com/extra_examples/ny

Lesson 12-3 Box-and-Whisker Plots **619**

Differentiated Instruction

• **Logical** Have students work backward to better understand box-and-whisker plots. Have students create a data set for each plot described.

a. The box is very short.   **b.** The box is very long.

c. The whiskers are very short.   **d.** The whiskers are very long.

e. The box is very short, and the left whisker is longer than the right whisker.

Have students compare their data.

3 **TREES** The average maximum height, in feet, for selected evergreen trees and deciduous trees is displayed. How do the heights of evergreen trees compare with the heights of deciduous trees?

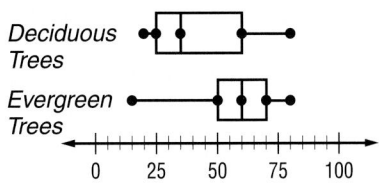

Deciduous Trees
Evergreen Trees

0   25   50   75   100

Source: ohioline.osu.edu
Most evergreen trees are taller than most deciduous trees.

3 Practice/Apply

Study Notebook

Have students—
• add the definition/example of the vocabulary term to their Vocabulary Builder Worksheets for Chapter 12.
• copy the box-and-whisker plot and its labels from p. 617 into their notebooks.
• include any other item(s) that they find helpful in mastering the skills in this lesson.

Answers

1. lower quartile, least value; upper quartile, greatest value

2. into fourths

3. Sample answer: {28, 30, 52, 68, 90, 92}

4.

19 21 23 25 27 29 31 33 35 37 39 41 43

5.

14 18 22 26 30 34 38 42 46 50

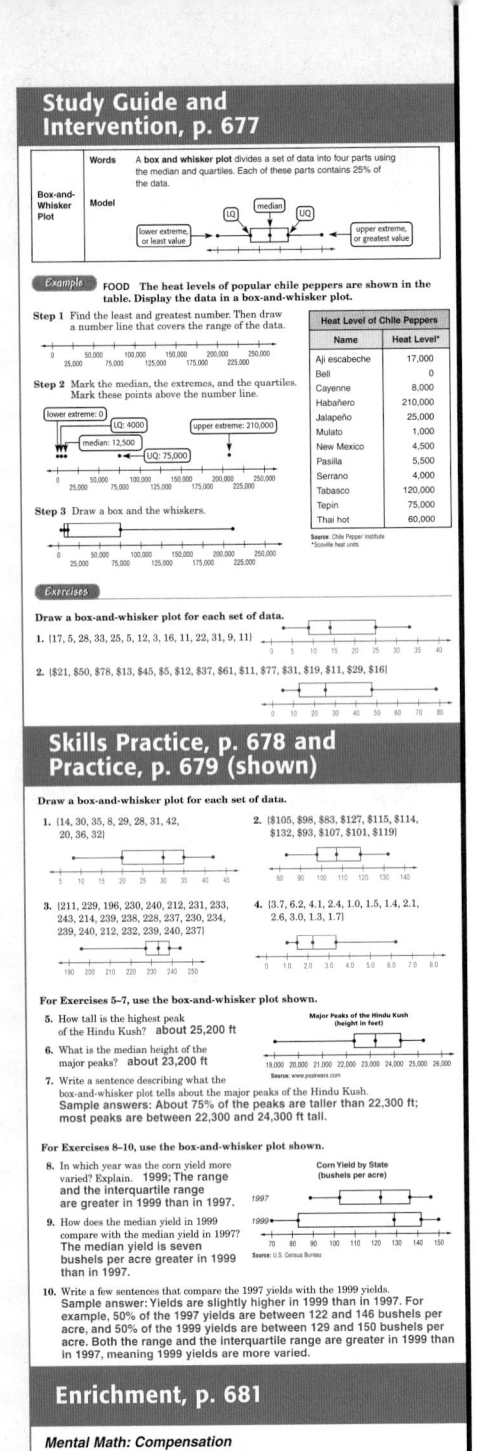

TRAVEL For Exercises 8 and 9, use the box-and-whisker plots shown.

Average Gas Mileage for Various Sedans and SUVs

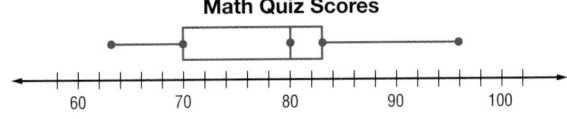

Source: www.classifieds2000.com

8. Which types of vehicles tend to be less fuel-efficient? **8–9. See pp. 665A–665F.**

9. Compare the most fuel-efficient SUV to the least fuel-efficient sedan.

★ indicates increased difficulty

Practice and Apply

Homework Help

For Exercises	See Examples
10–15	1
16–18	2
19	3

Extra Practice
See page 753.

Draw a box-and-whisker plot for each set of data. **10–15. See pp. 665A–665F.**

10. 65, 92, 74, 61, 55, 35, 88, 99, 97, 100, 96

11. 60, 60, 120, 80, 68, 90, 100, 69, 104, 99, 130

12. 80, 72, 42, 40, 63, 51, 55, 78, 81, 73, 77, 65, 67, 68, 59

13. $95, $105, $85, $122, $165, $55, $100, $158, $174, $162

★ 14.

Magnitudes of Recent Major Earthquakes		
6.8	6.2	6.2
5.9	6.1	6.8
6.9	6.5	6.7
6.1	6.9	7.4
7.5	6.3	5.9
6.1	5.8	7.6
7.3	7.8	7.9

Source: The World Almanac

★ 15.

Average Points Scored per Game for NBA Scoring Leaders		
33.1	37.1	29.8
30.7	35.0	29.3
32.3	32.5	30.4
28.4	33.6	29.6
30.6	31.5	28.7
32.9	30.1	26.8
30.3	32.6	29.7

Source: The World Almanac

SCHOOL For Exercises 16–18, use the box-and-whisker plot shown.

Math Quiz Scores

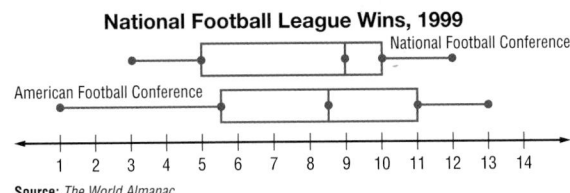

16. What was the highest quiz score? **96**

17. What percent of the students scored between 80 and 96? **50%**

18. Based on the plot, how did the students' scores vary? **See pp. 665A–665F.**

19. **SPORTS** The number of games won by the teams in each conference of the National Football League is displayed below. Write a few sentences that compare the data. **See pp. 665A–665F.**

National Football League Wins, 1999

Source: The World Almanac

620 Chapter 12 More Statistics and Probability

Connections Explain to students that box-and-whisker plots have many applications in the business world. They make immediately clear the range and interquartile range of a set of data. For example, a bakery manager knows that her store typically sells from 130 to 210 blueberry muffins per week, and might sell up to 260 muffins in a week. This way she knows how many to bake in order to make enough for the customers without creating too much waste. Making box-and-whisker plots for each of the 200 items her store makes would be a visual way of arranging such data.

20. CRITICAL THINKING Write a set of data that contains 12 values for which the box-and-whisker plot has no whiskers. **See margin.**

21. WRITING IN MATH   Answer the question that was posed at the beginning of the lesson. **See pp. 665A–665F.**

How can box-and-whisker plots help you interpret data?

Include the following in your answer:
- box-and-whisker plots that display the temperature data for each city,
- a description of the temperatures in Tampa and Caribou, and
- an advantage of displaying data in a box-and-whisker plot instead of in a table.

NEW YORK Test Practice

Standardized Test Practice
Ⓐ Ⓑ Ⓒ Ⓓ

For Exercises 22 and 23, use the box-and-whisker plot shown.

Highest Recorded Wind Speeds (mph) in the U.S.

40 45 50 55 60 65 70 75 80 85 90 95 100 105 110 115   230

Source: *The World Almanac*

22. What is the least highest recorded wind speed? **A**
  Ⓐ 40 mph   Ⓑ 55 mph   Ⓒ 70 mph   Ⓓ 230 mph

23. What percent of the wind speeds range from 40 to 70 mph? **C**
  Ⓐ 25%   Ⓑ 50%   Ⓒ 75%   Ⓓ 100%

Extending the Lesson
Data that are more than 1.5 times the interquartile range from the quartiles are called **outliers**. Consider the data set shown.

15 22 22 26 27 29 30 31 32 36 50

The interquartile range is $32 - 22$ or 10. The outliers are the values more than $1.5(10)$ or 15 from the quartiles.

$$22 - 15 = 7 \qquad 32 + 15 = 47$$

The limits for the outliers are 7 and 47. So, there is one outlier, 50.

Determine whether any outliers exist for each data set.

24. 67, 75, 89, 72, 56, 65, 70 **none**

25. 27, 30, 36, 35, 37, 46, 31, 4, 29, 38, 30 **4**

Maintain Your Skills

Mixed Review
26. 3.4; 1.8

For Exercises 26 and 27, use the set of data {2.4, 2.1, 4.8, 2.7, 1.4, 3.9}.

26. What is the range and interquartile range for the data?   *(Lesson 12-2)*

27. Display the data in a stem-and-leaf plot.   *(Lesson 12-1)* **See margin.**

Getting Ready for the Next Lesson

PREREQUISITE SKILL For Exercises 28 and 29, refer to the table shown.
(To review analyzing data, see pages 722 and 723.)

28. How many people were surveyed? **25**

29. How many people spend more than 7 hours a week on recreational activities? **14**

Weekly Recreation Time		
Time (h)	Tally	Frequency
0–3	III	3
4–7	⊞ III	8
8–11	⊞ IIII	9
12–15	⊞	5

Answers

20. Sample answer: {60, 60, 60, 60, 60, 70, 75, 80, 85, 85, 85, 85}

27.

Stem	Leaf
1	4
2	1 4 7
3	9
4	8

$2 | 4 = 2.4$

About the Exercises . . .

Organization by Objective
- **Display Data:** 10–15
- **Interpret Box-and-Whisker Plots:** 16–19

Odd/Even Assignments
Exercises 10–15 are structured so that students practice the same concepts whether they are assigned odd or even problems.

Assignment Guide
Basic: 11, 13, 16–23, 26–29
Average: 11–15 odd, 16–23, 26–29 (Optional: 24, 25)
Advanced: 10–14 even, 16–27 (Optional: 28, 29)

4 Assess

Open-Ended Assessment

Speaking Show students this plot. Ask students to state facts from the plot. For example, the median is 7, the interquartile range is 4, and so on.

0 1 2 3 4 5 6 7 8 9 10

Getting Ready for Lesson 12-4

PREREQUISITE SKILL Lesson 12-4 presents histograms, which utilize frequency tables. Exercises 28 and 29 should be used to determine your students' familiarity with frequency tables.

Assessment Options

Quiz (Lessons 12-1 through 12-3) is available on p. 727 of the *Chapter 12 Resource Masters*.

Getting Started

Know Your Calculator There are two types of box-and-whisker plots. In Step 2, the keystrokes will select MODBOXPLOT (modified box plot) rather than BOXPLOT (regular box plot). MODBOXPLOT will show outliers while BOXPLOT will not.

Clearing Data If more than one column in students' calculators have data, have students enter the keystrokes | STAT | 4 to select **ClrList** function and then enter list names.

Teach

- Have students double-check their lists after entering the data and edit them if necessary.
- As students work through Step 3, ask volunteers to identify the parts of the plot. Ask students why it may be easier to display data using a box-and-whisker plot.
- Have students complete Exercises 1–5.

Assess

After students answer Exercises 1–5, ask them how box-and-whisker plots help them interpret data using medians, quartiles, and extreme values. Have students reset the Xmin and Xmax values to create a greater range. Ask them how this change affects the appearance of the graph and how this might be misleading.

NEW YORK *Performance Indicator* **8.R.1 Use** physical objects, drawings, charts, **tables, graphs,** symbols, equations, **and objects created using technology as representations**

Box-and-Whisker Plots

You can use a TI-83 Plus graphing calculator to create box-and-whisker plots.

Example

The table shows the ages of the students in two karate classes.

Class	Age (years)													
A	39	33	37	26	39	25	39	40	27	25	35	31	29	28	35
B	19	26	40	19	20	32	16	24	24	16	27	23	22	25	16

Make box-and-whisker plots for the ages in Class A and in Class B.

Step 1 *Enter the data.*

- Clear any existing data.
  KEYSTROKES: | STAT | | ENTER | | ▲ | | CLEAR | | ENTER |

- Enter the Class A ages in L1 and the Class B ages in L2.
  KEYSTROKES: *Review entering a list on page 45.*

Step 2 *Format the graph.*

- Turn on two statistical plots.
  KEYSTROKES: *Review statistical plots on page 45.*

- For Plot 1, select the box-and-whisker plot and L1 as the Xlist.
  KEYSTROKES: | ▼ | | ▶ | | ▶ | | ▶ | | ENTER | | ▼ | | 2nd | L1 | ENTER |

- Repeat for Plot 2, using L2 as the Xlist, to make a box-and-whisker plot for Class B.

Step 3 *Graph the box-and-whisker plots.*

- Display the graph.
  KEYSTROKES: | ZOOM | 9

Press | TRACE |. Move from one plot to the other using the up and down arrow keys. The right and left arrow keys allow you to find the least value, greatest value, and quartiles.

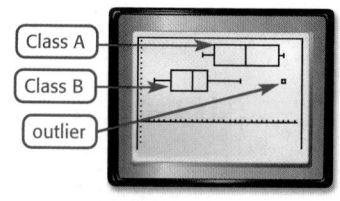

Exercises **1–5. See margin.**

1. What are the least, greatest, quartile, and median values for Classes A and B?

2. What is the interquartile range for Class A? Class B?

3. Are there any outliers? How does the graphing calculator show them?

4. a. Estimate the percent of Class A members who are high school students.
   b. Estimate the percent of Class B members who are high school students.

5. If you were a high school student, which class would you join? Explain.

 www.pre-alg.com/other_calculator_keystrokes

Answers

1. **Class A minimum: 25; Q1: 27; median: 33; Q3: 39; maximum: 40;**

   Class B minimum: 16; Q1: 19; median: 23; Q3: 26; maximum: 40

2. **Class A: 12; Class B: 7**

3. **Yes; a point is separated from the box-and-whisker plot.**

4a. **0%**

4b. **25%**

5. **Sample answer: Class B because there would be more members around my age.**

Histograms

NEW YORK *Performance Indicator* **8.R.1 Use** physical objects, drawings charts, **tables, graphs,** symbols, equations, and objects created using technology **as representations**

What You'll Learn

- Display data in a histogram.
- Interpret data in a histogram.

Vocabulary

histogram

Study Tip

Frequency Distribution
A frequency distribution is the organizing of data in a table using classes or intervals, and frequencies.

a. the totals in the row of tally marks

How are histograms similar to frequency tables?

The number of counties for each state in the United States is displayed in the table shown. This table is a *frequency table*.

a. What does each tally mark represent? **a state**

b. What does the last column represent?

c. What do you notice about the intervals that represent the counties? **They are equal.**

Number of Counties in Each State

Counties	Tally	Frequency
1–25	ЖЖ ЖЖ III	13
26–50	ЖЖ II	7
51–75	ЖЖ ЖЖ II	12
76–100	ЖЖ ЖЖ II	12
101–125	IIII	4
126–150		0
151–175	I	1
176–200		0
201–225		0
226–250		0
251–275	I	1

Source: *The World Almanac*

DISPLAY DATA Another type of graph that can be used to display data is a histogram. A **histogram** uses bars to display numerical data that have been organized into equal intervals.

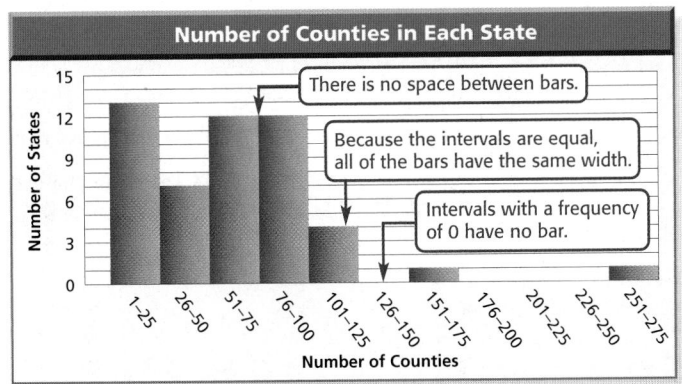

Number of Counties in Each State

- There is no space between bars.
- Because the intervals are equal, all of the bars have the same width.
- Intervals with a frequency of 0 have no bar.

Example 1 Draw a Histogram

WATER PARKS The frequency table shows certain water park admission costs. Display the data in a histogram.

Step 1 Draw and label a horizontal and vertical axis as shown. Include the title.

Water Park Admission

Cost ($)	Tally	Frequency
8–15	ЖЖ	5
16–23	ЖЖ II	7
24–31	IIII	4
32–39		0
40–47	II	2

(continued on the next page)

Workbooks and Reproducible Masters

Chapter 12 Resource Masters
- Study Guide and Intervention, p. 682
- Skills Practice, p. 683
- Practice, p. 684
- Reading to Learn Mathematics, p. 685
- Enrichment, p. 686

Parent and Student Study Guide Workbook, p. 101

---

1 Focus

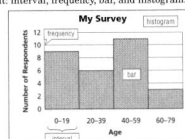 **5-Minute Check Transparency 12-4** Use as a quiz or review of Lesson 12-3.

Mathematical Background notes are available for this lesson on page 604D.

How are histograms similar to frequency tables?

The opening activity questions are repeated on page 685 of the *Chapter 12 Resource Masters*.

Reading to Learn Mathematics, p. 685 ELL

Pre-Activity *How are histograms similar to frequency tables?*
Do the activity at the top of page 623 in your textbook. Write your answers below.
  a. What does each tally mark represent? a state
  b. What does the last column represent?
     the totals in the row of tally marks
  c. What do you notice about the intervals that represent the counties?
     They are equal.

Reading the Lesson
Write a definition and give an example of the new vocabulary word.

	Vocabulary	Definition	Example
1.	histogram	See students' work.	

Complete the following statements about frequency tables and histograms.

2. If the first frequency interval goes from 1 to 50, the next frequency interval goes from **51–100**.

3. Because the intervals in a histogram are **equal**, all of the bars have the **same width**.

4. In a histogram, there is **no space between** bars.

5. Intervals that have a frequency of 0 have **no bar**.

6. The height of a bar in a histogram corresponds to the **frequency** of the data for that **interval**.

Helping You Remember

7. Label the following in the histogram at right: interval, frequency, bar, and histogram. Then make a frequency table showing the same information as the histogram.

My Survey		
Age	Tally	Frequency
0–19	ЖЖ IIII	9
20–39	ЖЖ I	6
40–59	ЖЖ ЖЖ I	11
60–79	III	3

Resource Manager

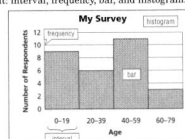 **Transparencies**

5-Minute Check Transparency 12-4
Answer Key Transparencies

Technology

Interactive Chalkboard

2 Teach

DISPLAY DATA

In-Class Example Power Point®

Teaching Tip Make sure that students know the difference between horizontal and vertical. Emphasize that a histogram is a type of bar graph.

1 TOURISM The frequency table shows the number of overseas visitors to certain U.S. cities in 1999. Display the data in a histogram.

Overseas Travelers		
Number of Visitors (1000s)	**Tally**	**Frequency**
0–1000	ⅢⅡ	5
1001–2000	|||	3
2001–3000	ⅢⅡ	5
3001–4000			1
4001–5000		0
5001–6000			1

Source: U.S. Department of Commerce

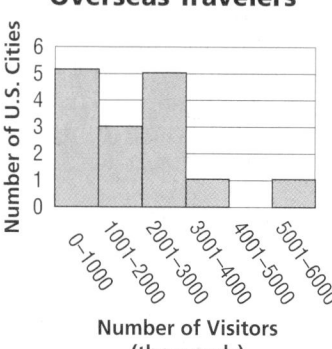

Overseas Travelers

Study Tip

Break in Scale
The symbol ∿ means there is a break in the scale. The scale from 0 to 7 has been omitted.

Reading Math

At Least
Recall that *at least* means *is greater than or equal to*.

Step 2 Show the intervals from the frequency table on the horizontal axis and an interval of 1 on the vertical axis.

Step 3 For each cost interval, draw a bar whose height is given by the frequency.

Water Park Admission

INTERPRET HISTOGRAMS A histogram gives a better visual display of data than a frequency table. Thus, it is easier to interpret data displayed in a histogram.

Example 2 Interpret Data

SCHOOL Refer to the histogram at the right.

a. **How many students are at least 69 inches tall?**

Since 30 students are 69–71 inches tall, and 10 students are 72–74 inches tall, 30 + 10 or 40 students are at least 69 inches tall.

b. **Is it possible to tell the height of the tallest student?**

No, you can only tell that the tallest student is between 72 and 74 inches.

Students' Heights

Histograms can also be used to compare data.

Example 3 Compare Two Sets of Data

OLYMPICS Use the histograms below to answer the question.

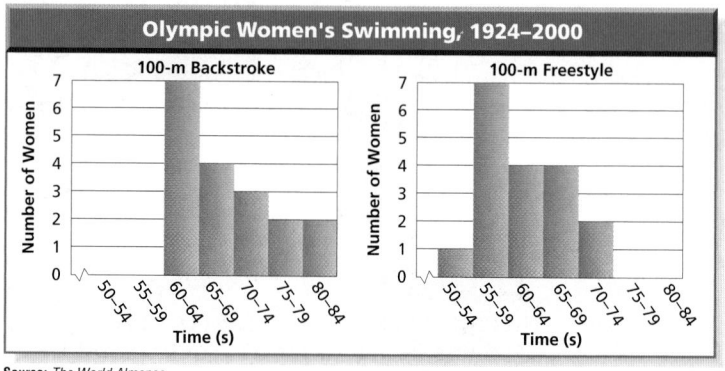

Olympic Women's Swimming, 1924–2000

Source: *The World Almanac*

Which event has more winning times less than 1 minute?

The 100-meter freestyle has 1 + 7 or 8 athletes with a winning time less than 1 minute while the 100-meter backstroke has none.

DAILY INTERVENTION

Differentiated Instruction

- **Auditory/Musical** Have students work in groups of four to compose a short piece of music inspired by the histograms in Example 3. Ask them to imagine that each bar on the histograms represents a range of notes in a musical scale. Have them assign musical intervals to each interval on the histograms and then "play" the graphs, using the heights of the bars as a guide for volume. Instruments such as the flute and the voice, which can play all of the notes in an interval in a sliding manner, lend themselves well to this activity.

Check for Understanding

Concept Check

1. **Explain** why there are no spaces between the bars of a histogram.

2. **OPEN ENDED** Tell how a histogram gives a better visual display than a frequency table. **1–2. See margin.**

Guided Practice

Display each set of data in a histogram. **3–4. See pp. 665A–665F.**

3.

Pet Survey		
Pets	Tally	Frequency
1–3	JHT JHT JHT JHT I	21
4–6	JHT II	7
7–9	II	2
10–12		0
13–15	I	1

4.

Test Scores		
Score	Tally	Frequency
95–100	JHT	5
89–94	JHT JHT II	12
83–88	JHT IIII	9
77–82	JHT I	6
71–76	IIII	4

Applications

ROLLER COASTERS For Exercises 5–8, use the histogram shown.

5. Describe the data.

6. Which interval has the most roller coasters? **0–9**

7. Why is there a jagged line in the vertical axis?

8. How many states have no roller coasters? Explain.

Source: The Roller Coaster Database

5. the number of states that have a certain number of roller coasters
7. The numbers between 10 and 34 are omitted.
8. See pp. 665A–665F.

 Online Research **Data Update** How has the number of roller coasters in the United States changed since 2000? Visit www.pre-alg.com/data_update to learn more.

VACATIONS For Exercises 9 and 10, use the histograms below.

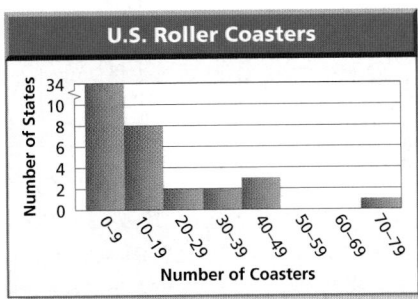

Source: www.infoplease.com

9. Are there more states with two or more national parks or two or more national monuments? **2 or more national monuments**

10. How many more states have either one or no national parks than either one or no national monuments? **4**

 www.pre-alg.com/extra_examples/ny

Lesson 12-4 Histograms **625**

Answers

1. Sample answer: Because the intervals are continuous.

2. Sample answer: By displaying the data in a histogram, it is much easier to see how the data in the intervals compare to each other.

In-Class Examples Power Point®

2 **ELEVATIONS** Use the histogram.

Highest Elevations in U.S.

a. How many states have highest points with elevations at least 3751 meters? **12**

b. Is it possible to tell the height of the tallest point? **No, you can only tell that the highest point is between 5001 and 6250 meters.**

3 **EMPLOYMENT** Use the histograms.

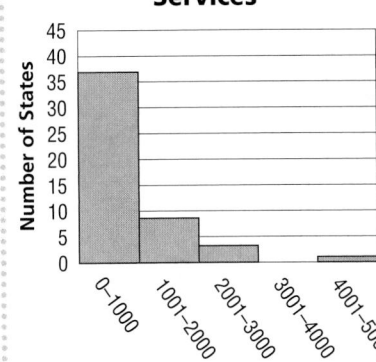

Which business sector has more states with between 1,001,000 and 3,000,000 employees? **services**

Lesson 12-4 Histograms **625**

Study Notebook

Have students—
- add the definition/example of the vocabulary term to their Vocabulary Builder Worksheets for Chapter 12.
- include their histograms for Exercises 3 and 4.
- include any other item(s) that they find helpful in mastering the skills in this lesson.

About the Exercises . . .

Organization by Objective
- **Display Data:** 11–14
- **Interpret Histograms:** 15–20

Odd/Even Assignments
Exercises 11–14 are structured so that students practice the same concepts whether they are assigned odd or even problems.

Assignment Guide

Basic: 11, 13, 18–28, 32–35
Average: 11, 13, 15–17, 18–28, 32–35 (Optional: 29, 30)
Advanced: 12, 14, 15–33 (Optional: 34, 35)
All: Practice Quiz 1 (1–5)

Answers

11. **Weekly Study Time**

★ indicates increased difficulty

Practice and Apply

Homework Help

For Exercises	See Examples
11–14	1
15–17	2
18–20	3

Extra Practice
See page 753.

Display each set of data in a histogram. **11. See margin.**

12–14. See pp. 665A–665F.

11.

Weekly Study Time		
Time (hr)	Tally	Frequency
0–3	II	2
4–6	III	3
7–9	JHT III	8
10–12	JHT JHT II	12
13–15	JHT JHT	10

12.

Weekly Allowance		
Amount	Tally	Frequency
$0–$5	JHT JHT I	11
$6–$11	JHT IIII	9
$12–$17	JHT III	8
$18–$23	III	3
$24–$29	JHT	5

13.

Touchdowns in a Season		
Amount	Tally	Frequency
80–96	JHT JHT	10
97–113	JHT	5
114–130	IIII	4
131–147	II	2
148–164		0
165–181	I	1

14.

Goals in a Season		
Amount	Tally	Frequency
65–69	JHT I	6
70–74	JHT II	7
75–79	III	3
80–84		0
85–89	III	3
90–94	I	1

FOOD For Exercises 15–17, use the data in the histogram.

15. How many restaurants sell chicken sandwiches that cost under $3? **13**

16. How many restaurants were surveyed? **16**

★ 17. What percent of the restaurants surveyed sell chicken sandwiches that cost between $2.00 and $2.49? **37.5%**

WebQuest

Frequency tables and histograms can help you analyze data. Visit www.pre-alg.com/webquest to continue work on your WebQuest project.

ARCHITECTURE For Exercises 18–20, use the histograms below.

18. Which city has more tall buildings? **Los Angeles**

19. Which city has the fewer number of buildings over 600 feet? **Dallas**

20. Compare the heights of the tall buildings in the two cities. **See margin.**

20. Sample answer: Whereas Dallas, Texas, has more buildings with a height of 400–499 feet, Los Angeles, California, has more buildings classified as tall buildings.

CRITICAL THINKING For Exercises 21–25, determine whether each statement is *true* or *false*.

21. You can determine the median from a box-and-whisker plot. **true**

22. You can determine the range from a stem-and-leaf plot. **true**

23. You can reconstruct the original data from a histogram. **false**

24. You can reconstruct the original data from a box-and-whisker plot. **false**

25. You can determine the interval in which the median falls in a histogram. **true**

26. **WRITING IN MATH** Answer the question that was posed at the beginning of the lesson. **See pp. 665A–665F.**

How are histograms similar to frequency tables?

Include the following in your answer:
- examples of a histogram and a frequency table, and
- an explanation describing how data are displayed in each.

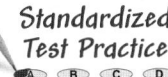

Standardized Test Practice
Ⓐ Ⓑ Ⓒ Ⓓ

The histogram shows the ages of the students in a drama club.

27. How old are the oldest students? **A**

   Ⓐ 18–19   Ⓑ 16–19

   Ⓒ 17–18   Ⓓ 16–18

28. What is the total number of students in the drama club? **C**

   Ⓐ 20   Ⓑ 22

   Ⓒ 24   Ⓓ 26

Drama Club Students

Extending the Lesson

In the frequency table shown, the frequencies 5, 6, 4, 3, and 2 are called the **absolute frequencies**.

To find the **relative frequencies**, divide each absolute frequency by the total number of items. For the data shown, the relative frequencies are $\frac{5}{20}$ or $\frac{1}{4}$, $\frac{6}{20}$ or $\frac{3}{10}$, $\frac{4}{20}$ or $\frac{1}{5}$, $\frac{3}{20}$, and $\frac{2}{20}$ or $\frac{1}{10}$.

Quiz Scores		
Score	Tally	Frequency
23–25	卌	5
20–22	卌 I	6
17–19	IIII	4
14–16	III	3
11–13	II	2

The **cumulative frequencies** are the sums of all preceding frequencies. For the data shown, the cumulative frequencies are 5, 5 + 6 or 11, 5 + 6 + 4 or 15, 5 + 6 + 4 + 3 or 18, and 5 + 6 + 4 + 3 + 2 or 20.

Find the absolute, relative, and cumulative frequency for each data set.

29–30. See margin.

29.

Record High Temperature (°F)		
Temp.	Tally	Frequency
100–104	II	2
105–109	卌 IIII	9
110–114	卌 卌 卌 II	17
115–119	卌 卌 II	12
120–124	卌 II	7
125–129	II	2

30.

Record Wind Speeds (mph)		
Speed	Tally	Frequency
30–36	卌 卌 I	11
37–43	卌 卌 卌 卌	20
44–50	卌 卌 卌 卌 I	21
51–57	卌 卌 II	12
58–64	I	1
65–71	I	1

Answers

29. absolute frequency: 2, 9, 17, 12, 7, 2;

relative frequency: $\frac{2}{49}, \frac{9}{49}, \frac{17}{49}, \frac{12}{49}, \frac{1}{7}$, $\frac{2}{49}$; cumulative frequency: 2, 11, 28, 40, 47, 49

30. absolute frequency: 11, 20, 21, 12, 1, 1;

relative frequency: $\frac{1}{6}, \frac{10}{33}, \frac{7}{22}, \frac{2}{11}, \frac{1}{66}$, $\frac{1}{66}$; cumulative frequency: 11, 31, 52, 64, 65, 66

4 Assess

Open-Ended Assessment

Writing Ask students to write a paragraph discussing the advantages of using a histogram to display data. Ask them to consider the types of information or statistics that could be depicted using a histogram.

Getting Ready for Lesson 12-5

PREREQUISITE SKILL Lesson 12-5 presents misleading line and bar graphs. Exercises 34 and 35 should be used to determine your students' familiarity with bar graphs.

Assessment Options

Practice Quiz 1 The quiz provides students with a brief review of the concepts and skills in Lessons 12-1 through 12-4. Lesson numbers are given to the right of exercises or instruction lines so students can review concepts not yet mastered.

Answers

31.

Average Length of U.S. States

Source: *The World Almanac*

35. **Sample answer: Brand B costs one-third more than brand C.**

When the middles of the intervals on a histogram are connected with line segments, a **frequency polygon** is formed. A frequency polygon is shown.

Tree Heights

31. Make a frequency polygon of the data shown below. **See margin.**

Average Length (mi) of U.S. States*									
330	1480	400	260	770	380	110	100	500	300
570	390	270	310	400	380	380	320	250	190
490	400	340	300	630	430	490	190	150	370
330	500	340	220	400	360	283	40	260	380
440	790	350	160	430	360	240	310	360	

Source: *The World Almanac*   * Hawaii is not listed.

Maintain Your Skills

Mixed Review   **PRESIDENTS**   For Exercises 32 and 33, use the data shown below.

Ages of Past Presidents at Time of Death

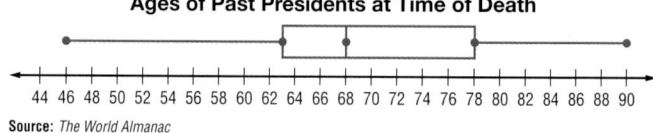

Source: *The World Almanac*

32. What percent of presidents died by the time they were 78 years old? *(Lesson 12-3)* **75%**

33. Find the range and interquartile range for the data. *(Lesson 12-2)* **44; 15**

Getting Ready for the Next Lesson   **PREREQUISITE SKILL**   For Exercises 34 and 35, use the graph shown.
*(To review **bar graphs**, see pages 722 and 723.)*

34. Which jeans cost the most? **Brand D**

35. How does the cost of Brand B compare to the cost of Brand C? **See margin.**

Cost of Certain Jeans

Practice Quiz 1   Lessons 12-1 through 12-4

For Exercises 1–5, use the data in the table.

1. Display the data in a stem-and-leaf plot. *(Lesson 12-1)*

2. Find the range and interquartile range. *(Lesson 12-2)* **73; 22**

3. Display the data in a box-and-whisker plot. *(Lesson 12-3)*

4. What percent of the costs were less than $20? *(Lesson 12-3)* **25%**

5. Display the data in a histogram. *(Lesson 12-4)* **1, 3, 5. See pp. 665A–665F.**

$20	$28	$18	$89	$55	$28
$30	$86	$19	$42	$19	$16
$26	$43	$28	$22	$32	$40

Graphing Calculator Investigation

A Follow-Up of Lesson 12-4

NEW YORK *Performance Indicator* **8.R.1 Use** physical objects, drawings charts, tables, **graphs,** symbols, equations, **and objects created using technology as representations**

Histograms

You can use a TI-83 Plus graphing calculator to make a histogram.

PRESIDENTS The list below shows the ages of the first 43 presidents at the time of inauguration.

57	61	57	57	58	57	61	54	68	51	49
64	50	48	65	52	56	46	54	49	50	47
55	55	54	42	51	56	55	51	54	51	60
62	43	55	56	61	52	69	64	46	54	

Make a histogram to show the age distribution.

Step 1 *Enter the data.*
- Clear any existing data in list L1.
  KEYSTROKES: STAT ENTER ▲ CLEAR ENTER
- Enter the ages in L1.
  KEYSTROKES: *Review entering a list on page 45.*

Step 2 *Format the graph.*
- Turn on the statistical plot.
  KEYSTROKES: 2nd [STAT PLOT] ENTER ENTER
- Select the histogram and L1 as the Xlist.
  KEYSTROKES: ▼ ▶ ▶ ENTER ▼ 2nd L1 ENTER

Step 3 *Graph the histogram.*
Set the viewing window so the *x*-axis goes from 40 to 75 in increments of 5, and the *y*-axis goes from −5 to 15 in increments of 1. So, [40, 75] scl: 5 by [−5, 15] scl: 1. Then graph.
  KEYSTROKES: WINDOW 40 ENTER 75 ENTER 5 ENTER −5 ENTER 15 ENTER 1 ENTER GRAPH

Exercises **1–7. See margin.**
1. Press Trace . Find the frequency of each interval using the right and left arrow keys.

2. Discuss why the domain is from 40 to 75 for this data set.

3. How does the graphing calculator determine the size of the intervals?

4. At inauguration, how many presidents have been at least 45, but less than 65?

5. What percent of presidents falls in the interval of Exercise 4?

6. Can you tell from the histogram how many presidents were inaugurated at age 52? Explain.

7. Refer to Example 2 on page 607. How does the stem-and-leaf plot compare to the histogram you have graphed here? Which graph is easier to read?

 www.pre-alg.com/other_calculator_keystrokes

Getting Started

Know Your Calculator When students are ready to format their graphs, some may receive error messages if **Plot 2** or **Plot 3** is turned on as well as **Plot 1**. Have them use **STAT PLOT** to turn them off. Alternatively, they can use the Y= , ENTER , and the arrow keys to turn off the extra plots.

Teach

- When students have finished entering the numbers into the list, have students choose a partner. Ask one student from each pair to read aloud the numbers from the list while the other student uses the arrow keys to scroll through the list and check that the numbers are entered correctly.
- After students have completed Steps 2 and 3, have them move through each bar on the histogram and record how many presidents are recorded on each bar.
- Have students complete Exercises 1–7.

Assess

Have students use the data on the number of electors in each state on p. 606 to make a histogram on the graphing calculator. Ask them to explain what numbers they used on the *x*-axis and how they determined the frequency.

Answers

1.

Interval	Frequency
40 up to 45	2
45 up to 50	6
50 up to 55	13
55 up to 60	12
60 up to 65	7
65 up to 70	3
70 up to 75	0

2. It contains all the possible ages.

3. It determines interval size by the scale factor of *x*.

4. 38

5. about 88%

6. No; the histogram shows the number of presidents for a range of ages, not the number of presidents for individual ages.

7. See students' work.

12-5 Misleading Statistics

1 Focus

5-Minute Check
Transparency 12-5 Use as a quiz or review of Lesson 12-4.

Mathematical Background
notes are available for this lesson on page 604D.

How can graphs be misleading?

The opening activity questions are repeated on page 690 of the *Chapter 12 Resource Masters*.

Reading to Learn Mathematics, p. 690

Pre-Activity **How can graphs be misleading?**

Do the activity at the top of page 630 in your textbook. Write your answers below.

a. Do both graphs show the same information? **yes**

b. Which graph suggests a dramatic increase in sales from May to June? **Graph B**

c. Which graph suggests steady sales? **Graph A**

d. How are the graphs similar? How are they different?
Sample answer: The graphs differ in that Graph A shows a gradual increase and decrease over the year; Graph B shows a drastic increase and decrease. They are similar in that each graph contains labeled axes and a title.

Reading the Lesson

Complete the following statements by filling in the blanks with the following words.

| different | gradually | horizontal | interval(s) |
| label(s) | rapidly | title(s) | vertical |

1. If two graphs showing the same information have different vertical scales, that means that on the **vertical** axis, the **intervals** are different.

2. If two graphs showing the same information have different horizontal scales, that means that on the **horizontal** axis, the intervals are **different**.

3. A graph can be misleading if it has no **title** or if it has no **labels** on the scales.

4. If a graph shows steady change, the plotted values should increase or decrease **gradually**.

5. If a graph shows dramatic change, the plotted values should increase or decrease **rapidly**.

Helping You Remember

6. Use a dictionary and a book of synonyms to rewrite the following sentence by replacing the underlined words with ones you are more familiar with.

Statistics or statistical graphs can be misleading when the same data are represented in different ways, so that each graph gives a different visual impression.

Sample answer: A collection of numerical information or statistical graphs can be deceptive when the same facts are shown in different ways, so that each graph gives a different effect to the eyes.

Teaching Tip Before starting the lesson, have students brainstorm ways in which groups may use partial data to mislead.

b. Graph B

Study Tip

Statistics
A graph is also misleading if there is no title, there are no labels on either scale, and the vertical axis does not include zero.

NEW YORK *Performance Indicator* Reinforcement of 7.S.7 Identify and explain misleading statistics and graphs

What You'll Learn

• Recognize when statistics are misleading.

How can graphs be misleading?

The graphs below show the monthly sales for one year for a company.

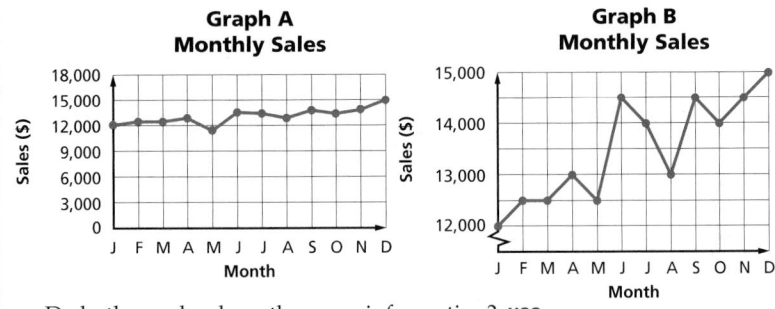

Graph A Monthly Sales

Graph B Monthly Sales

a. Do both graphs show the same information? **yes**

b. Which graph suggests a dramatic increase in sales from May to June?

c. Which graph suggests steady sales? **Graph A**

d. How are the graphs similar? How are they different? **See margin.**

MISLEADING GRAPHS   Two line graphs that represent the same data may look quite different. Consider the graphs above. Different vertical scales are used. So, each graph gives a different visual impression.

Example 1 *Misleading Graphs*

TRAVEL   The graphs show the growth of the cruise industry.

a. **Why do the graphs look different?**

The vertical scales differ.

b. **Which graph appears to show a greater increase in the growth of the cruise industry? Explain.**

Graph B; the size of the ship makes the increase appear more dramatic because both the height and width of the ship are increasing.

Cruise Industry Growth

Cruise Industry Growth

Resource Manager

 Workbooks and Reproducible Masters

Chapter 12 Resource Masters
• Study Guide and Intervention, p. 687
• Skills Practice, p. 688
• Practice, p. 689
• Reading to Learn Mathematics, p. 690
• Enrichment, p. 691
• Assessment, pp. 727, 729

Parent and Student Study Guide Workbook, p. 102

Transparencies
5-Minute Check Transparency 12-5
Real-World Transparency 12
Answer Key Transparencies

Technology
Interactive Chalkboard
Pre-AlgePASS: Tutorial Plus, Lesson 37
Multimedia Applications

Bar graphs can also be misleading.

Example 2 Misleading Bar Graphs

READING The graph shows the amount of time people spend reading the newspaper each day. Explain why the graph is misleading.

The inconsistent vertical scale and horizontal scale cause the data to be misleading.

The graph gives the impression that people aged 65 and up read the newspaper six times longer than those aged 18–24. By using the horizontal scale, you can see that it is only about 3.5 times longer.

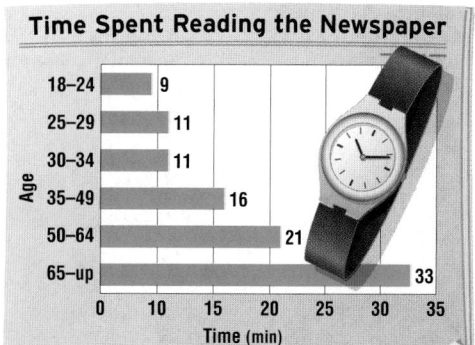

Time Spent Reading the Newspaper

Age	Time (min)
18–24	9
25–29	11
30–34	11
35–49	16
50–64	21
65–up	33

Check for Understanding

Concept Check

1. **Name** two ways a graph can be misleading. **See margin.**

2. **OPEN ENDED** Find an example of a misleading graph in a newspaper or magazine. Explain why it is misleading. **See students' work.**

Guided Practice

SCHOOL For Exercises 3 and 4, refer to the graphs below.

GUIDED PRACTICE KEY	
Exercises	Examples
3–5	1, 2

3. Graph A has a break in the vertical scale.
4. Graph A because the increase appears more drastic.

Jennifer's Science Grades Graph A

(bar graph: Grade vs Grading Period 1–5)

Jennifer's Science Grades Graph B

(bar graph: Grade vs Grading Period 1–5)

3. Explain why the graphs look different.

4. Which graph appears to show Jennifer's grades improving more? Explain.

Application

5. **COMMUNICATION** The graph shows how the number of area codes in the U.S. have increased over the years. Tell why the graph is misleading. **See margin.**

Increasing Area Codes

(bar graph: Number of Area Codes vs Year 1996, 1999)

Answers

1. Sample answer: inconsistent vertical scale and break in vertical scale

5. From the vertical scale, you can see that the number of area codes in 1999 is about 1.5 times the number of area codes in 1996. The graph is misleading because the drawing of the phone for 1999 is about 3 times the size of the phone for 1996. Also, there is a break in the vertical scale.

---

2 Teach

MISLEADING GRAPHS

In-Class Examples Power Point®

1 **FOOD** The graphs show the increase in the price of lemons. **Source:** U.S. Bureau of Labor Statistics

Price of Lemons Graph C

(line graph: Dollars per Pound vs Year '93–'99)

Price of Lemons Graph D

(line graph: Dollars per Pound vs Year '93 '95 '97 '99)

a. Why do the graphs look different? **The horizontal scales differ.**

b. Which graph appears to show a more rapid increase in the price of lemons after 1997? Explain. **Graph D; the slope of the line from 1997 to 1998 is steeper in Graph D.**

2 **INTERNET** Explain why the following graph is misleading.

Internet Users (%)

Age	Percent
18–24	58.7
25–34	53.3
35–44	53.8
45–54	54.8
55–64	35.1
65–up	10.7

The inconsistent horizontal and vertical scales cause the data to be misleading.

★ indicates increased difficulty

Homework Help

For Exercises	See Examples
6–10	1, 2

Extra Practice See page 754.

MOVIES For Exercises 6 and 7, refer to the graphs below.

 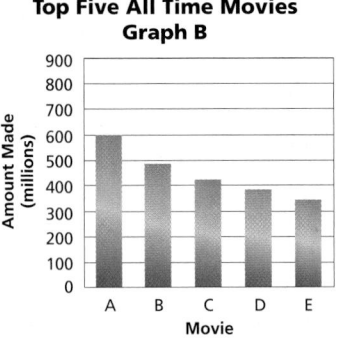

6. Which graph gives the impression that the top all-time movie made far more money than any other top all-time movie? **Graph A**

7. Which graph shows that movie C made nearly as much money as the other top movies? **Graph B**

JOBS For Exercises 8 and 9, use the graphs below.

8. What causes the graphs to differ in their appearance? **8–9. See margin.**

9. Which graph appears to show that unemployment rates have decreased rapidly since 1992? Explain your reasoning.

10. **TRAVEL** The distance adults drive each week is shown in the graph at the right. Is the graph misleading? Explain your reasoning. **See margin.**

Average Weekly Travel Distance

Source: Simmons

632 **Chapter 12** More Statistics and Probability

11. CRITICAL THINKING The table shows the number of yearly passengers on certain commuter trains.

a. Draw a graph that shows a slow increase in the number of passengers.

b. Redraw the graph so that it shows a rapid increase in the number of passengers. **a–b. See pp. 665A–665F.**

Commuter Train Passengers

Year	Amount (millions)
1996	45.9
1997	48.5
1998	54.0
1999	58.3

Source: Time Almanac

12. **WRITING IN MATH** Answer the question that was posed at the beginning of the lesson. **See pp. 665A–665F.**

How can graphs be misleading?

Include the following in your answer:
• an example of a graph that is misleading, and
• a discussion of how to redraw the graph so it is not misleading.

13. Which sentence is a true statement about the data in the graph? **B**

Ⓐ From 1995 to 1996, the amount spent on dining out doubled.

Ⓑ The amount spent in 1998 was about 1.2 times the amount spent in 1994.

Ⓒ The amount spent on dining out from 1995 to 1997 increased by three times.

Ⓓ From 1997 to 1998 the amount spent on dining out increased by about 20%.

Annual Spending on Dining Out

Maintain Your Skills

Mixed Review

14. Display the data shown in a histogram. *(Lesson 12-4)*

15. Draw a box-and-whisker plot for {56°, 43°, 38°, 42°, 50°, 47°, 41°, 55°}. *(Lesson 12-3)* **14–15. See pp. 665A–665F.**

Book Survey

Books Read	Tally	Frequency
0–2	卌 Ⅲ	8
3–5	ⅢⅠ	4
6–8	卌 卌	10
9–11	卌	5
12–14	Ⅲ	3

Find the area of each figure described. *(Lesson 10-5)*

16. triangle: base, 6 feet; height, 4.2 feet **12.6 ft²**

17. trapezoid: height, 5.8 meters; bases, 4 meters, 3 meters **20.3 m²**

Getting Ready for the Next Lesson

A bag contains 3 yellow marbles, 2 blue marbles, and 7 purple marbles. Suppose one marble is selected at random. Find the probability of each outcome. Express each probability as a fraction and as a percent.
(To review probability, see Lesson 6-9) **18–23. See pp. 665A–665F.**

18. P(yellow)   19. P(blue)   20. P(not purple)

21. P(not blue)   22. P(blue or purple)   23. P(yellow or not blue)

Study Notebook

Have students—
• list all of the ways a graph can be misleading that have been mentioned in the lesson or in class.
• include any other item(s) that they find helpful in mastering the skills in this lesson.

Assignment Guide

Basic: 7, 9, 11–23

Average: 7, 9, 11–23

Advanced: 6, 8–17

(Optional: 18–23)

4 Assess

Open-Ended Assessment

Modeling Have students make a list of ways that graphs can be misleading. Then have each student choose one way and create a misleading graph.

Getting Ready for Lesson 12-6

PREREQUISITE SKILL Lesson 12-6 presents the Fundamental Counting Principle and applies it to probability. Exercises 18–23 should be used to determine your students' familiarity with probability.

Assessment Options

Quiz (Lessons 12-4 and 12-5) is available on p. 727 of the *Chapter 12 Resource Masters.*

Mid-Chapter Test (Lessons 12-1 through 12-5) is available on p. 729 of the *Chapter 12 Resource Masters.*

Answers (p. 632)

8. The vertical scale of graph A goes from 0 to 8.0 whereas the vertical scale of graph B goes from 4.0 to 8.0. In addition, the actual distance between vertical scales is less than the distance used in Graph B.

9. Graph B; the vertical scale used makes the decrease in the unemployment rates appear more drastic.

10. Yes; the intervals are inconsistent and the horizontal scale has a break in it.

Reading Mathematics

Getting Started

You may wish to have students review "Taking a Survey" on p. 309 before beginning this activity. In particular, review the terms *random*, *sample*, and *unbiased*.

Teach

Surveys Many survey-taking organizations now use the Internet as an efficient way to gather responses from people all over the country. You may wish to print out some Web surveys for the students to examine. How are the questions worded? How is the survey data to be compiled? How much time would it take for a respondent to complete the survey? Have students discuss in what ways surveys on the Web could create or reduce bias.

Assess

Study Notebook

Ask students to write down an example for each of the four types of bias covered in the activity.

ELL English Language Learners may benefit from writing key concepts from this activity in their Study Notebooks in their native language and then in English.

Dealing with Bias

In statistics, a sample is biased if it favors certain outcomes or parts of the population over others. While taking a random survey is the best way to eliminate bias or favoritism, there are still many ways in which a survey and its responses can be biased.

Voluntary Response
Consider a survey where people call or write in. Those who take the time to voluntarily respond usually have strong opinions on an issue. This may result in bias.

Response Bias
Some surveys are biased because either the people participating in the survey are influenced by the interviewer or the people do not give accurate responses.

Nonresponse
Consider a survey where the selected individuals cannot be contacted or they refuse to cooperate. Since the survey does not include a portion of the population, bias results.

Poorly Worded Questions
A survey is biased if it contains questions that are worded to influence people's responses.

Reading to Learn **1–4. See margin.**
Tell whether each situation may result in bias. Explain your reasoning.

1. Suppose a bakery wants to know what percent of households makes baked goods from scratch. A sample is taken of 300 households. An interviewer goes from door to door between 9 A.M. and 4 P.M.

2. A telephone survey of 500 urban households is taken. The interviewer asks, "Does anyone in your household use public transportation?"

3. A radio station is conducting a survey as to whether people want a law that prohibits the use of computers for downloading music files. The radio announcer gives a number to call to answer *yes* or *no*. Of the responses, 85% said they do not want this law.

4. An interviewer states, "Due to heavy traffic, should another lane be added to Main Street?"

634 Chapter 12 More Statistics and Probability

Sample Answers

1. This situation may result in bias. Many people may not be at home during these hours and thus, the survey will not include a portion of the population.

2. Since many cities offer public transportation, people living in urban households may be more apt to use public transportation. Thus, this may be biased.

3. The survey may be biased. It is a voluntary response and those who call in may have strong opinions.

4. This survey is biased due to the wording of the question.

12-6 Counting Outcomes

NEW YORK *Performance Indicator* **8.PS.13 Set expectations and limits for possible solutions**

What You'll Learn

- Use tree diagrams or the Fundamental Counting Principle to count outcomes.
- Use the Fundamental Counting Principle to find the probability of an event.

Vocabulary

- tree diagram
- Fundamental Counting Principle

How can you count the number of skateboard designs that are available from a catalog?

The basic model of a skateboard has 5 choices for decks and 3 choices for wheel sets, as shown at the right. How many different skateboards are possible?

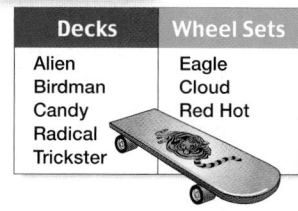

Decks	Wheel Sets
Alien	Eagle
Birdman	Cloud
Candy	Red Hot
Radical	
Trickster	

a. Write the names of each deck choice on 5 sticky notes of one color. Write the names of each type of wheel on 3 notes of another color.

b. Choose one deck note and one wheel note. One possible skateboard is Alien, Eagle. **a–b. See students' work.**

c. Make a list of all the possible skateboards. **See margin.**

d. How many different skateboard designs are possible? **15**

COUNTING OUTCOMES To solve the skateboard problem above, you can look at a simpler problem. Suppose there are only three deck choices, Birdman, Alien, or Candy, and only two wheel choices, Eagle or Cloud. You can draw a **tree diagram** to represent the possible outcomes.

Study Tip

Look Back
To review **outcomes**, see Lesson 6-9.

Example 1 Use a Tree Diagram to Count Outcomes

How many different skateboards can be made from three deck choices and two wheel choices?

You can draw a diagram to find the number of possible skateboards.

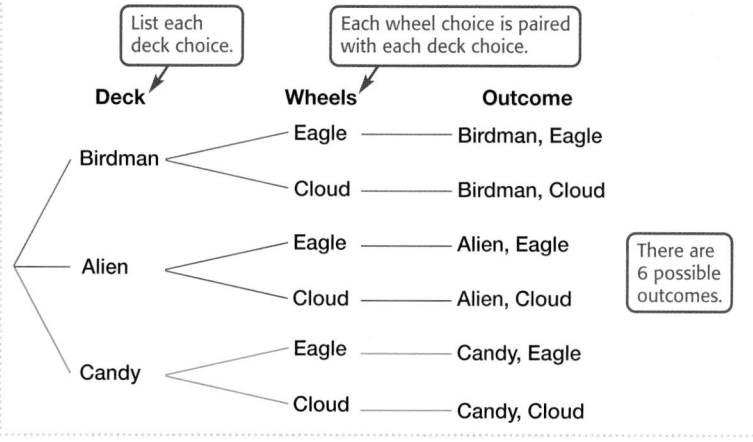

List each deck choice.

Each wheel choice is paired with each deck choice.

Deck	Wheels	Outcome
Birdman	Eagle	Birdman, Eagle
	Cloud	Birdman, Cloud
Alien	Eagle	Alien, Eagle
	Cloud	Alien, Cloud
Candy	Eagle	Candy, Eagle
	Cloud	Candy, Cloud

There are 6 possible outcomes.

12-6 Lesson Notes

1 Focus

5-Minute Check Transparency 12-6 Use as a quiz or review of Lesson 12-5.

Mathematical Background notes are available for this lesson on page 604D.

How can you count the number of skateboard designs that are available from a catalog?

The opening activity questions are repeated on page 695 of the *Chapter 12 Resource Masters*.

Reading to Learn Mathematics, p. 695 **ELL**

Pre-Activity *How can you count the number of skateboard designs that are available from a catalog?*

Do the activity at the top of page 635 in your textbook. Write your answers below.

a. Write the names of each deck choice on 5 sticky notes of one color. Write the names of each type of wheel on 3 notes of another color. **See students' work.**

b. Choose one deck note and one wheel note. One possible skateboard is Alien, Eagle. **See students' work.**

c. Make a list of all the possible skateboards. **alien-eagle, alien-cloud, alien-red hot, birdman-eagle, birdman-cloud, birdman-red hot, candy-eagle, candy-cloud, candy-red hot, radical-eagle, radical-cloud, radical-red hot, trickster-eagle, trickster-cloud, trickster-red hot**

d. How many different skateboard designs are possible? **15**

Reading the Lesson 1–2. See students' work.

Write a definition and give an example of each new vocabulary phrase.

Vocabulary	Definition	Example
1. tree diagram		
2. Fundamental Counting Principle		

Helping You Remember

3. Complete the two diagrams below by filling in each blank with one of the following words. Some words may be used more than once.

choices

favorable

outcomes

possible

Fundamental Counting Principle	m choices for event 1	×	n choices for event 2	=	number of possible outcomes

Probability	Probability =	number of favorable outcomes / number of possible outcomes

---

Resource Manager

Workbooks and Reproducible Masters

Chapter 12 Resource Masters
- Study Guide and Intervention, p. 692
- Skills Practice, p. 693
- Practice, p. 694
- Reading to Learn Mathematics, p. 695
- Enrichment, p. 696

Parent and Student Study Guide Workbook, p. 103
School-to-Career Masters, p. 23

 Transparencies
5-Minute Check Transparency 12-6
Answer Key Transparencies

 Technology
Interactive Chalkboard

COUNTING OUTCOMES

1 GREETING CARDS A greeting-card maker offers four birthday greetings in five possible colors, as shown in the table below. How many different cards can be made from four greeting choices and five color choices?

Greeting	Color
Humorous	Blue
Traditional	Green
Romantic	Orange
"From the Group"	Purple, Red

20

2 CELL PHONES A cell phone company offers 3 payment plans, 4 styles of phones, and 6 decorative phone wraps. How many phone options are available? **72**

FIND THE PROBABILITY OF AN EVENT

3 a. Henry rolls a number cube and tosses a coin. What is the probability that he will roll a 3 and toss heads? $\frac{1}{12}$

b. What is the probability of winning a multi-state lottery game where the winning number is made up of 6 numbers from 1 to 50 chosen at random? Assume all numbers are eligible each draw.

$\frac{1}{15,625,000,000}$

In Example 1, notice that the product of the number of decks and the number of types of wheels, $3 \cdot 2$, is the same as the number of outcomes, 6. The **Fundamental Counting Principle** relates the number of outcomes to the number of choices.

Key Concept — Fundamental Counting Principle

- **Words** If event M can occur in m ways and is followed by event N that can occur in n ways, then the event M followed by N can occur in $m \cdot n$ ways.

- **Example** If there are 5 possible decks and 3 possible sets of wheels, then there are $5 \cdot 3$ or 15 possible skateboards.

✓ **Concept Check** How many outcomes are possible if you toss a coin and roll a 6-sided number cube? $2 \cdot 6 = 12$

You can also use the Fundamental Counting Principle when there are more than two events.

Example 2 Use the Fundamental Counting Principle

SKIING When you rent ski equipment at Bridger Peaks Ski Resort, you choose from 4 different types of ski boots, 5 lengths of skis, and 2 types of poles. How many different outfits are possible?

Use the Fundamental Counting Principle.

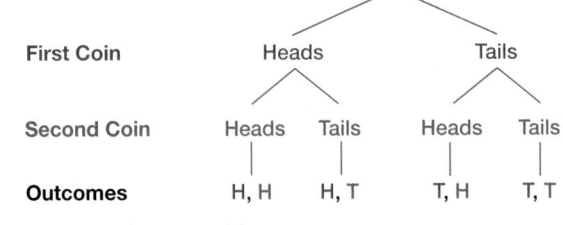

The number of types of boots	times	the number of lengths of skis	times	the number of types of poles	equals	the number of possible outcomes.
4	×	5	×	2	=	40

There are 40 possible different sets of boots, skis, and poles.

FIND THE PROBABILITY OF AN EVENT When you know the number of outcomes, you can find the probability that an event will occur.

Example 3 Find Probabilities

a. Jasmine is going to toss two coins. What is the probability that she will toss one head and one tail?

First find the number of outcomes.

First Coin		Heads		Tails	
Second Coin	Heads	Tails	Heads	Tails	
Outcomes	H, H	H, T	T, H	T, T	

There are four possible outcomes.

DAILY INTERVENTION — Differentiated Instruction

- **Kinesthetic** Have students work in groups of four or five to act out the number of different ways the students can be seated. Each student should have a chair. The students should keep a chart showing each of the arrangements of students and chairs. When each student in the group has sat in each of the chairs, the students should discuss their chart. They should then use the Fundamental Counting Principle to determine whether they recorded each possible arrangement once and only once.

Look at the tree diagram. There are two outcomes that have one head and one tail.

$$P(\text{one head, one tail}) = \frac{\text{number of favorable outcomes}}{\text{number of possible outcomes}}$$

$$= \frac{2}{4} \text{ or } \frac{1}{2}$$

The probability that Jasmine will toss one head and one tail is $\frac{1}{2}$.

Study Tip

Look Back
You can review
probability in Lesson 6-9.

b. **What is the probability of winning a state lottery game where the winning number is made up of four digits from 0 to 9 chosen at random?**

First, find the number of possible outcomes. Use the Fundamental Counting Principle.

choices for the 1st digit	times	choices for the 2nd digit	times	choices for the 3rd digit	times	choices for the 4th digit	equals	total number of outcomes
10	×	10	×	10	×	10	=	10,000

There are 10,000 possible outcomes. There is 1 winning number. So, the probability of winning with one ticket is $\frac{1}{10,000}$. This probability can also be written as a decimal, 0.0001, or a percent, 0.01%.

Check for Understanding

Concept Check

1. **Compare and contrast** using a tree diagram and using the Fundamental Counting Principle to find numbers of outcomes. **1–3. See margin.**

2. **OPEN ENDED** Give an example of a situation that would have 12 outcomes.

3. **Explain** how to find the probability of an order containing chicken filling from a choice of burrito or taco with chicken, beef, or bean filling.

Guided Practice

The spinner at the right is spun twice.

4. Draw a tree diagram to represent the situation. How many outcomes are possible? **See pp. 665A–665F.**

5. What is the probability of spinning two blues? $\frac{1}{16}$

A coin is tossed, and a six-sided number cube is rolled.

6. How many outcomes are possible? **12**

7. What is the probability of tails and an odd number? $\frac{1}{4}$

8. Four coins are tossed. How many outcomes are possible? **16**

GUIDED PRACTICE KEY	
Exercises	Examples
4	1
5, 7	3
6, 8, 9	2

Application

9. **FOOD SERVICE** Hastings Cafeteria serves toast, a muffin, or a bagel with coffee, milk, or orange juice. How many different breakfasts of one bread and one beverage are possible? **9**

Study Notebook

Have students—
• add the definitions/examples of the vocabulary terms to their Vocabulary Builder worksheets for Chapter 12.
• copy the tree diagram and the model using the Fundamental Counting Principle from Example 3.
• include any other item(s) that they find helpful in mastering the skills in this lesson.

About the Exercises . . .
Organization by Objective
• **Counting Outcomes:** 10–19, 24
• **Find the Probability of an Event:** 20–23

Odd/Even Assignments
Exercises 10–23 are structured so that students practice the same concepts whether they are assigned odd or even problems.

Assignment Guide
Basic: 11–25 odd, 27–42
Average: 11–25 odd, 27–42
Advanced: 10–22 even, 24–38 (Optional: 39–42)

Answers

1. Sample answer: Both methods find the number of outcomes. Using the Fundamental Counting Principle is faster and uses less space; using a tree diagram shows what each outcome is.

2. Sample answer: Choosing an outfit from 3 pairs of shorts and 4 T-shirts.

3. First find the number of outcomes possible. The possible outcomes are taco-chicken, taco-beef, taco-bean, burrito-chicken, burrito-beef, and burrito-bean, for a total of 6 outcomes. Two of the outcomes have chicken filling, so the probability of chicken filling is $\frac{2}{6}$ or $\frac{1}{3}$.

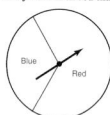
Practice and Apply

10–13. See pp. 665A–665F for tree diagrams.
12. 12 outcomes

Draw a tree diagram to find the number of outcomes for each situation.

10. Each spinner shown at the right is spun once. **24 outcomes**

11. Three coins are tossed. **8 outcomes**

12. A restaurant offers three types of pasta with two types of sauce and a choice of meatball or sausage.

13. Andrew has a choice of a blue, yellow, white, or striped shirt with a choice of black, navy, or tan pants. **12 outcomes**

Find the number of possible outcomes for each situation.

14. School sweatshirts come in four sizes and four colors. **16 outcomes**

15. A number cube is rolled twice. **36 outcomes**

16. Two coins are tossed and a number cube is rolled. **24 outcomes**

17. A car comes with two or four doors, a four- or six-cylinder engine, and a choice of six exterior colors. **24 outcomes**

18. A quiz has five true-false questions. **32 outcomes**

19. There are four answer choices for each of five multiple-choice questions on a quiz. **1024 outcomes**

Find the probability of each event. 20. $\frac{3}{8}$ 23. $\frac{1}{100,000}$

20. Three coins are tossed. What is the probability of two heads and one tail?

21. Two six-sided number cubes are rolled. What is the probability of getting a 3 on exactly one of the number cubes? $\frac{5}{18}$

22. An 8-sided die is rolled three times. What is the probability of getting three 7s? $\frac{1}{512}$

23. What is the probability of winning a lottery game where the winning number is made up of five digits from 0 to 9 chosen at random?

24. **SKATEBOARDS** How many different deluxe skateboards are possible from 10 choices of decks, 8 choices of trucks (the axles that hold the wheels on), and 12 choices of wheels? **960**

25. **GAMES** Suppose you play a game where each player rolls two number cubes and records the sum. The first player chooses whether to win with an even or an odd sum. Should the player choose even or odd? Explain your reasoning.

25. Either; the probability of rolling either odd or even is one-half.

26. **COMPUTERS** The table shows the features you can choose to customize a computer.

Processor	RAM	External Drive	Printer	Color
regular high-speed	64 MB 128 MB 256 MB	regular extra-capacity	basic standard deluxe fax edition	red gray green white lime

  a. How many customized computers include the deluxe printer? **60**
  b. How many customized computers include 256 MB of RAM and a high-speed processor? **40**

27. Sample answer: any two letters followed by any four digits

27. CRITICAL THINKING A certain state uses a system to design motor vehicle license plates that allows for 6,760,000 different plates using a total of six digits and letters. Find a way to use the digits 0–9 and letters A–Z to produce this exact number of arrangements.

28. WRITING IN MATH   Answer the question that was posed at the beginning of the lesson. **See margin.**

How can you count the number of skateboard designs that are available from a catalog?

Include the following in your answer:

- the strategy you used to find all possible skateboard designs,
- the relationship of the number of designs to the number of wheels and decks, and
- how the number of skateboards would change if the number of types of decks was doubled.

NEW YORK
Test Practice

Standardized Test Practice
Ⓐ Ⓑ Ⓒ Ⓓ

29. A 4-character password uses the letters of the alphabet. Each letter can be used more than once, but the letter I is not used at all. How many different passwords are possible? **D**

Ⓐ 100   Ⓑ 13,800
Ⓒ 303,600   Ⓓ 390,625

30. Elena has 6 sweaters, 4 pairs of pants, and 3 pairs of shoes. How many different outfits of one sweater, one pair of pants, and one pair of shoes can she make? **D**

Ⓐ 13   Ⓑ 24
Ⓒ 27   Ⓓ 72

Maintain Your Skills

Mixed Review

31. Sample answer: Vertical scale that does not start at zero.

31. STATISTICS Describe a situation that might cause a line graph to be misleading. *(Lesson 12-5)*

ANIMALS For Exercises 32–34, use the histogram. *(Lesson 12-4)*

32. How many years are there in each interval? **10 years**

33. Which interval has the greatest number of animals? **11–20**

34. How many of the animals have a life span more than 20 years? **3**

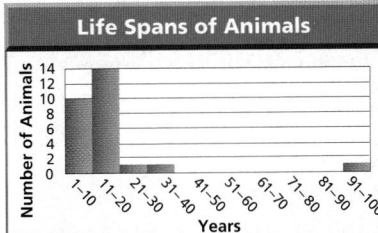
Life Spans of Animals
Number of Animals / Years
Source: *The World Almanac*

ALGEBRA Use the slope and the y-intercept to graph each equation. *(Lesson 8-3)* **35–38. See margin.**

35. $y = 3x + 1$ **36.** $y = \frac{1}{2}x - 2$ **37.** $y = 5$ **38.** $2x - y = 4$

Getting Ready for the Next Lesson

PREREQUISITE SKILL   Simplify. *(To review simplifying fractions, see Lesson 4-5.)*

39. $\frac{6 \cdot 5}{2 \cdot 1}$ **15**   **40.** $\frac{5 \cdot 4 \cdot 3}{3 \cdot 2 \cdot 1}$ **10**   **41.** $\frac{8 \cdot 7}{2 \cdot 1}$ **28**   **42.** $\frac{6 \cdot 5 \cdot 4 \cdot 3}{4 \cdot 3 \cdot 2 \cdot 1}$ **15**

www.pre-alg.com/self_check_quiz/ny   **Lesson 12-6** Counting Outcomes **639**

Open-Ended Assessment

Writing Have students write a paragraph comparing and contrasting tree diagrams and the Fundamental Counting Principle as methods for finding the number of outcomes of an event.

Getting Ready for Lesson 12-7

PREREQUISITE SKILL In Lesson 12-7, students will learn how to find the number of combinations of items by dividing the number of permutations of the set of items by the number of ways each smaller set can be arranged. Exercises 39–42 should be used to determine your students' familiarity with simplifying fractions.

Answers

28. Answers may include making a list pairing each deck choice with each wheel choice, making a tree diagram, multiplying the number of choices for deck times the number of choices for wheels. Answers should include the following.

- The strategy used by the student to count the possible designs is explained.
- The number of designs is the same as the product of the number of choices.
- The number of skateboards would double.

35.

 36.

 37.

 38.

Getting Started

Objective Explore the relationship between tossing coins and Pascal's triangle.

Materials
penny
dime
nickel
quarter

Teach

- After students have completed their tree diagrams in Collect Data, have them quickly switch papers and proof the diagrams before proceeding to the rest of the activity.

Assess

In **Exercises 1–6,** students should be able to work quickly once they have done one or two of the exercises. Watch for students who are taking too much time as they may need some intervention.

In **Exercises 7 and 8,** students should demonstrate that they have found the connections between Pascal's triangle and tossing coins.

Use **Exercise 9** to determine whether students have discovered the patterns in the triangle and understand why the patterns exist.

Study Notebook

You may wish to have students summarize this activity and what they learned from it.

Probability and Pascal's Triangle

Collect Data

Step 1 Copy and complete the tree diagram shown below listing all possible outcomes if you toss a penny and a dime.

Step 2 Make another tree diagram showing the possible outcomes if you toss a penny, a nickel, and a dime. **See pp. 665A–665F.**

Step 3 Make a third tree diagram to show the outcomes for tossing a penny, a nickel, a dime, and a quarter. **See pp. 665A–665F.**

Analyze the Data

1. For tossing two coins, how many outcomes are there? How many have one head and one tail? **4; 2**

2. Find P(two heads), P(one head, one tail) and P(two tails). Do not simplify. $\frac{1}{4}, \frac{2}{4}, \frac{1}{4}$

3. For tossing three coins, how many outcomes are there? How many have two heads and one tail? one head and two tails? **8; 3; 3**

4. Find P(three heads), P(two heads, one tail), P(one head, two tails), and P(three tails). Do not simplify. $\frac{1}{8}, \frac{3}{8}, \frac{3}{8}, \frac{1}{8}$

5. For tossing four coins, how many outcomes are there? How many have three heads and one tail? two heads and two tails? one head and three tails? **16; 4; 6; 4**

6. Find P(four heads), P(three heads, one tail), P(two heads, two tails), P(one head, three tails), and P(four tails). Do not simplify. $\frac{1}{16}, \frac{4}{16}, \frac{6}{16}, \frac{4}{16}, \frac{1}{16}$

Make a Conjecture

Pascal was a French mathematician who lived in the 1600s. He is known for the triangle of numbers at the right, called Pascal's triangle.

				1					Row 0
			1		1				Row 1
		1		2		1			Row 2
	1		3		3		1		Row 3
1		4		6		4		1	Row 4

7. Examine the rows of Pascal's triangle. Explain how the numbers in each row are related to tossing coins. (*Hint:* Row 2 relates to tossing two coins.) **See pp. 665A–665F.**

Extend the Activity

8. Use Pascal's triangle to find the probabilities for tossing five coins. **See pp. 665A–665F.**

9. Find other patterns in Pascal's triangle. **See students' work.**

Resource Manager

📁 *Teaching Pre-Algebra with Manipulatives*

- p. 151 (student recording sheet)

Permutations and Combinations

 NEW YORK *Performance Indicator* **8.PS.13**
Set expectations and limits for possible solutions

What You'll Learn

* Use permutations.
* Use combinations.

Vocabulary
* permutation
* factorial
* combination

Why is order sometimes important when determining outcomes?

Lenora, Michael, Ned, Olivia, and Patrick are running for president and treasurer of the class. How many pairs are possible for the two offices?

choices for president	times	choices for treasurer	equals	possible pairs		Use the Fundamental Counting Principle.
5	×	4	=	20	

There are 20 possible pairs. How is the number of pairs different for five students running for two student council seats, where order is not important?

a. Make a list of all possible pairs for class offices. (*Note:* Lenora-Michael is different than Michael-Lenora.) **See margin.**

b. How does the Fundamental Counting Principle relate to the number of pairs you found? **The results are the same.**

c. Make another list for student council seats. (*Note:* For this list, Lenora-Michael is the same as Michael-Lenora.) **See margin.**

d. The answer in part c equals the answer in part a divided by 2.

d. How does the answer in part **a** compare to the answer in part **c**?

Reading Math

Permutation

Root Word: Permute
Permute means to change the order or arrangement of, especially to arrange the order in all possible ways.

TEACHING TIP

Point out that the first factor is the number of things you are choosing from. The number of factors is the number of things that are chosen. Each factor is one less than the factor before it.

USE PERMUTATIONS An arrangement or listing in which order is important is called a **permutation**. The symbol $P(5, 2)$ represents the number of permutations of 5 things taken 2 at a time, as in 5 students running for 2 offices.

5 choices for president
4 choices left for treasurer

$$P(5, 2) = 5 \cdot 4$$

5 students — Choose 2.

Example 1 Use a Permutation

a. SWIMMING How many ways can six swimmers be arranged on a four-person relay team?

On a relay team, the order of the swimmers is important. This arrangement is a permutation.

6 swimmers — Choose 4.

$$P(6, 4) = 6 \cdot 5 \cdot 4 \cdot 3$$
$$= 360$$

| 6 choices for 1st person |
| 5 choices for 2nd person |
| 4 choices for 3rd person |
| 3 choices for 4th person |

There are 360 possible arrangements.

Workbooks and Reproducible Masters

Chapter 12 Resource Masters
* Study Guide and Intervention, p. 697
* Skills Practice, p. 698
* Practice, p. 699
* Reading to Learn Mathematics, p. 700
* Enrichment, p. 701
* Assessment, p. 728

Parent and Student Study Guide Workbook, p. 104
School-to-Career Masters, p. 24

12-7 **Lesson Notes**

1 Focus

 5-Minute Check Transparency 12-7 Use as a quiz or review of Lesson 12-6.

Mathematical Background notes are available for this lesson on page 604D.

Why is order sometimes important when determining outcomes?

The opening activity questions are repeated on page 700 of the *Chapter 12 Resource Masters*.

Reading to Learn Mathematics, p. 700 **ELL**

Pre-Activity *Why is order sometimes important when determining outcomes?*

Do the activity at the top of page 641 in your textbook. Write your answers below.

a. Make a list of all possible pairs for class offices. (*Note:* Lenora-Michael is different than Michael-Lenora.) Lenora-Michael, Lenora-Nate, Lenora-Olivia, Lenora-Patrick, Michael-Lenora, Michael-Nate, Michael-Olivia, Michael-Patrick, Nate-Michael, Nate-Lenora, Nate-Olivia, Nate-Patrick, Olivia-Michael, Olivia-Lenora, Olivia-Nate, Olivia-Patrick, Patrick-Lenora, Patrick-Michael, Patrick-Nate, Patrick-Olivia

b. How does the Fundamental Counting Principle relate to the number of pairs you found? The results are the same.

c. Make another list for student council seats. (*Note:* For this list, Lenora-Michael is the same as Michael-Lenora.) Lenora-Michael, Lenora-Nate, Lenora-Olivia, Lenora-Patrick, Michael-Nate, Michael-Olivia, Michael-Patrick, Nate-Olivia, Nate-Patrick, Olivia-Patrick

d. How does the answer in part **a** compare to the answer in part **c**? The answer in part c equals the answer in part a divided by 2.

Reading the Lesson 1–3. See students' work.

Write a definition and give an example of each new vocabulary word.

Vocabulary	Definition	Example
1. permutation		
2. factorial		
3. combination		

Helping You Remember

4. Complete the diagram at right by writing the words *combinations* and *permutations* in the correct blanks. Then write a sentence based on the diagram stating how to remember the difference between permutations and combinations. Sample answer: Permutations are all of the possible outcomes, and both start with the letter *p.* Because the set of permutations contains all possible outcomes, it must be the larger set. Therefore, the smaller set of outcomes must be the set of combinations.

Resource Manager

 Transparencies
5-Minute Check Transparency 12-7
Answer Key Transparencies

 Technology
Interactive Chalkboard

2 Teach

USE PERMUTATIONS

In-Class Examples Power Point®

1 a. **TRAVEL** The Reyes family will visit a complex of theme parks during its summer vacation. They have a four-day pass good at one park per day; they can choose from seven parks. How many different ways can they arrange their vacation schedule? **840**

b. How many five-digit numbers can be made from the digits 2, 4, 5, 8, and 9 if each digit is used only once? **120**

2 Find the value of 12!. **479,001,600**

USE COMBINATIONS

In-Class Examples Power Point®

Teaching Tip Have students check that they have listed all possible permutations by calculating the permutations as they did in Example 1.

3 **HATS** How many ways can a window dresser choose two hats out of a fedora, a bowler, and a sombrero? **3**

4 **PENS** How many ways can a customer choose two pens from a purple, orange, green, red, or black pen? **10**

---

b. **How many four-digit numbers can be made from the digits 1, 3, 5, and 7 if each digit is used only once?**

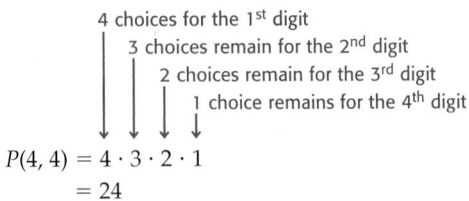

4 choices for the 1st digit
3 choices remain for the 2nd digit
2 choices remain for the 3rd digit
1 choice remains for the 4th digit

$P(4, 4) = 4 \cdot 3 \cdot 2 \cdot 1$
$= 24$

Reading Math

The Symbol !
Read 4! as *four factorial.*

The number of permutations in Example 1b can be written as 4!. It means $4 \cdot 3 \cdot 2 \cdot 1$. The notation n **factorial** means the product of all counting numbers beginning with n and counting backward to 1.

Example 2 Factorial Notation

Find the value of 5!.

$5! = 5 \cdot 4 \cdot 3 \cdot 2 \cdot 1$ Multiply 5 and all of the counting numbers less than 5.
$= 120$

USE COMBINATIONS Sometimes order is not important. For example, *pepperoni, mushrooms,* and *onions* is the same as *onions, pepperoni,* and *mushrooms* when you order a pizza. An arrangement or listing where order is *not* important is called a **combination**.

Example 3 Use a Combination

SCHOOL COLORS **How many ways can students choose two school colors from red, blue, white and gold?**

Since order is not important, this arrangement is a combination.

First, list all of the permutations of red, blue, white, and gold taken two at a time. Then cross off arrangements that are the same as another one.

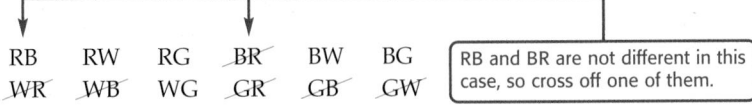

| RB | RW | RG | ~~BR~~ | BW | BG |
| ~~WR~~ | ~~WB~~ | WG | ~~GR~~ | ~~GB~~ | ~~GW~~ |

RB and BR are not different in this case, so cross off one of them.

There are only six *different* arrangements. So, there are six ways to choose two colors from a list of four colors.

Example 4 Counting Arrangements

FLOWERS **How many ways can three flowers be chosen from tulips, daffodils, lilies, and roses?**

The arrangement is a combination because order is not important.

TDL	TDR	TLR	~~TLD~~	~~TRD~~	~~TRL~~
DLR	~~DLT~~	~~DRT~~	~~DRL~~	~~DTL~~	~~DTR~~
~~LRT~~	~~LRD~~	~~LTD~~	~~LTR~~	~~LDR~~	~~LDT~~
~~RTD~~	~~RTL~~	~~RDL~~	~~RDT~~	~~RLT~~	~~RLD~~

First, list all of the permutations. Then cross off the arrangements that are the same.

There are 4 ways to choose three flowers from a list of four flowers.

DAILY INTERVENTION   **Differentiated Instruction**

• **Visual/Spatial** Pascal's triangle can be used to answer questions involving combinations. Show students this table and ask them to find the number of combinations of 6 things taken 4 at a time. **15**

Number Taken at a Time	0	1	2	3	4	5	6
Row 6	1	6	15	20	15	6	1

You can find the number of combinations of items by dividing the number of permutations of the set of items by the number of ways each smaller set can be arranged.

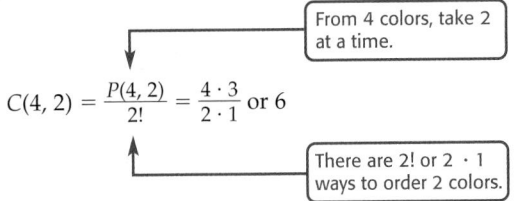

From 4 colors, take 2 at a time.

$$C(4, 2) = \frac{P(4, 2)}{2!} = \frac{4 \cdot 3}{2 \cdot 1} \text{ or } 6$$

There are 2! or 2 · 1 ways to order 2 colors.

Reading Math

Combination Notation
C(4, 2) is read *the number of combinations of 4 things taken 2 at a time.*

Example 5 *Use a Combination to Solve a Problem*

GEOMETRY **Find the number of line segments that can be drawn between any two vertices of an octagon.**

Explore An octagon has 8 vertices.

Plan The segment connecting vertex *A* to vertex *C* is the same as the segment connecting *C* to *A*, so this is a *combination*. Find the combination of 8 vertices taken 2 at a time.

Solve $C(8, 2) = \dfrac{P(8, 2)}{2!}$

$= \dfrac{8 \cdot 7}{2 \cdot 1} \text{ or } 28$

Examine Draw an octagon and all the segments connecting any two vertices. Check to see that there are 28 segments.

Be sure to count the sides of the octagon.

Check for Understanding

Concept Check 1. **OPEN ENDED** Write a problem that can be solved by finding the value of P(4, 3). **See margin.**

2. **Compare and contrast** 5 · 4 · 3 and 5!. **See margin.**

3. **FIND THE ERROR** Sindu thinks choosing five CDs from a collection of 30 to take to a party is a permutation. Sarah thinks it is a combination. Who is correct? Explain your reasoning. **See margin.**

Guided Practice 4. Find the value of 6!. **720**

GUIDED PRACTICE KEY	
Exercises	Examples
4	2
5, 6	1
7, 8	3, 4
9	5

Tell whether each situation is a *permutation* or *combination*. Then solve.

5. How many ways can 5 people be arranged in a line? **P; 120 ways**

6. How many programs of 4 musical pieces can be made from 8 possible pieces? **P; 1680 programs**

7. How many ways can a 3-player team be chosen from 9 students? **C; 84 ways**

8. How many ways can 6 different flowers be chosen from 12 different flowers? **C; 924 ways**

Application 9. **FOOD** A pizza shop has 12 toppings to choose from. How many different 3-topping pizzas can be ordered? **220 pizzas**

www.pre-alg.com/extra_examples/ny

In-Class Example Power Point®

5 **GEOMETRY** Find the number of line segments that can be drawn between any two vertices of a hexagon. **15**

3 Practice/Apply

Study Notebook

Have students—
• add the definitions/examples of the vocabulary terms to their Vocabulary Builder worksheets for Chapter 12.
• choose an example each of using a permutation and using a combination to label and add to their notebooks.
• include any other item(s) that they find helpful in mastering the skills in this lesson.

DAILY
INTERVENTION **FIND THE ERROR**
Students may confuse combinations and permutations. Emphasize each definition, model various situations, and ask whether order is important. It may also be helpful to have students make up memory tools for each definition.

Answers

1. Sample answer: How many 3-digit numbers can be made from the digits 1, 2, 3, and 4 if no digit is repeated?

2. Both expressions have 5, 4, and 3 as factors; 5! also has factors of 2 and 1.

3. Sarah; five CDs from a collection of 30 is a combination because order is not important.

Teaching Tip Have students divide a sheet of paper into two columns. They should head one column "Permutation: order important" and the other "Combination: order not important." As students complete Exercises 5–8 and 10–17, have them write the number of the exercise under the proper column.

Study Guide and Intervention, p. 697

	Words	An arrangement or listing in which order is important is called a **permutation**.
Permutations	Symbols	$P(m, n)$ means m number of choices taken n at a time.
	Example	$P(3, 2) = 3 \cdot 2 = 6$
	Words	An arrangement or listing where order is *not* important is called a **combination**.
Combinations	Symbols	$C(m, n) = \dfrac{P(m, n)}{n!}$
	Example	$C(6, 2) = \dfrac{P(6, 2)}{2!} = \dfrac{6 \cdot 5}{2 \cdot 1}$ or 15

Example 1 SPORTS How many ways can the top five finishers be arranged in a 20-person cross-country race?

Order is important.
So, this arrangement is a permutation.

20 choices for 1st place
19 choices for 2nd place
18 choices for 3rd place
17 choices for 4th place
16 choices for 5th place

$P(20, 5) = 20 \cdot 19 \cdot 18 \cdot 17 \cdot 16$
$= 1,860,480$ ways

Example 2 SCHOOL In a science class with 42 students, how many 3-person lab teams can be formed?

Order is not important.
So, this arrangement is a combination.

From 42 students, take 3 at a time.

$C(42, 3) = \dfrac{P(42, 3)}{3!}$

$= \dfrac{42 \cdot 41 \cdot 40}{3 \cdot 2 \cdot 1}$ or 11,480 lab teams

Exercises

Tell whether each situation is a *permutation* or *combination*. Then solve.

1. How many ways can three people be selected from a group of seven? **C; 35 ways**
2. How many ways can a 6-person kickball team be chosen from 27 students? **C; 296,010 ways**
3. How many ways can 15 actors fill 6 roles in a play? **P; 3,603,600 ways**
4. How many ways can 5 books be borrowed from a collection of 40 books? **C; 658,008 ways**
5. JOBS A telemarketing firm has 35 applicants for 8 identical entry-level positions. How many ways can the firm choose 8 employees? **C; 23,535,820 ways**
6. FOOD A pizza place sends neighbors a coupon for a 4 topping pizza of any size. If the pizzeria has 15 toppings and 3 sizes to choose from, how many possible pizzas could be purchased using the coupon? **C; 4,095 pizzas**

Skills Practice, p. 698 and Practice, p. 699 (shown)

Tell whether each situation is a *permutation* or *combination*. Then solve.

1. How many ways can you make a sandwich by choosing 4 of 10 ingredients? **C; 210**
2. How many ways can 11 photographs be arranged horizontally? **P; 39,916,800**
3. How many ways can you buy 2 software titles from a choice of 12? **C; 66 ways**
4. How many ways can a baseball manager make a 9-player batting order from a group of 16 players? **P; 4,151,347,200 ways**
5. How many ways can 30 students be arranged in a 4-student line? **P; 657,720 ways**
6. How many ways can 3 cookie batches be chosen out of 6 prize-winning batches? **C; 20 ways**
7. SCHOOL TRIPS Students are chosen in groups of 6 to tour a local business. How many ways can 6 students be selected from 3 classes totaling 53 students? **22,957,480 ways**
8. CONTESTS In a raffle, 5 winners get to choose from 5 prizes, starting with the first name drawn. If 87 people entered the raffle, how many ways can the winners be arranged? **4,433,982,840 ways**
9. RESTAURANTS A local restaurant specializes in simple and tasty meals.
   a. How many sandwiches are possible if the restaurant lets you build a sandwich by choosing any 4 of 10 sandwich ingredients? **210 sandwiches**
   b. If there are 6 soups to choose from, how many soup-and-build-a-sandwich specials are possible? **1260 specials**
10. SPORTS An inline skate has 4 wheels. How many ways could 4 replacement wheels be chosen from a pack of 10 wheels and fitted to a skate? **5040 ways**

GIFT WRAPPING For Exercises 11–14, use the following information.
An upscale department offers its customers free gift wrapping on any day that they spend at least $100. The store offers 5 box sizes (XS, S, M, L, XL), 6 wrapping themes (birthday, wedding, baby girl, baby boy, anniversary, and all-occasion), and 3 styles of bow (classic, modern, and jazzy).

11. How many ways can packages be gift-wrapped at the store? **90 ways**
12. What is the probability that any wrapped package will be in a large box? $\dfrac{1}{5}$
13. What is the probability that any wrapped package will *not* have a jazzy bow? $\dfrac{2}{3}$
14. What is the probability that a customer will request wrapping for a baby-boy gift? $\dfrac{1}{6}$

Enrichment, p. 701

Permutations and Combinations

An arrangement of objects *in a given order* is called a **permutation** of the objects. A symbol for the number of permutations is $P(n, x)$, where x represents the number of objects to be arranged in order and n reminds us that these objects are chosen from an original set of n objects.

$$P(n, x) = \dfrac{n!}{(n - x)!}$$

Example 1 If gold, silver, and bronze medals are to be awarded to the first 3 finishers in an 8-person race, in how many ways can the medals be awarded?

$P(8, 3) = \dfrac{8!}{5!}$

$= \dfrac{8 \cdot 7 \cdot 6 \cdot 5 \cdot 4 \cdot 3 \cdot 2 \cdot 1}{5 \cdot 4 \cdot 3 \cdot 2 \cdot 1}$

$= 8 \cdot 7 \cdot 6$

$= 336$ ways in which the medals may be awarded

A selection of x objects taken from a set of n objects *without regard for order* of the selection is called a **combination**. A symbol for the number of combinations is $C(n, x)$.

$$C(n, x) = \dfrac{n!}{x!(n - x)!}$$

Example 2 In how many ways can you choose 3 people from a group of 12 without regard for order?

$C(12, 3) = \dfrac{12!}{3!9!}$

$= \dfrac{12 \cdot 11 \cdot 10 \cdot 9 \cdot 8 \cdot 7 \cdot 6 \cdot 5 \cdot 4 \cdot 3 \cdot 2 \cdot 1}{(3 \cdot 2 \cdot 1)9 \cdot 8 \cdot 7 \cdot 6 \cdot 5 \cdot 4 \cdot 3 \cdot 2 \cdot 1}$

$= \dfrac{12 \cdot 11 \cdot 10}{3 \cdot 2}$

$= 220$ possible groups of 3 people

Find each value.

1. $P(7, 2)$ **42**
2. $P(7, 5)$ **2520**
3. $C(7, 2)$ **21**
4. $C(7, 5)$ **21**
5. $P(13, 2)$ **156**
6. $C(13, 11)$ **78**

★ indicates increased difficulty

Practice and Apply

Homework Help

For Exercises	See Examples
10–17	1, 3, 4
18–21	2
22, 23	5

Extra Practice See page 754.

Tell whether each situation is a *permutation* or *combination*. Then solve.

10. How many ways can 6 cars line up for a race? **P; 720 ways**
11. How many different flags can be made from the colors red, blue, green, and white if each flag has three vertical stripes? **P; 24 flags**
12. How many ways can 4 shirts be chosen from 10 shirts to take on a trip?
13. How many ways can you buy 2 DVDs from a display of 15? **C; 105 ways**
14. How many 3-digit numbers can you write using the digits 6, 7, and 8 exactly once in each number? **P; 6 numbers**
15. There are 12 paintings in a show. How many ways can the paintings take first, second, and third place? **P; 1320 ways**
16. How many 5-card hands can be dealt from a standard deck of 52 cards?
17. How many ways can you choose 3 flavors of ice cream from a choice of 14 flavors? **C; 364 ways**

12. C; 210 ways
16. C; 2,598,960 hands

Find each value.

18. 7! **5040**
19. 8! **40,320**
20. 10! **3,628,800**
21. 11! **39,916,800**

22. GEOMETRY Twelve points are marked on a circle. How many different line segments can be drawn between any two of the points? **66 line segments**
23. HANDSHAKES Nine people gather for a meeting. Each person shakes hands with every other person exactly once. How many handshakes will take place? **36 handshakes**

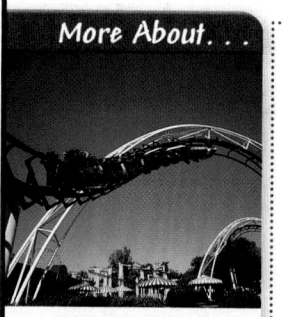

More About. . .

Amusement Parks

An amusement park in Ohio is known for its thrilling roller coasters. There are fourteen roller coasters at the park.
Source: www.cedarpoint.com

AMUSEMENT PARKS For Exercises 24 and 25, use the information at the left.

24. Suppose you only have time to ride eight of the coasters. How many ways are there to ride eight coasters if order is important? **121,080,960 ways**
25. How many ways are there to ride eight of the coasters if order is not important? **3003 ways**

26. LICENSE PLATES North Carolina issues general license plates with three letters followed by four numbers. (The first number cannot be zero.) Numbers can repeat, but letters cannot. How many license plates can North Carolina generate with this format? **140,400,000 license plates**

FLOWERS For Exercises 27–29, use the following information.
Three roses are to be placed in a vase. The color choices are red, pink, white, yellow, and orange. 27. **10 combinations**

27. How many different 3-rose combinations can be made from the 5 roses?
28. What is the probability that 3 roses selected at random will include pink, white, and yellow? $\dfrac{1}{10}$
★ 29. What is the probability that 3 roses selected at random will *not* include red? $\dfrac{2}{5}$

30. CRITICAL THINKING Is the value of $P(x, y)$ sometimes, always, or never greater than the value of $C(x, y)$? (Assume neither x nor y equals 1 and $x \neq y$.) **always**

Answer (p. 645)

31. When order is not important, duplicate arrangements are not included in the number of arrangements. Answers should include the following.
- When order was not important there were half as many pairs.
- Order is important when you arrange things in a line; order is not important when you choose a group of things.

31. WRITING IN MATH   Answer the question that was posed at the beginning of the lesson.

Why is order sometimes important when determining outcomes?
Include the following in your answer: **See margin.**
- how the number of pairs differed when order was not important, and
- an example of a situation where order is important and one where order is not important.

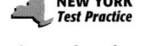
32. Refer to the table. How many different slates of officers could be made if a slate consists of one candidate for each office? **D**

President	Secretary	Treasurer
Tracy	Glenn	Ariel
Marta	Ling	Sherita
José		Wesley

Ⓐ 3 Ⓑ 6
Ⓒ 9 Ⓓ 18

33. Caitlyn knows a phone number begins with 444 and the last four digits are 3, 2, 1, and 0, but she does not remember in what order. What is the greatest number of calls she would have to make to get the right number?
Ⓐ 4 Ⓑ 12 Ⓒ 24 Ⓓ 72   **C**

Maintain Your Skills

Mixed Review

34. Draw a tree diagram to find the number of outcomes for rolling two number cubes. *(Lesson 12-6)* **36 outcomes; see pp. 665A–665F for diagram.**

35. Yes; the vertical axis does not include zero.

35. Is the graph at the right misleading? Explain your reasoning. *(Lesson 12-5)*

Name all of the sets of numbers to which each real number belongs. Let N = natural numbers, W = whole numbers, Z = integers, Q = rational numbers, and I = irrational numbers. *(Lesson 9-2)*

Ticket Sales

Number of Tickets — 100, 150, 200, 250, 300 — Class A, B, C

36. 5 **N,W,Z,Q**   **37.** 0.262626… **Q**
38. −81 **Z, Q**   **39.** √20 **I**

Getting Ready for the Next Lesson

PREREQUISITE SKILL   Write each ratio in simplest form.
*(To review **simplifying ratios**, see Lesson 6-1.)*
40. 16:14 **8:7**   **41.** 4:32 **1:8**   **42.** 4:48 **1:12**   **43.** 44:8 **11:2**   **44.** 45:55 **9:11**

Practice Quiz 2   Lessons 12-5 through 12-7

1. STATISTICS   Describe a situation that might cause a bar graph to be misleading. *(Lesson 12-5)* **Sample answer: Bars are different widths.**

2. Draw a tree diagram to represent the possible combinations of blue or tan shorts with a red, white, or yellow shirt. *(Lesson 12-6)* **See margin.**

3. How many outcomes are possible for a quiz with 8 true-false questions? *(Lesson 12-6)* **256 outcomes**

4. How many ways can the letters of the word STUDY be arranged? *(Lesson 12-7)* **120 ways**

5. GEOMETRY   Find the number of line segments that can be drawn between any two vertices of a hexagon. *(Lesson 12-7)* **15 segments**

Answer (Practice Quiz 2)

2.

Shorts: blue, tan
Shirt: red, white, yellow, red, white, yellow
Outfit: B, R B, W B, Y T, R T, W T, Y

4 Assess

Open-Ended Assessment
Modeling Have students work in small groups. Give each group seven different books. Have students model permutations and combinations if the books are used five at a time.

Getting Ready for Lesson 12-8
PREREQUISITE SKILL In Lesson 12-8, students learn how to find odds, for which they will need to simplify ratios. Exercises 40–44 should be used to determine your students' familiarity with simplifying ratios.

Assessment Options
Practice Quiz 2 The quiz provides students with a brief review of the concepts and skills in Lessons 12-5 through 12-7. Lesson numbers are given to the right of exercises or instruction lines so students can review concepts not yet mastered.

Quiz (Lessons 12-6 and 12-7) is available on p. 728 of the *Chapter 12 Resource Masters*.

About the Exercises . . .
Organization by Objective
- **Use Permutations:** 10–21
- **Use Combinations:** 10–17, 22, 23

Odd/Even Assignments
Exercises 10–23 are structured so that students practice the same concepts whether they are assigned odd or even problems.

Assignment Guide
Basic: 11–23 odd, 24, 25, 30–44
Average: 11–23 odd, 24–44
Advanced: 10–22 even, 24–39 (Optional: 40–44)
All: Practice Quiz 2 (1–5)

NEW YORK *Performance Indicator* **8.PS.13 Set expectations and limits for possible solutions**

1 Focus

5-Minute Check Transparency 12-8 Use as a quiz or review of Lesson 12-7.

Mathematical Background notes are available for this lesson on page 604D.

How are odds related to probability?

The opening activity questions are repeated on page 705 of the *Chapter 12 Resource Masters.*

Reading to Learn Mathematics, p. 705 **ELL**

Pre-Activity **How are odds related to probability?**
Do the activity at the top of page 646 in your textbook. Write your answers below.

a. Roll the number cubes 50 times. Record whether you win or lose each time. **See students' work.**

b. What is the experimental probability of winning the game based on your results in part a? **See students' work; theoretical probability is $\frac{5}{12}$.**

c. Write the ratio of wins to losses using your results in part a. **See students' work; based on theoretical probability, the ratio is 5:7.**

Reading the Lesson
Write a definition and give an example of the new vocabulary word.

Vocabulary	Definition	Example
1. odds	See students' work.	

2. The odds **in favor of** an outcome is the ratio of the number of successes to the number of failures.

3. The odds **against** an outcome is the ratio of the number of failures to the number of successes.

4. The number of successes added to the number of failures equals the number of **total possible** outcomes.

5. To find the **odds** of an outcome, compare the number of successes with the number of failures.

Helping You Remember
6. Study the spinner below, then complete the following.

The number of total possible outcomes = **8**
The odds in favor of spinning an even number = **1:1**
The probability of spinning an even number = **$\frac{1}{2}$**
The odds in favor of spinning a number less than 5 = **5:3**
The odds against spinning a number less than 5 = **3:5**

Vocabulary
- odds

a–b. See students' work; theoretical probability is $\frac{5}{12}$.
c. See students' work; based on theoretical probability, the ratio is 5:7.

Study Tip

Rolling Number Cubes
There are 36 ways to roll two 6-sided number cubes. 15 of the results have a sum of 6 or less. 21 results have a sum greater than 6. See Lesson 6-9 for a table of possible outcomes.

What You'll Learn
- Find the odds of a simple event.

How are odds related to probability?

Suppose you play the following game.
- Roll two number cubes.
- If the sum of the numbers you roll is 6 or less, you win. If the sum is *not* 6 or less, you lose.

Do you think you will win or lose more often? Play the game to find out.

a. Roll the number cubes 50 times. Record whether you win or lose each time.

b. What is the experimental probability of winning the game based on your results in part **a**?

c. Write the ratio of wins to losses using your results in part **a**.

FIND ODDS You can find theoretical probabilities for rolling a certain sum from two 6-sided number cubes.

$$P(6 \text{ or less}) = \frac{15}{36} \text{ or } \frac{5}{12} \qquad P(\text{not } 6 \text{ or less}) = \frac{21}{36} \text{ or } \frac{7}{12}$$

Another way to describe the chance of an event occurring is with odds. The **odds** in favor of an event is the ratio that compares the number of ways the event can occur to the ways that the event *cannot* occur.

ways to occur ⟶ ⟵ ways to not occur

odds of sum of 6 or less ⟶ 15:21 or 5:7

Read 15:21 as 15 to 21.

TEACHING TIP
Point out that the odds against an outcome is the reciprocal of the odds in favor of an outcome.

Key Concept — Definition of Odds

The odds in favor of an outcome is the ratio of the number of ways the outcome can occur to the number of ways the outcome cannot occur.

> Odds in favor = number of successes : number of failures

The odds against an outcome is the ratio of the number of ways the outcome cannot occur to the number of ways the outcome can occur.

> Odds against = number of failures : number of successes

✓ Concept Check If the odds in favor of an outcome are 2:3, what are the odds *against* the same outcome? **3:2**

646 Chapter 12 More Statistics and Probability

Resource Manager

 Workbooks and Reproducible Masters

Chapter 12 Resource Masters
- Study Guide and Intervention, p. 702
- Skills Practice, p. 703
- Practice, p. 704
- Reading to Learn Mathematics, p. 705
- Enrichment, p. 706

Parent and Student Study Guide Workbook, p. 105

 Transparencies
5-Minute Check Transparency 12-8
Answer Key Transparencies

Technology
Interactive Chalkboard

Example 1 Find Odds

a. Find the odds of a sum less than 4 if a pair of number cubes are rolled.

There are 6 · 6 or 36 sums possible for rolling a pair of number cubes.
There are 3 sums less than 4. They are (1, 1), (1, 2), and (2, 1).
There are 36 − 3 or 33 sums that are not less than 4.

Odds of rolling a sum less than 4

$$= \underbrace{3}_{\text{number of ways to roll a sum less than 4}} \text{ to } \underbrace{33}_{\text{number of ways to roll any other sum}}$$
$$= 3 : 33 \quad \text{or } 1{:}11$$

The odds of rolling a sum less than 4 are 1:11.

b. A bag contains 6 red marbles, 4 blue marbles, and 2 gold marbles. What are the odds against drawing a blue marble from the bag?

There are 12 − 4 or 8 marbles that are not blue.

Odds against drawing a blue marble

$$= \underbrace{8}_{\text{number of ways to draw a marble that is not blue}} \text{ to } \underbrace{4}_{\text{number of ways to draw a blue marble}}$$
$$= 8 : 4 \quad \text{or } 2{:}1$$

The odds *against* drawing a blue marble are 2:1.

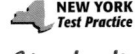

NEW YORK Test Practice

Standardized Test Practice
Ⓐ Ⓑ Ⓒ Ⓓ

Example 2 Use Odds

Multiple-Choice Test Item

> Enrico got positive results 6 out of the 18 times he conducted a science experiment. Based on these results, what are the odds that he will get a positive result the next time he conducts the experiment?
> Ⓐ 3 to 9
> Ⓑ 9 to 3
> Ⓒ 1 to 2
> Ⓓ 2 to 1

Read the Test Item

To find the odds, compare the number of success to the number of failures.

Solve the Test Item

The experiment was conducted 18 times.

6 results were positive.

18 − 6 or 12 results were not positive.

    successes : failures = 6 to 12 or 1 to 2

The answer is C.

Test-Taking Tip

Preparing for Tests
As part of your preparation for a standardized test, review basic definitions such as *odds* and *probability*.

www.pre-alg.com/extra_examples/ny

✓ **Concept Check** How do the number of successes and failures relate to the number of total possible outcomes?
successes + failures = total possible outcomes

In-Class Examples Power Point®

Teaching Tip To simplify finding the answer to In-Class Example 1a or to check it, have students find how many sums are less than or equal to 5, and subtract that number from the 36 possible sums.

1 a. Find the odds of a sum greater than 5 if a pair of number cubes are rolled. **13:5**

b. A bag contains 5 yellow marbles, 3 white marbles, and 1 black marble. What are the odds against drawing a white marble from the bag? **2:1**

2 Multiple-Choice Test Item
After 2 weeks, 8 out of 20 sunflower seeds that Tamara planted had sprouted. Based on these results, what are the odds that a sunflower seed will sprout under the same conditions? **C**

A 2 to 5   **B** 5 to 2

C 2 to 3   **D** 3 to 2

---

3 Practice/Apply

Study Notebook

Have students—
• add the definition/example of the vocabulary term to their Vocabulary Builder worksheets for Chapter 12.
• include any other item(s) that they find helpful in mastering the skills in this lesson.

DAILY

INTERVENTION

Differentiated Instruction

• **Naturalist** Have students find out the chance of precipitation for your town each day for a week. Then have students use the data to record the odds for and against precipitation each day onto one column of a chart. Then have students note what actually happened on another column of the chart and compare the actual results to the odds.

Study Guide and Intervention, p. 702

Odds

The **odds** in favor of an outcome is the ratio of the number of ways the outcome can occur to the number of ways the outcome cannot occur.

Odds in favor = number of successes : number of failures

The **odds** against an outcome is the ratio of the number of ways the outcome cannot occur to the number of ways the outcome can occur.

Odds against = number of failures : number of successes

Example 1 Find the odds of a sum of 11 if a pair of number cubes are rolled.

There are 6 · 6 or 36 sums possible for rolling a pair of number cubes. There are 2 sums of 11. They are (5, 6) and (6, 5). There are 36 − 2 or 34 sums that are not 11.

Odds of rolling a sum of 11

$$\underset{\text{a sum of 11}}{\underset{\text{ways to roll}}{\text{numbers of}}} : \underset{\text{any other sum}}{\underset{\text{ways to roll}}{\text{numbers of}}}$$

= 2 : 34
= 2:34 or 1:17

The odds of rolling an 11 are 1:17.

Example 2 In a bag of marbles, 30 are blue, 15 are orange, 20 are yellow, and 10 are green. What are the odds against drawing a green marble from the bag?

There are 75 − 10 marbles that are not green.

Odds against drawing a green marble

$$\underset{\text{that is not green}}{\underset{\text{to draw a marble}}{\text{numbers of ways}}} : \underset{\text{green marble}}{\underset{\text{to draw a}}{\text{numbers of ways}}}$$

= 65 : 10
= 65:10 or 13:2

The odds against drawing a green marble are 13:2.

Exercises

Find the odds of each outcome if a pair of number cubes are rolled.

1. *not* a sum of 7 **5:1**
2. a sum less than 5 or greater than 9 **1:2**
3. a sum that is a multiple of 3 **1:2**
4. a double number **1:5**
5. *not* a double number **5:1**
6. double twos **35:1**
7. A hockey team scores 6 goals for every 30 shots taken. What are the odds in favor of the next shot being a goal? **1:9**
8. A bookshelf holds 12 mysteries, 3 history books, 4 how-to books, and 11 self-help books. What are the odds of randomly picking a how-to book? **2:13**
9. A professional football team finished the season with a record of 10 wins and 6 losses. What were its odds that season of winning a game? **5:3**
10. After many sessions of playing rock-paper-scissors with Joe, you discover that he throws "rock" 55 percent of the time. What are the odds in favor of his next throw being "rock"? **11:9**

Skills Practice, p. 703 and Practice, p. 704 (shown)

Find the odds of each outcome if the spinner at the right is spun.

1. an odd number **1:1**
2. a number less than 6 **5:3**
3. *not* 7 or 8 **3:1**
4. a number greater than 5 **3:5**

A card is selected from a standard deck of 52 cards.

5. What are the odds of selecting a red king? **1:25**
6. What are the odds of selecting a 4 of diamonds? **1:51**
7. What are the odds of *not* selecting an even club (not a face card)? **47:5**
8. What are the odds of selecting a diamond or an 8 of spades? **7:19**
9. What are the odds of *not* selecting a queen of hearts? **51:1**
10. What are the odds of selecting a jack? **1:12**
11. SURVEYS One opinion poll revealed that 41 percent of Americans are completely satisfied with their jobs and that 44 percent are somewhat satisfied. What are the odds of an American worker, chosen at random, being completely satisfied? Somewhat satisfied? **Source:** www.gallup.com **41:59; 44:56**

SURVEYS For Exercises 12–14, use the information in the table at the right.

12. What are the odds against a randomly chosen respondent being a sports fan? **43:57**
13. What are the odds against a person having no opinion? **99:1**
14. Based on this poll, in a group of 1000 people, how many would you expect *not* to be sports fans? **420 people**

Gallup Poll, August 2001		
Sports Fan	Not a Fan	No Opinion
57%	42%	1%

Source: www.gallup.com

SCIENCE For Exercises 15–18, use the information in the table at the right. Assume that one sample is drawn randomly from a bag containing one sample of each of the minerals in the table.

15. What are the odds in favor of drawing a mineral harder than topaz? **1:4**
16. What are the odds in favor of drawing quartz? **1:9**
17. What are the odds against drawing a mineral softer than quartz? **2:3**
18. What are the odds against drawing a mineral harder than apatite? **1:1**

Mohs Scale of Mineral Hardness	
Mineral	Hardness (hardest rank is 10)
Diamond	10
Corundum	9
Topaz	8
Quartz	7
Orthoclase	6
Apatite	5
Fluorite	4
Calcite	3
Gypsum	2
Talc	1

Source: The Sizesaurus

Enrichment, p. 706

Odds

The **odds** for an event can be found as follows.

odds *for* an event = number of ways that event can occur : number of ways that event cannot occur

If a number cube is rolled once, find the odds for a 4.

1 → A 4 can occur only in one way.
5 → The other events are 1, 2, 3, 5, and 6.

The odds of rolling a 4 are 1 to 5 or 1:5.

odds *against* an event = number of ways that event cannot occur : number of ways that event can occur

Find the odds for spinning each of the following.

1. for a 6 **1:15**
2. *not* for a 13 **15:1**
3. for a prime number **3:5**
4. for a 4, 8, or 12 **3:13**
5. *not* for an odd number **1:1**
6. for a 7 or 9 **1:7**
7. for an odd number less than 14 **7:9**
8. *not* for a number greater than 11 **11:5**

A pair of number cubes are rolled. Find the odds for each of the following.

9. for a sum of 6 **5:31**
10. for a sum of 2 or 10 **1:8**
11. *not* for a sum of 3 **17:1**
12. for matching numbers (doubles) **1:5**
13. for a sum of 7, with a 2 on one die **1:17**
14. for a sum of 10 with a 4 on one die **1:17**
15. *not* for a sum greater than 9 **5:1**
16. for a sum greater than 9 **1:5**

Check for Understanding

Concept Check

1. **Explain** how to find the odds of an event occurring. **1–3. See margin.**

2. **OPEN ENDED** Describe a situation in real life that uses odds.

3. **FIND THE ERROR** Hoshi says that the probability of getting a 2 on one roll of a number cube is 1 out of 6. Nashoba says that the odds of getting a 2 on one roll of a number cube are 1:6. Who is correct? Explain your reasoning.

GUIDED PRACTICE KEY	
Exercises	Examples
4–7	1
8	2

Guided Practice

Find the odds of each outcome if a number cube is rolled.

4. a number less than 2 **1:5**
5. a multiple of 3 **1:2**
6. a number greater than 3 **1:1**
7. not a 5 **5:1**

NEW YORK Test Practice

Standardized Test Practice
Ⓐ Ⓑ Ⓒ Ⓓ

8. Ramon found that 2 out of 8 promotional cards at a fast-food restaurant were instant winners. Based on these results, what are the odds against the next card being an instant winner? **D**

Ⓐ 1 to 4   Ⓑ 4 to 1   Ⓒ 1 to 3   Ⓓ 3 to 1

★ indicates increased difficulty

Practice and Apply

Homework Help	
For Exercises	See Examples
9–25	1
26–29	2

Extra Practice See page 755.

Find the odds of each outcome if the spinner at the right is spun.

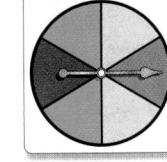

9. yellow **1:2**
10. orange **0**
11. not green **2:1**
12. not red or green **1:1**

Find the odds of each outcome if a pair of number cubes are rolled. **18. 7:5**

13. an odd sum **1:1**
14. an even sum **1:1**
15. a sum that is a multiple of 4 **1:3**
16. a sum less than 2 **0**
17. a sum that is a prime number **5:7**
18. a sum that is a composite number
19. *not* a sum of 8 **31:5**
20. not a sum of 9 or 10 **29:7**
★ 21. a sum of 6 with a 4 on one number cube **1:17**
★ 22. an even sum or a sum greater than 6 **5:1**
★ 23. a sum that is *not* 6, 7, or 8 **5:4**

TEACHING TIP

To complete Exercises 24 and 25, students will need to be familiar with the contents of a *standard deck of cards*. In this text, a standard deck of cards always includes 52 cards in 4 suits of 13 cards each.

A card is selected from a standard deck of 52 cards.

24. What are the odds of selecting a red queen? **1:25**
★ 25. What are the odds of *not* selecting a diamond *or* an ace? **9:4**

26. The probability of having all girls in an eight-child family is $\frac{1}{256}$. What are the odds in favor of an eight-girl family? the odds against? **1:255; 255:1**

27. A family had 13 children, and they were all boys. The odds in favor of this type of family are 1:8191. What is the probability of a 13-child family having all boys? $\frac{1}{8192}$

DAILY INTERVENTION FIND THE ERROR Be sure that students do not confuse probability and odds. If the odds of an event happening are 1:1, the probability is $\frac{1}{2}$. For odds of 1:3, the probability is $\frac{1}{4}$.

Answers

1. Write a ratio comparing the ways the event can occur to the ways the event cannot occur.

2. Sample answer: Prize contests list the odds of winning the grand prize.

3. Hoshi; The probability of rolling a 2 is 1 out of 6. The odds of rolling a 2 are 1 in 5.

•→ STATISTICS   For Exercises 28–30, use the graphic shown below.

★ 28. If you select a man at random from a group, what are the odds that he believes in aliens? **27:23**

★ 29. If you select a woman at random from a group, what are the odds that she does *not* believe in aliens? **47:53**

30. In a group of 500 men, how many can be expected to believe in aliens? **270**

31. **CRITICAL THINKING** A carnival game consists of rolling three 8-sided dice. The odds for winning are listed as 8:512. Do you think the odds given are correct? Explain. **See margin.**

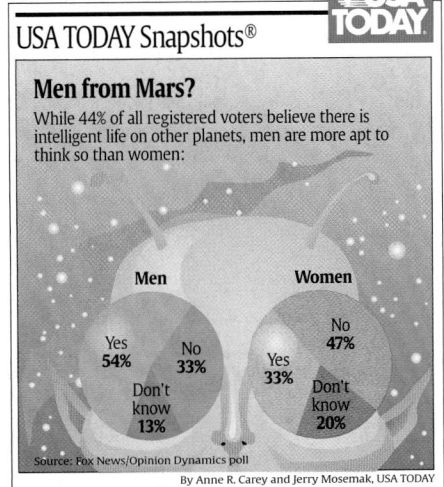

USA TODAY Snapshots®

Men from Mars?
While 44% of all registered voters believe there is intelligent life on other planets, men are more apt to think so than women:

Men
Yes **54%**   No **33%**   Don't know **13%**

Women
No **47%**   Yes **33%**   Don't know **20%**

Source: Fox News/Opinion Dynamics poll
By Anne R. Carey and Jerry Mosemak, USA TODAY

32. WRITING IN MATH   Answer the question that was posed at the beginning of the lesson. **See margin.**

How are odds related to probability?

Include the following in your answer:
• a comparison of your results from parts **b** and **c** on page 646, and
• an explanation of how you can find the odds of an event if you know its probability.

33. A set of cards is numbered 1 through 40. A card is drawn at random. What are the odds that the card drawn is greater than 25? **A**
   Ⓐ 3 to 5   Ⓑ 3 to 8   Ⓒ 5 to 3   Ⓓ 5 to 8

34. Judie made a basket 15 of the 25 times she shot the basketball. Based on this record, what would be the odds *against* Judie making a basket the next time she shoots the ball? **D**
   Ⓐ 3 to 5   Ⓑ 5 to 3   Ⓒ 3 to 2   Ⓓ 2 to 3

Maintain Your Skills

Mixed Review 35. How many ways can a family of four be seated in a row of four chairs at the theater if the father sits in the aisle seat? *(Lesson 12-7)* **6 ways**

36. How many outcomes are possible for rolling three number cubes? *(Lesson 12-6)* **216**

Solve each inequality. Then graph the solution on a number line. *(Lessons 7-5 and 7-6)* **37–39. See margin for graphs.**

37. $2a - 3 \geq 9$ $a \geq 6$ 38. $4c + 4 > 32$ $c > 7$ 39. $-2y + 3 < 9$ $y > -3$

Getting Ready for the Next Lesson **PREREQUISITE SKILL Find each product.**
*(To review **multiplying fractions**, see Lesson 5-3.)*
40. $\frac{1}{6} \cdot \frac{1}{3}$ $\frac{1}{18}$ 41. $\frac{2}{3} \cdot \frac{3}{6}$ $\frac{1}{3}$ 42. $\frac{1}{3} \cdot \frac{1}{3} \cdot \frac{1}{3}$ $\frac{1}{27}$ 43. $\frac{3}{8} \cdot \frac{2}{7} \cdot \frac{1}{6}$ $\frac{1}{56}$

www.pre-alg.com/self_check_quiz/ny   **Lesson 12-8 Odds 649**

Answers

31. No; 512 is the total number of possible outcomes, so it could not be a number in the odds of winning.

32. Odds and probability both express the likelihood of an event happening. Answers should include the following.

• The sum of the numbers in the odds ratio is the total number of outcomes in the probability ratio; the first number in the odds ratio is the same as the numerator in the probability ratio.

• You can find the odds of an event by using the numerator of its probability as the first number in the odds ratio and subtracting that number from the denominator to find the second number in the odds ratio.

NEW YORK *Performance Indicator* **8.PS.13** Set expectations and limits for possible solutions

1 Focus

Mathematical Background notes are available for this lesson on page 604D.

How are compound events related to simple events?

The opening activity questions are repeated on page 710 of the *Chapter 12 Resource Masters.*

Reading to Learn Mathematics, p. 710 **ELL**

Pre-Activity *How are compound events related to simple events?*

Do the activity at the top of page 650 in your textbook. Write your answers below.

a. What was your experimental probability for the red then white outcome? **See students' work; theoretical probability is $\frac{1}{4}$.**

b. Would you expect the probability to be different if you did not place the first counter back in the bag? Explain your reasoning. **Yes; by not replacing the first counter drawn, you affect the possibilities for the second draw.**

Reading the Lesson 1–4. See students' work.

Write a definition and give an example of each new vocabulary phrase.

Vocabulary	Definition	Example
1. compound events		
2. independent events		
3. dependent events		
4. mutually exclusive events		

You are finding the probability of choosing the following arrangements of counters from a bag containing red, orange, and blue counters. Label each situation with *independent events, dependent events,* or *mutually exclusive events.*

5. a red counter, which is replaced, followed by a blue counter **independent events**

6. an orange counter or a primary color **mutually exclusive events**

7. an orange counter, which is kept out of the bag, followed by a red counter **dependent events**

Helping You Remember

8. Complete the concept map below with the vocabulary phrases from this lesson.

What You'll Learn

- Find the probability of independent and dependent events.
- Find the probability of mutually exclusive events.

Vocabulary

- compound events
- independent events
- dependent events
- mutually exclusive events

a. See students' work; theoretical probability is $\frac{1}{4}$.

b. Yes; by not replacing the first counter drawn, you affect the possibilities for the second draw.

How are compound events related to simple events?

Place two red counters and two white counters in a paper bag. Then complete the following activity.

Step 1 Without looking, remove a counter from the bag and record its color. Place the counter back in the bag.

Step 2 Without looking, remove a second counter and record its color. The two colors are one trial. Place the counter back in the bag.

Step 3 Repeat until you have 50 trials. Count and record the number of times you chose a red counter, followed by a white counter.

a. What was your experimental probability for the red then white outcome?

b. Would you expect the probability to be different if you did not place the first counter back in the bag? Explain your reasoning.

PROBABILITIES OF INDEPENDENT AND DEPENDENT EVENTS

A **compound event** consists of two or more simple events. The activity above finds P(red *and* white), the probability of choosing a red counter, followed by a white counter.

The results from the activity above are independent events. In **independent events**, the outcome of one event does *not* influence the outcome of a second event.

$$P(\text{red on 1st draw}) = \frac{2}{4} \text{ or } \frac{1}{2}$$

> There are 4 counters and 2 of them are red.

$$P(\text{white on 2nd draw}) = \frac{2}{4} \text{ or } \frac{1}{2}$$

> You replaced the first counter. There are still 4 counters and 2 are white.

The probability of two independent events can be found by using multiplication.

Reading Math

Probability Notation

Read $P(A \text{ and } B)$ as the probability of A followed by B.

Key Concept *Probability of Two Independent Events*

- **Words** The probability of two independent events is found by multiplying the probability of the first event by the probability of the second event.

- **Symbols** $P(A \text{ and } B) = P(A) \cdot P(B)$

- **Example** $P(\text{red and white}) = \frac{1}{2} \cdot \frac{1}{2} \text{ or } \frac{1}{4}$

Resource Manager

Workbooks and Reproducible Masters

Chapter 12 Resource Masters
- Study Guide and Intervention, p. 707
- Skills Practice, p. 708
- Practice, p. 709
- Reading to Learn Mathematics, p. 710
- Enrichment, p. 711
- Assessment, p. 728

Graphing Calculator and Spreadsheet Masters, p. 42

Parent and Student Study Guide Workbook, p. 106

Science and Mathematics Lab Manual, pp. 27–30

 Transparencies
5-Minute Check Transparency 12-9
Answer Key Transparencies

 Technology
Interactive Chalkboard

Example 1 *Probability of Independent Events*

GAMES In some versions of the board game Parchisi, your piece returns to Start if you roll three doubles in a row. What is the probability of rolling three doubles in a row?

The events are independent since each roll of the number cubes does not affect the outcome of the next roll.

There are six ways to roll doubles, (1, 1), (2, 2), and so on, and there are 36 ways to roll two number cubes. So, the probability of rolling doubles on a toss of the number cubes is $\frac{6}{36}$ or $\frac{1}{6}$.

$P(\text{three doubles}) = P(\text{doubles on 1st roll}) \cdot P(\text{doubles on 2nd roll}) \cdot P(\text{doubles on 3rd roll})$

$$= \frac{1}{6} \cdot \frac{1}{6} \cdot \frac{1}{6}$$

$$= \frac{1}{216}$$

The probability of rolling three doubles in a row is $\frac{1}{216}$.

If the outcome of one event affects the outcome of a second event, the events are called **dependent events**. In the opening activity, if you do not replace the first counter, the events are dependent events.

$$P(\text{red on 1}^{\text{st}} \text{ draw}) = \frac{1}{2}$$

$$P(\text{white on 2}^{\text{nd}} \text{ draw}) = \frac{2}{3} \leftarrow$$

If you do not replace the counter, there are three counters left and two of them are white.

Key Concept — *Probability of Two Dependent Events*

- **Words** If two events, A and B, are dependent, then the probability of both events occurring is the product of the probability of A and the probability of B after A occurs.

- **Symbols** $P(A \text{ and } B) = P(A) \cdot P(B \text{ following } A)$

- **Example** $P(\text{red and white, without replacement}) = \frac{1}{2} \cdot \frac{2}{3}$ or $\frac{1}{3}$

✓ **Concept Check** How can you tell whether events are independent or dependent? If the outcome of one event does not influence the outcome of a second event, the events are independent.

Example 2 *Probability of Dependent Events*

Reiko takes two coins at random from the 3 quarters, 5 dimes, and 2 nickels in her pocket. What is the probability that she chooses a quarter followed by a dime?

$$P(\text{quarter and dime}) = \frac{3}{10} \cdot \frac{5}{9}$$

3 of 10 coins are quarters.

5 of 9 remaining coins are dimes.

$$= \frac{15}{90} \text{ or } \frac{1}{6}$$

---

2 Teach

Building on Prior Knowledge

In Chapter 6, students studied simple probability. In this lesson, they will add to this knowledge by learning about the probability of compound events.

PROBABILITIES OF INDEPENDENT AND DEPENDENT EVENTS

In-Class Examples Power Point®

1 **GAMES** In a popular dice game, the highest possible score in a single turn is a roll of five of a kind. After rolling one five of a kind, every other five of a kind you roll earns 100 points. What is the probability of rolling two five of a kinds in a row?
$$\frac{1}{1,679,616}$$

Reading Tip Tell students that in dependent events, you always assume you were successful on the first event.

2 Charlie's clothes closet contains 3 blue shirts, 10 white shirts, and 7 striped shirts. What is the probability that Charlie will reach in and randomly select a white shirt followed by a striped shirt?
$$\frac{7}{38}$$

Teaching Tip Show students that you can use Venn diagrams to show whether two events are mutually exclusive.

3 You draw a card from a standard deck of playing cards. What is the probability that the card will be a black nine or any heart? $\frac{15}{52}$

Teaching Tip Post a U.S. map. Have cooperative groups write probability problems relating independent information about the states. Trade and solve. For example, what is the probability that a state name begins with the letter "A" and that the state borders the Gulf of Mexico?

MUTUALLY EXCLUSIVE EVENTS If two events cannot happen at the same time, they are said to be **mutually exclusive**. For example, when you roll two number cubes, you cannot roll a sum that is both 5 and even.

Second Number Cube

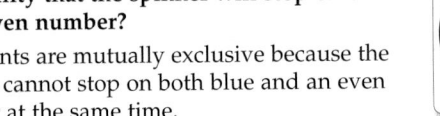

+	1	2	3	4	5	6
1	2	3	4	5	6	7
2	3	4	5	6	7	8
3	4	5	6	7	8	9
4	5	6	7	8	9	10
5	6	7	8	9	10	11
6	7	8	9	10	11	12

First Number Cube

The probability of two mutually exclusive events is found by adding.

$$P(5 \text{ or even}) = P(5) + P(\text{even})$$

There are 4 sums of five. | There are 18 even sums.

$$= \frac{4}{36} + \frac{18}{36}$$

$$= \frac{22}{36} \text{ or } \frac{11}{18}$$

Study Tip

Look Back
To review **adding fractions with like denominators**, see Lesson 5-5.

Key Concept — *Probability of Mutually Exclusive Events*

- **Words** The probability of one or the other of two mutually exclusive events can be found by adding the probability of the first event to the probability of the second event.

- **Symbols** $P(A \text{ or } B) = P(A) + P(B)$

- **Example** $P(5 \text{ or even}) = \frac{4}{36} + \frac{18}{36} \text{ or } \frac{11}{18}$

Example 3 *Probability of Mutually Exclusive Events*

The spinner at the right is spun. What is the probability that the spinner will stop on blue or an even number?

The events are mutually exclusive because the spinner cannot stop on both blue and an even number at the same time.

$P(\text{blue or even}) = P(\text{blue}) + P(\text{even})$

$$= \frac{1}{6} + \frac{1}{2}$$

$$= \frac{4}{6} \text{ or } \frac{2}{3}$$

The probability that the spinner will stop on blue or an even number is $\frac{2}{3}$.

✓ **Concept Check** Using the spinner in Example 3, are the events (green and even) mutually exclusive? Explain.
No; the spinner could land on 2, a space that is both green and even.

DAILY INTERVENTION **Unlocking Misconceptions**

- **Independent Events and Mutually Exclusive Events** Some students may think that all independent events are mutually exclusive events, or may mistake one term for the other. Reinforce that the results of a second independent event do not depend on the results of the first, and that these two events can occur at the same time. On the other hand, mutually exclusive events cannot happen at the same time.

Check for Understanding

Concept Check

2. See margin.

1. **Compare and contrast** independent and dependent events. **See margin.**

2. **OPEN ENDED** Write an example of two mutually exclusive events.

3. **Describe** how to find the probability of the second of two dependent events. **The result of the 1st event must be taken into account.**

Guided Practice

GUIDED PRACTICE KEY	
Exercises	Examples
4, 5	1
6, 7	2
8–10	3

A number cube is rolled and the spinner is spun. Find each probability.

 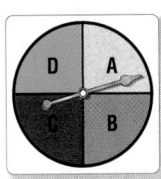

4. P(an odd number and a B) $\frac{1}{8}$

5. P(a composite number and a vowel) $\frac{1}{12}$

A card is drawn from a deck of eight cards numbered from 1 to 8. The card is not replaced and a second card is drawn. Find each probability.

6. P(5 and 2) $\frac{1}{56}$

7. P(two odd numbers) $\frac{3}{14}$

8. A card is drawn from a standard deck of 52 cards. What is the probability that it is a diamond or a club? $\frac{1}{2}$

9. There are 3 books of poetry, 5 history books, and 4 books about animals on a shelf. If a book is chosen at random, what is the probability of choosing a book about history or animals? $\frac{3}{4}$

Application

10. **GAMES** Jack is playing a board game that involves rolling two number cubes. He needs to roll a sum of 5 or 8 to land on an open space. What is the probability that he will land on an open space? $\frac{1}{4}$

★ indicates increased difficulty

Practice and Apply

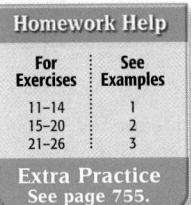

Homework Help	
For Exercises	See Examples
11–14	1
15–20	2
21–26	3

Extra Practice
See page 755.

A number cube is rolled and the spinner is spun. Find each probability.

11. P(3 and E) $\frac{1}{30}$

12. P(an even number and A) $\frac{1}{10}$

13. P(a prime number and a vowel) $\frac{1}{5}$

14. P(an odd number and a consonant) $\frac{3}{10}$

There are 3 red marbles, 4 green marbles, 2 yellow marbles, and 5 blue marbles in a bag. Once a marble is drawn, it is not replaced. Find the probability of each outcome.

15. two yellow marbles in a row $\frac{1}{91}$

16. two blue marbles in a row $\frac{10}{91}$

17. a blue then a green marble $\frac{10}{91}$

18. a yellow then a red marble $\frac{3}{91}$

★ 19. a blue marble, a yellow marble, and then a red marble $\frac{5}{364}$

★ 20. three green marbles in a row $\frac{1}{91}$

Lesson 12-9 Probability of Compound Events **653**

Study Notebook

Have students—

• complete the definitions/examples for the remaining terms on the Vocabulary Builder worksheets for Chapter 12.

• draw models illustrating independent events, dependent events, and mutually exclusive events.

• include any other item(s) that they find helpful in mastering the skills in this lesson.

About the Exercises . . .

Organization by Objective
• **Probabilities of Independent and Dependent Events:** 11–20
• **Mutually Exclusive Events:** 21–26

Odd/Even Assignments
Exercises 11–30 are structured so that students practice the same concepts whether they are assigned odd or even problems.

Assignment Guide

Basic: 11–17 odd, 21–27 odd, 31–34, 36–50

Average: 11–29 odd, 31–34, 36–50 (Optional: 35)

Advanced: 12–28 even, 29–50

Answers

1. Independent and dependent events are similar because both are a connection of two or more simple events, and the probability of the compound event is found by multiplying the probabilities of each simple event. They are different because the second event in a dependent event is influenced by the outcome of the first event. Therefore, the probability of the second event used in calculating the probability of the compound event is dependent on the outcome of the first event.

2. Sample answer: choosing an odd or composite number when rolling a die

An eight-sided die is rolled. Find the probability of each outcome.

21. $P(3 \text{ or even})$ $\frac{5}{8}$
22. $P(6 \text{ or prime})$ $\frac{5}{8}$

A card is drawn from the cards shown. Find the probability of each outcome.

23. $P(3 \text{ or multiple of 2})$ $\frac{3}{7}$
24. $P(4 \text{ or greater than 5})$ $\frac{4}{7}$
25. $P(\text{odd or even})$ **1**
26. $P(2 \text{ or } 6)$ $\frac{1}{7}$

27. A bag contains six blue marbles and three red marbles. A marble is drawn, it is replaced, and another marble is drawn. What is the probability of drawing a red marble and a blue marble in either order? $\frac{2}{9}$

28. **FAMILIES** Each time a baby is born, the chance for either a boy or a girl is one-half. Find the probability that a family of four children has four girls. $\frac{1}{16}$

•**INTERNET USE** For Exercises 29 and 30, use the graphic.

★ 29. What is the probability that a teen chosen at random has used the Internet for both games and studying in the last 30 days? Write the probability as a decimal to the nearest hundredth. **0.16**

★ 30. What is the probability that a teen chosen at random has used the Internet to both browse and use e-mail in the last 30 days? Write the probability as a percent to the nearest percent. **28%**

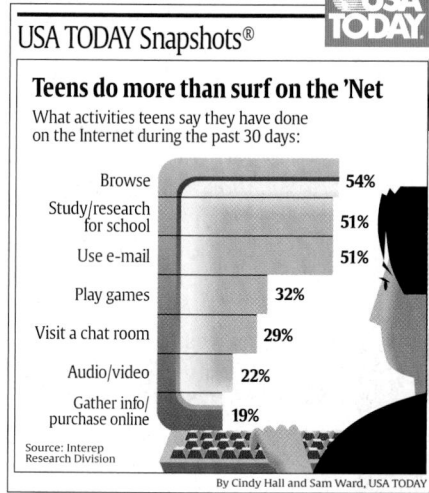

USA TODAY Snapshots®

Teens do more than surf on the 'Net

What activities teens say they have done on the Internet during the past 30 days:

Browse **54%**
Study/research for school **51%**
Use e-mail **51%**
Play games **32%**
Visit a chat room **29%**
Audio/video **22%**
Gather info/ purchase online **19%**

Source: Interep Research Division

By Cindy Hall and Sam Ward, USA TODAY

More About. . .

Internet •

It is estimated that by the year 2005, one billion people worldwide will be connected to the Internet.

Source: *The World Almanac*

31. **CRITICAL THINKING** There are 9 marbles in a bag. Some are red, some are white, and some are blue. The probability of selecting a red marble, a white marble, and then a blue marble is $\frac{1}{21}$.

a. How many of each color are in the bag? **a–b. See margin.**

b. Explain why there is more than one correct answer to part **a**.

32. WRITING IN MATH Answer the question that was posed at the beginning of the lesson. **See margin.**

How are compound events related to simple events?

Include the following in your answer:

• an explanation of how the results of drawing two counters relate to the probability for drawing one counter, and
• the difference between independent and dependent events.

33. A bag contains three green balls, two blue balls, four pink balls, and one yellow ball, all the same size. Marcus chooses a ball at random, then without replacing it chooses a second ball. What is the probability that Marcus chooses a blue ball followed by a yellow ball? **B**

(A) $\frac{1}{50}$ (B) $\frac{1}{45}$ (C) $\frac{2}{45}$ (D) $\frac{3}{20}$

34. If a card is drawn at random from a standard deck of 52 cards, what is the probability that the card drawn is a jack, queen, or king? **D**

(A) $\frac{1}{13}$ (B) $\frac{1}{12}$ (C) $\frac{3}{52}$ (D) $\frac{3}{13}$

*Extending ★
the Lesson*

35. When two events are *inclusive*, they can happen at the same time. To find the probability of inclusive events, add the probabilities of the events and subtract the probability of both events happening. Find P(green or even) for the spinner shown at the right. $\frac{2}{3}$

Maintain Your Skills

Mixed Review

A card is drawn from a standard deck of 52 cards. *(Lesson 12-8)*

36. Find the odds of selecting a red card. **1:1**

37. Find the odds of selecting a jack, queen, or king. **3:10**

38. How many different teams of 3 players can be chosen from 8 players? *(Lesson 12-7)* **56**

39. How many license plates can be made from 3 letters (A–Z) and 3 numbers (0–9)? *(Lesson 12-7)* **17,576,000**

In the figure at the right, $a \parallel b$. Find the measure of each angle. *(Lesson 10-1)*

40. ∠1 **25°**   **41.** ∠2 **65°**

42. ∠3 **115°**   **43.** ∠4 **65°**

44. ∠5 **115°**   **45.** ∠6 **90°**

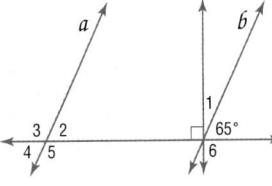

In a right triangle, if a and b are the measures of the legs and c is the measure of the hypotenuse, find each missing measure. Round to the nearest tenth. *(Lesson 9-5)*

46. $a = 6, b = 8$ **10**   **47.** $a = 7, b = 40$ **40.6**

48. $a = 8, c = 15$ **12.7**   **49.** $b = 63, c = 65$ **16**

50. BLOOD TYPES The distribution of blood types in a random survey is shown in the table. If there are 625 students at Ford Middle School, how many would you expect to have Type A blood? *(Lesson 6-7)* **250**

Distribution of Blood Types	
Type	Percent
A	40
B	9
AB	4
O	47

Lesson 12-9 Probability of Compound Events 655

Open-Ended Assessment

Speaking Use a standard deck of playing cards and have students describe how to determine each outcome. Then find the probability of that outcome.

- **Independent events, drawing a king and drawing a jack** Draw a card. Replace it. Draw again. $\frac{1}{169}$

- **Dependent events, drawing a king and drawing a jack** Draw a card. Do not replace it. Draw again. $\frac{4}{663}$

- **Mutually exclusive events, drawing a ten or drawing a face card** Draw one card. $\frac{4}{13}$

Assessment Options

Quiz (Lessons 12-8 and 12-9) is available on p. 728 of the *Chapter 12 Resource Masters.*

Answers (p. 654)

31a. Sample answer: 3 red, 2 white, and 4 blue

31b. Sample answer: The numerator must be 24. Any combination of 3, 2, and 4 will have a probability of $\frac{1}{21}$.

32. The probability of compound events is based on the probability of each simple event. Answers should include the following.

- The probability for two draws is the product of the probabilities of each single draw.

- Independent events do not affect one another; dependent events do.

Getting Started

Objective Use simulations to examine outcomes.

Materials
coin
number cube
red and white counters
blue and red marbles

Teaching Tip Ask students which would take less time to do—roll a number cube 100 times or run a computer program that simulates rolling a die 100 times.

Teach

Activity 1
- Be sure that students understand the difference between tossing a coin as a good simulation and tossing a coin as a way to take the quiz.
- After students complete collecting the data for Activity 1, poll the class to see whether anyone rolled enough correct answers to pass the quiz. Discuss how the experimental probability compares with the theoretical probability for passing the quiz this way.

Activity 2
- You may wish to have students collect the data in pairs or small groups.
- Review the terms *experimental probability* and *theoretical probability* from Lesson 6-9, p. 311.

Algebra Activity

Simulations

NEW YORK *Performance Indicator* **Reinforcement of 7.S.11 Design and conduct an experiment to test predictions, Reinforcement of 7.S.12 Compare actual results to predicted results**

You can use a **simulation** to act out a situation so that you can see outcomes. For many problems, you can conduct a simulation of the outcomes by using items such as a number cube, a coin, or a spinner. The items or combination of items used should have the same number of outcomes as the number of possible outcomes of the situation.

Activity 1

A quiz has 10 true-false questions. The correct answers are T, F, F, T, T, T, F, F, T, F. You need to correctly answer 7 or more questions to pass the quiz. Is tossing a coin to decide your answers a good strategy for taking the quiz?

Since two choices are available for each answer, tossing a coin is a reasonable activity to simulate guessing the answers.

Collect the Data

Step 1 Toss a coin and record the answer for each question. Write T(true) for tails and F(false) for heads.

Step 2 Repeat the simulation three times.

Step 3 Shade the cells with the correct answers. A sample for one simulation is shown in the table below.

Answers	T	F	F	T	T	T	F	F	T	F	Number Correct
Simulation 1	F	T	T	F	F	F	T	T	T	F	2
Simulation 2											
Simulation 3											

Analyze the Data

1. Based on the simulations, is tossing a coin a good way to take the quiz? Explain. **Sample answer: No; none of the simulations results in a passing grade.**

Extend the Activity

Use a simulation to act out the problem.

2. A restaurant includes prizes with children's meals. Six different prizes are available. There is an equally likely chance of getting each prize each time.

   a. Use a number cube to simulate this problem. Let each number represent one of the prizes. Conduct a simulation until you have one of each number. **See students' work.**

   b. Based on your simulation, how many meals must be purchased in order to get all six different prizes? **Sample answer: at least 6**

656   **Chapter 12**   More Statistics and Probability

Resource Manager

📁 Teaching Pre-Algebra with Manipulatives
- p. 157 (student recording sheet)
- p. 20 (die patterns)

Glencoe Mathematics Classroom Manipulative Kit
- counters
- marbles
- dice

Activity 2

Logan usually makes three out of every four free throws he attempts during a basketball game. Conduct the following experiment to simulate the probability of Logan's making two free throws in a row.

Collect the Data

Step 1 Put 20 red and white counters in a bag. Use red to represent a basket and white to represent a miss. The probability Logan will make a free throw is $\frac{3}{4}$, or $\frac{15}{20}$. So, use 15 red counters and 5 white counters.

Step 2 Conduct a simulation for 25 free throws.

Step 3 Without looking, draw a counter from the bag and record its color. Replace the counter and draw a second counter.

Step 4 Repeat 25 times and record the results of the simulation in a chart like the one shown below.

Misses the first shot	Makes the first shot, misses the second	Makes both shots

Analyze the Data

3. Calculate the experimental probability that Logan makes two free throws in a row. **See students' work. The probability should be about 56%.**

4. How do the results in Activity 2 compare to the theoretical probability that Logan will make two free throws in a row? (*Hint*: These are independent events.) **See students' work.**

Model the Data 5. 0.64 or 64%   6. 40 red, 10 blue; red represents a basket; blue a miss

5. Trevor usually makes four out of every five free throws he attempts. Calculate the theoretical probability that Trevor will make two free throws in a row.

6. To simulate the probability of Trevor making two free throws in a row, Drew puts 50 red and blue marbles in a bag. How many red and how many blue marbles should Drew use? Explain your reasoning.

7. Conduct a simulation for this situation. Compare the theoretical probability with the experimental probability. **See margin.**

Extend the Activity 8. No; the data suggests the number varies from machine to machine.

8. There are three gumball machines numbered 1, 2, and 3 in a video arcade. Each machine contains an equal number of gumballs, some orange, some red, and some green. Ali thinks that her chance of getting a green gumball is the same from each machine. She conducted an experiment in which she bought 20 gumballs from each of the three machines. She got 4 green gumballs from machine 1, 8 from machine 2, and 12 from machine 3. Does this data support Ali's hypothesis? Explain why or why not.

In **Exercises 1–7**, watch for students who estimate results or use theoretical probabilities rather than experimental probabilities. Emphasize the need for systematically setting up the experiments and then completing them to find the experimental probabilities.

You may want to have students devise more than one way of simulating the situations.

Use **Exercise 8** to evaluate whether students understand how using a simulation can help solve problems involving outcomes.

Study Notebook

You may wish to have students summarize this activity and what they learned from it.

Answer

7. See students' work. The theoretical probability and the experimental probability should be about the same.

Chapter 12 Study Guide and Review

Vocabulary and Concept Check

- This alphabetical list of vocabulary terms in Chapter 12 includes a page reference where each term was introduced.

- **Assessment** A vocabulary review/test for Chapter 12 is available on p. 726 of the *Chapter 12 Resource Masters*.

Lesson-by-Lesson Review

For each lesson,
- the main ideas are summarized,
- additional examples review concepts, and
- practice exercises are provided.

Vocabulary PuzzleMaker

ELL The Vocabulary PuzzleMaker software improves students' mathematics vocabulary using four puzzle formats—crossword, scramble, word search using a word list, and word search using clues. Students can work on a computer screen or from a printed handout.

MindJogger Videoquizzes

ELL MindJogger Videoquizzes provide an alternative review of concepts presented in this chapter. Students work in teams in a game show format to gain points for correct answers. The questions are presented in three rounds.

Round 1 Concepts (5 questions)
Round 2 Skills (4 questions)
Round 3 Problem Solving (4 questions)

Vocabulary and Concept Check

back-to-back stem-and-leaf plot (p. 607)	independent events (p. 650)	quartiles (p. 613)
box-and-whisker plot (p. 617)	interquartile range (p. 613)	range (p. 612)
combination (p. 642)	leaves (p. 606)	simulation (p. 656)
compound events (p. 650)	lower quartile (p. 613)	stem-and-leaf plot (p. 606)
dependent events (p. 651)	measures of variation (p. 612)	stems (p. 606)
factorial (p. 642)	mutually exclusive events (p. 652)	tree diagram (p. 635)
Fundamental Counting Principle (p. 636)	odds (p. 646)	upper quartile (p. 613)
histogram (p. 623)	permutation (p. 641)	

Choose the letter of the term that best matches each statement or phrase.

1. an arrangement or listing in which order is important **b**

2. the ratio of the number of ways an event can occur to the ways that the event cannot occur **e**

3. two or more events that cannot occur at the same time **c**

4. an arrangement or listing in which order is not important **a**

5. the median of the lower half of a set of data **d**

a. combination
b. permutation
c. mutually exclusive events
d. lower quartile
e. odds

Lesson-by-Lesson Review

12-1 *Stem-and-Leaf Plots*

See pages 606–611.

Concept Summary
- A stem-and-leaf plot can be used to organize and display data.

Example Display the data below in a stem-and-leaf plot.

Lobster Length (mm)			
75	76	80	77
77	77	79	84
80	76	78	69
79	66	84	85

Stem	Leaf
6	6 9
7	5 6 6 7 7 7 8 9 9
8	0 0 4 4 5

$7|6 = 76$ mm

Exercises Display each set of data in a stem-and-leaf plot.
(See Example 1 on pages 606 and 607.) **6–8. See margin.**

6.

Height of Girls on Soccer Team (in.)			
58	62	59	60
61	65	57	56
55	59	62	61

7.

Price of Juice (¢)			
85	45	75	60
60	50	55	75
45	50	60	60
55	75	85	60

8.

Theater Attendance			
110	112	140	124
128	145	119	129
118	124	140	123
146	142	120	114

 www.pre-alg.com/vocabulary_review

FOLDABLES™
Study Organizer

For more information about Foldables, see *Teaching Mathematics with Foldables.*

Have students review the statistical examples and vocabulary definitions on their Foldables for correctness.

Encourage students to refer to their Foldables while completing the Study Guide and Review and to use them in preparing for the Chapter Test.

12-2 Measures of Variation

See pages 612–616.

Concept Summary

- The range is the difference between the greatest and the least values of a data set.
- The interquartile range is the range of the middle half of a set of data.

Example   Find the range and interquartile range for the set of data {18, 11, 26, 28, 15, 21, 20, 20, 15, 23, 19}.

$$\overbrace{11, 15, 15, 18, 19,}^{\text{lower half}} 20, \overbrace{20, 21, 23, 26, 28}^{\text{upper half}} \quad \text{List the data from least to greatest.}$$

$$\underset{\text{LQ}}{\uparrow} \qquad \underset{\text{median}}{\uparrow} \qquad \underset{\text{UQ}}{\uparrow}$$

The range is 28 − 11 or 17. The interquartile range is 23 − 15 or 8.

Exercises   Find the range and interquartile range for each set of data.
(See Examples 1 and 2 on pages 612 and 613.)

9. {42, 45, 38, 27, 41, 39, 50}   **23; 7**
10. {7, 6, 1, 3, 4, 4, 5, 8, 11, 8, 5}   **10; 4**
11. {58°, 64°, 72°, 62°, 74°, 80°, 65°, 70°}
    22; 10

12.

Stem	Leaf
2	4 4 9
3	0 2 3 3 6 7
4	5 7 8 9 9 9

3|2 = 32   **25; 18**

12-3 Box-and-Whisker Plots

See pages 617–621.

Concept Summary

- A box-and-whisker plot separates data into four parts.

Example   Use the box-and-whisker plot shown to find the percent of New York City marathons that were held on days that had a high temperature greater than 72.5°F.

Each of the four parts represents 25% of the data, so 25% of the marathons had a high temperature greater than 72.5°F.

NYC Marathon High Temperatures (°F)

50 52 54 56 58 60 62 64 66 68 70 72 74 76 78 80

Source: *Chance*

Exercises   For Exercises 13–15, use the box-and-whisker plot shown above.
(See Example 2 on page 618.)

13. What was the highest temperature?   **80°F**
14. Half the marathons were held on days having at least what high temperature?   **62°F**
15. What percent of the marathons were held on days that had a high temperature between 54.5°F and 72.5°F?   **50%**

Answers (p. 658)

6.

Stem	Leaf
5	5 6 7 8 9 9
6	0 1 1 2 2 5

6 |1 = 61 in.

7.

Stem	Leaf
4	5 5
5	0 0 5 5
6	0 0 0 0 0
7	5 5 5
8	5 5

7 |5 = 75¢

8.

Stem	Leaf
11	0 2 4 8 9
12	0 3 4 4 8 9
13	
14	0 0 2 5 6

12 |4 = 124

Answers

16. Books Read in a Month

17. Graph A

18. Graph B

See pages 623–628.

12-4 Histograms

Concept Summary

- A histogram displays data that have been organized into equal intervals.

Example Display the set of data in a histogram.

Boys' 50-Yard Dash		
Time (s)	Tally	Frequency
6.0–6.4	|||	3
6.5–6.9	JHT		6
7.0–7.4	JHT |||	8
7.5–7.9	JHT |||	8
8.0–8.4	JHT	5

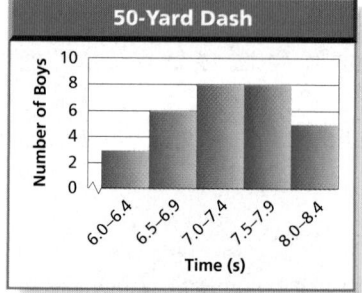

Exercises

16. The frequency table shows the results of a reading survey. Display the data in a histogram. *(See Example 1 on page 623.)* **See margin.**

Books Read in a Month		
Books	Tally	Frequency
0–1	JHT JHT JHT	15
2–3	JHT JHT JHT |||	18
4–5	JHT JHT ||	12

See pages 630–633.

12-5 Misleading Statistics

Concept Summary

- Graphs that do not have a title or labels on the scales may be misleading.
- Graphs that use different vertical scales may be misleading.

Example Explain why the graphs look different.

The vertical scales are different.

Weekly Allowance Graph A

Weekly Allowance Graph B

17–18. See margin.

Exercises Refer to the graphs shown. *(See Example 1 on page 630.)*

17. Which graph seems to show a slight increase in weekly allowances?

18. Which graph seems to show a dramatic increase in weekly allowance?

12-6 Counting

See pages 635–639.

Concept Summary

- The Fundamental Counting Principle relates the number of outcomes to the number of choices.

Example   **A number cube is rolled three times. Find the number of possible outcomes.**

Outcomes on the first roll	times	outcomes on the second roll	times	outcomes on the third roll	equals	possible outcomes.
6	×	6	×	6	=	216

There are 216 possible outcomes.

Exercises   Find the number of possible outcomes for each situation.
(See Example 2 on page 636.)

19. Four coins are tossed. **16 outcomes**

20. A tennis shoe comes in men's and women's sizes; cross training, walking, and running styles; blue, black, or white colors. **18 outcomes**

12-7 Permutations and Combinations

See pages 641–645.

Concept Summary

- Permutation: order is important.
- Combination: order is *not* important.

Examples   **1 How many ways can 8 horses place first, second, and third in a race?**

The order is important, so this is a permutation.

8 horses ⟶ ⟵ Choose 3.

$$P(8, 3) = 8 \cdot 7 \cdot 6$$

$$= 336$$

8 choices for first place
7 choices for second place
6 choices for third place

There are 336 ways for 8 horses to place first, second, and third.

2 An ice cream shop has 5 toppings from which to choose. How many different 2-topping sundaes are possible?

The order is not important, so this is a combination.

$$C(5, 2) = \frac{P(5, 2)}{2!} = \frac{5 \cdot 4}{2 \cdot 1} \text{ or 10 different sundaes}$$

Exercises   Tell whether each situation is a *permutation* or *combination*.
Then solve.   *(See Examples 1 and 3 on pages 641 and 642.)* **21. C; 364 ways**

21. How many ways can 3-person teams be chosen from 14 students?

22. How many 5-digit security codes are possible if each digit is a number from 0 to 9? **P; 100,000 codes**

C; 21 ways

23. How many ways can you choose 2 team colors from a total of 7 colors?

For More ... • Extra Practice, see pages 752–755.
• Mixed Problem Solving, see page 769.

Answers (p. 663)

1. permutation: the number of ways 7 different plants can be planted in a row; combination: the number of ways 6 different candy bars can be chosen from 10 different candy bars.

2. They cannot happen at the same time.

3.

Stem	Leaf
5	8 9
6	0 2 4 7 8 9
7	0 3 4 5 5 6 8
8	1

$5\ |\ 9 = 59$ in.

7. See below.

9.

Length of Bus Ride to School

11. permutation; 5040 ways

12. combination; 220 ways

16. $\frac{4}{7}$

17. $\frac{4}{7}$

18. 1

19. $\frac{3}{7}$

12-8 Odds

See pages 646–649.

Concept Summary

• The odds in favor of an event is the ratio that compares the number of ways the event can occur to the ways that the event *cannot* occur.

Example Find the odds of spinning a red if the spinner at the right is spun.

odds of spinning red

$= \dfrac{\text{number of ways to spin red}}{}$ to $\dfrac{\text{number of ways to spin any color other than red}}{}$

$= \quad 2 \quad : \quad 4$

$= 1:2$

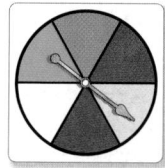

The odds of spinning a red are 1:2.

Exercises Find the odds of each outcome if the spinner at the right is spun.
(See Example 1 on page 647.)

24. yellow **1:7**   25. blue **3:5**

26. not green **3:1**   27. white or red **1:3**

12-9 Probability of Compound Events

See pages 650–655.

Concept Summary

• A compound event consists of two or more simple events.

• When the outcome of one event does *not* affect the outcome of a second event, these are called independent events.

• When the outcome of one event *does* affect the outcome of a second event, these are called dependent events.

Example There are 3 red, 4 purple, and 2 green marbles in a bag. Find the probability of randomly drawing a purple marble and then a green marble without replacement.

$P(\text{purple, then green}) = P(\text{purple on 1st draw}) \cdot P(\text{green on 2nd draw})$

$= \dfrac{4}{9} \cdot \dfrac{2}{8} \text{ or } \dfrac{1}{9}$

The probability of drawing a purple marble and then a green marble is $\dfrac{1}{9}$.

Exercises A card is drawn from a deck of six cards numbered from 1 to 6. Find each probability. *(See Examples 1 and 3 on pages 651 and 652.)*

28. $P(\text{odd number or 2})$ $\dfrac{2}{3}$

29. The card is not replaced, and a second card is drawn. Find $P(3 \text{ and } 6)$. $\dfrac{1}{30}$

30. The card is replaced, and a second card is drawn. Find $P(4 \text{ and } 2)$. $\dfrac{1}{36}$

7.

70 72 74 76 78 80 82 84 86 88 90 92 94 96 98 100

Vocabulary and Concepts

1. **OPEN ENDED** Describe a situation that involves a permutation and a situation that involves a combination. **1–2. See margin.**

2. **Explain** what it means when two events are mutually exclusive.

Skills and Applications

For Exercises 3–5, use the table shown.

Students' Heights (in.)							
70	81	59	69	78	68	75	73
76	62	67	74	75	64	60	58

3. Display the data in a stem-and-leaf plot. **3. See margin.**

4. What is the median height of the students? **4. 69.5 in.**

5. In which interval do most of the heights occur? **70 in.–79 in.**

For Exercises 6–8, use the stem-and-leaf plot shown.

Stem	Leaf
7	1 2 2 3 7
8	0 0 4 4 4 9
9	3 5 6 6 6 8 8 9

8 | 4 = $84

6. Find the range for the data. **$28**

7. Display the data in a box-and-whisker plot. **See margin.**

8. Find the interquartile range. **$19**

9. Display the data shown at the right in a histogram. **See margin.**

Length of Bus Ride to School		
Time (min)	Tally	Frequency
0–9	IIII	4
10–19	ЖН II	7
20–29	ЖН I	6

10. Find the number of possible outcomes for a choice of fish, chicken, pork, or beef and a choice of green beans, asparagus, or mixed vegetables. **12 outcomes**

Tell whether each situation is a *permutation* or *combination*. Then solve.

11. How many ways can 7 potted plants be arranged on a window sill? **11–12. See margin.**

12. A sand bucket contains 12 seashells. How many ways can you choose 3 of them?

13. Find the value of 4!. **24**

14. Find the odds of rolling a number greater than 4 if a ten-sided die is rolled. **3:2**

15. Four number cubes are tossed. What is the probability that all of them land on four? $\frac{1}{1296}$

A card is drawn from the cards shown. Find the probability of each outcome. 16–19. See margin.

| 1 | 5 | 4 | 3 |

| 2 | 9 | 8 |

16. P(5 or even)   17. P(even or 1)

18. P(odd or even)   19. P(2 or greater than 5)

20. **STANDARDIZED TEST PRACTICE** Refer to the box-and-whisker plot shown. What percent of the daily high temperatures range from 70° to 95°? **C**

Ⓐ 25%   Ⓑ 50%

Ⓒ 75%   Ⓓ 100%

Daily High Temperatures (°F)

50 55 60 65 70 75 80 85 90 95

www.pre-alg.com/chapter_test/ny

Portfolio Suggestion

Introduction Statistical displays make the interpretation of data easier. Each type of display has particular advantages.

Ask Students to include a stem-and-leaf plot, a box-and-whisker plot, and a histogram from their homework answers. Next to each example, have them write a sentence or two stating in what ways that type of statistical display makes the data easier to understand.

Assessment Options

Vocabulary Test A vocabulary review/test for Chapter 12 can be found on p. 726 of the *Chapter 12 Resource Masters.*

Chapter Tests There are six Chapter 12 Tests and an Open-Ended Assessment task available in the *Chapter 12 Resource Masters.*

Chapter 12 Tests			
Form	Type	Level	Pages
1	MC	basic	713–714
2A	MC	average	715–716
2B	MC	average	717–718
2C	FR	average	719–720
2D	FR	average	721–722
3	FR	advanced	723–724

MC = multiple-choice questions
FR = free-response questions

Open-Ended Assessment
Performance tasks for Chapter 12 can be found on p. 725 of the *Chapter 12 Resource Masters,* along with a sample scoring rubric for these tasks on p. A30.

ExamView® Pro

Use the networkable **ExamView® Pro** to:

- Create **multiple versions** of tests.
- Create **modified** tests for *Inclusion* students.
- **Edit** existing questions and **add** your own questions.
- Use built-in **state curriculum correlations** to create tests aligned with state standards.
- Change **English** tests to **Spanish** and vice versa.

These two pages contain practice questions in the various formats that can be found on the most frequently given standardized tests.

A practice answer sheet for these pages can be found on page A1 of the *Chapter 12 Resource Masters*.

Standardized Test Practice
Student Recording Sheet, p. A1

Part 1 Multiple Choice

Select the best answer from the choices given and fill in the corresponding oval.

1 Ⓐ Ⓑ Ⓒ Ⓓ   4 Ⓐ Ⓑ Ⓒ Ⓓ   7 Ⓐ Ⓑ Ⓒ Ⓓ   9 Ⓐ Ⓑ Ⓒ Ⓓ

2 Ⓐ Ⓑ Ⓒ Ⓓ   5 Ⓐ Ⓑ Ⓒ Ⓓ   8 Ⓐ Ⓑ Ⓒ Ⓓ   10 Ⓐ Ⓑ Ⓒ Ⓓ

8 Ⓐ Ⓑ Ⓒ Ⓓ   3 Ⓐ Ⓑ Ⓒ Ⓓ

Part 2 Short Response/Grid In

Solve the problem and write your answer in the blank.

For Questions 12 and 19, also enter your answer by writing each number or symbol in a box. Then fill in the corresponding oval for that number or symbol.

11
12   (grid in)
13
14
15
16
17
18
19   (grid in)

Part 3 Extended Response

Record your answers for Questions 20–21 on the back of this paper.

Additional Practice

• See pp. 731–732 of the *Chapter 12 Resource Masters* for additional standardized test practice.

NEW YORK
Test Practice

Part 1 | Multiple Choice

Record your answers on the answer sheet provided by your teacher or on a sheet of paper.

1. A package of 20 computer disks costs $18.40. How much does each individual disk cost? (Prerequisite Skill, p. 715) **B**

Ⓐ $0.46   Ⓑ $0.92

Ⓒ $1.60   Ⓓ $1.84

2. The point system for a basketball contest is shown below. **B**

basket made	basket missed
⬇	⬇
gain 3 points	lose 3 points

Suppose Shantelle made 8 baskets and missed 4 baskets, then what was her total score? (Lesson 1-2)

Ⓐ 4 points   Ⓑ 12 points

Ⓒ 24 points   Ⓓ 32 points

3. An office has 45 light fixtures. Each fixture uses two light bulbs and each bulb costs $0.89. Which expression could be used to find the total cost of replacing all of the bulbs in the office? (Lesson 1-2) **D**

Ⓐ 45(0.89)   Ⓑ 2(45 + 0.89)

Ⓒ $\frac{45}{2}$ (0.89)   Ⓓ 2(45)(0.89)

4. What is the value of m in the equation $\frac{5}{8} + m = \frac{3}{4}$? (Lesson 5-9) **D**

Ⓐ $\frac{1}{2}$ Ⓑ $\frac{2}{5}$

Ⓒ $\frac{3}{8}$ Ⓓ $\frac{1}{8}$

5. Rita makes $6.80 per hour. If she gets a 5% raise, what will be her new hourly rate? (Lessons 6-5 and 6-7) **C**

Ⓐ $0.34   Ⓑ $3.40

Ⓒ $7.14   Ⓓ $10.20

---

6. Juliet recorded the distance and the time she walked every day.

Day	Distance (mi)	Tim (mi
1	2	28
2	3	42
3	4	?

What is the best estimate of how many minutes it will take her to walk 4 miles? (Lesson 8-1) **C**

Ⓐ 48 min   Ⓑ 52 min

Ⓒ 56 min   Ⓓ 64 min

7. A line passes through the points at (4, 0) an (8, 8). Which of the following points also lie on the line? (Lesson 8-7) **B**

Ⓐ (2, −2)   Ⓑ (6, 4)

Ⓒ (6, 6)   Ⓓ (10, 6)

8. What is the surface area of the cube? (Lesson 11-4) **C**

Ⓐ 9 in²   Ⓑ 36 in²

Ⓒ 54 in²   Ⓓ 324 in²

Volume: 27 in³

9. How many different four-digit numbers can be formed using the digits 5, 6, 7, and 8 if each digit is used only once? (Lesson 12-7)

Ⓐ 26   Ⓑ 24

Ⓒ 12   Ⓓ 10

10. A bag contains 4 red marbles, 3 blue marbles, and 2 white marbles. One marble i chosen without replacement. Then another marble is chosen. What is the probability that the first marble is red and the second marble is blue? (Lesson 12-9) **C**

Ⓐ $\frac{7}{72}$ Ⓑ $\frac{4}{27}$

Ⓒ $\frac{1}{6}$ Ⓓ $\frac{4}{9}$

Test-Taking Tip

Questions 1–10
Eliminate the answer choices you know to be wrong. Then take your best guess from the choices that remain. If you can eliminate at least one answer choice, it is better to answer a question than to leave it blank.

ExamView® Pro

Special banks of standardized test questions similar to those on the SAT, ACT, TIMSS 8, NAEP 8, and Pre-Algebra End-of-Course tests can be found on this CD-ROM.

Part 2 Short Response/Grid In

Record your answers on the answer sheet provided by your teacher or on a sheet of paper.

11. What is the value of $(0.3)^4$? (Lesson 4-2) **0.0081**

12. Sixteen pounds of ground beef will be divided into patties measuring one-quarter pound each. How many patties can be made? (Lesson 5-6) **64**

13. Suppose the segment shown is translated 3 units to the left. What are the coordinates of the endpoints of the resulting segment? (Lesson 10-3)

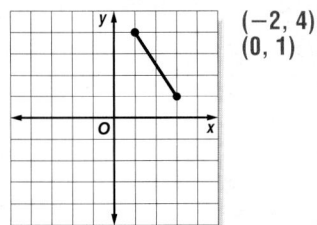 **(−2, 4) and (0, 1)**

14. What is the area of the trapezoid? (Lesson 10-5) **66 in²**

15. Use the formula $V = \frac{1}{3}\pi r^2 h$ to find the volume of a cone with a radius of 9 feet and a height of 12 feet. Round to the nearest tenth. (Lesson 11-3) **1017.9 ft³**

16. A can of soup is 12 cm high and has a diameter of 8 cm. A rectangular label is being designed for this can of soup. If the label will cover the surface of the can except for its top and bottom, what are the width and length of the label, to the nearest centimeter? (Lesson 11-4)

 12 cm; 25 cm

www.pre-alg.com/standardized_test/ny

For Exercises 17 and 18, use the following box-and-whisker plot.

Cost ($) of Various Scooters

17. What is the median price of the scooters? (Lesson 12-3) **about $105**

18. About what percent of these scooters cost less than $90? (Lesson 12-3) **25%**

19. Only two of the five school newspaper editors can represent the school at the state awards banquet. How many different combinations of two editors can be selected to go to the banquet? (Lesson 12-7) **10**

Part 3 Extended Response

Record your answers on a sheet of paper. Show your work. 20a–b. See margin.

20. The scores on a mathematics test are given in the frequency table. (Lesson 12-4)

Score	Tally	Frequency
60–69	I	1
70–79	IIII	4
80–89	IIII	5
90–99	II	2

a. Display the data in a histogram.

b. Which interval contains the greatest number of test scores?

21. If you order a "surprise pizza" special at a certain restaurant, the restaurant chooses two toppings at random. The available toppings are pepperoni, sausage, onions, green peppers, mushrooms, and black olives. (Lessons 12-6, 12-7, and 12-9)

a. List all of the possible "surprise pizzas."

b. How many different "surprise pizzas" are available at this restaurant?

c. If you order a "surprise pizza," what is the probability that it will have pepperoni or sausage on it?
a–c. See margin.

Chapter 12 Standardized Test Practice **665**

Evaluating Extended Response Questions

Extended Response questions are graded by using a multilevel rubric that guides you in assessing a student's knowledge of a particular concept.

Goal: Display and analyze data using a frequency table and a histogram, and explore the relationship between combinations and probability.

Sample Scoring Rubric: The following rubric is a sample scoring device. You may wish to add more detail to this sample to meet your individual scoring needs.

Score	Criteria
4	A correct solution that is supported by well-developed, accurate explanations
3	A generally correct solution, but may contain minor flaws in reasoning or computation
2	A partially correct interpretation and/or solution to the problem
1	A correct solution with no supporting evidence or explanation
0	An incorrect solution indicating no mathematical understanding of the concept or task, or no solution is given

Answer

20a.

Answers

20b. 80—89

21a. PS, PO, PG, PM, PB, SO, SG, SM, SB, OG, OM, OB, GM, GB, MB

21b. 15

21c. $\frac{3}{5}$ or 60%

Page 607, Lesson 12-1

(Concept Check) The stems are the greatest common values of the data. The leaves are the numbers in the next place value position.

Page 608, Lesson 12-1

3.

Stem	Leaf
0	6 7
1	2 5 5
2	0
3	5
4	0 1

$2 \mid 0 = 20$

4.

Stem	Leaf
2	2 3 9
3	
4	2 2 2 4
5	
6	1
7	
8	2
9	
10	3
11	
12	8

$12 \mid 8 = 128$

7. Sample answer: The lowest score was 50. The highest score was 99. Most of the scores were in the 70–79 interval.

Page 609, Lesson 12-1

13.

Stem	Leaf
0	6 6 8
1	0 1 4 6 8
2	0 2 5
3	2 7
4	
5	0

$3 \mid 7 = 37$

14.

Stem	Leaf
46	8
47	2 5 5 6 8 8
48	1 7
49	3 6
50	1 8
51	1 7
52	4 6
53	0 4
54	0
55	0
56	
57	6

$53 \mid 4 = 53.4$

15.

Stem	Leaf
40	0 0 5
41	
42	5
43	
44	
45	0 6
46	
47	
48	0 4 7
49	
50	
51	0
52	0
•	
•	
•	
62	5
•	
•	
•	
76	4
77	
78	9

$76 \mid 4 = 764$

Page 610, Lesson 12-1

28. Stem-and-leaf plots can help you understand an election by allowing you to see how the number of electors in the U.S. is distributed. Answers should include the following.

- Most of the states in the U.S. have 0 to 10 electors. However, there are some states that have 10–19, 20–29, 30–39, and 50–59 electors.

- A presidential candidate might use the display to determine the importance of each state when campaigning.

Stem	Leaf
0	3 3 3 3 3 3 3 3
	4 4 4 4 4 4 5 5
	5 5 6 6 7 7 7 8
	8 8 8 8 8 9 9
1	0 0 1 1 1 1 2 2
	3 3 4 5 8
2	1 2 3 5
3	2 3
4	
5	4

$3 \setminus 2 = 32$

Page 614, Lesson 12-2

1. The range describes how the entire set of data is distributed, while the interquartile range describes how the middle half of the data is distributed.

2. The lower quartile is the median of the lower half of the set of data. The upper quartile is the median of the upper half of the set of data.

3. Sample answer: {8, 9, 13, 25, 26, 26, 26, 27, 28, 30, 35, 40}

8. Sample answer: Since the length of a day ranges from 5832 − 10 or 5822 hours, the lengths of days for the planets vary greatly.

Page 615, Lesson 12-2

20. Sample answer: Since the measures of variation are about the same, we can conclude that the number of home runs hit by the leaders in each league is consistent. That is, neither league exceeds the other.

Page 616, Lesson 12-2

25.

Stem	Leaf
0	9
1	2 4 5 8
2	1 7
3	7

3|7 = $37

30. {4.3, 4.8, 4.9, 5.0, 5.3, 5.6}

31. {0.2, 0.3, 0.6, 0.8, 1.2, 1.4, 1.5}

32. {40.6, 45.2, 45.4, 46.0, 50.7}

33. {9.8, 9.9, 10.5, 10.9, 11.2, 11.4}

Page 619, Lesson 12-3

6. Summer Olympic Games 1924–2000
Winning Times for Men's Marathon

128 132 136 140 144 148 152 156 160

7. Sample answer: The length of the box-and-whisker plot shows that the winning times of the men's marathons are not concentrated around a certain time.

Page 620, Lesson 12-3

8. Since SUVs average the least miles per gallon, they tend to be less fuel-efficient.

9. The most fuel-efficient SUV and the least fuel-efficient sedan both average 22 miles per gallon.

10.

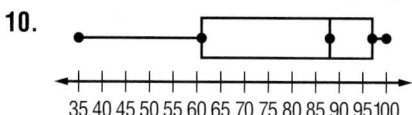

35 40 45 50 55 60 65 70 75 80 85 90 95 100

11.

60 70 80 90 100 110 120 130

12.

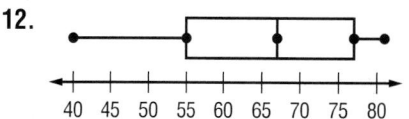

40 45 50 55 60 65 70 75 80

13.

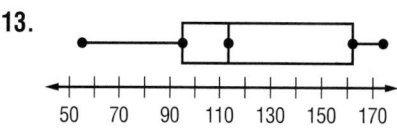

50 70 90 110 130 150 170

14.

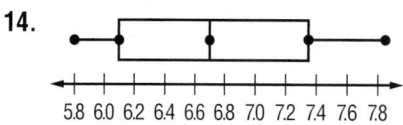

5.8 6.0 6.2 6.4 6.6 6.8 7.0 7.2 7.4 7.6 7.8

15.

26.0 28.0 30.0 32.0 34.0 36.0

18. Sample answer: Based on the plot, the students' overall scores are between 63 and 96.

19. Sample answer: The least number of games won for the NFC is 3 and the least number of games won for the AFC is 1. The most number of games won for the NFC is 12 and the most number of games won for the AFC is 13. In addition, for both conferences, the median number of games won is about 9.

Page 621, Lesson 12-3

21. A box-and-whisker plot would clearly display any upper and lower extreme temperatures and the median temperature. Answers should include the following.

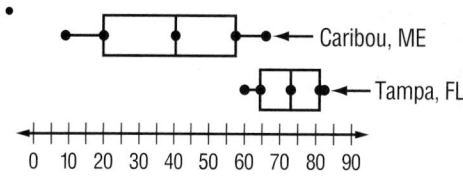

Caribou, ME

Tampa, FL

0 10 20 30 40 50 60 70 80 90

- Sample answer: Tampa has a median temperature of 73 and Caribou has a median temperature of 40.5. Whereas the highest average temperature for Tampa is 82, the highest average temperature for Caribou is 66.

- Sample answer: You can easily see how the temperatures vary.

Page 625, Lesson 12-4

3.

Pet Survey

Number of Participants vs *Number of Pets*

1–3: 21
4–6: 7
7–9: 2
10–12: (none shown)
13–15: 1

4.

Test Scores

8. No; the graph shows that 34 states have anywhere from 0 to 9 roller coasters, but it does not indicate how many states have none.

Page 626, Lesson 12-4

12.

Weekly Allowance

13.

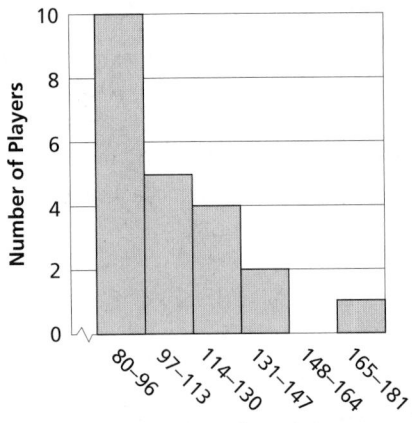

Touchdowns in a Season

14.

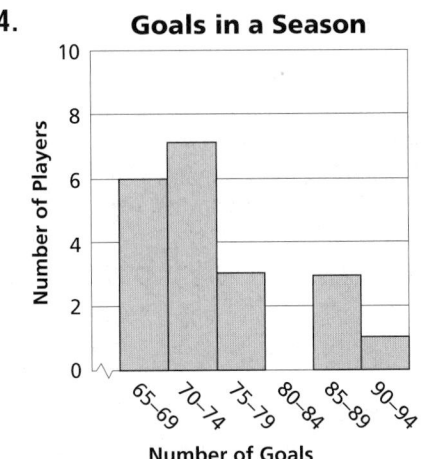

Goals in a Season

Page 627, Lesson 12-4

26. Histograms and frequency tables are similar in that they both categorize data using intervals. Answers should include the following.

-

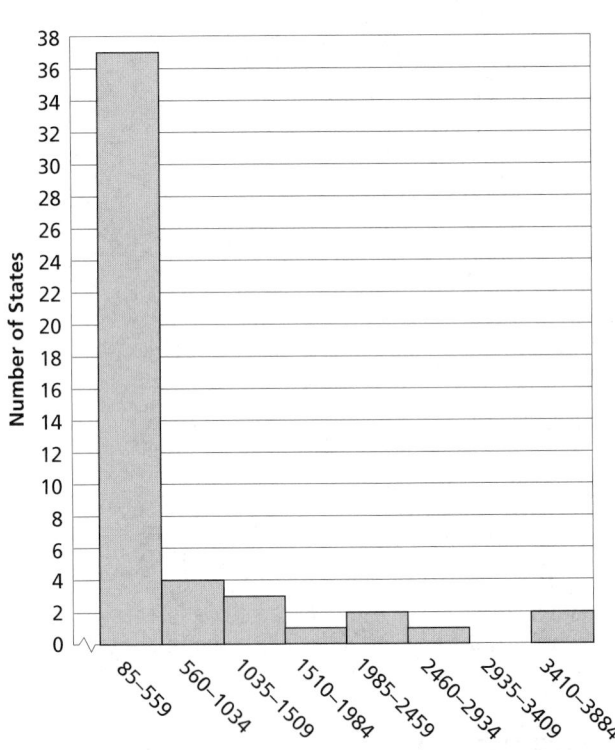

Size of U.S. Farms

Size of U.S. Farms		
Acres	**Tally**	**Frequency**
85–59	⊪⊪⊪⊪⊪⊪⊪ II	37
560–1034	IIII	4
1035–1509	III	3
1510–1984	I	1
1985–2459	II	2
2460–2934	I	1
2935–3409		0
3410–3884	II	2

- In the histogram, the size of the farm is shown on the horizontal axis and the number of states that contain a farm of that size is shown on the vertical axis. The bars are used to show the number of states that contain a farm of the given size. In the frequency table, the size of the farm is listed in the first column and the number of states that contain a farm of the given size is listed in the third column. The middle column is used for tallying the data.

Page 628, Lesson 12-4 (Practice Quiz)

1.
Stem	Leaf
1	6 8 9 9
2	0 2 6 8 8 8
3	0 2
4	0 2 3
5	5
6	
7	
8	6 9 5	5 = 55

3.

5.

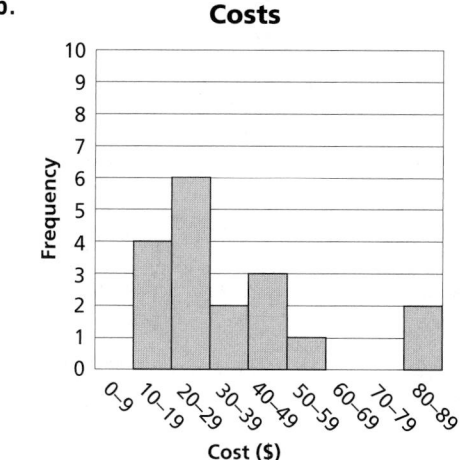

Page 633, Lesson 12-5

11a.

11b.

12. The use of inconsistent scales, broken scales, expanded and shortened axes will make the graph misleading. Answers should include the following.

-
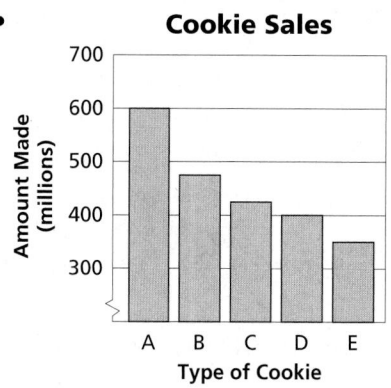

- This graph is misleading because the vertical axis does not start at zero. To redo the graph so that it is not misleading, you can redraw the vertical axis so that it does include zero and the intervals of the vertical axis are equal.

14.

15.

18. $\frac{1}{4}$ or 25%

19. $\frac{1}{6}$ or $16\frac{2}{3}$%

20. $\frac{5}{12}$ or $41\frac{2}{3}$%

21. $\frac{5}{6}$ or $83\frac{1}{3}$%

22. $\frac{3}{4}$ or 75%

23. $\frac{5}{6}$ or $83.\overline{3}$%

Page 637, Lesson 12-6

4.

16 outcomes

Page 638, Lesson 12-6

10.

11.

12.

13.

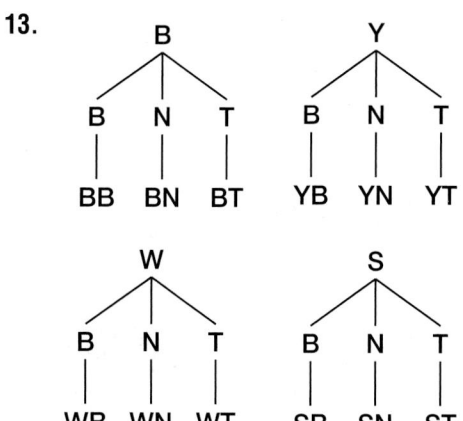

Page 640, Algebra Activity

Collect Data

Step 2.

Step 3.

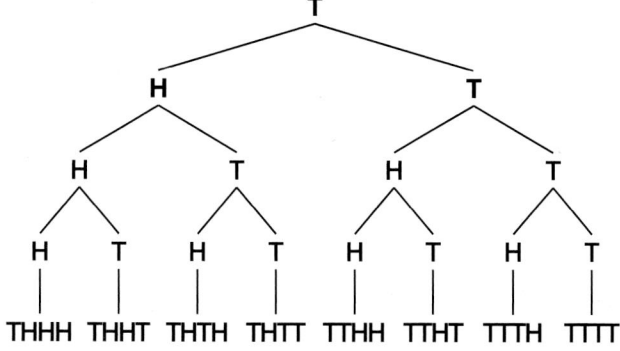

7. The sum of the numbers in each row is the number of outcomes for tossing a number of coins one less than the row number. The numbers in each row are the numerators for the probabilities for outcomes for the coin tossing connected with that row.

8. The numbers in the row are 1, 5, 10, 10, 5, 1. The number of outcomes is 32. The probabilities are:

$P(5 \text{ heads}) = \frac{1}{32}$, $P(4 \text{ heads}, 1 \text{ tail}) = \frac{5}{32}$, $P(3 \text{ heads},$

$2 \text{ tails}) = \frac{10}{32}$, $P(2 \text{ heads}, 3 \text{ tails}) = \frac{10}{32}$, $P(1 \text{ head}, 4 \text{ tails})$

$= \frac{5}{32}$; $P(5 \text{ tails}) = \frac{1}{32}$.

Page 645, Lesson 12-7

34.

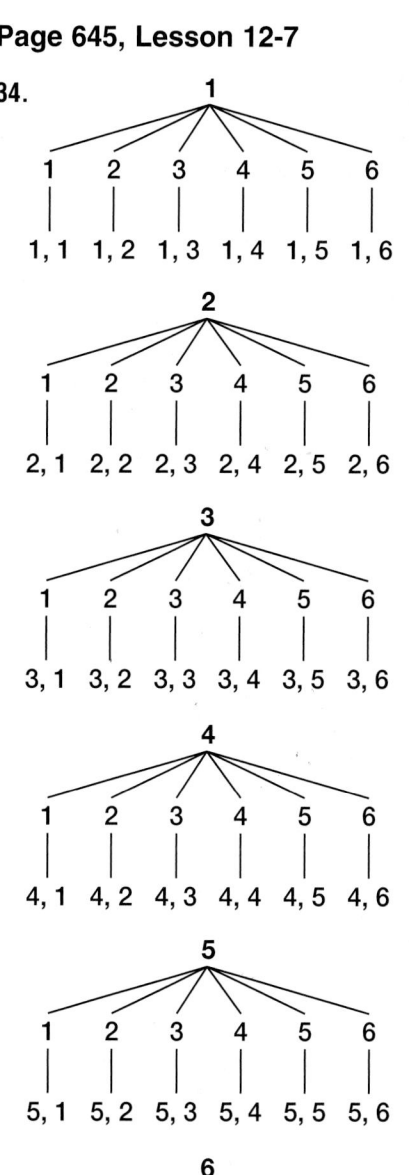

Polynomials and Nonlinear Functions
Chapter Overview and Pacing

Year-long pacing: pages T20–T21.

LESSON OBJECTIVES	PACING (days)			
	Regular		Block	
	Basic/ Average	Advanced	Basic/ Average	Advanced
13-1 Polynomials (pp. 669–673) • Identify and classify polynomials. • Find the degree of a polynomial. *Follow-Up:* Model polynomials with algebra tiles.	Optional	2 (with 13–1 Follow-Up)	Optional	1 (with 13–1 Follow-Up)
13-2 Adding Polynomials (pp. 674–677) • Add polynomials.	Optional	1	Optional	0.5
13-3 Subtracting Polynomials (pp. 678–681) • Subtract polynomials.	Optional	1	Optional	0.5
13-4 Multiplying a Polynomial by a Monomial (pp. 682–686) *Preview:* Model multiplication with algebra tiles. • Multiply a polynomial by a monomial.	Optional	2	Optional	1
13-5 Linear and Nonlinear Functions (pp. 687–691) • Determine whether a function is linear or nonlinear.	Optional	2	Optional	1
13-6 Graphing Quadratic and Cubic Functions (pp. 692–697) • Graph quadratic functions. • Graph cubic functions. *Follow-Up:* Graph families of quadratic functions.	Optional	3	Optional	1.5
Study Guide and **Practice Test** (pp. 698–701) **Standardized Test Practice** (pp. 702–703)	Optional	1	Optional	0.5
Chapter Assessment	Optional	1	Optional	0.5
TOTAL	0	13	0	6.5

*An electronic version of this chapter is available on **StudentWorks™**. This backpack solution CD-ROM allows students instant access to the Student Edition, lesson worksheet pages, and web resources.*

Chapter Resource Manager

CHAPTER 13 RESOURCE MASTERS						Prerequisite Skills Workbook	Applications*	Parent and Student Study Guide Workbook	5-Minute Check Transparencies	Interactive Chalkboard	Pre-AlgePASS: Tutorial Plus (lessons)	Materials
Study Guide and Intervention	Practice (Skills and Average)	Reading to Learn Mathematics	Enrichment	Assessment								
733	734–735	736	737					108	13-1	13-1		*Follow-Up:* algebra tiles
738	739–740	741	742	777				109	13-2	13-2		
743	744–745	746	747	777, 779			SC 25	110	13-3	13-3		
748	749–750	751	752				GCS 43	111	13-4	13-4	38	*Preview:* algebra tiles, product mat
753	754–755	756	757	778			SC 26	112	13-5	13-5		
758	759–760	761	762	778			GCS 44	113	13-6	13-6		*Follow-Up:* graphing calculator
				763–776 780–794								

* *Key to Abbreviations:* GCS = Graphing Calculator and Spreadsheet Masters
SC = School-to-Career Masters
SM = Science and Mathematics Lab Manual

ELL Study Guide and Intervention, Skills Practice, Practice, and Parent and Student Study Guide Workbooks are also available in Spanish.

Chapter 13

Mathematical Connections and Background

Continuity of Instruction

Prior Knowledge

In Chapter 2, students learned to add integers, using the additive inverse when necessary. In Chapter 3, they studied the Distributive Property and its use in simplifying mathematical expressions. In Chapter 4, students learned about monomials. In addition, they studied functions and rate of change and graphed linear equations and inequalities in Chapter 8.

This Chapter

Students expand their knowledge of polynomials to include expressions with more than one term, such as binomials and trinomials, and they learn to add, subtract, and multiply polynomials. Students compare the rates of change of several functions. They compare linear and nonlinear functions, learn the shapes of some nonlinear functions, and graph quadratic and cubic functions.

Future Connections

The material covered in this chapter is fundamental for future mathematics courses, particularly calculus. Many formulas contain monomials and polynomials, and solving problems involving these formulas will be a necessary skill in higher level courses such as physics and engineering.

13-1 Polynomials

Recall that a monomial is a number, a variable, or a product of numbers and/or variables such as 3x4. An algebraic expression that contains one or more monomials is called a polynomial. In a polynomial, there are no terms with variables in the denominator and no terms with variables under a radical sign. Polynomials can be classified by the number of terms contained in the expression. Therefore, a polynomial with two terms is called a binomial ($z^2 - 1$), and a polynomial with three terms is called a trinomial ($2y^3 + 4y^2 - y$).

Polynomials also can be classified by their degrees. The degree of a monomial is the sum of the exponents of its variables. The degree of a nonzero constant such as 6 or 10 is 0. The constant 0 has no degree. For example, the monomial $4b^5c^2$ has a degree of 7. The degree of a polynomial is the same as that of the term with the greatest degree. For example, the polynomial $3x^4 - 2y^3 + 4y^2 - y$ has a degree of 4.

13-2 Adding Polynomials

Monomials that contain the same variables to the same power are like terms. Like terms differ only by their coefficients. Polynomials can be added by combining like terms. When a polynomial has a minus sign, the coefficient following is a negative number. There are two methods for adding polynomials. In one method, the polynomials are stacked vertically with like terms aligned, as shown below.

$$2ab - 3b^2 - 8$$
$$\underline{(+) \quad ab + 6b^2 + 0}$$
$$3ab + 3b^2 - 8$$

When using the vertical method, it can be helpful to add zeros as placeholders when a term in one polynomial does not have a corresponding like term in another polynomial. In the other method, the polynomials are written horizontally and like terms are combined by using the Associative and Commutative Properties, as shown below.

$$(3xy + 4) + (xy - 2) = (3xy + xy) + (4 - 2)$$
$$= 4xy + 2$$

Polynomials often are used to represent measures of geometric figures. For example, a rectangle whose length is 3 times its width has the dimensions $x \times 3x$ and its perimeter is equal to $2x + 2(3x)$, or $8x$.

13-3 Subtracting Polynomials

Just as measurements are subtracted by subtracting like units, polynomials are subtracted by subtracting like terms. As with the addition of polynomials, polynomials can be subtracted vertically or horizontally. Recall that you can subtract a rational number by adding its additive inverse. Similarly, you can subtract a polynomial by adding its additive inverse. The additive inverse is found by multiplying the entire polynomial by –1. By the Distributive Property, this is done by multiplying each term of the polynomial by –1. For example, $-1(2a^2c + 4bc - 7) = -2a^2c - 4bc + 7$.

13-4 Multiplying a Polynomial by a Monomial

When multiplying a polynomial by a monomial, use the Distributive Property and then simplify, as shown below.

$$4y(2x^2y - 3x + 5) = 4y(2x^2y) + 4y(-3x) + 4y(5)$$
$$= 8x^2y^2 + (-12xy) + 20y$$

13-5 Linear and Nonlinear Functions

Linear functions have graphs that are straight lines. These graphs represent constant rates of change. In other words, the slope between any two points on the graph is the same. Nonlinear functions do not have constant rates of change. The slope changes along these graphs. Therefore, the graphs of nonlinear functions are *not* straight lines. Graphs of curves represent nonlinear functions. Recall that the equation for a linear function can be written in the form $y = mx + b$, where m represents the slope. Therefore, you can determine whether a function is linear by looking at its equation. For example, the equation $y = \dfrac{3}{x}$ is nonlinear because x is in the denominator and the equation cannot be written in the form $y = mx + b$. A nonlinear function does not increase or decrease at the same rate.

Some nonlinear functions are given special names. A quadratic function is a function that can be described by an equation of the form $y = ax^2 + bx + c$, where $a \neq 0$. The graph of a quadratic function has the shape of a parabola. A cubic function is a function that can be described by an equation of the form $y = ax^3 + bx^2 + cx + d$, where $a \neq 0$. Other nonlinear functions are exponential functions, such as $y = 4^x$, and inverse variation functions, such as $y = \dfrac{1}{x}$. See page 688 for examples of graphs of these four types of nonlinear functions.

13-6 Graphing Quadratic and Cubic Functions

Quadratic functions can be graphed using an equation or a table of values. For example, to graph $y = 3x^2 + 1$, substitute the values –1, –0.5, 0, 0.5, and 1 for x in the equation to yield the point coordinates (–1, 4), (–0.5, 1.75), (0, 1), (0.5, 1.75), and (1, 4). Plot these points on a coordinate grid and connect the points in the form of a parabola. Parabolas are symmetric with respect to a line drawn from the vertex to the focus of the parabola. Note that the graph of this example has a vertical line of reflection at $x = 0$. Parabolas with a horizontal line of reflection are not functions, since for every value x except the vertex, there are two values for y.

Cubic functions also can be graphed by making a table of values. Students sometimes will try to connect the points as a straight line. Note that the graph of any cubic function is a curve, and there is one point at which the curve changes from opening upward to opening downward, or vice versa. On the graph of the cubic function $y = 3x^3 + 1$, this point, called the point of inflection, is at (0, 1). At this point, the curve changes from being concave down to concave up.

Quick Review Math Handbook

Hot Words includes a glossary of terms while Hot Topics consists of explanations of key mathematical concepts with exercises to test comprehension. This valuable resource can be used as a reference in the classroom or for home study.

Lesson	Hot Topics Section	Lesson	Hot Topics Section
GS 13	1.4, 6.4	13-4	6.4, 6.7
13-1	6.2	13-5	6.4, 6.7, 6.8
13-3	6.2		

GS = Getting Started

 Additional mathematical information and teaching notes are available at www.pre-alg.com/key_concepts.

DAILY
INTERVENTION and Assessment

Key to Abbreviations:
TWE = Teacher Wraparound Edition; CRM = Chapter Resource Masters

	Type	Student Edition	Teacher Resources	Technology/Internet
INTERVENTION	Ongoing	Prerequisite Skills, pp. 667, 672, 677, 681, 686, 691 Practice Quiz 1, p. 681 Practice Quiz 2, p. 691	5-Minute Check Transparencies *Prerequisite Skills Workbook*, pp. 1–2, 21–24, 27–28, 31–32, 47–62 Quizzes, *CRM*, pp. 777, 778 Mid-Chapter Test, *CRM*, p. 779 Study Guide and Intervention, *CRM*, p. 733, 738, 743, 748, 753, 758	Pre-AlgePASS: Tutorial Plus, Lesson 38 www.pre-alg.com/ self_check_quiz www.pre-alg.com/ extra_examples
	Mixed Review	pp. 672, 677, 681, 686, 691, 696	Cumulative Review, *CRM*, p. 780	
	Error Analysis	Find the Error, pp. 671, 676	Find the Error, *TWE*, pp. 671, 676 Unlocking Misconceptions, *TWE*, p. 693	
	Standardized Test Practice	pp. 672, 677, 681, 686, 689, 691, 695, 702–703	*TWE*, pp. 702–703 Standardized Test Practice, *CRM*, pp. 781–872	Standardized Test Practice CD-ROM www.pre-alg.com/ standardized_test
ASSESSMENT	Open-Ended Assessment	Writing in Math, pp. 672, 677, 681, 686, 691, 695 Open Ended, pp. 670, 676, 680, 684, 689, 694 Standardized Test, p. 703	Speaking: *TWE*, pp. 680, 691 Writing: *TWE*, pp. 672, 695 Modeling: *TWE*, pp. 676, 685 Open-Ended Assessment, *CRM*, p. 775	
	Chapter Assessment	Study Guide, pp. 698–700 Practice Test, p. 701	Multiple-Choice Tests (Forms 1, 2A, 2B), *CRM*, pp. 763–768 Free-Response Tests (Forms 2C, 2D, 3), *CRM*, pp. 769–774 Vocabulary Test/Review, *CRM*, p. 776	ExamView® Pro (see below) MindJogger Videoquizzes www.pre-alg.com/ vocabulary_review www.pre-alg.com/chapter_test

For more information on Yearly ProgressPro, see p. 602.

Pre-Algebra Lesson	Yearly ProgressPro Skill Lesson
13-1	Simplifying Polynomials
13-2	Adding polynomials
13-3	Subtracting Polynomials
13-4	Multiplying Monomials and Polynomials
13-5	Linear and Non-Linear Function
13-6	Graphing Quadratic Functions

ExamView® Pro

Use the networkable **ExamView® Pro** to:
- Create **multiple versions** of tests.
- Create **modified** tests for *Inclusion* students.
- **Edit** existing questions and **add** your own questions.
- Use built-in **state curriculum correlations** to create tests aligned with state standards.
- Change **English** tests to **Spanish** and vice versa.

For more information on Intervention and Assessment, see pp. T8–T11.

Reading and Writing in Mathematics

Glencoe Pre-Algebra provides numerous opportunities to incorporate reading and writing into the mathematics classroom.

Student Edition

- Foldables™ Study Organizer, p. 667
- Reading Mathematics, p. 668
- Concept Check questions require students to verbalize and write about what they have learned in the lesson. (pp. 669, 670, 675, 676, 679, 680, 684, 689, 694)
- Writing in Math questions in every lesson, pp. 672, 677, 681, 689, 691, 695
- Reading Math, p. 678, 684, 688
- WebQuest, pp. 690, 696

Teacher Wraparound Edition

- Foldables™ Study Organizer, pp. 667, 698
- Study Notebook suggestions, pp. 668, 671, 673, 675, 680, 682, 684, 689, 694
- Modeling activities, pp. 676, 685
- Speaking activities, pp. 680, 691
- Writing activities, pp. 672, 695
- Differentiated Instruction (Verbal/Linguistic), p. 694
- **ELL** Resources, pp. 666, 668, 669, 674, 678, 683, 687, 692, 694, 698

Additional Resources

- Vocabulary Builder worksheets require students to define and give examples for key vocabulary terms as they progress through the chapter (*Chapter 13 Resource Masters*, pp. vii–viii)
- Reading to Learn Mathematics master for each lesson (*Chapter 13 Resource Masters*, pp. 736, 741, 746, 751, 756, 761)
- *Vocabulary PuzzleMaker* software creates crossword, jumble, and word search puzzles using vocabulary lists that you can customize.
- *Teaching Mathematics with Foldables* provides suggestions for promoting cognition and language.
- *Reading and Writing in the Mathematics Classroom*
- *WebQuest and Project Resources*

For more information on Reading and Writing in Mathematics, see pp. T6–T7.

PROJECT CRISS^{SM} **Study Skill**

A concept of definition map helps students organize information in a lesson or chapter around a major concept or idea.

The post-reading map at the right shows how students might describe what they learn about polynomials in Chapter 13. Concept of definition maps can be completed by the entire class, by a small group, or individually. They should contain at least three types of information the students feel will help them understand and explain the topic.

What is it?

An algebraic expression that is the sum or difference of one or more monomials

Examples

POLYNOMIAL

$(7b + 3) - (3b - 2) = 4b + 5$

$5n(n^3 - 8) = 5n^4 - 40n$

Strategies

To add/subtract: first combine like terms

To multiply/divide: use the Distributive Property and Product of Powers rule

CReating Independence Through Student-Owned Strategies

What You'll Learn

Have students read over the list of objectives and make a list of any words with which they are not familiar.

Why It's Important

Point out to students that this is only one of many reasons why each objective is important. Others are provided in the introduction to each lesson.

Chapter 13

Polynomials and Nonlinear Functions

What You'll Learn

- **Lesson 13-1** Identify and classify polynomials.
- **Lessons 13-2 through 13-4** Add, subtract, and multiply polynomials.
- **Lesson 13-5** Determine whether functions are linear or nonlinear.
- **Lesson 13-6** Explore different representations of quadratic and cubic functions.

Key Vocabulary

- polynomial (p. 669)
- degree (p. 670)
- nonlinear function (p. 687)
- quadratic function (p. 688)
- cubic function (p. 688)

Why It's Important

You have studied situations that can be modeled by linear functions. Many real-life situations, however, are not linear. These can be modeled using nonlinear functions. *You will use a nonlinear function in Lesson 13-6 to determine how far a skydiver falls in 4.5 seconds.*

Lesson	NCTM Standards	Local Objectives
13-1 Preview	2, 8, 10	
13-1	2, 9, 10	
13-1 Follow-Up	2, 3, 4, 7, 9, 10	
13-2	1, 2, 9, 10	
13-3	1, 2, 9, 10	
13-4 Preview	1, 2, 3, 4, 8, 9, 10	
13-4	1, 2, 9, 10	
13-5	2, 3, 9, 10	
13-6	2, 3, 9, 10	
13-6 Follow-Up	2, 3, 6, 7, 9, 10	

Key to NCTM Standards:

1=Number & Operations, 2=Algebra, 3=Geometry, 4=Measurement, 5=Data Analysis & Probability, 6=Problem Solving, 7=Reasoning & Proof, 8=Communication, 9=Connections, 10=Representation

Vocabulary Builder
ELL

The Key Vocabulary list introduces students to some of the main vocabulary terms included in this chapter. For a more thorough vocabulary list with pronunciations of new words, give students the Vocabulary Builder worksheets found on pages vii and viii of the *Chapter 13 Resource Masters*. Encourage them to complete the definition of each term as they progress through the chapter. You may suggest that they add these sheets to their study notebooks for future reference when studying for the Chapter 13 test.

Getting Started

Getting Started

▶ **Prerequisite Skills** To be successful in this chapter, you'll need to master these skills and be able to apply them in problem-solving situations. Review these skills before beginning Chapter 13.

For Lesson 13-1   Monomials

Determine the number of monomials in each expression. *(For review, see Lesson 4-1.)*

1. $2x^3$ **1**   **2.** $a + 4$ **2**   **3.** $8s - 5t$ **2**

4. $x^2 + 3x - 1$ **3**   **5.** $\frac{1}{t}$ **0**   **6.** $9x^3 + 6x^2 + 8x - 7$ **4**

For Lesson 13-4   Distributive Property

Use the Distributive Property to write each expression as an equivalent algebraic expression. *(For review, see Lesson 3-1.)*

7. $5(a + 4)$ **$5a + 20$**   **8.** $2(3y - 8)$ **$6y - 16$**   **9.** $-4(1 + 8n)$ **$-4 - 32n$**

10. $6(x + 2y)$ **$6x + 12y$**   **11.** $(9b - 9c)3$ **$27b - 27c$**   **12.** $5(q - 2r + 3s)$
                                                                               $5q - 10r + 15s$

For Lesson 13-5   Linear Functions

Determine whether each equation is linear. *(For review, see Lesson 8-2.)*

13. $y = x - 2$ **yes**   **14.** $y = x^2$ **no**   **15.** $y = -\frac{1}{2}x$ **yes**

 Study Organizer

Polynomials Make this Foldable to help you organize your notes. Begin with a sheet of 11" by 17" paper.

Step 1 **Fold**	**Step 2** **Fold Again**
Fold the short sides toward the middle. 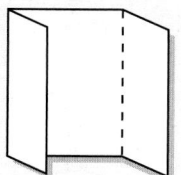	Fold the top to the bottom.
Step 3 **Cut**	**Step 4** **Label**
Open. Cut along the second fold to make four tabs.	Label each of the tabs as shown. 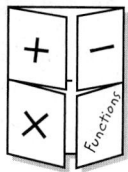

Reading and Writing As you read and study the chapter, write examples of each concept under each tab.

This section provides a review of the basic concepts needed before beginning Chapter 13. Page references are included for additional student help.

Prerequisite Skills, in the Getting Ready for the Next Lesson section at the end of each lesson, reviews a skill needed in the next lesson.

For Lesson	Prerequisite Skill
13-2	Properties of Addition (p. 672)
13-3	Additive Inverse (p. 677)
13-4	Multiplying Monomials (p. 681)
13-5	Using Tables to Find Ordered Pair Solutions (p. 686)
13-6	Graphing Equations (p. 691)

FOLDABLES™ **Study Organizer**

For more information about Foldables, see *Teaching Mathematics with Foldables.*

Expository Writing to Teach Others Under each tab of their Foldables, have students explain how to add, subtract, multiply, and divide polynomials and give several examples of each operation. Student expositions should be clear and concise so that someone who did not understand how to do these operations could read their explanations and learn from them. Encourage students to exchange and read their Foldables.

Reading Mathematics

Getting Started

Have students compare the list of *Monomials* to the list of *Not Monomials*. Ask what is different and the same about each list. Then ask which list $16jp^2r^3$ belongs in. Have them explain why.

Teaching Tip Point out to students that expressions like $\frac{1}{a}$ are not monomials.

Teach

Prefixes and Trinomials Have students think of as many words as they can that have the same prefix as *trinomial*. Write the words on the board as they say them. Examples include triad, triceps, tripod, trio, tricycle, trifocal, trimester, trinity, and triple. Have students discuss the meanings of the words and what they have in common.

Assess

Study Notebook

Have students copy their answers to Exercise 3 into their notebooks. Ask them to include at least one example for each definition.

ELL English Language Learners may benefit from writing key concepts from this activity in their Study Notebooks in their native language and then in English.

Prefixes and Polynomials

You can determine the meaning of many words used in mathematics if you know what the prefixes mean. In Lesson 4-1, you learned that the prefix *mono* means one and that a monomial is an algebraic expression with one term.

Monomials	Not Monomials
5	$x + y$
$2x$	$8n^2 - n + 1$
y^3	$a^3 + 4a^2 + a - 6$

The words in the table below are used in mathematics and in everyday life. They contain the prefixes *bi*, *tri*, and *poly*.

Prefix	Words	
bi	• bisect – to divide into two congruent parts • biannual – occurring twice a year • bicycle – a vehicle with two wheels	**bisect**
tri	• triangle – a figure with three sides • triathlon – an athletic contest with three phases • trilogy – a series of three related literary works, such as films or books	**triangle**
poly	• polyhedron – a solid with many flat surfaces • polychrome – having many colors • polygon – a figure with many sides	**polyhedron**

Reading to Learn **4.** Sample answer: $x + y$; $a^2 + a + 1$; $x^3 + x^2 + x + 1$

1. How are the words in each group of the table related? **Each group has 2, 3, or many items.**

2. What do the prefixes *bi*, *tri*, and *poly* mean? **Bi means two, tri means three, poly means many.**

3. Write the definition of *binomial*, *trinomial*, and *polynomial*. **See margin.**

4. Give an example of a binomial, a trinomial, and a polynomial.

5. **RESEARCH** Use the Internet or a dictionary to make a list of other words that have the prefixes *bi*, *tri*, and *poly*. Give the definition of each word. **See margin.**

668 Chapter 13 Polynomials and Nonlinear Functions

Answers

3. Sample answer: binomial, an expression with two terms; trinomial, an expression with three terms; polynomial, an expression with many terms

5. Sample answer: bicolored means two-colored; a trident is a spear with three prongs; polysyllable means having many syllables.

NEW YORK *Performance Indicator* Reinforcement of 7.A.3 Identify a polynomial as an algebraic expression containing one or more terms

What You'll Learn

- Identify and classify polynomials.
- Find the degree of a polynomial.

How are polynomials used to approximate real-world data?

Heat index is a way to describe how hot it feels outside with the temperature and humidity combined. Some examples are shown below.

Humidity (%)	Temperature (°F)		
	80	90	100
40	79	93	110
45	80	95	115
50	81	96	120

Heat Index

To calculate heat index, meteorologists use an expression similar to the one below. In this expression, x is the percent humidity, and y is the temperature.

$$-42 + 2x + 10y - 0.2xy - 0.007x^2 - 0.05y^2 + 0.001x^2y + 0.009xy^2 - 0.000002x^2y^2$$

a. How many terms are in the expression for the heat index? **9**

b. What separates the terms of the expression? **plus and minus signs**

CLASSIFY POLYNOMIALS Recall that a *monomial* is a number, a variable, or a product of numbers and/or variables. An algebraic expression that contains one or more monomials is called a **polynomial**. In a polynomial, there are no terms with variables in the denominator and no terms with variables under a radical sign.

A polynomial with two terms is called a **binomial**, and a polynomial with three terms is called a **trinomial**.

Polynomial	Number of Terms	Examples
monomial	1	$4, x, 2y^3$
binomial	2	$x + 1, a - 5b, c^2 + d$
trinomial	3	$a + b + c, x^2 + 2x + 1$

The terms in a binomial or a trinomial may be added or subtracted.

Example 1 Classify Polynomials

Determine whether each expression is a polynomial. If it is, classify it as a *monomial*, *binomial*, or *trinomial*.

a. $2x^3 + 5x + 7$

This is a polynomial because it is the sum of three monomials. There are three terms, so it is a trinomial.

b. $t - \dfrac{1}{t^2}$

The expression is *not* a polynomial because $\dfrac{1}{t^2}$ has a variable in the denominator.

Yes; it has two terms, so it is a binomial.

✔ **Concept Check** Is $0.5x + 10$ a polynomial? Explain.

Vocabulary
- polynomial
- binomial
- trinomial
- degree

Study Tip

Matrices
Another way to organize the data displayed in this table is with a *matrix*. To learn more about matrices, see page 705.

Study Tip

Classifying Polynomials
Be sure expressions are written in simplest form.
- $x + x$ is the same as $2x$, so the expression is a monomial.
- $\sqrt{25}$ is the same as 5, so the expression is a monomial.

TEACHING TIP

Explain that in a monomial, the exponent of a variable must be a whole number. $\dfrac{1}{t^2}$ is not a monomial because $\dfrac{1}{t^2} = t^{-2}$.

---

1 Focus

 5-Minute Check Transparency 13-1 Use as a quiz or review of Chapter 12.

Mathematical Background notes are available for this lesson on page 666C.

How are polynomials used to approximate real-world data?

The opening activity questions are repeated on page 736 of the *Chapter 13 Resource Masters*.

Reading to Learn Mathematics, p. 736   ELL

Pre-Activity *How are polynomials used to approximate real-world data?*

Do the activity at the top of page 669 in your textbook. Write your answers below.

a. How many terms are in the expression for the heat index? 9

b. What separates the terms of the expression?
plus and minus signs

Reading the Lesson 1–4. See students' work.

Write a definition and give an example of each new vocabulary word.

Vocabulary	Definition	Example
1. polynomial		
2. binomial		
3. trinomial		
4. degree		

Helping You Remember

5. Notice that the words *binomial, trinomial,* and *polynomial* contain the same root—*nomial,* but have different prefixes.

a. Find the definition of the prefix *bi-* in a dictionary. Write the definition. Explain how it can help you remember the meaning of *binomial.*
Two; a binomial contains two terms.

b. Find the definition of the prefix *tri-* in a dictionary. Write the definition. Explain how it can help you remember the meaning of *trinomial.*
Three; a trinomial contains three terms.

c. Find the definition of the prefix *poly-* in a dictionary. Write the definition. Explain how it can help you remember the meaning of *polynomial.*
Many; a polynomial contains many terms.

Resource Manager

Workbooks and Reproducible Masters

Chapter 13 Resource Masters
- Study Guide and Intervention, p. 733
- Skills Practice, p. 734
- Practice, p. 735
- Reading to Learn Mathematics, p. 736
- Enrichment, p. 737

Parent and Student Study Guide Workbook, p. 108

 Transparencies

5-Minute Check Transparency 13-1
Answer Key Transparencies

Technology

Interactive Chalkboard

2 Teach

CLASSIFY POLYNOMIALS

Teaching Tip Emphasize that when there is a variable in the denominator of a fraction, it cannot be a monomial. A variable can be in the numerator, such as $\frac{x}{2}$, because it can be written as $\frac{1}{2}x$.

In-Class Example Power Point®

1 Determine whether each expression is a polynomial. If it is, classify it as a *monomial*, *binomial*, or *trinomial*.

a. $\frac{-2}{x}$ **not a polynomial**

b. $x^2 - 12$ **yes; binomial**

DEGREES OF POLYNOMIALS

In-Class Examples Power Point®

2 Find the degree of each monomial.

a. $-10w^4$ **4**

b. $8x^3y^7z$ **11**

3 Find the degree of each polynomial.

a. $a^2b^5 - 4$ **7**

b. $2x^2y^2 + 7xy^6$ **7**

4 **AREA** The formula for the surface area (A) of a cube is $A = 6s^2$, where s is the side length. Find the degree of the polynomial. **2**

Career Choices

Ecologist
An ecologist studies the relationships between organisms and their environment.

Online Research
For more information about a career as an ecologist, visit:
www.pre-alg.com/careers

DEGREES OF POLYNOMIALS The **degree** of a monomial is the sum of the exponents of its variables. The degree of a nonzero constant such as 6 or 10 is 0. The constant 0 has no degree.

Example 2 Degree of a Monomial
Find the degree of each monomial.

a. $5a$

The variable a has degree 1, so the degree of $5a$ is 1.

b. $-3x^2y$

x^2 has degree 2 and y has degree 1. The degree of $-3x^2y$ is $2 + 1$ or 3.

A polynomial also has a degree. The degree of a polynomial is the same as that of the term with the greatest degree.

Example 3 Degree of a Polynomial
Find the degree of each polynomial.

a. $x^2 + 3x - 2$

term	degree
x^2	2
$3x$	1
2	0

The greatest degree is 2. So the degree of $x^2 + 3x - 2$ is 2.

b. $a^2 + ab^2 + b^4$

term	degree
a^2	2
ab^2	1 + 2 or 3
b^4	4

The greatest degree is 4. So the degree of $a^2 + ab^2 + b^4$ is 4.

Example 4 Degree of a Real-World Polynomial
ECOLOGY In the early 1900s, the deer population of the Kaibab Plateau in Arizona was affected by hunters and by the food supply. The population from 1905 to 1930 can be approximated by the polynomial $-0.13x^5 + 3.13x^4 + 4000$, where x is the number of years since 1900. Find the degree of the polynomial.

$$\underbrace{-0.13x^5}_{\text{degree 5}} + \underbrace{3.13x^4}_{\text{degree 4}} + \underbrace{4000}_{\text{degree 0}}$$

So, $-0.13x^5 + 3.13x^4 + 4000$ has degree 5.

☑ **Concept Check** Find the degree of the polynomial at the beginning of the lesson. **4**

Check for Understanding

Concept Check
1-2. See margin.

1. **Explain** how to find the degree of a monomial and the degree of a polynomial.

2. **OPEN ENDED** Write three binomial expressions. Explain why they are binomials.

Answers

1. The degree of a monomial is the sum of the exponents of its variables. The degree of a polynomial is the same as the degree of the term with the greatest degree.

2. Sample answer: $2x + 1$, $x - y$, $x^2 + x$; they are sums or differences of two monomials.

Interactive Chalkboard
PowerPoint® Presentations

This CD-ROM is a customizable Microsoft® Power-Point® presentation that includes:

- Step-by-step, dynamic solutions of each In-Class Example from the Teacher Wraparound Edition
- Additional, Your Turn exercises for each example
- The 5-Minute Check Transparencies
- Hot links to Glencoe Online Study Tools

3. Tanisha; the degree of a binomial is the degree of the term with the greater degree.

3. FIND THE ERROR Carlos and Tanisha are finding the degree of $5x + y^2$.

> **Carlos**
> $5x$ has degree 1.
> y^2 has degree 2.
> $5x + y^2$ has degree $1 + 2$ or 3.

> **Tanisha**
> $5x$ has degree 1.
> y^2 has degree 2.
> $5x + y^2$ has degree 2.

Who is correct? Explain your reasoning.

Guided Practice Determine whether each expression is a polynomial. If it is, classify it as a *monomial*, *binomial*, or *trinomial*.

GUIDED PRACTICE KEY

Exercises	Examples
4–9	1
10–15	2, 3
16, 17	4

4. -7 **yes; monomial**   5. $\dfrac{d}{2}$ **yes; monomial**   6. $\dfrac{1}{x} - x$ **no**

7. $a^5 + a^3$ **yes; binomial**   8. $y^2 - 4$ **yes; binomial**   9. $x^2 + xy^2 - y^2$ **yes; trinomial**

Find the degree of each polynomial.

10. $4b^2$ **2**   11. 121 **0**   12. $8x^3y^2$ **5**

13. $3x + 5$ **1**   14. $r^3 + 7r$ **3**   15. $d^2 + c^4$ **4**

Application **GEOMETRY** For Exercises 16 and 17, refer to the square at the right with a side length of x units.

16. $x(x - y)$ or $x^2 - xy$

16. Write a polynomial expression for the area of the small blue rectangle.

17. What is the degree of the polynomial you wrote in Exercise 16? **2**

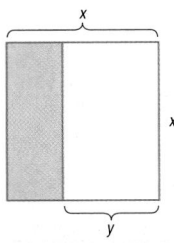

★ indicates increased difficulty

Practice and Apply

Homework Help

For Exercises	See Examples
18–29	1
30–41	2, 3
44–46	4

Extra Practice See page 755.

Determine whether each expression is a polynomial. If it is, classify it as a *monomial*, *binomial*, or *trinomial*. **20. yes; binomial   26. yes; trinomial**

18. 16 **yes; monomial**   19. $x^2 - 7x$ **yes; binomial**   20. $11a^2 + 4$

21. $-\dfrac{1}{3}w^2$ **yes; mono.**   22. $\sqrt{15c}$ **no**   23. $8 - \dfrac{2}{k}$ **no**

24. $r^4 + r^2s^2$ **yes; bi.**   25. $12 - n + n^4$ **yes; tri.**   26. $ab^2 + 3a - b^2$

27. $\sqrt{y} + y$ **no**   28. $\dfrac{ab}{c} - c$ **no**   29. $x^2 - \dfrac{1}{2}x + \dfrac{1}{3}$ **yes; trinomial**

Find the degree of each polynomial.

30. 3 **0**   31. 56 **0**   32. ab **2**

33. $12c^3$ **3**   34. xyz^2 **4**   35. $9s^4t$ **5**

36. $2 - 8n$ **1**   37. $g^5 + 5h$ **5**   38. $x^2 + 3x + 2$ **2**

39. $4y^3 + 6y^2 - 5y - 1$ **3**   ★40. $d^2 + c^4d^2$ **6**   ★41. $x^3 - x^2y^3 + 8$ **5**

42. Sometimes; $x^3 + xy + 5$ has degree 3; $x + xy + 5$ has degree 2.
43. Always; any number is a monomial.

Tell whether each statement is *always*, *sometimes*, or *never* true. Explain.

42. A trinomial has a degree of 3.   43. An integer is a monomial.

44. **MEDICINE** Doctors can study a patient's heart by injecting dye in a vein near the heart. In a normal heart, the amount of dye in the bloodstream after t seconds is given by $-0.006t^4 + 0.140t^3 - 0.53t^2 + 1.79t$. Find the degree of the polynomial. **4**

www.pre-alg.com/self_check_quiz/ny

LANDSCAPING For Exercises 45 and 46, use the information below and the diagram at the right.
Lee wants to plant flowers along the perimeter of his vegetable garden.

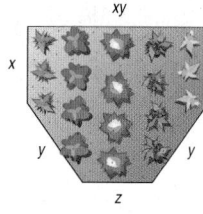

45. Write a polynomial that represents the perimeter of the garden in feet. **$2x + 2y + z + xy$**

46. What is the degree of the polynomial? **2**

★ 47. **RESEARCH** Suppose your grandparents deposited $100 in your savings account each year on your birthday. On your fifth birthday, there would have been approximately $100x^4 + 100x^3 + 100x^2 + 100x + 100$ dollars, where x is the annual interest rate plus 1. Research the current interest rate at your family's bank. Using that interest rate, how much money would you have on your next birthday? **See students' work.**

48. **CRITICAL THINKING** Find the degree of $a^{x+3} + x^x - 2b^3 + b^{x+2}$. **$x + 3$**

49. **WRITING IN MATH** Answer the question that was posed at the beginning of the lesson. **See pp. 703A–703D.**

How are polynomials used to approximate real-world data?

Include the following in your answer:
- a description of how the value of heat index is found, and
- an explanation of why a linear equation cannot be used to approximate the heat index data.

50. Choose the expression that is *not* a binomial. **D**
  Ⓐ $x^2 - 1$ Ⓑ $a + b$ Ⓒ $m^3 + n^3$ Ⓓ $7x + 2x$

51. State the degree of $4x^3 + xy - y^2$. **C**
  Ⓐ 1   Ⓑ 2   Ⓒ 3   Ⓓ 4

Maintain Your Skills

Mixed Review A number cube is rolled. Determine whether each event is *mutually exclusive* or *inclusive*. Then find the probability. *(Lesson 12-9)*

52. P(odd or greater than 3) **inclusive; $\frac{5}{6}$**
53. P(5 or even) **mut. exclusive; $\frac{2}{3}$**

54. A number cube is rolled. Find the odds that the number is greater than 2. *(Lesson 12-8)* **2:1**

Find the volume of each solid. If necessary, round to the nearest tenth. *(Lesson 11-3)*

55. **70 in³**
  7 in. / 6 in. / 5 in.

56. **189.3 m³**
  4 m / 11.3 m

Getting Ready for the Next Lesson

PREREQUISITE SKILL Rewrite each expression using parentheses so that the terms having variables of the same power are grouped together.
*(To review **properties of addition**, see Lesson 1-4.)*

57–62. See pp. 703A–703D.

57. $(x + 4) + 2x$
58. $3x^2 - 1 + x^2$
59. $(6n + 2) + (3n + 5)$
60. $(a + 2b) + (3a + b)$
61. $(s + t) + (5s - 3t)$
62. $(x^2 + 4x) + (7x^2 - 3x)$

4 Assess

Open-Ended Assessment

Writing Have students write an example of a second-degree trinomial. They should include an explanation.

Getting Ready for Lesson 13-2

Students will use the properties of addition to rewrite expressions to add polynomials in Lesson 13-2. Exercises 57–62 should be used to determine your students' familiarity with grouping terms having variables of the same power.

Algebra Activity

A Follow-Up of Lesson 13-1

NEW YORK *Performance Indicator* **8.A.5 Use physical models to perform operations with polynomials**

Modeling Polynomials with Algebra Tiles

In a set of algebra tiles, represents the integer 1, x represents the variable x,

and represents x^2. Red tiles are used to represent -1, $-x$, and $-x^2$.

You can use these tiles to model monomials.

$3x^2$ $-2x$ 7

You can also use algebra tiles to model polynomials. The polynomial $2x^2 - 3x + 4$ is modeled below.

$2x^2 - 3x + 4$

Model and Analyze

Use algebra tiles to model each polynomial. 1–4. See pp. 703A–703D.

1. $-3x^2$ **2.** $5x + 3$ **3.** $4x^2 - x$ **4.** $2x^2 + 2x - 3$

5. Explain how you can tell whether an expression is a monomial, binomial, or trinomial by looking at the algebra tiles. **See pp. 703A–703D.**

6. Name the polynomial modeled below. $-x^2 + 3x - 5$

7. Explain how you would find the degree of a polynomial using algebra tiles.
The degree of a polynomial is determined by the size of the largest algebra tile.

Getting Started

Objective Model polynomials with algebra tiles.

Materials
algebra tiles

Teaching Tip Show students how to model 4 and -4 and $2x$ and $-2x$. Have students demonstrate other monomials.

Teach

- Ask students to model several binomials using x and x^2 tiles.
- Have students work Exercises 1–5 in small groups.

Assess

After working **Exercises 1–5**, students should understand how to use algebra tiles to model polynomials and to recognize the model of a monomial, binomial, and trinomial.

In **Exercises 6–7**, students should be able to name a polynomial and identify the degree of a polynomial using algebra tiles.

Study Notebook

Have students—
- draw algebra tiles to represent 5, -5, $3x$, $-3x$, $2x^2$, and $-2x^2$. Then have them draw algebra tiles to represent $-3x^2 + 5x - 1$.
- write how algebra tiles help them understand polynomials.

Resource Manager

📁 **Teaching Pre-Algebra with Manipulatives**

- pp. 7–8 (masters for algebra tiles)
- p. 160 (student recording sheet)

Glencoe Mathematics Classroom Manipulative Kit

- algebra tiles

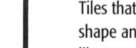

1 Focus

5-Minute Check
Transparency 13-2 Use as a quiz or review of Lesson 13-1.

Mathematical Background notes are available for this lesson on page 666C.

How can you use algebra tiles to add polynomials?

The opening activity questions are repeated on page 741 of the *Chapter 13 Resource Masters*.

Reading to Learn Mathematics, p. 741 ELL

Pre-Activity *How can you use algebra tiles to add polynomials?*

Do the activity at the top of page 674 in your textbook. Write your answers below.

a. Write the polynomial for the tiles that remain. $x^2 - 2x + 2$

b. Find the sum of $x^2 + 4x + 2$ and $7x^2 - 2x + 3$ by using algebra tiles. $8x^2 + 2x + 5$

c. Compare and contrast finding the sums of polynomials with finding the sum of integers. **The concept of the zero pairs is the same, but there are tiles that represent different terms in polynomials.**

Reading the Lesson

1. Draw a model that shows $(x^2 - 4x + 2) + (2x^2 + 2x - 3)$. Write the polynomial that shows the sum. $3x^2 - 2x - 1$

2. Show how to find the sum $(5x - 2) + (4x + 4)$ both vertically and horizontally.

Vertically	Horizontally
$5x - 2$	$(5x - 2) + (4x + 4)$
$(+)4x + 4$	$= (5x + 4x) + (-2 + 4)$
$9x + 2$	$= 9x + 2$

Helping You Remember

3. You have learned that you can combine like terms. On the left below, write three pairs of monomials that have like terms. On the right below, write three pairs of monomials that have unlike terms. Explain your answers. **Sample answers are given.**

Like Terms	Unlike Terms
1. $23a$ and $12a$	1. $2xy$ and $2x$
2. $4b^2c$ and b^2c	2. $3mn^2$ and $3m^2n$
3. xy^3 and $2xy^3$	3. $-8ab^3$ and $5ab^2$

---

b. $8x^2 + 2x + 5$
c. The concept of the zero pairs is the same, but there are tiles that represent different terms in polynomials.

Study Tip

Algebra Tiles
Tiles that are the same shape and size represent like terms.

13-2 Adding Polynomials

NEW YORK *Performance Indicator* **8.A.7 Add** and subtract **polynomials (integer coefficients)**

What You'll Learn

* Add polynomials.

How can you use algebra tiles to add polynomials?

Consider the polynomials $2x^2 - 3x + 4$ and $-x^2 + x - 2$ modeled below.

$$2x^2 - 3x + 4 \qquad\qquad -x^2 + x - 2$$

Follow these steps to add the polynomials.

Step 1 Combine the tiles that have the same shape.

Step 2 When a positive tile is paired with a negative tile that is the same shape, the result is called a *zero pair*. Remove any zero pairs.

$$2x^2 + (-x^2) \qquad + \qquad -3x + x \qquad + \qquad 4 + (-2)$$

a. Write the polynomial for the tiles that remain. $x^2 - 2x + 2$

b. Find the sum of $x^2 + 4x + 2$ and $7x^2 - 2x + 3$ by using algebra tiles.

c. **Compare and contrast** finding the sums of polynomials with finding the sum of integers.

ADD POLYNOMIALS Monomials that contain the same variables to the same power are *like terms*. Terms that differ only by their coefficient are called like terms.

Like Terms	**Unlike Terms**
$2x$ and $7x$	$-6a$ and $7b$
$-x^2y$ and $5x^2y$	$4ab^2$ and $4a^2b$

You can add polynomials by combining like terms.

Example 1 Add Polynomials

Find each sum.

a. $(3x + 5) + (2x + 1)$

Method 1 Add vertically.

$$\begin{array}{r} 3x + 5 \\ (+)\ 2x + 1 \\ \hline 5x + 6 \end{array}$$ Align like terms.
Add.

The sum is $5x + 6$.

Method 2 Add horizontally.

$(3x + 5) + (2x + 1)$
$= (3x + 2x) + (5 + 1)$
$= 5x + 6$

Associative and Commutative Properties

Resource Manager

 Workbooks and Reproducible Masters

Chapter 13 Resource Masters
* Study Guide and Intervention, p. 738
* Skills Practice, p. 739
* Practice, p. 740
* Reading to Learn Mathematics, p. 741
* Enrichment, p. 742
* Assessment, p. 777

Parent and Student Study Guide Workbook, p. 109

 Transparencies
5-Minute Check Transparency 13-2
Answer Key Transparencies

Technology
Interactive Chalkboard

b. $(2x^2 + x - 7) + (x^2 + 3x + 5)$

Method 1

$$\begin{array}{r} 2x^2 + \;\;x - 7 \\ (+)\;\; x^2 + 3x + 5 \qquad \text{Align like terms.} \\ \hline 3x^2 + 4x - 2 \qquad \text{Add.} \end{array}$$

Method 2

$(2x^2 + x - 7) + (x^2 + 3x + 5)$ Write the expression.

$= (2x^2 + x^2) + (x + 3x) + (-7 + 5)$ Group like terms.

$= 3x^2 + 4x - 2$ Simplify.

The sum is $3x^2 + 4x - 2$.

c. $(9c^2 + 4c) + (-6c + 8)$

$(9c^2 + 4c) + (-6c + 8)$ Write the expression.

$= 9c^2 + (4c - 6c) + 8$ Group like terms.

$= 9c^2 - 2c + 8$ Simplify.

The sum is $9c^2 - 2c + 8$.

d. $(x^2 + xy + 2y^2) + (6x^2 - y^2)$

$$\begin{array}{r} x^2 + xy + 2y^2 \\ (+)\; 6x^2 \qquad\;\; - \;\; y^2 \\ \hline 7x^2 + xy + \;\; y^2 \end{array}$$

Leave a space because there is no other term like xy.

The sum is $7x^2 + xy + y^2$.

✓ **Concept Check**   Name the like terms in $b^2 + 5b - ab + 9b^2$. b^2 and $9b^2$

Polynomials are often used to represent measures of geometric figures.

Example 2   *Use Polynomials to Solve a Problem*

• **GEOMETRY**   The lengths of the sides of golden rectangles are in the ratio 1:1.62. So, the length of a golden rectangle is approximately 1.62 times greater than the width.

x

$1.62x$

a. Find a formula for the perimeter of a golden rectangle.

$P = 2\ell + 2w$ Formula for the perimeter of a rectangle

$P = 2(1.62x) + 2x$ Replace ℓ with 1.62x and w with x.

$P = 3.24x + 2x$ or $5.24x$ Simplify.

A formula for the perimeter of a golden rectangle is $P = 5.24x$, where x is the measure of the width.

b. Find the length and the perimeter of a golden rectangle if its width is 8.3 centimeters.

length $= 1.62x$ Length of a golden rectangle

     $= 1.62(8.3)$ or 13.446 Replace x with 8.3 and simplify.

perimeter $= 5.24x$ Perimeter of a golden rectangle

     $= 5.24(8.3)$ or 43.492 Replace x with 8.3 and simplify.

The length of the golden rectangle is 13.446 centimeters, and the perimeter is 43.492 centimeters.

 www.pre-alg.com/extra_examples/ny   **Lesson 13-2**   Adding Polynomials   **675**

Teaching Tip   Have students compare the *Like Terms* column to the *Unlike Terms* column. Ask them how like terms can differ from one another.   **sign, coefficient**
Ask what must be the same. **variable(s), exponent**

ADD POLYNOMIALS

In-Class Examples   Power Point®

1   Find each sum.

a. $(9w - 4) + (w + 5)$ **10w + 1**

b. $(6x^2 - 3x + 1) + (x^2 + x - 1)$ **$7x^2 - 2x$**

c. $5a^3 + (2a - 4a) + 7$ **$5a^3 - 2a + 7$**

d. $(4x^2 - 3y^2) + (x^2 + 4xy + y^2)$ **$5x^2 + 4xy - 2y^2$**

Teaching Tip   Some students may benefit from turning their ruled papers horizontally and using the lines to align like terms vertically so they can add.

2   **GEOMETRY**   The length of a rectangle is $3x^2 + 2x - 5$ units and the width is $8x - 1$ units.

a. Find the perimeter.   **$6x^2 + 20x - 12$ units**

b. Find the length of the rectangle if $x = -3$.   **16 units**

3 Practice/Apply

Study Notebook

Have students—
• choose a problem from the Practice to help them explain how to add two polynomials.
• include any other item(s) that they find helpful in mastering the skills in this lesson.

About the Exercises . . .

Odd/Even Assignments
Exercises 11–25 are structured
so that students practice the
same concepts whether they
are assigned odd or even
problems.

Assignment Guide

Basic: 11–21 odd, 26–28, 32–48

Average: 11–25 odd, 26–28, 32–48

Advanced: 12–24 even, 29–42 (Optional: 43–48)

4 Assess

Open-Ended Assessment

Modeling Use algebra tiles
to find the sum of each of the
following.

  a. $(6) + (-2x^2)$ $-2x^2 + 6$

  b. $(3x + 4) + (x^2 - 2x - 2)$
  $x^2 + x + 2$

*Getting Ready
for Lesson 13-3*

PREREQUISITE SKILL Lesson
13-3 presents subtracting polynomials. One method uses the
additive inverse. Exercises 43–48
should be used to determine
your students' familiarity with
finding the additive inverse to
subtract polynomials.

Assessment Options

Quiz (Lessons 13-1 and 13-2)
is available on p. 777 of the
Chapter 13 Resource Masters.

Check for Understanding

Concept Check

1. **Name** the like terms in $(x^2 + 5x + 2) + (2x^2 - 4x + 7)$.
   x^2 and $2x^2$; $5x$ and $-4x$; 2 and 7

2. **OPEN ENDED** Write two binomials that share only one pair of like terms.
   Sample answer: $3x + 1$ and $4x + x^2$

3. **FIND THE ERROR** Hai says that $7xyz$ and $2zyx$ are like terms. Devin says
   they are not. Who is correct? Explain your reasoning.
   Hai; the terms have the same variables in a different order.

Guided Practice Find each sum. 9. $4x^2 + 3x - 2$

GUIDED PRACTICE KEY	
Exercises	Examples
4–9	1
10	2

4. $\begin{array}{r} 4x + 5 \\ (+) -x - 3 \\ \hline 3x + 2 \end{array}$

5. $\begin{array}{r} 3a^2 - 9a + 6 \\ (+)4a^2 \quad\quad -2 \\ \hline 7a^2 - 9a + 4 \end{array}$

6. $(x + 3) + (2x + 5)$ $3x + 8$

7. $(13x - 7y) + 3y$ $13x - 4y$

8. $(2x^2 + 5x) + (9 - 7x)$ $2x^2 - 2x + 9$

9. $(3x^2 - 2x + 1) + (x^2 + 5x - 3)$

Application 10. **GEOMETRY** Find the
perimeter of the figure
at the right.
$6x + 24$ units

★ indicates increased difficulty

Practice and Apply

Homework Help

For Exercises	See Examples
11–22	1
23–27	2

Extra Practice
See page 756.

Find each sum.

11. $\begin{array}{r} -5x + 4 \\ (+) 8x - 1 \end{array}$ $3x + 3$

12. $\begin{array}{r} 7b - 5 \\ (+)-9b + 8 \end{array}$ $-2b + 3$

13. $\begin{array}{r} 10x^2 + 5xy + 7y^2 \\ (+) \quad x^2 \quad\quad -3y^2 \\ \hline 11x^2 + 5xy + 4y^2 \end{array}$

14. $\begin{array}{r} 4a^3 + a^2 + 8a - 8 \\ (+) \quad\quad 2a^2 \quad + 6 \\ \hline 4a^3 + 3a^2 + 8a - 2 \end{array}$

15. $(3x + 9) + (x + 5)$ $4x + 14$

16. $(4x + 3) + (x - 1)$ $5x + 2$

17. $(6y - 5r) + (2y + 7r)$ $8y + 2r$

18. $(8m - 2n) + (3m + n)$ $11m - n$

20. $3a^2 + 2b^2 + 3a$

19. $(x^2 + y) + (4x^2 + xy)$ $5x^2 + xy + y$

20. $(3a^2 + b^2) + (3a + b^2)$

21. $(5x^2 + 6x + 4) + (2x^2 + 3x + 1)$
   $7x^2 + 9x + 5$

22. $(-2x^2 + x - 5) + (x^2 - 3x + 2)$
   $-x^2 - 2x - 3$

Find each sum. Then evaluate if $a = -3$, $b = 4$, and $c = 2$.

★ 23. $(3a + 5b) + (2a - 9b)$ $5a - 4b$; -31

★ 24. $(a^2 + 7b^2) + (5 - 3b^2) + (2a^2 - 7)$ $3a^2 + 4b^2 - 2$; 89

★ 25. $(3a + 5b - 4c) + (2a - 3b + 7c) + (-a + 4b - 2c)$ $4a + 6b + c$; 14

GEOMETRY For Exercises 26–28, refer to the triangle.

26. Find the sum of the measures of the angles. $(4x - 44)°$

27. The sum of the measures of the angles in
   any triangle is 180°. Find the value of x. **56**

28. Find the measure of each angle. **56°, 42°, 82°**

Answer (p. 677)

32. 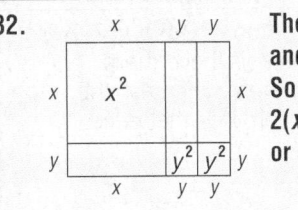 The length is $x + 2y$
    and the width is $x + y$.
    So, the perimeter is
    $2(x + 2y) + 2(x + y)$
    or $4x + 6y$.

FINANCE For Exercises 29–31, refer to the information below.
Jason and Will both work at the same supermarket and are paid the same hourly rate. At the end of the week, Jason's paycheck showed that he worked 23 hours and had \$12 deducted for taxes. Will worked 19 hours during the same week and had \$10 deducted for taxes. Let x represent the hourly pay.

9. $23x - 12$ ★ 29. Write a polynomial expression to represent Jason's pay for the week.

0. $19x - 10$ ★ 30. Write a polynomial expression to represent Will's pay for the week.

★ 31. Write a polynomial expression to represent the total weekly pay for Jason and Will. $42x - 22$

32. **CRITICAL THINKING** In the figure at the right, x^2 is the area of the larger square, and y^2 is the area of each of the two smaller squares. What is the perimeter of the whole rectangle? Explain.
$4x + 6y$; See margin for explanation.

33. **WRITING IN MATH** Answer the question that was posed at the beginning of the lesson. **See margin.**

How can you use algebra tiles to add polynomials?

Include the following in your answer:
- a description of algebra tiles that represent like terms, and
- an explanation of how zero pairs are used in adding polynomials.

Standardized Test Practice
Ⓐ Ⓑ Ⓒ Ⓓ

34. Choose the pair of terms that are *not* like terms. **C**
  Ⓐ $6cd$, $12cd$ Ⓑ $\frac{x}{2}$, $5x$ Ⓒ a^2, b^2 Ⓓ x^2y, yx^2

35. What is the sum of $11x + 2y$ and $x - 5y$? **B**
  Ⓐ $10x - 3y$ Ⓑ $12x - 3y$ Ⓒ $12x + 3y$ Ⓓ $12x - 5y$

Maintain Your Skills

Mixed Review Find the degree of each polynomial. *(Lesson 13-1)*
36. a^3b **4**   37. $3x - 5y + z^2$ **2**   38. $c^2 - 7c^3y^4$ **7**

A card is drawn from a standard deck of 52 playing cards. Find each probability. *(Lesson 12-9)*
39. $P(2 \text{ or jack})$ $\frac{2}{13}$ 40. $P(10 \text{ or red})$ $\frac{7}{13}$ 41. $P(\text{ace or black } 7)$ $\frac{3}{26}$

42. Determine whether the prisms are similar. Explain. *(Lesson 11-6)*
Yes; the corresponding dimensions are proportional.

Getting Ready for the Next Lesson **PREREQUISITE SKILL** Rewrite each expression as an addition expression by using the additive inverse. *(To review **additive inverse**, see Lesson 2-3.)*
43. $15c - 26$ $15c + (-26)$ 44. $x^2 - 7$ $x^2 + (-7)$ 45. $1 - 2x$ $1 + (-2x)$
46. $6b - 3a^2$ $6b + (-3a^2)$ 47. $(n + rt) - r^2$ $(n + rt) + (-r^2)$ 48. $(s + t) - 2s$ $(s + t) + (-2s)$

Lesson 13-2 Adding Polynomials **677**

Study Guide and Intervention, p. 738

Add polynomials by combining like terms, which are monomials that contain the same variables to the same power.

Example Find $(8x^2 - 7x + 1) + (x^2 + 5)$.
Method 1 Add vertically.
$8x^2 - 7x + 1$
$(+) x^2 \qquad + 5$
$9x^2 - 7x + 6$

Method 2 Add horizontally.
$(8x^2 - 7x + 1) + (x^2 + 5)$
$= (8x^2 + x^2) - 7x + (1 + 5)$
$= 9x^2 - 7x + 6$

Exercises
Find each sum.
1. $3x - 7$
   $(+) x + 1$
   $4x - 6$
2. $6d + 8$
   $(+) -4d + 1$
   $2d + 9$
3. $4w^2 - 6w + 3$
   $(+) w^2 \quad - 5$
   $5w^2 - 6w - 2$
4. $5a^2 - a$
   $(+) \qquad 2a - 5$
   $5a^2 + a - 5$
5. $(-m + 3) + (7m - 1)$
   $6m + 2$
6. $(9x^2 + 3x - 1) + (4x + 1)$
   $9x^2 + 7x$
7. $(2k^2 - k) + (k - 1)$
   $2k^2 - 1$
8. $(5a^2 + 6ab) + (-ab + b^2)$
   $5a^2 + 5ab + b^2$
9. $(4c^2 - 7) + (c^2 - 3c + 6)$
   $5c^2 - 3c - 1$
10. $(x^2 + y) + (xy + y)$
   $x^2 + xy + 2y$
11. $(12h - 6) + (h^2 - 8h + 6)$
   $h^2 + 4h$
12. $(10x^2 + x + 5) + (x - 10x^2)$
   $2x + 5$
13. $(6y^2 - y + 1) + (y^2 - 3y - 6)$
   $7y^2 - 4y - 5$
14. $(p^3 + 4) + (2p^2 - 2p + 3)$
   $p^3 + 2p^2 - 2p + 7$
15. $(3g^2 + 3g + 5) + (5g^2 - 3)$
   $8g^2 + 3g + 2$
16. $(5r^2 - 6) + (-r^2 - 4r + 7)$
   $4r^2 - 4r + 1$

Skills Practice, p. 739 and Practice, p. 740 (shown)

Find each sum.
1. $8q + 3$
   $(+) 4q - 2$
   $12q + 1$
2. $9f - 3$
   $(+) -f - 15$
   $8f - 18$
3. $4r^2 + 11r$
   $(+) 5r^2 - 3r - 7$
   $9r^2 + 8r - 7$
4. $n^2 - 3n$
   $(+) \qquad 3n - 10$
   $n^2 - 10$
5. $6u^2 + 2w + 7$
   $(+) 8w^2 + 3w - 9$
   $14w^2 + 5w - 2$
6. $8c^2 - 3c + 15$
   $(+) 3c^2 + 3c - 11$
   $11c^2 + 4$
7. $-5p^2 - 2p + 4$
   $(+) 5p^2 + 2p - 4$
   0
8. $7v^2 - 2v$
   $(+) 7v^2 - v + 5$
   $14v^2 - 3v + 5$
9. $5m^2 + 6m - 3$
   $(+) 8m^2 + 9m - 2$
   $13m^2 + 15m - 5$
10. $7d^2 + 8d - 3$
    $(+) d^2 + d + 3$
    $8d^2 + 9d$
11. $(r^2 + 9) + (-4r^2 + 6r + 10)$
    $-3r^2 + 6r + 19$
12. $(g^2 + 3g - 6) + (6g^2 - 6g + 1)$
    $7g^2 - 3g - 5$
13. $(-2m + 10) + (5m - 3)$
    $3m + 7$
14. $(4x^2 - 7x) + (8x + 5)$
    $4x^2 + x + 5$
15. $(3k^2 + 9k) + (k^2 - 2k - 4)$
    $4k^2 + 7k - 4$
16. $(2a^2 - 3ab) + (4ab - 8b^2)$
    $2a^2 + ab - 8b^2$
17. $(c + 4) + (c^2 - c + 6)$
    $c^2 + 10$
18. $(5x^2 - 3xy) + (2xy + 9y^2)$
    $5x^2 - xy + 9y^2$
19. $(2y^3 + y^2 + 5) + (2y^2 + 3y)$
    $2y^3 + 3y^2 + 3y + 5$
20. $(-5p^2 + 6p - 7) + (p^2 - 2)$
    $-4p^2 + 6p - 9$
21. $(3ab^2 - 2a - 1) + (a^2 + ab + 3)$
    $3ab^2 + a^2 - 2a + ab + 2$
22. $(6rs^3 + 4r) + (5rs^3 + 7)$
    $11rs^3 + 4r + 7$
23. **GEOMETRY** The lengths of the sides of a triangle are $(x^2 - 5)$, $(7x - 1)$, and x. Find the perimeter of the triangle. $x^2 + 8x - 6$

Enrichment, p. 742

Adding Polynomials
Can you make a sentence using these words?
A FRUIT TIME LIKE AN BUT FLIES BANANA ARROW LIKE FLIES
Add the polynomials. Then find the word in the table at the right that corresponds to the sum. Read the words in order down the column to discover the hidden saying.

		Word
1. $(2x^2 + 3x^2) + (5x^2 + x^2)$ $11x^2$	TIME	
2. $(2x^3 + 3x^3) + (5x^2 + x^2)$ $3x^3 + 8x^2$	FLIES	
3. $(2x^2 + x) + (xy + x)$ $2x^2 + 2x + xy$	LIKE	
4. $(x^3 + 2x^2) + (5x^3 + x)$ $6x^3 + 2x^2 + x$	AN	
5. $(x + xy) + (x^2 + xy)$ $x^2 + 2xy + x$	ARROW	
6. $(5x^2 + x) + (x + 2x^4)$ $2x^4 + 5x^2 + 2x$	BUT	
7. $(xy + y^2 + x^2) + (2xy + x^2)$ $2x^2 + 3xy + y^2$	FRUIT	
8. $(3x^2 + 2x^3) + (x^3 + x)$ $3x^3 + 3x^2 + x$	FLIES	
9. $(x + x^2) + x^3$ $x^3 + x^2 + x$	LIKE	
10. $(x^3 + x^3) + (x^3 + x^3)$ $4x^3$	A	
11. $2x^{12} + 2x^{12}$ $4x^{12}$	BANANA	

$4x^3$	A
$2x^3 + 3xy + y^2$	FRUIT
$11x^2$	TIME
$x^3 + x^2 + x$	LIKE
$6x^3 + 2x^2 + x$	AN
$2x^4 + 5x^2 + 2x$	BUT
$3x^3 + 8x^2$	FLIES
$4x^{12}$	BANANA
$x^2 + 2xy + x$	ARROW
$2x^2 + 2x + xy$	LIKE
$3x^3 + 3x^2 + x$	FLIES

Answer

33. Use algebra tiles to model each polynomial and combine the tiles that have the same size and shape. Answers should include the following.

  - Algebra tiles that represent like terms have the same size and shape.

  - When adding polynomials, a red tile and a white tile that have the same size and shape are zero pairs and may be removed. The result is the sum of the polynomials.

13-3 Lesson Notes

1 Focus

5-Minute Check Transparency 13-3 Use as a quiz or review of Lesson 13-2.

Mathematical Background notes are available for this lesson on page 666D.

How is subtracting polynomials similar to subtracting measurements?

The opening activity questions are repeated on page 746 of the *Chapter 13 Resource Masters.*

Reading to Learn Mathematics, p. 746   **ELL**

Pre-Activity   *How is subtracting polynomials similar to subtracting measurements?*

Do the activity at the top of page 678 in your textbook. Write your answers below.

a. What is the difference in degrees and the difference in minutes between the two stations? **4 degrees, 8.1 minutes**

b. Explain how you can find the difference in latitude between any two locations, given the degrees and minutes. **Subtract the degrees and subtract the minutes.**

c. The longitude of Station 1 is 162°16'36" and the longitude of Station 5 is 68°8'2". Find the difference in longitude between the two stations. **94°8'34"**

Reading the Lesson

1. Show how to find the difference $(3x^2 + x + 2) - (2x^2 - 7)$ by aligning like terms and by adding the additive inverse.

Like Terms	Additive Inverse
$3x^2 + x + 2$	$3x^2 + x + 2$
$(-) 2x^2 \quad - 7$	$(+)-2x^2 \quad + 7$
$x^2 + x + 9$	$x^2 + x + 9$

2. Which method do you prefer? Why? **Answers will vary.**

Helping You Remember

3. a. You have learned to subtract polynomials by adding the additive inverse. Look up *inverse* in the dictionary. What is its definition? How does this help you remember how to find the additive inverse? **Opposite; you change each sign to the opposite and then add instead of subtract.**

b. Write the additive inverses of the polynomials in the table below.

Polynomial	Additive Inverse
$x^2 + 2x - 3$	$-x^2 - 2x + 3$
$6x - 8$	$-6x + 8$
$5x^2 + 8y^2 - 2xy$	$-5x^2 - 8y^2 + 2xy$

Reading Math

Symbols
The symbol " in 68° 8' 2" is read as *seconds*.

b. Subtract the degrees and subtract the minutes.
c. 94° 8' 34"

13-3 Subtracting Polynomials

 NEW YORK *Performance Indicator* **8.A.7** Add and **subtract polynomials (integer coefficients)**

What You'll Learn

- Subtract polynomials.

How is subtracting polynomials similar to subtracting measurements?

At the North Pole, buoy stations drift with the ice in the Arctic Ocean. The table shows the latitudes of two North Pole buoys in April, 2000.

Station	Latitude
1	89° 35.4'N = 89 degrees 35.4 minutes
5	85° 27.3'N = 85 degrees 27.3 minutes

a. What is the difference in degrees and the difference in minutes between the two stations? **4 degrees, 8.1 minutes**

b. Explain how you can find the difference in latitude between any two locations, given the degrees and minutes.

c. The longitude of Station 1 is 162° 16' 36" and the longitude of Station 5 is 68° 8' 2". Find the difference in longitude between the two stations.

SUBTRACT POLYNOMIALS   When you subtract measurements, you subtract like units. Consider the subtraction of latitude measurements shown below.

$$
\begin{array}{r}
89 \text{ degrees } 35.4 \text{ minutes} \\
(-)\ 85 \text{ degrees } 27.3 \text{ minutes} \\
\hline
4 \text{ degrees } \quad 8.1 \text{ minutes}
\end{array}
$$

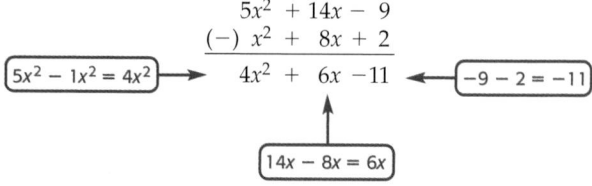

| 89 degrees − 85 degrees | | 35.4 minutes − 27.3 minutes |

Similarly, when you subtract polynomials, you subtract like terms.

$$
\begin{array}{r}
5x^2 + 14x - 9 \\
(-)\ x^2 + 8x + 2 \\
\hline
4x^2 + 6x - 11
\end{array}
$$

$5x^2 - 1x^2 = 4x^2$ → $\qquad$ ← $-9 - 2 = -11$

$14x - 8x = 6x$

Example 1   Subtract Polynomials

Find each difference.

a. $(5x + 9) - (3x + 6)$

$$
\begin{array}{r}
5x + 9 \\
(-)\ 3x + 6 \quad \text{Align like terms.} \\
\hline
2x + 3 \quad \text{Subtract.}
\end{array}
$$

The difference is $2x + 3$.

b. $(4a^2 + 7a + 4) - (3a^2 + 2)$

$$
\begin{array}{r}
4a^2 + 7a + 4 \\
(-)\ 3a^2 \qquad + 2 \quad \text{Align like terms.} \\
\hline
a^2 + 7a + 2 \quad \text{Subtract.}
\end{array}
$$

The difference is $a^2 + 7a + 2$.

Resource Manager

Workbooks and Reproducible Masters

Chapter 13 Resource Masters
- Study Guide and Intervention, p. 743
- Skills Practice, p. 744
- Practice, p. 745
- Reading to Learn Mathematics, p. 746
- Enrichment, p. 747
- Assessment, pp. 777, 779

Parent and Student Study Guide Workbook, p. 110
School-to-Career Masters, p. 25

Transparencies

5-Minute Check Transparency 13-3
Answer Key Transparencies

Technology

Interactive Chalkboard
Multimedia Applications

Recall that you can subtract a rational number by adding its *additive inverse*.

$$10 - 8 = 10 + (-8)$$ The additive inverse of 8 is -8.

You can also subtract a polynomial by adding its additive inverse. To find the additive inverse of a polynomial, multiply the entire polynomial by -1.

Polynomial	Multiply by -1	Additive Inverse
t	$-1(t)$	$-t$
$x + 3$	$-1(x + 3)$	$-x - 3$
$-a^2 + b^2 - c$	$-1(-a^2 + b^2 - c)$	$a^2 - b^2 + c$

Example 2 *Subtract Using the Additive Inverse*

Find each difference.

a. $(3x + 8) - (5x + 1)$

The additive inverse of $5x + 1$ is $(-1)(5x + 1)$ or $-5x - 1$.

$(3x + 8) - (5x + 1)$
$= (3x + 8) + (-5x - 1)$ To subtract $(5x + 1)$, add $(-5x - 1)$.
$= (3x - 5x) + (8 - 1)$ Group the like terms.
$= -2x + 7$ Simplify.

The difference is $-2x + 7$.

b. $(4x^2 + y^2) - (-3xy + y^2)$

The additive inverse of $-3xy + y^2$ is $(-1)(-3xy + y^2)$ or $3xy - y^2$.
Align the like terms and add the additive inverse.

$$\begin{array}{r} 4x^2 \qquad + y^2 \\ (-) \quad -3xy + y^2 \end{array} \quad \rightarrow \quad \begin{array}{r} 4x^2 \qquad + y^2 \\ (+) \qquad 3xy - y^2 \\ \hline 4x^2 + 3xy + 0 \end{array}$$

The difference is $4x^2 + 3xy$.

☑ Concept Check   What is the additive inverse of $a^2 + 9a - 1$? $-a^2 - 9a + 1$

Example 3 *Subtract Polynomials to Solve a Problem*

SHIPPING   The cost for shipping a package that weighs x pounds from Dallas to Chicago is shown in the table at the right. How much more does the Atlas Service charge for shipping the package?

Shipping Company	Cost ($)
Atlas Service	$4x + 280$
Bell Service	$3x + 125$

difference in cost = cost of Atlas Service $-$ cost of Bell Service
$= (4x + 280) - (3x + 125)$ Substitution
$= (4x + 280) + (-3x - 125)$ Add additive inverse.
$= (4x - 3x) + (280 - 125)$ Group like terms.
$= x + 155$ Simplify.

The Atlas Service charges $x + 155$ dollars more for shipping a package that weighs x pounds.

www.pre-alg.com/extra_examples/ny   **Lesson 13-3** Subtracting Polynomials **679**

---

2 Teach

Building on Prior Knowledge

In Lesson 2-3, students learned how to subtract an integer by adding its additive inverse. In this lesson, they will extend this knowledge to adding the additive inverse when subtracting polynomials.

SUBTRACT POLYNOMIALS

In-Class Examples   Power Point®

1 Find each difference.

a. $(7a + 4) - (9a + 2)$ $-2a + 2$

b. $(8b^2 + 6) - (3b^2 + 6b + 1)$
$5b^2 - 6b + 5$

2 Find each difference.

a. $(4x - 8) - (3x + 9)$ $x - 17$

b. $(7ab + 2b^2) - (3a^2 + ab + b^2)$
$-3a^2 + 6ab + b^2$

3 **GEOMETRY** The length of a rectangle is $x^2 - 9x + 10$ units. The width is $x^2 - x$ units. How much longer is the length than the width?
$-8x + 10$ units

☑ Skills Check

Subtract Polynomials Have students subtract $(2x^3 - 4x + 2)$ from $(8x^4 - 6x^3 + 2x^2 - x)$.
$8x^4 - 8x^3 + 2x^2 + 3x - 2$

DAILY INTERVENTION   **Differentiated Instruction**

- **Kinesthetic** To model $(2x^2 - 3x - 6) - (x^2 + 5x - 5)$, have students use algebra tiles to show $2x^2 - 3x - 6$. Remind them that subtracting is the same as adding the opposite. So, they should then add tiles to represent $-x^2 - 5x + 5$. Have them remove zero pairs, which results in $x^2 - 8x - 1$.

Study Notebook

Have students—
- write a paragraph comparing adding polynomials to subtracting them. Have them describe their similarities and differences.
- include any other item(s) that they find helpful in mastering the skills in this lesson.

About the Exercises . . .

Odd/Even Assignments
Exercises 10–25 are structured so that students practice the same concepts whether they are assigned odd or even problems.

Assignment Guide

Basic: 11–25 odd, 28–45

Average: 11–27 odd, 28–45

Advanced: 10–28 even, 29–39 (Optional: 40–45)

All: Practice Quiz 1 (1–10)

Open-Ended Assessment

Speaking Display a polynomial subtraction problem. Have students tell you everything you need to do to subtract. Be sure they mention aligning like terms and finding the additive inverse.

Getting Ready for Lesson 13-4

PREREQUISITE SKILL Lesson 13-4 presents using the Distributive Property to multiply a polynomial by a monomial. Exercises 40–45 should be used to determine your students' familiarity with multiplying monomials.

Check for Understanding

Concept Check
1. **Describe** how subtraction and addition of polynomials are related. See margin.
2. **OPEN ENDED** Write two polynomials whose difference is $x^2 + 2x - 4$.
   Sample answer: $2x^2 + 4x + 1$ and $x^2 + 2x + 5$

Guided Practice **Find each difference.**

GUIDED PRACTICE KEY	
Exercises	Examples
3, 4	1
5–8	2
9	3

3. $r^2 + 5r$
    $\underline{(-)\ r^2 +\ \ r}$
        $4r$

4. $3x^2 + 5x + 4$
    $\underline{(-)\ x^2\ \ \ \ \ - 1}$
      $2x^2 + 5x + 5$

5. $(9x + 5) - (4x + 3)$ $5x + 2$

6. $(2x + 4) - (-x + 5)$ $3x - 1$

7. $(3x^2 + x) - (8 - 2x)$ $3x^2 + 3x - 8$

8. $(6a^2 - 3a + 9) - (7a^2 + 5a - 1)$
   $-a^2 - 8a + 10$

Application
9. **GEOMETRY** The perimeter of the isosceles trapezoid shown is $16x + 1$ units. Find the length of the missing base of the trapezoid. **7x + 5 units**

★ indicates increased difficulty

Practice and Apply

Homework Help	
For Exercises	See Examples
10–15	1
16–25	2
26, 27	3

Extra Practice
See page 756.

Find each difference.

10. $8k + 9$
    $\underline{(-)\ k + 2}$
      $7k + 7$

11. $-n^2 + 1n$
    $\underline{(-)\ \ n^2 - 5n}$
     $-2n^2 + 6n$

12. $5a^2 + 9a - 12$
    $\underline{(-)\ -3a^2 + 5a -\ \ 7}$
      $8a^2 + 4a - 5$

13. $6y^2 - 5y + 3$
    $\underline{(-)\ 5y^2 + 2y - 7}$
      $y^2 - 7y + 10$

14. $5x^2 - 4xy$
    $\underline{(-)\ \ \ \ \ - 3xy + 2y^2}$
      $5x^2 - xy - 2y^2$

15. $9w^2\ \ \ \ \ + 7$
    $\underline{(-)-6w^2 + 2w - 3}$
     $15w^2 - 2w + 10$

16. $(3x + 4) - (x + 2)$ $2x + 2$

17. $(7x + 5) - (3x + 2)$ $4x + 3$

18. $(2y + 5) - (y + 8)$ $y - 3$

19. $(3t - 2) - (5t - 4)$ $-2t + 2$

21. $3a^2 + 2b^2$

20. $(2x + 3y) - (x - y)$ $x + 4y$

21. $(a^2 + 6b^2) - (-2a^2 + 4b^2)$

22. $(x^2 + 6x) - (3x^2 + 7)$ $-2x^2 + 6x - 7$

23. $(9n^2 - 8) - (n + 4)$ $9n^2 - n - 12$

24. $(6x^2 + 3x + 9) - (2x^2 + 8x + 1)$
    $4x^2 - 5x + 8$

25. $(3x^2 - 5xy + 7y^2) - (x^2 - 3xy + 4y^2)$
    $2x^2 - 2xy + 3y^2$

26. **GEOMETRY** Alyssa plans to trim a picture to fit into a frame. The area of the picture is $2x^2 + 11x + 12$ square units, but the area inside the frame is only $2x^2 + 5x + 2$ square units. How much of the picture will Alyssa have to trim so that it will fit into the frame? **6x + 10 square units**

★ 27. **TEMPERATURE** The highest recorded temperature in North Carolina occurred in 1983. The lowest recorded temperature in North Carolina occurred two years later. The difference between these two record temperatures is 68°F more than the sum of the temperatures. Write an equation to represent this situation. Then find the record low temperature in North Carolina. $x - y = 68 + (x + y)$; **−34°F**

28. **CRITICAL THINKING** Suppose A and B represent polynomials. If $A + B = 3x^2 + 2x - 2$ and $A - B = -x^2 + 4x - 8$, find A and B.
    $A = x^2 + 3x - 5$; $B = 2x^2 - x + 3$

Answers

1. Subtracting one polynomial from another is the same as adding the additive inverse.

39.
Stem	Leaf
5	4 9
6	4 6 8
7	0 1 1 2
8	5 9
9	1

$5|4 = 54$

29. `WRITING IN MATH` Answer the question that was posed at the beginning of the lesson. **See pp. 703A–703D.**

How is subtracting polynomials similar to subtracting measurements?

Include the following in your answer:
- a comparison between subtracting measurements with two parts and subtracting polynomials with two terms, and
- an example of a subtraction problem involving measurements that have two parts, and an explanation of how to find the difference.

30. What is $(5x - 7) - (3x - 4)$? **A**
Ⓐ $2x - 3$ Ⓑ $2x + 3$ Ⓒ $2x - 11$ Ⓓ $2x + 11$

31. Write the additive inverse of $-4h^2 - hk - k^2$. **B**
Ⓐ $4h^2 - hk - k^2$ Ⓑ $4h^2 + hk + k^2$
Ⓒ $-4h^2 + hk + k^2$ Ⓓ $-4h^2 + hk - k^2$

Maintain Your Skills

Mixed Review **Find each sum.** *(Lesson 13-2)*

32. $(2x - 3) + (x - 1)$ **$3x - 4$**

33. $(11x + 2y) + (x - 5y)$ **$12x - 3y$**

34. $(5x^2 - 7x + 9) + (3x^2 + 4x - 6)$
$8x^2 - 3x + 3$

35. $(4t - t^2) + (8t + 2)$
$-t^2 + 12t + 2$

Determine whether each expression is a polynomial. If it is, classify it as a monomial, binomial, or trinomial. *(Lesson 13-1)* **38. yes; trimonial**

36. $\dfrac{1}{5a^2}$ **no**

37. $x^2 + 9$ **yes; binomial**

38. $c^2 - d^3 + cd$

39. Make a stem-and-leaf plot for the set of data shown below. *(Lesson 12-1)*
72, 64, 68, 66, 70, 89, 91, 54, 59, 71, 71, 85 **See margin.**

Getting Ready for the Next Lesson **PREREQUISITE SKILL** **Simplify each expression.**
*(To review **multiplying monomials**, see Lesson 4-2.)*

40. $x(3x)$ **$3x^2$**

41. $(2y)(4y)$ **$8y^2$**

42. $(t^2)(6t)$ **$6t^3$**

43. $(4m)(m^2)$ **$4m^3$**

44. $(w^2)(-3w)$ **$-3w^3$**

45. $(2r^2)(5r^3)$ **$10r^5$**

Practice Quiz 1   Lessons 13-1 through 13-3

Find the degree of each polynomial. *(Lesson 13-1)*

1. cd^3 **4**

2. $a - 4a^2$ **2**

3. $x^2y + 7x^2 - 21$ **3**

Find each sum or difference. *(Lessons 13-2 and 13-3)*

4. $(2x - 8) + (x - 7)$ **$3x - 15$**

5. $(4x + 5) - (2x + 3)$ **$2x + 2$**

6. $(5d^2 - 3) - (2d^2 - 7)$ **$3d^2 + 4$**

7. $(3r + 6s) + (5r - 9s)$ **$8r - 3s$**

8. $(x^2 + 4x + 2) + (7x^2 - 2x + 3)$ **$8x^2 + 2x + 5$**

9. $(9x - 4y) - (12x - 9y)$ **$-3x + 5y$**

10. **GEOMETRY** The perimeter of the triangle is $8x + 3y$ centimeters. Find the length of the third side. *(Lessons 13-2 and 13-3)*
$3x + 2y$ cm

$4x - y$ cm $x + 2y$ cm

Assessment Options

Practice Quiz 1 The quiz provides students with a brief review of the concepts and skills in Lessons 13-1 through 13-3. Lesson numbers are given to the right of exercises or instruction lines so students can review concepts not yet mastered.

Quiz (Lesson 13-3) is available on p. 777 of the *Chapter 13 Resource Masters*.

Mid-Chapter Test (Lessons 13-1 through 13-3) is available on p. 779 of the *Chapter 13 Resource Masters*.

Study Guide and Intervention, p. 743

To subtract polynomials, subtract like terms.

Example Find $(x^2 + 3x - 6) - (4x^2 - 1)$.

Method 1 Subtract vertically.
$x^2 + 3x - 6$
$(-)\ 4x^2\qquad - 1$
$\overline{-3x^2 + 3x - 5}$

Method 2 Add the additive inverse of $4x^2 - 1$, which is $(-1)(4x^2 - 1)$ or $-4x^2 + 1$.
$= (x^2 + 3x - 6) - (4x^2 - 1)$
$= (x^2 + 3x - 6) + (-4x^2 + 1)$
$= (x^2 - 4x^2) + (3x) + (-6 + 1)$
$= -3x^2 + 3x - 5$

Exercises

Find each difference.

1. $4c + 7$
$(-)\ 3c + 3$
$\overline{c + 4}$

2. $2m + 5$
$(-)\ -8m + 1$
$\overline{10m + 4}$

3. $9h^2 - 4h + 5$
$(-)\quad h^2\quad - 5$
$\overline{8k^2 - 4h + 10}$

4. $3z^2 - z$
$(-)\qquad 3z - 5$
$\overline{3z^2 - 4z + 5}$

5. $(-6r + 3) - (7r + 2)$
$-13r + 1$

6. $(8f^2 - 7f - 3) - (2f + 4)$
$8f^2 - 9f - 7$

7. $(5n^2 - 2n) - (3n + 9)$
$5n^2 - 5n - 9$

8. $(a^2 + 5ab) - (-2ab - 3b^2)$
$a^2 + 7ab + 3b^2$

9. $(6g^2 + 8) - (5g^2 - 2g + 6)$
$g^2 + 2g + 2$

10. $(8x^2 - 3y) - (2xy + 3y)$
$8x^2 - 2xy - 6y$

11. $(n - 12) - (n^2 + n + 9)$
$-n^2 - 21$

12. $(h^2 - 2h + 1) - (3h - 7h^2)$
$8h^2 - 5h + 1$

13. $(y^2 + y + 1) - (y^2 - y + 1)$
$2y$

14. $(6p^2 - 5p - 1) - (2p - 4)$
$6p^2 - 7p + 3$

15. $(4q^2 + q) - (q^2 + 3)$
$3q^2 + q - 3$

16. $(6v^2 + 8) - (7v^2 + 2v - 5)$
$-v^2 - 2v + 13$

17. $(u^2 + u - 4) - (5u^2 - 4)$
$-4u^2 + u$

18. $(9b^2 + 2) - (-b^2 + b + 9)$
$10b^2 - b - 7$

Skills Practice, p. 744 and Practice, p. 745 (shown)

Find each difference.

1. $4y + 1$
$(-)\ 3y + 8$
$\overline{y - 7}$

2. $2k + 3$
$(-)\ 7k - 6$
$\overline{-5k + 9}$

3. $5j^2 + 2j - 2$
$(-)\ j^2 + 9j + 2$
$\overline{4j^2 - 7j - 4}$

4. $c^2 + 5c - 3$
$(-)\ -c^2 - 5c - 1$
$\overline{2c^2 + 10c - 2}$

5. $d^2 - 4d + 6$
$(-)\ d^2 + 3d - 8$
$\overline{-7d + 14}$

6. $2n^2 - 3n - 10$
$(-)\ -n^2 - 3n + 8$
$\overline{3n^2 - 18}$

7. $9m^2 - 4m + 13$
$(-)\ 7m^2 - 2m - 3$
$\overline{2m^2 - 2m + 16}$

8. $d^2 + 3d - 6$
$(-)\ d^2 + 3d + 6$
$\overline{-12}$

9. $-6q^2 - 3q + 2$
$(-)\ 3q^2 + 4q + 4$
$\overline{-9q^2 - 7q - 2}$

10. $v^2 - v$
$(-)\ 2v^2 - 9v - 3$
$\overline{-v^2 + 8v + 3}$

11. $(4n^2 - n - 6) - (-2n^2 - 3n - 14)$
$6n^2 + 2n + 8$

12. $(3k^2 + 9k) - (8k^2 - 12)$
$-5k^2 + 9k + 12$

13. $(k^2 - 7) - (k - 11)$
$k^2 - k + 4$

14. $(3h^2 - x - 2) - (3x^2 - x - 4)$
$6x^2 + 2$

15. $(k^2 - 12) - (k^2 + 6k - 9)$
$-6k - 3$

16. $(k^2 + 4kb) - (5kb + 2b^2)$
$k^2 - kb - 2b^2$

17. $(3u^2 - 9) - (u^2 + 21u + 2)$
$2u^2 - 21u - 11$

18. $(5m^2 - 4mn) - (4mn + 8n^2)$
$5m^2 - 8mn - 8n^2$

19. $(h^2 + 8h + 5) - (h^2 - 3h - 7)$
$11h + 12$

20. $(2x^2 - 4x - 8) - (2x - 8x^2)$
$10x^2 - 6x - 8$

21. $(6g^2 + 3g + 2) - (g^2 + g - 4)$
$5g^2 + 2g + 6$

22. $(b^3 + b^2 - ab) - (b^3 + 3b^2 + 5)$
$-2b^2 - ab - 5$

23. **POOLS** A swimming pool is $(4u^2 - 16)$ feet long and $(w - 16)$ feet wide. How much longer is the length than the width? **$4w^2 - w$ ft**

Enrichment, p. 747

Polynomials with Fractional Coefficients

Polynomials may have fractional coefficients in some or all of the terms. Computation with these types of polynomials is done in the same way as with whole-number coefficients.

Add or subtract. Write all coefficients as fractions.

1. Add $\frac{3}{4}x^2 + \frac{2}{5}y^2$ and $\frac{1}{6}x^2 - \frac{3}{5}y^2$. $\frac{11}{12}x^2 - \frac{14}{15}y^2$

2. From $\frac{1}{2}x^2 - \frac{1}{3}xy + \frac{1}{4}y^2$, take $\frac{1}{3}x^2 - \frac{1}{6}xy + \frac{5}{2}y^2$. $\frac{1}{6}x^2 - \frac{1}{6}xy + \frac{2}{3}xy - \frac{7}{12}y^2$

3. Add $\frac{3}{2}x - \frac{4}{3}x, -\frac{7}{8}x - \frac{6}{7}y$, and $y - \frac{1}{4}x$. $\frac{3}{8}x - \frac{25}{21}y$

4. Subtract $\frac{1}{6}x^2 + \frac{1}{8}x - \frac{1}{4}$ from $\frac{2}{3}x^2 + \frac{5}{8}x + \frac{1}{2}$. $\frac{1}{2}x^2 + \frac{1}{2}x + \frac{3}{4}$

5. Add $\frac{1}{3}xy + \frac{11}{12}y^2$ to $\frac{4}{9}xy - \frac{1}{6}y^2$. $\frac{7}{9}xy + \frac{3}{4}y^2$

6. Add $\frac{1}{5}x^2 - \frac{1}{8}x - \frac{1}{9}$ and $\frac{3}{10}x^2 + \frac{5}{8}x + \frac{1}{9}$. $\frac{1}{2}x^2 + \frac{1}{2}x - \frac{2}{9}$

7. From $\frac{1}{2} + \frac{2}{3}y + \frac{3}{4}y^2$, take $\frac{1}{8} + \frac{1}{6}y - \frac{5}{6}y^2$. $\frac{3}{8} + \frac{1}{2}y + \frac{19}{12}y^2$

8. Subtract $\frac{7}{12}x - \frac{1}{4}$ from $\frac{3}{4}x - \frac{1}{3}$. $\frac{1}{6}x - \frac{1}{12}$

9. Add $\frac{3}{8}x^2 - \frac{1}{3}xy + \frac{5}{9}y^2$ and $\frac{1}{2}x^2 - \frac{1}{2}xy - \frac{1}{3}y^2$. $\frac{7}{8}x^2 - \frac{5}{6}xy + \frac{2}{9}y^2$

10. Subtract $\frac{3}{4}y^2 + \frac{1}{2}y$ from $\frac{4}{3}y^2 + \frac{7}{8}y$. $\frac{7}{12}y^2 + \frac{3}{8}y$

Algebra Activity

A Preview of Lesson 13-4

Modeling Multiplication

Recall that algebra tiles are named based on their area. The area of each tile is the product of the width and length.

These algebra tiles can be placed together to form a rectangle whose length and width each represent a polynomial. The area of the rectangle is the product of the polynomials.

Use algebra tiles to find $x(x + 2)$.

Step 1 Make a rectangle with a width of x and a length of $x + 2$. Use algebra tiles to mark off the dimensions on a product mat.

Step 2 Using the marks as a guide, fill in the rectangle with algebra tiles.

Step 3 The area of the rectangle is $x^2 + x + x$. In simplest form, the area is $x^2 + 2x$. Therefore, $x(x + 2) = x^2 + 2x$.

Model and Analyze 1–8. See pp. 703A–703D for models.

Use algebra tiles to determine whether each statement is *true* or *false*.

1. $x(x + 1) = x^2 + 1$ **false**
2. $x(2x + 3) = 2x^2 + 3x$ **true**
3. $(x + 2)2x = 2x^2 + 4x$ **true**
4. $2x(3x + 1) = 6x^2 + x$ **false**

Find each product using algebra tiles.

5. $x(x + 5)$ $\mathbf{x^2 + 5x}$
6. $(2x + 1)x$ $\mathbf{2x^2 + x}$
7. $(2x + 4)2x$ $\mathbf{4x^2 + 8x}$
8. $3x(2x + 1)$ $\mathbf{6x^2 + 3x}$

9. There is a square garden plot that measures x feet on a side.

   a. Suppose you double the length of the plot and increase the width by 3 feet. Write two expressions for the area of the new plot. $\mathbf{2x(x + 3);\ 2x^2 + 6x}$

   b. If the original plot was 10 feet on a side, what is the area of the new plot? $\mathbf{260\ ft^2}$

Extend the Activity $(x + 3)(2x + 3) = 2x^2 + 9x + 9$

10. Write a multiplication sentence that is represented by the model at the right.

Getting Started

Objective Model multiplication with algebra tiles.

Materials
algebra tiles
product mat

Teach

- Have students work in small groups, taking turns modeling and recording the results.
- Make sure students follow the format of placing the x^2 tiles in the upper left corner and the unit tiles in the lower right corner of the rectangle. Also, the short end of the x-tile faces the upper or left perimeter.
- Make sure students understand that the factors are read from uppermost and leftmost perimeter, and that the area is read from the interior of the rectangle.

Assess

In **Exercises 1–9**, students should

- use algebra tiles to multiply a monomial and a binomial.
- write an expression to represent a length and width and use it to solve a problem.

In **Exercise 10**, students write a multiplication problem represented by a model.

Study Notebook

Have students write a paragraph and show diagrams of algebra tiles explaining how to find $2x(x + 1)$.

Resource Manager

 Teaching Pre-Algebra with Manipulatives
- pp. 7–8 (masters for algebra tiles)
- p. 14 (master for product mat)
- p. 161 (student recording sheet)

Glencoe Mathematics Classroom Manipulative Kit
- algebra tiles
- product mat

Multiplying a Polynomial by a Monomial

What You'll Learn

- Multiply a polynomial by a monomial.

How is the Distributive Property used to multiply a polynomial by a monomial?

The Grande Arche office building in Paris, France, looks like a hollowed-out prism, as shown in the photo at the right.

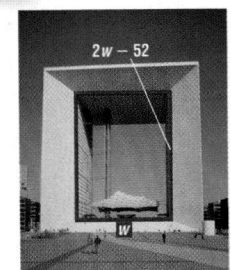

2w − 52

a. Write an expression that represents the area of the rectangular region outlined on the photo. $w(2w − 52)$ b. $2w^2 − 52w$

b. Recall that $2(4 + 1) = 2(4) + 2(1)$ by the Distributive Property. Use this property to simplify the expression you wrote in part **a**.

c. The Grande Arche is approximately w feet deep. Explain how you can write a polynomial to represent the volume of the hollowed-out region of the building. Then write the polynomial.

NEW YORK
Performance Indicator

8.A.8 Multiply a binomial by a monomial or a binomial (integer coefficients)

c. Use the Distributive Property to multiply $2w^2 − 52w$ by w; $2w^3 − 52w^2$.

MULTIPLY A POLYNOMIAL AND A MONOMIAL

You can model the multiplication of a polynomial and a monomial by using algebra tiles.

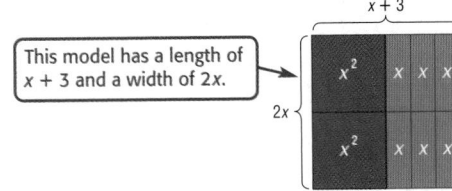

This model has a length of $x + 3$ and a width of $2x$.

$x + 3$

$2x$

Study Tip

Look Back

To review the **Distributive Property**, see Lesson 3-1.

The model shows the product of $2x$ and $x + 3$. The rectangular arrangement contains 2 x^2 tiles and 6 x tiles. So, the product of $2x$ and $x + 3$ is $2x^2 + 6x$. In general, the Distributive Property can be used to multiply a polynomial and a monomial.

Example 1 Products of a Monomial and a Polynomial

Find each product.

a. $4(5x + 1)$

$4(5x + 1) = 4(5x) + 4(1)$ Distributive Property
$= 20x + 4$ Simplify.

b. $(2x − 6)(3x)$

$(2x − 6)(3x) = 2x(3x) − 6(3x)$ Distributive Property
$= 6x^2 − 18x$ Simplify.

---

1 Focus

 5-Minute Check Transparency 13-4 Use as a quiz or review of Lesson 13-3.

Mathematical Background notes are available for this lesson on page 666D.

How is the Distributive Property used to multiply a polynomial by a monomial?

The opening activity questions are repeated on page 751 of the *Chapter 13 Resource Masters.*

Reading to Learn Mathematics, p. 751   **ELL**

Pre-Activity   *How is the Distributive Property used to multiply a polynomial by a monomial?*

Do the activity at the top of page 683 in your textbook. Write your answers below.

a. Write an expression that represents the area of the rectangular region outlined on the photo. $w(2w − 52)$

b. Recall that $2(4 + 1) = 2(4) + 2(1)$ by the Distributive Property. Use this property to simplify the expression you wrote in part **a**.
$2w^2 − 52w$

c. The Grande Arche is approximately w feet deep. Explain how you can write a polynomial to represent the volume of the hollowed-out region of the building. Then write the polynomial.
Use the Distributive Property to multiply $2w^2 − 52w$ by w; $2w^3 − 52w^2$.

Reading the Lesson

1. Draw a model that shows the product $x(x + 2)$. Write the polynomial that shows the product. See students' work. $x^2 + 2x$

2. Explain the Distributive Property and give an example of how it is used to multiply a polynomial by a monomial. Sample answer: Multiply each number inside the parentheses by the number outside the parentheses.
$2(3y + 2) = 2(3y) + 2(2)$
$= 6y + 4$

Helping You Remember

3. *Distribute* is a common word in the English language.
   a. Find the definition of *distribute* in a dictionary. Write the definition that most closely relates to this lesson. to deliver to members of a group
   b. Explain how this definition can help you remember how to use the Distributive Property to multiply a polynomial by a monomial. The number outside the parentheses is "distributed" to each number inside.

Resource Manager

Workbooks and Reproducible Masters

Chapter 13 Resource Masters
- Study Guide and Intervention, p. 748
- Skills Practice, p. 749
- Practice, p. 750
- Reading to Learn Mathematics, p. 751
- Enrichment, p. 752

Graphing Calculator and Spreadsheet Masters, p. 43
Parent and Student Study Guide Workbook, p. 111

 Transparencies
5-Minute Check Transparency 13-4
Answer Key Transparencies

 Technology
Interactive Chalkboard
Pre-AlgePASS: Tutorial Plus, Lesson 38

Building on Prior Knowledge

In Lesson 3-1, students used the Distributive Property to write equivalent numerical and algebraic expressions. In this lesson, they will extend this knowledge to using the Distributive Property to multiply a polynomial by a monomial.

MULTIPLY A POLYNOMIAL AND A MONOMIAL

In-Class Examples

1 Find each product.

a. $-8(3x + 2)$ $-24x - 16$

b. $(6x - 1)(-2x)$ $-12x^2 + 2x$

2 Find $4b(-a^2 + 5ab + 2b^2)$.
$-4a^2b + 20ab^2 + 8b^3$

Teaching Tip If students are having trouble using the Distributive Property, have them write one polynomial below the other and multiply each monomial as they would with numerical multiplication.

3 FENCES The length of a dog run is 4 feet more than three times its width. The perimeter of the dog run is 56 feet. What are the dimensions of the dog run?   **6 ft by 22 ft**

3 Practice/Apply

Study Notebook

Have students—

- write a paragraph explaining how to multiply a binomial and a monomial.
- include any other item(s) that they find helpful in mastering the skills in this lesson.

Study Tip

Look Back
To review **equations with grouping symbols**, see Lesson 3-1.

NEW YORK
Study Tip
You can also find the quotient of a polynomial and a monomial. For a lesson on dividing a polynomial by a monomial, see Lesson 13-4b on p. NY35.

2. Multiply x^3 by $4x$ and multiply -7 by $4x$. Then add.

Example 2 **Product of a Monomial and a Polynomial**

Find $3a(a^2 + 2ab - 4b^2)$.

$3a(a^2 + 2ab - 4b^2)$
$= 3a(a^2) + 3a(2ab) - 3a(4b^2)$ Distributive Property
$= 3a^3 + 6a^2b - 12ab^2$ Simplify.

✓ Concept Check What is the product of x^2 and $x + 1$? $x^3 + x^2$

Sometimes problems can be solved by simplifying polynomial expressions.

Example 3 **Use a Polynomial to Solve a Problem**

POOLS The world's largest swimming pool is the Orthlieb Pool in Casablanca, Morocco. It is 30 meters longer than 6 times its width. If the perimeter of the pool is 1110 meters, what are the dimensions of the pool?

Explore   You know the perimeter of the pool. You want to find the dimensions of the pool.

Plan   Let w represent the width of the pool. Then $6w + 30$ represents the length. Write an equation.

Perimeter	equals	twice	the sum of the length and width.
P	$=$	2	$(\ell + w)$

Solve

$P = 2(\ell + w)$	Write the equation.
$1110 = 2(6w + 30 + w)$	Replace P with 1110 and ℓ with $6w + 30$.
$1110 = 2(7w + 30)$	Combine like terms.
$1110 = 14w + 60$	Distributive Property
$1050 = 14w$	Subtract 60 from each side.
$75 = w$	Divide each side by 14.

The width is 75 meters, and the length is $6w + 30$ or 480 meters.

Examine   Check the reasonableness of the results by estimating.

$P = 2(\ell + w)$ Formula for perimeter of a rectangle
$P \approx 2(500 + 80)$ Round 480 to 500 and 75 to 80.
$P \approx 2(580)$ or about 1160

Since 1160 is close to 1110, the answer is reasonable.

Check for Understanding

Concept Check

1. **Determine** whether the following statement is *true* or *false*.

   If you change the order in which you multiply a polynomial and a monomial, the product will be different.

   Explain your reasoning or give a counterexample. **See margin.**

GUIDED PRACTICE KEY	
Exercises	Examples
4–9	1, 2
10	3

2. **Explain** the steps you would take to find the product of $x^3 - 7$ and $4x$.

3. **OPEN ENDED** Write a monomial and a polynomial, each having a degree no greater than 1. Then find their product. **Sample answer:**
   $2x(x + 1) = 2x^2 + 2x$

DAILY
INTERVENTION   **Differentiated Instruction**

- **Visual/Spatial** Have students work together in groups to draw diagrams of rectangles showing the lengths and widths in terms of x. Then have groups make up exercises involving their diagrams and the perimeters of the rectangles. After members of each group agree on the solutions to their own exercises, have them exchange diagrams and exercises with another group and solve that group's exercises. Encourage discussion of difficult problems.

Guided Practice   Find each product.   **9.** $-15x^2 + 35x - 45$

4. $(5y - 4)3$ $15y - 12$ **5.** $a(a + 4)$ $a^2 + 4a$ **6.** $t(7t + 8)$ $7t^2 + 8t$

7. $(3x - 7)4x$ $12x^2 - 28x$ **8.** $a(2a + b)$ $2a^2 + ab$ **9.** $-5(3x^2 - 7x + 9)$

Application   **10.** **TENNIS** The perimeter of a tennis court is 228 feet. The length of the court is 6 feet more than twice the width. What are the dimensions of the tennis court? **36 feet wide by 78 feet long**

★ indicates increased difficulty

Practice and Apply

Homework Help

For Exercises	See Examples
11–26	1, 2
27–30	3

Extra Practice
See page 756.

Find each product.

11. $7(2n + 5)$ $14n + 35$

12. $(1 + 4b)6$ $6 + 24b$

13. $t(t - 9)$ $t^2 - 9t$

14. $(x + 5)x$ $x^2 + 5x$

15. $-a(7a + 6)$ $-7a^2 - 6a$

16. $y(3 + 2y)$ $3y + 2y^2$

17. $4n(10 + 2n)$ $40n + 8n^2$

18. $-3x(6x - 4)$ $-18x^2 + 12x$

19. $3y(y^2 - 2)$ $3y^3 - 6y$

20. $ab(a^2 + 7)$ $a^3b + 7ab$

21. $5x(x + y)$ $5x^2 + 5xy$

22. $4m(m^2 - m)$ $4m^3 - 4m^2$

23. $-14x^2 + 35x - 77$ ★ **23.** $7(-2x^2 + 5x - 11)$

★ **24.** $-3y(6 - 9y + 4y^2)$

24. $-18y + 27y^2 - 12y^3$

★ **25.** $4c(c^3 + 7c - 10)$ $4c^4 + 28c^2 - 40c$ ★ **26.** $6x^2(-2x^3 + 8x + 1)$
$-12x^5 + 48x^3 + 6x^2$

Solve each equation.

★ **27.** $30 = 6(-2w + 3)$ -1

★ **28.** $-3(2a - 12) = 3a - 45$ 9

29. **BASKETBALL** The dimensions of high school basketball courts are different than the dimensions of college basketball courts, as shown in the table. Use the information in the table to find the length and width of each court.

	Basketball Courts	
Measure	**High School (ft)**	**College (ft)**
Perimeter	268	288
Width	w	w
Length	$2w - 16$	$(2w - 16) + 10$

high school, 84 ft by 50 ft; college, 94 ft by 50 ft

★ **30.** **BOXES** A box large enough to hold 43,000 liters of water was made from one large sheet of cardboard.

a. Write a polynomial that represents the area of the cardboard used to make the box. Assume the top and bottom of the box are the same. (Hint: $(2x + 2y)$ $(6x - 2y) = 12x^2 + 8xy - 4y^2$)

$2x + 2y$

$6x - 2y$

$2x$

x

b. If x is 1.2 meters and y is 0.1 meter, what is the total amount of cardboard in square meters used to make the box? **94 m²**   **30a.** $64x^2 + 16xy - 8y^2$

31. **CRITICAL THINKING** You have seen how algebra tiles can be used to connect multiplying a polynomial by a monomial and the Distributive Property. Draw a model and write a sentence to show how to multiply two binomials: $(a + b)(c + d)$. $(a + b)(c + d) = ac + ad + bc + bd$;
See margin for model.

 www.pre-alg.com/self_check_quiz/ny   **Lesson 13-4** Multiplying a Polynomial by a Monomial **685**

About the Exercises . . .
Odd/Even Assignments
Exercises 11–28 are structured so that students practice the same concepts whether they are assigned odd or even problems.

Assignment Guide
Basic: 11–21 odd, 29, 31–46
Average: 11–31 odd, 32–46
Advanced: 12–30 even, 31–43
(Optional: 44–46)

4 Assess

Open-Ended Assessment
Modeling Have students sketch algebra tiles that represent $4(3x + 2)$.

Getting Ready
for Lesson 13-5
PREREQUISITE SKILL Lesson 13-5 presents determining whether a function is linear or nonlinear. One way to determine this is to complete a function table and compare the rates of change. Exercises 44–46 should be used to determine your students' familiarity with using tables to find ordered pair solutions of functions.

Answers

1. False; the order in which numbers or terms are multiplied does not change the product, by the Commutative Property of Multiplication; $x(2x + 3) = 2x^2 + 3x$ and $(2x + 3)x = 2x^2 + 3x$.

31.

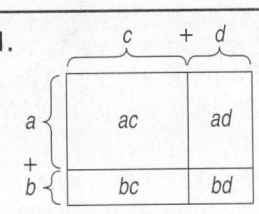

	c	$+$	d
a	ac		ad
$+$			
b	bc		bd

---

32. **WRITING IN MATH** 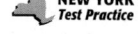 Answer the question that was posed at the beginning of the lesson. **See margin.**

How is the Distributive Property used to multiply a polynomial by a monomial?

Include the following in your answer:
- a description of the Distributive Property, and
- an example showing the steps used to multiply a polynomial and a monomial.

33. What is the product of $2x$ and $x - 8$? **D**
- Ⓐ $2x - 8$
- Ⓑ $2x^2 - 8$
- Ⓒ $2x^2 - 16$
- Ⓓ $2x^2 - 16x$

34. The area of the rectangle is 252 square centimeters. Find the length of the longer side. **A**
- Ⓐ 18 cm
- Ⓑ 16 cm
- Ⓒ 14 cm
- Ⓓ 10 cm

x cm
$2x - 10$ cm

Maintain Your Skills

Mixed Review Find each sum or difference. (Lessons 13-2 and 13-3)

36. $10a + 3a^2 + 4$
37. $4y^2 - 2y + 14$
40. $7n^2 + 6n$

35. $(2x - 1) + 5x$ $7x - 1$
37. $(y^2 + 6y + 2) + (3y^2 - 8y + 12)$
39. $(9x + 8y) - (x - 3y)$ $8x + 11y$

36. $(9a + 3a^2) + (a + 4)$
38. $(4x - 7) - (2x + 2)$ $2x - 9$
40. $(13n^2 + 6n + 5) - (6n^2 + 5)$

41. **STATISTICS** Describe two ways that a graph of sales of several brands of cereal could be misleading. (Lesson 12-5) **See margin.**

State whether each transformation of the triangles is a *reflection*, *translation*, or *rotation*. (Lesson 10-3)

42. translation

43. reflection

Getting Ready for the Next Lesson

PREREQUISITE SKILL Complete each table to find the coordinates of four points through which the graph of each function passes.
(To review **using tables to find ordered pair solutions**, see Lesson 8-2.)

44. $y = 4x$

x	$4x$	(x, y)
0	0	$(0, 0)$
1	4	$(1, 4)$
2	8	$(2, 8)$
3	12	$(3, 12)$

45. $y = 2x^2 - 3$

x	$2x^2 - 3$	(x, y)
0	-3	$(0, -3)$
1	-1	$(1, -1)$
2	5	$(2, 5)$
3	15	$(3, 15)$

46. $y = x^3 + 1$

x	$x^3 + 1$	(x, y)
0	1	$(0, 1)$
1	2	$(1, 2)$
2	9	$(2, 9)$
3	28	$(3, 28)$

Answers

32. To use the Distributive Property, multiply each term of the polynomial by the monomial. Answers should include the following.
- The Distributive Property combines multiplication and addition when used to find the product of a polynomial and a monomial.
- To find the product of $3x$ and $x + 2$, first find $3x \cdot x$. Then find $3x \cdot 2$. Finally, add the products, $3x^2 + 6x$.

41. Sample answer: The scales are labeled inconsistently or the bars on a bar graph are different widths.

Linear and Nonlinear Functions

What You'll Learn

- Determine whether a function is linear or nonlinear.

How can you determine whether a function is linear?

Vocabulary

- nonlinear function
- quadratic function
- cubic function

a. $x(40 - 2x)$ or $40x - 2x^2$

b. 168 ft², 192 ft², 200 ft², 192 ft², 168 ft²

NEW YORK
Performance Indicator

8.G.20 Distinguish between linear and nonlinear equations $ax^2 + bx + c$; $a = 1$ (only graphically)

The sum of the lengths of three sides of a new deck is 40 feet. Suppose x represents the width of the deck. Then the length of the deck is $40 - 2x$.

40 − 2x

a. Write an expression to represent the area of the deck.

b. Find the area of the deck for widths of 6, 8, 10, 12, and 14 feet.

c. Graph the points whose ordered pairs are (width, area). Do the points fall along a straight line? Explain. **See Reading Math mini in margin.**

NONLINEAR FUNCTIONS In Lesson 8-2, you learned that linear functions have graphs that are straight lines. These graphs represent constant rates of change. **Nonlinear functions** do not have constant rates of change. Therefore, their graphs are *not* straight lines.

Example 1 Identify Functions Using Graphs

Determine whether each graph represents a *linear* or *nonlinear* function. Explain.

a.
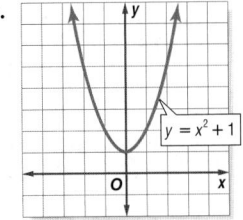

$y = x^2 + 1$

The graph is a curve, not a straight line, so it represents a nonlinear function.

b.
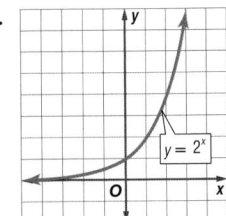

$y = 2^x$

This graph is also a curve, so it represents a nonlinear function.

Recall that the equation for a linear function can be written in the form $y = mx + b$, where m represents the constant rate of change. Therefore, you can determine whether a function is linear by looking at its equation.

Example 2 Identify Functions Using Equations

Determine whether each equation represents a *linear* or *nonlinear* function.

a. $y = 10x$

This is linear because it can be written as $y = 10x + 0$.

b. $y = \dfrac{3}{x}$

This is nonlinear because x is in the denominator and the equation cannot be written in the form $y = mx + b$.

1 Focus

5-Minute Check Transparency 13-5 Use as a quiz or review of Lesson 13-4.

Mathematical Background notes are available for this lesson on page 666D.

How can you determine whether a function is linear?

The opening activity questions are repeated on page 756 of the *Chapter 13 Resource Masters*.

Reading to Learn Mathematics, p. 756 **ELL**

Pre-Activity *How can you determine whether a function is linear?*

Do the activity at the top of page 687 in your textbook. Write your answers below.

a. Write an expression to represent the area of the deck.
$x(40 - 2x)$ or $40x - 2x^2$

b. Find the area of the deck for widths of 6, 8, 10, 12, and 14 feet.
168 ft², 192 ft², 200 ft², 192 ft², 168 ft²

c. Graph the points whose ordered pairs are (width, area). Do the points fall along a straight line? Explain.
No; the connected points fall along a curve.

Reading the Lesson 1–3. See students' work.

Write a definition and give an example of each new vocabulary phrase.

Vocabulary	Definition	Example
1. nonlinear function		
2. quadratic function		
3. cubic function		

Helping You Remember

4. You have learned about linear and nonlinear functions. Nonlinear functions include quadratic functions and cubic functions. Below, write three equations that represent each type of function given. For the nonlinear functions, include at least one quadratic function and one cubic function. **Sample answers are given.**

Linear
1. $y = x + 2$
2. $y = 2x + 1$
3. $y = \dfrac{x}{-5} - 5$

Nonlinear
1. $y = x^2 + 1$
2. $y = 5x^3$
3. $y = x^2 + 2x - 1$

Resource Manager

Workbooks and Reproducible Masters

Chapter 13 Resource Masters
- Study Guide and Intervention, p. 753
- Skills Practice, p. 754
- Practice, p. 755
- Reading to Learn Mathematics, p. 756
- Enrichment, p. 757
- Assessment, p. 778

Parent and Student Study Guide Workbook, p. 112
School-to-Career Masters, p. 26

Transparencies

5-Minute Check Transparency 13-5
Real-World Transparency 13
Answer Key Transparencies

Technology

Interactive Chalkboard

NONLINEAR FUNCTIONS

In-Class Examples

1 Determine whether each graph represents a *linear* or *nonlinear* function.

a.

linear

b.

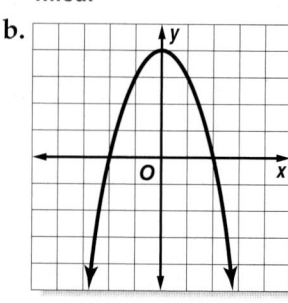

nonlinear

2 Determine whether each equation represents a *linear* or *nonlinear* function.

a. $y = -5x - 4$ **linear**

b. $y = 2x^2 + 3$ **nonlinear**

Teaching Tip Make sure students notice the degree of the equation in each case. Help them to discover that the degree of a linear equation must be 1.

3 Determine whether each table represents a *linear* or *nonlinear* function.

a.

x	y
2	25
4	17
6	9
8	1

linear

b.

x	y
5	2
8	4
11	8
14	16

nonlinear

The tables represent the functions in Example 2. Compare the rates of change.

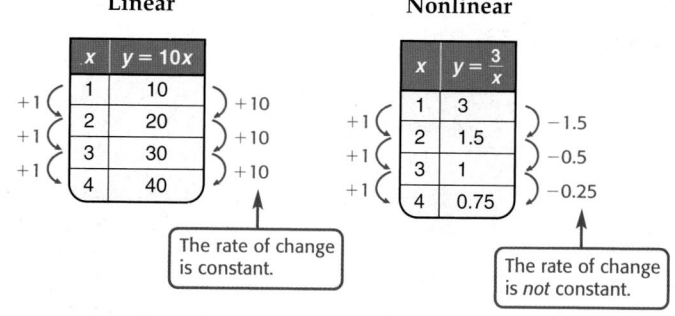

Linear

Nonlinear

The rate of change is constant.

The rate of change is *not* constant.

A nonlinear function does not increase or decrease at the same rate. You can check this by using a table.

Example 3 Identify Functions Using Tables

Determine whether each table represents a *linear* or *nonlinear* function.

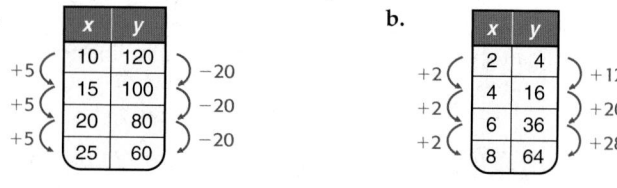

a.

As *x* increases by 5, *y* decreases by 20. So this is a linear function.

b.

As *x* increases by 2, *y* increases by a greater amount each time. So this is a nonlinear function.

Some nonlinear functions are given special names.

Reading Math

Cubic

Cubic means three-dimensional. A cubic function has a variable to the third power.

Key Concept — Quadratic and Cubic Functions

A **quadratic function** is a function that can be described by an equation of the form $y = ax^2 + bx + c$, where $a \neq 0$.

A **cubic function** is a function that can be described by an equation of the form $y = ax^3 + bx^2 + cx + d$, where $a \neq 0$.

Examples of these and other nonlinear functions are shown below.

Concept Summary — Nonlinear Functions

Quadratic	Cubic	Exponential	Inverse Variation
$y = x^2$	$y = x^3$	$y = 2^x$	$y = \frac{1}{x}$

DAILY INTERVENTION — Differentiated Instruction

• **Logical** Have students make a function table comparing altitude in feet (*x*) and temperature in °C (*y*). The altitudes are 0, 1500, 6000, and 9000 feet. The corresponding temperatures are 15, 5, −26, and −44°C. Have students graph the data and determine the altitude at which the temperature is −32°C.   **7000 ft**   Have them examine their graphs and discuss whether the function is linear or nonlinear.   **linear**

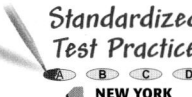
Example 4 Describe a Linear Function

Multiple-Choice Test Item

Which rule describes a linear function?
Ⓐ $y = 7x^3 + 2$　Ⓑ $y = (x - 1)5x$　Ⓒ $4x + 3y = 12$　Ⓓ $-2x^2 + 6y = 8$

Read the Test Item

A rule describes a relationship between variables. A rule that can be written in the form $y = mx + b$ describes a relationship that is linear.

Solve the Test Item

- $y = 7x^3 + 2 \rightarrow$ cubic equation　　The variable has an exponent of 3.
  $-2x^2 + 6y = 8 \rightarrow$ quadratic equation　The variable has an exponent of 2.

  You can eliminate choices A and D.

- $y = (x - 1)5x$
  $y = 5x^2 - 5x$　　This is a quadratic equation. Eliminate choice B.

The answer is C.

CHECK　$4x + 3y = 12 \rightarrow y = -\frac{4}{3}x + 4$

This equation is in the form $y = mx + b$. ✓

Check for Understanding

Concept Check

1. See pp. 703A–703D.
2. Exponential; for the long term, growth of profits would occur at a faster rate.

1. **Describe** two methods for determining whether a function is linear.
2. **Explain** whether a company would prefer profits that showed linear growth or exponential growth.
3. **OPEN ENDED** Use newspapers, magazines, or the Internet to find real-life examples of nonlinear situations. **Sample answer: population growth**

Guided Practice

Determine whether each graph, equation, or table represents a *linear* or *nonlinear* function. Explain.

4.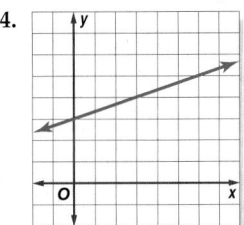
Linear; graph is a straight line.

5.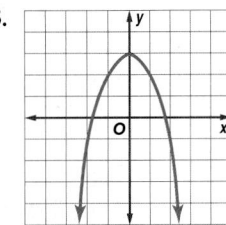
Nonlinear; graph is a curve.

8. Nonlinear; rate of change is not constant.

6. $y = \frac{x}{5}$
Linear; equation can be written as $y = \frac{1}{5}x + 0$.

7. $xy = 12$
Nonlinear; equation cannot be written as $y = mx + b$.

8.

x	y
−4	13
−2	0
0	4
2	0

9.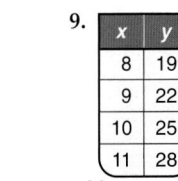

x	y
8	19
9	22
10	25
11	28

Linear; rate of change is constant.

10. Which rule describes a nonlinear function? **B**
Ⓐ $x + y = 100$　Ⓑ $y = \frac{8}{x}$　Ⓒ $9 = 11x - y$　Ⓓ $x = y$

In-Class Example　 Power Point®

4. **Multiple-Choice Test Item**
Which rule describes a linear function?　**B**

A $y = \frac{1}{x} + 3$

B $y = -9x$

C $y = x(x - 5)$

D $32 = 2x^2 + 3y$

✓ Skills Check

Nonlinear Functions What is the degree of a nonlinear function?　**greater than 1**

3 Practice/Apply

Study Notebook

Have students—
- add the definitions/examples of the vocabulary terms to their Vocabulary Builder worksheets for Chapter 13.
- include any other item(s) that they find helpful in mastering the skills in this lesson.

About the Exercises . . .

Odd/Even Assignments
Exercises 11–26 are structured so that students practice the same concepts whether they are assigned odd or even problems.

Assignment Guide

Basic: 11–25 odd, 28, 30–43
Average: 11–27 odd, 28–43
Advanced: 12–28 even, 31–39 (Optional: 40–43)
All: Practice Quiz 2 (1–5)

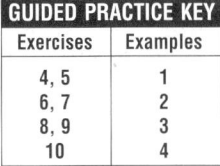
Example 4 Point out to students that they might quickly spot either choice B or choice C as the correct answer since neither has an exponent and neither has a variable as a denominator. Even if they are certain of their choice, they should look over other choices.

★ indicates increased difficulty

Practice and Apply

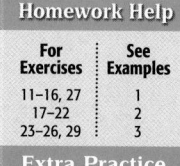

Homework Help

For Exercises	See Examples
11–16, 27	1
17–22	2
23–26, 29	3

Extra Practice See page 757.

11. nonlinear
12. linear
13. linear
14. nonlinear
15. nonlinear
16. nonlinear

17–26. See pp. 703A–703D for explanations.

27. Nonlinear; the points (year, applications) would lie on a curved line, not on a straight line. Or, the rate of change is not constant.

Determine whether each graph, equation, or table represents a *linear* or *nonlinear* function. Explain. 11–16. See margin for explanations.

11.

12.

13.

14.

15.

16.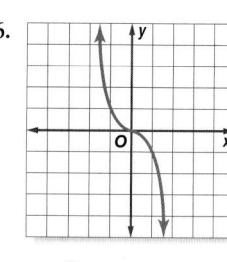

17. $y = 0.9x$ **linear**

18. $y = x^3 + 2$ **nonlinear**

19. $y = \frac{3x}{4}$ **linear**

20. $2x + 3y = 12$ **linear**

21. $y = 4^x$ **nonlinear**

22. $xy = -6$ **nonlinear**

23.

x	y
9	−2
11	−8
13	−14
15	−20

linear

24.

x	y
4	1
5	4
6	9
7	16

nonlinear

25.

x	y
−4	12
−2	0
0	4
2	0

nonlinear

26.

x	y
−10	20
−9	18
−8	16
−7	14

linear

★ 27. **TECHNOLOGY** The graph shows the increase of trademark applications for internet-related products or services. Would you describe this growth as linear or nonlinear? Explain.

 Online Research Data Update Is the growth of the Internet itself linear or nonlinear? Visit www.pre-alg.com/data_update to learn more.

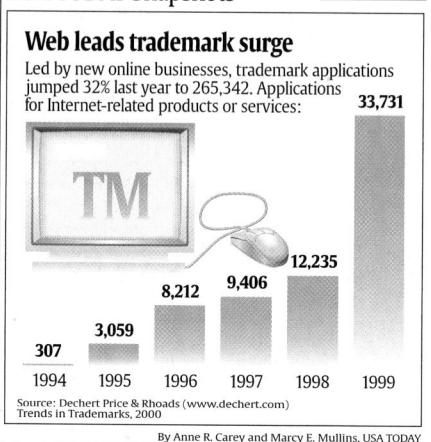

USA TODAY Snapshots®

Web leads trademark surge

Led by new online businesses, trademark applications jumped 32% last year to 265,342. Applications for Internet-related products or services:

Year	Applications
1994	307
1995	3,059
1996	8,212
1997	9,406
1998	12,235
1999	33,731

Source: Dechert Price & Rhoads (www.dechert.com) Trends in Trademarks, 2000

By Anne R. Carey and Marcy E. Mullins, USA TODAY

28. **CRITICAL THINKING** Are all graphs of straight lines linear functions? Explain. See pp. 703A–703D.

Teaching Tip Have students determine which functions in Exercises 11–22 appear to be quadratic, cubic, exponential, and inverse variations.

Answers

11. Graph is a curve.

12. Graph is a straight line.

13. Graph is a straight line.

14. Graph is a curve.

15. Graph is a curve.

16. Graph is a curve.

29. **PATENTS** The table shows the
★ years in which the first six million patents were issued. Is the number of patents issued a linear function of time? Explain. **No, the difference between the years varies, so the change is not constant.**

Year	Number of Patents Issued
1911	1 million
1936	2 million
1961	3 million
1976	4 million
1991	5 million
1999	6 million

Source: *New York Times*

30. WRITING IN MATH   Answer the question that was posed at the beginning of the lesson. **See margin.**

How can you determine whether a function is linear?

Include the following in your answer:

- a list of ways in which a function can be represented, and
- an explanation of how each representation can be used to identify the function as linear or nonlinear.

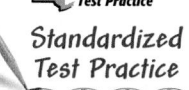

Standardized Test Practice
Ⓐ Ⓑ Ⓒ Ⓓ

31. Which equation represents a linear function? **A**

   Ⓐ $y = \frac{1}{2}x$ Ⓑ $3xy = 12$ Ⓒ $x^2 - 1 = y$ Ⓓ $y = x(x + 4)$

32. Determine which general rule represents a nonlinear function if $a > 1$. **C**

   Ⓐ $y = ax$ Ⓑ $y = \frac{x}{a}$ Ⓒ $y = a^x$ Ⓓ $y = a + x$

Maintain Your Skills

Mixed Review   **Find each product.**   *(Lesson 13-4)* **34.** $-5n + 15n^2$

33. $t(4 + 9t)$ **$4t + 9t^2$**   34. $5n(-1 + 3n)$ 35. $(a - 2b)ab$ **$a^2b - 2ab^2$**

Find each difference. *(Lesson 13-3)* **36.** $x + 8$ **38.** $-2a - a^2 - 3$

36. $(2x + 7) - (x - 1)$ 37. $(4x + y) - (5x + y)$ **$-x$** 38. $(6a - a^2) - (8a + 3)$

39. **GEOMETRY** Classify a 65° angle as *acute, obtuse, right,* or *straight.*
   (Lesson 9-3) **acute**

Getting Ready for the Next Lesson   **PREREQUISITE SKILL**   Use a table to graph each line.
*(To review **graphing equations**, see Lesson 8-3.)* **40–43. See pp. 703A–703D.**

40. $y = -x$ 41. $y = x - 4$ 42. $y = 2x + 2$ 43. $y = -\frac{1}{2}x + 3$

Practice Quiz 2   *Lessons 13-4 and 13-5*

Find each product.   *(Lesson 13-4)*

1. $c(2c^2 - 8)$ **$2c^3 - 8c$**   2. $(4x + 2)3x$ **$12x^2 + 6x$**   3. $a^2(5 + a + 2a^2)$ **$5a^2 + a^3 + 2a^4$**

Determine whether each equation represents a *linear* or *nonlinear* function.
Explain.   *(Lesson 13-5)*

4. $y = 9x$ **Linear; equation can be written as $y = 9x + 0$.**   5. $y = 0.25x^3$ **Nonlinear; equation cannot be written as $y = mx + b$.**

 www.pre-alg.com/self_check_quiz/ny   Lesson 13-5 Linear and Nonlinear Functions **691**

Answer

30. **A function is linear if it has a constant rate of change. This can be determined from graphs, equations, or tables of values. Answers should include the following.**

   - **Functions can be represented using graphs, equations, or tables.**

   - **A graph that is a straight line represents a linear function. An equation that can be written in the form $y = mx + b$ is a linear function. If a table of values shows a constant rate of change, the function is linear.**

4 Assess

Open-Ended Assessment

Speaking Have students read an equation to a partner and have the partner determine whether the equation is linear or nonlinear. Then have them switch roles.

Getting Ready for Lesson 13-6

PREREQUISITE SKILL Lesson 13-6 presents graphing nonlinear functions. Students will need to be able to make a table of values before graphing these functions. Exercises 40–43 should be used to determine your students' familiarity with using function tables to graph lines.

Assessment Options

Practice Quiz 2 The quiz provides students with a brief review of the concepts and skills in Lessons 13-4 and 13-5. Lesson numbers are given to the right of exercises or instruction lines so students can review concepts not yet mastered.

Quiz (Lessons 13-4 and 13-5) is available on p. 778 of the *Chapter 13 Resource Masters.*

NEW YORK *Performance Indicator* **8.G.21** Recognize the characteristic of quadratics in tables, graphs, equations and situations

1 Focus

 5-Minute Check Transparency 13-6 Use as a quiz or review of Lesson 13-5.

Mathematical Background notes are available for this lesson on page 666D.

How are functions, formulas, tables, and graphs related?

The opening activity questions are repeated on page 761 of the *Chapter 13 Resource Masters*.

Reading to Learn Mathematics, p. 761   **ELL**

Pre-Activity   *How are functions, formulas, tables, and graphs related?*

Do the activity at the top of page 692 in your textbook. Write your answers below.

a. The volume of cube *V* equals the cube of the length of an edge *a*. Write a formula to represent the volume of a cube as a function of edge length. $V = a^3$

b. Graph the volume as a function of edge length. (*Hint:* Use values of *a* like 0, 0.5, 1, 1.5, 2, and so on.)

Reading the Lesson

1. Write a quadratic function. Explain what makes it a quadratic function and what its graph would look like. **Sample answer:** $y = 2x^2 + 5$; This is a quadratic function because it has the form $y = ax^2 + bx + c, a \neq 0$. It is a parabola.

2. Write a cubic function. Explain what makes it a cubic function and what its graph would look like. **Sample answer:** $y = 3x^3 + 2$; This is a cubic function because it has the form $y = ax^3 + bx + cx, a \neq 0$. It is similar in appearance to $y = x^3$, only shifted up two units and increasing more rapidly.

Helping You Remember

3. You have learned to graph quadratic and cubic functions. Make a list of the steps you use to graph the two functions.

Make a table of values.

Plot the ordered pairs.

Connect the points with a curve.

Teaching Tip Discuss how to select "easy" values for *x* when making a function table. Suggest using numbers that will create whole numbers for *y* values.

What You'll Learn

- Graph quadratic functions.
- Graph cubic functions.

How are functions, formulas, tables, and graphs related?

You can find the area of a square *A* by squaring the length of a side *s*. This relationship can be represented in different ways.

Equation	Table	Graph

Equation

Area equals length of a side squared.

$A = s^2$

Table

s	s^2	*(s, A)*
0	$0^2 = 0$	(0, 0)
1	$1^2 = 1$	(1, 1)
2	$2^2 = 4$	(2, 4)

Graph

a. The volume of cube *V* equals the cube of the length of an edge *a*. Write a formula to represent the volume of a cube as a function of edge length. $V = a^3$

b. Graph the volume as a function of edge length. (*Hint*: Use values of *a* like 0, 0.5, 1, 1.5, 2, and so on.) **See margin.**

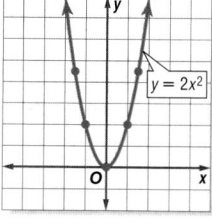

QUADRATIC FUNCTIONS   In Lesson 13-5, you saw that functions can be represented using graphs, equations, and tables. This allows you to graph quadratic functions such as $A = s^2$ using an equation or a table of values.

***Example* 1** *Graph Quadratic Functions*

Graph each function.

a. $y = 2x^2$

Make a table of values, plot the ordered pairs, and connect the points with a curve.

Study Tip

Graphing
It is often helpful to substitute decimal values of *x* in order to graph points that are closer together.

x	$2x^2$	*(x, y)*
−1.5	$2(-1.5)^2 = 4.5$	(−1.5, 4.5)
−1	$2(-1)^2 = 2$	(−1, 2)
0	$2(0)^2 = 0$	(0, 0)
1	$2(1)^2 = 2$	(1, 2)
1.5	$2(1.5)^2 = 4.5$	(1.5, 4.5)

Resource Manager

📁 Workbooks and Reproducible Masters

Chapter 13 Resource Masters
- Study Guide and Intervention, p. 758
- Skills Practice, p. 759
- Practice, p. 760
- Reading to Learn Mathematics, p. 761
- Enrichment, p. 762
- Assessment, p. 778

Graphing Calculator and Spreadsheet Masters, p. 44
Parent and Student Study Guide Workbook, p. 113

💡 Transparencies

5-Minute Check Transparency 13-6
Answer Key Transparencies

💿 Technology

Interactive Chalkboard

b. $y = x^2 - 1$

x	$x^2 - 1$	(x, y)
-2	$(-2)^2 - 1 = 3$	$(-2, 3)$
-1	$(-1)^2 - 1 = 0$	$(-1, 0)$
0	$(0)^2 - 1 = -1$	$(0, -1)$
1	$(1)^2 - 1 = 0$	$(1, 0)$
2	$(2)^2 - 1 = 3$	$(2, 3)$

c. $y = -x^2 + 3$

x	$-x^2 + 3$	(x, y)
-2	$-(-2)^2 + 3 = -1$	$(-2, -1)$
-1	$-(-1)^2 + 3 = 2$	$(-1, 2)$
0	$-(0)^2 + 3 = 3$	$(0, 3)$
1	$-(1)^2 + 3 = 2$	$(1, 2)$
2	$-(2)^2 + 3 = -1$	$(2, -1)$

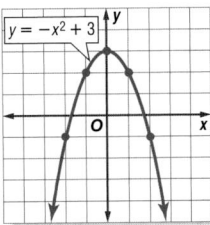

You can also write a rule from a verbal description of a function, and then graph.

Example 2 Use a Function to Solve a Problem

• **SKYDIVING** The distance in feet that a skydiver falls is equal to sixteen times the time squared, with the time given in seconds. Graph this function and estimate how far he will fall in 4.5 seconds.

Words   Distance is equal to sixteen times the time squared.

Variables   Let d = the distance in feet and t = the time in seconds.

Distance	is equal to	sixteen	times	the time squared.
d	$=$	16	$\cdot$	t^2

Equation

The equation is $d = 16t^2$. Since the variable t has an exponent of 2, this function is nonlinear. Now graph $d = 16t^2$. Since time cannot be negative, use only positive values of t.

t	$d = 16t^2$	(t, d)
0	$16(0)^2 = 0$	$(0, 0)$
1	$16(1)^2 = 16$	$(1, 16)$
2	$16(2)^2 = 64$	$(2, 64)$
3	$16(3)^2 = 144$	$(3, 144)$
4	$16(4)^2 = 256$	$(4, 256)$
5	$16(5)^2 = 400$	$(5, 400)$
6	$16(6)^2 = 576$	$(6, 576)$

By looking at the graph, we find that in 4.5 seconds, the skydiver will fall approximately 320 feet. You could find the exact distance by substituting 4.5 for t in the equation $d = 16t^2$.

More About...

Skydiving •
Skydivers fall at a speed of 110–120 miles per hour.
Source: www.aviation.about.com

---

2 Teach

QUADRATIC FUNCTIONS

In-Class Examples Power Point®

1 Graph each function.

a. $y = -2x^2$

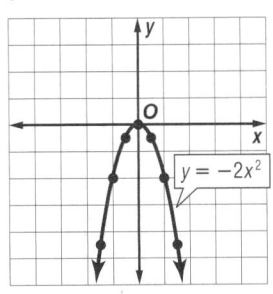

b. $y = \dfrac{x^2}{2} + 1$

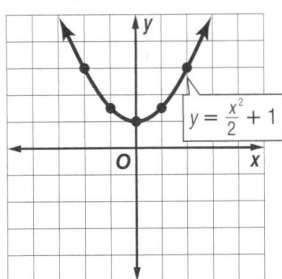

c. $y = -x^2 - 3$

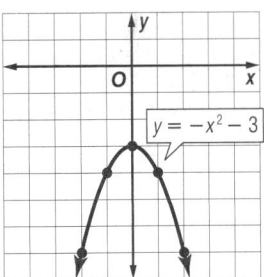

2 **GEOMETRY** The height of a triangle is 4 times its base. Write a formula for the area and graph it. Find the area of the triangle whose base is 3 units. $A = 2b^2$; 18 units²

DAILY INTERVENTION

Unlocking Misconceptions

• **Graphs of Quadratic Equations** Point out to students that not all quadratic equations have graphs that curve upward or downward. Equations like $x = y^2$ are quadratic but not quadratic functions. Their graphs open to the right or to the left.

CUBIC FUNCTIONS

Teaching Tip Remind students that a negative number cubed is also negative.

3 Graph each function.

a. $y = \dfrac{-x^3}{2}$

$y = -\dfrac{x^3}{2}$

b. $y = 2x^3 + 2$

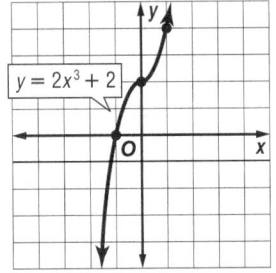

$y = 2x^3 + 2$

Study Notebook

Have students—

• explain how the graph of the equation $y = x^2 - 8$ compares to the graph of the equation $y = x^2$.

• include any other item(s) that they find helpful in mastering the skills in this lesson.

CUBIC FUNCTIONS You can also graph cubic functions such as the formula for the volume of a cube by making a table of values.

Example 3 Graph Cubic Functions

Graph each function.

a. $y = x^3$

x	$y = x^3$	(x, y)
-1.5	$(-1.5)^3 \approx -3.4$	$(-1.5, -3.4)$
-1	$(-1)^3 = -1$	$(-1, -1)$
0	$(0)^3 = 0$	$(0, 0)$
1	$(1)^3 = 1$	$(1, 1)$
1.5	$(1.5)^3 \approx 3.4$	$(1.5, 3.4)$

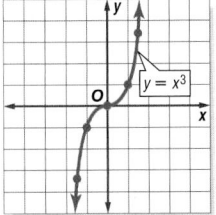

$y = x^3$

b. $y = x^3 - 1$

x	$y = x^3 - 1$	(x, y)
-1.5	$(-1.5)^3 - 1 \approx -4.4$	$(-1.5, -4.4)$
-1	$(-1)^3 - 1 = -2$	$(-1, -2)$
0	$(0)^3 - 1 = -1$	$(0, -1)$
1	$(1)^3 - 1 = 0$	$(1, 0)$
1.5	$(1.5)^3 - 1 \approx 2.4$	$(1.5, 2.4)$

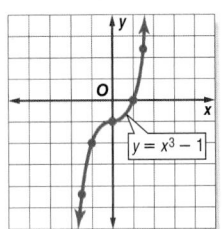

$y = x^3 - 1$

GUIDED PRACTICE KEY

Exercises	Examples
4–9	1, 3
10	2

Check for Understanding

Concept Check

1. Sample answer: The graph of $y = nx^2$ has line symmetry and the graph of $y = nx^3$ does not.

1. Describe one difference between the graph of $y = nx^2$ and the graph of $y = nx^3$ for any rational number n.

2. Explain how to determine whether a function is quadratic. **See margin.**

3. OPEN ENDED Write a quadratic function and explain how to graph it. **Sample answer:** $y = x^2 + 3$; make a table of values and plot the points.

Guided Practice Graph each function. **4–5. See margin. 6–9. See pp. 703A–703D.**

4. $y = x^2$ **5.** $y = -2x^2$ **6.** $y = x^2 + 1$

7. $y = -x^3$ **8.** $y = 0.5x^3$ **9.** $y = x^3 - 2$

Application   **10. GEOMETRY** A cube has edges measuring a units.

　　a. Write a quadratic equation for the surface area S of the cube. $S = 6a^2$

　　b. Graph the surface area as a function of a. (*Hint:* Use values of a like 0, 0.5, 1, 1.5, 2, and so on.) **See pp. 703A–703D.**

★ indicates increased difficulty

Practice and Apply

Graph each function. **11–22. See pp. 703A–703D.**

11. $y = 3x^2$ **12.** $y = 0.5x^2$ **13.** $y = -x^2$

14. $y = 3x^3$ **15.** $y = -2x^3$ **16.** $y = -0.5x^2$

17. $y = 2x^3$ **18.** $y = 0.1x^3$ **19.** $y = x^3 + 1$

20. $y = x^2 - 3$ ★ **21.** $y = \dfrac{1}{2}x^2 + 1$ ★ **22.** $y = \dfrac{1}{3}x^3 + 2$

694 Chapter 13 Polynomials and Nonlinear Functions

Answers

2. Sample answer: A function is quadratic if its equation contains one independent variable whose greatest exponent is 2.

4.

$y = x^2$

5.

$y = -2x^2$

23. See margin.

23. Graph $y = x^2 - 4$ and $y = -4x^3$. Are these equations functions? Explain.

24. Graph $y = x^2$ and $y = x^3$ in the first quadrant on the same coordinate plane. Explain which graph shows faster growth. **See margin for graph. For $x > 1$, $y = x^3$ shows faster growth; the graph has a steeper upward slope.**

The *maximum point* of a graph is the point with the greatest y value coordinate. The *minimum point* is the point with the least y value coordinate. Find the coordinates of each point.

25. the maximum point of the graph of $y = -x^2 + 7$ **(0, 7)**

26. the minimum point of the graph of $y = x^2 - 6$ **(0, -6)**

Graph each pair of equations on the same coordinate plane. Describe their similarities and differences. 27–30. See pp. 703A–703D for graphs.

27. Similar shape; $y = 3x^2$ is more narrow.

28. Similar shape; $y = 2x^3$ is more narrow.

29. Same shape; $y = -2x^2$ is $y = 2x^2$ reflected over the x-axis.

30. Same shape; $y = x^3 - 3$ is translated 3 units down from $y = x^3$.

27. $y = x^2$
$y = 3x^2$

28. $y = 0.5x^3$
$y = 2x^3$

29. $y = 2x^2$
$y = -2x^2$

30. $y = x^3$
$y = x^3 - 3$

CONSTRUCTION For Exercises 31–33, use the information below and the figure at the right.
A dog trainer is building a dog pen with a 100-foot roll of chain link fence.

x ft
50 − x ft

★ **31.** Write an equation to represent the area A of the pen. $A = 50x - x^2$

★ **32.** Graph the equation you wrote in Exercise 31. **See pp. 703A–703D.**

★ **33.** What should the dimensions of the dog pen be to enclose the maximum area inside the fence? (*Hint:* Find the coordinates of the maximum point of the graph.) **25 ft by 25 ft**

GEOMETRY Write a function for each of the following. Then graph the function in the first quadrant. 34–35. See pp. 703A–703D for graphs.

★ **34.** the volume V of a rectangular prism as a function of a fixed height of 2 units and a square base of varying lengths s $V = 2s^2$

★ **35.** the volume V of a cylinder as a function of a fixed height of 0.2 unit and radius r $V = 0.2\pi r^2$ or $V \approx 0.6r^2$

36. The solutions are the x-intercepts of the graph.

36. CRITICAL THINKING Describe how you can find real number solutions of the quadratic equation $ax^2 + bx + c = 0$ from the graph of the quadratic function $y = ax^2 + bx + c$.

37. WRITING IN MATH   Answer the question that was posed at the beginning of the lesson. **See pp. 703A–703D.**

How are functions, formulas, tables, and graphs related?

Include the following in your answer:
• an explanation of how to make a graph by using a rule, and
• an explanation of how to write a rule by using a graph.

Standardized Test Practice
Ⓐ Ⓑ Ⓒ Ⓓ

38. Which equation represents the graph at the right? **C**

Ⓐ $y = 4x^2$

Ⓑ $y = -4x^2$

Ⓒ $y = 4x^3$

Ⓓ $y = -4x^3$

About the Exercises . . .
Organization by Objective
• **Quadratic Functions:** 11–13, 16, 20, 21, 27, 29, 31–35
• **Cubic Functions:** 14, 15, 17–19, 22, 28, 30

Odd/Even Assignments
Exercises 11–30 are structured so that students practice the same concepts whether they are assigned odd or even problems.

Assignment Guide
Basic: 11–19 odd, 23–29 odd, 36–39, 42–48
Average: 11–29 odd, 36–39, 42–48 (Optional: 40, 41)
Advanced: 12–36 even, 37–48

Answers

23.

Both equations are functions because every value of x is paired with a unique value of y.

24.

---

39. For a certain frozen pizza, as the cost goes from \$2 to \$4, the demand can be modeled by the formula $y = -10x^2 + 60x + 180$, where x represents the cost and y represents the number of pizzas sold. Estimate the cost that will result in the greatest demand. **C**

A. \$0
B. \$2
C. \$3
D. \$8

Extending the Lesson Just as you can estimate the area of irregular figures, you can also estimate the area under a curve that is graphed on the coordinate plane. Estimate the shaded area under each curve to the nearest square unit.

40–41. Sample answers are given.

40. $y = -\frac{1}{2}x^2 + 3x - \frac{1}{2}$ **15 units²**

41. 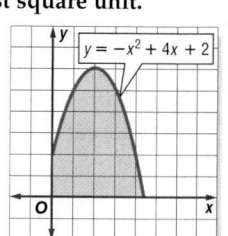 $y = -x^2 + 4x + 2$ **18 units²**

Maintain Your Skills

Mixed Review

42. **SCIENCE** The graph shows how water vapor pressure increases as the temperature increases. Is this relationship linear or nonlinear? Explain. *(Lesson 13-5)*
Nonlinear; the points on the graph do not lie on a straight line.

Water Vapor Pressure

Find each product. *(Lesson 13-4)*

43. $(2x - 4)5$ **$10x - 20$**
44. $n(n + 6)$ **$n^2 + 6n$**
45. $3y(8 - 7y)$ **$24y - 21y^2$**

Write an equation in slope-intercept form for the line passing through each pair of points. *(Lesson 8-7)*

46. $(3, 6)$ and $(0, 9)$
$y = -x + 9$

47. $(2, 5)$ and $(-1, -7)$
$y = 4x - 3$

48. $(-4, -3)$ and $(8, 6)$
$y = \frac{3}{4}x$

 WebQuest Internet Project

Family Farms
It is time to complete your project. Use the information and data you have gathered to prepare a Web page about farming or ranching in the United States. Be sure to include at least five graphs or tables that show statistics about farming or ranching and at least one scatter plot that shows a farming or ranching statistic over time, from which you can make predictions.

www.pre-alg.com/webquest

---

4 Assess

Open-Ended Assessment

Writing Have students write a paragraph explaining how the shape of the graph of $y = x^2$ differs from the graph of $y = x^3$.

Assessment Options

Quiz (Lesson 13-6) is available on p. 778 of the *Chapter 13 Resource Masters*.

Graphing Calculator Investigation

A Follow-Up of Lesson 13-6

NEW YORK *Performance Indicator* **8.G.21** Recognize the characteristics of quadratics in tables, graphs, equations and situations

Families of Quadratic Functions

A quadratic function can be described by an equation of the form $ax^2 + bx + c$, where $a \neq 0$. The graph of a quadratic function is called a **parabola**. Recall that families of linear graphs share the same slope or y-intercept. Similarly, families of parabolas share the same maximum or minimum point, or have the same shape.

Graph $y = x^2$ and $y = x^2 + 4$ on the same screen and describe how they are related.

Step 1 *Enter the function $y = x^2$.*

- Enter $y = x^2$ as Y1.
  KEYSTROKES: Y= | X,T,θ,n | x² | ENTER

Step 2 *Enter the function $y = x^2 + 4$.*

- Enter $y = x^2 + 4$ as Y2.
  KEYSTROKES: Y= | X,T,θ,n | x² | + | 4
  ENTER

Step 3 *Graph both quadratic functions on the same screen.*

- Display the graph.
  KEYSTROKES: ZOOM 6

The first function graphed is Y1 or $y = x^2$. The second is Y2 or $y = x^2 + 4$. Press TRACE and move along each function by using the right and left arrow keys. Move from one function to another by using the up and down arrow keys.

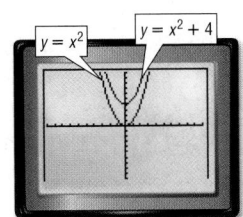

$y = x^2$ $y = x^2 + 4$

The graphs are similar in that they are both parabolas. However, the graph of $y = x^2$ has its vertex at $(0, 0)$, whereas the graph of $y = x^2 + 4$ has its vertex at $(0, 4)$.

Exercises 3. $y = x^2 - 8$, $y = x^2 + 1$, $y = x^2 + 6$

1. Graph $y = x^2$, $y = x^2 - 5$, and $y = x^2 - 3$ on the same screen and draw the parabolas on grid paper. Compare and contrast the three parabolas. **See pp. 703A–703D.**

2. **Make a conjecture** about how adding or subtracting a constant c affects the graph of a quadratic function. **It shifts the graph vertically c units.**

3. The three parabolas at the right are graphed in the standard viewing window and have the same shape as the graph of $y = x^2$. Write an equation for each, beginning with the lowest parabola.

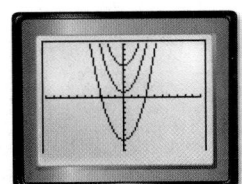

4. Clear all functions from the Y= menu. Enter $y = 0.4x^2$ as Y1, $y = x^2$ as Y2, and $y = 3x^2$ as Y3. Graph the functions in the standard viewing window on the same screen. Then draw the graphs on the same coodinate grid. How does the shape of the parabola change as the coefficient of x^2 increases? **See pp. 703A–703D for graphs.**
As the coefficient of x^2 increases, the parabola is narrower.
www.pre-alg.com/other_calculator_keystrokes

Graphing Calculator Investigation   697

Graphing Calculator Investigation

A Follow-Up of Lesson 13-6

Getting Started

Know Your Calculator In order for the graphs to display correctly, students may need to adjust the calculator settings. Have students use the arrow keys to place the cursor on any plot currently high-lighted, then press ENTER.

Graph Modes The mode settings determine what type of graph will result. If students' displays do not match those shown on this page, check that their mode settings are the following, in order from top to bottom: **Normal, Float, Radian, Func, Connected, Sequential, Real,** and **Full.**

Teach

- Before beginning Step 1, and again before doing Exercise 1, students should clear all functions from the Y= list.

- As students work through Step 3, you may wish to show them the TABLE function. Have them key in 2nd TBLSET and enter TblStart=0 and ΔTbl=.5. Then have them press 2nd TABLE and use the up and down arrows to explore the points of the two graphs.

- Have students complete Exercises 1–4.

Assess

After students answer Exercises 1–4, ask how the shape of the parabola would change if the coefficient of x^2 were $\frac{1}{2}$. Have them make a generalization to describe this.

The parabola would become wider; as the coefficient of x^2 decreases, the parabola becomes wider.

Chapter 13 Study Guide and Review

Vocabulary and Concept Check

- This alphabetical list of vocabulary terms in Chapter 13 includes a page reference where each term was introduced.

- **Assessment** A vocabulary review/test for Chapter 13 is available on p. 776 of the *Chapter 13 Resource Masters*.

Lesson-by-Lesson Review

For each lesson,

- the main ideas are summarized,
- additional examples review concepts, and
- practice exercises are provided.

Vocabulary PuzzleMaker

ELL The Vocabulary PuzzleMaker software improves students' mathematics vocabulary using four puzzle formats—crossword, scramble, word search using a word list, and word search using clues. Students can work on a computer screen or from a printed handout.

MindJogger Videoquizzes

ELL MindJogger Videoquizzes provide an alternative review of concepts presented in this chapter. Students work in teams in a game show format to gain points for correct answers. The questions are presented in three rounds.

Round 1 Concepts (5 questions)
Round 2 Skills (4 questions)
Round 3 Problem Solving (4 questions)

Vocabulary and Concept Check

binomial (p. 669)	nonlinear function (p. 687)	quadratic function (p. 688)
cubic function (p. 688)	polynomial (p. 669)	trinomial (p. 669)
degree (p. 670)		

Choose the correct term to complete each sentence.

1. A (binomial, <u>trinomial</u>) is the sum or difference of three monomials.
2. Monomials that contain the same variables with the same (<u>power</u>, sign) are like terms.
3. The function $y = 2x^3$ is an example of a (<u>cubic</u>, quadratic) function.
4. The equation $y = x^2 + 5x + 1$ is an example of a (cubic, <u>quadratic</u>) function.
5. x^2 and $4x^2$ are examples of (binomials, <u>like terms</u>).
6. The equation $y = 4x^3 + x^2 + 2$ is an example of a (quadratic, <u>cubic</u>) function.
7. The graph of a quadratic function is a (straight line, <u>curve</u>).
8. To multiply a polynomial and a monomial, use the (<u>Distributive</u>, Commutative) Property.

Lesson-by-Lesson Review

13-1 Polynomials

See pages 669–672.

Concept Summary

- A polynomial is an algebraic expression that contains one or more monomials.
- A binomial has two terms and a trinomial has three terms.
- The degree of a monomial is the sum of the exponents of its variables.

Example State whether $x^3 - 2xy$ is a *monomial, binomial,* or *trinomial.* **Then find the degree.**

The expression is the difference of two monomials. So it is a binomial. x^3 has degree 3, and $-2xy$ has degree $1 + 1$ or 2. So, the degree of $x^3 - 2xy$ is 3.

Exercises Determine whether each expression is a polynomial. If it is, classify it as a *monomial, binomial,* or *trinomial.* *See Example 1 on page 669.*

9. $c^2 + 3$ **yes; bi.** 10. -5 **yes; mono.** 11. $4t^4$ **yes; mono.** 12. $\frac{6}{a} + b$ **no**

13. $3x^2 + 4x - 2$ **yes; trinomial** 14. $x + y$ **yes; bi.** 15. $\sqrt{n}$ **no** 16. $1 + 3x + 5x^2$ **yes; trinomial**

Find the degree of each polynomial. *See Examples 2 and 3 on page 670.*

17. $2x$ **1** 18. $5xy$ **2** 19. $3a^2b$ **3** 20. $n^2 - 4$ **2**

21. $x^6 + y^6$ **6** 22. $2xy + 6yz^2$ **3** 23. $2x^5 + 9x + 1$ **5** 24. $x^2 + xy^2 - y^4$ **4**

 www.pre-alg.com/vocabulary_review

Study Organizer

For more information about Foldables, see *Teaching Mathematics with Foldables.*

Have students refer to their Foldable journals for Chapter 13 to review concepts before beginning the Study Guide and Review or while preparing for the Chapter Test.

13-2 Adding Polynomials

See pages 674–677.

Concept Summary

- To add polynomials, add like terms.

Example Find $(5x^2 - 8x + 2) + (x^2 + 6x)$.

$$5x^2 - 8x + 2$$
$$(+) \quad x^2 + 6x \quad \text{Align like terms.}$$
$$\overline{6x^2 - 2x + 2} \quad \text{Add.}$$

The sum is $6x^2 - 2x + 2$.

Exercises Find each sum. *See Example 1 on pages 674 and 675.*

25. $\quad 3b + 8 \quad$ **$8b + 3$**
    $\quad (+) \; 5b - 5$

26. $\quad 2x^2 + 3x - 4 \quad$ **26. $8x^2 + 2x + 1$**
    $\quad (+) \; 6x^2 - \;\; x + 5$

27. $\quad 4y^2 + 2y + 3 \quad$ **27. $5y^2 + 2y - 4$**
    $\quad (+) \; y^2 \qquad - 7$

28. $(9m - 3n) + (10m + 4n)$ **$19m + n$**

29. $(-3y^2 + 2) + (4y^2 - y - 3)$ **$y^2 - y - 1$**

13-3 Subtracting Polynomials

See pages 678–681.

Concept Summary

- To subtract polynomials, subtract like terms or add the additive inverse.

Example Find $(4x^2 + 7x + 4) - (x^2 + 2x + 1)$.

$$4x^2 + 7x + 4$$
$$(-) \quad x^2 + 2x + 1 \quad \text{Align like terms.}$$
$$\overline{3x^2 + 5x + 3} \quad \text{Subtract.}$$

The difference is $3x^2 + 5x + 3$.

30. $-2a^2 + 25$ 31. $3x^2 - 4x + 7$ 32. $16y^2 + 3y - 7$

Exercises Find each difference. *See Examples 1 and 2 on pages 678 and 679.*

30. $\quad a^2 + 15$
    $\quad (-) \, 3a^2 - 10$

31. $\quad 4x^2 - 2x + 3$
    $\quad (-) \;\; x^2 + 2x - 4$

32. $\quad 18y^2 + 3y - 1$
    $\quad (-) \; 2y^2 + \qquad + 6$

33. $(x + 8) - (2x + 7)$ **$-x + 1$**

34. $(3n^2 + 7) - (n^2 - n + 4)$ **$2n^2 + n + 3$**

13-4 Multiplying a Polynomial by a Monomial

See pages 683–686.

Concept Summary

- To multiply a polynomial and a monomial, use the Distributive Property.

Example Find $-3x(x + 8y)$.

$$-3x(x + 8y) = -3x(x) + (-3x)(8y) \quad \text{Distributive Property}$$
$$= -3x^2 - 24xy \quad \text{Simplify.}$$

Exercises Find each product. *See Example 1 on page 683.*

35. $5(4t - 2)$ **$20t - 10$**   36. $(2x + 3y)7$ **$14x + 21y$**   37. $k(6k + 3)$ **$6k^2 + 3k$**

38. $4d(2d - 5)$ **$8d^2 - 20d$**   39. $-2a(9 - a^2)$ 40. $6(2x^2 + xy + 3y^2)$

39. **$-18a + 2a^3$**   40. **$12x^2 + 6xy + 18y^2$**

Study Guide and Review

Chapter 13 For More ...
- Extra Practice, see pages 755–757.
- Mixed Problem Solving, see page 770.

Answers

44.

45.

46.

47.

48.

13-5 Linear and Nonlinear Functions

See pages 687–691.

Concept Summary

- Nonlinear functions do not have constant rates of change.

Example Determine whether each graph, equation, or table represents a *linear* or *nonlinear* function. Explain.

a.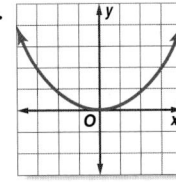

Nonlinear; graph is not a straight line.

b. $y = x + 12$

Linear; equation can be written as $y = mx + b$.

c.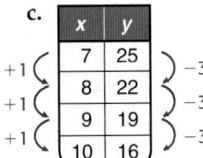

Linear; rate of change is constant.

Exercises Determine whether each graph, equation, or table represents a *linear* or *nonlinear* function. Explain. *See Examples 1–3 on pages 687 and 688.*

41.

42. $y = \dfrac{x}{2}$ Linear; equation can be written as $y = \dfrac{1}{2}x + 0$.

Linear; graph is a straight line.

43.

x	y
-6	3
-4	4
-2	6
0	9

Nonlinear; rate of change is not constant.

13-6 Graphing Quadratic and Cubic Functions

See pages 692–696.

Concept Summary

- Quadratic and cubic functions can be graphed by plotting points.

Example Graph $y = -x^2 + 3$.

x	$y = -x^2 + 3$	(x, y)
-2	$-(-2)^2 + 3 = -1$	(-2, -1)
-1	$-(-1)^2 + 3 = 2$	(-1, 2)
0	$-(0)^2 + 3 = 3$	(0, 3)
1	$-(1)^2 + 3 = 2$	(1, 2)
2	$-(2)^2 + 3 = -1$	(2, -1)

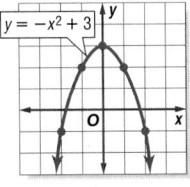

Exercises Graph each function. *See Examples 1 and 3 on pages 692–694.*

44. $y = x^2 + 2$
45. $y = -3x^2$
46. $y = x^3 - 2$
47. $y = x^3 + 1$
48. $y = -x^3$
49. $y = 2x^2 + 4$

44–49. See margin.

49.

Vocabulary and Concepts

1. **Define** polynomial. **an algebraic expression that contains one or more monomials**
2. **Explain** how the degree of a monomial is found. **Add the exponents of the variables.**
3. **OPEN ENDED** Draw the graph of a linear and a nonlinear function. **See students' drawings; the linear function should be a straight line and the nonlinear function should be a curve.**

Skills and Applications

Determine whether each expression is a polynomial. If it is, classify it as a *monomial*, *binomial*, or *trinomial*.

4. $3x^3 - 2x + 7$ **yes; trinomial**   5. $6 + \dfrac{5}{m}$ **no**   6. $\dfrac{3}{5}p^4$ **yes; monomial**

Find the degree of each polynomial.

7. $5ab^3$ **4**

8. $w^5 - 3w^3y^4 + 1$ **7**

Find each sum or difference. 11. $4m^3 - 2m^2 + 5m - 5$

9. $(5y + 8) + (-2y + 3)$ **$3y + 11$**

10. $(5a - 2b) + (-4a + 5b)$ **$a + 3b$**

11. $(-3m^3 + 5m - 9) + (7m^3 - 2m^2 + 4)$

12. $(6p + 5) - (3p - 8)$ **$3p + 13$**

13. $(5w - 3x) - (6w + 4x)$ **$-w - 7x$**

14. $(-2s^2 + 4s - 7) - (6s^2 - 7s - 9)$ **$-8s^2 + 11s + 2$**

Find each product.

15. $x(3x - 5)$ **$3x^2 - 5x$**

16. $-5a(a^2 - b^2)$ **$-5a^3 + 5ab^2$**

17. $6p(-2p^2 + 3p - 4)$
$-12p^3 + 18p^2 - 24p$

Determine whether each graph, equation, or table represents a *linear* or *nonlinear* function. Explain.

18.
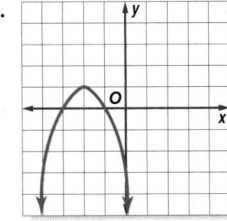

19. $5x - 6y = 2$ **Linear; equation can be written as $y = \dfrac{5}{6}x - \dfrac{1}{3}$.**

20.

x	y
1	10
3	7
5	3
7	-2

Nonlinear; rate of change is not constant.

Nonlinear; graph is a curve.

Graph each function. 21–23. See pp. 703A–703D.

21. $y = 2x^2$

22. $y = \dfrac{1}{2}x^3$

23. $y = -x^2 + 3$

24. **GEOMETRY** Refer to the rectangle.
   a. Write an expression for the perimeter of the rectangle. **$2x + 6$ in.**
   b. Find the value of x if the perimeter is 14 inches. **4**

$3x - 9$ in.
$12 - 2x$ in.

25. **STANDARDIZED TEST PRACTICE** The length of a garden is equal to 5 less than four times its width. The perimeter of the garden is 40 feet. Find the length of the garden. **D**
   (A) 1 ft   (B) 5 ft   (C) 10 ft   (D) 15 ft

Assessment Options

Vocabulary Test A vocabulary review/test for Chapter 13 can be found on p. 776 of the *Chapter 13 Resource Masters*.

Chapter Tests There are six Chapter 13 Tests and an Open-Ended Assessment task available in the *Chapter 13 Resource Masters*.

Chapter 13 Tests			
Form	Type	Level	Pages
1	MC	basic	763–764
2A	MC	average	765–766
2B	MC	average	767–768
2C	FR	average	769–770
2D	FR	average	771–772
3	FR	advanced	773–774

MC = multiple-choice questions
FR = free-response questions

Open-Ended Assessment
Performance tasks for Chapter 13 can be found on p. 775 of the *Chapter 13 Resource Masters*, along with a sample scoring rubric for these tasks on p. A22.

Unit 5 Test A unit test/review can be found on pp. 783–784 of the *Chapter 13 Resource Masters*.

End-of-Year Tests A Second Semester Test for Chapters 6–13 and a **Final Test** for Chapters 1–13 can be found on pp. 785–794 of the *Chapter 13 Resource Masters*.

ExamView® Pro

Use the networkable ExamView® Pro to:
- Create **multiple tests.**
- Create **modified** tests for *Inclusion* students.
- **Edit** existing questions and **add** your own questions.
- Use built-in **state curriculum correlations** to create tests aligned with state standards.
- Change **English** tests to **Spanish** and vice versa.

Portfolio Suggestion

Introduction Equations are used to solve many different types of problems. Sometimes special types of equations called formulas are used.

Ask Students to find a problem from their work in this chapter and explain how they used an equation or formula to solve it.

These two pages contain practice questions in the various formats that can be found on the most frequently given standardized tests.

A practice answer sheet for these two pages can be found on page A1 of the *Chapter 13 Resource Masters*.

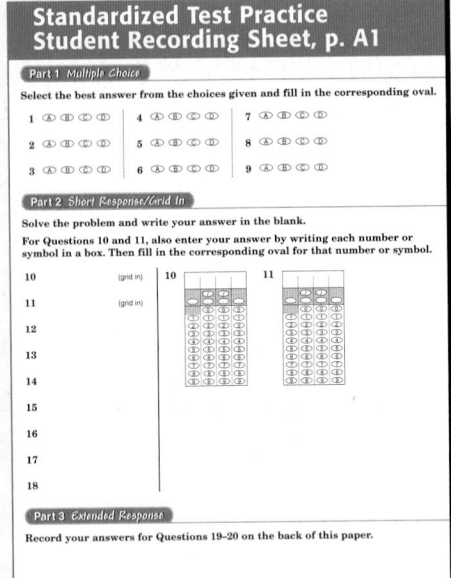

Additional Practice

• Additional Standardized Test Practice is available on pp. 781–782 of the Chapter 13 *Resource Masters*.

Part 1 Multiple Choice

Record your answers on the answer sheet provided by your teacher or on a sheet of paper.

1. If n represents a positive number, which of these expressions is equivalent to $n + n + n$? (Lesson 1-3) **B**

   (A) n^3 (B) $3n$

   (C) $n + 3$ (D) $3(n + 1)$

2. Connor sold 4 fewer tickets to the band concert than Miguel sold. Kylie sold 3 times as many tickets as Connor. If the number of tickets Miguel sold is represented by m, which of these expressions represents the number of tickets that Kylie sold? (Lesson 3-6) **D**

   (A) $m - 4$

   (B) $4 - 3m$

   (C) $3m - 4$

   (D) $3(m - 4)$

3. Melissa's family calculated that they drove an average of 400 miles per day during their three-day trip. They drove 460 miles on the first day and 360 miles on the second day. How many miles did they drive on the third day? (Lesson 5-7) **B**

   (A) 340   (B) 380

   (C) 410   (D) 420

4. What is the ratio of the length of a side of a square to its perimeter? (Lesson 6-1) **B**

   (A) $\dfrac{1}{16}$ (B) $\dfrac{1}{4}$

   (C) $\dfrac{1}{3}$ (D) $\dfrac{1}{2}$

Test-Taking Tip

Question 2
If you have time at the end of a test, go back to check your calculations and answers. If the test allows you to use a calculator, use it to check your calculations.

---

5. The table shows values of x and y, where x is proportional to y. What are the missing values, S and T? (Lesson 6-3) **B**

x	3	9	S
y	5	T	35

   (A) $S = 36$ and $T = 3$

   (B) $S = 21$ and $T = 15$

   (C) $S = 15$ and $T = 21$

   (D) $S = 3$ and $T = 36$

6. In the figure at the right, lines ℓ and m are parallel. Choose two angles whose measures have a sum of 180°. (Lesson 10-2) **C**

   (A) $\angle 1$ and $\angle 5$

   (B) $\angle 2$ and $\angle 8$

   (C) $\angle 2$ and $\angle 5$

   (D) $\angle 4$ and $\angle 8$

   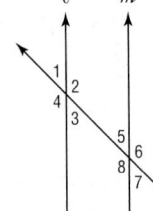

7. The point represented by coordinates $(4, -6)$ is reflected across the x-axis. What are the coordinates of the image? (Lesson 10-3) **D**

   (A) $(-6, 4)$ (B) $(-4, -6)$

   (C) $(-4, 6)$ (D) $(4, 6)$

8. If $2x^2 - 3x + 7$ is subtracted from $4x^2 + 6x - 3$, what is the difference? (Lesson 13-3) **A**

   (A) $2x^2 + 9x - 10$

   (B) $2x^2 + 3x + 4$

   (C) $-2x^2 + 3x + 4$

   (D) $-2x^2 - 9x + 10$

9. Which function includes all of the ordered pairs in the table? It may help you to sketch a graph of the points. (Lesson 13-6) **B**

x	-2	-1	1	2	3
y	4	2	-2	-4	-6

   (A) $y = -x^2$ (B) $y = -2x$

   (C) $y = -x + 2$ (D) $y = x^2$

ExamView® Pro

Special banks of standardized test questions similar to those on the SAT, ACT, TIMSS 8, NAEP 8, and Pre-Algebra End-of-Course tests can be found on this CD-ROM.

Part 2 Short Response/Grid In

Record your answers on the answer sheet provided by your teacher or on a sheet of paper.

10. The table shows the number of sandwiches sold during twenty lunchtimes. What is the mode?   (Lesson 5-8) **9**

Number of Sandwiches Sold				
9	8	10	14	12
16	9	7	10	11
11	8	9	8	7
12	14	8	9	9

11. One machine makes plastic containers at a rate of 360 containers per hour. A newer machine makes the same containers at a rate of 10 containers per minute. If both machines are run for four hours, how many containers will they make?   (Lesson 6-1) **3840**

12. What percent of 275 is 165?   (Lesson 6-5) **60%**

13. Mrs. Rosales can spend $8200 on equipment for the computer lab. Each computer costs $850 and each printer costs $325. Mrs. Rosales buys 8 computers. Write an inequality that can be used to find p, the number of printers she could buy.
(Lesson 7-6) **$8(850) + 325p \le 8200$**

14. What is the y-intercept of the graph shown at the right? Each square represents 1 unit.   (Lesson 8-6)
−3

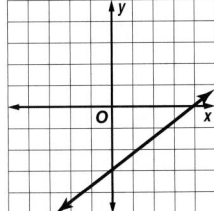

15. The area of a triangle is $\frac{1}{2}(b \times h)$. What is the area of the kite?   (Lesson 10-5)
315 in²

9 in.

35 in.

16. Brooke wants to fill her new aquarium two-thirds full of water. The aquarium dimensions are 20 inches by 20 inches by $8\frac{1}{2}$ inches. What volume of water, in cubic inches, is needed?   (Lesson 11-2) **about 2267 in³**

20 in.

20 in.

$8\frac{1}{2}$ in.

17. Let $s = 3x^2 - 2x - 1$ and $t = -2x^2 + x + 2$. Find $s + t$.   (Lesson 13-2) **$x^2 - x + 1$**

18. The perimeter of a soccer field is 1040 feet. The length of the field is 40 feet more than 2 times the width. What is the length of the field?   (Lesson 13-4) **360 ft**

Part 3 Extended Response

Record your answers on a sheet of paper. Show your work.

19. An artist created a sculpture using five cylindrical posts. Each post has a diameter of 12 inches. The heights of the posts are 6 feet, 5 feet, 4 feet, 3 feet, and 2 feet.   (Lesson 11-2)

  a. What is the total volume of all five posts? $V = \pi r^2 h$ is the formula for the volume of a cylinder. Use $\pi = 3.14$. **15.7 ft³**

  b. The posts are made of a material whose density is 12 pounds per cubic foot. How much does the sculpture weigh? **188.4 lb**

20. Refer to the table below.
(Lesson 13-6) **a–b. See margin.**

  a. Graph the ordered pairs in the table as coordinate points.

  b. Sketch a line or curve through the points.

  c. Write a quadratic function that includes all of the ordered pairs in the table.

$y = x^2 - 4$

x	y
−2	0
−1	−3
0	−4
1	−3
2	0

Chapter 13 Standardized Test Practice **703**

Evaluating Extended Response Questions

Extended Response questions are graded by using a multilevel rubric that guides you in assessing a student's knowledge of a particular concept.

Goal: Find volume and weight of a sculpture/Use a table of ordered pairs to draw a graph and write a quadratic function.

Sample Scoring Rubric: The following rubric is a sample scoring device. You may wish to add more detail to this sample to meet your individual scoring needs.

Score	Criteria
4	A correct solution that is supported by well-developed, accurate explanations
3	A generally correct solution, but may contain minor flaws in reasoning or computation
2	A partially correct interpretation and/or solution to the problem
1	A correct solution with no supporting evidence or explanation
0	An incorrect solution indicating no mathematical understanding of the concept or task, or no solution is given

Answer

20a–b.

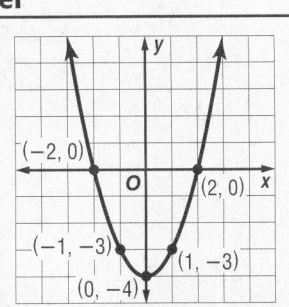

(−2, 0)

O

(2, 0)

(−1, −3)

(1, −3)

(0, −4)

Page 672, Lesson 13-1

49. Polynomials approximate real-world data by using variables to represent quantities that are related. Answers should include the following.

- Heat index is found by using a polynomial in which one variable represents the percent humidity and another variable represents the temperature.

- Heat index cannot be approximated using a linear equation because the values do not change at a constant rate.

57. $(x + 2x) + 4$

58. $(3x^2 + x^2) - 1$

59. $(6n + 3n) + (2 + 5)$

60. $(a + 3a) + (2b + b)$

61. $(s + 5s) + (t - 3t)$

62. $(x^2 + 7x^2) + (4x - 3x)$

Page 673, Algebra Activity

1.

2.

3.

4.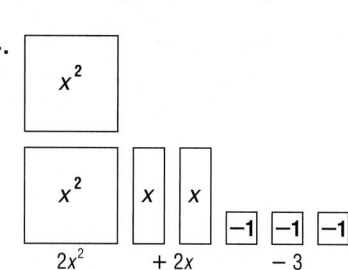

5. A monomial has tiles of one size, a binomial has tiles of two sizes, and a trinomial has tiles of three sizes.

Page 681, Lesson 13-3

29. In subtracting polynomials and in subtracting measurements, like parts are subtracted. Answers should include the following.

- To subtract measurements with two or more units, subtract the like units. To subtract polynomials with two or more terms, subtract the like terms.

- For example, to subtract 1 foot 5 inches from 3 feet 8 inches, subtract the feet $3 - 1$ and subtract the inches $8 - 5$. The difference is 2 feet 3 inches.

Page 682, Algebra Activity

1.

2.

3.

4.

5.

6.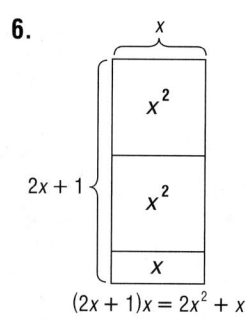

7. 2x

x^2	x^2
x^2	x^2
x	x
x	x
x	x
x	x

2x + 4

$(2x + 4)2x = 4x^2 + 8x$

8. 2x + 1

x^2	x^2	x
x^2	x^2	x
x^2	x^2	x

3x

$3x(2x + 1) = 6x^2 + 3x$

Page 689, Lesson 13-5

1. Sample answer: Determine whether an equation can be written in the form $y = mx + b$ or look for a constant rate of change in a table of values.

Page 690, Lesson 13-5

17. Equation can be written as $y = 0.9x + 0$.

18. Equation cannot be written as $y = mx + b$.

19. Equation can be written as $y = \frac{3}{4}x + 0$.

20. Equation can be written as $y = -\frac{2}{3}x + 4$.

21. Equation cannot be written as $y = mx + b$.

22. Equation cannot be written as $y = mx + b$.

23. Rate of change is constant.

24. Rate of change is not constant.

25. Rate of change is not constant.

26. Rate of change is constant.

28. No, a vertical line based on a rule such as $x = 3$ is not a function because there is more than one y value for the x value 3.

Page 691, Lesson 13-5

40.

41.

42.

43.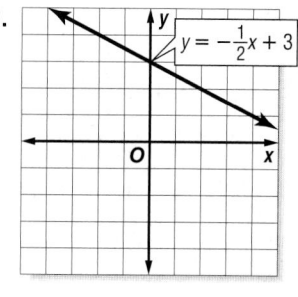

Page 694, Lesson 13-6

6.

7.

8.

9.

10b.

11.

12.

13.

14.

15.

16.

17.

18.

19.

20.

21.

22.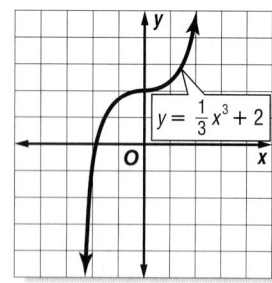

Page 695, Lesson 13-6

27.

28.

29.

30.

32.

34.

35.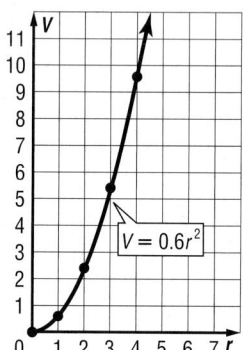

37. Formulas, tables, and graphs are interchangeable ways to represent functions. Answers should include the following.

- To make a graph, use a rule to make a table of values. Then plot the points and connect them to make a graph.

- To write a rule, find points that lie on a graph and make a table of values using the coordinates. Look for a pattern and write a rule that describes the pattern.

Page 697, Graphing Calculator Investigation

1.

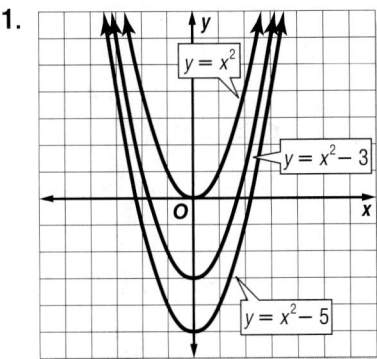

All the parabolas have the same shape. The graph of $y = x^2 - 5$ is shifted 5 units down from the graph of $y = x^2$. The graph of $y = x^2 - 3$ is shifted 3 units down from the graph of $y = x^2$.

4.

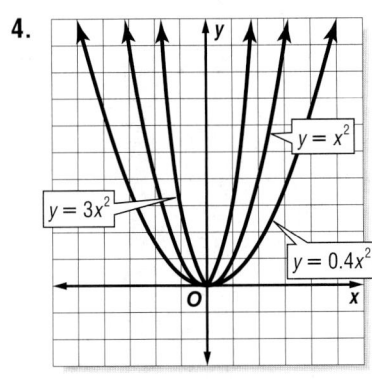

Page 701, Practice Test

21.

22.

23.

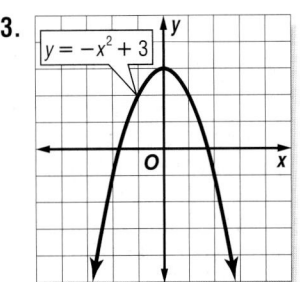

Student Handbook

Introduction to Matrices

Introduction
to Matrices

A **matrix** is a rectangular arrangement of numerical data in **rows** (horizontal) and **columns** (vertical) enclosed with brackets that visually organizes the information. Each number in a matrix is called an **element**. *Matrices* are identified by their **dimensions**, or the number of rows and columns, with the number of rows stated first. To display a data set in matrix form, sort the data into categories and assign those categories appropriate labels.

Example

Sue and Eva made a table of their science quiz grades during the grading period. Create a matrix organizing this information. Then state the dimensions of the matrix.

| Sue | B | C | A | B | A | B | A | C | B | A | B | C |
| Eva | A | B | B | A | A | C | B | B | A | A | B | B |

Sue received 4 A's, 5 B's, and 3 C's.
Eva received 5 A's, 6 B's, and 1 C.
Label the rows of the matrix with each girl's name and the columns with each letter grade. The dimensions of the resulting matrix are 2 by 3.

This matrix has 3 columns.

This matrix has 2 rows

$$\begin{array}{c} \\ \text{Sue} \\ \text{Eva} \end{array} \begin{array}{ccc} A & B & C \\ 4 & 5 & 3 \\ 5 & 6 & ① \end{array}$$

This element is in the second row and the third column.

2. 3 by 2; third row, first column   3. 4 by 3; second row, third column

State the dimensions of each matrix. Then identify the position of the circled element.

1. $\begin{bmatrix} 8 & 6 & 4 & ⊘2 \\ -3 & 7 & 2 & 1 \end{bmatrix}$
2 by 4; first row, fourth column

2. $\begin{bmatrix} -6 & 2 \\ 0 & -3 \\ ⑤ & -8 \end{bmatrix}$

3. $\begin{bmatrix} 14 & 10 & 11 \\ 9 & 7 & ⑮ \\ 16 & 4 & 10 \\ 21 & 17 & 13 \end{bmatrix}$

4. $\begin{bmatrix} -5 & 8 & -1 & 4 & ② & 7 \end{bmatrix}$
1 by 6; first row, fifth column

Create a matrix organizing each set of data. 5-7. See margin.

5. Three clubs participated in a fund-raiser. Club 1 sold 114 plain and 57 chocolate doughnuts. Club B sold 75 plain and 89 chocolate doughnuts. Club C sold 50 plain and 35 chocolate doughnuts.

6. At the end of the 2003 NFL regular season, the Steelers had 275 first downs, 33 touchdowns, and 23 field goals. The Bears had 264 first downs, 29 touchdowns, and 26 field goals. The Ravens had 258 first downs, 41 touchdowns, and 34 field goals. The Browns had 267 first downs, 27 touchdowns, and 23 field goals.

7. Three teammates either won (W), lost (L), or tied (T) each of 10 chess matches they played. The table indicates the results.

Hector	W	L	L	W	W	T	W	W	L	W
Tim	T	L	L	L	W	W	W	L	W	W
Malik	L	W	W	W	T	T	W	T	L	W

Introduction to Matrices 705

Answers

Sample Answers:

5.
	Plain	Chocolate
Club A	114	57
Club B	75	89
Club C	50	35

6.
	FD	TD	FG
Steelers	275	33	23
Bears	264	29	26
Ravens	258	41	31
Browns	267	27	23

7.
	W	L	T
Hector	6	3	1
Tim	5	4	1
Malik	5	2	3

Introduction
to Matrices

Intoduction to Matrices 705

Prerequisite Skills

1 Problem-Solving Strategy: Solve a Simpler Problem

One of the strategies you can use to solve a problem is to **solve a simpler problem**. To use this strategy, first solve a simpler or more familiar case of the problem. Then use the same concepts and relationships to solve the original problem.

Example 1 Find the sum of the numbers 1 through 500.

NEW YORK
Performance Indicator
8.PS.8 Understand how to break a complex problem into simpler parts or use a similar problem type to solve a problem

Consider a simpler problem. Find the sum of the numbers 1 through 10. Notice that you can group the addends into partial sums as shown below.

$$1 + 2 + 3 + 4 + 5 + 6 + 7 + 8 + 9 + 10 = 55$$

11
11
11
11
11

The number of sums is 5, or half the number of addends.

Each partial sum is 11, the sum of the first and last numbers.

The sum is 5×11 or 55.

Use the same concepts to find the sum of the numbers 1 through 500.

$$1 + 2 + 3 + \ldots + 499 + 500 = 250 \times 501$$
$$= 125{,}250$$

Multiply half the number of addends, 250, by the sum of the first and last numbers, 501.

A similar problem-solving strategy is to use subgoals.

Example 2 Two workers can make two chairs in two days. How many chairs can 8 workers working at the same rate make in 20 days?

First find how many chairs each worker can make in two days. Divide 2 chairs by 2 workers. ⟶ $2 \div 2 = 1$

So, each worker can make 1 chair in 2 days. To find how many chairs each worker can make in 20 days, divide 20 by 2. ⟶ $20 \div 2 = 10$

Now find how many chairs 8 workers can make by multiplying 8 by 10. ⟶ $8 \times 10 = 80$

So, 8 workers can make 80 chairs in 20 days.

Solve each problem by first solving a simpler problem.

1. Find the sum of the numbers 1 through 1000. **500,500**
2. Find the number of squares of any size in the game board shown at the right. **204 squares**
3. How many links are needed to join 30 pieces of chain into one long chain? **29 links**

Solve each problem by using subgoals.

4. Three people can pick six baskets of apples in one hour. How many baskets of apples can 12 people pick in one-half hour? **12 baskets**
5. A shirt shop has 112 orders for T-shirt designs. Three designers can make 12 shirts in 2 hours. How many designers are needed to complete the orders in 8 hours? **7 designers**

2 Problem-Solving Strategy: Work Backward

In most problems, a set of conditions or facts is given and an end result must be found. However, some problems start with the result and ask for something that happened earlier. The strategy of **working backward** can be used to solve problems like this. To use this strategy, start with the end result and *undo* each step.

Example

NEW YORK
Performance Indicator
S.9 Work backwards
m a solution

Paco spent half of the money he had this morning on lunch. After lunch, he loaned his friend a dollar. Now he has $1.50. How much money did Paco start with?

Start with the end result, $1.50, and work backward to find the amount Paco started with.

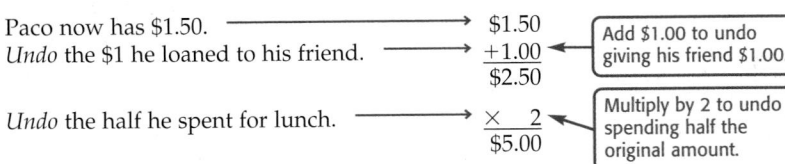

Paco now has $1.50.
Undo the $1 he loaned to his friend.

$1.50
$+1.00$ ← Add $1.00 to undo giving his friend $1.00.
$2.50

Undo the half he spent for lunch.

$\times\ \ 2$ ← Multiply by 2 to undo spending half the original amount.
$5.00

The amount Paco started with was $5.00.

CHECK Paco started with $5.00. If he spent half of that, or $2.50, on lunch and loaned his friend $1.00, he would have $1.50 left. This matches the amount stated in the problem, so the solution is correct.

Solve each problem by working backward.

1. Katie used half of her allowance to buy a ticket to the class play. Then she spent $1.75 for an ice cream cone. Now she has $2.25 left. How much is her allowance? **$8**

2. Michele put $15 of her paycheck in savings. Then she spent one-half of what was left on clothes. She paid $24 for a concert ticket and later spent one-half of what was then left on a book. When she got home, she had $14 left. What was the amount of Michele's paycheck? **$119**

3. A certain number is multiplied by 3, and then 5 is added to the result. The final answer is 41. What is the number? **12**

4. Mr. and Mrs. Jackson each own an equal number of shares of a stock. Mr. Jackson sells one-third of his shares for $2700. What was the total value of Mr. and Mrs. Jackson's stock before the sale? **$16,200**

5. A certain bacteria doubles its population every 12 hours. After 3 full days, there are 1600 bacteria in a culture. How many bacteria were there at the beginning of the first day? **25 bacteria**

6. Masao had some pieces of bubble gum. He gave one-fourth of the gum to Bob. Bob then gave half of his gum to Lisa. Lisa gave a third of her gum to Maria. If Maria has 3 pieces of gum, how many pieces of gum did Masao have in the beginning? **72 pieces**

7. To catch a 7:30 A.M. bus, Carla needs 30 minutes to get dressed, 30 minutes for breakfast, and 15 minutes to walk to the bus stop. What time should she wake up? **6:15 A.M.**

8. Justin rented three times as many DVDs as Cole last month. Cole rented four fewer than Maria, but four more than Paloma. Maria rented 10 DVDs. How many DVDs did each person rent? **Justin, 18; Cole, 6; Maria, 10; Paloma, 2**

3 Problem-Solving Strategy: Make a Table or List

One strategy for solving problems is to **make a table**. A table allows you to organize information in an understandable way.

Example 1 **A fruit machine accepts dollars, and each piece of fruit costs 65 cents. If the machine gives only nickels, dimes, and quarters, what combinations of those coins are possible as change for a dollar?**

The machine will give back $1.00 − $0.65 or 35 cents in change in a combination of nickels, dimes, and quarters.

NEW YORK
Performance Indicator

8.CM.4 Share organized mathematical ideas through the manipulation of objects, **numerical tables,** drawings, pictures, charts, graphs, **tables,** diagrams, models and symbols in written and verbal form

Make a table showing different combinations of nickels, dimes, and quarters that total 35 cents. Organize the table by starting with the combinations that include the most quarters.

The total for each combination of the coins is 35 cents. There are 6 combinations possible.

quarters	dimes	nickels
1	1	0
1	0	2
0	3	1
0	2	3
0	1	5
0	0	7

A similar strategy is to **list possibilities**. When you make a list, use an organized approach so you do not leave out important items.

Example 2 **How many ways can you receive change for a quarter if at least one coin is a dime?**

List the possibilities. Start with the ways that use the fewest number of coins.

1. dime, dime, nickel
2. dime, dime, 5 pennies
3. dime, nickel, nickel, nickel
4. dime, nickel, nickel, 5 pennies
5. dime, nickel, 10 pennies
6. dime, 15 pennies

There are 6 possibilities.

Solve each problem by making a table or list.

1. How many ways can you make change for a half-dollar using only nickels, dimes, and quarters? **10**

2. A number cube has faces numbered 1 to 6. If a red and a blue cube are tossed and the faces landing up are added, how many ways can you roll a sum less than 8? **21**

3. A penny, a nickel, a dime, and a quarter are in a purse. How many amounts of money are possible if you grab two coins at random? **6**

4. If the sides of a rectangular garden are whole numbers and the area of the garden is 48 square feet, how many combinations of side lengths are possible? **5**

5. Malcolm had 55 football cards. He traded 8 cards for 5 from Damon. He traded 6 more for 4 from Ines and 5 for 3 from Christopher. Finally, he traded 12 cards for 9 from Sam. How many cards does Malcolm have now? **45**

4 Problem-Solving Strategy: Guess and Check

To solve some problems, you can make a reasonable guess and then check it in the problem. You can then use the results to improve your guess until you find the solution. This strategy is called **guess and check**.

Example

NEW YORK
Performance Indicator

**S.5 Make
conjectures from
generalizations**

The product of two consecutive even integers is 1088. What are the integers?

The product is close to 1000.
Make a guess. Let's try 24 and 26. ⟶ $24 \times 26 = 624$ ← This product is too low.

Adjust the guess upward.
Try 30 and 32. ⟶ $30 \times 32 = 960$ ← This product is still too low.

Adjust the guess upward again.
Try 34 and 36. ⟶ $34 \times 36 = 1224$ ← This product is too high.

Try between 30 and 34.
Try 32 and 34. ⟶ $32 \times 34 = 1088$ ← This is the correct product.

The integers are 32 and 34.

Use the guess-and-check strategy to solve each problem.

1. The product of two consecutive odd integers is 783. What are the integers? **27, 29**

2. Paula is three times as old as Courtney. Four years from now she will be just two times as old as Courtney. How old are Paula and Courtney now? **12 and 4**

3. The product of a number and its next two consecutive whole numbers is 120. What is the number? **4**

4. Stamps for postcards cost $0.21, and stamps for first-class letters cost $0.34. Diego wants to send postcards and letters to 10 friends. If he has $2.75 for stamps, how many postcards and how many letters can he send? **5 postcards, 5 letters**

5. Each hand in the human body has 27 bones. There are 6 more bones in the fingers than in the wrist. There are 3 fewer bones in the palm than in the wrist. How many bones are in each part of the hand? **f: 14, w: 8, p: 5**

6. The Science Club sold candy bars and soft pretzels to raise money for an animal shelter. They raised a total of $62.75. They made 25¢ profit on each candy bar and 30¢ profit on each pretzel sold. How many of each did they sell? **Sample answer: 125 candy bars and 105 pretzels**

7. Luis has the same number of quarters, dimes, and nickels. In all he has $4 in change. How many of each coin does he have? **10**

8. Kelsey sold tickets to the school musical. She had 12 bills worth $175 for the tickets she sold. If all the money was in $5 bills, $10 bills, and $20 bills, how many of each bill did she have? **Sample answer: 3 $5-bills, 2 $10-bills, and 7 $20-bills**

9. You can buy standard-sized postcards in packages of 5 and large-sized postcards in packages of 3. How many packages of each should you buy if you need exactly 16 postcards? **two 5-card packages and two 3-card packages**

5 Comparing and Ordering Decimals

To determine which of two decimals is greater, you can compare the digits in each place-value position, or you can use a number line.

Method 1	Use place value.
	Line up the decimal points of the two numbers. Starting at the left, compare the digits in each place-value position. In the first position where the digits are different, the decimal with the greater digit is the greater decimal.
Method 2	Use a number line.
	Graph each number on a number line. On a number line, numbers to the right are greater than numbers to the left.

Example 1 Which is greater, 4.35 or 4.8?

Method 1 Use place value.

4.35   Line up the decimal points.
4.8   The digits in the tenths place are not the same.

8 tenths > 3 tenths, so 4.8 > 4.35.

Method 2 Use a number line.
Compare the decimals on a number line.

4.8 is to the right of 4.35. So 4.8 > 4.35.

Example 2 Order 0.8, 1.52, and 1.01 from least to greatest.
0.8 is less than both 1.52 and 1.01.
1.01 is less than 1.52.

Thus, the order from least to greatest is 0.8, 1.01, 1.52.

Replace each ● with < or > to make a true sentence.

1. 4.05 ● 4.45 <   **2.** 2.26 ● 2.28 <   **3.** 3.005 ● 3.05 <
4. 8.7 ● 82.1 <   **5.** 6.2 ● 6.008 >   **6.** 15.601 ● 16.9 <
7. 1.9 ● 1.96 <   **8.** 8.9 ● 7.99 >   **9.** 0.66 ● 0.582 >
10. 7.14 ● 7.2 <   **11.** 0.048 ● 0.11 <   **12.** 10.1 ● 1.01 >
13. 32.1 ● 3.215 >   **14.** 1.098 ● 2 <   **15.** 9.1 ● 9.005 >
16. 16.8 ● 16.791 >   **17.** 0.943 ● 0.4991 > **18.** 0.117 ● 0.95 <

Order each set of decimals from least to greatest.

19. {0.2, 0.01, 0.6} **0.01, 0.2, 0.6**
20. {1.2, 2.4, 0.04, 2.2} **0.04, 1.2, 2.2, 2.4**
21. {3.5, 0.6, 2.06, 0.28} **0.28, 0.6, 2.06, 3.5**
22. {0.8, 0.07, 1.001, 0.392} **0.07, 0.392, 0.8,**
23. {7.06, 7.026, 7.061, 7.009, 7.1}
      7.009, 7.026, 7.06, 7.061, 7.1
24. {0.82, 0.98, 0.103, 0.625, 0.809}
      0.103, 0.625, 0.809, 0.82, 0.98

6 Rounding Decimals

Rewriting a number to a certain place value is called **rounding**. Look at the digit to the right of the place being rounded.

- If the digit to the right is *less than or equal to* 4, the digit being rounded stays the same.

- If the digit to the right is *greater than or equal to* 5, the digit being rounded increases by one.

The place-value chart below shows how to round 3.81 to the nearest one (or whole number).

Tens	Ones	Tenths	Hundredths	Thousandths
	3 .	8	1	

- 3 is in the ones place

- 8 is to the right of 3

- $8 > 5$

So, 3.81 rounded to the nearest one (or whole number) is 4.

Example 1 Round each number to the nearest one (or whole number).

    a. 8.3
        8.3 rounds to 8.

    b. 9.6
        9.6 rounds to 10.

Example 2 Round each number to the nearest tenth.

    a. 16.08
        16.08 rounds to 16.1.

    b. 29.54
        29.54 rounds to 29.5.

Example 3 Round each number to the nearest hundredth.

    a. 50.345
        50.345 rounds to 50.35.

    b. 19.998
        19.998 rounds to 20.00.

Round each number to the nearest whole number.

1. 3.2 **3**
2. 64.8 **65**
3. 50.57 **51**
4. 16.08 **16**
5. 41.29 **41**
6. 38.726 **39**
7. 74.455 **74**
8. 86.299 **86**
9. 79.603 **80**

Round each number to the nearest tenth.

10. 16.57 **16.6**
11. 1.05 **1.1**
12. 43.827 **43.8**
13. 53.865 **53.9**
14. 80.349 **80.3**
15. 24.731 **24.7**
16. 49.5463 **49.5**
17. 131.9884 **132.0**
18. 68.3553 **68.4**

Round each number to the nearest hundredth.

19. 62.624 **62.62**
20. 44.138 **44.14**
21. 85.5639 **85.56**
22. 105.3582 **105.36**
23. 99.9862 **99.99**
24. 24.8715 **24.87**
25. 458.7625 **458.76**
26. 206.6244 **206.62**
27. 153.2965 **153.30**

Round each number to the nearest dollar.

28. $40.29 **$40**
29. $72.50 **$73**
30. $36.82 **$37**

7 Estimating Sums and Differences of Decimals

Estimation is often used to provide a quick and easy answer when an exact answer is not necessary. It is also an excellent way to quickly see if your answer is reasonable or not.

Example 1 Estimate each sum or difference to the nearest whole number.

a. $16.9 + 5.4$

$$\begin{array}{r} 16.9 \\ + 5.4 \end{array} \rightarrow \begin{array}{r} 17 \\ + 5 \\ \hline 22 \end{array}$$

Round to the nearest whole number.

b. $200.35 - 174.82$

$$\begin{array}{r} 200.35 \\ -174.82 \end{array} \rightarrow \begin{array}{r} 200 \\ -175 \\ \hline 25 \end{array}$$

Round to the nearest whole number.

You can also use rounding to estimate answers involving money.

Example 2 Estimate each sum or difference to the nearest dollar.

a. $\$67.07 + \$52.64 + \$0.85$

$$\begin{array}{r} \$67.07 \\ 52.64 \\ + \;\; 0.85 \end{array} \rightarrow \begin{array}{r} \$67.00 \\ 53.00 \\ + \;\; 1.00 \\ \hline \$121.00 \end{array}$$

Round to the nearest dollar.

b. $\$89.42 - \$8.94$

$$\begin{array}{r} \$89.42 \\ - \;\; 8.94 \end{array} \rightarrow \begin{array}{r} \$89.00 \\ - \;\; 9.00 \\ \hline \$80.00 \end{array}$$

Round to the nearest dollar.

NEW YORK——
Performance Indice
Reinforcement of 5.N.
Estimate sums,
differences, products,
and quotients **of**
decimals

Estimate each sum or difference to the nearest whole number.

1. $12.5 + 44.8$ **58**
2. $8.6 + 11.9$ **21**
3. $34.32 + 19.51$ **54**
4. $15.9 + 20.32$ **36**
5. $32 - 29.75$ **2**
6. $125.8 - 22.4$ **104**
7. $159.7 - 124.8$ **35**
8. $8.890 + 15.98$ **25**
9. $0.7 + 1.663$ **3**
10. $52.4 - 21.01$ **31**
11. $26.55 - 10$ **17**
12. $2.79 + 5.9 + 0.02$ **9**
13. $42.1 + 16.25 + 8.96$ **67**
14. $209.5 - 110$ **100**
15. $18 - 12.49$ **6**

Estimate each sum or difference to the nearest dollar.

16. $\$6.89 + \$1.20$ **$8**
17. $\$5.72 + \$4.35$ **$10**
18. $\$1.68 - \$0.99$ **$1**
19. $\$5.00 - \$2.56$ **$2**
20. $\$20.00 - \$15.34$ **$5**
21. $\$12.86 + \$3.33$ **$16**
22. $\$4.99 + \$3.29$ **$8**
23. $\$50.00 - \$39.89$ **$10**
24. $\$92.30 - \$40.00$ **$52**
25. $\$16.39 - \$11.80$ **$4**
26. $\$84.99 + \$5.52$ **$91**
27. $\$132.62 - \$45.81$ **$87**
28. $\$20.19 + \$3.60 + \$5.08$ **$29**
29. $\$4.80 + \$7.65 + \$2.59$ **$16**
30. $\$325.44 + \$125.10$ **$450**

31. Annual precipitation in Seattle, Washington, is about 37.19 inches. The city of Spokane receives only about 16.49 inches annually. About how much more precipitation does Seattle receive than Spokane? **about 21 in.**

32. The Adventure Club holds monthly aluminum can recycling drives. During the last three months, they collected $45.45, $45.19, and $44.95 from the drives. About how much did the club collect altogether? **about $135**

8 Adding and Subtracting Decimals

To add or subtract decimals, write the numbers in a column and line up the decimal points. Then add or subtract as with whole numbers, and bring down the decimal point.

Example 1 Find each sum or difference.

a. 8.2 + 3.4

$$\begin{array}{r} 8.2 \\ +\ 3.4 \\ \hline 11.6 \end{array}$$ Line up the decimal points. Then add.

b. 36.98 − 15.22

$$\begin{array}{r} 36.98 \\ -\ 15.22 \\ \hline 21.76 \end{array}$$ Line up the decimal points. Then subtract.

In some cases, you may want to *annex*, or place zeros at the end of the decimals, to help align the columns. Then add or subtract.

NEW YORK
Performance Indicator

Reinforcement of 5.N.23 Use a variety of strategies to add, subtract, multiply, and divide **decimals to thousandths**

Example 2 Find each sum or difference.

a. 21.43 + 5.2

$$\begin{array}{r} 21.43 \\ +\ 5.2 \end{array} \rightarrow \begin{array}{r} 21.43 \\ +\ 5.20 \\ \hline 26.63 \end{array}$$ Annex a zero to align the columns.

b. 7 − 1.75

$$\begin{array}{r} 7 \\ -\ 1.75 \end{array} \rightarrow \begin{array}{r} {}^{6\ 91}7.00 \\ -\ 1.75 \\ \hline 5.25 \end{array}$$ Annex two zeros to align the columns.

Find each sum or difference.

1. $\begin{array}{r} 42.3 \\ +\ 0.81 \end{array}$ **43.11**

2. $\begin{array}{r} 5.86 \\ -\ 1.51 \end{array}$ **4.35**

3. $\begin{array}{r} 13 \\ -\ 0.324 \end{array}$ **12.676**

4. 2.3 + 1.1 **3.4**

5. 11.5 + 4.2 **15.7**

6. 9.5 − 8.3 **1.2**

7. 24.8 − 3.6 **21.2**

8. 3.57 − 2.17 **1.40**

9. 7.43 − 5.34 **2.09**

10. 6.40 + 7.36 **13.76**

11. 15.20 + 0.16 **15.36**

12. 7.97 − 4.29 **3.68**

13. 8.70 + 0.64 **9.34**

14. 56.88 − 12.35 **44.53**

15. 4.192 + 1.255 **5.447**

16. 14.6 + 20.81 **35.41**

17. 5.2 − 3.01 **2.19**

18. 1.9 − 1.65 **0.25**

19. 6.38 − 1.1 **5.28**

20. 4.86 − 0.3 **4.56**

21. 9.43 + 1.8 **11.23**

22. 70.3 + 7.03 **77.33**

23. 0.5 + 1.674 **2.174**

24. 25 − 8.3 **16.7**

25. 18 − 12.31 **5.69**

26. 2.85 + 23.6 **26.45**

27. 0.8 + 9.612 **10.412**

28. 6.8 + 5.09 + 0.03 **11.92**

29. 0.5 + 2.41 + 6.7 **9.61**

30. 0.563 + 5.8 + 6.89 **13.253**

31. 41.30 + 0.28 + 6.15 **47.73**

32. 4.52 + 0.167 + 12.9 **17.587**

33. 23.4 + 9.865 + 18.26 **51.525**

34. Find the sum of 27.38 and 6.8. **34.18**

35. Add $26.59, $1.80, and $13. **$41.39**

36. Find the difference of 42.05 and 11.621. **30.429**

37. How much more than $102.90 is $115? **$12.10**

38. Karen plans to buy a softball for $6.50, a softball glove for $37.99, and sliders for $13.79. Find the cost of these items before tax is added. **$58.28**

9 Estimating Products and Quotients of Decimals

NEW YORK—
Performance Indic

Reinforcement of 5.N
Estimate sums, differences, **products, and quotients of decimals**

You can use rounding to estimate products and quotients of decimals.

Example 1 Estimate each product or quotient to the nearest whole number.

a. 3.8 × 2.1

$3.8 \times 2.1 \rightarrow 4 \times 2 = 8$ Round 3.8 to 4 and round 2.1 to 2.

3.8 × 2.1 is about 8.

b. 16.45 ÷ 3.92

$16.45 \div 3.92 \rightarrow 16 \div 4 = 4$ Round 16.45 to 16 and round 3.92 to 4.

16.45 ÷ 3.92 is about 4.

You can use mental math and compatible numbers to estimate products and quotients of decimals. **Compatible numbers** are rounded so it is easy to compute with them mentally.

Example 2 Estimate each product or quotient to the nearest whole number.

a. 7 × 98.24

$7 \times 98.24 \rightarrow 7 \times 100 = 700$ Even though 98.24 rounds to 98, 100 is a compatible number because it is easy to mentally compute 7×100.

7 × 98.24 is about 700.

b. 47.5 ÷ 5.23

$47.5 \div 5.23 \rightarrow 48 \div 6 = 8$ Even though 5.23 rounds to 5, 6 is a compatible number because 48 is divisible by 6.

47.5 ÷ 5.23 is about 8.

Rewrite each expression using rounding and compatible numbers. Then estimate each product or quotient. 1–12. Sample answers are given.

1. 9.2×4.89 **9 × 5 = 45**
2. 6.75×5.25 **7 × 5 = 35**
3. $12.19 \div 3.8$ **12 ÷ 4 = 3**
4. $39.79 \div 4.61$ **40 ÷ 5 = 8**
5. 11.2×6.25 **11 × 6 = 66**
6. $15.2 \div 2.7$ **15 ÷ 3 = 5**
7. $47.2 \div 5.1$ **45 ÷ 5 = 9**
8. $16.53 \div 8.36$ **16 ÷ 8 = 2**
9. $4.32(107.6)$ **4 × 100 = 4**
10. 26×10.9 **26 × 10 = 260**
11. $73.2 \div 6.99$ **70 ÷ 7 = 10**
12. $19.1(21.60)$ **20 × 20 = 4**

Estimate each product or quotient. 13–34. Sample answers are given.

13. 4.6×8.3 **5 × 8 = 40**
14. 5.12×5.9 **5 × 6 = 30**
15. $7.5 \div 4.2$ **8 ÷ 4 = 2**
16. $9.27 \div 3.31$ **9 ÷ 3 = 3**
17. $19.8(2.6)$ **20 × 3 = 60**
18. $41.75 \div 6$ **42 ÷ 6 = 7**
19. $36.24 \div 8.7$ **36 ÷ 9 = 4**
20. 5.85×7.55 **6 × 8 = 48**
21. $8.1 \div 2.2$ **8 ÷ 2 = 4**
22. $7.9(9.12)$ **8 × 9 = 72**
23. $6.1 \div 2.1$ **6 ÷ 2 = 3**
24. 9×96.42 **9 × 100 = 900**
25. 13×9.1 **13 × 10 = 130**
26. $10.1 \div 4.7$ **10 ÷ 5 = 2**
27. $28.6(5)$ **30 × 5 = 150**
28. $21 \div 7.6$ **21 ÷ 7 = 3**
29. $81 \div 10.5$ **80 ÷ 10 = 8**
30. $52.7 \div 5.3$ **50 ÷ 5 = 10**
31. 47.74×2 **50 × 2 = 100**
32. 204.5×3 **200 × 3 = 600**
33. $41.79 \div 7.23$ **42 ÷ 7 = 6**

34. The speed of the spine-tailed swift has been measured at 106.25 miles per hour. At that rate, about how far can it travel in 1.8 hours? **about 200 miles**

Multiplying and Dividing Decimals

To multiply decimals, multiply as with whole numbers. Then add the total number of decimal places in the factors. Place the same number of decimal places in the product, counting from right to left.

Example 1 Find each product.

a. 6.3(2.1)

$$
\begin{array}{r}
6.3 \quad \leftarrow 1 \text{ decimal place} \\
\times\ 2.1 \quad \leftarrow 1 \text{ decimal place} \\
\hline
63 \\
12\ 6 \\
\hline
13.23 \quad \leftarrow 2 \text{ decimal places}
\end{array}
$$

The product is 13.23.

b. 9.47(0.5)

$$
\begin{array}{r}
9.47 \quad \leftarrow 2 \text{ decimal places} \\
\times\ 0.5 \quad \leftarrow 1 \text{ decimal place} \\
\hline
4.735 \quad \leftarrow 3 \text{ decimal places}
\end{array}
$$

The product is 4.735.

To divide decimals, move the decimal point in the divisor to the right, and then move the decimal point in the dividend the same number of places. Align the decimal point in the quotient with the decimal point in the dividend.

Example 2 Find each quotient.

a. 1.20 ÷ 0.8

$$
\begin{array}{r}
1.5 \\
0.8\overline{)1.2\,0} \\
\underline{8} \\
4\,0 \\
\underline{4\,0} \\
0
\end{array}
$$
Move each decimal point right 1 place.

The quotient is 1.5.

b. 32 ÷ 0.25

$$
\begin{array}{r}
128 \\
0.25\overline{)32.00} \\
\underline{25} \\
70 \\
\underline{50} \\
200 \\
\underline{200} \\
0
\end{array}
$$
Move each decimal point right 2 places.

The quotient is 128.

Find each product or quotient.

1. 1.2(3) **3.6**
2. 8(3.4) **27.2**
3. 0.2 × 7.2 **1.44**
4. 1.4(6.1) **8.54**
5. 0.63 ÷ 0.9 **0.7**
6. 8.4 ÷ 0.4 **21**
7. 0.06 × 3 **0.18**
8. 42 ÷ 0.8 **52.5**
9. 3.9(8.2) **31.98**
10. 0.2(3.1) **0.62**
11. 27 ÷ 0.3 **90**
12. 64 ÷ 0.4 **160**
13. 0.4 ÷ 2 **0.2**
14. 14.4 ÷ 0.16 **90**
15. 15.6 × 38 **592.8**
16. 0.51 ÷ 0.03 **17**
17. 5.7(3.8) **21.66**
18. 7.07(4) **28.28**
19. 1.25 × 12 **15**
20. 62.9 ÷ 100 **0.629**
21. 6.5(0.13) **0.845**
22. 14.9(0.56) **8.344**
23. 0.384 ÷ 1.2 **0.32**
24. 4.2 ÷ 1.05 **4**
25. 25.9 ÷ 2.8 **9.25**
26. 0.47 × 3.01 **1.4147**
27. 1.01(6.2) **6.262**
28. 9 ÷ 0.375 **24**
29. 50 ÷ 0.25 **200**
30. 500 ÷ 3.2 **156.25**
31. 0.001(7.09) **0.00709**
32. 6.32 × 0.81 **5.1192**
33. 2.92 ÷ 0.002 **1460**

34. Find the product of 13.6 and 9.15. **124.44**

35. What is the quotient of 72.05 and 0.11? **655**

36. If one United States dollar can be exchanged for 128.46 Spanish pesetas, how many pesetas would you receive for $50? **6423 pesetas**

11 Estimating Sums and Differences of Fractions and Mixed Numbers

NEW YORK
Performance Indicat

Reinforcement of 6.N.16 Add and subtract fractions with unlike denominators

Reinforcement of 6.N.1 Add, subtract, multiply, and divide **mixed numbers** with unlike denominators

You can use rounding to estimate sums and differences of fractions and mixed numbers. To estimate the sum or difference of proper fractions, round each fraction to 0, $\frac{1}{2}$, or 1.

Example 1 Estimate each sum or difference.

a. $\frac{5}{8} + \frac{9}{10}$

$\frac{5}{8} + \frac{9}{10} \rightarrow \frac{1}{2} + 1 = 1\frac{1}{2}$

The sum of $\frac{5}{8}$ and $\frac{9}{10}$ is about $1\frac{1}{2}$.

b. $\frac{5}{6} - \frac{3}{8}$

$\frac{5}{6} - \frac{3}{8} \rightarrow 1 - \frac{1}{2} = \frac{1}{2}$

$\frac{5}{6} - \frac{3}{8}$ is about $\frac{1}{2}$.

To estimate the sum or difference of mixed numbers, round each mixed number to the nearest whole number or to the nearest $\frac{1}{2}$.

Example 2 Estimate each sum or difference.

a. $3\frac{3}{8} + 15\frac{15}{16}$

$3\frac{3}{8} + 15\frac{15}{16} \rightarrow 3\frac{1}{2} + 16 = 19\frac{1}{2}$

The sum of $3\frac{3}{8}$ and $15\frac{15}{16}$ is about $19\frac{1}{2}$.

b. $10\frac{3}{4} - 4\frac{1}{6}$

$10\frac{3}{4} - 4\frac{1}{6} \rightarrow 11 - 4 = 7$

$10\frac{3}{4} - 4\frac{1}{6}$ is about 7.

Round each fraction to 0, $\frac{1}{2}$, or 1.

1. $\frac{9}{10}$ 1 2. $\frac{1}{8}$ 0 3. $\frac{13}{25}$ $\frac{1}{2}$

4. $\frac{3}{14}$ 0 5. $\frac{9}{15}$ $\frac{1}{2}$ 6. $\frac{78}{81}$ 1

Estimate each sum or difference. 7–29. Sample answers given.

7. $\frac{8}{9} + \frac{1}{4}$ $1 + 0 = 1$

8. $\frac{14}{15} + \frac{5}{6}$ $1 + 1 = 2$

9. $\frac{47}{90} + \frac{3}{24}$ $\frac{1}{2} + 0 = \frac{1}{2}$

10. $\frac{11}{12} + \frac{4}{9}$ $1 + \frac{1}{2} = 1\frac{1}{2}$

11. $\frac{15}{16} + 9\frac{3}{4}$ $1 + 10 = 11$

12. $1\frac{5}{12} + \frac{7}{18}$ $1\frac{1}{2} + \frac{1}{2} = 2$

13. $5\frac{10}{11} + \frac{3}{5}$ $6 + \frac{1}{2} = 6\frac{1}{2}$

14. $21\frac{8}{9} + 6\frac{4}{25}$ $22 + 6 = 28$

15. $32\frac{3}{56} + 18\frac{2}{75}$ $32 + 18 =$

16. $\frac{4}{5} - \frac{1}{10}$ $1 - 0 = 1$

17. $\frac{7}{9} - \frac{13}{18}$ $1 - 1 = 0$

18. $\frac{9}{10} - \frac{3}{8}$ $1 - \frac{1}{2} = \frac{1}{2}$

19. $5\frac{1}{5} - 2\frac{3}{4}$ $5 - 3 = 2$

20. $8\frac{3}{5} - 2\frac{1}{8}$ $8\frac{1}{2} - 2 = 6\frac{1}{2}$

21. $16\frac{34}{35} - 3\frac{1}{6}$ $17 - 3 = 14$

22. $35\frac{7}{8} - 4\frac{1}{2}$ $36 - 4\frac{1}{2} = 31\frac{1}{2}$

23. $15\frac{4}{9} + 13\frac{9}{11}$ $15\frac{1}{2} + 14 = 29\frac{1}{2}$

24. $140\frac{4}{5} - 120\frac{2}{15}$ $141 - 12$

25. About how much longer than $\frac{5}{6}$ minute is $4\frac{1}{2}$ minutes? $4\frac{1}{2}$ min $- 1$ min $= 3\frac{1}{2}$ min

26. Estimate the sum $3\frac{3}{10} + 2\frac{4}{5} + 3\frac{1}{3}$. $3 + 3 + 3 = 9$

27. About how much more is $19\frac{3}{4}$ inches than $10\frac{7}{8}$ inches? 20 in. $- 11$ in. $= 9$ in.

28. Estimate the sum of $7\frac{1}{3}$, $6\frac{4}{5}$, $6\frac{3}{4}$, $7\frac{1}{10}$, and $6\frac{15}{16}$. $7 + 7 + 7 + 7 + 7 = 35$

29. A board that is $63\frac{5}{8}$ inches long is about how much longer than a board that is $62\frac{1}{4}$ inches long? $63\frac{1}{2}$ in. $- 62$ in. $= 1\frac{1}{2}$ in.

12 Estimating Products and Quotients of Fractions and Mixed Numbers

You can estimate products and quotients of fractions and mixed numbers using rounding and compatible numbers. Compatible numbers are rounded to make it easy to compute with them mentally.

NEW YORK
Performance Indicator

inforcement of 6.N.17
ltiply and divide
ctions with unlike
nominators

inforcement of 6.N.18
d, subtract, **multiply**,
d divide mixed
mbers with unlike
nominators

Example

Estimate each product or quotient.

a. $\dfrac{5}{16} \times 30$

$$\dfrac{5}{16} \times 30 \rightarrow \dfrac{1}{3} \times 30$$

$\dfrac{5}{16}$ is close to $\dfrac{5}{15}$ and $\dfrac{5}{15} = \dfrac{1}{3}$.

$\dfrac{1}{3}$ and 30 are compatible numbers.

Think: $\dfrac{1}{3} \times 30 = 10$

$\dfrac{5}{16} \times 30$ is about 10.

b. $9\dfrac{7}{8} \div 5$

$9\dfrac{7}{8} \div 5 \rightarrow 10 \div 5 = 2$ Round $9\dfrac{7}{8}$ to 10. 10 and 5 are compatible numbers.

$9\dfrac{7}{8} \div 5$ is about 2.

Estimate each product or quotient. 1–24. Sample answers given.

1. $\dfrac{1}{4} \cdot 11$ $\dfrac{1}{4} \cdot 12 = 3$

2. $\dfrac{1}{3}(20)$ $\dfrac{1}{3}(21) = 7$

3. $\dfrac{1}{3} \times 14$ $\dfrac{1}{3} \times 15 = 5$

4. $\dfrac{1}{4}(15)$ $\dfrac{1}{4}(16) = 4$

5. $\dfrac{7}{15} \times 120$ $\dfrac{1}{2} \times 120 = 60$

6. $\dfrac{11}{20}(62)$ $\dfrac{1}{2}(60) = 30$

7. $\dfrac{31}{40} \cdot 100$ $\dfrac{3}{4} \cdot 100 = 75$

8. $\dfrac{6}{13} \times 150$ $\dfrac{1}{2} \times 150 = 75$

9. $\dfrac{1}{5}(44)$ $\dfrac{1}{5}(45) = 9$

10. $1\dfrac{5}{6} \cdot 30$ $2 \cdot 30 = 60$

11. $2\dfrac{1}{4} \cdot 22$ $2 \times 22 = 44$

12. $4\dfrac{4}{5} \times 24$ $5 \times 25 = 125$

13. $5\dfrac{7}{8} \div 2$ $6 \div 2 = 3$

14. $8\dfrac{1}{4} \div 4$ $8 \div 4 = 2$

15. $14\dfrac{6}{7} \div 3$ $15 \div 3 = 5$

16. $50 \div 4\dfrac{7}{8}$ $50 \div 5 = 10$

17. $61 \div 2\dfrac{4}{5}$ $60 \div 3 = 20$

18. $148 \div 3\dfrac{1}{4}$ $150 \div 3 = 50$

19. $79 \div 1\dfrac{9}{10}$ $80 \div 2 = 40$

20. $75 \div 2\dfrac{11}{16}$ $75 \div 3 = 25$

21. $88 \div 2\dfrac{1}{8}$ $88 \div 2 = 44$

22. Kim needs $3\dfrac{1}{2}$ batches of cookies. If one recipe calls for $2\dfrac{1}{4}$ cups of flour, about how many cups of flour are needed? $4 \times 2 = 8$ **cups**

23. Mario wants to place photographs of people in one vertical row on a poster board that is $17\dfrac{1}{2}$ inches long. If each photograph is $2\dfrac{3}{4}$ inches long, about how many photographs can Mario place on the poster board? $18 \div 3 = 6$ **photographs**

24. A basketball hoop has a diameter of $18\dfrac{1}{2}$ inches. Estimate the circumference of the hoop. (*Hint:* To estimate the circumference of a circle, multiply the diameter by 3.) $18 \times 3 = 54$ **in.**

13 Converting Measurements within the Metric System

All units of length in the metric system are defined in terms of the meter (m). The diagram below shows the relationships between some common metric units.

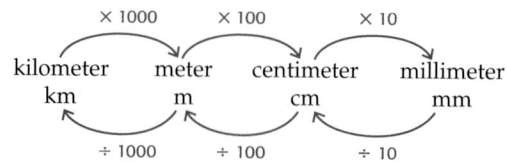

Comparing Metric and Customary Units of Length
1 mm ≈ 0.04 inch (height of a comma)
1 cm ≈ 0.4 inch (half the width of a penny)
1 m ≈ 1.1 yards (width of a doorway)
1 km ≈ 0.6 mile (length of a city block)

- To convert from larger units to smaller units, multiply.

- To convert from smaller units to larger units, divide.

There will be a greater number of smaller units than larger units.

Converting From Larger Units to Smaller Units	Converting From Smaller Units to Larger Units
1 km = 1 × 1000 = 1000 m	1 mm = 1 ÷ 10 = 0.1 cm
1 m = 1 × 100 = 100 cm	1 cm = 1 ÷ 100 = 0.01 m
1 cm = 1 × 10 = 10 mm	1 m = 1 ÷ 1000 = 0.001 km

There will be fewer larger units than smaller units.

Example 1 Complete each sentence.

a. 3 km = __?__ m

$3 \times 1000 = 3000$
3 km = 3000 m

To convert from kilometers to meters, multiply by 1000.

b. 9.75 cm = __?__ mm

$9.75 \times 10 = 97.5$
9.75 cm = 97.5 mm

To convert from centimeters to millimeters, multiply by 10.

c. 42 mm = __?__ cm

$42 \div 10 = 4.2$
42 mm = 4.2 cm

To convert from millimeters to centimeters, divide by 10.

The basic unit of capacity in the metric system is the liter (L). A liter and milliliter (mL) are related in a manner similar to meter and millimeter.

1 L = 1000 mL

Comparing Metric and Customary Units of Capacity
1 mL ≈ 0.03 ounce (drop of water)
1 L ≈ 1 quart (bottle of ketchup)

Example 2 Complete each sentence.

a. 2.5 L = __?__ mL

$2.5 \times 1000 = 2500$
2.5 L = 2500 mL

To convert from larger units to smaller units, multiply.

b. 860 mL = __?__ L

$860 \div 1000 = 0.86$
860 mL = 0.86 L

To convert from smaller units to larger units, divide.

The *mass* of an object is the amount of matter that it contains. The basic unit of mass in the metric system is the kilogram (kg). Kilogram, gram (g), and milligram (mg) are related in a manner similar to kilometer, meter, and millimeter.

> **Comparing Metric and Customary Units of Mass**
> 1 g ≈ 0.04 ounce (one raisin)
> 1 kg ≈ 2.2 pounds (textbook)

$$1 \text{ kg} = 1000 \text{ g} \qquad 1 \text{ g} = 1000 \text{ mg}$$

Example 3 Complete each sentence.

a. 3400 mg = __?__ g

3400 ÷ 1000 = 3.4   To convert from smaller units
3400 mg = 3.4 g   to larger units, divide.

b. 74.2 kg = __?__ g

74.2 × 1000 = 74,200   To convert from larger units
74.2 kg = 74,200 g   to smaller units, multiply.

State which metric unit you would probably use to measure each item. 4. **milliliter**

1. amount of water in a pitcher **liter**
2. distance between two cities **kilometer**
3. thickness of a coin **millimeter**
4. amount of water in a medicine dropper
5. length of a textbook **centimeter**
6. mass of a pencil **gram**
7. length of a football field **meter**
8. width of a quarter **centimeter**
9. thickness of a pencil **millimeter**
10. gas in the tank of a car **liter**
11. vanilla used in a cookie recipe **milliliter**
12. mass of a table tennis ball **milligram**
13. bag of sugar **kilogram**
14. mass of a horse **kilogram**

Complete each sentence.

15. 5 km = __?__ m **5000**
16. 3.5 cm = __?__ mm **35**
17. 6 L = __?__ mL **6000**
18. 370 mL = __?__ L **0.37**
19. 20 mm = __?__ cm **2**
20. 4000 g = __?__ kg **4**
21. 18 cm = __?__ mm **180**
22. 0.75 L = __?__ mL **750**
23. 935 cm = __?__ m **9.35**
24. 210 mm = __?__ cm **21**
25. 65 g = __?__ kg **0.065**
26. 2 m = __?__ cm **200**
27. 52.9 kg = __?__ g **52,900**
28. 800 m = __?__ km **0.8**
29. 9.05 kg = __?__ g **9050**
30. 0.62 km = __?__ m **620**
31. 1250 mL = __?__ L **1.25**
32. 20,000 mg = __?__ g **20**
33. 3100 m = __?__ km **3.1**
34. 2.6 m = __?__ cm **260**
35. 36 mg = __?__ g **0.036**
36. 7 mm = __?__ cm **0.7**
37. 0.085 L = __?__ mL **85**
38. 125.9 g = __?__ kg **0.1259**

39. The mass of a sample of rocks is 1.56 kilograms. How many grams are in 1.56 kilograms? **1560 g**
40. How many milliliters are in 0.09 liter? **90 mL**
41. Runners often participate in races that are 10 kilometers long. How many meters are in 10 kilometers? **10,000 m**
42. How many centimeters are in 0.58 meter? **58 cm**
43. A can holds 355 milliliters of soft drink. How many liters is this? **0.355 L**

14 Converting Measurements within the Customary System

The units of length in the customary system are inch, foot, yard, and mile. The table at the right shows the relationships among these units.

Customary Units of Length
1 foot (ft) = 12 inches (in.)
1 yard (yd) = 3 feet
1 mile (mi) = 5280 feet

- To convert from larger units to smaller units, multiply.

- To convert from smaller units to larger units, divide.

Larger Units		Smaller Units

$5 \text{ ft} = 5 \times 12 = 60 \text{ in.}$
$4 \text{ yd} = 4 \times 3 = 12 \text{ ft}$

There will be a greater number of smaller units than larger units.

Smaller Units		Larger Units

$24 \text{ in.} = 24 \div 12 = 2 \text{ ft}$
$15 \text{ ft} = 15 \div 3 = 5 \text{ yd}$

There will be fewer larger units than smaller units.

NEW YORK—
Performance Indicator

8.M.1 Solve equations/ proportions to convert to equivalent measurements within metric and customary measurement systems
Note: also allow Fahrenheit to Celsius and vice versa

Example 1 Complete each sentence.

a. **6 yd = ___?___ ft**

$6 \times 3 = 18$
$6 \text{ yd} = 18 \text{ ft}$ To convert from yards to feet, multiply by 3.

b. **1.5 mi = ___?___ ft**

$1.5 \times 5280 = 7920$
$1.5 \text{ mi} = 7920 \text{ ft}$ To convert from miles to feet, multiply by 5280.

c. **120 in. = ___?___ ft**

$120 \div 12 = 10$
$120 \text{ in.} = 10 \text{ ft}$ To convert from inches to feet, divide by 12.

The units of weight in the customary system are ounce, pound, and ton. The table at the right shows the relationships among these units.

Customary Units of Weight
1 pound (lb) = 16 ounces (oz)
1 ton (T) = 2000 pounds

- To convert from larger units to smaller units, multiply.

- To convert from smaller units to larger units, divide.

Larger Units		Smaller Units

$3 \text{ T} = 3 \times 2000 = 6000 \text{ lb}$
$2 \text{ lb} = 2 \times 16 = 32 \text{ oz}$

Smaller Units		Larger Units

$48 \text{ oz} = 48 \div 16 = 3 \text{ lb}$
$4000 \text{ lb} = 4000 \div 2000 = 2 \text{ T}$

Example 2 Complete each sentence.

a. **120 oz = ___?___ lb**

$120 \div 16 = 7.5$
$120 \text{ oz} = 7.5 \text{ lb}$ To convert from smaller units to larger units, divide.

b. **4 T = ___?___ lb**

$4 \times 2000 = 8000$
$4 \text{ T} = 8000 \text{ lb}$ To convert from larger units to smaller units, multiply.

Capacity is the amount of liquid or dry substance a container can hold. Customary units of capacity are fluid ounce, cup, pint, quart, and gallon. The relationships among these units are shown in the table.

As with units of length and units of weight, to convert from larger units to smaller units, multiply. To convert from smaller units to larger units, divide.

Customary Units of Capacity
1 cup (c) = 8 fluid ounces (fl oz)
1 pint (pt) = 2 cups
1 quart (qt) = 2 pints
1 gallon (gal) = 4 quarts

Example 3 Complete each sentence.

a. 3 gal = __?__ qt

$3 \times 4 = 12$ larger unit → smaller unit
3 gal = 12 qt

b. 2 c = __?__ fl oz

$2 \times 8 = 16$ larger unit → smaller unit
2 c = 16 fl oz

c. 12 pt = __?__ qt

$12 \div 2 = 6$ smaller unit → larger unit
12 pt = 6 qt

d. 8 c = __?__ qt

$8 \div 2 = 4$ First, convert cups to pints.
8 c = 4 pt

$4 \div 2 = 2$ Next, convert pints to quarts.
4 pt = 2 qt
So, 8 c = 2 qt.

Complete each sentence.

1. 5 ft = __?__ in. **60**
2. 2 gal = __?__ qt **8**
3. 96 oz = __?__ lb **6**
4. 2 T = __?__ lb **4000**
5. 9 ft = __?__ yd **3**
6. 6 c = __?__ pt **3**
7. 2 mi = __?__ ft **10,560**
8. 72 in. = __?__ ft **6**
9. 3 lb = __?__ oz **48**
10. 7 yd = __?__ ft **21**
11. 32 fl oz = __?__ c **4**
12. 15,840 ft = __?__ mi **3**
13. 2 qt = __?__ pt **4**
14. 5 pt = __?__ c **10**
15. 16 qt = __?__ gal **4**
16. 3000 lb = __?__ T **1.5**
17. 6 pt = __?__ qt **3**
18. 8 pt = __?__ c **16**
19. 14 pt = __?__ qt **7**
20. 8 yd = __?__ ft **24**
21. 5 gal = __?__ qt **20**
22. 36 qt = __?__ gal **9**
23. 5 c = __?__ fl oz **40**
24. 120 in. = __?__ ft **10**
25. 30 in. = __?__ ft **2.5**
26. 6.5 lb = __?__ oz **104**
27. 12 oz = __?__ lb **0.75**

Solve each problem by breaking it into simpler parts.

28. How many inches are in a yard? **36**
29. How many ounces are in a ton? **32,000**
30. How many cups are in a gallon? **16**

15 Displaying Data in Graphs

Statistics involves collecting, analyzing, and presenting information. The information that is collected is called data. Displaying **data** in graphs makes it easier to visualize the data.

- **Bar graphs** are used to compare the frequency of data. The bar graph below compares the amounts of recycled materials.

Source: Bureau of Mines

- **Double bar graphs** compare two sets of data. The double bar graph below shows movie preferences for men and women.

- **Line graphs** usually show how values change over a period of time. The line graph at the right shows the results of the women's Olympic high jump event from 1972 to 2000.

NEW YORK
Performance Indicator

Reinforcement of 6.S.4
Determine and justify the most appropriate graph to display a given set of data (pictograph, **bar graph, line graph,** histogram, or **circle graph)**

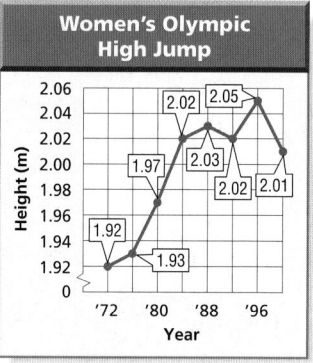

Source: *The World Almanac*

- **Double line graphs**, like double bar graphs, show two sets of data. The double line graph below compares the number of boys and the number of girls participating in high school athletics.

Source: Based on National Federation of State High School statistics

Circle graphs show how parts are related to the whole. The circle graph at the right shows how electricity is generated in the United States.

How America Powers Up

Gas 9.0%
Nuclear 21.2%
Hydropower 9.3%
Coal 56.9%
Oil 3.5%
Other 0.1%

Source: Energy Information Administration

Example

A newspaper wants to display the high temperature of the past week. Should they use a line graph, circle graph, or double bar graph?

Since the data would show how values change over a period of time, a line graph would give the reader a clear picture of what temperatures were and the changes in temperature.

–5. Sample answers are given. See margin for explanations.
etermine whether a bar graph, double bar graph, line graph, double line raph, or circle graph is the best way to display each of the following sets of ata. Explain your reasoning.

the number of people who have different kinds of pets **bar graph**

the percent of students in class who have 0, 1, 2, 3, or more than 3 siblings **circle graph**

the number of teens who attended art museums, symphony concerts, rock concerts, and athletic events in 1990 compared to the number who attended the same events this year **double bar graph**

the minimum wage every year from 1980 to the present **line graph**

the number of boys and the number of girls participating in volunteer programs each year from 1995 to the present **double line graph**

The table below shows the number of events at recent Olympic games. Would the data be best displayed using a line graph, circle graph, or double bar graph? Explain your reasoning. **Line graph; it is easier to see the increase in events over time.**

Olympic Year	1968	1972	1976	1980	1984	1988	1992	1996	2000
Number of Events	172	196	199	200	223	237	257	271	300

It shows how each age group makes up the whole group of Internet users. he graph at the right represents the age of Internet users.

Explain how the graph is useful in displaying the data.

Describe any advantages or disadvantages of using a different type of graph to display the data. **Sample answer: A bar graph would also compare the different age groups, but a circle graph is more useful in comparing the parts to the whole.**

Age of Internet Users

Over 40 9%
16–20 9%
36–40 12%
21–25 24%
31–35 16%
26–30 30%

Source: Time

Answers

Sample Answers:

1. A bar graph would show the different frequencies of the data.

2. A circle graph would show how each category compares to the whole class.

3. A double bar graph would make a side-by-side comparison of the two sets of data.

4. A line graph would show the wage's increase during those years.

5. A double line graph would show the changes in boys' and girls' participation over time.

Extra Practice

Lesson 1-1

(pages 6–10)

Solve.

1. **POSTAL SERVICE** The U.S. Postal Service offers air mail service to other countries. The rates for International Air Mail letters and packages are shown in the table at the right. Determine the air mail rate for a package that weighs 5.5 ounces. **d. See students' work.**

Weight not over (ounces)	Rate
0.5	$0.50
1.0	$0.95
1.5	$1.34
2.0	$1.73
2.5	$2.12
3.0	$2.51
3.5	$2.90
4.0	$3.29

   a. Write the *Explore* step. What do you know and what do you need to find? **know other rates, need to find rate for 5.5 oz**

   b. Write the *Plan* step. What strategy will you use? What do you estimate the answer to be? **sample answer: look for a pattern; $4.50**

   c. *Solve* the problem using your plan. What is your answer? **$4.46**

   d. *Examine* your solution. Is it reasonable? Does it answer the question?

2. **POSTAL SERVICE** In 1995, the state of Florida celebrated the 150th anniversary of its statehood. The U.S. Postal Service issued a stamp, the first to bear the 32-cent price, to honor the occasion. Ninety million of the commemorative stamps were issued. About how much postage did the stamps represent? **b. about $30 million**

   a. Which method of computation do you think is most appropriate for this problem? Justify your choice. **sample answer: estimation since the problem says "about"**

   b. Solve the problem using the four-step plan. Be sure to examine your solution.

Find the next term in each list.

3. 3, 8, 13, 18, 23, … **28**
4. 32, 29, 26, 23, 20, … **17**
5. 6, 7, 9, 12, 16, … **21**

Lesson 1-2

(pages 12–16)

Find the value of each expression.

1. $8 + 7 + 12 \div 4$ **18**
2. $20 \div 4 - 5 + 12$ **12**
3. $(25 \cdot 3) + (10 \cdot 3)$ **105**
4. $36 \div 6 + 7 - 6$ **7**
5. $30 \cdot (6 - 4)$ **60**
6. $(40 \cdot 2) - (6 \cdot 11)$ **14**
7. $\frac{86 - 11}{11 + 4}$ **5**
8. $\frac{12 + 84}{11 + 13}$ **4**
9. $\frac{5 \cdot 5 + 5}{5 \cdot 5 - 15}$ **3**
10. $(19 - 8)4$ **44**
11. $75 - 5(2 \cdot 6)$ **15**
12. $81 \div 27 \times 6 - 2$ **16**

13. Find the value of *thirty-two divided by the product of four and two.* **4**

Write a numerical phrase for each verbal phrase.

14. three increased by nine **3 + 9**
15. fifteen divided by three **15 ÷ 3**
16. six less than ten **10 − 6**

Lesson 1-3

(pages 17–21)

ALGEBRA Evaluate each expression if $a = 2$, $b = 4$, and $c = 3$.

1. $ba - ac$ **2**
2. $4b + a \cdot a$ **20**
3. $11 \cdot c - ab$ **25**
4. $4b - (a + c)$ **11**
5. $7(a + b) - c$ **39**
6. $8a + 8b$ **48**
7. $\frac{8(a + b)}{4c}$ **4**
8. $36 - 12c$ **0**
9. $\frac{9(b + a)}{c - 1}$ **27**
10. $abc - bc$ **12**
11. $28 - bc + a$ **18**
12. $a(b - c)$ **2**

ALGEBRA Translate each phrase into an algebraic expression.

13. nine more than a **$a + 9$**
14. eleven less than k **$k - 11$**
15. three times p **$3p$**
16. the product of some number and five **$5n$**
17. twice Shelly's score decreased by 18 **$2s - 18$**
18. the quotient of 16 and n **$16 \div n$**

Lesson 1-4

(pages 23–27)

Name the property shown by each statement. 2. Associative (+)

$1 \cdot 4 = 4$ **Mult. Identity**   **2.** $6 + (b + 2) = (6 + b) + 2$ **3.** $9(6n) = (9 \cdot 6)n$ **Associative (×)**

$8t \cdot 0 = 0 \cdot 8t$ **Commutative (×)**   **5.** $0(13n) = 0$ **Mult. Prop. of 0**   **6.** $7 + t = t + 7$ **Commutative (+)**

Find each sum or product mentally.

$6 + 8 + 14$ **28**   **8.** $5 \cdot 18 \cdot 2$ **180**   **9.** $0(13 \cdot 6)$ **0**

$8 + 4 + 12 + 16$ **40**   **11.** $8 \cdot 20 \cdot 10$ **1600**   **12.** $4 \cdot 14 \cdot 5$ **280**

ALGEBRA   Simplify each expression.

$(12 + x) + 9$ $x + 21$ **14.** $2 \cdot (6 \cdot x)$ **12x**   **15.** $(5 \cdot m) \cdot 3$ **15m**

Lesson 1-5

(pages 28–32)

ALGEBRA   Find the solution of each equation from the list given.

$16 - f = 11; 3, 5, 7$ **5**   **2.** $9 = \frac{72}{m}; 8, 9, 11$ **8**   **3.** $4b + 1 = 17; 3, 4, 5$ **4**

$17 + r = 25; 6, 7, 8$ **8**   **5.** $9 = 7n - 12; 3, 5, 7$ **3**   **6.** $67 = 98 - q; 21, 26, 31$ **31**

ALGEBRA   Solve each equation mentally.

$13 - u = 7$ **6**   **8.** $23 = w + 6$ **17**   **9.** $88 + y = 96$ **8**

$9z = 45$ **5**   **11.** $88 = 11d$ **8**   **12.** $5t = 0$ **0**

$13g = 39$ **3**   **14.** $\frac{x}{2} = 8$ **16**   **15.** $\frac{84}{h} = 12$ **7**

ALGEBRA   Define a variable. Then write an equation and solve.

The sum of a number and 8 is 14. $x + 8 = 14, 6$ **17.** Twelve less than a number is 50. $n - 12 = 50, 62$

The product of a number and ten is seventy.   **19.** A number divided by three is nine. $n \div 3 = 9, 27$
$10n = 70, 7$

Lesson 1-6

(pages 33–38)

Use the grid at the right to name the point for each ordered pair.

$(9, 7)$ **P**   **2.** $(5, 5)$ **N**

$(3, 1)$ **Q**   **4.** $(2, 7)$ **B**

$(8, 4)$ **S**   **6.** $(4, 0)$ **T**

Refer to the coordinate system shown at the right. Write the ordered pair that names each point.

R **(4, 8)**   **8.** P **(9, 7)**

W **(5, 1)**   **10.** C **(0, 6)**

D **(0, 8)**   **12.** F **(3, 4)**

Express each relation as a table and as a graph. Then determine the domain and range. 13–14. See margin for tables and graphs.

13. $\{(3, 6), (4, 9), (5, 1)\}$
$D = \{3, 4, 5\}; R = \{1, 6, 9\}$

14. $\{(2, 1), (4, 4), (6, 7), (4, 3)\}$
$D = \{2, 4, 6\}; R = \{1, 3, 4, 7\}$

13.

x	y
3	6
4	9
5	1

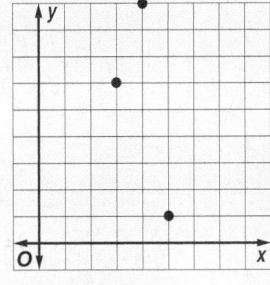

14.

x	y
2	1
4	4
6	7
4	3

4. **Puzzle Completion**

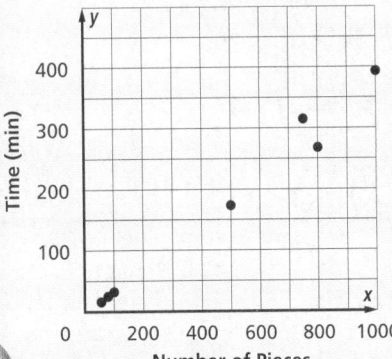

Number of Pieces

Lesson 1-7 *(pages 40–44)*

Determine whether a scatter plot of the data for the following might show a *positive*, *negative*, **or** *no* **relationship. Explain your answer.**

1. speed of airplane and miles traveled in three hours **positive**
2. weight and shoe size **no**
3. outside temperature and heating bill **negative**

GAMES For Exercises 4–6, use the following information. The number of pieces in a jigsaw puzzle and the number of minutes required for a person to complete it is shown below.

Number of Pieces	100	60	500	750	1000	800	75
Time (min)	35	20	175	315	395	270	25

4. Make a scatter plot of the data. **See margin.**
5. Does the scatter plot show any relationship? If so, is it positive or negative? Explain your reasoning. **Positive; as the number of pieces increases, the time increases.**
6. Suppose Dave purchases a puzzle having 650 pieces. Predict the length of time it will take him to complete the puzzle. **260 minutes**

Lesson 2-1 *(pages 56–61)*

Replace each ● with <, >, or = to make a true sentence.

1. $-4 ● -8$ **>**
2. $-6 ● 3$ **<**
3. $0 ● -5$ **>**
4. $-12 ● -9$ **<**
5. $12 ● -25$ **>**
6. $3 ● -7$ **>**
7. $0 ● -2$ **>**
8. $-15 ● 12$ **<**
9. $5 ● -7$ **>**
10. $|6| ● -2$ **>**
11. $-2 ● |-3|$ **<**
12. $|-7| ● |-4|$ **>**

Order the integers in each set from least to greatest. 16. **{−43, −40, −1, 8, 16, 27}**

13. $\{-1, 2, -5\}$ **{−5, −1, 2}**
14. $\{0, -2, 8, 5, -9\}$ **{−9, −2, 0, 5, 8}**
15. $\{100, -34, -86, 21, 0\}$ **{−86, −34, 0, 21, 100}**
16. $\{-1, 16, -43, 8, 27, -40\}$
17. $\{0, -23, 75, -15, 24\}$ **{−23, −15, 0, 24, 75}**
18. $\{-6, 6, -5, 18\}$ **{−6, −5, 6, 18}**

Evaluate each expression.

19. $|-3| + |9|$ **12**
20. $|-18| - |5|$ **13**
21. $|12 + 7|$ **19**
22. $-|6|$ **−6**
23. $|-8| + |4|$ **12**
24. $-|-20|$ **−20**
25. $|15 - 12|$ **3**
26. $|8 + 9|$ **17**
27. $-|4| \cdot |-5|$ **−20**
28. $|-6| \cdot |8|$ **48**
29. $-|12| \cdot |9|$ **−108**
30. $-\||-16| + |-22|\|$ **−38**

Lesson 2-2 *(pages 64–68)*

Find each sum.

1. $5 + (-6)$ **−1**
2. $-17 + 24$ **7**
3. $15 + (-29)$ **−14**
4. $-6 + 13$ **7**
5. $50 + (-14)$ **36**
6. $-21 + (-4)$ **−25**
7. $30 + (-7)$ **23**
8. $(-3) + (-10)$ **−13**
9. $-15 + 26$ **11**
10. $-17 + 4 + -2$ **−15**
11. $50 + (-16) + (-11)$ **23**
12. $-17 + 8 + (-14)$ **−23**
13. $-11 + 15 + -6$ **−2**
14. $23 + (-64)$ **−41**
15. $-1 + 14 + (-13)$ **0**
16. $33 + -18 + 7$ **22**
17. $-75 + (-13)$ **−88**
18. $26 + 14 + (-71)$ **−31**
19. $8 + (-9) + (-1)$ **−2**
20. $-16 + (-12) + 13$ **−15**
21. $35 + (-60)$ **−25**
22. $12 + -20 + 16$ **8**
23. $100 + (-54) + (-17)$ **29**
24. $11 + (-22) + (-33)$ **−44**

ind each difference.

1. $8 - 17$ **−9**
2. $-15 - 3$ **−18**
3. $10 - 21$ **−11**
4. $20 - (-5)$ **25**
5. $5 - (-9)$ **14**
6. $-12 - (-7)$ **−5**
7. $-19 - (-6)$ **−13**
8. $-16 - (-23)$ **7**
9. $-56 - 32$ **−88**
10. $-49 - (-52)$ **3**
11. $-6 - 9 - (-7)$ **−8**
12. $-6 - (-10) - 7$ **−3**
13. $17 - 33$ **−16**
14. $-21 - 19$ **−40**
15. $12 - (-24)$ **36**
16. $-35 - (-18)$ **−17**
17. $-54 - 27$ **−81**
18. $32 - (-18)$ **50**
19. $-26 - (-41)$ **15**
20. $99 - (-1)$ **100**
21. $-12 - (-25)$ **13**
22. $18 - (-43)$ **61**
23. $-66 - 13$ **−79**
24. $54 - 100$ **−46**

ALGEBRA Evaluate each expression if $x = 6$, $y = -8$, $z = -3$, and $w = 4$.

25. $y - z$ **−5**
26. $3 - z$ **6**
27. $y - 5$ **−13**
28. $x - y$ **14**
29. $14 - y - x$ **16**
30. $6 + x - z$ **15**
31. $y + z + w$ **−7**
32. $w - z + 11$ **18**

ind each product.

1. $-4(2)$ **−8**
2. $-8(-5)$ **40**
3. $13(-4)$ **−52**
4. $-5 \cdot 6 \cdot 10$ **−300**
5. $-6(-2)(-14)$ **−168**
6. $18(-3)(6)$ **−324**
7. $4(-10)(-3)$ **120**
8. $-9(3)(2)$ **−54**
9. $12(-8)$ **−96**

ALGEBRA Simplify each expression.

10. $-3 \cdot 5x$ **−15x**
11. $7(-8m)$ **−56m**
12. $-10(-3k)$ **30k**
13. $-4y(-8z)$ **32yz**
14. $(-2r)(-3s)$ **6rs**
15. $6(-2m)(3n)$ **−36mn**

ALGEBRA Evaluate each expression.

16. $-6t$, if $t = 15$ **−90**
17. $7p$, if $p = -9$ **−63**
18. $-4k$, if $k = -16$ **64**
19. aw, if $a = 0$ and $w = -72$ **0**
20. dk, if $d = -12$ and $k = 11$ **−132**
21. st, if $s = -8$ and $t = -10$ **80**
22. $3hp$, if $h = 9$ and $p = -3$ **−81**
23. $-5bc$, if $b = -6$ and $c = 2$ **60**
24. $-4wx$, if $w = -1$ and $x = -8$ **−32**

ind each quotient.

1. $-36 \div 9$ **−4**
2. $112 \div (-8)$ **−14**
3. $-72 \div 2$ **−36**
4. $-26 \div (-13)$ **2**
5. $-144 \div 6$ **−24**
6. $-180 \div (-10)$ **18**
7. $304 \div (-8)$ **−38**
8. $-216 \div (-9)$ **24**
9. $80 \div (-5)$ **−16**
10. $-105 \div 15$ **−7**
11. $120 \div (-30)$ **−4**
12. $-200 \div (-8)$ **25**
13. $42 \div (-6)$ **−7**
14. $144 \div (-12)$ **−12**
15. $-360 \div 9$ **−40**
16. $-84 \div -6$ **14**
17. $125 \div (-5)$ **−25**
18. $180 \div (-15)$ **−12**
19. $-400 \div 20$ **−20**
20. $72 \div (-9)$ **−8**
21. $-156 \div (-2)$ **78**

ALGEBRA Evaluate each expression if $x = -5$, $y = -3$, $z = 2$, and $w = 7$.

22. $25 \div x$ **−5**
23. $-42 \div w$ **−6**
24. $3 \div y$ **−1**
25. $2x \div z$ **−5**
26. $-3x \div y$ **−5**
27. $x \div (-1)$ **5**
28. $xyz \div 10$ **3**
29. $yz \div 2$ **−3**
30. $\dfrac{3y}{-3}$ **3**
31. $\dfrac{6 - y}{y}$ **−3**
32. $\dfrac{w}{-7}$ **−1**
33. $\dfrac{w - x}{y}$ **−4**

9.–14.

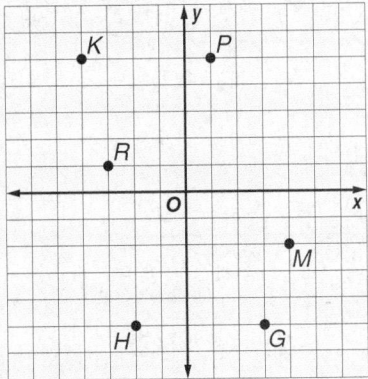

Name the point for each ordered pair graphed at the right.

1. $(-6, 8)$ **D**
2. $(1, -2)$ **J**
3. $(9, 2)$ **C**
4. $(1, 4)$ **L**
5. $(-3, -4)$ **B**
6. $(2, 5)$ **N**
7. $(3, 0)$ **K**
8. $(5, -1)$ **M**

Graph and label each point on a coordinate plane. Name the quadrant in which each point is located. **9–14. See margin for graph.**

9. $H(-2, -5)$ **III**
10. $P(1, 5)$ **I**
11. $R(-3, 1)$ **II**
12. $M(4, -2)$ **IV**
13. $K(-4, 5)$ **II**
14. $G(3, -5)$ **IV**

Extra Practice

Use the Distributive Property to write each expression as an equivalent expression. Then evaluate it.

1. $2(4 + 5)$ **$2 \cdot 4 + 2 \cdot 5$, 18**
2. $4(5 + 3)$ **$4 \cdot 5 + 4 \cdot 3$, 32**
3. $3(7 - 6)$ **$3 \cdot 7 - 3 \cdot 6$, 3**
4. $(2 + 5)9$ **$2 \cdot 9 + 5 \cdot 9$, 63**
5. $(10 - 4)3$ **$10 \cdot 3 - 4 \cdot 3$, 18**
6. $-6(1 + 3)$ **$-6 \cdot 1 - 6 \cdot 3$, -24**

ALGEBRA Use the Distributive Property to write each expression as an equivalent algebraic expression.

7. $3(m + 4)$ **$3m + 12$**
8. $(y + 7)5$ **$5y + 35$**
9. $-6(x + 3)$ **$-6x - 18$**
10. $(p - 4)5$ **$5p - 20$**
11. $-3(s - 9)$ **$-3s + 27$**
12. $5(x + y)$ **$5x + 5y$**
13. $b(c + 3d)$ **$bc + 3bd$**
14. $(a - b)(-5)$ **$-5a + 5b$**
15. $-6(v - 3w)$ **$-6v + 18w$**
16. $5(x + 12)$ **$5x + 60$**
17. $(m - 6)(4)$ **$4m - 24$**
18. $-2(a - b)$ **$-2a + 2b$**
19. $(8 - m)(-3)$ **$-24 + 3m$**
20. $8(p - 3q)$ **$8p - 24q$**
21. $(2x + 3y)(4)$ **$8x + 12y$**
22. $-5(9 - z)$ **$-45 + 5z$**
23. $21(k - 3)$ **$21k - 63$**
24. $(7 - 2h)(-3)$ **$-21 + 6h$**

Identify the like terms in each expression.

1. $3 + 4x + x$ **$4x, x$**
2. $5n + 2 - 3n$ **$5n, -3n$**
3. $6 + 1 + 7y$ **6, 1**
4. $2c + c + 8d$ **$2c, c$**
5. $3a - 9 + b$ **none**
6. $2 + 6k + 7 - 5k$ **2, 7; $6k, -5k$**

ALGEBRA Simplify each expression.

7. $8k + 2k + 7$ **$10k + 7$**
8. $3 + 2b + b$ **$3 + 3b$**
9. $t + 2t$ **$3t$**
10. $9(3 + 2x)$ **$27 + 18x$**
11. $4(y + 2) - 2$ **$4y + 6$**
12. $(6 + 3e)4$ **$24 + 12e$**
13. $4 + 9c + 3(c + 2)$ **$12c + 10$**
14. $5(7 + 2s) + 3(s + 4)$ **$13s + 47$**
15. $9(f + 2) + 14f$ **$23f + 18$**
16. $5a - 9a$ **$-4a$**
17. $-6 + 4x + 9 - 2x$ **$2x + 3$**
18. $6a + 11 + (-15) + 9a$ **$15a - 4$**
19. $2(8w - 7)$ **$16w - 14$**
20. $3(2d + 5) + 4d$ **$10d + 15$**
21. $2 + 4p - 6(p - 2)$ **$-2p + 14$**
22. $-3(b + 4)$ **$-3b - 12$**
23. $-6 + 3s + 11 - 5s$ **$-2s + 5$**
24. $3(x - 5) + 7(x + 2)$ **$10x - 1$**
25. $3q - r + q + 6r$ **$4q + 5r$**
26. $8(r + 1) + 7$ **$8r + 15$**
27. $3p - 2(p + 6q)$ **$p - 12q$**
28. $a + 2b + 4a$ **$5a + 2b$**
29. $9x - 12 + 12$ **$9x$**
30. $1 + g + 5g - 2$ **$-1 + 6g$**

ALGEBRA Solve each equation. Check your solution.

1. $y + 49 = 26$ **−23**
2. $d + 31 = -24$ **−55**
3. $q - 8 = 16$ **24**
4. $x - 16 = 32$ **48**
5. $40 = a + 12$ **28**
6. $b + 12 = -1$ **−13**
7. $21 = u + 6$ **15**
8. $-52 = p + 5$ **−57**
9. $-14 = 5 - g$ **19**
10. $121 = k + (-12)$ **133**
11. $-234 = m - 94$ **−140**
12. $110 = x + 25$ **85**
13. $f - 7 = 84$ **91**
14. $y - 864 = 652$ **1516**
15. $475 + z = -18$ **−493**
16. $x + 12 = -9$ **−21**
17. $15 - h = 11$ **4**
18. $16 = p + 21$ **−5**
19. $-13 + t = -2$ **11**
20. $86 = x + 43$ **43**
21. $y - 11 = -14$ **−3**

ALGEBRA Write and solve an equation to find each number.

22. The sum of −6 and a number is 8. $-6 + x = 8$; **14**
23. When 3 is subtracted from a number, the result is −5. $x - 3 = -5$; **−2**
24. When 7 is added to a number, the result is −9. $n + 7 = -9$; **−16**
25. When a number is decreased by 8, the result is 5. $w - 8 = 5$; **13**

ALGEBRA Solve each equation. Check your solution.

1. $-y = -32$ **32**
2. $7r = -56$ **−8**
3. $\frac{t}{-3} = 12$ **−36**
4. $4 = \frac{s}{-14}$ **−56**
5. $\frac{b}{47} = -2$ **−94**
6. $64 = -4n$ **−16**
7. $-144 = 12q$ **−12**
8. $\frac{r}{11} = -12$ **−132**
9. $-5g = -385$ **77**
10. $-16x = -176$ **11**
11. $-21 = \frac{y}{-4}$ **84**
12. $-372 = 31k$ **−12**
13. $84 = \frac{k}{5}$ **420**
14. $-b = 19$ **−19**
15. $\frac{v}{112} = -9$ **−1008**
16. $-3x = -27$ **9**
17. $\frac{p}{-12} = 4$ **−48**
18. $5q = -100$ **−20**
19. $\frac{d}{11} = -8$ **−88**
20. $-9n = -45$ **5**
21. $125 = -25z$ **−5**

ALGEBRA Write and solve an equation for each sentence.

22. The product of 8 and a number is −40. $8m = -40$; **−5**
23. The quotient of a number and −3 is 27. $\frac{w}{-3} = 27$; **−81**
24. When 6 is multiplied by a number, the result is −24. $6e = -24$; **−4**

ALGEBRA Solve each equation. Check your solution.

1. $3t - 13 = 2$ **5**
2. $-8j - 7 = 57$ **−8**
3. $9d - 5 = 4$ **1**
4. $6 - 3w = -27$ **11**
5. $\frac{k}{6} + 8 = 12$ **24**
6. $-4 = \frac{q}{8} - 19$ **120**
7. $15 - \frac{n}{7} = 13$ **14**
8. $44 = -4 + 8p$ **6**
9. $21 - h = -32$ **53**
10. $-19 = 11b - (-3)$ **−2**
11. $6 = 20 + \frac{x}{3}$ **−42**
12. $9 + 3a = -3$ **−4**
13. $2x - 8 = 10$ **9**
14. $\frac{m}{4} - 6 = 10$ **64**
15. $-12 + 3p = 3$ **5**
16. $-18 = 6a - 6$ **−2**
17. $\frac{t}{-3} + 11 = 23$ **−36**
18. $3 + 2v = 11$ **4**
19. $16 = \frac{k}{3} - 11$ **81**
20. $-6g - 12 = -60$ **8**
21. $15 - 4c = -21$ **9**

Lesson 3-6 (pages 126–130)

ALGEBRA Write and solve an equation for each sentence.

1. Five less than three times a number is 13. $3x - 5 = 13; 6$
2. The product of 2 and a number is increased by 9. The result is 17. $2p + 9 = 17; 4$
3. Ten more than four times a number is 46. $4z + 10 = 46; 9$
4. The quotient of a number and -8, less 5 is -2. $\frac{a}{-8} - 5 = -2; -24$
5. Three more than two times a number is 11. $2n + 3 = 11; 4$
6. The quotient of a number and six, increased by 2 is -5. $\frac{w}{6} + 2 = -5; -42$
7. The product of -3 and a number, decreased by 9 is 27. $-3x - 9 = 27; -12$

Lesson 3-7 (pages 131–136)

ALGEBRA Solve by replacing the variables with the given values.

1. $d = rt$, if $d = 366$ and $t = 3$. **122**
2. $S = (n - 2) \cdot 180$, if $n = 8$. **1080**
3. $A = bh$, if $A = 36$ and $h = 12$. **3**
4. $P = 4s$, if $P = 108$. **27**
5. $V = \ell wh$, if $\ell = 27$, $w = 5$, and $h = 2$. **270**
6. $h = 69 + 2F$, if $F = 42$. **153**

Find the perimeter and area of each rectangle.

7. a rectangle 23 centimeters long and 9 centimeters wide **64 cm, 207 cm²**
8. a 16-foot by 14-foot rectangle **60 ft, 224 ft²**
9. a rectangle with a length of 31 meters and a width of 3 meters **68 m, 93 m²**
10. a square with sides 7 meters long **28 m, 49 m²**

Find the missing dimension of each rectangle.

	Length	Width	Area	Perimeter
11.	9 ft	**14 ft**	126 ft²	46 ft
12.	**6 in.**	18 in.	108 in²	48 in.
13.	13 yd	**21 yd**	273 yd²	68 yd
14.	**14 cm**	12 cm	168 cm²	52 cm
15.	**54 m**	3 m	162 m²	114 m

16. The perimeter of a rectangle is 50 meters. Its width is 10 meters. Find the length. **15 m**
17. The area of a rectangle is 96 square inches. Its length is 12 inches. Find the width. **8 in.**

Lesson 4-1 (pages 148–152)

Use divisibility rules to determine whether each number is divisible by 2, 3, 5, 6, or 10.

1. 98 **2**
2. 243 **3**
3. 800 **2, 5, 10**
4. 252 **2, 3, 6**
5. 105 **3, 5**
6. 210 **2, 3, 5, 6, 10**
7. 225 **3, 5**
8. 180 **2, 3, 5, 6, 10**

List all the factors of each number.

9. 77 **1, 7, 11, 77**
10. 42 **1, 2, 3, 6, 7, 14, 21, 42**
11. 81 **1, 3, 9, 27, 81**
12. 132 **1, 2, 3, 4, 6, 11, 12, 22, 33, 44, 66, 13**

ALGEBRA Determine whether each expression is a monomial. Explain why or why not. **13. yes; the product of a number and a variable   14. No; terms are subtracted.**

13. $-6h$
14. $9 - v$
15. g **yes; a variable**
16. $3n + 9$ **No; two terms are added.**
17. 112 **yes; a number**
18. $2(x + 9)$ **No; two terms are added.**

Lesson 4-2

(pages 153–157)

ALGEBRA Write each expression using exponents.

1. $8 \cdot 8 \cdot 8 \cdot 8$ $\mathbf{8^4}$
2. 9 $\mathbf{9^1}$
3. $(-6)(-6)(-6)(-6)(-6)$ $\mathbf{(-6)^5}$
4. $(y \cdot y \cdot y) \cdot (y \cdot y \cdot y \cdot y)$ $\mathbf{y^7}$
5. $a \cdot b \cdot b$ $\mathbf{ab^2}$
6. $4 \cdot 4 \cdot 4 \cdot 4 \cdot x \cdot x \cdot x \cdot y$ $\mathbf{4^4 x^3 y}$
7. $3q \cdot 3q \cdot 3q \cdot 3q \cdot 3q \cdot 3q$ $\mathbf{(3q)^6}$
8. $\underbrace{n \cdot n \cdot n \cdot \ldots \cdot n}_{\text{17 factors}}$ $\mathbf{n^{17}}$
9. $(x + y)(x + y)$ $\mathbf{(x + y)^2}$

Express each number in expanded form. **12.** $(4 \times 10^3) + (0 \times 10^2) + (7 \times 10^1) + (5 \times 10^0)$

10. 56 $\mathbf{(5 \times 10^1) + (6 \times 10^0)}$
11. 231 $\mathbf{(2 \times 10^2) + (3 \times 10^1) + (1 \times 10^0)}$
12. 4075

ALGEBRA Evaluate each expression if $m = 3$, $n = 2$, and $p = -4$.

13. $3m^2$ $\mathbf{27}$
14. $n^0 + m$ $\mathbf{4}$
15. 7^4 $\mathbf{2401}$
16. -5^3 $\mathbf{-125}$
17. p^3 $\mathbf{-64}$
18. $2(m - p)^2$ $\mathbf{98}$
19. $-2n^3 + m$ $\mathbf{-13}$
20. $m - p^2$ $\mathbf{-13}$
21. $(m + n + p)^3$ $\mathbf{1}$
22. $5p - m^2$ $\mathbf{-29}$
23. $(n + p)^4$ $\mathbf{16}$
24. $(m - n)^8$ $\mathbf{1}$

Lesson 4-3

(pages 159–163)

Determine whether each number is *prime* or *composite*.

1. 57 **composite**
2. 369 **composite**
3. 116 **composite**
4. 125 **composite**
5. 83 **prime**
6. 99 **composite**
7. 91 **composite**
8. 79 **prime**

Write the prime factorization of each number. Use exponents for repeated factors.

9. 21 $\mathbf{3 \cdot 7}$
10. 44 $\mathbf{2^2 \cdot 11}$
11. 51 $\mathbf{3 \cdot 17}$
12. 65 $\mathbf{5 \cdot 13}$
13. 30 $\mathbf{2 \cdot 3 \cdot 5}$
14. 28 $\mathbf{2^2 \cdot 7}$
15. 117 $\mathbf{3^2 \cdot 13}$
16. 88 $\mathbf{2^3 \cdot 11}$
17. 54 $\mathbf{2 \cdot 3^3}$
18. 32 $\mathbf{2^5}$
19. 300 $\mathbf{2^2 \cdot 3 \cdot 5^2}$
20. 210 $\mathbf{2 \cdot 3 \cdot 5 \cdot 7}$

ALGEBRA Factor each number or monomial completely.

21. 40 $\mathbf{2 \cdot 2 \cdot 2 \cdot 5}$
22. $630a$ $\mathbf{2 \cdot 3 \cdot 3 \cdot 5 \cdot 7 \cdot a}$
23. 187 $\mathbf{11 \cdot 17}$
24. 310 $\mathbf{2 \cdot 5 \cdot 31}$
25. 510 $\mathbf{2 \cdot 3 \cdot 5 \cdot 17}$
26. 1589 $\mathbf{7 \cdot 227}$
27. $-18ab^2$ $\mathbf{-1 \cdot 2 \cdot 3 \cdot 3 \cdot a \cdot b \cdot b}$
28. $-117x^3$ $\mathbf{-1 \cdot 3 \cdot 3 \cdot 13 \cdot x \cdot x \cdot x}$
29. $105j^2k^5$ $\mathbf{3 \cdot 5 \cdot 7 \cdot j \cdot j \cdot k \cdot k \cdot k \cdot k \cdot k}$

Lesson 4-4

(pages 164–168)

ALGEBRA Find the GCF of each set of numbers or monomials.

1. $27, 45$ $\mathbf{9}$
2. $30, 12$ $\mathbf{6}$
3. $16, 40, 28$ $\mathbf{4}$
4. $18, 17, 15$ $\mathbf{1}$
5. $112, 216$ $\mathbf{8}$
6. $120, 245$ $\mathbf{5}$
7. $84k, 108k^2$ $\mathbf{12k}$
8. $135ab, 171b$ $\mathbf{9b}$
9. $185fg, 74f^2g$ $\mathbf{37fg}$
10. $44m, 60n$ $\mathbf{4}$
11. $90gh, 225k$ $\mathbf{45}$
12. $8, 28h$ $\mathbf{4}$
13. $16w, 28w^3$ $\mathbf{4w}$
14. $24a, 30ab, 66a^2$ $\mathbf{6a}$
15. $13z, 39yz, 52y$ $\mathbf{13}$

ALGEBRA Factor each expression.

16. $3m + 12$ $\mathbf{3(m + 4)}$
17. $5x + 15$ $\mathbf{5(x + 3)}$
18. $4 + 8b$ $\mathbf{4(1 + 2b)}$
19. $7x + 21$ $\mathbf{7(x + 3)}$
20. $2a + 100$ $\mathbf{2(a + 50)}$
21. $42 - 14b$ $\mathbf{14(3 - b)}$
22. $5f - 25$ $\mathbf{5(f - 5)}$
23. $11p - 66$ $\mathbf{11(p - 6)}$
24. $7y - 21$ $\mathbf{7(y - 3)}$
25. $48 + 12s$ $\mathbf{12(4 + s)}$
26. $18 - 2w$ $\mathbf{2(9 - w)}$
27. $24k + 96$ $\mathbf{24(k + 4)}$
28. $2y + 14$ $\mathbf{2(y + 7)}$
29. $42 - 7b$ $\mathbf{7(6 - b)}$
30. $13w + 39$ $\mathbf{13(w + 3)}$

Lesson 4-5

(pages 169–173)

Write each fraction in simplest form. If the fraction is already in simplest form, write *simplified*.

1. $\frac{3}{54}$ $\frac{1}{18}$

2. $\frac{3}{16}$ **simplified**

3. $\frac{6}{58}$ $\frac{3}{29}$

4. $\frac{15}{55}$ $\frac{3}{11}$

5. $\frac{10}{90}$ $\frac{1}{9}$

6. $\frac{20}{49}$ **simplified**

7. $\frac{8}{20}$ $\frac{2}{5}$

8. $\frac{99}{9}$ **11**

9. $\frac{18}{54}$ $\frac{1}{3}$

10. $\frac{21}{64}$ **simplified**

11. $\frac{40}{76}$ $\frac{10}{19}$

12. $\frac{49}{56}$ $\frac{7}{8}$

13. $\frac{22}{66}$ $\frac{1}{3}$

14. $\frac{42}{49}$ $\frac{6}{7}$

15. $\frac{110}{200}$ $\frac{11}{20}$

16. $\frac{b}{b^4}$ $\frac{1}{b^3}$

17. $\frac{16p}{24p}$ $\frac{2}{3}$

18. $\frac{21x^2y}{81y}$ $\frac{7x^2}{27}$

19. $\frac{32d^2}{6d}$ $\frac{16d}{3}$

20. $\frac{72ab}{8b}$ **9a**

21. $\frac{120z^3x}{18zx}$ $\frac{20z^2}{3}$

22. Fourteen inches is what part of 1 yard? $\frac{7}{18}$

23. Nine hours is what part of one day? $\frac{3}{8}$

Lesson 4-6

(pages 175–179)

ALGEBRA Find each product or quotient. Express using exponents.

1. $r^4 \cdot r^2$ r^6

2. $\frac{2^9}{2^3}$ 2^6

3. $\frac{b^{18}}{b^5}$ b^{13}

4. $12^3 \cdot 12^8$ 12^{11}

5. $x \cdot x^9$ x^{10}

6. $(2s^6)(4s^2)$ $8s^8$

7. $w^3 \cdot w^4 \cdot w^2$ w^9

8. $(-2)^2(-2)^5(-2)$ $(-2)^8$

9. $\frac{4^7}{4^6}$ 4

10. $3(f^{17})(f^2)$ $3f^{19}$

11. $(5k)^2 \cdot k^7$ $25k^9$

12. $\frac{6m^8}{3m^2}$ $2m^6$

13. $(3x^4)(-6x)$ $-18x^5$

14. $(4k^4)(-3k)^3$ $-108k^7$

15. $\left(\frac{42}{-6}\right)\left(\frac{g^{10}}{g^3}\right)$ $-7g^7$

Lesson 4-7

(pages 181–185)

ALGEBRA Write each expression using a positive exponent.

1. y^{-9} $\frac{1}{y^9}$

2. m^{-4} $\frac{1}{m^4}$

3. 5^{-3} $\frac{1}{5^3}$

4. 2^{-7} $\frac{1}{2^7}$

5. 6^{-3} $\frac{1}{6^3}$

6. a^{-11} $\frac{1}{a^{11}}$

Write each fraction as an expression using a negative exponent other than −1.

7. $\frac{1}{p^4}$ p^{-4}

8. $\frac{1}{b^9}$ b^{-9}

9. $\frac{1}{5^3}$ 5^{-3}

10. $\frac{1}{7^4}$ 7^{-4}

11. $\frac{1}{15^2}$ 15^{-2}

12. $\frac{1}{25}$ 5^{-2}

13. $\frac{1}{c^7}$ c^{-7}

14. $\frac{1}{64}$ $4^{-3}, 8^{-2},$ or 2^{-6}

Write each decimal using a negative exponent.

15. 0.01 10^{-2}

16. 0.00001 10^{-5}

17. 0.0001 10^{-4} or 100^{-2}

18. 0.001 10^{-3}

19. 0.1 10^{-1}

20. 0.000001 10^{-6}

Evaluate each expression if $x = 3$ and $y = -2$.

21. x^{-2} $\frac{1}{9}$

22. 9^y $\frac{1}{81}$

23. y^{-3} $-\frac{1}{8}$

24. x^{-3} $\frac{1}{27}$

25. y^{-4} $\frac{1}{16}$

26. $(xy)^{-2}$ $\frac{1}{36}$

Extra Practice (side tab)

xpress each number in scientific notation.

1. 9040 **9.04×10^3**
2. 0.015 **1.5×10^{-2}**
3. 6,180,000 **6.18×10^6**
4. 27,210,000 **2.721×10^7**
5. 0.00004637 **4.637×10^{-5}**
6. 0.00546 **5.46×10^{-3}**
7. 500,300,100 **5.003001×10^8**
8. −0.0000032 **-3.2×10^{-6}**

xpress each number in standard form.

9. -9.5×10^{-3} **−0.0095**
10. 8.245×10^{-4} **0.0008245**
11. 8.2×10^4 **82,000**
12. -9.102040×10^2 **−910.204**
13. 4.02×10^3 **4020**
14. 1.6×10^{-2} **0.016**
15. 2.41023×10^6 **2,410,230**
16. 4.21×10^{-5} **0.0000421**

Write each fraction or mixed number as a decimal. Use a bar to show a repeating ecimal.

1. $\frac{6}{10}$ **0.6**
2. $\frac{4}{25}$ **0.16**
3. $-\frac{1}{8}$ **−0.125**
4. $1\frac{3}{4}$ **1.75**
5. $\frac{5}{6}$ **$0.8\overline{3}$**
6. $\frac{9}{20}$ **0.45**
7. $-4\frac{7}{12}$ **$-4.58\overline{3}$**
8. $\frac{8}{11}$ **$0.\overline{72}$**
9. $3\frac{4}{18}$ **$3.\overline{2}$**
10. $-\frac{3}{16}$ **−0.1875**
11. $8\frac{36}{44}$ **$8.\overline{81}$**
12. $\frac{6}{15}$ **0.4**

eplace each ● with <, >, or = to make a true sentence.

13. $\frac{7}{8}$ ● $\frac{5}{6}$ **>**
14. 0.04 ● $\frac{5}{9}$ **<**
15. $\frac{1}{3}$ ● $\frac{2}{7}$ **>**
16. $\frac{3}{5}$ ● $\frac{12}{20}$ **=**
17. $\frac{1}{2}$ ● 0.75 **<**
18. 0.3 ● $\frac{1}{3}$ **<**
19. $\frac{2}{3}$ ● 0.64 **>**
20. $\frac{2}{20}$ ● 0.10 **=**
21. $0.\overline{5}$ ● $\frac{5}{9}$ **=**
22. $2.\overline{1}$ ● $2\frac{1}{10}$ **>**
23. $3\frac{7}{8}$ ● 3.78 **>**
24. $-\frac{6}{7}$ ● $-\frac{5}{6}$ **<**

Write each number as a fraction.

1. $3\frac{4}{5}$ **$\frac{19}{5}$**
2. $-1\frac{2}{9}$ **$-\frac{11}{9}$**
3. 15 **$\frac{15}{1}$**
4. $2\frac{3}{8}$ **$\frac{19}{8}$**
5. −13 **$-\frac{13}{1}$**
6. $2\frac{6}{7}$ **$\frac{20}{7}$**
7. 36 **$\frac{36}{1}$**
8. $-1\frac{3}{5}$ **$-\frac{8}{5}$**

Write each decimal as a fraction or mixed number in simplest form.

9. 0.6 **$\frac{3}{5}$**
10. 0.05 **$\frac{1}{20}$**
11. 0.38 **$\frac{19}{50}$**
12. 4.12 **$4\frac{3}{25}$**
13. 0.375 **$\frac{3}{8}$**
14. −3.24 **$-3\frac{6}{25}$**
15. 0.222... **$\frac{2}{9}$**
16. $-0.\overline{4}$ **$-\frac{4}{9}$**

dentify all sets to which each number belongs.

17. $-4\frac{2}{5}$ **Q**
18. 6 **N, W, I, Q**
19. $3\frac{1}{3}$ **Q**
20. −10 **I, Q**
21. 5.9 **Q**
22. $-\frac{3}{1}$ **I, Q**
23. $\frac{16}{8}$ **N, W, I, Q**
24. 7.02002000... **not rational**

Lesson 5-3

(pages 210–214)

Find each product. Write in simplest form.

1. $\frac{2}{5} \cdot \frac{3}{16}$ $\frac{3}{40}$

2. $3\frac{1}{4} \cdot \frac{2}{11}$ $\frac{13}{22}$

3. $\frac{3}{5}\left(-\frac{5}{12}\right)$ $-\frac{1}{4}$

4. $\frac{5}{8} \cdot \frac{2}{3}$ $\frac{5}{12}$

5. $-\frac{9}{10} \cdot \frac{5}{24}$ $-\frac{3}{16}$

6. $\frac{1}{7} \cdot \frac{21}{22}$ $\frac{3}{22}$

7. $\frac{4}{5} \cdot \frac{1}{8}$ $\frac{1}{10}$

8. $2\frac{2}{6} \cdot 6\frac{2}{7}$ $14\frac{2}{3}$

9. $2\left(-\frac{7}{12}\right)$ $-1\frac{1}{6}$

10. $1\frac{3}{7}\left(-9\frac{4}{5}\right)$ -14

11. $-\frac{6}{7}\left(-\frac{6}{7}\right)$ $\frac{36}{49}$

12. $\frac{6c}{10} \cdot \frac{2}{c}$ $\frac{6}{5}$

13. $\frac{p^3}{4} \cdot \frac{12}{p}$ $3p^2$

14. $\frac{ab}{9} \cdot \frac{3}{b^2}$ $\frac{a}{3b}$

15. $\frac{4x}{3y} \cdot \frac{12y^4}{x^2}$ $\frac{16y^3}{x}$

MEASUREMENT Complete.

16. ____?____ inches = $\frac{5}{12}$ yard **15**

17. ____?____ minutes = $\frac{1}{5}$ hour **12**

18. $\frac{3}{4}$ pound = ____?____ ounces **12**

19. $\frac{7}{8}$ day = ____?____ hours **21**

Lesson 5-4

(pages 215–219)

Find the multiplicative inverse of each number.

1. $\frac{4}{7}$ $\frac{7}{4}$

2. $-\frac{5}{9}$ $-\frac{9}{5}$

3. $\frac{1}{4}$ 4

4. $5\frac{3}{8}$ $\frac{8}{43}$

5. 6 $\frac{1}{6}$

6. -18 $-\frac{1}{18}$

7. $\frac{7}{10}$ $\frac{10}{7}$

8. 2.35 $\frac{20}{47}$

Find each quotient. Write in simplest form.

9. $\frac{4}{5} \div \frac{2}{5}$ 2

10. $-\frac{1}{3} \div \frac{6}{7}$ $-\frac{7}{18}$

11. $\frac{4}{9} \div \frac{1}{5}$ $2\frac{2}{9}$

12. $\frac{2}{3} \div \frac{1}{9}$ 6

13. $\frac{4}{5} \div \left(-\frac{8}{15}\right)$ $-1\frac{1}{2}$

14. $\frac{1}{12} \div \frac{3}{4}$ $\frac{1}{9}$

15. $\frac{3}{4} \div \frac{15}{16}$ $\frac{4}{5}$

16. $16 \div 1\frac{7}{8}$ $8\frac{8}{15}$

17. $2\frac{1}{6} \div \left(-1\frac{1}{5}\right)$ $-1\frac{29}{36}$

18. $-11 \div 3\frac{1}{7}$ $-3\frac{1}{2}$

19. $\frac{8}{45} \div \frac{10}{27}$ $\frac{12}{25}$

20. $-22 \div \left(-5\frac{1}{2}\right)$ 4

21. $\frac{w}{5} \div \frac{w}{35}$ 7

22. $\frac{ab}{12} \div \frac{b}{16}$ $\frac{4a}{3}$

23. $\frac{21y}{8x^2} \div \frac{7y}{16x}$ $\frac{6}{x}$

Lesson 5-5

(pages 220–224)

Find each sum or difference. Write in simplest form.

1. $\frac{2}{7} + \frac{3}{7}$ $\frac{5}{7}$

2. $\frac{8}{15} - \frac{4}{15}$ $\frac{4}{15}$

3. $\frac{3}{7} + \frac{4}{7}$ 1

4. $-\frac{8}{9} + \frac{1}{9}$ $-\frac{7}{9}$

5. $\frac{5}{6} - \frac{1}{6}$ $\frac{2}{3}$

6. $\frac{7}{12} - \frac{5}{12}$ $\frac{1}{6}$

7. $\frac{5}{12} + \frac{11}{12}$ $1\frac{1}{3}$

8. $-\frac{3}{14} - \frac{5}{14}$ $-\frac{4}{7}$

9. $3\frac{1}{4} + \left(-\frac{3}{4}\right)$ $2\frac{1}{2}$

10. $\frac{3}{8} - \left(-1\frac{1}{8}\right)$ $1\frac{1}{2}$

11. $4\frac{9}{10} - 1\frac{1}{10}$ $3\frac{4}{5}$

12. $-5\frac{3}{5} + \left(-2\frac{1}{5}\right)$ $-7\frac{4}{5}$

ALGEBRA Find each sum or difference. Write in simplest form.

13. $\frac{n}{5} + \frac{3n}{5}$ $\frac{4n}{5}$

14. $\frac{15}{k} - \frac{8}{k}, k \neq 0$ $\frac{7}{k}$

15. $12\frac{7}{8}s - 7\frac{3}{8}s$ $5\frac{1}{2}s$

16. $-6\frac{4}{9}t - 3\frac{2}{9}t$ $-9\frac{2}{3}t$

17. $6\frac{1}{4}g + \left(-6\frac{3}{4}g\right)$ $-\frac{1}{2}g$

18. $7\frac{2}{5}n - \left(-4\frac{2}{5}n\right)$ $11\frac{4}{5}n$

Lesson 5-6
(pages 226–230)

Find the least common multiple (LCM) of each set of numbers or monomials.

1. 30, 18 **90**   **2.** 4, 16 **16**   **3.** $3m$, 12 **$12m$**

4. $6a$, $17a^5$ **$102a^5$**   **5.** 2, 5, 7 **70**   **6.** $9x^2y$, $12xy^3$ **$36x^2y^3$**

Find the least common denominator (LCD) of each pair of fractions.

7. $\frac{2}{5}, \frac{6}{25}$ **25**   **8.** $\frac{3}{12}, \frac{4}{5}$ **60**   **9.** $\frac{4}{6}, \frac{7}{9}$ **18**   **10.** $\frac{5}{9}, \frac{7}{12}$ **36**

11. $\frac{1}{4}, \frac{5}{6}$ **12**   **12.** $\frac{11}{20}, \frac{3}{8}$ **40**   **13.** $\frac{3}{10p}, \frac{7}{5p^3}$ **$10p^3$**   **14.** $\frac{1}{a^2}, \frac{2}{3a^4}$ **$3a^4$**

Replace each ● with <, >, or = to make a true statement.

15. $\frac{2}{3}$ ● $\frac{3}{4}$ **<**   **16.** $-\frac{5}{8}$ ● $-\frac{3}{5}$ **<**   **17.** $\frac{4}{6}$ ● $\frac{7}{12}$ **>**

18. $\frac{11}{18}$ ● $\frac{33}{54}$ **=**   **19.** $\frac{4}{19}$ ● $\frac{8}{38}$ **=**   **20.** $\frac{9}{15}$ ● $\frac{1}{2}$ **>**

Lesson 5-7
(pages 232–236)

Find each sum or difference. Write in simplest form.

1. $\frac{1}{5} + \frac{2}{7}$ **$\frac{17}{35}$**   **2.** $\frac{4}{5} + \frac{7}{9}$ **$1\frac{26}{45}$**   **3.** $\frac{1}{9} - \frac{7}{12}$ **$-\frac{17}{36}$**

4. $\frac{8}{11} - \frac{4}{5}$ **$-\frac{4}{55}$**   **5.** $\frac{7}{12} - \left(-\frac{4}{11}\right)$ **$\frac{125}{132}$**   **6.** $-\frac{9}{14} + \frac{15}{16}$ **$\frac{33}{112}$**

7. $-\frac{3}{8} + \left(-1\frac{5}{12}\right)$ **$-1\frac{19}{24}$**   **8.** $-\frac{2}{15} - 3\frac{1}{5}$ **$-3\frac{1}{3}$**   **9.** $-5\frac{1}{3} + \left(-\frac{1}{6}\right)$ **$-5\frac{1}{2}$**

10. $3\frac{2}{5} + 2\frac{4}{7}$ **$5\frac{34}{35}$**   **11.** $-4\frac{1}{8} + 2\frac{5}{9}$ **$-1\frac{41}{72}$**   **12.** $-3\frac{3}{7} - 5\frac{1}{14}$ **$-8\frac{1}{2}$**

13. $11\frac{3}{5} - \left(-6\frac{5}{8}\right)$ **$18\frac{9}{40}$**   **14.** $\frac{5}{14} + \frac{2}{21}$ **$\frac{19}{42}$**   **15.** $2\frac{1}{7} - 3\frac{1}{3}$ **$-1\frac{4}{21}$**

Lesson 5-8
(pages 238–242)

Find the mean, median, and mode for each set of data. If necessary, round to the nearest tenth.

1. 82, 79, 93, 91, 95 **88; 91; none**   **2.** 88, 85, 76, 94, 85, 97 **87.5; 86.5; 85**

3. 23, 32, 19, 27, 41, 21, 26, 32, 23 **27.1; 26; 23 and 32**   **4.** 7.4, 8.3, 6.1, 5.4, 6.8, 7.1, 8.0, 9.2 **7.3; 7.3; none**

5. 0.57, 12.81, 12.6, 0.96, 6.1, 14.3, 4.1, 12.81, 0.96 **7.2; 6.1; 0.96 and 12.81**

6. **11.7; 12; 11**   **7.** **0.4; 0.4; 0.3**

8. POPULATION The population of the Canadian provinces and territories in 2000 is shown in the table. Find the mean, median, and mode of the data. If necessary, round to the nearest tenth. **2365.4; 941.0; none**

Province/Territory	Population (thousands)	Province/Territory	Population (thousands)
Newfoundland	538.8	Saskatchewan	1023.6
Prince Edward Island	138.9	Northwest Territories	42.1
Nova Scotia	941.0	Alberta	2997.2
New Brunswick	756.6	Yukon	30.7
Quebec	7372.4	British Columbia	4063.8
Ontario	11,669.3	Nunavut	27.7
Manitoba	1147.9		

Lesson 5-9

(pages 244–248)

ALGEBRA Solve each equation. Check your solution.

1. $a - 4.86 = 7.2$ **12.06**

2. $n + 6.98 = 10.3$ **3.32**

3. $87.64 = f - (-8.5)$ **79.14**

4. $x - \dfrac{2}{5} = -\dfrac{8}{15}$ $-\dfrac{2}{15}$

5. $3\dfrac{3}{4} + m = 6\dfrac{5}{8}$ $2\dfrac{7}{8}$

6. $4\dfrac{1}{6} = r + 6\dfrac{1}{4}$ $-2\dfrac{1}{12}$

7. $7\dfrac{1}{3} = c - \dfrac{4}{5}$ $8\dfrac{2}{15}$

8. $-4.62 = h + (-9.4)$ **4.78**

9. $w - 1\dfrac{1}{5} = \dfrac{2}{9}$ $1\dfrac{19}{45}$

10. $\dfrac{2}{3}w = \dfrac{1}{6}$ $\dfrac{1}{4}$

11. $6 = -\dfrac{3}{4}x$ -8

12. $-0.5m = -10$ **20**

13. $-\dfrac{1}{9}t = 7$ -63

14. $5\dfrac{2}{3} = y - \dfrac{1}{8}$ $5\dfrac{19}{24}$

15. $-14.8 = -7.1 + t$ -7.7

Lesson 5-10

(pages 249–252)

State whether each sequence is *arithmetic*, *geometric*, or *neither*. If it is arithmetic or geometric, state the common difference or common ratio and write the next three terms of the sequence.

1. $3.5, 4.3, 5.1, \ldots$ **arithmetic; 0.8; 5.9, 6.7, 7.5**

2. $125, 75, 45, \ldots$ **geometric; 0.6; 27, 16.2, 9.72**

3. $5, 10, 20, \ldots$ **geometric; 2; 40, 80, 160**

4. $2401, 49, 7, \ldots$ **neither**

5. $\dfrac{1}{2}, \dfrac{5}{6}, 1\dfrac{1}{6}$ **arithmetic;** $\dfrac{1}{3}$**;** $1\dfrac{1}{2}$**;** $1\dfrac{5}{6}$**;** $2\dfrac{1}{6}$

6. $-\dfrac{4}{5}, 2, -5, 12\dfrac{1}{2}, \ldots$ **geometric;** $-\dfrac{5}{2}$**;** $-31\dfrac{1}{4}, 78\dfrac{1}{8}, -195\dfrac{5}{16}$

7. $\dfrac{1}{4}, \dfrac{1}{2}, 1, 2, \ldots$ **geometric; 2; 4, 8, 16**

8. $23, 18, 13, \ldots$ **arithmetic; −5; 8, 3, −2**

9. $45, 43, 39, 33, \ldots$ **neither**

10. $2, 4, 8, 16, \ldots$ **geometric; 2; 32, 64, 128**

11. $100, 75, 50, \ldots$ **arithmetic; −25; 25, 0, −25**

12. $\dfrac{1}{5}, 1, 5, 25, \ldots$ **geometric; 5; 125, 625, 3125**

Lesson 6-1

(pages 264–268)

Express each ratio as a fraction in simplest form.

1. 15 vans out of 40 vehicles $\dfrac{3}{8}$

2. 6 pens to 14 pencils $\dfrac{3}{7}$

3. 12 dolls out of 18 toys $\dfrac{2}{3}$

4. 8 red crayons out of 36 crayons $\dfrac{2}{9}$

5. 18 boys out of 45 students $\dfrac{2}{5}$

6. 30 birds to 6 birds $\dfrac{5}{1}$

7. 98 ants to 14 ladybugs $\dfrac{7}{1}$

8. 140 dogs to 12 cats $\dfrac{35}{3}$

9. 321 pennies to 96 dimes $\dfrac{107}{32}$

10. 3 cups to 3 quarts $\dfrac{1}{4}$

Express each ratio as a unit rate. Round to the nearest tenth, if necessary.

11. 343.8 miles on 9 gallons **38.2 mi/gal**

12. $7.95 for 5 pounds **$1.60/lb**

13. $52 for 8 tickets **$6.50/ticket**

14. $43.92 for 4 CDs **$11/CD**

15. 450 miles in 8 hours **56.3 mi/h**

16. $3.96 for 12 cans of pop **$0.3/can**

17. $3.84 for 64 ounces **$0.06/oz**

18. 200 yards in 32.3 seconds **6.2 yd/s**

19. **MONEY** Which costs more per notebook, a 4-pack of notebooks for $3.98 or a 5-pack of notebooks for $4.99? Explain. **Since the 4-pack costs $0.995 per notebook and the 5-pack costs $0.998 per notebook, the 5-pack costs more per notebook.**

20. **ANIMALS** A cheetah can run 70 miles in 1 hour. How many feet is this per second? Round to the nearest whole number. **103 ft/s**

Lesson 6-2

(pages 270–274)

ALGEBRA Solve each proportion.

1. $\frac{7}{k} = \frac{49}{63}$ **9**

2. $\frac{s}{4.8} = \frac{30.6}{28.8}$ **5.1**

3. $\frac{6}{11} = \frac{19.2}{g}$ **35.2**

4. $\frac{8}{13} = \frac{b}{65}$ **40**

5. $\frac{x}{12} = \frac{26}{24}$ **13**

6. $\frac{21}{p} = \frac{3}{9}$ **63**

7. $\frac{6.5}{8} = \frac{w}{20}$ **16.25**

8. $\frac{10}{4.21} = \frac{7}{y}$ **2.947**

**Write a proportion that could be used to solve for each variable.
Then solve.**

9. 6 plums at \$1
10 plums at d $\frac{6}{\$1.00} = \frac{10}{d}$; **\$1.67**

10. 8 gallons at \$9.36
f gallons at \$17.55 $\frac{8}{\$9.36} = \frac{f}{\$17.55}$; **15**

11. 3 packages at \$53.67
7 packages at m $\frac{3}{\$53.67} = \frac{7}{m}$; **\$125.23**

12. 10 cards at \$7.50
p cards at \$18 $\frac{10}{\$7.50} = \frac{p}{\$18.00}$; **24**

13. 12 cookies at \$3.00
16 cookies at s $\frac{12}{\$3.00} = \frac{16}{s}$; **\$4.00**

14. 6 toy cars at \$4.50
c toy cars at \$6.75 $\frac{6}{\$4.50} = \frac{c}{\$6.75}$; **9**

Lesson 6-3

(pages 276–280)

On a set of architectural drawings for a school, the scale is
1 inch = 4 feet. Find the actual length of each room.

Room	Drawing Distance	
1. Classroom	5 inches	**40 ft**
2. Principal's Office	1.75 inches	**14 ft**
3. Library	$7\frac{1}{2}$ inches	**60 ft**
4. Cafeteria	$9\frac{1}{4}$ inches	**74 ft**
5. Gymnasium	12.2 inches	**97.6 ft**
6. Nurse's Office	1.3 inches	**10.4 ft**

Lesson 6-4

(pages 281–285)

**Express each decimal or fraction as a percent. Round to the nearest tenth percent,
if necessary.**

1. 0.42 **42%**

2. 0.06 **6%**

3. 1.35 **135%**

4. 0.001 **0.1%**

5. 0.99 **99%**

6. 3.6 **360%**

7. 0.8 **80%**

8. 0.0052 **0.52%**

9. 0.00009 **0.009%**

10. $\frac{17}{50}$ **34%**

11. $\frac{9}{25}$ **36%**

12. $\frac{12}{8}$ **150%**

13. $\frac{7}{40}$ **17.5%**

14. $\frac{11}{33}$ **33.3%**

15. $\frac{36}{27}$ **133.3%**

**Express each percent as a fraction or mixed number in simplest form and as a
decimal.**

16. 32% $\frac{8}{25}$; **0.32**

17. 15% $\frac{3}{20}$; **0.15**

18. $88\frac{1}{2}\%$ $\frac{177}{200}$; **0.885**

19. 250% $\frac{5}{2}$; **2.5**

20. 21% $\frac{21}{100}$; **0.21**

21. 64% $\frac{16}{25}$; **0.64**

22. 25% $\frac{1}{4}$; **0.25**

23. 131% $\frac{131}{100}$; **1.31**

24. 72.5% $\frac{29}{40}$; **0.725**

25. $66\frac{2}{3}\%$ $\frac{2}{3}$; **0.$\overline{6}$**

26. 0.06% $\frac{3}{5000}$; **0.0006**

27. 315% $3\frac{3}{20}$; **3.15**

9. fraction method: $\frac{3}{5} \times 50$ or 30

10. fraction method: $\frac{1}{5} \times 40$ or 8

11. fraction method: $\frac{8}{10} \times 60$ or 48

12. meaning of percent method: 125% means about 125 for every 100 or about 13 for every 10. 81 has about 8 tens. $8 \times 13 = 104$. So, 125% of 81 is about 104.

13. 1% method: Since 1% of 502 is about 5, $\frac{1}{2}$% of 502 is about $\frac{1}{2}$ of 5 or 2.5.

14. fraction method: $\frac{3}{10} \times 20$ or 6

Extra Practice

Lesson 6-5

(pages 288–292)

Use the percent proportion to solve each problem. Round to the nearest tenth.

1. What is 81% of 134? **108.5**
2. 52.08 is 21% of what number? **248**
3. 11.18 is what percent of 86? **13%**
4. What is 120% of 312? **374.4**
5. 140 is what percent of 400? **35%**
6. 430.2 is 60% of what number? **717**
7. 32 is what percent of 80? **40%**
8. What is 15% of 125? **18.8**
9. 22 is what percent of 110? **20%**
10. 9.4 is 40% of what number? **23.5**
11. What is 41.5% of 95? **39.4**
12. 17.92 is what percent of 112? **16%**

13. **FOOD** If 28 of the 50 soup cans on a shelf are chicken noodle soup, what percent of the cans are chicken noodle soup? **56%**

14. **SCHOOL** Of the students in a classroom, 60% are boys. If there are 20 students, how many are boys? **12**

Lesson 6-6

(pages 293–297)

Find the percent of each number mentally.

1. 40% of 60 **24**
2. 25% of 72 **18**
3. 50% of 96 **48**
4. $33\frac{1}{3}$% of 24 **8**
5. 150% of 42 **63**
6. $37\frac{1}{2}$% of 80 **30**
7. 200% of 125 **250**
8. $66\frac{2}{3}$% of 45 **30**

Estimate. Explain which method you used to estimate.

9. 60% of 49 **30**
10. 19% of 41 **8**
11. 82% of 60 **48**
12. 125% of 81 **104**
13. $\frac{1}{2}$% of 502 **2.5**
14. 31% of 19 **6**

9–14. Sample answers are given. See margin for explanations.

Lesson 6-7

(pages 298–302)

Solve each problem using an equation.

1. 9.28 is what percent of 58? **16%**
2. What number is 43% of 110? **47.3**
3. 80% of what number is 90? **112.5**
4. What number is 61% of 524? **319.64**
5. 126 is what percent of 90? **140%**
6. 52% of what number is 109.2? **210**
7. 62% of what number is 29.76? **48**
8. 54 is what percent of 90? **60%**
9. Find 78% of 125. **97.5**
10. What is 0.2% of 12? **0.024**
11. 66% of what number is 49.5? **75**
12. 36.45 is what percent of 81? **45%**

Find the discount to the nearest cent.

13. $35 skirt, 20% off **$7**
14. $108 lamp, 25% off **$27**

Find the interest to the nearest cent.

15. $1585 at 6% for 5 years **$475.50**
16. $2934 at 5.75% for $3\frac{1}{2}$ years **$590.47**

17. **BOOKS** A dictionary is on sale at a 15% discount. Find the sale price of the dictionary if it normally sells for $29.99. **$25.49**

Lesson 6-8

(pages 304–308)

State whether each change is a *percent of increase* or a *percent of decrease*. Then find the percent of change. Round to the nearest tenth, if necessary.

1. from $56 to $42 **D; −25%**
2. from $26 to $29.64 **I; 14%**
3. from $22 to $37.18 **I; 69%**
4. from $137.50 to $85.25 **D; −38%**
5. from $455 to $955.50 **I; 110%**
6. from $3 to $15 **I; 400%**
7. from $750.75 to $765.51 **I; 2%**
8. from $953 to $476.50 **D; −50%**
9. from $101.25 to $379.69 **I; 275%**
10. from $836 to $842.27 **I; $\frac{3}{4}$%**
11. from $18 to $24 **I; $33\frac{1}{3}$%**
12. from $250 to $100 **D; −60%**
13. from $107.50 to $92 **D; −14.4%**
14. from $365 to $394.20 **I; 8%**

15. **BASEBALL CARDS** A baseball card collection contains 340 baseball cards. What is the percent of change if 25 cards are removed from the collection? **−7.4%**

3. $\frac{6}{15}$; **40%** 4. $\frac{2}{15}$; **13%** 7. $\frac{10}{15}$; **67%** 8. $\frac{13}{15}$; **87%** 12. $\frac{9}{15}$; **60%**

Lesson 6-9

(pages 310–314)

There are 4 blue marbles, 6 red marbles, 3 green marbles, and 2 yellow marbles in a bag. Suppose you select one marble at random. Find the probability of each outcome. Express each probability as a fraction and as a percent. Round to the nearest percent.

1. P(green) $\frac{3}{15}$; **20%**
2. P(blue) $\frac{4}{15}$; **27%**
3. P(red)
4. P(yellow)
5. P(not green) $\frac{12}{15}$; **80%**
6. P(white) **0; 0%**
7. P(blue or red)
8. P(not yellow)
9. P(neither red nor green) $\frac{6}{15}$; **40%**
10. P(red or yellow) $\frac{8}{15}$; **53%**
11. P(not orange) **1; 100%**
12. P(neither blue nor yellow)
13. P(not red) $\frac{9}{15}$; **60%**
14. P(not green or yellow) $\frac{10}{15}$; **67%**

15. Suppose two number cubes are rolled. What is the probability of rolling a sum greater than 8? $\frac{5}{18}$ **or about 28%**

16. **COOKIES** A sample from a package of assorted cookies revealed that 20% of the cookies were sugar cookies. Suppose there are 45 cookies in the package. How many can be expected to be sugar cookies? **9**

Lesson 7-1

(pages 330–333)

ALGEBRA Solve each equation. Check your solution.

1. $-7h - 5 = 4 - 4h$ **−3**
2. $5t - 8 = 3t + 12$ **10**
3. $m + 2m + 1 = 7$ **2**
4. $2y + 5 = 6y + 25$ **−5**
5. $3z - 1 = 23 - 3z$ **4**
6. $5a - 5 = 7a - 19$ **7**
7. $5x + 12 = 3x - 6$ **−9**
8. $3x - 5 = 7x + 7$ **−3**
9. $5c + 9 = 8c$ **3**
10. $3p = 4 - 9p$ $\frac{1}{3}$
11. $6z + 5 = 4z - 7$ **−6**
12. $2a + 4.2 = 3a - 1.6$ **5.8**
13. $3.21 - 7y = 10y - 1.89$ **0.3**
14. $1.9s + 6 = 3.1 - s$ **−1**
15. $12b - 5 = 3b$ $\frac{5}{9}$
16. $9 + 11a = -5a + 21$ $\frac{3}{4}$
17. $6 - x = -5$ **11**
18. $2.8 - 3w = 4.6 - w$ **−0.9**
19. $2.9y + 1.7 = 3.5 + 2.3y$ **3**
20. $2.85a - 7 = 12.85a - 2$ $-\frac{1}{2}$

7.
1 2 3 4 5 6 7 8 9

8.
−8 −7 −6 −5 −4 −3 −2 −1 0

9.
−3 −2 −1 0 1 2 3 4 5

10.
−3 −2 −1 0 1 2 3 4 5

11.
−4 −3 −2 −1 0 1 2 3 4

12.
−6 −5 −4 −3 −2 −1 0 1 2

Extra Practice

Answers Lesson 8-1

1. Yes; each x value is paired with only one y value.
2. Yes; each x value is paired with only one y value.
3. No; 2 is paired with 9 and 36.
4. Yes; each x value is paired with only one y value.
5. No; 1 is paired with 0, 9, and 18.
6. Yes; each x value is paired with only one y value.
7. Yes; each x value is paired with only one y value.
8. No; −2 is paired with 4 and 8 and −1 is paired with 5 and 7.
9. Yes; each x value is paired with only one y value.
10. Yes; each x value is paired with only one y value.

Extra Practice

Lesson 7-2
(pages 334–338)

ALGEBRA Solve each equation. Check your solution.

1. $6(m − 2) = 12$ **4**
2. $4(x − 3) = 4$ **4**
3. $5(2d + 4) = 35$ **1.5**
4. $w + 6 = 2(w − 6)$ **18**
5. $3(b + 1) = 4b − 1$ **4**
6. $7w − 6 = 3(w + 6)$ **6**
7. $4(k − 6) = 6(k + 2)$ **−18**
8. $3x − 0.8 = 3x + 4$ **∅**
9. $\frac{5}{9}g + 8 = \frac{1}{6}g + 1$ **−18**
10. $\frac{s − 3}{7} = \frac{s + 5}{9}$ **31**

11. **ALGEBRA** Find the solution of $3(3x + 4) − 2 = 9x + 10$. **all numbers**

12. **NUMBER THEORY** Four times the sum of three consecutive integers is 48.
   a. Write an equation that could be used to find the integers. $4[x + (x + 1) + (x + 2)] = 48$
   b. What are the integers? **3, 4, 5**

Lesson 7-3
(pages 340–344)

ALGEBRA For the given value, state whether each inequality is *true* or *false*.

1. $5 \geq 2t − 12$; $t = 11$ **false**
2. $7 + n < 25$; $n = 4$ **true**
3. $6r − 18 > 0$; $r = 3$ **false**
4. $3n + 2 < 26$; $n = 3$ **true**
5. $h − 19 < 13$; $h = 28$ **true**
6. $20m \geq 10$; $m = 0$ **false**

ALGEBRA Graph each inequality on a number line. **7–12. See margin.**

7. $b \geq 4$
8. $x < −2$
9. $y > 2$
10. $m \leq 0$
11. $p > −1$
12. $q \geq −3$

ALGEBRA Write an inequality for each sentence.

13. At least 295 students attend Greenville Elementary School. $s \geq 295$
14. An electric bill increased by $15 is now more than $80. $b + 15 > 80$
15. If 8 times a number is decreased by 2, the result is less than 15. $8n − 2 < 15$
16. Citizens who are 18 years of age or older can vote. $a \geq 18$
17. One dozen jumbo eggs must weigh at least 30 ounces. $w \geq 30$
18. A healthful breakfast cereal should contain no more than 5 grams of sugar. $s \leq 5$

Lesson 7-4
(pages 345–349)

ALGEBRA Solve each inequality and check your solution.

1. $m + 9 < 14$ **$m < 5$**
2. $k + (−5) < −12$ **$k < −7$**
3. $−15 < v − 1$ **$−14 < v$**
4. $−7 + f \geq 47$ **$f \geq 54$**
5. $r > −15 − 8$ **$r > −23$**
6. $18 \geq s − (−4)$ **$14 \geq s$**
7. $38 < r − (−6)$ **$32 < r$**
8. $z − 9 \leq −11$ **$z \leq −2$**
9. $−16 + c \geq 1$ **$c \geq 17$**
10. $d + 1.4 < 6.8$ **$d < 5.4$**
11. $−3 + x > 11.9$ **$x > 14.9$**
12. $−0.2 \geq 0.3 + y$ **$y \leq −0.5$**
13. $h + 5.7 > 21.3$ **$h > 15.6$**
14. $t − 8.5 > −4.2$ **$t > 4.3$**
15. $−13.2 > w − 4.87$ **$w < −8.33$**
16. $a + \frac{5}{12} \geq \frac{7}{18}$ **$a \geq −\frac{1}{36}$**
17. $7\frac{1}{2} < n − \left(−\frac{7}{8}\right)$ **$6\frac{5}{8} < n$**
18. $\frac{2}{3} \leq a − \frac{5}{6}$ **$1\frac{1}{2} \leq a$**
19. $−7.42 \leq d − 5.9$ **$−1.52 \leq d$**

Lesson 7-5

(pages 350–354)

ALGEBRA Solve each inequality and check your solution.

1. $6p < 78$ **$p < 13$**
2. $\frac{m}{-3} > 24$ **$m < -72$**
3. $-18 < 3b$ **$b > -6$**

4. $-5k \geq 125$ **$k \leq -25$**
5. $-75 > \frac{a}{5}$ **$-375 > a$**
6. $\frac{w}{6} < -5$ **$w < -30$**

7. $8 < \frac{2}{3}c$ **$12 < c$**
8. $\frac{m}{1.3} \geq 0.5$ **$m \geq 0.65$**
9. $0.4y > -2$ **$y > -5$**

10. $-\frac{1}{2}d \leq -5\frac{1}{2}$ **$d \geq 11$**
11. $\frac{2}{7}t < 4$ **$t < 14$**
12. $\frac{1}{5}m \geq 4\frac{3}{5}$ **$m \geq 23$**

13. $\frac{y}{-13} > -20$ **$y < 260$**
14. $14t < 266$ **$t < 19$**
15. $\frac{g}{-25} \geq 8$ **$g \leq -200$**

16. The product of a number and -4 is greater than or equal to -20. What is the number? **$n \leq 5$**

Lesson 7-6

(pages 355–359)

ALGEBRA Solve each inequality and check your solution.

1. $2m + 1 < 9$ **$m < 4$**
2. $-3k - 4 \leq -22$ **$k \geq 6$**
3. $-2 > 10 - 2x$ **$6 < x$**

4. $-6a + 2 \geq 14$ **$a \leq -2$**
5. $3y + 2 < -7$ **$y < -3$**
6. $\frac{d}{4} + 3 \geq -11$ **$d \geq -56$**

7. $\frac{x}{3} - 5 < 6$ **$x < 33$**
8. $-5g + 6 < 3g + 26$ **$g > -2.5$**
9. $-3(m - 2) > 12$ **$m < -2$**

10. $\frac{r}{5} - 6 \leq 3$ **$r \leq 45$**
11. $\frac{3(n+1)}{7} \geq \frac{n+4}{5}$ **$n \geq 1.625$**
12. $\frac{n+10}{-3} \leq 6$ **$n \geq -28$**

13. Five plus three times a number is less than the difference of two times the same number and 4. What is the number? **$x < -9$**

Lesson 8-1

(pages 369–373)

Determine whether each relation is a function. Explain. **1–10. See margin for explanations.**

1. $\{(3, 6), (35, 64), (1, 1), (21, 7)\}$ **yes**
2. $\{(32, 24), (27, 24), (36, 24), (45, 24)\}$ **yes**

3. $\{(2, 9), (3, 18), (4, 27), (2, 36)\}$ **no**
4. $\left\{\left(\frac{1}{2}, 3\right), \left(\frac{1}{4}, 5\right), \left(\frac{1}{6}, 7\right), \left(\frac{1}{8}, 9\right), \left(\frac{1}{10}, 11\right)\right\}$ **yes**

5. $\{(1, 0), (1, 9), (1, 18)\}$ **no**
6. $\{(5, 5), (6, 6), (7, 7), (8, 7)\}$ **yes**

7. **yes**

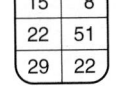

x	y
8	8
15	8
22	51
29	22

8. **no**

x	y
-2	4
-1	5
0	6
-1	7
-2	8

9. **yes**

10. **yes**

13.

14.

15.

16.

17.

18.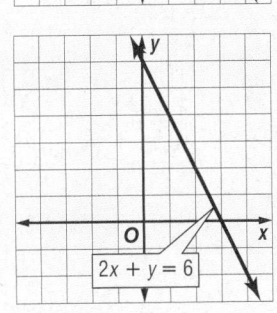

Answers Lesson 8-2

See page 741.

Answers Lesson 8-3

7.

8.

9.

10.

11.

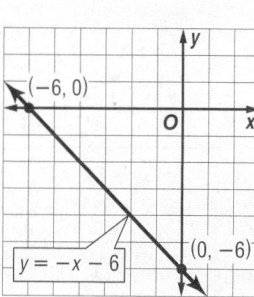

Lesson 8-2

(pages 375–379)

Find four solutions of each equation. Write the solutions as ordered pairs.

1. $x = 4$ **(4, 2), (4, 3), (4, 5), (4, 6)**
2. $y = 0$ **(1, 0), (5, 0), (6, 0), (0, 0)**
3. $x + y = 2$ **(2, 0), (1, 1), (0, 2), (−1, 3)**
4. $y = 2x − 6$ **(0, −6), (1, −4), (2, −2), (3, 0)**
5. $x − y = 5$ **(8, 3), (7, 2), (6, 1), (5, 0)**
6. $3x − y = 8$ **(3, 1), (4, 4), (0, −8), (2, −2)**
7. $y = \frac{1}{2}x − 3$ **(0, −3), (2, −2), (4, −1), (6, 0)**
8. $y = \frac{1}{3}x + 1$ **(0, 1), (3, 2), (−3, 0), (6, 3)**
9. $2x + y = −2$ **(1, −4), (0, −2), (−1, 0), (−2, 2)**
10. $2x + 3y = 12$ **(6, 0), (0, 4), (3, 2), (−3, 6)**
11. $x + 2y = −4$ **(0, −2), (2, −3), (−2, −1), (−4, 0)**
12. $2x − 4y = 8$ **(4, 0), (0, −2), (2, −1), (−2, −3)**

1–12. Sample answers are given.

ALGEBRA Graph each equation by plotting ordered pairs. 13–18. See margin.

13. $y = x + 4$
14. $y = 4x$
15. $x + y = 3$
16. $y = x − 3$
17. $y = −2x + 5$
18. $2x + y = 6$

Lesson 8-3

(pages 381–385)

Find the x-intercept and the y-intercept for the graph of each equation.

1. $y = x + 7$ **−7; 7**
2. $y = 3x + 12$ **−4; 12**
3. $4x + 3y = 24$ **6; 8**
4. $y = 8 − 2x$ **4; 8**
5. $−5x + y = −10$ **2; −10**
6. $y = \frac{2}{3}x − 7$ **$\frac{21}{2}$; −7**

ALGEBRA Graph each equation using the x- and y-intercepts. 7–12. See margin.

7. $2x + y = 6$
8. $−4x + y = 8$
9. $3x − 3y = −12$
10. $x + 2y = −4$
11. $y = −x − 6$
12. $y = −1$

Lesson 8-4

(pages 387–391)

Find the slope of each line.

1.   **3**

2. 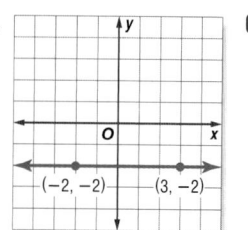 **0**

Find the slope of the line that passes through each pair of points.

3. $P(3, 8), Q(4, −3)$ **−11**
4. $D(4, 5), E(−3, −9)$ **2**
5. $L(−1, 2), M(0, 5)$ **3**
6. $J(6, 2), K(6, −4)$ **undefined**
7. $B(8, −3), C(−4, 1)$ **$−\frac{1}{3}$**
8. $D(1, 5), E(3, 10)$ **$\frac{5}{2}$**
9. $H(7, 2), I(−2, −2)$ **$\frac{4}{9}$**
10. $K(2, −4), L(5, −19)$ **−5**
11. $G(5, 6), H(7, 6)$ **0**
12. $A(−6, −3), B(−9, 4)$ **$−\frac{7}{3}$**
13. $P(−1, −6), Q(−5, −10)$ **1**
14. $B(5, 9), C(−4, −5)$ **$\frac{14}{9}$**

12.

Lesson 8-5

(pages 393–397)

ALGEBRA Find the rate of change for each linear function.

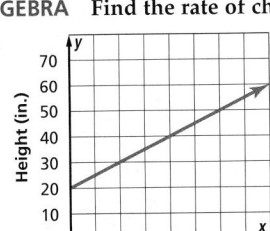

increase of
10 in. per year

2.

increase of
$\frac{1}{2}$ ft per s

Cookies Purchased	x	0	1	2	3
Balance ($)	y	6	5.6	5.2	4.8

decrease of $0.40 per cookie

Suppose y varies directly with x. Write an equation relating x and y.

4. $y = 12$ when $x = -3$ $\;$ $y = -4x$

5. $y = 45$ when $x = 15$ $\;$ $y = 3x$

6. $y = 8$ when $x = 18$ $\;$ $y = \frac{4}{9}x$

7. $y = 7.6$ when $x = 4$ $\;$ $y = 1.9x$

Lesson 8-6

(pages 398–401)

State the slope and the y-intercept for the graph of each equation.

1. $y = x + 9$ $\;$ **1; 9**

2. $y = 2x - 5$ $\;$ **2; −5**

3. $y = -6x$ $\;$ **−6; 0**

4. $y = \frac{3}{2}x$ $\;$ $\frac{3}{2}$**; 0**

5. $y = \frac{1}{3}x + 8$ $\;$ $\frac{1}{3}$**; 8**

6. $x + 2y = 12$ $\;$ $-\frac{1}{2}$**; 6**

Graph each equation using the slope and y-intercept. **7–14. See margin.**

7. $y = 3x - 2$

8. $x - 3y = 9$

9. $y = \frac{1}{2}x + 4$

10. $y = -\frac{2}{3}x - 1$

11. $x - y = -4$

12. $2x + 4y = -4$

13. $y = x + 5$

14. $3x + y = 9$

Lesson 8-7

(pages 404–408)

ALGEBRA Write an equation in slope-intercept form for each line.

1. slope = 3, y-intercept = −4 $\;$ $y = 3x - 4$

2. slope = $\frac{3}{4}$, y-intercept = 1 $\;$ $y = \frac{3}{4}x + 1$

3. slope = −7, y-intercept = −2 $\;$ $y = -7x - 2$

4. slope = $\frac{5}{8}$, y-intercept = 9 $\;$ $y = \frac{5}{8}x + 9$

5. slope = $-\frac{1}{2}$, y-intercept = 0 $\;$ $y = -\frac{1}{2}x$

6. slope = 0, y-intercept = −6 $\;$ $y = -6$

ALGEBRA Write an equation in slope-intercept form for the line passing through each pair of points.

7. (4, 7) and (0, 3) $\;$ $y = x + 3$

8. (3, −6) and (−1, 2) $\;$ $y = -2x$

9. (8, 7) and (0, 0) $\;$ $y = \frac{7}{8}x$

10. (1, 4) and (3, −6) $\;$ $y = -5x + 9$

11. (−2, 5) and (3, 9) $\;$ $y = \frac{4}{5}x + \frac{33}{5}$

12. (3, −1) and (5, −1) $\;$ $y = -1$

7.

$y = 3x - 2$

8.

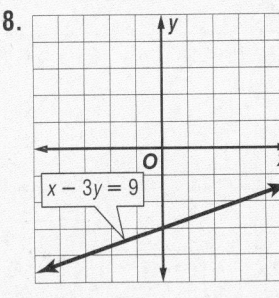

$x - 3y = 9$

9.

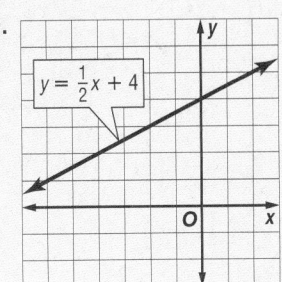

$y = \frac{1}{2}x + 4$

10.

$y = -\frac{2}{3}x - 1$

11.

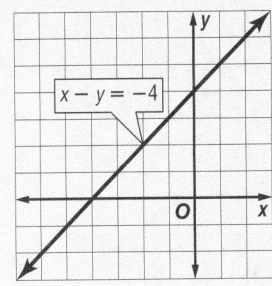

$x - y = -4$

12.

$2x + 4y = -4$

13.

$y = x + 5$

14.

$3x + y = 9$

Answer Lesson 8-8

1.

Answers Lesson 8-9

1.

2.

3.

4.

Lesson 8-8

(pages 409–413)

TECHNOLOGY For Exercises 1–3, use the table that shows the percent of U.S. households owning more than one television set.

Year	1955	1960	1965	1970	1975	1980	1985	1990	1995	2000
Percent	4	12	22	35	43	50	57	65	71	76

1. Make a scatter plot and draw a best-fit line. **See margin.**

2. Write an equation in slope-intercept form for the best-fit line. **Sample answer:** $y = 1.5x - 2925$

3. Use the equation to predict what percent of U.S. households will own more than one television set in 2010.
Sample answer: 90%

Lesson 8-9

(pages 414–418)

Solve each system of equations by graphing. **1–6. See margin for graphs.**

1. $x + 2y = 6$
$y = -0.5x + 3$ **infinitely many**

2. $y = -2$
$4x + 3y = 2$ **(2, −2)**

3. $y = x + 4$
$y = -2x + 4$ **(0, 4)**

4. $y = 4 + \frac{2}{3}x$
$2x = 3y$ **none**

5. $y = x - 2$
$y = -\frac{1}{3}x + 2$ **(3, 1)**

6. $y = \frac{1}{2}x + 6$
$2x + y = 1$ **(−2, 5)**

ALGEBRA Solve each system of equations by substitution.

7. $x + y = 4$
$y = 2$ **(2, 2)**

8. $2x + y = 8$
$x = 2$ **(2, 4)**

9. $y = x - 7$
$x = 7$ **(7, 0)**

10. $x = 3$
$y = 4$ **(3, 4)**

11. $y = 1$
$2y + x = 1$ **(−1, 1)**

12. $y = 2x + 3$
$y = 5$ **(1, 5)**

Lesson 8-10

(pages 419–422)

Graph each inequality. **1–9. See margin.**

1. $y > 2x - 2$ **2.** $y \geq x$ **3.** $y < 1$

4. $x + y \leq -1$ **5.** $y + 3x \leq 0$ **6.** $x < -3$

7. $2x + 3y \geq 12$ **8.** $-2x + y > -1$ **9.** $y \geq -4$

WORK For Exercises 10–12, use the following information.
Seth can tutor students and volunteer at a soup kitchen no more than 9 evenings per month.

10. Write an inequality to represent this situation. $x + y \leq 9$

11. Graph the inequality. **See margin.**

12. Use the graph to determine how many days each month that Seth could tutor and volunteer. List two possibilities. **Sample answer: tutor 4 h, volunteer 5 h; tutor 6 h, volunteer 3 h**

5.

6.

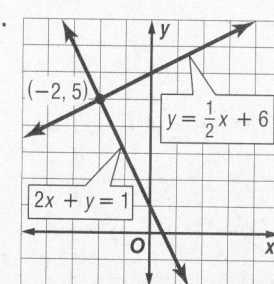

Lesson 9-1

(pages 436–440)

Find each square root, if possible.

1. $\sqrt{36}$ **6**
2. $-\sqrt{81}$ **−9**
3. $\sqrt{\frac{1}{4}}$ **$\frac{1}{2}$**
4. $-\sqrt{144}$ **−12**
5. $\sqrt{-25}$ **not possible**
6. $\sqrt{1.96}$ **1.4**
7. $\sqrt{-100}$ **not possible**
8. $-\sqrt{0.49}$ **−0.7**
9. $\sqrt{400}$ **20**

Use a calculator to find each square root to the nearest tenth.

10. $\sqrt{21}$ **4.6**
11. $\sqrt{99}$ **9.9**
12. $-\sqrt{60}$ **−7.7**
13. $\sqrt{124}$ **11.1**
14. $-\sqrt{350}$ **−18.7**
15. $\sqrt{18.6}$ **4.3**
16. $-\sqrt{42}$ **−6.5**
17. $-\sqrt{84.2}$ **−9.2**
18. $\sqrt{182}$ **13.5**

Estimate each square root to the nearest whole number. Do not use a calculator.

19. $\sqrt{21}$ **5**
20. $-\sqrt{85}$ **−9**
21. $\sqrt{7.3}$ **3**
22. $\sqrt{1.99}$ **1**
23. $-\sqrt{62}$ **−8**
24. $\sqrt{74.1}$ **9**
25. $\sqrt{810}$ **28**
26. $-\sqrt{88.8}$ **−9**
27. $\sqrt{1000}$ **32**

Lesson 9-2

(pages 441–445)

Name all of the sets of numbers to which each real number belongs.
Let N = natural numbers, W = whole numbers, Z = integers, Q = rational numbers, and I = irrational numbers.

1. 15 **N, W, Z, Q**
2. 0 **W, Z, Q**
3. $\frac{3}{8}$ **Q**
4. 0.666… **Q**
5. 1.75 **Q**
6. $\sqrt{2}$ **I**
7. 5.14726… **I**
8. $-\sqrt{36}$ **Z, Q**
9. 0.3535… **Q**

Replace each ● with <, >, or = to make a true statement.

10. $3\frac{3}{4}$ ● $\sqrt{15}$ **<**
11. $-\sqrt{41}$ ● −6.8 **>**
12. 5.2 ● $\sqrt{27.04}$ **=**
13. $-\sqrt{110}$ ● −10.5 **>**

ALGEBRA Solve each equation. Round to the nearest tenth, if necessary.

14. $x^2 = 14$ **3.7, −3.7**
15. $y^2 = 25$ **5, −5**
16. $34 = p^2$ **5.8, −5.8**
17. $55 = h^2$ **7.4, −7.4**
18. $225 = k^2$ **15, −15**
19. $324 = m^2$ **18, −18**
20. $d^2 = 441$ **21, −21**
21. $r^2 = 25{,}000$ **158.1, −158.1**
22. $10{,}000 = x^2$ **100, −100**

Lesson 9-3

(pages 447–451)

Use a protractor to find the measure of each angle.
Then classify each angle as *acute, right,* or *obtuse.*

1. $m\angle PQW$ **120°, obtuse**
2. $m\angle VQW$ **27°, acute**
3. $m\angle TQW$ **90°, right**
4. $m\angle SQW$ **140°, obtuse**
5. $m\angle SQR$ **40°, acute**
6. $m\angle VQR$ **153°, obtuse**

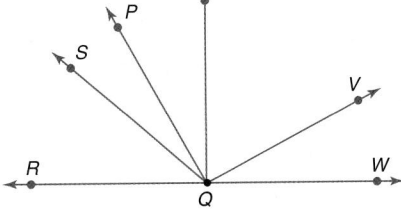

Use a protractor to draw an angle having each measurement. Then classify each angle as *acute, obtuse, right,* or *straight.* **7–12. See margin for drawings.**

7. 35° **acute**
8. 115° **obtuse**
9. 90° **right**
10. 160° **obtuse**
11. 180° **straight**
12. 18° **acute**

1.
2.
3.

4.

5.

6.

7.

8.

9.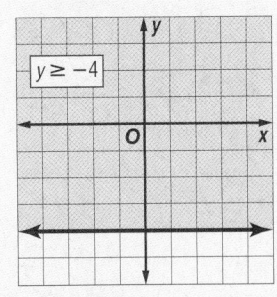

Answers for Lessons 8-10 and 9-3 are continued on the next page.

11.

$x + y \le 9$

Answers Lesson 9-3

7.

35°

8.

115°

9.

90°

10.

160°

11.

180°

12.

18°

Lesson 9-4

(pages 453–457)

Find the value of *x* in each triangle. Then classify each triangle as *acute, right,* **or** *obtuse.*

1. $x°$ 56°   **34°; right**

2. 42° 63° $x°$ **75°; acute**

3. 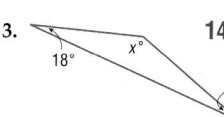 18° $x°$ 16°   **146°; obtuse**

4. 40° 95° $x°$ **45°; obtuse**

5. 31° $x°$ **59°; right**

6. 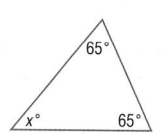 65° $x°$ 65°   **50°; acute**

7. ALGEBRA The measure of the angles of a triangle are in the ratio 1:2:3. What is the measure of each angle? **30°; 60°; 90°**

8. ALGEBRA Determine the measures of the angles of $\triangle ABC$ if the measures of the angles of a triangle are in the ratio 1:1:2. **45°; 45°; 90°**

9. ALGEBRA Suppose the measures of the angles of a triangle are in the ratio 1:9:26. What is the measure of each angle? **5°; 45°; 130°**

Lesson 9-5

(pages 460–464)

Find the length of the hypotenuse in each right triangle. Round to the nearest tenth, if necessary.

1. 4 ft, c ft, 3 ft   **5 ft**

2. 8 in., 6 in., c in.   **10 in.**

3. c m, 24 m, 10 m   **26 m**

If *c* is the measurement of the hypotenuse, find each missing measure. Round to the nearest tenth, if necessary.

4. $a = 7$ m, $b = 24$ m **25 m**

5. $a = 18$ in., $c = 30$ in. **24 in.**

6. $b = 10$ ft, $c = 20$ ft **17.3 ft**

7. $a = 3$ cm, $c = 9$ cm **8.5 cm**

8. $b = 8$ m, $c = 32$ m **31.0 m**

9. $a = 32$ yd, $c = 65$ yd **56.6 yd**

Lesson 9-6

(pages 466–470)

Find the distance between each pair of points. Round to the nearest tenth, if necessary.

1. $A(2, 6)$, $B(-4, 2)$ **7.2**

2. $C(-3, 9)$, $D(2, 4)$ **7.1**

3. $E(6, -4)$, $F(1, -6)$ **5.4**

4. $G(0, -1)$, $H(9, -1)$ **9**

5. $I(-8, -3)$, $J(2, 2)$ **11.2**

6. $K(3, 0)$, $L(-7, -2)$ **10.2**

The coordinates of the endpoints of a segment are given. Find the coordinates of the midpoint of each segment.

7. $M(3, 5)$, $N(7, 1)$ **(5, 3)**

8. $O(-6, 2)$, $P(0, 8)$ **(-3, 5)**

9. $Q(4, -9)$, $R(-2, 7)$ **(1, -1)**

10. $S(13, -1)$, $T(-5, -3)$ **(4, -2)**

Lesson 9-7

(pages 471–475)

In Exercises 1–4, the triangles are similar. Write a proportion to find each missing measure. Then find the value of x.

1.
$\frac{12}{8} = \frac{x}{6}$; 9 in.

2.
$\frac{20}{x} = \frac{8}{4}$; 10 m

3.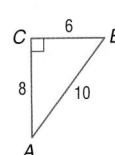
$\frac{9}{6} = \frac{x}{4}$; 6 cm

4.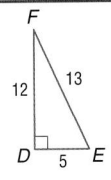
$\frac{18}{10} = \frac{12}{x}$; $6\frac{2}{3}$ in.

Lesson 9-8

(pages 477–481)

Find each sine, cosine, or tangent. Round to four decimal places, if necessary.

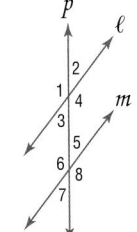

1. $\sin A$ **0.6**
2. $\sin B$ **0.8**
3. $\tan F$ **0.4167**
4. $\sin E$ **0.9231**
5. $\cos A$ **0.8**
6. $\tan A$ **0.75**

Use a calculator to find each value to the nearest ten thousandth.

7. $\sin 21°$ **0.3584**
8. $\tan 83°$ **8.1443**
9. $\cos 45°$ **0.7071**
10. $\tan 10°$ **0.1763**
11. $\sin 72°$ **0.9511**
12. $\cos 3°$ **0.9986**

Lesson 10-1

(pages 490–497)

In the figure at the right, ℓ is parallel to m and p is a transversal. If the measure of angle 2 is 38°, find the measure of each angle.

1. $\angle 1$ **142°**
2. $\angle 4$ **142°**
3. $\angle 3$ **38°**
4. $\angle 6$ **142°**
5. $\angle 5$ **38°**
6. $\angle 8$ **142°**

Find the value of x in each figure.

7. **32°**
8. **162°**
9. **38°**
10. 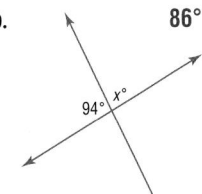 **86°**

Extra Practice

Answers Lesson 10-2

1. $\angle A \cong \angle D$; $\angle B \cong \angle F$; $\angle C \cong \angle E$;
$\overline{AB} \cong \overline{DF}$, $\overline{BC} \cong \overline{FE}$; $\overline{AC} \cong \overline{DE}$;
$\triangle ABC \cong \triangle DFE$

2. $\angle G \cong \angle K$; $\angle H \cong \angle J$; $\angle I \cong \angle I$;
$\overline{GH} \cong \overline{KJ}$, $\overline{HI} \cong \overline{JI}$; $\overline{GI} \cong \overline{KI}$;
$\triangle GHI \cong \triangle KJI$

Answers Lesson 10-3

1. $A'(1, 1)$, $B'(5, -1)$, $C'(1, -3)$

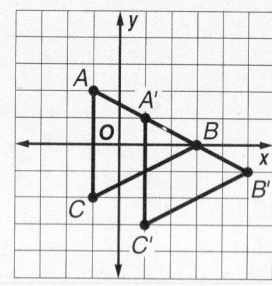

2. $K'(-3, 3)$, $L'(0, -2)$, $M'(-3, -4)$, $N'(-4, -2)$

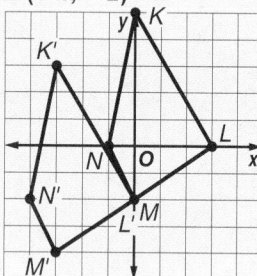

3. $J'(3, 3)$, $K'(1, 3)$, $I'(3, -3)$,

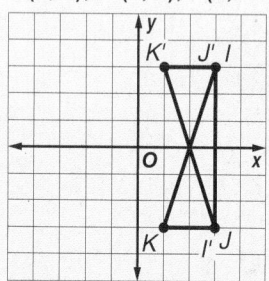

4. $D'(0, 4)$, $E'(-4, 2)$, $F'(-3, -4)$, $G'(0, 1)$

Lesson 10-2

(pages 500–504)

For each pair of congruent triangles, name the corresponding parts. Then complete the congruence statement. 1–2. See margin.

1.
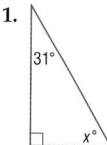

$\triangle ABC \cong \triangle$ __?__ **DFE**

2.

$\triangle GHI \cong \triangle$ __?__ **KJI**

Complete each congruence statement if $\triangle JKL \cong \triangle DGW$.

3. $\angle K \cong$ __?__ $\angle G$

4. $\overline{WG} \cong$ __?__ $\overline{LK}$

5. $\angle D \cong$ __?__ $\angle J$

6. $\overline{KL} \cong$ __?__ $\overline{GW}$

7. $\overline{DG} \cong$ __?__ $\overline{JK}$

8. $\angle W \cong$ __?__ $\angle L$

Lesson 10-3

(pages 506–511)

Find the coordinates of the vertices of each figure after the given translation. Then graph the translation image. 1–4. See margin.

1. $(2, -1)$

2. $(-3, -2)$

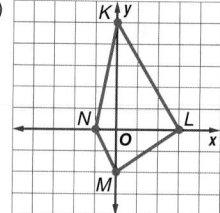

Find the coordinates of the vertices of each figure after a reflection over the given axis. Then graph the reflection image.

3. *x*-axis

4. *y*-axis

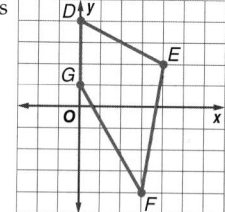

Lesson 10-4

(pages 513–517)

ALGEBRA Find the value of *x*. Then find the missing angle measure.

1.
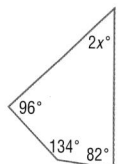
115; 115°

2.
110; 110°

3.

24; 48°

4.

88; 83°; 98°

nd the area of each figure.

 30 in²

2. **75.26 cm²**

10.6 cm

14.2 cm

. **18.125 ft²**

8.5 ft
2.5 ft
6 ft

4. **27 m²**

 9 m

6 m

. What is the height of a parallelogram with a base of 3.4 inches and an area of 32.3 inches? **9.5 in.**

. The bases of a trapezoid measure 8 meters and 12 meters. Find the measure of the height if the trapezoid has an area of 70 square meters. **7 m**

lassify each polygon. Then determine whether it appears to be regular or not egular.

1. **hexagon; regular**

2. **11-gon; not regular**

ind the sum of the measures of the interior angles of each polygon.

3. decagon **1440°**   4. pentagon **540°**   5. nonagon **1260°**

6. hexagon **720°**   7. octagon **1080°**   8. 15-gon **2340°**

ind the circumference and area of each circle. Round to the nearest tenth.

1. 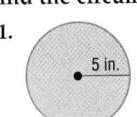 **31.4 in; 78.5 in²**

5 in.

2. **28.3 cm; 63.6 cm²**

9 cm

3. 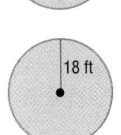 **113.1 ft; 1017.9 ft²**

18 ft

4. **22.9 cm; 41.9 cm²**

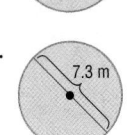 7.3 m

5. The radius is 8.2 feet. **51.5 ft; 211.2 ft²**   6. The diameter is 1.3 yd. **4.1 yd; 1.3 yd²**

7. The diameter is 5.2 yd. **16.3 yd; 21.2 yd²**   8. The radius is 4.8 cm. **30.2 cm; 72.4 cm²**

9. Find the diameter of a circle if its circumference is 18.5 feet. Round to the nearest tenth. **5.9 ft**

10. A circle has an area of 62.9 square inches. What is the radius of the circle? Round to the nearest tenth. **4.5 in.**

1. rectangular prism; bases: *ABCD*, *EFGH*, or *ADHE*, *BCGF*, or *ABFE*, *DCGH*; faces *ABCD*, *ADHF*, *DHGC*, *BCGF*, *ABFE*, *EFGH*; edges: $\overline{AB}$, $\overline{BC}$, $\overline{CD}$, $\overline{DA}$, $\overline{EF}$, $\overline{FG}$, $\overline{GH}$, $\overline{HE}$, $\overline{AE}$, $\overline{DH}$, $\overline{CG}$, $\overline{BF}$; vertices: *A, B, C, D, E, F, G, H*

2. triangular prism; bases: *HJK*, *LMN*; faces: *HJK*, *LMN*, *HJML*, *KJMN*, *HLNK*; edges: $\overline{HJ}$, $\overline{JK}$, $\overline{KH}$, $\overline{LM}$, $\overline{MN}$, $\overline{NL}$, $\overline{JM}$, $\overline{HL}$, $\overline{KN}$; vertices: *I, J, K, L, M, N*

Extra Practice

Lesson 10-8
(pages 539–543)

Find the area of each figure. Round to the nearest tenth.

1. **52.3 ft²**
2. **76.3 cm²**
3. **30.6 yd²**
4. 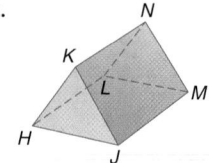 **99.3 in²**

Lesson 11-1
(pages 556–561)

Identify each solid. Name the bases, faces, edges, and vertices. 1–2. See margin.

1.
2.

For Exercises 3–5, use the figure in Exercise 2.

3. State whether $\overline{HK}$ and $\overline{KN}$ are *parallel, skew,* or *intersecting.* **intersecting**
4. Name a segment that is skew to $\overline{JM}$. **$\overline{HK}$ or $\overline{LN}$**
5. Identify two planes that appear to be parallel. ***HJK* and *LMN***

Lesson 11-2
(pages 563–567)

Find the volume of each solid. If necessary, round to the nearest tenth.

1. **1696.5 in³**
2. **180 m³**
3. **80 ft³**
4. **600 cm³**

5. rectangular prism: length $2\frac{1}{2}$ yd, width 7 yd, height 12 yd **210 yd³**

6. cylinder: diameter 9.2 mm, height 16 mm **1063.6 mm³**

7. triangular prism: base of triangle 3.1 cm, altitude of triangle 1.7 cm, height of prism 5.0 cm **13.2 cm³**

8. Find the height of a rectangular prism with a length of 13 inches, width of 5 inches, and volume of 292.5 cubic inches. **4.5 in.**

Lesson 11-3

(pages 568–572)

Find the volume of each solid. If necessary, round to the nearest tenth.

 167.6 ft³
10 ft
4 ft

2. **256 cm³**
12 cm
8 cm
8 cm

cone: diameter 10 yd, height 7 yd **183.3 yd³**

rectangular pyramid: length 6 in., width 6 in., height 9 in. **108 in³**

square pyramid: length $3\frac{1}{4}$ ft, height 12 ft **42.3 ft³**

cone: radius 3.6 cm, height 20 cm **271.4 cm³**

hexagonal pyramid: base area 185 m², height 7 m **431.7 m³**

Lesson 11-4

(pages 573–577)

Find the surface area of each solid. If necessary, round to the nearest tenth.

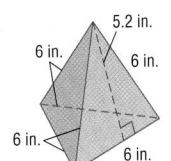 **980.2 in²**
6 in.
20 in.

2. **174 cm²**
3 cm
9 cm
5 cm

cube: side length 6 ft **216 ft²**

4. cylinder: diameter 8 m, height 12 m **402.1 m²**

cylinder: radius 2.5 cm, height 5 cm **117.8 cm²**

6. cube: side length 4.9 m **144.1 m²**

rectangular prism: length 7.6 mm, width 8.4 mm, height 7.0 mm **351.7 mm²**

triangular prism: right triangle 3 in. by 4 in. by 5 in., height of prism 10 in. **132 in²**

Lesson 11-5

(pages 578–582)

Find the surface area of each solid. If necessary, round to the nearest tenth.

 62.4 in²
5.2 in.
6 in.
6 in.
6 in.
6 in.

2. **578.1 cm²**
15 cm
8 cm

3. **88 ft²**
9 ft
4 ft
4 ft

4. **75.2 m²**
4.2 m
9.3 m

5. square pyramid: base side length 1.8 mm, slant height 3.0 mm **14.0 mm²**

6. cone: radius 4 in., slant height 7 in. **138.2 in²**

7. cone: diameter 15.2 cm, slant height 12.3 cm **475.1 cm²**

Answers Lesson 12-1

1.

Stem	Leaf
3	2 7
4	4 9
5	3 9
6	1 9

5 | 3 = 53

2.

Stem	Leaf
0	3 5 8
1	
2	1 4 6
3	0 5 5 8 9

2 | 1 = 21

3.

Stem	Leaf
0	5 6
⋮	
7	3 4 9
⋮	
15	3 7

7 | 3 = 7.3

Answers Lesson 12-1

1–3. See page 751.

4.

Stem	Leaf
17	1 2 9
18	1 1 2 6
19	3 8

$18|6 = 186$

5.

Stem	Leaf
5	5
6	2 7 9
7	1 4 5
8	0 1

$7|5 = 75$

6.

Stem	Leaf
9	8
10	6 9
11	1 7
12	1 5 6
13	2
14	2

$13|2 = 132$

7.

Stem	Leaf
1	7
2	1 4
3	7
4	
5	4
6	9
7	7
8	6
9	2

$8|6 = 86$

8.

Stem	Leaf
5	4 9
6	1 7
7	3 5
8	2 3 9
9	3
10	2

$6|7 = 6.7$

Lesson 11-6
(pages 584–588)

Determine whether each pair of solids is similar.

1. **no**

2.   **yes**

Find the missing measure of each pair of similar solids.

3. $x = 7$ ft

4. $x = 25$ yd

Determine whether each pair of solids is *sometimes*, *always*, or *never* similar. Explain.

5. two cylinders
Sometimes; radii and heights must be proportional.

6. a square pyramid and a triangular pyramid
never; different shapes

Lesson 11-7
(pages 590–594)

Determine the number of significant digits in each measure.

1. 625 ft **3**

2. 30 g **1**

3. 0.24 mm **2**

4. 36.83 L **4**

5. 6.0 in. **2**

6. 3900 ft **2**

7. 4.007 cm **4**

8. 0.0105 m **3**

9. 0.550 g **3**

Calculate. Round to the correct number of significant digits.

10. 32 yd + 16.9 yd **49 yd**

11. 14.36 in. − 9.4 in. **5.0 in.**

12. 20.86 cm − 0.375 cm **20.49 cm**

13. 9.600 m + 4.271 m **13.871 m**

14. 8 ft · 6.2 ft **50 ft²**

15. 7.50 m · 3.01 m **22.6 m²**

16. 41.61 in. + 18.4 in. − 3.65 in. + 7.371 in. **63.7 in.**

Lesson 12-1
(pages 606–611)

Display each set of data in a stem-and-leaf plot. **1–8. See margin.**

1. 37, 44, 32, 53, 61, 59, 49, 69

2. 3, 26, 35, 8, 21, 24, 30, 39, 35, 5, 38

3. 15.7, 7.4, 0.6, 0.5, 15.3, 7.9, 7.3

4. 172, 198, 181, 182, 193, 171, 179, 186, 181

5. 55, 62, 81, 75, 71, 69, 74, 80, 67

6. 121, 142, 98, 106, 111, 125, 132, 109, 117, 126

7. 17, 54, 37, 86, 24, 69, 77, 92, 21

8. 7.3, 6.1, 8.9, 6.7, 8.2, 5.4, 9.3, 10.2, 5.9, 7.5, 8.3

For Exercises 9–11, use the stem-and-leaf plot shown at the right.

9. What is the greatest value? **98**

10. In which interval do most of the values occur? **80–89**

11. What is the median value? **82.5**

Stem	Leaf
7	2 2 3 5 9
8	0 1 1 4 6 6 8 9
9	3 4 8

$9|4 = 94$

Lesson 12-2

(pages 612–616)

Find the range and interquartile range for each set of data.

1. {44, 37, 23, 35, 61, 95, 49, 96} **73; 42**

2. {30, 62, 35, 80, 12, 24, 30, 39, 53, 38} **68; 23**

3. {7.15, 4.7, 6, 5.3, 30.1, 9.19, 3.2} **26.9; 4.49**

4. {271, 891, 181, 193, 711, 791, 861, 818} **710; 607.5**

5.
Stem	Leaf
2	0 1 1 2 4 7 9
3	3 3 6 8 8 8
4	2 4 5 7 9 9
5	2 9

39; 20.5

$3|6 = 36$

6.
Stem	Leaf
4	0 2 2 3 4 5 6 6 7 8
5	1 2 5 5 5 9
6	4 7 8 8
7	0 0 1 4 9 9 9
8	1 7 9
9	0 0 1 3 5

55; 32

$8|7 = 87$

Lesson 12-3

(pages 617–621)

Draw a box-and-whisker plot for each set of data. 1–4. See margin.

1. 32, 54, 88, 17, 29, 73, 65, 52, 99, 103, 43, 13, 8, 59, 40, 37, 23

2. 42, 23, 31, 27, 32, 48, 37, 25, 19, 26, 30, 41, 32, 29

3. 124, 327, 215, 278, 109, 225, 186, 134, 251, 308, 179

4. 126, 432, 578, 312, 367, 400, 275, 315, 437, 299, 480, 365, 278

VOLLEYBALL For Exercises 5–7, use the box-and-whisker plot shown.

Heights (in.) of Players on Volleyball Team

5. What is the height of the tallest player? **68 in.**

6. What percent of the players are between 56 and 68 inches tall? **75%**

7. Explain what the length of the box-and-whisker plot tells us about the data. **The values are spread out.**

Lesson 12-4

(pages 623–628)

Display each set of data in a histogram. 1–4. See margin.

1.
Weekly Exercise Time		
Time (h)	Tally	Frequency
0–2	ⅢⅢ Ⅲ	8
3–5	ⅢⅠ	4
6–8	Ⅱ	2
9–11	Ⅲ	3

2.
Weekly Grocery Bill		
Amount ($)	Tally	Frequency
0–49	ⅢⅠ	6
50–99	ⅢⅢ Ⅱ	12
100–149	ⅢⅢ	8
150–199	ⅢⅠ	4
200–249	Ⅱ	2

3.
Daily High Temperatures in August		
Temperature (°F)	Tally	Frequency
60–69	Ⅱ	2
70–79	ⅢⅢ	10
80–89	ⅢⅠ	6
90–99	Ⅲ	3

4.
Score on Math Test		
Score	Tally	Frequency
50–59	Ⅱ	2
60–69	Ⅰ	1
70–79	ⅢⅢ	8
80–89	ⅢⅢ ⅢⅠ	14
90–99		0

Answers Lesson 12-4

1. **Weekly Exercise Time**

2. **Weekly Grocery Bill**

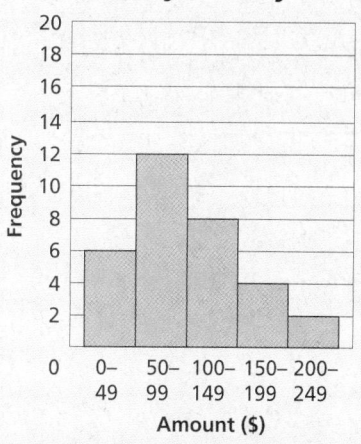

3. **Daily High Temperatures in August**

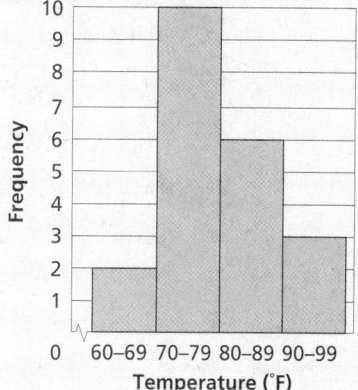

(continued on the next page)

Answers Lesson 12-3

1.

2.

3.

4.

4. **Math Test Scores**

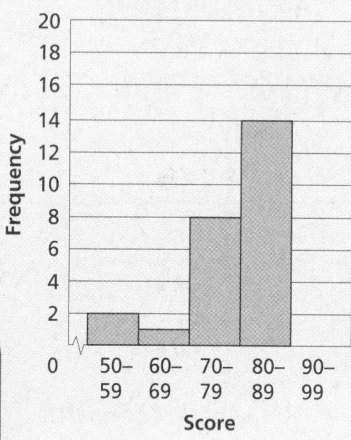

Lesson 12-5

(pages 630–633)

MONEY For Exercises 1–2, refer to the graphs below.

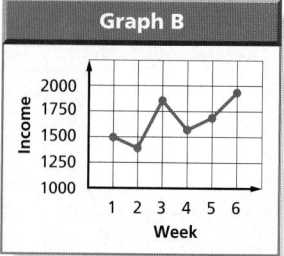

1. Explain why the graphs look different. **Different scales are used.**

2. Which graph appears to show that the income has been fairly consistent?
   Explain your reasoning. **Graph A; It shows a less dramatic increase and decrease.**

Lesson 12-6

(pages 635–639)

Find the number of possible outcomes for each situation.

1. Engagement rings come in silver, gold, and white gold. The diamond can weigh
   $\frac{1}{2}$ karat, $\frac{1}{3}$ karat, or $\frac{1}{4}$ karat. The diamond can have 4 possible shapes. **36**

2. A dress can be long, tea-length, knee-length, or mini. It comes in 2 colors and the dress
   can be worn on or off the shoulders. **16**

3. The first digit of a 7 digit phone number is a 2. The last digit is a 3. **100,000**

4. A chair can be a rocker, recliner, swivel, or straight back. It is available in fabric, vinyl,
   or leather. **12**

Find the probability of each event.

5. Three coins are tossed. What is the probability of three tails? $\frac{1}{8}$

6. Two six-sided number cubes are rolled. What is the probability of getting an
   odd sum? $\frac{1}{2}$

7. A ten-sided die is rolled and a coin is tossed. Find the probability of the coin landing
   on tails and the die landing on a number greater than 3. $\frac{7}{20}$

Lesson 12-7

(pages 641–645)

Tell whether each situation is a *permutation* or a *combination*. Then solve.

1. Seven people are running for four seats on student council. How many ways can the
   students be elected? **C; 35**

2. How many ways can the letters of the word ISLAND be arranged? **P; 720**

3. How many ways can five candles be arranged in three candlesticks? **C; 10**

4. How many ways can six students line up for a race? **P; 720**

5. How many ways can you select three books from a shelf containing 12 books? **C; 220**

6. **GEOMETRY** Determine the number of line segments that can be drawn between
   any two vertices of a pentagon. **10**

(pages 646–649)

nd the odds of each outcome if the spinner below is spun.

. blue **1:5**

2. a color with less than 5 letters **1:2**

. a color that begins with a consonant **5:1**

4. red, yellow, or blue **1:1**

nd the odds of each outcome if a 10-sided die is rolled.

. number less than 7 **3:2**

6. odd number **1:1**

. composite number **1:1**

8. number divisible by 3 **3:7**

(pages 651–655)

deck of Euchre cards consists of 4 nines, 4 tens, 4 jacks, 4 queens,
kings, and 4 aces. Suppose one card is selected and not replaced.
ind the probability of each outcome.

1. 3 nines in a row $\frac{1}{506}$

2. a black jack and a red queen $\frac{1}{138}$

3. a nine of clubs, a black king, and a red ace $\frac{1}{3036}$

4. 4 face cards in a row $\frac{15}{322}$

number from 6 to 19 is drawn. Find the probability.

5. P(13 or even) $\frac{4}{7}$

6. P(13 or less than 7) $\frac{1}{7}$

7. P(even or odd) **1**

8. P(14 or greater than 20) $\frac{1}{14}$

9. P(even or less than 10) $\frac{9}{14}$

10. P(odd or greater than 10) $\frac{11}{14}$

(pages 669–672)

Determine whether each expression is a polynomial. If it is, classify it as a
monomial, binomial, or *trinomial.*

1. $3x^2 + 5$ **yes; binomial**

2. $\frac{6}{x} + 9x$ **no**

3. $\frac{2}{3}p^4$ **yes; monomial**

4. $-6x^2 + 3x - 5$ **yes; trinomial**

5. $\sqrt{w} - 6$ **no**

6. $16 - 3m + m^3$ **yes; trinomial**

7. $\frac{d}{15}$ **yes; monomial**

8. $t^2 - 2$ **yes; binomial**

9. $\frac{x}{y} + z$ **no**

Find the degree of each polynomial.

10. 38 **0**

11. $4b + 9$ **1**

12. cd **2**

13. $4x$ **1**

14. $a^2 - 6$ **2**

15. $11r + 5s$ **1**

16. x^2y **3**

17. $n^2 - n$ **2**

18. $6a^2b^2$ **4**

19. $3y^2 - 2$ **2**

20. $9cd^3 - 5$ **4**

21. $-5p^3 + 8q^2$ **3**

22. $w^2 + 2x - 3y^3 - 7z$ **3**

23. $\frac{x^3}{6} - x$ **3**

24. $-17n^2p - 11np^3$ **4**

1. Nonlinear; the graph is a curve.

2. Linear; the graph is a straight line.

3. Nonlinear; the graph is a curve.

4. Linear; the graph is a straight line.

5. Linear; the graph is a straight line.

6. Nonlinear; the graph is a curve.

7. Linear; the graph is a straight line.

8. Linear; the graph is a straight line.

9. Nonlinear; the graph is a curve.

10. Nonlinear; the graph is a curve

11. Linear; as x increases by 2, y increases by 2.

12. Linear; as x increases by 5, y increases by 6.

Lesson 13-2

(pages 674–677)

Find each sum.

1.
$$\begin{array}{r} -6m + 7 \\ (+)\ 9m - 2 \\ \hline \mathbf{3m + 5} \end{array}$$

2.
$$\begin{array}{r} 12y - 4 \\ (+)\ -8y + 9 \\ \hline \mathbf{4y + 5} \end{array}$$

3.
$$\begin{array}{r} 5x + y \\ (+)\ 9x - 2y \\ \hline \mathbf{14x - y} \end{array}$$

4.
$$\begin{array}{r} 7c^2 - 10c + 5 \\ (+)\ 4c^2 - 4c - 8 \\ \hline \mathbf{11c^2 - 14c - 3} \end{array}$$

5.
$$\begin{array}{r} 2a^2 + 5ab + 6b^2 \\ (+)\ 3a^2 \qquad - b^2 \\ \hline \mathbf{5a^2 + 5ab + 5b^2} \end{array}$$

6.
$$\begin{array}{r} 3d^3 + 2d^2 + 6d - 4 \\ (+)\quad -4d^2 \quad - 3 \\ \hline \mathbf{3d^3 - 2d^2 + 6d - 7} \end{array}$$

7. $(3a + 4) + (a + 2)$ $\mathbf{4a + 6}$

8. $(8m - 3) + (4m + 1)$ $\mathbf{12m - 2}$

9. $(5x - 3y) + (2x - y)$ $\mathbf{7x - 4y}$

10. $(8p^2 - 2p + 3) + (-3p^2 - 2)$ $\mathbf{5p^2 - 2p + 1}$

11. $(-11r^2 + 3s) + (5r^2 - s)$ $\mathbf{-6r^2 + 2s}$

12. $(3a^2 + 5a + 1) + (2a^2 - 3a - 6)$ $\mathbf{5a^2 + 2a - 5}$

Find each sum. Then evaluate if $m = -2$, $n = 4$, and $p = 3$.

13. $(3m - 5n) + (-6m + 8n)$ $\mathbf{-3m + 3n}$; **18**

14. $(m^2 + 2p^2) + (-4m^2 - 6p^2)$ $\mathbf{-3m^2 - 4p^2}$; **−48**

15. $(-2m + 3n + 4p) + (5m - 6n - 8p)$ $\mathbf{3m - 3n - 4p}$; **−30**

Lesson 13-3

(pages 678–681)

Find each difference.

1.
$$\begin{array}{r} 2a + 7 \\ (-)\ a + 3 \\ \hline \mathbf{a + 4} \end{array}$$

2.
$$\begin{array}{r} -3k^2 + 6k \\ (-)\ 4k^2 + k \\ \hline \mathbf{-7k^2 + 5k} \end{array}$$

3.
$$\begin{array}{r} 6x^2 - 4x + 11 \\ (-)\ 5x^2 + 5x - 4 \\ \hline \mathbf{x^2 - 9x + 15} \end{array}$$

4.
$$\begin{array}{r} 9r^2 \qquad + 1 \\ (-)\ 2r^2 + 3r - 7 \\ \hline \mathbf{7r^2 - 3r + 8} \end{array}$$

5.
$$\begin{array}{r} 8n^2 + 3mn - 9 \\ (-)\ 4n^2 + 2mn \\ \hline \mathbf{4n^2 + mn - 9} \end{array}$$

6.
$$\begin{array}{r} -5b^2 - 2ab \\ (-)\quad - 10ab + 6a^2 \\ \hline \mathbf{-5b^2 + 8ab - 6a^2} \end{array}$$

7. $(3n + 2) - (n + 1)$ $\mathbf{2n + 1}$

8. $(-3c + 2d) - (7c - 6d)$ $\mathbf{-10c + 8d}$

9. $(4x^2 + 1) - (3x^2 - 4)$ $\mathbf{x^2 + 5}$

10. $(5a - 4b) - (-a + b)$ $\mathbf{6a - 5b}$

11. $(-12a + 9b) - (3a - 7b)$ $\mathbf{-15a + 16b}$

12. $(3w^3 + 5w - 6) - (5w^3 - 2w + 5)$ $\mathbf{-2w^3 + 7w -}$

13. $(2t^2 - 5) - (t + 8)$ $\mathbf{2t^2 - t - 13}$

14. $(x^2 + xy - 9y^2) - (3x^2 - xy + 3y^2)$
$\mathbf{-2x^2 + 2xy - 12y^2}$

Lesson 13-4

(pages 683–686)

Find each product. 19. $\mathbf{-10x^3 + 15x^2 - 5x}$

1. $2(3a - 7)$ $\mathbf{6a - 14}$

2. $(8c + 1)4$ $\mathbf{32c + 4}$

3. $n(5n + 6)$ $\mathbf{5n^2 + 6n}$

4. $t(2 - t)$ $\mathbf{2t - t^2}$

5. $(3k - 5)k$ $\mathbf{3k^2 - 5k}$

6. $(a + b)a$ $\mathbf{a^2 + ab}$

7. $4n(5n - 3)$ $\mathbf{20n^2 - 12n}$

8. $-3x(4 - x)$ $\mathbf{-12x + 3x^2}$

9. $6m(-m^2 + 3)$ $\mathbf{-6m^3 + 18m}$

10. $5(3x - 2)$ $\mathbf{15x - 10}$

11. $(2p + 9)8$ $\mathbf{16p + 72}$

12. $m(3m - 4)$ $\mathbf{3m^2 - 4m}$

13. $-2w(6 - w)$ $\mathbf{-12w + 2w^2}$

14. $ab(a + b)$ $\mathbf{a^2b + ab^2}$

15. $7t(-3t + 4w)$ $\mathbf{-21t^2 + 28tw}$

16. $4x(2x + y)$ $\mathbf{8x^2 + 4xy}$

17. $(c^2 - 3d)2c$ $\mathbf{2c^3 - 6cd}$

18. $-5z(z^2 - 9z)$ $\mathbf{-5z^3 + 45z^2}$

19. $-5x(2x^2 - 3x + 1)$

20. $7r(r^2 - 3r + 7)$
$\mathbf{7r^3 - 21r^2 + 49r}$

21. $-3az(2z^2 + 4az + a^2)$
$\mathbf{-6az^3 - 12a^2z^2 - 3a^3z}$

Lesson 13-5

(pages 687–691)

Determine whether each graph, equation, or table represents a *linear* or a *nonlinear* function. Explain. 1–12. See margin.

1.

2.

3.

4.
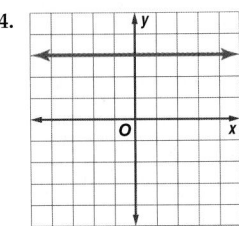

5. $y = -3x$

6. $y = 2x^3 - 5$

7. $-2x + 5y = 10$

8. $x = 7y$

9. $y = (-2)^x$

10. $y = \frac{6}{x}$

11.

x	y
2	5
4	7
6	9
8	11

12.

x	y
5	7
10	13
15	19
20	25

Lesson 13-6

(pages 692–696)

Graph each function. 1–9. See margin.

1. $y = 3x^2$

2. $y = -2x^2$

3. $y = \frac{1}{2}x^2$

4. $y = x^3$

5. $y = 0.3x^3$

6. $y = x^3 - 2$

7. $y = x^2 + 4$

8. $y = \frac{1}{3}x^2 - 3$

9. $y = -0.5x^2 + 1$

Answers Lesson 13-6

1.

$y = 3x^2$

2.

$y = -2x^2$

3.

$y = \frac{1}{2}x^2$

4.

$y = x^3$

5.

$y = 0.3x^3$

6.

$y = x^3 - 2$

7.

$y = x^2 + 4$

8.
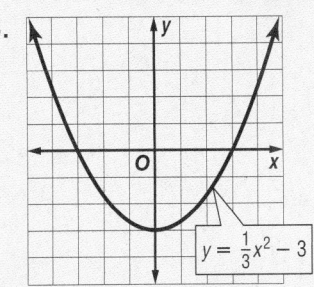
$y = \frac{1}{3}x^2 - 3$

9.

$y = -0.5x^2 + 1$

12.

Graph: Temperature (°C) vs Depth (km). Points plotted at (0, 20), (2, 90), (4, 160).

14.

Graph: Width (cm) vs Length (cm). Points plotted approximately at (1.0, 1.0), (1.9, 1.5), (3.1, 2.3), (5.0, 3.3), (8.6, 5.8).

Mixed Problem Solving

Chapter 1   The Tools of Algebra

(pages 4–53)

1. PATTERNS   How many cubes are in the tenth figure if the pattern below continues? *(Lesson 1-1)* **37 cubes**

figure 1   figure 2   figure 3

2. SPACE EXPLORATION   On one flight, the space shuttle *Endeavour* traveled 6.9 million miles and circled Earth 262 times. About how many miles did the shuttle travel on each trip around Earth? *(Lesson 1-1)* **about 7 million ÷ 250 or 28,000 mi**

3. TREES   A conservation group collects seeds from trees at historic homes, grows them into saplings, and sells them to the public. Each sapling costs $35, and $7 is added to each order for shipping and handling. Write and then evaluate an expression for the total cost of one order of six saplings. *(Lesson 1-2)* **35(6) + 7; $217**

4. SALES   For a school fund-raiser, Sophia sold 15 white chocolate hearts at $4.25 each, 36 milk chocolate hearts at $3.75 each, and 22 milk chocolate assortments at $7.45 each. How much money did Sophia raise? *(Lesson 1-2)* **$362.65**

SPACE   For Exercises 5 and 6, use the following information.
Objects weigh six times more on Earth than they do on the moon because the force of gravity is greater. *(Lesson 1-3)*

5. Write an expression for the weight of an object on Earth if its weight on the moon is *x*. **6x**

6. A scientific instrument weighs 34 pounds on the moon. How much does the instrument weigh on Earth? **204 lb**

VOLLEYBALL   For Exercises 7 and 8, use the following information.
A volleyball net is 3 feet 3 inches tall. The bottom of the net is to be set 4 feet 8 inches from the floor. *(Lesson 1-4)*

7. Write an expression for the distance from the floor to the top of the net. **(3 ft + 3 in.) + (4 ft + 8 in.)**

8. Find the distance from the floor to the top of the net. **7 ft 11 in.**

9. NEWSPAPERS   Nick sold 86 newspapers on Monday, 79 on Tuesday, 68 on Wednesday, and 8 on Friday. How many newspapers did Nick sell on Thursday if he sold a total of 391 in the five days? *(Lesson 1-5)* **75**

10. FOOD   Kristin is planning to buy twice as man blueberry bagels as plain bagels for a staff meeting. Write a relation to show the different possibilities. *(Lesson 1-6)* **Sample answer: {(6, 3), (8, 4), (10, 5), (12, 6)}**

GEOLOGY   For Exercises 11 and 12, use the following information.
The underground temperature of rocks in degrees Celsius is estimated by the expression 35x + 20, where *x* is the depth in kilometers. *(Lesson 1-6)*

11. Make a list of ordered pairs in which the *x*-coordinate represents the depth and the *y*-coordinate represents the temperature for depths of 0, 2, and 4 kilometers.

12. Graph the ordered pairs. **See margin.**
11. (0, 20), (2, 90), (4, 160)

13. EMPLOYMENT   The scatter plot shows the years of experience and salaries of twenty peopl Do the data show a *positive*, *negative*, or *no* relationship? Explain. *(Lesson 1-7)*

Scatter plot: Salary ($ thousands) vs Years of Experience.

Positive; a experienc increases salaries increase.

14. BIRDS   The table shows the average lengths an widths of five bird eggs.

Bird	Length (cm)	Width (cm)
Canadian goose	8.6	5.8
robin	1.9	1.5
turtledove	3.1	2.3
hummingbird	1.0	1.0
raven	5.0	3.3

Source: *Animals as Our Companions*

Make a scatter plot of the data and predict the width of an egg 6 centimeters long. *(Lesson 1-7)* **See margin for graph, 4 cm.**

ASTRONOMY Mars is about 228 million kilometers from the Sun. Earth is about 150 million kilometers from the Sun. Write two inequalities that compare the two distances. *(Lesson 2-1)* **228 > 150, 150 < 228**

GAMES In a popular television game show, one contestant finished the regular round with a score of −200, and another contestant finished with a score of −500. Write two inequalities that compare their scores. *(Lesson 2-1)* **−200 > −500, −500 < −200**

MONEY Tino had $250 in his checking account at the beginning of April. During the month he wrote checks in the amounts of $72, $37, and $119. He also made one deposit of $45. Find Tino's account balance at the end of April. *(Lesson 2-2)* **$67**

ASTRONOMY At noon, the average temperature on the moon is 112°C. During the night, the average temperature drops 252°C. What is the average temperature of the moon's surface during the night? *(Lesson 2-2)* **−140° C**

SUBMARINES The research submarine *Alvin* is located at 1500 meters below sea level. It descends another 1250 meters to the ocean floor. How far below sea level is the ocean floor? *(Lesson 2-3)* **2750 m**

METEOROLOGY Windchill factor is an estimate of the cooling effect the wind has on a person in cold weather. If the outside temperature is 10°F and the wind makes it feel like −25°F, what is the difference between the actual temperature and how cold it feels? *(Lesson 2-3)* **−35°F**

GEOGRAPHY The highest point in Africa is Mount Kilimanjaro. Its altitude is 5895 meters. The lowest point on the continent is Lake Assal. Its altitude is −155 meters. Find the difference between these altitudes. *(Lesson 2-3)* **6050 m**

8. **GEOLOGY** In December, 1994, geologists found that the Bering Glacier had come to a stop. The glacier had been retreating at a rate of about 2 feet per day. If the retreat resumes at the old rate, what integer represents how far the glacier will have advanced after 28 days? *(Lesson 2-4)* **−56**

9. **SPORTS** The Wildcat football team was penalized the same amount of yardage four times during the third quarter. The total of the four penalties was 60 yards. If −60 represents a loss of 60 yards, write a division sentence to represent this situation. Then express the number of yards of each penalty as an integer. *(Lesson 2-5)* **−60 ÷ 4 = y, −15**

10. **AEROSPACE** To simulate space travel, NASA's Lewis Research Center in Cleveland, Ohio, uses a 430-foot shaft. If the free fall of an object in the shaft takes 5 seconds to travel the −430 feet, on average how far does the object travel in each second? *(Lesson 2-5)* **−86 feet per second**

11. **MAPS** A map of a city can be created by placing the following buildings at the given coordinates: City Hall (1, 2), High School (−3, 6), Fire Department (4, −2), Recreation Center (0, 3). Draw and label the map. *(Lesson 2-6)* **See margin.**

GEOMETRY For Exercises 12 and 13, use the following information.
A vertex of a polygon is a point where two sides of the polygon intersect.

12. Identify the coordinates of the vertices in the triangle below. **A(2, 2), B(−3, −1), C(3, −3)**

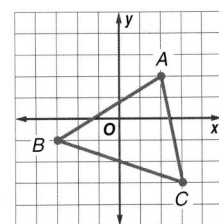

13. Add 2 to each *x*-coordinate. Graph the new ordered pairs. Describe how the position of the new triangle relates to the original triangle. *(Lesson 2-6)* **The triangle is moved two units right; see margin for graph.**

Answers

11.

13.

1. **BUSINESS** A local newspaper can be ordered for delivery on weekdays or Sundays. A weekday paper is 35¢, and the Sunday edition is $1.50. The Stadlers ordered delivery of the weekday papers. The month of March had 23 weekdays and April had 20. How much should the carrier charge the Stadlers for those two months? *(Lesson 3-1)* **$15.05**

SHOPPING For Exercises 2 and 3, use the following information.
One pair of jeans costs $23, and one T-shirt costs $15. *(Lesson 3-1)* **2. 3(23 + 15), 3 · 23 + 3 · 15**

2. Write two equivalent expressions for the total cost of 3 pairs of jeans and 3 T-shirts.

3. Find the total cost. **$114**

4. **ENTERTAINMENT** Kyung bought 3 CDs that each cost x dollars, 2 tapes that each cost $10, and a video that cost $14. Write an expression in simplest form that represents the total amount that Kyung spent. *(Lesson 3-2)* **$3x + 34$**

TRANSPORTATION For Exercises 5 and 6, use the following information.
A minivan is rated for maximum carrying capacity of 900 pounds.

5. If the luggage weighs 100 pounds, what is the maximum weight allowable for passengers? **800 lb**

6. What is the maximum average weight allowable for each of 5 passengers? *(Lesson 3-3)* **160 lb**

7. **GEOMETRY** The perimeter of any square is 4 times the length of one of its sides. If the perimeter of a square is 72 centimeters, what is the length of each side of the square? *(Lesson 3-4)* **18 cm**

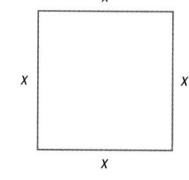

8. **PURCHASING** Mr. Rockwell bought a television set. The price was $362. He paid $75 down and will pay the balance in 7 equal payments. How much is each payment? *(Lesson 3-5)* **$41**

9. **SPORTS** Marcie paid $75 to join a tennis club for the summer. She will also pay $10 for each hour that she plays. If Marcie has budgeted $22. to play tennis this summer, how many hours ca she play tennis? *(Lesson 3-5)* **15 h**

FENCING For Exercises 10 and 11, use the following information.
Wanda uses 130 feet of fence to enclose a rectangula flower garden. She also used the 50-foot wall of her house as one side of the garden. What is the width o the garden? *(Lesson 3-6)* **10. $2w + 50 = 130$**

10. Write an equation that represents this situation.

11. Solve the equation to find the width of the garden. **40 ft**

WORKING For Exercises 12 and 13, use the following information.
Kate worked a 40-hour week and was paid $410. Th amount included a $50 bonus. *(Lesson 3-6)*

12. Write an equation that represents this situation.

13. What was Kate paid per hour? **$9**
12. $40x + 50 = 410$

14. **GEOMETRY** The perimeter of the triangle below is 27 yards.

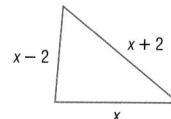

Find the lengths of the sides of the triangle. *(Lesson 3-7)* **7 yd, 9 yd, 11 yd**

15. **TRAVEL** The Flynn family plans to drive 600 miles for their summer vacation. The speed limit on the highways they plan to use is 55 mile per hour. If they do not exceed the speed limit, how many hours of driving should it take them? *(Lesson 3-7)* **10.9 h**

SCIENCE For Exercises 16 and 17, use the following information.
Acceleration is the rate at which velocity is changing with respect to time. To find the acceleration, find the change in velocity by subtracting the starting velocity s from the final velocity, f. Then divide by the time, t. *(Lesson 3-7)*

16. Write the formula for acceleration, a. $a = \dfrac{f - s}{t}$

17. A motorcycle goes from 2 m/s to 14 m/s in 6 seconds. Find its acceleration. **2 m/s²**

LUNCHTIME A group of 136 sixth graders needs to be seated in the cafeteria for lunch. If all of the tables need to be full, should the school use tables that seat 6, 8, or 10 students each? (Lesson 4-1) **8**

PATTERNS In a pattern, the number of colored tiles used in row x is 3^x. Find the number of tiles used in rows 4, 5, and 6 of the pattern. (Lesson 4-2) **81, 243, 729**

ELECTRICITY The amount of power lost in watts P can be found by using the formula $P = I^2R$, where I is current in amps, and R is resistance in ohms. The resistance of the wire leading from the source of power to a home is 2 ohms. If an electric stove causes a current of 41 amps to flow through the wire, find the power lost from the wire powering the stove. (Lesson 4-2) **3362 watts**

CODES Prime numbers are used to code and decode information. Suppose two prime numbers p and q are chosen so that $n = pq$. Then the key to the code is n. Find p and q if $n = 1073$. (Lesson 4-3) **29 and 37**

INTERIOR DESIGN Mrs. Garcia has two different fabrics to make square pillows for her living room. One fabric is 48 inches wide, and the other fabric is 60 inches wide. How long should each side of the pillows be if they are all the same size and no fabric is wasted? (Lesson 4-4) **12 in.**

ECONOMICS The graph below shows how each dollar spent by the Federal Government is used.

Government Spending

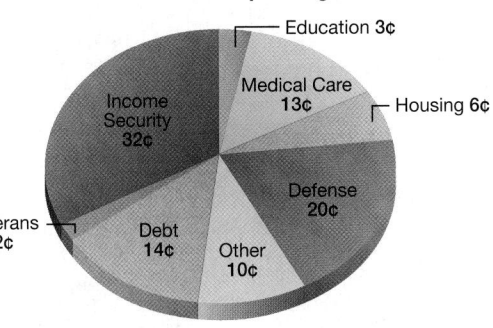

- Education 3¢
- Medical Care 13¢
- Housing 6¢
- Income Security 32¢
- Defense 20¢
- Debt 14¢
- Other 10¢
- erans 2¢

Source: The Tax Foundation

Write a fraction in simplest form comparing the amount spent on housing assistance and the total amount spent. (Lesson 4-5) $\dfrac{3}{50}$

7. **BASKETBALL** Sydney made 8 out of 14 free throws in her last basketball game. Write her success as a fraction in simplest form. (Lesson 4-5) $\dfrac{4}{7}$

8. **TRANSPORTATION** Cameron spends 18 minutes traveling to work. What fraction of the day is this? (Lesson 4-5) $\dfrac{1}{80}$

9. **EARTHQUAKES** The table below describes different earthquake intensities.

Earthquake	Richter Scale	Intensity
A	8	10^7
B	4	10^3

Find $10^7 \div 10^3$ to determine how much more intense Earthquake A was than Earthquake B. (Lesson 4-6) 10^4 **or 10,000 times**

ASTRONOMY For Exercises 10 and 11, use the following information. 10. $\dfrac{6.67}{10^{11}}$
Any two objects in space have an attraction that can be calculated by using a formula that includes the universal gravitational constant, 6.67×10^{-11} Nm^2/kg^2. (N is newtons.) (Lesson 4-7)

10. Write the universal gravitational constant using positive exponents.

11. Write the constant as a decimal. **0.0000000000667**

12. $\dfrac{1}{10^7}$ m

BIOLOGY For Exercises 12 and 13, use the following information.
Deoxyribonucleic acid, or DNA, contains the genetic code of an organism. The length of a DNA strand is about 10^{-7} meter. (Lesson 4-7)

12. Write the length of a DNA strand using positive exponents.

13. Write the length of a DNA strand as a decimal. **0.0000001 m**

14. **SCIENCE** Atoms are extremely small particles about two millionths of an inch in diameter. Write this measure in standard form and in scientific notation. (Lesson 4-8)
0.000002; 2.0 $\times 10^{-6}$

15. **BUSINESS** A large corporation estimates its yearly revenue at 4.72×10^8. Write this number in standard form. (Lesson 4-8) **$472,000,000**

Mixed Problem Solving **761**

1. **FURNITURE**   A shelf $16\frac{5}{8}$ inches wide is to be placed in a space that is $16\frac{3}{4}$ inches wide. Will the shelf fit in the space? Explain. *(Lesson 5-1)*
yes; $16\frac{5}{8} < 16\frac{3}{4}$

2. **MEASUREMENT**   A piece of metal is 0.025 inch thick. What fraction of an inch is this? *(Lesson 5-2)*
$\frac{1}{40}$ **in.**

3. **HEALTH**   You can stay in the Sun 15 times longer than usual without burning by applying SPF number 15. If you usually burn after $\frac{1}{4}$ hour in the Sun, how long could you stay in the Sun using SPF 15 lotion? *(Lesson 5-3)* $3\frac{3}{4}$ **h**

4. **MONEY**   A dollar bill remains in circulation about $1\frac{1}{4}$ years. A coin lasts about $22\frac{1}{2}$ times longer. How long is a coin in circulation?
(Lesson 5-3) $28\frac{1}{8}$ **yr**

5. **FOOD**   If each guest at a party eats two-thirds of a small pizza, how many guests would finish 12 small pizzas? *(Lesson 5-4)* **18 guests**

6. **PUBLISHING**   A magazine page is 8 inches wide. The articles are printed in three columns with $\frac{1}{4}$ inch of space in between and $\frac{3}{8}$-inch margins on each side, as shown below.

How wide should an author set the columns on her computer so that they are the same width as in the magazine? *(Lesson 5-4)* $2\frac{1}{4}$ **in.**

7. **REMODELING**   In their basement, the Jacksons installed $\frac{3}{8}$-inch thick paneling over a layer of dry wall that is $\frac{5}{8}$ inch thick. How thick are the wall coverings? *(Lesson 5-5)* **1 in.**

8. **COLLEGE**   In a college dormitory, $\frac{3}{8}$ of the residents are from Ohio, and $\frac{2}{5}$ of the residents are from New York. Which state has a greater representation? *(Lesson 5-6)* **New York**

9. **NUTRITION**   A survey found that $\frac{1}{6}$ of American households bought bottled water in 2000. Only $\frac{}{}$ of American households bought bottled water in 1993. What fraction of the population bought bottled water in 2000 that did not in 1993?
(Lesson 5-7) $\frac{11}{102}$

10. **EMPLOYMENT**   The table below shows the earnings per woman for every $100 earned by a man in the same occupation for two years.
(Lesson 5-8)

Occupation	Earnings ($)	
	Year 1	Year 2
Nurse	99.50	104.70
Teacher	88.60	90.30
Police Officer	91.20	94.20
Food Service	102.50	105.60
Postal Clerk	93.40	94.60

Find the mean, median, and mode of the earnings for each year. **Year 1: 95.04; 93.40; none; Year 2: 97.88; 94.60; none**

11. **OIL PRODUCTION**   Texas and Alaska produced a total of 1372.2 million barrels of oil. Alaska produced 684.0 million barrels. How many barrels of oil were produced in Texas? *(Lesson 5-9)*
688.2 million

12. **ON-LINE SERVICE**   The cost of using an Internet service provider for 5, 6, 7, and 8 hours is given by the sequence $9.95, $12.90, $15.85, and $18.80, respectively. Is the cost an arithmetic or geometric sequence? Explain. *(Lesson 5-10)* **Arithmetic; the common difference is $2.95.**

SHOPPING   Best buys in grocery stores are generally found by comparing unit rates such as cents per ounce. Which bag of nachos shown in the table at the right is the better buy? *(Lesson 6-1)*

Size	Price
16-oz	$2.49
32-oz	$3.69

32-oz bag at $3.69

COOKING   A recipe that makes 72 cookies calls for $4\frac{1}{2}$ cups of flour. How many cups of flour would be needed to make 48 cookies? *(Lesson 6-2)* **3 c**

FERRIS WHEEL   In a scale model of a Ferris wheel, the diameter of the wheel is 5 inches. If the actual height of the wheel is 55 feet, what is the scale of the model? *(Lesson 6-3)* **1 in. = 11 ft**

BUSINESS   An executive of a marshmallow company said that marshmallows are 80% air. What fraction of a marshmallow is air? *(Lesson 6-4)* $\frac{4}{5}$

HEALTH   Doctors estimate that 3 babies out of every 1000 are likely to get a cold during their first month. What percent is this? *(Lesson 6-4)* **0.3%**

NUTRITION   Refer to the nutritional label from a bag of pretzels shown below.

Nutrition Facts
Serving Size 1 package (46.8g)
Servings per container 1

Amount per serving
Calories 190 Calories from Fat 15

	% Daily Value*
Total Fat 1.5g	3%
Saturated Fat 0g	0%
Cholesterol 0mg	0%
Sodium 760mg	32%
Total Carbohydrate 37g	12%

The 760 milligrams of sodium (salt) in one serving is 32% of the recommended daily value. What is the total recommended daily value of sodium? *(Lesson 6-5)* **about 2375 mg or 2.375 g**

7. **FAST FOOD**   A certain hamburger has 560 Calories, and 288 of these are from fat. About what percent of the Calories are from fat? *(Lesson 6-6)* **about 50%**

8. **MONEY**   If Simone wants to leave a tip of about 15% on a dinner check of $23.85, how much should she leave? *(Lesson 6-6)* **$3.60**

9. **BUSINESS**   Many car dealers offer special interest rates as incentives to attract buyers. How much interest would a person pay for the first month of a $5500 car loan if the monthly interest rate is 0.24%? *(Lesson 6-7)* **$13.20**

10. **PETS**   Hedgehogs are becoming so popular as pets that some breeders have reported a 250% increase in sales in recent years. If a breeder sold 50 hedgehogs one year before the increase, how many should he or she expect to sell a year from now? *(Lesson 6-8)* **175**

11. **BRAND NAMES**   The graph below shows the results of a survey.

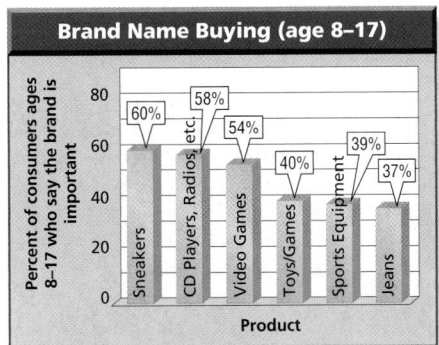

Brand Name Buying (age 8–17)

Source: International Mass Retail Association

How many of a class of 423 ninth grade students would you expect to say that they consider brand name when buying jeans? *(Lesson 6-9)* **157**

12. **CANDY**   In a small bag of colored chocolate candies, there are 15 green, 23 red, and 18 yellow candies. What is the probability of selecting a red candy if one is taken from the bag at random? *(Lesson 6-9)* $\frac{23}{56}$

CENSUS   For Exercises 1–3, use the following information.

The table below shows the 2000 populations and the average rates of change in population in the 1990s for Buffalo, New York, and Corpus Christi, Texas. Suppose the population of each city continued to increase or decrease at these rates. *(Lesson 7-1)*

City	Population in 2000	Yearly Rate of Change
Buffalo, NY	293,000	−3500
Corpus Christi, TX	277,000	+2000

1. Write an expression for the population of Buffalo after x years. **293,000 − 3500x**

2. Write an expression for the population of Corpus Christi after x years. **277,000 + 2000x**

3. In how many years would the population of the two cities be the same? **about 3 yr**

4. **INTERNET**   One Internet provider charges $19.95 a month plus $0.21 per minute, and a second provider charges $24.95 a month plus $0.16 per minute. For how many minutes is the cost of the plans the same? *(Lesson 7-1)* **100 min**

5. **GEOMETRY**   The length of a rectangle is three times the difference between its width and two. Find the width if the length is 15 inches. *(Lesson 7-2)* **7 in.**

6. **SPORTS**   More than 100,000 fans attended the opening football game of the season. Write an inequality for the number of people who attended. *(Lesson 7-3)* **$f > 100,000$**

7. **SCHOOL**   Julie has math and English homework tonight. She has no more than 90 minutes to spend on her homework. Suppose Julie spends 35 minutes completing her math homework. Write and solve an inequality to find how much time she can spend on her English homework. *(Lesson 7-4)* **$e + 35 \leq 90$; at most 55 minutes**

8. **SAVINGS**   Curtis is saving money to buy a new mountain bike. The bikes that he likes start at $375, and he has already saved $285. Write and solve an inequality to find the amount he must still save. *(Lesson 7-4)* **$x + 285 \geq 375$; at least $90**

9. **STATISTICS**   The Boston Marathon had more than 2,600,000 spectators along its 26-mile route. Write and solve an inequality to find the average number of spectators per mile. *(Lesson 7-5)* **$26x > 2,600,000$; more than 100,000 spectators**

10. **GROCERY SHOPPING**   Mrs. Hiroshi spends at least twice as much on her weekly grocery shopping as she did one year ago. Last year, she spent $54 each week. How much is Mrs. Hiroshi now spending each week on groceries? *(Lesson 7-5)* **at least $108**

11. **GEOMETRY**   An *acute angle* has a measure less than 90°. If the measure of an acute angle is $2x$, write and solve an inequality to find the possible values of x. *(Lesson 7-5)* **$2x < 90$; less than 45°**

12. **SHOPPING**   Luis plans to spend at most $85 on jeans and shirts. He bought 2 shirts for $15.30 each. How much can he spend on jeans? *(Lesson 7-6)* **at most $54.40**

13. **CAR SALES**   A car salesperson receives a monthly salary of $1000 plus a 3% commission on every car sold. For what amount of monthly sales will the salesperson earn more than $2500? *(Lesson 7-6)* **$s > $50,000**

14. **SCHOOL**   Dave has earned scores of 73, 85, 91, and 82 on the first four of five math tests for the grading period. He would like to finish the grading period with a test average of at least 82. What is the minimum score Dave needs to earn on the fifth test in order to achieve his goal? *(Lesson 7-6)* **79**

SHIPPING RATES   For Exercises 1–3, use the following information.
The shipping costs for mail-order merchandise are given in the table below. *(Lesson 8-1)*

Total Price of Merchandise	Shipping Cost
$0–$30.00	$4.25
$30.01–$70.00	$5.75
$70.01 and over	$6.95

1. What is the shipping cost of merchandise totaling $75? **$6.95**

2. For what price of merchandise is the shipping cost $5.75? **$30.01–$70.00**

3. Does the table represent a function? Explain.
Yes, each price has a unique shipping cost.

PHYSICS   For Exercises 4 and 5, use the following information.
As a thunderstorm approaches, you see lightning as it occurs, but you hear the accompanying thunder a short time afterward. The distance y in miles that sound travels in x seconds is given by $y = 0.21x$. *(Lesson 8-2)* **4. (1, 0.21), (2, 0.42), (3, 0.63)**

4. Find three ordered pairs that relate x and y.

5. How far away is lightning when thunder is heard 2.5 seconds after the lightning is seen?
about 0.525 mi

AVIATION   For Exercises 6 and 7, use the following information.
The steady descent of a jetliner is represented by the equation $a = 24{,}000 - 1500t$, where t is the time in minutes and a is the altitude in feet. *(Lesson 8-3)* **6. 16**

6. Name the x-intercept of the graph of the equation.

7. What does the x-intercept represent? **Time when the altitude is zero and the jet has landed.**

8. **KITES**   Drew is flying a kite in the park. The kite is a horizontal distance of 20 feet from Drew's position and a vertical distance of 70 feet. Find the slope of the kite string. *(Lesson 8-4)* $\dfrac{7}{2}$

9. **FUEL**   The cost of gasoline varies directly as the number of gallons bought. If it costs $27.80 to fill a 20-gallon tank, what would it cost to fill a 12-gallon tank? *(Lesson 8-5)* **$16.68**

10. **BUSINESS**   A company's monthly cost y is given by $y = 1500 + 12x$, where x represents the number of items produced. State the slope and y-intercept of the graph of the equation and describe what they represent. *(Lesson 8-6)*
12, cost per item; 1500, cost when no items are produced

CAR RENTAL   For Exercises 11 and 12, use the following information.
It costs $59 per day plus $0.12 per mile driven to rent a minivan. *(Lesson 8-7)*

11. Write an equation in slope-intercept form that shows the cost y for renting a minivan for one day and driving x miles. $y = 59 + 0.12x$

12. Find the daily rental cost if 30 miles are driven.
$62.60

13. **NUTRITION**   The graph below shows energy bar sales in the United States during the month of October.

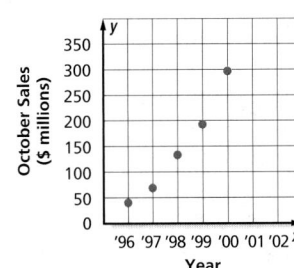

Source: ACNielsen

Use the graph to predict energy bar sales during October 2002. *(Lesson 8-8)*
Sample answer: $375 million

14. **SCHOOL CONCERT**   Tickets for the fall concert cost $3 for students and $5 for nonstudents. If a total of 140 tickets were sold and $590 was collected, how many of each type of ticket was sold? *(Lesson 8-9)* **55 student, 85 nonstudent**

FINANCE   For Exercises 15–17, use the following information. 15–17. See margin.
Silvina earns $3.50 per hour for weeding the garden and $5.00 per hour for mowing the lawn. Suppose she wants to earn at least $35 this week. *(Lesson 8-10)*

15. Write an inequality to represent this situation. Let x represent the number of hours she weeds and let y represent the number of hours she mows.

16. Graph the inequality.

17. Determine two possible ways that she can earn at least $35 this week.

Answers

15. $3.5x + 5y \geq 35$

16.

17. Sample answer: weed 4 hours, mow 6 hours; weed 8 hours, mow 2 hours

Mixed Problem Solving

Answer

5.

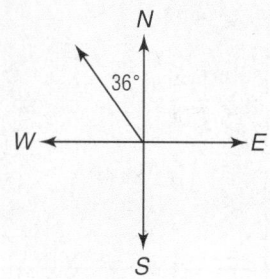

1. **CONSTRUCTION** A banquet facility must allow at least 4 square feet for each person on the dance floor. Reston's Hotel is adding a square dance floor that will be large enough for 100 people. How long should it be on each side? *(Lesson 9-1)* **20 ft**

2. **PHYSICS** The time t in seconds that it takes an object to fall d feet can be estimated by using $d = 0.5gt^2$. In this formula, g is acceleration due to gravity, 32 ft/s². If a ball is dropped from the top of a 55-foot building, how long does it take to hit the ground? *(Lesson 9-2)* **about 1.85 s**

BOOKS For Exercises 3 and 4, use the following information.
The graph shows the results of a survey, which asked which types of books people buy the most. *(Lesson 9-3)*

Books Americans Buy

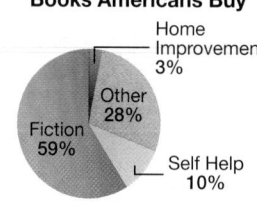

Source: *USA TODAY*

3. Classify the angle labeled Self Help as *acute, obtuse, right,* or *straight*. **acute**

4. Find the measure of the angle labeled Fiction. **212.4°**

5. **AVIATION** Airplane flight paths can be described using angles and compass directions. The path of a particular airplane is described as 36° west of north. Draw a diagram that represents this path. *(Lesson 9-3)* **See margin.**

6. **UTILITIES** A support cable is sometimes attached to give a utility pole stability. If the cable makes an angle of 65° with the ground, what is the measure of the angle formed by the cable and the pole? *(Lesson 9-4)* **25°**

7. **BASEBALL** A baseball diamond is actually a square with 90 feet between the bases. What is the distance between home plate and second base? *(Lesson 9-5)* **about 127.3 ft**

8. **SAILING** A rope from the top of a sailboat mast is attached to a point 6 feet from the base of the mast. If the rope is 24 feet long, how high is the mast? *(Lesson 9-5)* **about 23.2 ft**

9. **TRAVEL** Matt's home is at $(-4, 9)$ on the map. His friend Carlos' home is at $(6, 3)$ on the same map. They want to meet halfway between their two homes. What are the coordinates on the map where they should plan to meet? *(Lesson 9-6)* **(1, 6)**

10. **HISTORY** The largest known pyramid is Khufu's pyramid. At a certain time of day, a yardstick casts a shadow 1.5 feet long, and the pyramid casts a shadow 241 feet long. Use shadow reckoning to find the height of the pyramid. *(Lesson 9-7)* **482 ft**

11. **SURVEYING** A surveyor needs to find the distance across a river and draws the sketch shown below.

Find the distance across the river. *(Lesson 9-7)* **32 m**

12. **RECREATION** Maxine is flying a kite on a 75-yard string. The string is making a 45° angle with the ground. How high above the ground is the kite? *(Lesson 9-8)* **53 yd**

13. **MAINTENANCE** A 15-foot ladder is propped against a house. The angle it forms with the ground is 60°. To the nearest foot, how far up the side of the house does the ladder reach? *(Lesson 9-8)* **13 ft**

Mixed Problem Solving

Mixed Problem Solving

TRANSPORTATION   The angle at the corner where two streets intersect is 125°. If a bus cannot make a turn at an angle of less than 70°, can bus service be provided on a route that includes turning that corner in both directions? Explain. *(Lesson 10-1)*

No; the corresponding angle has a measure of only 55°.

BRIDGES   For Exercises 2 and 3, use the following information.
The figure below shows part of the support structure of a bridge. Name a triangle that seems to be congruent to each triangle below. *(Lesson 10-2)*

$\triangle AFB$ **$\triangle CFB$**   3. $\triangle CHG$ **$\triangle ADE$**

MOVING   A historic house in the shape of a rectangle has coordinates $A(-3, 5)$, $B(4, 5)$, $C(4, -3)$, and $D(-3, -3)$ on a map. The house is going to be moved to a new site 3 units east and two units north. Find the coordinates of the house once it reaches the new site. *(Lesson 10-3)*
$A'(0, 7)$, $B'(7, 7)$, $C'(7, -1)$, $D'(0, -1)$

SHAPES   Name three items in your room that are quadrilaterals. Classify the shapes. *(Lesson 10-4)*
See students' work.

6. GEOGRAPHY   The state of Indiana is shaped almost like a trapezoid. Estimate the area of the state. *(Lesson 10-5)*
about 33,600 mi²

SIGNS   For Exercises 7 and 8, use the following information.
Part of a driver's license exam includes identifying road signs by color and by shape. Identify the shape of each road sign pictured below. *(Lesson 10-6)*

7.
octagon

8.
square

MANUFACTURING   For Exercises 9 and 10, use the following information.
Some cafeteria trays are designed so that four people can place their trays around a square table without bumping corners, as shown below. The top and bottom of the tray are parallel. *(Lesson 10-6)*

9. What is the shape of the tray? **trapezoid**

10. Find the measure of each angle of the tray so that the trays will fit side-to-side around the table.
45°, 45°, 135°, 135°

11. **PUBLIC SAFETY**   A tornado warning system can be heard for a 2-mile radius. Find the area that will benefit from the warning. *(Lesson 10-7)*
about 13 mi²

12. **CITY PLANNING**   The circular region inside the streets at DuPont Circle in Washington, D.C., is 250 feet across. What is the area of the region? *(Lesson 10-7)* **49,087.4 ft²**

13. **GEOMETRY**   Find the area of a figure that is formed using a rectangle having width equal to 8 feet and length equal to 5 feet and a half circle with a diameter of 6 feet. *(Lesson 10-8)* **54.14 ft²**

1. **PRESENTS** Mateo received a gift wrapped in the shape of a rectangular pyramid. How many faces, edges, and vertices are on the gift box? *(Lesson 11-1)* **5; 8; 5**

2. **PET CARE** Tina has an old fish tank in the shape of a circular cylinder. The tank is 2 feet in diameter and 6 feet high. How many cubic feet of water does it hold? Round to the nearest cubic foot. *(Lesson 11-2)* **19 ft³**

3. **CHEMISTRY** A quartz crystal is a hexagonal prism. It has a base area of 1.41 square centimeters and a volume of 4.64 cubic centimeters. What is its height? If necessary, round to the nearest hundredth. *(Lesson 11-2)* **3.29 cm**

4. **BAKING** A rectangular cake pan is 30 centimeters by 21 centimeters by 5 centimeters. A round cake pan has a diameter of 21 centimeters and a height of 4 centimeters. Which holds more batter, the rectangular pan or two round pans? *(Lesson 11-2)* **rectangular pan**

5. **MONUMENTS** The top of the Washington Monument is a square pyramid 54 feet high and 34 feet long on each side. What is the volume of this top part of the monument? *(Lesson 11-3)* **20,808 ft³**

6. **MANUFACTURING** A carton of canned fruit holds 24 cans. Each can has a diameter of 7.6 centimeters and a height of 10.8 centimeters. Approximately how much paper is needed to make the labels for the 24 cans? If necessary, round to the nearest tenth. *(Lesson 11-4)* **6188.7 cm²**

7. **CAMPING** How much canvas was used to make the A-frame tent shown below? (*Hint:* Be sure to include the floor of the tent.) *(Lesson 11-4)* **94 ft²**

8. **HISTORY** The Pyramid of Cestius is a monument in Rome. It is a square pyramid with the dimensions shown below.

What is its lateral area? If necessary, round to the nearest tenth. *(Lesson 11-5)* **2394.0 m²**

9. **TEPEES** The largest tepee in the United States is in the shape of a cone with a diameter of 42 feet and a slant height of about 47.9 feet. How much canvas was used for the cover of the tepee? If necessary, round to the nearest tenth. *(Lesson 11-5)* **3160.1 ft²**

10. **SHIPPING** Are the two packing tubes shown below similar solids? *(Lesson 11-6)* **yes**

11. **MODELS** A miniature greenhouse is a rectangular prism with a volume of 16 cubic feet. The scale factor of this greenhouse to a larger greenhouse of the same shape is $\frac{1}{4}$. What is the volume of the larger greenhouse? (*Hint:* scale factor $= \frac{a}{b}$, ratio of volumes $= \frac{a^3}{b^3}$) *(Lesson 11-6)* **1024 ft³**

12. **DECORATING** Alicia is wallpapering a wall that is 8.25 feet high and 23.7 feet wide. What is the area of the wall? Round to the correct number of significant digits. *(Lesson 11-7)* **195.5 ft²**

1. ARCHITECTURE   *The World Almanac* lists fifteen tall buildings in New Orleans, Louisiana. The number of floors in each of these buildings is listed below.

51	53	45	39	36
47	42	33	32	31
33	28	28	25	23

Make a stem-and-leaf plot of the data.
(Lesson 12-1) **See margin.**

2. WORLD CULTURES   Many North American Indians hold conferences called *powwows*, to celebrate their culture and heritage through various ceremonies and dances. The ages of participants and observers in a Menominee Indian powwow are shown in the chart below.

Participants	20, 18, 12, 13, 14, 72, 65, 23, 25, 43, 67, 35, 68, 13, 56
Observers	43, 55, 70, 63, 15, 41, 9, 42, 75, 25, 16, 18, 51, 80, 75, 39, 23, 55, 50, 54, 60, 43

Find the range and interquartile range for each group. *(Lesson 12-2)*
participants: 60, 51; observers: 71, 35

3. CONSUMERISM   The average retail price for one gallon of unleaded gasoline at a certain station are shown in the table below.

Year	1	2	3	4	5
Price ($)	1.21	1.20	0.92	0.95	0.95
Year	6	7	8	9	10
Price ($)	1.02	1.16	1.14	1.13	1.11

Make a box-and-whisker plot of the data.
(Lesson 12-3) **See margin.**

4. HOMEWORK   The frequency table below shows the amount of time students spend doing homework each week.

Weekly Homework Time		
Number of Hours	Tally	Frequency
0–3	IIII	5
4–7	JHT JHT IIII	14
8–11	JHT JHT JHT III	18
12–15	JHT JHT I	11

Display the data in a histogram. *(Lesson 12-4)*
See margin.

5. ENTERTAINMENT   The graph below displays data about movie attendance.

Tell why the graph appears to be misleading.
(Lesson 12-5) **See margin.**

6. BUSINESS   The Yogurt Oasis advertises that there are 1512 ways to enjoy a one-topping sundae. They offer six flavors of frozen yogurt, six different serving sizes, and several different toppings. How many toppings do they offer? *(Lesson 12-6)* **42 toppings**

7. VOLLEYBALL   How many different 6-player starting squads can be formed from a volleyball team of 15 players? *(Lesson 12-7)* **5005 teams**

8. TELEVISION   The odds in favor of a person in North America appearing on television sometime in their lifetime is 1:3. If there are 32 students in your class, predict how many will appear on television. *(Lesson 12-8)* **8 students**

9. BUSINESS   An auto dealer finds that of the cars coming in for service, 70% need a tune up and 50% need a new air filter. What is the probability that a car brought in for service needs both a tune up and a new air filter? *(Lesson 12-9)* **0.35**

10. ECONOMICS   Thirty-one percent of minimum-wage workers are between 16 and 19 years old. Twenty-two percent of the minimum-wage workers are between 20 and 24 years old. If a person who makes minimum wage is selected at random, what is the probability that he or she will be between 16 and 24 years old? *(Lesson 12-9)*
53%

Answers

1.

Stem	Leaf					
2	3	5	8	8		
3	1	2	3	3	6	9
4	2	5	7			
5	1	3				

$4 \mid 2 = 42$

3.

4.   Weekly Homework Time

5. There is no title or labels on either scale and the vertical axis does not include zero.

Answer

10.

$y = 2x^3$

ARCHITECTURE   For Exercises 1 and 2, use the following information.

The polynomial $2xy + 2y^2 + 2yz$ represents the total area of the first floor shown in the plan below. *(Lesson 13-1)*

1. Find the degree of the polynomial. **2**

2. Find an expression to represent the area of the living room. Then classify the expression as a *monomial, binomial,* or *trinomial.* **4xy; monomial**

3. CONSTRUCTION   A standard unit of measurement for a window is the *united inch.* You can find the united inches of a window by adding the length and width of the window. If the length of a window is $3x - 5$ inches and the width is $x + 7$ inches, what is the size of the window in united inches? *(Lesson 13-2)* **4x + 2 united inches**

4. GEOMETRY   The perimeter of the triangle below is $4x + 4$ centimeters. Find the length of the hypotenuse of the triangle. *(Lesson 13-3)* **x + 5 cm**

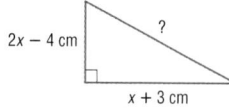

2x − 4 cm   ?

x + 3 cm

5. GEOMETRY   Find the area of the shaded region. Write in simplest form. *(Lesson 13-4)*
3s² − 3s units²

2s   s

s   3

MANUFACTURING   For Exercises 6 and 7, use the following information.

The figure below shows a pattern for a cardboard b before it has been cut and folded. *(Lesson 13-4)*

2x + 1

x   x

2x + 1

x   x

6. Find the area of each rectangular region and add to find a formula for the number of square inche of cardboard needed. **12x² + 8x + 1 units²**

7. Find the surface area if x is 2.5 inches. **96 in²**

8. PRODUCTION   The XYZ Production Company states that the cost y of producing x items is give by the equation $y = 2500 + 3.2x$. Does this equation represent a *linear* or *nonlinear* function? *(Lesson 13-5)* **linear**

9. INTERNET   The graph below shows the increas in electronic mailboxes in the United States.

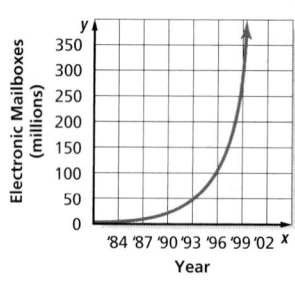

Source: Messaging Online

Does this graph represent a *linear* or *nonlinear* function? Explain. *(Lesson 13-5)*
Nonlinear; the graph is a curve.

10. POPULATION   The population growth of a particular species of insect is given by the equation $y = 2x^3$, where x represents time elapse in days and y represents the population size. Graph this equation. *(Lesson 13-6)* **See margin.**

Mixed Problem Solving

Preparing For Standardized Tests Ⓐ Ⓑ Ⓒ Ⓓ

Becoming a Better Test-Taker NEW YORK Test Practice

At some time in your life, you will probably have to take a standardized test. Sometimes this test may determine if you go on to the next grade level or course, or even if you will graduate from high school. This section of your textbook is dedicated to making you a better test-taker.

TYPES OF TEST QUESTIONS In the following pages, you will see examples of four types of questions commonly seen on standardized tests. A description of each type is shown in the table below.

Type of Question	Description	See Pages
multiple choice	Four or five possible answer choices are given from which you choose the best answer.	772–775
gridded response	You solve the problem. Then you enter the answer in a special grid and shade in the corresponding circles.	776–779
short response	You solve the problem, showing your work and/or explaining your reasoning.	780–783
extended response	You solve a multi-part problem, showing your work and/or explaining your reasoning.	784–788

PRACTICE After being introduced to each type of question, you can practice that type of question. Each set of practice questions is divided into five sections that represent the concepts most commonly assessed on standardized tests.

- Number and Operations
- Algebra
- Geometry
- Measurement
- Data Analysis and Probability

USING A CALCULATOR On some tests, you are permitted to use a calculator. You should check with your teacher to determine if calculator use is permitted on the test you will be taking, and if so, what type of calculator can be used.

TEST-TAKING TIPS In addition to the Test-Taking Tips like the one shown on the right, here are some additional thoughts that might help you.

- Get a good night's rest before the test. Cramming the night before does not improve your results.

- Budget your time when taking a test. Don't dwell on problems that you cannot solve. Just make sure to leave that question blank on your answer sheet.

- Watch for key words like NOT and EXCEPT. Also look for order words like LEAST, GREATEST, FIRST, and LAST.

> **Test-Taking Tip**
> If you are allowed to use a calculator, make sure you are familiar with how it works so that you won't waste time trying to figure out the calculator when taking the test.

Multiple-choice questions are the most common type of question on standardized tests. These questions are sometimes called *selected-response questions*. You are asked to choose the best answer from four or five possible answers.

To record a multiple-choice answer, you may be asked to shade in a bubble that is a circle or an oval or to just write the letter of your choice. Always make sure that your shading is dark enough and completely covers the bubble.

To make sure you have the correct solution, you must check to make sure that your answer satisfies the conditions of the original problem.

Incomplete Shading
Ⓐ Ⓑ Ⓒ Ⓓ

Too light shading
Ⓐ Ⓑ Ⓒ Ⓓ

Correct shading
Ⓐ Ⓑ Ⓒ Ⓓ

Example 1

Nathan wants to save $500 for a season ski pass. He has $200 and can save $25 per week. About how many months will he need to save in order to have enough money?

Ⓐ 20 months

Ⓑ 15 months

Ⓒ 12 months

Ⓓ 8 months

Ⓔ 3 months

Notice that the problem gives the amount that Nathan can save each *week*, but asks for the time it will take to save the money in *months*. Since Nathan can save $25 per week and there are about 4 weeks in a month, he can save about $4 \cdot \$25$ or $100 each month.

Let x represent the number of months. So, the amount he will have after x months is $200 + 100x$. Since Nathan wants to save $500, set the expression equal to 500. Write the equation $500 = 200 + 100x$.

Strategy

You can use backsolving to find the correct answer.

Next, test each value given in the answer choices.

$500 = 200 + 100x$
$500 \stackrel{?}{=} 200 + 100(20)$ Replace x with 20.
$500 \neq 2200$

$500 = 200 + 100x$
$500 \stackrel{?}{=} 200 + 100(15)$ Replace x with 15.
$500 \neq 1700$

$500 = 200 + 100x$
$500 \stackrel{?}{=} 200 + 100(12)$ Replace x with 12.
$500 \neq 1400$

$500 = 200 + 100x$
$500 \stackrel{?}{=} 200 + 100(8)$ Replace x with 8.
$500 \neq 1000$

$500 = 200 + 100x$
$500 = 200 + 100(3)$ Replace x with 3.
$500 = 500$ ✓

The answer is E.

Preparing for Standardized Tests

Many multiple-choice questions do not include a diagram. Drawing a diagram for the situation can help you to answer the question.

Example 2

Isabelle and Belinda take a hiking trip. They want to get to Otter's pond but cannot walk directly to it. They start from the beginning of the trail and follow the trail for 4 miles to the west. Then they turn south and walk 6 miles. How far is Otter's Pond from the start of the trail? Round to the nearest tenth of a mile.

    (A) 1.4 mi   (B) 4.5 mi   (C) 6.3 mi   (D) 7.2 mi

Strategy

Whenever possible, use a drawing to help you solve a problem.

Draw a diagram of the hiking trip. Isabelle and Belinda have walked in a path that creates a right triangle.

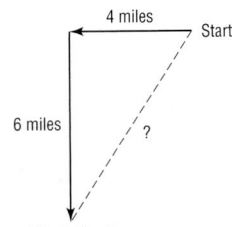

Looking at the diagram, you can eliminate 1.4 miles since it is too small.

The legs of the right triangle are 4 and 6. Use the Pythagorean Theorem to find the hypotenuse.

$$c^2 = a^2 + b^2 \qquad \text{Pythagorean Theorem}$$
$$c^2 = 6^2 + 4^2 \qquad \text{Replace } a \text{ with 6 and } b \text{ with 4.}$$
$$c^2 = 36 + 16 \qquad \text{Evaluate } 6^2 + 4^2.$$
$$c^2 = 52 \qquad \text{Add 36 and 16.}$$
$$\sqrt{c^2} = \sqrt{52} \qquad \text{Take the square root of each side.}$$
$$c \approx 7.2 \qquad \text{Round to the nearest tenth.}$$

The answer is D, 7.2 miles.

Often multiple-choice questions require you to convert measurements to solve. Pay careful attention to each unit of measure in the question and the answer choices.

Example 3

Malik is planning to draw a large map of his neighborhood for a school project. He wants the scale for the map to be 1 inch = 8800 feet. His house is 2.5 miles from school. How far on the map will his house be from the school?

    (A) 0.5 in.   (B) 0.8 in.   (C) 1.0 in.   (D) 1.5 in.   (E) 1.8 in.

The actual distance from Malik's house to the school is given in miles, and the scale is given in feet. You need to convert from miles to feet to solve the problem.

Since 1 mile is equal to 5280 feet, 2.5 miles = 2.5(5280) or 13,200 feet.

Now use the scale factor to find the distance.

$$13{,}200 \text{ ft} \times \frac{1 \text{ in.}}{8800 \text{ ft}} \text{ or 1.5 inches}$$

Strategy

Have you really answered the question?

On the map, Malik's house will be 1.5 inches from the school. Choice D is the answer.

Multiple-Choice Practice

Choose the best answer.

Number and Operations

1. In 2001, the population of China was approximately 1,273,000,000. Write the population in scientific notation. **D**

- (A) 12.73×10^1
- (B) 1273.0×10^6
- (C) 1.27×10^9
- (D) 1.273×10^9

2. Tyler uses 4 gallons of stain to cover 120 square feet of fence. He still has 520 square feet left to cover. Which proportion could he use to calculate how many more gallons of stain he will need? **B**

- (A) $\dfrac{120}{520} = \dfrac{x}{4}$
- (B) $\dfrac{4}{120} = \dfrac{x}{520}$
- (C) $\dfrac{120}{x} = \dfrac{520}{4}$
- (D) $\dfrac{4}{520} = \dfrac{120}{x}$

3. If 1.5 cups of nuts are in a bag of trail mix that serves 6 people, how many cups of nuts will be needed for a trail mix that will serve 9 people? **C**

- (A) 1 c
- (B) 1.5 c
- (C) 2.25 c
- (D) 2.5 c

4. Hannah has a roll of ribbon for wrapping presents that is 10 yards long. If it takes $\dfrac{2}{3}$ yard of ribbon to wrap each present, how many presents can she wrap with the 10 yards? **C**

- (A) 8
- (B) 10
- (C) 15
- (D) 20

Algebra

5. Ms. Blackwell needs to rent a car for her family vacation. She has found a company that offers the following two options.

Plan	Flat Rate	Cost per Mile
Option A	$40	$0.25
Option B	$30	$0.35

How many miles must the Blackwells drive for the plans to cost the same? **D**

- (A) 0 mi
- (B) 10 mi
- (C) 25 mi
- (D) 100 mi

6. Six friends go to a movie and each buys a large container of popcorn. If a movie ticket costs $8.75 and a large popcorn costs $2.25, which expression can be used to find the total cost for all six people? **C**

- (A) $2.25(8.75 + 5)$
- (B) $2.25 + 8.75(6)$
- (C) $6(8.75 + 2.25)$
- (D) $6(2.25) + 8.75$

7. Midtown Printing Company charges $50 to design a flyer and $0.25 per flyer for printing. y is the total cost in dollars and x is the number of fliers, which equation describes the relationship between x and y? **C**

- (A) $y = 50 - 0.25x$
- (B) $y = 50x + 0.25$
- (C) $y = 50 + 0.25x$
- (D) $y = 0.25x - 50$

8. The simple interest formula, $I = Prt$, gives the interest I earned for an amount of money invested P at a given rate r for t years. If Nicholas invests $2100 at an annual interest rate of 7.5%, how long will it take him to earn $3000? Round to the nearest year. **B**

- (A) 3 yr
- (B) 19 yr
- (C) 20 yr
- (D) 52 yr

Geometry

9. Alyssa wants to redecorate her room. She makes a scale diagram of her room on paper. She then cuts out scale pictures of her bed, dresser, and desk. If she slides her dresser along the wall, what type of transformation is this? **D**

- (A) reflection
- (B) rotation
- (C) dilation
- (D) translation

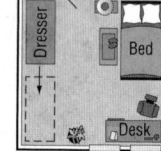

Test-Taking Tip (A) (B) (C) (D)

Question 8
Some multiple-choice questions have you use a formula to solve a problem. You can check your solution by replacing the variables with the given values and your answer. The answer choice that results in a true statement is the correct answer.

10. To get to work from her house, Amanda walks 6 blocks west then turns and walks 11 blocks south. If she could walk directly home from work, how many blocks would she need to walk? Round to the nearest block. **C**

- Ⓐ 9 blocks
- Ⓑ 12 blocks
- Ⓒ 13 blocks
- Ⓓ 15 blocks

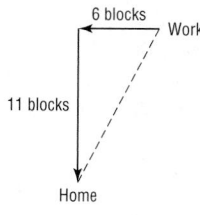

11. Andrés plans to lay sod in his yard. How many square feet of sod will he need? **B**

- Ⓐ 5100 ft²
- Ⓑ 8925 ft²
- Ⓒ 9000 ft²
- Ⓓ 9650 ft²

Measurement

12. The world's largest ball of Sisal Twine is located in Cawker City, Kansas. It consists of about 7,009,942 feet of twine. How many miles of twine is this? **B**

- Ⓐ 586,080 mi
- Ⓑ 1328 mi
- Ⓒ 1402 mi
- Ⓓ 37,012,493,760 mi

13. The world's largest pizza was made on October 11, 1987 by Lorenzo Amato and Louis Piancone. The pizza measured 140 feet across. If a regular size pizza at a local restaurant measures 12 inches across, how many times more area does the largest pizza cover than the regular pizza? **D**

- Ⓐ about 12 times
- Ⓑ about 136 times
- Ⓒ 140 times
- Ⓓ 19,600 times

14. A cookie recipe requires 6 cups of chocolate chips. The recipe serves 20 people. How many cups of chocolate chips would be needed to serve 35 people? **A**

- Ⓐ 10.5 c
- Ⓑ 11 c
- Ⓒ 12 c
- Ⓓ 15 c

15. Shopper's Mart sells two sizes of Corn Crunch cereal. The 16-ounce box costs $4.95. The 12-ounce box costs $3.55. What is true about these two cereals? **B**

- Ⓐ The 16-ounce box is a better buy.
- Ⓑ The 12-ounce box is a better buy.
- Ⓒ They are the same cost per ounce.
- Ⓓ None of these statements are true.

Test-Taking Tip Ⓐ Ⓑ Ⓒ Ⓓ
Question 15
Always read every answer choice, particularly in questions that ask what is true about a given situation.

Data Analysis and Probability

16. The graph below shows the number of hours that students in Mr. Cardona's math class watch television and the number of hours that they exercise in the same week. Based on the trend in the scatter plot, what number of hours of exercise would you expect a student to get that watches 15 hours of television each week? **A**

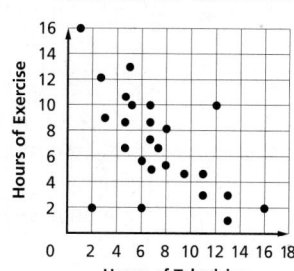

- Ⓐ 2 h
- Ⓑ 6 h
- Ⓒ 10 h
- Ⓓ 15 h

17. Mika received the following scores on 4 of his five social studies exams: 89, 75, 82, and 77. What score does he need on his fifth exam to ensure that he receives at least an average of 85? Note that a score cannot be over 100. **D**

- Ⓐ 75
- Ⓑ 85
- Ⓒ 95
- Ⓓ not possible

Gridded-Response Questions

Gridded-response questions are another type of question on standardized tests. These questions are sometimes called *student-produced response* or *grid in*.

For gridded response, you must mark your answer on a grid printed on an answer sheet. The grid contains a row of four or five boxes at the top, two rows of ovals or circles with decimal and fraction symbols, and four or five columns of ovals, numbered 0–9. At the right is an example of a grid from an answer sheet.

Example 1   **Solve the equation $10 - 4a = -38$ for a.**

What value do you need to find?

You need to find the value of a.

$$10 - 4a = -38$$ Original equation

$$10 - 4a - 10 = -38 - 10$$ Subtract 10 from each side.

$$-4a = -48$$ Simplify.

$$\frac{-4a}{-4} = \frac{-48}{-4}$$ Divide each side by -4.

$$a = 12$$ Simplify.

How do you fill in the answer grid?

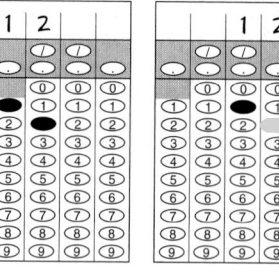

- Print your answer in the answer boxes.
- Print only one digit or symbol in each answer box.
- Do not write any digits or symbols outside the answer boxes.
- You may print your answer with the first digit in the left answer box, or with the last digit in the right answer box. You may leave blank any boxes you do not need on the right or the left side of your answer.
- Fill in only one bubble for every answer box that you have written in. Be sure not to fill in a bubble under a blank answer box.

Many gridded-response questions result in an answer that is a fraction or a decimal. These values can also be filled in on the grid.

Example 2   **A recipe for orange chicken calls for 1 cup of orange juice and serves 6 people. If Emily needs to serve 15 people, how many cups of orange juice will she need?**

What value do you need to find?

You need to find the number of cups of orange juice Emily will need for 15 servings.

Write and solve a proportion for the problem. Let s represent the number of cups.

$$\frac{1 \text{ cup}}{6 \text{ servings}} = \frac{s \text{ cups}}{15 \text{ servings}}$$

$\dfrac{1}{6} = \dfrac{s}{15}$ Write the proportion.

$15 = 6s$ Find the cross products.

$\dfrac{15}{6} = \dfrac{6s}{6}$ Divide each side by 6.

$\dfrac{5}{2} = s$ Simplify.

How do you fill in the answer grid?

You can either grid the fraction $\frac{5}{2}$, or rewrite it as 2.5 and grid the decimal. Be sure to write the decimal point or fraction bar in the answer box. The following are acceptable answer responses that represent $\frac{5}{2}$ and 2.5.

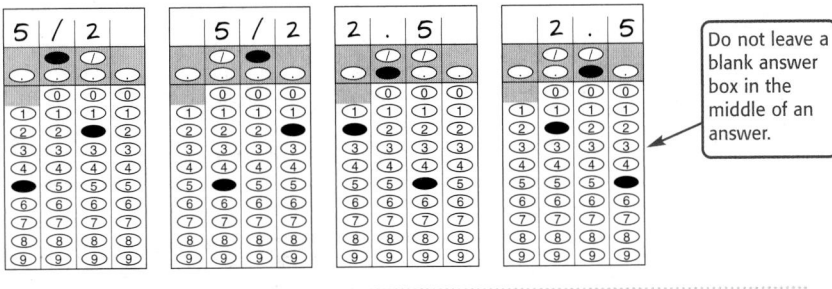

Do not leave a blank answer box in the middle of an answer.

Some problems may result in an answer that is a mixed number. Before filling in the grid, change the mixed number to an equivalent improper fraction or decimal. For example, if the answer is $1\frac{1}{2}$, do not enter 11/2, as this will be interpreted as $\frac{11}{2}$. Instead, enter 3/2 or 1.5.

Example 3

The Corner Candy Store sells 16 chocolates in a gift box. For Mother's Day the store offers the chocolates in boxes of 20. What is the percent of change?

Write the ratio for percent of change.

$\text{percent of change} = \dfrac{\text{new amount} - \text{original amount}}{\text{original amount}}$

Remember percent of change has the original amount as the denominator.

$= \dfrac{20 - 16}{16}$ Substitution

$= \dfrac{4}{16}$ Subtraction

$= 0.25$ Rewrite as a decimal.

$= 25\%$

Since the question asks for the percent, be sure to grid 25, not 0.25.

Gridded-Response Practice

Solve each problem. Then copy and complete a grid like the one shown on page 776.

Number and Operations

1. The Downtown Department Store has a 75% markup on all clothing items. A certain sweater cost the store $20. What will be the selling price of the sweater in dollars? **35**

2. The following table shows the number of billionaires in the following countries in the year 2000.

Country	Number of Billionaires
USA	70
Germany	18
Japan	12
China	8
France/Mexico/Saudi Arabia	7

   What percent of the billionaires were in the USA? Round to the nearest percent. **61**

3. Pepperoni is the most popular pizza topping. Each year approximately 251,770,000 pounds of pepperoni are eaten. If this number were written in scientific notation, what would be the power of 10? **8**

4. Dylan wants to buy an ice cream cone with three different flavors of ice cream. He has 18 flavors from which to choose. How many different ways can he have his cone? **4896**

5. Ignacio has $40 to spend at the mall. He spends half of it on a CD. He then spends $6 for lunch. Later he decides to go to a movie that costs $5.75. How much money does he have left in dollars? **8.25**

6. There are 264 tennis players and 31 coaches at a sports camp. What is the ratio of tennis players to coaches as a decimal rounded to the nearest tenth? **8.5**

Algebra

7. Find the x-intercept of the graph of the equation $2x + y = 5$. **2.5**

8. Solve $4x - 5 = 2x + 3$ for x. **4**

9. Ayana has $125 dollars to spend on CDs and DVDs. CDs cost $20. The equation $y = 125 - 20c$ represents the amount she has left to buy DVDs. If she buys 3 CDs, how much money in dollars will she have to buy DVDs? **65**

10. For her birthday, Allison and her five friends went out for pizza. They ate an entire pizza that was cut into 16 pieces. If two of her friends ate 4 pieces, one of her friends ate 3 pieces and two of her friends ate 1 piece, how many pieces did Allison eat? **3**

11. A parking garage has two different pay parking options. You can pay $11 for the day or $2 for the first hour and $0.75 for each additional half hour. How many hours would you need to stay for both rates to be the same? **7**

Geometry

12. The bridge over the Hoover Dam in Lake Mead, Nevada, stretches 1324 feet. A model is built that is 60 feet long. What is the scale factor of the model to the actual bridge? Round to the nearest hundredth. **0.05**

13. Use the figure to find the value of x. **55**

14. Quadrilateral $ABCD$ is translated 2 units to the right and 3 units down to get $A'B'C'D'$. What is the y-coordinate of A'? **0**

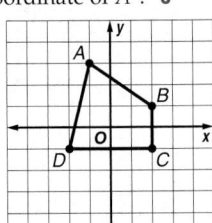

5. Toshiro swam across a river that was 20 feet wide. When he got across the river, the current had pushed him 40 feet farther down stream than when he had started. How far did he travel? Round to the nearest tenth of a foot. **44.7**

6. A building casts a shadow that is 210 feet long. If the angle of elevation from the end of the shadow to the top of the building is 40°, how tall is the building? Round to the nearest foot. **176**

Measurement

17. The Student Council held a car wash for a fund-raiser. On Saturday, approximately 8 containers of car wash were used to wash 52 cars. Assuming the rate stayed the same, how many cars did they wash if they used 11 containers on Sunday? **72**

18. Ethan wants to know how much water his sister's swimming pool holds. If the pool is 1 foot high and 6 feet across, what is the volume in cubic feet? Use π = 3.14 and round to the nearest tenth of a cubic foot. **28.3**

19. Marisa needs to make tablecloths for a wedding party. Each table is a rectangle measuring 8 feet by 3 feet. She wants the tablecloth to extend 1 foot on each of the four sides. In square feet, what will be the area of each tablecloth? **50**

20. Darnell's commute takes 1.5 hours. He drove at 20 miles per hour for 0.75 hour, and the rest of the time he drove at 50 miles per hour. In miles, how far is his work from his house? **52.5**

21. A juice company wants to make cylinder-shaped juice cans that hold approximately 196 cubic inches of juice. The base has to have a diameter of 5 inches. What will be the height of the can in inches? Use π = 3.14 and round to the nearest whole number. **10**

Data Analysis and Probability

22. The following table shows the average number of vacation days per year for people in selected countries. What is the mean number of vacation days per year for these countries? Round to the nearest whole day.

Average Number of Vacation Days per Year for 2000	
Country	Number of Days
Korea	25
Japan	25
United States	13
Brazil	34
Italy	42
France	37

Source: *The World Almanac*

29

23. Kaya and her family went on a vacation for spring break. The following table shows the distance traveled for each hour. What is the rate of change between hours 3 and 4?

Time (hours)	Distance (miles)
1	60
2	132
3	208
4	273
5	328

65

24. If a standard six-sided die is rolled, what is the probability of rolling a multiple of 2? **1/2**

Test-Taking Tip Ⓐ Ⓑ Ⓒ Ⓓ

Question 24
Fractions do not have to be written in simplest form. Any equivalent fraction that fits the grid is correct.

Short-response questions require you to provide a solution to the problem, as well as any method, explanation, and/or justification you used to arrive at the solution. These are sometimes called *constructed-response, open-response, open-ended, free-response,* or *student-produced questions.*

The following is a sample **rubric**, or scoring guide, for scoring short-response questions.

Credit	Score	Criteria
Full	2	Full credit: The answer is correct and a full explanation is provided that shows each step in arriving at the final answer.
Partial	1	Partial credit: There are two different ways to receive partial credit. • The answer is correct, but the explanation provided is incomplete or incorrect. • The answer is incorrect, but the explanation and method of solving the problem is correct.
None	0	No credit: Either an answer is not provided or the answer does not make sense.

> On some standardized tests, no credit is given for a correct answer if your work is not shown.

Example

In the first four events of a gymnastics competition, Nicole scored 7.6, 7.9, 8.5, and 8. Sandra scored 9.3, 7.4, 8.5, 7.9, and 8.1 after five events. If the entire competition consists of five events, what does Nicole need to get on her fifth event to score higher than Sandra?

Full Credit Solution

First find the total number of points that Nicole has scored so far.

$$7.6 + 7.9 + 8.5 + 8 = 32$$

Let x represent the score that Nicole will receive on her final event. Then Nicole's total score will be $32 + x$.

Next, find the total number of points that Sandra has scored.

$$9.3 + 7.4 + 8.5 + 7.9 + 8.1 = 41.2$$

> The steps, calcu[lations] and reasoning a[re] clearly stated.

Since Nicole needs to get a higher score than Sandra, we can write and solve an inequality.

Nicole's score > Sandra's score

$$32 + x > 41.2 \quad \text{Substitution}$$

$$x > 9.2 \quad \text{Subtract 32 from each side.}$$

> The solution of the problem is clearly stated.

In order to score higher than Sandra in the competition, Nicole must score higher than a 9.2 on her fifth event.

Partial Credit Solution

In this sample solution, the answer is correct; however there is no justification for any of the calculations.

$$9.3 + 7.4 + 8.5 + 7.9 + 8.1 = 41.2$$

$$32 + x > 41.2$$

$$x > 9.2$$

Nicole will need to score higher than 9.2.

> There is not an explanation of how 32 was obtained.

Partial Credit Solution

In this sample solution, the answer is incorrect because the student added Nicole's points incorrectly. However, after this error, the calculations and reasoning are correct. An equation is used in this solution and the student reasons that the score must be greater than 9.7 in the final answer.

First find the total number of points that Nicole has scored so far.

$$7.6 + 7.9 + 8.5 + 8 = 31.5$$

Let x represent the score that Nicole will receive on her final event. Then Nicole's total score will be $32 + x$. Next, find the total number of points that Sandra has scored.

$$9.3 + 7.4 + 8.5 + 7.9 + 8.1 = 41.2$$

Now we can write an equation to solve.

$$31.5 + x = 41.2$$

$$x = 9.7$$

In order to score higher than Sandra in the competition, Nicole must score higher than a 9.7.

> The answer is incorrect, but the reasoning used to find the answer is correct.

No Credit Solution

$$7.6 + 7.9 + 8.5 + 8 = 32$$

$$9.3 + 7.4 + 8.5 + 7.9 + 8.1 = 41.2$$

$$\frac{41.2 + 32}{10} = 7.32$$

Nicole needs a 7.32.

> The student averaged all of the scores demonstrating no understanding of the problem.

Solve each problem. Show all your work.

Number and Operations

1. Crispy Crunch cereal has a new box that says it is 25% larger than the original size. If the original box had 16 ounces, how many ounces does the new box have? **20 oz**

2. Austin has $\frac{1}{3}$ of a gallon of paint to paint his go cart. He knows that he will need $3\frac{1}{2}$ gallons to paint his entire cart. How many more gallons does he need? **$3\frac{1}{6}$ gal**

3. In 1999, the United States took in 6.206×10^9 from Canadian tourists. Express this value in standard notation. **$6,206,000,000**

4. Prairie High School assigns every student a student identification code. The codes consist of one letter and five digits. What is the greatest number of students that can attend Prairie High School before codes will need to be reused? **2,600,000**

5. Jacob works at a computer factory making $8.50 per hour. The company has not been selling as many computers lately so they have decreased each employee's wage by 6%. What will Jacob's new hourly wage be? **$7.99**

Algebra

6. Francisca ran for 1.25 hours at an average rate of 5 miles per hour. What distance did Francisca run? (Use the formula $d = rt$, where d represents distance, r represents rate, and t represents time.) **6.25 mi**

7. Simplify the expression $-2(y + 4) - 3$. **$-2y - 11$**

8. Tariq plans to go to Raging Waters Water Park. The park charges a $12 admission and rents inner tubes for $1.50 per hour. If he has $15, for how many hours can he rent an inner tube? **2 h**

9. $m > -\frac{7}{2}$

$-5\ -4\ -3\ -2\ -1\quad 0\quad 1\quad 2\quad 3\quad 4$

9. Solve and graph the inequality $6 - 2m < 13$.

10. Roller Way Amusement park closes the park for a day and allows only schools to visit. The schools must bring students in buses that carry 30 students. If 32 buses are at the park, write an equation to represent the total number of students S that are at the park that day. **$S = 30(32)$**

Geometry

11. Triangle RST is translated 3 units up and 1 unit to the left. Find the coordinates of translated $\triangle R'S'T'$. **$R'(3, 4)$, $S'(4, 1)$, $T'(1, 2)$**

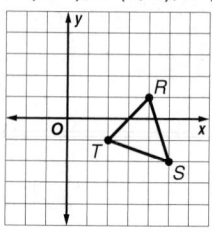

12. Chi-Yo wants to make a quilt pattern using similar triangles as shown. What is the length of the third side of the larger triangle? **7.5 in.**

13. Lawana has a window planter in the shape of a cylinder cut in half. She needs to fill it with dirt before she can plant flowers. What is the volume of the planter? Use $\pi = 3.14$ and round to the nearest tenth of a cubic foot. **21.2 ft³**

Test-Taking Tip Ⓐ Ⓑ Ⓒ Ⓓ

Question 13
After finding the solution, always go back and read the problem again to make sure your solution answers what the problem is asking.

4. $\angle KLM$ and $\angle XYZ$ are complementary. If $m\angle KLM = 3x - 1$ and $m\angle XYZ = x + 7$, find the measure of each angle. **$m\angle KLM = 62$, $m\angle XYZ = 28$**

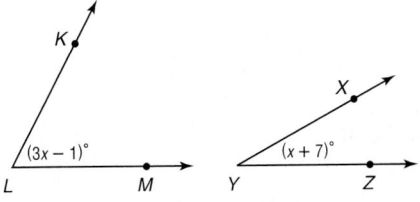

5. A cylindrical grain bin holds approximately 28,260 cubic feet of grain. If the bin has a diameter of 50 feet, what is the bin's height? Use $\pi = 3.14$ and round to the nearest tenth of a foot. **14.4 ft**

$V = 28,260 \text{ ft}^3$

50 ft

Measurement

6. One kilometer is equal to about 0.62 mile. Tito is running a 10-kilometer race. How many miles is this? **6.2 mi**

7. Jordan wants to make cone-shaped candles as shown in the diagram. What is the volume of one candle? Use $\pi = 3.14$ and round to the nearest tenth of a cubic inch. **75.4 in³**

8 in.

← 6 in. →

8. Abigail is planning a cookout at her house. She wants to put trim around the edges of round tables. If the diameter of each table is 8 feet, how much trim will she need for each table? Use $\pi = 3.14$ and round to the nearest tenth of a cubic foot. **25.1 ft**

9. At Oakwood Lawncare Service, a lawn crew can do 5 jobs in 3 days. At this rate, how many days would it take the crew to do 20 jobs? **12 days**

20. In a recent bicycle race, Kevin rode his bike at a pace of 16 miles per hour. How many feet per minute is this? **1408 ft/min**

21. Mateo wants to fill the cylindrical container shown with water. How many pints of water will he need? (*Hint:* One pint of liquid is equivalent to 28.875 cubic inches.) Use $\pi = 3.14$ and round to the nearest pint. **2.4 pt**

10 in.

3 in.

Data Analysis and Probability

22. Theo needs a four digit Personal Identification Number (PIN) for his checking account. If he can choose any digit from 0 to 9 for each of the digits, how many different PIN numbers are possible? **10,000**

23. Matthew is choosing some CDs to take on a long car drive. He has 10 jazz CDs, 3 classical CDs, and 9 soundtracks. If he chooses two CDs without replacement, what is the probability that the first CD is a soundtrack and the second CD is a jazz CD? **$\frac{15}{77}$**

24. Nikki is playing a game in which you spin the spinner below and then roll a six-sided die labeled 1 through 6. Each section of the spinner is equal in size. What is the probability that the spinner lands on blue and the die lands on an even number? **$\frac{3}{16}$**

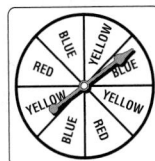

25. Two cards are drawn from a hand of eight cards numbered 1 to 8. The first card is not replaced after it is drawn. What is the probability that a 2 and a 5 are drawn? **$\frac{1}{28}$**

Extended-Response Questions

Extended-response questions are often called *open-ended* or *constructed-response questions*. Most extended-response questions have multiple parts. You must answer all parts to receive full credit.

Extended-response questions are similar to short-response questions in that you must show all of your work in solving the problem and a rubric is used to determine whether you receive full, partial, or no credit. The following is a sample rubric for scoring extended-response questions.

Credit	Score	Criteria
Full	4	Full credit: A correct solution is given that is supported by well-developed, accurate explanations.
Partial	3, 2, 1	Partial credit: A generally correct solution is given that may contain minor flaws in reasoning or computation or an incomplete solution. The more correct the solution, the greater the score.
None	0	No credit: An incorrect solution is given indicating no mathematical understanding of the concept, or no solution is given.

On some standardiz tests, no credit is giv for a correct answer your work is not sho

Make sure that when the problem says to *Show your work*, you show every aspect of your solutio including figures, sketches of graphing calculator screens, or reasoning behind computations.

Example

Northern Sofa Store's delivery charges depend upon the distance furniture is delivered. The graph shows the charge for deliveries according to the distance.

a. Write an equation to show the relationship between delivery cost y and distance from the store x.

b. Name the y-intercept and slope of the line that models the data. Explain what each means in this situation.

c. Suppose Mr. Hawkins wants a sofa delivered. His house is 21 miles from the store. What will be the cost of delivery?

Delivery Rate

Full Credit Solution

Part a   A complete solution for writing the equation shows all the computations needed and the reasoning behind those computations.

> To write the equation, first I need to find the slope. I will use the two points marked on the graph, $(0, 50)$ and $(10, 55)$.

$$m = \frac{y_2 - y_1}{x_2 - x_1} \qquad \text{slope formula}$$

$$= \frac{55 - 50}{10 - 0} \qquad (x_i, y_i) = (0, 50) \text{ and } (x_2, y_2) = (10, 55)$$

$$= \frac{5}{10} \text{ or } 0.5$$

The slope of the line is 0.5 and the y-intercept is 50.

$$y = mx + b \qquad \text{Slope-intercept form}$$

$$y = 0.5x + 50 \qquad m = 0.5 \text{ and } b = 50.$$

So an equation that fits the data is $y = 0.5x + 50$.

> The calculations and reasoning are clearly stated. The solution of the problem is also clearly stated.

Part b   In this sample answer, the student demonstrates clear understanding of the y-intercept and slope of the graph.

> I can see from the graph that the y-intercept is 50 which means \$50. This is the initial charge for any delivery and then additional money is charged for each mile. The slope of the line that I found in Part a is 0.5 which means \$0.50. This is the additional charge per mile to deliver the furniture.

Part c   In this sample answer, the student knows how to use the equation to find the delivery cost for a given distance.

> I will substitute 21 for x into the equation since Mr. Hawkins lives 21 miles from the store.
>
> $$y = 0.5x + 50$$
> $$y = 0.5(21) + 50$$
> $$y = 60.50$$
>
> The cost of delivery will be \$60.50.

Partial Credit Solution

Part a   This sample answer includes no explanations for the calculations performed. However, partial credit is given for correct calculations and a correct answer.

$$m = \frac{y_2 - y_1}{x_2 - x_1} = \frac{55 - 50}{10 - 0} = \frac{1}{2}$$

$$y = \frac{1}{2}x + 50$$

> The equation is correct because $\frac{1}{2}$ is the same as 0.5.

> More credit would have been given if an explanation had been given.

Part b   This part receives full credit because the student demonstrates understanding of the y intercept and slope.

> The y-intercept 50 is the charge for just making any delivery. It means $50. The slope $\frac{1}{2}$ is the charge per mile which is 50 cents.

Part c   Partial credit is given for Part c because the student makes a calculation error.

> To get the delivery cost, substitute 21 miles into the equation.
>
> $y = \frac{1}{2}x + 50$
>
> $y = \frac{1}{2}(21) + 50$
>
> $y = 42 + 50 = 92$
>
> The cost is $92.

This sample answer might have received a score of 2, depending on the judgment of the scorer. Had the student gotten Part c correct, the score would probably have been a 3.

No Credit Solution

Part a   The student demonstrates no understanding of how to write an equation for a line.

> If I use the points (0, 50) and (10, 55), an equation is $10y = 10x + 55$.

Part b   The student does not understand the meaning of the y-intercept or the slope.

> The y-intercept is 0 because that is when the truck leaves the store. The slope is 10 because that is the distance from the store in miles when the truck makes its first stop.

Part c   The student does not understand how to read the graph to find the cost or how to use an equation to find the cost.

> $21, because it is 21 miles from the store.

Solve each problem. Show all your work.

Number and Operations

1. In a recent survey, Funtime Amusement Park found that 6 out of 8 of their customers had been to the park before. In one week, 4500 people attended the park.

a. What percent of customers have been to the park before? **75%**

b. How many of the park goers in that week had been there before? **3375**

c. If 3000 people were at the park the next week, how many would you expect had *not* been there before? **750**

2. The following table shows the number of people of each age living in the U.S. in the year 2000.

Age	Number of People
Under 15	60,253,375
15 to 24	39,183,891
25 to 34	39,891,724
35 to 44	44,148,527
45 to 64	61,952,636
65 and over	34,991,753

Source: U.S. Census Bureau

a. To the nearest million, how many people were under age 25? **99 million**

b. What percent of people were under 15? Round to the nearest percent. **21%**

c. What is the total population of the United States? Write in scientific notation.
2.80421906×10^8

Algebra

3. Victoria needs to study for a math exam. The exam is in 18 days. She has decided to begin right away by studying 15 minutes the first night and increasing her study time by 5 minutes each day. **a. $T = 15 + 5d$**

a. Write an expression for the total number of minutes that Victoria will study T for a given time d days from today.

b. If she has 18 days to study, how many minutes will she study on the last day before the exam? **100 min**

c. Victoria begins to study on a Monday, 18 days before the exam. On what day will she study exactly one hour? **Wednesday**

4. Jasmine wants to get her portrait taken for her senior pictures. She finds that three different portrait studios charge a sitting fee and charge a separate fee for each ordered picture. The table below shows their prices.

Studio	Sitting Fee	Cost per Portrait
Famous Photos	$50	$10
Picture Perfect	$80	$8
Timeless Portraits	$45	$15

a. For each studio, write an equation that represents the total cost. In each of the three equations, use C to represent the total cost and p to represent the number of pictures. **See margin.**

b. If Jasmine wants to order 30 portraits, which studio would be the least expensive?
Picture Perfect

c. How many portraits will she need to order for Famous Photos and Picture Perfect to cost the same? **15**

Geometry

5. Rodrigo stands 50 yards away from the base of a building. From his eye level of 5 feet, Rodrigo sees the top of the building at an angle of elevation of 25°.

a. What is the height of the building? Round to the nearest tenth of a foot. **74.9 ft**

b. If Rodrigo moved back 15 more yards, how would the angle of elevation to the top of the building change? **smaller**

c. If the building were taller, would the angle of elevation be greater than or less than 25°?
greater

Test-Taking Tip Ⓐ Ⓑ Ⓒ Ⓓ
Question 5
Be sure to use a trigonometric ratio that includes the measurement you are asked to find in order to solve the problem correctly.

Preparing for Standardized Tests

6a. G' (-3, -4), H' (-1, -5), I' (-1, 1), J' (-3, -2)

6b.

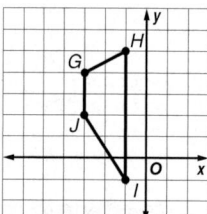
$I'(-1, 1)$
$J'(-3, 2)$
$G'(-3, -4)$
$H'(-1, -5)$

6. The diagram below shows polygon *GHIJ*.
6a–b. See margin.

G H
J
I O x

a. Find the coordinates of the vertices of quadrilateral $G'H'I'J'$ after a reflection of quadrilateral *GHIJ* in the *x*-axis.

b. Graph $G'H'I'J'$ after a reflection of quadrilateral *GHIJ* in the *x*-axis.

c. If *ABCD* is the image of *GHIJ* dilated by a scale factor of $\frac{1}{4}$ with respect to the origin, what are the coordinates of *C*? $\left(-\frac{1}{4}, -\frac{1}{4}\right)$

Measurement

7. The diagram shows a pattern for a garden that Marie plans to plant. Use $\pi = 3.14$.

8 ft
20 ft

a. What is the area of the garden in square feet? **210.24 ft²**

b. What is the area of the garden in square yards? **23.36 yd²**

c. Marie wants to put a stone border around the outside of the garden. What is the perimeter of the garden? **65.12 ft**

8. The table below shows the speeds of several animals.

Animal	Speed (mph)
Cheetah	70
Zebra	40
Reindeer	32
Cat (domestic)	30
Wild Turkey	15

Source: *World Book*

a. What is the rate of the cat in feet per minute? **2640 feet per minute**

b. How many times faster is the cheetah than the wild turkey? Round to the nearest tenth. **4.7**

Data Analysis and Probability

9. The table shows the life expectancy in years of people in different countries. The figures are for the year 2000.

Country	Life Expectancy (yr)
Afghanistan	45.9
Australia	79.8
Brazil	62.9
Canada	79.4
France	78.8
Haiti	49.2
Japan	80.7
Madagascar	55.0
Mexico	71.5
United States	77.1

Source: U.S. Census Bureau **a. 74.3 yr**

a. What is the median life expectancy?

b. What is the mean life expectancy? **68.03 yr**

c. In 2000, Cambodians had a life expectancy of 56.5. If Cambodia was added to the table how would the mean be affected? **Sample answer: It would go down.**

10. The table shows the average cost for a year of higher education for all public institutions.

Year	Cost ($)
1997-1998	$6813
1998-1999	$7107
1999-2000	$7310
2000-2001	$7621

Source: *World Book*

a. What was the rate of change between the 1999-2000 year and the 2000-2001 school year? **$311 per year**

b. What was the rate of change in dollars per year between the 1997-1998 year and the 2000-2001 year? **$269.33 per year**

c. Between what two years was the rate of change the greatest? **1999-2000 and 2000-2001**

d. Find the mean annual increase in tuition cost between 1997 and 2001. Round to the nearest dollar. **$269**

e. Based on your answer in part d, what might you expect the cost of education to be in the 2009–2010 school year if the average increase remains constant? **$10,042**

Glossary/Glosario

Cómo usar el glosario en español:

1. Busca el término en inglés que desees encontrar.

2. El término en español, junto con la definición, se encuentran en la columna de la derecha.

English

Español

A

absolute value (58) The distance a number is from zero on the number line.

valor absoluto Distancia que un número dista de cero en la recta numérica.

accuracy (589) The degree of conformity of a measurement with the true value.

exactitud Grado de conformidad de una medida con el valor verdadero.

acute angle (449) An angle with a measure greater than 0° and less than 90°.

ángulo agudo Ángulo con una medida mayor que 0° y menor que 90°.

acute triangle (454) A triangle that has three acute angles.

triángulo acutángulo Triángulo que posee tres ángulos agudos.

adjacent angles (493) Two angles that have the same vertex, share a common side, and do *not* overlap.

ángulos adyacentes Dos ángulos que poseen el mismo vértice, comparten un lado y *no* se traslapan.

algebraic expression (17) An expression that contains sums and/or products of variables and numbers.

expresión algebraica Expresión que contiene sumas y/o productos de números y variables.

algebraic fraction (170) A fraction with one or more variables in the numerator or denominator.

fracción algebraica Fracción con una o más variables en el numerador o denominador.

alternate exterior angles (492) Nonadjacent exterior angles found on opposite sides of the transversal. In the figure below, ∠1 and ∠7, ∠2 and ∠8 are alternate exterior angles.

ángulos alternos externos Ángulos exteriores no adyacentes que se encuentran en lados opuestos de una transversal. En la siguiente figura, ∠1 y ∠7, ∠2 y ∠8 son ángulos alternos externos.

alternate interior angles (492) Nonadjacent interior angles found on opposite sides of the transversal. In the figure above, ∠4 and ∠6, ∠3 and ∠5 are alternate interior angles.

ángulos alternos internos Ángulos interiores no adyacentes que se encuentran en lados opuestos de una transversal. En la figura anterior, ∠4 y ∠6, ∠3 y ∠5 son ángulos alternos internos.

altitude (520) A line segment that is perpendicular to the base of a figure with endpoints on the base and the side opposite the base.

altura Segmento de recta perpendicular a la base de una figura y cuyos extremos yacen en la base y en el lado opuesto de la base.

angle (447) Two rays with a common endpoint form an angle. The rays and vertex are used to name an angle. The angle below is ∠ABC.

ángulo Dos rayos con un punto común forman un ángulo. Los rayos y el vértice se usan para identificar el ángulo. El siguiente ángulo es ∠ABC.

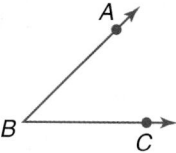

area (132) The measure of the surface enclosed by a geometric figure.

área Medida de la superficie que encierra una figura geométrica.

arithmetic sequence (249) A sequence in which the difference between any two consecutive terms is the same.

average (82) The sum of data divided by the number of items in the data set, also called the mean.

sucesión aritmética Sucesión en que la diferencia entre dos términos consecutivos cualesquiera es siempre la misma.

promedio Suma de los datos dividida entre el número de elementos en el conjunto de datos. También llamado media.

B

back-to-back stem-and-leaf plot (607) Used to compare two sets of data. The leaves for one set of data are on one side of the stem and the leaves for the other set of data are on the other side.

bar graph (722) A graphic form using bars to make comparisons of statistics.

bar notation (201) In repeating decimals the line or bar placed over the digits that repeat. For example, $2.\overline{63}$ indicates the digits 63 repeat.

base (153) In 2^4, the base is 2. The base is used as a factor as many times as given by the exponent (4). That is, $2^4 = 2 \times 2 \times 2 \times 2$.

base (288) In a percent proportion, the whole quantity, or the number to which the part is being compared.

$$\frac{\text{part}}{\text{base}} = \frac{\text{percent}}{100}$$

base (520, 521, 522) The base of a parallelogram or a triangle is any side of the figure. The bases of a trapezoid are the parallel sides.

base (557) The bases of a prism are any two parallel congruent faces.

best-fit line (409) On a scatter plot, a line drawn that is very close to most of the data points. The line that best fits the data.

binomial (669) A polynomial with exactly two terms.

boundary (419) A line that separates a graph into half planes.

box-and-whisker plot (617) A diagram that divides a set of data into four parts using the median and quartiles. A box is drawn around the quartile values and whiskers extend from each quartile to the extreme data points.

diagrama de tallo y hojas consecutivo Se usa para comparar dos conjuntos de datos. Las hojas de uno de los conjuntos de datos aparecen en un lado del tallo y las del otro al otro lado de éste.

gráfica de barras Tipo de gráfica que usa barras para comparar estadísticas.

notación de barra En decimales periódicos, la línea o barra que se escribe encima de los dígitos que se repiten. Por ejemplo, en $2.\overline{63}$ la barra encima del 63 indica que los dígitos 63 se repiten.

base En 2^4, la base es 2. La base se usa como factor las veces que indique el exponente (4). Es decir, $2^4 = 2 \times 2 \times 2 \times 2$.

base En una proporción porcentual, toda la cantidad o número al que se compara la parte.

$$\frac{\text{parte}}{\text{base}} = \frac{\text{por ciento}}{100}$$

base La base de un paralelogramo o de un triángulo es cualquier lado de la figura. Las bases de un trapecio son los lados paralelos.

base Las bases de un prisma son cualquier par de caras paralelas y congruentes.

recta de ajuste óptimo En una gráfica de dispersión, una recta que está muy cercana a la mayoría de los puntos de datos. La recta que mejor se ajusta a los datos.

binomio Polinomio con exactamente dos términos.

frontera Recta que divide una gráfica en semiplanos.

diagrama de caja y patillas Diagrama que divide un conjunto de datos en cuatro partes usando la mediana y los cuartiles. Se dibuja una caja alrededor de los cuartiles y se extienden patillas de cada uno de ellos a los valores extremos.

C

center (533) The given point from which all points on the circle are the same distance.

centro Punto dado del cual equidistan todos los puntos de un círculo.

circle (533) The set of all points in a plane that are the same distance from a given point called the center.

circle graph (723) A type of statistical graph used to compare parts of a whole.

circumference (533) The distance around a circle.

coefficient (103) The numerical part of a term that contains a variable.

combination (642) An arrangement or listing in which order is not important.

common difference (249) The difference between any two consecutive terms in an arithmetic sequence.

common multiples (226) Multiples that are shared by two or more numbers. For example, some common multiples of 4 and 6 are 0, 12, and 24.

common ratio (250) The ratio between any two consecutive terms in a geometric sequence.

compatible numbers (714) Numbers that have been rounded so when the numbers are divided by each other, the remainder is zero.

complementary (493) Two angles are complementary if the sum of their measures is 90°.

composite number (159) A whole number that has more than two factors.

compound event (650) Two or more simple events.

cone (569) A three-dimensional figure with one circular base. A curved surface connects the base and vertex.

congruent (455, 493, 500) Line segments that have the same length, or angles that have the same measure, or figures that have the same size and shape.

conjecture (7) An educated guess.

constant (103) A term without a variable.

constant of variation (394) The slope, or rate of change, in the equation $y = kx$, represented by k.

converse (462) The statement formed by reversing the phrases after *if* and *then* in an if-then statement.

círculo Conjunto de todos los puntos del plano que están a la misma distancia de un punto dado del plano llamado centro.

gráfica circular Tipo de gráfica estadística que se usa para comparar las partes de un todo.

circunferencia Longitud del contorno de un círculo.

coeficiente Parte numérica de un término que contiene una variable.

combinación Arreglo o lista en que el orden no es importante.

diferencia común Diferencia entre dos términos consecutivos cualesquiera de una sucesión aritmética.

múltiplos comunes Múltiplos compartidos por dos o más números. Por ejemplo, algunos múltiplos comunes de 4 y 6 son 0, 12 y 24.

razón común Razón entre dos términos consecutivos cualesquiera de una sucesión geométrica.

números compatibles Números redondeados de modo que cuando se dividen, el residuo es cero.

complementarios Dos ángulos son complementarios si la suma de sus medidas es 90°.

número compuesto Número entero que posee más de dos factores.

evento compuesto Dos o más eventos simples.

cono Figura tridimensional con una base circular, la cual posee una superficie curva que une la base con el vértice.

congruentes Segmentos de recta que tienen la misma longitud o ángulos que tienen la misma medida o figuras que poseen la misma forma y tamaño.

conjetura Suposición informada.

constante Término sin variables.

constante de variación La pendiente, o tasa de cambio, en la ecuación $y = kx$, representada por k.

recíproca Un enunciado que se forma intercambiando los enunciados que vienen a continuación de *si-entonces* en un enunciado *si-entonces*.

coordinate (57) A number that corresponds with a point on a number line.

coordinate plane (33) Another name for the coordinate system.

coordinate system (33) A coordinate system is formed by the intersection of two number lines that meet at right angles at their zero points, also called a coordinate plane.

corresponding angles (492) Angles that have the same position on two different parallel lines cut by a transversal. In the figure, $\angle 1$ and $\angle 5$, $\angle 2$ and $\angle 6$, $\angle 3$ and $\angle 7$, $\angle 4$ and $\angle 8$ are corresponding angles.

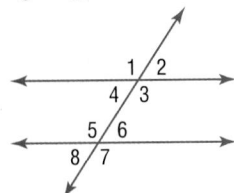

corresponding parts (500) Parts of congruent or similar figures that match.

cosine (477) If $\triangle ABC$ is a right triangle and A is an acute angle,

$$\text{cosine } \angle A = \frac{\text{measure of the leg adjacent to } \angle A}{\text{measure of the hypotenuse}}$$

counterexample (25) An example that shows a conjecture is not true.

cross products (270) If $\frac{a}{c} = \frac{b}{d}$, then $ad = bc$. If $ad = bc$, then $\frac{a}{c} = \frac{b}{d}$.

cubic function (688) A function that can be described by an equation of the form $y = ax^3 + bx^2 + cx + d$, where $a \neq 0$.

cylinder (565) A solid that has two parallel, congruent bases (usually circular) connected with a curved side.

coordenada Número que corresponde a un punto en la recta numérica.

plano de coordenadas Otro nombre para el sistema de coordenadas.

sistema de coordenadas Un sistema de coordenadas se forma de la intersección de dos rectas numéricas perpendiculares que se intersecan en sus puntos cero. También llamado plano de coordenadas.

ángulos correspondientes Ángulos que tienen la misma posición en dos rectas paralelas distintas cortadas por una transversal. En la figura, $\angle 1$ y $\angle 5$, $\angle 2$ y $\angle 6$, $\angle 3$ y $\angle 7$, $\angle 4$ y $\angle 8$ son ángulos correspondientes.

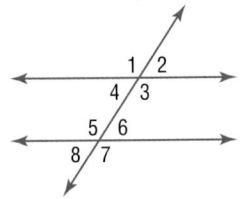

partes correspondientes Partes de figuras congruentes o semejantes que se corresponden mutuamente.

coseno Si $\triangle ABC$ es un ángulo rectángulo y A es uno de sus ángulos agudos,

$$\text{coseno } \angle A = \frac{\text{medida del cateto adyacente a } \angle A}{\text{medida de la hipotenusa}}$$

contraejemplo Ejemplo que muestra que una conjetura no es verdadera.

productos cruzados Si $\frac{a}{c} = \frac{b}{d}$, entonces $ad = bc$. Si $ad = bc$, entonces $\frac{a}{c} = \frac{b}{d}$.

función cúbica Función que puede describirse por una ecuación de la forma $y = ax^3 + bx^2 + cx + d$, donde $a \neq 0$.

cilindro Sólido que posee dos bases congruentes y paralelas (por lo general circulares) unidas por un lado curvo.

D

deductive reasoning (25) The process of using facts, properties, or rules to justify reasoning or reach valid conclusions.

defining a variable (18) Choosing a variable and a quantity for the variable to represent in an equation.

razonamiento deductivo Proceso de usar hechos, propiedades o reglas para justificar un razonamiento o para sacar conclusiones válidas.

definir una variable Seleccionar una variable y una cantidad para la variable psts representst en una ecuación.

degree (448) The most common unit of measure for angles.

grado La unidad de medida angular más común.

degree (670) The sum of the exponents of the variables of a monomial.

grado Suma de los exponentes de las variables de un monomio.

dependent events (651) Two or more events in which the outcome of one event does affect the outcome of the other event(s).

eventos dependientes Dos o más eventos en que el resultado de uno de ellos afecta el resultado del otro o de los otros eventos.

diagonal (528) A line segment that joins two nonconsecutive vertices of a polygon.

diagonal Segmento de recta que une dos vértices no consecutivos de un polígono.

diameter (533) The distance across a circle through its center.

diámetro Distancia de un lado a otro de un círculo medida a través de su centro.

dilation (512) A transformation that alters the size of a figure but not its shape.

dilatación Transformación que altera el tamaño de una figura, pero no su forma.

dimensional analysis (212) The process of including units of measurement when computing.

análisis dimensional Proceso que incorpora las unidades de medida al hacer cálculos.

direct variation (394) A special type of linear equation that describes rate of change. A relationship such that as x increases in value, y increases or decreases at a constant rate.

variación directa Tipo especial de ecuación lineal que describe tasas de cambio. Relación en que a medida que x aumenta de valor, y aumenta o disminuye a una tasa constante .

discount (299) The amount by which the regular price of an item is reduced.

descuento Cantidad por la que se reduce el precio normal de un artículo.

Distance Formula (466) The distance between two points, with coordinates (x_1, y_1) and (x_2, y_2), is given by $d = \sqrt{(x_2 - x_1)^2 + (y_2 - y_1)^2}$.

Fórmula de la distancia La distancia entre dos puntos, con coordenadas (x_1, y_1) y (x_2, y_2), se calcula con $d = \sqrt{(x_2 - x_1)^2 + (y_2 - y_1)^2}$.

divisible (148) A number is divisible by another if, upon division, the remainder is zero.

divisible Un número es divisible entre otro si, al dividirlos, el residuo es cero.

domain (35) The domain of a relation is the set of all x-coordinates from each pair.

dominio El dominio de una relación es el conjunto de coordenadas x de todos los pares .

E

edge (556) Where two planes intersect in a line.

arista Recta en donde se intersecan dos planos.

empty set (336) A set with no elements shown by the symbol { } or $\varnothing$.

conjunto vacío Conjunto que carece de elementos y que se denota con el símbolo { } o $\varnothing$.

equation (28) A mathematical sentence that contains an equals sign (=).

ecuación Enunciado matemático que contiene el signo de igualdad (=).

equilateral triangle (455) A triangle with all sides congruent.

triángulo equilátero Un triángulo cuyos lados son todos congruentes.

equivalent equations (111) Two or more equations with the same solution. For example, $x + 4 = 7$ and $x = 3$ are equivalent equations.

ecuaciones equivalentes Dos o más ecuaciones con las mismas soluciones. Por ejemplo, $x + 4 = 7$ y $x = 3$ son ecuaciones equivalentes.

equivalent expressions (98) Expressions that have the same value.

evaluate (12) Find the numerical value of an expression.

expanded form (154) A number expressed using place value to write the value of each digit in the number.

experimental probability (311) What actually occurs in a probability experiment.

exponent (153) In 2^4, the exponent is 4. The exponent tells how many times the base, 2, is used as a factor. So, $2^4 = 2 \times 2 \times 2 \times 2$.

exterior angles (492, 531) Four of the angles formed by the transversal and two parallel lines. Exterior angles lie outside the two parallel lines.

expresiones equivalentes Expresiones que tienen el mismo valor.

evaluar Calcular el valor numérico de una expresión.

forma desarrollada Número que se escribe usando el valor de posición para indicar el valor de cada dígito de un número.

probabilidad experimental Lo que realmente sucede en un experimento probabilístico.

exponente En 2^4, el exponente es 4. El exponente indica cuántas veces se usa la base, 2, como factor. Así, $2^4 = 2 \times 2 \times 2 \times 2$.

ángulos exteriores Cuatro de los ángulos formados por una transversal y dos rectas paralelas. Los ángulos exteriores yacen fuera de las dos rectas paralelas.

F

face (556) A flat surface, the side or base of a prism.

factorial (642) The expression *n factorial* (*n*!) is the product of all counting numbers beginning with *n* and counting backward to 1.

factors (148) Two or more numbers that are multiplied to form a product.

factor tree (160) A way to find the prime factorization of a number. The factors branch out from the previous factors until all the factors are prime numbers.

formula (131) An equation that shows a relationship among certain quantities.

frequency table (623) A chart that indicates the number of values in each interval.

function (369) A function is a special relation in which each element of the domain is paired with exactly one element in the range.

Fundamental Counting Principle (636) If event *M* can occur in *m* ways and is followed by event *N* that can occur in *n* ways, then the event *M* followed by event *N* can occur in $m \cdot n$ ways.

cara Superficie plana, el lado o la base de un prisma.

factorial La expresión *n factorial* (*n*!) es el producto de todos los números naturales, comenzando con *n* y contando al revés hasta llegar al 1.

factores Dos o más números que se multiplican para formar un producto.

árbol de factores Forma de encontrar la factorización prima de un número. Los factores se ramifican de los factores anteriores hasta que todos los factores son números primos.

fórmula Ecuación que muestra la relación entre ciertas cantidades.

tabla de frecuencias Tabla que indica el número de valores en cada intervalo.

función Una función es una relación especial en que a cada elemento del dominio le corresponde un único elemento del rango.

Principio fundamental de contar Si el evento *M* puede ocurrir de *m* maneras y lo sigue un evento *N* que puede ocurrir de *n* maneras, entonces el evento *M* seguido del evento *N* puede ocurrir de $m \cdot n$ maneras.

G

geometric sequence (250) A sequence in which the ratio between any two consecutive terms is the same.

graph (34) A dot at the point that corresponds to an ordered pair on a coordinate plane.

sucesión geométrica Sucesión en que la razón entre dos términos consecutivos cualesquiera es siempre la misma.

gráfica Marca puntual en el punto que corresponde a un par ordenado en un plano de coordenadas.

greatest common factor (GCF) (164) The greatest number that is a factor of two or more numbers.

greatest possible error (594) One-half the precision unit, used to describe the actual measure.

máximo común divisor (MCD) El número mayor que es factor de dos o más números.

error máximo posible La mitad de la unidad de precisión. Se usa para describir la medida exacta.

H

half plane (419) The region that contains the solution for an inequality.

histogram (623) A histogram uses bars to display numerical data that have been organized into equal intervals.

hypotenuse (460) The side opposite the right angle in a right triangle.

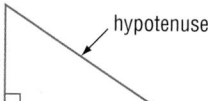

semiplano Región que contiene la solución de una desigualdad.

histograma Un histograma usa barras para exhibir datos numéricos que han sido organizados en intervalos iguales.

hipotenusa Lado opuesto al ángulo recto en un triángulo rectángulo.

I

identity (336) An equation that is true for every value of the variable.

independent events (650) Two or more events in which the outcome of one event does *not* influence the outcome of the other event(s).

indirect measurement (472) Using the properties of similar triangles to find measurements that are difficult to measure directly.

inductive reasoning (7) Reasoning based on a pattern of examples or past events.

inequality (57, 340) A mathematical sentence that contains $<$, $>$, $\neq$, $\leq$, or $\geq$.

integers (56) The whole numbers and their opposites.
$\ldots, -3, -2, -1, 0, 1, 2, 3, \ldots$

interior angles (492, 528) Four of the angles formed by the transversal and two parallel lines. Interior angles lie between the two parallel lines.

interquartile range (613) The range of the middle half of a set of data. It is the difference between the upper quartile and the lower quartile.

inverse operations (110) Operations that undo each other, such as addition and subtraction.

irrational number (441) A number that cannot be expressed as $\frac{a}{b}$, where a and b are integers and b does not equal 0.

identidad Ecuación que es verdadera para cada valor de la variable.

eventos independientes Dos o más eventos en que el resultado de uno de ellos *no* afecta el resultado del otro o de los otros eventos .

medición indirecta Uso de las propiedades de triángulos semejantes para hacer mediciones que son difíciles de realizar directamente.

razonamiento inductivo Rezonamiento basada en un patrón de ejemplos o de sucesos pasados.

desigualdad Enunciado matemático que contiene $<$, $>$, $\neq$, $\leq$ o $\geq$.

enteros Los números enteros y sus opuestos.
$\ldots, -3, -2, -1, 0, 1, 2, 3, \ldots$

ángulos interiores Cuatro de los ángulos formados por una transversal y dos rectas paralelas. Los ángulos interiores yacen entre las dos rectas paralelas.

amplitud intercuartílica Amplitud de la mitad central de un conjunto de datos. Es la diferencia entre el cuartil superior y el inferior.

operaciones inversas Operaciones que se anulan mutuamente, como la adición y la sustracción.

número irracional Número que no puede escribirse como $\frac{a}{b}$, donde a y b son enteros y b no es igual a 0.

isosceles triangle (455) A triangle that has at least two congruent sides.

triángulo isósceles Triángulo que posee por lo menos dos lados congruentes.

L

lateral area (578) The sum of the areas of the lateral faces of a solid.

área lateral Suma de las àreas de las caras laterales de un sólido.

lateral faces (578) The lateral faces of a prism, cylinder, pyramid, or cone are all the surface of the figure except the base or bases.

caras laterales Las caras laterales de un prisma, cilindro, pirámide o cono son todas las superficies de la figura, excluyendo la base o las bases.

least common denominator (LCD) (227) The least common multiple of the denominators of two or more fractions.

mínimo común denominador (mcd) El mínimo común múltiplo de los denominadores de dos o más fracciones.

least common multiple (LCM) (226) The least of the nonzero common multiples of two or more numbers. The LCM of 4 and 6 is 12.

mínimo común múltiplo (mcm) El menor de los múltiplos comunes no nulos de dos o más números. El MCM de 4 y 6 es 12.

leaves (606) In a stem-and-leaf plot, the next greatest place value of the data after the stem forms the leaves.

hojas En un diagrama de tallo y hojas, las hojas las forma el segundo valor de posición mayor después del tallo.

legs (460) The sides that are adjacent to the right angle of a right triangle.

catetos Lados adyacentes al ángulo recto de un triángulo rectángulo.

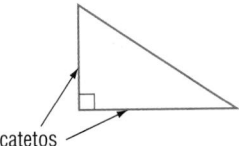

like terms (103, 674) Expressions that contain the same variables to the same power, such as $2n$ and $5n$ or $6xy^2$ and $4xy^2$.

términos semejantes Expresiones que tienen las mismas variables elevadas a los mismos exponentes, como $2n$ y $5n$ ó $6xy^2$ y $4xy^2$.

line (447) A never-ending straight path.

recta Trayectoria rectilínea interminable.

line graph (722) A type of statistical graph used to show how values change over a period of time.

gráfica lineal Tipo de gráfica estadística que se usa para mostrar cómo cambian los valores durante un período de tiempo.

line of symmetry (506) Each half of a figure is a mirror image of the other half when a line of symmetry is drawn.

eje de simetría Cuando se traza un eje de simetría, cada mitad de una figura es una imagen especular de la otra mitad.

line segment (453) Part of a line containing two endpoints and all the points between them.

segmento de recta Parte de una recta que contiene dos extremos y todos los puntos entre éstos.

linear equation (375) An equation in which the variables appear in separate terms and neither variable contains an exponent other than 1. The graph of a linear equation is a straight line.

ecuación lineal Ecuación en que las variables aparecen en términos separados y en la cual ninguna de ellas tiene un exponente distinto de 1. La gráfica de una ecuación lineal es una recta.

lower quartile (613) The median of the lower half of a set of data, indicated by LQ.

cuartil inferior Mediana de la mitad inferior de un conjunto de datos, se denota con CI.

mean (82, 238) The sum of data divided by the number of items in the data set, also called the average.

measures of central tendency (238) For a list of numerical data, numbers that can represent the whole set of data.

measures of variation (612) Used to describe the distribution of statistical data.

median (238) In a set of data, the middle number of the ordered data, or the mean of the two middle numbers.

midpoint (468) On a line segment, the point that is halfway between the endpoints.

Midpoint Formula (468) On a coordinate plane, the coordinates of the midpoint of a segment whose endpoints have coordinates at (x_1, y_1) and (x_2, y_2) are given by $\left(\frac{x_1 + x_2}{2}, \frac{y_1 + y_2}{2}\right)$.

mixed number (200) The indicated sum of a whole number and a fraction. For example, $3\frac{1}{2}$.

mode (238) The number or numbers that occurs most often in a set of data.

monomial (150) An expression that is a number, a variable, or a product of numbers and/or variables.

multiple (226) The product of a number and a whole number.

mutually exclusive events (652) Two or more events that cannot happen at the same time.

media Suma de los datos dividida entre el número de elementos en el conjunto de datos. También llamada promedio.

medidas de tendencia central Números que pueden representar todo el conjunto de datos en una lista de datos numéricos.

medidas de variación Se usan para describir la distribución de datos estadísticos.

mediana En un conjunto de datos, el número central de los datos ordenados numéricamente o la media de los dos números centrales.

punto medio En un segmento de recta, el punto que equidista de ambos extremos.

Fórmula del punto medio En el plano de coordenadas, el punto medio de un segmento cuyos extremos son (x_1, y_1) y (x_2, y_2) se calcula con la fórmula $\left(\frac{x_1 + x_2}{2}, \frac{y_1 + y_2}{2}\right)$.

número mixto Suma de un entero y una fracción. Por ejemplo, $3\frac{1}{2}$.

moda Número o números de un conjunto de datos que aparecen más frecuentemente.

monomio Expresión que es un número, una variable y/o un producto de números y variables.

múltiplo Producto de un número por un número entero.

eventos mutuamente exclusivos Dos o más eventos que no pueden ocurrir simultáneamente.

negative number (56) A number less than zero.

nonlinear function (687) A function with a graph that is not a straight line.

null set (336) A set with no elements shown by the symbol { } or $\varnothing$.

numerical expression (12) A combination of numbers and operations such as addition, subtraction, multiplication, and division.

número negativo Número menor que cero.

función no lineal Función cuya gráfica no es una recta.

conjunto vacío Conjunto que carece de elementos y que se denota con el símbolo { } o $\varnothing$.

expresión numérica Combinación de números y operaciones, como adición, sustracción, multiplicación y división.

obtuse angle (449) An angle with a measure greater than 90° but less than 180°.

ángulo obtuso Ángulo que mide más de 90°, pero menos de 180°.

obtuse triangle (454) A triangle with one obtuse angle.

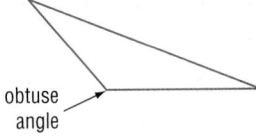

obtuse
angle

triángulo obtusángulo Triángulo que posee un ángulo obtuso.

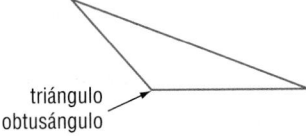

triángulo
obtusángulo

odds (646) A way to describe the chance of an event occurring.

posibilidades Una manera de describir la oportunidad de que ocurra un evento.

open sentence (28) An equation that contains a variable.

enunciado abierto Ecuación que contiene una variable.

opposites (66) Two numbers with the same absolute value but different signs.

opuestos Dos números que tienen el mismo valor absoluto, pero que tienen distintos signos.

ordered pair (33) A pair of numbers used to locate any point on a coordinate plane.

par ordenado Par de números que se usa para ubicar cualquier punto en un plano de coordenadas.

order of operations (12)

1. Simplify the expressions inside grouping symbols.
2. Evaluate all powers.
3. Do all multiplications and/or divisions from left to right.
4. Do all additions and/or subtractions from left to right.

orden de las operaciones

1. Reduce las expresiones dentro de símbolos de agrupamiento.
2. Evalúa todas las potencias.
3. Ejecuta todas las multiplicaciones y/o divisiones de izquierda a derecha.
4. Ejecuta todas las adiciones y/o sustracciones de izquierda a derecha.

origin (33) The point at which the number lines intersect in a coordinate system.

origen Punto de intersección de las rectas numéricas de un sistema de coordenadas.

outcomes (310) Possible results of a probability event.

resultado Resultados posibles de un experimento probabilístico.

outliers (621) Data that are more than 1.5 times the interquartile range from the quartiles.

valores atípicos Datos que distan de los cuartiles más de 1.5 veces la amplitud intercuartílica.

P

parallel lines (492) Two lines in the same plane that do not intersect.

rectas paralelas Dos rectas en el mismo plano que no se intersecan.

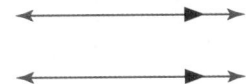

parallelogram (514) A quadrilateral with opposite sides parallel and congruent.

paralelogramo Cuadrilátero con lados opuestos congruentes y paralelos.

part (288) In a percent proportion, the number being compared to the whole quantity.

parte En una proporción porcentual, el número que se compara con la cantidad total.

percent (281) A ratio that compares a number to 100.

por ciento Razón que compara un número con 100.

percent equation (298) An equivalent form of percent proportion, where % is written as a decimal.

Part = Percent × Base

ecuación porcentual Forma equivalente a la proporción porcentual en que el % se escribe como decimal.

Parte = Por ciento × Base

percent of change (304) The ratio of the increase or decrease of an amount to the original amount.

porcentaje de cambio Razón del aumento o disminución de una cantidad a la cantidad original.

percent of decrease (306) The ratio of an amount of decrease to the previous amount, expressed as a percent. A negative percent of change.

percent of increase (305) The ratio of an amount of increase to the original amount, expressed as a percent.

percent proportion (288)

$$\frac{\text{part}}{\text{base}} = \frac{\text{percent}}{100} \text{ or } \frac{a}{b} = \frac{p}{100}$$

perfect squares (436) Rational numbers whose square roots are whole numbers. 25 is a perfect square because $\sqrt{25} = 5$.

perimeter (132) The distance around a geometric figure.

period (201) In a repeating decimal, the digit or digits that repeats. The period of $0.\overline{6}$ is 6.

permutation (641) An arrangement or listing in which order is important.

perpendicular lines (494) Lines that intersect to form a right angle.

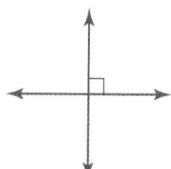

pi, π (533) The ratio of the circumference of a circle to the diameter of the circle. Approximations for π are 3.14 and $\frac{22}{7}$.

plane (556) A two-dimensional flat surface that extends in all directions and contains at least three noncollinear points.

point (447) A specific location in space with no size or shape.

polygon (527) A simple closed figure in a plane formed by three or more line segments.

polyhedron (556) A solid with flat surfaces that are polygons.

polynomial (669) An algebraic expression that contains the sums and/or products of one or more monomials.

power (153) A number that is expressed using an exponent.

precision (590) The exactness to which a measurement is made.

prime factorization (160) A composite number expressed as a product of prime factors. For example, the prime factorization of 63 is $3 \times 3 \times 7$.

porcentaje de disminución Razón de la cantidad de disminución a la cantidad original, escrita como por ciento. Un por ciento de cambio negativo.

porcentaje de aumento Razón de la cantidad de aumento a la cantidad original, escrita como por ciento.

proporción porcentual

$$\frac{\text{parte}}{\text{base}} = \frac{\text{por ciento}}{100} \text{ o } \frac{a}{b} = \frac{p}{100}$$

cuadrados perfectos Números racionales cuyas raíces cuadradas son números racionales. 25 es un cuadrado perfecto porque $\sqrt{25} = 5$.

perímetro Longitud alrededor de una figura geométrica.

período En un decimal periódico, el dígito o dígitos que se repiten. El período de $0.\overline{6}$ es 6.

permutación Arreglo o lista en que el orden es importante.

rectas perpendiculares Rectas que se intersecan formando un ángulo recto.

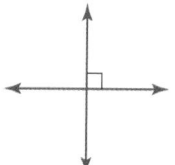

pi, π Razón de la circunferencia de un círculo al diámetro del mismo. 3.14 y $\frac{22}{7}$ son aproximaciones de π.

plano Superficie plana bidimensional que se extiende en todas direcciones y que contiene por lo menos tres puntos no colineales.

punto Ubicación específica en el espacio sin tamaño o forma.

polígono Figura simple y cerrada en el plano formada por tres o más segmentos de recta.

poliedro Sólido con superficies planas que son polígonos.

polinomio Expresión algebraica que contiene sumas y/o productos de uno o más monomios.

potencia Número que puede escribirse usando un exponente.

precisión Exactitud con que se realiza una medida.

factorización prima Número compuesto escrito como producto de factores primos. Por ejemplo, la factorización prima de 63 es $3 \times 3 \times 7$.

prime number (159) A whole number that has exactly two factors, 1 and itself.

principle (300) The amount of money in an account.

prism (557) A polyhedron that has two parallel, congruent bases in the shape of polygons.

rectangular prism   triangular prism

probability (310) The ratio of the number of ways a certain event can occur to the number of possible outcomes.

$$P(\text{event}) = \frac{\text{number of favorable outcomes}}{\text{number of possible outcomes}}$$

properties (23) Statements that are true for any numbers.

proportion (270) A statement of equality of two or more ratios.

protractor (448) An instrument used to measure angles.

pyramid (557) A polyhedron that has a polygon for a base and triangles for sides.

Pythagorean Theorem (460) If a triangle is a right triangle, then the square of the length of the hypotenuse is equal to the sum of the squares of the lengths of the legs or $c^2 = a^2 + b^2$.

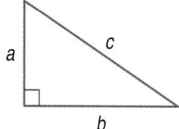

número primo Número entero que sólo tiene dos factores, 1 y sí mismo.

capital Cantidad de dinero en una cuenta.

prisma Poliedro que posee dos bases congruentes y paralelas en forma de polígonos.

prisma rectangular   prisma triangular

probabilidad La razón del número de maneras en que puede ocurrir el evento al número de resultados posibles.

$$P(\text{evento}) = \frac{\text{número de resultados favorables}}{\text{número de resultados posibles}}$$

propiedades Enunciados que son verdaderos para cualquier número.

proporción Enunciado de la igualdad de dos o más razones.

transportador Instrumento que se usa para medir ángulos.

pirámide Poliedro cuya base es un polígono y cuyos lados son triángulos.

Teorema de Pitágoras Si un triángulo es rectángulo, entonces el cuadrado de la longitud de la hipotenusa es igual a la suma de los cuadrados de las longitudes de los catetos, o $c^2 = a^2 + b^2$.

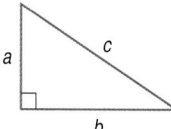

Q

quadrants (86) The four regions into which the x-axis and y-axis separate the coordinate plane.

quadratic function (688) A function that can be described by an equation of the form $y = ax^2 + bx + c$, where $a \neq 0$.

quadrilateral (513) A closed figure with four sides and four vertices, including squares, rectangles, and trapezoids.

cuadrantes Las cuatro regiones en que los ejes x y y dividen el plano de coordenadas.

función cuadrática Función que puede describirse por una ecuación de la forma $y = ax^2 + bx + c$, donde $a \neq 0$.

cuadrilátero Figura cerrada de cuatro lados y cuatro vértices, incluyendo cuadrados, rectángulos y trapecios.

quartiles (613) The values that divide a set of data into four equal parts.

cuartiles Valores que dividen un conjunto de datos en cuatro partes iguales.

---

radical sign (436) The symbol $\sqrt{}$ used to indicate a nonnegative square root.

signo radical El símbolo $\sqrt{}$ que se usa para indicar la raíz cuadrada no negativa.

radius (533) The distance from the center to any point on the circle.

radio Distancia del centro a cualquier punto de un círculo.

range (35) The range of a relation is the set of all *y*-coordinates from each ordered pair.

rango El rango de una relación es el conjunto de coordenadas *y* de todos los pares.

range (612) A measure of variation that is the difference between the least and greatest values in a set of data.

amplitud Medida de variación que es la diferencia entre los valores máximo y mínimo de un conjunto de datos.

rate (265) A ratio of two measurements having different units.

tasa Razón de dos medidas que tienen unidades distintas.

rate of change (393) A change in one quantity with respect to another quantity.

tasa de cambio Cambio de una cantidad con respecto a otra.

ratio (264) A comparison of two numbers by division. The ratio of 2 to 4 can be stated as 2 out of 4, 2 to 4, 2:4, or $\frac{2}{4}$.

razón Comparación de dos números mediante división. La razón de 2 a 4 puede escribirse como 2 de cada 4, 2 a 4, 2:4 ó $\frac{2}{4}$.

rational number (205) A number that can be written as a fraction in the form $\frac{a}{b}$, where *a* and *b* are integers and $b \neq 0$.

número racional Número que puede escribirse como una fracción de la forma $\frac{a}{b}$ donde *a* y *b* son enteros y $b \neq 0$.

ray (447) A part of a line that extends indefinitely in one direction.

rayo Parte de una recta que se extiende indefinidamente en una dirección.

real numbers (441) The set of rational numbers together with the set of irrational numbers.

números reales El conjunto de los números racionales junto con el de números irracionales.

reciprocal (215) Another name for a multiplicative inverse.

recíproco Otro nombre del inverso multiplicativo.

rectangle (514) A parallelogram with four right angles.

rectángulo Paralelogramo con cuatro ángulos rectos.

reflection (506) A transformation where a figure is flipped over a line. Also called a flip.

reflexión Transformación en que una figura se voltea a través de una recta.

regular polygon (529) A polygon having all sides congruent and all angles congruent.

polígono regular Polígono cuyos lados son todos congruentes y cuyos ángulos son también todos congruentes.

relation (35) A set of ordered pairs.

relación Conjunto de pares ordenados.

repeating decimal (201) A decimal whose digits repeat in groups of one or more. Examples are 0.181818... and 0.8333... .

decimal periódico Decimal cuyos dígitos se repiten en grupos de uno o más. 0.181818... y 0.8333... son ejemplos de este tipo de decimales.

rhombus (514) A parallelogram with four congruent sides.

rombo Paralelogramo con cuatro lados congruentes.

right angle (449) An angle that measures 90°.

right triangle (454) A triangle with one right angle.

rotation (506) A transformation where a figure is turned around a fixed point. Also called a turn.

ángulo recto Ángulo que mide 90°.

triángulo rectángulo Triángulo que tiene un ángulo recto.

rotación Transformación en que una figura se hace girar alrededor de un punto fijo. También se llama vuelta.

S

sample (309) A subgroup or subset of a population used to represent the whole population.

sample space (311) The set of all possible outcomes.

scale (276) The relationship between the measurements on a drawing or model and the measurements of the real object.

scale drawing (276) A drawing that is used to represent an object that is too large or too small to be drawn at actual size.

scale factor (277) The ratio of a length on a scale drawing or model to the corresponding length on the real object.

scale model (276) A model used to represent an object that is too large or too small to be built at actual size.

scalene triangle (455) A triangle with no congruent sides.

scatter plot (40) A graph that shows the relationship between two sets of data.

scientific notation (186) A number in scientific notation is expressed as $a \times 10^n$, where $1 \le a < 10$ and n is an integer. For example, $5,000,000 = 5.0 \times 10^6$.

sequence (249) An ordered list of numbers, such as, 0, 1, 2, 3, or 2, 4, 6, 8.

sides (447) The two rays that make up an angle.

significant digits (590) The digits recorded from measurement, indicating the precision of the measurement.

similar solids (584) Solids that have the same shape but not necessarily the same size.

similar triangles (471) Triangles that have the same shape but not necessarily the same size.

muestra Subgrupo o subconjunto de una población que se usa para representarla.

espacio muestral Conjunto de todos los resultados posibles.

escala Relación entre las medidas de un dibujo o modelo y las medidas de la figura verdadera.

dibujo a escala Dibujo que se usa para representar una figura que es demasiado grande o pequeña como para ser dibujada de tamaño natural.

factor de escala Razón de la longitud en un dibujo a escala o modelo a la longitud correspondiente en la figura verdadera.

modelo a escala Modelo que se usa para representar una figura que es demasiado grande o pequeña como para ser construida de tamaño natural.

triángulo escaleno Triángulo que no tiene lados congruentes.

gráfica de dispersión Gráfica en que se muestra la relación entre dos conjuntos de datos.

notación científica Un número en notación científica se escribe como $a \times 10^n$, donde $1 \le a < 10$ y n es un entero. Por ejemplo, $5,000,000 = 5.0 \times 10^6$.

sucesión Lista ordenada de números, como 0, 1, 2, 3 ó 2, 4, 6, 8.

lados Los dos rayos que forman un ángulo.

dígitos significativos Los dígitos de una medición que indican la precisión de la medición.

sólidos semejantes Sólidos que tienen la misma forma, pero no necesariamente el mismo tamaño.

triángulos semejantes Triángulos que tienen la misma forma, pero no necesariamente el mismo tamaño.

simple event (310) One outcome or a collection of outcomes.

simple interest (300) The amount of money paid or earned for the use of money.

$$I = prt \quad \text{(Interest = principal} \times \text{rate} \times \text{time)}$$

simplest form (104) An algebraic expression in simplest form has no like terms and no parentheses.

simplest form (169) A fraction is in simplest form when the GCF of the numerator and the denominator is 1.

simplify (25) To write an expression in a simpler form.

simulation (656) The process of acting out a situation to see possible outcomes.

sine (477) If $\triangle ABC$ is a right triangle and A is an acute angle,

$$\text{sine } \angle A = \frac{\text{measure of the leg opposite } \angle A}{\text{measure of the hypotenuse}}.$$

skew lines (558) Lines that are neither intersecting nor parallel. Skew lines lie in different planes.

slant height (578) The length of the altitude of a lateral face of a regular pyramid.

slope (387) The ratio of the rise, or vertical change, to the run, or horizontal change. The slope describes the steepness of a line.

$$\text{slope} = \frac{\text{rise}}{\text{run}}$$

slope-intercept form (398) A linear equation in the form $y = mx + b$, where m is the slope and b is the y-intercept.

solution (28) A value for the variable that makes an equation true. For $x + 7 = 19$, the solution is 12.

solving the equation (28) The process of finding a solution to an equation.

solving a right triangle (461) Using the Pythagorean Theorem to find the length of the third side of a right triangle, if the lengths of the other two sides are known.

square (514) A parallelogram with all sides congruent and four right angles.

square root (436) One of the two equal factors of a number. The square root of 25 is 5 since $5^2 = 25$.

standard form (154) A number is in standard form when it does not contain exponents. The standard form for seven hundred thirty-nine is 739.

evento simple Resultado o colección de resultados.

interés simple Cantidad que se paga o que se gana por usar el dinero.

$$I = crt \quad \text{(Interés = capital} \times \text{rédito} \times \text{tiempo)}$$

forma reducida Una expresión algebraica reducida no tiene ni términos semejantes ni paréntesis.

forma reducida Una fracción está reducida si el MCD de su numerador y denominador es 1.

reducir Escribir una expresión en forma más simple.

simulación Proceso de representación de una situación para averiguar los resultados posibles.

seno Si $\triangle ABC$ es un triángulo rectángulo y A es un ángulo agudo,

$$\text{seno } \angle A = \frac{\text{medida del cateto opuesto a } \angle A}{\text{medida de la hipotenusa}}.$$

rectas alabeadas Rectas que no se intersecan y que no son paralelas. Las rectas alabeadas yacen en distintos planos.

altura oblicua En una pirámide regular, la longitud de la altura de una cara lateral.

pendiente Razón de la elevación o cambio vertical al desplazamiento o cambio horizontal. La pendiente describe la inclinación de una recta.

$$\text{pendiente} = \frac{\text{elevación}}{\text{desplazamiento}}$$

forma pendiente-intersección Una ecuación lineal de la forma $y = mx + b$, donde m es la pendiente y b es la intersección y.

solución Valosss y que posee cuatro ángulos rectos.

resolver la ecuación (28) Proceso de hallar una solución a una ecuación.

resolver un triángulo rectángulo Uso del Teorema de Pitágoras para hallar la longitud de un tercer lado de un triángulo rectángulo, si se conocen las longitudes de los otros dos lados.

cuadrado Paralelogramo cuyos lados son todos congruentes y que posee cuatro ángulos rectos.

raíz cuadrada Uno de los dos factores iguales de un número. Una raíz cuadrada de 25 es 5 porque $5^2 = 25$.

forma estándar Un número está en forma estándar si no contiene exponentes. Por ejemplo, la forma estándar de setecientos treinta y nueve es 739.

stem-and-leaf plot (606) A system used to condense a set of data where the greatest place value of the data forms the stem and the next greatest place value forms the leaves.

stems (606) The greatest place value common to all the data values is used for the stem of a stem-and-leaf plot.

straight angle (449) An angle with a measure equal to 180°.

supplementary (494) Two angles are supplementary if the sum of their measures is 180°.

surface area (573) The sum of the areas of all the surfaces (faces) of a 3-dimensional figure.

system of equations (414) A set of equations with the same variables. The solution of the system is the ordered pair that is a solution for all of the equations.

diagrama de tallo y hojas Sistema que se usa para condensar un conjunto de datos, en que el valor de posición máximo de los datos forma el tallo y el segundo valor de posición máximo forma las hojas.

tallos Máximo valor de posición común a todos los datos que se usa como el tallo en un diagrama de tallo y hojas.

ángulo llano Ángulo que mide 180°.

suplementarios Dos ángulos son suplementarios si sus medidas suman 180°.

área de superficie Suma de las áreas de todas las superficies (caras) de una figura tridimensional.

sistema de ecuaciones Conjunto de ecuaciones con las mismas variables. La solución del sistema es el par ordenado que resuelve ambas ecuaciones.

T

tangent (477) If $\triangle ABC$ is a right triangle and A is an acute angle,

$$\text{tangent } \angle A = \frac{\text{measure of the leg opposite } \angle A}{\text{measure of the leg adjacent to } \angle A}$$

term (103) When plus or minus signs separate an algebraic expression into parts, each part is a term.

term (249) Each number within a sequence is called a term.

terminating decimal (200) A decimal whose digits end. Every terminating decimal can be written as a fraction with a denominator of 10, 100, 1000, and so on.

theoretical probability (311) What should occur in a probability experiment.

transformation (506) A movement of a geometric figure.

translation (506) A transformation where a figure is slid from one position to another without being turned. Also called a slide.

transversal (492) A line that intersects two parallel lines to form eight angles.

trapezoid (514) A quadrilateral with exactly one pair of parallel sides.

tree diagram (635) A diagram used to show the total number of possible outcomes.

tangente Si $\triangle ABC$ es un triángulo rectángulo y A es un ángulo agudo,

$$\text{tangente } \angle A = \frac{\text{medida del cateto opuesto al } \angle A}{\text{medida del cateto adyacente a } \angle A}$$

término Cada una de las partes de una expresión algebraica separadas por los signos de adición o sustracción.

término Cada número de una sucesión se llama término.

decimal terminal Decimal cuyos dígitos terminan. Todo decimal terminal puede escribirse como una fracción con un denominador de 10, 100, 1000, etc.

probabilidad teórica Lo que debería ocurrir en un experimento probabilístico.

transformación Desplazamiento de una figura geométrica.

translación Transformación en que una figura se desliza sin girar, de una posición a otra. También se llama deslizamiento.

transversal Recta que interseca dos rectas paralelas formando ocho ángulos.

trapecio Cuadrilátero con sólo un par de lados paralelos.

diagrama de árbol Diagrama que se usa para mostrar el número total de resultados posibles.

triangle (453) A polygon having three sides.

trigonometric ratio (477) A ratio of the lengths of two sides of a right triangle. The tangent, sine, and cosine ratios are three trigonometric ratios.

trigonometry (477) The study of the properties of triangles. Trigonometry means *angle measurement*.

trinomial (669) A polynomial with three terms.

two-step equation (120) An equation that contains two operations.

triángulo Polígono de tres lados.

razón trigonométrica Razón de las longitudes de dos lados de un triángulo rectángulo. La tangente, el seno y el coseno son tres razones trigonométricas.

trigonometría Estudio de las propiedades de los triángulos. La palabra significa *medida de ángulos*.

trinomio Polinomio de tres términos.

ecuación de dos pasos Ecuación que contiene dos operaciones.

U

unit rate (265) A rate simplified so that it has a denominator of 1.

upper quartile (613) The median of the upper half of a set of data, indicated by UQ.

tasa unitaria Tasa reducida que tiene denominador igual a 1.

cuartil superior Mediana de la mitad superior de un conjunto de datos, denotada por CS.

V

variable (17) A placeholder for any value.

Venn diagram (164) A diagram that is used to show the relationships among sets of numbers or objects by using overlapping circles in a rectangle.

vertex (447) The common endpoint of the rays forming an angle.

vertex (453) A vertex of a polygon is a point where two sides of the polygon intersect.

vertex (556) Where three or more planes intersect in a point.

vertical angles (493) Two pairs of opposite angles formed by two intersecting lines. The angles formed are congruent. In the figure, the vertical angles are ∠1 and ∠3, ∠2 and ∠4.

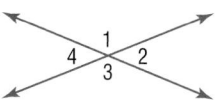

vertical line test (370) If any vertical line drawn on the graph of a relation passes through no more than one point on the graph for each value of x in the domain, then the relation is a function.

volume (563) The measure of space occupied by a solid region.

variable Marcador de posición para cualquier valor.

diagrama de Venn Diagrama que se usa para mostrar las relaciones entre conjuntos de números o elementos mediante círculos, que pueden traslaparse, dentro de un rectángulo.

vértice Extremo común de los dos rayos que forman un ángulo.

vértice El vértice de un polígono es un punto en que se intersecan dos lados del mismo.

vértice Punto en que se intersecan tres o más planos.

ángulos opuestos por el vértice Dos pares de ángulos opuestos formados por dos rectas que se intersecan. Los ángulos que resultan son congruentes. En la figura, los ángulos opuestos por el vértice son ∠1 y ∠3, ∠2 y ∠4.

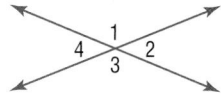

prueba de la recta vertical Si todas las rectas verticales trazadas en la gráfica de una relación no pasan por más un punto para cada valor de x en el dominio, entonces la relación es una función.

volumen Medida del espacio que ocupa un sólido.

X

x-axis (33) The horizontal number line which helps to form the coordinate system.

eje x Recta numérica horizontal que forma parte de un sistema de coordenadas.

x-coordinate (33) The first number of an ordered pair.

x-intercept (381) The x-coordinate of a point where a graph crosses the x-axis.

coordenada x El primer número de un par ordenado.

intersección x La coordenada x de un punto en que una gráfica interseca el eje x.

Y

y-axis (33) The vertical number line which helps to form the coordinate system.

y-coordinate (33) The second number of an ordered pair.

y-intercept (381) The y-coordinate of a point where a graph crosses the y-axis.

eje y Recta numérica vertical que forma parte de un sistema de coordenadas.

coordenada y El segundo número en un par ordenado.

intersección y La coordenada y de un punto en que una gráfica interseca el eje y.

Glossary/Glosario

Selected Answers

Chapter 1   The Tools of Algebra

Page 5   Chapter 1 Getting Started
1. 14.8   **3.** 3.1   **5.** 2.95   **7.** 3.55   **9.** 7.88   **11.** Sample answer: 1200   **13.** Sample answer: 120   **15.** Sample answer: 20,000   **17.** Sample answer: 220   **19.** Sample answer: 14   **21.** Sample answer: $5   **23.** Sample answer: 120   **25.** Sample answer: 4   **27.** Sample answer: 10

Pages 9–10   Lesson 1-1
1. when an exact answer is not needed   **3.** 1:33 P.M.   **5.** 17   **7.** 3072   **9.** 178 beats per min   **11.** 17   **13.** 25   **15.** 34   **17.** 27
19.

21. Since $68 + $15 + $20 + $16 = $119, Ryan does not have enough money for the ski trip.   **23.** about 5 h   **25.** Sample answer: about 21,800 transplants   **27a.** There are more even products. Since any even number multiplied by any number is even, and only an odd number multiplied by an odd number is odd, there are more even products in the table. There are about 3 times as many evens as odds.
27b. Yes; in the addition table, there is only one more even number than odd.   **29.** B   **31.** 3   **33.** 35   **35.** 109

Pages 14–16   Lesson 1-2
1. Sample answer: $(8 - 3) \cdot 2$ **3.** Emily; she followed the order of operations and divided first.   **5.** ÷; 20   **7.** −; 66   **9.** ×; 15   **11.** $12 - 9$ **13.** 4   **15.** 25   **17.** 38   **19.** 2   **21.** 55   **23.** 24   **25.** 64   **27.** 180   **29.** 50   **31.** $6 - 3$ **33.** 9×5 **35.** $24 \div 6$ **37.** $3 \times 6 **39.** $(4 \times 2) + (2 \times 13)$
41. $(3 \times 57) + (2 \times 12)$ **43.** $61 - (15 + 3) = 43$
45. $56 \div (2 + 6) - 4 = 3$
47. $(50 \times 25) + (7 \times 24) + (4 \times 22) + (3 \times 16)$
49. 0-07-825200-8   **51.** Sample answer: $111 - (1 + 1 + 1) \times (11 + 1)$ **53.** C   **55.** 64   **57.** 28
59. $275   **61.** Sample answer: about 26 compact cars
63. 126   **65.** 563

Pages 19–21   Lesson 1-3
1. Sample answer: $7n$ and $3x - 1$; $2 + 3$ and 3×8
3. Sample answer: $4 \times c \times d$ **5.** 6   **7.** 17   **9.** $g - 5$
11. $7 + n \div 8$ **13.** 11   **15.** 38   **17.** 2   **19.** 9   **21.** 27   **23.** 56
25. 53   **27.** 44   **29.** 32   **31.** 71°F   **33.** $s + 200 **35.** $h - 6$
37. $5q - 4$ **39.** $n \div 6 + 9$ **41.** $17 - 4w$ **43.** 10   **45.** $x + 3$
47. $p - 4$ **49.** $s = c + m - d$ **51.** 1   **53.** D   **55.** 7   **57.** 9
59. 36   **61.** 22

Page 21   Practice Quiz 1
1. 14   **3.** 79   **5.** 22

Pages 26–27   Lesson 1-4
1. Sample answer: $3 \cdot 4 = 4 \cdot 3$ **3.** Kimberly; the Associative Property only holds true if all numbers are added or all numbers are multiplied, not a combination of the two.   **5.** Additive Identity   **7.** 28   **9.** 45   **11.** $n + 13$
13. $42; To find the total cost, add the three costs together.

Since the order in which the costs are added does not matter, the Commutative Property of Addition holds true and makes the addition easier. By adding 4 and 26, the result is 30, and $30 + 12$ is 42.   **15.** Multiplicative Identity   **17.** Commutative Property of Multiplication   **19.** Associative Property of Addition   **21.** Additive Identity   **23.** Associative Property of Multiplication
25. Commutative Property of Addition   **27.** 55   **29.** 40
31. 990   **33.** 0   **35.** false; $(100 \div 10) \div 2 \neq 100 \div (10 \div 2)$
37. false; $9 - 3 \neq 3 - 9$ **39.** $m + 12$ **41.** $a + 27$ **43.** $12y$
45. $48c$ **47.** $75s$
49. There are many real-life situations in which the order in which things are completed does not matter. Answers should include the following.
• Reading the sports page and then the comics, or reading the comics and then the sports page. No matter the order, both parts of the newspaper will be read.
• When washing clothes, you would add the detergent and then wash the clothes, not wash the clothes and then add the detergent. Order matters.
51. B   **53.** 36   **55.** $w - 12$ **57.** 35   **59.** 15, 21   **61.** 296
63. 1050   **65.** 7493

Pages 30–32   Lesson 1-5
1. Sample answer: $b + 7 = 12$ and $8 - h = 3$ **3.** 6   **5.** 5
7. 6   **9.** Symmetric   **11.** Let $n =$ the number; $n + 8 = 23$; 15
13. C   **15.** 11   **17.** 12   **19.** 5   **21.** 15   **23.** 9   **25.** always
27. 15   **29.** 0   **31.** 15   **33.** 17   **35.** 11   **37.** 9   **39.** 3   **41.** 4
43. Let $h =$ the number; $h - 10 = 27$; 37   **45.** Let $w =$ the number; $9 + w = 36$; 27   **47.** Let $x =$ the number; $3x = 45$; 15   **49.** $8   **51.** Symmetric Property of Equality
53. Symmetric Property of Equality   **55.** 3   **57.** Sample answer: Once the variable(s) are replaced in the open sentence, the order of operations is used to find the value of the expression. Answers should include the following.
• To evaluate an expression, replace the variable(s) with the given values, and then find the value of the expression.
• To solve an open sentence, find the value of the variable that makes the sentence true.
59. B   **61.** $23 + d$ **63.** $10 - n$ **65.** 11   **67.** 42   **69.** 18
71. 50   **73.** 90

Page 32   Practice Quiz 2
1. Identity (×)   **3.** $24h$ **5.** 8

Pages 36–38   Lesson 1-6
1. Sample answer: (3, 5); the x-coordinate is 3 and the y-coordinate is 5.   **3.** The domain of a relation is the set of x-coordinates. The range is the set of y-coordinates.
5.

7. (6, 5)

9.

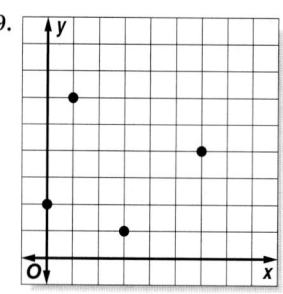

x	y
1	6
6	4
0	2
3	1

domain = {1, 6, 0, 3};
range = {6, 4, 2, 1}

11.

13.

15.

17.

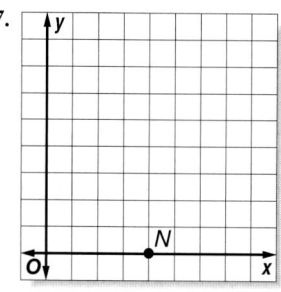

19. (7, 3)   **21.** (6, 6)
23. (3, 4)   **25.** on the *x*-axis;
on the *y*-axis

27. Speed of a House Mouse

29. Science Experiment

31.

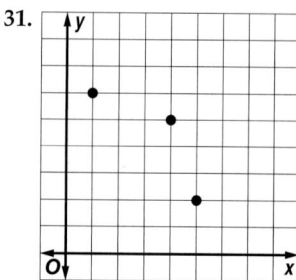

x	y
4	5
5	2
1	6

domain = {4, 5, 1};
range = {5, 2, 6}

33.

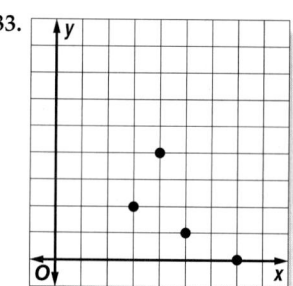

x	y
7	0
3	2
4	4
5	1

domain = {7, 3, 4, 5};
range = {0, 2, 4, 1}

35.

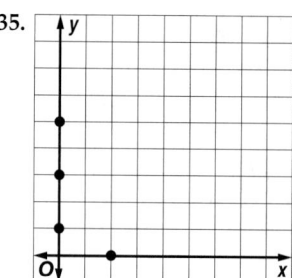

x	y
0	1
0	3
0	5
2	0

domain = {0, 2};
range = {1, 3, 5, 0}

37. (0, 14.7), (1, 10.2), (2, 6.4), (3, 4.3), (4, 2.7), (5, 1.6)
39. domain = {0, 1, 2, 3, 4, 5}; range = {14.7, 10.2, 6.4, 4.3,
2.7, 1.6}   **41.** {(0, 100), (1, 95), (2, 90), (3, 85), (4, 80), (5, 75)}
43. about 93°C; about 96°C   **45.** Ordered pairs can be used
to graph real-life data by expressing the data as ordered
pairs and then graphing the ordered pairs. Answers should
include the following.
• The *x*- and *y*-coordinate of an ordered pair specifies the
  point on the graph.
• longitude and latitude lines.

47. D **49a.**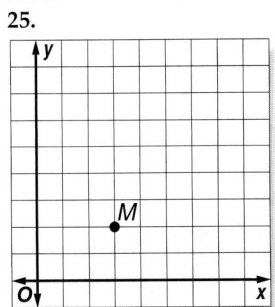

49b. triangle
49c. (4, 2), (4, 8), (10, 2)
49d. triangle
49e. The figures have the same shape but not the same size.

51. 6 **53.** Multiplicative Identity **55.** 7 **57.** 10 · 30 **59.** 12
61. 28 **63.** 7 **65.** 9

Pages 42–44 Lesson 1-7

1. Sample answer: make predictions, draw conclusions, spot trends **3.** negative, positive, and none **5.** No; hair color is not related to height. **7.** Since the points appear to be random, there is no relationship. **9.** The number of songs on a CD usually does not affect the cost of the CD; no. **11.** As speed increases, distance traveled increases; positive. **13.** The size of a television screen and the number of channels it receives are not related; no. **15.** The number decreases.

17.

Player Statistics

(scatter plot: Field Goal Attempts vs. Minutes Played; y-axis 0–1300, x-axis 0–3000)

19. about 800 **21.** Sample answer: Yes; as more emphasis is placed on standardized tests, students will become more comfortable taking the tests, and the scores will increase.
23. C

25. *(graph with point M)* **27.** *(graph with point K)*

29. (0, 4) **31.** domain = {0, 4, 2, 6}; range = {9, 8, 3, 1}
33. 7 **35.** b + 18 **37.** 31

Pages 47–50 Chapter 1 Study Guide and Review

1. d **3.** e **5.** c **7.** 20 **9.** 22 **11.** 22 **13.** 16 **15.** 12
17. 14 **19.** 10 **21.** 25 **23.** Commutative Property of

Addition **25.** Multiplicative Property of Zero **27.** 10
29. 17 **31.** 6
33.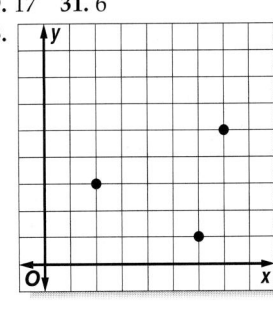

x	y
2	3
6	1
7	5

domain: {2, 6, 7};
range: {3, 1, 5}

35. Positive; as the height increases, the circumference increases.

Chapter 2 Integers

Page 55 Chapter 2 Getting Started
1. 22 **3.** 42 **5.** 8 **7.** 4 **9.** T **11.** V **13.** Q

Pages 59–61 Lesson 2-1
1. Draw a number line. Draw a dot at −4. **3.** The absolute value of a number is its distance from 0 on a number line.
5. +15 *(number line: 8 9 10 11 12 13 14 15 16)*

7. −4 < 2; 2 > −4 **9.** < **11.** > **13.** 10 **15.** 21 **17.** 3
19. −54, −52, −45, −37, −36, −34, −27, −27, −2
21. −6 *(number line: −8 −7 −6 −5 −4 −3 −2 −1 0)*

23. +9 *(number line: 5 6 7 8 9 10 11 12 13)*

25. −5 *(number line: −8 −7 −6 −5 −4 −3 −2 −1 0)*

27. *(number line: −3 −2 −1 0 1 2 3 4 5)*

29. *(number line: −8 −6 −4 −2 0 2 4 6 8)*

31. −5 > −10; −10 < −5 **33.** 248 < 425; 425 > 248
35. 212 > 32; 32 < 212 **37.** > **39.** > **41.** > **43.** >
45. {−15, −4, −2, −1} **47.** {−60, −57, 38, 98, 188} **49.** 46
51. −5 **53.** 7 **55.** 2 **57.** 9 **59.** −20 **61.** 4 **63.** 40 **65.** 3
67.

(number line with −54 marked: −90 −70 −50 −30 −10)

69. −54 > −70 **71.** 7 **73.** Sometimes; if A and B are both positive, both negative, or one is 0, it is true. If one number is negative and the other is positive, it is false. **75.** B
77. Positive; as height increases, so does arm length.
79.

x	y
3	2
3	4
2	1
2	4

{(3, 2), (3, 4), (2, 1), (2, 4)}

81. Commutative Property of Multiplication
83. Commutative Property of Multiplication **85.** 388
87. 17 **89.** 1049

Pages 67–68   Lesson 2-2

1a. Negative; both addends are negative.   **1b.** Positive; $|12| > |-2|$.   **1c.** Negative; $|-11| > |9|$.   **1d.** Positive; both addends are positive.   **3.** -6 **5.** 5 **7.** 3 **9.** 4
11. $4 + (-5) = -1$ **13.** -7 **15.** -11 **17.** -16 **19.** -21
21. -66 **23.** 2 **25.** -2 **27.** 6 **29.** -26 **31.** 21 **33.** -2
35. -6 **37.** -3 **39.** 0 **41.** -5 **43.** 8 **45.** 40
47. $+107{,}680$
49. To add integers on a number line, start at 0. Move right to show positive integers and left to show negative integers. Answers should include the following.

- Sample answer:

- Sample answer:

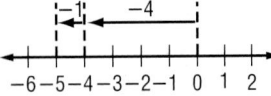

51. D   **53.** $\{-12, -9, -8, 0, 3, 14\}$ **55.** no relationship
57. 6 **59.** 20 **61.** 25 **63.** 42 **65.** 65

Pages 72–74   Lesson 2-3

1. Sample answer: $5, -5; -9, 9$ **3.** -3 **5.** 9 **7.** -2 **9.** 20
11. 21 **13.** Utah, Washington, Wisconsin, or Wyoming
15. -1 **17.** -3 **19.** -9 **21.** -12 **23.** 10 **25.** 12 **27.** 3
29. -9 **31.** -14 **33.** -28 **35.** 239 **37.** 1300 **39.** $14{,}776$ ft
41. 24 **43.** -36 **45.** -9 **47.** -20 **49.** -23 **51.** -17
53. $-10{,}822$ **55a.** False; $3 - 4 \neq 4 - 3$ **55b.** False;
$(5 - 2) - 1 \neq 5 - (2 - 1)$ **57.** A   **59.** -2450 **61.** 3 **63.** 7
65. $\frac{x}{5}$ **67.** $\frac{86}{b}$ **69.** 20 **71.** 75 **73.** 120

Page 74   Practice Quiz 1

1. $-80, -70, -69$ **3.** 6 **5.** -7 **7.** 32 **9.** -9

Pages 77–79   Lesson 2-4

1. $3(-5) = -15$ **3.** Sample answer: $(-4)(9)(2)$ **5.** -40
7. 28 **9.** -540 **11.** $-21y$ **13.** 120 **15.** A   **17.** -42
19. -72 **21.** -70 **23.** 128 **25.** 45 **27.** 130 **29.** -308
31. 528 **33.** -1344 **35.** $-56°F$ **37.** $-96y$ **39.** $-55b$
41. $108mn$ **43.** $-135xy$ **45.** $-88bc$ **47.** $-90jk$ **49.** -99
51. 80 **53.** -216 **55.** 248 ft   **57a.** True; $3(-5) = -5(3)$
57b. True; $-2(3 \cdot 5) = (-2 \cdot 3)(5)$ **59.** B   **61.** -16 **63.** 4
65. 10 **67.** $126°F$ **69.** -14 **71.** $(6, 2)$ **73.** $(1, 5)$ **75.** $(5, 5)$
77. 480 **79.** 550 **81.** 6 **83.** 15 **85.** 4

Pages 83–84   Lesson 2-5

1. Sample answer: $-16 \div 4 = -4$ **3.** 11 **5.** -3 **7.** -10
9. -13 **11.** 0 **13.** 9 **15.** 8 **17.** 10 **19.** -50 **21.** -11
23. -11 **25.** 19 **27.** -12 **29.** -13 **31.** 16 **33.** 49 points
35. 61 **37.** Sample answer: $x = -144; y = 12; z = -12$
39. When the signs of the integers are the same, both a product and a quotient are positive; when the signs are different, the product and quotient are negative. Answers should include the following.

- Sample answer: $4 \cdot (-6) = -24$ and $-24 \div 4 = -6$;
  $-3 \cdot 2 = -6$ and $-6 \div (-3) = 2$
- Sample answers: same sign: $-30 \div (-5) = 6, 30 \div 5 = 6$;
  different signs: $-24 \div 8 = -3, 24 \div (-8) = -3$

41. B   **43.** -39 **45.** $-50cd$ **47.** B   **49.** D

Page 84   Practice Quiz 2

1. -84 **3.** -126 **5.** -31 **7.** -25 **9.** $-20xy$

Pages 87–89   Lesson 2-6

1. Sample answer: (3, 6) represents a point 3 units to the right and 6 units up from the origin. (6, 3) represents a point 6 units to the right and 3 units up from the origin.
3. Keisha; a point in Quadrant I has two positive coordinates. Interchanging the coordinates will still result in two positive coordinates, and the point will be in Quadrant I.   **5.** $(1, 3)$ **7.** $(5, -4)$ **9.** II   **11.** III   **13.** $(-2, 4)$
15. $(4, -2)$ **17.** $(2, 2)$ **19.** $(0, -2)$ **21.** $(-3, -5)$

23–34.

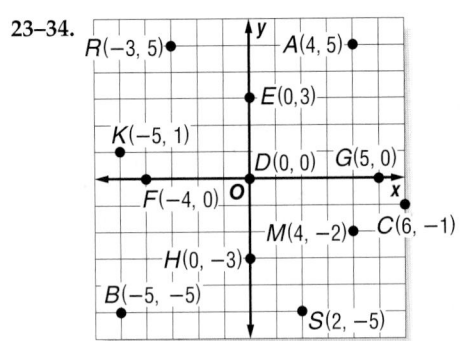

23. I   **25.** IV   **27.** IV   **29.** none   **31.** none   **33.** none

35. Sample answer:

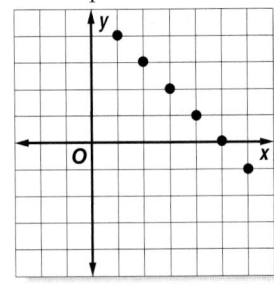

x	y
1	4
2	3
3	2
4	1
5	0
6	-1

The points are along a line slanting down to the right, crossing the y-axis at 5 and the x-axis at 5.

37. Sample answer:

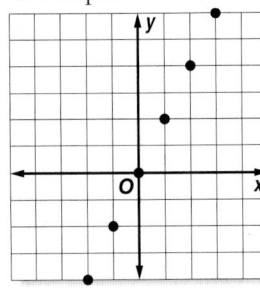

x	y
-2	-4
-1	-2
0	0
1	2
2	4
3	6

The points are along a line slanting up, through the origin.

39. Sample answer:

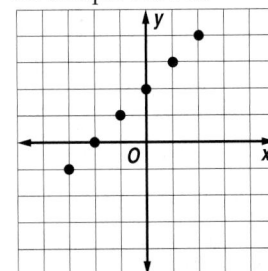

x	y
-3	-1
-2	0
-1	1
0	2
1	3
2	4

The points are along a line slanting up, crossing the y-axis at 2 and the x-axis at -2.

41. 5-point star

40–43.

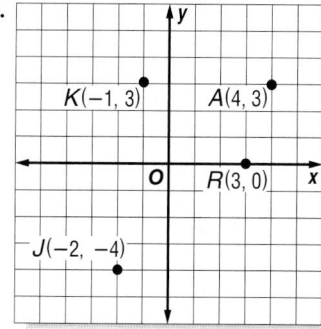

41. III **43.** None

43. Sample answer:

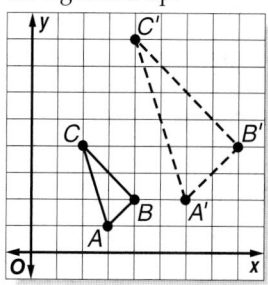

The graph can include any integer pairs where $x > 3$ or $x < -3$.

45. The new triangle is twice the size of the original triangle, and is moved to the right and up.

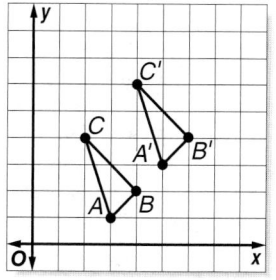

47. The new triangle is translated right 2 units and up 2 units; it is the same size as the original triangle.

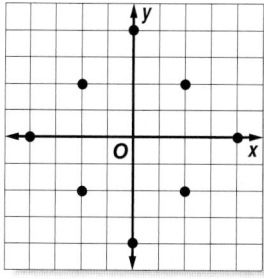

51. Sample answer:

The points lie outside a rhombus defined by (0, 4), (4, 0), (0, −4), and (−4, 0).

53. D **55.** −3 **57.** 8 **59.** −96 **61.** 13°F **63.** 24h **65.** 45b
67. 0

Pages 90–92 Chapter 2 Study Guide and Review
1. negative number **3.** coordinate **5.** integers
7. inequality **9.** = **11.** > **13.** 25 **15.** 22 **17.** −5 **19.** −4
21. −10 **23.** −8 **25.** 5 **27.** −4 **29.** 9 **31.** −66 **33.** 48
35. 7 **37.** −4 **39.** 2

Chapter 3 Equations

Page 97 Chapter 3 Getting Started
1. −6 **3.** 10 **5.** 5 + (−7) **7.** −5 + (−9) **9.** −3 **11.** 0
13. 5 + 2n **15.** n − 3

Pages 100–102 Lesson 3-1
1. Sample answer: 2(3 + 4) = 2 · 3 + 2 · 4 **3.** 5 · 7 + 5 · 8, 75 **5.** 2 · 6 + 4 · 6, 36 **7.** 3n + 6 **9.** −6x + 30 **11.** $56.25
13. 5 · 7 + 5 · 3, 50 **15.** 4 · 3 + 3 · 3, 21 **17.** 8 · 2 + 8 · 2, 32
19. 6 · 8 + 6(−5), 18 **21.** −3 · 9 + (−3)(−2), −21
23. 10(−5) − 3(−5), −35 **25.** 12($15 + $10 + $8), 12($15) + 12($10) + 12($8); $396 **27.** 5$y$ + 30 **29.** 7y + 56
31. 10y + 20 **33.** 10 + 5x **35.** 9m − 18 **37.** 15s − 45
39. 12x − 36 **41.** 2w − 20 **43.** −5a − 50 **45.** −5w + 40
47. −5a + 30 **49.** 3a + 3b **51.** $488.75 **53.** No;
3 + (4 · 5) = 23, (3 + 4)(3 + 5) = 56 **55.** C
57. 8(20 + 3) = 184 **59.** 16(10 + 1) = 176
61. 9(100 + 3) = 927 **63.** 12(1000 + 4) = 12,048 **65.** 6
67. 4 **69.** 21, 25, 29 **71.** 80, 160, 320 **73.** −8 + (−4)
75. 3 + (−9) **77.** −7 + (−10)

Pages 105–107 Lesson 3-2
1. terms that contain the same variable or are constants
3. Koko; 5x + x = 6x, not 5x. **5.** terms: 2m, −1n, 6m; like terms: 2m, 6m; coefficients: 2, −1, 6: constant: none **7.** 8a
9. 7c + 12 **11.** 9y **13.** −3y − 16 **15.** 4x + 12y **17.** terms: 3, 7x, 3x, x; like terms: 7x, 3x, x; coefficients: 7, 3, 1; constant: 3 **19.** terms 2a, 5c, −1a, 6a; like terms: 2a, −1a, 6a; coefficients: 2, 5, −1, 6; constant: none **21.** terms: 6m, −2n, 7; like terms: none; coefficients: 6, −2; constant: 7 **23.** 7x
25. 11y **27.** 7a + 3 **29.** 7y + 9 **31.** 2x **33.** −y
35. −4x + 8 **37.** 8y **39.** −x + 12 **41.** 5b + 6 **43.** −4a − 6
45. −8 **47.** 16m + 2n **49.** −9c + 2d **51.** 3s + 80
53. 5d − 2 **55.** 6x + 2 **57a.** Distributive Property
57b. Commutative Property **57c.** Substitution Property of Equality **57d.** Distributive Property **59.** C **61.** −2y − 16
63. III **65.** 17 **67.** 2 **69.** −11 **71.** −5 **73.** −13

Page 107 Practice Quiz 1
1. 6x + 12 **3.** 7y − 4 **5.** 2m + 15

Pages 113–114 Lesson 3-3
1. Addition Property of Equality **3.** 11 **5.** −4 **7.** 55
9. ←—┼——●——┼——┼——┼——┼——┼——┼——→
　　　−3 −2 −1　0　1　2　3　4
11. C **13.** 13 **15.** −8 **17.** −15 **19.** −1 **21.** 15 **23.** 24
25. 36 **27.** −4 **29.** −31 **31.** 118 **33.** n + 9 = −2; −11
35. n − 3 = −6; −3
37. ←—┼——●——┼——┼——┼——┼——┼——┼——→
　　　−6 −5 −4 −3 −2 −1　0　1

39.
(number line: points from 5 to 12, dot at 10)

41.
(number line: from −4 to 3, dot at −4)

43. $12 = x - 20$; 32   **47.** 17 million   **49.** When you solve an equation, you perform the same operation on each side so that the two sides remain equal. Answers should include the following.

• In an equation, both sides are equal. In a balance scale, the weight of the items on both sides are equal.
• The Addition and Subtraction Properties of Equality allow you to add or subtract the same number from each side of an equation. The two sides of the equation remain equal.

51. C   **53.** $3t + 12$ **55.** $-4z + 4$ **57.** $-4m - 1$
59. Additive Inverse Property   **61.** 84   **63.** −25   **65.** −9
67. −4

Pages 117–119   Lesson 3-4
1. Multiplication Property of Equality   **3.** Sample answer: $-5x = -20$ **5.** −5   **7.** 27   **9.** 66   **11.** 7   **13.** −8
15. 8   **17.** 24   **19.** 14   **21.** −33   **23.** 9   **25.** −43   **27.** −135
29. 130   **31.** 29   **33.** −168   **35.** $6x = -42$; −7
37. $\frac{x}{-4} = 8$; −32

39.
(number line: from −9 to −2, dot at −7)

41.
(number line: from −3 to 4, dot at 3)

43.
(number line: from 30 to 37, dot at 35)

45. $12,000 = 5x$; 2400 mi²   **47.** $6p = 24$, 4 painters
49a. True; one pyramid balances two cubes, so this is the same as adding one cube to each side.   **49b.** True; one pyramid and one cube balance three cubes, which balance one cylinder.   **49c.** False; one cylinder and one pyramid balance five cubes.   **51.** B   **53.** 13   **55.** −28   **57.** $7y + 6$
59. −36   **61.** 10   **63.** −2   **65.** 2   **67.** −19   **69.** −27

Pages 122–124   Lesson 3-5
1. You undo the operations in reverse order.   **3.** 8   **5.** −2
7. −40   **9.** −4   **11.** 10   **13.** 2   **15.** 4   **17.** 8   **19.** 13   **21.** 3
23. 28   **25.** 64   **27.** 65   **29.** 21   **31.** 11   **33.** 30   **35.** 33
37. −13   **39.** 5   **41.** 5   **43.** −2   **45.** 10   **47.** 3 h   **49.** 131 bikes
51. $5x - 2 = 8$ **53.** C   **55.** −7   **57.** −2   **59.** −2
61. $-5y - 15$ **63.** $-9y + 36$ **65.** $-8r + 40$ **67.** (2, −3)
69. (−3, −4)   **71.** $x \div 15$ **73.** $2x + 10$

Pages 128–130   Lesson 3-6
1. is, equals, is equal to   **3.** Ben; *Three less than* means that three is subtracted *from* a number.   **5.** $2n - 4 = -2$, 1
7. $2x + 5 = 37$, 21 yr   **9.** $3n + 20 = -4$, −8
11. $10n - 8 = 82$, 9   **13.** $\frac{n}{-4} - 8 = -42$, 136
15. $3n - 8 = -2$, 2   **17.** $17 - 2n = 5$, 6
19. $4n + 3n + 5 = 47$, 6   **21.** $8 - 5x = -7$, 3 h   **23.** $2x + 2 = 12$. 5 million people   **25.** Sample answer: By 2020, Texas is expected to have 10 thousand more people age 85 or older than New York will have. Together, they are expected to have 846 thousand people age 85 or older. Find the expected number of people age 85 or older in New York by 2020.   **27.** Two-step equations can be used when you start

with a certain amount and increase or decrease at a certain rate. Answers should include the following.
• You've been running 15 minutes each day as part of a fitness program. You plan to increase your time by 5 minutes each week. After how many weeks do you plan to run 30 minutes each day? ($5w + 15 = 30$, 3 weeks)
• You are three years older than your sister is. Together the sum of your ages is 21. How old is your sister? ($2x + 3 = 21$, 9 years old)
29. D   **31.** 4   **33.** 5   **35.** −11   **37.** −4   **39.** −5   **41.** 6

Page 130   Practice Quiz 2
1. −13   **3.** −18   **5.** $3n + 20 = 32$, 4

Pages 133–136   Lesson 3-7
1. $d = rt$ **3.** Sample answer:

5 in.
4 in.

5. 34 km, 30 km²   **7.** 4 in.   **9.** 8 h   **11.** 15 mph   **13.** 54 cm, 162 cm²   **15.** 136 in., 900 in²   **17.** 48 m, 144 m²   **19.** 20 m, 25 m²   **21.** 11 yd   **23.** 5 m   **25.** 39 ft   **27.** 19 yd   **29.** 390 yd, 9000 yd²   **31.** $d = 2r$ **33.** 4300 ft²   **35.** ≈ 23.5 mph
37.
4 ft
3 ft
39.
4 cm
4 cm

41. Sometimes; a 3-inch by 4-inch rectangle has a perimeter of 14 inches and an area of 12 square inches; a 6-inch by 8-inch rectangle has a perimeter of 28 inches and an area of 48 square inches.   **43.** Formulas are important in math and science because they summarize the relationships among quantities. Answers should include the following.
• Sample answer: The formula to find acceleration is $a = \dfrac{v_f - v_i}{t}$ where v_f is the final velocity and v_i is the initial velocity.
• You can find the acceleration of an automobile with this formula.
45. C   **47.** −9   **49.** −8   **51.** $-4x + 9$ **53a.** {(1870, 14), (1881, 600), (1910, 1000), (2000, 1500)}   **53b.** domain: {1870, 1881, 1910, 2000}, range: {14, 600, 1000, 1500}

Pages 138–140   Chapter 3 Study Guide and Review
1. like terms   **3.** Multiplication Property of Equality
5. Distributive Property   **7.** coordinate   **9.** constant
11. $3h + 18$ **13.** $-5k - 5$ **15.** $9t - 45$ **17.** $-2b + 8$
19. $9a$ **21.** $-2n - 8$ **23.** 3   **25.** 5   **27.** 8   **29.** −18
31. 1   **33.** −6   **35.** $2n + 3 = 53$; 25   **37.** 34 ft, 72 ft²

Chapter 4   Factors and Fractions

Page 147   Chapter 4 Getting Started
1. $2x + 2$ **3.** $-2k - 16$ **5.** $12c + 24$ **7.** $7a + 7b$ **9.** 14
11. 28   **13.** 63   **15.** 30   **17.** 45   **19.** 78   **21.** 0.39   **23.** 0.005

Pages 150–152   Lesson 4-1
1. Use the rules for divisibility to determine whether 18,450 is divisible by both 2 and 3. If it is, then the number is also divisible by 6 and there is no remainder.   **3a.** Sample

answer: 102 **3b.** Sample answer: 1035 **3c.** Sample answer: 343 **5.** 2 **7.** 2, 5, 10 **9.** 1, 2, 4, 5, 8, 10, 16, 20, 40, 80 **11.** yes; a number **13.** No; two terms are added. **15.** 2000, 2004, and 2032 are leap years. **17.** 3, 5 **19.** 2, 3, 5, 6, 10 **21.** 2 **23.** 5 **25.** 2, 3, 6 **27.** 2, 5, 10 **29.** 1, 2, 3, 6, 19, 38, 57, 114 **31.** 1, 5, 13, 65 **33.** 1, 2, 4, 31, 62, 124 **35.** 1, 3, 5, 9, 15, 27, 45, 135 **37.** yes; a number **39.** No; one term is subtracted from another term. **41.** No; two terms are added. **43.** No; one term is subtracted from another term. **45.** yes; the product of a number and a variable **47.** yes; the product of numbers and variables **49.** 6 ways; 1×72, 2×36, 3×24, 4×18, 6×12, 8×9 **51.** Alternating rows of a flag contain 6 stars and 5 stars, respectively. Fifty is not divisible by a number that would make the arrangement of stars in an appropriate-sized rectangle. **53.** Never; a number that has 10 as a factor is divisible by $2 \cdot 5$, so it is always divisible by 5. **55a.** 24 cases **55b.** 36 bags **55c.** Sample answer: 12 cases, 18 bags; 14 cases, 15 bags; 16 cases, 12 bags **57.** The side lengths or dimensions of a rectangle are factors of the number that is the area of the rectangle. Answers should include the following.
- A rectangle with dimensions and area labeled; for example, a 4×5 rectangle would have length 5 units, width 4 units, and area 20 square units.
- Factors are numbers that are multiplied to form a product. The dimensions of a rectangle are factor pairs of the area since they are multiplied to form the area.

59. C **61.** 34 in., 60 in^2 **63.** $5n - 2 = 3; 1$ **65.** 2 **67.** 64 **69.** -27 **71.** 2304

Pages 155–157   Lesson 4-2

1. Sample answer: 2^5, x^5 **3.** When n is even, $1^n = (-1)^n = 1$. When n is odd, $1^n = 1$ and $(-1)^n = -1$. **5.** 7^2 **7.** $(2 \times 10^3) + (6 \times 10^2) + (9 \times 10^1) + (5 \times 10^0)$ **9.** -11 **11.** 13^2 **13.** 6^1 **15.** $(-8)^4$ **17.** $(-t)^3$ **19.** m^4 **21.** $2x^2y^2$ **23.** $9(p + 1)^2$ **25.** $(8 \times 10^2) + (0 \times 10^1) + (3 \times 10^0)$ **27.** $(2 \times 10^4) + (3 \times 10^3) + (7 \times 10^2) + (8 \times 10^1) + (1 \times 10^0)$ **29.** 1000 **31.** -32 **33.** 81 **35.** -54 **37.** 13 **39.** 9 **41.** 243 **43.** $81 = 9^2$ or 3^4, $64 = 8^2$ or 4^3 or 2^6 **45.** $(-8)^3$; $(-8)(-8)(-8); -512$ **47.** Always; the product of two negative numbers is always positive. **49.** $2^1, 2^2, 2^3, 2^4, 2^5$ **51.** After 10 folds, the noodles are $5(2^{10}) = 5(1024)$ or 5120 feet long, which is slightly less than a mile. So, after 11 folds the length of the noodles will be greater than a mile. **53.** $=$ **55.** $6 \cdot 3^2$ cm^2 **57.** No; the surface area is multiplied by 4. The volume is multiplied by 8. **59.** As the capacity of computer memory increases, the factors of 2 in the number of megabytes increases. Answers should include the following.
- Computer data are measured in small units that are based on factors of 2.
- In describing the amount of memory in modern computers, it would be impractical to list all the factors of 2. Using exponents is a more efficient way to describe and compare computer data.

61. B **63.** 2, 5, 10 **65.** 150 mph **67.** 4 **69.** $3y + 8$ **71.** 1, 5 **73.** 1, 2, 4, 8, 16 **75.** 1, 5, 7, 35

Pages 161–163   Lesson 4-3

1. A prime number has exactly two factors: 1 and itself. A composite number has more than two factors. **3.** Francisca; 4 is not prime. **5.** prime **7.** $2 \cdot 3^2$ **9.** $2 \cdot 5^2$ **11.** $5 \cdot a \cdot a \cdot b$ **13.** 3 and 5, 5 and 7, 11 and 13, 17 and 19, 29 and 31, 41 and 43 **15.** composite **17.** composite **19.** composite **21.** prime **23.** 3^4 **25.** $3^2 \cdot 7$ **27.** $2^2 \cdot 5^2$

29. $2 \cdot 5 \cdot 11$ **31.** $3 \cdot 3 \cdot t \cdot t$ **33.** $-1 \cdot 5 \cdot 5 \cdot z \cdot z \cdot z$ **35.** $-1 \cdot 2 \cdot 19 \cdot m \cdot n \cdot p$ **37.** $3 \cdot 7 \cdot g \cdot h \cdot h \cdot h$ **39.** $2 \cdot 2 \cdot 2 \cdot 2 \cdot 2 \cdot 2 \cdot n \cdot n \cdot n$ **41.** $-1 \cdot 2 \cdot 2 \cdot 2 \cdot 3 \cdot 5 \cdot r \cdot r \cdot s \cdot t \cdot t \cdot t$ **43.** Sample answer: $-25x$ **45.** The number of rectangles that can be modeled to represent a number indicate whether the number is prime or composite. Answers should include the following.
- If a number is prime, then only one rectangle can be drawn to represent the number. If a number is composite, then more than one rectangle can be drawn to represent the number.
- If a model has a length or width of 1, then the number may be prime or composite. If a model does not have a length or width of 1, then the number must be composite.

47. C **49.** $(-5)^3h^2k$ **51.** yes **53.** no **55.** -9 **57.** -28 **59.** $5x - 35$ **61.** $10a + 60$ **63.** $72 - 8y$

Page 163   Practice Quiz 1

1. 3, 5 **3.** none **5.** 37 **7.** $7 \cdot 11 \cdot x$ **9.** $-1 \cdot 23 \cdot n \cdot n \cdot n$

Pages 166–168   Lesson 4-4

1. Sample answer: Find the prime factorization of each number. Multiply the factors that are common to both. **3.** Jack; the common prime factors of the expressions are 2 and 11, so the GCF is $2 \cdot 11$ or 22. **5.** 3 **7.** 14 **9.** 36 **11.** $14n$ **13.** $3(n + 3)$ **15.** $5(3 + 4x)$ **17.** 4 **19.** 8 **21.** 10 **23.** 9 **25.** 8 **27.** 5 **29.** 4 **31.** 3 **33.** 4 **35.** $4x$ **37.** $2s$ **39.** $14b$ **41.** $4n$ **43.** Sample answer: $2x, 6x^2$ **45.** $3(r + 4)$ **47.** $3(2 + y)$ **49.** $7(2 + 3c)$ **51.** $4(y - 4)$ **53a.** 7; Sample answer:

7	14	21	28	35
↓	↓	↓	↓	↓
7(1)	7(2)	7(3)	7(4)	7(5)

The terms increase by a factor of 7.
53b. 42, 49 **55a.** 6-in. squares **55b.** 20 tiles **57.** Yes; the GCF of 2 and 8 is 2. **59.** D **61.** yes **63.** no **65.** yes **67.** $3 \cdot 3 \cdot n$ **69.** $-1 \cdot 5 \cdot j \cdot k$ **71.** 92 **73.** -6 **75.** -10 **77.** 36 **79.** 24 **81.** 1000

Pages 171–173   Lesson 4-5

1. The GCF of the numerator and denominator is 1. **3.** $\frac{1}{7}$ **5.** simplified **7.** $\frac{16}{17}$ **9.** $\frac{a}{2}$ **11.** simplified **13.** B **15.** $\frac{5}{6}$ **17.** $\frac{2}{9}$ **19.** $\frac{9}{22}$ **21.** simplified **23.** $\frac{1}{3}$ **25.** $\frac{5}{12}$ **27.** $\frac{19}{20}$ **29.** $\frac{3}{92}$ **31.** $\frac{y^2}{1}$ or y^2 **33.** $\frac{20}{21}$ **35.** $\frac{1}{8t}$ **37.** $\frac{7z^2}{4}$ **39.** simplified **41.** $\frac{gh}{3}$ **43.** $\frac{24}{25}$ **45a.** yes; $\frac{330}{440} = \frac{3}{4}$ **45b.** No; $\frac{294}{349}$ cannot be simplified. **45c.** yes; $\frac{264}{528} = \frac{1}{2}$ **47.** $\frac{31}{50}$ **49.** $\frac{7}{10}$ **51.** Fractions represent parts of a whole. So, measurements that contain parts of units can be represented using fractions. Answers should include the following.
- Measurements can be given as parts of a whole because smaller units make up larger units. For example, inches make up feet.
- Twelve inches equals 1 foot. So, 3 inches equals $\frac{3}{12}$ or $\frac{1}{4}$ foot.

53. A **55.** 2 **57.** 5 **59.** composite **61.** prime **63.** 27 **65.** $(6 \cdot 7)(k^3)$ **67.** $(3 \cdot -5)(x^4 \cdot x^2)$

1. Neither; the factors have different bases.   3. Sample answer: $5 \cdot 5^2 = 5^3$ 5. a^6 7. $-12x^5$ 9. 10^2 11. a^4 13. 3^5 15. d^{10} 17. n^9 19. 9^9 21. $18y^5$ 23. $8a^3b^{10}$ 25. 5^3 27. b^3 29. m^{12} 31. $(-2)^1$ or -2 33. n^6 35. k^2m 37. 9^7 39. 7^9 41. 10^2 or 100 times   43. 3   45. 2 times   47. 8   49. 5   51. Each level on the Richter scale is 10 times greater than the previous level. So, powers of 10 can be used to compare earthquake magnitudes. Answers should include the following.

• On the Richter scale, each whole-number increase represents a 10-fold increase in the magnitude of seismic waves.

• An earthquake of magnitude 7 is 10^5 times greater than an earthquake of magnitude 2 because $10^7 \div 10^2 = 10^{7-2}$ or 10^5.

53. B   55. simplified   57. $\dfrac{3x}{2y}$ 59. 2   61. a 63. Positive; as the high temperature increases, the amount of electricity that is used also increases.   65. $-\dfrac{1}{10}$ 67. $-\dfrac{1}{20}$ 69. $\dfrac{1}{64}$

1. To get each successive power, divide the previous power by 3. Therefore, $3^0 = 3 \div 3$ or 1.   3. $\dfrac{1}{5^2}$ 5. $\dfrac{1}{t^6}$ 7. 3^{-4} 9. 7^{-2} 11. $\dfrac{1}{32}$ 13. 10^{-3} 15. $\dfrac{1}{5^3}$ 17. $\dfrac{1}{(-3)^3}$ 19. $\dfrac{1}{10^4}$ 21. $\dfrac{1}{a^{10}}$ 23. $\dfrac{1}{q^4}$ 25. x^2 27. $\dfrac{1}{5^4}$; 0.0016   29. 5^{-5} 31. 13^{-2} 33. 9^{-2} 35. 2^{-4} or 4^{-2} 37. 10^{-2} or 100^{-1} 39. 10^{-5} 41. $-\dfrac{1}{128}$ 43. $\dfrac{1}{729}$ 45. 128 times   47. x^{-5} 49. x^{-3} 51. a^3b^{-2} or $\dfrac{a^3}{b^2}$

53. Yes; $(x^3)^{-2} = \dfrac{1}{(x^3)^2}$
$$= \dfrac{1}{x^3 \cdot x^3} \text{ or } \dfrac{1}{x^6}$$
$(x^{-2})^3 = (x^{-2})(x^{-2})(x^{-2})$
$$= x^{-6} \text{ or } \dfrac{1}{x^6}$$

55. C   57. 9×10^{-1} 59. $(1 \times 10^{-1}) + (7 \times 10^{-2}) + (3 \times 10^{-3})$ 61. 3^7 63. 5^3 65. $8y + 48$ 67. $5n - 15$ 69. 720   71. 40.5   73. 0.0005

1. 5   3. $2a$ 5. $\dfrac{2}{5}$ 7. $-2n^7$ 9. $\dfrac{1}{b^6}$

1. Sample answer: Numbers that are greater than 1 can be expressed as the product of a factor and a positive power of 10. So, these numbers are written in scientific notation using positive exponents. Numbers between 0 and 1 cannot be expressed as the product of a factor and a whole number power of 10, so they are written in scientific notation using negative exponents.   3. 0.000308   5. 849,500   7. 6.97×10^5 9. 1.0×10^{-3} 11. Mars, Venus, Earth   13. 57,200   15. 0.005689   17. 0.0901   19. 2505   21. 2.0×10^6 23. 6.0×10^{-3} 25. 5.0×10^7 27. 5.894×10^6 29. 4.25×10^{-4} 31. 6.25×10^6 33. 7.53×10^{-7} 35. 2.3×10^5 37. 5000   39. Arctic, Indian, Atlantic, Pacific   41. 6.1×10^{-5}, 0.0061, 6.1×10^{-2}, 6100, 6.1×10^4 43. 48,396   45. 2.52×10^5; 252,000   47. Bezymianny; Santa Maria; Agung; Mount St. Helens tied with Hekla 1947; Hekla, 1970; Ngauruhoe   49. 3.14   51. B   53. $\dfrac{1}{81}$ 55. $\dfrac{1}{49}$ 57. $15a^4$ 59. $c + \$2.50$

1. true   3. true   5. true   7. true   9. 3   11. 5   13. 2, 3, 6   15. 2, 5, 10   17. 27   19. 25   21. 90   23. 112   25. $3^2 \cdot 5$ 27. $2^2 \cdot 17$ 29. $7 \cdot 7 \cdot k$ 31. $2 \cdot 13 \cdot p \cdot p \cdot p$ 33. 6   35. n 37. $2(t + 10)$ 39. $2(15 + 2n)$ 41. $\dfrac{3}{5}$ 43. $\dfrac{10}{17}$ 45. simplified   47. $\dfrac{5c^2}{8b}$ 49. c^4 51. r^2 53. $\dfrac{1}{7^2}$ 55. $\dfrac{1}{b^4}$ 57. $\dfrac{1}{(-4)^3}$ 59. 0.0029   61. 70,450   63. 8.0×10^{-3} 65. 4.571×10^7

Chapter 5 Rational Numbers

1. 0.6   3. 34   5. 0.2   7. -75 9. -1.7 11. $\dfrac{3}{5}$ 13. $\dfrac{18}{25}$ 15. 6   17. -13 19. 15   21. 9

1. Sample answer: write the fractions as decimals and then compare.   3. Sample answer: $0.\overline{14}$ 5. 2.08   7. $0.2\overline{6}$ 9. $<$ 11. $>$ 13. 0.2   15. 0.32   17. 7.3   19. 5.125   21. $0.\overline{1}$ 23. $-0.\overline{45}$ 25. $0.1\overline{6}$ 27. 0.3125   29. $0.8\overline{3}$ 31. $\dfrac{7}{9}$, 0.8, $\dfrac{7}{8}$ 33. $<$ 35. $<$ 37. $>$ 39. $=$ 41. $>$ 43. $>$ 45. Sample answer: 0.7 and $0.\overline{7}$; $\dfrac{1}{6} = 0.1\overline{6}$ and $\dfrac{8}{9} = 0.\overline{8}$; 0.7 and $0.\overline{7}$ are both greater than $0.1\overline{6}$ and less than $0.\overline{8}$.   47. This is greater than those who chose English in the survey because $\dfrac{1}{7} \approx 0.14$, and $0.14 > 0.13$.   49. All coins were made with a fraction of silver that was contained in a silver dollar. Answers should include the following.

• A quarter had one-fourth the amount of silver as a silver dollar, a dime had one-tenth the amount, and a nickel had one-twentieth the amount.

• It is easier to perform arithmetic operations using decimals rather than using fractions.

51. D   53. 7.7×10^{-2} 55. 9.25×10^5 57. $\dfrac{1}{(-2)^7}$ 59. $\dfrac{1}{y^3}$ 61. 29   63. -32 65. 56   67. $\dfrac{1}{13}$ 69. $\dfrac{2}{3}$ 71. $\dfrac{4}{7}$ 73. $\dfrac{1}{8}$

1. any number that can be written as a fraction   3. $-\dfrac{7}{3}$ 5. $\dfrac{4}{5}$ 7. $-\dfrac{7}{9}$ 9. I, Q   11. $\dfrac{39}{1,000,000}$ 13. $-\dfrac{11}{7}$ 15. $\dfrac{60}{1}$ 17. $\dfrac{9}{100}$ 19. $1\dfrac{17}{25}$ 21. $8\dfrac{1}{250}$ 23. $-\dfrac{1}{3}$ 25. $5\dfrac{2}{3}$ 27. $2\dfrac{25}{99}$ 29. $\dfrac{3}{50}$ 31. $\dfrac{59}{200}$ 33. $\dfrac{4}{25}$ 35. I, Q   37. N, W, I, Q   39. Q   41. not rational   43. $200\dfrac{19}{100}$ 45. Sometimes; $\dfrac{1}{2}$ and 2 are both rational numbers, but only 2 is an integer.   47. $\dfrac{1}{1250}$ in.   49. Yes; $2\dfrac{3}{8} = 2.375$ and $2.375 > 2.37$.   51. The set of rational numbers includes the set of natural numbers, whole numbers, and integers. In the same way, natural numbers are part of the set of whole numbers and the set of whole numbers is part of the set of integers. Answers should include the following.

• The number 5 belongs to the set of natural numbers, whole numbers integers, and rational numbers.

• The number $\dfrac{1}{2}$ belongs only to the set of rational numbers.

53. C   55. -7.8 57. $2.\overline{5}$ 59. 3,050,000   61. 0.01681   63. $(4 \times 10^2) + (8 \times 10^1) + (3 \times 10^0)$ 65. 24 cm; 27 cm^2

67. $8 \cdot 2 + 1 \cdot 2$ **69.** $7x + 28$ **71.** Sample answer: $-5 \cdot 4 = -20$ **73.** Sample answer: $7 \cdot 2 = 14$ **75.** Sample answer: $16 \cdot 2 = 32$

Pages 212–214   Lesson 5-3
1. Sample answer: $\frac{1}{2}, \frac{1}{3}$ **3.** $\frac{3}{20}$ **5.** $\frac{5}{9}$ **7.** $\frac{13}{22}$ **9.** $\frac{6}{7}$ **11.** $\frac{8}{t}$
13. $\frac{12}{49}$ **15.** $-\frac{1}{40}$ **17.** $\frac{8}{45}$ **19.** $\frac{1}{3}$ **21.** $-\frac{1}{4}$ **23.** $\frac{3}{8}$ **25.** $1\frac{1}{6}$
27. $3\frac{1}{3}$ **29.** $14\frac{2}{3}$ **31.** 10   **33.** $-4\frac{4}{9}$ **35.** 6   **37.** 27   **39.** 27
41. $\frac{8c}{11}$ **43.** $\frac{xz^2}{3}$ **45.** $\frac{9}{25}$ **47.** $\frac{11}{60}$ **49.** 12.7   **51.** 10.257
53a. Sample answer: $\frac{8}{4} \times \frac{3}{5}$ **53b.** Sample answer: $\frac{3}{4} \times \frac{5}{6}$
55. A   **57.** $\frac{5}{8}$ **59.** $\frac{13}{32}$ **61.** $-\frac{1}{5}$ **63.** $\frac{7}{9}$ **65.** $0.1\overline{6}$ **67.** -4.875
69. $8n$ **71.** $2t$ **73.** 9

Pages 217–219   Lesson 5-4
1. Dividing by a fraction is the same as multiplying by its reciprocal.   **3.** $\frac{5}{4}$ **5.** $\frac{8}{25}$ **7.** $\frac{4}{5}$ **9.** $1\frac{7}{15}$ **11.** $-1\frac{29}{36}$ **13.** $\frac{3a}{2}$
15. 6 boards   **17.** $-\frac{5}{1}$ or -5 **19.** $\frac{1}{24}$ **21.** $-\frac{9}{29}$ **23.** $\frac{8}{9}$
25. $-\frac{15}{22}$ **27.** $\frac{15}{16}$ **29.** -1 **31.** $1\frac{1}{2}$ **33.** -10 **35.** $1\frac{1}{3}$ **37.** 2
39. $-6\frac{1}{4}$ **41.** $\frac{4}{3}$ **43.** $\frac{5}{6r}$ **45.** $\frac{16}{t^5}$ **47.** 6 ribbons   **49.** $\frac{81}{256}$
51. 8 days   **53.** Dividing by a fraction is the same as multiplying by its reciprocal. Answers should include the following.
• For example, a model of two circles, each divided into four sections, represents $2 \div \frac{1}{4}$. Since there are 8 sections, $2 \div \frac{1}{4} = 8$.
• Division of fractions and multiplication of fractions are inverse operations. So, $2 \div \frac{1}{4}$ equals $2 \cdot 4$ or 8.
55. C   **57.** $\frac{5}{24}$ **59.** $-\frac{10}{21}$ **61.** Q   **63.** not rational   **65.** 7
67. $1\frac{1}{7}$ **69.** $6\frac{1}{4}$ **71.** $3\frac{2}{3}$ **73.** $1\frac{2}{3}$

Pages 222–224   Lesson 5-5
1.

3. Kayla; Ethan incorrectly left out the negative sign on the first term.   **5.** $\frac{4}{7}$ **7.** $-\frac{3}{4}$ **9.** $8\frac{1}{2}$ **11.** $\frac{8r}{11}$ **13.** $-\frac{1}{3x}$ **15.** $\frac{3}{5}$
17. $\frac{2}{3}$ **19.** $-\frac{1}{2}$ **21.** $-1\frac{1}{2}$ **23.** $-\frac{2}{9}$ **25.** $11\frac{4}{5}$ **27.** $9\frac{1}{3}$ **29.** $\frac{3}{4}$
31. $4\frac{6}{7}$ **33.** $8\frac{1}{8}$ **35.** $2\frac{3}{5}$ **37.** $\frac{1}{5}$ **39.** $\frac{5x}{8}$ **41.** $\frac{3}{m}$ **43.** $2\frac{3}{7}c$
45. $5\frac{3}{8}$ in.   **47.** 38 ft   **49.** When you use a ruler or a tape measure, measurements are usually a fraction of an inch. Answers should include the following.
• The marks on a ruler represent $\frac{1}{16}$ of an inch, $\frac{1}{8}$ of an inch, $\frac{1}{4}$ of an inch, and $\frac{1}{2}$ of an inch.
• Fractional measures are used in sewing and construction.
51. A   **53.** $-1\frac{7}{8}$ **55.** $\frac{3}{10}$ **57.** $1\frac{1}{3}$ **59.** 42 cm; 90 cm^2
61. $5^2 \cdot 7$ **63.** $2^2 \cdot 3 \cdot n$ **65.** $2 \cdot 3 \cdot 7 \cdot a^2 \cdot b$

1. 0.16   **3.** 3.125   **5.** $\frac{3}{25}$ **7.** $\frac{2}{27}$ **9.** $\frac{5}{12}$

Pages 228–230   Lesson 5-6
1. The LCM involves the common multiples of a set of numbers; the LCD is the LCM of the denominators of two or more fractions.   **3.** 24   **5.** 70   **7.** 48   **9.** 8   **11.** $100x$
13. $=$ **15.** front gear: 5; back gear: 13   **17.** 60   **19.** 48
21. 84   **23.** 100   **25.** 96   **27.** 84   **29.** 630   **31.** $112a^2b$
33. $75n^4$ **35.** 15   **37.** 35   **39.** 24   **41.** $16c^2d$ **43.** 60 s   **45.** $<$
47. $>$ **49.** $=$ **51.** $>$ **53.** amphibians   **55.** 12 and 18
57. Never; sample answer: 5 and 6 do not contain any factors in common, and the LCM of 5 and 6 is 30.   **59a.** If two numbers are relatively prime, then their LCM is the product of the two numbers. For example, the LCM of 4 and 5 is $2^2 \cdot 5$ or 20; the LCM of 6 and 25 is $2 \cdot 3 \cdot 5^2$ or 150.   **59b.** Always; the LCM contains all of the factors of both numbers. Therefore, it must contain any common factors.
61. B   **63.** $\frac{1}{2}$ **65.** $1\frac{1}{7}$ **67.** 3   **69.** $\frac{ad}{5}$ **71.** $7 + 2n = 11$; 2
73. -20 **75.** Sample answer: $0 + 1 = 1$ **77.** Sample answer: $1 + 2 = 3$ **79.** Sample answer: $8 + 7 = 15$

Pages 234–236   Lesson 5-7
1. Find the least common denominator.   **3.** José; he finds a common denominator by multiplying the denominators. Daniel incorrectly adds the numerators and the denominators of unlike fractions.   **5.** $\frac{2}{9}$ **7.** $-\frac{5}{6}$ **9.** $-4\frac{1}{4}$
11. $\frac{9}{10}$ **13.** $\frac{5}{28}$ **15.** $1\frac{1}{16}$ **17.** $\frac{1}{8}$ **19.** $-\frac{1}{8}$ **21.** $1\frac{1}{15}$ **23.** $-7\frac{5}{9}$
25. $-11\frac{7}{9}$ **27.** $-14\frac{5}{8}$ **29.** $3\frac{11}{36}$ **31.** $5\frac{3}{5}$ lb   **33.** $8\frac{3}{4}$ in.
35. Sample answer: Fill the $\frac{1}{2}$-cup. From the $\frac{1}{2}$-cup, fill the $\frac{1}{3}$-cup. $\frac{1}{6}$ cup will be left in the $\frac{1}{2}$-cup because $\frac{1}{2} - \frac{1}{3} = \frac{1}{6}$.
37. Find the LCM of the denominators. Then rename the fractions as like fractions with the LCM as the denominators. Answers should include the following.
• For example, the LCM of 4 and 6 is 12. So, $\frac{1}{4} + \frac{5}{6} = \frac{3}{12} + \frac{10}{12} = \frac{13}{12}$ or $1\frac{1}{12}$.
• Writing the prime factorization of the denominators is the first step in finding the LCM of the denominators, which is the LCD. Then the fractions can be added or subtracted.
39. B   **41.** Sample answer: $\frac{1}{2} + \frac{1}{10}$ **43.** 36   **45.** $6n^3$ **47.** $9\frac{1}{2}$
49. $2\frac{4}{5}$ **51.** $1\frac{4}{5}$ **53.** 27   **55.** -9

Pages 241–242   Lesson 5-8
1. Mean; when an extreme value is added to the other data, it can raise or lower the sum, and therefore the mean.
3. 12.4; 8; none   **5.** 3.6; 3.5; 4   **7.** Sample answer: 13 could be an extreme value because it is 12 less than the next value. It lowers the mean by 2.1.   **9.** 98   **11.** 8.9; 8; 8
13. 7.6; 7.5; 7.1 and 7.4   **15.** 4.3; 4.2; 4.1 and 4.2   **17.** Sample answer: the median, 95, or the modes, 95 and 97, because most students scored higher than mean, which is 91.
19. Sample answer: The median home price would be useful because it is not affected by the cost of the very expensive homes. The cost of half the homes in the county would be greater than the median cost and half would be less.   **21.** C   **23.** $9\frac{5}{6}$ **25.** $-3\frac{7}{8}$ **27.** $>$ **29.** 18   **31.** -5
33. 7.9   **35.** 3

1. Subtraction Property of Equality   **3.** Ling; dividing 0.3 by 3 does not isolate the variable on one side.   **5.** 18.7
7. $1\frac{13}{30}$ **9.** $-2\frac{1}{12}$ **11.** −90   **13.** 29.15 in.   **15.** −2.4   **17.** 12.24
19. 5.9   **21.** $-\frac{31}{36}$ **23.** $6\frac{7}{9}$ **25.** $-\frac{2}{15}$ **27.** $-2\frac{3}{10}$ **29.** 4
31. 5   **33.** −32   **35.** $1\frac{1}{4}$ **37.** $5\frac{3}{4}$ **39.** $2\frac{7}{8}$ **41.** $13\frac{1}{2}$ in. by $21\frac{1}{2}$ in.   **43.** $16.66   **45.** $2\frac{1}{4}$ ft   **47.** Equations with fractions can be written to represent the number of vibrations per second for different notes. To solve, multiply each side of the equation by the reciprocal of the fraction. Answers should include the following.
- For example, if n vibrations per second produce middle C, then $\frac{5}{4}n$ vibrations per second produce the note E above middle C.
- The equation $\frac{5}{3}n = 440$ represents the number of vibrations per second to produce middle C. To solve, multiply each side by the reciprocal of $\frac{5}{3}$, $\frac{3}{5}$.

49. D   **51.** 13; 12; 11 and 12   **53.** 70.8; 66; 60   **55.** $\frac{17}{24}$ **57.** $\frac{17}{36}$
59. $7\frac{11}{15}$ **61.** $\frac{3}{8}$ **63.** −6   **65.** −6   **67.** 5   **69.** $-\frac{1}{3}$

Page 248   Practice Quiz 2
1. 72   **3.** 10   **5.** $\frac{13}{16}$ **7.** $1\frac{2}{3}$ **9.** 32.4; 30.5; 29

1. Arithmetic sequences have a common difference and the terms can be found by adding or subtracting. Geometric sequences have a common ratio and the terms can be found by multiplying or dividing.   **3.** A; 4; 19, 23, 27
5. neither   **7.** A; $-\frac{1}{3}, \frac{5}{3}, \frac{4}{3}, 1$ **9.** $11,027.36   **11.** A; 11; 38, 49, 60   **13.** G; 3; 162, 486, 1458   **15.** A; −3; 13, 10, 7
17. G; $-\frac{1}{5}; -\frac{1}{125}, \frac{1}{625}, -\frac{1}{3125}$ **19.** A; $\frac{1}{6}, \frac{2}{3}, \frac{5}{6}, 1$ **21.** A; −0.5, 2.5, 2, 1.5   **23.** neither   **25.** G; $-\frac{1}{3}, \frac{2}{9}, -\frac{2}{27}, \frac{2}{81}$
27. G; $\frac{1}{2}, \frac{1}{32}, \frac{1}{64}, \frac{1}{128}$ **29a.** Arithmetic; the common difference is $3.   **29b.** $48   **31.** Find the pattern, continue the sequence, and use the new values to make predictions. Answers should include the following.
- The difference between any two consecutive terms in an arithmetic sequence is the common difference. To find the next value in such a sequence, add the common difference to the last term. The ratio of any two consecutive terms in a geometric sequence is the common ratio. So, to find the next value in such a sequence, multiply the last term by the common ratio.
- Sequences occurring in nature include geysers spouting every few minutes, the arrangement of geese in migration patterns, and ocean tides.

33. A   **35.** 56   **37.** −5.28   **39.** 10   **41.** 3.3; 3.3; 3.6
43. $102\frac{7}{8}$ in.   **45.** b^3 **47.** 6   **49.** 15

1. rational   **3.** algebraic fraction   **5.** LCD   **7.** reciprocal
9. arithmetic   **11.** 0.45   **13.** $-0.4\overline{6}$ **15.** $6.3\overline{6}$ **17.** $\frac{3}{5}$ **19.** $\frac{1}{8}$
21. $4\frac{11}{25}$ **23.** $\frac{5}{9}$ **25.** $1\frac{7}{9}$ **27.** $3\frac{4}{11}$ **29.** $-\frac{7}{27}$ **31.** $6\frac{2}{5}$ **33.** $1\frac{1}{3}$
35. −3   **37.** $9\frac{4}{9}$ **39.** x **41.** −6   **43.** $-3\frac{3}{4}$ **45.** $-4\frac{1}{5}$ **47.** $\frac{4}{21x}$

49. $\frac{5}{9}$ **51.** $1\frac{1}{3}$ **53.** $2\frac{3}{5}$ **55.** $\frac{4}{3x}$ **57.** 120   **59.** $21c^2$ **61.** <
63. >   **65.** $1\frac{2}{3}$ **67.** $2\frac{5}{6}$ **69.** $1\frac{11}{15}$ **71.** $3\frac{1}{6}$ **73.** 6.0; 6.5; 3.6 and 7.2   **75.** 3.25   **77.** $-2\frac{1}{2}$ **79.** G; 3; 81, 243, 729
81. neither

Chapter 6   Ratio, Proportion, and Percent

1. 24   **3.** 10,560   **5.** 480   **7.** 4000   **9.** 6   **11.** 580
13. 50   **15.** 15,000   **17.** 48.8   **19.** 13.44   **21.** 0.18
23. 3.04   **25.** $\frac{1}{3}$ **27.** simplified   **29.** simplified   **31.** $\frac{3}{4}$

1. Sample answer:

3. Sample answer: $12 per person   **5.** $\frac{5}{8}$ **7.** $\frac{1}{3}$
9. 0.75 inch/hour   **11.** 24.2 miles/gallon   **13.** 576
15. No; the ratio will be 2 to 3.   **17.** $\frac{2}{5}$ **19.** $\frac{3}{7}$ **21.** $\frac{9}{32,000}$
23. $\frac{1760}{1}$ **25.** $\frac{17}{118}$ **27.** $\frac{3}{1}$ **29.** 0.10 cents/pencil
31. 4.5 m/sec   **33.** 7.8 ft/h   **35.** 39 pages/week   **37.** The 6-pack of soda costs $0.37 per can. The 12-pack of soda costs $0.35 per can. So, the 12-pack is less expensive.
39. 26.4   **41.** 19.2   **43.** 72   **45.** 105   **47.** about 579 mi/h
49. $9   **51.** C   **53b.** The ratios should be close in value.
53c. Sample answer: Pyramid of Khufu in Giza, Egypt; The Taj Mahal in India; The Lincoln Memorial in Washington, D.C.   **55.** arithmetic; 0.3; 13.3, 13.6, 13.9
57. $-\frac{1}{12}$ **59.** $13\frac{1}{3}$ **61.** 5.2×10^7 **63.** 3.8×10^{-2} **65.** 30
67. 40   **69.** 13

1. A statement of equality of two ratios.   **3.** Yes   **5.** 15
7. 4.2   **9.** yes   **11.** no   **13.** yes   **15.** 4   **17.** 20   **19.** 15
21. 1.4   **23.** 7.5   **25.** 0.94   **27.** 0.8   **29.** 15   **31.** 26
33. $\frac{12}{3} = \frac{72}{m}$; 18   **35.** $\frac{5}{6.25} = \frac{d}{8.75}$; 7   **37.** about 360.8 ft
39. $22.47   **41.** chocolate pieces: 3 c; peanuts: $1\frac{1}{2}$ c
43. $\frac{a}{c} = \frac{b}{d}, \frac{b}{a} = \frac{d}{c}$, or $\frac{c}{a} = \frac{d}{b}$ **45.** C   **47.** 57.3 mph
49. 4   **51.** $\frac{4}{7y}$ **53.** 102   **55.** 6.5

1. 1 unit   3 units   **3.** 40 mi   **5.** 1 in. = 5 ft

7.
0.5 in. = 10 ft

9. 12 ft   **11.** 24.6 ft   **13.** 11.4 ft
15. $49\frac{1}{2}$ ft   **17.** $\frac{2}{3}$
19. 1 cm = 0.25 cm

21. A scale factor less than 1 means that the drawing or model is drawn smaller than actual size. A scale factor of 1 means that the drawing or model is drawn actual size. A scale factor greater than 1 means the drawing or model is drawn larger than actual size. **23.** B **25a.** $\frac{1}{2}$ **25b.** $\frac{1}{4}$

25c. The perimeter of a 3-inch by 5-inch rectangle is 16 inches. The area is 15 square inches. For a 6-inch by 10-inch rectangle, the perimeter should be double the 3-inch by 5-inch rectangle. That is, 16×2 or 32 inches. The area should be 4 times the area of the 3-inch by 5-inch rectangle. That is, 4×15 or 60 square inches. Since the perimeter of the 6-inch by 10-inch rectangle is 32 and its area is 60, the conjecture is true. **27.** 3.5 **29.** 21.6 **31.** $6\frac{1}{12}$

33. $18t^5$ **35.** $\frac{4m^3}{3}$ **37.** $\frac{1}{20}$ **39.** $\frac{2}{5}$ **41.** $\frac{39}{50}$ **43.** $\frac{41}{50}$

Pages 283–285 Lesson 6-4

1. Sample answer: write an equivalent fraction with a denominator of 100 or express the fraction as a decimal and then express the decimal as a percent. A fraction is greater than 100% if it is greater than 1. It is less than 1% if it is less than $\frac{1}{100}$. **3.** $\frac{3}{10}$, 0.3 **5.** $1\frac{1}{4}$, 1.25 **7.** $1\frac{7}{20}$, 1.35 **9.** 45%

11. 0.8% **13.** 133.3% **15.** daily newspaper **17.** $\frac{22}{25}$, 0.88

19. $\frac{7}{8}$, 0.875 **21.** $3\frac{1}{2}$, 3.5 **23.** $\frac{61}{100}$, 0.61 **25.** $2\frac{23}{100}$, 2.23

27. $\frac{53}{10,000}$, 0.0053 **29.** 9% **31.** 270% **33.** 0.06% **35.** 22.5%

37. 175% **39.** 1.7% **41.** $\frac{37}{1000}$ **43.** 0.45 **45.** 19%

47. 61%, $\frac{2}{3}$, 0.69 **49.** 0.4 **51.** There are only two possibilities that satisfy the conditions, $\frac{1}{4}$ and $\frac{2}{5}$.

53. Percents are related to fractions and decimals because they can be expressed as them. Answers should include the following.

25%   30%

40%

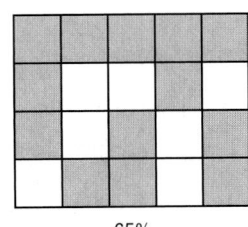

65%

• $25\% = \frac{1}{4} = 0.25$; $30\% = \frac{3}{10} = 0.3$; $40\% = \frac{2}{5} = 0.4$;

$65\% = \frac{13}{20} = 0.65$ **55.** A **57.** $\frac{1}{12}$ **59.** $\frac{11}{21}$ **61.** $1\frac{3}{13}$
63. composite **65.** composite **67.** 800 **69.** 0.94 **71.** 320

Pages 291–292 Lesson 6-5

1. $\frac{\text{number correct}}{50} = \frac{\%}{100}$ **3.** 40% **5.** 104 **7.** 60% **9.** 45%
11. 50 **13.** 77 **15.** 36% **17.** 112 **19.** 0.2% **21.** 16%
23. about 70% **25.** 26.8 lbs
27. In real-world situations, percents are important because they show how something compares to the whole. Answers should include the following.

• For example, the outer layer of the new state quarters is an alloy of 3 parts copper to 1 part nickel.
• Thus, there are 4 parts to the outer layer (copper, copper, copper, nickel). The outer layer is $\frac{3}{4}$ or 75% copper and $\frac{1}{4}$ or 25% nickel.

29. $\frac{21}{50}$ **31.** $1\frac{1}{5}$ **33.** $\frac{7}{9}$ **35.** $3\frac{1}{2}$ **37.** 8 **39.** 6 **41.** 25

Page 292 Practice Quiz 1
1. $0.14 per can **3.** 1 ft = 3069 ft **5.** 19.5

Pages 295–297 Lesson 6-6

1. 18% is about 20% or $\frac{1}{5}$. 216 is about 220. $\frac{1}{5}$ of 220 is 44. So, 18% of 216 is about 44. **5.** Sample answer: 13

7. Sample answer: 72 **9.** Sample answer: 8; fraction method: $\frac{1}{3} \times 24$ or 8 **11.** Sample answer: 21; meaning of percent method: 152% means about 150 for every 100 or about 15 for every 10. 14 has 1 tens. $1 \times 15 = 15$. So, 152% of 14 is about 21. **13.** Sample answer: 14 **15.** Sample answer: 33 **17.** Sample answer: 49 **19.** Sample answer: 4 **21.** Sample answer: 90 **23.** Sample answer: 375

25. Sample answer: $\frac{1}{4} \times 8$ or 2 billion **27.** Sample answer: 27; fraction method: $\frac{3}{10} \times 90$ or 27 **29.** Sample answer: 36; fraction method: $\frac{2}{5} \times 90$ or 36 **31.** Sample answer: 2; 1% method: Since 1% of 806 is about 8, $\frac{1}{4}$% of 806 is about $\frac{1}{4}$ of 8 or 2. **33.** Sample answer: 78; meaning of percent: 127% means about 130 for every 100 or about 13 for every 10. 64 has 6 tens. $6 \times 13 = 78$. So, 127% of 64 is about 78. **35.** Sample answer: 450; meaning of percent: 295% means about 300 for every 100 or about 30 for every 10. 145 has one 100 and about 5 tens. $(300 \times 1) + (30 \times 5) = 300 + 150$ or 450. **37.** Sample answer: Pluto and Mars, or Neptune and Jupiter **39.** Sample answer: $\frac{1}{3} \times 90,000$ or 30,000 miles **41.** about 10% **43.** 7 to 8 **45.** C **47.** 21 **49.** Maine: 31,813 sq mi; New Hampshire: 8238 sq mi; West Virginia: 18,779 sq mi; Vermont: 7279 sq mi; Alabama: 35,071 sq mi **51.** 160% **53.** 0.77 **55.** 4.21 **57.** 8.9 **59.** -21 **61.** 0.5 **63.** 0.25 **65.** 0.07

Pages 300–302 Lesson 6-7

1. Use the percent equation in any situation where the rate and base are known. **3.** I = interest; p = principal; r = annual interest rate; t = time in years **5.** 50 **7.** 3% **9.** $1680 **11.** 1.5 years **13.** 95% **15.** 50 **17.** 63 **19.** 37.5% **21.** 14.52 **23.** 218% **25.** 0.9% **27.** 13.2 **29.** $25.49 **31.** $17 **33.** $18.50 **35.** $1113.75 **37.** $244.76 **39.** 16 **41.** $1.20 **43.** If you know two of the three values, you can use the percent proportion to solve for the missing value. Answers should include the following.

• To find the amount of tax on an item, you can use the percent proportion or the percent equation.
• For example, the following methods can be used to find 6% tax on $24.99.
Method 1: Percent Proportion

$$\frac{x}{24.99} = \frac{6}{100}$$

Method 2: Percent Equation

$$n = 0.06(24.99)$$

Using either method, $x = 1.50$. The amount of tax is $1.50.
45. B **47.** Sample answer: 250; meaning of percent method: 126% means about 125 for every 100 and 12.5 for every 10.

198 has about 2 one-hundreds. $125 \times 2 = 250$. So, 126% of 198 is about 250. **49.** 121 **51.** 41 **53.** 38 cm **55.** $8w - 24$ **57.** 89% **59.** 156% **61.** 22.4%

Pages 306–308 Lesson 6-8

1. If the amount increases, it is a percent of increase. If the amount decreases, it is a percent of decrease. **3.** Mark; he divided the difference of the new amount and the original amount by the original amount. **5.** -60%; D **7.** 10.1%; I **9.** A **11.** 170%; I **13.** -12%; D **15.** -5.4%; D **17.** 164%; I **19.** 10.1% **21.** -14.3% **23.** 150% **25.** The amount by which a rectangle is increased or decreased can be represented by a percent. Answers should include the following.

• If the size of the new rectangle is greater than the size of the original rectangle, the percent of increase is greater than 100%.

• **Original Rectangle**   **Less than 100%**

Greater than 100%

27. D **29.** \$149.85 **31.** \$13.46 **33.** Sample answer: 63; fraction method: $\frac{9}{10} \times 70$ or 63 **35.** integer, rational **37.** rational **39.** 20% **41.** $83\frac{1}{3}\%$

Page 308 Practice Quiz 2

1. Sample answer: 28; fraction method: $\frac{2}{5} \times 70$ or 28 **3.** \$14.50 **5.** 158%

Pages 312–314 Lesson 6-9

1. The event will not happen. **3.** Sample answer: Spinning the spinner shown and having it land on 4.

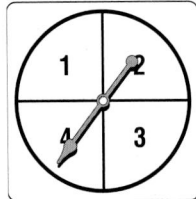

5. $\frac{1}{2}$; 50% **7.** $\frac{2}{5}$; 40% **9.** 1; 100% **11.** 75 **13.** $\frac{1}{4}$; 25% **15.** $\frac{1}{2}$; 50% **17.** 0; 0% **19.** $\frac{7}{8}$; 87.5% **21.** $\frac{2}{9}$; 22.2% **23.** $\frac{11}{18}$; 61.1% **25.** $\frac{1}{3}$; $33\frac{1}{3}\%$ **27.** 1; 100% **29.** $\frac{1}{6}$ **31.** $\frac{1}{16}$ **33.** $\frac{1}{4}$ **35.** 0.05; 5% **37.** 444 **39.** Once the probability or likeliness of something happening is known, then you can use the probability to make a prediction. For example, in football, if you know the number of field goals a player has made in the past, you can use the information to predict the number of field goals he/she will make in upcoming games. Answers should include the following.

• E: $\frac{12}{100}$ or 12%; A, I: $\frac{9}{100}$ or 9%; O: $\frac{8}{100}$ or 8%; N, R, T: $\frac{6}{100}$ or 6%; D, L, S, U: $\frac{4}{100}$ or 4%; G: $\frac{3}{100}$ or 3%; B, C, F, H, M, P, V, W, Y, blank: $\frac{2}{100}$ or 2%; J, K, Q, X, Z: $\frac{1}{100}$ or 1%

41. 146.9% **43.** 23.9 **45.** $2x^5$ **47.** $\frac{18n^2}{7}$

Pages 316–320 Chapter 6 Study Guide and Review

1. proportion **3.** scale factor **5.** experimental probability **7.** $\frac{3}{4}$ **9.** $\frac{1}{4}$ **11.** $\frac{20}{9}$ **13.** 30 **15.** 0.9 **17.** 45.6 ft **19.** $\frac{7}{20}$; 0.35 **21.** $\frac{2}{25}$; 0.08 **23.** $1\frac{1}{5}$; 1.2 **25.** $\frac{5}{8}$; 0.625 **27.** 24% **29.** 45.2% **31.** 40% **33.** 7.5% **35.** 40% **37.** 25 **39.** 50 **41.** 43 **43.** 9 **45.** 8 **47.** Sample answer: 16; fraction method: $\frac{1}{2} \times 32$ or 16 **49.** Sample answer: 10; fraction method: $\frac{1}{5} \times 50$ or 10 **51.** Sample answer: 1; 1% method: Since 1% of 304 is about 3, $\frac{1}{3}\%$ of 304 is about $\frac{1}{3}$ of 3 or 1. **53.** 48% **55.** 94.5 **57.** 200 **59.** D; -70% **61.** I; 86.2% **63.** $\frac{1}{3}$ **65.** $\frac{2}{3}$ **67.** 0

Chapter 7 Equations and Inequalities

Page 327 Chapter 7 Getting Started

1. 4 **3.** 24 **5.** -44 **7.** 11 **9.** -17 **11.** 16 **13.** -14 **15.** -15 **17.** 72 **19.** -5 **21.** 1

Pages 332–333 Lesson 7-1

1. Subtraction Property of Equality **3.** -8 **5.** 3 **7.** 0.3 **9.** 75 miles **11.** 13 **13.** -7 **15.** -0.5 **17.** -6 **19.** $\frac{4}{3}$ **21.** 3 **23.** 4.2 **25.** 0.3 **27.** 3.4 **29.** $3y - 14 = y$; 7 **31.** -16 **33.** 72 **35.** 70 min **37.** 29 **39.** A **41.** $-40°$ **43.** 12.5% **45.** 6.48 **47.** 70 **49.** $6a + 27$ **51.** $2.4c + 28$ **53.** $\frac{1}{2}n - \frac{9}{2}$

Pages 336–338 Lesson 7-2

1. Multiply 4 times $(x - 1)$. Subtract $2x$ from each side. Add 4 to each side. Divide each side by 2. **3.** 11 **5.** 13 **7.** $\varnothing$ **9.** $\ell = 7$ ft; $w = 3$ ft; $A = 21$ ft² **11.** 6 **13.** 2.5 **15.** 18 **17.** 3 **19.** 35 **21.** $\varnothing$ **23.** all numbers **25.** 6 **27.** all numbers **29.** 0 **31.** 70 yd by 150 yd **33.** w: 3 ft; ℓ: 13 ft; A: 39 ft² **35.** triangle: 7, 8, 9; rectangle, 4, 8; perimeter: 24 **37.** 2 gal **39.** Many equations include grouping symbols. You must use the Distributive Property to correctly solve the equation. Answers should include the following.

• The Distributive Property states that $a(b + c) = ab + ac$.

• You use the Distributive Property to remove the grouping symbols when you are solving equations.

41. D **43.** 0.4 **45.** 40% **47.** 0.375 **49.** 3.24 **51.** -7 **53.** -24 **55.** -8

Page 338 Practice Quiz 1

1. $2x = 5x - 150$; 50 **3.** $3.\overline{1}$ **5.** all numbers

Pages 342–344 Lesson 7-3

1. An inequality represents all numbers greater or less than a given number. A number line graph can represent all those numbers. **3.** $n + 14 \geq 25$ **5.** true

7.
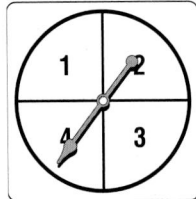
—2 —1 0 1 2 3 4 5 6

9.
1 2 3 4 5 6 7 8 9

11. $x \geq -20$ **13.** $f > 18{,}000$ **15.** $86 \geq 2w$ **17.** true **19.** false **21.** true

23.
−1 0 1 2 3 4 5 6 7

25.
4 5 6 7 8 9 10 11 12

27.
6 7 8 9 10 11 12 13 14

29.
−2 −1 0 1 2 3 4 5 6

31.
−6 −5 −4 −3 −2 −1 0 1 2

33.
−8 −7 −6 −5 −4 −3 −2 −1 0

35. $x > 13$ **37.** $x \le -3$ **39.** $x \ge -32$ **41.** $m \ge 6.4$
43. $b + 14{,}600 > 30{,}000$; $b > 15{,}400$ **45.** Symmetric: If $a < b$, then $b < a$; not true. Sample counterexample: $4 < 5$, but $5 \not< 4$. Transitive: If $a < b$ and $b < c$, then $a < c$; true.
47. B

49a.
−3 −2 −1 0 1 2 3 4 5

49b.
−3 −2 −1 0 1 2 3 4 5

51. 5   **53.** $4n - 6 = 3n + 2$; 8   **55.** G: $-16, 32, -64$ **57.** 13
59. -7 **61.** 19.8

Pages 347–349   Lesson 7-4

1. Use addition to undo subtraction; use subtraction to undo addition.   **3.** Sample answer: Joanna works part-time at a clothing store. Part-time workers must work fewer than 30 hours a week. If Joanna has already worked 8 hours this week, how many hours can she still work?   **5.** $y \ge -7$
7. $a > 11$ **9.** $t > -3$

11. $x \le 10$
7 8 9 10 11 12 13 14 15

13. $p < 2$ **15.** $b \le -22$ **17.** $y \le 5$ **19.** $r \le 7$ **21.** $j \le -4$
23. $w < 6$ **25.** $y \le 1.4$ **27.** $f \ge 5.4$ **29.** $b < 3\frac{1}{4}$
31. $n < 5$
1 2 3 4 5 6 7 8 9

33. $p > 2$
1 2 3 4 5 6 7 8 9

35. $x \le -5$
−7 −6 −5 −4 −3 −2 −1 0 1

37. $m \ge 27$
23 25 27 29 31

39. $b < 1\frac{3}{4}$
0 $\frac{1}{2}$ 1 $1\frac{1}{2}$ 2

41. $s \le 4\frac{2}{3}$
3 4 5

43. 980 lb   **45.** $42 + x \ge 74$; $x \ge 32$; at least 32 mph
47. Always; subtracting x gives $-1 < 0$, which is always true.   **49.** C   **51.** F   **53.** F   **55.** 3 cm, 9 cm   **57.** $8 + 32$
59. $5x - 17.5$ **61.** -3 **63.** -15 **65.** -2 **67.** -4 **69.** -48

Pages 353–354   Lesson 7-5

1. Multiply each side by -12 and reverse the inequality symbol.   **3.** Tamika is correct. She divided each side of the inequality by 9. Since 9 is a positive number, she did not reverse the inequality symbol.

5. $x \ge -2$
−4 −3 −2 −1 0 1 2 3 4

7. $a > 50$
10 30 50 70 90

9. $m \ge -8.4$
−9 −8.6 −8.2 −7.8 −7.4

11. $y \ge -72$
−80 −76 −72 −68 −64

13. C

15. $y > 9$
5 6 7 8 9 10 11 12 13

17. $b \ge -3$
−4 −3 −2 −1 0 1 2 3 4

19. $t \le 5$
1 2 3 4 5 6 7 8 9

21. $h \le 98$
90 94 98 102 106

23. $z \ge 3$
1 2 3 4 5 6 7 8 9

25. $w \le 2$
−4 −3 −2 −1 0 1 2 3 4

27. $r > 4$
1 2 3 4 5 6 7 8 9

29. $k > -18$
−20 −18 −16 −14 −12

31. $t \ge -16$
−20 −18 −16 −14 −12

33. $n \le 4$
1 2 3 4 5 6 7 8 9

35. $y > 5.7$
5 5.2 5.4 5.6 5.8

37. $b < 72$
70 74 78 82 86

39a. $40m \ge 2000$ **39b.** at least 50 min   **41.** Inequalities can be used to compare the weights of objects on different planets. Answers should include the following.
- Comparing the weight of an astronaut in a space suit on Mars to the same astronaut on the moon: $113 > 50$.
- If you multiply or divide the astronaut's weight by the same number, the inequality comparing the weights on different planets would still be true.

43. 40   **45.** $c \le -20$ **47.** $2n \le 14$ **49.** $-\frac{5}{21}$ **51.** $\frac{2a}{c}$ **53.** 4
55. -9 **57.** 32

1.
```
◄──●┼┼┼┼┼┼┼┼──►
  -4-3-2-1 0 1 2 3 4
```

3. $a \le 40$ **5.** $n \ge 124$ **7.** $r < -225$ **9.** $g \le 7$

Pages 357–359   Lesson 7-6

1. Check the solution by replacing the variable with a number in the solution. If the inequality is true, the solution checks.   **3.** Jerome is correct. By the Distributive Property $2(2y + 3) = 4y + 6$ not $4y + 3$.

5. $n > 2$
```
┼┼○┼┼┼┼┼┼──►
1 2 3 4 5 6 7 8 9
```

7. $c > 1$
```
┼┼┼┼┼○┼┼┼──►
-4-3-2-1 0 1 2 3 4
```

9. $x \ge 8$
```
┼┼┼┼┼┼┼●┼──►
1 2 3 4 5 6 7 8 9
```

11. $d < -9\frac{1}{2}$
```
◄──○┼┼┼┼┼┼──►
 -10  -9  -8  -7  -6
```

13. $x > 8$
```
┼┼┼┼┼┼┼○┼──►
1 2 3 4 5 6 7 8 9
```

15. $c > -4$
```
◄○┼┼┼┼┼┼┼┼──►
-4-3-2-1 0 1 2 3 4
```

17. $x > 3$
```
┼┼┼┼┼┼┼○┼──►
-4-3-2-1 0 1 2 3 4
```

19. $k \ge -5$
```
┼┼●┼┼┼┼┼┼──►
-7-6-5-4-3-2-1 0 1
```

21. $n < -5$
```
◄┼○┼┼┼┼┼┼┼──►
-7-6-5-4-3-2-1 0 1
```

23. $b \le 2$
```
◄─────────●┼┼──►
-4-3-2-1 0 1 2 3 4
```

25. $y \ge 30$
```
┼┼●┼┼┼┼┼┼──►
10  30  50  70  90
```

27. $c < -4$
```
◄┼┼┼┼┼○┼┼──►
-10  -8  -6  -4  -2
```

29. $n > 7$

31. $n \le 4.5$
```
◄─────●┼┼┼┼──►
1 2 3 4 5 6 7 8 9
```

33. $t \le -1$
```
◄─────●┼┼┼┼──►
-4-3-2-1 0 1 2 3 4
```

35. $c < -4$
```
◄┼┼┼┼┼○┼┼──►
-10  -8  -6  -4  -2
```

37. $0.55c + 0.35 \le 2$; 3 candy bars   **39.** $2s + 10 \ge 40$, 15 subscriptions   **41.** $x < 200$; Sample explanation: The inequality finds at what mileage Able's charge is greater than Baker's charge.   **43.** more than 100 minutes   **45.** $k < 3$ and $k > -3$, or $k = \{-2, -1, 0, 1, 2\}$ **47.** D   **49.** $-5 < x < 1$ **51.** $y \ge 37$ **53.** $n \le 5$ **55.** $a < -18.6$ **57.** 0.5% **59.** 16.6 mpg   **61.** \$1.25 an issue   **63.** 6 m

Pages 360–362   Chapter 7 Study Guide and Review

1. true   **3.** false; identity   **5.** false; inequality   **7.** true   **9.** false; is greater than or equal to   **11.** 3   **13.** 4   **15.** 1   **17.** -1 **19.** -1.2 **21.** 9   **23.** 16   **25.** all numbers   **27.** true

29. $b \ge 17$
```
┼┼┼●┼┼┼┼┼──►
14  16  18  20  22  24
```

31. $t < 3\frac{1}{2}$
```
◄──────○┼┼┼
0   1   2   3   4   5
```

33. $k \le 5.1$
```
◄──────────●┼┼┼──►
-1 0 1 2 3 4 5 6 7 8 9
```

35. $y \le -7$
```
◄──────●┼┼┼──►
-12  -10  -8  -6  -4
```

37. $a \ge -2\frac{2}{5}$
```
┼●┼┼┼┼┼┼──►
-4   -2   0   2   4   6
```

39. $n \le 4$ **41.** $t > -12$ **43.** $b > -4\frac{1}{4}$

Chapter 8   Functions and Graphing

Page 367   Chapter 8 Getting Started

1.

x	y
0	4
-3	3

domain = $\{0, -3\}$; range = $\{4, 3\}$

3.

x	y
6	8
7	10
8	12

domain = $\{6, 7, 8\}$; range = $\{8, 10, 12\}$

5.

x	y
-8	5
7	-1
6	1
1	-2

domain = $\{-8, 7, 6, 1\}$; range = $\{5, -1, 1, -2\}$

7. E **9.** A **11.** F **13.** true   **15.** true   **17.** true

Pages 371–373   Lesson 8-1

1. Sample answer: a set of ordered pairs: $\{(1, 2), (4, 3), (-2, -1), (-3, 3)\}$

a table:

x	y
1	2
4	3
-2	-1
-3	3

a graph:

3. Sample answer: This graph does not represent a function because when x equals 1, there are two y values, 0 and 2.

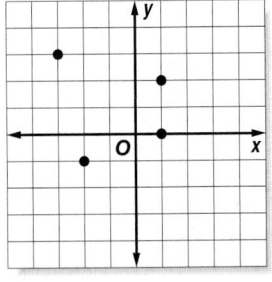

5. Yes; each x value is paired with only one y value. **7.** No; 5 is paired with 4 and 14. **9.** Yes; any vertical line passes through no more than one point of the graph. **11.** As wind speed increases, the windchill temperature decreases.
13. Yes; each x value is paired with only one y value.
15. No; 5 in the domain is paired with -4 and -1 in the range. **17.** No; -2 in the domain is paired with 5 and 1 in the range. **19.** Yes; each x value is paired with only one y value. **21.** No; a vertical line passes through more than one point. **23.** Yes; any vertical line passes through no more than one point of the graph. **25.** Generally, as the years progress, the number of farms decreases. An exception is in the year 2000. **27.** Generally, as the years progress, the size of farms increases. An exception is in the year 2000. **29.** Generally, as foot length increases, height increases. **31.** Sometimes; a relation that has a member of the domain paired with more than one member in the range is not a function.
33. For a given wind speed, there is only one windchill temperature for each actual temperature. So, the relationship between actual temperatures and windchill temperatures is a function. Answers should include the following.
- For a given wind speed, as the actual temperature increases, the windchill temperature increases.
- Since the relationship between actual temperatures and windchill temperatures is a function, there cannot be two different windchill temperatures for the same actual temperature when the wind speed remains the same.

35. A **37.** $a < -21$ **39.** $x < 6$ **41.** ∅ **43.** 18 **45.** 75 **47.** 13 **49.** 5 **51.** 0

Pages 377–379 Lesson 8-2
1. Sample answer: Infinitely many values can be substituted for x, or the domain.
3.

x	x + 5	y
-3	-3 + 5	2
-1	-1 + 5	4
0	0 + 5	5
1	1 + 5	6

$(-3, 2), (-1, 4), (0, 5), (1, 6)$

5. Sample answer: $(-1, -4), (0, 0), (1, 4), (2, 8)$ **7.** Sample answer: $(-1, 1), (0, 6), (1, 11), (2, 16)$
9.
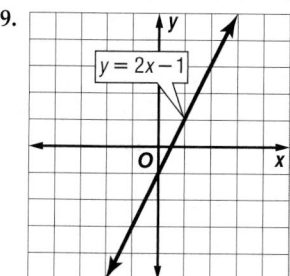

11. Sample answer: (1, 186,000) means that light travels 186,000 miles in 1 second. (2, 372,000) means that light travels 372,000 miles in 2 seconds.
13.

x	2x + 6	y
-4	2(-4) + 6	-2
0	2(0) + 6	6
2	2(2) + 6	10
4	2(4) + 6	14

$(-4, -2), (0, 6), (2, 10), (4, 14)$

15. Sample answer: $(-1, -8), (0, -7), (1, -6), (2, -5)$
17. Sample answer: $(-1, 5), (0, 0), (1, -5), (2, -10)$
19. Sample answer: $(-1, -2), (0, 1), (1, 4), (2, 7)$
21. Sample answer: $(-1, -5), (0, -6), (1, -7), (2, -8)$
23. Sample answer: $(-1, -13), (0, -10), (1, -7), (2, -4)$
25. Sample answer: $(-1, 0), (-1, 1), (-1, 2), (-1, 3)$
27. 6.2 mi **29.** Quadrant I; a person cannot have a negative age or heart rate.

31.

33.

35.

37.

39.

41.

43.
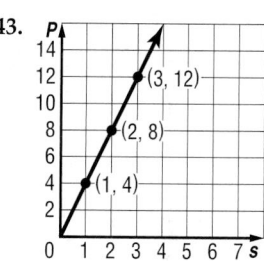

45. Yes; the points lie on a straight line. **47.** Yes; the points lie on a straight line. **49.** No; the exponent of x is not 1.
51. Sample answer: In the first table, as the x values increase by 1, the y values increase by 2. In the second table, as the x values increase by 1, the y values do not change by a constant amount. **53.** B **55.** Yes; each x value is paired with only one y value. **57.** No; 11 in the domain is paired with 8 and 21 in the range.
59. $x < 4$;

61. $\dfrac{6}{7}$ **63.** 3 **65.** 4

Pages 384–385   Lesson 8-3

1. To find the x-intercept, let $y = 0$ and solve for x. To find the y-intercept, let $x = 0$ and solve for y.   **3.** -1; -3
5. -4; 4 **7.** 3; 2

9.

11.

The y-intercept 3 represents the base fee of $3.

13. 1; 1 **15.** none; -5 **17.** -5; 5 **19.** none; -4 **21.** 8; -4
23. 5; 4

25.

27.

29.

31.

33.

35.

The x-intercept 6 represents the number of books that she can buy with no money left over. The y-intercept 18 represents the money she has before she buys any books.
37. The x- and y-intercept are both 0. Therefore, the line passes through the origin. Since two points are needed to graph a line, $y = 2x$ cannot be graphed using only the intercepts.

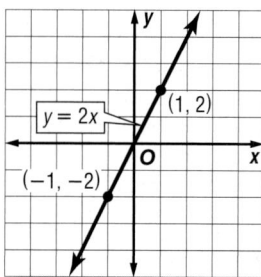

39. B   **41.** Sample answer:
$(-1, 5)$, $(0, 7)$, $(1, 9)$, $(2, 11)$
43. Sample answer: $(-1, 1)$,
$(0, 5)$, $(1, 9)$, $(2, 13)$ **45.** no
47. $n > 12$ **49.** 2.8%
51. -16 **53.** 25

Pages 389–391   Lesson 8-4

1. Sample answer: horizontals do not rise, so
slope $= \dfrac{\text{rise}}{\text{run}} = \dfrac{0}{\text{run}}$ or 0.   **3.** Mike; Chloe should have
subtracted -2 from 11 in the denominator.   **5.** $-\dfrac{2}{3}$ **7.** 2
9. 0   **11.** B   **13.** 4   **15.** $-\dfrac{3}{4}$ **17.** 0   **19.** 1   **21.** $-\dfrac{3}{2}$
23. undefined   **25.** $-\dfrac{3}{4}$ **27.** It decreased; negative slope.
29. Slope can be used to describe the steepness of roller coaster hills. Answers should include the following.
• Slope is the steepness of a line or incline. It is the ratio of the rise to the run.
• An increase in rise with no change in run makes a roller coaster hill steeper. An increase in run with no change in rise makes a roller coaster less steep.
31. A   **33.** 2; 6   **35.** Sample answer: $(-1, 3)$, $(0, 5)$, $(1, 7)$, $(2, 9)$ **37.** Sample answer: $(-1, 8)$, $(0, 7)$, $(1, 6)$, $(2, 5)$
39. $y = -2x$ **41.** $y = \dfrac{1}{3}x$

Pages 395–397   Lesson 8-5

1. The slope is 60, the rate of change is 60 units for every 1 unit, and the constant of variation is 60.   **3.** Justin; any linear function, including direct variations, has a rate of change.   **5.** increase of $12 per hour   **7.** $y = 6x$ **9.** increase of 12 in./ft   **11.** decrease of 2°F/min
13. Sample answer: The population of wild condors decreased from 1966 to 1990. Then the population increased from 1990 to 1996. The population of condors in captivity

increased slowly from 1966 to 1982, then increased more rapidly from 1982 to 1996.

| Interval | Rate of Change (number per year) | |
	Condors in the Wild	Condors in Captivity
1966–1982	−2.25	0.1875
1982–1990	−3	4.625
1990–1992	0	8
1992–1994	1.5	14.5
1994–1996	12.5	3.5

15. $y = -5x$ **17.** $y = 0.75x$ **19.** $y = 2.54x$ **21.** A line representing the relationship between time and distance has a slope that is equal to the speed. Answers should include the following.

- Sample drawing:

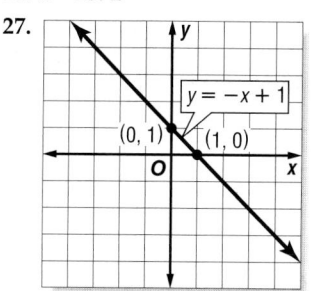

- As speed increases, the slope of the graph becomes steeper.

23. B **25.** 2

27.

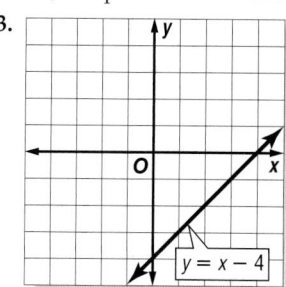

29. 14 **31.** $y = 1 - 3x$

Page 397 Practice Quiz 1

1. No; 1 is paired with 2 and −3.

3.

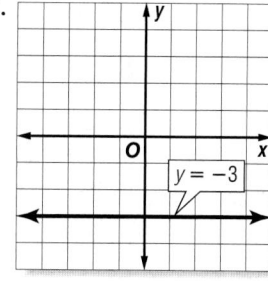

5. −9; 9 **7.** 5; −4 **9.** −2

Pages 400–401 Lesson 8-6

1. a **3.** Alex; the equation in slope-intercept form is $y = -\frac{1}{2}x + 4$. **5.** −1; 0

7.

9.

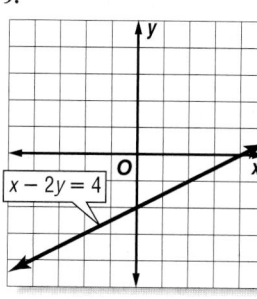

11. The y-intercept 25 represents the charge for a basic cake. Slope 1.5 represents the cost per additional slice.
13. 2; −4 **15.** −2; −3 **17.** 0; 4

19.

21.

23.

25.

27.

29.

31.

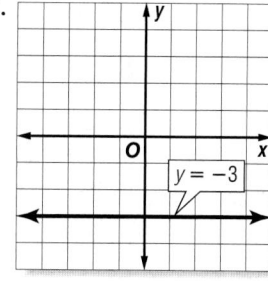

33. slope = −50, the descent in feet per minute; y-intercept = 300, initial altitude **35.** $-\frac{b}{m}$. Replace y with 0

in $y = mx + b$ and solve for x.　**37.** B　**39.** $y = -4x$　**41.** 2
43. 4　**45.** $6x = 2x + 28; 7$　**47.** $-\frac{3}{5}$　**49.** 29　**51.** 11

Pages 407–408　Lesson 8-7
1. Sample answer: Find the y-intercept b and another point on the line. Use the points to determine the slope m. Then substitute these values in $y = mx + b$ and write the equation.

3. $y = \frac{1}{2}x + 1$　**5.** $y = -2x + 3$　**7.** $y = \frac{1}{2}x + 1$

9. $y = \frac{3}{4}x - 1$　**11.** $y = 2x + 6$　**13.** $y = 5$　**15.** $y = -\frac{1}{3}x + 8$

17. $y = 2x + 3$　**19.** $y = -2.5$　**21.** $y = -\frac{1}{2}x$　**23.** $y = x + 1$

25. $y = -x$　**27.** $y = 7$　**29.** $y = 4x - 3$　**31.** $y = 1088x$; The speed of sound is 1088 feet per second.
33a. $d = 0.5(0.7c \times 1.06)$ or $d = 0.371c$　**33b.** $18.55　**35.** C
37. 6; 7　**39.** 3; -2　**41.** positive

Pages 410–413　Lesson 8-8
1. Sample answer: Use a ruler to extend the line so that it passes through the x value for which you want to predict. Locate the x value on the line and determine the corresponding y value. Or, write an equation for the best-fit line and substitute the desired value of x to find the corresponding value of y.
3. Sample answer:

5. $y = 20x + 320$
7. Sample answer:

9. Sample answer:

11. No, the equation gives a negative value for barometric pressure, which is not possible. Also, the data in the scatter plot do not appear to be linear.　**13.** Sample answer: 238 in.
15. As latitude increases, temperature decreases.
17. Sample answer: 61.3°F　**19.** The data describing the life expectancy for past generations can be displayed using a scatter plot. Then a line is drawn as close to as many of the points as possible. Then the line can be extended and used to predict the life expectancy for future generations. Answers should include the following.
- A best-fit line is a line drawn as close to as many of the data points as possible.
- Although the points may not be exactly linear, a best-fit line can be used to approximate the data set.

21. A　**23.** $y = -2x + 2$　**25.** $y = -4$

27.

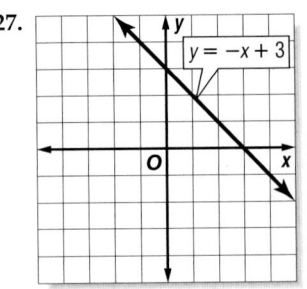

29. $n \le 7$　**31.** $d > -\frac{3}{2}$　**33.** 2　**35.** 4.5　**37.** 3　**39.** -1
41. -2

Pages 416–418　Lesson 8-9
1. Sample answer: A group of two or more equations form a system of equations. The solution is the ordered pair that satisfies all the equations in the system. If the equations are graphed, the solution is the coordinates of the point where the graphs intersect. The system has infinitely many solutions if the equations are the same and the graphs coincide.　**3.** $(-5, -4)$

5. no solution

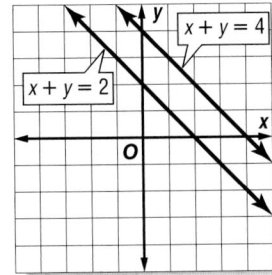

7. $(2, 6)$　**9.** $(3, -2)$　**11.** infinitely many

13. $(3, 3)$

15. infinitely many

17. $(-2, 4)$

19. $(-2, 0)$ **21.** $(-4, 10)$ **23.** $(3, 6)$ **25.** $(6, 11)$; an order of 6 pounds will cost the same, $11.00, for both sites.

27a. Sample answer: No; since slope represents rate, the slopes of the graphs are the same. Therefore, the runners will never meet.

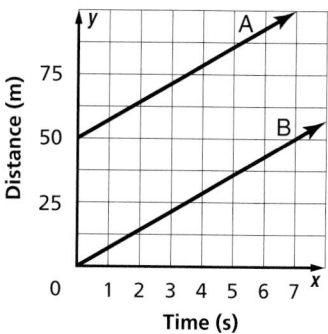

27b. Sample answer: The line representing runner B has a steeper slope than the line representing runner A. The intersection point represents the time and distance at which runner B catches up to runner A.

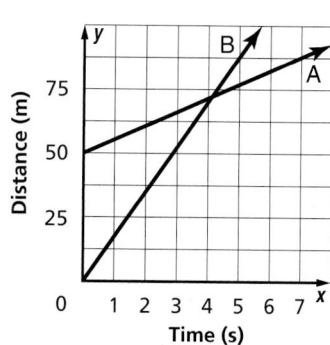

29. C **31.** positive slope **33.** $y = -3x$ **35.** yes **37.** no
39. yes

Page 418 Practice Quiz 2
1. $-1; 8$ **3.** $-\frac{1}{2}; 3$ **5.** $y = 1$

7. Sample answer:

9. $(0, 5)$

Pages 421–422 Lesson 8-10
1. $y < -x + 3$ **3a.** Sample answer: $(0, -1)$, $(1, 0)$, $(2, 1)$
3b. Sample answer: $(0, 0)$, $(1, 1)$, $(2, 2)$

5.

7.

9.

Sample answer:
5 adults, 30 children;
10 adults, 22 children;
15 adults, 15 children

11.

13.

15.

17.

19.

21.

23.

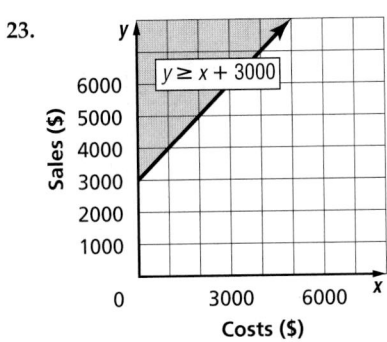

25. No; the number of sales and the costs cannot be negative. **27.** $10x + 25y \leq 1440$ **29.** Sample answer: 25 small, 45 large; 50 small, 30 large; 100 small, 10 large

31.

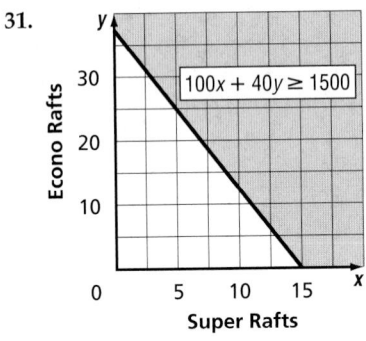

33a. $y > x - 1, y \leq -\frac{3}{2}x + 2$

33b. Sample answers: $(0, 2), (-1, 2), (-3, -2)$ **35.** C

37. $(0, 3)$

39. $(2, -5)$

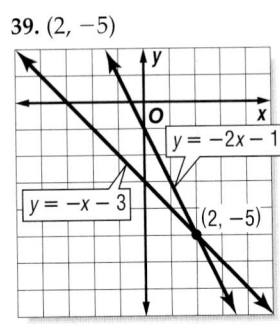

41. 0.4 **43.** $-0.\overline{5}$

Pages 424–428 Chapter 8 Study Guide and Review

1. d **3.** h **5.** a **7.** f **9.** c **11.** Yes; each x value is paired with only one y value. **13.** Yes; each x value is paired with only one y value.

15.

17.

19.

21.

23.

25.

27.

29.

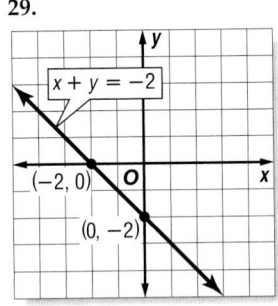

31. 1 **33.** $\frac{7}{8}$ **35.** undefined **37.** increase of 8 m/s

39.

41.

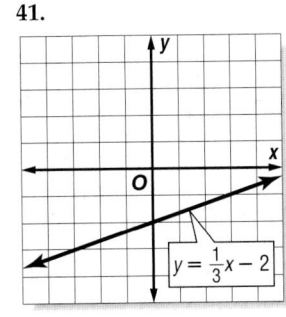

43. $y = -x + 3$

45. Sample answer:

47. (3, 3)

49. no solution

51. (4, 4)

53.

55.

Chapter 9   Real Numbers and Right Triangles

Page 435   Chapter 9 Getting Started
1. <   **3.** <   **5.** >   **7.** <   **9.** 8   **11.** 60   **13.** 9   **15.** 11   **17.** 8
19. 34   **21.** 97

Pages 438–440   Lesson 9-1
1. A positive number squared results in a positive number, and a negative number squared results in a positive number.   **3.** Sample answer: $-\sqrt{1.69}$

5. −8   **7.** 3.9   **9.** 8   **11.** 44.9 mi   **13.** 6   **15.** −5   **17.** not possible   **19.** 14   **21.** 18, −18   **23.** 1.5   **25.** 7.5   **27.** −9.3
29. 15.8   **31.** −1.7   **33.** 70.7   **35.** 9   **37.** −7   **39.** 14
41. −17   **43.** −2   **45.** 6   **47.** 14.8 mi   **49.** 9; Since $64 < 65 < 81$, $\sqrt{64} < \sqrt{65} < \sqrt{81}$. Thus it follows that $8 < \sqrt{65} < 9$. So, 9 is greater than $\sqrt{65}$.   **51a.** 10.4 in.; 41.6 in.   **51b.** 14.2 cm; 56.8 cm   **51c.** 8.4 m; 33.6 m
53. 10   **55.** 2   **57.** Sample answer: A number that has a rational square root will have an ending digit of 0, 1, 4, 5, 6, or 9. The last digit is the ending digit in one of the squares from 1–100. There are just six ending digits.   **59.** D
61. Sample answer: addition and subtraction   **63.** a

65.

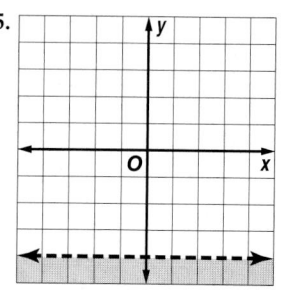

67. (5, 7)   **69.** (−4, −3)
71. $\frac{2}{3}$ **73.** 9   **75.** It can be written as a fraction.
77. It can be written as $\frac{3}{4}$.
79. It can be written as $\frac{6}{1}$.

Pages 443–445   Lesson 9-2
1. Whereas rational numbers can be expressed in the form $\frac{a}{b}$, where a and b are integers and b does not equal 0, irrational numbers cannot.   **3.** N, W, Z, Q   **5.** Q   **7.** <
9. $\frac{10}{3}, 3\frac{3}{5}, \sqrt{13}, 3.\overline{7}$ **11.** 8.6, −8.6   **13.** N, W, Z, Q   **15.** Q
17. Q   **19.** I   **21.** I   **23.** Z, Q   **25.** Q   **27.** Z, Q   **29.** always
31. always   **33.** >   **35.** <   **37.** =   **39.** $\frac{6}{5}, \sqrt{4}, 2.\overline{1}, 5\frac{1}{4}$
41. $-10\frac{1}{2}, -\sqrt{105}, -10, -1.05$ **43.** Sample answer: $\sqrt{4}$
and $\sqrt{49}$ **45.** 7, −7   **47.** 4.7, −4.7   **49.** 12, −12   **51.** 11.3, −11.3   **53.** 1.3, −1.3   **55.** 1.9, −1.9   **57.** 12 or −12
59. 4 or −4   **61.** 36

63. If a square has an area that is not a perfect square, the lengths of the sides will be irrational. Answers should include the following.

Area = 56 in^2 Area = 64 in^2

65. B   **67.** 2621.2 ft^2 **69.** 7   **71.** 3   **73.** Sample answer: (0, 5), (1, 6), (−6, 2)   **75.** $x > 5$ **77.** $0.53/cupcake

79.

3:00

81.

10:00

83.

7:45

Pages 449–451   Lesson 9-3
1. N; $\overrightarrow{NM}, \overrightarrow{NP}$; ∠1, ∠MNP, ∠PNM, ∠N   **3.** 20°; acute
5. 70°; acute   **7.** acute   **9.** straight angle

55°

11. 15°; acute   **13.** 85°; acute   **15.** 135°; obtuse
17. 60°; acute   **19.** 90°

21.

acute
40°

23.

acute
65°

25.

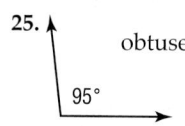
obtuse
95°

27.
obtuse
155°

29.

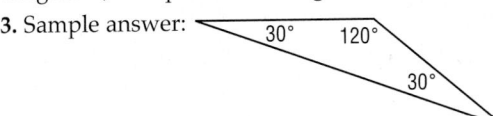

acute
38°

31a. obtuse **31b.** right **31c.** acute
33. Intense: about 68°; Moderate: about 104°; Light: 72°; No standard routine: about 47°; Don't exercise regularly: about 68° **35.** 24
37. C **39.** Z, Q **41.** I **43.** 4 **45.** $x - 7 \geq 22$ **47.** 99
49. 60 **51.** 18

Page 451 Practice Quiz 2
1. 6 **3.** 8.2, −8.2 **5.** obtuse

Pages 455–457 Lesson 9-4
1. Whereas an isosceles triangle has at least two sides congruent, an equilateral triangle has three sides congruent.
3. Sample answer:

5. 90; right **7.** right isosceles **9.** acute isosceles
11. 27; right **13.** 112; obtuse **15.** 90; right **17.** 20°, 60°, 100°
19. acute equilateral **21.** right scalene **23.** acute scalene
25. always **27.** obtuse **29.** acute **31.** not possible
33. not possible **35.** 45°; 50°; 85° **37.** 10, 15, 21 **39.** B
41. 180°; straight **43.** 145°; obtuse **45.** 9, −9 **47.** 9.2, −9.2
49. 144 **51.** 324 **53.** 729

Pages 462–464 Lesson 9-5
1. Sample answer: 8, 15, 17 **3.** 25 **5.** 15 **7.** no **9.** B
11. 26 **13.** 12.5 **15.** 18.9 **17.** 23 in. **19.** 12 **21.** 12.1
23. 37.3 **25.** 28 **27.** 33.5 **29.** yes **31.** no **33.** no
35. 32 in.
37. There is enough information to find the lengths of the legs. Since the right triangle is an isosceles right triangle, we know that the lengths of the legs are equal. So, in the Pythagorean Theorem, we can say that $a = b$. In addition, we know that $c = 8$.

$c^2 = a^2 + b^2$ *Pythagorean Theorem*
$8^2 = a^2 + a^2$ *a = b and c = 8*
$8^2 = 2a^2$ *Add a^2 and a^2.*
$64 = 2a^2$ *Evaluate 8^2.*
$\dfrac{64}{2} = \dfrac{2a^2}{2}$ *Divide each side by 2.*
$32 = a^2$ *Simplify.*
$\sqrt{32} = a$ *Take the square root of each side.*

39. D **41.** 17 units **45.** 90; right **49.** $n \geq -9$ **51.** 5

Pages 468–470 Lesson 9-6
1. the point halfway between two endpoints
3. Sample answer:

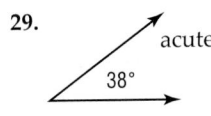

; The coordinates of the midpoint of $\overline{AB}$ are $\left(-\frac{1}{2}, 0\right)$.
5. 11.2 **7.** (2, −5) **9.** 9.2
11. 10.2 **13.** 16.6 **15.** 4.8
17. 19.2 **19.** (1, 3) **21.** (4, −2)
23. (2, 2) **25.** (3, −4)
27. $\left(11\frac{1}{2}, -5\right)$

29. Yes; $\overline{PM}$ and $\overline{MN}$ have equal measures. **31.** (−2, 3)
33. C **35.** 9.2 **37.** 35.1 **39.** 2, 1 **41.** −4, −6 **43.** 28
45. 21 **47.** 59

Page 470 Practice Quiz 2
1. obtuse isosceles **3.** Yes; $34^2 = 30^2 + 16^2$ **5.** (−1, 5)

Pages 473–475 Lesson 9-7
1. Sample answer:

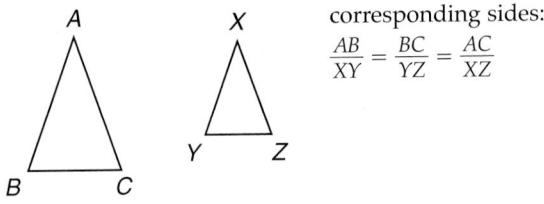

corresponding sides:
$\dfrac{AB}{XY} = \dfrac{BC}{YZ} = \dfrac{AC}{XZ}$

3. $\dfrac{x}{15} = \dfrac{6}{9}$; 10 **5.** 6 km **7.** $\dfrac{x}{4} = \dfrac{10}{5}$; 8 **9.** $\dfrac{x}{18} = \dfrac{20}{15}$; 24
11. $\dfrac{x}{3} = \dfrac{7}{4.2}$; 5 **13.** always **15.** 68 yd **17.** 6 ft
19. No, triangles ABC and DEF are not similar since the corresponding sides are not proportional. **21.** A **23.** 3.6
25. 7.1 **27.** 77.4 **29.** $\frac{1}{4}$ **31.** $1\frac{1}{2}$ **33.** 0.7143 **35.** 0.225

Pages 479–481 Lesson 9-8
1. The sine ratio compares the measure of the leg opposite the angle to the measure of the hypotenuse. The cosine ratio compares the measure of the leg adjacent to the angle to the measure of the hypotenuse. The tangent ratio compares the measure of the leg opposite the angle to the measure of the leg adjacent to the angle. **3.** 0.8824
5. 1.875 **7.** 0.9455 **9.** 25.6 **11.** 7.8 **13.** 0.9231 **15.** 0.7241
17. 2.4 **19.** 0.8944; 0.4472; 2.0 **21.** 0.1045 **23.** 0.8572
25. 0.2126 **27.** 6.8 **29.** 24.9 **31.** 97.6 **33.** about 21 m
35. about 44 m **37.** 24.0 **39.** 40.4 **41.** sin 45° = cos 45°; sin 60° = cos 30°; sin 30° = cos 60° **43.** To find heights of buildings. Answers should include the following.
- If two of the three measures of the sides of a right triangle are known, you can use the Pythagorean Theorem to find the measure of the third side. If the measure of an acute angle and the length of one side of a right triangle are known, trigonometric ratios can be used to find the missing measures.

•

6°   19 ft   x ft

$\sin 6° = \dfrac{x}{19}$
$19(\sin 6°) = x$
$2.0 \approx x$

The height of the ramp is about 2 feet.
45. C **47.** $\left(1\frac{1}{2}, \frac{1}{2}\right)$ **49.** (−3, −4) **51.** $a < -6$

Pages 483–486 Chapter 9 Study Guide and Review
1. real numbers **3.** obtuse **5.** hypotenuse
7. trigonometric ratio **9.** 6 **11.** −9 **13.** not possible
15. 9, −9 **17.** 1.2, −1.2 **19.** 90°; right **21.** 35°; acute
23. obtuse isosceles **25.** 13.7 **27.** 15.9 **29.** 9.4 **31.** (3, 5)
33. (0, −2) **35.** $\dfrac{AB}{HJ} = \dfrac{BC}{JK}$; 10 **37.** 1.3333

Chapter 10 Two-Dimensional Figures

Page 491 Chapter 10 Getting Started
1. 44 **3.** 51 **5.** 28 **7.** 39 **9.** 44 **11.** 71.8 **13.** 12.5
15. 10.7 **17.** $10\frac{1}{6}$ **19.** $3\frac{7}{8}$ **21.** $5\frac{3}{8}$ **23.** $6\frac{2}{9}$

Pages 495–497 Lesson 10-1
1. Complementary angles have a sum of 90° and supplementary angles have a sum of 180°. **3.** 56° **5.** 124°
7. 28 **9.** D **11.** 127° **13.** 53° **15.** 127° **17.** 148 **19.** 175

21. 9 **23.** 41° **25.** 73° **27.** 112° **29.** 5 **31.** 9 **33.** They are supplementary. **35.** A **37.** Sample answer: Both graphs intersect to form right angles. **39.** Sample answer: The slopes of the graphs of perpendicular lines are negative reciprocals of each other. **41.** 0.8910 **43.** 7.5 **45.** −9m

47.

45°

49.

145°

Pages 502–504 Lesson 10-2

1. They have the same size and shape. **3.** $\angle J \cong \angle C$, $\angle K \cong \angle B$, $\angle M \cong \angle G$, $\overline{KM} \cong \overline{BG}$, $\overline{MJ} \cong \overline{GC}$, $\overline{KJ} \cong \overline{BC}$; $\triangle BGC$ **5.** $\angle M$ **7.** $\overline{MN}$ **9.** 15 ft **11.** $\angle K \cong \angle N$, $\angle J \cong \angle P$, $\angle M \cong \angle M$, $\overline{KJ} \cong \overline{NP}$, $\overline{JM} \cong \overline{PM}$, $\overline{KM} \cong \overline{NM}$; $\triangle NPM$ **13.** $\angle Z \cong \angle S$, $\angle W \cong \angle T$, $\angle Y \cong \angle R$, $\overline{ZW} \cong \overline{ST}$, $\overline{WY} \cong \overline{TR}$, $\overline{ZY} \cong \overline{SR}$; $\triangle STR$ **15.** sometimes **17.** 30° **19.** $\angle F$ **21.** $\angle A$ **23.** $\overline{HF}$ **25.** $\overline{DC}$ **27.** 20 **29.** 6 **31.** Sample answer: $\triangle ZQN$ **33.** Sample answer: $\triangle WQO$ **35.** Congruent triangles can be found on objects in nature like leaves and animals. Answers should include the following.

- Congruent triangles are triangles with the same angle measures and the same side lengths.
- Sample answer: A bird's wings when extended are an example of congruent angles. Another example of congruent angles would be the wings of a butterfly.

37. D **39.** 0.1219 **41.** 1.1585 **43.** −6

45–49.

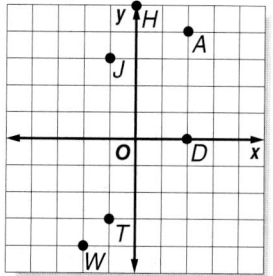

Pages 509–511 Lesson 10-3

1. The figure is moved 5 units to the right and 2 units down.

3.

5.

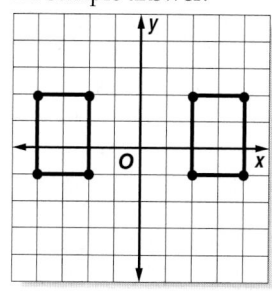

7. $A'(-2, 5)$, $B'(1, 3)$, $C'(-2, 0)$;

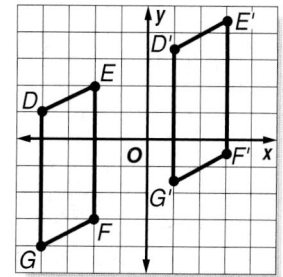

9. $D'\left(1, 3\frac{1}{2}\right)$, $E'\left(3, 4\frac{1}{2}\right)$, $G'\left(1, -1\frac{1}{2}\right)$, $F'\left(3, -\frac{1}{2}\right)$;

11. $R'(-4, -3)$, $S'(0, -3)$, $T'(-4, 1)$;

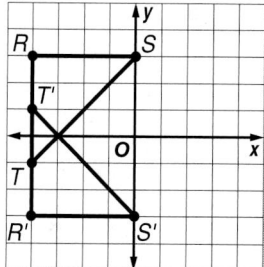

13. $M'(-1, -2)$, $N'(4, -4)$, $O'(3, -2)$, $P'(3, 0)$, $Q'(0, 0)$;

15.

17.

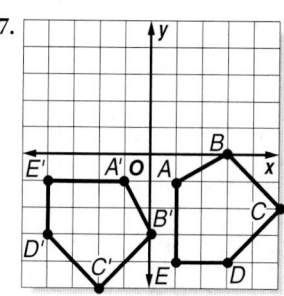

19. translation

21. Sample answer:

; The image of the figure's reflection is the same as the image of its translation to the right 6 units.

23. reflection **25.** Since many of the movements used in recreational activities involve rotating, sliding, and flipping, they are examples of transformations. Answers should include the following.

- a translation is a slide, a reflection is a mirror-image, and a rotation is a turn.
- sample answer: the swing represents a rotation, the scooter represents a translation, and the skateboard represents reflection.

27. C **29.** $\overline{DF}$ **31.** 110°

33. $x \geq 9.6$;

```
    7.0   8.0   9.0   10.0
```

35. 113 **37.** 47 **39.** 106

Pages 515–517 Lesson 10-4

1. Sample answer: A textbook is an example of a quadrilateral; the tiles in a shuffleboard scoring region are examples of parallelograms; a "dead end" road sign is an example of a rhombus; and a floppy disk is an example of a square. **3.** 110; 110° **5.** rectangle **7.** trapezoids, parallelograms **9.** 102; 102° **11.** 60; 60°; 60°; 120° **13.** 70; 70°; 80°; 120° **15.** Sample answer: A chessboard; it is a square because it is a parallelogram with 4 congruent sides and 4 right angles. **17.** square **19.** parallelogram **21.** rhombus **23.** always **25.** sometimes **27.** quadrilateral

29a. Yes; a rhombus is equilateral but may not be equiangular.

29b. Yes; a rectangle is equiangular but may not be equilateral.

31. B **33.**

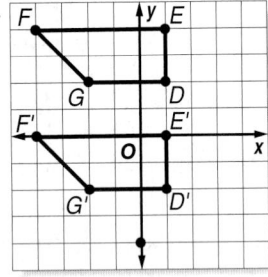

35. $\overline{MA}$ **37.** 14.4
39. 28.52

Page 517   Practice Quiz 1
1. 35° **3.** $Q'(3, -3)$, $R'(5, -6)$, $S'(7, -3)$ **5.** 60; 60°; 120°

Pages 523–525   Lesson 10-5
1. Sample answer:

3 in.

8 in.

3. 8 ft² **5.** 60 m² **7.** 11 m² **9.** 90 cm² **11.** 43.99 cm²
13. 28 in² **15.** 22.8 yd² **17.** 36.75 m² **19.** about 95,284 mi²
21. 147 km² **23.** 57 ft² **25.** 5 bags **27.** 16 in. **29.** 24.5%
31. The area of a parallelogram is found by multiplying the base and the height of the parallelogram. The area of a rectangle is found by multiplying the length and the width of the rectangle. Since in a parallelogram, the base is the length of the parallelogram, and the height is the width of the parallelogram, both areas are found by multiplying the length and the width. Answers should include the following.

• Parallelograms and rectangles are similar in that they are quadrilaterals with opposite sides parallel and opposite sides congruent. They are different in that rectangles always have 4 right angles.

•

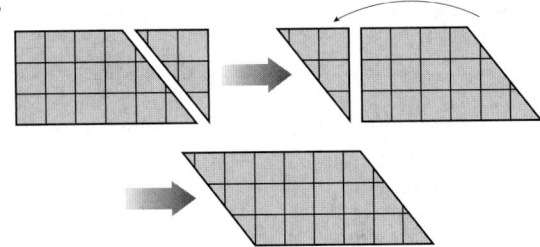

33. B **35.** 24; 24°; 96° **37.** 30 **39.** 26 **41.** 900 **43.** 1260

Pages 529–531   Lesson 10-6
1.

3. The number of triangles is 2 less than the number of sides. **5.** octagon; regular **7.** 128.6° **9.** hexagon; regular **11.** nonagon; not regular **13.** decagon, not regular **15.** 540° **17.** 1440°

19. 2880° **21.** Sample answer: hexagon, triangle, decagon, quadrilateral, and pentagon **23.** 140° **25.** 135° **27.** 150°
29. octagons, squares **31.** 180 cm **33.** 58.5 in.
35. In tessellations, polygons are fit together to create a pattern such that there are no gaps or spaces. Answers should include the following.
• Sample answer:

• Sample answer:

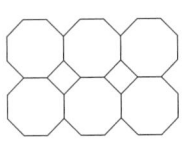

37. B **39.** 120° **41.** 60° **43.** 30° **45.** 18 cm²
47. quadrilateral **49.** 16.4x **51.** 33.9 **53.** 18.1

Pages 536–538   Lesson 10-7
1. Multiply 2 times π times the radius. **3.** Mark; since the diameter of the circle is 7 units, its radius is 3.5 units. Thus, the area of the circle is $\pi \cdot (3.5)^2$ or 38.5 square units.
5. 50.3 m; 201.1 m² **7.** 8.2 km; 5.3 km² **9.** about 9.1 mi²
11. 40.8 in.; 132.7 in² **13.** 131.9 km; 1385.4 km² **15.** 79.8 m; 506.7 m² **17.** 22.9 cm; 41.9 cm² **19.** 96.6 in; 742.6 in²
21. 1.5 m **23.** 13 cm **25.** about 3979 mi **27.** d **29.** a
31. about 26 times **33.** are safe: 25.4 in²; are unsafe: 24.2 in²; don't know: 14.0 in² **35.** 4 **37.** C **39.** 125° **41.** 235°
43. 125° **45.** 62.5° **47.** Sample answer: $\overline{SP}$, $\overline{SQ}$, $\overline{RP}$
49. 144° **51.** 38 m² **53.** $x < -7$ **55.** 150.5

Page 538   Practice Quiz 2
1. 112.86 cm² **3.** 32 m² **5.** 29.5 in.; 69.4 in²

Pages 541–543   Lesson 10-8
1. Sample answer:

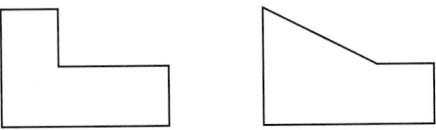

3. 49.5 yd² **5.** 2 **7.** 72 ft² **9.** 56.1 cm² **11.** 18.3 in²
13. 45 ft² **15.** 86.8 yd² **17.** 85 units² **19.** 6963.5 yd²
21. Sample answer: Separate the area into a rectangle and a trapezoid. **23.** 68,679 mi² **25.** You can use polygons to find the area of an irregular figure by finding the area of each individual polygon and then finding the total area of the irregular figure. Answers should include the following.

•

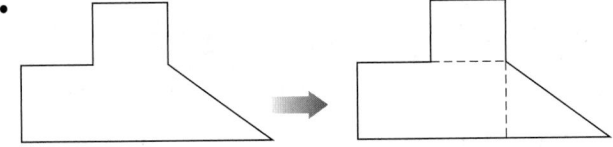

• To find the area of the irregular figure shown above, the figure can be separated into two rectangles and a triangle.
27. C **29.** 44.0 cm, 153.9 cm² **31.** 540° **33.** 1080°
35. $-24xy$

Pages 544–548   Chapter 10 Study Guide and Review
1. supplementary **3.** corresponding angles **5.** equilateral
7. 109° **9.** 71° **11.** $\angle H$ **13.** $\overline{RS}$ **15.** $\overline{GF}$

17.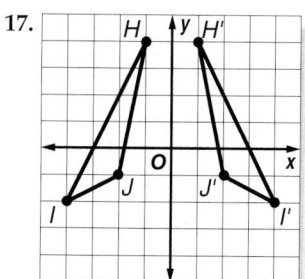

19. 112; 112° **21.** 70; 70°; 70° **23.** 11 yd^2
25. hexagon; 720°
27. decagon; 1440°
29. 13.2 m; 13.9 m^2
31. 118 in^2 **33.** 863.4 cm^2

Chapter 11 Three-Dimensional Figures

Page 553 Chapter 11 Getting Started
1. yes; triangle **3.** no **5.** 17 **7.** 7 **9.** 155 **11.** yes **13.** yes
15. yes

Pages 559–561 Lesson 11-1
1. Five planes form a square pyramid because the solid has five faces. An edge is formed when two planes intersect; a vertex is formed when three or four planes intersect.
3. triangular pyramid; any one of the following faces can be considered a base: RST, QRS, QST, QRT; $\overline{QR}$, $\overline{QS}$, $\overline{QT}$, $\overline{RT}$, $\overline{RS}$, $\overline{ST}$; Q, R, S, T **5.** intersecting

7. top   front   side

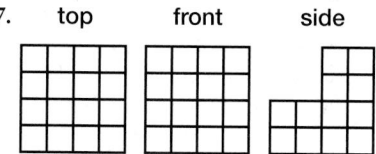

9. rectangular prism; $LMNP$, $QRST$ or $LPTQ$, $MNSR$ or $PNST$, $LMRQ$; $LMNP$, $QRST$, $LPTQ$, $MNSR$, $PNST$, $LMRQ$; $\overline{LM}$, $\overline{MN}$, $\overline{NP}$, $\overline{PL}$, $\overline{LQ}$, $\overline{MR}$, $\overline{NS}$, $\overline{PT}$, $\overline{QR}$, $\overline{RS}$, $\overline{ST}$, $\overline{TQ}$; L, M, N, P, Q, R, S, T **11.** triangular pyramid; any one of the following faces can be considered a base: WXY, WYZ, WZX, XYZ; $\overline{WX}$, $\overline{WY}$, $\overline{WZ}$, $\overline{XZ}$, $\overline{XY}$, $\overline{YZ}$; W, X, Y, Z **13.** $\overline{WR}$
15. skew **17.** top **19.** rectangular and pentagonal prisms
23. Never; only three or more planes can intersect in a single point. **25.** Sometimes; three planes may intersect in a line. Or, the planes may be parallel and not intersect at all.
27. Two-dimensional figures form three-dimensional figures. Answers should include the following.
- Two-dimensional figures have length and width and therefore lie in a single plane. Three-dimensional figures have length, width, and depth.
- Two-dimensional figures form the faces of three-dimensional figures.
29. D **31.** 37.7 cm; 113.1 cm^2 **33.** 0.5000 **35.** $c < 8$
37. $n > -11$ **39.** $y < 1\frac{3}{4}$ **41.** 14 in^2 **43.** 6.5 cm^2

Pages 565–567 Lesson 11-2
1. Sample answer: Finding how much sand is needed to fill a child's rectangular sandbox; measure the length, width, and height, and then multiply to find the volume.
3. 183.6 cm^3 **5.** 1608.5 ft^3 **7.** 282.7 yd^3 **9.** 198.9 ft
11. 512 cm^3 **13.** 748 in^3 **15.** 88.0 ft^3 **17.** 225 mm^3
19. 18.6 m^3 **21.** 6.2 m **23.** 1728 **25.** 1,000,000 **27.** 11.5 in.
29. The volume will be greater if the height is $8\frac{1}{2}$ inches.

By using the formula for circumference, you can find the radius and volume of each cylinder. If the height is $8\frac{1}{2}$ inches, the volume is 86.5 in^3; if the height is 11 inches, the volume is 67.7 in^3. **31.** C **33.** Sample answer: $\overline{QT}$ and $\overline{YZ}$ **35.** $x > -8$ **37.** 25 **39.** 4 **41.** 28

Pages 570–572 Lesson 11-3
1. The base is a circle.
3. Sample answer:
$V = 134.0$ cm^3

5. 37.7 cm^3 **7.** 378 ft^3 **9.** 91,636,272 ft^3
11. 412 cm^3 **13.** 150 in^3 **15.** 78.5 m^3
17. 270.8 cm^3 **19.** 565.5 m^3 **21.** 44.0 m^3
23a. 2.4 ft^3 **23b.** 314.4 lb

25. The volume of a pyramid is one-third the volume of a prism with the same base and height. Answers should include the following.
- The height of the pyramid and prism are equal. The bases of the pyramid and prism are squares with equal side lengths. Therefore, their base areas are equal.
- The formula for the volume of a pyramid is one-third times the formula for the volume of a prism.
27. B **29.** 904.8 cm^3 **31.** 107.5 mm^3 **33.** 10.1 in^3
35. 7.8 **37.** 36

Page 572 Practice Quiz 1
1. triangular prism **3.** 12.6 cm^3 **5.** $\approx$11,545,353 ft^3

Pages 575–577 Lesson 11-4
1. Sample answer: The surface of a solid is two-dimensional. Its area is the sum of the face areas, which are given in square units. **3.** 150 ft^2 **5.** 571.8 in^2 **7.** 140.7 mm^2
9. 282 in^2 **11.** 264 m^2 **13.** 1885.0 ft^2 **15.** 294 ft^2
17. 628.3 in^2 **19.** 264.0 in^2 **21.** 754 ft^2 **23.** The surface area is 4 times greater. **25.** D **27.** square or rectangle
29. rectangle **31.** 565.5 in^3 **33.** 15.21 **35.** 1.3 **37.** $3\frac{1}{4}$

Pages 580–582 Lesson 11-5
1. Slant height is the altitude of a triangular face of a pyramid; it is the length from the vertex of a cone to the edge of its base. Height of a pyramid or cone is the altitude of the whole solid. **3.** Sample answer: An architect might use the formulas to calculate the amount of materials needed for parts of a structure. **5.** 42.9 m^2 **7.** 336 ft^2
9. 96.3 in^2 **11.** 62.4 in^2 **13.** 339.3 in^2 **15.** 311.9 m^2
17. 506.6 mm^2 **19.** Style 8M has 29 in^2 more plastic.
21. 339 ft^2; 4 squares **23.** Many building materials are priced and purchased by square footage. Architects use surface area when designing buildings. Answers should include the following.
- Surface area is used in covering building exteriors and in designing interiors.
- It is important to know surface areas so the amounts and costs of building materials can be estimated.
25. C **27.** 5541.8 mm^2 **29.** 7 ft^2 **31.** 25.1 in^3 **33.** infinitely many solutions **35.** 3 **37.** 3 **39.** 3.15

Pages 586–588 Lesson 11-6
1. Sample answer:
The cones are similar because the ratios comparing their radii and slant heights are equal: $\frac{2}{3} = \frac{5}{7.5}$.

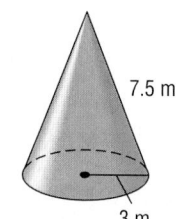

3. no   **5.** $x = 33\frac{1}{3}$ ft   **7.** 525 m   **9.** 2,976,750 m³   **11.** yes
13. yes   **15.** $x = 7$ m, $y = 18$ m   **17.** Sometimes; bases must be the same polygon and the corresponding side lengths must be proportional.   **19.** always; same shape, diameters or radii are proportional   **21.** 200^3 or 8,000,000 times greater   **23.** If the ratios of corresponding linear dimensions are equal, the solids are similar. Answers should include the following.
• For example, if the ratio comparing the heights of two cylinders equals the ratio comparing their radii, then the cylinders are similar.
• A cone and a prism are not similar.
25. C   **27.** 184 ft²   **29.** 65°   **31.** $-\frac{5}{9}$ **33.** 19.3   **35.** 6.0
37. 9.4

Page 588   Practice Quiz 2
1. 166 mm²   **3.** 9.4 m²   **5.** Yes; their corresponding dimensions are proportional.

Pages 592–594   Lesson 11-7
1. Josh; the first two 0s are not significant because they are placeholders for the decimal point. The 0 between 2 and 5 is significant because it is between two significant digits and shows the actual value in the thousandths place.
3. Sample answer: 0.012 or 2500   **5.** 3   **7.** 3   **9.** 7.1 L
11. 544.5 in²   **13.** $\frac{1}{32}$ in.   **15.** 3   **17.** 2   **19.** 1   **21.** 4
23. 45 in.   **25.** 2 ft²   **27.** 84.47 m   **29.** 49.5 cm   **31.** 26 m²
33. b; The precision unit of ruler a is $\frac{1}{8}$ inch. The precision unit of ruler b is $\frac{1}{16}$ inch.   **35.** No, the numbers are estimated to the nearest 0.1 million.   **37.** 12,400,000; 3
39. Not necessarily, because the actual size of the 2.0 mm wrench can range from 1.95 mm to 2.05 mm and the actual size of the 2 mm bolt can range from 1.5 mm to 2.5 mm. So, the bolts could be larger than the corresponding wrenches.
41. A   **43.** 0.05 mi; between 132.75 mi and 132.85 mi
45. 26.5 cm²   **47.** 14.8 m²

Pages 595–598   Chapter 11 Study Guide and Review
1. false; lateral area   **3.** false; slant height   **5.** false; cylinder
7. true   **9.** rectangular prism; $QRST$, $UVWX$ or $QTXU$, $RSWV$ or $QRVU$, $TSWX$; $QRST$, $UVWX$, $QTXU$, $RSWV$, $QRVU$, $TSWX$; $\overline{QR}$, $\overline{RS}$, $\overline{ST}$, $\overline{TZ}$, $\overline{UV}$, $\overline{VW}$, $\overline{WX}$, $\overline{XU}$, $\overline{QU}$, $\overline{TX}$, $\overline{SW}$, $\overline{RV}$; Q, R, S, T, U, V, W, X **11.** rectangular pyramid; $YNPZ$; AYZ, AZP, ANP, ANY, $YNPZ$; $\overline{AY}$, $\overline{AZ}$, $\overline{AP}$, $\overline{AN}$, $\overline{YZ}$, $\overline{ZP}$, $\overline{PN}$, $\overline{NY}$; A, Y, Z, P, N **13.** 0.8 mm³   **15.** 4 ft³
17. 1721.9 cm³   **19.** 548.7 mm²   **21.** 45 in²   **23.** 37.1 in²
25. yes   **27.** 19.0 cm   **29.** 0.9 m   **31.** 973 ft²

Chapter 12   More Statistics and Probability

Page 605   Chapter 12 Getting Started
1. 16; 15; none   **3.** 5.3, 5.8, 6.5   **5.** $\frac{1}{3}$ **7.** $\frac{1}{2}$ **9.** $\frac{1}{2}$ **11.** $\frac{1}{2}$
13. $\frac{1}{8}$ **15.** $\frac{1}{6}$ **17.** $\frac{1}{6}$

Pages 608–611   Lesson 12-1
1. Sample answer: The age of the youngest President at the time of his inauguration was 42 and the age of the oldest President to be inaugurated was 69. However, most of the Presidents were 50 to 59 years old at the time of their inauguration.

3.

Stem	Leaf
0	6 7
1	2 5 5
2	0
3	5
4	0 1 $2\,|\,0 = 20$

5. 50, 99   **7.** Sample answer: The lowest score was 50. The highest score was 99. Most of the scores were in the 70–79 interval.
9. Chicken; whereas chicken sandwiches have 8–20 grams of fat, burgers have 10–36 grams of fat.

11.

Stem	Leaf
1	3
2	6 8
3	4 9
4	
5	2 3
6	2 2 7
7	7 9
8	4 $7\,|\,7 = 77$

13.

Stem	Leaf
0	6 6 8
1	0 1 4 6 8
2	0 2 5
3	2 7
4	
5	0 $3\,|\,7 = 37$

15.

Stem	Leaf
40	0 0 5
41	
42	5
43	
44	
45	0 6
46	
47	
48	0 4 7
49	
50	
51	0
52	0
⋮	
62	5
⋮	
76	4
77	
78	9 $76\,|\,4 = 764$

17. never   **19.** 35%   **21.** Sample answer: In the most populated U.S. cities, about 27 to 35% of the people exercise daily.   **23.** 5
25. The average number of games won by the teams in the Big East Conference is less than the average number of games won by the teams in the Big Ten Conference.   **29a.** Sample answer: It would be easier to find the median in a stem-and-leaf plot because the data are arranged in order from least to greatest.   **29b.** Sample answer: It would be easier to find the mean in a table because once you find the sum, it may be easier to count the number of items in a table.

29c. Sample answer: It would be easier to find the mode in a stem-and-leaf plot because the value or values that occur most often are grouped together.   **31.** C   **33.** no
35. 62.8 ft; 314.2 ft²   **37.** 247%   **39.** 0.65%   **41.** 57.1%
43. 1.6%   **45.** 6   **47.** 1.1

Pages 614–616   Lesson 12-2
1. The range describes how the entire set of data is distributed, while the interquartile range describes how the middle half of the data is distributed.   **3.** Sample answer: {8, 9, 13, 25, 26, 26, 26, 27, 28, 30, 35, 40}   **5.** 27; 6   **7.** 24 h
9. 77; 39   **11.** 50; 10   **13.** 25; 15.5   **15.** 22   **17.** Feb.: 13.5; July: 8   **19.** National League: 42, 44, 48, 38, 10; American League: 39, 44, 49, 39, 10   **21a.** Sample answer: {43, 49, 50, 50, 58, 60, 60, 66, 70, 70, 71, 78}   **21b.** Sample answer: {15, 18, 20, 20, 44, 60, 60, 64, 70, 70, 75, 79}   **21c.** Sample answer: The first set of data has a smaller interquartile range, thus the data in the first set are more tightly clustered around the median and the data in the second are more spread out over the range.   **23.** C

25.

Stem	Leaf
0	9
1	2 4 5 8
2	1 7
3	7 $3\,|\,7 = \$37$

27. 461.8 cm³   **29.** 1.6 ft
31. {0.2, 0.3, 0.6, 0.8, 1.2, 1.4, 1.5}
33. {9.8, 9.9, 10.5, 10.9, 11.2, 11.4}

Pages 619–621   Lesson 12-3

1. lower quartile, least value; upper quartile, greatest value
3. Sample answer: {28, 30, 52, 68, 90, 92}

5.

14 18 22 26 30 34 38 42 46 50

7. Sample answer: The length of the box-and-whisker plot shows that the winning times of the men's marathons are not concentrated around a certain time.   **9.** The most fuel-efficient SUV and the least fuel-efficient sedan both average 22 miles per gallon.

11.

60   70   80   90 100 110 120 130

13.

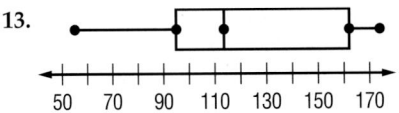

50   70   90   110   130   150   170

15.

26.0   28.0   30.0   32.0   34.0   36.0

17. 50%   **19.** Sample answer: The least number of games won for NFC is 3 and the least number of games won for the AFC is 1. The most number of games won for the NFC is 12 and the most number of games won for the AFC is 13. In addition, for both conferences, the median number of games won is about 9.   **21.** A box-and-whisker plot would clearly display any upper and lower extreme temperatures and the median temperature. Answers should include the following.

•

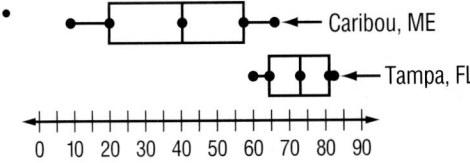

← Caribou, ME

← Tampa, FL

0   10   20   30   40   50   60   70   80   90

• Sample answer: Tampa has a median temperature of 73 and Caribou has a median temperature of 40.5. Whereas the highest average temperature for Tampa is 82, the highest average temperature for Caribou is 66.
• Sample answer: You can easily see how the temperatures vary.

23. C   **25.** 4

27. Stem	Leaf
1	4
2	1 4 7
3	9
4	8 2|4 = 24

29. 14

Pages 625–628   Lesson 12-4

1. Sample answer: Because the intervals are continuous.

3.

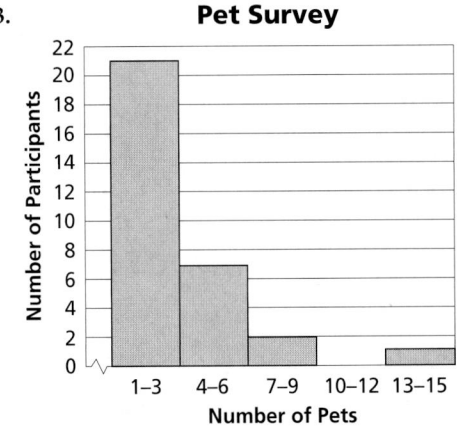

Pet Survey

5. the number of states that have a certain number of roller coasters   **7.** The numbers between 10 and 34 are omitted.   **9.** 2 or more national monuments

11.

Weekly Study Time

13.

Touchdowns in a Season

15. 13   **17.** 37.5%   **19.** Dallas   **21.** true   **23.** false   **25.** true
27. A   **29.** absolute frequency: 2, 9, 17, 12, 7, 2; relative frequency: $\frac{2}{49}, \frac{9}{49}, \frac{17}{49}, \frac{12}{49}, \frac{1}{7}, \frac{2}{49}$; cumulative frequency: 2, 11, 28, 40, 47, 49

31.

Average Length of U.S. States

Source: *The World Almanac*

33. 44; 15 **35.** Sample answer: Brand B costs one-third more than brand C.

Page 628   Practice Quiz 1

1.

Stem	Leaf
1	6 8 9 9
2	0 2 6 8 8 8
3	0 2
4	0 2 3
5	5
6	
7	
8	6 9

$5|5 = 55$

3.

5.

Costs

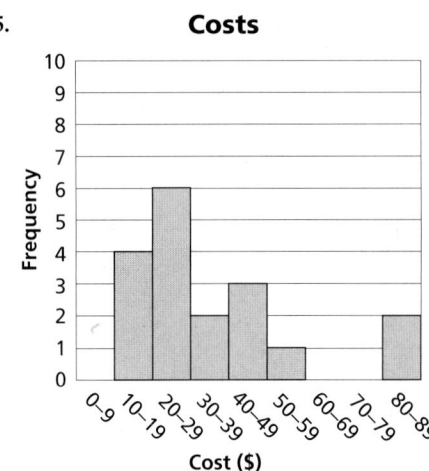

Pages 631–633   Lesson 12-5

1. Sample answer: inconsistent vertical scale and break in vertical scale **3.** Graph A has a break in the vertical scale.
5. From the vertical scale, you can see that the number of

area codes in 1999 is about 1.5 times the number of area codes in 1996. The graph is misleading because the drawing of the phone for 1999 is about 3 times the size of the phone for 1996. Also, there is a break in the vertical scale.
7. Graph B   **9.** Graph B; the vertical scale used makes the decrease in the unemployment rates appear more drastic.
11a. Sample answer:

Commuter Train Passengers

11b. Sample answer:

Commuter Train Passengers

13. B

15.

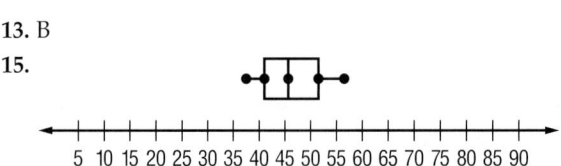

17. 20.3 m²   **19.** $\frac{1}{6}$ or $16\frac{2}{3}$%   **21.** $\frac{5}{6}$ or $83\frac{1}{3}$%

23. $\frac{5}{6}$ or $83.\overline{3}$%

Pages 637–639   Lesson 12-6
1. Sample answer: Both methods find the number of outcomes. Using the Fundamental Counting Principle is faster and uses less space; using a tree diagram shows what each outcome is.   **3.** First find the number of outcomes possible. The possible outcomes are taco-chicken, taco-beef,

taco-bean, burrito-chicken, burrito-beef, and burrito-bean, for a total of 6 outcomes. Two of the outcomes have chicken filling, so the probability of chicken filling is $\frac{2}{6}$ or $\frac{1}{3}$. **5.** $\frac{1}{16}$
7. $\frac{1}{4}$ **9.** 9

11.

8 outcomes

13.

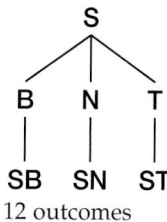

12 outcomes

15. 36 outcomes **17.** 24 outcomes
19. 1024 outcomes **21.** $\frac{5}{18}$ **23.** $\frac{1}{100,000}$
25. Either; the probability of rolling either odd or even is one-half.
27. Sample answer: any two letters followed by any four digits **29.** D
31. Sample answer: Vertical scale that does not start at zero. **33.** 11–20

35.

37.

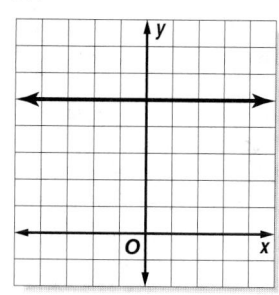

39. 15 **41.** 28

Pages 643–645 Lesson 12-7
1. Sample answer: How many 3-digit numbers can be made from the digits 1, 2, 3, and 4 if no digit is repeated?
3. Sarah; five CDs from a collection of 30 is a combination because order is not important. **5.** P; 120 ways **7.** C; 84 ways **9.** 220 pizzas **11.** P; 24 flags **13.** C; 105 ways
15. P; 1320 ways **17.** C; 364 ways **19.** 40,320
21. 39,916,800 **23.** 36 handshakes **25.** 3003 ways
27. 10 combinations **29.** $\frac{2}{5}$ **31.** When order is not important, duplicate arrangements are not included in the number of arrangements. Answers should include the following.
• When order was not important there were half as many pairs.
• Order is important when you arrange things in a line; order is not important when you choose a group of things.

33. C **35.** Yes; the vertical axis does not include zero.
37. Q **39.** I **41.** 1:8 **43.** 11:2

Page 645 Practice Quiz 2
1. Sample answer: Bars are different widths.
3. 256 outcomes **5.** 15 segments

Pages 648–649 Lesson 12-8
1. Write a ratio comparing the ways the event can occur to the ways the event cannot occur. **3.** Hoshi; the probability of rolling a 2 is 1 out of 6. The odds of rolling a 2 are 1 in 5.
5. 1:2 **7.** 5:1 **9.** 1:2 **11.** 2:1 **13.** 1:1 **15.** 1:3 **17.** 5:7
19. 31:5 **21.** 1:17 **23.** 5:4 **25.** 9:4 **27.** $\frac{1}{8192}$ **29.** 47:53
31. No; 512 is the total number of possible outcomes, so it could not be a number in the odds of winning. **33.** A
35. 6 ways
37.

$$\begin{array}{c} \longleftarrow\!\!+\!\!-\!\!+\!\!-\!\!+\!\!-\!\!+\!\!-\!\!+\!\!-\!\!+\!\!-\!\!+\!\!\longrightarrow \\ \quad 3\ \ 4\ \ 5\ \ 6\ \ 7\ \ 8\ \ 9\ \ 10 \end{array}\ ; a \geq 6$$

39.

$$\begin{array}{c} \longleftarrow\!\!+\!\!-\!\!+\!\!-\!\!+\!\!-\!\!\oplus\!\!-\!\!+\!\!-\!\!+\!\!-\!\!+\!\!\longrightarrow \\ -6\ -5\ -4\ -3\ -2\ -1\ \ 0\ \ 1\ \ 2 \end{array}\ ; y > -3$$

41. $\frac{1}{3}$ **43.** $\frac{1}{56}$

Pages 653–655 Lesson 12-9
1. Independent and dependent events are similar because both are a connection of two or more simple events and the probability of the compound event is found by multiplying the probabilities of each simple event. They are different because the second event in a dependent event is influenced by the outcome of the first event. Therefore, the probability of the second event used in calculating the probability of the compound event is dependent on the outcome of the first event. **3.** The result of the 1st event must be taken into account. **5.** $\frac{1}{12}$ **7.** $\frac{3}{14}$ **9.** $\frac{3}{4}$ **11.** $\frac{1}{30}$
13. $\frac{1}{5}$ **15.** $\frac{1}{91}$ **17.** $\frac{10}{91}$ **19.** $\frac{5}{364}$ **21.** $\frac{5}{8}$ **23.** $\frac{3}{7}$ **25.** 1 **27.** $\frac{2}{9}$
29. 0.16 **31a.** Sample answer: 3 red, 2 white, and 4 blue
31b. Sample answer: The numerator must be 24. Any combination of 3, 2, and 4 will have a probability of $\frac{1}{21}$.
33. B **35.** $\frac{2}{3}$ **37.** 3:10 **39.** 17,576,000 **41.** 65° **43.** 65°
45. 90° **47.** 40.6 **49.** 16

Pages 658–662 Chapter 12 Study Guide and Review
1. b **3.** c **5.** d **7.**

Stem	Leaf
4	5 5
5	0 0 5 5
6	0 0 0 0 0
7	5 5 5
8	5 5 $7|5 = 75¢$

9. 23; 7 **11.** 22; 10 **13.** 80°F **15.** 50% **17.** Graph A
19. 16 outcomes **21.** C; 364 ways **23.** C; 21 ways **25.** 3:5
27. 1:3 **29.** $\frac{1}{30}$

Chapter 13 Polynomials and Nonlinear Functions

Page 667 Chapter 13 Getting Started
1. 1 **3.** 2 **5.** 0 **7.** $5a + 20$ **9.** $-4 - 32n$ **11.** $27b - 27c$
13. yes **15.** yes

Pages 670–672 Lesson 13-1
1. The degree of a monomial is the sum of the exponents of its variables. The degree of a polynomial is the same as the degree of the term with the greatest degree. **3.** Tanisha; the degree of a binomial is the degree of the term with the greater degree. **5.** yes; monomial **7.** yes; binomial
9. yes; trinomial **11.** 0 **13.** 1 **15.** 4 **17.** 2 **19.** yes; binomial **21.** yes; monomial **23.** no **25.** yes; trinomial
27. no **29.** yes; trinomial **31.** 0 **33.** 3 **35.** 5 **37.** 5 **39.** 3
41. 5 **43.** Always; any number is a monomial.
45. $2x + 2y + z + xy$ **49.** Polynomials approximate real-world data by using variables to represent quantities that are related. Answers should include the following.
• Heat index is found by using a polynomial in which one variable represents the percent humidity and another variable represents the temperature.
• Heat index cannot be approximated using a linear equation because the values do not change at a constant rate.
51. C **53.** mutually exclusive; $\frac{2}{3}$ **55.** 70 in^3
57. $(x + 2x) + 4$ **59.** $(6n + 3n) + (2 + 5)$
61. $(s + 5s) + (t - 3t)$

Pages 676–677 Lesson 13-2
1. x^2 and $2x^2$; $5x$ and $-4x$; 2 and 7 **3.** Hai; the terms have the same variables in a different order. **5.** $7a^2 - 9a + 4$
7. $13x - 4y$ **9.** $4x^2 + 3x - 2$ **11.** $3x + 3$
13. $11x^2 + 5xy + 4y^2$ **15.** $4x + 14$ **17.** $8y + 2r$
19. $5x^2 + xy + y$ **21.** $7x^2 + 9x + 5$ **23.** $5a - 4b$; -31
25. $4a + 6b + c$; 14 **27.** 56 **29.** $23x - 12$ **31.** $42x - 22$
33. Use algebra tiles to model each polynomial and combine the tiles that have the same size and shape. Answers should include the following.
• Algebra tiles that represent like terms have the same size and shape.
• When adding polynomials, a red tile and a white tile that have the same size and shape are zero pairs and may be removed. The result is the sum of the polynomials.
35. B **37.** 2 **39.** $\frac{2}{13}$ **41.** $\frac{3}{26}$ **43.** $15c + (-26)$
45. $1 + (-2x)$ **47.** $(n + rt) + (-r^2)$

Pages 680–681 Lesson 13-3
1. Subtracting one polynomial from another is the same as adding the additive inverse. **3.** $4r$ **5.** $5x + 2$
7. $3x^2 + 3x - 8$ **9.** $7x + 5$ units **11.** $-2n^2 + 6n$
13. $y^2 - 7y + 10$ **15.** $15w^2 - 2w + 10$ **17.** $4x + 3$
19. $-2t + 2$ **21.** $3a^2 + 2b^2$ **23.** $9n^2 - n - 12$
25. $2x^2 - 2xy + 3y^2$ **27.** $x - y = 68 + (x + y)$; $-34°F$
29. In subtracting polynomials and in subtracting measurements, like parts are subtracted. Answers should include the following.
• To subtract measurements with two or more units, subtract the like units. To subtract polynomials with two or more terms, subtract the like terms.
• For example, to subtract 1 foot 5 inches from 3 feet 8 inches, subtract the feet $3 - 1$ and subtract the inches $8 - 5$. The difference is 2 feet 3 inches.
31. B **33.** $12x - 3y$ **35.** $-t^2 + 12t + 2$ **37.** yes; binomial

39. Stem | Leaf

Stem	Leaf
5	4 9
6	4 6 8
7	0 1 1 2
8	5 9
9	1 5	4 = 54

41. $8y^2$ **43.** $4m^3$ **45.** $10r^5$

Page 681 Practice Quiz 1
Page 681 Practice Quiz 1
1. 4 **3.** 3 **5.** $2x + 2$ **7.** $8r - 3s$ **9.** $-3x + 5y$

Pages 684–686 Lesson 13-4
1. False; the order in which numbers or terms are multiplied does not change the product, by the Commutative Property of Multiplication; $x(2x + 3) = 2x^2 + 3x$ and $(2x + 3)x = 2x^2 + 3x$. **3.** Sample answer: $2x(x + 1) = 2x^2 + 2x$ **5.** $a^2 + 4a$ **7.** $12x^2 - 28x$
9. $-15x^2 + 35x - 45$ **11.** $14n + 35$ **13.** $t^2 - 9t$
15. $-7a^2 - 6a$ **17.** $40n + 8n^2$ **19.** $3y^3 - 6y$ **21.** $5x^2 + 5xy$
23. $-14x^2 + 35x - 77$ **25.** $4c^4 + 28c^2 - 40c$ **27.** -1
29. high school, 84 ft by 50 ft; college, 94 ft by 50 ft

31.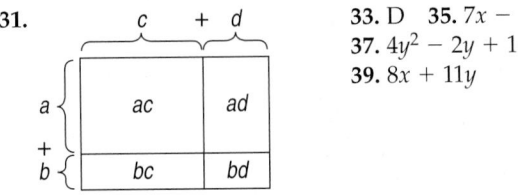

33. D **35.** $7x - 1$
37. $4y^2 - 2y + 14$
39. $8x + 11y$

$(a + b)(c + d) = ac + ad + bc + bd$
41. Sample answer: The scales are labeled inconsistently or the bars on a bar graph are different widths.
43. reflection

45.

x	2x² – 3	(x, y)
0	−3	(0, −3)
1	−1	(1, −1)
2	5	(2, 5)
3	15	(3, 15)

Pages 689–691 Lesson 13-5
1. Sample answer: Determine whether an equation can be written in the form $y = mx + b$ or look for a constant rate of change in a table of values. **3.** Sample answer: population growth **5.** Nonlinear; graph is a curve. **7.** Nonlinear; equation cannot be written as $y = mx + b$. **9.** Linear; rate of change is constant. **11.** Nonlinear; graph is a curve.
13. Linear; graph is a straight line. **15.** Nonlinear; graph is a curve. **17.** Linear; equation can be written as $y = 0.9x + 0$. **19.** Linear; equation can be written as $y = \frac{3}{4}x + 0$. **21.** Nonlinear; equation cannot be written as $y = mx + b$. **23.** Linear; rate of change is constant.
25. Nonlinear; rate of change is not constant.
27. Nonlinear; the points (year, applications) would lie on a curved line, not on a straight line. Or, the rate of change is not constant. **29.** No, the difference between the years varies, so the change is not constant. **31.** A **33.** $4t + 9t^2$
35. $a^2b - 2ab^2$ **37.** $-x$ **39.** acute

41.

43.
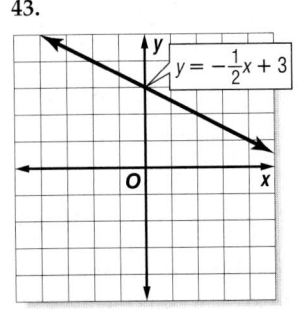

Page 691 Practice Quiz 2

1. $2c^3 - 8c$ **3.** $5a^2 + a^3 + 2a^4$ **5.** Nonlinear; equation cannot be written as $y = mx + b$.

Pages 694–696 Lesson 13-6

1. Sample answer: The graph of $y = nx^2$ has line symmetry and the graph of $y = nx^3$ does not. **3.** Sample answer: $y = x^2 + 3$; make a table of values and plot the points.

5.   **7.**

9.   **11.**

13.   **15.**

17.   **19.**

21.

23.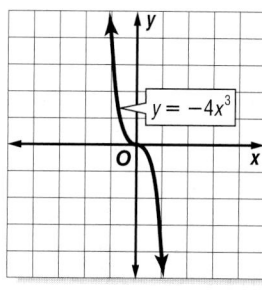

Both equations are functions because every value of x is paired with a unique value of y.

25. $(0, 7)$

27. 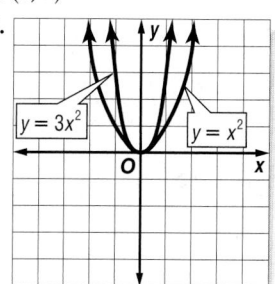 Similar shape; $y = 3x^2$ is more narrow.

29. 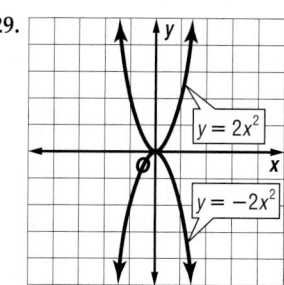 Same shape; $y = -2x^2$ is $y = 2x^2$ reflected over the x-axis.

31. $A = 50x - x^2$ **33.** 25 ft by 25 ft
35. $V = 0.2\pi r^2$ or $V \approx 0.6r^2$

37. Formulas, tables, and graphs are interchangeable ways to represent functions. Answers should include the following.
- To make a graph, use a rule to make a table of values. Then plot the points and connect them to make a graph.
- To write a rule, find points that lie on a graph and make a table of values using the coordinates. Look for a pattern and write a rule that describes the pattern.

39. C **41.** Sample answer: 18 units² **43.** $10x - 20$
45. $24y - 21y^2$ **47.** $y = 4x - 3$

Pages 698–700 Chapter 13 Study Guide and Review

1. trinomial **3.** cubic **5.** like terms **7.** curve **9.** yes; binomial **11.** yes; monomial **13.** yes; trinomial **15.** no

17. 1   **19.** 3   **21.** 6   **23.** 5   **25.** $8b + 3$ **27.** $5y^2 + 2y - 4$
29. $y^2 - y - 1$ **31.** $3x^2 - 4x + 7$ **33.** $-x + 1$ **35.** $20t - 10$
37. $6k^2 + 3k$ **39.** $-18a + 2a^3$ **41.** Linear; graph is a straight line.   **43.** Nonlinear; rate of change is not constant.

45.

47.

49.

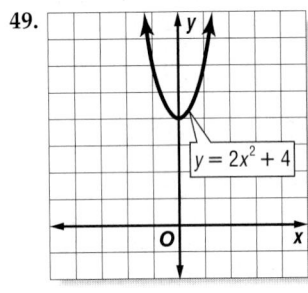

Photo Credits

About the Cover

The Great Bear at Hersheypark in Hershey, Pennsylvania, is an inverted coaster – that is, you ride below it, not above it. With four inversions, including loops, twists, and rolls, this ride reaches a speed of almost 60 miles per hour and at one point falls 124 feet. Roller coasters use math in their design and operation from beginning to end. Their designers want to make the tallest, fastest, most exciting coasters ever!

Index

Index

Index

Symbols and Properties

Symbols

+	plus or positive	°	degree
−	minus or negative	!	factorial
±	plus or minus	$\overline{AB}$	line segment AB
× or ·	times	AB	measure of $\overline{AB}$
÷	divided by	$-a$	opposite or additive inverse of a
=	is equal to	(a, b)	ordered pair a, b
≠	is not equal to	O	origin
>	is greater than	%	percent
<	is less than	π	pi
≥	is greater than or equal to	$P(A)$	probability of A
≤	is less than or equal to	$a{:}b$	ratio of a to b
≈	is approximately equal to	$0.7\overline{5}$	repeating decimal $0.75555\ldots$
$|a|$	absolute value of a	$\sqrt{a}$	square root of a
∠	angle	△	triangle

Addition and Multiplication Properties

Additive Identity	For any number a, $a + 0 = 0 + a = a$.
Multiplicative Identity	For any number a, $a \cdot 1 = 1 \cdot a = a$.
Additive Inverse	For any number a, there is exactly one number $-a$ such that $a + (-a) = 0$.
Multiplicative Inverse	For any number $\frac{a}{b}$, where $a, b \neq 0$, there is exactly one number $\frac{b}{a}$ such that $\frac{a}{b} \cdot \frac{b}{a} = 1$.
Commutative (+)	For any numbers a and b, $a + b = b + a$.
Commutative (×)	For any numbers a and b, $a \cdot b = b \cdot a$.
Associative (+)	For any numbers a, b, and c, $(a + b) + c = a + (b + c)$.
Associative (×)	For any numbers a, b, and c, $(a \cdot b) \cdot c = a \cdot (b \cdot c)$.
Distributive	For any numbers a, b, and c, $a(b + c) = ab + ac$ and $a(b - c) = ab - ac$.

Formulas and Measures

Formulas

Midpoint on a coordinate plane		$M = \left(\dfrac{x_1 + x_2}{2}, \dfrac{y_1 + y_2}{2}\right)$
Distance on a coordinate plane		$d = \sqrt{(x_2 - x_1)^2 + (y_2 - y_1)^2}$
Perimeter of a rectangle		$P = 2\ell + 2w$ or $P = 2(\ell + w)$
Circumference of a circle		$C = 2\pi r$ or $C = \pi d$
Area	rectangle	$A = \ell w$
	parallelogram	$A = bh$
	triangle	$A = \frac{1}{2}bh$
	trapezoid	$A = \frac{1}{2}h(b_1 + b_2)$
	circle	$A = \pi r^2$
Surface Area	cube	$S = 6s^2$
	prism	$S = Ph + 2B$
	cylinder	$S = 2\pi rh + 2\pi r^2$
	regular pyramid	$S = \frac{1}{2}P\ell + B$
	cone	$S = \pi r\ell + \pi r^2$
Volume	cube	$V = s^3$
	prism	$V = Bh$
	cylinder	$V = \pi r^2 h$
	regular pyramid	$V = \frac{1}{3}Bh$
	cone	$V = \frac{1}{3}\pi r^2 h$

Measures

Measure	Metric	Customary
Length	kilometer (km) = 1000 meters (m) 1 meter = 100 centimeters (cm) 1 centimeter = 10 millimeters (mm)	1 mile (mi) = 1760 yards (yd) 1 mile = 5280 feet (ft) 1 yard = 3 feet 1 foot = 12 inches (in.) 1 yard = 36 inches
Volume and Capacity	1 liter (L) = 1000 milliliters (mL) 1 kiloliter (kL) = 1000 liters	1 gallon (gal) = 4 quarts (qt) 1 gallon = 128 fluid ounces (fl oz) 1 quart = 2 pints (pt) 1 pint = 2 cups (c) 1 cup = 8 fluid ounces
Weight and Mass	1 kilogram (kg) = 1000 grams (g) 1 gram = 1000 milligrams (mg) 1 metric ton (t) = 1000 kilograms	1 ton (T) = 2000 pounds (lb) 1 pound = 16 ounces (oz)